Glencoe Science

EARTH SCIENCE
Geology, the Environment, and the Universe

Features and Benefits

		Sample Pages
Dynamic Instructional Strategies	**...accommodate students of all ability levels.**	
	■ *Differentiated Instruction* and student activities that help meet students' special needs.	**20T-21T**
	■ *Cultural Diversity* connections allow teachers to show successful scientists from diverse ethnic backgrounds, allowing students to understand how people from different cultures approach and solve problems.	**58** **481**
Variety of Labs and Demos	**...get students excited about being involved in chemistry.**	
	■ Each chapter in the Student Edition includes a *Discovery Lab*, a *Problem-Solving Lab*, a *MiniLab*, and a *GeoLab*.	**3, 234, 504-505, 568**
	■ The Teacher Wraparound Edition provides more hands-on activities in the form of quick *Demos*.	**228-229, 604-605**
	■ The *Laboratory Manual, GeoLab and MiniLab Worksheets*, and *Exploring Environmental Problems* provide additional opportunities to practice laboratory techniques.	**22T-23T**
Teacher Resources	**...provide innovative strategies to help new and experienced teachers.**	
	■ *Chapter Organizer* helps teachers reduce preparation time and add variety and interest to the classroom presentation.	**4A-4B**
	■ *National Geographic Expeditions* provide additional material on topics that are unusual or informative to inform, excite, and motivate students.	**4T-5T**
	■ *Content Background* offers in-depth background on section material and expands on the section subject with more information at a higher level.	**576C-576D**
	■ *Teacher Classroom Resources* contain reproducible masters and transparencies.	
Online Resources	**...enrich the learning experience with the click of a mouse.**	
	■ Link to earthgeu.com for *National Geographic Society, Teacher Forum, Extending the Content*, and *NASA's Picture of the Day*.	**31T**
	■ Students can build vocabulary through word scrambles, word jumbles, and crosswords at **earthgeu.com/vocabulary_puzzlemaker**.	**143, 519**
Technology	**...provides time-saving products to help teachers creatively engage their students.**	
	■ Easy-to-edit *Interactive Chalkboard Microsoft® PowerPoint®* CD-ROM presentations include step-by-step lessons, an image bank, transparencies, animations, video, and audio.	**152, 746**
	■ *ExamView® Pro Testmaker* CD-ROM allows teachers to quickly create tests for the desired difficulty level.	**25, 521**
	■ *TeacherWorks™* CD-ROM is a teacher's all-in-one resource center that helps plan and organize lessons.	**52B, 384B**

Topographic Map Symbols

ROADS AND RAILROADS

Primary highway, hard surface

Secondary highway, hard surface

Light-duty road, hard or improved surface

Unimproved road

Railroad: single track and multiple track

Railroads in juxtaposition

BUILDINGS AND STRUCTURES

Buildings

School, church, and cemetery

Barn and warehouse

Wells, not water (with labels)   o oil   o gas

Tanks: oil, water, etc.

(labeled if water)

Open-pit mine, quarry, or prospect

Tunnel

Benchmark   BM Δ 293

Bridge

Campsite

HABITATS

Marsh (swamp)

Wooded marsh

Woods or brushwood

Vineyard

Submerged marsh

Mangrove

Coral reef, rocks

Orchard

Urban area

Perennial streams

Elevated aqueduct

Water well and spring

Small rapids

Large rapids

Intermittent lake

Intermittent stream

Glacier

Large falls

Dry lake bed

SURFACE ELEVATIONS

Spot elevation   x 7369

Water elevation   670

Index contour   100

Intermediate contour

Depression contour

BOUNDARIES

National

State

County, parish, municipal

Civil township, precinct, town, barrio

Incorporated city, village, town, hamlet

Reservation, national or state

Small park, cemetery, airport, etc.

Land grant

Township or range line, United States land survey

Township or range line, approximate location

HANDBOOK
FOR NEW YORK TEACHERS

Contents

Correlations

FEATURES FOR NEW YORK TEACHERS

Earth Science: Geology, the Environment, and the Universe provides a variety of handy, effective teaching tools for making sure your students have a successful learning experience in Earth Science.

Effective Use of Your Time

You hold in your hands all the information you need for planning a complete Earth Science course for the New York core curriculum—quickly and efficiently. Glencoe's *Earth Science: Geology, the Environment, and the Universe* provides extensive teaching help on lesson pages, chapter planning guides, and in the *New York Lesson Plans and Block Scheduling* books that clearly support your New York Regents Physical Setting/Earth Science Core Curriculum. Turn to any of these handy references when working on your curriculum goals, and you will be able to plan lessons that will enable all of your students to master Earth Science concepts successfully.

New York Regents Physical Setting/ Earth Science Core Curriculum

Correlations of the standards and key ideas found in the New York Regents Physical Setting/Earth Science Core Curriculum are provided on individual lesson pages, making it easy for you to be sure that you have covered the core curriculum related to your lesson plan. In addition, a complete correlation in this book gives you an overview of the Regents coverage.

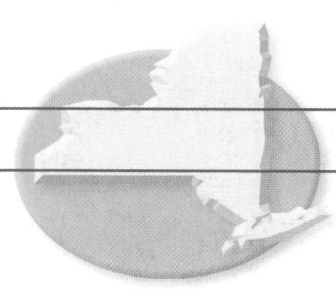

YOUR STUDENT EDITION

Hands-on Learning

The *Earth Science: Geology, the Environment, and the Universe* program is filled with hands-on activities and labs that will more than meet your lab requirements. Each chapter has one 2-page GeoLab in addition to a Discovery Lab, a MiniLab, and a Problem-Solving Lab. "Design Your Own GeoLabs" enable students to plan and conduct their own investigations. For students who have difficulty designing their own experiments, *Earth Science: Geology, the Environment, and the Universe* offers several lab alternatives. The *Student Edition* contains "Mapping GeoLabs" that allow students to use and interpret a map to solve a geologic problem, "Internet GeoLabs" that allow students to use the Internet to gather and share geologic data, and Traditional "GeoLabs" that allow students to conduct controlled experiments aimed at increasing the understanding of geologic concepts. Various demos in the *Teacher Wraparound Edition* provide yet another opportunity for hands-on learning. In addition, the *Laboratory Manual* provides more than 60 additional Earth Science labs.

Skill Development and Reinforcement

Every Section Assessment has a Skill Review question that reinforces process skills. Frequent assessments in the *Teacher Wraparound Edition* give you additional ideas for determining the mastery of the process skills in Discovery Labs, MiniLabs, Problem-Solving Labs, and GeoLabs. GeoDigests at the end of each unit provide a content overview and supply an additional opportunity for skill development and reinforcement. Test Practice and various skills activities in each Chapter Assessment round out the skill development strand. For students who want extra help, a Skill Handbook is provided at the back of the *Student Edition*.

Applications to Everyday Life

When students can relate classroom concepts with everyday life, they become more motivated. Features in the *Student Edition* such as Science & Math, Science & Technology, Science in the News, and Science & the Environment provide a connection between Earth Science and everyday life. In addition, Environmental Connections throughout the *Student Edition* provide an additional link between Earth Science and the environment. The National Geographic Society's Expeditions connect Earth Science with news-worthy events. Other features focus on Cultural Diversity and reflections of Earth Science in various other disciplines, such as history and physics.

All of the components of the *Earth Science: Geology, the Environment, and the Universe* program support your efforts to make learning Earth Science a realistic and achievable goal for all students of all abilities. The *Study Guide for Content Mastery* and two kinds of transparency overheads—*Section Focus* and *Teaching*—strengthen knowledge of basic information. The *Study Guide for Content Mastery* is referenced in both the *English Audiocassettes* and the *Spanish Audiocassettes*. Students are prompted to pause the tape and complete the worksheets in the *Study Guide for Content Mastery* booklet. Listed below are descriptions of other important program resources.

- *Exploring Environmental Problems:* These activities encourage the use of Earth Science concepts from the student text to the application of real-world environmental problems and issues. These computer-based labs (CBL) and Global Positioning System (GPS) labs also provide an interesting opportunity for students to use a variety of equipment used widely in the environmental field.

- *Vocabulary Puzzlemaker (Windows and Macintosh):* This online program allows you to create crossword, word search, and jumble puzzles using vocabulary terms from the student text, thereby reinforcing your students' Earth Science vocabulary.

- *Chapter Assessment:* Chapter Assessment includes a four-part assessment with questions of different levels for every chapter. Unique case studies require students to apply the scientific method to an interesting geologic or environmental problem.

- *Performance Assessment in Earth Science:* Includes the philosophy and strategies for assessing both the processes and products of Earth Science classes. This booklet contains two performance assessment activities for each of the units in the student text. Also included are performance assessment task lists and rubrics for helping you and your students evaluate their progress toward attaining the goals of the New York Regents Physical Setting/Earth Science Core Curriculum.

- *MindJogger VideoQuizzes (VHS and DVD):* The interactive quiz-show format of MindJogger VideoQuizzes provides fun for your students while reviewing core concepts for every chapter.

- *ExamView™ Pro CD-ROM (Windows and Macintosh):* Design and create your own test instruments with the ExamView™ Pro CD-ROM. Select test items by objective from different levels of difficulty or write and edit your own. All questions are correlated to the New York Regents Physical Setting/Earth Science Core Curriculum.

- *5 Days to the Regents Exam, Student and Teacher Editions:* This practice test includes questions all correlated to the New York Regents Physical Setting/Earth Science Core Curriculum. Students are provided hints on test-taking techniques as they answer various questions. A five-day plan gives students a specific schedule to follow in preparation for the Regents examination in Physical Setting/Earth Science. The teacher edition contains correlations to the New York Regents Physical Setting/Earth Science Core Curriculum and answers to all questions.

- *Review Handbook for Regents Earth Science Exam:* This handbook, organized by topics, will provide an alternative resource for your students as they prepare to take the Regents Earth science exam. Content reviews, practice problems in the style of the Regents test questions, and a full-length practice examination, all correlated to the New York Regents Physical Setting/Earth Science Core Curriculum and to the *Student Edition*, are included. In addition, a glossary and copies of the Earth Science Reference Tables provide a useful tool to your students. When used in conjunction with the *5 Days to the Regents Exam* booklet and the *Student Edition*, your students will have all that they need to successfully prepare for the Regents Earth Science exam.

New York Regents Core Curriculum

Correlation of Standards and Key Ideas for Physical Setting/Earth Science	Student Edition Pages
STANDARD 1—Analysis, Inquiry, and Design Students will use mathematical analysis, scientific inquiry, and engineering design, as appropriate, to pose questions, seek answers, and develop solutions.	
Mathematical Analysis	
(KI 1) Abstraction and symbolic representation are used to communicate mathematically.	14–16, 18, 20–21, 24–26, 28–29, 35–36, 42–43, 46–47, 94, 110, 172, 206, 217–218, 226, 239, 247, 253, 278, 282–283, 302–303, 305–307, 310–311, 319, 326–327, 344, 350, 357, 363, 386, 390–392, 394–396, 399, 464–465, 486, 492, 516–517, 610, 658, 665, 672, 695, 699, 702, 704–705, 748, 768–770, 777–779, 791–792, 798–799, 802–803, 806, 810–812, 815–817, 826–827, 830–831, 833, 842–843, 845–846, 850, 856–857
(KI 2) Deductive and inductive reasoning are used to reach mathematical conclusions.	26, 28, 31, 35–36, 42–44, 46–47, 57, 63, 80, 94, 96–97, 110, 112, 129, 161, 172, 204–206, 217–218, 226, 239, 247, 253, 263, 278–280, 283–284, 310, 318, 327, 329, 344, 348, 350, 353, 357, 360, 363, 365, 385, 388–389, 391–392, 394–396, 399, 464–465, 486, 492, 524, 586, 637, 644, 665, 698–699, 702, 704–705, 770, 777–780, 783, 786, 791–792, 797–799, 802–803, 806, 810, 815–817, 826–827, 830–831, 833, 843, 845–846, 850–851
(KI 3) Critical thinking skills are used in the solution of mathematical problems.	28, 31, 35–36, 42–44, 46–47, 94, 96–97, 129, 141, 172, 204–206, 217, 226, 237, 239, 247, 253, 263, 279–280, 283–284, 318, 344, 348, 350, 357, 360, 363, 365, 391–392, 394–395, 428, 464–465, 486, 492, 516–517, 521, 526, 542, 586, 590, 637, 665, 695, 698–699, 704–705, 770, 777–779, 791–792, 798–799, 810, 816–817, 826–827, 830–831, 833, 843, 845–846, 850
Scientific Inquiry	
(KI 1) The central purpose of scientific inquiry is to develop explanations of natural phenomena in a continuing, creative process.	4–5, 11–13, 17–19, 21, 23–25, 48–49, 71, 88, 92–93, 99, 108, 114–115, 121, 132, 138–140, 153, 163, 174–175, 181, 204–205, 211, 229, 232–233, 239, 254, 284, 292–293, 299, 302, 329, 359, 376–379, 385, 406–407, 413, 428, 430, 443, 471, 474, 495, 540, 553, 558, 576, 587, 618–619, 625, 642, 674, 689, 704–705, 711, 734–735, 756, 757, 768, 775–792, 794–797, 800–803, 805–857
(KI 2) Beyond the use of reasoning and consensus, scientific inquiry involves the testing of proposed explanations involving the use of conventional techniques and procedures and usually requiring considerable ingenuity.	5, 71, 92–93, 99, 108, 114–115, 121, 126–127, 140, 153, 163, 174–175, 181, 211, 229, 232–233, 239, 254, 271, 284, 290, 293, 299, 302, 359, 376–379, 385, 406–407, 428, 471, 474, 495, 558, 576, 601, 625, 642, 655, 676–677, 688, 704–705, 711, 768–769, 783, 785, 790, 793, 800, 816–817, 830–831, 833–834, 837, 840–843, 846, 848–853, 855–857
(KI 3) The observations made while testing proposed explanations, when analyzed using conventional and invented methods, provide new insights into phenomena.	53, 77, 92–93, 99, 108, 114–115, 121, 123, 126, 140, 142, 153, 163, 174–175, 181, 211, 229, 232–233, 239, 254, 271, 290, 293, 299, 302, 329, 352–354, 359, 376–379, 385, 394, 406–407, 413, 428, 471, 474, 558, 576, 587, 596, 625, 683, 688, 699, 704–705, 768, 776–777, 783, 800, 805–810, 812, 817, 819, 826–828, 835, 837–845, 847–849, 851–857
Engineering Design	
(KI 1) Engineering design is an iterative process involving modeling and optimization (finding the best solution within given constraints); this process is used to develop technological solutions to problems within given constraints.	26, 28–36, 42–43, 45–46, 108, 110, 114–115, 166, 243, 260, 284, 316, 321, 377, 466, 511–512, 520, 671, 676–677, 679–681, 691, 700–705, 708–709, 717, 720, 722–723, 729, 732–735, 749–752, 798–799, 810–811, 817, 833, 837, 842, 847, 850–855

New York Regents Core Curriculum

Correlation of Standards and Key Ideas for Physical Setting/Earth Science	Student Edition Pages
STANDARD 2 Students will access, generate, process, and transfer information, using appropriate technologies.	
Information Systems	
(KI 1) Information technology is used to retrieve, process, and communicate information as a tool to enhance learning.	10, 22, 26, 37–41, 46, 49, 72, 200, 311, 313–316, 319, 324, 352–354, 385–386, 410, 439, 488–490, 542, 706, 775, 800, 805, 828, 852–854, 858
(KI 2) Knowledge of the impacts and limitations of information systems is essential to its effective and ethical use.	200, 314–316, 319, 324, 352–353, 385–386, 706, 800, 828, 852–854
(KI 3) Information technology can have positive and negative impacts on society, depending upon how it is used.	40–41, 46, 200, 206, 221, 236–237, 313–316, 319, 324, 339–340, 346, 349–353, 385–386, 488–490, 706, 775, 800, 828, 854
STANDARD 6—Interconnectedness: Common Themes Students will understand the relationships and common themes that connect mathematics, science, and technology and apply the themes to these and other areas of learning.	
Systems Thinking	
(KI 1) Through systems thinking, people can recognize the commonalities that exist among all systems and how parts of a system interrelate and combine to perform specific functions.	4–7, 9, 23–24, 76, 81–83, 91, 93, 95–100, 107–113, 117–119, 138–141, 143, 145, 161, 165–175, 177–179, 184–188, 190, 195, 199–201, 203–205, 207–208, 210–231, 235–259, 261–263, 271, 273–275, 285–293, 296–298, 300–302, 304–311, 316, 318, 320–323, 325–346, 348–351, 355–357, 364–374, 381–383, 391, 399–408, 410–411, 470, 472–475, 479–487, 491–493, 681–682, 697, 699–703, 707–709, 712–713, 721, 776–779, 793–800, 814–815, 819–825, 829–831, 838–839, 843, 846–847, 851, 855–857
Models	
(KI 2) Models are simplified representations of objects, structures, or systems used in analysis, explanation, interpretation, or design.	18, 26–27, 32–36, 42–43, 45, 49, 79, 106, 108, 110, 113–115, 126, 149, 161, 166, 172, 179, 190, 194, 203–205, 208–209, 217, 221, 227, 229, 231–233, 237, 243, 248, 253–254, 260, 290–291, 293, 299, 302, 311, 316–318, 322–323, 325–327, 329, 368, 374, 376, 380, 383, 385, 401, 406–407, 411, 423, 430, 458, 464–465, 471, 474, 493, 495–496, 502, 504, 508–509, 516–517, 521, 523, 525–526, 533, 535–538, 541, 544–545, 554, 558, 560, 577–578, 587, 594, 601, 603, 610, 613, 616, 623, 625, 636, 646, 658, 665, 672, 680, 688–689, 704–705, 708–709, 711, 713–714, 718, 727–728, 730, 738, 748, 757, 761, 766–767, 772, 776–780, 782–785, 787–795, 798–799, 801–803, 805, 811, 813, 815–816, 818–825, 829–833, 836–837, 839–843, 847–857
Magnitude and Scale	
(KI 3) The grouping of magnitudes of size, time, frequency, and pressures or other units of measurement into a series of relative order provides a useful way to deal with the immense range and the changes in scale that affect the behavior and design of systems.	26–36, 42–43, 45, 174–175, 204–205, 327, 385, 423, 430, 443, 458, 464–465, 501, 503–508, 519, 521, 526, 533, 536, 570–571, 594, 602, 610, 623, 626, 635, 747, 768–769, 786, 790–792, 795, 798–799, 805–806, 810–811, 814–816, 819–821, 824–827, 829–831, 833–834, 836, 839–843, 845, 851–853, 855–857

New York Regents Core Curriculum

Correlation of Standards and Key Ideas for Physical Setting/Earth Science	Student Edition Pages
Equilibrium and Stability	
(KI 4) Equilibrium is a state of stability due either to a lack of change (static equilibrium) or a balance between opposing forces (dynamic equilibrium).	101–106, 152–175, 177, 180–205, 207–209, 222–227, 235–237, 304, 327, 330, 334–335, 337, 340, 355–357, 388, 393–394, 487, 525, 533, 543, 656–657, 659–660, 664–665, 670–674, 679, 685, 703, 707, 716, 718, 764, 783, 787–788, 790–797, 800–803, 807–809, 821–825, 828–829, 831, 834, 836, 838, 842–851, 855–857
Patterns of Change	
(KI 5) Indentifying patterns of change is necessary for making predictions about future behavior and conditions.	6, 66, 71, 101–106, 114–115, 117–119, 121–125, 127, 130–131, 133–135, 138–141, 143–145, 277, 285, 293, 297, 304, 318–323, 326, 328, 331, 333, 338, 340, 344, 346–347, 351, 356–357, 359–360, 363, 369, 371–383, 388, 393–394, 396–408, 410–411, 428, 470–471, 473, 475–479, 486–493, 510, 513–517, 519, 521, 630, 632, 657, 665, 682, 685, 687–689, 697, 707, 710, 713–715, 719, 724–725, 730–731, 736–739, 742–743, 773, 797, 800, 808–809, 813, 818, 822–825, 829–831, 843, 846–851, 855–857
Optimization	
(KI 6) In order to arrive at the best solution that meets criteria within constraints, it is often necessary to make trade-offs.	90, 176, 178–179, 197, 204–205, 207–208, 234, 237, 257–259, 659, 673, 675, 682, 685, 687, 690–705, 708–710, 717, 720, 723, 737–739
STANDARD 7–Interdisciplinary Problem Solving **Students will apply the knowledge and thinking skills of mathematics, science, and technology to address real-life problems and make informed decisions.**	
Connections	
(KI 1) The knowledge and skills of mathematics, science, and technology are used together to make informed decisions and solve problems, especially those relating to issues of science/technology/society, consumer decision making, design, and inquiry into phenomena.	32–43, 45–47, 94, 97, 129, 142, 176–179, 189–190, 204–206, 258–259, 281–284, 294, 311, 316, 319, 321, 340, 346, 348, 350–351, 358, 386–387, 398, 407, 464–465, 586, 663, 671–674, 680, 685, 687, 690–705, 707–710, 717, 720, 722–723, 728, 732, 734–735, 748–752
Strategies	
(KI 2) Solving interdisciplinary problems involves a variety of skills and strategies, including effective work habits; gathering and processing information; generating and analyzing ideas; realizing ideas; making connections among the common themes of mathematics, science, and technology; and presenting results.	69, 234, 257–259, 283, 298, 312–313, 315–316, 321, 324, 350–351, 408, 488–490, 665, 690–705, 707–710, 717, 720, 722, 734–735

New York Regents Core Curriculum

Correlation of Standards and Key Ideas for Physical Setting/Earth Science	Student Edition Pages
STANDARD 4 Students will understand and apply scientific concepts, principles, and theories pertaining to the physical setting and living environment and recognize the historical development of ideas in science.	
(KI 1) The Earth and celestial phenomena can be described by principles of relative motion and perspective.	
(PI 1.1) Explain complex phenomena, such as tides, variations in day length, solar insolation, apparent motion of the planets, and annual traverse of the constellations.	
(1.1a) Most objects in the solar system are in regular and predictable motion.	384, 402–403, 405, 409–410, 758–767, 771–785, 787–792, 796–799, 801–803, 815, 818
• These motions explain such phenomena as the day, the year, seasons, phases of the moon, eclipses, and tides.	384, 402–403, 405, 409–410, 758–767, 771–785, 787–792, 796–799, 801–803, 815, 818
• Gravity influences the motions of celestial objects. The force of gravity between two objects in the universe depends on their masses and the distance between them.	402–403, 405, 409–410, 764, 771, 774, 778, 803, 813–814
(1.1b) Nine planets move around the Sun in nearly circular orbits.	753, 771, 775–780, 783, 791, 798–799, 801–803, 813, 832, 859
• The orbit of each planet is an ellipse with the Sun located at one of the foci.	775–780, 791, 798–799, 801–803, 832
• Earth is orbited by one moon and many artificial satellites.	753, 771, 775, 783, 798–799, 813, 859
(1.1c) Earth's coordinate system of latitude and longitude, with the equator and prime meridian as reference lines, is based upon Earth's rotation and our observation of the Sun and stars.	27–29, 45, 362, 760–761, 771, 783, 815
(1.1d) Earth rotates on an imaginary axis at a rate of 15 degrees per hour. To people on Earth, this turning of the planet makes it seem as though the Sun, the moon, and the stars are moving around Earth once a day. Rotation provides a basis for our system of local time; meridians of longitude are the basis for time zones.	30–31, 45, 402, 758–759, 772, 774, 776, 783, 794–795, 813, 815, 818, 858
(1.1e) The Foucault pendulum and the Coriolis effect provide evidence of Earth's rotation.	404, 410, 758, 772, 783
(1.1f) Earth's changing position with regard to the Sun and the moon has noticeable effects.	362, 373–374, 402–403, 684, 690–692, 746, 759–762, 765–766, 771–773, 776, 809, 813, 815, 858
• Earth revolves around the Sun with its rotational axis tilted at 23.5 degrees to a line perpendicular to the plane of its orbit, with the North Pole aligned with Polaris.	362, 373–374, 746, 759–762, 771–773, 813, 858
• During Earth's one-year period of revolution, the tilt of its axis results in changes in the angle of incidence of the Sun's rays at a given latitude; these changes cause variation in the heating of the surface. This produces seasonal variation in weather.	362, 373–374, 402–403, 684, 690–692, 746, 759–762, 765–766, 771–773, 776, 809, 813, 815, 858

New York Regents Core Curriculum

Correlation of Standards and Key Ideas for Physical Setting/Earth Science	Student Edition Pages
(1.1g) Seasonal changes in the apparent positions of constellations provide evidence of Earth's revolution.	760–761, 770, 813
(1.1h) The Sun's apparent path through the sky varies with latitude and season.	668, 758–762, 771–773, 776, 810, 815
(1.1i) Approximately 70 percent of Earth's surface is covered by a relatively thin layer of water, which responds to the gravitational attraction of the moon and the Sun with a daily cycle of high and low tides.	385, 389–391, 400–403, 405, 409–410, 412, 438–439, 523, 669, 758, 764, 771, 783, 858
(PI 1.2) Describe current theories about the origin of the universe and solar system.	
(1.2a) The universe is vast and estimated to be over ten billion years old. The current theory is that the universe was created from an explosion called the Big Bang. Evidence for this theory includes:	774, 793, 801–803, 832, 836–837, 845–851, 854–857, 860–861
• cosmic background radiation.	847–851, 854–857, 860–861
• a red-shift (the Doppler effect) in the light from very distant galaxies.	845–846, 848–851, 854–857, 860–861
(1.2b) Stars form when gravity causes clouds of molecules to contract until nuclear fusion of light elements into heavier ones occurs. Fusion releases great amounts of energy over millions of years.	793–795, 804–805, 809, 811–812, 814–827, 829–838, 841–843, 846, 855–857, 859–861
• The stars differ from each other in size, temperature, and age.	793–795, 814–827, 829–831, 833–838, 859–861
• Our Sun is a medium-sized star within a spiral galaxy of stars known as the Milky Way. Our galaxy contains billions of stars, and the universe contains billions of such galaxies.	804–805, 830–838, 841–843, 846, 855–857, 859–861
(1.2c) Our solar system formed about five billion years ago from a giant cloud of gas and debris. Gravity caused Earth and the other planets to become layered according to density differences in their materials.	387, 409, 597–598, 756, 774, 780, 783–799, 801–803, 812, 832, 836–837, 839, 854–857, 861
• The characteristics of the planets of the solar system are affected by each planet's location in relationship to the Sun.	387, 409, 597–598, 756, 774, 780, 783–799, 801–803, 812, 832, 836–837, 839, 854–857, 861
• The terrestrial planets are small, rocky, and dense. The Jovian planets are large, gaseous, and of low density.	597–598, 756, 774, 780, 783–799, 801–803, 832, 854–857, 861
(1.2d) Asteroids, comets, and meteors are components of our solar system.	387, 409, 565, 579, 589, 596, 633–634, 754–755, 784, 789, 792–793, 795–799, 801, 803
• Impact events have been correlated with mass extinction and global climatic change.	634
• Impact craters can be identified in Earth's crust.	633
(1.2e) Earth's early atmosphere formed as a result of the outgassing of water vapor, carbon dioxide, nitrogen, and lesser amounts of other gases from its interior.	388, 409–410, 576, 584, 587–589, 598–599, 651, 664, 740, 783

Correlation of Standards and Key Ideas for Physical Setting/Earth Science	Student Edition Pages
(1.2f) Earth's oceans formed as a result of precipitation over millions of years. The presence of an early ocean is indicated by sedimentary rocks of marine origin, dating back about four billion years.	384, 387–388, 391, 409, 432, 438, 576, 588, 597–598
(1.2g) Earth has continuously been recycling water since the outgassing of water early in its history. This constant recirculation of water at and near Earth's surface is described by the hydrologic (water) cycle.	8, 24, 48, 210–221, 234–259, 261–263, 265–267, 270, 290–291, 388, 395, 420, 436, 588, 669, 679–680, 683, 692–693, 708–709
• Water is returned from the atmosphere to Earth's surface by precipitation. Water returns to the atmosphere by evaporation or transpiration from plants. A portion of the precipitation becomes runoff over the land or infiltrates into the ground to become stored in the soil or groundwater below the water table. Soil capillarity influences these processes.	8, 24, 210–212, 235, 238–259, 261–263, 266–267, 270, 290–291, 388, 395, 420, 436, 588, 669, 679–680, 683, 692–693, 708-709
• The amount of precipitation that seeps into the ground or runs off is influenced by climate, slope of the land, soil, rock type, vegetation, land use, and degree of saturation.	212–221, 235–237, 240–259, 261–263, 265
• Porosity, permeability, and water retention affect runoff and infiltration.	212–221, 234–235, 237, 240–259, 261–263
(1.2h) The evolution of life caused dramatic changes in the composition of Earth's atmosphere. Free oxygen did not form in the atmosphere until oxygen-producing organisms evolved.	576, 585–586, 588, 590–591, 597–598, 649–651, 781
(1.2i) The pattern of evolution of life-forms on Earth is at least partially preserved in the rock record.	22, 126–127, 132, 143, 554–556, 564, 566–569, 572–575, 577, 585–586, 591–593, 596–597, 599, 604, 609–611, 615–618, 620–623, 628–634, 636, 639–641, 645–650
• Fossil evidence indicates that a wide variety of life-forms has existed in the past and that most of these forms have become extinct.	22, 126–127, 132, 143, 554–556, 564, 566–569, 572–575, 577, 585–586, 592–593, 596–597, 599, 604, 609–611, 615–618, 620–623, 628–634, 636, 639, 645–650
• Human existence has been very brief compared to the expanse of geologic time.	577, 585, 591, 597, 640–641, 648–650

Correlation of Standards and Key Ideas for Physical Setting/Earth Science	Student Edition Pages
(1.2j) Geologic history can be reconstructed by observing sequences of rock types and fossils to correlate bedrock at various locations.	76, 120, 127, 132–134, 145, 369, 444–446, 450, 552–556, 558–563, 565–567, 573–578, 581, 585–586, 592–596, 604–606, 609, 613–615, 617, 620–623, 626, 628–631, 633, 636, 639–640, 646–650, 668, 687
• The characteristics of rocks indicate the processes by which they formed and the environments in which these processes took place.	76, 120, 127, 132–134, 145, 369, 444–446, 450, 552–556, 573–578, 581, 585–586, 604–606 613–614, 621–623, 648–650
• Fossils preserved in rocks provide information about past environmental conditions.	120, 127, 369, 445, 552–556, 566–567, 573–577, 592–593, 596, 609, 615, 617, 620, 621–623, 636, 646, 648–650
• Geologists have divided Earth history into time units based upon the fossil record.	552–556, 573–577, 604–606, 609, 613–615, 617, 620–621, 623, 626, 628–631, 633, 639–640, 647–650
• Age relationships among bodies of rocks can be determined using principles of original horizontality, superposition, inclusions, cross-cutting relationships, contact metamorphism, and unconformities. The presence of volcanic ash layers, index fossils, and meteoritic debris can provide additional information.	132, 552–556, 558–561, 573–577, 594–595, 648–649
• The regular rate of nuclear decay (half-life time period) of radioactive isotopes allows geologists to determine the absolute age of materials found in some rocks.	562–563, 565, 573, 578, 648–649, 668, 687
(KI 2) Many of the phenomena that we observe on Earth involve interactions among components of air, water, and land.	
(PI 2.1) Use the concepts of density and heat energy to explain observations of weather patterns, seasonal changes, and the movements of Earth's plates.	
(2.1a) Earth systems have internal and external sources of energy, both of which create heat.	101, 117, 154, 278, 295, 300, 303, 420, 436, 471–472, 578–580, 597–598, 670, 682, 684–688, 690–691, 693, 697–698, 707–709, 741, 743
(2.1b) The transfer of heat energy within the atmosphere, the hydrosphere, and Earth's interior results in the formation of regions of different densities. These density differences result in motion.	278, 288, 295–298, 300–301, 303–304, 331–332, 473, 476–479, 482–487, 580–581, 598, 690–692, 694, 708–709, 809–810
(2.1c) Weather patterns become evident when weather variables are observed, measured, and recorded. These variables include air temperature, air pressure, moisture (relative humidity and dewpoint), precipitation (rain, snow, hail, sleet, etc.), wind speed and direction, and cloud cover.	278–284, 287–289, 291, 295, 298–300, 304, 306, 312–321, 325–326, 328–346, 352–355, 359–362, 374, 376–379, 381, 412, 436, 439, 694, 809
(2.1d) Weather variables are measured using instruments such as thermometers, barometers, psychrometers, precipitation gauges, anemometers, and wind vanes.	312–316, 325–326, 378–379, 436
(2.1e) Weather variables are interrelated. For example:	281–292, 295–297, 307–311, 325–327, 329–340, 348–351, 355–357, 436
• temperature and humidity affect air pressure and probability of precipitation	281–292, 295–297, 311, 326–327, 329–335, 340, 348–349, 351, 355–357, 436
• air pressure gradient controls wind velocity	281–292, 295–296, 307–311, 325–327, 336–340, 348–351, 355–357, 436

New York Regents Core Curriculum

Correlation of Standards and Key Ideas for Physical Setting/Earth Science	Student Edition Pages
(2.1f) Air temperature, dewpoint, cloud formation, and precipitation are affected by the expansion and contraction of air due to vertical atmospheric movement.	240, 279–281, 285–286, 288–292, 295–297, 307, 325–326, 332–335, 337, 356–357, 368, 382–383, 436
(2.1g) Weather variables can be represented in a variety of formats including radar and satellite images, weather maps (including station models, isobars, and fronts), atmospheric cross-sections, and computer models.	298, 309–311, 314–319, 322–323, 325–327, 340, 352–353, 436, 439
(2.1h) Atmospheric moisture, temperature and pressure distributions; jet streams, wind; air masses and frontal boundaries; and the movement of cyclonic systems and associated tornadoes, thunderstorms, and hurricanes occur in observable patterns. Loss of property, personal injury, and loss of life can be reduced by effective emergency preparedness.	240, 436, 439
(2.1i) Seasonal changes can be explained using concepts of density and heat energy. These changes include the shifting of global temperature zones, the shifting of planetary wind and ocean current patterns, the occurrence of monsoons, hurricanes, flooding, and severe weather.	220–221, 294, 297, 302–306, 325–328, 334, 341–351, 355–357, 359–360, 365–366, 369–374, 381–383, 400, 405, 408–409, 411, 684, 690–692, 694, 697, 708–709, 810
(2.1j) Properties of Earth's internal structure (crust, mantle, inner core, and outer core) can be inferred from the analysis of the behavior of seismic waves (including velocity and refraction).	462, 487, 498–505, 509, 514–515, 518–521, 525, 543, 547, 597
• Analysis of seismic waves allows the determination of the location of earthquake epicenters and the measurement of earthquake magnitude; this analysis leads to the inference that Earth's interior is composed of layers that differ in composition and states of matter.	462, 487, 498–505, 509, 514–515, 518–521, 525, 543, 547, 597
(2.1k) The outward transfer of Earth's internal heat drives convective circulation in the mantle that moves the lithospheric plates comprising Earth's surface.	420, 427, 460–462, 467, 546–547, 549, 580–581, 597, 708–709
(2.1l) The lithosphere consists of separate plates that ride on the more fluid asthenosphere and move slowly in relationship to one another, creating convergent, divergent, and transform plate boundaries. These motions indicate Earth is a dynamic geologic system.	8, 24–25, 48, 422, 434–435, 442–444, 447–448, 455–456, 459, 461, 463, 467–469, 472, 478–481, 484–485, 487–495, 513, 525, 528–535, 537, 542–549, 581–583, 598–599, 648, 693
• These plate boundaries are the sites of most earthquakes, volcanoes, and young mountain ranges.	8, 442–444, 455–456, 459, 461, 463, 467–469, 472, 478–481, 485, 487, 491–495, 528–534, 537, 542–549, 582–583, 598–599, 693
• Compared to continental crust, ocean crust is thinner and denser. New ocean crust continues to form at mid-ocean ridges.	422, 434–435, 447–448, 523, 535, 537, 543–549, 581, 599
• Earthquakes and volcanoes present geologic hazards to humans. Loss of property, personal injury, and loss of life can be reduced by effective emergency preparedness.	484, 487–490, 492, 494–495, 513, 548

New York Regents Core Curriculum

Correlation of Standards and Key Ideas for Physical Setting/Earth Science	Student Edition Pages
(2.1m) Many processes of the rock cycle are consequences of plate dynamics. These include the production of magma (and subsequent igneous rock formation and contact metamorphism) at both subduction and rifting regions, regional metamorphism within subduction zones, and the creation of major depositional basins through down-warping of the crust.	98, 101, 422, 427, 451, 460–461, 467, 470–475, 491–493, 522, 530–531, 535–536, 546–547, 549, 580, 582, 597, 607, 647, 687
(2.1n) Many of Earth's surface features such as mid-ocean ridges/rifts, trenches/subduction zones/island arcs, mountain ranges (folded, faulted, and volcanic), hot spots, and the magnetic and age patterns in surface bedrock are a consequence of forces associated with plate motion and interaction.	422–423, 425–428, 433–435, 444, 449–454, 456–459, 461, 463, 467–470, 476–481, 486–487, 491–493, 495–497, 499, 509–510, 512, 518–521, 523, 527–539, 542–549, 557, 582–583, 598–599, 602, 607, 609, 614–615, 621–623, 625–627, 635–638, 645–647
(2.1o) Plate motions have resulted in global changes in geography, climate, and the patterns of organic evolution.	422–426, 433–435, 442, 455, 459, 463, 467–469, 487, 490, 528, 532–534, 542–548, 557, 581–583, 600–601, 611, 621, 624–626, 635, 638, 647, 687
(2.1p) Landforms are the result of the interaction of tectonic forces and the processes of weathering, erosion, and deposition.	267, 281, 413–414, 418, 421, 423, 425, 433–435, 523, 525, 527–528, 580, 582, 597–599, 608, 612, 626, 636–637, 645, 651
(2.1q) Topographic maps represent landforms through the use of contour lines that are isolines connecting points of equal elevation. Gradients and profiles can be determined from changes in elevation over a given distance.	523–524
(2.1r) Climate variations, structure, and characteristics of bedrock influence the development of landscape features including mountains, plateaus, plains, valleys, ridges, escarpments, and stream drainage patterns.	158–160, 170–171, 173, 178, 192, 197, 214–215, 220, 222–225, 227–229, 235–237, 543–545, 635
(2.1s) Weathering is the physical and chemical breakdown of rocks at or near Earth's surface. Soils are the result of weathering and biological activity over long periods of time.	152–159, 161, 167–168, 173–175, 177–178, 264, 267
(2.1t) Natural agents of erosion, generally driven by gravity, remove, transport, and deposit weathered rock particles. Each agent of erosion produces distinctive changes in the material that it transports and creates characteristic surface features and landscapes. In certain erosional situations, loss of property, personal injury, and loss of life can be reduced by effective emergency preparedness.	152–153, 162–163, 168, 176–179, 181–182, 185–193, 196, 200–205, 207–208, 221, 264–265, 267, 414, 416–419, 424, 428, 433–435, 526, 602, 647, 660, 662, 679

New York Regents Core Curriculum

Correlation of Standards and Key Ideas for Physical Setting/Earth Science	Student Edition Pages
(2.1u) The natural agents of erosion include:	124, 164–166, 168, 176–189, 191–208, 215, 217–219, 222–225, 227, 232–233, 235–237, 264–265, 267, 414–419, 428, 433–435, 636, 647
• *Streams (running water):* Gradient, discharge, and channel shape influence a stream's velocity and the erosion and deposition of sediments. Sediments transported by streams tend to become rounded as a result of abrasion. Stream features include V-shaped valleys, deltas, flood plains, and meanders. A watershed is the area drained by a stream and its tributaries.	124, 164, 168, 177–179, 215, 217–219, 222–225, 227, 232–233, 235–237, 264, 267, 647
• *Glaciers (moving ice):* Glacial erosional processes include the formation of U-shaped valleys, parallel scratches, and grooves in bedrock. Glacial features include moraines, drumlins, kettle lakes, finger lakes, and outwash plains.	124, 165, 168, 177–180, 198–203, 206–208, 264–265, 267, 636
• *Wave Action:* Erosion and deposition cause changes in shoreline features, including beaches, sandbars, and barrier islands. Wave action rounds sediments as a result of abrasion. Waves approaching a shoreline move sand parallel to the shore within the zone of breaking waves.	124, 164, 176, 178–179, 264, 267, 414–419, 428, 433–435
• *Wind:* Erosion of sediments by wind is most common in arid climates and along shorelines. Wind-generated features include dunes and sand-blasted bedrock.	124, 164–166, 168, 176–180, 191–197, 207–208, 264–265, 267
• *Mass Movement:* Earth materials move downslope under the influence of gravity.	124, 177–189, 204–205, 207–208, 264, 267
(2.1v) Patterns of deposition result from a loss of energy within the transporting system and are influenced by the size, shape, and density of the transported particles. Sediment deposits may be sorted or unsorted.	163, 202, 216, 226, 235–237, 264, 415–417, 428, 603, 636
(2.1w) Sediments of inorganic and organic origin often accumulate in depositional environments. Sedimentary rocks form when sediments are compacted and/or cemented after burial or as the result of chemical precipitation from seawater.	231, 428, 602, 604, 606, 613, 621–623, 627, 636, 686–687, 689, 696–697, 707–709

Correlation of Standards and Key Ideas for Physical Setting/Earth Science	Student Edition Pages
(PI 2.2) Explain how incoming solar radiation, ocean currents, and land masses affect weather and climate.	

(2.2a) Insolation (solar radiation) heats Earth's surface and atmosphere unequally due to variations in:	270–271, 275–277, 295–296, 300, 303–305, 327, 341, 355, 357–358, 362–363, 367–375, 381–383, 436–437, 683–684, 690–694, 697, 707–708, 807, 809–810
• the intensity caused by differences in atmospheric transparency and angle of incidence, which vary with time of day, latitude, and season	270–271, 275–277, 295–296, 300, 304, 341, 355, 357–358, 362–363, 369–375, 381–383, 436–437, 683–684, 690–694, 697, 707–708, 807, 809–810
• characteristics of the materials absorbing the energy such as color, texture, transparency, state of matter, and specific heat	271, 276, 296, 304, 367–368, 375, 381–383, 436–437, 690–694, 697, 707, 809–810
• duration, which varies with seasons and latitude.	303–305, 327, 362–363, 370, 375, 381–383, 436–437, 690–694, 697, 707
(2.2b) The transfer of heat energy within the atmosphere, the hydrosphere, and Earth's surface occurs as the result of radiation, convection, and conduction.	9, 272, 275–277, 295–297, 301, 303–305, 327, 329–330, 333, 341–346, 356–357, 362, 366–377, 381–384, 403–405, 408–411, 436, 460, 467, 587, 684, 690, 693–694, 697, 707–709, 807, 810, 812
• Heating of Earth's surface and atmosphere by the Sun drives convection within the atmosphere and oceans, producing winds and ocean currents.	9, 272, 275–277, 295–297, 301, 303–305, 327, 329–330, 333, 341–346, 356–357, 384, 403–405, 408–411, 436, 460, 467, 587
(2.2c) A location's climate is influenced by latitude, proximity to large bodies of water, ocean currents, prevailing winds, vegetative cover, elevation, and mountain ranges.	271, 275–277, 295, 297, 300–301, 304–305, 311, 325–327, 341–346, 356–358, 361–374, 378–379, 381–384, 403–405, 408–411, 437, 439, 684, 690–691, 694, 697, 708–709
(2.2d) Temperature and precipitation patterns are altered by:	320–321, 341, 358, 369–377, 380–383, 411, 437, 664, 666–667, 724–728, 737
• natural events such as El Niño and volcanic eruptions	320–321, 341, 358, 369–377, 381–383, 411, 437
• human influences including deforestation, urbanization, and the production of greenhouse gases such as carbon dioxide and methane.	358, 375–377, 380–383, 664, 666–667, 724–728, 737
(KI 3) Matter is made up of particles whose properties determine the observable characteristics of matter and its reactivity.	
(PI 3.1) Explain the properties of materials in terms of the arrangement and properties of the atoms that compose them.	
(3.1a) Minerals have physical properties determined by their chemical composition and crystal structure.	52–56, 59, 67, 76–79, 82–97, 99–113, 117–119, 122, 132, 135–149, 156–160, 174–175, 177, 393–394, 451–452, 621–622, 661
• Minerals can be identified by well-defined physical and chemical properties, such as cleavage, fracture, color, density, hardness, streak, luster, crystal shape, and reaction with acid.	52–56, 59, 67, 76–79, 82–89, 91–97, 99–113, 117–119, 122, 135–147, 149, 156–160, 174–175, 177, 393–394, 621, 661
• Chemical composition and physical properties determine how minerals are used by humans.	53, 76–79, 89–95, 132, 136–137, 145–145, 147–148, 177, 451–452, 622, 661

Correlation of Standards and Key Ideas for Physical Setting/Earth Science	Student Edition Pages
(3.1b) Minerals are formed inorganically by the process of crystallization as a result of specific environmental conditions. These include:	52, 58, 65, 67, 70, 76–80, 83, 95–96, 100–106, 114–115, 117–119, 124–125, 128, 130, 132–140, 143–149, 429, 476, 567, 661, 681
• cooling and solidification of magma	52, 76–80, 83, 95–96, 100–106, 114–115, 117–119, 133–140, 143–147, 476, 661, 681
• precipitation from water caused by such processes as evaporation, chemical reactions, and temperature changes	52, 58, 65, 70, 76–80, 83, 95–96, 101–106, 117–119, 124–125, 128, 130, 132–140, 143–145, 148–149, 429, 661, 681
• rearrangement of atoms in existing minerals subjected to conditions of high temperature and pressure	52, 58, 67, 76–80, 83, 95–96, 101–106, 117–119, 124–125, 133–140, 143–145, 148–149, 567, 661, 681
(3.1c) Rocks are usually composed of one or more minerals.	52, 53, 55, 58–59, 68, 70, 76, 80–81, 95–96, 98–100, 102–113, 116–120, 122, 128–129, 131–132, 134–141, 143–149, 155, 686–689, 695–697, 707–709
• Rocks are classified by their origin, mineral composition, and texture.	53, 55, 68, 70, 76, 80–81, 95–96, 98–100, 102–113, 116–120, 128–129, 132, 134–141, 143–149
• Conditions that existed when a rock formed can be inferred from the rock's mineral content and texture.	52, 58–59, 70, 95–96, 98–100 ,102–113, 117–120, 128–129, 131–132, 136–141, 143–145, 148
• The properties of rocks determine how they are used and also influence land usage by humans.	70, 98, 116–120, 122, 128–129, 131–132, 136–137, 139, 145, 147–149, 155, 686–689, 695–697, 707–709

Correlation to Physical Setting/Earth Science Core Curriculum

Earth Science: Geology, the Environment, and the Universe Student Edition

Contents	Pages	New York Regents Standards
Chapter 1 The Nature of Science		
1.1 Earth Science	4–10	St 1 Science KI 1 & 2, St 2 KI 1, St 4 KI 1.2 g, 2.1l, & 2.2b, St 6 KI 1 & 5
1.2 Methods of Scientists	11–16	St 1 Math KI 1 & Science KI 1
1.3 Communicating in Science	17–25	St 1 Math KI 1 & Science KI 1, St 4 KI 1.2g, 1.2l, and 2.1l, St 6 KI 1 & 2
Chapter 2 Mapping Our World		
2.1 Latitude and Longitude	26–31	St 1 Math KI 1, 2, 3, & Engin KI 1, St 2 KI 1, St 4 KI 1.1c & 1.1d, St 6 KI 2 & 3
2.2 Types of Maps	32–36	St 1 Math KI 1, 2, 3, & Engin KI 1, St 6 KI 2 & 3, St 7 KI 1
2.3 Remote Sensing	37–47	St 1 Math KI 1, 2, 3, & Engin KI 1, St 2 KI 1 & 3, St 4 KI 1.1c & 1.1d, St 6 KI 2 & 3, St 7 KI 1
Chapter 3 Matter and Atomic Structure		
3.1 What are elements?	52–59	St 1 Math KI 2, & Science KI 3, St 4 KI 3.1a, 3.1b, & 3.1c
3.2 How Atoms Combine	60–66	St 1 Math KI 2, St 4 KI 3.1b, St 6 KI 5
3.3 States of Matter	67–75	St 1 Math KI 1, 2, 3, Science KI 1 & 2, St 2 KI 1, St 4 KI 3.1a, 3.1b, & 3.1c, St 6 KI 5, St 7 KI 2
Chapter 4 Minerals		
4.1 What is a mineral?	76–83	St 1 Math KI 2 & Science KI 3, St 4 KI 1.2j, 3.1a, 3.1b, & 3.1c, St 6 KI 1 & 2
4.2 Identifying Minerals	84–97	St 1 Math KI 1, 2, 3, Science KI 1, 2, & 3, St 4 KI 3.1a, 3.1b, & 3.1c, St 6 KI 1 & 6, St 7 KI 1
Chapter 5 Igneous Rocks		
5.1 What are igneous rocks?	98–106	St 1 Science KI 1, 2, & 3, St 4 KI 2.1a, 2.1m, 3.1a, 3.1b, & 3.1c, St 6 KI 1, 2, 4, & 5
5.2 Classifying Igneous Rocks	107–119	St 1 Math KI 1, 2, 3, Science KI 1, 2, 3, & Engin KI 1, St 4 KI 2.1a, 3.1a, 3.1b, & 3.1c, St 6 KI 1, 2, & 5
Chapter 6 Sedimentary and Metamorphic Rocks		
6.1 Formation of Sedimentary Rocks	120–127	St 1 Science KI 1, 2, & 3, St 4 KI 1.2i, 1.2j, 3.1a, 3.1b, & 3.1c, St 6 KI 2 & 5
6.2 Types of Sedimentary Rocks	128–132	St 1 Math KI 2, 3, & Science KI 1, St 4 KI 1.2i, 1.2j, 3.1a, 3.1b, & 3.1c, St 6 KI 5, St 7 KI 1
6.3 Metamorphic Rocks	133–145	St 1 Math KI 3, Science KI 1, 2, & 3, St 4 KI 1.2i, 1.2j, 3.1a, 3.1b, & 3.1c, St 6 KI 1 & 5, St 7 KI 1
Chapter 7 Weathering, Erosion, and Soil		
7.1 Weathering	152–161	St 1 Math KI 2, Science KI 1, 2, & 3, St 4 KI 2.1a, 2.1r, 2.1s, 2.1t, 3.1a, & 3.1c, St 6 KI 1, 2, 4, & 5
7.2 Erosion and Deposition	162–166	St 1 Science KI 1, 2, 3, & Engin KI 1, St 4 KI 2.1t & 2.1v, St 6 KI 1, 2, 4, & 5
7.3 Formation of Soil	167–179	St 1 Math KI 1, 2, 3, Science KI 1, 2, & 3, St 4 KI 2.1r, 2.1s, 2.1t, 2.1u, & 3.1a, St 6 KI 1, 2, 3, 4, 5, & 6, St 7 KI 1

Correlation to Physical Setting/Earth Science Core Curriculum

Earth Science: Geology, the Environment, and the Universe Student Edition

Contents	Pages	New York Regents Standards
Chapter 8 Mass Movements, Wind, and Glaciers		
8.1 Mass Movements at Earth's Surface	180–190	St 1 Science KI 1, 2, & 3, St 4 KI 2.1t & 2.1u, St 6 KI 1, 2, 4, & 5, St 7 KI 1
8.2 Wind	191–197	St 4 KI 2.1r, 2.1t, & 2.1u, St 6 KI 1, 2, 4, 5, & 6
8.3 Glaciers	198–209	St 1 Math KI 1, 2, 3, Science KI 1, 2, & 3, St 2 KI 1, 2, & 3, St 4 KI 2.1t, 2.1u, & 2.1v, St 6 KI 1, 2, 3, 4, 5, & 6, St 7 KI 1
Chapter 9 Surface Water		
9.1 Surface Water Movement	210–221	St 1 Math KI 1, 2, 3, Science KI 1, 2, & 3, St 2 KI 3, St 4 KI 1.2g, 2.1i, 2.1r, 2.1u, & 2.1v, St 6 KI 1, 2, & 5
9.2 Stream Development	222–227	St 1 Math KI 1, 2, & 3, St 4 KI 2.1r, 2.1u, & 2.1v, St 6 KI 1, 2, 4, & 5
9.3 Lakes and Freshwater Wetlands	228–237	St 1 Math KI 2, Science KI 1, 2, & 3, St 2 KI 3, St 4 KI 1.2g, 2.1r, 2.1u, 2.1v, & 2.1w, St 6 KI 1, 2, 4, 5, & 6, St 7 KI 2
Chapter 10 Groundwater		
10.1 Movement and Storage of Groundwater	238–243	St 1 Math KI 1, 2, 3, Science KI 1, 2, 3, & Engin KI 1, St 4 KI 1.2g, 2.1f, & 2.1h, St 6 KI 1, 2, & 5
10.2 Groundwater Erosion and Deposition	244–248	St 1 Math KI 1, 2, & 3, St 4 KI 1.2g, St 6 KI 1, 2, & 5
10.3 Groundwater Systems	249–263	St 1 Math KI 1, 2, 3, Science KI 1, 2, 3, & Engin KI 1, St 4 KI 1.2g, St 6 KI 1, 2, 5, & 6, St 7 KI 1 & 2
Chapter 11 Atmosphere		
11.1 Atmospheric Basics	270–277	St 1 Science KI 2 & 3, St 4 KI 1.2g, 2.2a, 2.2b, & 2.2c, St 6 KI 1
11.2 State of Atmosphere	278–284	St 1 Math KI 1, 2, 3, Science KI 1, 2, & Engin KI 1, St 4 KI 2.1a, 2.1b, 2.1c, 2.1e, & 2.1f, St 7 KI 1 & 2
11.3 Moisture in the Atmosphere	285–297	St 1 Science KI 1, 2, & 3, St 4 KI 1.2g, 2.1a, 2.1b, 2.1c, 2.1e, 2.1f, 2.1i, 2.2a, 2.2b, & 2.2c, St 6 KI 1, 2, & 5, St 7 KI 1
Chapter 12 Meteorology		
12.1 The Causes of Weather	298–304	St 1 Math KI 1, Science KI 1, 2, & 3, St 4 KI 2.1a, 2.1b, 2.1c, 2.1g, 2.1i, 2.2a, 2.2b, & 2.2c, St 6 KI 1, 2, 4, & 5, St 7 KI 2
12.2 Weather Systems	305–311	St 1 Math KI 1 & 2, St 2 KI 1, St 4 KI 2.1c, 2.1e, 2.1f, 2.1g, & 2.2c, St 6 KI 1 & 2, St 7 KI 1
12.3 Gathering Weather Data	312–316	St 1 Engin KI 1, St 2 KI 1, 2, & 3, St 4 KI 2.1c, 2.1d, & 2.1g, St 6 KI 1 & 2, St 7 KI 1 & 2
12.4 Weather Analysis	317–327	St 1 Math KI 1, 2, 3, & Engin KI 1, St 2 KI 1, 2, & 3, St 4 KI 2.1c, 2.1d, 2.1e, 2.1f, 2.1g, 2.1i, 2.2b, 2.2c, & 2.2d, St 6 KI 1, 2, 3, 4, & 5, St 7 KI 1 & 2

Correlation to Physical Setting/Earth Science Core Curriculum

Earth Science: Geology, the Environment, and the Universe Student Edition

Contents	Pages	New York Regents Standards
Chapter 13 The Nature of Storms		
13.1 Thunderstorms	328–333	St 1 Math KI 2, Science KI 1, & 3, St 4 KI 2.1b, 2.1c, 2.1e, 2.1f, 2.1i, & 2.2b, St 6 KI 1, 2, 4, & 5
13.2 Severe Weather	334–340	St 2 KI 3, St 4 KI 2.1c, 2.1e, 2.1f, 2.1i, & 2.2b, St 6 KI 1, 4, & 5, St 7 KI 1
13.3 Tropical Storms	341–346	St 1 Math KI 1, 2, & 3, St 2 KI 3, St 4 KI 2.1b, 2.1c, 2.1i, 2.2a, 2.2b, 2.2c, & 2.2d, St 6 KI 1 & 5, St 7 KI 1
13.4 Recurring Weather	347–357	St 1 Math KI 1, 2, 3, Science KI 1, 2, & 3, St 2 KI 1, 2, & 3, St 4 KI 2.1c, 2.1e, 2.1f, 2.1g, 2.1i, 2.2a, 2.2b, 2.2c, & 2.2d, St 6 KI 1, 4, & 5, St 7 KI 1 & 2
Chapter 14 Climate		
14.1 What is climate?	358–363	St 1 Math KI 1, 2, 3, Science KI 1, 2, & 3, St 4 KI 1.1c, 1.1f, 2.1c, 2.1i, 2.2a, 2.2b, 2.2c, & 2.2d, St 6 KI 5, St 7 KI 1
14.2 Climate Classification	364–368	St 1 Math KI 2 & 3, St 4 KI 2.1f, 2.1i, 2.2a, 2.2b, & 2.2c, St 6 KI 1 & 2
14.3 Climatic Changes	369–374	St 4 KI 1.1f, 1.2j, 2.1c, 2.1i, 2.2a, 2.2b, 2.2c, & 2.2d, St 6 KI 1, 2, & 5
14.4 The Human Factor	375–383	St 1 Science KI 1, 2, 3, & Engin KI 1, St 4 KI 2.1c, 2.1d, 2.1f, 2.1i, 2.2a, 2.2b, 2.2c, & 2.2d, St 6 KI 1, 2, & 5
Chapter 15 Physical Oceanography		
15.1 The Oceans	384–391	St 1 Math KI 1, 2, 3, Science KI 1, 2, & 3, St 2 KI 1, 2, & 3, St 4 KI 1.1a, 1.1i, 1.2c, 1.2d, 1.2e, 1.2f, 1.2g, 2.2b, & 2.2c, St 6 KI 1, 2, 3, 4, & 5, St 7 KI 1
15.2 Seawater	392–398	St 1 Math KI 1, 2, 3, & Science KI 3, St 2 KI 1, 2, & 3, St 4 KI 1.2g & 3.1a, St 6 KI 4 & 5, St 7 KI 1
15.3 Ocean Movements	399–411	St 1 Math KI 1, 2, Science KI 1, 2, & 3, St 2 KI 1, St 4 KI 1.1a, 1.1d, 1.1e, 1.1f, 1.1i, 1.2a, 1.2d, 1.2e, 1.2f, 2.1i, 2.2b, 2.2c, & 2.2d, St 6 KI 1, 2, & 5, St 7 KI 1 & 2
Chapter 16 The Marine Environment		
16.1 Shoreline Features	412–421	St 1 Math KI 1 & Science KI 3, St 4 KI 1.1i, 1.2g, 2.1a, 2.1c, 2.1p, 2.1t, 2.1u, & 2.1v
16.2 The Seafloor	422–435	St 1 Math KI 3, Science KI 1, 2, & 3, St 4 KI 1.2f, 2.1k, 2.1l, 2.1m, 2.1n, 2.1o, 2.1p, 2.1t, 2.1u, 2.1v, 2.1w, & 3.1b, St 6 KI 2, 3, & 5
Chapter 17 Plate Tectonics		
17.1 Drifting Continents	442–447	St 1 Science KI 1, St 4 KI 1.2j, 2.1l, 2.1n, & 2.1o, St 6 KI 3
17.2 Seafloor Spreading	448–454	St 4 KI 2.1l, 2.1m, 2.1n, & 3.1a
17.3 Theory of Plate Tectonics	455–459	St 4 KI 2.1l, 2.1n, & 2.1o, St 6 KI 2 & 3
17.4 Causes of Plate Motion	460–469	St 1 Math KI 1, 2, & 3, St 2 KI 1, St 4 KI 2.1j, 2.1k, 2.1l, 2.1m, 2.1n, 2.1o, & 2.2b, St 6 KI 2 & 3, St 7 KI 1

Correlation to Physical Setting/Earth Science Core Curriculum

Earth Science: Geology, the Environment, and the Universe Student Edition

Contents	Pages	New York Regents Standards
Chapter 18 Volcanic Activity		
18.1 Magma	470–475	St 1 Science KI 1, 2, & 3, St 2 KI 1, 2, & 3, St 4 KI 2.1a, 2.1b, 2.1l, 2.1m, & 2.1n, St 6 KI 1, 2, & 5
18.2 Intrusive Activity	476–479	St 4 KI 2.1b, 2.1l, 2.1n, & 3.1b, St 6 KI 1 & 5
18.3 Volcanoes	480–493	St 1 Math KI 1, 2, 3, & Science KI 1, St 2 KI 1 & 3, St 4 KI 2.1b, 2.1j, 2.1l, 2.1m, 2.1n, 2.1o, & 2.1p, St 6 KI 1, 2, 4, & 5, St 7 KI 2
Chapter 19 Earthquakes		
19.1 Forces Within the Earth	494–499	St 1 Science KI 1 & 2, St 4 KI 2.1j, 2.1l, & 2.1n, St 6 KI 2
19.2 Seismic Waves and Earth's Interior	500–504	St 4 KI 2.1j, St 6 KI 2 & 3
19.3 Measuring and Locating Earthquakes	505–510	St 4 KI 2.1j & 2.1n, St 6 KI 2, 3, & 5
19.4 Earthquakes and Society	511–521	St 1 Math KI 1, 3, Engin KI 1, St 4 KI 2.1j, 2.1l, & 2.1n, St 6 KI 2, 3, & 5
Chapter 20 Mountain Building		
20.1 Crust-Mantle Relationships	522–527	St 1 Math KI 2 & 3, St 4 KI 1.1i, 2.1j, 2.1l, 2.1n, 2.1o, 2.1p, 2.1q, & 2.1t, St 6 KI 2, 3, & 4
20.2 Convergent-Boundary Mountains	528–534	St 4 KI 2.1l, 2.1m, 2.1n, 2.1o, & 2.1p, St 6 KI 2, 3, 4, & 5
20.3 Other Types of Mountains	535–545	St 1 Science KI 1 & Math KI 3, St 2 KI 1, St 4 KI 2.1l, 2.1m, 2.1n, 2.1o 2.1p, & 2.1r, St 6 KI 2, 4, & 6
Chapter 21 Fossils and the Rock Record		
21.1 The Geologic Time Scale	552–556	St 1 Science KI 1, St 4 KI 1.2i & 1.2j, St 6 KI 2
21.2 Relative Age-Dating of Rocks	557–561	St 1 Science KI 1, 2, & 3, St 4 KI 1.2j, 2.1n, & 2.1o, St 6 KI 2
21.3 Absolute-Age Dating of Rocks	562–565	St 4 KI 1.2d, 1.2i, & 1.2j
21.4 Remains of Organisms in the Rock Record	566–575	St 4 KI 1.2i, 1.2j, & 3.1b, St 6 KI 3
Chapter 22 The Precambrian Earth		
22.1 The Early Earth	576–579	St 1 Science KI 1, 2 & 3, St 4 KI 1.2d, 1.2e, 1.2f, 1.2h, 1.2i, 1.2j, & 2.1a, St 6 KI 2 & 3
22.2 Formation of the Crust and Continents	580–583	St 4 KI 1.2j, 2.1a, 2.1b, 2.1k, 2.1l, 2.1m, 2.1n, 2.1o, & 2.1p
22.3 Formation of the Atmosphere and Oceans	584–588	St 1 Math KI 2 & 3, St 4 KI 1.2e, 1.2f, 1.2g, 1.2h, 1.2i, 1.2j, & 2.2c, St 6 KI 2 & 3
22.4 Early Life on Earth	589–599	St 1 Science KI 3 & Math KI 3, St 4 KI 1.2c, 1.2d, 1.2e, 1.2f, 1.2h, 1.2i, 1.2j, & 2.1a, 2.1b, 2.1k, 2.1l, 2.1m, 2.1n, & 2.1p, St 6 KI 2 & 3
Chapter 23 The Paleozoic Era		
23.1 The Early Paleozoic	600–604	St 1 Science KI 2, St 4 KI 2.1l, 2.1n, 2.1o, 2.1t, 2.1v, & 2.1w, St 6 KI 2 & 3
23.2 The Middle Paleozoic	605–611	St 1 Math KI 1, St 4 KI 1.2i, 1.2j, 2.1m, 2.1n, 2.1o, 2.1w, & 3.1a, St 6 KI 2 & 3
23.3 The Late Paleozoic	612–623	St 1 Science KI 1, St 4 KI 1.2i, 1.2j, 2.1n, 2.1w, & 3.1a, St 6 KI 2 & 3

Correlation to Physical Setting/Earth Science Core Curriculum

Earth Science: Geology, the Environment, and the Universe Student Edition

Contents	Pages	New York Regents Standards
Chapter 24 The Mesozoic and Cenozoic Eras		
24.1 Mesozoic Paleogeography	624–627	St 1 Science KI 1, 2, & 3, St 4 KI 1.2j, 2.1n, 2.1o, 2.1p, & 2.1w, St 6 KI 2 & 3
24.2 Mesozoic Life	628–634	St 4 KI 1.2i & 1.2j, St 6 KI 5
24.3 Cenozoic Paleogeography	635–638	St 1 Math KI 2 & 3, St 4 KI 1.2l, 1.2j, 2.1n, 2.1o, 2.1p, 2.1r, 2.1u, 2.1v, & 2.1w, St 6 KI 2 & 3
24.4 Cenozoic Life	639–647	St 1 Math KI 2, Science KI 1, & 2, St 4 KI 1.2i, 1.2j, 2.1m, 2.1n, 2.1o, 2.1p, 2.1t, & 2.1u
Chapter 25 Earth Resources		
25.1 What are resources?	654–658	St 1 Math KI 1 & Science KI 2, St 6 KI 2, 4, & 5
25.2 Land Resources	659–663	St 4 KI 2.1t, 3.1a, & 3.1b, St 6 KI 4 & 6, St 7 KI 1
25.3 Air Resources	664–668	St 1 Math KI 1, 2, & 3, St 4 KI 1.2e & 2.2d, St 6 KI 2, 4, & 5, St 7 KI 2
25.4 Water Resources	669–681	St 1 Science KI 1, 2, & Engin KI 1, St 4 KI 1.1i, 1.2g, 2.1a, & 3.1b, St 6 KI 1, 2, 4, & 6, St 7 KI 1
Chapter 26 Energy Resources		
26.1 Conventional Energy Resources	682–689	St 1 Science KI 1, 2, & 3, St 4 KI 1.1f, 1.2g, 1.2j, 2.1a, 2.1i, 2.1m, 2.1o, 2.1w, 2.2a, 2.2b, 2.2c, & 3.1c, St 6 KI 1, 2, 4, 5, & 6, St 7 KI 1
26.2 Alternative Energy Resources	690–697	St 1 Math KI 1, 3, & Engin KI 1, St 4 KI 1.1f, 1.2g, 2.1a, 2.1b, 2.1c, 2.1i, 2.1l, 2.1w, 2.2a, 2.2b, 2.2c, & 3.1c, St 6 KI 1, 5, & 6, St 7 KI 1 & 2
26.3 Conservation of Energy Resources	698–709	St 1 Math KI 1, 2, 3, Science KI 1, 2, 3, & Engin KI 1, St 2 KI 1, 2, & 3, St 4 KI 1.2g, 2.1a, 2.1b, 2.1i, 2.1k, 2.1w, 2.2a, 2.2b, 2.2c, & 3.1c, St 6 KI 1, 2, 4, 5, & 6, St 7 KI 1 & 2
Chapter 27 Human Impact on Earth Resources		
27.1 Populations and the Use of Natural Resources	710–715	St 1 Science KI 1 & 2, St 6 KI 1, 2, 5, & 6, St 7 KI 1 & 2
27.2 Human Impact on Land Resources	716–723	St 1 Engin KI 1, St 6 KI 1, 2, 4, 5, & 6, St 7 KI 1 & 2
27.3 Human Impact on Air Resources	724–729	St 1 Engin KI 1, St 4 KI 2.2d, St 6 KI 2 & 5, St 7 KI 1
27.4 Human Impact on Water Resources	730–739	St 1 Science KI 1 & Engin KI 1, St 4 KI 2.2d, St 6 KI 2, 5, & 6, St 7 KI 1 & 2
Chapter 28 The Sun-Earth-Moon System		
28.1 Tools of Astronomy	747–752	St 1 Math KI & Engin KI 1, St 4 KI 1.1f, St 6 KI 3, St 7 KI 1
28.2 The Moon	753–757	St 1 Science KI 1, St 4 KI 1b, St 4 KI 1.1b, 1.2c, & 1.2d, St 6 KI 2
28.3 The Sun-Earth-Moon System	758–773	St 1 Math KI 1, 2, 3, & Science KI 2, St 4 KI 1.1a, 1.1c, 1.1d, 1.1e, 1.1f, 1.1g, 1.1h, & 1.1i, St 6 KI 2, 3, 4, & 5

Correlation to Physical Setting/Earth Science Core Curriculum

Teacher Wraparound Edition

Glencoe Science

EARTH SCIENCE

*Geology, the Environment,
and the Universe*

New York Physical Setting/
Earth Science Edition

NATIONAL
GEOGRAPHIC
SOCIETY

ny.earthgeu.com

McGraw Hill **Glencoe**

New York, New York   Columbus, Ohio   Chicago, Illinois   Peoria, Illinois   Woodland Hills, California

Earth Science: Geology, the Environment, and the Universe

Teacher Classroom Resources

Visit the Earth Science Web site at <u>earthgeu.com</u>

You'll find:

Online Student Edition, Chapter Resources,
Extending the Content, Problem of the Week,
Science Fair Ideas, NASA's Picture ofthe Day,
Internet Geolabs, Web Links,
Interactive Tutor, Online Quizzes
and much more!

NATIONAL GEOGRAPHIC The National Geographic features were designed and developed by the National Geographic Society's Education Division. Copyright ©National Geographic Society. The name "National Geographic Society" and the Yellow Border Rectangle are trademarks of the Society, and their use, without prior written permission, is strictly prohibited.

Send all inquiries to:
Glencoe/McGraw-Hill
8787 Orion Place
Columbus, OH 43240

Special Consultants:
David R. McCleary, B.S., Inclusion Consultant
Eric J. Pyle, Ph.D., Misconceptions Consultant
Kenneth R. Roy, Ph.D., Safety Consultant

ISBN 0-07-868352-1
Printed in the United States of America.

1 2 3 4 5 6 7   071/043   10 09 08 07 06 05 04

Contents in Brief

NATIONAL GEOGRAPHIC
eXpeditions!

Finding the *Titanic*

Plunging Into History

"God himself could not sink this ship," boasted a crewman aboard the R.M.S. *Titanic*. Famous last words. Many aboard the sumptuous liner—the largest and most expensive ship of her era—shared the sailor's optimism. As the ship left England on her maiden voyage, she seemed the very emblem of technological triumph.

Probably most people in America know the unhappy ending. The *Titanic* hit an iceberg at 11:40 P.M. on April 14, 1912. She sank about two hours later, killing 1522 people. (The ship's lifeboats saved 705 others.) The "unsinkable" ship didn't survive a single Atlantic crossing.

Yet by sinking, the *Titanic* achieved gruesome immortality. When scientists found the shipwreck in 1985, they earned attention seldom given to marine exploration.

● **ABOVE:** A proud and allegedly unsinkable R.M.S. *Titanic* departs her berth in Southampton, England, in April 1912, on her fateful maiden voyage to the North Atlantic.

● **LEFT:** The ghostly hulk of the *Titanic* lies in her grave more than two miles deep, her bow festooned by decades of rust and sediment.

DEADLY DECISION

Fred Fleet was on lookout duty the night the *Titanic* sank. From his perch in the crow's nest, he spotted an iceberg directly in the ship's path, only a quarter of a mile away. He phoned the bridge with a terse, terrifying warning: "Iceberg right ahead!"

The officer-in-charge tried to reverse engines while turning hard to starboard (to the right)—a combination that proved fatal. Because the ship was in reverse, the change in steering actually moved her to port

880

881

Some topics of Earth science deserve more attention than others because they're unusual, informative, or just plain interesting. **National Geographic Society** has created visually exciting multipage Expeditions! features that inform, excite, and motivate your students. **Expeditions!** features are relevant to the Earth Science content of the student edition. Assign them as a lead-in to special research projects and in-depth studies for extra credit. Use them as a basis for colorful visual displays and bulletin boards.

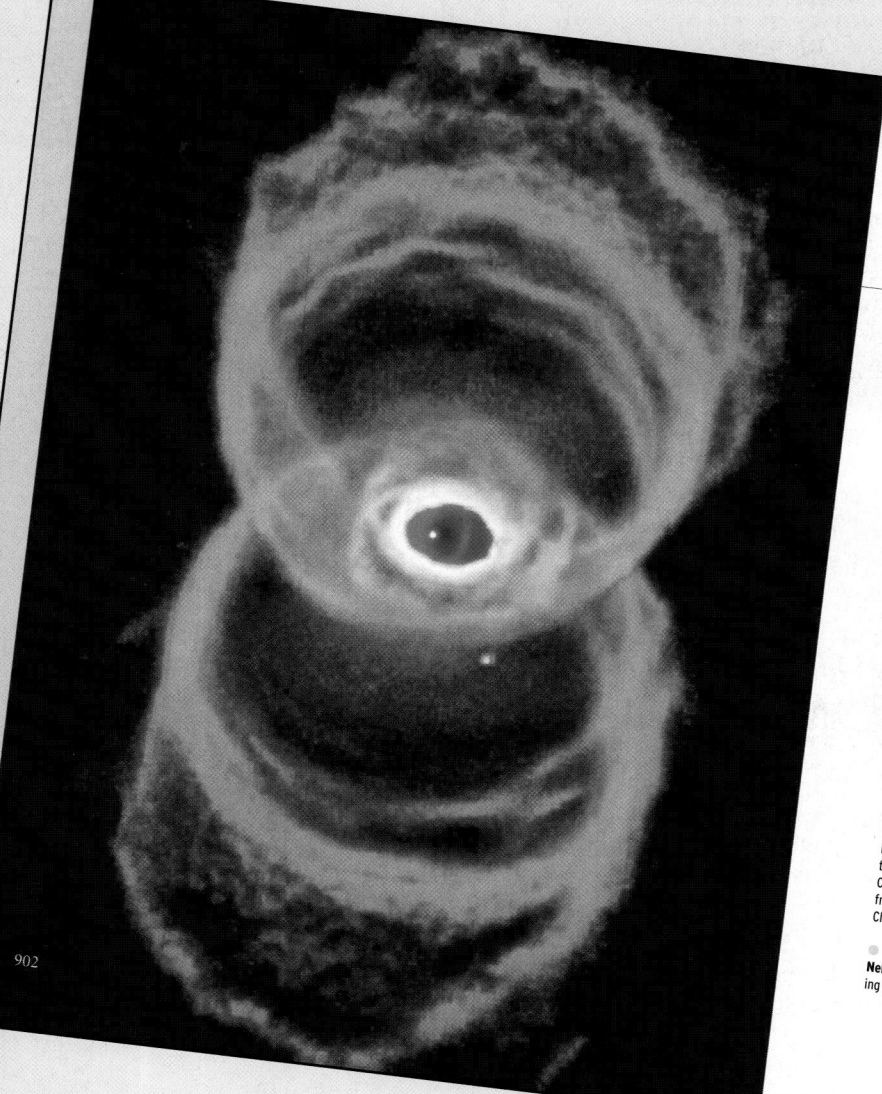

NASA's Eye in the Sky

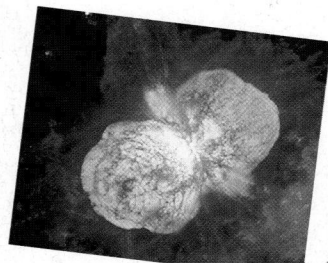

Hermann Oberth was frustrated.
The German scientist yearned to explore space, but even the best telescopes available to him—to anyone—were hampered by Earth's atmosphere. The gases that make the planet habitable also distort our views of the heavens. Oberth's frustration sparked a bold idea: Why not design a telescope that could orbit the planet? It could offer an unparalleled view of the universe. But would it ever exist?

Oberth conceived his orbiting telescope in 1923. Air travel was still new; space travel was still science fiction. As the saying goes, he was ahead of his time—by decades. NASA launched two small space telescopes in the 1960s and 1970s, but neither came close to being the marvel that Oberth and others yearned for.

ASTRONOMY'S DREAM MACHINE

Five, four, three, two, one—blastoff! In April 1990, four months after Hermann Oberth's death, the shuttle *Discovery* set the *Hubble Space Telescope (HST)* into orbit 595 kilometers (370 miles) above Earth's surface. Named for American astronomer Edwin Hubble, the telescope would finally offer scientists the undistorted images for which they had waited so long. *Hubble* promised to be, as headlines and hype put it, a "window on the universe."

The new telescope could create images that were ten times sharper than anything seen from Earth-based observatories. That's

ABOVE: Clouds of gas and dust pour out from the exploding star **Eta Carinae** at 2.4 million kilometers (1.5 million miles) per hour. Still burning five million times brighter than our Sun, Eta Carinae illuminates the clouds from the inside, like frosted Christmas bulbs.

LEFT: The **Etched Hourglass Nebula** is a shell of gas expanding from a dying star.

902

903

NATIONAL GEOGRAPHIC

For additional information on **National Geographic Expeditions!** topics, connect through the Earth Science Web site at <u>ny.earthgeu.com</u>.

ENVIRONMENTAL CONNECTIONS

ENVIRONMENTAL CONNECTIONS show the relevancy of Earth science to modern issues, the application of chapter lessons, and a connection between classroom information and the contemporary world.

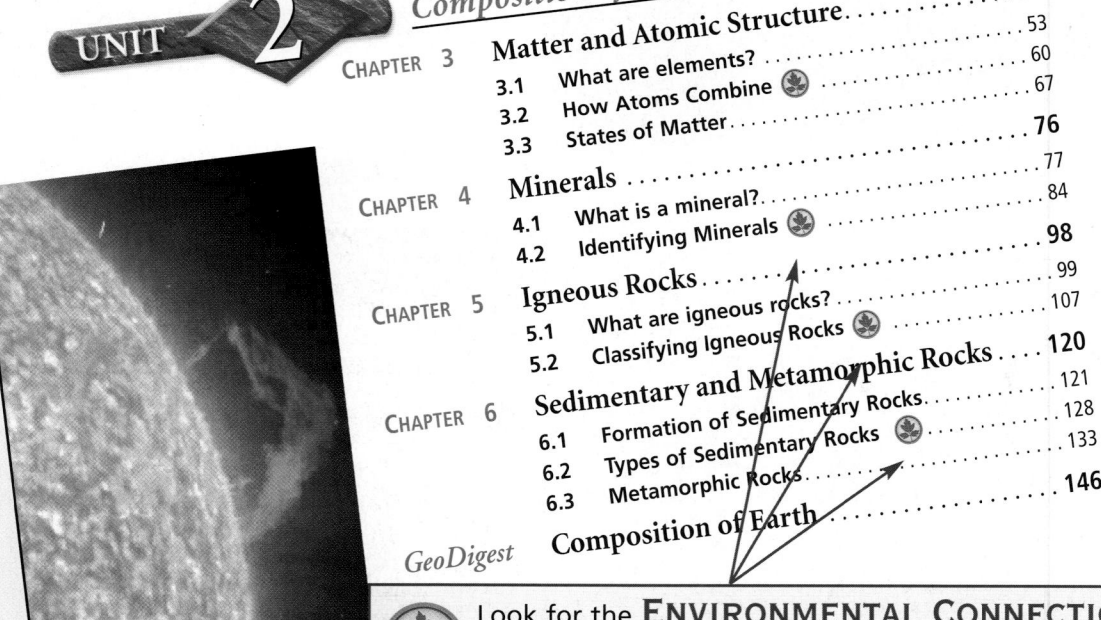

Table of Contents

Look for the **ENVIRONMENTAL CONNECTION** logo to point out chapters, sections, and activities with an emphasis on environmental applications.

Pesticides A variety of pesticides, including fungicides and insecticides, have played an important role in boosting food production worldwide by eliminating organisms that destroy crops. However, the use of pesticides has drawbacks. Some pesticides remain in the environment for long periods of time. As they slowly accumulate in the food chain, they may harm beneficial organisms, such as fishes and birds. Some pesticides also kill beneficial insect predators along with destructive insects. When pesticides kill decomposers, such as worms, the overall fertility of topsoil deteriorates. In addition, insect populations can quickly develop resistance to an insecticide, causing some farmers to use ever-increasing amounts in an attempt to control pests. Further problems are created when wind and rain carry pesticides away from a farm and cause pollution in nearby waterways.

Topsoil It can take thousands of years for topsoil to form, and thus, once it is lost, it is hard to replace. Erosion of topsoil occurs when forests or grasslands are cleared for the first time, but even established farms can suffer from the loss of topsoil. As shown in **Figure 27-10,** whenever fields are plowed and the [roots hold the soil] [to] erosion by wind [s]ome of the nutri-[...] are other sub-[...] Topsoil contains [...rms,] which aer-[...y, and] nitrogen-[...r] and make it [...] organic matter, [...ve in] the soil and dead [...] insects. As organic matter

The Teacher Wraparound Edition contains an **ENVIRONMENTAL CONNECTION** activity or information that provides additional resources for environmental teaching.

[...]ms such as grasses and [...] decomposes, it releases nutrients back into the soil.

Cultural Diversity

Ronald Brooks (1935–1989) A[...] American chemist, Dr. Ronald Brooks led [...] units at General Electric to develop oil-ea[...] microorganisms that cleaned up environ[...] damaging oil spills in ocean environments[...] digesting microbes helped to metabolize, [...] down, the hydrocarbons in petroleum into [...]

Environmental Connection

In the late 1990s, the government of New York City had to choose between spraying pesticides in populated areas or risking an outbreak of potentially fatal mosquito-borne diseases. Ask students what they would have chosen to do under these circumstances. Ask them what they think the government of New York City decided to do. Government officials of New York City chose aerial spraying of pesticides to control mosquitoes.

Activity

Visual-Spatial Have groups of students make posters or data tables showing different ways that fertilizer and pesticides can enter the environment. L2 P

Environmental Connection

In the late 1990s, the government of New York City had to choose between spraying pesticides in populated areas or risking an outbreak of potentially fatal mosquito-borne diseases. Ask students what they would have chosen to do under these circumstances. Ask them what they think the government of New York City decided to do. Government officials of New York City chose aerial spraying of pesticides to control mosquitoes.

Using Scientific Terms

Have students find the origin and meaning of *mono.* It is of Greek origin and means "one" or "alone." Challenge students to compile a list of words that have the prefix *mono-.* Students may not have heard the word *monograph,* but they probably are familiar with words such as *monocle, monologue, monorail,* and *monotone.*

NY Core Curriculum Standards
Page 718: St 6 KI 2 & 4
Page 719: St 6 KI 5

Program Overview

The *National Science Education Standards*, published by the National Research Council and representing the contribution of thousands of educators and scientists, offer a comprehensive vision of a scientifically literate society. The standards describe not only what students should know but also offer guidelines for Earth science teaching and assessment. If you are using, or plan to use, the standards to guide changes in your curriculum, you can be assured that ***Earth Science: Geology, the Environment, and the Universe*** aligns with the *National Science Education Standards*.

Earth Science: Geology, the Environment, and the Universe is an example of how Glencoe's commitment to effective science education is changing the materials used in classrooms today. More than just a collection of facts in a textbook, ***Earth Science: Geology, the Environment, and the Universe*** is a program that provides numerous opportunities for students, teachers, and school districts to meet the *National Science Education Standards*.

National Science Content Standards

Correlations in each Chapter Organizer and GeoDigest show the close alignment between ***Earth Science: Geology, the Environment, and the Universe*** and the content standards. Correlations are designated according to the numbering system in the table of science content standards shown on the opposite page. The approach of ***Earth Science: Geology, the Environment, and the Universe*** allows students to discover concepts within each of the content standards, giving them opportunities to make connections between Earth science concepts and the real world. Hands-on labs and inquiry-based lessons reinforce the science processes emphasized in the standards.

Teaching Standards

Alignment with the *National Science Education Standards* requires much more than alignment with the outcomes in the content standards. The way in which concepts are presented is critical to effective learning. The teaching standards within the *National Science Education Standards* recommend an inquiry-based program facilitated and guided by teachers. ***Earth Science: Geology, the Environment, and the Universe*** provides such opportunities through activities and discussions that allow students to discover critical concepts by inquiry and apply the knowledge they've constructed to their own lives. Throughout the program, students are building critical skills that will be available to them for lifelong learning. The ***Teacher Wraparound Edition*** helps you make the most of every instructional moment. It offers an abundance of effective strategies and suggestions for guiding students as they explore Earth science.

Assessment Standards

The assessment standards are supported by many of the components that make up the ***Earth Science: Geology, the Environment, and the Universe*** program. The Teacher Wraparound Edition and Teacher Classroom Resources provide multiple chances to assess students' understanding of important concepts as well as their abilities to perform a wide range of skills. Ideas for portfolios, performance assessment, written reports, and other assessment activities accompany every lesson. For more suggestions about assessment ideas and resources, see pages 34T-35T of the Teacher Guide.

Philosophy and Themes

In ***Earth Science: Geology, the Environment, and the Universe***, there is an emphasis on five themes, as adapted from the Unifying Concepts and Processes of the *National Science Education Standards*. These themes are: Systems, order, and organization; Evidence, models, and explanation; Change, constancy, and measurement; Evolution and equilibrium; and Form and function. Emphasis on themes contributes to the big picture by focusing learning on connections among major ideas and concepts. The thematic approach contributes to students' comprehension of fundamental Earth science processes, ability to integrate facts with concepts, and appreciation of how scientists work.

National Science Content Standards

Unifying Concepts and Processes (UCP)

UCP.1 Systems, order, and organization
UCP.2 Evidence, models, and explanation
UCP.3 Change, constancy, and measurement
UCP.4 Evolution and equilibrium
UCP.5 Form and function

Science as Inquiry

A.1 Abilities necessary to do scientific inquiry
A.2 Understandings about scientific inquiry

Physical Science

B.1 Structure of atoms
B.2 Structure and properties of matter
B.3 Chemical reactions
B.4 Motions and forces
B.5 Conservation of energy and increase in disorder
B.6 Interactions of energy and matter

Life Science

C.1 The cell
C.2 Molecular basis of heredity
C.3 Biological evolution
C.4 Interdependence of organisms
C.5 Matter, energy, and organization in living systems
C.6 Behavior of organisms

Earth and Space Science

D.1 Energy in the Earth system
D.2 Geochemical cycles
D.3 Origin and evolution of the Earth system
D.4 Origin and evolution of the universe

Science and Technology

E.1 Abilities of technological design
E.2 Understandings about science and technology

Science in Personal and Social Perspectives

F.1 Personal and community health
F.2 Population growth
F.3 Natural resources
F.4 Environmental quality
F.5 Natural and human-induced hazards
F.6 Science and technology in local, national, and global challenges

History and Nature of Science

G.1 Science as a human endeavor
G.2 Nature of scientific knowledge
G.3 Historical perspectives

Student Edition: *Program Tour*

Student Edition

Feature	Location	Suggestions for Use
Activities	In every chapter At the point where concept is taught	Use to strengthen key concepts Provide visual learning element
MiniLab	In every chapter At the point where concept is taught	Assign to groups in a lab setting Use as homework or in-class work
GeoLab Design Your Own GeoLab Internet GeoLab Mapping GeoLab	At the end of the chapter	Assign to groups in a lab setting Help reinforce understanding of scientific methods Help students learn science process
Discovery Lab	At the beginning of each chapter	Introduce students to chapter subject Get attention with initial activity
Problem-Solving Lab	At the point where concept is taught	Reinforce scientific methods Allow students to evaluate other experiments
Test-Taking Tips	In the Chapter Assessment	Prepare students for standardized testing
Science & the Environment Science & Math Science & Technology Science in the News	At the end of the chapter	Connect Earth science to related topics Expand chapter subject to daily life
Earth Science Online	In every chapter At the point where concept is taught	Integrate the Internet with chapter material Expand activities and homework Allow students to share data online with other classes
GeoDigest	At the end of each unit	Provide a summary of the unit Can be used as a review or overview of the unit Contains additional assessments
National Geographic Expeditions	Special section following the final chapter	Provides exciting extra material that strengthens Earth science concepts

Getting Students Involved

What You'll Learn
Introduces the main concepts of the chapter before students begin to study the material.

Why It's Important
Provides an answer to the "Why do we have to learn this?" question that students ask.

Chapter 18

Volcanic Activity

What You'll Learn
• How magma forms.
• What kinds of features form as the result of igneous activity within Earth.
• How volcanoes form and how they can be classified.

Why It's Important
Many of Earth's internal processes help to shape our planet's surface. Igneous activity deep within Earth and at its surface produce many of the mountains and rock formations on Earth.

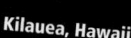

Earth Science Online
To learn more about volcanic activity, visit the Earth Science Web Site at earthgeu.com

470

Kilauea, Hawaii

Earth Science Online
Connects students to the resources available on the Earth Science Web Site. Encourages individual Internet research on science topics at home, or in class for those who finish the lesson early. Assign a different site to each student group for group reports, and use to update text information.

Student Edition: *Program Resources*

Hands-on Experience

Working in the lab is often the most enjoyable part of Earth science. **Discovery Labs** open each chapter with an activity. When students feel inquisitive but there's a shortage of time, assign a **MiniLab. GeoLabs** give your students an opportunity to act like geologists, develop their own plans for studying a question or problem, and share their data with others. Whether they're designing experiments or following well-tested procedures, they'll have fun doing these lab activities.

GeoLab Guide students in following the procedure steps to arrive at the answer to the lab problem. Labs can also be set up as teacher demos if time or materials are short.

Design Your Own GeoLab Challenge your students to design an experiment that provides an answer to the lab problem. Labs can also be used as a source for science fair projects.

Mapping GeoLab Students utilize maps in a practical, classroom exercise.

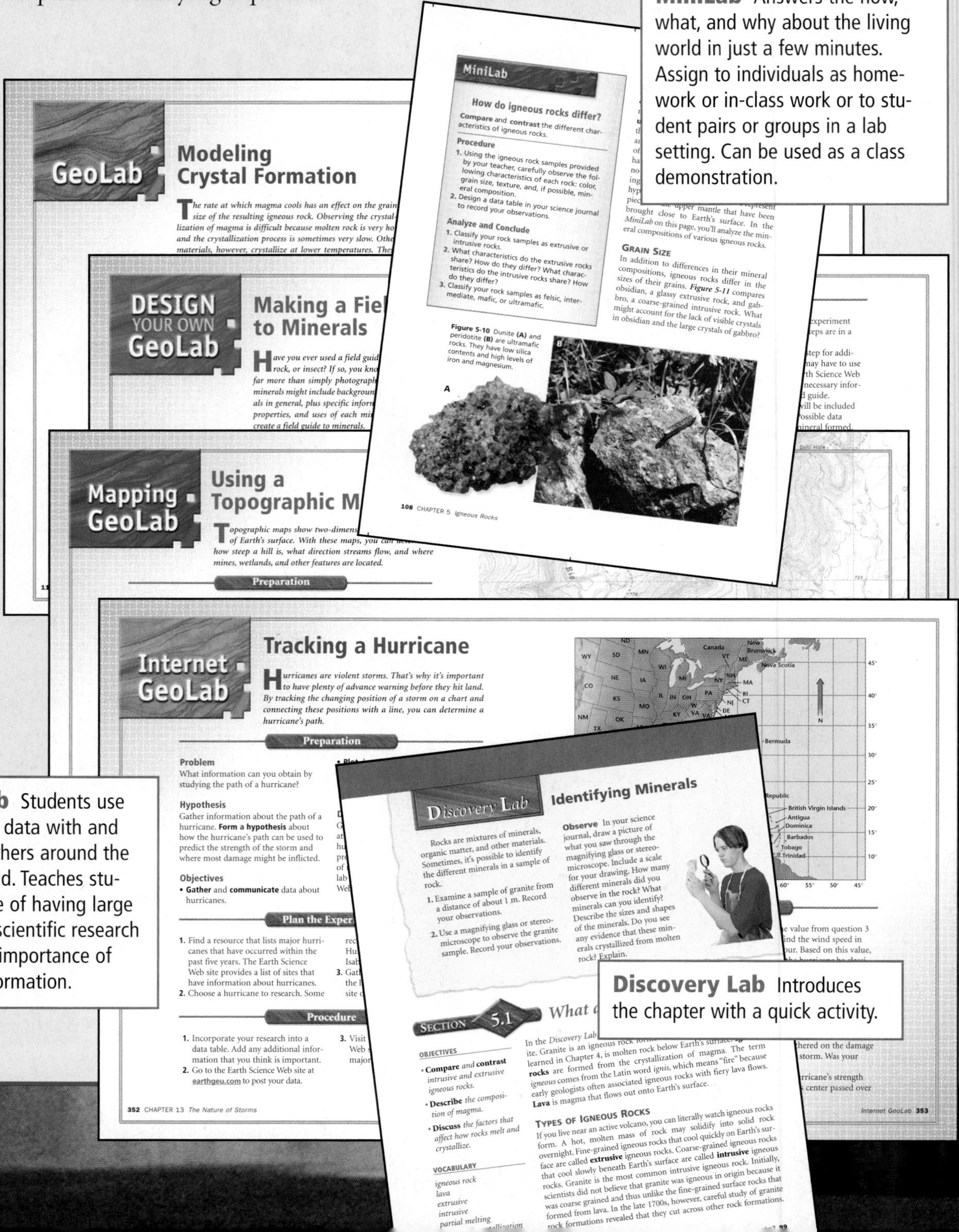

Internet GeoLab Students use the Internet to share data with and retrieve data from others around the country and the world. Teaches students the importance of having large numbers of trials in scientific research and emphasizes the importance of sharing scientific information.

MiniLab Answers the how, what, and why about the living world in just a few minutes. Assign to individuals as homework or in-class work or to student pairs or groups in a lab setting. Can be used as a class demonstration.

Discovery Lab Introduces the chapter with a quick activity.

GeoLab — Modeling Crystal Formation

The rate at which magma cools has an effect on the grain size of the resulting igneous rock. Observing the crystallization of magma is difficult because molten rock is very hot, and the crystallization process is sometimes very slow. Other materials, however, crystallize at lower temperatures. These

DESIGN YOUR OWN GeoLab — Making a Field Guide to Minerals

Have you ever used a field guide to identify a rock, or insect? If so, you know that a field guide is far more than simply photographs. Field guides for minerals might include background information about minerals in general, plus specific information about properties, and uses of each mineral. In this GeoLab, create a field guide to minerals.

Mapping GeoLab — Using a Topographic Map

Topographic maps show two-dimensional images of Earth's surface. With these maps, you can tell how steep a hill is, what direction streams flow, and where mines, wetlands, and other features are located.

Preparation

Internet GeoLab — Tracking a Hurricane

Hurricanes are violent storms. That's why it's important to have plenty of advance warning before they hit land. By tracking the changing position of a storm on a chart and connecting these positions with a line, you can determine a hurricane's path.

Preparation

Problem
What information can you obtain by studying the path of a hurricane?

Hypothesis
Gather information about the path of a hurricane. **Form a hypothesis** about how the hurricane's path can be used to predict the strength of the storm and where most damage might be inflicted.

Objectives
• **Gather** and **communicate** data about hurricanes.

Plan the Experiment

1. Find a resource that lists major hurricanes that have occurred within the past five years. The Earth Science Web site provides a list of sites that have information about hurricanes.
2. Choose a hurricane to research. Some

Procedure

1. Incorporate your research into a data table. Add any additional information that you think is important.
2. Go to the Earth Science Web site at earthgeu.com to post your data.

3. Visit the Earth Science Web site to find out the major

352 CHAPTER 13 *The Nature of Storms*

MiniLab — How do igneous rocks differ?

Compare and **contrast** the different characteristics of igneous rocks.

Procedure
1. Using the igneous rock samples provided by your teacher, carefully observe the following characteristics of each rock: color, grain size, texture, and, if possible, mineral composition.
2. Design a data table in your science journal to record your observations.

Analyze and Conclude
1. Classify your rock samples as extrusive or intrusive rocks.
2. What characteristics do the extrusive rocks share? How do they differ? What characteristics do the intrusive rocks share? How do they differ?
3. Classify your rock samples as felsic, intermediate, mafic, or ultramafic.

Figure 5-10 Dunite (A) and peridotite (B) are ultramafic rocks. They have low silica contents and high levels of iron and magnesium.

108 CHAPTER 5 *Igneous Rocks*

Discovery Lab — Identifying Minerals

Rocks are mixtures of minerals, organic matter, and other materials. Sometimes, it's possible to identify the different minerals in a sample of rock.

1. Examine a sample of granite from a distance of about 1 m. Record your observations.
2. Use a magnifying glass or stereomicroscope to observe the granite sample. Record your observations.

Observe In your science journal, draw a picture of what you saw through the magnifying glass or stereomicroscope. Include a scale for your drawing. How many different minerals did you observe in the rock? What minerals can you identify? Describe the sizes and shapes of the minerals. Do you see any evidence that these minerals crystallized from molten rock? Explain.

SECTION 5.1 — What

In the Discovery Lab... ite. Granite is an igneous rock learned in Chapter 4, is molten rock below Earth's surface. The term **rocks** are formed from the crystallization of magma. The term igneous comes from the Latin word *ignis*, which means "fire" because early geologists often associated igneous rocks with fiery lava flows.
Lava is magma that flows out onto Earth's surface.

TYPES OF IGNEOUS ROCKS
If you live near an active volcano, you can literally watch igneous rocks form. A hot, molten mass of rock may solidify into solid rock overnight. Fine-grained igneous rocks that cool quickly on Earth's surface are called **extrusive** igneous rocks. Coarse-grained igneous rocks that cool slowly beneath Earth's surface are called **intrusive** igneous rocks. Granite is the most common intrusive igneous rock. Initially, scientists did not believe that granite was igneous in origin because it was coarse grained and thus unlike the fine-grained surface rocks that formed from lava. In the late 1700s, however, careful study of granite rock formations revealed that they cut across other rock formations.

OBJECTIVES
• **Compare** and **contrast** intrusive and extrusive igneous rocks.
• **Describe** the composition of magma.
• **Discuss** the factors that affect how rocks melt and crystallize.

VOCABULARY
igneous rock
lava
extrusive
intrusive
partial melting

Internet GeoLab 353

Skills

Skill Handbook *Earth Science: Geology, the Environment, and the Universe* encourages the interaction between content and critical-thinking processes and experiences with scientific methods. All the labs and activities require students to make observations and collect a variety of data. Section Assessment questions at the end of each section and in the Chapter Assessment provide students with another opportunity to practice the thinking processes relevant to the material they are studying. The *Skill Handbook* provides students with examples of all the process skills that they need to practice during these activities.

Skill Handbook

Thinking Critically

COMPARING AND CONTRASTING

You can analyze and then organize your observations by noting the similarities and differences between two or more objects or events. When you examine objects or events to determine their similarities, you are comparing them. When you examine similar objects or events to determine their differences, you are contrasting them.

Suppose you are asked to compare and contrast the minerals halite and quartz. You could begin by making observations of each type of mineral. Then, you could divide a piece of paper into two columns and list the ways in which the two minerals are similar in one column and the ways in which they are different in the other column. After completing your list, you could organize your findings in a data table or a graph.

Similarities you might point out are that both minerals are solids that occur as crystals, and both are inorganic compounds. Differences might include that halite has a cubic crystal structure, whereas quartz has a hexagonal crystal structure. You could further investigate these two minerals by testing for hardness, luster, color, streak, and cleavage or fracture.

RECOGNIZING CAUSE AND EFFECT

Have you ever seen something happen, and then tried to figure out why or how it happened? If so, you observed an event and inferred a reason for the event. The event or result of an action is an effect, and the reason for the event is the cause.

Suppose that you take a 2-L bottle of soda pop out of the refrigerator and accidentally drop it on the floor. You pick the bottle up, then unscrew the cap and take it off. Immediately, the soda pop fizzes up and spills out of the bottle all over the counter. What was the effect, and what would you infer was the cause? The effect was the soda pop fizzing up and spilling out of the open bottle.

SKILL HANDBOOK **925**

Problem-Solving Lab

Using Graphs

Predict how sediments move in a stream The velocity of water affects the transport of different-sized particles.

Analysis

1. Study the graph at right.
2. At what velocity would flowing water pick up a pebble?
3. At what velocity would flowing water drop a pebble?

Thinking Critically

4. Infe___
wo___
ran___
egg___
ter___

Stream Velocity and Particle Size

Particle diameter (cm) vs (m/s)

- Boulders 25.6 cm
- Cobbles 6.4 cm
- Pebbles
- 0.2 cm
- Sand
- 0.006 cm
- Silt
- 0.0004 cm
- Clay

100.0, 10.0, 1.0, 0.1, 0.01, 0.001, 0.0001, 0.00001

0 100 200 300 400 500 600 700 800

Problem-Solving Labs *Problem-Solving Labs* offer a unique opportunity for students to evaluate another scientist's experiments and data without bench mess. Can be assigned as homework or class work. Use these labs to reinforce the steps of scientific methods.

Test-Taking Tips *Test-Taking Tips* help prepare students for taking the tests that are an integral part of their school experience. Found in every Chapter Assessment, these tips can be collected in a journal by students and reviewed before they take end-of-course, PSAT, or state exams.

Test-Taking Tip

BEAT THE CLOCK—AND THEN GO BACK

As you take a practice test, pace yourself to finish each section just a few minutes early so you can go back and check over your work. You will sometimes find a mistake or two.

Student Edition: *Program Resources*

Science & the Environment, Science & Math, Science & Technology, Science in the News

Help students to realize that Earth science is connected to all their courses and that it impacts their lives and society as a whole. These features cover topics that students hear about from the media. **Science & the Environment** presents environmental issues that impact science. **Science & Math** provides mathematical challenges in Earth science. **Science & Technology** shows students how technology may affect their lives, and **Science in the News** provides the opportunity to understand science as related to current or historical topics.

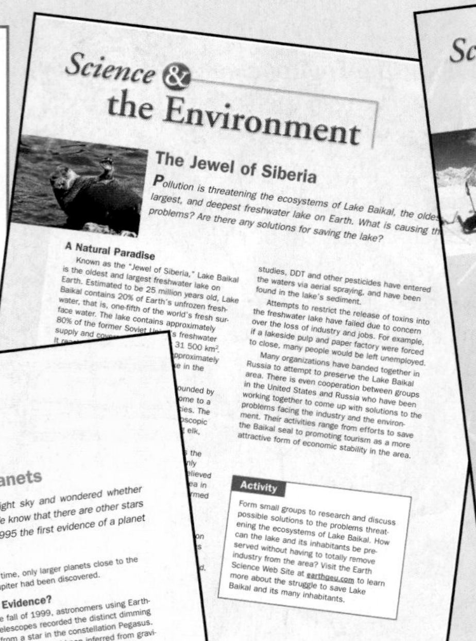

Science & the Environment

The Jewel of Siberia

*P*ollution is threatening the ecosystems of Lake Baikal, the oldest, largest, and deepest freshwater lake on Earth. What is causing the problems? Are there any solutions for saving the lake?

A Natural Paradise

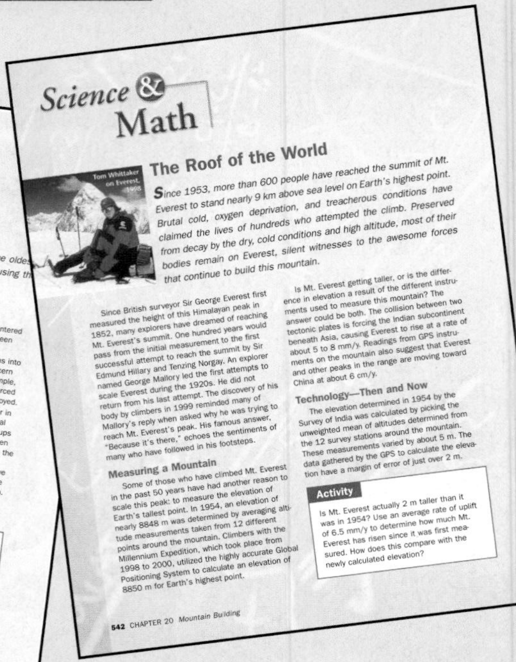

Known as the "Jewel of Siberia," Lake Baikal is the oldest and largest freshwater lake on Earth. Estimated to be 25 million years old, Lake Baikal contains 20% of Earth's unfrozen freshwater, that is, one-fifth of the world's fresh surface water. The lake contains approximately 80% of the former Soviet Union's freshwater supply and contains approximately [...] in the [...]

studies, DDT and other pesticides have entered the waters via aerial spraying, and have been found in the lake's sediment.

Attempts to restrict the release of toxins into the freshwater lake have failed due to concern over the loss of industry and jobs. For example, if a lakeside pulp and paper factory were forced to close, many people would be left unemployed.

Many organizations have banded together in Russia to attempt to preserve the Lake Baikal area. There is even cooperation between groups in the United States and Russia who have been working together to come up with solutions to the problems facing the industry and the environment. Their activities range from efforts to save the Baikal seal to promoting tourism as a more attractive form of economic stability in the area.

Activity

Form small groups to research and discuss possible solutions to the problems threatening the ecosystems of Lake Baikal. How can the lake and its inhabitants be preserved without having to totally remove industry from the area? Visit the Earth Science Web Site at earthgeu.com to learn more about the struggle to save Lake Baikal and its many inhabitants.

Science & Math

The Roof of the World

*S*ince 1953, more than 600 people have reached the summit of Mt. Everest to stand nearly 9 km above sea level on Earth's highest point. Brutal cold, oxygen deprivation, and treacherous conditions have claimed the lives of hundreds who attempted the climb. Preserved from decay by the dry, cold conditions and high altitude, most of their bodies remain on Everest, silent witnesses to the awesome forces that continue to build this mountain.

Since British surveyor Sir George Everest first measured the height of this Himalayan peak in 1852, many explorers have dreamed of reaching Mt. Everest's summit. One hundred years would pass from the initial measurement to the first successful attempt to reach the summit by Sir Edmund Hillary and Tenzing Norgay. An explorer named George Mallory led the first attempts to scale Everest during the 1920s. He did not return from his last attempt. The discovery of his body by climbers in 1999 reminded many of Mallory's reply when asked why he was trying to reach Mt. Everest's peak. His famous answer, "Because it's there," echoes the sentiments of many who have followed in his footsteps.

Measuring a Mountain

Some of those who have climbed Mt. Everest in the past 50 years have had another reason to scale this peak: to measure the elevation of Earth's tallest point. In 1954, an elevation of nearly 8848 m was determined by averaging altitude measurements taken from 12 different points around the mountain. Climbers with the Millennium Expedition, which took place from 1998 to 2000, utilized the highly accurate Global Positioning System to calculate an elevation of 8850 m for Earth's highest point.

Is Mt. Everest getting taller, or is the difference in elevation a result of the different instruments used to measure this mountain? The answer could be both. The collision between two tectonic plates is forcing the Indian subcontinent beneath Asia, causing Everest to rise at a rate of about 5 to 8 mm/y. Readings from GPS instruments on the mountain also suggest that Everest and other peaks in the range are moving toward China at about 6 cm/y.

Technology—Then and Now

The elevation determined in 1954 by the Survey of India was calculated by picking the unweighted mean of altitudes obtained from the 12 survey stations around the mountain. These measurements varied by about 5 m. The data gathered by the GPS to calculate the elevation have a margin of error of just over 2 m.

Activity

Is Mt. Everest actually 2 m taller than it was in 1954? Use an average rate of uplift of 6.5 mm/y to determine how much Mt. Everest has risen since it was first measured. How does this compare with the newly calculated elevation?

542 CHAPTER 20 Mountain Building

Science in the News

Discovering New Planets

*H*ave you ever looked up at the night sky and wondered whether there are other Earth-like planets? We know that there are other stars similar to the Sun in the galaxy. In 1995 the first evidence of a planet was discovered.

In 1995, after a year of careful measurements, Swiss astronomers announced the discovery of a planet orbiting around the star 51 Pegasi. A planet found outside of our solar system is called an extrasolar planet. Shortly after the discovery of the first extrasolar planet, several more were discovered. More than 100 extrasolar planets have been detected, with the number of discoveries increasing with every [...]

Direct Evidence?

In the fall of 1999, astronomers using Earth-based telescopes recorded the distinct dimming of light from a star in the constellation Pegasus. Previously, a planet had been inferred from gravitational effects, but astronomers did not have direct evidence. However, the dimming of light where the gravitational effects predicted a planet to be. This dimming was caused by light from the star being blocked out by the solar planet passing in front of the star, and provided direct evidence of an extrasolar planet.

No Earth-sized planets have yet been discovered, but scientists theorize that the [...] NASA missions, the Space Interferometry (SIM) and the Terrestrial Planet Finder (TPF), will be used to study the orbiting around a single star. On April 15, astronomers announced the discovery of planets orbiting around the star Upsilon Andromedae. This discovery was significant because scientists then had evidence of a multi-planet system, similar to our solar system. On March 29, 2000, planets smaller than Saturn were discovered.

Activity

Visit your library or the Earth Science Web Site at earthgeu.com to find links to the most recent extrasolar planet discoveries. Present your findings in the form of a poster or in an oral report.

CHAPTER 29 Our Solar System

Science & Technology

Extreme Magnification

*S*tudents from Malibu, California, to Atlanta, Georgia, are collecting bugs with more enthusiasm than usual. They are sending insects to a project called Bugscope. Bugscope workers use a scanning electron microscope (SEM) to take close-up photographs of these amazing animals. The photographs are then posted on the Internet. The photos provide detailed information about the structure and composition of matter in our world.

Electron Microscopy

Microscopes have been used by scientists to magnify objects since the 1600s. Traditional light microscopes, however, have limitations: they can magnify objects only up to 2000 times their size, and there is a limit to how clear these microscopes can make objects appear. In the early 1930s, German scientists developed a new type of microscope that could magnify objects 10 000 times their size. This microscope did not use light for the examination of objects; instead, it used a beam of high-energy electrons. Today, electron microscopes scan material to create detailed, three-dimensional, black-and-white images of objects that are magnified up to 100 000 times.

Applications

When a scanning electron microscope is used to examine an object, a beam of electrons is directed over the object's surface. As scanning coils move the electron beam over the object in a gridlike pattern, the beam causes electrons to be knocked off the object's surface. An image is created on a fluorescent screen by the calculation of the number of electrons that are bounced off each spot on the object. Electron microscopes provide information about the properties of matter being examined, including its reactivity,

strength, and reflectivity. Currently, scientists are using electron microscopes to further research in areas ranging from combating leukemia to searching for evidence of product tampering to developing better ways to process and store food.

Activity

The photographs on this page are SEM images. What does each image represent? Go to earthgeu.com to find links to SEM images of solids and create an image gallery. Present your images, along with clues about their identities, to your classmates, and see how many they can identify.

72 CHAPTER 3 Matter and Atomic Structure

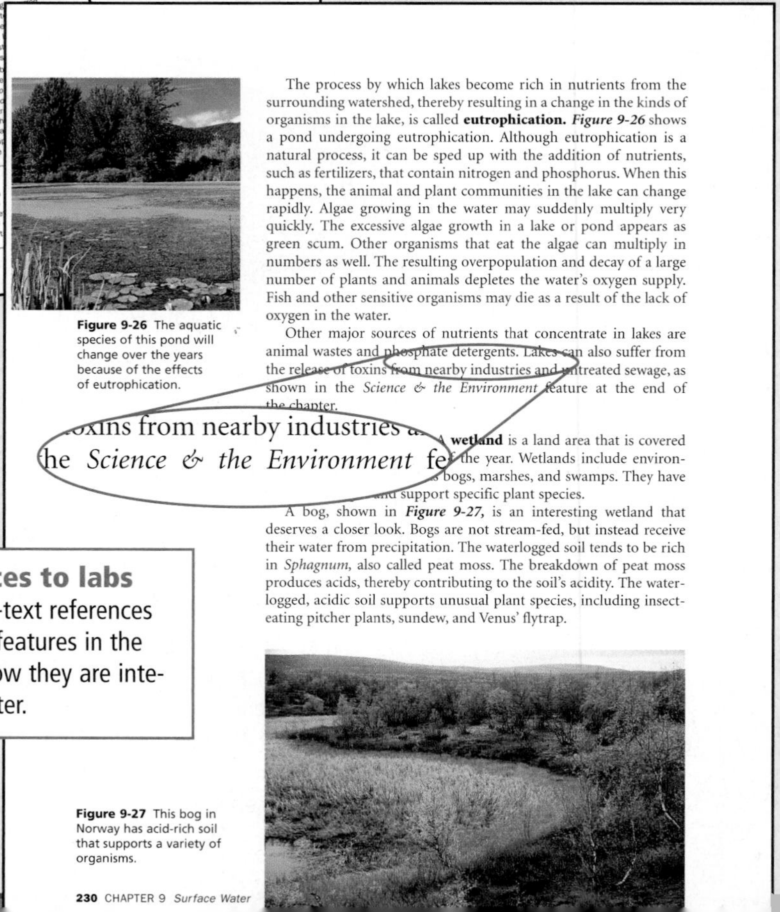

Magnification 13×

Magnification 15×

Magnification 140×

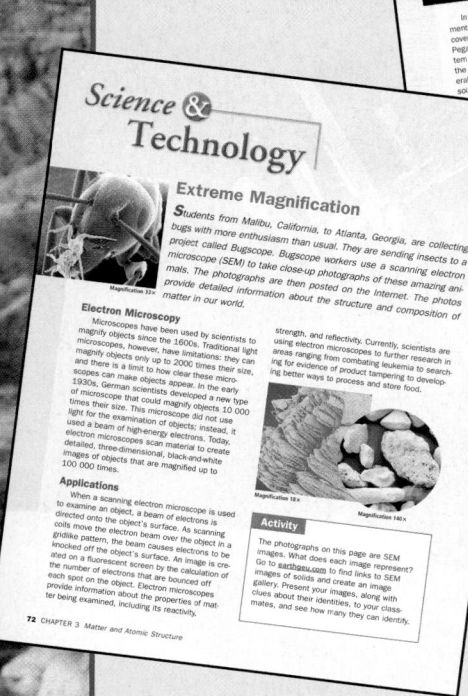

In-text references to labs and features

In-text references call out all labs and features in the chapter and show how they are integrated into the chapter.

The process by which lakes become rich in nutrients from the surrounding watershed, thereby resulting in a change in the kinds of organisms in the lake, is called **eutrophication.** *Figure 9-26* shows a pond undergoing eutrophication. Although eutrophication is a natural process, it can be sped up with the addition of nutrients, such as fertilizers, that contain nitrogen and phosphorus. When this happens, the animal and plant communities in the lake can change rapidly. Algae growing in the water may suddenly multiply very quickly. The excessive algae growth in a lake or pond appears as green scum. Other organisms that eat the algae can multiply in numbers as well. The resulting overpopulation and decay of a large number of plants and animals depletes the water's oxygen supply. Fish and other sensitive organisms may die as a result of the lack of oxygen in the water.

Other major sources of nutrients that concentrate in lakes are animal wastes and phosphate detergents. Lakes can also suffer from the release of toxins from nearby industries and untreated sewage, as shown in the *Science & the Environment* feature at the end of the chapter.

Toxins from nearby industries and the *Science & the Environment* feature.

A **wetland** is a land area that is covered [...] the year. Wetlands include environments [...] bogs, marshes, and swamps. They have [...] and support specific plant species.

A bog, shown in *Figure 9-27*, is an interesting wetland that deserves a closer look. Bogs are not stream-fed, but instead receive their water from precipitation. The waterlogged soil tends to be rich in *Sphagnum*, also called peat moss. The breakdown of peat moss produces acids, thereby contributing to the soil's acidity. The waterlogged, acidic soil supports unusual plant species, including insect-eating pitcher plants, sundew, and Venus' flytrap.

Figure 9-26 The aquatic species of this pond will change over the years because of the effects of eutrophication.

Figure 9-27 This bog in Norway has acid-rich soil that supports a variety of organisms.

230 CHAPTER 9 Surface Water

Student Edition: *Program Resources*

GeoDigest

Use the **GeoDigests** as an introduction or a summary of a unit.

UNIT 3
GeoDigest

For a **preview** of Earth's surface processes, study this GeoDigest before you read the chapters. After you have studied the chapters, you can use the GeoDigest to **review** the unit.

Surface Processes on Earth

Weathering, Erosion, and Soil
Chemical and mechanical weathering break down Earth materials. Chemical weathering causes a change in the composition of a rock. Agents of chemical weathering include hydrolysis, oxidation, acids from decaying organic matter, and acid precipitation. Each of these processes or substances combines with Earth materials, resulting in new combinations of minerals or in other substances. Mechanical weathering causes a change only in a rock's size and shape. Temperature and pressure are the major factors in mechanical weathering. Temperature changes can cause rocks to split. Pressure changes can cause rocks to crack or break apart.

Yosemite Nati...

Erosion and Deposition
Gravity is the driving force behind all agents of erosion, the process by which weathered pieces of rock are moved to new locations. Other agents of erosion include moving water, wind, and glaciers. Deposition occurs when the movement of transported materials slows down and they are dropped in a new location.

Formation of Soil
Soils vary with climate and are classified as polar, temperate, desert, or tropical. A single centimeter of soil takes hundred of years to develop, but can erode away in just seconds. Soil is made of weathered rock and decayed organic matter called humus. Residual soil remains on top of its parent bedrock. Transported soil is moved away from its parent bedrock by weathering agents. A cross section of layers of ...
soil profile. The top of l...

soil. Horizons ...
is solid bedroc...
conditions det...
ture is determi...
sand, and silt th...
soil's ability to grow crops. ... soil fertility is a
through methods that include wind barriers.

Use the **GeoDigests** to give students a quick overview of important information in a unit.

Mass Movements, Wind, and Glaciers
The landscape is changed by mass movements, wind, and glaciation. Mass movement refers ...
movement of Earth materials d...
of gravity. Almost ...
mass...

264 UNIT 3

GeoDigest — Surface Processes on Earth

saturation, its resistance to sliding, and sometimes, a trigger such as an earthquake. Mass movements can cause great damage and loss of life.

Wind
Limited precipitation and scarce vegetation, conditions common to arid, semi-arid, and seashore environments, contribute to wind erosion. Wind-carried sediment causes abrasive action which wears down or polishes the sides of rocks that face the wind. Wind-formed Earth features include deflation blowouts, desert pavement, and sand dunes. Dunes are classified by shape as barchan, transverse, longitudinal, or parabolic. Wind-deposited soils called loess contain minerals and nutrients and are highly fertile.

Sand overwhelms building, Namibia

Glaciers
...ving masses of ice called ...th's poles and high in mountains ...eratures keep fallen snow ...g. Over time, the weight of ... downward pressure to ... snow to recrystallize into ...ude U-shaped valleys, hang... ...ins in the mountains; moraines, drumlins, and kettles in outwash plains; and a variety of glacially formed lakes. Valley glaciers

form in mountains and move downslope. Valley glaciers are much smaller than continental glaciers, which form over broad regions and spread out from their centers.

Surface Water
Many landscape features on Earth are produced and changed by surface water. The amount of water in the ground depends on the number and sizes of pores in a particular Earth material and the amount of vegetation. A watershed or drainage...
land area drained by a...
which a...

Tahquamenon River, Mi...

Beyond Earth — GeoDigest

Galaxies
The Milky Way The Milky Way consists of a nuclear bulge, a disk, and a halo; much of its mass is not visible. In the galaxy, Population I stars contain small amounts of heavy elements and are located in the arms and disk. Population II stars are located in the bulge and halo, and contain only trace amounts of heavy elements. Because Earth is inside the Milky Way, it has been difficult to determine the size and shape of the galaxy, and also where Earth is located within it.

Other Galaxies Most galaxies occur in clusters that are further organized into superclusters. Galaxies are classified according to their shapes as normal spirals, barred spirals, ellipticals, or irregulars. Some galaxies have energetic objects or activities at their cores called active galactic nuclei. The universe is expanding, as measured by the Hubble constant. When astronomers observe distant galaxies, they are looking back in time because the light takes so long to reach Earth.

Cosmology Cosmology is the study of the universe as a whole. The Big Bang model proposes that

Star trails around Polaris

the universe began as a single point and has been expanding ever since. The universe is filled with cosmic background radiation that is left over from the early, hot stages in the Big Bang's expansion. According to the Big Bang model, the universe could be open, closed, or flat. The steady state theory of cosmology, which proposed that the universe is and always will be the same, is not accepted among most astronomers. The inflationary theory explains the walls and voids in the distribution of galaxies. Current observations indicate that the expansion of the universe is accelerating.

FOCUS ON CAREERS

Cosmologist
Cosmologists study the universe as a whole in an attempt to discover how it formed and how it will end. They usually obtain doctoral degrees in physics, astronomy, or both and have a strong background in math and computer analysis. Cosmologists usually work and teach at universities, or other research institutions.

Vital Statistics

The Sun's Nearest Neighbors

Star	Distance from the Sun
1. Proxima Centauri	4.22 ly
2. Alpha Centauri	4.39 ly
3. Barnard's Star	5.94 ly
4. Wolf 359	7.80 ly
5. Lalande 21185	8.31 ly
6. Luyten 726-8	8.57 ly
7. Sirius	8.59 ly
8. Ross 154	9.67 ly
9. Ross 248	10.33 ly

860 UNIT 8

Beyond Earth

ASSESSMENT

Understanding Main Ideas

1. A telescope that uses mirrors rather than lenses to bring light to a focus is what kind of telescope?
   a. refracting
   b. reflecting
   c. electromagnetic
   d. probing

2. What is one theory about how the Moon formed?
   a. Numerous asteroids were pulled together.
   b. Earth and Mars collided.
   c. Earth and a Mars-sized body collided.
   d. Earth captured an existing moon from Mars.

3. The planets formed from a collapsing interstellar cloud that flattened into a disk. From which part of the disk did terrestrial planets form?
   a. the inner section of the disk
   b. the outer section of the disk
   c. the exact center of the disk
   d. sections throughout the entire disk

4. Which planets have low densities, no solid surfaces, ring systems, and many moons?
   a. the terrestrial planets
   b. the gas giants
   c. Pluto and Mercury
   d. Mars and Earth

5. The atmosphere of which object in the solar system is made up of the photosphere, the chromosphere, and the corona?
   c. Venus

6. What tool of astronomy relates the class, mass, temperature, magnitude, diameter, and luminosity of stars?
   a. parallax
   b. absolute magnitude
   c. absolute brightness
   d. the Hertzsprung-Russell diagram

7. Stars that are 8 to 20 times more massive than the Sun end up as what kind of stars?
   a. red giants   c. neutron stars
   b. white dwarfs   d. black holes

8. Where are Population II stars located in the Milky Way?
   a. in the bulge and halo
   b. in the arms
   c. in the disk
   d. in the heavy elements

Eskimo Nebula, NGC 2392

9. How are galaxies classified?
   a. by size
   b. by closeness to Earth
   c. by shape
   d. by the Hubble constant

10. What is the study of the universe as a whole?
    a. astronomy   c. physics
    b. cosmology   d. astrometry

Thinking Critically

1. Compare lunar and solar eclipses.
2. Sequence the following star outcomes in order of the mass of the original star, with the smallest mass first: neutron star, white dwarf, and black hole.
3. Explain the Big Bang model of the formation of the universe.

GeoDigest **861**

Can be used as a year-end review for exams by assigning a different **GeoDigest** to each student group for a report to afford quick coverage.

Teacher Wraparound Edition: *Program Tour*

Teacher Wraparound Edition

Feature	Location	Suggestions for Use
Chapter Organizer	At the beginning of each chapter	Preview chapter subject content Correlate all materials, resources, and activities
Activity Materials	At the beginning of each chapter	Plan materials for activities
Key to Teaching Strategies	At the beginning of each chapter	Correlate activities to learning levels and strategies
Multiple Learning Styles	At the beginning of each chapter	Use to develop teaching strategies for various learning styles
✔ Assessment Additional Resources	At the beginning of each chapter	Correlate Teacher Classroom Resources for each chapter
NGS Teacher's Corner Glencoe Technology box	At the beginning of each chapter	Reference additional materials
Resource Manager box	At the point of use	Correlate subject matter to Teacher Classroom Resources
Section Focus	At the beginning of each section	Focus students' attention with opening transparency
Earth Science Online	In every chapter At the point where concept is taught	Integrate the Internet with chapter material Expand activities and homework Allow students to share data online
Demos	At the point where concept is taught	Help students visualize Earth science concepts
Cultural Diversity	One per chapter	Introduce diversity into Earth science topics
Differentiated Instruction	One per section	Use to develop teaching strategies for special needs students
✔ Assessment box	At point of use and in all labs	Use to assess students' understanding of material Use skill, performance, knowledge, and portfolio teaching strategies
Assessment Planner	At the beginning of each chapter	Correlate the assessments in each chapter

Classroom Management

Out of Time The *Out of Time* logo on the Chapter Opener page reminds you to use the GeoDigest if time does not permit teaching the entire chapter.

Resource Manager

Section Focus Transparency 13 L1 ELL

Study Guide for Content Mastery, pp. 31–32 L2

Resource Manager boxes *Resource Manager* boxes located at point of use show you where to integrate the many *Teacher Classroom Resources* materials into your lessons.

⏱ 0:00 Out of Time?

If time does not permit teaching the entire chapter, use the Chapter Summary on page 491 and the GeoDigest found at the end of the unit as an overview.

UNIT 5
GeoDigest

Prepare

Purpose
This GeoDigest can be used as an overview of plate tectonics and the processes and features associated with tectonism. If time is limited, you may wish to use this unit summary to teach the concepts presented in the chapters in Unit 5.

Key Concepts
Students are introduced to plate tectonics and some of the processes associated with tectonism, such as ridge push, slab pull, volcanism, seismicity, and orogeny.

1 Focus

Section Focus
Kinesthetic As you read the information about the three types of plate boundaries aloud, have students use their hands to model the movement associated with each boundary. L1 ELL

⏱ 0:00 Out of Time?
If time does not permit teaching the entire unit, use this GeoDigest as an overview.

546 UNIT 5

UNIT 5
GeoDigest

For a **preview** of Unit 5, study this GeoDigest before you read. After you have studied these chapters, you can use the Geo...

The Dynamic Earth

Plate Tectonics
Drifting Continents and Seafloor Spreading Continental drift, first hypothesized by Alfred Wegener, states that Earth's continents were once joined as a single landmass that broke up and drifted apart. Wegener used matching coastlines of Earth's continents, similar rocks and fossils, and ancient climatic data to support his hypothesis. Wegener, however, couldn't explain how or why the continents moved. The answer, seafloor spreading, was found by studying ocean-floor rocks and sediments. Magnetic patterns of ocean-floor rocks are symmetric in relation to ocean ridges, which indicates that oceanic crust on either side of the ridge is moving away from the ridge. Seafloor spreading occurs as magma rises toward the crust, cools and hardens to fill the gap that forms, and becomes a new section of oceanic crust.

The Theory of Plate Tectonics Earth's crust and the top of the upper mantle are broken into large slabs of rock called plates, which move at different rates over Earth's surface. Interactions occur at plate boundaries. At a divergent boundary, plates move apart; high heat flow, volcanism, and earthquakes are associated with divergent boundaries. At a convergent boundary, plates come together; deep-sea trenches, island arcs, and folded mountain ranges are associated with this type of boundary. At a transform boundary, plates slide past one another horizontally; faults and shallow earthquakes are associated with transform boundaries. Convection currents in Earth's mantle are related to

Soufrière, a composite con...

plate movements. Convection currents transfer energy through the movement of matter. Heat causes matter to expand and decrease in density. Warm matter is thus forced upward and cool matter is pulled downward. Ridge push is a tectonic process that occurs when the weight of an ocean ridge pushes a plate toward a subduction zone. Slab pull is a tectonic process that occurs when the weight of the subducting plate pulls a plate into a subduction zone.

Volcanic Activity
Magma The composition of magma is affected by temperature, pressure, and the presence of water. There are three main types of magma— basaltic, andesitic, and rhyolitic— that differ in the source rock from which they form, and also in composition, viscosity, silica content, amount of dissolved gases, and explosiveness.

Multiple Learning Styles
Look for the following icons for strategies that emphasize different learning modalities.
Kinesthetic Section Focus, p. 546
Visual-Spatial Project, p. 547
Linguistic Reteach, p. 549

GLENCOE Technology
Videodisc
The Infinite Voyage:
To the Edge of the Earth
Chapter 3: Exploring Volcanoes:
To the Center of the Earth 10:00

Section Focus The first step to teaching any set of concepts or skills is to focus the students' attention. Each numbered section begins with a *Section Focus* suggestion for using a *Section Focus Transparency* to focus the class on the key topic of the text section. A reduced transparency in the teacher margin lets you preview the transparency.

1 Focus

Section Focus

Before presenting the lesson, display **Section Focus Transparency 13** on the overhead projector. L1 ELL

Section Focus Transparency **13** OBSIDIAN
Use with Chapter 5, Section 5.2

❶ How would you describe the texture of this type of igneous rock?
❷ How do you think this type of rock formed? Why?

Section Focus Transparency   Earth Science: Geology, the Environment, and the Universe

Earth Science Online

Note Internet addresses that you find useful in the space below for quick reference.

_____

_____

_____

_____

For internet tips, see Glencoe's **Using the Internet in the Science Classroom.**

Earth Science Online Do you jot down interesting web sites on little scraps of paper, only to lose them before you can use them? The *Teacher Wraparound Edition* provides several *Earth Science Online* boxes at the bottom of the teacher margin of the chapter where you can write down those URLs you want to investigate.

Teacher Wraparound Edition: *Program Resources*

Interleaf Pages

Expanded Format The *Teacher Wraparound Edition* features a new, expanded four-page interleaf section. These expanded interleaves offer you an easy reference to all materials within the chapter, as well as extra content background for every section, including a unit *Identifying Misconceptions* feature.

Chapter Organizer Each chapter is preceded by a *Chapter Organizer,* a complete planning guide which lists the objectives, text features, and laboratory activities for each numbered section. Also correlated to each section are all the components of the Teacher Classroom Resources. In addition, National Science Content Standards correlated to each numbered section ensure that your lessons align well with the guidelines.

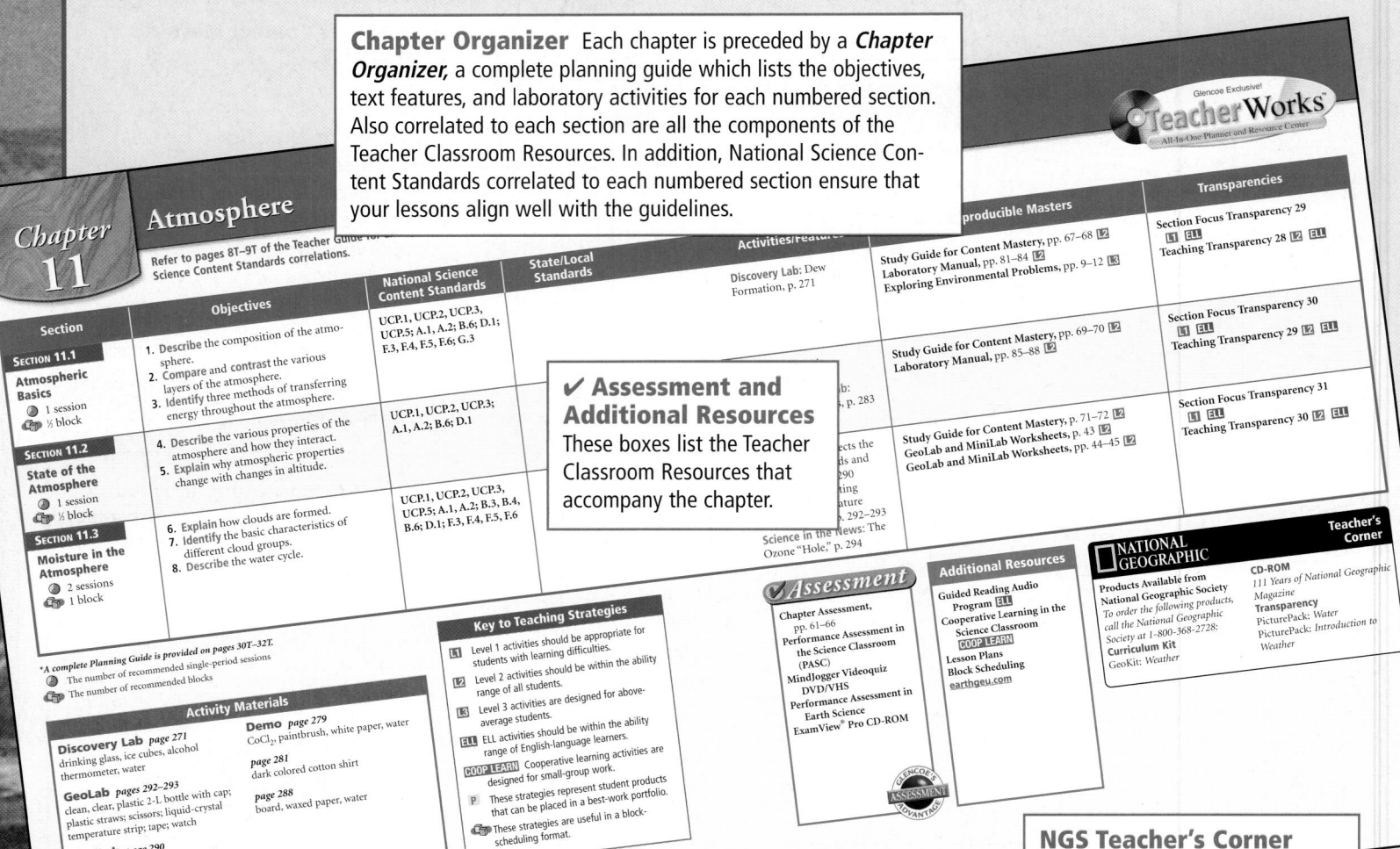

✔ Assessment and Additional Resources These boxes list the Teacher Classroom Resources that accompany the chapter.

Activity Materials This list of materials you will need for all the labs in the chapter is conveniently located at the point where you plan your lessons.

Key to Teaching Strategies The activities in the *Teacher Wraparound Edition* are broken down into three levels to accommodate all student ability levels. In addition, certain teaching strategies are designated as suitable for English-language learners or cooperative learning groups. Finally, strategies that produce work suitable for placement in student portfolios and strategies that are useful in a block scheduling format are called out with easy-to-find icons. Use this coding to select strategies and reproducible masters or transparencies for different learners.

NGS Teacher's Corner Handy *National Geographic Society* references can be used for group or individual reports or extra-credit work. Use them to check out or purchase appropriate materials for each chapter. Create a library corner in your classroom by asking your school librarian to locate back issues and other materials for student use.

Teacher Wraparound Edition: *Program Resources*

Content Background Every section is covered by a *Content Background*, which offers in-depth content on section material. This material expands on the section subject with more information at a higher level to assist the teacher in covering the chapter.

Identifying Misconceptions Presents common erroneous ideas that students often have about chapter subject material, including the correct information and suggestions for teaching it effectively. See page 33T for further explanation of *Identifying Misconceptions*.

Chapter 11 Atmosphere

Content Background

Earth's Primitive Atmosphere
Section 11.1

Earth's original atmosphere was probably composed mainly of methane and ammonia. In the first billion years after Earth formed, its surface was much more volcanically active than it is today. Thus, its primitive atmosphere changed over geologic time as erupting volcanoes emitted gases such as water vapor, chlorine, carbon dioxide, hydrogen, and nitrogen. Over millions of years, as the young planet cooled, the water vapor condensed and absorbed most of the carbon dioxide. Storm clouds formed and torrential rains began to fall. Scientists hypothesize that this water filled low basins on Earth's surface and ultimately formed the planet's first oceans. Oxygen was probably formed from the dissociation of water molecules and by photosynthesis of primitive cyanobacteria.

Smog
Section 11.1

In addition to gases and microscopic solids, the atmosphere contains smog, a form of pollution. Exhaust from cars and other vehicles expels nitrogen oxides and unburned hydrocarbons into the air. These pollutants mix with oxygen and other chemicals in the presence of sunlight to form photochemical smog, a type of brown smog common in Los Angeles and Mexico City. Sulfur oxides from burning fossil fuels such as coal and oil produce a gray smog known as sulfurous smog. The burning of fossil fuels releases sulfur compounds, dust, and smoke particles into the air. Sulfurous smog forms when these substances collect in areas where there's little or no wind. In such a case, a blanket of gray smog may hang over a city for several days.

The Transfer of Energy
Section 11.1

The transfer of energy by radiation does not involve matter. In theory, the transfer of energy by convection distributes energy until equilibrium is reached. On Earth, however, equilibrium is never attained. The tropics always receive more radiant energy than the rest of Earth. Therefore, energy transfer is always occurring in the atmosphere.

Properties of Air
Section 11.2

Because air is composed of matter, it has many properties. Air can absorb and retain heat, move, hold moisture, and exert pressure. The main source of atmospheric heat is Earth's surface. Thus, the air near the surface is usually warmest, and temperature usually decreases with height through the troposphere. The moisture that air holds can be present in varying amounts and in all three states of matter. The density of air varies, depending on how many molecules of air are present in a certain space. The weight of a parcel of air is dependent on its density and temperature, so changes in these properties affect how much pressure air exerts.

The Water Cycle
Section 11.3

Worldwide each year, about 500 000 km^3 of water evaporates. About 110 000 km^3 of this water eventually falls on land as precipitation; the rest falls as rain, snow, or sleet into the oceans. Some of the water that falls on land is absorbed by plants, filters into the soil, fills lakes, or becomes runoff that eventually flows to the oceans. During evaporation, heat energy causes the water molecules to move apart. The water then changes from a liquid to a gas. During condensation, water molecules lose energy and move closer together. The water changes from a gas to a liquid.

Identifying Misconceptions

Because air cannot, for the most part, be readily detected by our senses, it is natural for students to believe that Earth's atmosphere is composed of basically nothing. Help them to understand that air is matter, and thus it is made up of different substances with distinct physical and chemical properties. Explain that even though we can't readily detect air, it has physical and chemical properties, many of which can be measured. Have students compare the weights of an inflated balloon and a noninflated balloon to demonstrate that air has mass.

Multiple Learning Styles

- **Kinesthetic** Demo, p. 272
- **Visual-Spatial** Activity, p. 275; Modeling, p. 276; Demo, pp. 279, 288
- **Linguistic** Reteach, p. 277; Earth Science Journal, p. 280; Applying Earth Science, p. 283
- **Interpersonal** Activity, p. 285; Collaborative Learning, p. 289

GLENCOE Technology

The following multimedia resources are available from Glencoe.

The Infinite Voyage Series
Crisis in the Atmosphere
Secrets from a Frozen World
Vocabulary Puzzlemaker
TeacherWorks™ CD-ROM
MindJogger Videoquizzes DVD/VHS
ExamView® Pro CD-ROM
Interactive Chalkboard CD-ROM

 Assessment

Portfolio Assessment
Assessment, TWE, pp. 277, 291

Performance Assessment
Discovery Lab, SE, p. 271
Discovery Lab, TWE, p. 271
MiniLab, SE, p. 290
GeoLab, SE, pp. 292–293

Knowledge Assessment
Assessment, TWE, pp. 276, 281, 284, 289
Problem-Solving Lab, TWE, p. 283
GeoLab, TWE, pp. 292–293
Section Assessment, SE, pp. 277, 284, 291
Chapter Assessment, SE, pp. 296–297

Skill Assessment
MiniLab, TWE, p. 290

Earth Science Online
Be sure to check the Earth Science Web Site for links to chapter material: earthgeu.com

270C CHAPTER 11

270D

Glencoe Technology box A *Glencoe Technology* box for each chapter summarizes the technology materials available for the chapter from Glencoe. Look for more detailed information about these technology materials at point of use in the margins of the *Teacher Wraparound Edition*.

Teacher Wraparound Edition: *Program Resources*

Diversity in the Classroom

In an effort to provide all students with a positive science experience, *Earth Science: Geology, the Environment, and the Universe Teacher Wraparound Edition* offers a variety of ways for students to interact with materials so that they use their preferred method of learning.

Multiple Learning Styles

Kinesthetic MiniLab, p. 474

Visual-Spatial Discovery Lab, p. 471, Modeling, p. 481

Interpersonal Collaborative Learning, p. 482, Project, p. 484, Reteach, pp. 475, 479, 487

Linguistic Using Scientific Terms, pp. 477, 484

Logical-Mathematical Enrichment, p. 478

Multiple Learning Styles The *Teacher Wraparound Edition* provides a number of strategies for encouraging students with diverse learning styles. Look for the various learning style icons that identify strategies suitable for each style of learning. Strategies in each chapter are summarized in the Multiple Learning Styles box at the bottom of the chapter opener page.

Differentiated Instruction

Gifted Salt is mined from regions of the world other than those discussed in this section. Have students conduct research to discover where else salt is mined. Have them compare the different geological and environmental settings where these salt deposits occur. **L3**

Differentiated Instruction

Behaviorally Disordered To encourage students who are behaviorally disordered to learn the section content, ask them to find additional information about the Paleozoic sedimentary rocks of the Grand Canyon. Encourage students to use the library and the Earth Science Web Site at **earthgeu.com** to collect both descriptive and visual materials. Students can also contact the National Park System for more information.

Differentiated Instruction
Use these teaching strategies and student activities to structure the learning environment in your classroom to meet students' special needs.

Cultural Diversity Respond to diversity by sharing with students the *Cultural Diversity* connections found at the bottom of the page in every chapter of the *Teacher Wraparound Edition.*

Cultural Diversity

Estella Leopold (1927–) Paleoecology is the study of prehistoric organisms and their environments. Estella Leopold attempts to re-create ancient landscapes by comparing modern assemblages of pollen, spores, and leaves to fossilized vegetation. In this way, she creates images of past landscapes.

After graduating from Yale in 1955, Leopold worked for the U. S. Geological Survey and studied rocks in the Rocky Mountains to reconstruct the evolution of ancient forests. Leopold found that

patterns of evolution a climatic changes. She of trees lived in mode erate climates were m older species.

Leopold has won man Science Foundation fo served on such conser National Audubon Soc and the Colorado Wild

Teacher Wraparound Edition: *Program Resources*

✓ Assessment

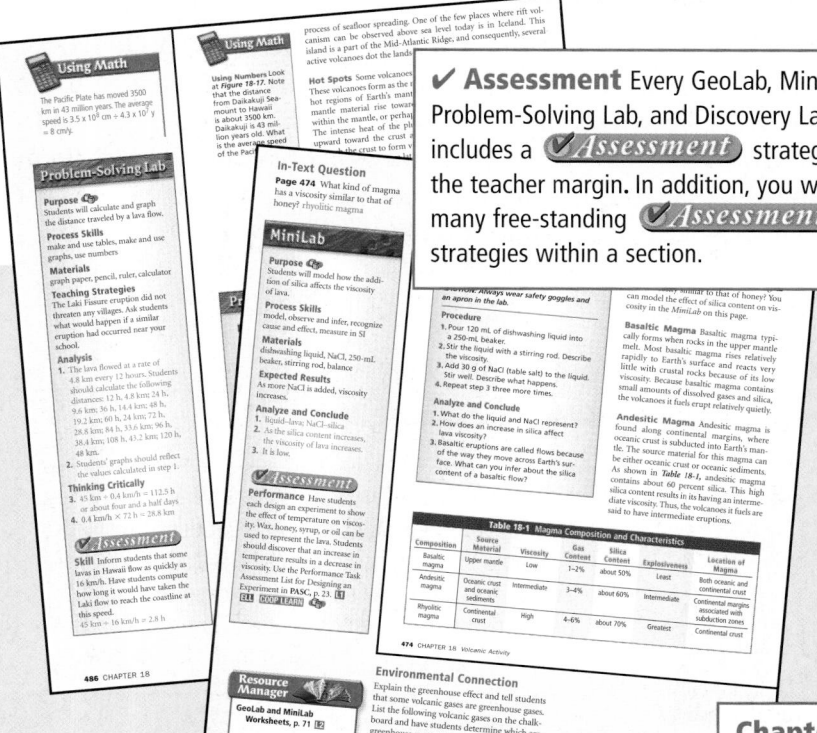

✔ **Assessment** Every GeoLab, MiniLab, Problem-Solving Lab, and Discovery Lab includes a ✓*Assessment* strategy in the teacher margin. In addition, you will find many free-standing ✓*Assessment* strategies within a section.

NY Core Curriculum Standards Correlations to the New York Core Curriculum standards have been placed on each two-page spread of the *Teacher Wraparound Edition* so you can be sure that the concepts on those pages meet your state guidelines.

NY Core Curriculum Standards

Page 546: St 4 KI 2.1j, 2.1l, 2.1m, 2.1n, & 2.1p

Page 547: St 4 KI 2.1j, 2.1k, 2.1m, 2.1n, & 2.1p

Chapter Assessments All Chapter Assessment questions and answers have been validated for accuracy. All Chapter Assessment questions have been checked against the chapter's objectives to ensure that the objectives are adequately tested. You can be sure when you assign a Chapter Assessment question that it reflects the content of the chapter in an accurate and suitable way for your class.

✓ Assessment

Assessment, TWE p. 479

Discovery Lab, SE and TWE p. 471
MiniLab, SE and TWE p. 474
Assessment, TWE p. 475
Problem-Solving Lab, SE p. 486
GeoLab, SE and TWE pp. 488–489

Assessment, TWE p. 478
Section Assessment, SE pp. 475, 479, 487
Chapter Assessment, SE pp. 492–493

Discovery Lab, SE p. 471
MiniLab, SE p. 474
Problem-Solving Lab, SE p. 486
Section Assessment, SE pp. 475, 479, 487
Chapter Assessment, SE pp. 492–493

Assessment Planner All the assessments in a chapter are summarized in the *Assessment Planner* located on the D page at the beginning of every chapter. A variety of Skill, Knowledge, Performance, and Portfolio assessment strategies provide more than enough for you to know exactly how much of the lesson each student understands.

21T

Teacher Classroom Resources: *Program Resources*

Resources for All Your Needs

In addition to the wide array of instructional options provided in the student and teacher editions, *Earth Science: Geology, the Environment, and the Universe* offers an extensive list of support materials and program resources. Some of these materials offer alternative ways of presenting your Earth Science program, others provide tools for reinforcing core concepts and evaluating student learning, and still others will help you extend and enrich your course. You won't have time to use them all, but the ones you use will help you make the best use of the time you have.

Hands-On Learning

GeoLab and MiniLab Worksheets Each of the GeoLabs and MiniLabs in the student text is also available in copymaster form in *GeoLab and Mini-Lab Worksheets.* As students proceed with a lab, have them copy their observations and data on the expanded data tables provided in these worksheets.

Laboratory Manual, Student Edition and Teacher Edition If you want more hands-on options, the *Laboratory Manual* offers two more labs for each chapter. Choose from a selection of traditional labs, Design Your Own labs, and mapping labs to provide students with a variety of laboratory experiences that reinforce the Earth science principles in the text.

Enrichment and Application

Exploring Environmental Problems, Student Edition and Teacher Edition
Exploring Environmental Problems incorporates several of the environmental issues covered daily by the media into research-based labs. These activities will allow students to use the Global Positioning System (GPS) and a variety of computer-based instruments to solve problems.

Teacher Classroom Resources: *Program Resources*

✔ Assessment

Review Handbook for Regents Earth Science Exam This handbook includes content summaries and questions that reflect the major concepts and themes of the text. These review questions serve as preparation for the end-of-course test. Each question has been correlated to the New York standards and key ideas.

Chapter Assessment *Chapter Assessment* includes a four-part assessment tool for every chapter that helps you assess process as well as content objectives. Unique simulations require students to analyze experimental designs and interpret data.

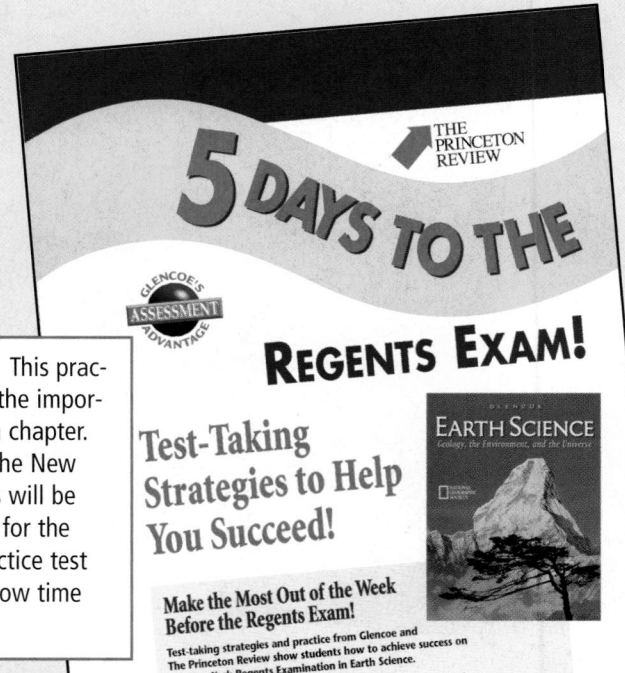

5 Days to the Regents Exam This practice test includes questions that cover the important concepts and processes from each chapter. Each question has been correlated to the New York standards and key ideas. Students will be able to gain insight on what to expect for the actual end-of-course test. Give the practice test one week prior to the actual test to allow time for you to answer students' questions.

Teacher Classroom Resources: *Program Resources*

✔ Assessment

Multimedia Assessment Options (MindJogger, ExamView® Pro Test Bank, PuzzleMaker)
Multimedia Assessment Options offer you assessment options in the form of MindJogger Videoquizzes, ExamView® Pro Test Bank, and Vocabulary PuzzleMaker computer software. You will never have to write another test question with the options you have.

Review and Reinforcement

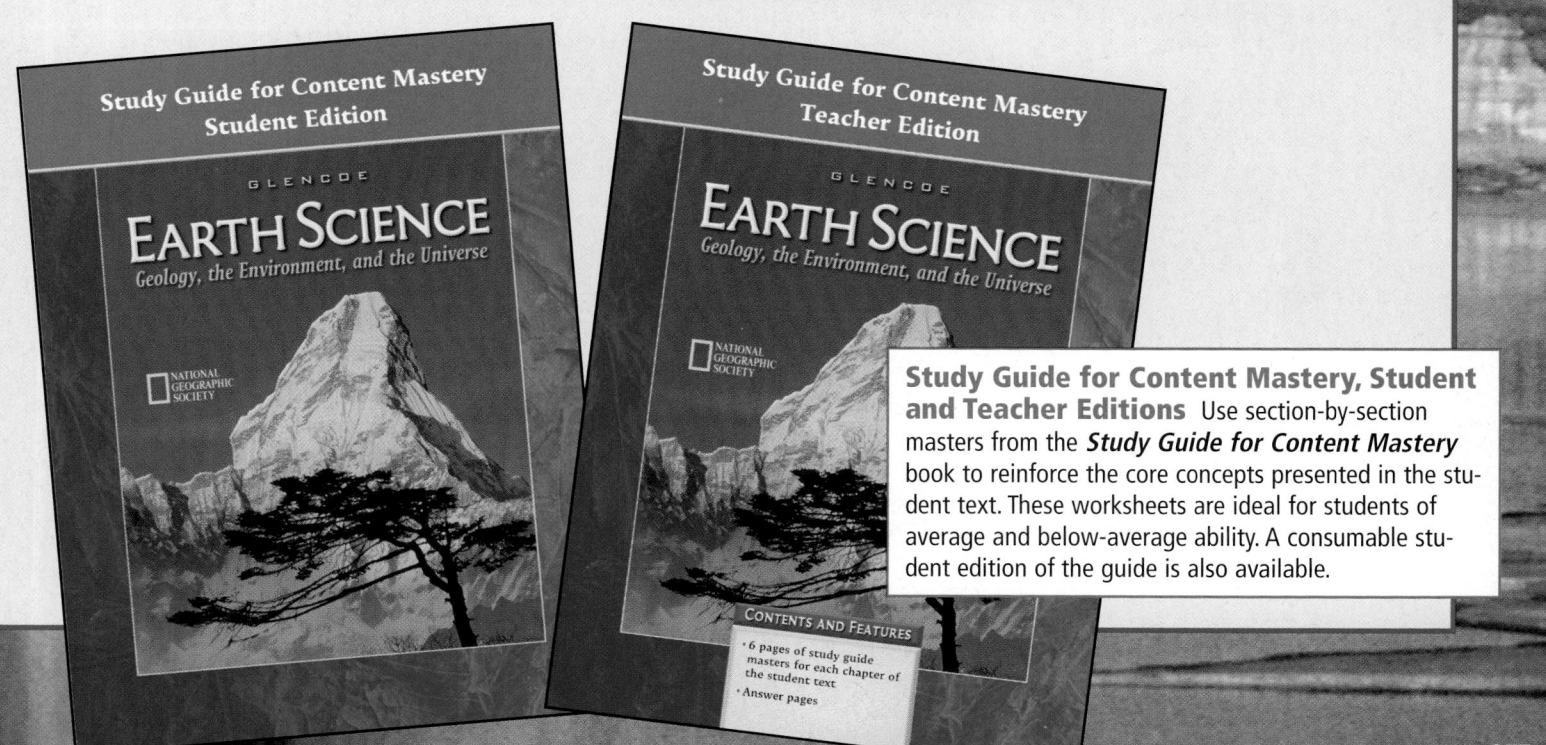

Study Guide for Content Mastery, Student and Teacher Editions Use section-by-section masters from the *Study Guide for Content Mastery* book to reinforce the core concepts presented in the student text. These worksheets are ideal for students of average and below-average ability. A consumable student edition of the guide is also available.

Teacher Classroom Resources: *Program Resources*

Teaching Aids

Lesson Plans and Block Scheduling *Lesson Plans* offer you a complete planning resource by correlating objectives, activities, and program resources for every lesson. Each plan is geared to the teaching cycle employed in the *Teacher Wraparound Edition* and contains a complete list of all the resources available for that numbered section. If you use block scheduling, the *Block Scheduling* book offers the same resources for your schedule.

Section Focus Transparencies and Masters The full-color transparencies in the *Section Focus Transparency Package* provide a way for you to begin each lesson by capturing the attention of your students with simple questions. Each numbered section begins with a strategy that shows a photo of the Section Focus Transparency for that section. The package also contains a booklet of blackline masters of all transparencies.

Glencoe Exclusive!

TeacherWorks™ *TeacherWorks™* provides instant access to all classroom resources, including transparencies, allowing you to quickly and efficiently preview chapters and lessons to reduce preparation time.

Teaching Transparencies and Masters These full-color teaching transparencies reinforce concepts taught in the student text. Each transparency is accompanied by a worksheet and blackline master.

Glencoe Technology

Glencoe's *Earth Science: Geology, the Environment, and the Universe* offers a broad array of new technology to enhance your students' Earth science experience.

Guided Reading Audio Program

Comprehensive chapter overviews in Spanish and English are a way for auditory learners, students with reading difficulties, and ELL students to review key chapter concepts. Students can listen individually during class or check out tapes and use them at home. Audio CDs can be used to provide effective responses to questions in the *Study Guide for Content Mastery*.

ExamView® Pro Test Bank Design and create your own test instruments from our *ExamView® Pro Test Bank* for Windows and Macintosh. Select your own test items by objective from two different levels of difficulty, or write and edit your own.

MindJogger Videoquizzes The interactive quiz-show format of *Earth Science: Geology, the Environment, and the Universe MindJogger Videoquizzes* provides fun for your students while reviewing core concepts for every chapter. Available in VHS and DVD formats.

Earth Science Web Site The Earth Science Web Site provides students and teachers with a wide range of materials. On the student site, links to other web sites provide more information on the topics being studied. Projects give students an opportunity to research and share data with other students. The Interactive Tutor provides online worksheets for study and review. The teacher site contains professional development resources for teaching Earth Science.

Glencoe Technology

Earth Science Web Site: ny.science.glencoe.com
Internet Support for Your Earth Science Classroom

In-text Earth Science Online boxes at point of use in the unit and chapter direct students to use Web curriculum as part of an integrated study of chapter content.

Science Home   Product Info   Site Map   Search   Contact Us

Science Earth Science:
Geology, the Environment, and

Be sure to check out the Online Study Tools!

- Chapter Resources
- Internet GeoLabs
- Extending The Content
- Online Study Tools
- National Geographic Society

You Need:	Current Content
We Provide:	Updated Information and Current Event Resources via the Web
You Need:	Help with Assessment
We Provide:	Self-Check Quizzes, Skill Review, Interactive Puzzles and Problems
You Need:	Integration of Web Resources into Your Lessons
We Provide:	Internet Labs, Post Data, Interactive Games and Activities, Teacher Strategies, and Additional Links

Use our Web site for additional resources. All essential content is covered in the Student Edition.

Our Pledge to You Glencoe is committed to providing textbooks that are as error-free and as accurate as possible. As part of this commitment, we will be updating critical time-sensitive data such as charts, graphs, and statistics along with the latest information in the field of Earth Science on our Web site. In this way, you and your students will always have access to the most accurate information possible.

ny.science.glencoe.com monitors all links and updates them to maintain chapter relevancy

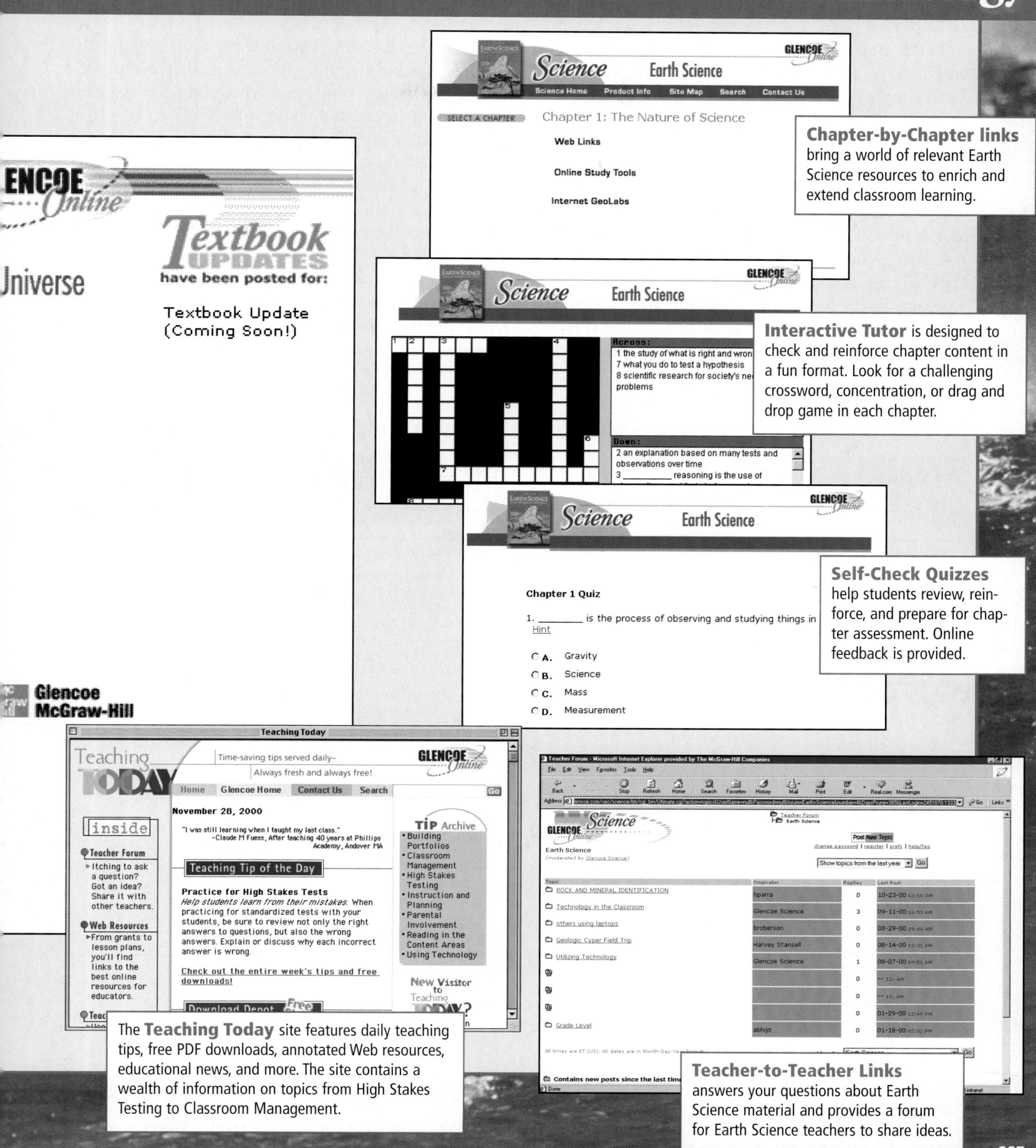

Chapter-by-Chapter links bring a world of relevant Earth Science resources to enrich and extend classroom learning.

Interactive Tutor is designed to check and reinforce chapter content in a fun format. Look for a challenging crossword, concentration, or drag and drop game in each chapter.

Self-Check Quizzes help students review, reinforce, and prepare for chapter assessment. Online feedback is provided.

The **Teaching Today** site features daily teaching tips, free PDF downloads, annotated Web resources, educational news, and more. The site contains a wealth of information on topics from High Stakes Testing to Classroom Management.

Teacher-to-Teacher Links answers your questions about Earth Science material and provides a forum for Earth Science teachers to share ideas.

Course Planning Guide

Earth Science: Geology, the Environment, and the Universe provides a complete selection of core concepts that are presented in a way to meet the needs of all your students. As the teacher, you are in the best position to design an Earth Science course that meets the needs of individual students and classes, sets the pace at which the content is covered, and determines what material should be given the most emphasis. To assist you in planning the course, the following course planning guide is provided.

Earth Science: Geology, the Environment, and the Universe may be used in a full-year, two semesters program that is comprised of 165 periods of approximately 45 minutes each. This type of schedule is represented in the table under the heading of Single-class Scheduling. This table also outlines a plan under the heading Block Scheduling for schools that use a block scheduling system. With block scheduling, it is assumed that the course will be taught for 90 class periods of approximately 90 minutes each. Both single-class and block scheduling times also appear in the Chapter Organizer, located in the interleaf pages of the *Teacher Edition.* Time allotment for the Chapter Assessment is added to the last section of the chapter in the Chapter Organizer.

Please remember that the planning guide is provided as an aid in planning the best course for your students. Use this guide in relation to your curriculum and the ability levels of the classes you teach.

Course Planning Guide for
Earth Science: Geology, the Environment, and the Universe

Chapter/Session	Single-class Scheduling (165 days)	Block Scheduling (90 days)
1 The Nature of Science	**3**	**$1\frac{1}{2}$**
1.1 Earth Science	1	$\frac{1}{2}$
1.2 Methods of Scientists	$\frac{1}{2}$	$\frac{1}{4}$
1.3 Communicating in Science	$\frac{1}{2}$	$\frac{1}{4}$
Chapter Assessment	1	$\frac{1}{2}$
2 Mapping Our World	**4**	**2**
2.1 Latitude and Longitude	1	$\frac{1}{2}$
2.2 Types of Maps	1	$\frac{1}{2}$
2.3 Remote Sensing	1	$\frac{1}{2}$
Chapter Assessment	1	$\frac{1}{2}$
GeoDigest Earth Science	**1**	**$\frac{1}{2}$**
3 Matter and Atomic Structure	**3**	**$1\frac{1}{2}$**
3.1 What are elements?	$\frac{1}{2}$	$\frac{1}{4}$
3.2 How Atoms Combine	$\frac{1}{2}$	$\frac{1}{4}$
3.3 States of Matter	1	$\frac{1}{2}$
Chapter Assessment	1	$\frac{1}{2}$
4 Minerals	**5**	**$2\frac{1}{2}$**
4.1 What is a mineral?	1	$\frac{1}{2}$
4.2 Identifying Minerals	3	$1\frac{1}{2}$
Chapter Assessment	1	$\frac{1}{2}$

Chapter/Session	Single-class Scheduling (165 days)	Block Scheduling (90 days)
5 Igneous Rocks	**5**	**3**
5.1 What are igneous rocks?	$1\frac{1}{2}$	1
5.2 Classifying Igneous Rocks	$2\frac{1}{2}$	$1\frac{1}{2}$
Chapter Assessment	1	$\frac{1}{2}$
6 Sedimentary and Metamorphic Rocks	**5**	**3**
6.1 Formation of Sedimentary Rocks	$1\frac{1}{2}$	1
6.2 Types of Sedimentary Rocks	1	$\frac{1}{2}$
6.3 Metamorphic Rocks	$1\frac{1}{2}$	1
Chapter Assessment	1	$\frac{1}{2}$
GeoDigest Composition of Earth	**1**	**$\frac{1}{2}$**
7 Weathering, Erosion, and Soil	**5**	**3**
7.1 Weathering	1	$\frac{1}{2}$
7.2 Erosion and Deposition	1	$\frac{1}{2}$
7.3 Formation of Soil	2	$\frac{1}{2}$
Chapter Assessment	1	$\frac{1}{2}$
8 Mass Movements, Wind, and Glaciers	**5**	**$2\frac{1}{2}$**
8.1 Mass Movement at Earth's Surface	2	1
8.2 Wind	1	$\frac{1}{2}$

Chapter/Session	Single-class Scheduling (165 days)	Block Scheduling (90 days)
8.3 Glaciers	1	$\frac{1}{2}$
Chapter Assessment	1	$\frac{1}{2}$
9 Surface Water	**6**	**3**
9.1 Surface Water Movement	2	1
9.2 Stream Development	$1\frac{1}{2}$	1
9.3 Lakes and Freshwater Wetlands	$1\frac{1}{2}$	1
Chapter Assessment	1	$\frac{1}{2}$
10 Groundwater	**5**	**3**
10.1 Movement and Storage of Groundwater	2	$1\frac{1}{4}$
10.2 Groundwater Erosion and Deposition	$1\frac{1}{2}$	1
10.3 Groundwater Systems	$\frac{1}{2}$	$\frac{1}{4}$
Chapter Assessment	1	$\frac{1}{2}$
GeoDigest **Surface Processes on Earth**	**1**	$\frac{1}{2}$
11 Atmosphere	**4**	**2**
11.1 Atmospheric Basics	1	$\frac{1}{2}$
11.2 State of the Atmosphere	1	$\frac{1}{2}$
11.3 Moisture in the Atmosphere	1	$\frac{1}{2}$
Chapter Assessment	1	$\frac{1}{2}$
12 Meteorology	**5**	**3**
12.1 The Causes of Weather	1	$\frac{1}{2}$
12.2 Weather Systems	2	1
12.3 Gathering Weather Data	$\frac{1}{2}$	$\frac{1}{2}$
12.4 Weather Analysis	$\frac{1}{2}$	$\frac{1}{2}$
Chapter Assessment	1	$\frac{1}{2}$
13 The Nature of Storms	**5**	$2\frac{1}{2}$
13.1 Thunderstorms	1	$\frac{1}{2}$
13.2 Severe Weather	1	$\frac{1}{2}$
13.3 Tropical Storms	1	$\frac{1}{2}$
13.4 Recurring Weather	1	$\frac{1}{2}$
Chapter Assessment	1	$\frac{1}{2}$
14 Climate	**5**	**3**
14.1 What is climate?	$\frac{1}{2}$	$\frac{1}{4}$
14.2 Climate Classification	$\frac{1}{2}$	$\frac{1}{4}$
14.3 Climate Changes	$1\frac{1}{2}$	1
14.4 The Human Factor	$1\frac{1}{2}$	1
Chapter Assessment	1	$\frac{1}{2}$
15 Physical Oceanography	**6**	$3\frac{1}{2}$
15.1 The Oceans	$1\frac{1}{2}$	1
15.2 Seawater	$1\frac{1}{2}$	1
15.3 Ocean Movements	2	1
Chapter Assessment	1	$\frac{1}{2}$
16 The Marine Environment	**4**	$2\frac{1}{2}$
16.1 Shoreline Features	1	$\frac{1}{2}$
16.2 The Seafloor	2	$1\frac{1}{2}$
Chapter Assessment	1	$\frac{1}{2}$
GeoDigest **The Atmosphere and the Oceans**	**1**	$\frac{1}{2}$
17 Plate Tectonics	**6**	$3\frac{1}{2}$
17.1 Drifting Continents	1	$\frac{1}{2}$
17.2 Seafloor Spreading	$1\frac{1}{2}$	1
17.3 Theory of Plate Tectonics	$1\frac{1}{2}$	1
17.4 Causes of Plate Motion	1	$\frac{1}{2}$
Chapter Assessment	1	$\frac{1}{2}$
18 Volcanic Activity	**6**	$2\frac{1}{2}$
18.1 Magma	$1\frac{1}{2}$	$\frac{1}{2}$
18.2 Intrusive Activity	$1\frac{1}{2}$	1
18.3 Volcanoes	2	1
Chapter Assessment	1	$1\frac{1}{2}$
19 Earthquakes	**6**	$3\frac{1}{2}$
19.1 Forces Within Earth	1	$1\frac{1}{2}$
19.2 Seismic Waves and Earth's Interior	$1\frac{1}{2}$	1
19.3 Measuring and Locating Earthquakes	$1\frac{1}{2}$	1
19.4 Earthquakes and Society	1	$\frac{1}{2}$
Chapter Assessment	1	$\frac{1}{2}$
20 Mountain Building	**6**	**3**
20.1 Crust-Mantle Relationships	1	$\frac{1}{2}$
20.2 Convergent-Boundary Mountains	1	$\frac{1}{2}$
20.3 Other Types of Mountains	3	$1\frac{1}{2}$
Chapter Assessment	1	$\frac{1}{2}$
GeoDigest The Dynamic Earth	**1**	$\frac{1}{2}$

Course Planning Guide

Chapter/Session	Single-class Scheduling (165 days)	Block Scheduling (90 days)
21 Fossils and the Rock Record	6	3
21.1 The Geologic Time Scale	2	1
21.2 Relative-Age Dating of Rocks	$\frac{1}{2}$	$\frac{1}{4}$
21.3 Absolute-Age Dating of Rocks	$1\frac{1}{2}$	$\frac{3}{4}$
21.4 Remains of Organisms in the Rock Record	1	$\frac{1}{2}$
Chapter Assessment	1	$\frac{1}{2}$
22 The Precambrian Earth	4	2
22.1 The Early Earth	$\frac{1}{2}$	$\frac{1}{4}$
22.2 Formation of the Crust and Continents	1	$\frac{1}{2}$
22.3 Formation of the Atmosphere and Oceans	$\frac{1}{2}$	$\frac{1}{2}$
22.4 Early Life on Earth	1	$\frac{1}{2}$
Chapter Assessment	1	$\frac{1}{2}$
23 The Paleozoic Era	5	2
23.1 The Early Paleozoic	1	$\frac{1}{2}$
23.2 The Middle Paleozoic	1	$\frac{1}{2}$
23.3 The Late Paleozoic	2	$\frac{1}{2}$
Chapter Assessment	1	$\frac{1}{2}$
24 The Mesozoic and Cenozoic Eras	5	$2\frac{1}{2}$
24.1 Mesozoic Paleogeography	1	$\frac{1}{2}$
24.2 Mesozoic Life	1	$\frac{1}{2}$
24.3 Cenozoic Paleogeography	1	$\frac{1}{2}$
24.4 Cenozoic Life	1	$\frac{1}{2}$
Chapter Assessment	1	$\frac{1}{2}$
GeoDigest Geologic Time	**1**	$\frac{1}{2}$
25 Earth Resources	6	$3\frac{1}{2}$
25.1 What are resources?	1	$\frac{1}{2}$
25.2 Land Resources	$1\frac{1}{2}$	1
25.3 Air Resources	$1\frac{1}{2}$	1
25.4 Water Resources	1	$\frac{1}{2}$
Chapter Assessment	1	$\frac{1}{2}$
26 Energy Resources	5	$2\frac{1}{2}$
26.1 Conventional Energy Resources	2	1
26.2 Alternative Energy Resources	1	$\frac{1}{2}$
26.3 Conservation of Energy Resources	1	$\frac{1}{2}$

Chapter/Session	Single-class Scheduling (165 days)	Block Scheduling (90 days)
Chapter Assessment	1	$\frac{1}{2}$
27 Human Impact on Earth Resources	5	3
27.1 Populations and the Use of Natural Resources	1	1
27.2 Human Impact on Land Resources	1	$\frac{1}{2}$
27.3 Human Impact on Air Resources	1	$\frac{1}{2}$
27.4 Human Impact on Water Resources	1	$\frac{1}{2}$
Chapter Assessment	1	$\frac{1}{2}$
GeoDigest Resources and the Environment	**1**	$\frac{1}{2}$
28 The Sun-Earth-Moon System	5	3
28.1 Tools of Astronomy	1	$\frac{1}{2}$
28.2 The Moon	1	$\frac{1}{2}$
28.3 The Sun-Earth-Moon System	2	$1\frac{1}{2}$
Chapter Assessment	1	$\frac{1}{2}$
29 Our Solar System	6	$3\frac{1}{2}$
29.1 Overview of Our Solar System	$1\frac{1}{2}$	1
29.2 The Terrestrial Planets	1	$\frac{1}{2}$
29.3 The Gas Giant Planets	1	$\frac{1}{2}$
29.4 Formation of Our Solar System	$1\frac{1}{2}$	1
Chapter Assessment	1	$\frac{1}{2}$
30 Stars	6	$3\frac{1}{2}$
30.1 The Sun	1	$\frac{1}{2}$
30.2 Measuring the Stars	2	$1\frac{1}{2}$
30.3 Stellar Evolution	2	1
Chapter Assessment	1	$\frac{1}{2}$
31 Galaxies and the Universe	5	3
31.1 The Milky Way Galaxy	1	$\frac{1}{2}$
31.2 Other Galaxies in the Universe	$1\frac{1}{2}$	1
31.3 Cosmology	$1\frac{1}{2}$	1
Chapter Assessment	1	$\frac{1}{2}$
GeoDigest Beyond Earth	**1**	$\frac{1}{2}$
Total sessions	**165**	**90**

Identifying Misconceptions

Earth Science: Geology, the Environment, and the Universe contains many opportunities to find, explore, and correct misconceptions about Earth science that students may have.

Each chapter begins with an Identifying Misconceptions that has been reviewed by an expert in science misconceptions. This introductory element anticipates erroneous ideas that students may bring to the chapter before material is presented.

Identifying Misconceptions

Because air cannot, for the most part, be readily detected by our senses, it is natural for students to believe that Earth's atmosphere is composed of basically nothing. Help them to understand that air is matter, and thus it is made up of different substances with distinct physical and chemical properties. Explain that even though we can't readily detect air, it has physical and chemical properties, many of which can be measured. Have students compare the weights of an inflated balloon and a noninflated balloon to demonstrate that air has mass.

Identifying Misconceptions

Some students might think that the basic shapes of continental coastlines have remained unchanged since the break-up of Pangaea.

Uncover the Misconception
Have students make a sketch of what they think North America looked like when the Atlantic Ocean started to open, about 200 M.Y.B.P.

Demonstrate the Concept
If necessary, help students identify North America in the series of sketches in **Figure 17-1.** Have students compare their sketches with those in the figure.

Assess New Knowledge
Have students make a series of sketches of North America using **Figure 17-1.** Ask students to sequence the sketches from oldest to most recent and write three or four sentences that describe how the overall shape of the continent has changed over the past 200 million years.

Each chapter contains a four-part Identifying Misconceptions.

Introductory paragraph explains the misconception that students may have concerning the chapter topic.

Uncover the Misconception explores the origin of the misconception.

Demonstrate the Concept provides new information to correct the current misconception and replace it with sound, scientific knowledge.

Assess New Knowledge has students demonstrate their grasp of the correct information.

Teaching Strategies

Assessment

The *Earth Science: Geology, the Environment, and the Universe* program has been designed to provide you with a variety of assessment tools, both formal and informal, to help you develop a clearer picture of your students' progress.

Performance Assessment

Various methods of assessing individual student performance are becoming more common in today's schools. These performance assessments differ in formality and complexity, but in most cases, the teacher observes a student or group of students involved in an activity and rates the performance and/or the products that result from the activity. Background information and specific examples of performance assessment are included in Glencoe's *Alternate Assessment in the Science Classroom.*

Earth Science: Geology, the Environment, and the Universe provides numerous opportunities to observe student behavior both in informal and formal settings. Each *Geolab, Problem-Solving Lab, MiniLab,* and *Discovery Lab* contains suggestions that will enable you to assess students' understanding of both concepts and process skills. Another approach for assessing student mastery of concepts and skills in the laboratory is provided in Glencoe's *Performance Assessment in Earth Science.* It features two activities per unit that enable you to evaluate students' skills and knowledge.

Group Performance Assessment

Recent research has shown that cooperative learning structures produce improved student learning outcomes for students of all ability levels. *Earth Science: Geology, the Environment, and the Universe* provides many opportunities for cooperative learning and, as a result, many opportunities to observe group work processes and products. Glencoe's *Cooperative Learning in the Science Classroom* provides strategies and resources for implementing and evaluating group activities.

In cooperative group assessment, all members of the group contribute to the work process and its products. For example, if a mixed-ability, four-member laboratory work group conducts an activity, you can use a rating scale or checklist to assess the quality of both group interaction and work skills. All four members of the group are expected to review and agree on the data sheet produced by the group. You can require each member to certify the group's results by signing the data sheet or lab report. In this approach, all members of the group receive the same grade on the work product. Research shows that cooperative group assessment is as valid as individual assessment. Additionally, it reduces the marking and grading workload of the teacher.

Portfolios: Putting It All Together

The purpose of a student or cooperative group portfolio is to present examples of the individual's or group's work in a nontesting environment. A portfolio is simply a method for assembling and presenting selected examples of work products. The process of assembling the portfolio should be both integrative (of process and content) and reflective. The performance portfolio is not a complete collection of all worksheets and other assignments for a grading period.

At its best, the portfolio should include integrated performance products that show growth in concept attainment and skill development. You can structure the portfolio development process by establishing categories and other limiting specifications. An essential component in portfolio development is the composition of a submission letter or reflective paper that lists the contents of the portfolio and discusses growth in knowledge, attitudes, and skills.

Earth Science: Geology, the Environment, and the Universe presents a wealth of opportunities for performance portfolio development. Each chapter contains projects; enrichment activities; laboratory investigations; skill reviews; suggestions for library research; features with critical-thinking opportunities; and connections to life, social studies, and the arts. Each of these student activities results in a product. A mixture of these products can be used to document student growth during the grading period.

In addition, *Earth Science: Geology, the Environment, and the Universe* strongly suggests the use of student journals. Students are encouraged to write observations, descriptions, and reflections in their journals. They are also encouraged to include diagrams and drawings. Excerpts from the student journal can be included in an individual or group portfolio. Additionally, as many writers have discovered, the journal will be an excellent resource for developing the reflective submission letter or paper.

Content Assessment

The *Earth Science: Geology, the Environment, and the Universe* program contains numerous strategies and an assortment of traditional aids for evaluating student progress toward mastery of science concepts. Concluding each numbered section in the *Student Edition, Section Assessment* questions are presented. This spaced review process helps build learning bridges that allow all students to progress confidently from one lesson to the next.

After instruction for the chapter is completed, a summation of the major concepts is presented. Small groups of students can research the major concepts in the chapter and present restatements of their meaning in writing and as oral reports to the class.

After the main idea presentations, the formal review process for the written content assessment can begin. *Earth Science: Geology, the Environment, and the Universe* presents a two-page *Chapter Assessment* at the end of each chapter. By evaluating the student responses to this extensive review, you can determine whether any substantial reteaching is needed.

For the formal content assessment, a six-page test is provided in the *Chapter Assessment* booklet for each chapter. If your individual assessment plan requires a test that differs from this test in the resource package, customized tests can be easily produced using the *ExamView Pro*™ *Test Bank,* available in various computer formats.

Skill Assessment

The *Earth Science: Geology, the Environment, and the Universe* program contains many assessment strategies that require students to use skills such as making and using graphs, tables, and concept maps. The *Skill Handbook,* located at the back of the *Student Edition,* can help students master these skills.

Chapter Assessment

All *Chapter Assessment* questions and answers have been validated for accuracy and suitability. In addition, each *Chapter Assessment* contains additional assessment questions and a test-taking tip that will aid students in preparing for and taking tests.

Teaching Strategies

Glencoe's Assessment Advantage

Glencoe has worked to align its texts with state and national tests. Alignment gets students prepared for these tests without the need for extensive "cram sessions" or expensive tutoring at the end of the year. Preparation is built in, not added on, to the instructional process.

- The textbook's end-of-chapter reviews are written to the same standards as those of the tests themselves.

- Standardized Test Practice workbooks give students practice drills tied to state and national tests.

- Without sacrificing your instructional objectives, you can guide your students toward state goals.

- Textbook alignment ensures that the skills and concepts students learn are the skills and concepts that are tested.

Integrated, cumulative test preparation throughout the year reduces test anxiety and improves student performance.

Glencoe's Test-Taking Tips prepare students for exams in other disciplines, as well as Earth science.

CHAPTER 15
Assessment

Understanding Main Ideas

1. Which of the following is used to measure ocean depth?
   - **a.** bottom dredges
   - **b.** nets
   - **c.** sonar
   - **d.** tidal patterns

2. Which of the following are the most common gases emitted by volcanoes?
   - **a.** hydrogen and helium
   - **b.** oxygen and nitrogen
   - **c.** water vapor and carbon dioxide
   - **d.** chlorine and hydrogen

3. What is the average depth of the oceans?
   - **a.** 380 m
   - **b.** 38 m
   - **c.** 3800 m
   - **d.** 3 km

4. What is the average salinity of seawater?
   - **a.** 100 ppt
   - **b.** 50 ppt
   - **c.** 35 ppt
   - **d.** 3.5 ppt

5. What is the average temperature of deep water below the thermocline?
   - **a.** 15°C
   - **b.** more than 4°C
   - **c.** less than 4°C
   - **d.** 0°C

6. What basic motion does water follow during the passage of a wave?
   - **a.** forward
   - **b.** backward
   - **c.** up and down
   - **d.** circular

7. Which of the following does not affect wave height in deep water?
   - **a.** wavelength
   - **b.** wind duration
   - **c.** wind speed
   - **d.** fetch

8. Which type of seawater has the greatest density?
   - **a.** warm, with low salinity
   - **b.** warm, with high salinity
   - **c.** cold, with low salinity
   - **d.** cold, with high salinity

9. To what average depth does light penetrate in the ocean?
   - **a.** 1 m
   - **b.** 10 m
   - **c.** 100 m
   - **d.** 1000 m

10. What type of high tides occur during a full Moon?
    - **a.** spring tides
    - **b.** neap tides
    - **c.** tidal ranges
    - **d.** tidal cycles

11. What is the the densest water mass in the Atlantic Ocean?
    - **a.** North Atlantic Deep Water
    - **b.** surface water
    - **c.** Antarctic Bottom Water
    - **d.** Antarctic Intermediate Water

12. The Arctic Ocean is the northern part of which body of water?
    - **a.** Atlantic Ocean
    - **b.** Pacific Ocean
    - **c.** Bering Sea
    - **d.** Indian Ocean

13. Explain why the Moon exerts a greater tidal influence than the Sun.

14. What distinguishes a sea from an ocean?

15. Where in the oceans are the highest values of salinity found? Explain.

16. What would be the wave base for a wave that is 200 m long?

17. Which gyre would have clockwise circulation: the North Pacific, the South Pacific, the South Atlantic, or the Indian Ocean? Explain.

Test-Taking Tip

MAXIMIZE YOUR SCORE If possible, find out how your standardized test will be scored. In order to do your best, you need to know if there is a penalty for guessing, and if so, how much of one. If there is no random-guessing penalty, you should always fill in an answer.

earthgeu.com/chapter_test

Test-Taking Tip

MAXIMIZE YOUR SCORE If possible, find out how your standardized test will be scored. In order to do your best, you need to know if there is a penalty for guessing, and if so, how much of one. If there is no random-guessing penalty, you should always fill in an answer.

Applying Main Ideas

18. Why does a wave break?

19. Copy the illustration on this page. Then use the following terms to label the characteristics of an ocean wave: *crest, trough, wave height,* and *wavelength.*

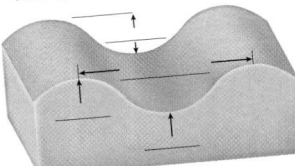

20. Cold water masses are generally denser than warm water masses, yet warm water from the Mediterranean Sea sinks to a depth of more than 1000 m when it flows into the Atlantic Ocean. Why?

Thinking Critically

21. One of the effects of El Niño, which you learned about in the previous chapter, is that the trade winds reverse direction. Predict how this might affect upwelling off the coast of Peru.

22. Based on what you have learned about water density, describe the movement of freshwater from a river as it flows into the sea.

23. Surface currents can affect coastal climates. Would the Gulf Stream and the Peru Current, both of which are surface currents, have the same effect on coastal climate? Explain.

24. Use your knowledge of global warming to hypothesize why sea level is rising.

earthgeu.com/standardized_test

Standardized Test Practice

1. Which sea was the first to be mapped?
a. the Bering Sea
b. the Caribbean Sea
c. the Gulf of Mexico
d. the Mediterranean Sea

2. Which region's seawater is most likely to have the highest concentration of dissolved salts?
a. an equatorial region
b. a subtropical region
c. a polar region
d. a delta where rivers empty into oceans

INTERPRETING SCIENTIFIC ILLUSTRATIONS
Use the illustration below to answer questions 3 and 4.

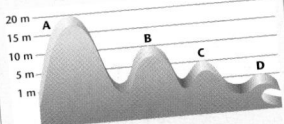

3. Which wave is most likely caused by a strong hurricane?
a. A   c. C
b. B   d. D

4. Why is Wave D most likely collapsing?
a. friction from the ocean floor
b. storm activity
c. increased crest-to-crest wavelength
d. opposing tidal movement

5. Which ocean movement is slow-moving and occurs in deep waters?
a. surface currents   c. density currents
b. upwelling   d. gyres

Assessment **411**

Princeton Review Test Practices are consistent with standardized tests and proficiency exams on state and national levels.

Test Practice

1. Which sea was the first to be mapped?
a. the Bering Sea
b. the Caribbean Sea
c. the Gulf of Mexico
d. the Mediterranean Sea

2. Which region's seawater is most likely to have the highest concentration of dissolved salts?
a. an equatorial region
b. a subtropical region
c. a polar region
d. a delta where rivers empty into oceans

SECTION ASSESSMENT

1. What is the most abundant salt in seawater? How do salts enter the ocean?

2. How does the salinity of seawater affect its density?

3. The salinity of seawater is higher in subtropical regions than at the equator. Why?

4. Explain why North Atlantic Deep Water and Antarctic Intermediate Water override Antarctic Bottom Water.

5. Which is more dense, cold freshwater or warm seawater? Explain.

6. Thinking Critically Why do red fish look black at ocean water depths greater than about 10 m?

SKILL REVIEW

7. Recognizing Cause and Effect Based on what you have learned about the freezing point of seawater, explain why salt is often used to de-ice roads in the winter. For more help, refer to the *Skill Handbook.*

Section Assessment questions and answers are reviewed by The Princeton Review and authenticated as effective ties to Earth Science lesson objectives.

Cracking the Regents Earth Science 2000
Specifically for students preparing for the Regents' examinations, this review includes score-raising techniques and is the only guide updated annually.

- Includes seven actual Regents exams (six for traditional curriculum; one for the modified curriculum).

- Teaches several important test-taking techniques for multiple choice questions and contains 25 key reference tables

THE PRINCETON REVIEW

2000

CRACKING THE REGENTS

EARTH SCIENCE

5 Actual Exams with Answers Explained
— Plus the August 1999 exam —
■ Test-taking techniques and study strategies to help you score higher
■ Reviewed by New York State high school teachers

Kim Magloire

Teaching Strategies: *Differentiated Instruction*

	Description	Sources of Help/Information
Learning Disabled	All learning disabled students have an academic problem in one or more areas, such as academic learning, language, perception, social-emotional adjustment, memory, or attention.	*Journal of Learning Disabilities* *Learning Disability Quarterly*
Behaviorally Disordered	Children with behavior disorders deviate from standards or expectations of behavior and impair the functioning of others and themselves. These children may also be gifted or learning disabled.	*Exceptional Children* *Journal of Special Education*
Physically Challenged	Children who are physically challenged fall into two categories—those with orthopedic impairments and those with other health impairments. Orthopedically impaired children have the use of one or more limbs severely restricted, so the use of wheelchairs, crutches, or braces may be necessary. Children with other health impairments may require the use of respirators or other medical equipment.	Batshaw, M.L. and M.Y. Perset. *Children with Handicaps: A Medical Primer.* Baltimore: Paul H. Brooks, 1981. Hale, G. (Ed.). *The Source Book for the Disabled.* New York: Holt, Rinehart & Winston, 1982. *Teaching Exceptional Children*
Visually Impaired	Children who are visually impaired have partial or total loss of sight. Individuals with visual impairments are not significantly different from their sighted peers in ability range or personality. However, blindness may affect cognitive, motor, and social development, especially if early intervention is lacking.	*Journal of Visual Impairment and Blindness* *Education of Visually Handicapped* *American Foundation for the Blind*
Hearing Impaired	Children who are hearing impaired have partial or total loss of hearing. Individuals with hearing impairments are not significantly different from their hearing peers in ability range or personality. However, the chronic condition of deafness may affect cognitive, motor, and social development if early intervention is lacking. Speech development also is often affected.	*American Annals of the Deaf* *Journal of Speech and Hearing Research* *Sign Language Studies*
English-Language Learners	Multicultural and/or bilingual children often speak English as a second language or not at all. The customs and behavior of people in the majority culture may be confusing for some of these students. Cultural values may inhibit some of these students from full participation.	*Teaching English as a Second Language Reporter* R.L. Jones (Ed.). *Mainstreaming and the Minority Child.* Reston, VA: Council for Exceptional Children, 1976.
Gifted	Although no formal definition exists, these students can be described as having above-average ability, task commitment, and creativity. Gifted students rank in the top 5% of their class. They usually finish work more quickly than other students, and are capable of divergent thinking.	*Journal for the Education of the Gifted* *Gifted Child Quarterly* *Gifted Creative/Talented*

Teaching Strategies

Tips for Instruction

1. Provide support and structure; clearly specify rules, assignments, and duties.
2. Practice skills frequently. Use games and drills to help maintain student interest.
3. Allow students to record answers on tape and allow extra time to complete tests and assignments.
4. Provide outlines or tape lecture material.
5. Pair students with peer helpers, and provide class time for pair interaction.

1. Provide a clearly structured environment with regard to scheduling, rules, room arrangement, and safety.
2. Clearly outline objectives and how you will help students obtain objectives. Seek input from them about their strengths, weaknesses, and goals.
3. Reinforce appropriate behavior and model it for students.
4. Do not expect immediate success. Instead, work for long-term improvement.
5. Balance individual needs with group requirements.

1. Openly discuss with the student any uncertainties you have about when to offer aid.
2. Ask parents or therapists and students what special devices or procedures are needed, and whether any special safety precautions need to be taken.
3. Allow physically challenged students to do everything their peers do, including participating in field trips, special events, and projects.
4. Help nondisabled students and adults understand physically challenged students.

1. As with all students, help the student become independent. Some assignments may need to be modified.
2. Teach classmates how to serve as guides.
3. Limit unnecessary noise in the classroom.
4. Encourage students to use their sense of touch. Provide tactile models whenever possible.
5. Describe people and events as they occur in the classroom.
6. Provide taped lectures and reading assignments.
7. Team the student with a sighted peer for laboratory work.

1. Seat students where they can see your lip movements easily, and avoid visual distractions.
2. Avoid standing with your back to the window or light source.
3. Using an overhead projector allows you to maintain eye contact while writing.
4. Seat students where they can see speakers.
5. Write all assignments on the board, or hand out written instructions.
6. If the student has a manual interpreter, allow both student and interpreter to select the most favorable seating arrangements.

1. Remember that students' ability to speak English does not reflect their academic ability.
2. Try to incorporate the student's cultural experience into your instruction. The help of a bilingual aide may be effective.
3. Include information about different cultures in your curriculum to help build students' self-image. Avoid cultural stereotypes.
4. Encourage students to share their cultures in the classroom.

1. Make arrangements for students to take selected subjects early and to work on independent projects.
2. Let students express themselves in art forms such as drawing, creative writing, or acting.
3. Make public services available through a catalog of resources, such as agencies providing free and inexpensive materials, community services and programs, and people in the community with specific expertise.
4. Ask "what if" questions to develop high-level thinking skills. Establish an environment safe for risk taking.
5. Emphasize concepts, theories, ideas, relationships, and generalizations.

The *Student Edition* and *Teacher Wraparound Edition* contain a variety of strategies for addressing the differentiated instruction of students:

- **Differentiated Instruction** strategies
- Both structured and open-ended **GeoLabs**
- Introductory **Discovery Labs**
- Hands-on **MiniLabs**
- **Demos**
- **Internet Connections**
- **Visual Learning strategies**

The following Glencoe products also can help you tailor your instruction to meet the individual needs of your students:

- **Study Guide for Content Mastery**
- **Section Focus Transparencies**
- **MindJogger Videoqizzes**
- **PuzzleMaker Software**
- **English/Spanish Audiocassettes**

Teaching Strategies

Cultural Diversity

> **"** *Multicultural education is an idea stating that all students, regardless of the groups to which they belong, such as those related to gender, ethnicity, race, culture, social class, religion, or exceptionality, should experience education equality in the schools* **"**
>
> — James Banks

Diverse Cultural Heritages

American classrooms reflect the rich and diverse cultural heritages of the American people. Students come from different ethnic backgrounds and different cultural experiences into a common classroom that must assist all of them to learn. The diversity itself is an important focus of the learning experience. Diversity can be repressed, creating a hostile environment; or appreciated, creating a receptive and productive environment.

Cultural Diversity in *Earth Science: Geology, the Environment, and the Universe*

Responding to diversity and approaching it as a part of every curriculum may be challenging to a teacher, experienced or not. The goal of science is understanding. The goal of multicultural education is to promote an understanding of how people from different cultures approach and solve the basic problems all humans have in living and learning.

Earth Science: Geology, the Environment, and the Universe addresses this issue by including numerous *Cultural Diversity* connections in the **Teacher Wraparound Edition**, by showing successful scientists from diverse ethnic backgrounds and by showing Earth science topics reflected in other cultures and historical settings.

These features offer opportunities to integrate multicultural materials that relate to the topics presented in each chapter into the curriculum. By providing these opportunities, **Earth Science: Geology, the Environment, and the Universe** is helping to meet the five major goals of multicultural education:

1. Promoting the strength and value of cultural diversity
2. Promoting the human rights of and respect for those who are different from oneself
3. Promoting alternative life choices for people
4. Promoting social justice and equal opportunity for all people
5. Promoting equity in the distribution of power among groups

Readings

Some books that provide additional information on multicultural education are:

Atwater, Mary, et al. *Multicultural Education: Inclusion of All*. Athens, Georgia: University of Georgia Press, 1994.

Banks, James A., *Multicultural Education: Issues and Perspectives*. Boston: Allyn and Bacon, 1989.

Banks, James A., *Curriculum Guidelines for Multiethnic Education*. Washington, DC: National Council for the Social Studies, 1977.

Selin, Helaine. *Science Across Cultures: An Annotated Bibliography of Books on Non-Western Science, Technology and Medicine*. New York: Garland, 1992.

Safety Symbols

The **Earth Science: Geology, the Environment, and the Universe** program uses safety symbols to alert you and your students to possible laboratory dangers. These symbols are provided in the student text in Appendix B and are explained below. Be sure your students understand each symbol before they begin an activity that displays a symbol.

SAFETY SYMBOLS	HAZARD	EXAMPLES	PRECAUTION	REMEDY
DISPOSAL	Special disposal procedures need to be followed.	certain chemicals, living organisms	Do not dispose of these materials in the sink or trash can.	Dispose of wastes as directed by your teacher.
BIOLOGICAL	Organisms or other biological materials that might be harmful to humans	bacteria, fungi, blood, unpreserved tissues, plant materials	Avoid skin contact with these materials. Wear mask or gloves.	Notify your teacher if you suspect contact with material. Wash hands thoroughly.
EXTREME TEMPERATURE	Objects that can burn skin by being too cold or too hot	boiling liquids, hot plates, dry ice, liquid nitrogen	Use proper protection when handling.	Go to your teacher for first aid.
SHARP OBJECT	Use of tools or glassware that can easily puncture or slice skin	razor blades, pins, scalpels, pointed tools, dissecting probes, broken glass	Practice common-sense behavior and follow guidelines for use of the tool.	Go to your teacher for first aid.
FUME	Possible danger to respiratory tract from fumes	ammonia, acetone, nail polish remover, heated sulfur, moth balls	Make sure there is good ventilation. Never smell fumes directly. Wear a mask.	Leave foul area and notify your teacher immediately.
ELECTRICAL	Possible danger from electrical shock or burn	improper grounding, liquid spills, short circuits, exposed wires	Double-check setup with teacher. Check condition of wires and apparatus.	Do not attempt to fix electrical problems. Notify your teacher immediately.
IRRITANT	Substances that can irritate the skin or mucous membranes of the respiratory tract	pollen, moth balls, steel wool, fiberglass, potassium permanganate	Wear dust mask and gloves. Practice extra care when handling these materials.	Go to your teacher for first aid.
CHEMICAL	Chemicals can react with and destroy tissue and other materials	bleaches such as hydrogen peroxide; acids such as sulfuric acid, hydrochloric acid; bases such as ammonia, sodium hydroxide	Wear goggles, gloves, and an apron.	Immediately flush the affected area with water and notify your teacher.
TOXIC	Substance may be poisonous if touched, inhaled, or swallowed.	mercury, many metal compounds, iodine, poinsettia plant parts	Follow your teacher's instructions.	Always wash hands thoroughly after use. Go to your teacher for first aid.
FLAMMABLE	Flammable chemicals may be ignited by open flame, spark, or exposed heat.	alcohol, kerosene, potassium permanganate	Avoid open flames and heat when using flammable chemicals.	Notify your teacher immediately. Use fire safety equipment if applicable.
OPEN FLAME	Open flame in use, may cause fire.	hair, clothing, paper, synthetic materials	Tie back hair and loose clothing. Follow teacher's instruction on lighting and extinguishing flames.	Notify your teacher immediately. Use fire safety equipment if applicable.

Eye Safety
Proper eye protection should be worn at all times by anyone performing or observing science activities.

Clothing Protection
This symbol appears when substances could stain or burn clothing.

Animal Safety
This symbol appears when safety of animals and students must be ensured.

Handwashing
After the lab, wash hands with soap and water before removing goggles.

Laboratory

The activities in **Earth Science: Geology, the Environment, and the Universe** are designed to minimize dangers in the laboratory. Careful planning and preparation as well as being aware of hazards can keep accidents to a minimum. Practice good laboratory housekeeping and management by observing these guidelines.

Personal Protection

The use of personal protection equipment is required when potentially hazardous material is present. Personal protection equipment includes eyewear, laboratory aprons, laboratory coats, and protective gloves.

Eyewear

Eyewear should meet the ANSI Standard Z87.1-*Practice for Occupational and Educational Eye and Face Protection*. Eyewear meeting this standard will bear markings such as "Z87.1" on the frames and the lens will be marked with the manufacturer's trademark.

Safety goggles are required for science laboratory and field activities involving any hazardous chemical, which could damage the eye if the chemical splashed into the eye or rubbed onto the eye. Goggles provide eye protection from fine dusts, liquids, splashes, mists, and sprays. They also prevent splashes and sprays from body fluids or dangerous chemicals.

Safety goggles should be large enough to protect and form a seal around the eyes. If not able to seal, goggles should contain side shields to prevent contamination to the eyes.

Eye protection may also be provided with safety glasses. Safety glasses with sideshields will not provide adequate protection for chemical splashes. These are designed primarily to protect the eyes from flying objects.

Protective Gloves

Gloves protect hands from heat, absorb perspiration, and provide a shield from corrosive chemicals, body fluids, and prevent the transmission of microorganisms from person to person. Always check gloves to be sure that there are no tears, punctures, or holes. When removing gloves, peel the gloves off your hand, starting at the wrists and working toward the fingers. Keep the working surface of the gloves from contact with the skin during removal.

Laboratory Aprons and Coats

Laboratory aprons and coats are designed to protect clothing and skin from splashed and spilled chemicals and biological materials. They should fit the wearer properly to provide maximum protection. A laboratory coat or apron should be worn at all times in the laboratory.

Aprons are usually listed as "bib type," which are suitable for laboratory use. Aprons should be worn over clothing that covers the arms and body.

Laboratory coats are usually fire retardant and made of cotton or paper. They are good for protection against flying objects, sharp or rough edges, splashes and spills, and fire.

Fire Protection

Fire is one of the most frequent mishaps in the science laboratory. The first line of defense from a fire is fire prevention. Effective fire prevention centers on thorough understanding of combustion and the required ingredients. As long as air is present, oxygen will be available for combustion to take place. The areas where prevention measures are best exercised are the fuel and ignition sources.

Fires are classified by the chemical properties of the fuel.

The basic classifications are grouped as follows:

- Class A – Ordinary combustible (i.e., paper, wood, etc.)

- Class B – Organic solvents (i.e., acetone, alcohols, ethers)

- Class C – Electrical wiring or static charges

- Class D – Active metals (i.e., sodium, potassium, magnesium)

These symbols are accepted for the different classifications of fire. They are applied to fire extinguishers and extinguisher locations to indicate their suitability in extinguishing the different types of fires.

The following precautions should be taken to prevent fires from occurring in the science classroom, laboratory, storage, and preparation area.

- Be aware of ignition sources in your laboratory area (open flames, heat, and electrical equipment).

- Purchase and store flammable reagents in the smallest quantities possible.

- Do not store flammable liquids in standard refrigerators (an explosion-proof refrigerator should be used).

- Store flammable liquids in appropriate safety cabinets and/or safety cans.

- Make sure that all electrical cords are in good condition. All electrical outlets should be grounded and should accommodate a 3-pronged plug.

Each science classroom, laboratory, storage, and preparation area should have a fire blanket and an appropriate fire extinguisher.

Fire Extinguishers

In most school environments, hand-held, portable fire extinguishers are the first fire-extinguishing agent used. Therefore, a multipurpose ABC fire extinguisher must be located in each science classroom, laboratory, storage room, and preparation area. Extinguishers must be:

- Located to be easily seen and the area around them kept clear.

- Inspected on a regular basis

- Used by well-trained teachers and students

Fire extinguishers are labeled in accordance with NFPA standards.

Fire Blankets

Actual fire control revolves around proper types of control devices such as a fire blanket. Fire blankets are made of specially treated fabric and should be located at strategic areas for all science laboratories where hazardous chemicals are stored and used. Fire blankets can be used if one is unable to reach the safety shower.

Safety in the Laboratory material used with permission from Texas Safety Standards, produced by the Texas Education Agency.

Laboratory

These easy-to-use tables of equipment and consumable materials can help you prepare for your Earth science classes for the year. Quantities listed for Geolabs, MiniLabs, and Discovery Labs are the maximum quantities you will need for one student group for the year. The pages on which each item is used are listed in parentheses after the quantities. Refer to the Chapter Organizer in front of each chapter for a list of equipment and materials used for each laboratory activity in the chapter.

Non-Consumables

Item	GeoLab	MiniLab	Discovery Lab
baby food jar with lid	3 (p. 676)	6 (p. 674)	
beaker, 100-mL	1 (p. 140)	7 (p. 394)	1 (pp. 121, 471)
beaker, 150-mL		1 (p. 587)	
beaker, 250-mL	2 (pp. 20, 70, 114)	1 (p. 474)	2 (pp. 53, 153, 471, 577, 683)
beaker, 1-L		1 (p. 394)	1 (p. 625)
book		1 (p. 254)	
bottle, small		7 (p. 394)	
bowl, clear plastic		1 (p. 290)	
brick, unglazed			1 (p. 601)
catch basin		1 (p. 163)	
compass, drafting	1 (pp. 430, 516)	1 (p. 761)	1 (p. 747)
copper sample	1 (p. 92)		
coverslip			1 (p. 413)
drinking glass			1 (p. 271)
dropper	1 (pp. 92, 406)	1 (p. 674)	1 (pp. 471, 577, 601)
encyclopedia	1 (p. 553)		
file, steel	1 (p. 92)		
flashlight		1 (p. 302)	
fossil bivalves, different	4 (p. 618)		
fossil brachiopods, different	4 (p. 618)		
geologic time scale	1 (p. 553)		
glass dish, shallow	1 (p. 70)		
glass plate	1 (p. 92)		
globe		1 (p. 29)	1 (p. 385)
graduated cylinder, 50-mL		1 (p. 587)	
graduated cylinder, 100-mL		1 (p. 674)	
graduated cylinder, 250-mL		1 (pp. 428, 688)	2 (pp. 181, 239)
graduated cylinder, 500-mL	1 (p. 406)		
graduated cylinder, 1-L		1 (p. 394)	
granite sample			1 (p. 99)

Non-Consumables *(continued)*

Item	GeoLab	MiniLab	Discovery Lab
halite sample			1 (p. 77)
hand lens	1 (pp. 92, 114, 140)		1 (pp. 53, 77, 99)
hole punch	1 (p. 232)		
hose	1 (p. 232)		
hurricane-tracking chart	1 (p. 354)		
ice-cube tray		1 (p. 348)	
igneous rock samples		1 (p. 108)	
jar, 1-L glass		3 (p. 636)	
jar, glass		1 (p. 376)	
jar, plastic with lid	1 (p. 174)		
jar, tall with lid			1 (p. 121)
lamp	1 (pp. 676, 704)		
liquid-crystal temperature strip	1 (p. 294)		2 (p. 299)
magnet, small	1 (p. 92)		1 (p. 53)
map, physiographic, Atlantic Ocean floor		1 (p. 536)	
map, physiographic, United States		1 (p. 536)	
map, topographic	1 (p. 430)		
map, topographic of Forest City, Florida	1 (p. 258)		
map, wind erosion		1 (p. 194)	
map, world		1 (pp. 29, 456)	
measuring tape	1 (pp. 572, 798)		
microscope slide			1 (p. 413)
mineral samples, set of	1 (p. 92)	1 (p. 79)	
Mohs hardness scale	1 (p. 92)		
mortar and pestle			1 (p. 413)
objects, small assorted			10 (p. 5)
pan, large glass	1 (p. 676)		
pan, large metal	3 (p. 676)		
personal items, assorted			1 (p. 711)
petri dish, glass			1 (p. 553)
petri dish, plastic	4 (p. 114)		
photographs of dinosaur or reptile footprints		3 (p. 126)	
plumb bob	1 (p. 232)		
protractor	1 (p. 232)	1 (pp. 761, 817)	
psychrometer	1 (p. 378)		
quartz sample			1 (p. 77)

Laboratory

Non-Consumables *(continued)*

Item	GeoLab	MiniLab	Discovery Lab
reference books, set	1 (p. 570)		
relative humidity chart	1 (p. 378)		
ring stand with clamp	1 (p. 232)		
rock samples, assorted small	5 (p. 20)		
rock, medium size			2 (p. 359)
rocks, sedimentary	5 (p. 140)		
rocks, metamorphic	5 (p. 140)		
rolling pin			1 (p. 53)
round objects, assorted size	1 (p. 798)		
sandstone			1 (p. 601)
screen, window			2 (p. 211)
shoe box, clear plastic		4 (pp. 229, 254)	2 (p. 211)
sieves, set of		1 (p. 428)	
spoon		1 (p. 587)	
spring scale	1 (p. 20)		
stirring rod	1 (p. 70)	1 (pp. 394, 474)	2 (pp. 153, 577)
streak plate	1 (p. 92)		
thermometer	1 (pp. 114, 378, 406, 704)	4 (pp. 12, 376)	1 (p. 271)
thumbtack		5 (p. 777)	10 (p. 495)
tub, plastic			1 (p. 523)
tweezers			1 (p. 553)
umbrella			1 (p. 359)
watch glass		1 (p. 587)	
wood block, (12 cm × 12 cm × 4 cm)			2 (p. 495)
wood block, hardwood, (8 cm × 8 cm × 2 cm)			1 (p. 523)
wood block, softwood, (8 cm × 8 cm × 2 cm)			1 (p. 523)
wood block, softwood, (8 cm × 8 cm × 4 cm)			1 (p. 523)

Consumables

Item	GeoLab	MiniLab	Discovery Lab
aluminum foil (30 cm × 60 cm)	1 (p. 704)		
bag, brown paper lunch			1 (p. 329)
bag, self-sealing plastic		1 (p. 290)	
balloon		1 (p. 845)	

Consumables *(continued)*

Item	GeoLab	MiniLab	Discovery Lab
bleach, household		15 mL (p. 587)	
bottle, 2-L plastic with cap	1 (p. 292)		
bottle, dishwashing-detergent with twist cap		1 (p. 348)	
box, sturdy cardboard	3 (p. 704)	1 (p. 376)	
cardboard (30 cm × 30 cm)		1 (p. 777)	1 (p. 181)
cereal, iron-fortified			20 g (p. 53)
chalk, natural			2 g (p. 413)
clay		6 kg (pp. 229, 254, 636)	
clay, white modeling		500 g (p. 616)	
clay, yellow modeling		250 g (p. 616)	
cupcake, cream-filled, frosted		2 (p. 718)	
dishwashing liquid		120 mL (p. 474)	
fabric (30 cm × 60 cm)	1 (p. 704)		
foamboard (60 cm × 60 cm)	1 (p. 704)	1 (p. 79)	
food coloring	1 mL (p. 406)		2 mL (pp. 471, 577)
glue	10 mL (p. 704)	10 mL (p. 79)	
gravel		6 kg (pp. 229, 636)	
gravel, colored aquarium		60 g (p. 688)	
halite chips	100 g (p. 174)		
knife, plastic		1 (p. 718)	
labels		6 (p. 674)	
milk jug, 1 gallon plastic		2 (p. 12)	
mirrors, assorted small	10 (p. 704)		
napkin, paper		2 (p. 718)	
oil, cooking		300 mL (pp. 428, 688)	175 mL (p. 577)
paint, assorted colors	60 mL each (p. 704)		
paper clip	1 (p. 92)		
paper towels	10 (pp. 114, 174)		
paper, dark colored construction, sheet	1 (p. 114)	1 (p. 302)	2 (p. 359)
paper, graph, sheet of	5 (pp. 20, 258, 406, 430, 540)	2 (pp. 376, 817)	1 (p. 27)
paper, tracing, sheet	3 (pp. 258, 464, 516)	1 (p. 536)	
pie plate, aluminum			3 (p. 181)
plastic sheet, clear (30 cm × 30 cm)	4 (pp. 676, 704)		
plastic wrap (30 cm × 30 cm)	1 (p. 70)	1 (p. 290)	1 (p. 53)
plasticine			10 g (p. 625)
plate, paper		1 (p. 718)	

Laboratory

Consumables (continued)

Item	GeoLab	MiniLab	Discovery Lab
posterboard (50 cm $\times$ 75 cm)	1 (p. 570)		
salt water	50 mL (p. 676)		
sand		3 kg (pp. 254, 636, 688)	500 g (p. 239)
sand, dry		5 kg (p. 229)	100 g (p. 181)
sand, white		100 g (p. 587)	
sand grains and small pebbles		5 (p. 428)	
sand-microfossil mixture			25 g (p. 553)
sandpaper, coarse, sheet			2 (p. 495)
silt		500 g (p. 636)	
soap, bar of		1 (p. 163)	
soap, liquid		1 mL (p. 674)	
sod clump (8 cm $\times$ 16 cm)			1 (p. 211)
soil		2 kg (p. 12)	200 g (p. 121)
soil clump (8 cm $\times$ 16 cm)			1 (p. 211)
steel wool		2 g (p. 587)	
stones, small	10 (p. 704)		
straw, clear plastic drinking	4 (p. 292)	3 (p. 254)	
string	1m (pp. 20, 42)	10 m (pp. 777, 817, 845)	1 m (p. 385)
sugar cube			1 (p. 153)
sugar, granulated			5 g (p. 153)
tape, masking	50 cm (p. 798)	10 cm (p. 12)	10 cm (p. 53)
tape, transparent	100 cm (p. 704)		
tape, vinyl gutter	1 m (p. 232)		
toothpick		1 (p. 163)	
water samples, different		5 (p. 674)	

Chemicals

Item	GeoLab	MiniLab	Discovery Lab
5% HCl	1 mL (p. 92)		
alum ($KAl(SO_4)_2 \cdot 12H_2O$)	50 g (p. 114)		
baking soda ($NaHCO_3$)		0.2 g (p. 394)	
calcium chloride ($CaCl_2$)		1.1 g (p. 394)	
magnesium chloride ($MgCl_2$)		5.0g (p. 394)	
potassium bromide (KBr)		0.1 g (p. 394)	
potassium chloride (KCl)		0.7g (p. 394)	
sodium chloride (NaCl)	70 g (pp. 70, 406)	55 g (pp. 394, 474)	
sodium sulfate (Na_2SO_4)		4.0 g (p. 394)	

The standard list of equipment is made up of a set of equipment that is generally found in a science laboratory. For all lab activities in this program, it is assumed that your classroom is equipped with these items. They are listed in the table below with the page numbers of major corresponding labs for your convenience.

Standard Equipment

Item	GeoLab	MiniLab	Discovery Lab
balance, beam-type	140		
balance, laboratory	20, 70, 174	163, 474	523
calculator	258, 406, 430, 516, 570, 798, 826	428, 616	833
colored pencils, assorted colors	464, 570, 594	559	27
hot plate	70, 114, 676		683
Internet access	352, 488, 642, 852		805
markers, felt, assorted colors	798	845	385
meterstick	232, 570, 798, 826	777, 845	747
microscope			413
pen, grease	232		
refrigerator	70		
ruler, metric	42, 204, 258, 322, 406, 430, 464, 516, 540, 594, 734, 826	79, 163, 348, 456, 536, 559, 616, 761, 777	385, 443, 523, 833
scissors	292, 704	79, 456, 559,	747
stereomicroscope			99
stopwatch, watch, or timer	174, 232, 292, 798	428	153, 211

Laboratory

Chemical Storage and Disposal

General Guidelines

Be sure to store all chemicals properly. The following are guidelines commonly used. Your school, city, county, or state may have additional requirements for handling chemicals. It is the responsibility of each teacher to become informed as to what rules or guidelines are in effect in his or her area.

1. Separate chemicals by reaction type. Strong acids should be stored together. Likewise, strong bases should be stored together and should be separated from acids. Oxidants should be stored away from easily oxidized materials, and so on.

2. Be sure all chemicals are stored in labeled containers indicating contents, concentration, source, date purchased (or prepared), any precautions for handling and storage, and expiration date.

3. Dispose of any outdated or waste chemicals properly according to accepted disposal procedures.

4. Do not store chemicals above eye level.

5. Wood shelving is preferable to metal. All shelving should be firmly attached to the wall and should have anti-roll edges.

6. Store only those chemicals that you plan to use.

7. Hazardous chemicals require special storage containers and conditions. Be sure to know what those chemicals are and the accepted practices for your area. Some substances must even be stored outside the building.

8. When working with chemicals or preparing solutions, observe the same general safety precautions that you would expect from students. These include wearing an apron and goggles. Wear gloves and use the fume hood when necessary. Students will want to do as you do whether they admit it or not.

9. If you are a new teacher in a particular laboratory, it is your responsibility to survey the chemicals stored there to be sure they are stored properly, or they should be disposed of. Consult the rules and laws in your area concerning what chemicals can be kept in your classroom. For disposal, consult up-to-date disposal information from the state and federal governments.

Disposal of Chemicals

Local, state, and federal laws regulate the proper disposal of chemicals. These laws should be consulted before chemical disposal is attempted. Although most substances encountered in high school laboratories can be flushed down the drain with plenty of water, it is not safe to assume that this is always true. It is recommended that teachers who use chemicals consult the following book from the National Research Council:

Prudent Practices in the Laboratory. Washington, DC: National Academy Press, 1995.

This book is useful and was revised in 1995. Current laws in your area would, of course, supersede the information in this book.

Disclaimer Glencoe Publishing Company makes no claims as to the completeness of this discussion of laboratory safety and chemical storage. The material presented is not all-inclusive, nor does it address all of the hazards associated with handling, storage, and disposal of chemicals, or with laboratory management.

Suppliers

Equipment Suppliers

American Science & Surplus
P.O. Box 1030
Skokie, IL 60076
(800) 647-0011
www.gciplus.com

Bio-Rad Laboratories
2000 Alfred Nobel Dr.
Life Science Group
Hercules, CA 94547
(800) 424-6723
www.bio-rad.com

Carolina Biological Supply Co.
2700 York Road
Burlington, NC 27215
(800) 334-5551
www.carolina.com

Edmund Scientific Company
60 Pearce Ave.
Tonawanda, NY 14150
(800) 728-6999
scientificsonline.com

Fisher Science Education
Educational Materials Division
4500 Turnberry Dr.
Hanover Park, IL 60133
(800) 955-1177
www.fisheredu.com

Nasco Science
901 Janesville Avenue,
P.O. Box 901
Fort Atkinson, WI 53538-0901
(800) 558-9595
www.enasco.com

Nebraska Scientific
3823 Leavenworth St.
Omaha, NE 68105-1180
(800) 228-7117
nebraskascientific.com

PASCO Scientific
10101 Foothills Blvd.
P.O. Box 619011
Roseville, CA 95747
(800) 772-8700
www.pasco.com

Sargent-Welch/VWR Scientific Products
P.O. Box 5229
Buffalo Grove, IL 60089-5229
(800) 727-4368
www.SargentWelch.com

Science Kit and Boreal Laboratories
777 East Park Dr.
P.O. Box 5003
Tonawanda, NY 14150
(800) 828-7777
www.sciencekit.com

WARD's Natural Science Est.
5100 W. Henrietta Road, P.O. Box 92912
Rochester, NY 14692-9012
(800) 962-2660
www.wardsci.com

Audiovisual Distributors

Bullfrog Films
P.O. Box 149
Oley, PA 19547
(800) 543-FROG
www.bullfrogfilms.com

Coronet/MTI Film & Video
2349 Chaffee Dr.
St Louis, MO 63146
(800) 221-1274

Discovery Channel School
1 Discovery Place
Silver Springs, MD 20910
(240) 662-2000
www.discoveryschool.com

Films for the Humanities and Sciences
P.O. Box 2053
Princeton, NJ 08543
(800) 257-5126

Flinn Scientific
P.O. Box 219
770 N. Raddant Rd.
Batavia, IL 60510
(800) 452-1261
www.flinnsci.com

Frey Scientific, Div. of Beckley Cardy
100 Paragon Parkway
Mansfield, OH 44903
(800) 235-3739
www.freyscientific.com

Media Design Associates
1731 15th St.
Suite 220
Boulder, CO 80302
(800) 546-9151
www.indra.com

National Geographic Society
Educational Services
1145 17th Street, N.W.
Washington, DC 20036
(800) 368-2728
www.nationalgeographic.com

Optical Data School Media
512 Means St., N.W.
Atlanta, GA 30318
(800) 524-2481
www.opticaldata.com

Scholastic, Inc.
555 Broadway
New York, NY 10012-3999
(800) 325-6149
www.scholastic.com

Time-Life Education
P.O. Box 85026
Richmond, VA 23285-5026
(800) 449-2010

Videodiscovery
920 N. 34th St.
Suite 300
Seattle, WA 98103
(800) 548-3472
www.videodiscovery.com

Software Distributors

Boreal Laboratories, Ltd.
399 Vansickle Rd.
St. Catharines, Ontario,
L2S 3T4
Canada
(800) 387-9393
boreal.com

Educational Activities, Inc.
1937 Grand Ave.
Baldwin, NY 11510
P.O. Box 87
(800) 645-3739
www.edact.com

IBM Global Education
4111 Northside Parkway
Atlanta, GA 30301-2150
(800) 426-4968
www.solutions.ibm.com/k12

J. Weston Walch, Publisher
321 Valley St.
P.O. Box 658
Portland, ME 04104-0658
(800) 341-6094
www.walch.com

Scholastic, Inc.
555 Broadway
New York, NY 10012-3999
(8000 325-6149
www.scholastic.com

Sunburst Communications
1550 Executive Dr.
Elgin, IL 60123
(800) 321-7511
www.SUNBURST.com

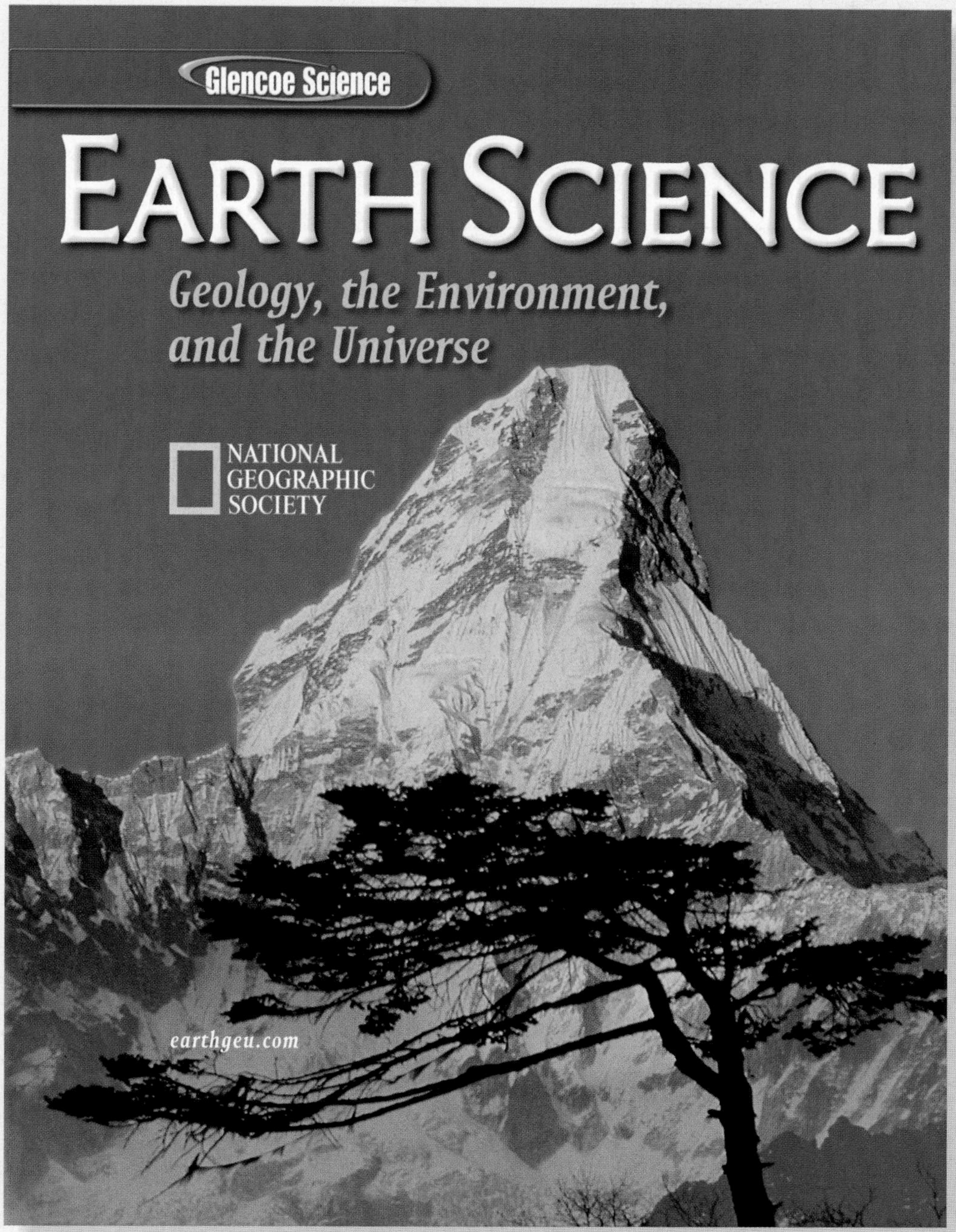
Glencoe Science
EARTH SCIENCE
Geology, the Environment, and the Universe
NATIONAL GEOGRAPHIC SOCIETY
earthgeu.com

McGraw Hill Glencoe

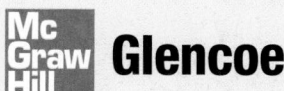

New York, New York Columbus, Ohio Chicago, Illinois Peoria, Illinois Woodland Hills, California

A Glencoe Program

Earth Science: Geology, the Environment, and the Universe

Visit the Earth Science Web site at <u>earthgeu.com</u>

You'll find:

Online Student Edition, Online Study Tools, Interactive Tutor, Online Quizzes, Internet Geolabs, National Geographic, Extending the Content, Problem of the Week, Web Links, Science Fair Ideas, NASA's Picture of the Day **and much more!**

NATIONAL GEOGRAPHIC The National Geographic features were designed and developed by the National Geographic Society's Education Division. Copyright © National Geographic Society. The name "National Geographic Society" and the Yellow Border Rectangle are trademarks of the Society, and their use, without prior written permission, is strictly prohibited.

Cover photo is the peak Ama Dablan (6747.9 m) in Nepal.

Send all inquiries to:
Glencoe/McGraw-Hill
8787 Orion Place
Columbus, OH 43240

ISBN 0-07-866423-3
Printed in the United States of America.

1 2 3 4 5 6 7   027/043   10 09 08 07 06 05 04

Frances Scelsi Hess teaches Earth science at Cooperstown High School in New York. She received her B.S. and M.S. in Science Education from the State University at Oneonta, and her Ed.D from Columbia University. Dr. Hess is a Fellow of the Science Teachers Association of New York State, and has received numerous teaching awards, including the Phi Delta Kappa Reed Travel Scholarship to Australia and New Zealand.

Gerhard Kunze is professor emeritus of Geology at the University of Akron in Ohio. He has a B.S. in Science and a Ph.D in Geophysics from Penn State University. He was an NRC research associate at Johnson Space Center, Houston, Texas from 1973-1974. In 1990, Dr. Kunze was awarded a senior Fulbright scholarship to teach geophysics at the Institute of Geophysics, a department of the University of Kiel in Germany.

Stephen A. Leslie is an associate professor of Geology in the Department of Earth Sciences at the University of Arkansas in Little Rock. His areas of research include paleontology, stratigraphy, and the evolution of early life on Earth. He has a B.S. in Geology from Bowling Green State University, an M.S. in Geology from the University of Idaho, and a Ph.D. in Geology from The Ohio State University.

Steve Letro has been a meteorologist for the National Weather Service, the media, and private industry since 1971. He currently serves as the Meteorologist-in-Charge of the National Weather Service office in Jacksonville, Florida. He received his B.S. in Meteorology from Florida State University with an emphasis in tropical meteorology. He is a member of the National Hurricane Center's Hurricane Liaison Team, and has received numerous awards, including an award for his role in restructuring the National Weather Service.

Clayton Millage has been teaching general science to eighth-graders at Lynden Middle School in Lynden, Washington, for six years. Prior to that, he taught marine science and astronomy at Cypress Creek High School in Houston, Texas. Mr. Millage has a B.A. in Geology from Occidental College, an M.S. in Geology from Stanford University, and an M.Ed. in Science Education from the University of Houston.

Len Sharp has taught Earth science at Liverpool High School, New York, for 26 years. He has a B.S. in Secondary Education and an M.S. in Science Education from Syracuse University. Mr. Sharp was president of the Science Teachers Association of New York in 1991-1992, and president of the National Earth Science Teachers Association from 1992-1994. He was a Presidential Awardee in 1995, and received the Fulbright Memorial Fund Fellowship to study in Japan in 1999.

Theodore Snow is a professor of Astronomy at the University of Colorado. He has a B.A. from Yale University, and an M.S. and Ph.D from the University of Washington. Dr. Snow is a founder and former director of the Center for Astrophysics and Space Astronomy at the University of Colorado, which conducts research on planets, stars, and galaxies. He has published numerous papers and several textbooks, and is a Fellow of the Royal Astronomical Society.

NATIONAL GEOGRAPHIC

National Geographic Society, founded in 1888 for the increase and diffusion of geographic knowledge, is the world's largest nonprofit scientific and educational organization. The School Publishing Division supports the Society's mission by developing innovative educational programs—ranging from print materials to multimedia programs, including CD-ROMS, DVDs, and software.

Safety Consultants

Anne B. Davidson
Assistant Principal for Instruction
Madison County High School
Madison, Alabama

John Longo
Coordinator of Laboratory Instruction
St. Joseph's University
Philadelphia, Pennsylvania

Kenneth Russell Roy, Ph.D.
Director of Science and Safety
Glastonbury Public Schools
Glastonbury, Connecticut

Teacher Reviewers

Frank Blatnik, M.S.
Science Facilitator
Swanton High School
Swanton, OH

Martha Boyd Buchanan
Freedom High School
Morganton, NC

Robert Ellyson, M.S.
Great Bridge High School
Chesapeake, VA

Kimberly Harmelink
Commerce High School
Commerce, GA

Regina Huffman, M. A.
Uniondale High School
Uniondale, NY

Al Janulaw
Creekside Middle School
Rohnert Park, CA

Bill Martin, M.Ed.
Fort Payne Middle School
Fort Payne. AL

Heather Monteleone
Page County High School
Shenandoah, VA

La Moine Motz, Ph.D.
Coordinator of Science Education
Oakland County Schools
Waterford, MI

Teresa Potter, M.A.
Science Department Chairperson
Rio Rico High School
Rio Rico, AZ

Katherine Richter
Athens Drive High School
Raleigh, NC

RevaBeth Russell
Science Department Chairperson
Lehi High School
Lehi, UT

Elsie Santiago, M.S.
Benjamin Cardoza High School
Bayside, NY

Robert Smith
Science Department Chairperson
Terry Parker High School
Jacksonville, FL

Gina Watkiss, M.A., M.S.
Science Coordinator
The Heritage School
Newnan, GA

Activity Testers

Gregory Beckway
Glenbrook North High School
Northbrook, IL

Paul Craft
Upper Arlington High School
Upper Arlington, OH

Georgia O'Hara
Centennial High School
Columbus, OH

Contents in Brief

NATIONAL GEOGRAPHIC

Table of Contents

= ENVIRONMENTAL CONNECTION

UNIT 3 *Surface Processes on Earth* **150**

 = ENVIRONMENTAL CONNECTION

Table of Contents

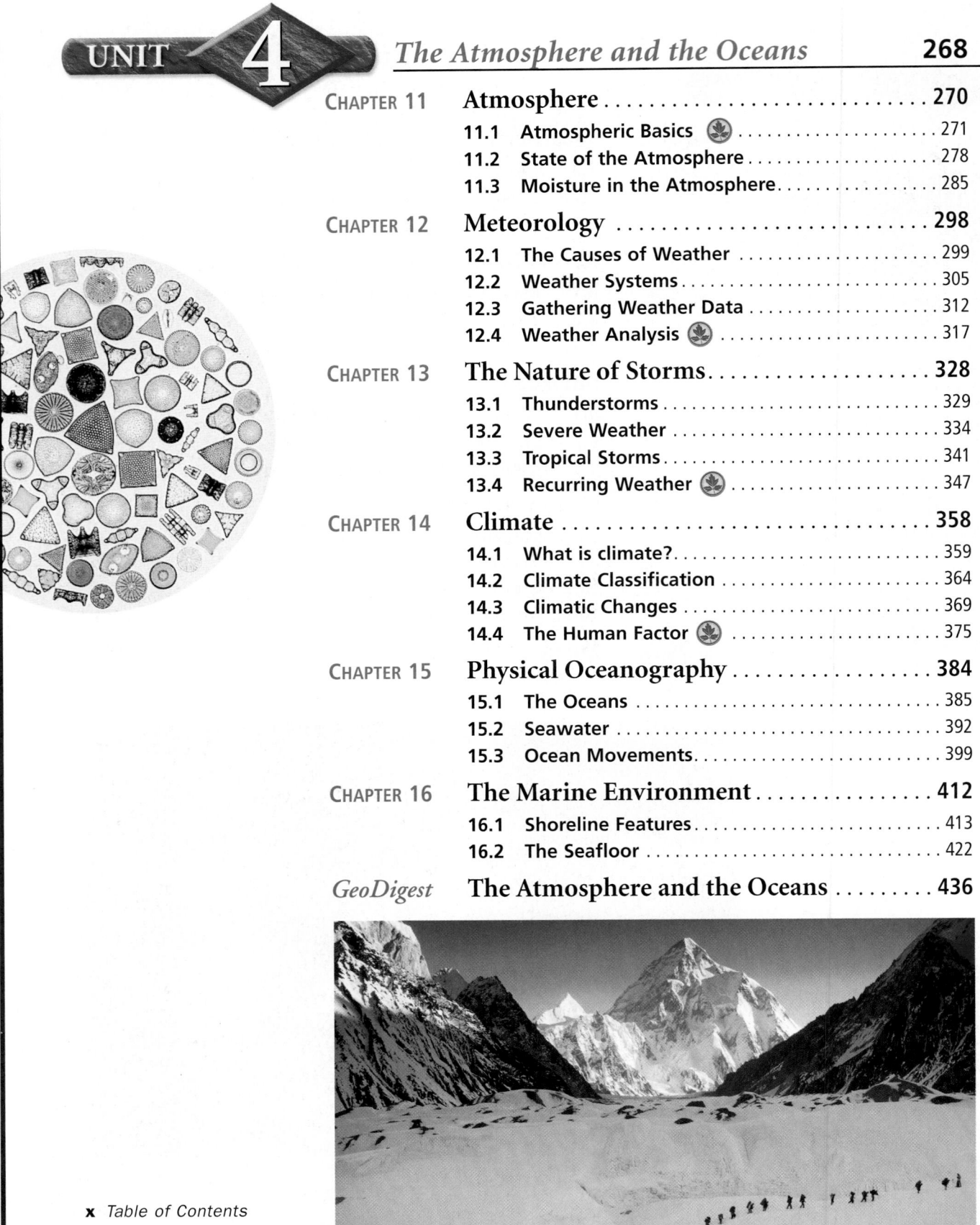

 = ENVIRONMENTAL
CONNECTION

Table of Contents

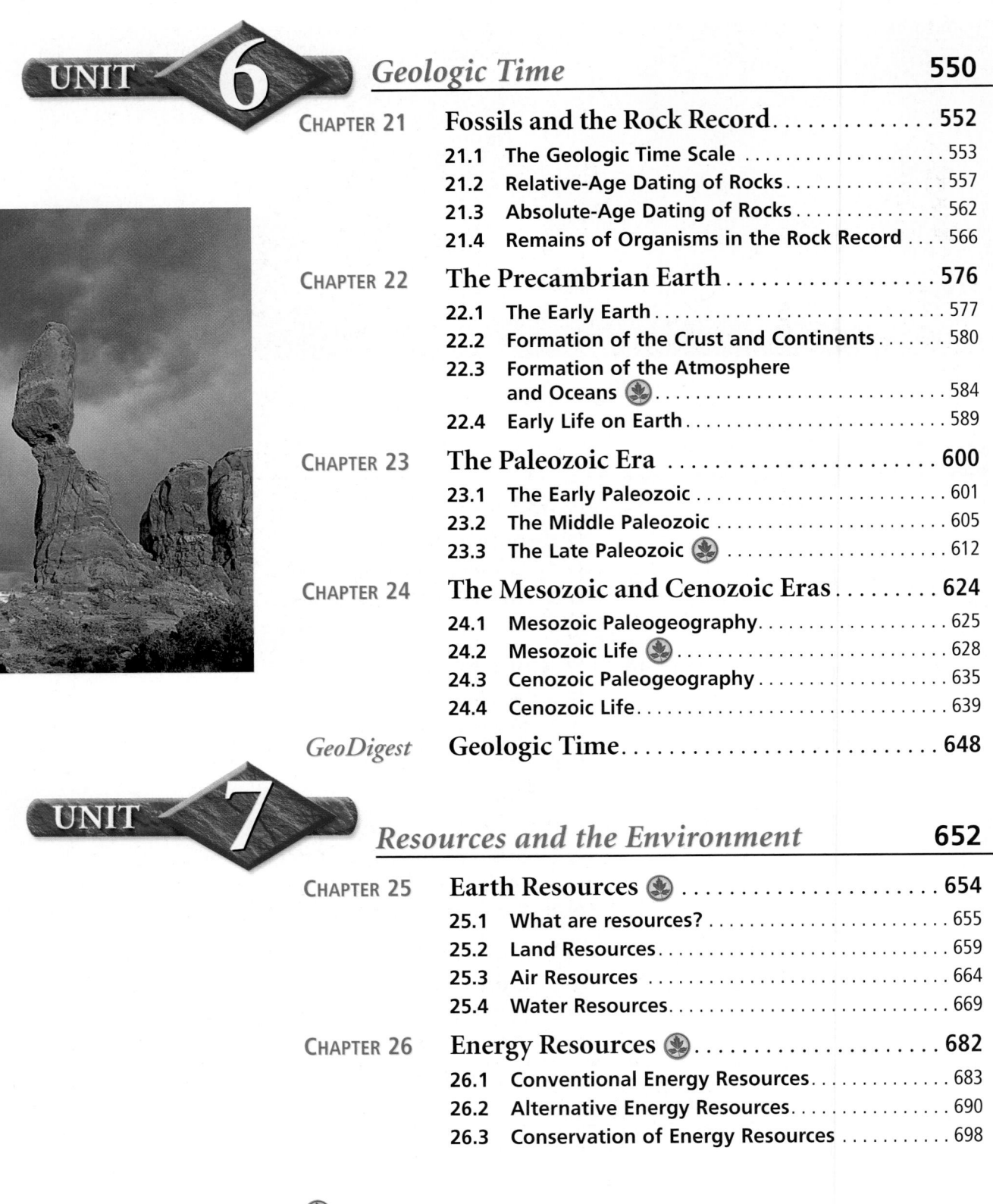
◉ = ENVIRONMENTAL
    CONNECTION

NATIONAL GEOGRAPHIC

Table of Contents

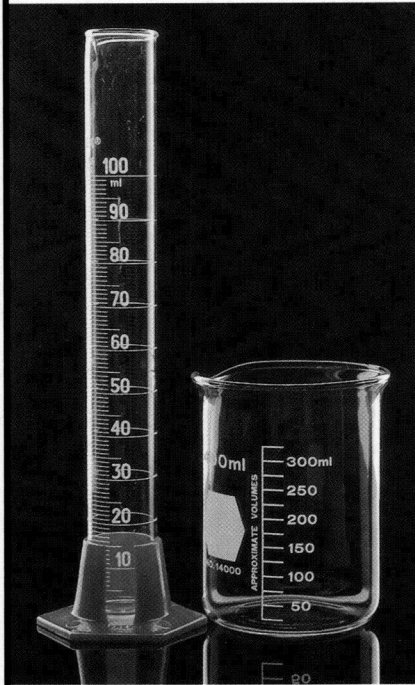

MiniLabs

Each chapter has one MiniLab. These short activities use simple materials and can be tried on your own at home or with help from a teacher at school.

GeoLabs

Each chapter contains a two-page GeoLab. There are four types of labs: GeoLab, Internet GeoLab, Design Your Own GeoLab, and Mapping GeoLab.

GeoLab

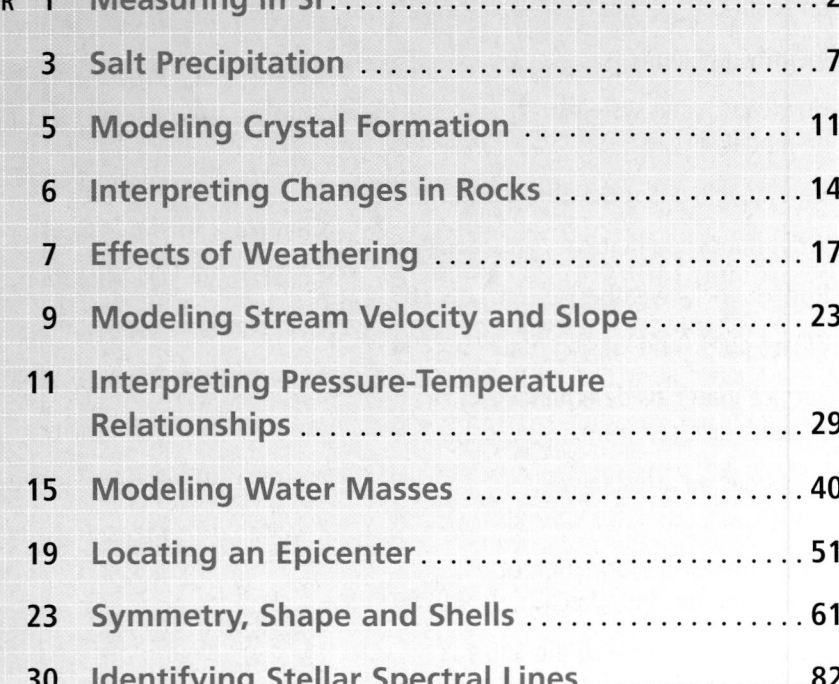

Internet GeoLab

Mapping GeoLab

DESIGN YOUR OWN GeoLab

Discovery Labs

Each chapter has one Discovery Lab. These activities are used to introduce the students to the chapter content.

Problem-Solving Labs

Each chapter has one Problem-Solving Activity. These activities are math-based skill activities, and often require data interpretation and graphing.

Features

Each chapter has one Feature. These features expand and extend the chapter content.

Science & Technology

Science & Math

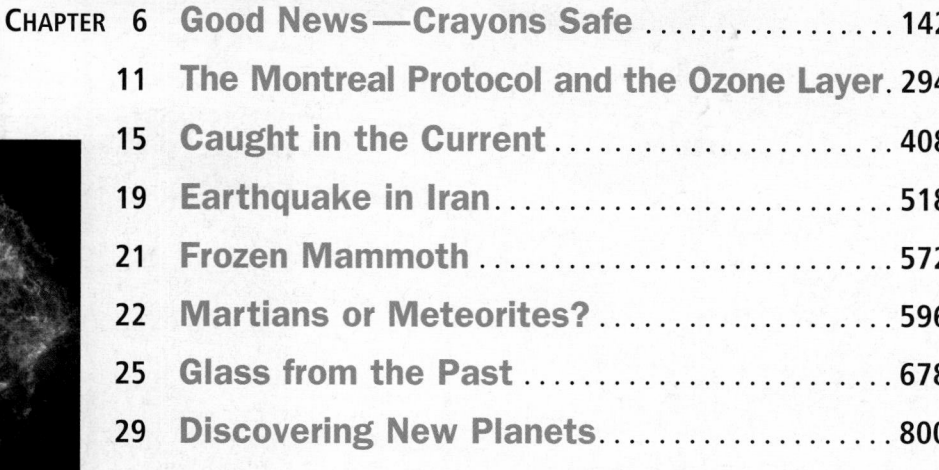

Science & the Environment

NATIONAL GEOGRAPHIC
eXpeditions!

Explore the *Titanic*...
Tame the mighty Colorado River...
Dig for Dinosaurs...

What is it like to map the highest mountain on Earth? Or to explore the ghostly wreck of the unsinkable *Titanic?* The **National Geographic Expeditions** allow you to share in the excitement and adventures of explorers, scientists, and lovers of the environment as they delve into the unknown. You can explore the sparkling beauty of a cave in a river of ice. Or watch the explosion of a dying star. Each Expedition will take you on a journey that reaches from the distant galaxies to the depths of the oceans.

As you learn about our dynamic planet, you can use the **National Geographic Expeditions** to extend your knowledge and challenge yourself. To learn more about the Expeditions, go to the **Earth Science Web Site** (earthgeu.com) and click on the **National Geographic Expeditions** link. Or read the original **National Geographic Society** magazine articles to find out how geologists work to discover how a volcano erupts and try to predict future eruptions. The goal is to save lives! It's explorers and scientists like these that discovered the fascinating topics you are studying in your Glencoe **Earth Science: Geology, the Environment, and the Universe** textbook.

xxii

National Geographic Expeditions! are referenced within the chapters at point of use, to support or extend chapter content.

Table of Contents

1

Earth Science

Unit Overview

The Study of Earth In Unit 1, students will learn that Earth science is actually a blend of several other sciences. Major fields of Earth science include astronomy, meteorology, oceanography, and geology. Scientists in these fields study Earth using organized procedures called scientific methods. Based on their studies, scientists develop models and propose theories. Theories can explain scientific laws, which describe the behavior of natural phenomena.

Chapter Breakdown In Chapter 1, students will learn about some of the fields of Earth science, as well as about Earth's four major systems—the lithosphere, the hydrosphere, the atmosphere, and the biosphere— and how they interact with one another. Scientific methods of problem solving are also discussed in Chapter 1. Different types of maps, which are models of Earth, are discussed in detail in Chapter 2.

0:00 *Out of Time?*

If time does not permit teaching the entire unit, use the GeoDigest at the end of the unit as an overview.

Earth Science

Earth science is a blend of many different sciences, including geology, meteorology, oceanography, and astronomy. Earth scientists in these different specialties study and model the processes that change our planet. Some of these changes take place in a matter of seconds; others take millions of years to occur. The rocks and structures shown here formed millions of years ago as a result of many interactions among some of Earth's systems. In this unit, you'll learn about some of the methods used by Earth scientists, how various parts of Earth interact to produce changes, and how our planet can be represented by models known as maps.

Unit Contents

1. The Nature of Science
2. Mapping Our World

 NATIONAL GEOGRAPHIC

Go to the National Geographic Expedition on page 864 to learn more about topics that are connected to this unit.

2

 NATIONAL GEOGRAPHIC

e**X**peditions!

Mapping Mount Everest Some topics of Earth science deserve more attention than others because they're unusual, informative, or just plain interesting. The National Geographic Society has created visually exciting, multipage *Expeditions!* features that will inform, excite, and motivate your students. *Expeditions!* features are relevant to the content of the student edition. Assign them as lead-ins to special research projects and in-depth studies for extra credit. Use them as a basis for colorful visual displays and bulletin boards.

Sunset Arch, Grand Staircase—
Escalante Wilderness, Utah

3

Introducing the Unit

Our Dynamic Planet The structure in the photograph is the Sunset Arch, which was carved into sandstone, a sedimentary rock, in the Grand Staircase-Escalante National Monument in Utah. The mountain in the background at left is Navajo Mountain; the cliffs are the Straight Cliffs of the Kaiparowitz Plateau. These rocks are parts of one of Earth's major systems: the lithosphere. Earth's lithosphere continuously changes as it interacts with the atmosphere, the hydrosphere, and organisms of the biosphere. Have students speculate about how interactions among Earth's major systems change the planet.

Making Models Ask students to describe how the features shown in the photo could be represented on a piece of paper. Discuss how a two-dimensional representation would differ from the actual three-dimensional scene. Have a variety of maps available for students to study as you teach the information presented in Chapter 2.

Earth Science Online Note Internet addresses that you find useful in the space below for quick reference.

_____

_____

_____

_____

_____

For Internet tips, see Glencoe's **Using the Internet in the Science Classroom.**

Chapter 1

The Nature of Science

Refer to pages 8T–9T of the Teacher Guide for an explanation of the National Science Content Standards correlations.

Section	Objectives	National Science Content Standards	State/Local Standards
SECTION 1.1 **Earth Science** 🕐 1 session 📦 ½ block	1. **Differentiate** among the four major branches of Earth science. 2. **Contrast** the four systems of Earth. 3. **Discuss** how Earth science affects your daily life.	UCP.1; A.1, A.2; C.4, C.5; D.2, D.3; E.1, E.2; G.1, G.2, G.3	St 1 Science KI 1 & 2, St 2 KI 1, St 4 KI 1.2g, 2.1l, & 2.2b, St 6 KI 1 & 5
SECTION 1.2 **Methods of Scientists** 🕐 1 session 📦 ½ block	4. **List** the steps used in a scientific method. 5. **Compare** and **contrast** experimental variables and controls. 6. **Identify** basic SI units. 7. **Explain** how to write numbers using scientific notation.	A.1, A.2; B.2, B.6; G.2	St 1 Math KI 1 & Science KI 1
SECTION 1.3 **Communicating in Science** 🕐 1½ sessions 📦 ¾ block	8. **List** several ways in which scientific information is communicated. 9. **Differentiate** between a scientific theory and a scientific law.	UCP.2, UCP.3; A.1, A.2; B.2; C.3, C.5; D.1, D.2, D.3, D.4; E.1, E.2; G.1, G.2, G.3	St 1 Math KI 1 & Science KI 1, St 4 KI 1.2g, 1.2i, & 2.1l, St 6 KI 1 & 2

A complete Planning Guide is provided on pages 30T–32T.

🕐 The number of recommended single-period sessions

📦 The number of recommended blocks

Activity Materials

Discovery Lab *page 5*
objects such as small rocks or mineral samples, coins, buttons, and game pieces; pencil; paper

GeoLab *pages 20–21*
water, 250-mL beaker, graph paper, balance, string, spring scale, rock samples

MiniLab *page 12*
soil; water; bottoms of clean, empty, plastic milk jugs (2); thermometers (4); masking tape

Need materials? Contact Science Kit at 1-800-828-7777 or at 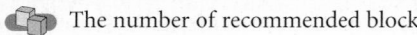www.sciencekit.com on the Internet. For alternate materials, see the activity on the listed page.

Key to Teaching Strategies

L1 Level 1 activities should be appropriate for students with learning difficulties.

L2 Level 2 activities should be within the ability range of all students.

L3 Level 3 activities are designed for above-average students.

ELL ELL activities should be within the ability range of English-language learners.

COOP LEARN Cooperative learning activities are designed for small-group work.

P These strategies represent student products that can be placed in a best-work portfolio.

📦 These strategies are useful in a block-scheduling format.

Chapter Organizer

Glencoe Exclusive!
TeacherWorks™
All-In-One Planner and Resource Center

Activities/Features	Reproducible Masters	Transparencies
Discovery Lab: Scientific Communication, p. 5	**Study Guide for Content Mastery,** pp. 1–2 **L2** **Laboratory Manual,** pp. 1–4 **L2**	**Section Focus Transparency 1** **L1** **ELL** **Teaching Transparency 1** **L2** **ELL**
MiniLab: How do soil and water absorb and release heat? p. 12 **Using Math:** Measuring, p. 14	**Study Guide for Content Mastery,** pp. 3–4 **L2** **GeoLab and MiniLab Worksheets,** p. 1 **L2** **Laboratory Manual,** pp. 5–8 **L2** **Exploring Environmental Problems,** pp. 5–8 **L2**	**Section Focus Transparency 2** **L1** **ELL** **Teaching Transparency 2** **L2** **ELL**
Problem-Solving Lab: Making and Using Graphs, p. 18 **GeoLab:** Measuring in SI, pp. 20–21 **Science & Technology:** Willo, Sue, and Technology, Too, p. 22	**Study Guide for Content Mastery,** pp. 5–6 **L2** **GeoLab and MiniLab Worksheets,** pp. 2–4 **L2**	**Section Focus Transparency 3** **L1** **ELL** **Teaching Transparency 3** **L2** **ELL**

✓Assessment

Chapter Assessment, pp. 1–6
Performance Assessment in the Science Classroom (PASC)
MindJogger Videoquiz DVD/VHS
Performance Assessment in Earth Science
ExamView® Pro CD-ROM
5 Days to the Regents Exam

GLENCOE'S
ASSESSMENT
ADVANTAGE

Additional Resources

Guided Reading Audio Program **ELL**
Cooperative Learning in the Science Classroom **COOP LEARN**
Lesson Plans
Block Scheduling
earthgeu.com
NY Lesson Plans
NY Block Scheduling
Review Handbook for Regents Earth Science Exam

☐ NATIONAL GEOGRAPHIC
Teacher's Corner

Products Available from National Geographic Society
To order the following products, call the National Geographic Society at 1-800-368-2728:

Videos
Our Dynamic Earth
Earth Alive

Content Background

A Dynamic Planet
Section 1.1

The idea that Earth is a dynamic rather than a static planet gained support in the 1700s. Detailed observations of the landscape around him led a Scottish physician, farmer, and amateur geologist named James Hutton to propose that processes such as erosion could alter Earth over time. Hutton concluded that Earth is much different today from how it was in the geologic past. His hypothesis that our planet changes very gradually as the result of Earth processes became known as the principle of uniformitarianism. Hutton was correct in his hypothesis that Earth changes, but incorrect in his assumption that only gradual changes occur. Most Earth scientists today agree that Earth evolves sporadically, with some changes, such as earthquakes and volcanic eruptions, taking place more rapidly than others, such as weathering and erosion.

Le Système International d'Unités (SI)
Section 1.2

To critically evaluate the merit and validity of scientific research and experiments, it is essential that scientists communicate using the same system of measurement. Most scientists use le Système International d'Unités, or SI. The basic units in this system are the kilogram, the meter, and the second. Originally, the kilogram and meter were defined by prototype samples—a kilogram mass and a platinum meterstick, both of which were kept in a vault in France. Copies of these standards were made and distributed so that scientists everywhere could use identical measurements. However, because this proved to be impractical, in 1983, the meter was redefined as the distance that light travels in a vacuum during the time period of one $1/c$, where c is the speed of light, 299 732 458 m/s. Nothing could be done about the kilogram, however, and this unit is still defined by the prototype block in the vault in France. The second, which was originally defined on the basis of astronomical time, is now defined by the rate of vibration of a cesium atom, such as that used in atomic clocks. The value of defining a meter in relation to the speed of light and the second by atomic vibrations is that the same values can be used as standards in any laboratory around the globe.

Multiple Learning Styles

- **Visual-Spatial** Modeling, p. 8
- **Interpersonal** Collaborative Learning, p. 8
- **Intrapersonal** Earth Science Journal, p. 6
- **Linguistic** Using Scientific Terms, p. 6
- **Logical-Mathematical** Project, p. 13, Demo, p. 15
- **Naturalist** Environmental Connection, p. 9

GLENCOE
Technology

The following multimedia resources are available from Glencoe.

Vocabulary Puzzlemaker
TeacherWorks™ CD-ROM
MindJogger Videoquizzes DVD/VHS
ExamView® Pro CD-ROM
Interactive Chalkboard CD-ROM

Chapter Organizer

Communicating in Science
Section 1.3

Communication is essential in professional scientific research. When a scientist develops a theory or makes a discovery, the results are scrutinized by the scientist's peers as part of the processes of testing and validation. Normally, the scientist who formulates the new model or makes the discovery writes a paper describing the work, which can be published in a professional journal. Before the paper is published, however, it is reviewed by other scientists in the same field who determine whether the work is new and whether there are any flaws in the logic or errors in the analysis of the data. Once the paper passes this often-stringent review process, it is published in a scientific journal, where other scientists can read it and either verify the work or challenge it. Thus, scientific research is a self-regulating process aimed at ensuring that only viable models and theories are put forward.

Identifying Misconceptions

People often use the terms *hypothesis* and *theory* synonymously. A scientific hypothesis is a suggested explanation for an observation or a statement of an anticipated outcome. A theory is an explanation based on many observations made during repeated experiments.

✓Assessment

Portfolio Assessment
Assessment, TWE, p. 9

Performance Assessment
Assessment, TWE, p. 10
MiniLab, SE, p. 12
GeoLab, SE, pp. 20–21
Discovery Lab, SE, p. 5

Knowledge Assessment
Discovery Lab, TWE, p. 5
Assessment, TWE, pp. 13, 16, 19
MiniLab, TWE, p. 12
GeoLab, TWE, pp. 20–21

Section Assessment, SE, pp. 10, 16, 19
Chapter Assessment, SE, pp. 24–25

Skill Assessment
Assessment, TWE, p. 15
Problem-Solving Lab, TWE, p. 18

Earth Science Online

Be sure to check the Earth Science Web Site for links to chapter material: earthgeu.com

GLENCOE'S ASSESSMENT ADVANTAGE

The Nature of Science

Introducing the Chapter

Ask students how they think Earth science affects their everyday lives. Answers might include observing clouds and relating these observations to changes in weather; seeing loose materials slide down a hillside and wondering why this happens; and observing that soils in different places vary in color and texture; among others.

Interpreting the Photo

The concretions on Bowling Ball Beach formed as the result of weathering and erosion of sedimentary rocks. Simulate these processes by burying marbles in a slab of modeling clay. Have volunteers pour water over the clay daily and observe that, over time, the clay will wash away, leaving "concretions" behind.

PowerPoint® Presentations

This CD is an editable Microsoft® PowerPoint® presentation that includes:
- Section presentations
- Section checks
- Image bank
- Links to Earth Science Online
- All transparencies
- Animations
- Audio

The Nature of Science

What You'll Learn

- How Earth science is a blend of sciences.
- How Earth's four major systems interact.
- What is involved in carrying out scientific experiments.
- Why it is important to communicate scientific methods and results accurately.

Why It's Important

In order to better understand Earth and how its processes affect our lives and the environment, it is necessary to learn about its major systems, the methods used by Earth scientists, and how scientific work is done.

Earth Science Online

To find out more about the planet on which you live, visit the Earth Science Web Site at earthgeu.com

4

Discovery Lab

Process Skills

describe, communicate **L1** **ELL**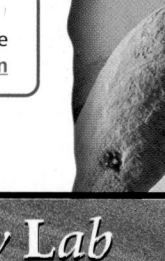

Preparation

- Collect a number of small objects that students can describe, such as rocks, minerals, buttons, coins, and game pieces.
- Make sure that each student has a science journal in which to record the results of this lab as well as

other labs and activities that will be conducted throughout this course.

Procedure

Troubleshooting

If objects are similar, use a permanent marker to identify them with small numbers so that students can distinguish their objects from similar ones.

Communicate

The revised descriptions should be more succinct than the original ones.

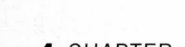

Discovery Lab

Scientific Communication

Have you ever explained something to someone only to later find out that what you thought was a crystal-clear explanation was confusing, misleading, or even incorrect? Communication is a very important skill both in everyday life and in science. In this activity, you will work with a partner to describe objects provided by your teacher.

1. Obtain an object from your teacher. Don't show it to your partner.

2. Write only one sentence that accurately describes the object in detail without actually saying what the object is.

3. Give your partner the description and allow him or her a few minutes to try to determine what your object is.

4. Now use your partner's description to determine what his or her object is.

Communicate Work together to rewrite each description in your science journals to make them as succinct as possible. Trade the new descriptions with another pair of students. Did this pair of students have an easier time at determining the objects than you and your partner did? Why or why not?

SECTION 1.1 — Earth Science

OBJECTIVES

- **Differentiate** *among the four major branches of Earth science.*
- **Contrast** *the four systems of Earth.*
- **Discuss** *how Earth science affects your daily life.*

VOCABULARY

astronomy
meteorology
geology
oceanography
lithosphere
asthenosphere
hydrosphere
atmosphere
biosphere

It is easy to see from the photograph on page 4 why this strip of the California coast is called Bowling Ball Beach. These round structures are concretions—masses of rock that form as the result of processes at work on Earth's surface. In this book, you'll learn about Earth and the processes and forces that change it, the materials from which it is made, its long history, and its place in the universe.

THE SCOPE OF EARTH SCIENCE

The scope of Earth science is vast. Dinosaur bones on display at museums were once embedded in the rocks that make up some of Earth's cliffs and canyons. Mining certain rocks produces some of the gold used by jewelers and dentists. Computer models simulate the flow of the blanket of air that surrounds Earth so that scientists better understand stormy weather. Ocean-floor exploration has led to the discovery of bizarre creatures that never see the light of day, while the study of objects in space has revealed much about our own planet.

1.1 Earth Science **5**

Assessment

Knowledge Have students use the results of this lab to discuss the importance of logical and objective communication in science.

Out of Time?

If time does not permit teaching the entire chapter, use the Chapter Summary on page 23 and the GeoDigest found at the end of the unit as an overview.

Resource Manager

Study Guide for Content Mastery, pp. 1–2 L2

Section Focus Transparency 1 L1 ELL

Section 1.1

1 Focus

Section Focus

Before presenting the lesson, display **Section Focus Transparency 1** on the overhead projector. L1 ELL

Section Focus Transparency — 1 — EARTH SYSTEMS
Use with Chapter 1, Section 1.1

① What parts of Earth are made of gases, liquids, and solids?
② In what parts of Earth are living things found?

Section Focus Transparency

Earth Science: Geology, the Environment, and the Universe

Activity

Show students a photo of Earth taken from space. Have students describe the planet on which they live from this perspective and contrast the view with that from your classroom window.

Chapter Themes

The following themes from the National Science Content Standards are covered in this chapter. Refer to page 8T of the Teacher Guide for an explanation of the correlations.
Systems, order, and organization (UCP.1); Evidence, models, and explanation (UCP.2); Change, constancy, and measurement (UCP.3)

NY Core Curriculum Standards

Page 4: St 1 Science KI 1, St 6 KI 1

Page 5: St 1 Science KI 1 & 2, St 6 KI 1

Using Scientific Terms

Linguistic Have students use their dictionaries to find out that the word part *-ology* is Greek in origin and means "the study of." Challenge students to determine the meanings of the following word parts used on these two pages: *meteor-, geo-, climat-, paleo-, hydro,* and *eco-.* Inform students that all of these terms come from the Greek language and reflect the pioneering exploration of many sciences during the time of the Greek empire, over 2000 years ago. L2

Enrichment

Ask each student to choose one of the subspecialties of Earth science and write a brief summary of what people in that field do. In addition to describing the type of work done in the selected discipline, each student summary should include a description of the educational background needed in the field and the kinds of institutions where most people in that field are employed. This activity will make students aware of the possibilities for careers in Earth science and what is necessary to prepare for such careers. P

Figure 1-1 Astronomy includes the study of Earth, its neighbors, and distant stars. The Keck Telescope in Hawaii, shown here, is used to study stars trillions of kilometers from Earth.

Figure 1-2 Some oceanographers study how human activities affect Earth's oceans. This oil spill occurred off the coast of Wales in 1996.

As you can see, there are many different areas of Earth science. This broad field can be broken into four major areas of specialization: astronomy, meteorology, geology, and oceanography.

Astronomy **Astronomy** is the study of objects beyond Earth's atmosphere. Prior to the invention of sophisticated instruments, such as the telescope shown in *Figure 1-1,* many astronomers merely described the locations of objects in space in relation to one another. Today, these Earth scientists study the universe and everything in it, including Earth, its neighbors, and other bodies in the universe.

Meteorology The branch of Earth science that studies the air that surrounds our planet is called **meteorology.** Meteorologists study the forces and processes that cause the atmosphere to change to produce weather. These Earth scientists also try to predict the weather and how changes in weather might affect Earth's climate.

Geology The study of the materials that make up Earth and the processes that form and change these materials is the branch of Earth science known as **geology.** Geologists identify rocks, study glacial movements, interpret clues to Earth's 4.6 billion-year history, and determine how forces change our planet, among many other things.

Oceanography The study of Earth's oceans, which cover nearly three-fourths of the planet, is called **oceanography.** Oceanographers study the creatures that inhabit salty water, measure different physical and chemical properties of the oceans, and observe various processes in these bodies of water. Some oceanographers study the effects of human activities on Earth's saltwater bodies. The oil shown in *Figure 1-2* is just a very small portion of the 70 000 tonnes that were spilled off the coast of Wales in 1996.

Earth Science Journal

Science Field Book

Intrapersonal Ask each student to find at least three examples of Earth science applications in the news or in their daily lives and to write a description of each application in their science journals. Examples might include weather reports, construction projects, obtaining resources, global warming, pollution, and astronomical discoveries in the news. L1

Differentiated Instruction

Learning Disabled Earth processes that are very violent and abrupt typically hold most students' attention. Have students with learning disabilities find pictures or reports of cataclysmic events related to Earth science, such as volcanic eruptions, storms, floods, and earthquakes. Suggest that students paste the pictures or reports in their science journals and highlight any facts in the reports that they find interesting. L1

The study of our planet is a broad endeavor, and thus it requires a variety of subspecialties of the four major areas of Earth science. Some of these subspecialties are listed in *Table 1-1.* What kinds of things does a paleontologist study? Which subspecialty is concerned with the environment? What types of things are studied by scientists specializing in tectonics? What might a hydrologist study?

EARTH'S SYSTEMS

Scientists who study Earth have identified four main Earth systems: the lithosphere, the hydrosphere, the atmosphere, and the biosphere. Each system is unique, yet each interacts with the others. None of Earth's systems is independent of the others, nor of the global system of Earth itself.

Table 1-1 Some Subspecialties of Earth Science

Subspecialty	Subjects Studied	Subspecialty	Subjects Studied
Climatology	Patterns of weather over a long period of time; effects of human activities on weather and climate	Ecology	Habitats of organisms and how organisms interact with each other and their environments
Paleontology	Remains of organisims that once lived on Earth; ancient environments	Geochemistry	Earth's composition and the processes that change it
Hydrology	Water flow on and below Earth's surface; sources of and solutions to water pollution	Tectonics	Effects of internal processes on Earth's surface, including earthquakes and mountain building

Content Background

Studies in many of the subdisciplines of modern Earth science would not be possible without extremely sophisticated and expensive technology, such as Earth-orbiting satellites, deep-sea robotic probes, scanning microscopes, and spacecraft. Only a very limited view of Earth and its systems would be possible without the necessary funds and expertise to develop these technologies.

In-Text Questions

Page 7 What kinds of things does a paleontologist study? remains of organisms and ancient environments Which subspecialty is concerned with the environment? ecology What types of things are studied by scientists specializing in tectonics? the effects of internal processes on Earth's surface What might a hydrologist study? water flow and the sources of and solutions to water pollution

Interpreting the Photo

Table 1-1 Inform students that the photograph at the top of the second column is that of a bog—a freshwater pond partially or completely filled with organic matter from living and decayed plants. Over geologic time, the organic material in a bog may undergo physical and chemical changes to become the fossil fuel called coal.

Cultural Diversity

Written in the Stars Some Egyptologists hypothesize that the positions of various pyramids coincide with certain constellations. The relative positions of the Giza pyramids, for example, echo the positions of the stars that form the belt of the hunter, Orion. Also, the chamber of Pharaoh Khufu points directly to Polaris. Have interested students research the importance of astronomy in the Mayan, Anasazi, and Aztec civilizations.

NY Core Curriculum Standards

Page 6: St 6 KI 1 & 5
Page 7: St 6 KI 1

Modeling

Visual-Spatial Use a globe and a simple scale diagram on the chalkboard to show the relative thicknesses of Earth's systems. Earth's lithosphere is roughly 100 km thick, or about 1.5 percent of Earth's radius. For a globe with a radius of 0.2 m, the lithosphere would be about 3 mm thick. The atmosphere would be about 50 km thick, or about 0.7 percent of Earth's radius. On a globe with a radius of 0.2 m, the atmosphere's thickness scales to about 2 mm. The depth of the hydrosphere, including the deepest oceanic trenches, is about 10 km, 0.0016 of Earth's radius, or about 0.33 mm for a globe with a radius of 0.2 m. The biosphere, which extends roughly from the ocean's greatest depth to the upper atmosphere, has a thickness of about 60 km, or 0.9 percent of Earth's radius.

Content Background

The biosphere extends farther into Earth's crust than was previously thought. Not only are there organisms in the deepest oceanic trenches, but also, strange microscopic life-forms have been found in rock at depths as great as 3.5 km. Some of these organisms live under conditions of very high temperature and pressure, and thus, they are called extremophiles.

The Lithosphere Earth's **lithosphere** is the rigid outer shell of the planet and includes the crust and the solid, uppermost part of the layer below the crust, the mantle. There are two kinds of crust: continental crust and oceanic crust. Earth's continental crust is made mostly of a rock called granite. Oceanic crust is mainly basalt, a rock that is denser than granite. Earth's mantle is mainly composed of a rock called peridotite. Some of Earth's upper mantle behaves like a rigid solid while other parts of this layer are partially molten and flow like a soft plastic. This partially molten layer is the **asthenosphere.**

Beneath Earth's mantle is the core, which can be divided into two parts: an outer, liquid part and a solid, inner part. Earth's core is thought to be made of iron and nickel. While Earth's core and asthenosphere are not parts of the lithosphere, they do interact with this system of Earth to produce many of the features at the planet's surface. You'll learn how the lithosphere and asthenosphere interact to produce volcanoes, mountains, and earthquakes in Unit 5.

The Hydrosphere The water in Earth's oceans, seas, lakes, rivers, and glaciers, as well as the water in the atmosphere, makes up the **hydrosphere.** About 97 percent of Earth's water exists as salt water; the remaining 3 percent is freshwater contained in glaciers, in lakes and rivers, and beneath Earth's surface as groundwater. About three fourths of all freshwater is contained in glaciers and icebergs, such as the one shown in *Figure 1-3;* most of the rest of this freshwater is groundwater. On a fraction of Earth's total amount of freshwater is in lakes and rivers. You'll find out more about Earth's hydrosphere in Units 3, 4, and 7.

Topic: Earth's Systems
To learn more about Earth's four major systems, visit the Earth Science Web Site at earthgeu.com

Activity: Write a study question for each of the Earth's four major systems based on your new knowledge.

Figure 1-3 Most of Earth's freshwater is contained in glaciers. The iceberg shown here broke off of one of the glaciers that covers nearly all of the continent of Antarctica.

8 CHAPTER 1 *The Nature of Science*

Collaborative Learning

Interpersonal Divide the class into four groups and have each group prepare a report, which should include illustrations and photographs, about one of the four major Earth systems. Have each group also prepare a brief oral presentation on its findings that includes an explanation of how its Earth system interacts with the others.
COOP LEARN P

Figure 1-4 The biosphere, hydrosphere, atmosphere, and lithosphere are interdependent systems of Earth.

The Atmosphere The blanket of gases that surrounds our planet is called the **atmosphere.** Among other things, Earth's atmosphere is necessary for respiration by most living things, protects Earth's inhabitants from harmful radiation from the Sun, and helps to keep the planet at a temperature suitable for life. Earth's atmosphere contains about 78 percent nitrogen and 21 percent oxygen. The remaining 1 percent of gases in the atmosphere include water vapor, argon, carbon dioxide, and other trace gases. You will learn more about Earth's atmosphere and how parts of this system interact to produce weather in Unit 4.

The Biosphere The **biosphere** includes all organisms on Earth as well as the environments in which they live. Most organisms exist within a few meters of Earth's surface, but some live deep beneath the ocean's surface, and others live high atop Earth's mountains. Earth's biosphere appears to be unique in that scientists have not yet found any confirmed evidence of life on other planets in our solar system or elsewhere in the galaxy.

As you can see in *Figure 1-4,* Earth's biosphere, lithosphere, hydrosphere, and atmosphere are interdependent systems. Earth's present atmosphere, for example, formed millions of years ago as a result of volcanic activity, respiration and transpiration by ancient organisms, and photosynthesis. Today's organisms, including humans, continue to change the atmosphere through their life processes and activities. You'll explore interactions among Earth's biosphere and other systems, both past and present, in Units 3, 4, 6, and 7.

1.1 *Earth Science* **9**

9

Check for Understanding

Reinforcement

Ask pairs of students to summarize the components and compositions of each of Earth's four major systems in a data table. Major points should include: **1.** lithosphere—crust and rigid upper mantle; rocks and minerals; **2.** atmosphere—clouds; gases and liquids; **3.** hydrosphere—lakes, rivers, oceans, seas, glaciers; water; **4.** biosphere—living things and their environments.

Reteach

Show students a photograph from a nature magazine that shows components of Earth's major systems. Have students identify the components of each system and explain how components in each system interact with components in other systems.

✓Assessment

Performance Ask small groups of students to debate whether or not astronomy should be included as a field of Earth science. Use the Performance Task Assessment List for Oral Presentation in **PASC,** p. 71. Reasons for include that astronomy is the study of Earth's place in space and that the study of other planets can help in the understanding of Earth and its origin. One reason against is that astronomy is the study of the environments beyond our planet.

Figure 1-5 Computers, calculators, telephones, and electricity are technological advances used by many people in their daily lives.

EARTH SCIENCE IN YOUR EVERYDAY LIFE

You and the billions of other life-forms that live on Earth are part of the biosphere. Together with many of these creatures, you live on Earth's crust, which is part of the lithosphere, and breathe the gases in Earth's atmosphere. You also depend in many ways on the substance that covers nearly three-fourths of Earth—water, which makes up the hydrosphere. In what other ways is Earth science a part of your everyday life?

Technology While you might not realize it, the study of science, including Earth science, has led to the discovery of many things that you use every day. This application of scientific discoveries is called technology. Freeze-dried foods, ski goggles, micro-fabrics, and the ultra-light materials used to make many pieces of sports equipment are just a few examples of technological advances developed as a result of scientific study. Today, these items, along with those shown in *Figure 1-5,* are common.

Technology is transferable, which means that it can be applied to new situations. The technological developments just described were first developed for use in space. Later, they were modified for use here on Earth. In the *Science & Technology* feature at the end of this chapter, you'll find out how medical technology has been used to study dinosaurs!

SECTION ASSESSMENT

1. Name and briefly describe the four branches of Earth science.

2. What does a geologist study?

3. What does a geochemist study?

4. Compare and contrast Earth's lithosphere and asthenosphere.

5. Describe the subdivisions of Earth's hydrosphere.

6. Thinking Critically What kinds of interactions do you think occur between Earth's hydrosphere and atmosphere?

SKILL REVIEW

7. Outlining Outline the main ideas of this section. For more help, refer to the *Skill Handbook.*

earthgeu.com/self_check_quiz

NY Core Curriculum Standards

Page 10: St 2 KI 1
Page 11: St 1 Science KI 1

SECTION ASSESSMENT

1. astronomy—phenomena beyond Earth's atmosphere; meteorology—Earth's atmosphere; geology—Earth and the processes that change it; oceanography—the oceans

2. rocks, glaciers, Earth's history, and forces that change the planet, among others

3. the composition of Earth and the processes that change Earth's composition

4. Both are layers of Earth. The lithosphere is the rigid outer shell of Earth that includes the crust and the uppermost part of the mantle. The asthenosphere is the partly molten layer of the mantle.

5. salty water in the oceans; freshwater in air, lakes, rivers, and glaciers; and the water beneath Earth's surface

6. Students should describe various processes involved in the water cycle.

7. Outlines should include the boldface heads in the section.

Are you a scientist? Have you ever picked up a rock and peered at it for clues about its origin? Have you ever made a decision about what to wear after having observed the clouds in the sky? Have you wondered where soil comes from, or where it goes during a heavy rain? While you might not be a scientist, if you answered *yes* to any of these or similar questions, you have thought like a scientist. What makes scientific methods different from other methods of problem solving?

THE NATURE OF SCIENTIFIC INVESTIGATIONS

A scientific method is a planned, organized approach to solving a problem. While the steps taken to solve the problem can vary, the first step involved in scientific problem solving, as shown in *Figure 1-6,* is usually identifying the problem, or determining what it is you want to know. Often, scientific problem solving involves researching the problem. Once the problem is defined and research is complete, a **hypothesis,** or suggested explanation for an observation, is made. Often, a hypothesis is stated in the form of a question that can be answered by the results of a test or an experiment.

OBJECTIVES

- **List** *the steps used in a scientific method.*
- **Compare** *and* **contrast** *experimental variables and controls.*
- **Identify** *basic SI units.*
- **Explain** *how to write numbers using scientific notation.*

VOCABULARY

hypothesis
independent variable
dependent variable
control
Le Système International d'Unités (SI)
scientific notation

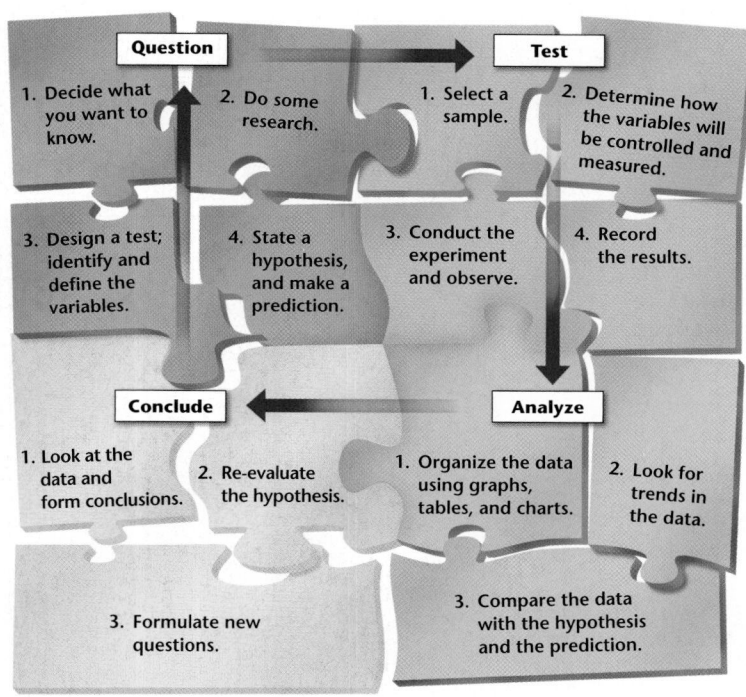

Question

1. Decide what you want to know.
2. Do some research.

Test

1. Select a sample.
2. Determine how the variables will be controlled and measured.

3. Design a test; identify and define the variables.
4. State a hypothesis, and make a prediction.

3. Conduct the experiment and observe.
4. Record the results.

Conclude

1. Look at the data and form conclusions.
2. Re-evaluate the hypothesis.
3. Formulate new questions.

Analyze

1. Organize the data using graphs, tables, and charts.
2. Look for trends in the data.
3. Compare the data with the hypothesis and the prediction.

Figure 1-6 Various steps and processes are involved in a scientific approach to problem solving.

Using an Analogy

Lead a discussion relating the problems associated with missing jigsaw puzzle pieces and the illustration shown in **Figure 1-6.** Students should conclude that the missing pieces in either case result in an incomplete picture.

Resource Manager

Study Guide for Content Mastery, pp. 3–4 **L2**

Laboratory Manual, pp. 1–4 **L2**

Section Focus Transparency 2 **L1** **ELL**

Section 1.2

Prepare

Section Background

For section content background, refer to **Le Système International d'Unités (SI)** on page 4C.

Preplanning

Refer to the Chapter Organizer on pages 4A–B.

1 Focus

Section Focus

Before presenting the lesson, display **Section Focus Transparency 2** on the overhead projector. **L1** **ELL**

❶ Which objects in this photograph are used for measuring?
❷ For what kind of measurement is each object used?

Tying to Previous Knowledge

Discuss television commercial claims for various products such as soaps, detergents, and paper towels. Have students propose how they might test an advertiser's claims about the effectiveness of the same product made by different manufacturers.

11

MiniLab

Purpose

Students will manipulate variables to measure heat transfer and retention in soil and water.

Process Skills

observe; recognize cause and effect; use variables, constants, and controls

Safety Precautions

If mercury thermometers are used, stress to students that if a thermometer breaks, they should NOT touch the mercury but should alert you immediately. Find out where to properly dispose of this toxic substance.

Materials

soil, water, the bottoms of clean plastic milk jugs, four thermometers per group, masking tape

Teaching Strategies

- If direct sunlight is not available, use a 150-W floodlight as the light source.
- Have students make multiple line graphs of their results.

Expected Results

The soil will heat up and cool down faster than water.

Analyze and Conclude

1. The soil absorbed heat faster than the water did; that is, the temperature of the soil rose faster than the temperature of the water did.
2. The soil cooled more quickly than the water did when the containers were removed from the heat source.
3. The independent variable was the medium—soil or water. The dependent variable was temperature.

✔Assessment

Knowledge Ask students to hypothesize what would have happened if both containers had been left in sunlight so long that the

---

MiniLab

How do soil and water absorb and release heat?

Experiment to determine the relationship between variables.

Procedure

1. Obtain the materials for this lab from your teacher.
2. Put soil into one container until it is half full. Put water into other container until it is half full.
3. Place one thermometer in the soil so that the bulb is barely covered. Use masking tape to secure another thermometer about 1 cm from the top of the soil.
4. Repeat step 3 with the container of water.
5. Put the containers on a very sunny windowsill. Record the temperature shown on each thermometer. Write these values in a table. Then record temperature readings every 5 minutes for half an hour.
6. Remove the containers from the windowsill and immediately record the temperature on each thermometer every 5 minutes for half an hour.

Analyze and Conclude

1. Which substance absorbed heat faster?
2. Which substance lost heat faster?
3. What was your independent variable? Your dependent variable?

Experimentation A hypothesis is tested by conducting an experiment, which is an organized procedure that involves making measurements and observations. A good scientific experiment tests only one variable, or changeable factor, at a time. The **independent variable** in an experiment is the factor that is manipulated by the experimenter. A **dependent variable** is a factor that can change if the independent variable is changed. Constants are factors that do not change during an experiment. A **control** is used in an experiment to show that the results of an experiment are actually a result of the condition being tested. Refer to the *Skill Handbook* for more information on variables. You will experiment with variables in the *MiniLab* on this page and in many other activities throughout this book.

Safety in the Science Classroom Some of the labs and activities in this book will require that you handle various materials and equipment, including those shown in *Figure 1-7*. When conducting any scientific investigation, it is important to use all materials and equipment only as instructed. Follow the safety rules listed in *Table 1-2* to

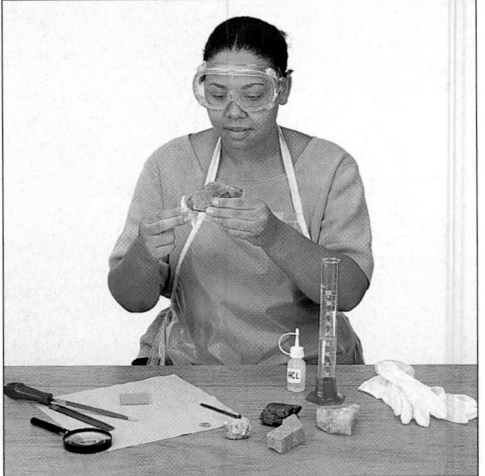

Figure 1-7 Safety goggles and a lab apron should be worn during any activity or experiment in the science lab.

---

temperature in both the soil and the water reached a steady-state value. The water would have had a higher steady-state temperature because water has a higher heat capacity, which means that it can store more heat per cubic meter than soil can.

Resource Manager

GeoLab and MiniLab Worksheets, p. 1 L2
Laboratory Manual, pp. 5–8 L2
Exploring Environmental Problems, pp. 5–8 L2

Table 1-2 Some Important Safety Rules for the Science Lab

1. Before beginning any investigation, understand the safety symbols noted by referring to the symbols and their meanings in *Appendix B*.

2. Wear safety goggles and a safety apron during all investigations that involve heating, pouring, or using chemicals.

3. Tie back long hair and loose clothing before you begin any investigation.

4. Always slant test tubes away from yourself and others when heating the tubes. Keep all materials away from open flames.

5. Never eat or drink in the lab and never use laboratory glassware as food or drink containers.

6. Never inhale chemicals, and never taste any substance used in the lab. Also, don't draw any material into a tube with your mouth.

7. Know what to do in case of fire. Also, know the location and proper use of the fire extinguisher, safety shower, fire blanket, first-aid kit, and fire alarm.

8. Report any spill, accident, or injury to your teacher immediately.

9. When cleaning up, dispose of chemicals and other materials only as directed by your teacher.

10. Always wash your hands thoroughly with soap after working in the lab.

help prevent injury to you and others in the lab as well as make you aware of possible hazards in a science lab. Refer to *Appendix B* for additional safety information and a table of symbols that will alert you to potential hazards.

Analysis and Conclusions During a scientific experiment, all data, including measurements and observations, are carefully recorded. Once an experiment is complete, the data must be formatted so that they can be studied, or analyzed. Graphs, tables, and charts are commonly used to format and display scientific data, which are then analyzed so that a conclusion can be drawn. Sometimes, a conclusion is contrary to the original hypothesis. In such a case, because the conclusion is supported by the data, the hypothesis, *not* the conclusion or the data, must be re-evaluated.

It is important to note, as shown in *Figure 1-6,* that scientific methods are not rigid, step-by-step outlines to solve problems. Scientists can take many different approaches to solving a scientific problem. In many scientific investigations, for example, scientists form new ideas after observing unexpected results. Sometimes, during the process of investigating one problem, an experimenter might encounter a different problem and choose to pursue the new problem rather than the original hypothesis.

Project

Logical-Mathematical Have pairs of students design their own experiments to test some aspect of Earth science. Have students describe in writing how they would carry out their experiments. Each description should clearly indicate the purpose, the hypothesis, the independent and dependent variables, and the expected results. Some students might wish to actually perform the experiments. Make sure to pre-approve any experiment before it is conducted. **L3** **COOP LEARN**

Using an Analogy

Explain that a scientific experiment can be likened to the work of a detective solving a crime. A detective's purpose is to determine who committed the crime, and at some point, the detective forms a hypothesis, which can be tested by logical analysis. Sometimes, a detective will even make predictions about where evidence may be hidden or what the suspect in a crime might do next. Finally, a detective, like a scientist, must be prepared to reject a hypothesis that is found to be inconsistent with known facts or that is not supported by further investigation.

Assessment

Knowledge

Ask: What happens when an experimental conclusion is not supported by the data that have been gathered?

a. The conclusion is changed.

b. The hypothesis is re-evaluated.

c. The data are changed.

d. The prediction is changed.

The correct answer is **b.**

Differentiated Instruction

Gifted Ask students to each find a description of an actual scientific experiment in an Earth science technical journal. Have students identify the purpose, the hypothesis, the procedure, the independent and dependent variables, and the conclusions of the experiment. **L3**

NY Core Curriculum Standards

Page 12: St 1 Science KI 1
Page 13: St 1 Science KI 1

In-Text Questions

Page 14 How many millimeters are in a meter? 1000 How many centimeters are in a kilometer? 100 000

Identifying Misconceptions

Students often use the terms *mass* and *weight* synonymously.

Uncover the Misconception
Ask students how the weight of an astronaut changes when he or she travels to the Moon.

Demonstrate the Concept
Remind students that weight is the force exerted on an object by the local gravitational field. An astronaut on the Moon weighs one-sixth of his or her sea-level weight on Earth, but has the same mass. Mass is the quantity of matter contained in an object and does not depend on the position of the object.

Assess New Knowledge
Ask students to explain why the standard conversion of 1 kg to 2.2 lb can be used everywhere on Earth and why this conversion would be invalid on the Moon.

Topic: SI Measurements
To learn more about SI, visit the Earth Science Web Site at **earthgeu.com**
Activity: List three facts about the history of SI.

Using Math

Measuring Use a metric ruler to measure the length of the following objects in both millimeters and centimeters: this book, a small paper clip, and your pencil. Would you use these same units to measure the length of your classroom? Why or why not?

Figure 1-8 The gravitational force exerted by the Moon is less than the gravitational force exerted by Earth. Thus, when this astronaut visited the Moon in 1969, he weighed less than he did on Earth.

MEASUREMENT

Scientific experiments often involve making measurements. A measurement, as you already know, includes both a number that identifies how many units there are and a unit of measure. Most scientific studies and experiments use a standard system of units called **Le Système International d'Unités,** or **SI** for short. This system is a modern version of the metric system. SI is based on a decimal system that uses the number 10 as the base unit. You will make various measurements in SI in the *GeoLab* at the end of this chapter.

Length The standard SI unit to measure length is the meter (m). The distance from a doorknob to the floor is about 1 m. A guitar is also about 1 m long. The meter is divided into 100 equal parts called centimeters (cm). Thus, 1 cm is 1/100 of 1 m. One millimeter (mm) is smaller than 1 cm. There are 10 mm in 1 cm. How many millimeters are in 1 m? Long distances are measured in kilometers (km). There are 1000 m in 1 km. How many centimeters are in 1 km?

Weight and Mass Weight is a measure of the gravitational force on an object. Weight is typically measured with some type of scale. Unlike mass, weight varies with location. For example, the weight of the astronaut shown in *Figure 1-8* while on the Moon is about one-sixth the astronaut's weight on Earth. This is because the gravitational force exerted by the Moon on the astronaut is one-sixth the force exerted by Earth on the astronaut. Weight is a force, and the SI unit for force is the newton (N). The SI unit of mass is the kilogram (kg). A half-cup of water with a mass of 4 ounces weighs about 1 N, and a person with a mass of 60 kg weighs about 600 N.

Mass is the amount of matter in an object and depends on the number and kinds of atoms that make up the object. The mass of an

Across the Curriculum

History Have students research the history of the metric system and report on significant steps in its development and adoption around the world. Students will find that the U.S. played a significant role in the development of the metric system. The U.S. was the first nation to adopt a decimal currency, and a federal law was passed in 1866 urging the use of the metric system for weights and measures. Challenge students to find out why the U.S. is the only major nation resisting full-scale adoption of the metric system.

Resource Manager

Teaching Transparency 2 L2 ELL

object, unlike weight, does not change with an object's position. Mass can be measured with a balance like the one shown in *Figure 1-9*.

Area and Volume Some measurements, such as area, require a combination of SI units. Area is the amount of surface included within a set of boundaries and is expressed in square units of length, such as square meters (m^2) or square centimeters (cm^2). Determine the area, in square centimeters, of this book by multiplying the length of the book by its width.

The amount of space occupied by an object is the object's volume. The SI units for volume, like those of area, are derived from the SI units used to measure length. The basic SI unit of volume for a regularly shaped, solid object is the cubic meter (m^3). SI measurements for liquid volumes are usually made in milliliters (mL) or liters (L). Volume can also be expressed in cubic centimeters (cm^3); 1 cm^3 equals 1 mL.

Density Density is a measure of the amount of matter that occupies a given space. Density is calculated by dividing the mass of the matter by its volume. Density is often expressed in grams per cubic centimeter (g/cm^3), grams per milliliter (g/mL), or kilograms per cubic meter (kg/m^3).

Time Time is the interval between two events and is usually measured with a watch or clock. The clock shown in *Figure 1-10* is an atomic clock, which provides the most precise measure of time. The SI unit of time is the second (s). In the activities in this book, you will generally measure time in seconds or minutes.

Temperature Temperature is a measure of the average vibrations of the particles that make up a material. A mass made up of particles that vibrate quickly has a higher temperature than a mass whose particles vibrate more slowly. Temperature is measured in degrees with a thermometer. In science, temperature is often measured on the Celsius (C) scale. On the Celsius scale, a comfortable room temperature is about 25°C, and the normal temperature of the human body is about 37°C. In SI, temperature is measured on the Kelvin scale. On this scale, the coldest possible temperature is absolute zero, or 0 K, which is equal to –273°C.

Figure 1-9 Mass is measured with a balance.

Figure 1-10 Atomic clocks provide much more precise measures of time than ordinary clocks.

Content Background

Despite the adoption of the Celsius temperature scale by most countries, in the U.S., the Fahrenheit scale is more commonly used. To convert from Celsius to Fahrenheit, multiply by 9/5 and then add 32°. To convert from Fahrenheit to Celsius, subtract 32°, then multiply by 5/9.

Skill Have students make the following conversions between the Celsius and absolute temperature scales: 50°C to K; -49°C to K; 77 K to °C; 500 K to °C. 50°C = 323 K; -49°C = 224 K; 77 K = -196°C; 500 K = 227°C

Interpreting the Illustration

Figure 1-9 Point out that the mass of the mineral shown here is 140.54 g. Ask students to compute the weight of the amethyst specimen on Earth.
2.2 lb/1 kg × 1 kg/1000 g × 140.54 g/? = 0.31 lb or about 5 oz

In-Text Question

Page 15 Determine the area, in square centimeters, of this book by multiplying the length of the book by its width. $529 cm^2$

Content Background

Uncertainty in measurement is unavoidable and must be accounted for when drawing conclusions. Experimental error can be reduced by making repeated measurements of the same quantity and averaging the results to cancel random errors. Make students aware of this as they do experiments and activities throughout this course.

Demo

Logical-Mathematical
To illustrate that experimental error is always present in measurements, have students take turns measuring the same quantity, such as the width of a desk or tabletop, with a meterstick. Have each student record his or her value. Compile the results on the chalkboard so that students can see that there is some variation in measured values. Make sure that students wear safety goggles during this entire activity.
COOP LEARN

NY Core Curriculum Standards

Page 14: St 1 Math KI 1
Page 15: St 1 Math KI 1

Check for Understanding

Activity

Ask students to go through an entire day using SI units. Have students convert every quantitative value that they encounter into SI units, including weather report temperatures, distances traveled, speeds of vehicles, distances and masses encountered in a physical education class or on an athletic field, and so on. Each student should record all of these quantities in his or her science journal.

Reteach

Have students name the SI unit for each of the following quantities: mass, temperature, weight, length, area, volume, time, and density.

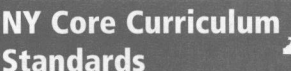

Knowledge Have students write the following values in scientific notation: 299 792 490 m/s (the speed of light) and 0.000 000 000 000 000 000 000 000 000 000 911 kg (the mass of an electron). $2.99\ 792\ 490 \times 10^8$ and 9.11×10^{-31} kg

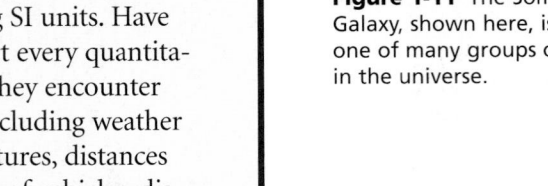

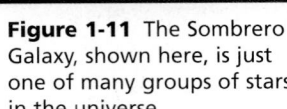

Figure 1-11 The Sombrero Galaxy, shown here, is just one of many groups of stars in the universe.

SCIENTIFIC NOTATION

In many branches of science, some numbers are very small, while others are quite large. To conveniently express these numbers, scientists use a type of shorthand called **scientific notation** to express the number as a multiplier and a power of 10.

In scientific notation, a number is expressed as a value between 1 and 10 multiplied by a power of 10. The power of 10 is the number of places the decimal point must be shifted so that only a single digit remains either to the left or right of the decimal point. If the decimal point must be shifted to the left, the exponent of 10 is positive. For example, the approximate number of stars in the Sombrero Galaxy, some of which are shown in *Figure 1-11,* is 90 000 000 000. In scientific notation, this number is written as 9×10^{10}. The mass of Earth, which is 5 974 200 000 000 000 000 000 000 kg, is written as 5.9742×10^{24} kg in scientific notation. If the decimal point in a number must be shifted to the right, then the exponent of 10 is negative. The diameter of an atom in meters, for example, which is approximately 0.0000000001 m, is written as 1×10^{-10} m.

All of the quantities discussed in this section and the units used to measure them are summarized in *Appendix A.* You can also refer to *Appendix A* for explanations of how to convert between the units you are familiar with, such as feet and pounds, and SI units. In the next section, you will learn about other ways in which scientific information is communicated.

SECTION ASSESSMENT

1. Describe the steps used in a scientific method.
2. Contrast dependent and independent variables.
3. What is the purpose of a control in a scientific experiment?
4. Explain how to write a large number using scientific notation.
5. **Thinking Critically** An increase in the temperature of matter generally results in a decrease in its density. Water is an exception to this rule. What do you think happens to water when it freezes?

SKILL REVIEW

6. **Concept Mapping** Use the terms below to make a concept map that summarizes the units used to measure each quantity discussed in this section. For help, refer to the *Skill Handbook.*

(time) (density) (temperature) (volume)

(mass) (weight) (length) (area)

(°C) (g/mL) (km) (s)

(cm³) (m²) (kg) (N)

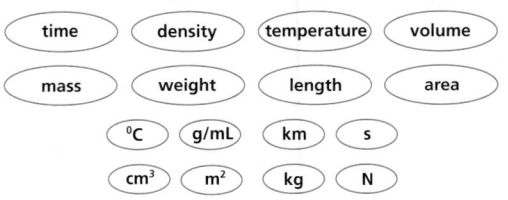

SECTION ASSESSMENT

1. define problem; develop hypothesis; make prediction; conduct experiment; reach conclusion regarding hypothesis
2. A dependent variable is a quantity whose value is determined by other quantities. An independent variable is a quantity whose value may vary without depending on other quantities, but which may determine the values of other quantities.
3. A control is a standard for comparison.
4. In scientific notation, a number is expressed as a value between 1 and 10 multiplied by a power of 10. The power of 10 is the number of places that the decimal point must be shifted so that only a single digit remains either to the left or right of the decimal point. If the decimal point is shifted left, the exponent is positive. If the decimal point is shifted right, the exponent is negative.
5. Water decreases in density. Hence, ice floats.
6. time: s; density: g/mL; temperature: °C; volume: cm³; mass: kg; weight: N; length: km; area: m²

Communicating in Science

There are many ways to communicate the same information, as you found out in the *Discovery Lab* at the beginning of this chapter. Scientists generally communicate through laboratory reports and research papers. Often, scientists propose models to try to explain ideas or systems. When an explanation withstands the test of repeated experiments, a theory might be proposed. Scientific models and theories can be modified when new observations and data are collected.

COMMUNICATING RESULTS

One important goal of science is to make results available to others. Communicating scientific data and results allows others to learn of new discoveries, to possibly verify what has been reported, and to conduct new experiments using the information. From the laboratory reports that you will generate as you use this book to scientific papers published in professional journals, scientific results are communicated in many ways.

Lab Reports Throughout this book, you will conduct many Earth science experiments and activities. During and after each activity or experiment, you will be asked to record and analyze the information that you collected and to draw conclusions based on your data. Your resulting lab report, similar to the one shown in *Figure 1-12,* will be used by your teacher to assess your understanding of the activity or experiment. You might also be asked to compare your results with the results of other students to help you find both similarities and differences among the results.

Graphs You will be asked to graph the results of many experiments and activities in this book. As you will find out in the *Problem-Solving Lab* on page 18, a line graph is a visual display that shows how two variables are related. On a line graph, the independent variable is plotted on the horizontal (*x*) axis, and the dependent

OBJECTIVES

- **List** *several ways in which scientific information is communicated.*
- **Differentiate** *between a scientific theory and a scientific law.*

VOCABULARY

theory
law

Figure 1-12 The results of laboratory experiments and the answers to questions posed in the experiment should be recorded neatly in your science journal.

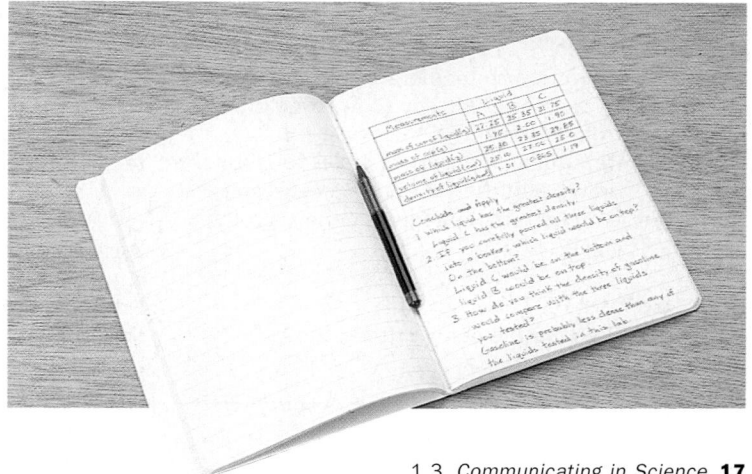

Resource Manager

Study Guide for Content Mastery,
   pp. 5–6 L2
Section Focus Transparency 3 L1 ELL
Teaching Transparency 3 L2 ELL

Section Background

For section content background, refer to **Communicating in Science** on page 4D.

Preplanning

Refer to the Chapter Organizer on pages 4A–B.

1 Focus

Section Focus

Before presenting the lesson, display **Section Focus Transparency 3** on the overhead projector.
L1 ELL

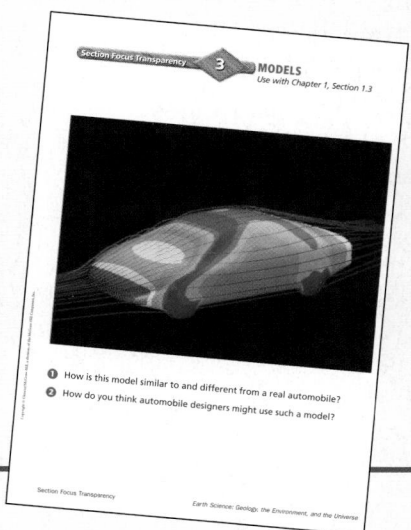

Tying to Previous Knowledge

Have students define and use the terms *theory* and *law* in everyday vernacular. Have students develop working definitions of these terms as they apply to Earth science. Correct any errors in the definitions as you teach this section.

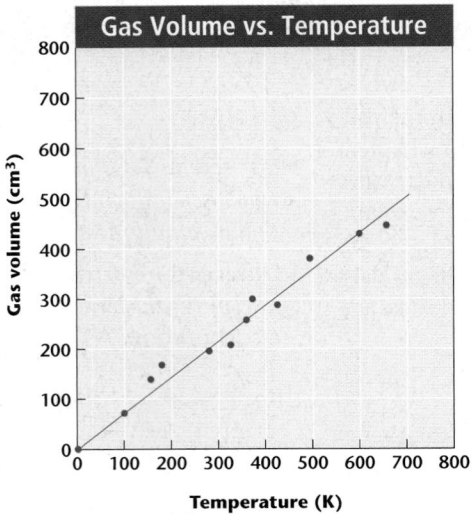

2 Teach

In-Text Questions

Page 18 What is the independent variable? temperature The dependent variable? gas volume

Interpreting the Illustration

Figure 1-13 Ask: How are these two variables related? An increase in temperature results in an increase in the volume of the gas.

Problem-Solving Lab

Purpose

Students will make and use a line graph.

Process Skills

make and use a graph, interpret data

Materials

graph paper, pencil

Teaching Strategies

If necessary, help students determine appropriate scales for the graph's axes.

Procedure

1. Temperature is converted from K to degrees Celsius by subtracting 273 from each value.
2. Scale should be sufficient to space data points appropriately.

Analysis

3. Temperature increases as the year increases.
4. The graph shows a steady rise in Earth's surface temperature since 1500.

Thinking Critically

5. Earth's surface temperature in 1980 was about 286.8°C.
6. In 2100, Earth's surface temperature will be about 287.4°C.

✓Assessment

Skill Have students extrapolate the data to determine what Earth's surface temperature might be every 100 years for the next 1000 years.

Gas Volume vs. Temperature

Figure 1-13 A line graph shows the relationship between two variables. Refer to the *Skill Handbook* for other types of graphs.

variable is plotted on the vertical (*y*) axis. Refer to the line graph in *Figure 1-13.* What is the independent variable? The dependent variable?

MODELS

In some of the activities and experiments in this book, you will be making and using models. A scientific model is an idea, a system, or a mathematical expression that is similar to the idea being explained. While a model might not have all of the components of a given idea, it should be a fairly accurate representation. Models can change when more data are gathered. Early astronomers, for example, thought that Earth was the center of the solar system, as shown in *Figure 1-14A.* This model was changed as the result of careful observations of the motions of the Sun and the planets in the night sky that showed that the planets in our solar system orbit the Sun, as shown in *Figure 1-14B.*

Problem-Solving Lab

Making and Using Graphs

Make and use a graph that shows how the annual, average surface temperature of Earth has varied over the past 500 years. The data in the table are global, average surface temperatures, in Kelvins, starting in the year 1500.

Procedure

1. Convert each temperature from kelvins to degrees Celsius by subtracting 273 from each value.
2. Determine appropriate scales for your graph. Plot the year on the *x*-axis and temperature, in degrees Celsius, on the *y*-axis.

Analysis

3. Describe the general trend shown by the data.

Average Surface Temperatures	
Year	Average Surface Temperature (K)
1500	285.8
1600	285.9
1700	286.0
1800	286.2
1900	286.5
2000	286.9

4. How has Earth's average surface temperature changed with time?

Thinking Critically

5. Use the graph to determine the average surface temperature for 1980.
6. Extrapolate the data to predict what the average surface temperature will be in the year 2100.

Content Background

The increase in Earth's surface temperature is called global warming and is thought to be mainly the result of the burning of fossil fuels.

Differentiated Instruction

Visually Impaired Provide students who are visually impaired with enlarged copies of the completed Problem-Solving graph to assist them in interpreting the data.

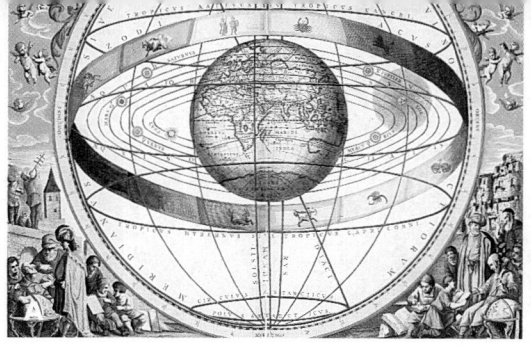

Figure 1-14 Some early astronomers thought that the Sun and other planets orbited Earth **(A).** It is now known that Earth and its eight neighbors orbit a star we call the Sun **(B).**

THEORIES AND LAWS

A scientific **theory** is an explanation based on many observations during repeated experiments. A scientific theory is valid only if it is consistent with observations, makes predictions that can be tested, and is the simplest explanation of observations. Like a scientific model, a theory can be changed or modified with the discovery of new data.

A scientific **law** is a basic fact that describes the behavior of a natural phenomenon. A scientific law can be thought of as a "rule of nature," even though the cause of the law may not be known. The events described by a law are observed to be the same every time. An example of a scientific law is Sir Isaac Newton's first law of motion, which states that an object at rest or in motion stays at rest or in motion unless it is acted upon by an outside force. This law explains why Earth and eight other planets remain in orbit around the Sun. Theories are often used to explain scientific laws.

In this book, you will communicate your observations and draw conclusions based on scientific data. You will also find out about many of the models, theories, and laws used by Earth scientists to explain the various processes and phenomena that make Earth unique among its celestial neighbors.

SECTION ASSESSMENT

1. What is the purpose of communicating scientific information?

2. What is the purpose of writing lab reports for experiments and activities in this book?

3. How are data plotted on a line graph?

4. What is a scientific model?

5. Contrast scientific theories and laws.

6. **Critical Thinking** When ice is heated, it melts. Is this a theory or a law? Explain.

SKILL REVIEW

7. **Recognizing Cause and Effect** Refer to *Figure 1-13.* Explain the relationship between the independent and dependent variables. For more help, refer to the *Skill Handbook*.

Check for Understanding
Activity
Have each student write a short paragraph that compares and contrasts the following scientific terms: *model, theory,* and *law.* Allow a few volunteers to read their paragraphs aloud. Have other students constructively critique the paragraphs.

Reteach

Provide students with an incomplete concept map that summarizes the information presented in this section. Allow students to work in pairs to complete their maps. **P**

✔Assessment

Knowledge Ask students to compare the format of their lab reports with the elements of a scientific method. Students will discover that the formats are very similar. Most student lab-report guidelines call for a sequence of steps, starting with a statement of the problem, a hypothesis, an experiment to test the hypothesis, and a conclusion. These steps closely parallel the main steps of a scientific method.

SECTION ASSESSMENT

1. to make results available to others so that they can check and evaluate the results

2. to help the teacher assess performance, to allow comparisons among results, and to learn how scientific results are communicated

3. The independent variable is plotted on the *x*-axis; the dependent variable is plotted on the *y*-axis.

4. an idea, system, or mathematical expression that represents a concept

5. A scientific theory is the best available explanation of a phenomenon. A scientific law is a rule of nature whose cause is not always understood but which is accepted based on observations or experiments.

6. The melting of ice is a law, or "rule" of nature that has been observed numerous times. The change of water from a solid to a liquid is observed to be the same every time ice melts.

7. An increase in temperature results in an increase in the volume of the gas.

NY Core Curriculum Standards

Page 18: St 1 Math KI 1 & Science KI 1, St 6 KI 2
Page 19: St 1 Science KI 1

19

Time Allotment

60 minutes

Process Skills

measure in SI; use numbers; collect, organize, and interpret data

Safety Precautions

Remind students to handle glassware carefully. Stress to students that the rocks must be gently lowered into glass beakers to prevent the beakers from breaking.

Preparation

- Review the basic SI units that will be used in this lab.
- Demonstrate how to properly use the balance and the spring scale.

Procedure

Teaching Strategies

- This is an appropriate activity for groups of two or three students, but it can also be done individually if sufficient equipment and rock samples are available.
- Explain that measuring the areas of the outlines of the rock samples requires counting squares because the shapes are irregular. You may need to review this procedure with students.

NY Core Curriculum Standards

Page 20: St 1 Math KI 1
Page 21: St 1 Math KI 1 & Science KI 1

GeoLab Measuring in SI

Suppose someone asked you to measure the area of your classroom in square cubits. What would you use? A cubit is an ancient unit of length equal to the distance from the elbow to the tip of the middle finger. Since this length varies among individuals, the cubit is not a standard unit of measure. SI units are standard units, which means that they are exact quantities that have been agreed upon to use for comparison. In this GeoLab, you will use SI units to measure various properties of rock samples.

Preparation

Problem

Measure various properties of rocks and use the measurements to explain the relationships among the properties.

Materials

water
250-mL beaker
graph paper
balance
pieces of string
spring scale
rock samples

Objectives

In this GeoLab, you will:
- **Measure** the area, volume, mass, and weight of several rock samples.
- **Calculate** the density of each sample.
- **Explain** the relationships among the quantities.

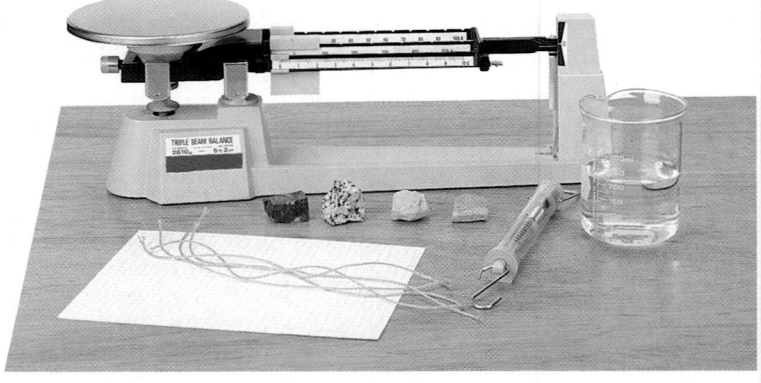

Troubleshooting

Tell students to make multiple measurements and average their results as a means of checking for errors and improving accuracy.

Data and Observations

Students should record their measurements in their data tables as they do the lab activity, including multiple measurements that can later be averaged.

Analyze

1. Differences among measurements will depend on the orientation of the sample when its outline is traced and on the ability of students to accurately count squares to measure the area of an irregular solid.
2. Volumes measured by different students for the same samples should agree, except for measurement errors, which should be small. Any large deviations are indications of serious mistakes in measurement.

Procedure

1. Use the information in the *Skill Handbook* to design a data table in which to record the following measurements for each sample: area, volume, mass, weight, and density.
2. Obtain rock samples from your teacher. Carefully trace the outline of each rock onto the graph paper. Determine the area of each sample and record the values in your data table.
3. Pour water into the beaker until it is half full. Record this volume in the table. Tie a piece of string securely around one rock sample. Slowly lower the sample into the beaker. Record the volume of the water. Subtract the two values to determine the volume of the rock sample.
4. Repeat step 3 for the other rocks. Make sure the original volume of water is the same as when you measured your first sample.
5. Follow your teacher's instructions about how to use the balance to determine the mass of each rock. Record the measurements in your table.
6. Again, secure each rock with a piece of dry string. Make a small loop in the other end of the string. Place the loop over the hook of the spring scale to determine the weight of each rock sample. Record the values in your data table.

Analyze

1. Compare the area of each of your samples with the areas determined by other students for the same samples. Explain any differences.
2. Compare the volume of each of your samples with the volumes determined by other students for the same samples. Explain any differences.
3. Compare the weight and mass of each of your samples with the values for these quantities determined by other students. Again, explain any differences.
4. Use your measurements to calculate the density of each sample using this formula: *density = mass/volume*. Record these values in your data table.

Conclude & Apply

1. How accurate do you think your measurement of the area of each sample is? Explain.
2. What were the variables you used to determine the volume of each sample?
3. How could you find the volume of a rock such as pumice, which floats in water?
4. Does mass depend on the size or shape of a rock? Explain.

Analyze *(continued)*

3. The weights and masses for the same samples as measured by different students should agree. Any differences should represent only standard margins of error in measurement.
4. Allow students to use calculators, if necessary, to do the computations.

Conclude & Apply

1. The measurements of area will be both inaccurate and variable as a result of the orientation of the samples when they were traced.
2. The variables were the size of the samples and the change in the level of the water in the beaker.
3. To find the volume of an object that floats on water, one could use a lower-density liquid, such as alcohol, or use a narrow stick to hold the sample below the water level and record the volume change. In the second method, one must assume that the volume of the stick is negligible compared to the volume of the sample.
4. Mass depends only on the size of the sample, not its shape, because mass is a measure of the quantity of matter in a sample.

Resource Manager

GeoLab and MiniLab Worksheets, pp. 2–4 **L2**

✓ *Assessment*

Knowledge Ask students to discuss the role of measurement error in the results of this GeoLab. Students should find that small errors in measurement can lead to equivalent errors in their results. For example, a 10-percent error in the measurement of mass would convert directly to a 10-percent error in the calculation of density, assuming that the volume was measured precisely. In fact, measurement uncertainties in both the mass and the volume add to the uncertainty in determining density.

Purpose

Students will recognize the value of technology in Earth science, even in long-established disciplines such as paleontology. Students also will learn how technologies developed for one purpose may sometimes cross over and become important for completely different applications from those that were originally envisioned.

Content Background

Computer technology has allowed sophisticated 3-D models of fossils to be made. A process called stereolithography uses digital data to cure a light-sensitive resin to form a model of a scanned specimen. This process, used to make prototypes of products, does not reveal inner structures, but it does allow large fossils to be scaled down and small fossils to be scaled up to aid in the assembly and study of organisms.

Teaching Strategies

- Have students compare a Web-based experience at a virtual museum with a visit to a museum where they have seen dinosaur bones or other fossils in person. Have them discuss the value of each experience.
- Have interested students research the life story of Sue Hendrickson, who found the skeleton of the *T. rex* Sue.
- Have students research medical and nonmedical uses of CT scans, MRI, X rays, and sonograms.

Science & Technology

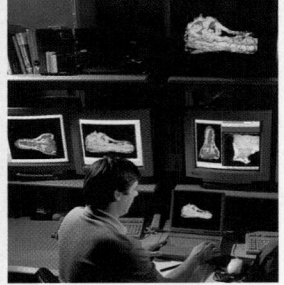

Willo, Sue, and Technology, Too

Paleontology, the area of Earth science that studies ancient life forms, has long been associated with hands-on work—digging, cleaning, and handling fossils. However, technology is playing an increasing role in this area. Technologies borrowed from medicine, manufacturing, and the aerospace industry are leading to new discoveries about dinosaurs—especially Willo and Sue.

Willo, the fossil remains of a 66-million year old *Thescelosaurus,* and Sue, the nearly complete skeleton of a 66-million year old *Tyrannosaurus rex,* were both studied using computerized tomographic scanning, or CT scans. A CT scan is a type of scan in which X rays move through a specimen at different rates depending on the density of the tissues encountered. A CT scan produces a picture of a very thin slice of a portion of a specimen. A computer is used to record and process the rates to produce an image on the screen. Multiple CT slices can be stacked to generate a three-dimensional image of the complete specimen.

A Dinosaur with Heart

Willo was found by paleontologist Michael Hammer in Harding County, South Dakota, in 1993. Willo was a plant-eater about the size of a pony. A CT scan of a dark mass of rock found in Willo's chest cavity revealed a structure that appears to be a heart—a four-chambered heart. A four-chambered heart would strongly support a relatively new hypothesis that dinosaurs were warm-blooded rather than cold-blooded animals.

Sue's Sniffer

Sue, the most complete skeleton of a *T. rex* ever recovered, was put on display at the Field Museum in Chicago, Illinois, in May 2000. Sue was found and excavated by amateur paleontolo-gist Sue Hendrickson in the South Dakota Badlands in 1990. The skull of Sue was sent for CT scanning to a company that makes jet airplane engines because medical scanners couldn't accommodate the skull's 1.6-meter length! The scan, which is shown above and is on display with a cast of the skull, revealed that the ferocious carnivore had a much more acute sense of smell than had been expected. The scan of Sue's skull showed olfactory bulbs the size of grapefruits! The discovery of these scent-sensing organs would never have been made without the use of CT technology.

Technology is changing how discoveries are made in Earth science, but also how they are shared. The images from CT scans are digital. They can be e-mailed and downloaded by scientists and students all over the world. The ease of access to important data will, in turn, lead to more exciting discoveries.

Internet

For more information on the use of CT scans in the area of paleontology, visit the Earth Science Web Site at **earthgeu.com**. Compare and contrast scanned skulls of meat-eating dinosaurs with those of plant-eating dinosaurs. Present your findings in a table.

22 CHAPTER 1 *The Nature of Science*

Internet

Students will find that meat-eating dinosaurs had sharper teeth and larger jaws than the plant-eating dinosaurs did.

Summary

SECTION 1.1
Earth Science

Main Ideas

- There are four major areas in Earth science. Astronomy is the study of objects beyond Earth's atmosphere. Meteorology is the branch of Earth science that deals with Earth's atmosphere. The study of the materials that make up Earth and the processes that form and change these materials is known as geology. The study of Earth's oceans is called oceanography.
- Earth can be divided into four main systems. The lithosphere includes the rocks that make up the crust and rigid, upper mantle. The atmosphere is the blanket of gases that surrounds Earth. Earth's hydrosphere is the system of all of the water on the planet. The biosphere is Earth's inhabitants and their environments.
- All of Earth's systems interact. You are part of the biosphere and you live on the crust, which is part of the lithosphere. You breathe the gases in that atmosphere and depend in many ways on the water in the hydrosphere.

Vocabulary

asthenosphere (p. 8)
astronomy (p. 6)
atmosphere (p. 9)
biosphere (p. 9)
geology (p. 6)
hydrosphere (p. 8)
lithosphere (p. 8)
meteorology (p. 6)
oceanography (p. 6)

SECTION 1.2
Methods of Scientists

Main Ideas

- The order of steps in a scientific method can vary. Most scientific methods to solving a problem, however, include defining the problem, stating a hypothesis, testing the hypothesis, analyzing the results of the test, and drawing conclusions.
- Variables are factors that change in an experiment. A dependent variable can change in response to changes in the independent variable. A control is a standard for comparison.
- Basic units used in SI include the liter, the meter, the second, the kilogram, the Newton, and degrees Celsius.
- In scientific notation, a number is expressed as a multiplier and a power of 10.

Vocabulary

control (p. 12)
dependent variable (p. 12)
hypothesis (p. 11)
independent variable (p. 12)
Le Système International d'Unités (SI) (p. 14)
scientific notation (p. 16)

SECTION 1.3
Communicating in Science

Main Ideas

- Scientific information is communicated through lab reports, professional papers, tables and graphs, and models.
- A scientific theory is an explanation based on many observations during repeated experiments. A scientific theory is valid only if it is consistent with observations, makes predictions that can be tested, and is the simplest explanation of observations. A theory can be changed or modified if it is found to be incorrect.
- A scientific law is a basic fact that describes the behavior of a natural phenomenon. A scientific law can be thought of as a "rule of nature," even though the cause of the law may not be known.

Vocabulary

law (p. 19)
theory (p. 19)

 earthgeu.com/vocabulary_puzzlemaker

Study Guide **23**

Main Ideas

Summary statements can be used by students to review the major concepts of the chapter.

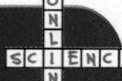

VOCABULARY PuzzleMaker

For additional help with vocabulary, have students access the Vocabulary Puzzlemaker online.

earthgeu.com/
vocabulary_puzzlemaker

0:00 *Out of Time?*

If time does not permit teaching the entire chapter, use the GeoDigest at the end of the unit as an overview.

Earth Science Online

Be sure to check the Earth Science Web Site for links to chapter material:
earthgeu.com

GLENCOE
Technology

Videotape/DVD
MindJogger Videoquizzes
Chapter 1: *The Nature of Science*
Have students work in groups as they play the videoquiz game to review key chapter concepts.

Resource Manager

Chapter Assessment, pp. 1–6
MindJogger Videoquizzes DVD/VHS
ExamView® Pro CD-ROM
Performance Assessment in Earth Science

NY Core Curriculum Standards

Page 22: St 2 KI 1, St 4 KI 1.2i
Page 23: St 1 Science KI 1, St 6 KI 1
Page 24: St 1 Math KI 1 & Science KI 1, St 4 KI 1.2g & 2.1l, St 6 KI 1
Page 25: St 1 Math KI 1 & Science KI 1, St 4 KI 2.1l

Understanding Main Ideas

1. c
2. d
3. a
4. a
5. c
6. c
7. d
8. Technology is the application of scientific discoveries. Science is the understanding of natural phenomena.
9. State the problem; develop a hypothesis; make predictions based on the hypothesis; perform experiments or make observations to test the predictions; reach conclusions about the validity of the hypothesis; modify the hypothesis, if necessary.
10. A hypothesis is a proposed explanation of some phenomenon. A theory is an explanation that has been tested and found to be consistent with observations.
11. The dependent variable is a quantity whose value is determined by the independent variable. The value of the independent variable may be set by the experimenter or it may change naturally. Its value determines the value of the dependent variable.
12. mass of apple (g or kg); length of beetle (mm); weight of Jupiter (N); volume of soft drink (L or mL); volume of sugar cube (cm^3)
13. Area and volume are quantities related to the size of an object. Area is the amount of surface included within a set of boundaries. Volume is the amount of space occupied by

---

1. Which area of Earth science includes the study of ancient organisms?
   a. astronomy
   b. meteorology
   c. paleontology
   d. geology

2. Which area of Earth science includes the study of stars?
   a. meteorology
   b. hydrology
   c. geology
   d. astronomy

3. What is geology?
   a. the study of the processes that form and change Earth
   b. the study of Earth's oceans
   c. the study of objects beyond Earth's atmosphere
   d. the systematic study of weather and climate

4. Which of the following is NOT a part of Earth's lithosphere?
   a. the inner core
   b. the crust
   c. the upper mantle
   d. rocks on the surface

5. What is Earth's hydrosphere?
   a. the gases in the air
   b. the solid, rocky part of Earth
   c. all of the water on the planet
   d. the study of Earth's atmosphere

6. What are the two most common gases in the atmosphere?
   a. hydrogen and oxygen
   b. nitrogen and water vapor
   c. oxygen and nitrogen
   d. hydrogen and nitrogen

7. Which of the following scientists would most likely study Earth's past biosphere?
   a. hydrologist
   b. geochemist
   c. meteorologist
   d. paleontologist

---

8. What is technology, and how is it different from science?
9. List the steps involved in a scientific approach to solving a problem.
10. What is a hypothesis, and how is it different from a scientific theory?
11. What is a dependent variable in a scientific investigation? How does it differ from an independent variable?
12. List the SI units that would be used to measure the following quantities: the mass of an apple, the length of a beetle, the weight of the planet Jupiter, the volume of a medium-sized soft drink, and the volume of a cube of sugar.
13. How are area and volume alike? How do they differ?
14. Complete the table below. Once you have made the conversions, express each answer in scientific notation.

Some SI Conversions		
1 m	____ mm	____ km
1 g	____ mg	____ kg
1 cm^3	____ m^3	____ mL
3.5 km	____ m	____ cm
18.6 cm	____ km	____ m

15. Refer to *Appendix B*. What are the safety symbols for a biological hazard, an electrical hazard, an open flame, and the need to wear safety goggles?

Test-Taking Tip

PREPARING FOR A TEST As soon as you find out about an upcoming test, ask which concepts and topics will be tested. When you study for the test, make sure you cover all of the material on which you may be tested.

earthgeu.com/chapter_test

---

an object.

14.

1000 mm	1.0 $\times 10^3$	0.0001 km	1.0 $\times 10^{-4}$
1000 mg	1.0 $\times 10^3$	0.0001 kg	1.0 $\times 10^{-4}$
0.001 m^3	1.0 $\times 10^{-3}$	1 mL	—
3500 m	3.5 $\times 10^3$	350 000 cm	3.5 $\times 10^5$
0.0186 km	1.86 $\times 10^{-2}$	0.186 m	1.86 $\times 10^{-1}$

15. overlapping, partial circles; plug; fire with overlapping circle; safety goggles
16. A theory can be explained and understood based on laws of nature and is verified through experimentation and/or

observation. A law is derived from observations but may not be understood. The theory of evolution is a theory; Newton's laws of motion are laws.
17. independent variable on the *x*-axis; dependent variable on the *y*-axis
18. A scientific model is an idea, a system, or a mathematical expression that represents a concept.

16. Compare and contrast scientific theories and laws. Give an example of each.
17. Explain how variables are plotted on a line graph.
18. What is a scientific model?

Applying Main Ideas

19. Which of the safety symbols in *Appendix B* would be shown in an activity in which you were asked to test the acidity of several liquids?
20. Explain how you might test which of three paper towels is most absorbent.
21. Suppose you were testing the effects of the amount of fertilizer needed to produce tall grass. What would be your independent variable? Your dependent variable? Your control?
22. A doctor is testing a new cancer drug. She chooses 50 patients who have the particular cancer to take part in the study. She gives 25 patients the new drug and the other 25 patients a placebo, which is a substance that contains no active ingredients. What is the purpose of this second group in the doctor's study?

Thinking Critically

23. Suppose you want to find out whether doubling the amount of potassium in a soil will increase the yield of tomato plants. Describe how you would test this hypothesis. What would be your variables? What would you use as a control?
24. How might elements in Earth's hydrosphere interact with Earth's lithosphere?
25. Explain your dependence on each of Earth's four systems.
26. When air or helium is added to a balloon, the balloon expands. Suggest a model that could be used to explain why this happens.

earthgeu.com/standardized_test

Standardized Test Practice

1. Which of the following lists Earth's layers from the inside out?
   a. inner core, outer core, mantle, crust
   b. crust, mantle, outer core, inner core
   c. crust, inner core, outer core, mantle
   d. mantle, outer core, inner core, crust

2. A block is 2 cm wide, 5.4 cm deep, and 3.1 cm long. The density of the block is 8.5 g/cm³. What is the mass of the block?
   a. 33.48 g   c. 399.3 g
   b. 85.10 g   d. 284.58 g

USING GRAPHS Use the graph below to answer questions 3 and 4.

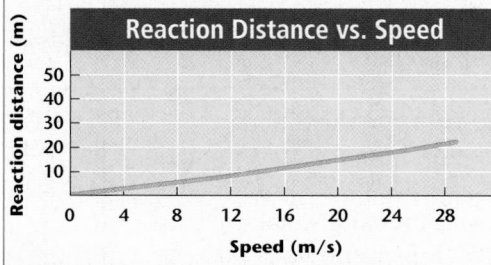

3. The distance a car travels between the time the driver decides to stop the car and the time the driver puts on the brakes is called the reaction distance. How does the reaction distance change with speed?
   a. Reaction distance decreases with speed.
   b. Reaction distance is the same as speed.
   c. Reaction distance increases with speed.
   d. You cannot tell from this graph.

4. What is the reaction distance of a driver traveling 20 m/s?
   a. 3 m   c. 20 m
   b. 15 m   d. 28 m

Assessment **25**

Applying Main Ideas

19. glove or overturned bottle
20. Measure three equal volumes of water and pour them onto a surface, then apply three different paper towels of equal area to absorb the water and measure the time required for each towel to absorb the water.
21. independent variables: amount and type of fertilizer; dependent variable: height of grass after a specified time; control: grass to which no fertilizer was applied
22. The second group was the control.

Thinking Critically

23. Several groups of plants would be grown under the same conditions; only the amount of potassium would change—the independent variable. The dependent variable would be the yield of the plants; the control would be plants to which no potassium was added.
24. Water changes the lithosphere by dissolving it as well as by transporting bits of it from one place to another. Water drops rocks when it loses energy.
25. lithosphere for resources; atmosphere for air to breathe; hydrosphere for water; biosphere for sources of food
26. For the balloon to be stable, that is, to stop expanding or contracting, the pressure inside the balloon must equal the pressure on the outside. The balloon will expand until this occurs.

Standardized Test Practice

1. a
2. d
3. c
4. b

Chapter 2

Mapping Our World

Refer to pages 8T–9T of the Teacher Guide for an explanation of the National Science Content Standards correlations.

Section	Objectives	National Science Content Standards	State/Local Standards
SECTION 2.1 **Latitude and Longitude** 🕐 1 session 📦 ½ block	1. **Compare** and **contrast** latitude and longitude. 2. **Describe** how time zones vary.	**UCP.1, UCP.2, UCP.3, UCP.5; A.1, A.2; E.1, E.2; F.6; G.3**	St 1 Math KI 1, 2, 3, & Engin KI 1, St 2 KI 1, St 4 KI 1.1c & 1.1d, St 6 KI 2 & 3
SECTION 2.2 **Types of Maps** 🕐 1 session 📦 ½ block	3. **Compare** and **contrast** different map projections. 4. **Analyze** topographic maps. 5. **Describe** map characteristics, such as map scales and map legends.	**UCP.3, UCP.5; A.1; E.1; F.6**	St 1 Math KI 1, 2, 3, & Engin KI 1, St 6 KI 2 & 3, St 7 KI 1
SECTION 2.3 **Remote Sensing** 🕐 2 sessions 📦 1 block	6. **Compare** and **contrast** the different forms of radiation in the electromagnetic spectrum. 7. **Discuss** how satellites and sonar are used to map Earth's surface and its oceans. 8. **Describe** the Global Positioning System.	**UCP.1, UCP.3, UCP.5; A.1; B.4; C.6; E.1, E.2; F.6; G.3**	St 1 Math KI 1, 2, 3, & Engin KI 1, St 2 KI 1 & 3, St 4 KI 1.1c & 1.1d, St 6 KI 2 & 3, St 7 KI 1

A complete Planning Guide is provided on pages 30T–32T.

🕐 The number of recommended single-period sessions

📦 The number of recommended blocks

Activity Materials

Discovery Lab *page 27*
graph paper, colored pencils

GeoLab *pages 42–43*
metric ruler, pencil, string

MiniLab *page 29*
world map or globe, pencil, paper

Demo *page 32*
assorted maps

page 37
prism, light source

Need materials? Contact Science Kit at 1-800-828-7777 or at www.sciencekit.com on the Internet. For alternate materials, see the activity on the listed page.

Key to Teaching Strategies

L1 Level 1 activities should be appropriate for students with learning difficulties.

L2 Level 2 activities should be within the ability range of all students.

L3 Level 3 activities are designed for above-average students.

ELL ELL activities should be within the ability range of English-language learners.

COOP LEARN Cooperative learning activities are designed for small-group work.

P These strategies represent student products that can be placed in a best-work portfolio.

📦 These strategies are useful in a block-scheduling format.

Chapter Organizer

Glencoe Exclusive!
Teacher Works™
All-In-One Planner and Resource Center

Activities/Features	Reproducible Masters	Transparencies
Discovery Lab: Make and Use a Map, p. 27 **Using Math:** Using Numbers, p. 28 **MiniLab:** How can you locate places on Earth?, p. 29	**Study Guide for Content Mastery,** pp. 7–8 L2 **GeoLab and MiniLab Worksheets,** p. 5 L2 **Exploring Environmental Problems,** pp. 49–52 L3 **Exploring Environmental Problems,** pp. 57–60 L3	**Section Focus Transparency 4** L1 ELL **Teaching Transparency 4** L2 ELL
Problem-Solving Lab: Calculating Gradients, p. 35	**Study Guide for Content Mastery,** pp. 9–11 L2 **Laboratory Manual,** pp. 9–12 L2 **Exploring Environmental Problems,** pp. 53–56 L3	**Section Focus Transparency 5** L1 ELL **Teaching Transparency 5** L2 ELL
Mapping GeoLab: Using a Topographic Map, pp. 42–43 **Science & Math:** Thriving in the Arctic, p. 44	**Study Guide for Content Mastery,** p. 12 L2 **Laboratory Manual,** pp. 13–16 L2 **GeoLab and MiniLab Worksheets,** pp. 6–8 L2 **Exploring Environmental Problems,** pp. 45–48 L3 **Exploring Environmental Problems,** pp. 61–64 L3	**Section Focus Transparency 6** L1 ELL **Teaching Transparency 6** L2 ELL

 **Assessment**

Chapter Assessment,
  pp. 7–12
**Performance Assessment in
  the Science Classroom
  (PASC)**
**MindJogger Videoquiz
  DVD/VHS**
**Performance Assessment in
  Earth Science**
ExamView® Pro CD-ROM
5 Days to the Regents Exam

Additional Resources

**Guided Reading Audio
  Program** ELL
**Cooperative Learning in the
  Science Classroom**
  COOP LEARN
Lesson Plans
Block Scheduling
earthgeu.com
NY Lesson Plans
NY Block Scheduling
Review Handbook for
  Regents Earth Science
  Exam

 **NATIONAL GEOGRAPHIC**

Teacher's Corner

**Products Available from
National Geographic Society**
*To order the following products,
call the National Geographic
Society at 1-800-368-2728:*
CD-ROM
PictureShow: *U.S. Regional
Geography Library*

Transparency Set
MapPack: *Continents Series*
MapPack: *U.S.A. Regions Series*
Videos
Latitude and Longitude
United States Geography Series
(3 Videos)

Content Background

The Celestial Grid System
Section 2.1

Celestial objects can be located using a grid system that is somewhat similar to the system of latitude and longitude used to locate places on Earth. In the celestial grid system, the celestial sphere is the imaginary dome on which the stars and planets appear in the night sky. To locate a celestial object, a person must first know his or her zenith. Each person's zenith is the imaginary point on the celestial sphere located directly above his or her head. An imaginary line drawn from the northern horizon up through the zenith and then down to the southern horizon traces the celestial meridian. The celestial meridian can then be used to locate constellations and planets throughout the year.

The USGS
Section 2.2

In the United States, the main publisher of topographic maps is the United States Geological Survey (USGS). Other U.S. map publishers include the Department of Defense, the Department of Agriculture, and the Forest Service. Standard maps produced by the USGS are called quadrangles. The boundaries of quadrangle maps are formed by lines of latitude and longitude. The maps are named for obvious features within the area shown on the map. No two quadrangles of the same series in the same state can have the same name.

The USGS uses standard colors to represent natural or cultural features in topographic maps. Black is used for human-made features such as houses and other buildings, and for the names of places. Green represents wooded or heavily vegetated areas. Red is used to mark important highways. Blue is used for all bodies of water, including rivers, ponds, reservoirs, swamps, lakes, and oceans. The contour lines that indicate the elevations of hills and valleys are brown. Topographic maps are periodically updated. Purple is used on updated maps to reflect any changes in the landscape, such as new bridges and buildings, that may have occurred since the maps were originally created.

Multiple Learning Styles

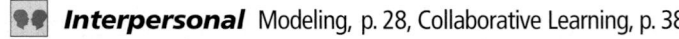

Interpersonal Modeling, p. 28, Collaborative Learning, p. 38

Intrapersonal Tying to Previous Knowledge, p. 30

Visual-Spatial Project, p. 30, Earth Science Journal, p. 35

Linguistic Reteach, p. 36, Activity, p. 40

Naturalist Environmental Connection, p. 39

GLENCOE Technology

The following multimedia resources are available from Glencoe.

Vocabulary Puzzlemaker

TeacherWorks™ CD-ROM

MindJogger Videoquizzes DVD/VHS

ExamView® Pro CD-ROM

Interactive Chalkboard CD-ROM

Chapter Organizer

Aerial Photography
Section 2.3

Aerial photography is a form of remote-sensing that can generate wide-angle views of Earth's surface. Thus, various surface features are shown in the photographs in their proper positions relative to other features. Accurate measurements of the features are obtained by placing the photographs in photogrammetric machines. To obtain a three-dimensional model of the features, cartographical technicians place pairs of overlapping aerial photographs in the photogrammetric machine using established control data as parameters. The resulting model can be used to determine the exact distances and positions of the photographed features. These data are then used by a cartographer to create a map.

Identifying Misconceptions

Many people assume that Earth's 24 time zones are of equal shapes and widths, and that they strictly follow lines of longitude. In reality, time zones are not divided evenly. Rather, they often conform to national and local boundaries. To help students understand this point, first remind them that Earth takes 24 hours to rotate. Thus, each time zone differs by one hour. In addition, because Earth is nearly a sphere and can be divided into 360°, each time zone is roughly 15° ($360° \div 24 = 15°$). Have students examine a world map that shows time zones. Tell students to trace the boundaries of several time zones. Students will observe that many time-zone boundaries do not follow lines of longitude. Tell students that these boundaries vary for geographical and political reasons.

✔ Assessment

Portfolio Assessment
Assessment, TWE, pp. 31, 36, 41

Performance Assessment
Discovery Lab, SE, p. 27
MiniLab, SE, p. 29
MiniLab, TWE, p. 29
GeoLab, SE, pp. 42–43
GeoLab, TWE, pp. 42–43

Knowledge Assessment
Section Assessment, SE, pp. 31, 36, 41
Chapter Assessment, SE, pp. 46–47

Skill Assessment
Discovery Lab, TWE, p. 27
Problem-Solving Lab, TWE, p. 35

Be sure to check the Earth Science Web Site for links to chapter material: earthgeu.com

GLENCOE'S
ASSESSMENT
ADVANTAGE

Chapter 2

Mapping Our World

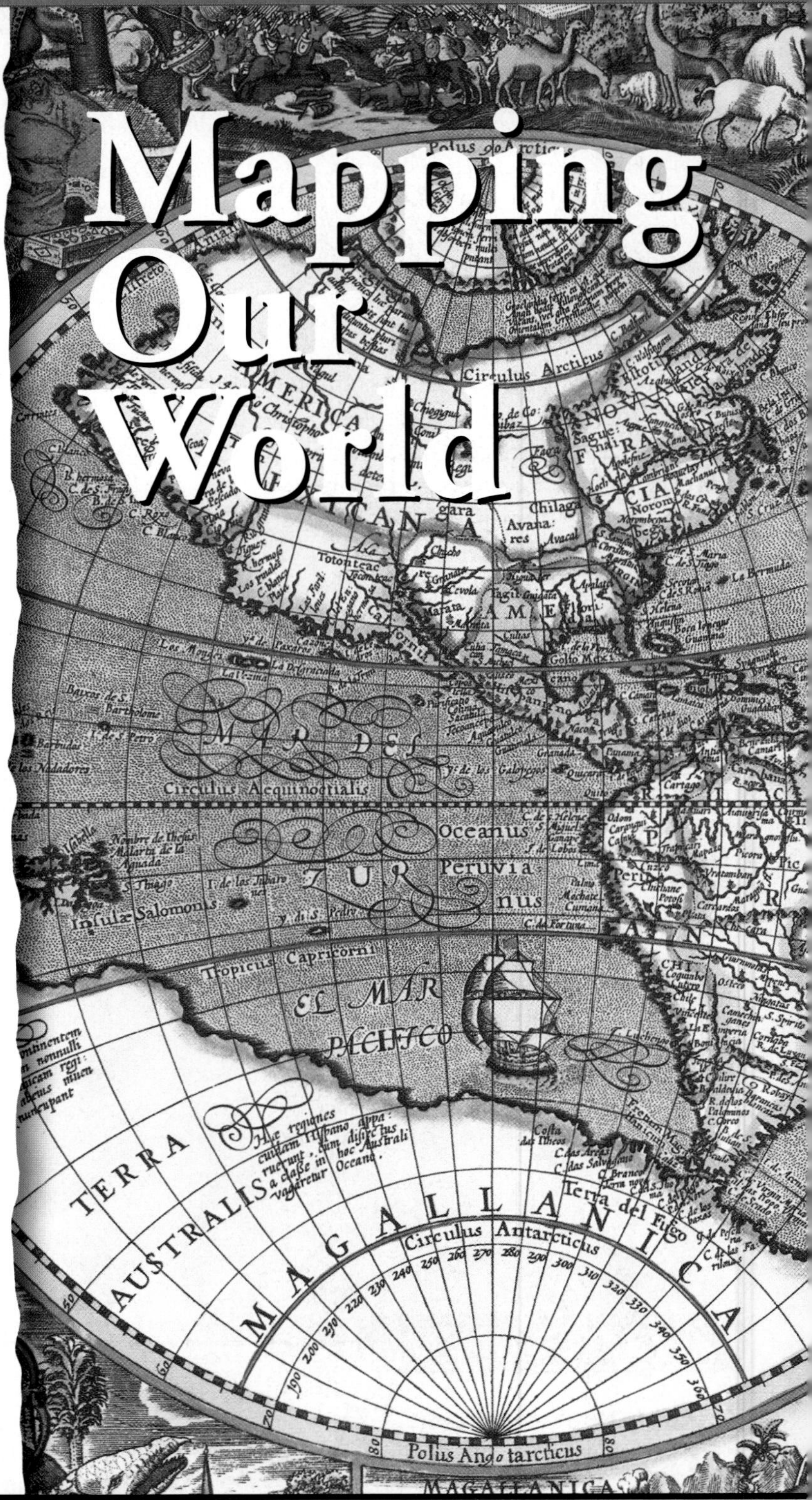

Introducing the Chapter

Have students describe the various ways in which they have used maps. Help students understand that maps have broad applications in many disciplines, such as geology, astronomy, environmental studies, land-use planning, climatology, and meteorology.

Interpreting the Photo

The chapter-opening photograph shows a portion of an elaborate world map drawn in 1607 by Petro Kærio. Have students compare and contrast this early map and a modern world map. Students should note that early maps contained many fanciful details based on legends, while modern maps are based on scientific knowledge.

INTERACTIVE CHALKBOARD with Image Bank

PowerPoint® Presentations

This CD is an editable Microsoft® PowerPoint® presentation that includes:
- Section presentations
- Section checks
- Image bank
- Links to Earth Science Online
- All transparencies
- Animations
- Audio

Chapter 2

What You'll Learn

- How latitude and longitude are used to locate places on Earth.
- How maps are made, and what types of maps are best suited to particular purposes.
- What technology is used to map Earth from space.

Why It's Important

Maps help us to locate exact places on Earth. All forms of transportation, including ships, planes, cars, and trucks, rely on accurate maps for guidance.

Earth Science Online

To find out more about maps, visit the Earth Science Web Site at earthgeu.com

26

Discovery Lab

Process Skills

model, communicate, observe and infer, compare and contrast, analyze data **L1** **ELL**

Preparation

You may find that most students already know where their classmates live. In this case, have students map local destinations, such as a park or the county courthouse, relative to the school.

Procedure

Teaching Strategies

Select several good examples of student maps. Make transparencies of these maps or draw them on the chalkboard.

Observe

Students should find that the maps were more helpful than the verbal directions in locating particular places. This is true in part because maps are visual models that can be referred to repeatedly, while verbal directions must be remembered. Answers will vary, but students may have included buildings, roads, railroads, and rivers, among other features.

Mapping Our World

Discovery Lab

Make and Use a Map

Have you ever been asked for directions? If so, you know that it's important to include as much detail as possible so that the person asking for directions will not get lost. You also may have realized that it helps to draw a detailed map of the destination in question.

1. Give verbal directions from your school to your home to a classmate who does not know where you live. Include as much detail as possible in your description.

2. Use a sheet of graph paper and colored pencils to draw a map from your school to your home. Include landmarks and other details. Share this map with your classmate.

3. Have your classmate also give you a description of where his or her home is located in relation to your school. Your classmate should then draw a map to his or her home for you to examine.

Observe Which did you find more helpful, the verbal directions or the map? Explain your answer. What kind of information did you include in your map? With your classmate, discuss how you could improve your maps. What details would you add?

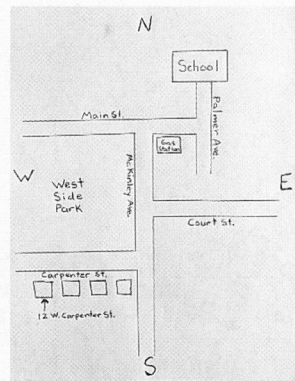

SECTION 2.1

Latitude and Longitude

OBJECTIVES

- **Compare** and **contrast** latitude and longitude.
- **Describe** how time zones vary.

VOCABULARY

cartography
equator
latitude
longitude
prime meridian
International Date Line

For thousands of years people have used maps such as the one shown at left to define borders and to find places. We still rely on maps for a variety of purposes. The science of mapmaking is called **cartography.** Cartographers use an imaginary grid of parallel lines and vertical lines to locate points on Earth exactly. In this grid, the **equator** circles Earth halfway between the north and south poles. The equator separates Earth into two equal halves called the northern hemisphere and the southern hemisphere.

LATITUDE

Lines running parallel to the equator are called lines of latitude. **Latitude** is the distance in degrees north or south of the equator. The equator, which serves as the reference point for latitude, is numbered 0° latitude. The poles are each numbered 90° latitude. Latitude is thus measured from 0° at the equator to 90° at the poles. Locations

---

Students also may have included scale and direction, and used color to represent various features. Students may say that they could improve their maps by developing a system for illustrating elevation or making a legend to illustrate map symbols.

✓ Assessment

Skill Have students compare and contrast their maps of particular areas and actual maps of the areas. Students should write brief reports in their science journals describing how the maps differ.

Resource Manager

Section Focus Transparency 4 L1 ELL

Study Guide for Content Mastery, pp. 7–8 L2

Exploring Environmental Problems, pp. 49–52 L3

---

1 Focus

Section Focus

Before presenting the lesson, display **Section Focus Transparency 4** on the overhead projector.
L1 ELL

Chapter Themes

The following themes from the National Science Education Standards are covered in this chapter. Refer to page 8T of the Teacher Guide for an explanation of the correlations.
Systems, order, and organization (UCP.1); Evidence, models, and explanation (UCP.2); Change, constancy, and measurement (UCP.3)

⏱ 0:00 *Out of Time?*

If time does not permit teaching the entire chapter, use the Chapter Summary on page 45 and the GeoDigest found at the end of the unit as an overview.

Modeling

Interpersonal Have students work in pairs to research how latitude can be determined using the North Star and a sextant. Show students photographs of a sextant or have one available in class for students to examine. Then have student pairs construct a sextant using a pin, a protractor, string, and a straw, and explain how it works. Students should wear safety goggles and take care when handling sharp pins. Models will vary. Students may pin the straw to the protractor so that the straw pivots at the center point of the protractor. Then they could hold the protractor up to their eyes so that its base is parallel to the ground. Next, they could sight along the straw to find the North Star. The angle made by the straw is their latitude. **L2** **COOP LEARN**

Using Math

The difference between 30°N and 42°N is 12°. Each degree of latitude equals 111 km. Thus, 12° multiplied by 111 km equals 1332 km.

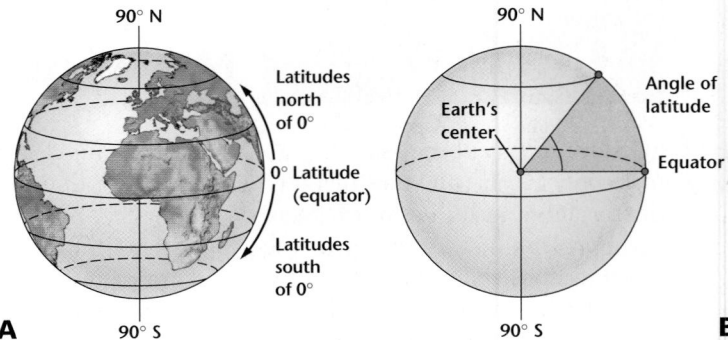

Figure 2-1 Lines of latitude are parallel to the equator **(A).** The value in degrees of each line of latitude is determined by measuring the imaginary angle created between the equator, the center of Earth, and the line of latitude **(B).**

north of the equator are referred to by degrees north latitude (N). Locations south of the equator are referred to by degrees south latitude (S). For example, Syracuse, New York, is located at 43° north latitude, and Christchurch, New Zealand, is located at 43° south latitude. Lines of latitude are illustrated in *Figure 2-1.*

Degrees of Latitude Each degree of latitude is equivalent to about 111 km on Earth's surface. How did cartographers determine this distance? Earth is a sphere, and can be divided into 360 degrees. The circumference of Earth is about 40 000 km. To find the distance of each degree of latitude, cartographers divide 40 000 km by 360°. To locate positions on Earth more precisely, cartographers break down degrees of latitude into 60 smaller units, called minutes. The symbol for a minute is ′. The actual distance on Earth's surface of each minute of latitude is 1.85 km, which is obtained by dividing 111 km by 60′. A minute of latitude can be further divided into seconds, which are represented by the symbol ″. Longitude, which is discussed next, is also divided into degrees, minutes, and seconds.

Using Math

Using Numbers Your plane has flown from 30° north latitude to 42° north latitude. Approximately how many kilometers have you traveled?

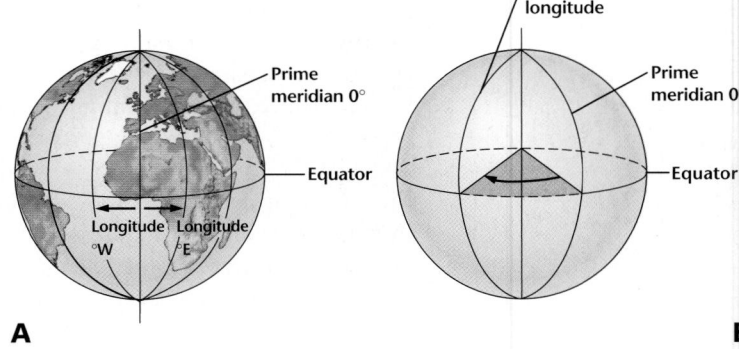

Figure 2-2 The reference line for longitude is the prime meridian **(A).** The degree value of each line of longitude is determined by measuring the imaginary angle created between the prime meridian, the center of Earth, and the line of longitude **(B).**

Across the Curriculum

History Have students research and write reports about how the ancient Polynesians of the Marshall Islands of the South Pacific navigated from one island to another without the aid of instruments. The early Polynesians used their knowledge of winds, waves, and currents to navigate. They also developed maps of star positions and ocean currents.

Differentiated Instruction

Learning Disabled Have students with learning disabilities carefully tape precut pieces of string over the lines of latitude and longitude on a world map. Then have students with visual impairments trace these lines with their fingers. This should help both groups of students acquire a deeper understanding of the grid system used to locate places on Earth.

LONGITUDE

To locate positions in east and west directions, cartographers use lines of longitude, also known as meridians. As shown in *Figure 2-2*, **longitude** is the distance in degrees east or west of the prime meridian, which is the reference point for longitude. The **prime meridian** represents 0° longitude. In 1884, astronomers decided that the prime meridian should go through Greenwich, England, home of the Royal Naval Observatory. Points west of the prime meridian are numbered from 0° to 180° west longitude (W); points east of the prime meridian are numbered from 0° to 180° east longitude (E).

Semicircles Unlike lines of latitude, lines of longitude are not parallel. Instead, they are large semicircles that extend vertically from pole to pole. For instance, the prime meridian runs from the north pole through Greenwich, England, to the south pole. The line of longitude on the opposite side of Earth from the prime meridian is the 180° meridian. There, east lines of longitude meet west lines of longitude. This meridian is also known as the International Date Line, as you'll learn later in this section.

Degrees of Longitude Degrees of latitude cover relatively consistent distances. The distances covered by degrees of longitude, however, vary with location. Refer back to *Figure 2-2*. As you can see, lines of longitude converge at the poles into a point. Thus, one degree of longitude varies from about 111 km at the equator to essentially the distance covered by a point at the poles.

Locating Places with Coordinates Both latitude and longitude are needed to precisely locate positions on Earth, as you'll see in the *MiniLab* on this page. For example, it is not sufficient to say that New Orleans,

---

MiniLab

How can you locate places on Earth?

Determine latitude and longitude for specific places.

Procedure

1. Use a world map or globe to locate the prime meridian and the equator.
2. Take a few moments to become familiar with the grid system. Examine lines of latitude and longitude on the map or globe.

Analyze and Conclude

1. Use a map to find the latitude and longitude of the following places.
   Mount St. Helens, Washington
   Niagara Falls, New York
   Mt. Everest, Nepal
   Great Barrier Reef, Australia
2. Use the map to find the name of the places with the following coordinates.
   0°03'S, 90°30'W
   27°07'S, 109°22'W
   41°10'N, 112°30'W
   35°02'N, 111°02'W
   3°04'S, 37°22'E
3. Find the latitude and longitude of your hometown, the nearest national or state park, and your state capital.

MiniLab

Purpose

Students will use lines of latitude and longitude to locate specific places on Earth's surface.

Process Skills

observe and infer, interpret scientific illustrations, communicate

Materials

world map or globe, pencil, paper

Teaching Strategies

- Have students work in groups of three or four.
- Obtain an atlas that lists places by latitude and longitude to assess student answers.
- Obtain enough world maps for each group of students.

Expected Results

Students will be able to locate places on Earth's surface using lines of latitude and longitude.

Analyze and Conclude

1. Mount St. Helens, Washington: 46°12'N, 122°11'W; Niagara Falls, New York: 43°05'N, 79°03'W; Mt. Everest, Nepal: 27°59'N, 86°56'E; Great Barrier Reef, Australia: 18°00'S, 145°50'E
2. 0°03'S, 90°30'W: Galápagos Islands, Ecuador; 27°07'S, 109°22'W: Easter Island, Chile; 41°10'N, 112°30'W: Great Salt Lake, Utah; 35°02'N, 111°02'W: Meteor Crater, Arizona; 3°04'S, 37°22'E: Mt. Kilimanjaro, Tanzania
3. Answers will vary depending upon students' location.

Assessment

Performance Give students reduced copies of world maps that show only lines of latitude and longitude and unlabeled continents. No countries, states, oceans, islands, or cities should be labeled. Have students use their answers from the Analyze and Conclude questions to locate the places listed in the MiniLab. Use the Performance Task Assessment List for Display in **PASC**, p. 63.

Interpreting the Illustrations

Figures 2-1 and **2-2** Have students compare and contrast latitude and longitude. Students should mention that latitude is distance in degrees north and south of the equator, and longitude is distance in degrees east and west of the prime meridian. Students also may mention that lines of latitude are parallel, while lines of longitude are semicircles.

Resource Manager

Teaching Transparency 4 L2 ELL
GeoLab and MiniLab Worksheets, p. 5 L2
Exploring Environmental Problems, pp. 57–60 L3

Content Background

The use of the equator as the reference line for latitude was established at least as early as A.D. 150, when it appeared in a world atlas by Ptolemy, an Egyptian astronomer. The use of the prime meridian as the reference point for longitude came into practice in the late 1700s after the publication of the *Nautical Almanac* by English royal astronomer Nevil Maskelyne.

Tying to Previous Knowledge

 **Intrapersonal** Show students a map of their city or any city that has a well-defined grid system of streets and avenues. Tell students that lines of latitude and longitude make up a similar grid system on a much larger scale.

Project

Visual-Spatial Have students work in pairs to draw and label the 24 time zones on a world map. Students should locate their town or city on the map. Have students use their location as a reference point and calculate the time in various places around the world. **L2** **ELL**

In-Text Question

Page 30 What time is it in Chicago, Illinois? 9 A.M.

NY Core Curriculum Standards

Page 30: St 1 Engin KI 1, St 4 KI 1.1d, St 6 KI 3
Page 31: St 1 Math KI 2, 3, & Engin KI 1, St 4 KI 1.1d, St 6 KI 3

Figure 2-3 The precise location of New Orleans is 29°57′N, 90°04′W.

Figure 2-4 Earth is divided into 24 time zones. Each zone represents a different hour.

Louisiana, is located at 29°57′ north latitude because that measurement includes any place on Earth located along the 29°57′ line of north latitude. The same is true of the longitude of New Orleans—90°04′ west longitude could be any point along that longitude from pole to pole. To precisely locate New Orleans, we use its complete coordinates, latitude and longitude, as shown in *Figure 2-3*. Note that latitude comes first in reference to the coordinates of a particular location.

TIME ZONES

As *Figure 2-4* shows, Earth is divided into 24 time zones. Why 24? Earth takes about 24 hours to rotate once on its axis. Thus, there are 24 times zones, each representing a different hour. Because Earth is constantly spinning, time is always changing. Each time zone is 15° wide, corresponding roughly to lines of longitude. For convenience's sake, however, time zone boundaries have been adjusted in local areas. For example, if a city were split by a time zone, confusion would result. In such a situation, the time zone boundary is moved outside of the city. Large countries, however, often have several times zones. There are six different time zones in the United States, as shown in *Figure 2-5*. When it's 10 A.M. in Atlanta, Georgia, it's 7 A.M. in Los Angeles, California. What time is it in Chicago, Illinois?

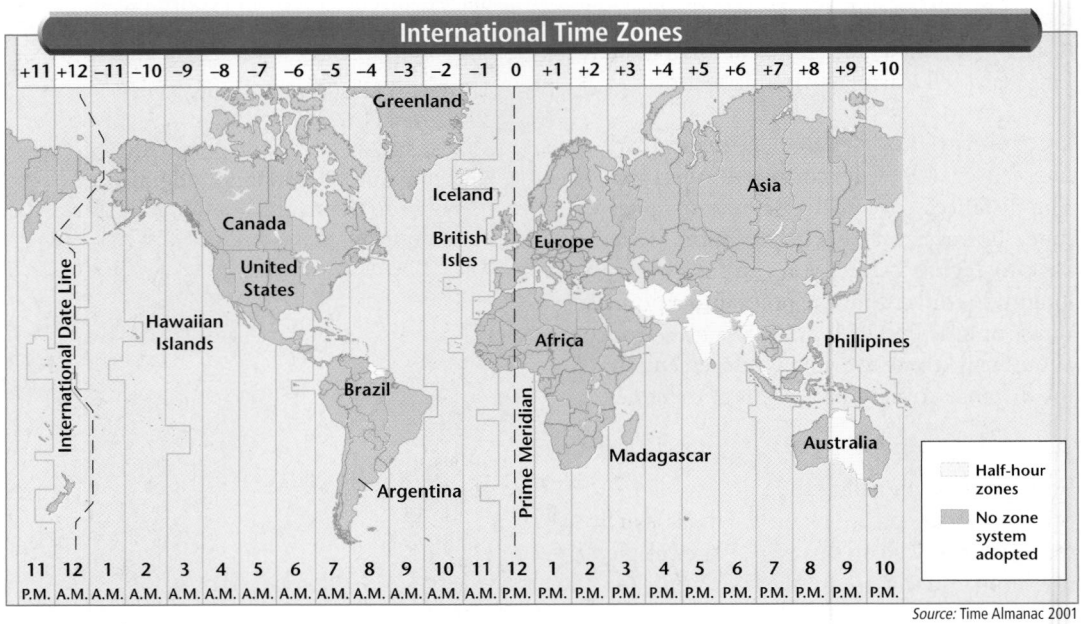

Source: Time Almanac 2001

Cultural Diversity

Polar Explorer Mathew Hensen, an African-American explorer, was the first American to reach the north pole and officially map its location. He went to sea at age 12 and learned the skills of an explorer: navigation, mathematics, and cartography. At age 21, Hensen met a fellow explorer, Robert Peary, who hired him as an assistant. Together, in 1907, they set off to achieve a lifelong dream to chart the north pole. To survive in the rugged, unfamiliar climate, the Americans relied on Inuit guides. Hensen learned much about Inuit culture, language, and survival skills. On April 9, 1909, Hensen became the first American to reach the north pole, followed by Peary and the Inuit guides. At the time, Peary, the leader of the expedition, was given credit for this accomplishment. Hensen's role in the expedition was officially recognized in 1988.

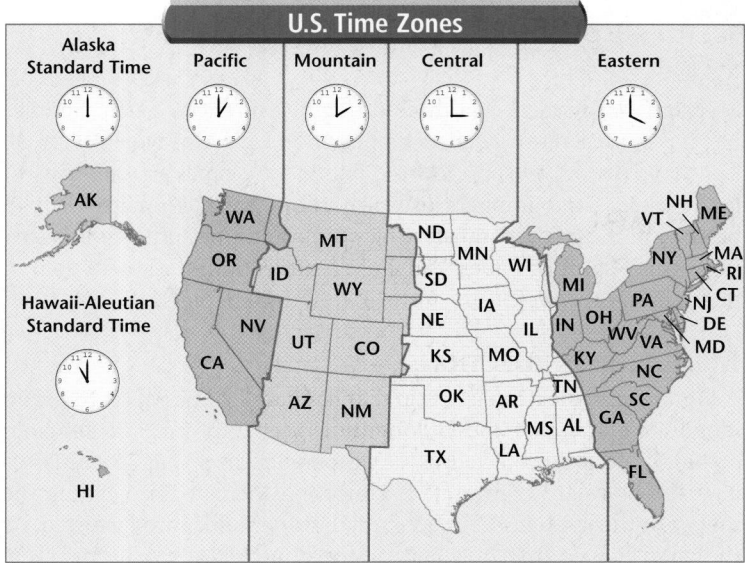

Figure 2-5 Large countries such as the United States are often split into multiple time zones. The United States has six time zones, including Alaska and Hawaii.

Calendar Dates Each day ends and the next day begins at the stroke of midnight. Every time zone experiences this transition from one day to the next, with the calendar advancing to the next day at midnight. Each time you travel through a time zone, you gain or lose time until, at some point, you gain or lose an entire day. The **International Date Line,** or 180° meridian, serves as the transition line for calendar days. If you were traveling west across the International Date Line, you would advance your calendar one day. If you were traveling east, you would move your calendar back one day.

SECTION ASSESSMENT

1. What is cartography?

2. Compare and contrast latitude and longitude. What is the reference point for lines of latitude? What is the reference point for lines of longitude?

3. What is the International Date Line? If it is 3 P.M. on Thursday, July 4, in Salt Lake City, Utah, what time and day is it in Tokyo, Japan? Use *Figure 2-4* for help.

4. Estimate the time difference between your home and places that are 60° east and west longitude of your home.

5. **Critical Thinking** If you were flying directly south from the north pole and reached 70° north latitude, how many more degrees of latitude would be left to pass over before you reached the south pole?

SKILL REVIEW

6. **Comparing and Contrasting** Describe how the distance of a degree of longitude varies from the equator to the poles. For more help, refer to the *Skill Handbook.*

SECTION ASSESSMENT

1. Cartography is the science of mapmaking.
2. Latitude is distance in degrees north and south of the equator. Longitude is distance in degrees east and west of the prime meridian. The reference points for lines of latitude and longitude are the equator and prime meridian, respectively.
3. The International Date Line, located at the 180° meridian, is the transition line for calendar days. The time and date in Tokyo would be 7 A.M., Friday, July 5.
4. $60° \div 15°/h = 4$ h
5. The south pole is located at 90°S. Thus, if you were at 70°N, you would need to travel another 160° latitude before reaching the south pole ($90° + 70° = 160°$).
6. One degree of longitude varies from about 111 km at the equator to essentially the distance covered by a point at the poles.

3 Assess

Check for Understanding

Reinforcement

Ask students the following question. If it is 2 P.M. in New York, New York, what time is it in Quito, Peru? 2 P.M. because Quito is in the same time zone as New York

Reteach

Have students explain why time zone boundaries do not strictly follow lines of longitude. The boundaries of time zones are sometimes adjusted for geographical and political reasons.

✓ Assessment

Portfolio Have pairs of students model lines of latitude. Each pair will need a sheet of 8" x 11" paper, a compass, a ruler marked with 1/4" graduations, and scissors. Have students draw a horizontal line halfway down the paper and label it *equator*. Next, students should draw nine parallel lines both above and below the equator at intervals of 1/4". Each line should be labeled in 10° increments starting with 0° at the equator and going up to 90°N above the equator and down to 90°S below the equator. Tell students to place the compass point in the center of the equator and open the compass so that the tip of the pencil touches 90°N. Have students draw a circle and cut it out. Students can then add continents and oceans to their models.

31

Prepare

Section Background

For section content background, refer to **The USGS** on page 26C.

Preplanning

Refer to the Chapter Organizer on pages 26A–B.

1 Focus

Section Focus

Before presenting the lesson, display **Section Focus Transparency 5** on the overhead projector. L1 ELL

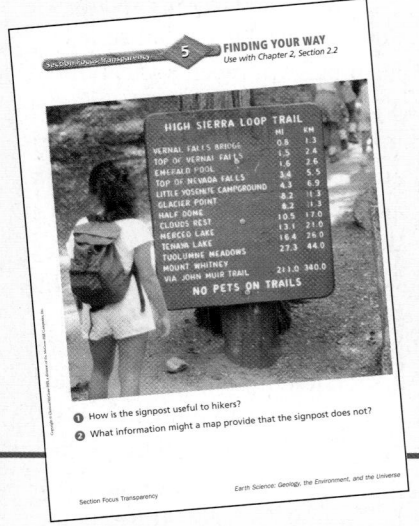

Demo

Obtain several examples of different types of map projections, such as Mercator, conic, gnomonic, Robinson, and azimuthal. Tape the maps to the chalkboard. Discuss the advantages and disadvantages of each map projection. Have students outline the main ideas of the discussion in their science journals.

OBJECTIVES

- **Compare** and **contrast** *different map projections.*
- **Analyze** *topographic maps.*
- **Describe** *map characteristics, such as map scales and map legends.*

VOCABULARY

Mercator projection
conic projection
gnomonic projection
topographic map
contour line
contour interval
map legend
map scale

Maps are flat models of a three-dimensional object, Earth. Because Earth is curved, it's difficult to represent on a piece of paper. Thus, all flat maps distort to some degree either the shapes or the areas of landmasses. Cartographers use projections to make maps. A map projection is made by transferring points and lines on a globe's surface onto a sheet of paper. You'll use a projection of a world map in the *Science & Math* feature at the end of this chapter.

MERCATOR PROJECTIONS

A **Mercator projection** is a map that has parallel lines of latitude and longitude. Recall that lines of longitude meet at the poles. When lines of longitude are projected as being parallel on a map, landmasses near the poles are exaggerated. Thus, in a Mercator projection, the shapes of the landmasses are correct, but their areas are distorted. As shown in *Figure 2-6,* Greenland appears much larger than Australia. In reality, Greenland is much smaller than Australia. Because Mercator projections show the correct shapes of landmasses and also clearly indicate direction in straight lines, they are used for the navigation of planes and ships.

CONIC PROJECTIONS

A **conic projection** is made by projecting points and lines from a globe onto a cone, as shown in *Figure 2-7.* The cone touches the globe at a particular line of latitude. There is very little distortion in the areas or shapes of landmasses that fall along this line of latitude. Distortion is evident, however, near the top and bottom of the projection. Because conic projections have a high degree of accuracy for limited areas, they are excellent for mapping small areas. Hence, they are used to make road maps and weather maps.

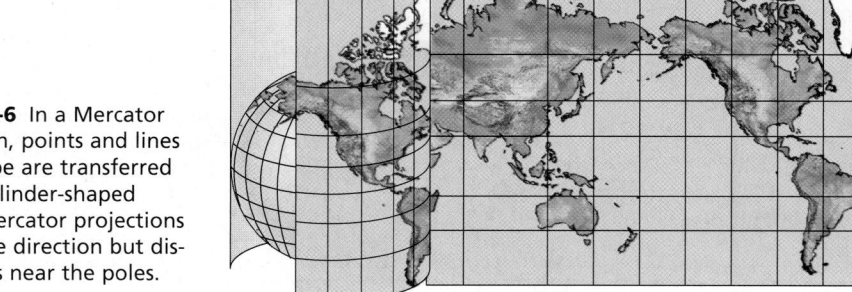

Figure 2-6 In a Mercator projection, points and lines on a globe are transferred onto a cylinder-shaped paper. Mercator projections show true direction but distort areas near the poles.

32 CHAPTER 2 *Mapping Our World*

Differentiated Instruction

Gifted Assign each student a different type of map projection to research, such as gnomonic, Mercator, conic, azimuthal, or Robinson. Ask students to each write a report describing how the projection is made, the best uses of the projection, and problems associated with its use. Have students construct models of their projections and share their results with the class. L3 P

Resource Manager

Section Focus Transparency 5 L1 ELL
Study Guide for Content Mastery, pp. 9–11 L2
Laboratory Manual, pp. 13–16 L2
Exploring Environmental Problems, pp. 53–56 L3

GNOMONIC PROJECTIONS

A **gnomonic projection** is made by projecting points and lines from a globe onto a piece of paper that touches the globe at a single point. As shown in *Figure 2-8,* gnomonic projections distort direction and distance between landmasses. However, they are useful in plotting long-distance trips by air and by sea. To understand why, you must understand the concept of a great circle. Great circles are imaginary lines that divide Earth into two equal halves. The equator is a great circle, as are any two lines of longitude that connect at the poles to form a complete circle. On a sphere such as Earth, the shortest distance between two points lies along a great circle. Navigators connect points on gnomonic projections to plot great-circle routes.

TOPOGRAPHIC MAPS

Detailed maps showing the hills and valleys of an area are called topographic maps. **Topographic maps** show changes in elevation of Earth's surface. They also show mountains, rivers, forests, and bridges, among other features. Topographic maps use lines, symbols, and colors to represent changes in elevation and features on Earth's surface.

Contour Lines Elevation on a topographic map is represented by a contour line. A **contour line** connects points of equal elevation. Elevation refers to the distance of a location above or below sea level. Because contour lines connect points of equal elevation, they never cross. If they did, it would mean that the point where they crossed had two different elevations, which would be impossible.

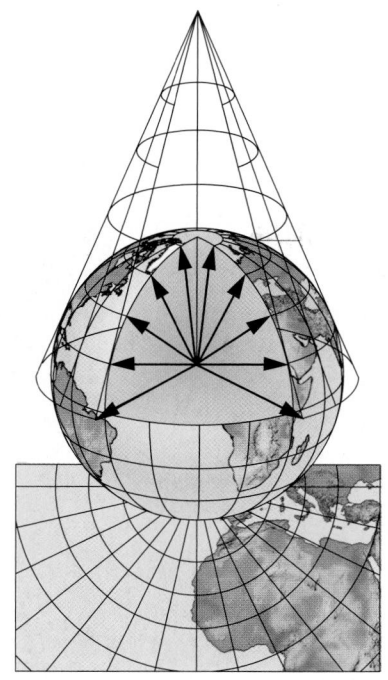

Figure 2-7 In a conic projection, points and lines on a globe are projected onto a cone-shaped paper. Along the line of latitude touched by the paper, there is little distortion.

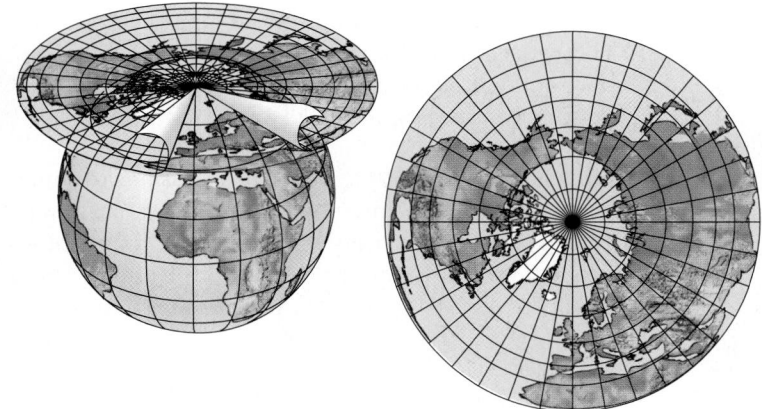

Figure 2-8 In a gnomonic projection, points and lines from a globe are projected onto paper that touches the globe at a single point.

Interpreting the Illustration

Figure 2-7 Have students answer the following questions. How is a conic map projection made? Points and lines from a globe are projected onto a cone that touches the globe at one line of latitude. What are conic projections used for, and why? Because conic projections have a high degree of accuracy for limited areas, they are used to map small areas and thus make excellent road maps and weather maps.

Content Background

Maps are two-dimensional models of Earth. Geologists, however, often need to know what Earth looks like in three dimensions. With computers, topographic maps are digitized to make the top or surface layer of three-dimensional maps of Earth. Digitizing is a process by which points are located on a coordinate grid. Geologists use data obtained from drilling into Earth's crust to generate the other layers of three-dimensional maps.

Differentiated Instruction

Visually Impaired Have topographic relief maps available for students with visual impairments. These students can touch the maps to discern changes in elevation. Be sure to tell students the scale of the map they are touching.

Applying Earth Science

Invite a local orienteering club member to visit your class. Ask the person to explain how orienteering involves the use of a compass and map to find specific locations. If possible, arrange a field trip on a local trail so students can apply their new knowledge.

NY Core Curriculum Standards

Page 32: St 1 Engin KI 1, St 6 KI 2 & 3, St 7 KI 1
Page 33: St 1 Engin KI 1, St 6 KI 2 & 3, St 7 KI 1

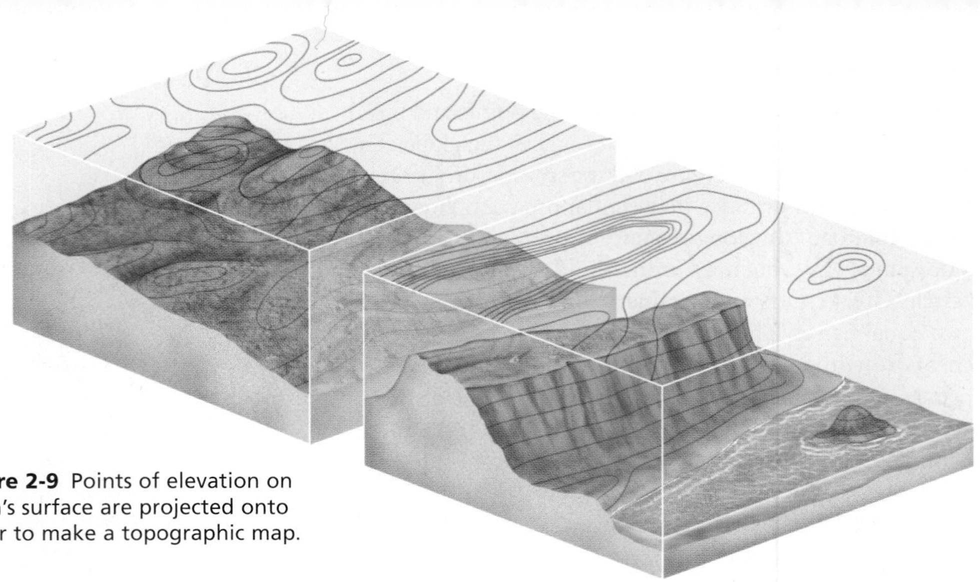

Figure 2-9 Points of elevation on Earth's surface are projected onto paper to make a topographic map.

Contour Intervals As *Figure 2-9* shows, topographic maps use contour lines to show changes in elevation. The difference in elevation between two side-by-side contour lines is called the **contour interval.** The contour interval is dependent on the terrain. For mountains, the contour lines might be very close together, and the contour interval might be as great as 100 m. This would indicate that the land is quite steep because there is a large change in elevation between lines. You'll learn more about topographic maps in the *Problem-Solving Lab* on the next page and in the *Mapping GeoLab* at the end of this chapter.

Figure 2-10 The depression contour lines shown here indicate that the center of the area has a lower elevation than the outer portion of the area.

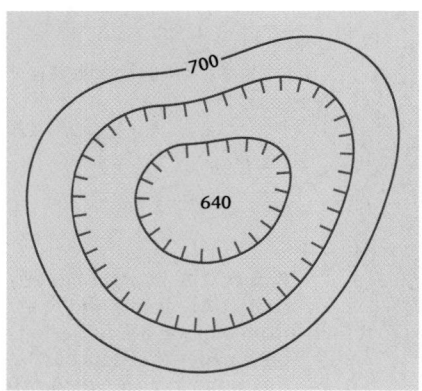

Index Contours To aid in the interpretation of topographic maps, some contour lines are marked by numbers representing their elevations. These are index contours, and they are used hand-in-hand with contour intervals. If a contour interval on a map is 5 m, you can determine the elevations represented by other lines around the index contour by adding or subtracting 5 m from the elevation indicated on the index contour.

Depression Contour Lines The elevations of some features such as volcanic craters and mines are lower than that of the surrounding landscape. Depression contour lines are used to represent such features. On a map, depression contour lines have *hachures*, or short lines at right angles to the contour line, to indicate depressions. The hachures point toward lower elevations, as shown in *Figure 2-10*.

34 CHAPTER 2 *Mapping Our World*

MAP LEGENDS

Topographic maps and most other maps include both human-made and natural features that are located on Earth's surface. These features are represented by symbols, such as black dotted lines for trails, solid red lines for highways, and small black squares and rectangles for buildings. A **map legend,** such as the one shown in *Figure 2-11,* explains what the symbols represent. For more information about the symbols in map legends, see *Appendix D.*

MAP SCALES

When using a map, you need to know how to measure distances. This is accomplished by using a map scale. A **map scale** is the ratio between distances on a map and actual distances on the surface of Earth. There are three types of map scales: verbal scales, graphic scales, and fractional scales. A verbal scale expresses distance as a statement, such as "One centimeter is equal to one kilometer." This means that one centimeter on the map represents one kilometer on Earth's surface. A graphic scale consists of a line that represents a certain distance, such as 5 km or 5 miles. The line is broken down into sections, with each section representing a distance on Earth's surface. For instance, a graphic scale of 5 km may be broken down into five sections, with each section representing 1 km.

Highway	
Trail	
Bridge	
Railroad	+++++++
Buildings	▪ ◼
School, church	♪ ♰
Spot elevation	BM △ 283
Contour line	
Depression contour lines (hachures)	
Stream	
Marsh	

Figure 2-11 Map legends explain what the symbols on maps represent.

Problem-Solving Lab

Calculating Gradients

Analyze changes in elevation
Gradient refers to the steepness of a slope. To measure gradient, divide the change in elevation between two points on a map by the distance between the points. Use the map to answer the questions; convert your answers to SI.

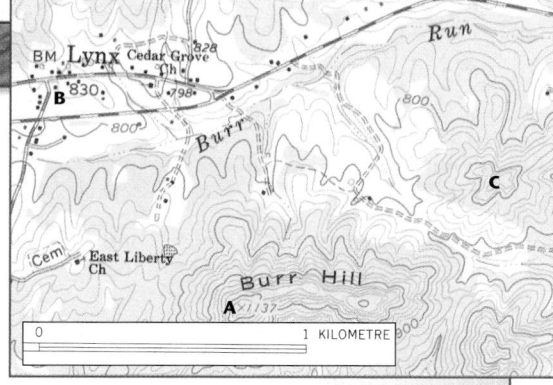

Analysis

1. Use the map scale and a ruler to determine the distance from point A to point B. Record the change in elevation between the two points.
2. If you were to hike this distance, what would be the gradient of your climb?

Thinking Critically

3. Calculate the gradient from point B to point C. Would it be more difficult to hike from point A to point B, or from point B to point C? Explain.
4. Between point A and point C, where is the steepest part of the hike? How do you know?

Problem-Solving Lab

Purpose
Students will use a topographic map to analyze changes in elevation in terms of gradients.

Process Skills
interpret scientific illustrations, predict, use numbers, observe and infer, interpret data, analyze data, communicate

Materials
map included in lab, ruler, pencil

Teaching Strategies
- Remind students that the contour intervals on USGS maps are in English units. Because the map scale is given in SI units, students will need to convert the measured distances to English units.
- If possible, take students outside and show them an actual slope. Have one student stand at the top of the slope and another student stand at the bottom. Tell students that the gradient of the slope can be found by dividing the change in elevation between the two students by the distance between the two students.

Analysis
1. The distance between point A and point B is approximately 0.5 mi. The change in elevation is 1137 ft − 830 ft = 307 ft.
2. 307 ft ÷ 0.5 mi = 614 ft/mi

Thinking Critically
3. The distance between point B and point C is approximately 1 mi. The change in elevation is 960 ft − 830 ft = 130 ft. The gradient is 130 ft ÷ 1 mi = 130 ft. Answers will vary. The hike from point B to point C would be less steep, but longer than the hike from point A to point B.
4. The steepest part of the hike would be from the 900-ft contour line to point A. The close contour lines indicate a sharp rise in elevation.

Earth Science Journal

Visual-Spatial Have students compare and contrast how quarries and gravel pits are represented on topographic maps.
A quarry is symbolized by a pair of crossed picks, and a gravel pit is represented by a pair of crossed shovels. Both quarries and gravel pits are shown by depression contour lines. **L1**

✓*Assessment*

Skill Ask students to calculate the gradient of a region with an elevation that rises from sea level to a height of 4800 m over a distance of 8 km. gradient (G) = change in elevation ÷ change in distance = 4800 m ÷ 8 km = 600 m/km

Check for Understanding

Discussion

Have students describe the differences among verbal, graphic, and fractional map scales. Students should give examples of each type of scale.

Reteach

 **Linguistic** Have students outline the main ideas of this section in their science journals. Ask students to provide specific examples in support of each main idea. **L2**

✓*Assessment*

Portfolio Place students in groups of three. Obtain enough topographic maps so that each group has one. Have groups answer the following questions about their maps. What symbols are included on the map? What do the symbols represent? What is the fractional scale of the map? What is the contour interval? What are the highest and lowest elevations on the map? What is the gradient between the highest and lowest places? Answers will vary depending on maps used.

Figure 2-12 The map scale and legend shown here are from a map of the Rocky Mountain area in Montana.

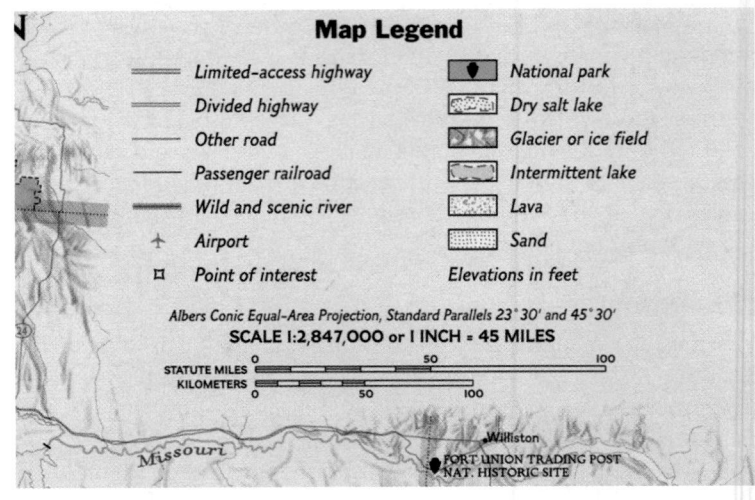

A fractional scale expresses distance as a ratio, such as 1:63 500. This means that one unit on the map represents 63 500 units on Earth's surface. One centimeter on a map, for instance, would be equivalent to 63 500 cm on Earth's surface. The unit of distance may be feet or meters or any other measure of distance. However, the units on each side of the ratio must always be the same. A large ratio indicates that the map represents a large area, while a small ratio indicates that the map represents a small area. A map with a large fractional scale such as 1:100 000 would therefore show less detail than a map with a small fractional scale such as 1:1000. *Figure 2-12* shows the map scale and legend found on a typical map.

SECTION ASSESSMENT

1. Compare and contrast Mercator and gnomonic projections. What are these projections most commonly used for?

2. How is a conic projection made? Why is this type of projection best suited for mapping small areas?

3. What is a contour line? How are areas of depression represented on a topographic map?

4. A topographic map has a fractional scale of 1:80 000. The units are in centimeters. If two cities are 3 km apart, how far apart would they be on the map?

5. **Thinking Critically** The equator is the only line of latitude that is a great circle. Why?

SKILL REVIEW

6. **Interpreting Scientific Illustrations** Use *Appendix D* to draw symbols in their appropriate colors for the following features: barn, school, church, orchard, woods, perennial stream, marsh, and primary highway. For more help, refer to the *Skill Handbook*.

earthgeu.com/self_check_quiz

SECTION ASSESSMENT

1. A Mercator projection is made by projecting points and lines from a globe onto a cylinder. It is widely used for the navigation of planes and ships. A gnomonic projection is made by projecting points and lines from a globe onto a piece of paper that touches the globe at a single point. It is also used for navigation purposes.

2. A conic projection is made by projecting points and lines from a globe onto a cone that touches the globe at a particular line of latitude. There is very little distortion along this line of latitude. Thus, conic projections are excellent for mapping limited areas.

3. A contour line connects points of equal elevation. Areas of depression are represented on a topographic map by depression contour lines that have hachures, or short lines at right angles to the contour lines, to indicate depressions.

4. 1 cm = 80 000 cm
80 000 cm ÷ 100 000 cm/km = 0.8 km
3 km ÷ 0.8 km/cm = 3.75 cm

5. The equator is the only line of latitude that divides Earth into two equal halves.

6. Student drawings should correspond to the symbols shown in Appendix D.

Until recently, mapmakers had to go on-site to collect the data needed to make maps. Today, advanced technology has changed the way maps are made. The process of collecting data about Earth from far above Earth's surface is called **remote sensing.** Let's examine how satellites, which use remote sensing, gather information about Earth's surface.

THE ELECTROMAGNETIC SPECTRUM

Satellites, such as the one being launched in *Figure 2-13,* detect different wavelengths of energy reflected or emitted from Earth's surface. This energy has both electric and magnetic properties. Thus, it is referred to as electromagnetic radiation. Visible light is a form of electromagnetic radiation. Other types include gamma rays, X rays, ultraviolet waves, infrared waves, radio waves, and microwaves.

Wave Characteristics All electromagnetic waves travel at the speed of 300 000 km/s in a vacuum, a value commonly referred to as the speed of light. In addition, electromagnetic waves have distinct

OBJECTIVES

- **Compare** and **contrast** *the different forms of radiation in the electromagnetic spectrum.*

- **Discuss** *how satellites and sonar are used to map Earth's surface and its oceans.*

- **Describe** *the Global Positioning System.*

VOCABULARY

remote sensing
electromagnetic spectrum
frequency
Landsat satellite
Topex/Poseidon satellite
Global Positioning System
sonar

Figure 2-13 *Landsat 7,* launched in 1999, is equipped to measure differences in thermal energy emitted by features on Earth's surface.

2.3 *Remote Sensing* **37**

Resource Manager

Section Focus Transparency 6 L1 ELL

Study Guide for Content Mastery,
p. 12 L2

Laboratory Manual, pp. 13–16 L2

Exploring Environmental Problems,
pp. 61–64 L3

Prepare

Section Background

For section content background, refer to **Aerial Photography** on page 26D.

Preplanning

Refer to the Chapter Organizer on pages 26A–B.

1 Focus

Section Focus

Before presenting the lesson, display **Section Focus Transparency 6** on the overhead projector. L1 ELL

Demo

Pass a beam of white light through a prism so that the colors of light bend to form a spectrum. Tell students that all colors in the visible spectrum have varying wavelengths, which bend through different angles and disperse to form spectra. Violet light has the shortest wavelength and thus bends the most. Red light has the longest wavelength and thus bends the least.

37

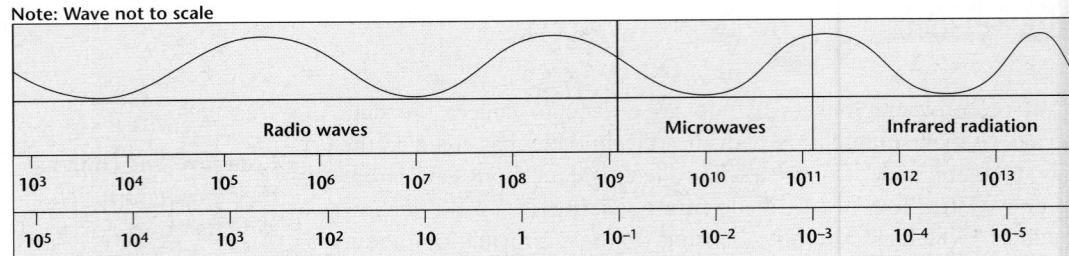

Figure 2-14 In the electromagnetic spectrum, the waves with the longest wavelengths have the lowest frequencies.

Collaborative Learning

Interpersonal Place students in groups of four. Assign each group a remote-sensing device to research, such as the *Topex/Poseidon* satellite, *MOLA*, the *GOES* satellite, the *Hubble Space Telescope, Landsat 7,* or Sea Beam. Have each group write a report that explains the system's design, how it uses electromagnetic frequencies, and its applications. Groups should share their reports with the class.

COOP LEARN

Concept Development

Download images and photographs from remote-sensing technology from NASA's Web site at **earthgeu.com**. Show students the type of information that is being sent back to Earth for analysis. Ask students to compare and contrast the images and photographs of various remote-sensing devices. For instance, some remote-sensing satellites use infrared imagery, while others use visible-light imagery. Students should observe an appreciable difference in the images.

Figure 2-15 The blue area in this *Landsat 7* image shows the range of a fire that occurred in Los Alamos, New Mexico, in May 2000.

wavelengths. The arrangement of electromagnetic radiation according to wavelengths is called the **electromagnetic spectrum,** as shown in *Figure 2-14.* Gamma rays have wavelengths of less than 0.000 000 000 01 m, while radio waves have wavelengths of 100 000 m. An electromagnetic wave also can be described according to its **frequency,** which refers to the number of waves that pass a particular point each second. Gamma rays have the highest frequencies and radio waves have the lowest. The wavelengths, speeds, and frequencies of electromagnetic waves help determine how the energy is used by different satellites to map Earth.

LANDSAT SATELLITES

A **Landsat satellite** receives reflected wavelengths of energy emitted by Earth's surface, including some wavelengths of visible light and infrared radiation. Features on Earth's surface, such as rivers and forests, radiate warmth at slightly different frequencies. Thus, these features show up as different colors in images such as the one in *Figure 2-15.* To obtain such images, each Landsat satellite is equipped with a moving mirror that scans Earth's surface. This mirror has rows of detectors that measure the intensity of energy received from Earth. This information is then converted by computers into digital images that show landforms in great detail. *Landsat 7,* launched in 1999, maps 185 km at a time and scans the entire surface of the planet in 16 days. Landsat data also are used to study the movements of Earth's plates, rivers, earthquakes, and pollution.

38 CHAPTER 2 *Mapping Our World*

NY Core Curriculum Standards

Page 36: St 1 Math KI 1, 2, 3, & Engin KI 1, St 6 KI 2 & 3, St 7 KI 1

Page 37: St 2 KI 1, St 7 KI 1

Differentiated Instruction

Behaviorally Disordered Rather than writing reports about remote-sensing technology as suggested in the Collaborative Learning item on this page, students with behavioral disorders can make posters that illustrate remote-sensing devices that have been used or are being used to collect data about the solar system. Examples might include the Voyager space probes, the *Hubble Space Telescope,* and the *Martian Rover.* Encourage students to choose topics that pique their interest.

Interpreting the Illustration

Figure 2-14 Have students describe the relationship between frequency and wavelength. Because all forms of electromagnetic radiation travel at the same speed, shorter wavelengths have higher frequencies—that is, more waves pass a particular point each second.

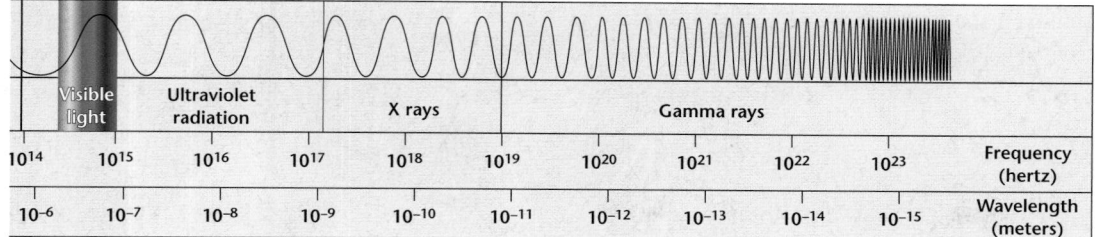

Visible light	Ultraviolet radiation		X rays		Gamma rays					
10^{14}	10^{15}	10^{16}	10^{17}	10^{18}	10^{19}	10^{20}	10^{21}	10^{22}	10^{23}	Frequency (hertz)
10^{-6}	10^{-7}	10^{-8}	10^{-9}	10^{-10}	10^{-11}	10^{-12}	10^{-13}	10^{-14}	10^{-15}	Wavelength (meters)

TOPEX/POSEIDON SATELLITE

Other satellites, such as the *Topex/Poseidon* **satellite,** shown in *Figure 2-16,* use radar to map features on the ocean floor. *Topex* stands for "topography experiment." Radar uses high-frequency signals that are transmitted from the satellite to the surface of the ocean. A receiving device then picks up the returning echo as it is reflected off the water. The distance to the water's surface is calculated using the known speed of light and the time it takes for the signal to be reflected. Variations in time indicate the presence of certain features on the ocean floor. For instance, ocean water bulges over seafloor mountains and forms depressions over seafloor valleys. These changes are reflected in satellite-to-sea measurements. Based on these data, computers create maps of ocean-floor features. The *Topex/Poseidon* satellite also has been used to study tidal changes and global ocean currents.

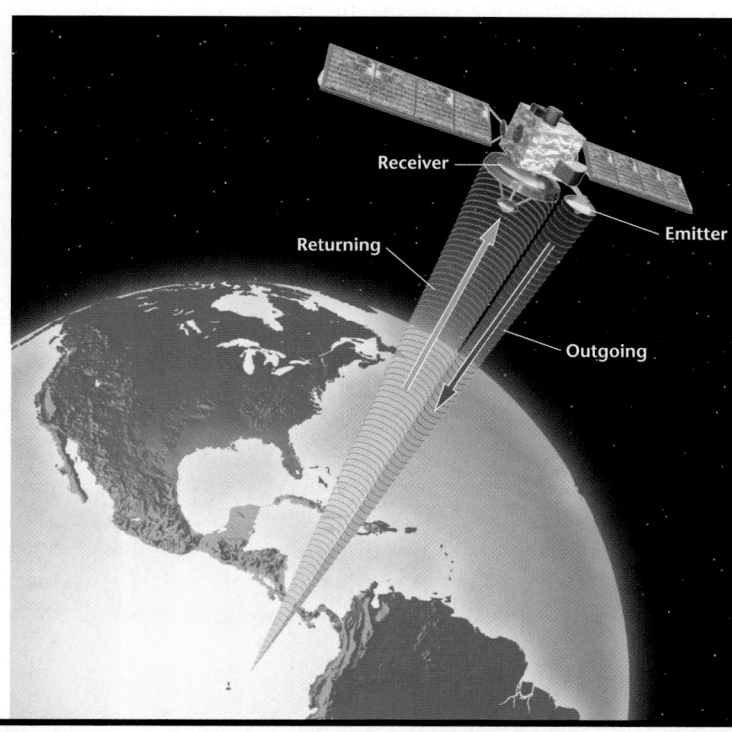

Figure 2-16 In the *Topex/Poseidon* satellite, an emitter sends an outgoing signal to the surface of the ocean. A receiver times the returning signal. The distance to the ocean's surface is calculated using the known speed of light and the return time.

Receiver

Returning

Emitter

Outgoing

Resource Manager

Teaching Transparency 6 L2 ELL

Exploring Environmental Problems, pp. 45–48 L3

Environmental Connection

Naturalist Ask students to research how the Landsat satellites have been used in environmental studies. Students should find that images from Landsat have been used to study the causes and effects of El Niño, to locate mineral resources, to plot changes in vegetation, to study ecological conditions following natural and human-made hazards, and to study the effects of overpopulation. Accept all reasonable answers. L2

Interpreting the Illustration

Figure 2-16 Have students describe the roles of the emitter and the receiver in the *Topex/ Poseidon* satellite. The emitter sends out high-frequency signals that are beamed from the satellite to the surface of an ocean. The receiver picks up the returning echo of the signal after it bounces off the ocean's surface.

NY Core Curriculum Standards

Page 38: St 2 KI 1, St 7 KI 1
Page 39: St 2 KI 1, St 7 KI 1

Activity

Linguistic Have students research and write reports about the Global Positioning System (GPS). Students can use the Glencoe Science Web Site and traditional library media sources for their reports. Students' reports should include information about the system's operation, its accuracy, the number of satellites in the system, its orbiting distance above Earth, and uses of the system. You may want to direct students to *Integrating GIS and the Global Positioning System,* by Karen Steede-Terry, ESRI Press, Redlands, CA, 2000. L2

Content Background

Sonar (*sound navigation and ranging*) was first used in World War I to detect submarines using echoes that bounced off their hulls. Today, it is widely used to calculate ocean depth. In addition, a type of sonar called side-scan sonar can be used to map ocean-floor features. Side-scan sonar directs sound waves to the seafloor at an angle, so that the sides of underwater hills and other topographic features can be mapped.

Figure 2-17 This hiker is using a hand-held, GPS receiver.

NATIONAL GEOGRAPHIC

To learn more about mapping, go to the National Geographic Expedition on page 864.

THE GLOBAL POSITIONING SYSTEM

The **Global Positioning System** (GPS) is a radio-navigation system of at least 24 satellites that allows its users to determine their exact position on Earth. Each satellite orbits Earth and transmits high-frequency microwaves that contain information about the satellite's position and the time of transmission. The orbits of the satellites are arranged so that signals from several satellites can be picked up at any given moment by a GPS user equipped with a hand-held receiver, as shown in *Figure 2-17.* The receiver calculates the user's precise latitude and longitude by processing the signals emitted by multiple satellites. The satellites also can relay information about elevation, direction, and speed. GPS technology is used extensively for navigation by airplanes and ships. However, it is also used to detect earthquakes, create maps, and track wildlife. Lately, it has become increasingly popular among hikers, backpackers, and other travelers.

SEA BEAM

Sea Beam technology is similar to the *Topex/Poseidon* satellite in that it is used to map the ocean floor. However, Sea Beam is located on a ship rather than on a satellite. To map ocean-floor features, Sea Beam relies on **sonar,** which is the use of sound waves to detect and measure objects underwater. First, a sound wave is sent from a ship toward the ocean floor, as shown in *Figure 2-18.* A receiving device then picks up the returning echo when it bounces off the seafloor. Computers on the ship calculate the distance to the ocean bottom

Across the Curriculum

Math Sonar uses the speed of sound in water to calculate the depth of the ocean floor or to map ocean-floor features. A sound wave travels much faster in water than in air because the water molecules are closer together. The velocity of sound at 0°C in dry air is about 332 m/s. In freshwater, it is 1454 m/s.

NY Core Curriculum Standards

Page 40: St 2 KI 1 & 3, St 7 KI 1
Page 41: St 2 KI 1 & 3, St 7 KI 1

Figure 2-18 In a ship equipped with Sea Beam, a sound wave is sent to the ocean floor. The wave bounces off the seafloor and its returning echo is recorded by a receiver on the ship. The distance to the ocean floor is then calculated using the known speed of sound in water and the return time of the sound wave.

Check for Understanding

Discussion

Ask students to define remote-sensing and to explain how the electromagnetic spectrum is used to collect data about Earth.

Reteach

Obtain a hand-held GPS unit. Take students outside, turn on the GPS unit, and walk around the school grounds. Pause every 50 m or so to show students that the latitude and longitude values change as the position of the GPS user changes. Have students explain why the coordinates constantly change. The hand-held GPS unit continually receives information from an array of satellites in space. This information is used to continually update the user's position.

✔Assessment

Portfolio Have students use a computer graphics program to create diagrams of the electromagnetic spectrum. Diagrams should include wave frequencies and wavelengths, and should be appropriately labeled.

using the speed of sound in water and the time it takes for the sound to be reflected. A ship equipped with Sea Beam has more than a dozen sonar devices aimed at different parts of the sea. Sea Beam technology is used by fishing fleets, deep-sea drilling operations, and scientists such as oceanographers, volcanologists, and archaeologists.

SECTION ASSESSMENT

1. What is the electromagnetic spectrum? Sequence the forms of electromagnetic radiation from longest wavelength to shortest wavelength.

2. How do Landsat satellites collect and analyze data to map Earth's surface?

3. What features are mapped by the *Topex/Poseidon* satellite? Describe the mapping process.

4. Describe the Global Positioning System.

5. **Thinking Critically** Explain why electromagnetic waves with short wavelengths have higher frequencies than electromagnetic waves with long wavelengths.

SKILL REVIEW

6. **Concept Mapping** Use the following words and phrases to complete a concept map about remote sensing. For more help, refer to the *Skill Handbook*.

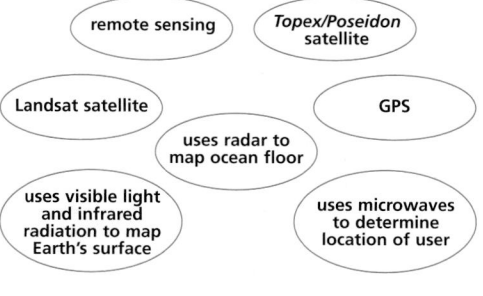

SECTION ASSESSMENT

1. The electromagnetic spectrum shows the arrangement of electromagnetic radiation, radio waves, microwaves, infrared radiation, visible light, ultraviolet light, X rays, and gamma rays.

2. Landsat satellites receive reflected wavelengths of energy emitted by features on Earth's surface.

3. The *Topex/Poseidon* satellite uses radar to map the seafloor. Signals are sent from the satellite to the ocean's surface. A receiver on the satellite picks up the returning signal. The distance to the water's surface is calculated using the known speed of light and the return time of the signal.

4. The Global Positioning System is a satellite system that allows users to determine their exact positions.

5. If a type of radiation has a short wavelength, then more of its waves pass a particular point per second compared with radiation of a longer wavelength.

6. first level: remote sensing; second level in any order: *Topex/Poseidon* satellite, Landsat satellite, and GPS; third level: uses radar to map ocean floor should be connected to *Topex/Poseidon* satellite, uses visible light and infrared radiation to map Earth's surface should be connected to Landsat satellite, and uses microwaves to determine location of user should be connected to GPS

Mapping GeoLab

Time Allotment

45 minutes

Process Skills

interpret scientific illustrations, use numbers, communicate, analyze data, draw conclusions

Preparation

Special Instructions

Refer students to Appendix D to view topographic map symbols. They'll need this appendix to answer question 1 under Conclude & Apply.

Procedure

Teaching Strategies

- To increase student proficiency in SI, have them give their answers in both English units and SI units.
- Team students with visual impairments with students who can easily discern small print.
- If possible, make a transparency of the map to enhance the class discussion following the activity.
- Remind students that gradient is found by dividing the change in elevation by the change in distance.

Mapping GeoLab

Using a Topographic Map

Topographic maps show two-dimensional representations of Earth's surface. With these maps, you can determine how steep a hill is, what direction streams flow, and where mines, wetlands, and other features are located.

Preparation

Problem

How can you use a topographic map to interpret information about an area?

Materials

ruler   string
pencil

Procedure

1. Use the map to answer the following questions. Be sure to check the map's scale.
2. Use the string to measure distances between two points that are not in a straight line. Lay the string along the curves, and then measure the distance by laying the string along the ruler.
3. Remember that elevations on United States Geological Survey maps are given in feet.

Analyze

1. What is the contour interval?
2. Calculate the stream gradient of Big Wildhorse Creek from the Gravel Pit in section 21 to where the creek crosses the road in section 34.
3. What is the highest elevation of the jeep trail? If you followed the jeep trail from the highest point to where it intersects an unimproved road, what would be your change in elevation?
4. If you started at the bench mark (BM) on the jeep trail and hiked along the trail and the road to the Gravel Pit in section 21, how far would you have hiked?
5. What is the straight line distance between the two points in question 4? What is the change in elevation?

Conclude & Apply

1. Does Big Wildhorse Creek flow all year round? Explain your answer.
2. What is the shortest distance along roads from the Gravel Pit in section 21 to the secondary highway?
3. Draw a profile of the land surface from the bench mark in section 22 to the Gravel Pit in section 33.

Data and Observations

Students will measure distances, interpret map symbols, and draw a profile of a topographic map. Have students record their data and profiles in their science journals.

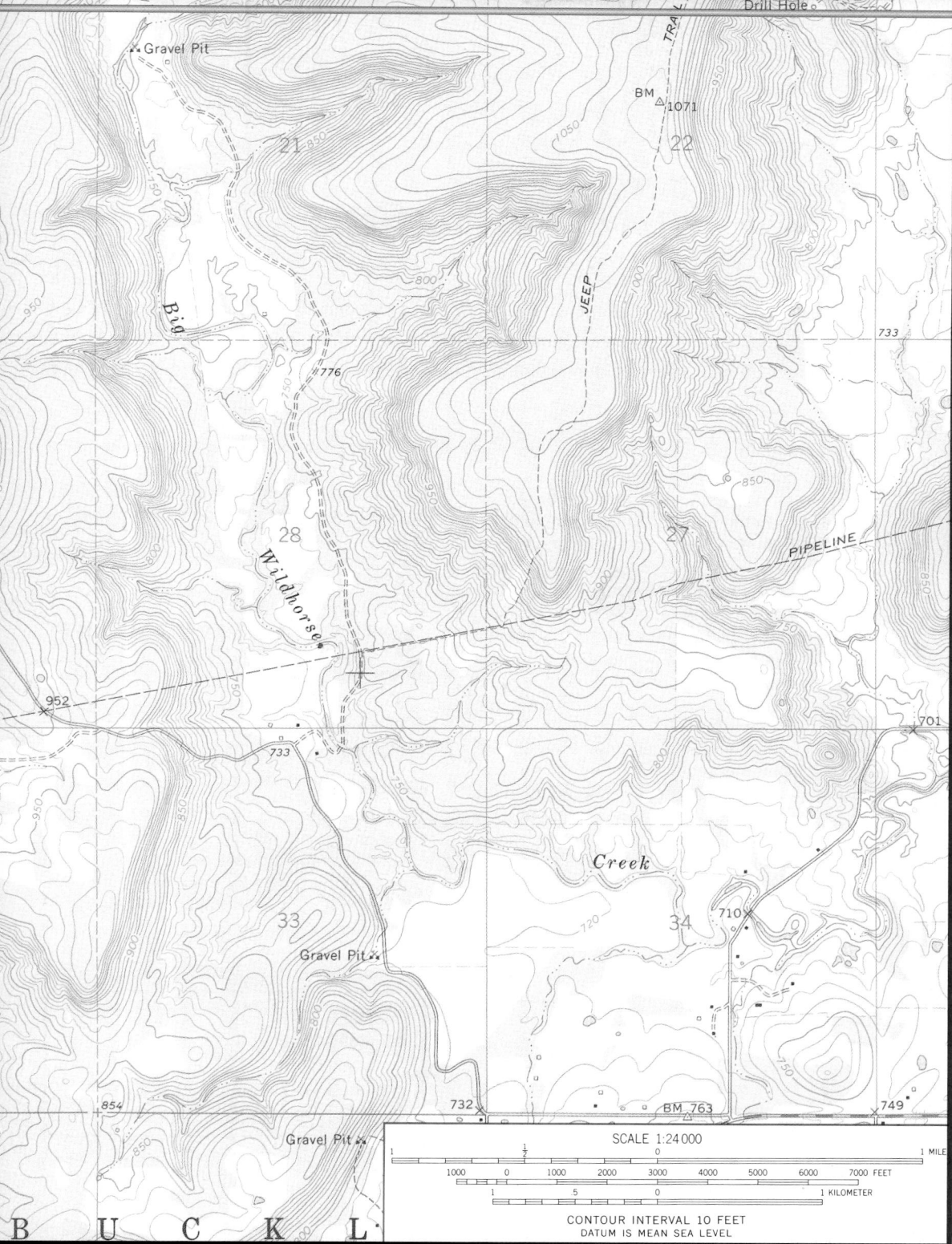

SCALE 1:24 000

1   1/2   0   1 MILE

1000   0   1000   2000   3000   4000   5000   6000   7000 FEET

1   5   0   1 KILOMETER

CONTOUR INTERVAL 10 FEET
DATUM IS MEAN SEA LEVEL

Analyze

1. The contour interval is 10 ft.
2. change in elevation is
   750 ft – 710 ft = 40 ft; change
   in distance is 4 mi; stream gradient is 40 ft ÷ 4 mi = 10 ft/mi
3. highest elevation = 1071 ft;
   change in elevation = 1071 ft
   – 740 ft = 331 ft
4. You would have hiked approximately 5.25 mi.
5. straight-line distance = 2 mi;
   change in elevation = 1071 ft
   – 750 ft = 321 ft

Conclude & Apply

1. No; the topographic map symbol for the stream indicates
   that it is an intermittent
   stream.
2. The shortest distance is slightly
   more than 3 mi.
3. Student profiles should show a
   relatively flat, high elevation,
   followed by a steep decline in
   elevation of nearly 300 ft, ending with a gentle increase in
   elevation of roughly 80 ft.

✓Assessment

Performance Have students
use modeling clay to make models of the profiles they created in
Conclude & Apply. Students
should write short descriptions
of the land surfaces they modeled. Use the Performance Task
Assessment List for Model in
PASC, p. 51.

Resource Manager

GeoLab and MiniLab Worksheets,
pp. 6–8 L2

NY Core Curriculum Standards

**Page 42: St 1 Math KI 1, 2, 3,
& Engin KI 1, St 6 KI 2 & 3,
St 7 KI 1**
**Page 43: St 1 Math KI 1, 2, 3,
& Engin KI 1, St 6 KI 2 & 3,
St 7 KI 1**

Purpose

Polar bears are found in all polar regions in the northern hemisphere, including Russia, Norway, Greenland, the United States, and Canada. This feature discusses the physical characteristics of polar bears that help them to survive in the arctic environment. Students will learn about polar bear ranges and calculate the distances these animals can travel on land and in the water.

Content Background

The home range of an animal is the area over which it travels to find food, find a mate, and care for its young. Polar bears are great roamers and have very large home ranges. Because polar bears do not mark or defend their territory, the ranges of polar bears often overlap. Also, their ranges vary greatly from season to season because their sea-ice environment is in constant flux.

Teaching Strategies

Have students answer the following questions before they attempt the Procedure and Challenge portions of this feature.

- How do conditions in the Arctic Ocean immediately surrounding the north pole differ from conditions around the southern boundaries of this region? The southern boundaries are less harsh and teem with life.
- Describe some physical adaptations that help polar bears survive in this environment. long necks, huge forepaws, white fur, and hollow hairs
- Compare a polar bear's walking and swimming speeds.

Polar bear

Thriving in the Arctic

How do you envision conditions in the arctic circle, which surrounds the north pole? Barren of life? Not quite! More than 20 000 polar bears live in this region, along with many other species. These hardy animals have unique adaptations that allow them to survive the harsh climate.

The Ring of Life

The borders of five countries—Russia, Norway, Greenland, Canada, and the United States—meet in a rough U-shape around the Arctic Ocean. The vast majority of this region is covered with ice some 2 m thick. In a climate where average winter temperatures hover around −35°C, survival is tenuous. The southern boundaries of this region, however, teem with life. Polar bears, walruses, beluga whales, fish, birds, and seals make the arctic circle their home.

Animal Adaptations

Polar bears in particular thrive where the ocean meets the shoreline, an area of constant freezing and thawing. Supremely adapted to this environment, they have long necks that help them keep their heads above water and huge forepaws that act as paddles. Light-colored fur provides camouflage to help them hunt, and an outer coat of hollow hairs makes the half-ton bears fairly buoyant in the water.

Traveling Bears

Polar bears can swim for an average of approximately 96.5 km without stopping for a rest. They have been tracked on land traveling 30 km a day for several days in a row. A polar bear's home range—the area in which it hunts, mates, and cares for its young—may be around 259 000 km². The home ranges of polar bears vary in size from 50 000 km² to as much as 350 000 km². Polar bear ranges are much greater than those of other mammals because the sea ice on which they live changes from season to season and year to year.

Procedure

1. Calculate the range of a polar bear that travels for six hours a day for seven days at a speed of 5.5 km/h.
2. Calculate how far a polar bear could swim in six hours at a speed of 10 km/h.
3. Convert your answers for questions 1 and 2 into U.S. units.

Challenge

1. Assume that polar bears do equal amounts of swimming and walking, and that they travel an average of four hours a day. Use your calculations and a world map or globe to determine whether a polar bear could travel around the circumference of Greenland in a year.

What is the most efficient means of travel for a polar bear? swimming

Procedure

1. 5.5 km/h × 6 h/day × 7 days = 231 km
2. 10 km/h × 6 h = 60 km
3. 143 mi and 37.2 mi, respectively

Challenge

Students should average polar-bear walking and swimming speeds. The average speed is 7.75 km/h, or 4.8 mi/h. Traveling an average of four hours per day, a polar bear would cover 11 284 km/y, or 6989 mi/y. Greenland has approximately 44 000 km, or 27 342 mi, of coastline. A polar bear could travel roughly one-fourth of this distance in a year.

Summary

CHAPTER 2
Study Guide

SECTION 2.1

Latitude and Longitude

Main Ideas

- Cartographers use a grid system to locate exact positions on Earth. Lines of latitude refer to distances north and south of the equator. Lines of longitude refer to distances east and west of the prime meridian.
- Earth is divided into 24 time zones. Each zone represents a different hour. The International Date Line, or 180° meridian, is the transition line for calendar days. The calendar advances to the next day in each time zone at midnight.

Vocabulary

cartography (p. 27)
equator (p. 27)
International Date Line (p. 31)
latitude (p. 27)
longitude (p. 29)
prime meridian (p. 29)

SECTION 2.2

Types of Maps

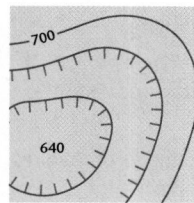

Main Ideas

- Maps are flat models of Earth's surface. All maps contain some sort of distortion in the shapes or areas of landmasses.
- Maps are made by transferring points and lines on a globe onto paper. Mercator projections and gnomonic projections are commonly used for navigation by ships and planes. Conic projections are best suited for mapping small areas.
- Topographic maps show changes in elevation of Earth's surface. Contour lines connect points of equal elevation. A map legend explains the symbols on a map. A map scale shows the relationship between distances on a map and actual distances on Earth.

Vocabulary

conic projection (p. 32)
contour interval (p. 34)
contour line (p. 33)
gnomonic projection (p. 33)
map legend (p. 35)
map scale (p. 35)
Mercator projection (p. 32)
topographic map (p. 33)

SECTION 2.3

Remote Sensing

Main Ideas

- The process of gathering data about Earth from far above the planet is called remote sensing. The electromagnetic spectrum shows the arrangement of electromagnetic radiation, which is often used by remote-sensing devices to map Earth.
- Landsat satellites use visible light and infrared radiation to map Earth's surface. The *Topex/Poseidon* satellite uses radar to map features on the ocean floor.
- The Global Positioning System is a satellite-based navigation system that allows a user to pinpoint his or her exact location on Earth.

Vocabulary

electromagnetic spectrum (p. 38)
frequency (p. 38)
Global Positioning System (p. 40)
Landsat satellite (p. 38)
remote sensing (p. 37)
sonar (p. 40)
Topex/Poseidon satellite (p. 39)

 earthgeu.com/vocabulary_puzzlemaker

Main Ideas

Summary statements can be used by students to review the major concepts of the chapter.

VOCABULARY PuzzleMaker

 For additional help with vocabulary, have students access the Vocabulary Puzzlemaker online.

earthgeu.com/ vocabulary puzzlemaker

0:00 *Out of Time?*

If time does not permit teaching the entire chapter, use the GeoDigest at the end of the unit as an overview.

Earth Science Online

Be sure to check the Earth Science Web Site for links to chapter material:
earthgeu.com

GLENCOE
Technology

Videotape/DVD
MindJogger Videoquizzes
Chapter 2: *Mapping Our World*
Have students work in groups as they play the videoquiz game to review key chapter concepts.

Resource Manager

Chapter Assessment, pp. 7–12
MindJogger Videoquizzes DVD/VHS
ExamView® Pro CD-ROM
Performance Assessment in Earth Science

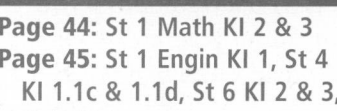
NY Core Curriculum Standards

Page 44: St 1 Math KI 2 & 3
Page 45: St 1 Engin KI 1, St 4 KI 1.1c & 1.1d, St 6 KI 2 & 3, St 7 KI 1

Understanding Main Ideas

1. b
2. c
3. d
4. b
5. c
6. a
7. b
8. c
9. The Global Positioning System (GPS) uses a system of satellites to help users find their exact positions on Earth. A hiker can use a hand-held GPS unit to determine the latitude and longitude of his or her position, and compare these coordinates with known latitude and longitude values to orient himself or herself.
10. A verbal scale expresses distance as a statement, such as "One centimeter equals one kilometer." A graphic scale consists of a line that represents units, such as 10 km or 10 mi. The line is broken down into sections, with each section representing a distance on Earth's surface. A fractional scale expresses distance as a ratio, such as 1:150 000. This means that 1 unit on a map represents 150 000 units on Earth's surface.
11. A topographic map of the Great Plains would have a large contour interval because the Great Plains are relatively flat.
12. Contour lines connect points of equal elevation. If two contour lines crossed, it would mean that the point where they crossed had two

Understanding Main Ideas

1. What feature on a map shows the ratio of map distance to actual distance on Earth?
   a. map legend   c. map symbol
   b. map scale   d. contour line

2. What type of map shows changes in elevation on Earth's surface?
   a. Mercator projection   c. topographic map
   b. gnomonic projection   d. GPS

3. Which of the following is NOT true of lines of longitude?
   a. They are semicircles.
   b. They measure distances east and west of the prime meridian.
   c. They run from pole to pole.
   d. They are parallel lines.

4. What technology is used to map seafloor features?
   a. conic projections
   b. *Topex/Poseidon* satellite
   c. the Global Positioning System
   d. Landsat satellite

5. What is the main disadvantage of a Mercator projection?
   a. It distorts areas near the equator.
   b. It distorts the shapes of landmasses.
   c. It distorts areas near the poles.
   d. It does not show true direction.

6. What is the reference point for lines of latitude?
   a. the equator
   b. the prime meridian
   c. the International Date Line
   d. the 180° meridian

7. What is the distance of one degree of latitude?
   a. 11 km   c. 40 000 km
   b. 111 km   d. 1.85 km

8. Some areas have lower elevations than the surrounding land. Which of the following represents these areas on a topographic map?
   a. index contours
   b. contour intervals
   c. depression contour lines
   d. map legends

9. What is the Global Positioning System? Describe how it might be used by a hiker lost in the woods.

10. Compare and contrast a verbal scale, a graphic scale, and a fractional scale.

11. Would a topographic map of the Great Plains have a large or small contour interval? Explain.

12. Why can't two contour lines overlap?

13. How could you leave home on Monday to go sailing, sail for an hour on Sunday, and return home on Monday?

14. What is a map legend? Give examples of features found in a map legend.

Applying Main Ideas

15. What type of map would best show true direction?

16. Do closely spaced contour lines indicate a steep slope or a gradual slope? Explain.

Test-Taking Tip

WHERE HAVE I HEARD THAT BEFORE? If you don't know the definition of a word, you can usually work through the question by thinking about how you've heard the word used before. Think about the context in which the word was used. This will narrow its meaning.

earthgeu.com/chapter_test

different elevations, which is impossible.
13. If you lived just west of the International Date Line, you could leave Monday, travel east across the 180th meridian and sail for an hour on Sunday, then return west across the date line on Monday night.
14. A map legend explains what the symbols on a map represent. Answers will vary.

Applying Main Ideas

15. A Mercator projection would be best because it shows true direction.
16. Closely spaced contour lines indicate a steep slope.
17. There is a 12° difference between Orlando, Florida, and Cleveland, Ohio. One degree of latitude is equal to 111 km/degree. 12° × 111 km/° = 1332 km
18. The time in Athens would be approximately 4 P.M.

17. Approximately how many kilometers separate Orlando, Florida, at 29° north latitude and Cleveland, Ohio, at 41° north latitude?

18. If it is 10 A.M. in Syracuse, New York, at 76° west longitude, what time is it in Athens, Greece, at 24° east longitude?

Use the map to answer questions 19–21.

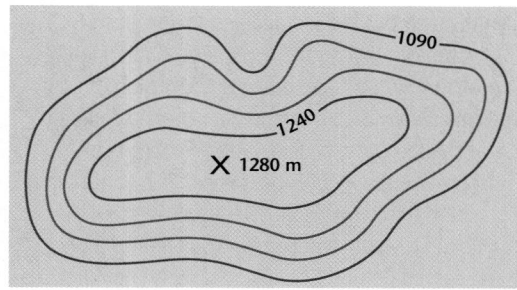

19. Copy the map shown here. What is its contour interval?

20. Based on the contour interval, label the elevations of all the contour lines.

21. Does the map represent a flat or hilly terrain? Explain.

Thinking Critically

22. Would a person flying from Virginia to California have to set his or her watch backward or forward? Explain.

23. If you wanted to study detailed features of a volcano on the island of Hawaii, would you use a map with a scale of 1:150 or 1:150 000? Why?

24. Based on what you have learned in this chapter, infer how astronomers map objects in the night sky.

25. Which direction would you travel along Earth's surface so that your longitude would not change? Explain your answer.

earthgeu.com/standardized_test

Standardized Test Practice

1. What is the reference point for lines of longitude?
a. the equator
b. the prime meridian
c. the International Date Line
d. the 360th meridian

2. Which would be most useful if you were lost in the Sahara desert?
a. Landsat satellite
b. *Topex/Poseidon* satellite
c. Global Positioning System
d. topographic map of Africa

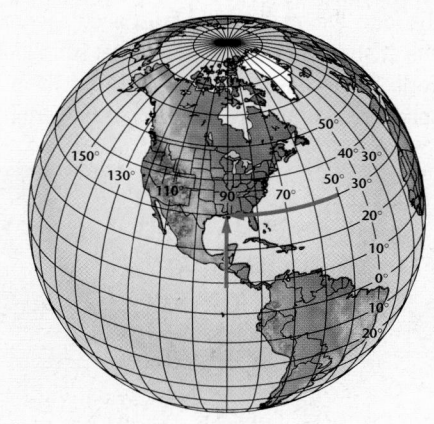

USING MAPS Use the map to answer questions 3 and 4.

3. Roughly how many degrees of longitude does the United States cover?
a. 10°   **b.** 20°   **c.** 30°   **d.** 40°

4. Roughly how many degrees of latitude does the United States cover?
a. 10°   **b.** 15°   **c.** 20°   **d.** 25°

Assessment **47**

19. 50 m

20. From the outermost line inward, the lines should be labeled 1090, 1140, 1190, and 1240.

21. There is a relatively large increase in elevation, so the map represents hilly terrain.

Thinking Critically

22. A person flying from Virginia to California would have to set his or her watch back because California is west of Virginia and thus is in an earlier time zone.

23. The map with a scale of 1:150 would be better because it would show more detail.

24. Astronomers can use a grid system similar to the system of latitude and longitude to locate objects in the night sky.

25. North or south; lines of longitude run from pole to pole. If you traveled east or west, you would change longitude.

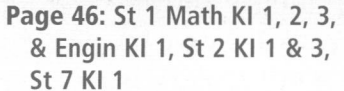
EXAMVIEW® PRO

Use Exam*View*® Pro Testmaker CD-ROM to:

- Create **multiple versions** of tests.
- Create **modified** tests with one mouse click for struggling students.
- **Edit** existing questions and add your own questions.
- **Build** tests based on national curriculum standards.

Standardized Test Practice

1. b
2. c
3. d
4. d

NY Core Curriculum Standards

Page 46: St 1 Math KI 1, 2, 3, & Engin KI 1, St 2 KI 1 & 3, St 7 KI 1
Page 47: St 1 Math KI 1, 2, & 3, St 7 KI 1

Prepare

Purpose

This GeoDigest can be used as an overview of Earth science concepts and maps. If time is limited, you may wish to use this unit summary to teach these concepts in place of the chapters in Unit 1.

Key Concepts

Students are introduced to the nature of Earth science and maps. They learn about Earth's systems, the scientific method, latitude and longitude, and different types of maps.

1 Focus

Section Focus

 Intrapersonal Before beginning the lesson, pass around a globe. Ask students to find their location on the globe. How would they describe their location to someone who does not know where they live? Answers will vary. Students may say that they could describe landmarks or draw maps. Some students will know about latitude and longitude and may offer coordinates that describe their location. **L1** **ELL**

NY Core Curriculum Standards

Page 48: St 1 Science KI 1, St 4 KI 1.2g, & 2.1l
Page 49: St 1 Science KI 1, St 2 KI 1, St 6 KI 2

For a **preview** of Earth science, study this GeoDigest before you read the chapters. After you have studied the unit, you can use the GeoDigest to **review**.

Earth Science

The Nature of Science

Earth Science Earth science is divided into four areas of specialization. Astronomy studies objects beyond Earth's atmosphere. Meteorology studies the atmosphere. Geology studies the materials of Earth and the processes that form them. Oceanography studies the oceans. The application of scientific discoveries is technology. Earth is made up of interacting systems. The lithosphere includes the rocks that make up the crust and upper mantle. The atmosphere is the gas layer that surrounds Earth. The hydrosphere is Earth's water. The biosphere is all of the life and habitats on Earth.

Methods and Communication Most scientific methods include defining the problem, stating a hypothesis, testing the hypothesis, analyzing the results of the test, and drawing conclusions. In the testing step, variables are factors in an experiment that change. A dependent variable changes in response to the independent variable. A control is a standard for comparison. Scientists use standard units of SI—liter, meter, second, kilogram, Newton, and degree Celsius. Scientists also use scientific notation, in which a number is expressed as a multiplier and a power of ten. Scientists communicate in reports and papers, and use tables, graphs, and models. A scientific theory is an explanation based on observations from repeated experiments. It is valid only if it is consistent with observations, leads to testable predictions, and is the simplest explanation. Scientific theories are changed if they are found to be incorrect. A scientific law is a basic fact that describes the behavior of a natural phenomenon.

FOCUS ON CAREERS

Science Teacher
Science teachers often provide a student's first exposure to science and may spark a life-long interest in a particular topic. High school science teachers must have at least a bachelor's degree, often from a five-year program, with an emphasis in their area of interest, such as Earth science.

48 UNIT 1

Multiple Learning Styles

 Intrapersonal Section Focus, p. 48

 Visual-Spatial Reteach, p. 49

Differentiated Instruction

English-Language Learners Have students whose first language is not English use world atlases to research statistics about their native country and the state they currently live in. Students can compare and contrast the locations, sizes, populations, landforms, climates, vegetation, soils, and agriculture of the two places. This will help students become familiar with their new home.

 **GeoDigest**

Mapping Our World
Latitude, Longitude, and Maps

Cartographers use a grid system of latitude and longitude to locate exact positions on Earth. Latitude refers to distances north and south of the equator. Longitude refers to distances east and west of the prime meridian. Earth is divided into 24 time zones, with each zone representing a different hour. The International Date Line, or the 180° meridian, is the transition line for calendar days. Maps are flat models of Earth's round surface, thus all maps contain some sort of distortion. Maps are made by transferring points and lines on a globe onto paper. A map legend explains map symbols. A map scale shows how distances on a map and actual distances on Earth are related. Mercator and gnomonic projections are used for aircraft and ship navigation. Conic projections are suited to mapping small areas. Topographic maps show changes in elevation of Earth's surface. Gathering data about

Earth from far above is called remote sensing. Examples of remote-sensing devices include *Landsat* satellites, the *Topex-Poseidon* satellite, and the Global Positioning System. These different types of technology can be used to map Earth's surface and oceans, and to locate places on Earth.

Vital Statistics

Earth's Land Area

Continent	Area in km²
Asia, Middle East	44 579 000
Africa	30 065 000
North America	24 256 000
South America, Central America, and Caribbean	17 819 000
Antarctica	13 209 000
Europe	9 938 000
Australia and Oceania	7 687 000
Earth Total	**148 429 000**

ASSESSMENT

Understanding Main Ideas

1. Which of the following is an area of specialization in Earth science?
   a. hydrosphere   **c.** meteorology
   b. Mercator projection   **d.** remote sensing

2. What happens if a scientific theory is found to be incorrect?
   a. It is published.
   b. It is changed.
   c. It becomes a scientific law.
   d. It becomes a control.

3. Which type of map shows changes in elevation of Earth's surface?
   a. conic projection   **c.** topographic map
   b. gnomonic projection **d.** latitude map

4. What does a map legend contain?
   a. contour lines
   b. longitude lines
   c. latitude lines
   d. the symbols used in a map

5. What is the application of science called?
   a. technology   **c.** scientific law
   b. latitude   **d.** theory

Thinking Critically

1. Describe the steps commonly used in scientific methods.
2. Why isn't a conic projection used to navigate a ship or aircraft?

2 Teach

Content Background
People often describe the shape of Earth as a perfect sphere. Earth is actually an oblate ellipsoid. Thus, it bulges slightly at the equator and is somewhat flattened at the poles. If possible, obtain a cross-sectional view of Earth through the poles. Students will see that Earth is not a perfect circle. It is ellipsoidal because of the centrifugal force of its rotation.

3 Assess

Check for Understanding
Reinforcement
Have students use the Vital Statistics box to make a bar graph of Earth's land area. As an added challenge, students can calculate the percentage of total land area that each continent represents.
L2

Reteach
Visual-Spatial Have students each make a map of the school. Maps should include map scales and map legends. Make sure students understand that larger scales show less detail than smaller scales do.

✓*Assessment*
Portfolio Have students make posters that illustrate the four areas of specialization of Earth science: astronomy, geology, oceanography, and meteorology.
P

ASSESSMENT

Understanding Main Ideas
1. c
2. b
3. c
4. d
5. a

Thinking Critically
1. Most scientific methods include defining the problem, stating a hypothesis, testing the hypothesis, analyzing the results, and drawing conclusions.
2. Ship and air navigation involves long distances, and a conic projection is only accurate for small areas.

Composition of Earth

Unit Overview

Rock Chemistry In Unit 2, students are introduced to matter and atomic structure and will learn how the chemical structure of elements and compounds determines their behavior. Students will then relate this information to the chemical composition of the various elements and compounds that make up the rocks and minerals found on Earth's surface and in the crust.

Chapter Breakdown Chapter 3 introduces chemical formulas and reactions to help students understand how the chemical natures of rocks and minerals are related to their structures. The properties and structures of minerals are discussed in Chapter 4. Chapter 5 introduces igneous rocks and explains how these rocks are related to internal forces in Earth's mantle and crust. Finally, the structures of sedimentary and metamorphic rocks are discussed in Chapter 6. Students are presented with a scientific overview of the development of sedimentary rocks, which will help them understand how different layers of rock represent different time periods and how fossils form.

0:00 **Out of Time?**

If time does not permit teaching the entire unit, use the GeoDigest at the end of the unit as an overview.

Unit 2

Composition of Earth

In the setting Sun, the giant monolith called Uluru by the Aborigines of the Northern Territory of Australia glows a fiery red. Uluru, also known as Ayers Rock, is 2.5 km long, 1.6 km wide, and oval in shape. This rock is a conglomerate, a type of sedimentary rock composed of large, rounded chunks of rocks and minerals. Uluru is a solitary rock that rises nearly 350 m above the surrounding desert plain. How did such a huge sedimentary rock form in a desert? In this unit, you will explore the geologic forces that formed Uluru and also shape rocks and minerals.

Unit Contents

3 **Matter and Atomic Structure**

4 **Minerals**

5 **Igneous Rocks**

6 **Sedimentary and Metamorphic Rocks**

Go to the National Geographic Expedition on page 870 to learn more about topics that are connected to this unit.

50

NATIONAL GEOGRAPHIC

The Remaking of a River Some topics of Earth science deserve more attention than others because they're unusual, informative, or just plain interesting. The National Geographic Society has created visually exciting, multipage *Expeditions!* features that inform, excite, and motivate your students. *Expeditions!* features are relevant to the Earth science content of the student edition. Assign them as a lead-in to special research projects and in-depth studies for extra credit. Use them as a basis for colorful visual displays and bulletin boards.

Ayers Rock, Australia

51

Introducing the Unit

Precambrian Rock This photograph shows a view of Ayers Rock, located in the Northern Territory of Australia. Ayers Rock, named Mount Uluru by the native Aborigines, is believed to have had its orgin in the Precambrian, more than 550 million years ago. Ask students what types of environmental or geologic events could have resulted in the present condition of Ayers Rock. Ask whether they see any evidence in this photo of volcanic activity or erosion by wind or water. What kind of material do students think this rock is made of? Is Ayers Rock made of different parent material from that of the surrounding plain?

Geology of Ayers Rock

Geologists hypothesize that enormous mountain ranges in Australia were pushed up, then eroded away over the next 200 million years, leaving the Mann, Musgrave, and Petermann Ranges in Central Australia. The sediments from these ranges were laid down on the Amadeus Basin, and further Earth movements about 300 million years ago, along with continual erosion, resulted in Ayers Rock.

A Red Rock Ayers Rock consists of arkose, a coarse-grained sandstone rich in feldspar. The famous red color of Ayers Rock is caused by iron oxide, the result of oxidation of iron in the arkose. In this unit, students will learn about the geologic forces that form, and rearrange chemically and physically, the rocks and minerals found on Earth.

Earth Science Online

Note Internet addresses that you find useful in the space below for quick reference.

_____

_____

_____

_____

_____

_____

For Internet tips, see Glencoe's **Using the Internet in the Science Classroom.**

Chapter 3

Matter and Atomic Structure

Refer to pages 8T–9T of the Teacher Guide for an explanation of the National Science Content Standards correlations.

Section	Objectives	National Science Content Standards	State/Local Standards
SECTION 3.1 **What are elements?** ½ session ¼ block	1. **Describe** the particles within atoms and the structure of atoms. 2. **Relate** the energy levels of atoms to the chemical properties of elements. 3. **Define** the concept of isotopes.	**A.1; B.1, B.2, B.3**	St 1 Math KI 2 & Science KI 3, St 4 KI 3.1a, 3.1b, & 3.1c
SECTION 3.2 **How Atoms Combine** ½ session ¼ block	4. **Describe** the chemical bonds that unite atoms to form compounds. 5. **Relate** the nature of chemical bonds that hold compounds together to the physical structures of compounds. 6. **Distinguish** among different types of mixtures and solutions.	**UCP.2, UCP.3; B.1, B.2, B.3**	St 1 Math KI 2, St 4 KI 3.1b, St 6 KI 5
SECTION 3.3 **States of Matter** 2 sessions 1 block	7. **Describe** the states of matter on Earth. 8. **Explain** the reasons that matter exists in these states. 9. **Relate** the role of thermal energy to changes of state in matter.	**UCP.1, UCP.3, UCP.5; A.1, A.2; B.1, B.2, B.3, B.6; E.1, E.2**	St 1 Math KI 1, 2, 3, Science KI 1, & 2, St 2 KI 1, St 4 KI 3.1a, 3.1b, & 3.1c, St 6 KI 5, St 7 KI 2

A complete Planning Guide is provided on pages 30T–32T.

- The number of recommended single-period sessions
- The number of recommended blocks

Activity Materials

Discovery Lab *page 53*
250-mL beaker, iron-fortified cereal, pencil, magnet, tape, plastic bag, rolling pin, hand lens, water

GeoLab *pages 70–71*
halite (sodium chloride), 250-mL glass beakers (2), distilled water, plastic wrap, laboratory scale, hot plate, shallow glass baking dish, refrigerator, glass stirring rod

MiniLab *page 55*
iron tools, file cabinets, keys, paper clips, coins, earrings, metal doorknobs,

pencils, electrical wires, chrome-plated fixtures, soft-drink cans, fluorescent lights

Demo *page 54*
glass rod, silk cloth, metallic object

page 60
100-mL beaker, hydrogen gas, matches

page 63
salt, solid shortening, metal spatulas (2), laboratory burner

Need materials? Contact Science Kit at 1-800-828-7777 or at <u>www.sciencekit.com</u> on the Internet. For alternate materials, see the activity on the listed page.

Key to Teaching Strategies

L1 Level 1 activities should be appropriate for students with learning difficulties.

L2 Level 2 activities should be within the ability range of all students.

L3 Level 3 activities are designed for above-average students.

ELL ELL activities should be within the ability range of English-language learners.

COOP LEARN Cooperative learning activities are designed for small-group work.

P These strategies represent student products that can be placed in a best-work portfolio.

These strategies are useful in a block-scheduling format.

Chapter Organizer

Glencoe Exclusive!
Teacher Works™
All-In-One Planner and Resource Center

Activities/Features	Reproducible Masters	Transparencies
Discovery Lab: Fortified Cereals, p. 53 **MiniLab:** Identifying Elements, p. 55 **Using Math:** Using Numbers, p. 58	**Study Guide for Content Mastery,** pp. 15–16 L2 **GeoLab and MiniLab Worksheets,** p. 9 L2	**Section Focus Transparency 7** L1 ELL **Teaching Transparency 7** L2 ELL
Problem-Solving Lab: Interpreting Scientific Illustrations, p. 63	**Study Guide for Content Mastery,** pp. 17–18 L2 **Exploring Environmental Problems,** pp. 25–28 L2 **Laboratory Manual,** pp. 21–24 L2	**Section Focus Transparency 8** L1 ELL **Teaching Transparency 8** L2 ELL
GeoLab: Salt Precipitation, pp. 70–71 **Science & Technology:** Extreme Magnification, p. 72	**Study Guide for Content Mastery,** pp. 19–20 L2 **GeoLab and MiniLab Worksheets,** pp. 10–12 L2 **Laboratory Manual,** pp. 17–20 L2	**Section Focus Transparency 9** L1 ELL

✔Assessment

Chapter Assessment, pp. 13–18
Performance Assessment in the Science Classroom (PASC)
MindJogger Videoquiz DVD/VHS
Performance Assessment in Earth Science
ExamView® Pro CD-ROM
5 Days to the Regents Exam

GLENCOE'S
ASSESSMENT
ADVANTAGE

Additional Resources

Guided Reading Audio Program ELL
Cooperative Learning in the Science Classroom COOP LEARN
Lesson Plans
Block Scheduling
earthgeu.com
NY Lesson Plans
Block Scheduling
Review Handbook for Regents Earth Science Exam

▢ NATIONAL GEOGRAPHIC

Teacher's Corner

Products Available from National Geographic Society
To order the following products, call the National Geographic Society at 1-800-368-2728:

Videos
What's the Earth Made of?
Our Dynamic Earth
Recycling: The Endless Circle

Content Background

Electron Shells
Section 3.1

Energy levels in atoms correspond to electron shells. Electron shells, in turn, consist of subshells, designated as s, p, d, and f. The lowest energy level of an atom consists of only one subshell, the 1s subshell. The second energy level contains two subshells, 2s and 2p. Higher energy levels consist of the 3s, 3p, 3d, and 4s, 4p, 4d, and 4f subshells. All s subshells can hold 2 electrons, p subshells can hold 6 electrons, and d and f subshells can hold 10 and 14 electrons, respectively. Therefore, the first energy level can hold 2 electrons, the second can hold 8 electrons, and the third and fourth can hold 18 and 32 electrons, respectively. The inert gases Ne, Ar, Kr, Xe, and Rn have filled s and p subshells (8 electrons) in their outer shells. Iron has filled 1s, 2s, 2p, 3s, 3p, and 4s subshells, and 6 electrons in the 3d subshell, for a total of 26 electrons.

Radioactive Decay
Section 3.1

There are three common types of radioactive decay: alpha decay, beta decay, and electron capture. During alpha decay, an alpha particle (alpha ray) is emitted from the decaying nucleus. An alpha particle consists of two protons and two neutrons—it is actually a helium nucleus. The radioactive isotope, therefore, loses two protons and two neutrons, which lowers its atomic number by 2 and its mass number by 4. Uranium-238 decays in this manner to thorium-234. During beta decay, a neutron of the decaying nucleus splits into a proton and an electron. The electron is emitted as a beta particle, or beta ray. The decaying nucleus, therefore, loses a neutron and gains a proton—a neutron converts to a proton. This increases the atomic number by 1, but the mass number remains unchanged because the beta particle has negligible mass. An example of beta decay is the decay of radioactive carbon-14 (atomic number 6) to nitrogen-14 (atomic number 7). The third type of decay, electron capture, is the exact opposite of beta decay: a proton of the nucleus combines with an orbital electron to form a neutron. The decaying nucleus thus gains a neutron and loses a proton; its atomic number decreases by 1 while its mass number remains unchanged. Potassium-14 decays in this manner to argon-14.

The Formation of Ions
Section 3.2

The most stable electron configurations are those of the inert gases. Inert gases have either filled outer energy levels, as helium and neon do, or eight electrons in their outer energy levels. All inert gases except helium have eight electrons in their outer energy levels—that is, they have filled s and p subshells. Atoms of other elements can achieve the same stable electron configuration either by sharing electrons or by forming ions.

Multiple Learning Styles

Kinesthetic Modeling, p. 62

Visual-Spatial Demo, pp. 54, 60, 63

Interpersonal Collaborative Learning, p. 64, Project, p. 67, Activity, p. 68,

Logical-Mathematical Activity, p. 62

GLENCOE
Technology

The following multimedia resources are available from Glencoe.

The Infinite Voyage Series
Unseen Worlds

Vocabulary Puzzlemaker

TeacherWorks™ CD-ROM

MindJogger Videoquizzes DVD/VHS

ExamView® Pro CD-ROM

Interactive Chalkboard CD-ROM

Chapter Organizer

Atoms whose outer energy levels contain fewer than four electrons tend to lose their outer electrons and form positive ions. For example, a magnesium atom (atomic number 12) has two electrons in its first energy level, eight electrons in its second energy level, and two electrons in its third energy level. By losing the two outer electrons, a magnesium atom becomes a magnesium ion with two electrons in its first energy level and eight electrons in its second (outer) energy level. Magnesium ions have the same electron configuration as the inert gas neon. However, because these ions each contain 12 protons but only 10 electrons, they have a net electrical charge of +2. Atoms whose outer energy levels contain more than four electrons tend to gain additional electrons and form negative ions. For example, an oxygen atom (atomic number 8) has two electrons in its first energy level and six electrons in its second energy level. By gaining two additional electrons in its outer energy level, an oxygen atom becomes a negative ion with the same stable electron

configuration as neon. Its net charge is −2 (eight protons and ten electrons). Iron is a special case. It can form +2 ions by losing its outer 4s electrons, or +3 ions by losing its 4s electrons and one 3d electron.

States of Matter
Section 3.3

Water on Earth occurs in three states of matter: solid, liquid, and gaseous. Ice is an open, rigid, three-dimensional framework of water molecules bound together by hydrogen bonds. Liquid water consists of clusters of molecules held together temporarily by hydrogen bonds. In water vapor, all hydrogen bonds are broken and the molecules move about independently. Changes of state involve the breaking of hydrogen bonds and require energy. The latent heat of fusion is the energy required to break enough hydrogen bonds of ice to liquefy it. The latent heat of vaporization is the energy required to break all hydrogen bonds of liquid water.

Identifying Misconceptions

Most students dislike chemistry. Chemistry has the reputation of being difficult and of dealing with strange, smelly, and possibly poisonous substances. Ask students what the word *chemistry* means to them. Explain that chemistry involves a lot of common sense, that it involves common, everyday substances, and that it is used every day in such activities as cooking and washing. Students might also associate chemistry with dramatic or dangerous chemical reactions, such as cannon fire or fireworks. Tell students that chemistry is also used to produce new types of makeup and video games.

✓Assessment

Portfolio Assessment
Assessment, TWE, p. 69

Performance Assessment
GeoLab, TWE, pp. 70–71
GeoLab, SE, pp. 70–71
MiniLab, SE, p. 55
Discovery Lab, TWE, p. 53
Discovery Lab, SE, p. 53

Knowledge Assessment
Section Assessment, SE, pp. 59, 66, 69
Chapter Assessment, SE, pp. 74–75
MiniLab, TWE, p. 55
Assessment, TWE, p. 66

Skill Assessment
Assessment, TWE, p. 59
Problem-Solving Lab, TWE, p. 63

Be sure to check the Earth Science Web Site for links to chapter material: earthgeu.com

Matter and Atomic Structure

Introducing the Chapter

Show the class several centimeter-sized crystals of halite. Describe the major properties of the crystals. Smash one of the crystals to a powder, place some of the powder under a microscope, and let students observe it. Ask students whether the pieces still look like salt. Then ask whether the pieces could be split into smaller and smaller fragments indefinitely.

Interpreting the Photo

Gold is a precious metal. Have students describe the appearance of the gold in the photograph and ask them the following question. How did the jeweler know that this is gold and not brass? from its properties

PowerPoint® Presentations

This CD is an editable Microsoft® PowerPoint® presentation that includes:
- Section presentations
- Section checks
- Image bank
- Links to Earth Science Online
- All transparencies
- Animations
- Audio

Matter and Atomic Structure

What You'll Learn
- What the basic structures are of the elements that make up Earth.
- How atoms interact to form compounds.
- What states of matter occur on Earth.

Why It's Important

Earth consists of many elements and compounds. Understanding how rocks and minerals form requires a basic knowledge of chemistry, the science of matter.

To find out more about matter and atomic structure, visit the Earth Science Web Site at earthgeu.com

52

Discovery Lab

Process Skills

observe and infer, interpret data L1 ELL

Disposal

Have students return all materials to you for disposal.

Procedure

Make sure students stir the cereal-water mixture very slowly for the last minute to allow the iron particles to adhere to the magnet.

Troubleshooting

The amount of iron collected on the magnet will depend upon the type of cereal used. Have students test several different brands of cereal and share their data with the class.

Observe

Small particles of iron will be found on the pencil-magnet stirrers. Explain to students that iron is an essential element in our diets because hemoglobin, the compound in red blood cells that enables them to carry oxygen, contains a substantial amount of

Discovery Lab

Fortified Cereals

Advertisements for breakfast cereals often indicate that they are fortified with substances that increase their nutritional value. In this activity, you will identify one substance that is added to cereals.

1. Tape a small strong magnet to the eraser end of a pencil.

2. Pour a sample of dry, fortified cereal into a small plastic bag. Smooth the bag as you close it.

3. Using a rolling pin, thoroughly crush the cereal in the plastic bag.

4. Pour the crushed cereal into a 250-mL glass beaker. Add 150 mL of tap water to the beaker.

5. Using the pencil-magnet stirrer, stir the cereal/water mixture for 10 minutes, stirring slowly for the last minute.

6. Remove the stirrer from the mixture and examine the magnet end of the stirrer with a hand lens.

Observe In your science journal, describe what you see on the end of the pencil stirrer. Study the cereal box to determine what the substance on the magnet might be.

What are elements?

OBJECTIVES

- **Describe** *the particles within atoms and the structure of atoms.*
- **Relate** *the energy levels of atoms to the chemical properties of elements.*
- **Define** *the concept of isotopes.*

VOCABULARY

element
atom
nucleus
proton
neutron
atomic number
mass number
electron
energy level
valence electron
isotope
atomic mass
radioactivity

When a jewelry designer plans a new piece, he or she often chooses to work in gold. Gold is soft and easy to work with. It can be molded, hammered, sculpted, or made into wire. But whatever shape the jewelry takes, the gold remains the same. Gold is a type of matter. The jewelry designer also is made up of matter. The physical world that surrounds you and all living things are composed of matter. What exactly is matter? Matter is anything that has volume and mass. On Earth, matter usually can be found as a solid, liquid, or gas.

ELEMENTS

All matter—that is, everything on Earth and beyond—is made of substances called elements. An **element** is a substance that cannot be broken down into simpler substances by physical or chemical means. For example, gold is still gold whether it has been melted, pulled into wire, hammered into a thin sheet, or divided into small particles.

Ninety-two elements occur naturally on Earth and in the stars. Other elements have been produced in laboratory experiments. Each element is identified by a one-, two-, or three-letter abbreviation known as a chemical symbol. For example, the symbol H represents

3.1 What are Elements **53**

---

iron. This is why iron is often added to cereal and other food products.

✓Assessment

Performance Ask students to make comprehensive lists of vitamin and mineral additives, carbohydrates, fats, and Calories contained in the various brands of cereals tested. Have students post the lists so teams of students can study them and reach a conclusion about the most healthful brand. Use the Performance Task Assessment List for Display in **PASC**, p. 63 **L1** **COOP LEARN**

Resource Manager

Study Guide for Content Mastery,
   pp. 15–16 **L2**

Section Focus Transparency 7 **L1** **ELL**

Section 3.1

1 Focus

Section Focus

Before presenting the lesson, display **Section Focus Transparency 7** on the overhead projector.
L1 **ELL**

> Section Focus Transparency **7** ELEMENTS
> *Use with Chapter 3, Section 3.1*
>
> ❶ Why do you think neon signs are used in advertising?
> ❷ Why do you think neon lights give off different bright colors?
>
> Section Focus Transparency
> *Earth Science: Geology, the Environment, and the Universe*

Chapter Themes

The following themes from the National Science Content Standards are covered in this chapter. Refer to page 8T of the Teacher Guide for an explanation of the correlations.
Systems, order, and organization (UCP.1); Evidence, models, and explanation (UCP.2); Form and function (UCP.5)

0:00 Out of Time?

If time does not permit teaching the entire chapter, use the Chapter Summary on page 73 and the *GeoDigest* at the end of the unit as an overview.

NY Core Curriculum Standards

Page 52: St 4 KI 3.1a, 3.1b, & 3.1c
Page 53: St 1 Science KI 3, St 4 KI 3.1a

Content Background

Tell students that they can figure out the names of many elements from their chemical symbols, for example O for oxygen and Al for aluminum. Explain the Latin origin of the chemical symbols Na, K, Au, Ag, and Fe, for sodium, potassium, gold, silver, and iron, respectively: natrium, kalium, aurum, argentum, and ferrum. Note that the mass numbers given in **Table 3-2** and the neutrons shown in **Figure 3-1** represent the most common isotope of each element.

Demo

Visual-Spatial Charge a glass rod with static electricity by rubbing it with a silk cloth. The silk cloth will remove electrons. Produce electrical sparks by holding the rod close to a metallic object. Explain that these sparks consist of electrons attracted by the positively charged rod. Also show that the rod can pick up small bits of paper by electrostatic attraction.

Earth Science Online

Topic: Elements
To find out more about the elements, visit the Earth Science Web Site at earthgeu.com

Activity: Choose three elements. Design a chart that describes how each element was discovered, and its common uses.

Table 3-1 Chemical Symbols of Some Elements

Element	Symbol	Element	Symbol	Element	Symbol
Hydrogen	H	Helium	He	Lithium	Li
Beryllium	Be	Boron	B	Carbon	C
Nitrogen	N	Oxygen	O	Fluorine	F
Neon	Ne	Sodium	Na	Magnesium	Mg
Aluminum	Al	Silicon	Si	Phosphorus	P
Sulfur	S	Chlorine	Cl	Argon	Ar
Potassium	K	Calcium	Ca	Gold	Au
Silver	Ag	Mercury	Hg	Copper	Cu

Sulfur

Mercury

Copper

the element hydrogen, C represents carbon, and O represents oxygen. Elements known in ancient times, such as gold and mercury, have symbols that reflect their Latin origins. For example, gold is identified by the symbol Au, for its Latin name, *aurum*. The chemical symbols of some elements are shown in *Table 3-1*.

ELEMENTS ARE MADE OF ATOMS

Each element has distinct characteristics. You've already learned some of the characteristics of the element gold. Aluminum has different characteristics from gold, but both aluminum and gold are elements that are made up of atoms. An **atom** is the smallest particle of an element that has all of the characteristics of that element.

All atoms consist of even smaller particles: protons, neutrons, and electrons. The center of an atom is called the nucleus (*plural*, nuclei). A **nucleus** of an atom is made up of protons and neutrons. A **proton** (p^+) is a tiny particle that has mass and a positive electrical charge. A **neutron** (n^0) is a particle with about the same mass as a proton, but it is electrically neutral; that is, it has no electrical charge. All atomic nuclei have a positive charge because they are composed of protons with positive electrical charges and neutrons that have no electrical charges.

The number of protons and neutrons in different atoms varies widely. The lightest of all atoms is the hydrogen atom, which has only one proton in its nucleus. The heaviest naturally occurring atoms are those of uranium. Uranium-238 has 92 protons and 146 neutrons in its nucleus. The number of protons in an atom's nucleus is its **atomic number.** The combined number of protons and neutrons is its **mass number.** For example, the atomic number of uranium is 92 and its mass number is 238 (92 + 146). The atomic numbers and mass

Resource Manager

Teaching Transparency 7 L2 ELL
GeoLab and MiniLab Worksheets, p. 9 L2

Across the Curriculum

History In the Middle Ages, alchemists attempted to make gold from other substances through various chemical reactions. All these attempts failed. Have students discuss why trying to obtain gold in this way is impossible. Chemical reactions don't affect the nuclei of elements.

numbers of 14 naturally occurring elements are shown in **Table 3-2.** You can explore the elements that you can find in your classroom in the *MiniLab* on this page. For a complete list of the elements arranged according to their chemical properties, see the Periodic Table of the Elements in *Appendix G* on page 917.

Surrounding the nucleus of an atom are smaller particles called electrons. An **electron** (e^-) has little mass, but it has a negative electrical charge that is exactly the same magnitude as the positive charge of a proton. An atom has an equal number of protons and electrons; thus, the electrical charge of an electron cancels the positive charge of a proton to produce an atom that has no overall charge.

Have you ever let a jawbreaker melt in your mouth? It may have started out as a large, red sphere, but as it melted, you may have observed layers of yellow, green, blue, and so on, until you reached the candy center. If you think of a jawbreaker's candy center as the nucleus of an atom, you can think of the various colored layers as the energy levels where electrons can be found. An **energy level** represents the area in an atom where an electron is most likely to be found.

MiniLab

Identifying Elements

Describe Most substances on Earth occur in the form of chemical compounds. Around your classroom, there are numerous objects or substances that consist mostly of a single element.

Procedure

1. Name three of these objects and the three different elements of which they are made.
2. List the atomic numbers of these elements and describe some of their properties.

Article	Element	Atomic Number	Properties

Analyze and Conclude

1. Matter can be solid, liquid, or gaseous. Give one example of a solid, liquid, and gaseous object or substance.
2. How does a liquid differ from a solid? How does a gas differ from a liquid?

Table 3-2 Atomic Structure of 14 Elements							
Element	Symbol	Atomic Number	Mass Number	Element	Symbol	Atomic Number	Mass Number
Hydrogen	H	1	1	Calcium	Ca	20	40
Helium	He	2	4	Iron	Fe	26	56
Oxygen	O	8	16	Sulfur	S	16	32
Carbon	C	6	12	Sodium	Na	11	23
Neon	Ne	10	20	Chlorine	Cl	17	35
Nitrogen	N	7	14	Potassium	K	19	39
Magnesium	Mg	12	24	Argon	Ar	18	40

MiniLab

Purpose
Students will identify common elements in their surroundings.

Process Skills
collect and interpret data, compare and contrast, classify

Materials
iron or steel tools, file cabinets, keys, paper clips, electrical wires, coins, earrings, metal doorknobs, chrome-plated fixtures, pencils, soft-drink cans, fluorescent lights

Teaching Strategies
Have students work in groups of three. Have the groups exchange their information.

Expected Results
Students will identify the atomic number of several elements as well as objects that contain those elements. Possible answers include iron, atomic number 26: tools, file cabinets, keys, paper clips; copper, atomic number 27: wires, pennies, doorknobs; nickel, atomic number 28: coins (nickels); aluminum, atomic number 13: soft-drink cans; carbon, atomic number 6: pencil lead; chromium, atomic number 24: fixtures; neon, atomic number 10: fluorescent lights.

Analyze and Conclude
1. Some examples include solids: most metals; liquids: mercury, water, and gasoline; and gases: neon, helium, and air.
2. Solids have definite shapes and resist deformation, liquids deform readily and flow, and gases expand and fill all available space.

Knowledge Ask students to describe the physical properties of all the elements investigated in this lab.

Differentiated Instruction

English-Language Learners Ask students to compare the English names of the listed elements in **Tables 3-1** and **3-2** with the names of those elements in their native language. Have students list the elements whose English and non-English names are similar or identical. **ELL**

NY Core Curriculum Standards
Page 54: St 4 KI 3.1a
Page 55: St 4 KI 3.1a

Interpreting the Illustration

Figures 3-1 and 3-2 show conceptual models of atoms. Real atoms do not look like this. The relative sizes of the protons, neutrons, and electrons are greatly exaggerated. For example, the actual size of a proton or neutron is about 10^{-15} m, and the diameter of a hydrogen atom is about 10^{-10} m. If the protons in these atoms are represented by 1-mm spheres, then the model hydrogen atom should have a diameter of about 100 m, roughly the length of a football field. However, scientists aren't sure whether protons are actually spherical.

Content Background

An electron can occupy only specific energy levels. These energy levels are numbered starting with 1 and proceeding to higher numbers. The number of the energy level, *n*, is called the *principal quantum number*. The principal quantum number corresponds to the energy levels 1, 2, 3, and so on. The greatest number of electrons possible in any one level is $2n^2$. Thus, the number of electrons possible in energy level 1 is $2(1)^2 = 2$. The number of electrons possible in energy level 2 is $2(2)^2 = 8$, and so on, to energy level 7, where $2(7)^2 = 98$.

Figure 3-1 Electrons move around the nucleus of an atom.

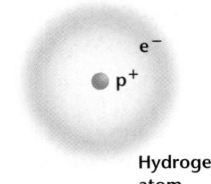

Hydrogen atom

A Hydrogen has just one proton in its nucleus and one electron in its innermost energy level.

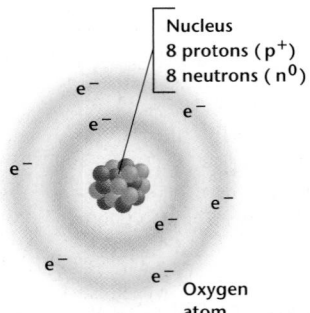

Nucleus
8 protons (p^+)
8 neutrons (n^0)

Oxygen atom

B Oxygen has eight protons and eight neutrons in its nucleus. Two electrons fill the innermost energy level; six electrons are found in the second energy level.

C An aluminum atom has a nucleus that is composed of 13 protons and 13 neutrons. The nucleus is surrounded by 13 electrons.

Figure 3-1 shows models of several atoms with their energy levels represented as cloudlike regions. Notice that the volume of an atom is mostly empty space. Because the electrons have little mass, the *mass* of an atom depends mostly upon the number of protons and neutrons in its nucleus. However, the *size* of an atom depends upon the number and arrangement of its electrons. You can explore how electrons can be used to produce images of objects in the *Science & Technology* feature at the end of this chapter.

ELECTRONS IN ENERGY LEVELS

Study **Figure 3-1**. Note that electrons are distributed over one or more energy levels in a predictable pattern. Each energy level can hold only a limited number of electrons. For example, the smallest, innermost energy level can hold only two electrons, as illustrated by the oxygen atom shown in **Figure 3-1B**. The second energy level is larger, and it can hold up to eight electrons. The third energy level is larger still; it can hold up to 18 electrons. The fourth energy level can hold up to 32 electrons. Depending upon the element, an atom may have electrons in as many as seven energy levels surrounding its nucleus.

Electrons tend to occupy the lowest available energy level. For example, the aluminum (Al) atom in **Figure 3-1C** has 13 protons in its nucleus and 13 electrons in its energy levels. The first energy level in an aluminum atom is filled by two electrons. The second energy level is also filled, by eight electrons. The third energy level has only three electrons, so it is not filled.

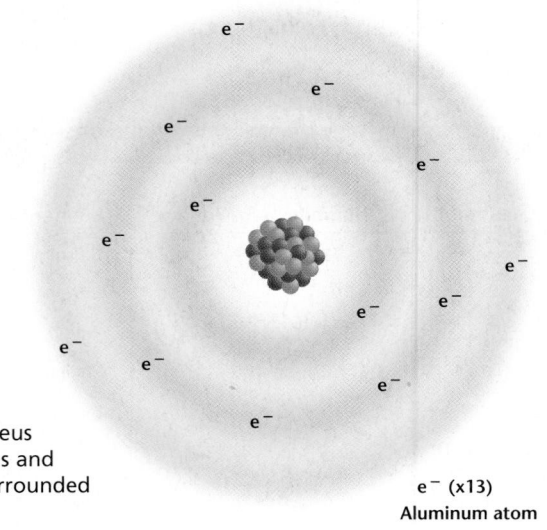

e^- (x13)
Aluminum atom

Across the Curriculum

Biology Our bodies consist mostly of the following elements: oxygen, 65%; carbon, 18.5%; hydrogen, 0.5%; nitrogen, 3.3%; calcium, 1.5%; phosphorus, 1.0%; potassium, 0.4%; sulfur, 0.3%; sodium, 0.2%; chlorine, 0.2%; and magnesium, 0.1%.

Note that four of these elements—oxygen, carbon, hydrogen, and nitrogen—make up over 96 percent of the human body. Most of the oxygen and hydrogen in our bodies is in the form of water. Our bodies contain traces of iron, zinc, copper, iodine, fluorine and many other elements.

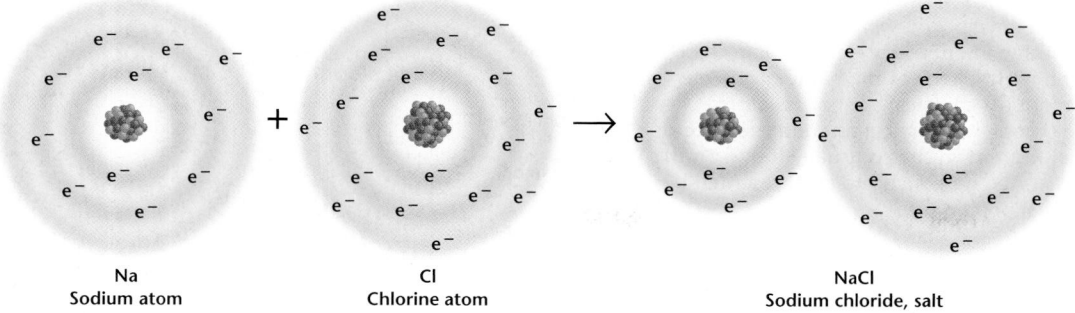

Na
Sodium atom

Cl
Chlorine atom

NaCl
Sodium chloride, salt

Figure 3-2 A sodium (Na) atom, with one valence electron, combines with a chlorine (Cl) atom, with seven valence electrons, to form a common substance, table salt (NaCl). The new substance forms when the sodium atom loses its valence electron to the chlorine atom.

The electrons in the outermost energy level determine the chemical behavior of the different elements. These outermost electrons are called **valence electrons.** Elements with the same number of valence electrons have similar chemical properties. For example, a sodium (Na) atom, with the atomic number 11, and a potassium (K) atom, with the atomic number 19, both have just one valence electron. Thus, both sodium and potassium are highly reactive metals, which means that they combine easily with other elements. *Figure 3-2* illustrates how the common substance table salt is formed when sodium combines with the element chlorine.

Elements such as helium (He), neon (Ne), and argon (Ar) are inert, which means that they do not easily combine with other elements. This is because they have full outermost energy levels. For example, a neon atom has ten electrons in its energy levels. The innermost energy level is filled with two electrons, and the second energy level, which is the outermost energy level, also is filled, with eight electrons. With a filled outermost energy level, neon is unlikely to combine chemically with other elements.

ISOTOPES

You have learned that all atoms of an element have the same number of protons. However, the number of neutrons in the nuclei of an element's atoms can vary. For example, all chlorine atoms have 17 protons in their nuclei, but they may have either 18 or 20 neutrons. This means that there are two types of chlorine atoms: one with a mass number of 35 (17 protons + 18 neutrons) and one with a mass number of 37 (17 protons + 20 neutrons). When atoms of the same

Identifying Misconceptions

A common misconception is that isotopes are radioactive substances.

Uncover the Misconception
Ask students what they think isotopes are. Also ask whether all isotopes are radioactive.

Demonstrate the Concept
Explain that many elements are mixtures of isotopes, and that most isotopes are not radioactive. Examples of radioactive isotopes are the isotopes of uranium. Examples of nonradioactive isotopes are carbon-12 and carbon-13.

Assess New Knowledge
Ask students to define the concept of an isotope and to give examples of nonradioactive isotopes.

Content Background

For many years after their discovery, inert gases were believed to be chemically unreactive. However, in 1962, the first inert compound was synthesized. Because inert compounds can now be made fairly easily, inert gases are now known as the noble gases.

Cultural Diversity

St. Elmo Brady (1884–1966) St. Elmo Brady was the first African-American to earn a Ph.D. in chemistry. He received his bachelor's degree from Fisk University in Tennessee in 1904 and his Ph.D. from the University of Illinois in 1916. His research on the diatomic oxygen molecule contributed greatly to his field. Brady had a long and distinguished academic career and was responsible for creating or greatly improving the science departments of several historically African-American colleges such as Howard and Fisk, where he became head of the chemistry departments and taught both general and organic chemistry. At Tougaloo College in Mississippi, he designed a completely new chemistry program and attracted an outstanding faculty. These are some of the examples of how he established many opportunities for other African-American scientists.

NY Core Curriculum Standards
Page 56: St 4 KI 3.1a
Page 57: St 1 Math KI 2

Content Background

The radioactive isotope U-238 decays by alpha decay to Th-234. However, Th-234 is also radioactive and decays by beta decay to Pa-235. Pa-235 is also radioactive and decays further. The result is a so-called radioactive decay chain (with eight alpha-decay and six beta-decay steps) that ends with the stable (nonradioactive) isotope Pb-206. A similar decay chain with seven alpha-decay and four beta-decay steps starts with U-235 and ends with Pb-207. Radioactive radon is an intermediate decay product of these decay chains.

Using Math

Uranium-235 contains 92 protons and 143 neutrons. Subtracting 2 protons and 2 neutrons (in the helium-4 nucleus) leaves 90 protons and 141 neutrons. The new element, thorium, has the atomic number 90.

Environmental Connection

The inert gas radon is radioactive. It is produced by the radioactive decay of uranium in soil and bedrock. Radon gas is heavier than air, and in some areas, it seeps into and accumulates in basements of houses. High concentrations of radioactive radon have been linked to cancer.

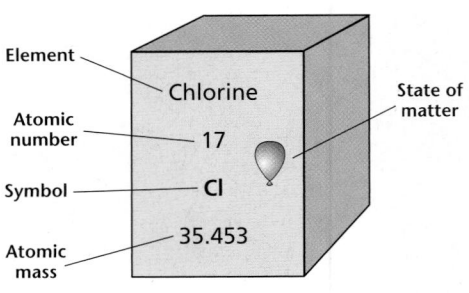

Figure 3-3 The Periodic Table of the Elements in *Appendix G* provides information about every element. Each block on the table gives the name of the element, its chemical symbol, its atomic number, its atomic mass, and the state of matter in which it is usually found. In this text, the gaseous state is represented by a balloon.

Using Math

Using Numbers As the radioactive isotope uranium-235 (atomic number 92) decays, it emits two protons and two neutrons. How many protons and neutrons are left in the nucleus after these neutrons and protons have been ejected? What is the atom's new atomic number? What is the name of this element?

element have different mass numbers, they are known as **isotopes** of that element. The element chlorine has two isotopes: chlorine-35 and chlorine-37. Naturally occurring chlorine is a mixture of these two isotopes. Many elements are mixtures of isotopes. Because the number of electrons in an atom equals the number of protons, isotopes of an element have the same chemical properties.

If many elements are mixtures of isotopes, how do scientists know how many neutrons are found in an element's atoms? Scientists have measured the mass of atoms of elements and found an average atomic mass for each element. The **atomic mass** of an element is the average of the mass numbers of the isotopes of an element. For example, in *Figure 3-3,* note that the atomic mass of chlorine is 35.453. This number is the average of the mass numbers of the naturally occurring isotopes of chlorine-35 and chlorine-37.

The nuclei of some isotopes are unstable and release radiation. **Radioactivity** is the spontaneous process through which unstable nuclei emit radiation. During radioactive decay, a nucleus can lose protons and neutrons, change a proton to a neutron, or change a neutron to a proton. Because the number of protons in a nucleus identifies an element, decay changes the identity of an element. For example, the isotope uranium-238 decays over time into lead-206, so uranium originally present in a rock gradually and predictably is replaced by lead. By measuring the amount of uranium and lead in rocks, scientists can calculate their age. You will find out more about the radioactive dating of rocks in Chapter 21.

WHAT ELEMENTS ARE MOST ABUNDANT?

Astronomers have identified the two most abundant elements in the universe as hydrogen and helium. All other elements account for less than one percent of all atoms in the universe, as you can see in *Figure 3-4A.* Analyses of the composition of rocks and minerals on Earth indicate that the percentages of elements in Earth's crust

Differentiated Instruction

Gifted Have students research how U-238 or U-235 decays to Pb-206 or Pb-207, respectively. Have them report their findings in the form of a decay chain, including intermediate radioisotopes as well as alpha-decay and beta-decay steps, to the class. **L3**

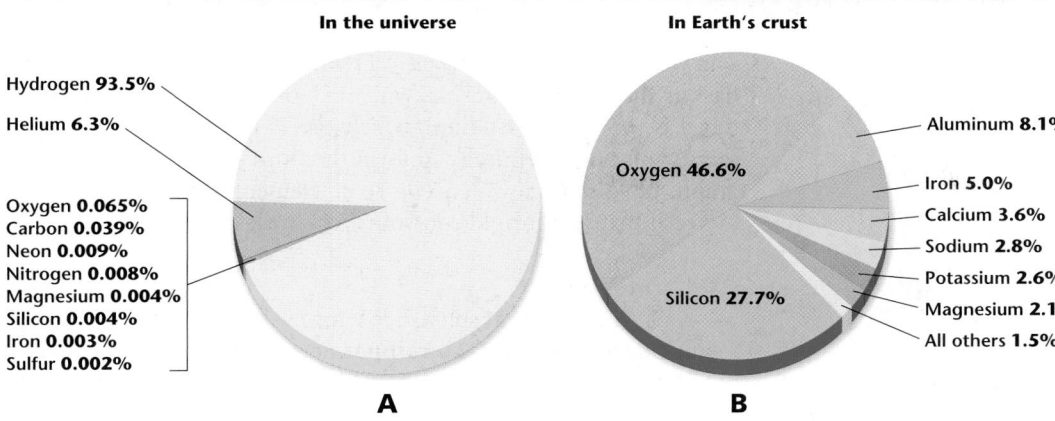

Abundance of Elements

In the universe

Hydrogen **93.5%**
Helium **6.3%**
Oxygen **0.065%**
Carbon **0.039%**
Neon **0.009%**
Nitrogen **0.008%**
Magnesium **0.004%**
Silicon **0.004%**
Iron **0.003%**
Sulfur **0.002%**

A

In Earth's crust

Aluminum **8.1%**
Oxygen **46.6%**
Iron **5.0%**
Calcium **3.6%**
Sodium **2.8%**
Potassium **2.6%**
Silicon **27.7%**
Magnesium **2.1%**
All others **1.5%**

B

Figure 3-4 The most abundant elements in the universe are hydrogen and helium **(A)**. The most abundant elements in Earth's crust are oxygen, silicon, and aluminum **(B)**.

differ from the percentages in the universe. The circle graph in *Figure 3-4B* shows the percentages of elements in Earth's crust. Note that 98.5 percent of Earth's crust is made up of only eight elements, and that two elements, oxygen and silicon, account for almost 75 percent of the crust. This means that most of the rocks and minerals on Earth contain oxygen and silicon. You might wonder how rocks can contain oxygen, as you usually think of oxygen as a gas in the atmosphere. Oxygen is a reactive element that is mostly found in chemical combinations with other elements. In the next section, you'll learn how elements combine to form compounds.

SECTION ASSESSMENT

1. Name the three particles that make up an atom of an element and discuss their relative masses.

2. The elements magnesium and calcium have similar chemical properties. Explain why.

3. The atomic mass for the element carbon (C) is 12.011. Explain how this number indicates that carbon is a mixture of isotopes. What is the mass number of the most common, naturally occurring isotope of carbon?

4. **Thinking Critically** Oxygen is often found in chemical combinations with other

elements, such as magnesium. Using the concepts of valence electrons and energy levels, explain why oxygen might combine easily with magnesium.

SKILL REVIEW

5. **Applying Concepts** The element copper (Cu) has 29 electrons. Draw a diagram of an atom of copper that shows the placement of its electrons in the correct energy levels and the number of protons it has. For more help, refer to the *Skill Handbook*.

earthgeu.com/self_check_quiz

Check for Understanding
Reinforcement
Ask students the following questions. How many protons, neutrons, and electrons are in a sodium-23 atom? 11 protons, 12 neutrons, 11 electrons Which energy levels are those electrons in? 2 in innermost energy level, 8 in next energy level, 13 in outermost energy level

Reteach
Ask students to explain how isotopes, for example He-3 and He-4, differ from each other, and why they have the same chemical behavior. **L2**

Assessment

Skill Have students draw models of the electron configurations of the first 12 elements in the periodic table. Ask them to compare and contrast the models and to record their work in their science journals.

SECTION ASSESSMENT

1. Protons, neutrons, and electrons; protons and neutrons have about equal masses; electrons have negligible masses.

2. Both magnesium and calcium have two valence electrons.

3. The atomic mass is the average of the mass numbers of the isotopes of an element. If all carbon atoms had the same mass numbers, the atomic mass would be a whole number. With an atomic mass of 12.011, carbon's most common naturally occurring isotope must be carbon-12.

4. Students should be able to identify that magnesium, atomic number 12, has two valence electrons, whereas oxygen, atomic number 8, has 6 valence electrons. Magnesium loses its two electrons to become a positive ion, Mg^{2+}. Oxygen gains two electrons and becomes a negative ion, O^{2-}. The new ionic compound is MgO.

5. Student drawings should indicate that copper has 2, 8, and 18 electrons in the first, second, and third energy levels, respectively, and 1 electron in its fourth energy level.

NY Core Curriculum Standards
Page 58: St 4 KI 3.1b & 3.1c
Page 59: St 4 KI 3.1a & 3.1c

Section Background

For section content background, refer to **The Formation of Ions** on pages 52C–D.

Preplanning

Refer to the Chapter Organizer on pages 52A–B.

1 Focus

Section Focus

Before presenting the lesson, display **Section Focus Transparency 8** on the overhead projector.
L1 **ELL**

8 MIXTURES
Use with Chapter 3, Section 3.2

❶ How many substances were used to make this building? Name some of these substances.

❷ How many substances make up the ocean water? Name some of these substances.

Section Focus Transparency   Earth Science: Geology, the Environment, and the Universe

Demo

Visual-Spatial Wear safety goggles and use a safety shield for this demo. Fill an inverted 100-mL beaker with one part hydrogen and three parts air. Carefully ignite the mixture—it will explode! Let the beaker cool. Ask students what the liquid condensate is. Explain that the oxygen and hydrogen atoms combined to form water. **ELL**

SECTION 3.2 *How Atoms Combine*

OBJECTIVES

• **Describe** *the chemical bonds that unite atoms to form compounds.*

• **Relate** *the nature of chemical bonds that hold compounds together to the physical structures of compounds.*

• **Distinguish** *among different types of mixtures and solutions.*

VOCABULARY

compound
chemical bond
covalent bond
molecule
ion
ionic bond
chemical reaction
solution
acid
base

Can you identify the materials in *Figure 3-5?* The greenish gas in the flask is the element chlorine, which is poisonous. The solid, silvery metal is the element sodium, which also is toxic. Yet these two elements combine chemically to form the third material in the photograph: table salt. How can two toxic elements combine to form a material that you sprinkle on your french fries?

COMPOUNDS

Table salt is a common substance. However, table salt is not an element, but a compound. A **compound** is a substance that is composed of atoms of two or more different elements that are chemically combined. Water is another example of a compound, because it is composed of two elements, hydrogen and oxygen. Most compounds have totally different properties from the elements of which they are composed. For example, both oxygen and hydrogen are gases at room temperature, but in combination they form water, a liquid.

For most elements, an atom is chemically stable when its outermost energy level is full. We know this is true because the most stable elements are the gases helium, neon, and argon. A state of stability is achieved by other elements through **chemical bonds,** which are the forces that hold the elements together in a compound.

Covalent Bonds One way in which atoms fill their outermost energy levels is by sharing electrons. For example, two hydrogen atoms can combine with each other by sharing electrons. Individual atoms of hydrogen each have just one electron. Each atom becomes more stable when it shares its electron with another hydrogen atom so that each atom has two electrons in its outermost energy level. How do these two atoms stay together? The nucleus of each atom has one proton with a positive charge, and the two positively charged protons attract the two negatively charged electrons. This attraction of two atoms for a shared pair of electrons that holds the atoms together is called a **covalent bond.**

Figure 3-5 Two elements, sodium and chlorine, combine chemically to form table salt, a compound also known as halite.

Resource Manager

Study Guide for Content Mastery, pp. 17–18 **L2**

Section Focus Transparency 8 **L1** **ELL**

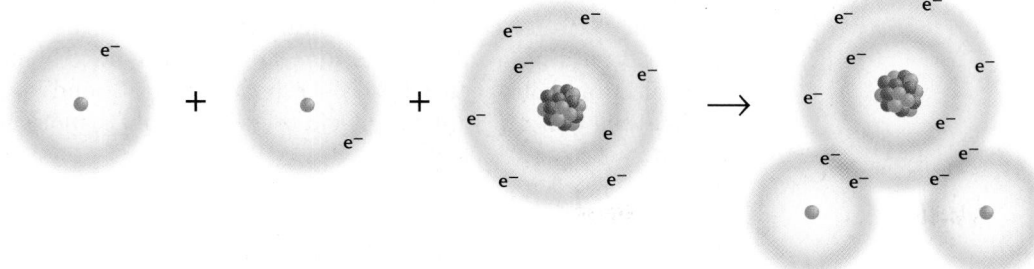

Figure 3-6 A water molecule forms when two hydrogen atoms share electrons with one oxygen atom by covalent bonding.

A **molecule** is composed of two or more atoms held together by covalent bonds. Molecules have no overall electrical charge because the total number of electrons equals the total number of protons. Molecules are represented in chemistry by chemical formulas that include the symbol for each element followed by a subscript number that stands for the number of atoms of that element in the molecule. If there is only one atom of an element, no subscript number follows the symbol. The chemical formula for hydrogen gas is written H_2 because two atoms of hydrogen make up one molecule of hydrogen gas. Water is an example of a compound whose atoms are held together by covalent bonds, as illustrated in *Figure 3-6.* The chemical formula for a water molecule is H_2O because, in this molecule, two atoms of hydrogen are combined with one atom of oxygen. A compound comprised of molecules is called a molecular compound.

Polar Molecules Although water molecules are held together by covalent bonds, the atoms do not share electrons equally. As shown in *Figure 3-7,* the shared electrons in a water molecule are attracted

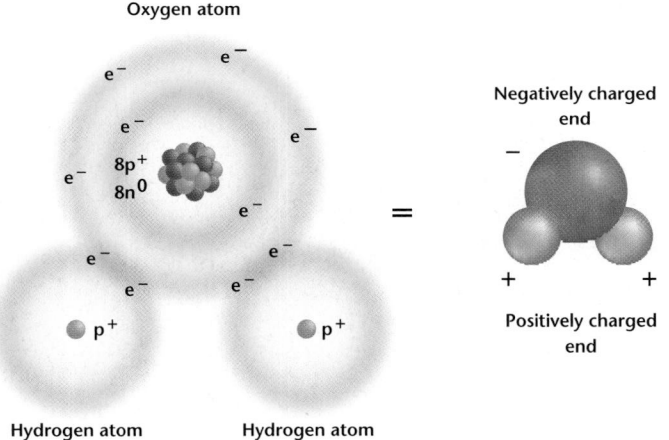

Oxygen atom

$8p^+$
$8n^0$

Hydrogen atom   Hydrogen atom

=

Negatively charged end

Positively charged end

Figure 3-7 At one end of a water molecule, the hydrogen atoms have a positive charge, while at the opposite end, the oxygen atom has a negative charge.

3.2 *How Atoms Combine* **61**

Interpreting the illustration

Figure 3-6 illustrates covalent bonding. For the atoms in a covalent compound to share electrons, their outermost energy levels must overlap.

Content Background

Inert gases have either full outer energy levels or eight electrons (filled s and p subshells) in their outer energy levels. Other elements are stable if they have the same electron configuration as the nearest inert gas in the periodic table. Such a configuration can be achieved by the gain or loss of electrons (the formation of ions) or by the sharing of electrons (covalent bonding). For instance, the ions O^{2-}, F^-, Na^+, Mg^{2+}, and Al^{3+} and the inert gas Ne all have the same electron configuration: two electrons in the first energy level and eight electrons in the second (outer) energy level.

Concept Development

There are two accepted definitions of the term *molecule.* The smallest unit of a compound with the properties of that compound is sometimes called a molecule. However, ionic compounds don't consist of molecules. More precisely, molecules are basic units consisting of two or more atoms bound together by covalent bonds, such as H_2O. These molecules can exist in the solid, liquid, or gaseous state. Solids consisting of such "real" molecules are called molecular compounds. This is not the same as a covalent compound, in which all the atoms are held together by covalent bonds, as in diamond. In molecular compounds, the molecules are held together by other, weaker bonds, such as hydrogen bonds in ice.

NY Core Curriculum Standards

Page 60: St 6 KI 4
Page 61: St 6 KI 2

Concept Development

A silicate ion consists of a small silicon (Si^{4+}) ion surrounded by four large oxygen (O^{2-}) ions in the form of a tetrahedron. The net charge of a silicate ion is, therefore, −4 (+4 −2 −2 −2 −2). Silicate ions are the building blocks of most of Earth's minerals. They are discussed further in the next chapter.

Modeling

Kinesthetic Have students build models of a silicate ion and a sodium chloride crystal (with 64 ions) out of large and small plastic foam spheres. The large NaCl crystal could be assembled from eight subcrystals, each containing eight ions built by several (up to eight) groups of students. **L2** **ELL**

Content Background

Chemical formulas of compounds follow the convention of writing the symbol(s) of the positive (metal) ion(s) first, and the symbol(s) of the negative ion(s) last, for exampe, NaCl, not ClNa, and Mg_2SiO_4, not SiO_4Mg_2.

Activity

Logical-Mathematical Have students analyze the following chemical formulas: NaCl, $MgCl_2$, CaO, K_2O, Al_2O_3, Fe_2O_3, $CaCO_3$, and Mg_2SiO_4. Have students list the chemical symbols and the charges of the positive and negative ions involved. This activity could also be a collaborative learning exercise or a homework assignment. **L2**

---

more strongly by the oxygen atom than by the hydrogen atoms. As a result, the electrons spend more time near the oxygen atom than they do near the hydrogen atoms. When atoms in a covalent bond do not share electrons equally, they form polar bonds. A polar bond has a positive end and a negative end. The overall shape of a molecule indicates whether it is polar.

IONS

Not all atoms bond by sharing electrons. Sometimes, atoms gain or lose electrons from their outermost energy levels. An atom that gains or loses an electron is a charged particle called an **ion.** In general, an atom in which the outermost energy level is less than half-full—that is, it has fewer than four valence electrons—tends to lose its valence electrons. When an atom loses its valence electrons, it becomes positively charged. In chemistry, a positive ion is indicated by a superscript plus sign. For example, a sodium ion is represented by Na^+. If an ion results from the loss of more than one electron, the number of electrons lost is placed before the plus sign. A magnesium ion, which forms when a magnesium atom has lost two electrons, is thus represented by Mg^{2+}.

An atom in which the outermost energy level is more than half-full—that is, it has more than four valence electrons—tends to fill its outermost energy level by adding one or more needed electrons. Such an atom forms a negative ion. By including additional electrons, negative ions, such as O^{2-} and Cl^-, tend to be larger than positive ions. If the outermost energy level is exactly half-full, an atom may form either a positive or negative ion.

Some compounds contain ions made up of covalently bonded atoms. Two such compounds that are important in forming the materials at Earth's surface are silicate ions (SiO_4^{4-}) and carbonate ions (CO_3^{2-}).

Figure 3-8 The positive charge of a sodium ion attracts the negative charge of a chlorine ion. The two ions are held together by an ionic bond. Note that the negative chlorine ion is slightly larger than the positive sodium ion.

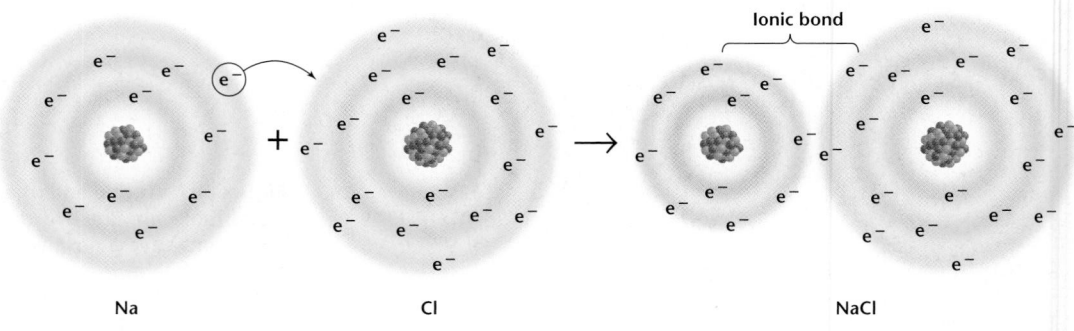

Na   Cl   NaCl

Differentiated Instruction

Visually Impaired Have students with visual impairments handle the plastic foam models constructed in the Modeling activity above. Explain the role of the different-sized spheres to them. **L1** **ELL**

Resource Manager

Teaching Transparency 8 **L2** **ELL**

Ionic Bonds As you might expect, positive and negative ions attract each other. The attractive force between two ions of opposite charge is known as an **ionic bond.** *Figure 3-8* illustrates an ionic bond between a positive ion of sodium and a negative ion of chlorine. Common table salt (NaCl) consists of equal numbers of sodium (Na^+) ions and chlorine (Cl^-) ions. Note that positive ions are always written first in chemical formulas.

Within the compound NaCl, there are as many positive as negative ions; therefore, the positive charge on the sodium ion cancels the negative charge on the chloride ion, and the net electrical charge of the compound NaCl is zero. Magnesium and oxygen ions combine in a similar manner to form the compound magnesium oxide (MgO), one of the most common compounds on Earth. Compounds formed by ionic bonding are known as ionic compounds. You can determine if elements form ionic compounds in the *Problem-Solving Lab* on this page.

Other ionic compounds have different proportions of ions. For example, oxygen and sodium ions combine in the ratio shown by the chemical formula for sodium monoxide, Na_2O, in which there are two sodium ions to each oxygen ion. With any other ratio of sodium ions and oxygen ions, the electrical charges wouldn't cancel, as you can prove by adding up the ionic charges.

Problem-Solving Lab

Interpreting Scientific Illustrations

Forming compounds Many atoms gain or lose electrons in order to have eight electrons in the outermost energy level. In the diagram, energy levels are indicated by the circles around the nucleus of each element. The colored spheres in the energy levels represent electrons, and the spheres in the nucleus represent protons and neutrons.

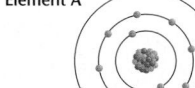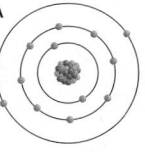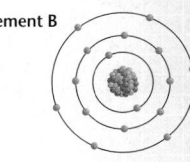

Element A   Element B

Analysis

1. What is the name and symbol of element A?
2. What is the name and symbol of element B?
3. How many electrons are present in atoms of element A? Element B?

Thinking Critically

4. Can these elements form ions? If so, how many protons would be present in the nuclei of these ions? What would be the electrical charges (magnitude and sign) and chemical symbols of these ions?
5. Can these two elements form a compound? If so, what is the chemical formula of the compound?

Problem-Solving Lab

Purpose
Students will identify the formation of positive and negative ions, and of ionic compounds.

Process Skills
compare and contrast, predict, communicate

Materials
pencil, paper

Teaching Strategies
Discuss the formation of ions before assigning this lab. Have students use the periodic table to get started.

Analysis
1. magnesium, Mg
2. sulfur, S
3. A: 12 electrons; B: 16 electrons

Thinking Critically
4. Yes. A has 12 protons; it loses 2 electrons and thus becomes a positive ion; Mg^{2+}. B has 16 protons; it gains 2 electrons and thus becomes a negative ion; S^{2-}.
5. yes; MgS

✓Assessment

Skill Ask students to draw model diagrams of magnesium and sulfur ions, and of argon atoms. Have them do the same with sodium, fluorine, and neon for homework.

Demo

Visual-Spatial Ionic compounds are characterized by high melting points, whereas covalent compounds are characterized by low melting points. Demonstrate the difference between these two types of compounds by melting salt, an ionic compound, and solid shortening, a covalent compound. Wear safety goggles, an apron, and heat-resistant gloves and use a safety shield for this demonstration. Place a small amount of each substance on the end of a metal spatula and place it in the flame of a laboratory burner. Salt does not melt at this temperature, but solid shortening does. Point out that ionic bonds give substances the property of high melting points.

METALLIC BONDS

Most compounds on Earth are held together by ionic or covalent bonds, or by a combination of these two types of bonds. However, there are other types of bonds. In metals, for example, the valence electrons are shared by all the atoms, not just by adjacent atoms, as in covalent compounds. You could think of a metal as a group of positive ions floating in a sea of negative electrons. The positive ions of the metal are held together by the negative electrons between them. This type of bond, known as a metallic bond, allows metals to conduct electricity because the electrons can move freely throughout the entire solid metal.

CHEMICAL REACTIONS

You have learned that atoms gain, lose, or share electrons to become more stable, and that these atoms form compounds. Sometimes, compounds break down into simpler substances. The change of one or more substances into other substances is called a **chemical reaction.** Chemical reactions are described by chemical equations. For example, water is formed by the chemical reaction between hydrogen gas (H_2) and oxygen gas (O_2). The formation of water can be described by the following equation.

$$2H_2 + O_2 \rightarrow 2H_2O$$

Figure 3-9 Rust, shown magnified in the top photo, forms on metals that contain iron when they are exposed to moist air.

Magnification 680×

A chemist reads this chemical equation as "Two molecules of hydrogen and one molecule of oxygen react to yield two molecules of water." In this reaction, hydrogen and oxygen are the reactants, and water is the product. When you write a chemical equation, you must balance the equation by showing an equal number of atoms for each element on each side of the equation. This is because the same amount of matter is present both before and after the reaction. Note that there are four hydrogen atoms on each side of the above equation ($2 + 2 = 4$). There are also two oxygen atoms on each side of the reaction.

Another example of a chemical reaction, one that takes place between iron (Fe) and oxygen (O), is represented by the following chemical equation.

$$4Fe + 3O_2 \rightarrow 2Fe_2O_3$$

This reaction forms the mineral hematite, an important iron ore. You may be more familiar with another form of this compound shown in *Figure 3-9*—rust!

64 CHAPTER 3 *Matter and Atomic Structure*

Resource Manager

Laboratory Manual, pp. 21–24 **L2**

Exploring Environmental Problems, pp. 25–28 **L2**

MIXTURES AND SOLUTIONS

Unlike a compound, in which the constituent atoms combine and lose their identities, a *mixture* is a combination of two or more components that retain their identities. When a mixture's components are easily recognizable, it is called a heterogeneous mixture. For example, soil, as shown in *Figure 3-10A*, is a heterogeneous mixture because its components are still recognizable: bits of minerals such as quartz and feldspar, clay particles, fragments of plants, and so on. In contrast, in a homogeneous mixture, the component particles cannot be distinguished, even though they still retain their original properties. Brewed coffee is an example of a homogeneous mixture, which is also called a **solution.**

A solution may be liquid, gaseous, or solid. Seawater is a liquid solution consisting of water molecules and ions of many elements that exist on Earth. You will investigate liquid solutions in the *GeoLab* at the end of this chapter. Magma is also a liquid solution; it is composed of ions representing all atoms that were present in the crystals of the rock before it melted. Air is a solution of gases, mostly nitrogen and oxygen molecules together with other atoms and molecules. Metal alloys, such as bronze and brass, are also solutions. Bronze is a homogeneous mixture of copper and tin atoms; brass is a similar mixture of copper and zinc atoms. Such solid homogeneous mixtures are called *solid solutions.* You will learn more about solid solutions in Chapters 4 and 5.

Acids and Bases Many chemical reactions that occur on Earth involve solutions called acids and bases. An **acid** is a solution containing a substance that produces hydrogen ions (H^+) in water. Recall that a hydrogen atom consists of one proton and one electron. When a hydrogen atom loses its electron, it becomes simply a proton. The most common acid in our environment is carbonic acid, which is produced when carbon dioxide is dissolved in water by the following reaction.

$$H_2O + CO_2 \longrightarrow H_2CO_3$$

Some of the carbonic acid molecules in the water dissociate, or break apart, into hydrogen ions and bicarbonate ions, as represented by the following equation.

$$H_2CO_3 \longrightarrow H^+ + HCO_3^-$$

These two equations play a major role in the dissolution and precipitation of limestone and the formation of caves, discussed in Chapter 10. Many of the reaction rates involved in geological

Figure 3-10 Soil is a heterogeneous mixture in which the component parts are easily recognizable **(A).** Coffee is a homogeneous mixture, called a solution, in which the component parts cannot be distinguished **(B).**

ENVIRONMENTAL CONNECTION

Discussion

Have students draw model diagrams of the following ions: Na^+, Li^+, and H^+. Have them discuss their diagrams, specifically their H^+ models. Ask students what the difference is between the H^+ ion and the other ions. The H^+ ion has no electrons. Ask students exactly what an H^+ ion is. a proton Then ask what makes it so extremely reactive. Because of its small size, it can penetrate and disrupt any structure.

Enrichment

One of the reactions most important to our environment is photosynthesis, the conversion of water and carbon dioxide into sugar and free oxygen by green plants using the energy of sunlight:
$6H_2O + 6CO_2 \rightarrow C_6H_{12}O_6 + 6O_2$.
Have students check this equation for proper balancing, research the role of photosynthesis in the development of Earth's present atmosphere, and present their findings to the class.

Content Background

Double arrows in chemical equations signify that chemical reactions can go in either direction. For instance, even as CO_2 and H_2O combine to form carbonic acid molecules, some of these H_2CO_3 molecules break apart into CO_2 and H_2O molecules.

Earth Science
Journal

Seawater is a solution that contains many different salts. Have students research and list the six most abundant ions in seawater (Cl^-, Na^+, SO_4^{2-}, Mg^{2+}, Ca^{2+}, and K^+) and their relative abundances. Also ask students to name several possible ionic compounds that could form when seawater evaporates, and to write their formulas.

NY Core Curriculum Standards

Page 64: St 6 KI 4 & 5
Page 65: St 4 KI 3.1b

Reinforcement
Ask students the following questions. What does the superscript in Ca^{2+} mean? The superscript 2+ means that this calcium ion has lost two valence electrons. What do the superscript and subscript in CO_3^{2-} mean? The subscript means that this compound is formed by one carbon and three oxygen atoms. The superscript means that the compound acts as an ion that has gained two electrons. What is the chemical formula of calcium carbonate? $CaCO_3$

Reteach

Starting with the atomic number of calcium, explain to students the electron structure and the number of valence electrons of calcium, as well as the formation of a calcium ion and its charge. Do the same thing for the element chlorine. Explain the chemical equation that shows the formation of calcium chloride: $Ca^{2+} + 2Cl^- \rightarrow CaCl_2$.

Assessment

Knowledge Have students determine what ions are formed by oxygen, sodium, and magnesium. O^{2-}, Na^+, and Mg^{2+} Also have them determine the formulas of sodium and magnesium oxide. Na_2O and MgO Have students explain the step-by-step procedure used in these determinations and record all of their responses in their science journals. L2

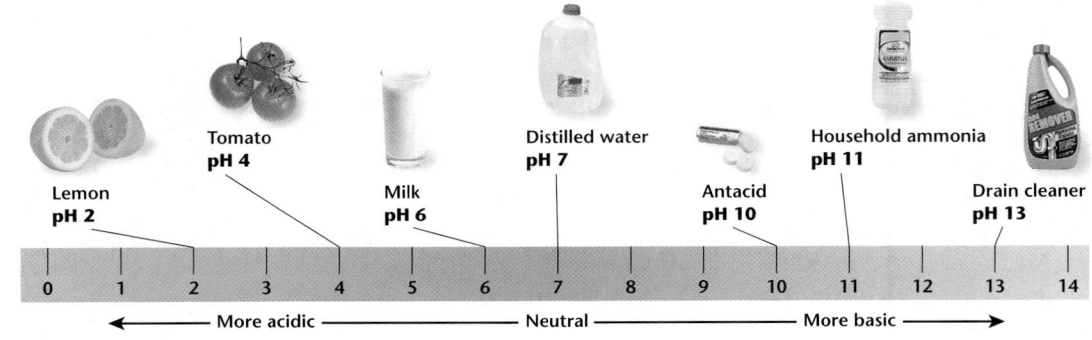

Figure 3-11 The pH values of some common substances are shown on this scale. Treated pH paper can be used to determine the acidity of a solution.

processes are exceedingly slow. For example, it may take thousands of years for the carbonic acid in groundwater to break down limestone to form a cave.

Bases produce hydroxide ions (OH^-) in solution. A base can neutralize an acid by combining with hydrogen ions of the acid to form water through the following reaction.

$$H^+ + OH^- \longrightarrow H_2O$$

The pH scale measures the hydrogen and hydroxide ions in solutions, with 7 being neutral. A solution with a pH reading below 7 is considered to be acidic. The lower the number, the more acidic the solution is. A solution with a reading above 7 is considered to be basic. The higher the number, the more basic the solution is. Distilled water usually has a pH of 7, but rainwater is slightly acidic, having a pH of 5.0 to 5.6. The pH values of some common substances are shown in **Figure 3-11**.

SECTION ASSESSMENT

1. What is the smallest unit of a molecular compound with the properties of that compound?

2. Why are negative ions usually larger than positive ions?

3. Explain why molecules held together by covalent bonds don't have electrical charges.

4. **Thinking Critically** Whole milk consists of microscopic fat globules suspended in a solution of nutrients. Is milk a homogeneous or a heterogeneous mixture? Explain.

SKILL REVIEW

5. **Predicting** What kind of bond forms between the nitrogen atoms and hydrogen atoms in ammonia (NH_3)? For more help, refer to the *Skill Handbook*.

earthgeu.com/self_check_quiz

SECTION ASSESSMENT

1. a molecule
2. Negative ions have more electrons than comparable positive ions do.
3. Individual molecules contain as many electrons as protons.

4. Milk is a heterogeneous mixture. Milk fat is in the form of fat globules, not molecules.
5. covalent bond; nitrogen shares the three valence electrons of the hydrogen atoms

SECTION 3.3 *States of Matter*

An iceberg floating in the ocean beneath a blue sky not only captures the beauty of nature, but it also illustrates three states of matter found on Earth. Matter may be solid, like the iceberg; liquid, like the ocean; or gaseous, like the water vapor in the air. But are these the only states in which matter can exist? At room temperature and standard atmospheric pressure, matter normally exists in one of these three states. However, there is another state of matter found on Earth, called plasma, which you will learn more about later in this section.

SOLIDS

What do ice crystals, table-salt crystals, and diamonds have in common? All of these substances are solids, and all of them form crystals. Solids are substances with densely packed particles, which may be ions, atoms, or molecules, depending upon the substance. The particles of a solid are arranged in a definite pattern; thus, a solid has both a definite shape and a definite volume. Most solids have a **crystalline structure,** in which the particles are arranged in regular geometric patterns, as illustrated in *Figure 3-12.* Crystals form symmetrical solid objects with flat faces and straight edges between faces. The angles between the faces depend upon the internal arrangement of the particles. For example, vanadium and quartz crystals look different from table-salt crystals because of the different internal arrangements of their particles. Magnesium, quartz, and many other substances have hexagonal crystals.

Figure 3-12 Crystals of table salt are cubic, whereas vanadium crystals are hexagonal.

Salt crystals

Chlorine
Sodium (Na)

Magnification: 290×

Vanadium crystals

Vanadium (V)

Magnification: 1×

OBJECTIVES

- **Describe** *the states of matter on Earth.*
- **Explain** *the reasons that matter exists in these states.*
- **Relate** *the role of thermal energy to changes of state in matter.*

VOCABULARY

crystalline structure
glass
evaporation
sublimation
plasma
condensation

Section 3.3

Prepare

Section Background

For section content background, refer to **States of Matter** on page 52D.

Preplanning

Refer to the Chapter Organizer on pages 52A–B.

1 Focus

Section Focus

Before presenting the lesson, display **Section Focus Transparency 9** on the overhead projector.
L1 ELL

Project

Interpersonal Have student groups research the properties of metals, including melting and boiling points, crystal type, and uses. Have each group display a poster of its results. L2 COOP LEARN P

NY Core Curriculum Standards

Page 66: St 6 KI 5
Page 67: St 4 KI 3.1a & 3.1b

Differentiated Instruction

Learning Disabled Have students arrange marbles in a neat, hexagonal pattern in a saucepan or similar container. Tell them that this is the way atoms are arranged in solids, such as magnesium. Next, have students shake the container so that the marbles roll around randomly, and explain that the marbles represent atoms in a liquid. Then have students stop shaking the container so that the marbles come to rest in a disorderly pattern. Explain to students that this pattern represents atoms in a glass. L1

Resource Manager

Study Guide for Content Mastery, pp. 19–20 L2

Section Focus Transparency 9 L1 ELL

Activity

 **Interpersonal** Have students wear safety goggles and aprons for this activity. Divide students into small groups. Give each group a small beaker that contains a small amount of water and an ice cube. Have a student from each group measure the temperature of the water in the beaker. Have students record their data in a table with these headings: Group, Time, Temperature, and Ice? (Y or N). Have the class discuss the results. Water temperature should stay near 0°C until the ice melts.

L1 **COOP LEARN**

Content Background

Many students may be unfamiliar with the concept of heat. Explain to students that temperature is not heat. Temperature is a measure of the average kinetic energy of the vibrating or moving atoms or molecules in a substance. Higher temperatures correspond to more vigorous motion. The lowest possible temperature, absolute zero, is the temperature at which all atomic motion stops. Heat, on the other hand, is the total kinetic energy of all atoms and molecules in a material. An iceberg, therefore, contains more heat than a small, red-hot piece of iron.

Enrichment

The Fahrenheit scale of temperature measurement, still used in this country, was invented in Germany by Gabriel D. Fahrenheit (1686–1736). Have interested students research the origins of the Fahrenheit and Celsius scales and the relationship between the scales. Have students record their research in their science journals and present their findings in class.

Figure 3-13 Granite, which is abundant in Earth's crust, is a mass of intergrown crystals.

Figure 3-14 Because the particles in liquids slide past each other, liquids have no definite shape **(A)**. Dry ice, which is solid carbon dioxide (CO_2), sublimates from a solid directly into a gas **(B)**.

A

B

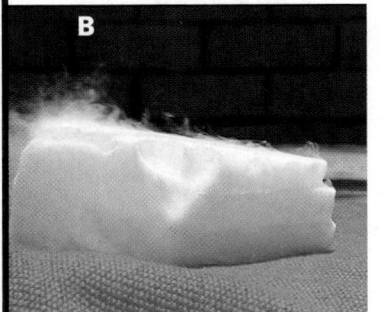

Well-formed crystals are rare. When many crystals form in the same space at the same time, mutual interference prevents the formation of regular crystals with smooth boundaries. The result is a mass of intergrown crystals, called a polycrystalline solid. Most solid substances on Earth, including rocks, are polycrystalline materials. *Figure 3-13* shows the polycrystalline nature of the rock granite.

Some solid materials have no regular internal patterns. **Glasses** are solids that consist of densely packed atoms arranged at random. Glasses form when molten material is chilled so rapidly that atoms don't have enough time to arrange themselves into a regular pattern. These solids do not form crystals, or their crystals are so small that they cannot be seen. Window glass consists mostly of disordered silicon and oxygen with the chemical composition SiO_2.

LIQUIDS

At any temperature above absolute zero ($-273°C$), the atoms in solids vibrate. Because these vibrations increase with increasing temperature, they are called thermal vibrations. At the melting point of the material, these vibrations become sufficiently vigorous to break the forces holding the solid together. The particles can then slide past each other, and the substance becomes liquid. Liquids do not have their own shape; they take the shape of the container they are placed in, as you can see in *Figure 3-14A.* However, liquids do have definite volume.

GASES

The particles in liquids vibrate vigorously, and individual particles may gain sufficient energy to escape the liquid. This process of change from a liquid to a gas is called **evaporation,** or vaporization. When any liquid reaches its boiling point, it vaporizes quickly and becomes a gas. However, some evaporation takes place even below the boiling point. In fact, thermal vibrations can enable individual atoms or molecules to escape even from a solid. You may have noticed that even on winter days with temperatures below freezing, snow gradually disappears. This slow change of state from a solid, ice crystals, to a gas, water vapor, without an intermediate liquid state is called **sublimation,** as illustrated in *Figure 3-14B.*

In gases, the particles are separated by relatively large distances and move about at extremely high speeds. Gas particles move independently of each other and travel randomly. They travel in one direction until they bump into another gas particle or the walls of a container. Gases, like liquids, have no definite shape. Gases also have no definite volume and can expand into any space available, unless they are restrained by a container or a force such as gravity. Earth's gravity keeps the gases in the atmosphere from escaping into space.

Interpreting the Photo

Figure 3-13 shows the igneous rock granite, an intergrown mass of mostly quartz, feldspar (K-spar and plagioclase), and hornblende crystals. Ask students how many different types of crystals they see in this image.

Resource Manager

Laboratory Manual, pp. 17–20

PLASMA

When matter is heated to temperatures greater than 5000°C, the collisions between particles are so violent that electrons are knocked away from atoms. Such extremely high temperatures exist in stars, and, as a result, the gases of stars consist entirely of positive ions and free electrons. These hot, highly ionized, electrically conducting gases are called **plasmas.** *Figure 3-15* shows the plasma that forms the Sun's corona. You have seen matter in the plasma state if you have ever seen lightning or a neon sign. Both lightning and the matter inside a neon tube are in the plasma state.

CHANGES OF STATE

Solids melt when they absorb thermal energy and their temperatures rise. When a liquid absorbs thermal energy from the environment, it evaporates. This actually has a cooling effect on the surrounding environment. What do you suppose happens when a liquid freezes? The same thermal energy is then released back into the environment. Finally, when a gas is cooled, it releases thermal energy in the process of **condensation,** the change from a gas to a liquid.

CONSERVATION OF MATTER AND ENERGY

The identity of matter can be changed through chemical reactions and nuclear processes, and its state can be changed under different thermal conditions. However, matter cannot be created or destroyed but can change from one form to another. This fundamental fact is called the law of conservation of matter. Like matter, energy cannot be created or destroyed but it can be changed from one form to another. This law of the conservation of energy is also called the first law of thermodynamics.

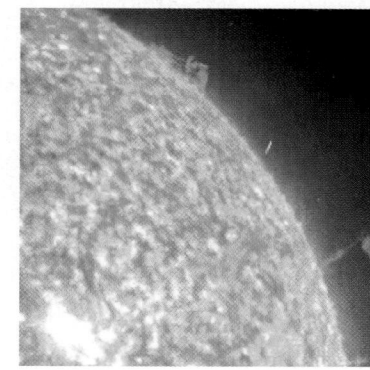

Figure 3-15 The corona around the Sun is formed from hot, glowing plasma.

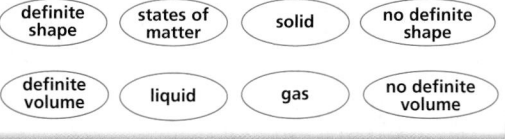
SECTION ASSESSMENT

1. What shape do salt crystals have? What determines the shape of a crystal?

2. Why is the puddle underneath a melting ice cube as cold as the ice cube itself?

3. Contrast what happens to thermal energy in evaporation and condensation.

4. **Thinking Critically** Water boils at 100°C at sea level. What do you think its boiling point would be if water molecules were not polar molecules?

SKILL REVIEW

5. **Concept Mapping** Use the following terms to construct a concept map to compare and contrast the three common states of matter. You may use some terms more than once. For more help, refer to the *Skill Handbook.*

definite shape   states of matter   solid   no definite shape

definite volume   liquid   gas   no definite volume

SECTION ASSESSMENT

1. cubic; the crystal shape is determined by the internal arrangement of the Na and Cl ions

2. The heat energy is used to break hydrogen bonds and melt the ice, not raise its temperature.

3. Thermal energy is needed for evaporation to occur. In condensation, thermal energy is released.

4. much lower; the reason for the high boiling point of water is that hydrogen bonds prevent the water molecules from leaving the liquid.

If the water molecules were nonpolar, these hydrogen bonds wouldn't exist.

5. Student concept maps should have lines drawn from *solid* to *definite shape* and *definite volume;* from *liquid* to *no definite shape* and *definite volume;* and from *gas* to *no definite shape* and *no definite volume.*

Check for Understanding

Discussion

Ask the class what happens to the water in a wet beach towel that is hung out to dry. The water evaporates. Also ask where the water goes. into the atmosphere as water vapor Then ask why the water vaporizes at temperatures below the boiling point. because some molecules vibrate vigorously enough to break loose from others

Reteach

In solid ice, all molecules are bound into an orderly, 3-D framework by hydrogen bonds. In liquid water, enough of these bonds are broken so that the molecules can slide around. In gaseous water vapor, all bonds between molecules are broken. Bonds break because of thermal vibrations. At the boiling point, the vibrations are vigorous enough to break all bonds.

✔Assessment

Portfolio Have students each assemble a collage of pictures showing examples of the states of water, for example, glaciers, icebergs, snowflakes, hoar frost, dew, fog, clouds, streams, the sea, and so on. L1 ELL P

NY Core Curriculum Standards

Page 68: St 4 KI 3.1c
Page 69: St 7 KI 2

GeoLab

Time Allotment
30–40 minutes (check results after one or two days)

Process Skills
observe and infer, draw conclusions, recognize cause and effect, compare and contrast, communicate

Safety Precautions
Advise students to be careful with hot plates. Remind them to wear safety goggles.

Disposal
Dispose of salt solutions and salt crystals in a sink.

Preparation
Don't use regular table salt that contains iodine.

Procedure

Teaching Strategies
Have students work in groups of three.

Tying to Previous Knowledge
Remind students that sugar dissolves much more readily in hot tea than in iced tea.

NY Core Curriculum Standards
Page 70: St 4 KI 3.1b & 3.1c
Page 71: St 1 Science KI 1 & 2, St 6 KI 5

GeoLab | Salt Precipitation

Many rocks on Earth form from salts precipitating out of seawater. Salt ions precipitate when a salt solution becomes saturated. Solubility is the ability of a substance to dissolve in a solution. When a solution is saturated, no more of that substance can be dissolved. What is the effect of temperature and evaporation on salt precipitation? How do precipitation rates affect the size of crystals?

Preparation

Problem
Under what conditions do salt solutions become saturated and under what conditions does salt precipitate out of solution?

Materials
halite (sodium chloride)
250-mL glass beakers (2)
distilled water
plastic wrap
laboratory scale
hot plate
shallow glass baking dish
refrigerator
glass stirring rod

Objectives
In this GeoLab, you will:
- **Observe** salt dissolving and precipitating from a saturated salt solution.

- **Identify** the precipitated salt crystals.
- **Compare** the salt crystals that precipitate out under different conditions.
- **Hypothesize** why different conditions produce different results.

Safety Precautions
Always wear safety goggles and an apron in the lab. Wash your hands after handling salt solutions. Use care in handling hot solutions. Use protection handling hot glassware.

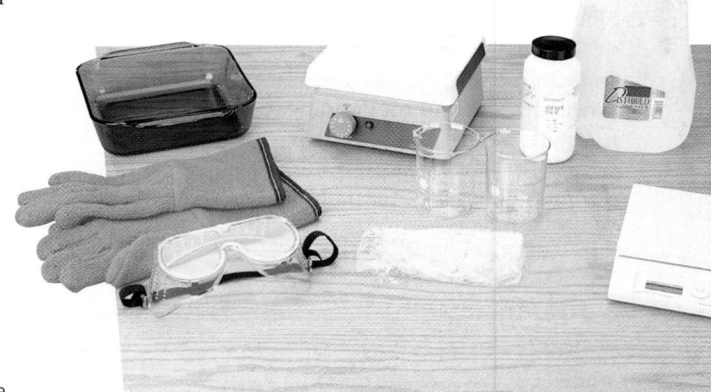

Troubleshooting
Salt crystals may not be able to nucleate in the beakers even if the salt solution becomes supersaturated. If this happens, add some small seed crystals and explain the problem to students.

Data and Observations
Students will observe that at room temperature, 150 mL of water can dissolve only about 52 g of salt. Students will note that large salt crystals, several millimeters in size, form in the beakers, while small salt crystals, only a fraction of a millimeter, form in the baking dish.

Procedure

1. Pour 150 mL of distilled water into a 250-mL glass beaker.
2. Measure 54 g of sodium chloride. Add the sodium chloride to the distilled water in the beaker and stir until only a few grains remain on the bottom of the beaker.
3. Place the beaker on the hot plate and turn the hot plate on. As the solution inside the beaker heats up, stir it until the last few grains of sodium chloride dissolve. The salt solution will then be saturated.
4. Pour 50 mL of the warm, saturated solution into the second 250-mL glass beaker. Cover this beaker with plastic wrap so that it forms a good seal. Put this beaker in the refrigerator.
5. Pour 50 mL of the saturated solution into the shallow glass baking dish. Place the dish on the hot plate and heat the salt solution until all the liquid evaporates. *CAUTION: The baking dish will be hot. Handle with care.*
6. Place the original beaker with 50 mL of the remaining solution on a shelf or windowsill. Do not cover the beaker.
7. Observe both beakers one day later. If crystals have not formed, wait another day to make your observations and conclusions.
8. Once crystals have formed in all three containers, observe the size and shape of the precipitated crystals. Describe your observations in your science journal.

Analyze

1. What is the shape of the precipitated crystals in the three containers? Does the shape of the crystals alone identify them as sodium chloride?
2. Why didn't all of the salt solution dissolve in step 2 above? How did heating affect the solubility of sodium chloride? Why did heating have the observed effect? Explain.
3. What effect does cooling have on the solubility of salt?
4. What happens when a salt solution evaporates? What effect does evaporation have on the solubility of salt?
5. Suppose you have two samples of volcanic rock of identical chemical composition but different crystal sizes. What conclusions can you make about the conditions under which each rock sample cooled?

Conclude & Apply

1. What are the sizes of the crystals in the different containers? Which container has the smallest crystals? Which crystals formed in the shortest time interval?
2. Why does salt precipitate from solution? How is crystal size related to precipitation rate?
3. Design an experiment to separate a heterogeneous mixture of different salts, such as NaCl and $MgCl_2$, into its components, by dissolving and precipitation.

GeoLab **71**

Resource Manager

GeoLab and MiniLab Worksheets, pp. 10–12 **L2**

Analyze

1. The crystals are cubic, and some may be in the form of flattened squares. No; compounds other than NaCl may have similar crystals.
2. The solution was saturated before all the salt could dissolve. Heating increased the solubility because increased thermal energy keeps salt ions from precipitating.
3. Cooling decreases the solubility of salt.
4. When a salt solution evaporates, only the water molecules evaporate. The concentration of salt ions in the remaining liquid increases, the solution becomes supersaturated, and salt crystals precipitate.
5. The rocks must have cooled under different temperatures or at different rates.

Conclude & Apply

1. The crystals in the beakers are large—several millimeters in size. The smallest crystals formed in the baking dish in the shortest time interval.
2. Salt precipitates from solution whenever the electrostatic attraction between salt ions overcomes the disruptive effect of thermal vibrations, either when the concentration of salt ions is high enough or the temperature is low enough. Slow precipitation rates allow the growth of large crystals.
3. Different salts have different solubilities. To separate two salts, dissolve a portion of the mixture. The solution will be enriched in one of the salts. Evaporate the solution and dissolve a portion of the residue. This will further enrich the solution in the more soluble salt. Repeat until the desired concentration is reached.

Purpose

The scanning electron microscope is a valuable tool used by scientists who explore the nature of matter. Students will learn how electron microscopes differ from traditional light microscopes, and how electron microscopes are used in science.

Content Background

Scanning electron microscope (SEM) images can be found on the Internet. Direct students to **earthgeu.com** to find links to sites that contain SEM images. Students may be able to find library books that have SEM images as well. Students may find images of common, everyday items as well as tiny organisms that live on their own bodies, including organisms that live in their eyelashes and other hair follicles.

Teaching Strategies

Have students focus on the following questions as they read the article. What makes an electron microscope more powerful than even the best light microscopes? What areas of research are enhanced by electron microscopy?

Science & Technology

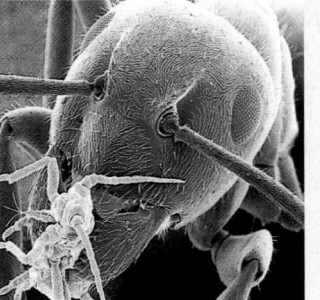

Magnification 33×

Extreme Magnification

Students from Malibu, California, to Atlanta, Georgia, are collecting bugs with more enthusiasm than usual. They are sending insects to a project called Bugscope. Bugscope workers use a scanning electron microscope (SEM) to take close-up photographs of these amazing animals. The photographs are then posted on the Internet. The photos provide detailed information about the structure and composition of matter in our world.

Electron Microscopy

Microscopes have been used by scientists to magnify objects since the 1600s. Traditional light microscopes, however, have limitations: they can magnify objects only up to 2000 times their size, and there is a limit to how clear these microscopes can make objects appear. In the early 1930s, German scientists developed a new type of microscope that could magnify objects 10 000 times their size. This microscope did not use light for the examination of objects; instead, it used a beam of high-energy electrons. Today, electron microscopes scan material to create detailed, three-dimensional, black-and-white images of objects that are magnified up to 100 000 times.

Applications

When a scanning electron microscope is used to examine an object, a beam of electrons is directed onto the object's surface. As scanning coils move the electron beam over the object in a gridlike pattern, the beam causes electrons to be knocked off the object's surface. An image is created on a fluorescent screen by the calculation of the number of electrons that are bounced off each spot on the object. Electron microscopes provide information about the properties of matter being examined, including its reactivity,

strength, and reflectivity. Currently, scientists are using electron microscopes to further research in areas ranging from combating leukemia to searching for evidence of product tampering to developing better ways to process and store food.

Magnification 18×

Magnification 140×

Activity

The photographs on this page are SEM images. What does each image represent? Go to **earthgeu.com** to find links to SEM images of solids and create an image gallery. Present your images, along with clues about their identities, to your classmates, and see how many they can identify.

72 CHAPTER 3 *Matter and Atomic Structure*

Activity

Prepare students for Internet research of electron microscope images by having them examine the photos on the student page. Give students hints about these images to help them hypothesize what each represents. The images included on the student page are an ant with an aphid, beach sand, and the clay mineral, vermiculite. For help finding electron microscope images, have students explore the links to this chapter and feature at **earthgeu.com**

Summary

SECTION 3.1
What are elements?

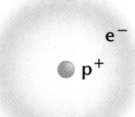

Hydrogen atom

Main Ideas
- The basic building blocks of matter are atoms. Atoms consist of protons, neutrons, and electrons.
- Protons have a positive electrical charge, electrons have a negative electrical charge, and neutrons are electrically neutral. Protons and neutrons make up the nucleus of an atom; electrons surround the nucleus in energy levels.
- An element is a substance consisting of atoms with a specific number of protons in their nuclei. Isotopes of an element differ by the number of neutrons in their nuclei. Many elements are mixtures of isotopes.
- The number of electrons in the outermost energy levels of atoms determines their chemical behavior. Elements with the same number of electrons in their outermost energy levels have similar chemical properties.

Vocabulary
atom (p. 54)
atomic mass (p. 58)
atomic number (p. 54)
electron (p. 55)
element (p. 53)
energy level (p. 55)
isotope (p. 58)
mass number (p. 54)
neutron (p. 54)
nucleus (p. 54)
proton (p. 54)
radioactivity (p. 58)
valence electron (p. 57)

SECTION 3.2
How Atoms Combine

Main Ideas
- Atoms of different elements combine to form compounds.
- Atoms held together by the sharing of electrons in covalent bonds form molecular compounds.
- Ions are electrically charged atoms or groups of atoms. Positive and negative ions attract each other and form ionic compounds.
- Acids are solutions containing hydrogen ions. Bases are solutions containing hydroxide ions. Acids and bases can neutralize each other.
- A mixture is a combination of components that retain their identities. A solution is a mixture in which the components can no longer be distinguished as separate. Solutions can be liquid, solid, gaseous, or combinations.

Vocabulary
acid (p. 65)
base (p. 66)
chemical bond (p. 60)
chemical reaction (p. 64)
compound (p. 60)
covalent bond (p. 60)
ion (p. 62)
ionic bond (p. 63)
molecule (p. 61)
solution (p. 65)

SECTION 3.3
States of Matter

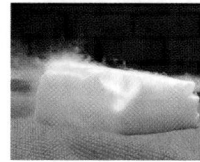

Main Ideas
- Matter on Earth exists in three common physical states: solid, liquid, or gaseous. Matter in the universe includes plasma.
- Most solids have a crystalline structure.
- Liquids are densely packed arrangements of particles.
- Gases consist of widely separated, individual particles. Plasmas are hot, highly ionized, electrically conducting gases.
- Changes of state involve thermal energy.

Vocabulary
condensation (p. 69)
crystalline structure (p. 67)
evaporation (p. 68)
glass (p. 68)
plasma (p. 69)
sublimation (p. 68)

 earthgeu.com/vocabulary_puzzlemaker

Study Guide **73**

Main Ideas

Summary statements can be used by students to review the major concepts of the chapter.

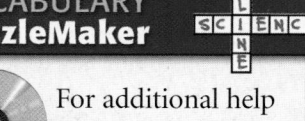
VOCABULARY PuzzleMaker

For additional help with vocabulary, have students access the Vocabulary Puzzlemaker online.

earthgeu.com/ vocabulary puzzlemaker

(0:00) Out of Time?

If time does not permit teaching the entire chapter, use the GeoDigest at the end of the unit as an overview.

Earth Science Online

Be sure to check the Earth Science Web Site for links to chapter material:
earthgeu.com

GLENCOE
Technology

Videotape/DVD
MindJogger Videoquizzes
Chapter 3: *Matter and Atomic Structure*
Have students work in groups as they play the videoquiz game to review key chapter concepts.

Resource Manager

Chapter Assessment, pp. 13–18
MindJogger Videoquizzes DVD/VHS
ExamView® Pro CD-ROM
Performance Assessment in Earth Science

NY Core Curriculum Standards

Page 72: St 2 KI 1
Page 73: St 4 KI 3.1a, 3.1b, & 3.1c

Understanding Main Ideas

1. d
2. c
3. c
4. c
5. b
6. b
7. a
8. b
9. a
10. Na + F → NaF
11. an ionic compound, which consists of ions
12. d
13. b
14. b
15. b
16. The valence electrons in metals are not bound to a single atom.

Understanding Main Ideas

1. What particles make up the nucleus of an atom?
   a. protons only
   b. neutrons only
   c. neutrons and electrons
   d. protons and neutrons

2. Which of these makes up an atom's mass number?
   a. number of protons
   b. number of neutrons
   c. neutrons and protons
   d. protons and electrons

3. Which is the average of the mass numbers of an element's isotopes?
   a. atomic number
   b. energy levels
   c. atomic mass
   d. valence electrons

4. What is the lightest of all the elements?
   a. helium
   b. lithium
   c. hydrogen
   d. magnesium

5. One of the isotopes of chlorine (atomic number 17) has a mass number of 35. How many neutrons does this isotope have in its nucleus?
   a. 17   b. 18   c. 35   d. 53

6. Which is NOT an element?
   a. hydrogen
   b. water
   c. argon
   d. uranium

7. What element is the final (nonradioactive) decay product of uranium?
   a. lead
   b. neon
   c. plutonium
   d. hydrogen

8. Many musical instruments are made of brass, which consists of copper and zinc atoms. What is brass an example of?
   a. an ionic compound
   b. a solid solution
   c. a chemical reaction
   d. a base

9. What are formed when sodium ions and chlorine ions combine to form NaCl?
   a. ionic bonds
   b. solid solutions
   c. isotopes
   d. covalent bonds

Use the following diagram to answer questions 10 and 11.

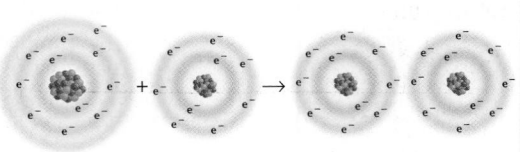

10. Write the chemical equation that the diagram represents.

11. Is the compound formed in the diagram a molecular compound or an ionic compound? Explain your answer.

12. What is the most abundant element in Earth's crust?
    a. hydrogen
    b. uranium
    c. silicon
    d. oxygen

13. Which chemical formula represents a polar molecule?
    a. MgO   b. H_2O c. SiO_2 d. NaCl

14. If an atom gains electrons, what does it become?
    a. a positive ion
    b. a negative ion
    c. a different element
    d. a heavier isotope

15. What kind of ions characterize an acid?
    a. hydroxide ions
    b. hydrogen ions
    c. oxygen ions
    d. negative ions

16. Why do metals conduct electricity?

Test-Taking Tip

TERMS If a test question involves a term that you don't remember, see if you can figure out its meaning from the question. Sometimes standardized tests will give a definition or example right in the question.

earthgeu.com/chapter_test

17. What happens to the thermal energy of a gas when it condenses and forms a liquid?

18. How are coffee and air chemically alike?

19. Explain the differences between a molecular compound and an ionic compound.

20. What is a molecule?

Applying Main Ideas

21. How many valence electrons do beryllium atoms (atomic number 4) have? Explain your answer.

22. Name two elements with chemical properties that are similar to those of sodium.

23. What is the charge on ions of fluorine (atomic number 9)?

24. List two elements that have ions with a 2+ charge.

25. What compound do the ions Al^{3+} and O^{2-} form?

26. Explain why the mass numbers of elements in the Periodic Table of Elements rarely are whole numbers.

Thinking Critically

27. Why don't gases such as neon and argon combine chemically with other elements?

28. Suppose you want to find out if the elements copper (atomic number 29) and sulfur (atomic number 16) could combine into a compound. How could you check this before you proceeded to do an experiment in the laboratory?

earthgeu.com/standardized_test

Standardized Test Practice

INTERPRETING DATA Use the table below to answer the following questions.

Atomic Structure		
Element	Atomic Number	Atomic Mass
Beryllium	4	9.01
Calcium	20	40.08
Silicon	14	28.09
Scandium	21	44.96
Titanium	22	47.88
Zirconium	40	91.22

1. If titanium has 22 protons in its nucleus, how many neutrons are present in the nucleus of its most common isotope?
- **a.** 48
- **b.** 26
- **c.** 60
- **d.** 28

2. If the most common isotope of scandium has 24 neutrons in its nucleus, how many protons does scandium have?
- **a.** 66
- **b.** 45
- **c.** 21
- **d.** 13

3. If calcium's most common isotope has 20 neutrons in its nucleus, how many neutrons can be found in another naturally occurring isotope of calcium?
- **a.** 60
- **b.** 41
- **c.** 30
- **d.** 21

4. How many valence electrons does oxygen have?
- **a.** 2
- **b.** 4
- **c.** 6
- **d.** 9

5. Does silicon have any isotopes? Explain your answer.

Answers

17. The thermal energy is released as heat.

18. Coffee and air are homogeneous mixtures.

19. The constituent particles of molecular compounds are molecules, and those of ionic compounds are ions.

20. A molecule is the smallest unit of a compound with the properties of that compound.

Applying Main Ideas

21. two valence electrons; the other two electrons fill the first energy level

22. lithium and potassium

23. Fluorine ions have a -1 charge.

24. Be, Mg, and Ca

25. Al_2O_3

26. Elements are mixtures of isotopes. Mass numbers of elements are the average mass numbers of their isotopes.

Thinking Critically

27. Inert gases have no valence electrons.

28. Determine what ions are formed by copper and sulfur, and which combination of copper and sulfur ions is electrically neutral (Cu_2S).

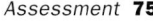

EXAM**VIEW**® PRO

Use Exam**View**® Pro Testmaker CD-ROM to:
- Create **multiple versions** of tests.
- Create **modified** tests with one mouse click for struggling students.
- **Edit** existing questions and add your own questions.
- **Build** tests based on national curriculum standards.

Standardized Test Practice

1. b   **3.** d
2. c   **4.** c
5. Silicon has an atomic mass of 28.09. Silicon does have isotopes, but they are rare.

NY Core Curriculum Standards

Page 74: St 1 Math KI 1, 2, 3, & Science KI 1
Page 75: St 1 Math KI 1, 2, 3, Science KI 1, & 2

Refer to pages 8T–9T of the Teacher Guide for an explanation of the National Science Content Standards correlations.

Section	Objectives	National Science Content Standards	State/Local Standards
SECTION 4.1 **What is a mineral?** 🕐 1 session 📦 ½ block	1. **Define** a mineral. 2. **Describe** how minerals form. 3. **Identify** the most common elements in Earth's crust.	UCP.1, UCP.3, UCP.5; A.1, A.2; B.2; D.2, D.3; F.3; G.3	St 1 Math KI 2 & Science KI 3, St 4 KI 1.2j, 3.1a, 3.1b, & 3.1c, St 6 KI 1 & 2
SECTION 4.2 **Identifying Minerals** 🕐 4 sessions 📦 2 blocks	4. **Classify** minerals according to their physical and chemical properties. 5. **Identify** different types of minerals. 6. **Discuss** how minerals are used.	UCP.1, UCP.2, UCP.3, UCP.5; A.1, A.2; B.2, B.3; D.3; E.2; F.3, F.4, F.6; G.3	St 1 Math KI 1, 2, 3, Science KI 1, 2, & 3, St 4 KI 3.1a, 3.1b, & 3.1c, St 6 KI 1 & 6, St 7 KI 1

*A complete Planning Guide is provided on pages 30T–32T.

🕐 The number of recommended single-period sessions

📦 The number of recommended blocks

Activity Materials

Discovery Lab *page 77*
halite, hand lens, quartz, paper, pencil

GeoLab *pages 92–93*
mineral samples, hand lens, glass plate, streak plate, Mohs scale, 5% HCl, dropper, steel file, copper piece, paper clip, magnet

MiniLab *page 79*
foam board, scissors, glue, mineral samples, ruler

Demo *page 84*
calcite, dilute HCl

Need materials? Contact Science Kit at 1-800-828-7777 or at www.sciencekit.com on the Internet. For alternate materials, see the activity on the listed page.

Key to Teaching Strategies

L1 Level 1 activities should be appropriate for students with learning difficulties.

L2 Level 2 activities should be within the ability range of all students.

L3 Level 3 activities are designed for above-average students.

ELL ELL activities should be within the ability range of English-language learners.

COOP LEARN Cooperative learning activities are designed for small-group work.

P These strategies represent student products that can be placed in a best-work portfolio.

📦 These strategies are useful in a block-scheduling format.

Chapter Organizer

Glencoe Exclusive!
TeacherWorks™
All-In-One Planner and Resource Center

Activities/Features	Reproducible Masters	Transparencies
Discovery Lab: Observing Mineral Shapes, p. 77 **MiniLab:** How can crystal systems be modeled?, p. 79 **Using Math:** Using Numbers, p. 80	**Study Guide for Content Mastery,** pp. 21–22 **L2** **GeoLab and MiniLab Worksheets,** pp. 13–14 **L2**	**Section Focus Transparency 10** **L1** **ELL** **Teaching Transparency 9** **L2** **ELL**
Problem-Solving Lab: Making and Using Tables, p. 88 **Design Your Own GeoLab:** Making a Field Guide to Minerals, pp. 92–93 **Science & Math:** The Price of Diamonds, p. 94	**Study Guide for Content Mastery,** pp. 23–26 **L2** **GeoLab and MiniLab Worksheets,** pp. 15–18 **L2** **Laboratory Manual,** pp. 25–28 **L2**	**Section Focus Transparency 11** **L1** **ELL** **Teaching Transparency 10** **L2** **ELL**

✓Assessment

Chapter Assessment,
    pp. 19–24
Performance Assessment in
    the Science Classroom
    (PASC)
MindJogger Videoquiz
    DVD/VHS
Performance Assessment in
    Earth Science
ExamView® Pro CD-ROM
5 Days to the Regents Exam

Additional Resources

Guided Reading Audio
    Program **ELL**
Cooperative Learning in the
    Science Classroom
    COOP LEARN
Lesson Plans
Block Scheduling
earthgeu.com
NY Lesson Plans
NY Block Scheduling
Review Handbook for
    Regents Earth Science
    Exam

☐ NATIONAL GEOGRAPHIC

Teacher's Corner

Products Available from
National Geographic Society
To order the following products,
call the National Geographic
Society at 1-800-368-2728:
Curriculum Kits
GeoKit: *Rocks and Minerals*
GeoKit: *Earth's History*

CD-ROM
111 years of National Geographic
Magazine
Videos
Our Dynamic Earth
Fossils: Clues to the Past

Content Background

Mineral Resources
Section 4.1

Many nations' economies depend on their supplies of natural resources, such as gold, silver, platinum, iron, copper, uranium, aluminum, tin, and other economically important substances that are obtained from minerals. Many of the materials needed to make numerous objects are obtained from minerals. For instance, minerals play a role in the manufacture of furniture, computers, televisions, stereos, automobiles, airplanes, sports equipment, cosmetics, and telephones. Earth's supply of minerals, however, is limited. The recycling of materials that contain iron, tin, copper, and aluminum helps extend our limited supply of these resources. However, recycling does not guarantee that certain minerals will not ultimately be depleted. Thus, scientists continually seek new sources of raw materials to satisfy the demand for consumer goods. The research and development process focuses on finding new deposits of minerals within Earth's crust, developing better methods of extracting low-grade ores, and developing more cost-effective ways to recycle metals. In addition, the conservation of minerals is aided by government policies that encourage reduced consumption of minerals at both the personal and industrial levels.

Hard Diamonds
Section 4.2

Diamonds have a hardness of 10 on the Mohs scale of mineral hardness. Because diamonds are so hard, they are often used to coat the tips of drill bits and other cutting instruments. These diamond-tipped instruments can cut through steel and rock. Scientists use methane gas and microwaves to make the synthetic diamonds used on the cutting instruments. Each methane molecule contains a carbon atom and four hydrogen atoms. Microwaves are used to strip the hydrogen atoms from the molecules. The carbon atoms then bond on the surface of the cutting instrument and form tiny rows of diamonds. This process is used to make diamond-tipped scalpels, dental drills, and computer parts.

Multiple Learning Styles

Interpersonal Project, pp. 80, 89; Earth Science Journal, p. 81; Collaborative Learning, p. 86; Environmental Connection, p. 90

Kinesthetic Modeling, p. 81; Reinforcement, p. 86

Linguistic Project, p. 82; Earth Science Journal, p. 90; Reteach, p. 91

Visual-Spatial Activity, pp. 85, 89

GLENCOE
Technology

The following multimedia resources are available from Glencoe.

The Infinite Voyage Series
The Future of the Past

Vocabulary Puzzlemaker

TeacherWorks™ CD-ROM

MindJogger Videoquizzes DVD/VHS

ExamView® Pro CD-ROM

Interactive Chalkboard CD-ROM

Chapter Organizer

Mineral Identification
Section 4.2

Color, texture, luster, streak, hardness, crystal shape, density, specific gravity, fracture, and cleavage are physical properties that all minerals have. These properties are commonly used to identify minerals. However, some minerals have undergone severe weathering or erosion, or their crystal development may have been altered by restrictive environmental conditions. In these and other cases, geologists may rely on a mineral's special properties for identification purposes. Special properties include a tendency to react with certain acids, radioactivity, magnetism, fluorescence, phosphorescence, piezoelectricity, and double refraction. In addition, the presence of natural inclusions can be used to distinguish real gems from synthetic gems. Many special properties are found only in one or two specific minerals. Thus, these properties are highly reliable forms of mineral identification. However, there are 3000 known minerals and there is no one simple way to identify them all.

Identifying Misconceptions

Show students samples of quartz, mica, salt, amber, pearl, coal, and sugar. Ask students to classify the samples as minerals or nonminerals. Write their answers in table form on the chalkboard. Then tell students the definition of minerals: minerals are naturally occurring, inorganic solids with definitive crystal structures and chemical compositions. Refer again to the samples and have students discuss whether the samples fit the definition of minerals. Should any of the samples be reclassified? Students may have classified amber as a mineral, for example. Amber, which is often used in jewelry, forms from organic tree sap, so it is not a mineral. Tell students that many substances, such as pearls, coal, ivory, coral, and synthetic gems, are often erroneously classified as minerals.

✔Assessment

Portfolio Assessment
Assessment, TWE, p. 91
GeoLab, TWE, pp. 92–93

Performance Assessment
Discovery Lab, SE, p. 77
MiniLab, SE, p. 79
MiniLab, TWE, p. 79
GeoLab, SE, pp. 92–93

Knowledge Assessment
Discovery Lab, TWE, p. 77
Assessment, TWE, p. 83
Section Assessment, SE, pp. 83, 91
Chapter Assessment, SE, pp. 96–97

Skill Assessment
Problem-Solving Lab, TWE, p. 88

Be sure to check the Earth Science Web Site for links to chapter material: earthgeu.com

Chapter 4

Minerals

Introducing the Chapter

Tell students that relatively few of the 3000 minerals found in Earth's crust have economic value. However, these few minerals are widely used for a variety of purposes. Have students write descriptions of seven objects around the classroom that contain minerals or that were obtained from minerals. Tell them to refer to Appendix H for guidance.

Interpreting the Photo

The chapter-opening photograph shows a spectacular crystal containing albite, watermelon tourmaline, and smoky quartz. Tell students the definition of a mineral: a naturally occurring, inorganic solid with a definite crystal structure and chemical composition. Have students explain how the crystal fits the definition of a mineral.

Chapter 4

Minerals

What You'll Learn

- How minerals form, and which are most common in Earth's crust.
- Which properties can be used to identify and classify minerals.
- Why certain minerals are ores and gems.

Why It's Important

Many products used in daily life are made directly or indirectly from minerals. Minerals also play a vital role in the processes that shape Earth. Some minerals form crystals that are valued for their beauty. The crystals shown here consist of albite, watermelon tourmaline, and smoky quartz.

Earth Science Online

To find out more about minerals, visit the Earth Science Web Site at earthgeu.com

76

Discovery Lab

Process Skills

observe and infer, communicate, compare and contrast 🄻🄻 🄴🄻🄻 📦

Procedure

- Do not use sugar as an alternate material. Sugar is organic and thus not a mineral.
- Premeasure the salt. Place a container on a table for students to use to dispose of the salt. The salt can be stored and reused in other activities.

Observe

Both the halite and quartz have distinctive crystal shapes. However, the halite is cubic, whereas the quartz crystal clearly shows a hexagonal shape. Answers will vary. Students may know that the environmental conditions under which the minerals formed and the internal structure or atomic arrangement of the minerals are different. Students may recognize other mineral properties such as color, luster, and texture.

Discovery Lab

Observing Mineral Shapes

Although there are thousands of minerals in Earth's crust, each type of mineral has unique characteristics. These characteristics are clues to a mineral's chemical composition and to the way it formed. Physical properties can also be used to distinguish one type of mineral from another.

1. Place a few grains of table salt—the mineral halite—on a microscope slide. Place the slide on the microscope stage and separate the grains. Or, simply observe the grains with a magnifying glass.

2. Focus on one grain at a time. Count the number of sides each grain has. Make sketches of the grains.

3. Next, examine a sample of quartz with the microscope or magnifying glass. Count the number of sides in the quartz sample. Sketch the shape of the quartz sample.

Observe Compare and contrast the shapes of the samples of halite and quartz. What might account for the differences you observed? In your science journal, describe some other physical properties of your mineral samples.

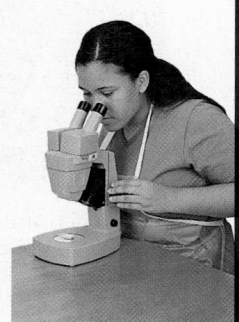

Section Focus

Before presenting the lesson, display **Section Focus Transparency 10** on the overhead projector. **L1** **ELL**

Section Focus Transparency 10 — NATURAL BEAUTIES
Use with Chapter 4, Section 4.1

❶ What are the objects in this photograph?
❷ How do the objects differ from one another?

SECTION 4.1

What is a mineral?

OBJECTIVES

- **Define** *a mineral.*
- **Describe** *how minerals form.*
- **Identify** *the most common elements in Earth's crust.*

VOCABULARY

mineral
crystal
magma
silicate

Earth's crust is composed of about 3000 minerals. Minerals play important roles in forming rocks and in shaping Earth's surface, and a select few have played—and continue to play—a role in shaping civilization. For example, great leaps in prehistory were made when early humans began making tools from iron. Calcite is the mineral that forms the 2 million limestone blocks that make up the Great Pyramid in Egypt. It is also the primary mineral in the marble found in the Parthenon in Greece. Throughout history, wars have been fought and empires have crumbled over minerals such as gold and silver.

MINERAL CHARACTERISTICS

Look around your classroom. The metal in your desk, the graphite in your pencil, and the glass in the windows are just three examples of how modern humans use products made from minerals. But what exactly is a mineral? A **mineral** is a naturally occurring, inorganic solid with a specific chemical composition and a definite crystalline structure. Let's examine each part of this definition in turn.

4.1 *What is a mineral?* **77**

Chapter Themes

The following themes from the National Science Content Standards are covered in this chapter. Refer to page 8T of the Teacher Guide for an explanation of the correlations.
Systems, order, and organization (UCP.1); Evidence, models, and explanation (UCP.2); Change, constancy, and measurement (UCP.3)

Assessment

Knowledge Have groups compare and contrast their lists of the physical properties of the samples. Write a comprehensive list of the mineral properties on the chalkboard. Have students discuss which properties are more easily recognizable than others.

Resource Manager

Section Focus Transparency 10 **L1** **ELL**
Study Guide for Content Mastery, pp. 21–22 **L2**

0:00 Out of Time?

If time does not permit teaching the entire chapter, use the Chapter Summary on page 95 and the GeoDigest found at the end of the unit as an overview.

Content Background

The largest mineral group is the silicates, which make up almost 96 percent of the known minerals. Feldspar and quartz, both silicates, are the first- and second-most abundant minerals found in Earth's crust, respectively. Other common silicates are muscovite, biotite, talc, serpentine, zircon, and topaz.

Enrichment

Tell students that there have been several gold rushes in American history. Assign half the class to research the 1849 Gold Rush at Sutter's Mill, California. The other half of the class should research the Alaskan Gold Rush of the 1890s. Students should write individual reports that include the following information: dates of discovery, location of gold fields, methods of extraction, and human-interest stories about life in the gold camps. Students should illustrate their reports with photographs, if possible, and share their research with the class.

Figure 4-1 The chemical composition of olivine varies within a limited range.

Naturally Occurring and Inorganic To say that minerals are naturally occurring simply means that they are formed by natural processes, which you'll learn about later in this section. Thus, synthetic diamonds and other substances developed in labs are not minerals. Secondly, all minerals are inorganic. That is, they aren't alive and never were alive during any part of their existence. Based on this criterion, salt is a mineral, but sugar, which is harvested from plants, is not. What about coal? According to the scientific definition of minerals, coal is not a mineral because hundreds of millions of years ago, it formed from organic processes.

Solids with Specific Compositions The third characteristic of minerals is that they all are solids. Solids have definite shapes and volumes. Liquids and gases do not. Thus, no gas or liquid can be considered a mineral. Next, each type of mineral has a chemical composition unique to that mineral. A few minerals, such as copper, silver, and sulfur, are composed of single elements. The vast majority, however, are made from compounds. The mineral quartz, for instance, is a combination of two atoms of oxygen and one atom of silicon. Although other minerals may contain silicon and oxygen, the arrangement and proportion of these elements in quartz are unique to quartz.

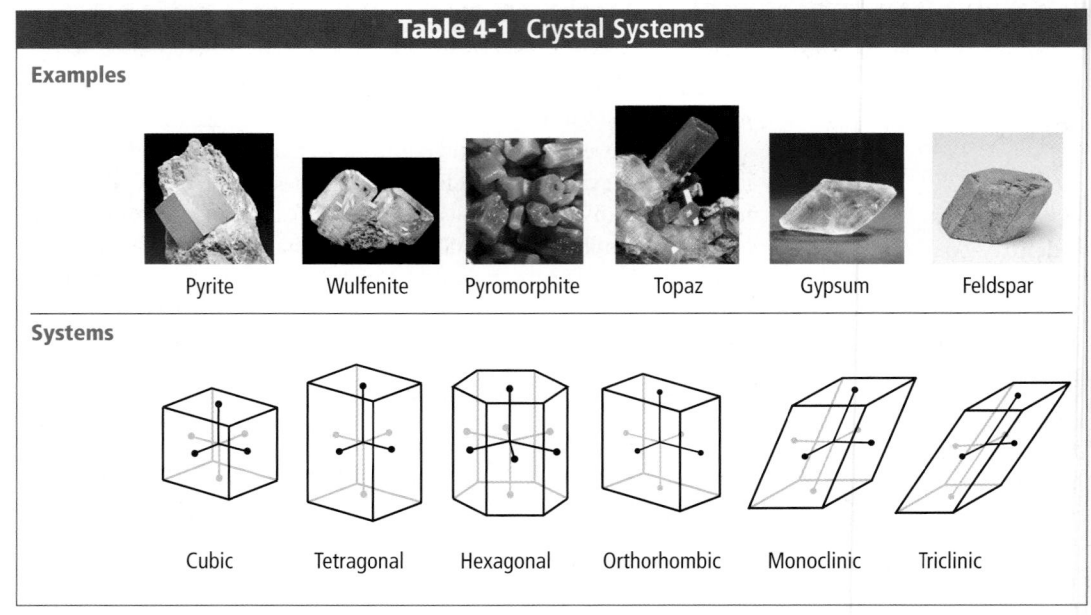

Table 4-1 Crystal Systems

Examples

| Pyrite | Wulfenite | Pyromorphite | Topaz | Gypsum | Feldspar |

Systems

| Cubic | Tetragonal | Hexagonal | Orthorhombic | Monoclinic | Triclinic |

Interpreting the Illustration

Table 4-1 Assign students a specific crystal system to research. Ask students to find at least ten minerals that are characteristic of their crystal system. Students should sketch color diagrams of the minerals and describe the minerals' physical properties. This project can be performed individually or in groups.

NY Core Curriculum Standards

Page 76: St 4 KI 1.2j, 3.1a, 3.1b, & 3.1c, St 6 KI 1
Page 77: St 1 Science KI 3, St 4 KI 3.1a & 3.1b
Page 78: St 4 KI 3.1a & 3.1b
Page 79: St 4 KI 3.1a & 3.1b, St 6 KI 2

Resource Manager

Teaching Transparency 9 L2 ELL
GeoLab and MiniLab Worksheets, pp. 13–14 L2

In some minerals, such as the one shown in *Figure 4-1,* chemical composition may vary within a certain range. For instance, the amount of individual iron and magnesium atoms in the mineral olivine may vary, with some forms of olivine containing more iron than others. But the ratio of the total amount of iron and magnesium atoms to the amount of silicon atoms in olivine is always the same. Thus, the chemical composition of this mineral varies, but only within a well-defined range.

Definite Crystalline Structure The last part of the definition of minerals relates to crystalline structures. The atoms in minerals are arranged in regular geometric patterns that are repeated again and again. A **crystal** is a solid in which the atoms are arranged in repeating patterns. At times, a mineral will form in an open space and grow into one large crystal. The resulting mineral crystal may take the shape of one of the six major crystal systems shown in *Table 4-1.* You'll model crystal systems in the *MiniLab* on this page. The well-defined crystal shapes shown in the table are fairly rare. More commonly, the internal atomic arrangement of a mineral is not so readily apparent because the mineral formed in a restricted space. *Figure 4-2* compares a crystal that grew in an open space with one that grew in a restricted space.

A   **B**

Figure 4-2 The well-shaped crystals of this sample of watermelon tourmaline indicate that it grew in an open space **(A).** This sample of watermelon tourmaline does not have well-defined crystals and thus grew in a restricted space **(B).**

4.1 *What is a mineral?* **79**

MiniLab

How can crystal systems be modeled?

Model the six major crystal systems, then classify mineral samples according to these systems.

Procedure

1. Using *Table 4-1* for guidance, cut pieces of foam board into geometric shapes. Your largest geometric shape should be no more than about 8 cm in length. Your group will need about 38 various shapes.
2. Tape or glue the geometric shapes into models of the six major crystal systems. Again, use *Table 4-1* for guidance.
3. Use the mineral samples provided by your teacher to classify minerals according to their crystal shapes.

Analyze and Conclude

1. What geometric shapes did you use to model the crystal systems?
2. Was the crystal structure readily apparent in all mineral samples? Infer why or why not.
3. Use *Appendix H* to identify your minerals. Besides crystal shape, what properties did you use for identification purposes?

MiniLab

Purpose 🎲
Students will create models of the six basic crystal systems.

Process Skills
observe and infer, model, classify, compare and contrast, interpret data, measuring in SI units, analyze data

Materials
Table 4-1, Appendix H, foam board, scissors, tape or glue, mineral samples, metric ruler

Alternate Materials
Stiff cardboard can be used as an alternative to foam board.

Teaching Strategies
- Have students work in groups of three or four. Students should record their observations and analyses in their science journals. Afterwards, display the models along with the mineral samples for other classes to observe.
- The following mineral samples can be used as examples of the six crystal systems: corundum (hexagonal), gypsum (monoclinic), albite (triclinic), halite (cubic), wulfenite (tetragonal), and topaz (orthorhombic).

Expected Results
Students will model the geometric shapes of the six basic crystal systems of minerals that form under ideal environmental conditions. Students will compare and contrast the crystal models with examples of actual minerals, and use their observations to identify the mineral samples.

Analyze and Conclude
1. squares, rectangles, hexagons, and triangles
2. Most minerals grow in restricted spaces; thus, their crystals are not well defined. Conversely, a mineral with a reasonably clear crystal structure probably formed in an unrestricted space.
3. Answers will vary depending on the samples used.

Using Math

Using Numbers Of the 3000 known minerals, ten make up about 90 percent of the rocks in Earth's crust. What percentage of the total number of minerals do these ten minerals represent?

MINERALS FROM MAGMA

Minerals can form from the cooling of magma. **Magma** is molten material found beneath Earth's surface. Density differences can force magma upward into cooler layers of Earth's interior, where the magma cools. The compounds in the magma no longer move freely in the cooling material, and they may begin to interact chemically to form minerals. The type and amount of elements present in the magma help determine which minerals will form, while the rate at which the magma cools determines the size of the mineral crystals. If the magma cools slowly within Earth's heated interior, the atoms have time to arrange themselves into large crystals. If the magma reaches Earth's surface, comes in contact with air or water, and cools quickly, the atoms don't have time to arrange themselves into large crystals. Thus, small crystals form from rapidly cooling magma and large crystals form from slowly cooling magma. You'll learn more about crystal size in Chapter 5.

MINERALS FROM SOLUTION

A given volume of water in a solution can dissolve only so much of a solid before the water becomes saturated. At that point, the saturated water cannot dissolve any more of the solid. In nature, if a solution becomes supersaturated, or overfilled, with another substance, mineral crystals may begin to precipitate, or drop out of solution. This is one way that minerals can form from a supersaturated solution.

Minerals can also form when elements dissolve in a supersaturated solution. When liquid evaporates from the solution, the elements remain behind and may begin to arrange into crystals. *Figure 4-3* shows gypsum deposits that were formed from the evaporation of water. This is the second way that minerals form from a supersaturated solution.

MINERAL GROUPS

Earlier, we said that 3000 minerals are found in Earth's crust. However, only about 30 of these minerals are common. The most common minerals are often referred to as rock-forming minerals

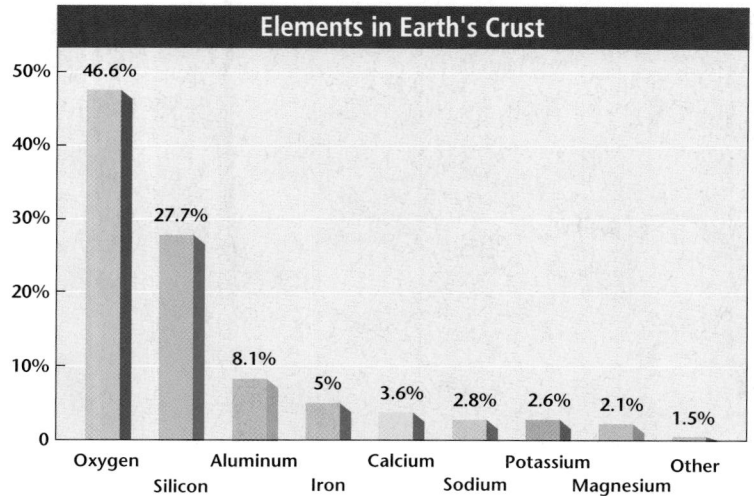

Elements in Earth's Crust

- Oxygen: 46.6%
- Silicon: 27.7%
- Aluminum: 8.1%
- Iron: 5%
- Calcium: 3.6%
- Sodium: 2.8%
- Potassium: 2.6%
- Magnesium: 2.1%
- Other: 1.5%

Figure 4-4 Oxygen is the most common element in Earth's crust, followed by silicon. The eight most common elements make up most minerals.

because they make up most of the rocks found in Earth's crust. Elements also are present in Earth's crust. About 90 known elements occur naturally in the crust. The vast majority of minerals are made up of the eight most common elements. *Figure 4-4* shows the percentages by weight of the common elements in Earth's crust.

Silicates Oxygen (O) is the most abundant element in Earth's crust, followed by silicon (Si). Minerals that contain silicon and oxygen, and usually one or more other elements, are known as **silicates.** Silicates make up approximately 96 percent of the minerals found in Earth's crust. The most common minerals, feldspar and quartz, are silicates.

Figure 4-5 shows how one silicon atom attaches to four oxygen atoms to form a silica tetrahedron. A tetrahedron is a three-dimensional shape structured like a pyramid. The basic silica tetrahedron has the ability to share oxygen atoms with other tetrahedron molecules. This unique structure allows molecules to combine chemically and

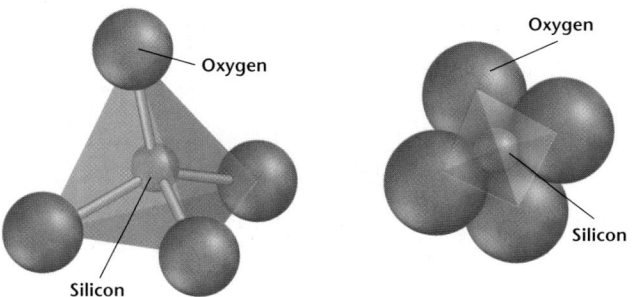

Figure 4-5 A silica tetrahedron is made up of one silicon atom bonded to four oxygen atoms.

4.1 *What is a mineral?* **81**

Activity

Have students use a computer graphics program to make graphs that show the relative percentages of the eight most common elements in Earth's crust.

Concept Development

All silicate rock-forming minerals contain silicon and oxygen. Thus, the chemical formulas for many common rock-forming minerals are somewhat similar. Have students compare and contrast the chemical formulas for the following minerals: quartz (SiO_2), orthoclase feldspar ($KAlSi_3O_8$), olivine ($(Mg, Fe)_2(SiO_4)$), and topaz ($Al_2SiO_4(F, OH)_2$).

Modeling

Kinesthetic Supply students with a box of straws and a ball of string. Have students work with partners to construct models of basic silica-oxygen tetrahedrons. Students should use **Figure 4-5** as a guide. Foam balls of different sizes and pipe cleaners for connectors can also be used to construct tetrahedral models. For an added challenge, students can refer to **Figure 4-6** and assemble models of other silica tetrahedral arrangements, such as sheets or networks. **L1** **ELL**

Science Field Book

Earth Science

Journal

Interpersonal Have students work in groups to compile lists of objects and materials that contain or are obtained from the following mineral groups: native elements, silicates, carbonates, and oxides. Have a field guide to minerals available for students to use. Students should record their findings in their science journals. **L2** **COOP LEARN**

NY Core Curriculum Standards

Page 80: St 1 Math KI 2, St 4 KI 3.1b & 3.1c
Page 81: St 4 KI 3.1c, St 6 KI 1

Using Scientific Terms

Have students use chemical compositions to distinguish the following groups of minerals: silicates, carbonates, sulfates, native elements, and oxides. Students should list mineral examples for each group. Have students write their responses in their science journals.

Project

Linguistic Assign each student a specific state to research. Instruct students to use the Glencoe Science Web Site to find the Web sites for their respective state's Department of Natural Resources office. Ask students to list the major minerals found in their state and their uses. Also, ask students to contact the National Mineralogical Society to request assistance in obtaining mineral samples. Students should share their results with the class. Keep an ongoing record of the major minerals for each state. After the reports have been completed, have students construct a U.S. map that shows the major minerals in each state. Then, have student groups review the map for patterns. For instance, is a particular mineral found exclusively in one state or one region? Are some minerals found throughout the country?

L2

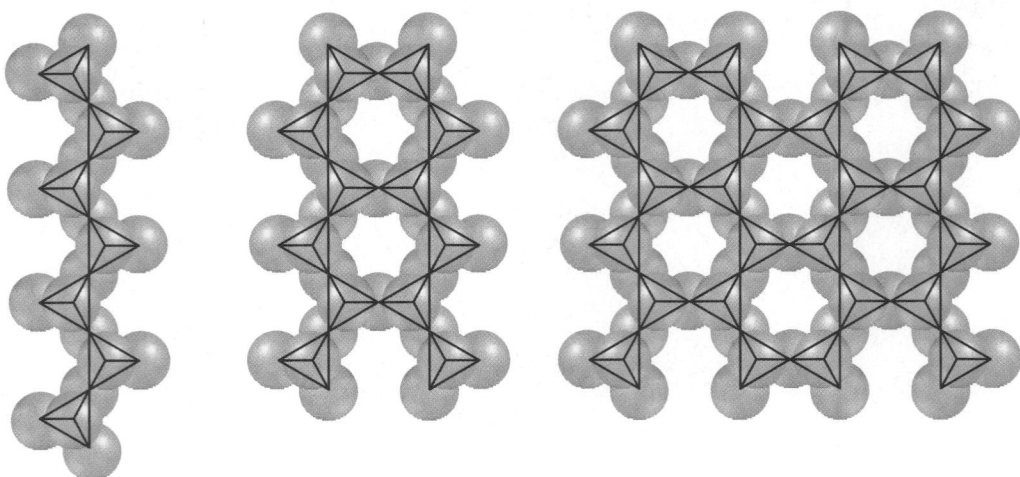

Single chain   Double chain   Sheet

Figure 4-6 Silica tetrahedrons can combine in many ways, including single chains, double chains, and sheets. The different structural combinations account for the diversity of silicates.

structurally in a vast number of ways, which accounts for the diversity of silicates. *Figure 4-6* shows some possible arrangements formed by silica tetrahedrons, including single chains, double chains, and sheets. The bonds between the atoms help determine several mineral properties, including the way a mineral splits. Minerals generally split along planes of weak bonds. For instance, mica is an example of a sheet tetrahedron, wherein an atom of aluminum (Al) or potassium (K) bonds sheets together. Mica separates easily into sheets because the attraction between the tetrahedrons and the atom of aluminum or potassium is weak. Quartz, on the other hand, has an intricate network. Quartz is highly resistant to weathering and does not break easily along any planes because its atoms are strongly bonded together.

Table 4-2 Mineral Groups	
Group	**Example**
Native elements	Copper metal (Cu)
Oxides and hydroxides	Hematite (Fe_2O_3) Brucite ($Mg[OH]_2$)
Halides	Halite (NaCl)
Carbonates	Calcite ($CaCO_3$)
Sulfates	Anhydrite ($CaSO_4$)
Silicates	Olivine (Mg_2SiO_4)
Sulfides	Pyrite (FeS_2)

82 CHAPTER 4 *Minerals*

Interpreting the Illustration

Figure 4-6 Have students describe in their own words how the bonds between silica tetrahedrons affect mineral properties, such as the way a mineral splits.

NY Core Curriculum Standards

Page 82: St 4 KI 3.1a, St 6 KI 1
Page 83: St 4 KI 3.1a & 3.1b, St 6 KI 1

Carbonates Oxygen easily combines with many other elements and thus forms other mineral groups, such as the carbonates and the oxides. Carbonates are minerals composed of one or more metallic elements with the carbonate compound CO_3. Examples of carbonates are calcite, dolomite, and rhodochrosite. Carbonates are the primary minerals found in rocks such as limestone, coquina, and marble. Some carbonates have distinctive colorations, such as the greenish hue of malachite and the blue of azurite, shown in *Figure 4-7.*

Oxides Oxides are compounds of oxygen and a metal. Hematite (Fe_2O_3) and magnetite (Fe_3O_4) are common iron oxides and good sources of iron. The mineral uraninite is valuable because it is the major source of uranium, which is used to generate nuclear power.

Other major mineral groups are sulfides, sulfates, halides, and native elements. Sulfides such as pyrite (FeS_2) are compounds of sulfur and one or more elements. Sulfates such as anhydrite ($CaSO_4$) are composed of elements with the sulfate compound SO_4. Halides such as halite (NaCl) are made up of chloride or fluoride along with calcium, sodium, or potassium. A native element such as silver (Ag) or copper (Cu) is made up of one element only. *Table 4-2* on the previous page summarizes the mineral groups. *Appendix H* contains further information about individual minerals. In the next section, you'll learn how to identify some of the minerals discussed thus far.

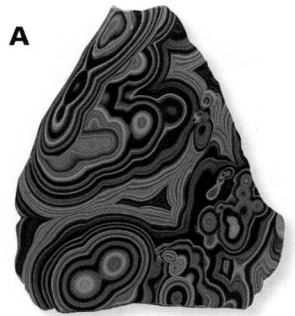
A

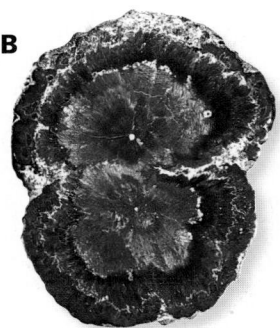
B

Figure 4-7 The carbonates malachite **(A)** and azurite **(B)** have distinct colorations.

3 Assess

Check for Understanding
Discussion
Have students explain why a synthetic diamond is not a mineral. A synthetic diamond is not naturally occurring.

Reteach
Review the definition of a mineral. Provide a visual illustration of each characteristic. For instance, use a mineral sample with large crystals to illustrate that minerals have crystalline structures.

✓Assessment

Knowledge Have students answer the following questions.
1. What is the most abundant element found in Earth's crust? oxygen
2. What is the second-most abundant element found in Earth's crust? silicon
3. What is the most abundant mineral group found in Earth's crust? the silicates
4. What are the two most abundant minerals found in Earth's crust? feldspar and quartz.

SECTION ASSESSMENT

1. Define a mineral. Give two reasons why petroleum is not a mineral.
2. How do minerals form from solution? How do they form from magma?
3. What are the two most abundant elements in Earth's crust? What mineral group do these elements form?
4. Identify the other major mineral groups.
5. Describe a crystal. What determines the size of a mineral crystal formed from magma?
6. **Thinking Critically** Water is an inorganic substance formed by natural processes on Earth. It has a unique chemical composition. Under what conditions, if any, could water be considered a mineral?

SKILL REVIEW

7. **Concept Mapping** Use the following terms and *Appendix H* to construct a concept map of the six major crystal systems. For more help, refer to the *Skill Handbook.*

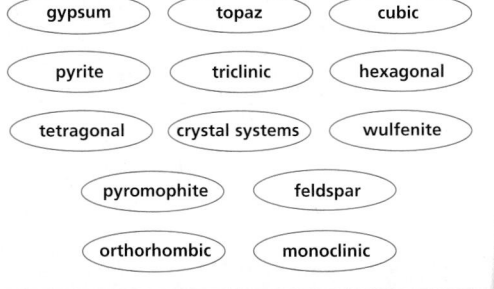

(gypsum) (topaz) (cubic)
(pyrite) (triclinic) (hexagonal)
(tetragonal) (crystal systems) (wulfenite)
(pyromophite) (feldspar)
(orthorhombic) (monoclinic)

earthgeu.com/self_check_quiz

SECTION ASSESSMENT

1. A mineral is a naturally occurring, inorganic solid with a definite crystal shape and a specific chemical composition. Petroleum is not a mineral because it is a liquid and lacks a definitive crystal shape.
2. Minerals form as a result of the evaporation of salts from a supersaturated lake or sea. Minerals also form when magma cools beneath or on Earth's surface.
3. oxygen and silicon; they make up the silicates

4. carbonates, oxides, sulfates, halides, sulfides, and native elements
5. A crystal is a solid in which the atoms are arranged in a specific, repeating pattern. The size and shape of a crystal formed from magma depends on cooling time.
6. Water might be considered a mineral in its frozen state because it satisfies the criteria for a mineral.
7. In the first level: crystal systems; in the second level, in any order: cubic, triclinic,

hexagonal, tetragonal, orthorhombic, and monoclinic; in the third level, pyrite should be connected to cubic, feldspar should be connected to triclinic, pyromophite should be connected to hexagonal, wulfenite should be connected to tetragonal, topaz should be connected to orthorhombic, and gypsum should be connected to monoclinic.

Prepare

Section Background

For section content background, refer to **Hard Diamonds** and **Mineral Identification** on pages 76C–D.

Preplanning

Refer to the Chapter Organizer on pages 76A–B.

1 Focus

Section Focus

Before presenting the lesson, display **Section Focus Transparency 11** on the overhead projector. **L1** **ELL**

Demo

Place a drop of cold, dilute hydrochloric acid on a sample of calcite. **CAUTION:** *Wear safety goggles, safety gloves, and an apron.* Have students describe the chemical reaction. Tell them that calcite is calcium carbonate (CaCo₃). The acid reacts with the calcium carbonate and produces carbon dioxide in the form of fizzing bubbles.

SECTION 4.2

Identifying Minerals

OBJECTIVES

- **Classify** *minerals according to their physical and chemical properties.*
- **Identify** *different types of minerals.*
- **Discuss** *how minerals are used.*

VOCABULARY

luster
streak
hardness
cleavage
fracture
specific gravity
ore
gem

At the beginning of this chapter, we discussed just a few of the many ways in which humans use minerals. Before a mineral can be used, it must first be identified. With more than 3000 minerals in Earth's crust, this presents a problem. How does one go about identifying an unknown mineral?

MINERAL IDENTIFICATION

Geologists rely on several relatively simple tests to identify minerals. These tests are based upon a mineral's physical and chemical properties. As you'll see in the *Design Your Own GeoLab* at the end of this chapter, it's usually best to use a combination of tests rather than just one to identify minerals.

Color One of the most noticeable characteristics of a mineral is its color. Color is sometimes caused by the presence of trace elements or compounds within a mineral. For example, quartz can be found in a variety of colors, as shown in *Figure 4-8*, and these different colors are the result of different trace elements in the quartz samples. Red jasper has trace elements of iron oxides, purple amethyst contains ferric iron, orange citrine contains iron hydrates, and rose quartz contains manganese or titanium. The appearance of milky quartz, on the other hand, is caused by the numerous bubbles of gas and liquid trapped within the crystal. In general, color is one of the least reliable clues to a mineral's identity.

Luster The way that a mineral reflects light from its surface is called **luster.** Luster is described as being either metallic or nonmetallic. Silver, gold, copper, and galena have shiny surfaces that reflect light like the chrome trim on cars. Thus, they are said to have a metallic luster.

Figure 4-8 Orange citrine **(A)**, purple amethyst **(B)**, and red jasper **(C)** are all varieties of quartz. The different colors are caused by trace elements.

A

B

Nonmetallic minerals, such as calcite, gypsum, sulfur, and quartz, do not shine like metals. Their lusters might be described as dull, pearly, waxy, or silky. Differences in luster, shown in *Figure 4-9,* are caused by differences in the chemical compositions of minerals.

Texture Texture describes how a mineral feels to the touch. Like luster and color, texture is often used in combination with other tests to identify a mineral. The texture of a mineral might be described as smooth, rough, ragged, greasy, soapy, or glassy. For example, fluorite has a smooth texture, while the texture of talc is greasy.

Streak A mineral rubbed across an unglazed porcelain plate will sometimes leave a colored powdered streak on the surface of the plate. **Streak** is the color of a mineral when it is broken up and powdered. Sometimes, a mineral's streak does not match the mineral's external color, as shown in *Figure 4-10.* For example, pyrite, which is also known as fool's gold because it looks like gold, leaves a greenish-black streak. Gold, on the other hand, leaves a yellow streak. Thus, streak is one of the main tests used to distinguish pyrite from gold.

A mineral's streak rarely changes, even if it is weathered or its external color varies slightly. For example, fluorite can be purple, yellow, green, or blue, but its streak is always white. The streak test can be used only on minerals that are softer than a porcelain plate. Thus, this test cannot be used to identify all minerals.

Earth Science Online

Topic: Minerals
To find out more about mineral identification, visit the Earth Science Web Site at earthgeu.com

Activity: Choose three minerals. Describe their color, luster, texture, and hardness.

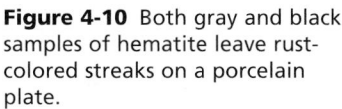

Figure 4-10 Both gray and black samples of hematite leave rust-colored streaks on a porcelain plate.

---

2 Teach

Activity

Visual-Spatial To illustrate that color is not the most reliable way to identify a mineral, obtain samples of colorless and different-colored calcite, such as orange, blue, green, and reddish-brown. Do not identify the samples for students yet. Instead, ask students to compare and contrast the physical properties of the samples. Then tell students that the minerals are all calcite. The color of each sample differs because of the presence of trace elements in the minerals.
L2

Content Background

Some motor oil is dark gray. The color is caused by the mineral graphite. Graphite is added to the motor oil because its softness makes it a good lubricant for the moving parts in motors. Graphite also can be used to lubricate moving parts in door locks. A powdered form of the mineral is squeezed into the door mechanism.

Differentiated Instruction

Learning Disabled Obtain or construct wooden, plastic, or paper models of the six basic crystal systems. Have students with learning disabilities practice taking the models apart and putting them back together. If the models do not come apart, let students handle and examine them. Have mineral samples that represent each crystal system available for students to examine.

Across the Curriculum

Math Have students work with partners to find the density of several minerals. Students should show their work and record their data in a table format. Also, tell students the density of a mineral, and have them calculate the mass of the sample, then solve for volume.

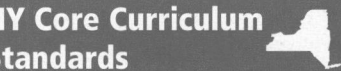

Reinforcement

Kinesthetic Have a student demonstrate how the Mohs scale of hardness can be used to identify an unknown mineral. Give the student samples of fluorite, apatite, and calcite, but do not identify which sample is which. By scratching the minerals against one another, the student should be able to identify the samples. For instance, the apatite will scratch both the fluorite and the calcite. The fluorite will scratch the calcite, but not the apatite. The calcite will not scratch the fluorite or the apatite.

Collaborative Learning

Interpersonal Have students work with partners to examine the following samples of quartz: amethyst, citrine, agate, crystalline quartz, and smoky quartz. Ask students to list the physical properties of each sample in a data table. At a minimum, data tables should include crystal shape, color, texture, and luster. Have pairs of students share their data with other pairs.
L2 COOP LEARN

Hardness One of the most useful tests for identifying minerals is hardness. **Hardness** is a measure of how easily a mineral can be scratched. German geologist Friedrich Mohs developed a scale in which an unknown mineral's hardness can be compared to the known hardnesses of ten minerals. The minerals in the Mohs scale of mineral hardness were selected because they are easily recognized and —with the exception of diamond—readily found in nature. Talc is one of the softest minerals and can be scratched by a fingernail; thus, talc represents 1 on the Mohs scale of hardness. In contrast, diamond is so hard that it can be used as a sharpener and cutting tool; diamond represents 10 on the Mohs scale of hardness. The scale, shown in *Table 4-3,* works like this: any mineral with a greater hardness than another mineral will scratch that softer mineral. For example, topaz will scratch quartz but not corundum. Hardness, which is one of the most reliable tests of mineral identification, is determined by the arrangement of a mineral's atoms.

Cleavage and Fracture Atomic arrangement also determines how a mineral will break. Minerals break along planes where atomic bonding is weak. A mineral that splits relatively easily and evenly along one or more flat planes is said to have **cleavage.** To identify a mineral by cleavage, geologists count the number of cleaved planes and study the angle or angles between them. For instance, mica, shown in *Figure 4-11A,* has perfect cleavage in one direction. It breaks in sheets because of weak atomic bonds, as you learned in the earlier discussion about silica tetrahedrons. Halite has a cubic cleavage,

Table 4-3	Mohs Hardness Scale		
	Hardness		**Hardness of Common Objects**
Talc	1	(softest)	
Gypsum	2		fingernail (2.5)
Calcite	3		piece of copper (3.5)
Fluorite	4		iron nail (4.5)
Apatite	5		glass (5.5)
Feldspar	6		steel file (6.5)
Quartz	7		streak plate (7)
Topaz	8		scratches quartz
Corundum	9		scratches topaz
Diamond	10	(hardest)	scratches all common materials

Resource Manager

Laboratory Manual, pp. 25–28 L2
Teaching Transparency 10 L2 ELL

Interpreting the Illustration

Table 4-3 Provide an unglazed porcelain streak plate for students to use to assess the hardness of mineral samples. Minerals softer than the streak plate will leave a streak on the streak plate. Minerals harder than the streak plate will scratch it.

Figure 4-11 Mica has perfect cleavage in one direction **(A)**. Quartz breaks along rough or jagged edges **(B)**. The rock obsidian fractures into arc-like patterns **(C)**.

which means that it breaks in three directions along planes of weak atomic attraction. Quartz, shown in *Figure 4-11B,* breaks unevenly along jagged edges because of its tightly bonded atoms. Minerals that break with rough or jagged edges are said to have **fracture.** Flint, chalcedony, and the rock obsidian share a unique fracture with arc-like patterns resembling clam shells, as shown in *Figure 4-11C.* This is called conchoidal fracture.

Density and Specific Gravity Sometimes, two minerals of the same size may feel quite different when they are lifted—one is much heavier than the other. Differences in weight are the result of differences in density, which is defined as mass per unit of volume. Density is expressed as a ratio of the mass of a substance divided by its volume, or $D = M/V$. Pyrite, for instance, has a density of 5.2 g/cm^3, and gold has a density of 19.0 g/cm^3.

Density reflects the atomic weight and structure of a mineral. Because density is not dependent on the size or shape of a mineral, it is a particularly useful identification tool. Often, however, differences in density are too small to be distinguished by simply lifting different minerals and estimating their perceived weights. Thus, for accurate mineral identification, density must be measured. The most common measure of density used by geologists is **specific gravity,** which is the ratio of the weight of a substance to the weight

Identifying Misconceptions

Many people mistakenly believe that diamond is the only mineral hard enough to scratch glass, and that this ability to scratch glass is a foolproof way to identify diamond.

Uncover the Misconception
Ask students whether they believe that only diamond can scratch glass. A number of students will likely say yes. Tell the class that glass has a hardness of 5.5 on the Mohs scale of mineral hardness. Therefore, any mineral with a hardness greater than 5.5 will scratch a glass surface.

Demonstrate the Concept
Rake a sample of crystalline quartz across a piece of glass. Have students observe the scratch left on glass by the quartz.

Assess New Knowledge
Tell students to use a field guide to minerals or Appendix H to create a list of minerals that will scratch glass. Possible minerals include diamond, feldspar, topaz, corundum, quartz, and amethyst.

Earth Science

Journal

Show students relatively large samples of muscovite or biotite. Demonstrate how the samples cleave. Tell students that these minerals are often called "books." Ask students to infer why. They should write their explanations in their science journals. Have students include sketches of the cleaved samples in their explanations. Large samples of muscovite or biotite are called books because the individual sheets of mica can be separated along one cleavage plane, similar to the pages in a book.

NY Core Curriculum Standards
Page 86: St 4 KI 3.1a
Page 87: St 4 KI 3.1a

Purpose

Students will complete a mineral identification chart.

Process Skills

make and use tables, predict, observe and infer, interpret data, classify, compare and contrast

Materials

Appendix H, pencil, data table included in lab

Teaching Strategies

- Ask students whether they have ever had to identify an unknown object. Have students describe the process that they used.
- Some students may have mineral collections. Have these students share their collections with the class. Students should describe how they acquired the samples in their collection.

Analysis

1. The minerals, in descending order in the table, are copper, hematite, gold, garnet, feldspar, and corundum.
2. Student data tables should match the data table below.

Thinking Critically

3. Corundum will scratch quartz. It has a hardness of 9 and quartz has a hardness of only 7.
4. Hematite is used in paint pigments. Iron or steel in desks would be made from hematite, the major iron ore.
5. Answers will vary. The table could have included luster, texture, density, and special properties. In addition, the mineral's chemical formulas could have been included in the table.

✓Assessment

Skill Have students identify a mineral based on the following data. The mineral is colorless, has a hardness of 7, a hexagonal crystal system, and a conchoidal breakage pattern. quartz

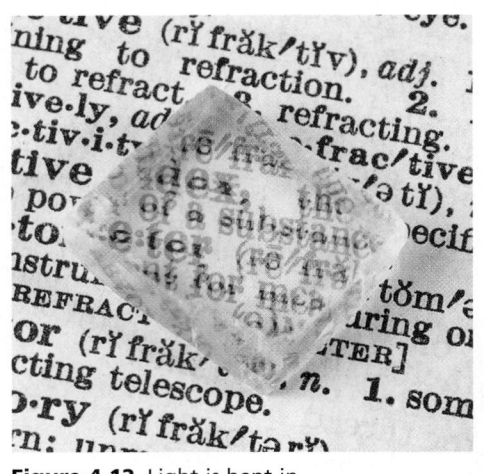

Figure 4-12 Light is bent in two directions when it passes through a sample of Iceland spar. The refraction creates the appearance of two images.

of an equal volume of water at 4°C. Do the *Problem-Solving Lab* to learn how specific gravity and other mineral properties are used to identify minerals.

SPECIAL PROPERTIES

Several special properties of minerals also can be used for identification purposes. For instance, the arrangement of atoms in a type of calcite called Iceland spar causes light to be bent in two directions when it passes through the mineral. The refraction of the single ray of light into two rays creates the appearance of two images, as shown in *Figure 4-12*. This process is known as double refraction. Double refraction is also a property of the mineral zircon.

Calcite exhibits another special property as a result of its chemical composition. Calcite ($CaCO_3$) fizzes when it comes into contact with hydrochloric acid (HCl). HCl reacts with calcite to release CO_2 in the form of bubbling gas. In this reaction, shown below, calcium chloride ($CaCl_2$) also forms.

$$CaCO_3 + 2HCl \longrightarrow CaCl_2 + H_2O + CO_2$$

Problem-Solving Lab

Making and Using Tables

Complete a mineral identification table Minerals can be identified by their physical and chemical properties. Common properties include color, streak, hardness, specific gravity, and crystalline structure.

Analysis

1. Copy the data table shown here. Use *Appendix H* to complete the table.
2. Expand the table to include the names of the minerals, information about breakage patterns, and mineral uses.

Thinking Critically

3. Which of these minerals will scratch quartz? How do you know?
4. Which of these minerals might be found in a painting? Which might be found in your desk?
5. What other information could you have included in the table?

Mineral Identification Chart

Mineral Color	Streak	Hardness	Specific Gravity	Crystal System
copper red		3	8.5–9	cubic
	red or reddish brown	6	5.3	hexagonal
pale to golden yellow	yellow			cubic
	colorless	7.5	3.5	
gray, green or white			2.5	triclinic
	colorless		4.0	hexagonal

Name	Fracture	Use	Color	Streak	Hardness	SG	Crystal System
copper	hackly fracture	coins, pipes, wiring	copper red	copper red	3	8.5–9	cubic
hematite	irregular fracture	source of iron	black or reddish brown	red or reddish brown	6	5.3	hexagonal
gold	hackly	jewelry, medicines	pale to golden yellow	yellow	2.5–3	19.3	cubic
garnet	conchoidal fracture	jewelry	deep yellow-red	colorless	7.5	3.5	cubic
feldspar	two cleavage planes	manufacture of porcelain	gray, green or white	colorless	6	2.5	triclinic
corundum	fracture	gemstones, abrasives	varies widely	colorless	9	4.0	hexagonal

Other special properties are exhibited by magnetite, an iron ore. Magnetite is naturally magnetic. Lodestone, a form of magnetite, will pick up nails like a magnet, as shown in *Figure 4-13*. The mineral sphalerite produces a distinctive rotten-egg odor when it is rubbed vigorously across a streak plate. The smell is the result of the presence of sulfide in the mineral.

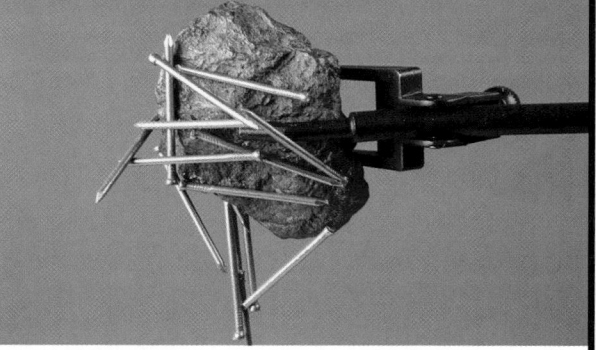

Figure 4-13 Magnetite can pick up iron nails because it is naturally magnetic.

MINERAL USES

There's a good chance that as you read these words, you're sitting on minerals, wearing minerals, and perhaps even eating minerals. Minerals are virtually everywhere. They are used to make computers, cars, televisions, desks, roads, buildings, jewelry, beds, paints, sports equipment, and medicines. This list is by no means exhaustive. In fact, it barely touches upon the many ways in which people use minerals.

Ores Many of the items mentioned above are made from ores. A mineral is an **ore** if it contains a useful substance that can be mined at a profit. Hematite, for instance, is a useful ore that contains the element iron. Look around the room. Are any items made of iron? If so, their original source may have been the mineral hematite. Are any items in the room made of aluminum? The element aluminum is found in the ore bauxite. Another mineral and its use are shown in *Figure 4-14.*

ENVIRONMENTAL CONNECTION

Figure 4-14 The ore rutile **(A)** contains the element titanium, a durable, lightweight metal often used in sports equipment **(B).**

Cultural Diversity

Ancient Peruvian Gold Before the 1500s, the world's most precious metal, gold, was mainly mined in Greece and Italy. When these supplies of gold became limited, European explorers sought gold in the Americas. When the Spanish invaded Peru, they encountered cultures such as the Chimu, the Chavin, the Nazca, and the Inca, who were experienced miners and goldsmiths. These cultures had found gold in the rivers of the Andes Mountains as early as 1200 B.C.; they later developed complex mining techniques. By 500 B.C., Chavin artisans were hammering gold into fine sheets and engraving it. The Chimu further developed this art and used sophisticated casting and filigree techniques, which involved intricate openwork designs. In 1531, Francisco Pizarro invaded Peru and had the gold artifacts melted down to ship them back to Spain; thus, very few treasures of the ancient American cultures exist. However, more than 10 000 specimens of the ancient gold artifacts are preserved in the Museo de Oro in Bogotá, Colombia.

Environmental Connection

Interpersonal Divide the class into groups of four. Assign each group an ore to research in the library or on the Glencoe Science Web Site. Possible research topics include ores that are mined for gold, zinc, iron, silver, aluminum, sulfur, tin, and uranium. Student reports should include the uses of the ore, where is the ore found, and methods of extracting the ore. Encourage students to develop multimedia presentations to share their results. **COOP LEARN**

P

Enrichment

If possible, arrange a guided field trip to a local quarry or mine. Have students come up with questions beforehand to ask the person conducting the tour. If no mine or quarry is within driving distance, have students contact and interview a mining expert via the Glencoe Science Web Site. Encourage students to ask a wide variety of questions. For instance, in addition to questions about extraction methods, students can ask about safety and reclamation issues.

Figure 4-15 The open-pit mine in the background, located in Carajas, Brazil, is the world's largest iron mine.

Mines Ores that are located deep within Earth's crust are removed by underground mining. Ores that are near Earth's surface are obtained from large, open-pit mines, such as the one shown in *Figure 4-15.* When a mine is excavated, unwanted rock and dirt, known as waste material, are dug up along with the valuable ore. The waste material must be separated from the ore before the ore can be used. Removing the waste material can be expensive and, in some cases, harmful to the environment, as you'll learn in later chapters. If the cost of removing the waste material becomes higher than the value of the ore itself, then the mineral will no longer be classified as an ore. It would no longer be economical to mine it.

The classification of a mineral as an ore may also change if the supply of or demand for that mineral changes. Consider a mineral that is used to make computers. Engineers might develop a more efficient design or a less costly alternative material. In either of these cases, the mineral would no longer be used in computers. Demand for the mineral would drop substantially, and the mineral would no longer be considered an ore.

GEMS

What makes a ruby more valuable than mica? Rubies are much rarer and more visually pleasing than mica. Rubies are thus considered gems. **Gems** are valuable minerals that are prized for their rarity and beauty. Gems such as rubies, emeralds, and diamonds are cut, polished, and used for jewelry. *Figure 4-16* shows a raw

Earth Science
Journal

Science Field Book

Linguistic Have students access the Glencoe Science Web Site to visit the Smithsonian Museum of Natural History—specifically, the Hall of Minerals. Have students explore the different ways that gems and minerals have been used by artists. Students should write brief reports describing their research.

Resource Manager

GeoLab and MiniLab Worksheets, pp. 15–18 **L2**

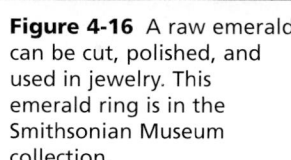

Figure 4-16 A raw emerald can be cut, polished, and used in jewelry. This emerald ring is in the Smithsonian Museum collection.

emerald and a polished emerald. Because of their rareness, rubies and emeralds are actually more valuable than diamonds. You'll learn more about diamonds in the *Science and Math* feature at the end of this chapter.

In some cases, the presence of trace elements can make one variety of a mineral more colorful and thus more prized than other varieties of the same mineral. Amethyst, for instance, is the gem form of quartz. Amethyst contains trace minerals, which give the gem a lovely purple color. The mineral corundum, which is often used as an abrasive, also can be found as rubies and sapphires. Rubies contain trace amounts of chromium; sapphires contain trace amounts of cobalt or titanium.

SECTION ASSESSMENT

1. Explain why color is not a good test for distinguishing between pyrite and gold. What test is most reliable for identifying these two minerals?

2. What is a mineral's texture? List several words that are used to describe texture.

3. Compare and contrast cleavage and fracture. Give an example of a mineral with cleavage and a mineral with fracture.

4. Describe the chemical reaction that takes place when hydrochloric acid comes in contact with calcite.

5. What is the hardness of a mineral if it scratches a penny but will not scratch glass?

6. What is an ore?

7. Why are some minerals classified as gems? List several gems.

8. **Critical Thinking** The mineral fluorite can be found in a variety of colors, yet its streak is always white. Why?

SKILL REVIEW

9. **Making and Using Tables** Use *Appendix H* and reference materials to make a data table that includes examples of minerals with the following special properties: magnetism, double refraction, reaction to acid, and smell. For more help, refer to the *Skill Handbook*.

4.2 *Identifying Minerals* **91**

Check for Understanding

Demo

Place samples of minerals on a table at the front of the classroom. Have student volunteers identify and describe the mineral samples. Students should explain what criteria they used to identify the samples.

Reteach

Linguistic Have students outline the main ideas of this chapter in their science journals. Ask students to provide specific examples in support of each main idea. L2

Portfolio Have students research and write reports about mining. Students can access the Glencoe Science Web Site for more information about mining operations and reclamation policies. Students also can contact the U.S. Environmental Protection Agency. Student reports should include photographs, diagrams, ore samples, and references.

SECTION ASSESSMENT

1. The minerals are similar in color. The best test to distinguish between pyrite and gold is streak.

2. Texture is the way a mineral feels to the touch. *Rough, smooth, greasy, glassy, soapy,* and *ragged* describe texture.

3. Both cleavage and fracture describe how minerals split. Minerals with cleavage split relatively easily and evenly along one or more planes. An example is mica. Minerals with fracture break unevenly along rough

and jagged edges. An example is quartz.

4. The acid reacts with the calcite to release carbon dioxide in the form of bubbling gas.

5. A penny (copper) has a hardness of about 3.5. A piece of glass has a hardness of about 5.5. A mineral that will scratch a penny but not a piece of glass has a hardness greater than 3.5 but less than 5.5.

6. a mineral that contains a useful substance that can be mined at a profit

7. They are rare and beautiful. Rubies, emeralds, and diamonds are gems.

8. A mineral's streak reflects its internal chemical composition, and is usually not affected by weathering, erosion, or trace elements.

9. Student tables will vary but should reflect information shown in Appendix H.

91

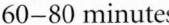

Making a Field Guide to Minerals

Have you ever used a field guide to identify a bird, flower, rock, or insect? If so, you know that field guides include far more than simply photographs. A typical field guide for minerals might include background information about minerals in general, plus specific information about the formation, properties, and uses of each mineral. In this activity, you'll create a field guide to minerals.

Time Allotment

60–80 minutes

Process Skills

observe and infer, classify, model, analyze data, compare and contrast, communicate, interpret data, interpret scientific illustrations

Preparation

Some of the data for this lab can be found in Appendix H.

Possible Hypotheses

Students may hypothesize that a combination of properties can be used to identify minerals. Students may note that these properties, along with other special properties, should be included in a field guide to aid in mineral identification.

Plan the Experiment

Teaching Strategies

- In addition to their testing the samples, encourage students to access additional data from the library, the Glencoe Science Web Site, museums, and mineral collectors.
- Have a variety of field guides available for students to examine. The field guides will help students decide what type of information to include in their own field guides.

Possible Procedures

Students will devise tests for the mineral samples based on the materials listed in the lab. Students may begin by scratching

Preparation

Problem

How would you go about identifying minerals? What physical and chemical properties would you test? Which of these properties should be included in a field guide to help others to identify unknown minerals?

Possible Materials

mineral samples
hand lens
glass plate
streak plate
Mohs scale of
  mineral hardness
5 percent hydrochloric
  acid (HCl) with dropper

Appendix H
steel file or nail
piece of copper
paper clip
magnet

Hypothesis

As a group, form a hypothesis about which property or properties might be most useful in identifying minerals.

Objectives

In this GeoLab, you will:

- **Conduct** tests on unknown minerals to determine their physical and chemical properties.
- **Identify** minerals based on the results of your tests.
- **Design** a field guide for minerals.

Safety Precautions

Review the safe use of acids. HCl may cause burns. If a spill occurs, rinse your skin with water and notify your teacher immediately.

each mineral with the piece of copper, the glass plate, the steel file or nail, and the paper clip to establish the mineral's hardness. Then, students may use the streak plate to determine the streak of each mineral. Students also may separate the minerals by color, luster, or heft (specific gravity). Students will likely use the hydrochloric acid and a magnet to test for special properties. Students will use their results to make a field guide to minerals. The field guide will include information about

how each mineral formed, its uses, its chemical formula, and a photograph or sketch of the mineral.

Data and Observations

Students should find that certain properties, such as hardness, are more reliable than others, such as color. Also, students should discover that a combination of properties is the best way to identify minerals.

Plan the Experiment

1. As a group, list the steps that you will take to test your hypothesis. Keep the available materials in mind as you plan your procedure. Be specific, describing exactly what you will do at each step. Properties that you may want to test include luster, color, reaction to HCl, magnetism, cleavage, fracture, texture, hardness, streak, double refraction, and density.
2. Should you test any of the properties more than once for any of the minerals? How will you determine whether certain properties indicate a specific mineral?
3. Design a data table to summarize your results. You can use this table as the basis for your field guide.

4. Read over your entire experiment to make sure that all steps are in a logical order.
5. Have you included a step for additional research? You may have to use the library or the Earth Science Web Site to gather all the necessary information for your field guide.
6. What information will be included in the field guide? Possible data include how each mineral formed, its uses, its chemical formula, and a labeled photograph or drawing of the mineral.
7. Make sure your teacher approves your plan before you proceed with your experiment.

Analyze

1. **Interpreting Results** Which properties were most reliable for identifying minerals? Which properties were least reliable? Discuss reasons why one property is more useful than others.
2. **Defending Your Hypothesis** Was your hypothesis supported? Why or why not?
3. **Thinking Critically** How could you use a piece of paper, a steel knife, and a glass bottle to distinguish between Iceland spar and quartz?

4. **Observing and Inferring** What mineral reacted with the HCl? Why did the mineral bubble? Write the balanced equation that describes the chemical reaction that took place between the mineral and the acid.
5. **Conducting Research** What information did you include in the field guide? What resources did you use to gather your data? Describe the layout of your field guide.

Conclude & Apply

1. Compare and contrast your field guide with those of other groups. How could you improve your field guide?

2. What are the advantages and disadvantages of field guides?
3. Based on your results, is there any one definitive test that can always be used to identify a mineral? Explain.

Design Your Own GeoLab **93**

Conclude & Apply (continued)

is that it offers information in an abridged form.
3. Students will likely find that a combination of tests worked better than any one particular test.

✓ Assessment

Portfolio Have students each create a collage representing the major groups of minerals: oxides, carbonates, sulfates, halides, sulfides, silicates, and native elements. Collages might include photos, sketches, or diagrams. **P**

Analyze

1. Answers will vary. Special properties are most reliable for mineral identification because usually only one or two minerals share specific special properties. The least reliable properties for identification of a mineral are color, luster, and texture because many minerals share these same properties.
2. Answers will vary.
3. The Iceland spar will tear the paper but it will not scratch the knife or glass. The quartz will tear the paper, and scratch the steel knife and glass bottle. This indicates that the quartz is harder than the Iceland spar.
4. Calcite reacts with HCl. The HCl and calcium carbonate found in the calcite react to release carbon dioxide gas in the form of bubbles. The equation is $CaCO_3 + 2HCl \rightarrow CaCl_2 + H_2O + CO_2$.
5. Students should have included the name of each mineral, its properties, its uses, its chemical formula, and a photograph or sketch of the mineral. Students likely collected data from their tests, the library, the Internet, magazines, field guides, and mineral collections. Layouts should be clear and easy to follow.

Conclude & Apply

1. Answers will vary greatly. Use this opportunity to encourage a lively class discussion about the best features to include in a field guide to minerals.
2. Answers will vary. The main advantage of a field guide is that it can be used to identify and classify objects using both physical and chemical properties. The main disadvantage

Purpose

Students will learn how diamonds are valued based on their color, cut, clarity, and weight, which is measured in carats.

Content Background

Diamonds are found imbedded in certain igneous rocks or as loose stones in sands and eroded gravels. Diamond-bearing igneous rocks occur as pipes that may extend all the way to Earth's mantle. Most diamonds form at great depths and are carried to Earth's surface by the molten rock.

Teaching Strategies

Some minerals have very complex chemical formulas. The chemical formula for diamond, however, is very simple: pure carbon. Another mineral, graphite, is also pure carbon. Diamond and graphite seem about as different as two minerals can be, yet chemically, they are exactly the same. Have students research why the minerals are different. The differences in the physical properties of the minerals are caused by the internal arrangements of the carbon atoms. In graphite, the atoms are linked into sheets. The sheets can easily slide over one another, which makes graphite a good lubricant. The sheets are also easily separated, even when graphite is rubbed against a substance as soft as paper. This causes the graphite in a so-called lead pencil to leave a mark. In diamond, on the other hand, the atoms of carbon are tightly linked in all directions. This makes diamond the hardest natural substance. In fact,

The Price of Diamonds

*F*or centuries people have valued diamonds for their beauty, sparkle, and hardness. The cost of a diamond in a jewelry store depends mainly on four things, often called the four Cs.

Color and Cut

Diamonds come in many colors. Colorless diamonds cost more than those with a slight yellowish tinge, but stones with a deep, rich color, such as the famous blue Hope Diamond, are the most valued of all. The different colors are caused by minor impurities.

Diamonds are cut into many shapes. Some of the most common shapes are the round brilliant; the rose, which is round with a flat-bottom and pointed top; the marquis, which is an oval with pointed ends; and the emerald cut, which is rectangular with rounded corners. The cut of a diamond affects how it reflects light and thus how much it sparkles. An uncut diamond crystal looks like a greasy piece of glass.

Clarity and Carat Weight

Clarity refers to the presence or absence of visible flaws and impurities in the diamond. A diamond is considered flawless if no such defects are visible under a magnification power of ten. Dozens of minerals occur in diamonds, the most common being olivine, garnet, and clinopyroxene. Bubbles of liquid or gas are also found within diamond crystals.

The weight of a diamond is represented by an ancient unit of measurement called the carat. A carat is 1/5 of a gram, or 1/142 of an ounce. The name probably came

from the tropical carob tree, which has quite uniform seeds.

Comparing the Costs

Because the combination of the four Cs varies among diamonds, there is no set price for a diamond. A 1-carat diamond may cost $7500. How does that compare with the cost of other items you buy?

Procedure

1. The data table lists some items you may frequently buy, along with their estimated price and mass. Copy the table, then calculate and record the weight in carats of each item.

Challenge

1. Calculate and record the cost per carat of each item in the data table.
2. The price of a 1-carat diamond may be $7500. How much would the items in the data table cost if they were priced at $7500 per carat?

Cost Comparison					
Item	Price	Mass (g)	Weight (carats)	Cost/ Carat	Cost at $7500/ carat
music CD	$14.00	16	80	17.5¢	$600,000
magazine	$3.99	148	740	0.5¢	$5.55 million
can of soda	.75¢	355	1775	0.04¢	$13.3 million
gallon of milk	$1.89	3629	18144	0.01¢	$136 million

the word *diamond* comes from the Greek word *adamas*, meaning "invincible."

Data and Observations

Students should find that everyday items would be horrendously expensive if they cost the same per carat as diamonds do.

Sources of Error

Make sure that students use the proper formula to calculate their cost comparisons.

Challenge

1. See data table on the student page for answers.
2. See data table on the student page for answers.

Summary

SECTION 4.1

What is a mineral?

Main Ideas

- A mineral is a naturally occurring, inorganic solid with a specific chemical composition and a definite crystalline structure. There are at least 3000 known minerals in Earth's crust.
- A crystal is a solid in which the atoms are arranged in repeating patterns. The six main crystal systems are cubic, tetragonal, hexagonal, orthorhombic, monoclinic, and triclinic.
- Minerals form from magma or from supersaturated solution. Most minerals are formed from the eight most common elements in Earth's crust.
- Oxygen readily combines with other elements to form a diverse group of minerals, including silicates, carbonates, and oxides. A silica tetrahedron is a three-dimensional shape structured like a pyramid. In a silica tetrahedron one silicon atom attaches to four oxygen atoms.
- Other major mineral groups include sulfides, sulfates, halides, and native elements. Native elements such as silver or copper are made of one element only.

Vocabulary

crystal (p. 79)
magma (p. 80)
mineral (p. 77)
silicate (p. 81)

SECTION 4.2

Identifying Minerals

Main Ideas

- Minerals can be identified based on their physical and chemical properties. The most reliable way to identify a mineral is by using a combination of several tests.
- A mineral's color is generally the result of trace elements within the mineral. Texture describes how a mineral feels, and luster describes how a mineral reflects light. Cleavage and fracture describe how minerals break.
- A mineral's streak, hardness, and density are reliable methods of identification. Special properties of minerals such as magnetism also can be used for identification purposes.
- An ore contains a useful substance that can be mined at a profit. If the cost of mining the ore becomes higher than the value of the ore, then the mineral is no longer classified as an ore. The classification of a mineral as an ore may also change if the supply of or demand for the mineral changes.
- Gems are valuable minerals that are prized for their rarity and beauty. Trace elements can make one variety of a mineral more valuable than other varieties of the same mineral.

Vocabulary

cleavage (p. 86)
fracture (p. 87)
gem (p. 90)
hardness (p. 86)
luster (p. 84)
ore (p. 89)
specific gravity (p. 87)
streak (p. 85)

 earthgeu.com/vocabulary_puzzlemaker

CHAPTER 4
Study Guide

Main Ideas

Summary statements can be used by students to review the major concepts of the chapter.

VOCABULARY PuzzleMaker

For additional help with vocabulary, have students access the Vocabulary Puzzlemaker online.

earthgeu.com/ vocabulary puzzlemaker

(0:00) Out of Time?

If time does not permit teaching the entire chapter, use the GeoDigest at the end of the unit as an overview.

Earth Science Online

Be sure to check the Earth Science Web Site for links to chapter material:
earthgeu.com

GLENCOE Technology

Videotape/DVD
MindJogger Videoquizzes

Chapter 4: *Minerals*
Have students work in groups as they play the videoquiz game to review key chapter concepts.

 **Resource Manager**

Chapter Assessment, pp. 19–24
MindJogger Videoquizzes DVD/VHS
ExamView® Pro CD-ROM
Performance Assessment in Earth Science

 **NY Core Curriculum Standards**

Page 92: St 1 Science KI 1, 2, & 3, St 4 KI 3.1a
Page 93: St 1 Science KI 1, 2, & 3, St 4 KI 3.1a, St 6 KI 1
Page 94: St 1 Math KI 1, 2, & 3, St 4 KI 3.1a, St 7 KI 1
Page 95: St 4 KI 3.1a, 3.1b, & 3.1c, St 6 KI 1

Understanding Main Ideas

1. c
2. d
3. a
4. b
5. b
6. d
7. b
8. b
9. a
10. a
11. a
12. Some minerals such as magnetite have the property of magnetism and are therefore able to attract magnets. Other special properties of minerals include double refraction and reaction to acid.
13. The four minerals all have the cubic crystal shapes.
14. The crystal shape is determined by the internal arrangement of a mineral's atoms. Examples will vary but may include pyrite (cubic), graphite (hexagonal), feldspar (triclinic), topaz (orthorhombic), muscovite (monoclinic), and bornite (tetragonal).
15. Trace elements give the samples different colors.

Understanding Main Ideas

1. How many minerals are found in Earth's crust?
   a. 1000   c. 3000
   b. 2000   d. 4000

2. Which of the following is part of the definition of a mineral?
   a. liquid   c. synthetic
   b. organic   d. inorganic

3. What element is the most abundant in Earth's crust?
   a. oxygen   c. silicon
   b. aluminum   d. potassium

4. What property causes the mineral galena to break into tiny cubes?
   a. its density
   b. the internal arrangement of its atoms
   c. its hardness
   d. its luster

5. What mineral fizzes when it comes in contact with hydrochloric acid?
   a. quartz   c. gypsum
   b. calcite   d. fluorite

6. A student rubs a mineral across an unglazed porcelain plate. What mineral property is the student testing?
   a. hardness   c. color
   b. luster   d. streak

7. A mineral has a mass of 100 g and a volume of 50 cm³. What is its density?
   a. 5000 g   c. 5 g/cm³
   b. 2 g/cm³   d. 150 g/cm³

8. *Dull, silky, waxy,* and *pearly* are descriptive terms that best describe which property of minerals?
   a. color   c. streak
   b. luster   d. cleavage

9. What would you use the Mohs scale of hardness for?
   a. to identify a mineral
   b. to find the mass of a mineral
   c. to calculate the density of a mineral
   d. to determine a mineral's fracture

10. The streak of which mineral is different from its external color?
   a. pyrite   c. copper
   b. gold   d. magnetite

11. What is an ore?
   a. a mineral that contains a useful substance
   b. a mineral found in food
   c. a mineral that has streak, but no color
   d. a mineral for which there is no demand

12. Why do some minerals attract magnets? What are some other special properties of minerals?

13. What property do the minerals copper, galena, magnetite, and pyrite have in common? Use *Appendix H* for help.

14. Why do minerals have different crystal shapes? Give examples of minerals that exhibit each of the six main crystal systems.

15. Sapphires and rubies are both forms of the mineral corundum, but they are different colors. Why?

earthgeu.com/chapter_test

Applying Main Ideas

16. The word *geology* would appear to be written twice. The light rays are bent in two different directions when they pass through the Iceland spar. This double refraction of light is caused by the internal arrangement of atoms.
17. The mineral in the photo is magnetite.
18. Student tables should correspond to the following table.

Property	Diamond	Graphite
composition	carbon	carbon
hardness	10	1
crystal shape	cubic	hexagonal
breakage pattern	cleavage	basal cleavage
specific gravity	4.5 to 5.5	2.3
streak	white	black to gray

Applying Main Ideas

16. A student places a clean, transparent sample of Iceland spar on top of the word *geology* in a textbook. How will the word *geology* appear to the student? Explain.

17. Use *Appendix H* to identify the mineral in the photo below. It contains iron, has a metallic luster, and has a streak that is the same color as the mineral itself.

18. Make a data table that compares and contrasts the chemical and physical properties of graphite and diamond. Use *Appendix H* and reference materials for help.

19. Calculate the density of copper if the volume of a sample is 30 cm³ and the mass is 267 g.

Thinking Critically

20. Topaz will not leave a streak on an unglazed porcelain plate. Why? What method could you use to observe the streak of topaz?

21. Other than diamond, what mineral would be best for making a sandpaper product? Why? Use *Appendix H* for help.

22. Infer how early prospectors used density to determine whether they had found gold or pyrite.

23. When would a mineral no longer be an ore? Explain.

earthgeu.com/standardized_test

Standardized Test Practice

1. What is the second most abundant element in Earth's crust?
- **a.** magma
- **b.** oxygen
- **c.** silicon
- **d.** carbon

Use the table below to answer questions 2–3.

Mineral Characteristics			
Mineral	**Hardness**	**Specific Gravity**	**Luster/ Color**
Feldspar	6–6.5	2.5–2.8	nonmetallic/ colorless or white
Fluorite	4	3–3.3	nonmetallic/ yellow, blue, purple, rose, green, or brown
Galena	2.5–2.75	7.4–7.6	metallic/ grayish black
Quartz	7	2.65	nonmetallic/ colorless in pure form

2. What is the hardest mineral in the table?
- **a.** feldspar
- **b.** fluorite
- **c.** galena
- **d.** quartz

3. Which mineral most likely has a shiny appearance?
- **a.** feldspar
- **b.** fluorite
- **c.** galena
- **d.** quartz

4. Which is the most reliable clue to a mineral's identity?
- **a.** color
- **b.** streak
- **c.** hardness
- **d.** luster

Assessment **97**

19. $d = m/v$
$d = 267\text{ g} \div 30\text{ cm}^3 = 8.9\text{ g/cm}^3$

Thinking Critically

20. The porcelain plate has a hardness of 6. Topaz has a hardness of 8. Topaz is harder than the streak plate and therefore will scratch the porcelain plate. Answers will vary. To observe the streak of topaz, students may suggest scratching the topaz on a harder mineral.

21. Corundum has a hardness of 9 and thus would make excellent sandpaper products.

22. Gold has a greater density than pyrite and the miners compared the perceived weights of the minerals.

23. A mineral will no longer be classified as an ore when the cost of mining the mineral exceeds profits.

EXAM*VIEW*® PRO

Use Exam*View*® Pro Testmaker CD-ROM to:

- Create **multiple versions** of tests.
- Create **modified** tests with one mouse click for struggling students.
- **Edit** existing questions and add your own questions.
- **Build** tests based on national curriculum standards.

Standardized Test Practice

1. c
2. d
3. c
4. c

NY Core Curriculum Standards

Page 96: St 1 Math KI 2 & 3, St 4 KI 3.1a, 3.1b, & 3.1c, St 6 KI 1

Page 97: St 1 Math KI 2 & 3, St 4 KI 3.1a, St 6 KI 1, St 7 KI 1

Chapter 5

Igneous Rocks

Refer to pages 8T–9T of the Teacher Guide for an explanation of the National Science Content Standards correlations.

Section	Objectives	National Science Content Standards	State/Local Standards
SECTION 5.1 **What are igneous rocks?** 🕐 1½ sessions 📦 1 block	1. **Compare** and **contrast** intrusive and extrusive igneous rocks. 2. **Describe** the composition of magma. 3. **Discuss** the factors that affect how rocks melt and crystallize.	UCP.1, UCP.2, UCP.3, UCP.4, UCP.5; A.1, A.2; B.2; D.1, D.2, D.3; F.3; G.3	St 1 Science KI 1, 2, & 3, St 4 KI 2.1a, 2.1m, 3.1a, 3.1b, & 3.1c, St 6 KI 1, 2, 4, & 5
SECTION 5.2 **Classifying Igneous Rocks** 🕐 3½ sessions 📦 2 blocks	4. **Classify** different types and textures of igneous rocks. 5. **Recognize** the effects of cooling rates on the grain sizes of igneous rocks. 6. **Describe** some uses of igneous rocks.	UCP.1, UCP.2, UCP.3, UCP.5; A.1, A.2; B.2; D.1, D.2; E.1, E.2; F.3	St 1 Math KI 1, 2, 3, Science KI 1, 2, 3, & Engin KI 1, St 4 KI 2.1a, 3.1a, 3.1b, & 3.1c, St 6 KI 1, 2, & 5

A complete Planning Guide is provided on pages 30T–32T.

🕐 The number of recommended single-period sessions

📦 The number of recommended blocks

Activity Materials

Discovery Lab *page 99*
magnifying glass or stereomicroscope, sample of granite

MiniLab *page 108*
igneous rock samples, pencil, paper

GeoLab *pages 114–115*
clean, plastic petri dishes; saturated alum solution; 200-mL glass beaker; magnifying glass; piece of dark-colored construction paper; thermometer; paper towels; water; hot plate

Need materials? Contact Science Kit at 1-800-828-7777 or at www.sciencekit.com on the Internet. For alternate materials, see the activity on the listed page.

Key to Teaching Strategies

L1 Level 1 activities should be appropriate for students with learning difficulties.

L2 Level 2 activities should be within the ability range of all students.

L3 Level 3 activities are designed for above-average students.

ELL ELL activities should be within the ability range of English-language learners.

COOP LEARN Cooperative learning activities are designed for small-group work.

P These strategies represent student products that can be placed in a best-work portfolio.

📦 These strategies are useful in a block-scheduling format.

Chapter Organizer

Glencoe Exclusive!
TeacherWorks™
All-In-One Planner and Resource Center

Activities/Features	Reproducible Masters	Transparencies
Discovery Lab: Identifying Minerals, p. 99	**Study Guide for Content Mastery,** pp. 27–30 **L2** **Laboratory Manual,** pp. 33–36 **L2**	**Section Focus Transparency 12** **L1** **ELL** **Teaching Transparency 11** **L2** **ELL**
MiniLab: How do igneous rocks differ?, p. 108 **Problem-Solving Lab:** Interpreting Scientific Illustrations, p. 110 **Using Math:** Using Numbers, p. 112 **GeoLab:** Modeling Crystal Formation, pp. 114–115 **Science & Technology:** Cutting-Edge Surgery, p. 116	**Study Guide for Content Mastery,** pp. 31–32 **L2** **GeoLab and MiniLab Worksheets,** p. 19 **L2** **GeoLab and MiniLab Worksheets,** pp. 20–22 **L2** **Laboratory Manual,** pp. 37–40 **L2**	**Section Focus Transparency 13** **L1** **ELL** **Teaching Transparency 12** **L2** **ELL**

 Assessment

Chapter Assessment, pp. 25–30
Performance Assessment in the Science Classroom (PASC)
MindJogger Videoquiz DVD/VHS
Performance Assessment in Earth Science
ExamView® Pro CD-ROM
5 Days to the Regents Exam

GLENCOE'S ASSESSMENT ADVANTAGE

 Additional Resources

Guided Reading Audio Program ELL
Cooperative Learning in the Science Classroom COOP LEARN
Lesson Plans
Block Scheduling
earthgeu.com
NY Lesson Plans
NY Block Scheduling
Review Handbook for Regents Earth Science Exam

◻ NATIONAL GEOGRAPHIC

Products Available from National Geographic Society
To order the following products, call the National Geographic Society at 1-800-368-2728:
Curriculum Kits
GeoKit: *Rocks and Minerals*
CD-ROM
111 years of National Geographic Magazine

Teacher's Corner

Video
Every Stone Has a Story
Book
National Geographic Desk Reference

Content Background

The First Rocks
Section 5.1

Igneous rocks were the first type of rocks to form on Earth as its molten surface cooled and solidified. In the billions of years since then, those original rocks have been slowly changed into other rock types, sedimentary and metamorphic rocks. These rock types are covered in succeeding chapters. Although geologists have learned much about igneous rocks over the years, questions still remain about how magma crystallizes. While the formation of extrusive igneous rocks can be observed, no one completely understands the conditions that exist in a magma chamber deep underground. Laboratory experiments can provide important clues, but certain factors such as magma movement and chemical reactions over long time periods can only be approximated.

Layered Intrusions
Section 5.1

Layered mafic and ultramafic intrusions are very rare igneous features. They are important nonetheless because they sometimes contain large amounts of extremely rare and valuable metals, such as chromium, platinum, palladium, vanadium, and rhodium. Other metals found in layered intrusions include copper, nickel, and gold. Typically, the metals are concentrated in well-defined layers that range from a few centimeters to 5 m thick. The best-known examples of metal-rich layered intrusions are the Bushveld Complex in South Africa and the Stillwater Complex in Montana. The Bushveld Complex is estimated to contain about 86 percent of the world's platinum and 83 percent of the world's chromium. Its layers extend for hundreds of kilometers. By contrast, the Stillwater Complex is only 42 km long and 8 km wide. It is the only source of platinum in the United States. Platinum is a critical metal in catalytic converters, which are used to reduce polluting emissions from motor vehicles.

Multiple Learning Styles

Interpersonal Collaborative Learning, p. 102

Logical-Mathematical Enrichment, p. 103, Activity, p. 105

Visual-Spatial Project, p. 104, Enrichment, p. 111

Intrapersonal Applying Earth Science, p. 111

Linguistic Reteach, p. 113

GLENCOE *Technology*

The following multimedia resources are available from Glencoe.

Vocabulary Puzzlemaker

TeacherWorks™ CD-ROM

MindJogger Videoquizzes DVD/VHS

ExamView® Pro CD-ROM

Interactive Chalkboard CD-ROM

Pegmatites
Section 5.2

The large, beautiful mineral specimens on display at natural history museums often come from pegmatites. Pegmatites are usually associated with granitic intrusions, which are formed from rhyolitic magmas with high water and volatile contents. Pegmatites form during the final stages of magma crystallization and are characterized by extremely coarse-grained textures. The large crystals are caused by special conditions that exist during this phase. For example, geologists hypothesize that pegmatites form while temperatures are 400 to 600°C and thus still fairly high. The remaining fluid portion of the magma at this stage has very low viscosity because of the increasing concentration of volatiles, gases, and other liquids. This low viscosity, combined with high temperatures, results in the rapid growth of large crystals. Quartz crystals that are more than 3 m long have been found in pegmatites in Brazil. Other giant pegmatite crystals include a 5.7-m beryl crystal and a 14-m spodumene crystal found in the Black Hills of South Dakota.

Diamonds
Section 5.2

Most of us associate gemstones with diamonds. It's true that diamonds are quite beautiful and are highly valued as jewels. But diamonds also are valued because of their hardness. Most mined diamonds are used for cutting, grinding, and polishing applications. Only a very small percentage of mined diamonds are of gemstone quality.

Identifying Misconceptions

Because students are familiar with volcanoes and lava flows, they may think that all igneous rocks form at Earth's surface. Explain that lava is magma that reaches Earth's surface. The magma, however, actually formed beneath Earth's surface, and not all of it passes through the crust during an eruption. The magma that remains underground also can cool to form igneous rocks.

✔ *Assessment*

Portfolio Assessment
Assessment, TWE, p. 113

Performance Assessment
Discovery Lab, SE, p. 99
MiniLab, SE, p. 108
Problem-Solving Lab, TWE, p. 110
GeoLab, SE, pp. 114–115
GeoLab, TWE, pp. 114–115

Knowledge Assessment
Discovery Lab, TWE, p. 99
Assessment, TWE, p. 102
Section Assessment, SE, pp. 106, 113
Chapter Assessment, SE, pp. 118–119

Skill Assessment
Assessment, TWE, p. 106
MiniLab, TWE, p. 108

Be sure to check the Earth Science Web Site for links to chapter material: earthgeu.com

Igneous Rocks

Introducing the Chapter

Show students a container of gravel or sand. Ask them to write down what they think would happen if the material was heated to its melting temperature and then allowed to slowly cool. After students have completed this chapter, have them review their predictions.

Interpreting the Photo

This polarized-light photomicrograph of a thin section of gabbro came from the Frankenstein Range in Hessia, Germany. Show students a sample of gabbro. Tell them that the rock's dark color is caused mainly by its mineral composition—gabbro is rich in iron and magnesium. Also, mention that gabbro is made up of different minerals, including plagioclase feldspar, pyroxene, biotite, amphibole, and olivine.

INTERACTIVE CHALKBOARD
with Image Bank

PowerPoint® Presentations

This CD is an editable Microsoft® PowerPoint® presentation that includes:
- Section presentations
- Section checks
- Image bank
- Links to Earth Science Online
- All transparencies
- Animations
- Audio

Chapter 5

Igneous Rocks

What You'll Learn
- How magma melts and crystallizes to form igneous rocks.
- How igneous rocks are classified.
- How igneous rocks are used.

Why It's Important

This photograph shows a microscopic view of gabbro, a type of igneous rock. Igneous rocks are the most abundant rocks in Earth's crust. Many important mineral and metal deposits are associated with igneous rocks.

Earth Science Online

To find out more about igneous rocks, visit the Earth Science Web Site at earthgeu.com

Discovery Lab

Process Skills

observe and infer, compare and contrast, communicate L1 ELL

Preparation

- Obtain enough samples of coarse-grained granite and magnifying glasses for each pair of students in the class.
- If they are available, set up stereomicroscopes around the room for students to use.

Procedure
Teaching Strategies

A local company that sells granite kitchen counters may be willing to give you broken samples or scraps that each have one polished surface.

Observe

Student sketches will vary. Typically, granite contains four to five different minerals. Quartz is clear to gray, orthoclase feldspar is pinkish, biotite is black, and plagioclase feldspar is usually white. Another black mineral, hornblende, is often present. It looks similar to biotite. Biotite, however, can be scratched by a metal pin; hornblende cannot. Most of the minerals

Rocks are mixtures of minerals, organic matter, and other materials. Sometimes, it's possible to identify the different minerals in a sample of rock.

1. Examine a sample of granite from a distance of about 1 m. Record your observations.

2. Use a magnifying glass or stereo-microscope to observe the granite sample. Record your observations.

Observe In your science journal, draw a picture of what you saw through the magnifying glass or stereo-microscope. Include a scale for your drawing. How many different minerals did you observe in the rock? What minerals can you identify? Describe the sizes and shapes of the minerals. Do you see any evidence that these minerals crystallized from molten rock? Explain.

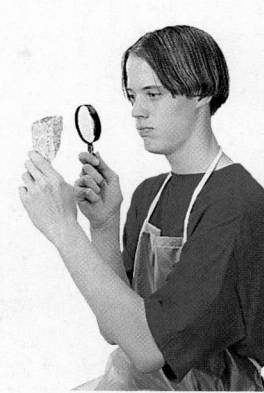

Section Focus

Before presenting the lesson, display **Section Focus Transparency 12** on the overhead projector. L1 ELL

Chapter Themes

The following themes from the National Science Content Standards are covered in this chapter. Refer to page 8T of the Teacher Guide for an explanation of the correlations.
Systems, order, and organization (UCP.1); Evidence, models, and explanation (UCP.2); Change, constancy, and measurement (UCP.3)

SECTION 5.1

What are igneous rocks?

OBJECTIVES

- **Compare** *and* **contrast** *intrusive and extrusive igneous rocks.*

- **Describe** *the composition of magma.*

- **Discuss** *the factors that affect how rocks melt and crystallize.*

VOCABULARY

igneous rock
lava
extrusive
intrusive
partial melting
fractional crystallization
Bowen's reaction series

In the *Discovery Lab,* you examined the minerals in a piece of granite. Granite is an igneous rock formed from magma, which, as you learned in Chapter 4, is molten rock below Earth's surface. **Igneous rocks** are formed from the crystallization of magma. The term *igneous* comes from the Latin word *ignis,* which means "fire" because early geologists often associated igneous rocks with fiery lava flows. **Lava** is magma that flows out onto Earth's surface.

TYPES OF IGNEOUS ROCKS

If you live near an active volcano, you can literally watch igneous rocks form. A hot, molten mass of rock may solidify into solid rock overnight. Fine-grained igneous rocks that cool quickly on Earth's surface are called **extrusive** igneous rocks. Coarse-grained igneous rocks that cool slowly beneath Earth's surface are called **intrusive** igneous rocks. Granite is the most common intrusive igneous rock. Initially, scientists did not believe that granite was igneous in origin because it was coarse grained and thus unlike the fine-grained surface rocks that formed from lava. In the late 1700s, however, careful study of granite rock formations revealed that they cut across other rock formations.

5.1 *What are igneous rocks?* **99**

---

will be about the same size and have a blocky shape.

Assessment

Knowledge Ask students the following questions. Which mineral in granite has the greatest hardness? quartz Based on the minerals you identified, what are the most abundant elements in granite? silicon, oxygen, and aluminum

Resource Manager

Section Focus Transparency 12 L1 ELL
Study Guide for Content Mastery, pp. 27–30 L2

0:00 Out of Time?

If time does not permit teaching the entire chapter, use the Chapter Summary on page 117 and the GeoDigest found at the end of the unit as an overview.

Enrichment

Have students research how glass is made and answer the following questions. What minerals are used? Glass is often made from quartz sand and sodium. How is the process of glass formation similar to the formation of an igneous rock? Glass formation is similar to the formation of an igneous rock in that molten materials solidify in both processes.

Identifying Misconceptions

Students may think that a rock melts all at the same time, like an ice cube.

Uncover the Misconception
Ask students to describe what they think would happen if the granite sample from the Discovery Lab was slowly heated to 1200°C.

Demonstrate the Concept
Explain that minerals have different melting temperatures. Minerals with low melting temperatures will melt before minerals with higher melting temperatures. Because rocks are made up largely of minerals, they do not melt all at once.

Assess New Knowledge
After you complete this section, have students list the melting order for the minerals in granite.

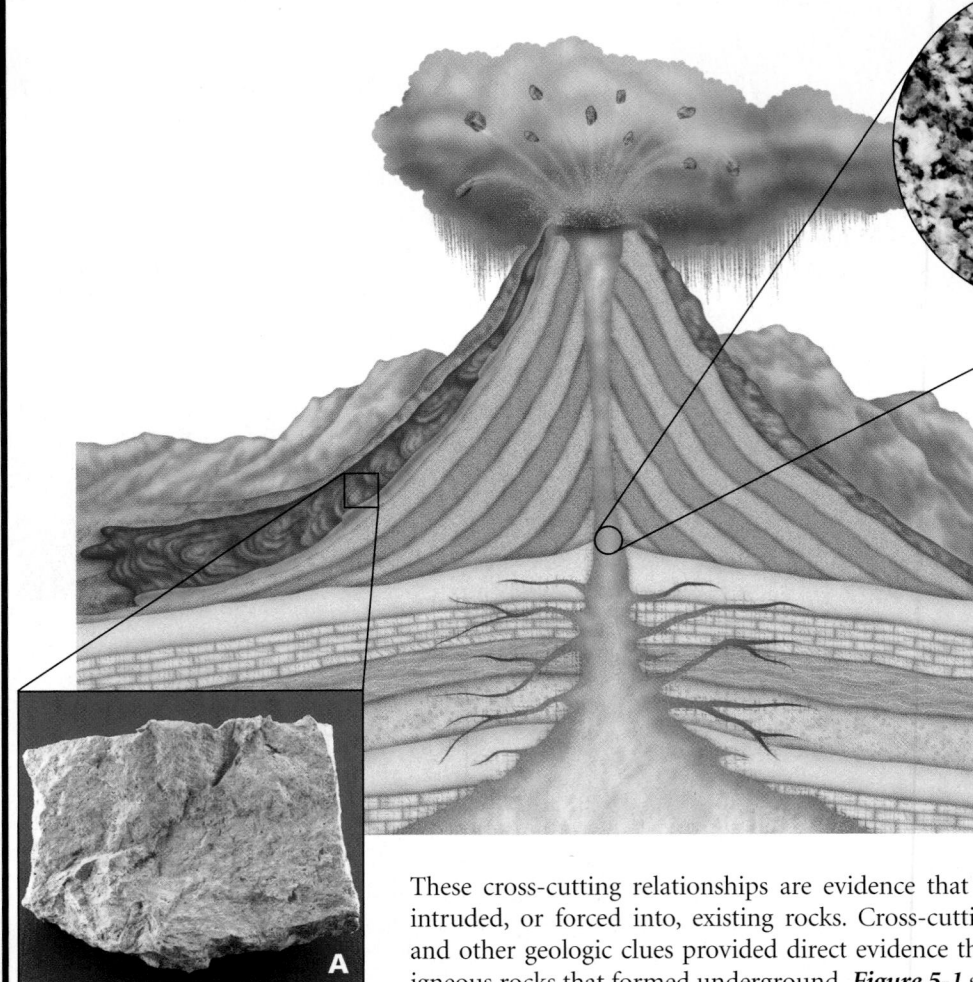

Figure 5-1 Lava cools quickly on Earth's surface and forms fine-grained igneous rocks such as rhyolite **(A).** Magma cools slowly beneath Earth's surface and forms coarse-grained igneous rocks such as granite. **(B).**

These cross-cutting relationships are evidence that the granite was intruded, or forced into, existing rocks. Cross-cutting relationships and other geologic clues provided direct evidence that granites were igneous rocks that formed underground. *Figure 5-1* shows the conditions under which granite and other igneous rocks form.

COMPOSITION OF MAGMA

Magma is often a slushy mix of molten rock, gases, and mineral crystals. The elements found in magma are the same major elements found in Earth's crust: oxygen (O), silicon (Si), aluminum (Al), iron (Fe), magnesium (Mg), calcium (Ca), potassium (K), and sodium (Na). Of all the compounds found in magma, silica (SiO_2) is the most abundant and has the greatest effect on magma characteristics. As summarized in *Table 5-1,* magmas are classified as basaltic, andesitic, and rhyolitic, based on the amount of SiO_2 they contain. Silica content affects melting temperature and also impacts how quickly magma flows.

100 CHAPTER 5 *Igneous Rocks*

Differentiated Instruction

English-Language Learners Have students use a dictionary to look up the origins of the words *intrusive* and *extrusive.* Ask students to explain why these terms aptly describe the two types of igneous rock. The Latin meaning of *intrusive* is "to thrust in," while the Latin meaning of *extrusive* is "to thrust out." The words are appropriate because intrusive rocks are formed inside Earth and extrusive rocks are formed on Earth's surface. ELL

ORIGINS OF MAGMA

In the laboratory, most rocks must be heated to temperatures of 800°C to 1200°C before they melt. In nature, these temperatures are found in the upper mantle and lower crust. Where does this heat come from? Scientists theorize that the remaining energy from Earth's molten formation and the heat generated from the decay of radioactive elements are the sources of Earth's thermal energy.

Factors That Affect Magma Formation The main factors involved in the formation of magma are temperature, pressure, water content, and mineral composition. Temperature generally increases with depth in Earth's crust. This temperature increase, known as the geothermal gradient, is plotted in *Figure 5-2A.* Oil-well drillers and miners, such as those shown in *Figure 5-2B,* have firsthand experience with the geothermal gradient. Temperatures encountered when drilling deep oil wells can exceed 200°C.

Pressure also increases with depth. This is a result of the weight of overlying rock. Laboratory experiments show that as pressure on a rock increases, its melting point also increases. Thus, a rock may melt at 1100°C at Earth's surface, but the same rock will melt at 1400°C under the intense pressure found at a depth of 100 km.

The third factor that affects the formation of magma is water content. Rocks and minerals often contain small percentages of water, which changes the melting point of the rocks. As water content increases, the melting point decreases.

Table 5-1 Types of Magma	
Group	**SiO₂ content**
Rhyolitic	70 percent
Andesitic	60 percent
Basaltic	50 percent

Table 5-1 Types of Magma

Group	SiO_2 content
Rhyolitic	70 percent
Andesitic	60 percent
Basaltic	50 percent

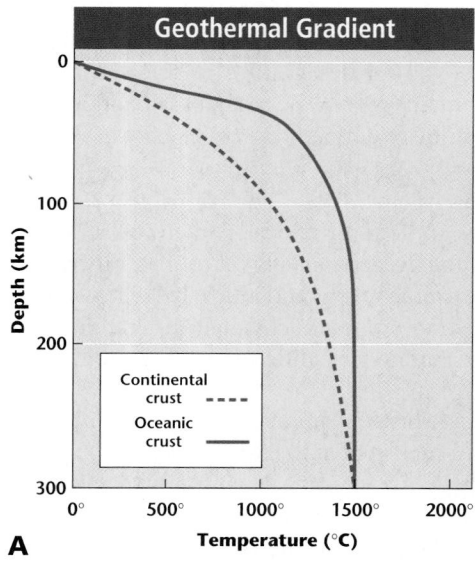

A

Figure 5-2 Differences in mineral composition cause the geothermal gradient to be higher in oceanic crust than in continental crust **(A)**, as you'll learn on the next page. Also, the geothermal gradient causes temperatures in deep mines to be quite high **(B).**

B

Content Background

Deep-mining operations are designed with pressure and temperature conditions in mind. Both pressure and temperature increase with depth. While the high temperatures make working conditions uncomfortable, the high pressures are far more dangerous. Pressure can cause rock to shatter and blow out into the mine tunnel from the roof and walls. Steel plates are sometimes bolted to the roof and walls to control this problem.

Using an Analogy

Relate increasing pressure with depth inside Earth to increasing pressure with depth in a swimming pool. Tell students that when someone dives to the bottom of a pool, the weight of the overlying water presses in on the diver's eardrum and sinus membranes, causing uncomfortable pressure. In a similar way, the weight of overlying rocks inside Earth presses down on the rocks below.

Across the Curriculum

Chemistry Review what happens to atoms and molecules when matter changes state from a solid to a liquid. Ask students to explain why increasing pressure causes the melting temperatures of rocks to increase. When matter changes from a solid to a liquid, atoms and molecules loosen their bonds and move farther apart. High pressure makes it more difficult for this to occur, and thus more thermal energy—or a higher melting temperature—is required for the matter to change state.

NY Core Curriculum Standards

Page 98: St 4 KI 2.1m & 3.1c, St 6 KI 1
Page 99: St 1 Science KI 1, 2, & 3, St 4 KI 3.1a & 3.1c, St 6 KI 1
Page 100: St 4 KI 3.1a, 3.1b, & 3.1c, St 6 KI 1
Page 101: St 4 KI 2.1a, 2.1m, 3.1a, & 3.1b, St 6 KI 4 & 5

Discussion

Discuss the factors that affect how rocks melt, particularly water content. Ask students to infer how water can exist in rocks at the high temperatures required for melting. Water can be locked inside the crystal structure of the minerals or be present in a gaseous state (water vapor) rather than a liquid state.

Collaborative Learning

Interpersonal Have groups of students brainstorm other mixtures besides wax and ice that might model the partial melting behavior of rocks. One example is ice cream with chocolate chips. **L1** **COOP LEARN**

Environmental Connection

Toxic chemicals can be destroyed by incineration at high temperatures. Incinerators often contain ceramic burners, which are made from fired clay minerals. Have interested students research the types of minerals used to make ceramic burners.

Figure 5-3 Granite's higher water content and mineral composition cause it to melt at lower temperatures than basalt.

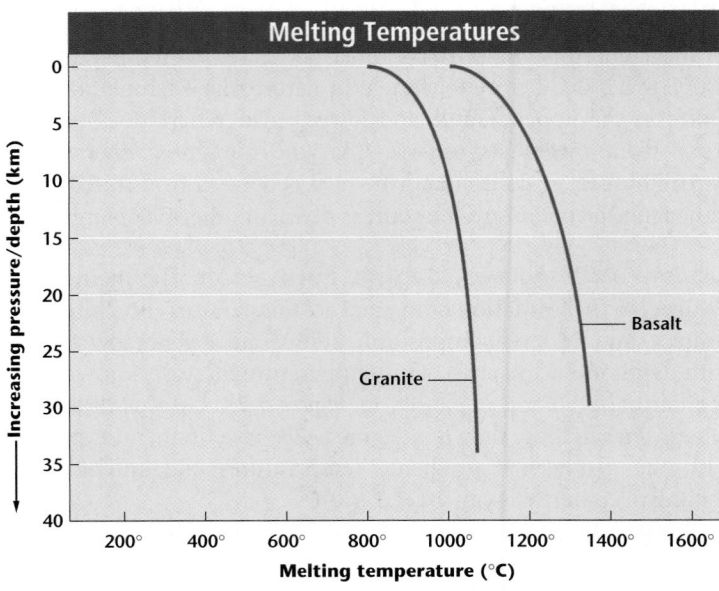

Mineral content also impacts how magma is formed. Different minerals have different melting points. For example, rocks formed of olivine, calcium feldspar, and pyroxene melt at higher temperatures than rocks containing quartz and potassium feldspar. In general, oceanic crust is rich in iron and magnesium and therefore melts at higher temperatures than continental crust, which contains higher levels of silicon and aluminum. Rocks melt only under certain conditions—the right combination of temperature, pressure, and composition must be present. *Figure 5-3* shows the melting curves of both granite and basalt. As you can see, granite has a lower melting point. This is because it contains more water than basalt and is made up of minerals that melt at lower temperatures.

HOW ROCKS MELT

Suppose you froze bits of candle wax and water in an ice-cube tray. If you took the tray out of the freezer and left it at room temperature, the ice would melt but the candle wax would not. Why? The two substances have different melting points. Rocks melt in a similar way because the minerals they contain have different melting points.

Partial Melting Because different minerals have different melting points, not all parts of a rock melt at the same time. This explains why magma is often a slushy mix of crystals and molten rock. The process whereby some minerals melt at low temperatures while other minerals remain solid is called **partial melting.** Partial melting is

✓Assessment

Knowledge Have students answer the following question. Which of the following factors does not affect magma formation?
a. pressure
b. radioactivity
c. mineral composition
d. water content
The answer is b, radioactivity.

Resource Manager

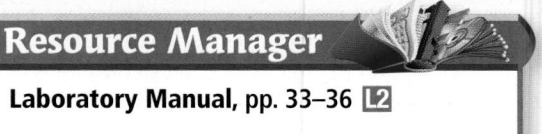

Laboratory Manual, pp. 33–36 **L2**

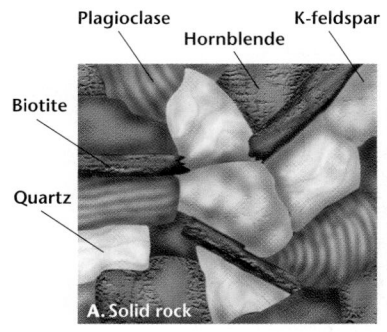

Plagioclase
Hornblende
K-feldspar
Biotite
Quartz
A. Solid rock

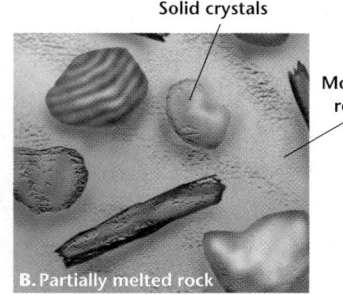

Solid crystals
Molten rock
B. Partially melted rock

Figure 5-4 A rock is made up of different minerals that melt at different temperatures **(A).** Thus, during the melting process, some minerals are molten while others remain solid **(B).**

illustrated in *Figure 5-4.* As each group of minerals melts, different elements are added to the magma "stew," thereby changing its composition. If temperatures are not great enough to melt the entire rock, the resulting magma will have a different chemistry from that of the original rock. This is one way in which different types of igneous rocks form.

Fractional Crystallization When magma cools, it crystallizes in the reverse order of partial melting—the first minerals to crystallize from magma are the last minerals to melt during partial melting. The process wherein different minerals form at different temperatures is called **fractional crystallization.** This process, which is illustrated in *Figure 5-5,* is similar to partial melting in that the composition of magma may change. However, during fractional crystallization, the changes occur because as each group of minerals crystallizes, it removes elements from the remaining magma instead of adding new elements.

BOWEN'S REACTION SERIES

In the early 1900s, Canadian geologist N. L. Bowen demonstrated that as magma cools, minerals form in predictable patterns. **Bowen's reaction series** illustrates this relationship between cooling magma and mineral formation. Bowen discovered two main patterns, or branches, of crystallization. The first pattern is characterized by a continuous, gradual change of mineral compositions in the feldspar group. The second pattern is characterized by an abrupt change of mineral type in the iron-magnesium groups. *Figure 5-6* on page 104 illustrates Bowen's reaction series.

Feldspars In Bowen's reaction series, the right branch represents the feldspar minerals, which undergo a continuous change of composition.

Figure 5-5 Magma is made up of different minerals that crystallize at different temperatures **(A).** Thus, during the crystallization process, some minerals become solid while others remain molten **(B).**

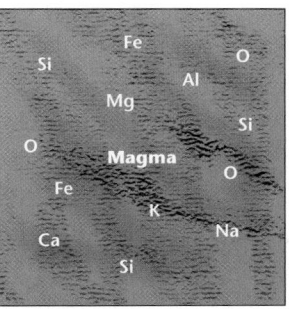

A

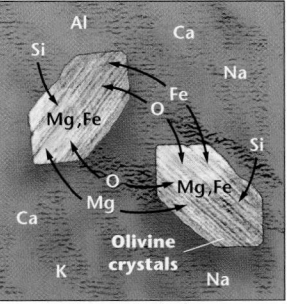

B

Modeling

Have students perform the analogy about wax and ice described on page 102 in the student text. Students should freeze bits of wax crayon and water in an ice tray, then melt the resulting ice cubes in a beaker placed on a hot plate. **CAUTION:** *Students should wear safety goggles and thermal mitts.* The wax and water will melt at different rates, thus modeling partial melting.

Concept Development

Have students each write an explanation of why the first minerals to crystallize are the last to melt when a rock is heated. The minerals that crystallize first have high melting temperatures. It takes a great deal of thermal energy to keep these minerals in a molten state. Thus, when temperatures decrease, these minerals are the first to crystallize. Conversely, temperatures must be very high for the minerals to melt.

Enrichment

Logical-Mathematical
Ask students to design ways to demonstrate how the concept of partial melting might be used to separate the components of a mixture. Designs will vary. Students may say that they could carefully heat the mixture until one component melts, and then filter out the remaining solid portion. **L2**

Across the Curriculum

Chemistry Have students research and list in their science journals the melting points of the eight most common elements in Earth's crust. Si, 1410°C; O, –218°C; Al, 660°C; Fe, 1535°C; Mg, 648°C; Ca, 839°C; K, 63.6°C; Na, 97.8°C

Science Field Book

Earth Science
Journal

Have students answer the following question in their science journals. What would happen to a calcium-rich plagioclase if it was placed in magma containing sodium-rich plagioclase? The calcium-rich plagioclase would react with the magma and would become more sodium-rich.

NY Core Curriculum Standards

Page 102: St 4 KI 3.1a, 3.1b, & 3.1c, St 6 KI 4 & 5

Page 103: St 4 KI 3.1a, 3.1b, & 3.1c, St 6 KI 4 & 5

Interpreting the Illustration

Figure 5-6 The plagioclase continuous reaction series is a very complex feedback system involving crystallizing plagioclase and magma. The first plagioclase crystals that form are always rich in calcium, which causes the magma to lose calcium and become enriched in sodium. The crystals then react with the sodium-rich magma, lose calcium, and gain sodium. This causes the calcium content of the magma to increase slightly. As more crystals form, the calcium-sodium composition of both the magma and the plagioclase crystals changes back and forth. The new and old crystals both react with the magma so that all the crystals that exist at a particular time have the same composition. At the point of complete solidification, all the crystals have a uniform calcium-sodium composition identical to that of the original magma.

Project

 Visual-Spatial Have groups of students each make a poster of Bowen's reaction series. Then, have students choose one of the three types of magma and illustrate the crystallization sequence for an intrusive igneous rock formed from that magma.

P

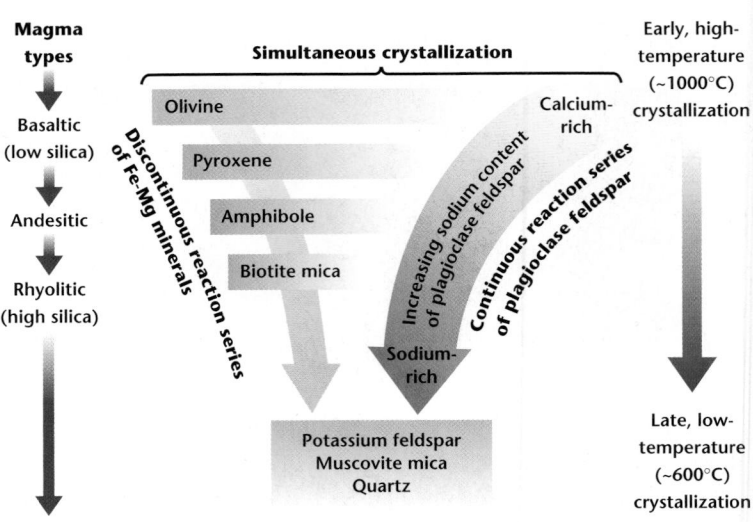

Figure 5-6 In the left branch of Bowen's reaction series, Fe-Mg minerals change to different minerals during the crystallization process. In the right branch, calcium-rich feldspars change gradually to sodium-rich feldspars.

Figure 5-7 When magma cools quickly, a feldspar crystal may not have time to react completely with the magma and it retains a calcium-rich core **(A)**. The result is a crystal with distinct zones **(B)**.

As magma cools, the first feldspars to form are rich in calcium. As cooling continues, these feldspars react with magma, and their calcium-rich compositions change to sodium-rich compositions. In some instances, as when magma cools rapidly, the calcium-rich cores are unable to react completely with the magma. The result is a zoned crystal that has sodium-rich outer layers and calcium-rich cores, as shown in *Figure 5-7*.

Iron-Rich Minerals The left branch of Bowen's reaction series represents the iron-rich minerals. These minerals undergo abrupt changes during fractional crystallization. For example, when a

A

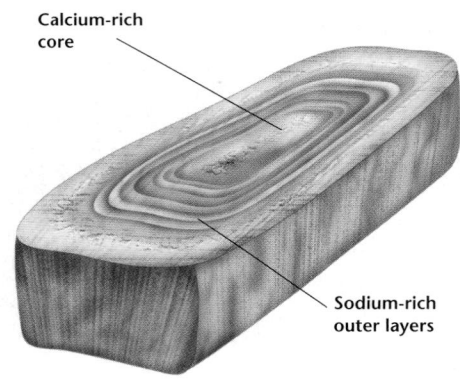

Calcium-rich core

Sodium-rich outer layers

B

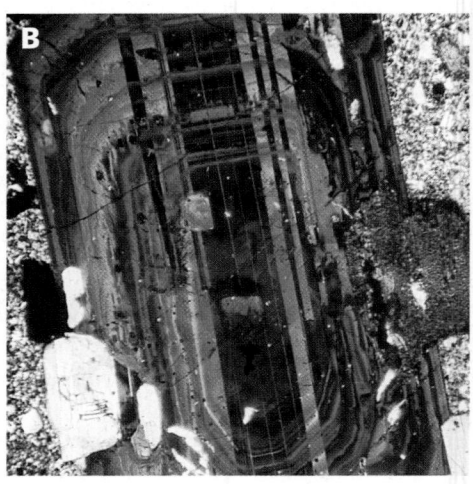

Differentiated Instruction

Learning Disabled Pair students with learning disabilities with other students. Have student pairs draw diagrams of four nested rectangles to represent a zoned plagioclase crystal. Students should label the zones with the following compositions: core: 80 percent Ca, 20 percent Na; first layer: 60 percent Ca, 40 percent Na; second layer: 50 percent Ca, 50 percent Na; outer rim: 40 percent Ca, 60 percent Na. Have students shade the zones to represent the changing element content.

Figure 5-8 Quartz, the last mineral to crystallize, often forms in rock veins when the remaining magma is squeezed into rock fractures and cools.

magma rich in iron and magnesium cools to around 1800°C, olivine begins to crystallize. Olivine continues to form until the temperature drops to 1557°C. At that temperature, a completely new mineral, pyroxene, begins to form. All the olivine that previously formed reacts with the magma and is converted to pyroxene. Similar mineral changes have been observed in amphiboles and biotite.

As minerals form in the order shown in Bowen's reaction series, elements are removed from the remaining magma. Silica and oxygen, the most abundant elements in magma, are left over at the end of the reaction series. When the remaining melt, enriched with silica and oxygen, finally crystallizes, quartz is formed. Quartz often occurs in veins, as shown in *Figure 5-8,* because it crystallizes as the last liquid portion of magma is squeezed into rock fractures.

Crystal Separation As is often the case with scientific inquiry, Bowen's reaction series led to more questions. For example, if olivine converts to pyroxene during cooling, why is olivine found in rock? Geologists hypothesize that under certain conditions, newly formed crystals are separated from magma, and the chemical reactions between the magma and the minerals stop. Crystal separation can occur when crystals settle to the bottom of the magma body, and when liquid magma is squeezed from the crystal mush to form two distinct igneous bodies with different compositions.

Layered Intrusions In some magma bodies, the minerals form into distinct bands in the order shown in Bowen's reaction series. The result

Topic: Bowen's Reaction
To find out more about Bowen's reaction series, visit the Earth Science Web Site at <u>earthgeu.com</u>

Activity: Explain which types of minerals weather more quickly than others. What unique rocks demonstrate this weathering process?

5.1 *What are igneous rocks?* **105**

Discussion

Ask students how it might be possible to have an olivine crystal with a rim of pyroxene. If the magma solidifies before all the olivine changes to pyroxene, a rim of pyroxene around an olivine core could form.

Reinforcement

Ask students the following questions. Which elements are removed first from a solidifying magma? the elements found in the iron-magnesium minerals and the calcium-rich plagioclase In the wax-ice analogy on page 102, which material represents the quartz-rich portion of crystallizing magma? Why? the ice, because it crystallizes last

Activity

Logical-Mathematical Write the chemical formulas of olivine and the common mineral augite on the chalkboard. Then, have students determine the compositional changes that would need to occur for olivine to be converted to augite. The chemical formula of olivine is $(Mg,Fe)_2SiO_4$. The chemical formula of augite is $(Ca,Na)(Mg,Fe,Al)(Si,Al)_2O_6$. For olivine to be converted to augite, additional Ca, Na, and Al would have to be added. **L3** **COOP LEARN**

Resource Manager

Teaching Transparency 11 **L2** **ELL**

Cultural Diversity

Early Tools Archaeologists have learned much about the cultures of ancient Native Americans through the study of tools made of obsidian. The early Hopewell people, for instance, used the volcanic glass to butcher game and to make arrowheads, spear points, and large ceremonial objects. Archaeological records show that obsidian tools were used more than 10 000 years ago. Scientists have found evidence of vast trade networks that ranged from Wyoming to Hopewell settlements in the Midwest.

NY Core Curriculum Standards

Page 104: St 4 KI 3.1a, 3.1b, & 3.1c, St 6 KI 4 & 5
Page 105: St 4 KI 3.1a, 3.1b, & 3.1c, St 6 KI 4 & 5

Check for Understanding

Reinforcement

Ask students to describe how temperature and pressure would change as a mass of magma moved upward through Earth's crust. Temperature and pressure would both decrease. What effect would this have on crystallization? The decrease in pressure would lower the melting temperature of the molten material. The decrease in temperature would cause the magma to solidify.

Reteach

Have students use the headings in the textbook to outline the major points in this section.

✓Assessment

Skill Assess students' critical-thinking skills by having students answer the following question. If a rhyolitic magma with low levels of iron and magnesium crystallized, which minerals in Bowen's reaction series would you not expect to form? olivine, pyroxene, amphibole, and biotite

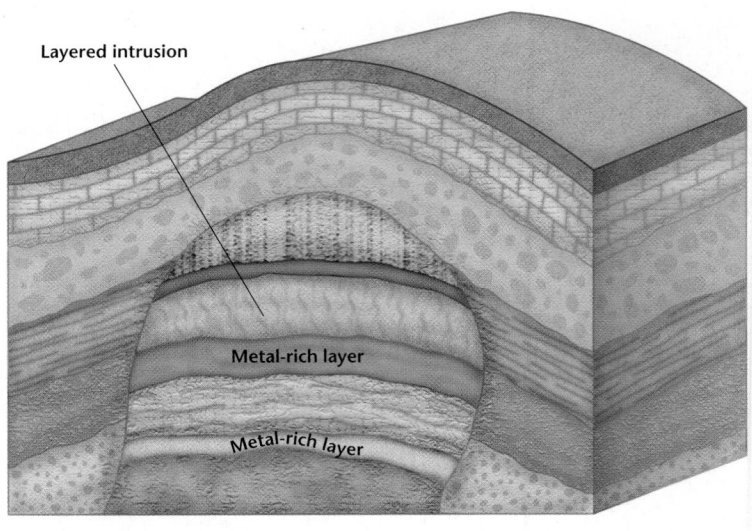

Figure 5-9 The settling of crystals, flowing currents in magma, and temperature differences may cause the formation of a layered intrusion, which sometimes has metal-rich layers.

is a layered intrusion, as shown in **Figure 5-9.** Geologists are uncertain how these layers form. The settling of crystals, flowing currents in the magma, and temperature gradients within the magma chamber may all play a role. Layered igneous intrusions can be valuable sources of rare metals. Some have very high concentrations of elements such as platinum, chromium, nickel, or gold. For instance, a layered intrusion in Montana called the Stillwater Complex is the only source of platinum in the United States. Platinum is a critical component in catalytic converters, which are used to reduce the amount of pollutants that vehicles emit.

SECTION ASSESSMENT

1. Compare and contrast magma and lava. What two types of igneous rock are formed as each cools?

2. Make a data table that lists the eight major elements found in most magma. Include the chemical symbol of each element.

3. What are the factors that affect the formation of magma?

4. Compare the ways in which iron-magnesium minerals and feldspars crystallize from magma.

5. **Thinking Critically** Geologists have found zoned pyroxene crystals that have magnesium-rich cores and iron-rich outer layers. Which has a higher melting temperature, magnesium-rich pyroxene or iron-rich pyroxene? Explain your reasoning.

SKILL REVIEW

6. **Comparing and Contrasting** Compare and contrast how partial melting and fractional crystallization can change the composition of magma. For more help, refer to the *Skill Handbook*.

earthgeu.com/self_check_quiz

SECTION ASSESSMENT

1. Magma is molten rock beneath Earth's surface; lava is magma that has flowed out onto Earth's surface. Magma forms intrusive igneous rocks; lava forms extrusive igneous rocks.

2. Students data tables should include the following elements: oxygen, O; silicon, Si; aluminum, Al; iron, Fe; magnesium, Mg; calcium, Ca; sodium, Na; potassium, K.

3. Four factors affect the formation of magma: temperature, pressure, water content, and mineral composition.

4. Feldspars continually react with the magma and change in composition from calcium-rich to sodium-rich. However, they remain feldspar. Minerals rich in iron and magnesium react with the magma and change into other minerals.

5. Magnesium-rich pyroxene has a higher melting temperature. Because this mineral forms the core of the crystal, it must have crystallized first at a higher temperature.

6. During partial melting, different elements are added to the magma as minerals melt at different temperatures. During fractional crystallization, different elements are removed from the magma as minerals crystallize at different temperatures. Both these processes change the chemical composition of the magma.

SECTION 5.2 · Classifying Igneous Rocks

Igneous rocks are broadly classified as intrusive or extrusive. However, geologists further classify these rocks by their mineral compositions. In addition, physical properties such as grain size and texture serve as clues for the identification of various igneous rocks.

MINERAL COMPOSITION

As shown in *Table 5-2,* the three main groups of igneous rocks—felsic, mafic, and intermediate—are classified according to their mineral compositions. **Felsic** rocks such as granite are light-colored, have high silica contents, and contain quartz and the feldspars orthoclase and plagioclase. **Mafic** rocks such as gabbro are dark-colored, have lower silica contents, and are rich in iron and magnesium. Mafic rocks contain plagioclase, biotite, amphibole, pyroxene, and olivine. Diorite is a good example of an intermediate rock with moderate amounts of biotite, amphibole, and pyroxene.

OBJECTIVES

- **Classify** *different types and textures of igneous rocks.*
- **Recognize** *the effects of cooling rates on the grain sizes of igneous rocks.*
- **Describe** *some uses of igneous rocks.*

VOCABULARY

felsic   porphyritic
mafic   pegmatite
ultramafic   kimberlite

Table 5-2 Classification of Igneous Rocks					
	Felsic	**Intermediate**	**Mafic**	**Ultramafic**	**Texture**
Extrusive	Obsidian		Basaltic glass		Glassy (non-crystalline)
	Rhyolite	Andesite	Basalt		Fine-grained
Intrusive	Granite	Diorite	Gabbro	Peri-dotite / Dun-ite	Coarse-grained
	Pegmatite				Very coarse-grained

Mineral composition (percentage by volume):
- 100%
- Potassium feldspar (pink to white)
- Quartz (clear to white)
- Plagioclase feldspar (white to gray)
- 75%
- 50%
- Pyroxene (green)
- Biotite (black)
- 25%
- Amphibole (black)
- Olivine (green)
- 0%

5.2 *Classifying Igneous Rocks* **107**

Interpreting the Illustration

Table 5-2 Have students describe the mineral compositions of several different types of igneous rocks. For instance, granite, an intrusive igneous rock, contains potassium feldspar, quartz, plagioclase feldspar, biotite, and amphibole.

Resource Manager

Section Focus Transparency 13 L1 ELL
Study Guide for Content Mastery, pp. 31–32 L2

Prepare

Section Background

For section content background, refer to **Pegmatites** and **Diamonds** on page 98D.

Preplanning

Refer to the Chapter Organizer on pages 98A–B.

1 Focus

Section Focus

Before presenting the lesson, display **Section Focus Transparency 13** on the overhead projector. L1 ELL

Section Focus Transparency 13 OBSIDIAN
Use with Chapter 5, Section 5.2

① How would you describe the texture of this type of igneous rock?
② How do you think this type of rock formed? Why?

Section Focus Transparency   Earth Science: Geology, the Environment, and the Universe

Tying to Previous Knowledge

Have students refer back to Bowen's reaction series in the previous section. Ask students to explain which type of igneous rock would have the highest melting temperature: a felsic, intermediate, mafic, or ultramafic rock. an ultramafic rock, because it contains the minerals with the highest melting temperatures

MiniLab

Purpose
Students will compare and contrast the different characteristics of igneous rocks.

Process Skills
observe and infer, compare and contrast, make and use tables, classify

Teaching Strategies
- Samples should be labeled. If materials are limited, have students work in pairs to describe and classify one sample at a time.
- Emphasize the need for careful observation and comprehensive descriptions. Students need to look very closely at the samples to observe differences.

Troubleshooting
The dark minerals in the mafic samples may be difficult to see. Tell students that light should reflect off the cleavage surfaces of the samples.

Expected Results
Students will produce a data table with four to five columns that list the name of each sample, its color, grain size, texture, and mineral composition.

Analyze and Conclude
1. Answers will vary depending on the samples used. The coarse-grained samples such as granite, diorite, and gabbro are intrusive. The fine-grained samples such as obsidian, rhyolite, andesite, and basalt are extrusive.
2. Extrusive rocks are fine grained. They differ in color and some may show a porphyritic texture. Intrusive rocks are coarse grained. They differ in color and mineral composition.
3. Answers will vary depending on the samples used. Light-colored samples such as granite and rhyolite are felsic. Medium-colored samples are intermediate, and dark-colored samples—other than obsidian—are mafic.

MiniLab

How do igneous rocks differ?
Compare and **contrast** the different characteristics of igneous rocks.

Procedure
1. Using the igneous rock samples provided by your teacher, carefully observe the following characteristics of each rock: color, grain size, texture, and, if possible, mineral composition.
2. Design a data table in your science journal to record your observations.

Analyze and Conclude
1. Classify your rock samples as extrusive or intrusive rocks.
2. What characteristics do the extrusive rocks share? How do they differ? What characteristics do the intrusive rocks share? How do they differ?
3. Classify your rock samples as felsic, intermediate, mafic, or ultramafic.

Figure 5-10 Dunite **(A)** and peridotite **(B)** are ultramafic rocks. They have low silica contents and high levels of iron and magnesium.

A

B

Ultramafic Rocks Two unusual igneous rocks, peridotite and dunite, have low silica contents and very high levels of iron and magnesium, and thus, they are classified as **ultramafic** rocks. Some scientists theorize these ultramafic rocks, shown in *Figure 5-10,* are formed by the fractional crystallization of olivine and pyroxene. The minerals may have been separated from magma and did not convert to another mineral upon reaching a particular temperature. Another hypothesis is that ultramafic rocks represent pieces of the upper mantle that have been brought close to Earth's surface. In the *MiniLab* on this page, you'll analyze the mineral compositions of various igneous rocks.

GRAIN SIZE
In addition to differences in their mineral compositions, igneous rocks differ in the sizes of their grains. *Figure 5-11* compares obsidian, a glassy extrusive rock, and gabbro, a coarse-grained intrusive rock. What might account for the lack of visible crystals in obsidian and the large crystals of gabbro?

✓ Assessment
Skill Have students use **Table 5-2** to estimate the percentages of the minerals in diorite. approximately 55 percent plagioclase feldspar, 15 percent biotite, 25 percent amphibole, and 5 percent quartz

Resource Manager
Teaching Transparency 12 L2 ELL
GeoLab and MiniLab Worksheets, p. 19 L2

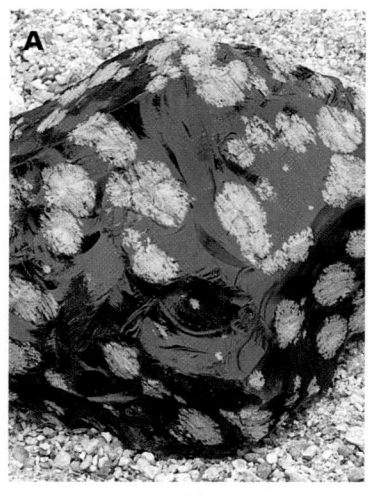

A

B

Figure 5-11 Obsidian cools quickly and has no visible mineral grains **(A)**. The white patches that characterize this snowflake obsidian are mineral crystals that formed from impurities as the obsidian cooled. Gabbro cools slowly and thus large mineral grains form **(B)**.

Cooling Rates When lava flows on Earth's surface, it is exposed to air and moisture. Under these conditions, the lava cools quickly, and there is not enough time for large crystals to form. Thus, extrusive igneous rocks such as obsidian have no visible mineral grains. In contrast, when magma cools slowly beneath Earth's surface, there is sufficient time for large crystals to form. Thus, intrusive igneous rocks such as gabbro may have crystals larger than 1 cm. You'll investigate the effects of cooling rate on crystal size in the *GeoLab* at the end of this chapter.

TEXTURE

Often, it's easier to observe the sizes of mineral grains than it is to observe their shapes. Geologists solve this problem by making thin sections, which are slices of rock so thin that light can pass through them. As shown in the thin section in *Figure 5-12,* many mineral grains have interlocking edges. As the grains crystallize from magma, they grow together and form these irregular edges. Although irregular crystal shapes are characteristic of many igneous rocks, well-shaped crystals can form under certain conditions. During fractional crystallization, the minerals that form early in the process float in a liquid and have space in which to grow distinct crystal shapes.

Figure 5-12 The interlocking edges of mineral grains are evident in this thin section of diorite.

Discussion

Ask students whether every diorite has the same composition. no Have groups of students list the mineral compositions of two rocks that represent the extreme range of the diorite group. Rock 1: quartz—10 percent, plagioclase—50 percent, biotite—15 percent, amphibole—20 percent, pyroxene—0 percent; Rock 2: quartz—0 percent, plagioclase—60 percent, biotite—5 percent, amphibole—30 percent, pyroxene—5 percent

Content Background

Volcanic glass has no mineral grains and therefore cannot be classified based on mineral percentage. Chemical analysis is used to classify volcanic glasses. Some typical chemical compositions are as follows. Rhyolite glass is made up of 76 percent SiO_2, 12 percent Al_2O_3, 1 percent FeO, and 0.1 percent MgO. Andesite glass is made up of 58 percent SiO_2, 17 percent Al_2O_3, 4 percent FeO, and 3 percent MgO. Basaltic glass is made up of 46 percent SiO_2, 9 percent Al_2O_3, 10 percent FeO, and 15 percent MgO.

Differentiated Instruction

Gifted Have students research the use of polarized light to identify minerals in thin sections. Students should explain the relationship between light and color in thin sections that are viewed through crossed-polarizing filters. Light travels at different speeds through crystals, depending upon the orientation of individual crystals. This causes certain wavelengths to interfere with and cancel each other. The remaining wavelengths show up as different colors in thin sections. L3

NY Core Curriculum Standards

Page 106: St 4 KI 3.1a, 3.1b, & 3.1c, St 6 KI 2, 4, & 5

Page 107: St 4 KI 3.1a & 3.1c, St 6 KI 1

Page 108: St 1 Science KI 1, 2, 3, & Engin KI 1, St 4 KI 3.1a & 3.1c, St 6 KI 1 & 2

Page 109: St 4 KI 3.1a & 3.1c, St 6 KI 1

Figure 5-13 The sample of
granite has crystals of the
same size **(A)**. In contrast,
the other granite sample has
a porphyritic texture with
crystals of different sizes **(B)**.

Problem-Solving Lab

Purpose

Students will use a diagram of a thin
section to estimate the mineral composition of an igneous rock.

Process Skills

make and use tables, apply concepts,
think critically, interpret scientific
illustrations, identify

Teaching Strategies

• Remind students that their estimated percentages should add up
  to 100 percent.
• Emphasize that mineral composition is being estimated, not the
  number of mineral grains. The
  areas of the mineral grains should
  be taken into consideration when
  estimating mineral composition.

Analysis

1. Methods will vary. Students may
   use a grid to plot the mineral at
   each intersection point. They also
   might estimate the areas of the
   mineral grains. Accept all reasonable methods.
2. Student data tables should accurately reflect the minerals shown
   in the thin section.

Thinking Critically

3. Students may say that the thin
   section represents the intermediate igneous rocks andesite
   or diorite. Both answers are correct because students cannot tell
   whether the rock is fine grained
   or coarse grained from the
   diagram.
4. Answers will vary depending on
   student estimations. Possible
   sources of error include too few
   data points, difficulty in estimating the area of different mineral
   shapes, and errors in calculation.
5. Usually, the more data points
   used, the more accurate the
   estimate.

Assessment

Performance Ask students to
infer why an accurate estimation of
minerals in a thin section may not
accurately reflect the actual mineral

Porphyritic Texture Compare the crystal textures of the rocks
shown in *Figure 5-13.* One of the rocks has grains of two different
sizes. This rock has a **porphyritic** texture, which is characterized by
large, well-formed crystals surrounded by finer-grained crystals of
the same mineral or different minerals.

What causes minerals to form both large and small crystals in the
same rock? Porphyritic textures indicate a complex cooling history
wherein a slowly cooling magma suddenly began cooling rapidly.
Imagine a magma body cooling slowly deep in Earth's crust. As it
cools, the resulting crystals grow large. If this magma were to be

Problem-Solving Lab

Interpreting Scientific Illustrations

Estimate mineral composition
Igneous rocks are classified by their mineral
compositions. In this activity, you'll estimate the different percentages of minerals
in an igneous sample, then use your results
to classify the rock.

Analysis

1. Using the diagram of the thin section
   shown here, design a method to estimate the percentages of the minerals
   in the rock sample.
2. Make a data table that lists the minerals and their estimated percentages.

Thinking Critically

3. Use *Table 5-2* to determine which
   type of igneous rock the thin section
   represents.

4. Compare your estimates of the percentages of minerals in the rock with
   those of your classmates. Hypothesize
   why the estimates vary. What are some
   possible sources of error?
5. What could you do to improve the
   accuracy of your estimate?

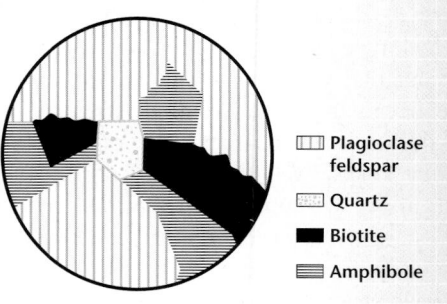

Plagioclase feldspar
Quartz
Biotite
Amphibole

composition of the rock. The minerals may
not be uniformly distributed throughout the
rock, so the thin section may not be representative of the whole rock. Also, if the thin section is perpendicular to needle-shaped
minerals, the true volume of the mineral will
be greatly underestimated. Use the Performance Task Assessment List for Making
Observations and Inferences in **PASC,** p. 17.

suddenly intruded higher in the crust, or if it erupted onto Earth's surface, the remaining magma would cool quickly and form smaller crystals. You'll explore other characteristics of igneous rocks in the *Problem-Solving Lab* on the previous page.

IGNEOUS ROCKS AS RESOURCES

Igneous rocks have several characteristics that make them especially useful as building materials. The interlocking grain textures of igneous rocks help to give them strength. In addition, many of the minerals found in igneous rocks are resistant to weathering. Granite is among the most durable of igneous rocks. Some common construction uses of granite are shown in *Figure 5-14.* You'll learn more about uses of other igneous rocks in the *Science & Technology* feature at the end of this chapter.

ORE DEPOSITS

As you learned in Chapter 4, ores are minerals that contain a useful substance that can be mined at a profit. Valuable ore deposits are often associated with igneous intrusions. Sometimes, these ore deposits are found within igneous rock, such as the layered intrusions mentioned earlier. Other times, ore minerals are found in the rocks surrounding intrusions. These type of deposits sometimes occur as veins.

Veins Recall from Bowen's reaction series that the fluid left during magma crystallization contains high levels of silica and water. This fluid also contains any leftover elements that

ENVIRONMENTAL CONNECTION

Figure 5-14 The columns in the Rhodes Memorial in Cape Town, South Africa **(A);** the kitchen tiles **(B);** and the Vietnam Memorial in Washington, D.C. **(C)** are all made of granite.

Enrichment

Visual-Spatial Show students a mafic porphyritic rock with large plagioclase feldspars surrounded by finer-grained feldspars. Have students infer how the compositions of the two different-sized feldspars might differ. The larger crystals may be more rich in calcium if they did not have time to react with the melt while the finer-grained crystals were forming.

Discussion

Ask students which mineral would more likely form porphyritic textures and why: plagioclase feldspar or orthoclase feldspar. Plagioclase feldspar would be more likely to form porphyritic textures; it crystallizes earlier. The large crystals found in porphyritic textures must form early in the crystallization sequence.

Applying Earth Science

Intrapersonal Have students investigate their homes and yards to see whether any igneous rocks have been used for decorative or construction purposes. Students should describe the rocks and how they are being used in their science journals. L1 ELL

Resource Manager

Laboratory Manual, pp. 37–40 L2

Differentiated Instruction

Gifted Have students research the crystal structure of quartz. Have them explain how the structure of quartz is related to its high resistance to weathering. Each silicon atom is tightly bonded to four oxygen atoms in a three-dimensional tetrahedral arrangement. The tight atomic bonds make quartz highly resistant to weathering. L3

NY Core Curriculum Standards

Page 110: St 1 Math KI 1, 2, 3, & Engin KI 1, St 4 KI 3.1a & 3.1c, St 6 KI 1 & 2
Page 111: St 4 KI 3.1a & 3.1c, St 6 KI 1

Content Background

Although most diamonds come from South African kimberlite pipes, diamonds have been found on every continent except Antarctica. In the United States, the largest number of diamonds have been found in Arkansas. Geologic studies indicate the presence of buried kimberlite pipes in Arkansas.

Enrichment

Graphite has a hardness of 1–2 on the Mohs scale of mineral hardness. Diamond has a hardness of 10. Both minerals are composed of pure carbon. Have students research the crystal structure of these minerals and explain how their structures are related to their hardnesses. The carbon atoms in graphite are bonded in six-atom rings that form flat sheets. The bonds between these sheets are weak. Carbon atoms in diamonds form strong covalent bonds with four other carbon atoms in a three-dimensional network of tetrahedrons. This is an extremely strong arrangement.

Figure 5-15 This sample of gold-bearing quartz came from El Dorado County, California.

Using Math

Using Numbers
A granite slab has a density of 2.7 g/cm³. What is the mass of a 2-cm thick countertop that is 0.6 m x 2.5 m? How many pounds is this?

were not incorporated into the common igneous minerals. Some important metallic elements that are not included in common minerals are gold, silver, lead, and copper. These elements, along with the dissolved silica, are released at the end of magma crystallization in a hot, mineral-rich fluid that fills cracks and voids in the surrounding rock. This fluid solidifies to form metal-rich quartz veins, such as the gold-bearing veins found in the Sierra Nevada mountains of California. An example of gold-bearing quartz is shown in **Figure 5-15**.

Pegmatites Vein deposits may contain other valuable resources in addition to metals. Veins of extremely large-grained minerals, such as the one shown in **Figure 5-16A,** are called **pegmatites.** Ores of rare elements such as lithium and beryllium are found in pegmatites. In addition to ores, pegmatites can produce beautiful crystals. Because these veins fill cavities and fractures in rock, minerals grow into voids and retain their shapes. Some of the world's most beautiful minerals have been found in pegmatites. An example is shown in **Figure 5-16B.**

Figure 5-16 Pegmatites are veins of extremely large-grained minerals **(A).** Stunning crystals such as this garnet are often found in pegmatites **(B).**

Across the Curriculum

History The Sierra Nevada were formed by large granitic intrusions that in turn formed large numbers of gold-rich quartz veins. Ask students to research and write reports about how these geologic features affected the westward migration and settlement of California.

Figure 5-17 Diamonds are found in kimberlites **(A),** such as those in the Kimberly Diamond Mine in South Africa **(B).**

Kimberlites Diamond is a valuable mineral found in rare, ultramafic rocks known as **kimberlites,** named after Kimberly, South Africa, where the intrusions were first identified. These unusual rocks are a variety of peridotite. They likely form deep in the crust at depths of 150 to 300 km or in the mantle because diamond and other minerals found in kimberlites can form only under very high pressures.

Geologists hypothesize that kimberlite magma is intruded rapidly upwards towards Earth's surface, where it forms long, narrow, pipelike structures. These structures extend several kilometers into the crust, but they are only 100 to 300 m in diameter. Most of the world's diamonds come from South African mines, such as the one shown in *Figure 5-17.*

SECTION ASSESSMENT

1. Describe the three major groups of igneous rocks. What are ultramafic rocks?

2. Why does rhyolite have smaller crystals than granite?

3. What chemical property is most commonly used to classify igneous rocks? List two physical properties that you could use to identify igneous rocks.

4. Why is gold often found in veins of quartz that are in and around igneous intrusions?

5. **Thinking Critically** Would quartz or plagioclase be more likely to form a well-shaped crystal in an igneous rock? Explain.

SKILL REVIEW

6. **Concept Mapping** Use the following terms to construct a concept map about igneous rock classification. For more help, refer to the *Skill Handbook.*

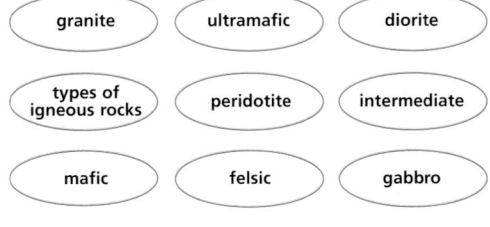

granite ultramafic diorite

types of igneous rocks peridotite intermediate

mafic felsic gabbro

SECTION ASSESSMENT

1. Felsic rocks are light-colored, have high silica levels, and contain quartz and feldspars. Intermediate rocks are medium-colored, have intermediate silica contents, and contain moderate amounts of biotite, amphibole, and pyroxene. Mafic rocks are dark colored, have low silica contents, and contain abundant iron-magnesium minerals such as biotite, pyroxene, amphibole, and olivine. Ultramafic rocks have low silica contents and very high levels of iron and magnesium.

2. Rhyolite cooled faster. The crystals did not have time to grow large.

3. Percentage of silica is the chemical property. The physical properties may be color, grain size, or texture.

4. Gold is not incorporated into the common igneous minerals. Therefore, it becomes concentrated in the leftover silica-rich fluids that form the quartz veins in and around igneous intrusions.

5. Plagioclase would form well-shaped crystals because it forms early and there is room in the liquid magma for the crystals to grow. Quartz crystallizes later and fills in the spaces between previously formed mineral grains.

6. "Types of igneous rocks" should be the main heading and should be linked to these four pairs: felsic–granite; intermediate–diorite; mafic–gabbro; ultramafic–peridotite.

GeoLab

GeoLab

Modeling Crystal Formation

Process Skills

analyze data, design an experiment, observe and infer, compare and contrast

Safety Precautions

The alum solution will be very hot. Students should not try to move the petri dishes after the solution has been poured. They should wear safety goggles and aprons.

Disposal

Allow the water to evaporate from the petri dishes over the course of several days. Dispose of solid wastes in the garbage. Collect the alum in a labeled container for reuse.

Preparation

- Prepare the saturated solution by dissolving as much alum as possible in a large beaker of nearly boiling water. Use approximately 400–500 mL of alum for each 1000 mL of water.
- The solution may become cloudy if it boils. This will not affect the crystallization process.

The rate at which magma cools has an effect on the grain size of the resulting igneous rock. Observing the crystallization of magma is difficult because molten rock is very hot and the crystallization process is sometimes very slow. Other materials, however, crystallize at lower temperatures. These materials can be used to model crystal formation.

Preparation

Problem
Model the crystallization of minerals from magma.

Materials
clean, plastic petri dishes
saturated alum solution
200-mL glass beaker
magnifying glass
piece of dark-colored
  construction paper
thermometer
paper towels
water
hot plate

Objectives
In this GeoLab, you will:
- **Determine** the relationship between cooling rate and crystal size.
- **Compare** and **contrast** different crystal shapes.

Safety Precautions

The alum mixture can cause skin irritation and will be hot when it is first poured into the petri dishes. If splattering occurs, wash skin with cold water. Always wear safety goggles and an apron in the lab.

Procedure

1. As a group, plan how you could change the cooling rate of a hot solution poured into a petri dish. For instance, you may want to put one sample in a freezer or refrigerator for a designated period of time. Assign each group member a petri dish to observe during the experiment.
2. Place a piece of dark-colored construction paper on a level surface where it won't be disturbed. Place the petri dishes on top of the paper.

Procedure

Teaching Strategies

Discuss the concept of saturated solutions. Hot water can dissolve more material than cold water can. As a hot, saturated solution cools, the water molecules lose energy and cannot keep the alum atoms in solution. The atoms bind together in a set pattern, forming solid crystals with a characteristic shape.

Troubleshooting

Drop a few grains of alum into a dish to trigger crystallization.

Data and Observations

Students will observe crystals growing. Students can use various methods to alter the cooling rate, such as using layers of paper towels for insulation or blowing on the liquid surface to cool it. The solution that cools more slowly will have larger crystals.

3. Carefully pour a saturated alum solution that is about 95°C to 98°C, or just below boiling temperature, into each petri dish so that it is half-full. Use caution when pouring the hot liquid to avoid splatters and burns.
4. Observe the petri dishes. Record your observations in your science journal.

Draw what you observe happening in the petri dish assigned to you.
5. Every 5 minutes for 30 minutes, record your observations of your petri dish. Make accurate, full-sized drawings of any crystals that begin to form.

Analyze

1. How did you vary the cooling rate of the solutions in the petri dishes? Compare your methods with those of other groups. Did one method appear to work better than others? Explain.
2. Use a magnifying glass or binocular microscope to observe your alum crystals. What do the crystals look like? Are all the crystals the same size?

3. Compare your drawings and petri dish with those of other students in your group. Which petri dish had the smallest average crystal size? Describe the conditions under which that petri dish cooled.
4. Do all the crystals have the same shape? Draw the most common shape. Share your drawings with other groups. Describe any patterns that you see.

Conclude & Apply

1. What factors affected the size of the crystals in the different petri dishes? How do you know?
2. Infer why the crystals changed shape as they grew.
3. How is this experiment different from magma crystallization? How is it the same?
4. Describe the relationship between cooling rate and crystal formation.

GeoLab **115**

✓Assessment

Performance Have students each design an experiment using alum that will create a porphyritic texture. If time allows, have them conduct their experiments. Use the Performance Task Assessment List for Designing an Experiment in **PASC,** p. 23.

Resource Manager

GeoLab and MiniLab Worksheets, pp. 20–22 L2

Analyze

1. Answers will vary depending on the cooling method used. Possible methods are listed under Data and Observations.
2. Alum crystals are tabular and have six sides. They look like triangles with the corners cut off. The crystals may be different sizes.
3. The petri dish that cooled most quickly will have the smallest crystals. The conditions under which the petri dish cooled will vary, depending on the cooling method used.
4. The majority of the crystals will have the same shape until they begin to grow together.

Conclude & Apply

1. The cooling rate affected the crystal size. This is evident because it is the only variable tested.
2. The crystals grew larger but maintained a similar shape until they began to interfere with each other. Their shapes became distorted as they grew together.
3. The experiment is different from magma crystallization in that magma crystallization involves the cooling of melted minerals, whereas this experiment involves the cooling of a hot solution containing dissolved minerals. The experiment is similar to magma crystallization in that the cooling rate affected crystal size in both cases, and the crystals grew by adding atoms to their surfaces.
4. A fast cooling rate results in small crystals; a slow cooling rate results in large crystals.

Purpose

Students will learn that the ancient art of knapping is still practiced today.

Content Background

Like their early counterparts, modern knappers still make knives. However, a select few make scalpels from obsidian. These scalpels are extremely efficient and are often used for plastic surgery.

Teaching Strategies

- Some students may have arrowhead collections. If so, have these students share their collections with the class, or arrange a field trip to a natural science museum to view ancient arrowheads.

- Ask students which they believe has a sharper edge: a handmade obsidian scalpel or a manufactured stainless-steel scalpel. Most students will likely say that the stainless-steel scalpel is sharper. After students have read this feature, reopen the topic. Students should have learned that the atomic structure of obsidian gives it a superior cutting edge.

Science & Technology

Cutting-Edge Surgery

When we hear the word technology, we often envision complicated gadgets. But one of the earliest forms of technology centered around common rocks. To better hunt their prey, for instance, our early ancestors created razor-sharp arrowheads and spears from the igneous rock obsidian. Today, there's a new use for this old rock: plastic surgery.

Knapping

Knapping is the process of shaping a rock by using a mallet-like instrument to break off pieces of the rock. For thousands of years, this technique has been used to shape obsidian into tools and decorative pieces. This fast-cooling, extrusive rock has a conchoidal fracture, which allows the rock to break in predictable ways. Knappers use three techniques, sometimes in combination, to shape obsidian. Percussion flaking involves using a hammer or mallet to shape the rock. Pressure flaking involves using specially designed tools to pry off flakes of the rock. Lastly, in indirect percussion, a tool called a punch is placed on the edge of the rock. Flaking results when the punch is struck by a hammer or mallet.

Obsidian Scalpels

Knapping is carried on today by skilled artisans. Some of these modern knappers have taken their craft into the medical field, and are creating scalpels made from obsidian. Because obsidian scalpels are handmade, their surfaces look somewhat rough compared with traditional stainless steel scalpels. However, obsidian scalpels actually have a much sharper, smoother edge than stainless steel scalpels. When viewed under an electron microscope, the edges of an obsidian scalpel meet at a single point, which gives the scalpel its fine, sharp edge. This sharpness allows the scalpel to "divide" rather than tear flesh. Unlike the stainless steel scalpel, the obsidian scalpel creates such a small incision it barely leaves a scar. For this reason, obsidian scalpels are particularly well-suited to plastic surgery.

Disadvantages

At present, only a few doctors use obsidian scalpels, largely because these handmade-tools are relatively expensive. The price of the scalpels is high because only a few knappers are producing the scalpels, and each scalpel takes days or even weeks to complete. The average obsidian scalpel may cost $20. In contrast, stainless steel scalpels, which can be mass-produced, cost approximately $2 each.

Reading Analysis

In addition to scalpels, obsidian is used to make knives. Other igneous rocks, such as granite, are used in the construction industry. Go to the Earth Science Web Site at **earthgeu.com** to research and write a report about some common uses for igneous rocks.

Reading Analysis

Reports will vary. Students may note that granite kitchen countertops are becoming quite popular in homes. Other uses for igneous rocks include tiles, building faces, block walls, and tombstones. Accept all reasonable answers.

Summary

SECTION 5.1

What are igneous rocks?

Main Ideas

- Igneous rocks are formed by the cooling and crystallization of magma. Intrusive rocks form inside Earth's crust, and extrusive rocks form on Earth's surface. Extrusive rocks, which cool more rapidly than intrusive rocks, are generally more fine grained.
- Magma is a slushy mix of molten rock, gases, and mineral crystals. The elements found in magma are the same major elements found in Earth's crust: oxygen (O), silicon (Si), aluminum (Al), iron (Fe), magnesium (Mg), calcium (Ca), potassium (K), and sodium (Na).
- Silica (SiO_2) is the most abundant compound in magma. Magmas are classified as basaltic, andesitic, and rhyolitic, based on the amount of SiO_2 they contain.
- Different minerals melt and crystallize at different temperatures in the processes of partial melting and fractional crystallization. Minerals crystallize from magma in a sequential pattern known as Bowen's reaction series.

Vocabulary

Bowen's reaction series (p. 103)
extrusive (p. 99)
fractional crystallization (p. 103)
igneous rock (p. 99)
intrusive (p. 99)
lava (p. 99)
partial melting (p. 102)

Main Ideas

Summary statements can be used by students to review the major concepts of the chapter.

VOCABULARY PuzzleMaker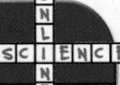

For additional help with vocabulary, have students access the Vocabulary Puzzlemaker online.

earthgeu.com/ vocabulary puzzlemaker

SECTION 5.2

Classifying Igneous Rocks

Main Ideas

- Igneous rocks are classified as felsic, mafic, intermediate, and ultramafic, depending upon their mineral compositions. Felsic rocks such as granite are light-colored, have high silica contents, and contain quartz and feldspars. Mafic rocks such as gabbro are dark-colored, have lower silica contents, and are rich in iron and magnesium. Intermediate rocks have moderate silica levels. Ultramafic rocks have low silica contents and very high levels of iron and magnesium. Igneous groups can be further identified by crystal size and texture.
- Early forming minerals may have well-shaped crystals, while later-forming minerals have irregular shapes. Porphyritic textures contain both large and small crystals.
- Igneous rocks such as granite are often used as building materials because of their strength, durability, and beauty.
- Valuable ore deposits and gems are often associated with igneous intrusions. Ores of rare elements such as lithium and beryllium are found in veins of extremely large-grained minerals called pegmatites. Diamonds are found in rare types of igneous intrusions known as kimberlites.

Vocabulary

felsic (p. 107)
kimberlite (p. 113)
mafic (p. 107)
pegmatite (p. 112)
porphyritic (p. 110)
ultramafic (p. 108)

0:00 Out of Time?

If time does not permit teaching the entire chapter, use the GeoDigest at the end of the unit as an overview.

Earth Science Online

Be sure to check the Earth Science Web Site for links to chapter material:
earthgeu.com

 earthgeu.com/vocabulary_puzzlemaker

GLENCOE *Technology*

 **Videotape/DVD MindJogger Videoquizzes**

Chapter 5: *Igneous Rocks*
Have students work in groups as they play the videoquiz game to review key chapter concepts.

Resource Manager

Chapter Assessment, pp. 25–30
MindJogger Videoquizzes DVD/VHS
ExamView® Pro CD-ROM
Performance Assessment in Earth Science

NY Core Curriculum Standards

Page 116: St 4 KI 3.1c
Page 117: St 4 KI 2.1a, 3.1a, 3.1b, & 3.1c, St 6 KI 1 & 5

Understanding Main Ideas

1. b
2. c
3. c
4. b
5. b
6. d
7. c
8. a
9. b
10. b
11. c
12. Answers will vary. Students may say kitchen countertops, floors, monuments, and walls. Accept all reasonable answers.
13. Diamonds require very high pressure to form.
14. The three main types of magma are basaltic, andesitic, and rhyolitic. These classifications are based on silica content.
15. Bowen's reaction series describes the relationship between mineral crystallization and cooling magma. The left branch contains minerals rich in iron and magnesium. The right branch contains the feldspars.
16. Both minerals crystallize early at high temperatures.

Understanding Main Ideas

1. What term describes igneous rocks that crystallize inside Earth?
   a. magma
   b. intrusive
   c. lava
   d. extrusive

2. What magma type contains the greatest amount of SiO_2?
   a. basaltic
   b. andesitic
   c. rhyolitic
   d. peridotitic

3. What igneous rock has no visible crystals as a result of rapid cooling?
   a. gabbro
   b. andesite
   c. obsidian
   d. pegmatite

4. What type of ultramafic rock sometimes contains diamond?
   a. pegmatite
   b. kimberlite
   c. granite
   d. rhyolite

5. What minerals are associated with the right branch of Bowen's reaction series?
   a. olivine and pyroxene
   b. feldspars
   c. mica and feldspars
   d. quartz and biotite

6. What is the last mineral to crystallize from magma?
   a. biotite
   b. plagioclase
   c. olivine
   d. quartz

7. What are veins of extremely coarse-grained igneous rocks called?
   a. gabbros
   b. layered intrusions
   c. pegmatites
   d. crystals

8. What effect does a fast cooling rate have on grain size in igneous rocks?
   a. It forms fine-grained crystals.
   b. It forms large-grained crystals.
   c. It forms light crystals.
   d. It forms dark crystals.

9. What term describes magma that flows out onto Earth's surface?
   a. layered intrusion
   b. lava
   c. crystallization
   d. ultramafic

10. Which of the following affects the melting temperature of magma?
    a. ore deposits
    b. silica content
    c. oxygen content
    d. potassium content

11. Which of the following does not affect the formation of magma?
    a. temperature
    b. pressure
    c. volume
    d. mineral composition

12. What are some uses of igneous rocks in the construction industry?

13. Why do scientists theorize that kimberlites originate deep within Earth's crust or mantle?

14. What are the three main types of magma? What factor determines these classifications?

15. Describe Bowen's reaction series. Be sure to discuss the two branches of the series.

16. Why are olivine and calcium-rich plagioclase often found together in igneous rocks?

Test-Taking Tip

GET TO THE ROOT OF THINGS. If you don't know the definition of a word, you can infer its meaning by examining its roots, prefixes, and suffixes. For instance, words that start with *non-, un-, a-, dis-,* and *in-* generally reverse what the rest of the word means. Words that end in *-ly* are usually adverbs, and thus, are descriptive terms.

earthgeu.com/chapter_test

Standardized Test Practice

1. d
2. c
3. a
4. c

NY Core Curriculum Standards

Page 118: St 4 KI 3.1a, 3.1b, & 3.1c, St 6 KI 1 & 5
Page 119: St 4 KI 3.1a, 3.1b, & 3.1c, St 6 KI 1 & 5

Applying Main Ideas

17. Why is magma usually a slushy mixture of crystals and molten rock?

18. What is unusual about peridotite and dunite?

Use the table below to answer questions 19-21.

Rock Composition				
Mineral	Mineral Percentage			
	Rock 1	Rock 2	Rock 3	Rock 4
Quartz	5	35	0	0
Potassium feldspar	0	15	0	0
Plagioclase feldspar	55	25	0	55
Biotite	15	15	0	10
Amphibole	25	10	0	30
Pyroxene	0	0	40	5
Olivine	0	0	60	0

19. Which rock is most likely granite?

20. Which rock is an ultramafic rock?

21. Rock 4 is fine grained. What type of rock is it?

22. What characteristics of igneous rocks make them good building materials?

Thinking Critically

23. How is it possible for magma to have a higher silica content than the rock from which it formed?

24. Would you expect to find plagioclase feldspar or biotite in a greater variety of igneous rocks? Explain.

25. Which would make a lighter-colored kitchen counter, granite or gabbro? Why?

26. Why are mineral deposits often found around the perimeter of igneous intrusions?

 earthgeu.com/standardized_test

Standardized Test Practice

1. Which of the following is most abundant in magma and has the greatest effect on its characteristics?
 a. O
 b. Ca
 c. Al
 d. SiO$_2$

2. Which process describes how different minerals form at different rates?
 a. partial melting
 b. Bowen's reaction series
 c. fractional crystallization
 d. geothermal gradient

USING TABLES Use the table to answer questions 3 and 4.

Characteristics of Rocks			
	Color	Silica Content	Composition
Rock A	light	high	quartz and feldspars
Rock B	dark	low	iron and magnesium

3. Rock A is most likely what kind of rock?
 a. felsic
 b. mafic
 c. ultramafic
 d. intermediate

4. Which type of rock is rock B?
 a. granite
 b. diorite
 c. gabbro
 d. pegmatite

Applying Main Ideas

17. Minerals melt and crystallize at different temperatures. Thus, some minerals may remain solid, while others melt.

18. Peridotite and dunite are ultramafic rocks that contain high levels of iron and magnesium and low levels of silica.

19. rock 2

20. rock 3

21. andesite

22. Answers will vary. Students may say interlocking grain textures, minerals that are resistant to weathering, and massive structures with few zones of weaknesses. Accept all reasonable answers.

Thinking Critically

23. This is possible during partial melting. The first minerals to melt may have a high silica content and will thus generate magma with more silica than the parent rock.

24. plagioclase feldspar; it crystallizes over a much wider range of temperatures than biotite does

25. Granite is lighter in color; thus, it would make a lighter-colored counter. Gabbro contains a higher percentage of dark-colored iron and magnesium minerals.

26. Metallic elements are often concentrated in the final fluids during magma crystallization. These fluids invade the fractures surrounding an intrusion and form mineral deposits.

EXAM*VIEW*® PRO

Use Exam*View*® Pro Testmaker CD-ROM to:

- Create **multiple versions** of tests.
- Create **modified** tests with one mouse click for struggling students.
- **Edit** existing questions and add your own questions.
- **Build** tests based on national curriculum standards.

119

Chapter 6

Sedimentary and Metamorphic Rocks

Refer to pages 8T–9T of the Teacher Guide for an explanation of the National Science Content Standards correlations.

Section	Objectives	National Science Content Standards	State/Local Standards
Section 6.1 **Formation of Sedimentary Rocks** 1½ sessions 1 block	1. **Sequence** the formation of sedimentary rocks. 2. **Explain** the formation and classification of clastic sediments. 3. **Describe** features of sedimentary rocks.	UCP.2, UCP.3; A.1, A.2; B.2, B.3, B.4; C.6; F.3	St 1 Science KI 1, 2, & 3, St 4 KI 1.2i, 1.2j, 3.1a, 3.1b, & 3.1c, St 6 KI 2 & 5
Section 6.2 **Types of Sedimentary Rocks** 1 session ½ block	4. **Describe** the types of clastic sedimentary rocks. 5. **Explain** how chemical sedimentary rocks form. 6. **Describe** organic sedimentary rocks. 7. **Recognize** the importance of sedimentary rocks.	UCP.1, UCP.3; A.1, A.2; B.2, B.3, B.4; F.3	St 1 Math KI 2 & 3, Science KI 1, St 4 KI 1.2i, 1.2j, 3.1a, 3.1b, & 3.1c, St 6 KI 5, St 7 KI 1
Section 6.3 **Metamorphic Rocks** 2½ sessions 1½ blocks	8. **Compare** and **Contrast** the different types and causes of metamorphism. 9. **Distinguish** among metamorphic textures. 10. **Explain** how mineral and compositional changes occur during metamorphism. 11. **Understand** how rocks continuously change from one type to another in the rock cycle.	UCP.1, UCP.2, UCP.3, UCP.5; A.1, A.2; B.2, B.4; D.2; E.2; F.1, F.3, F.5, F.6	St 1 Math KI 3, Science KI 1, 2, & 3, St 4 KI 1.2i, 1.2j, 3.1a, 3.1b, & 3.1c, St 6 KI 1 & 5, St 7 KI 1

*A complete Planning Guide is provided on pages 30T–32T.

The number of recommended single-period sessions

 The number of recommended blocks

Activity Materials

Discovery Lab *page 121*
soil, 100-mL graduated cylinder or beaker, tall jar with lid, water

GeoLab *pages 140–141*
Sedimentary rocks and their metamorphic equivalents, magnifying glass or hand lens, paper, pencil, beam balance, 100-mL graduated cylinder or beaker

Demo *page 125*
coarse gravel, clear container

Key to Teaching Strategies

L1 Level 1 activities should be appropriate for students with learning difficulties.

L2 Level 2 activities should be within the ability range of all students.

L3 Level 3 activities are designed for above-average students.

ELL ELL activities should be within the ability range of English-language learners.

COOP LEARN Cooperative learning activities are designed for small-group work.

P These strategies represent student products that can be placed in a best-work portfolio.

These strategies are useful in a block-scheduling format.

Need materials? Contact Science Kit at 1-800-828-7777 or at www.sciencekit.com on the Internet. For alternate materials, see the activity on the listed page.

Chapter Organizer

Glencoe Exclusive!
Teacher Works™
All-In-One Planner and Resource Center

Activities/Features	Reproducible Masters	Transparencies
Discovery Lab: Model Sediment Layering, p. 121 **MiniLab:** What happened here? p. 126	**Study Guide for Content Mastery,** pp. 33–34 **L2** **GeoLab and MiniLab Worksheets,** p. 23 **L2** **Laboratory Manual,** pp. 41–44 **L2**	**Section Focus Transparency 14** **L1** **ELL** **Teaching Transparency 13** **L2** **ELL**
Using Math: Using Percentages, p. 129	**Study Guide for Content Mastery,** p. 35 **L2** **Laboratory Manual,** pp. 45–48 **L2**	**Section Focus Transparency 15** **L1** **ELL** **Teaching Transparency 14 L2 ELL**
Problem-Solving Lab: Interpreting Scientific Illustrations, p. 138 **GeoLab:** Interpreting Changes in Rocks, pp. 140–141 **Science in the News:** Good News–Crayons Safe, p. 142	**Study Guide for Content Mastery,** pp. 36–38 **L2** **GeoLab and MiniLab Worksheets,** pp. 24–25 **L2**	**Section Focus Transparency 16** **L1** **ELL** **Teaching Transparency 15 L2 ELL**

✓Assessment

Chapter Assessment, pp. 31–36
Performance Assessment in the Science Classroom (PASC)
MindJogger Videoquiz DVD/VHS
Performance Assessment in Earth Science
ExamView® Pro CD-ROM
5 Days to the Regents Exam

GLENCOE'S
ASSESSMENT
ADVANTAGE

Additional Resources

Guided Reading Audio Program ELL
Cooperative Learning in the Science Classroom COOP LEARN
Lesson Plans
Block Scheduling
earthgeu.com
NY Lesson Plans
NY Block Scheduling
Review Handbook for Regents Earth Science Exam

NATIONAL GEOGRAPHIC

Teacher's Corner

Products Available from National Geographic Society
To order the following products, call the National Geographic Society at 1-800-368-2728:
Curriculum Kits
GeoKit: *Rocks and Minerals*
CD-ROM
111 years of National Geographic Magazine

Video
Every Stone Has a Story
Book
National Geographic Desk Reference

Content Background

Turbidites
Section 6.1

Geologists have found thick sedimentary sequences containing multiple layers of graded bedding. These rhythmic alternations of thin sandstone and thin shale can be thousands of meters thick, with each layer ranging from 1 cm to 1 m. Each sandstone layer has a sharp base with an upward-fining sequence capped by a shale layer. In the mid-1900s, it was realized that these rocks were formed by underwater turbidity flows. An underwater landslide, possibly triggered by an earthquake or a slump, formed a mass of muddy water that behaved like a heavy liquid and flowed downhill under water for great distances. As the current waned, deposition progressed in such a manner as to form an upward-fining sequence of graded bedding. At some later time, another turbidite flow covered the preceding flow with another graded sequence. Because each layer was deposited in deep water, there was little disturbance between events. Turbidite sequences have been identified in rocks of all ages and are forming today along the continental shelves. Turbidite deposits may have great importance to oil and gas exploration in offshore regions.

Karst Topography
Section 6.2

Under certain conditions, thick sequences of limestone can be deposited. These deposits can be biologic in origin, as coral reefs are, or they can form from chemical processes in evaporite basins.

When these limestone layers are uplifted near Earth's surface, a peculiar type of topography, known as karst topography, can be formed. Karst topography is characterized by closed drainages, sinkholes, caves, streams that suddenly disappear underground and then reappear, and other unusual features. All of these conditions are caused by the dissolution of limestone by groundwater. Rainwater absorbs CO_2 from the atmosphere and also from decaying organic material. This produces a weak carbonic acid. As the acidic water seeps through cracks and fissures in the limestone, the water slowly dissolves and enlarges the openings. Eventually, large caves and underground river channels can develop. Parts of Kentucky, Tennessee, and Florida are underlain by thick layers of limestone and are characterized by karst topography.

Multiple Learning Styles

- **Kinesthetic** Modeling, pp. 130, 136, Activity, pp. 130, 131
- **Visual-Spatial** Demo, pp. 128, 135, Project, p. 136
- **Interpersonal** Project, p. 125, Collaborative Learning, pp. 131, 135
- **Linguistic** Reteach, p. 127, Reteach, p. 132
- **Logical-Mathematical** Activity, p. 123
- **Naturalist** Environmental Connection, p. 131

GLENCOE Technology

The following multimedia resources are available from Glencoe.

Vocabulary Puzzlemaker
TeacherWorks™ CD-ROM
MindJogger Videoquizzes DVD/VHS
ExamView® Pro CD-ROM
Interactive Chalkboard CD-ROM

Chapter Organizer

Skarn Deposits
Section 6.3

Contact metamorphism occurs whenever rocks are intruded by magma. The type of minerals found in the contact aureole, the area around the intrusion, depends on the type of rocks that are intruded. A special type of contact metamorphism, called a skarn deposit, occurs when a siliceous magma intrudes dirty carbonate rocks, such as silty limestone or calcareous shale. In this geologic setting, there are a great variety of minerals and elements to react with each other, causing significant changes to occur between the magma and the carbonate rocks. Skarn deposits are usually unevenly grained rocks rich in calcium and silica, primarily garnet and pyroxene. The Si–Ca ratio and the concentration of aluminum typically increase towards the intrusive contact. This indicates that the limestone contains components from the magma. Some skarns contain valuable concentrations of metals. Important sources of Fe, Au, Cu, Zn, and W have been found in skarn deposits.

Identifying Misconceptions

Many students may think that in order to become cemented into rock, sediments must be buried. Some sedimentary rocks are composed of smaller, broken pieces of other, pre-existing rocks. When these pieces are deposited, compacted and lithified, they become one form of sedimentary rocks. Other types of sedimentary rocks are precipitated from a water solution, caused by a change in water chemistry, biological action, or evaporation.

✔Assessment

Portfolio Assessment
Discovery Lab, TWE, p. 121

Performance Assessment
Assessment, TWE, p. 132
Discovery Lab, SE, p. 121
MiniLab, SE, p. 126
GeoLab, SE, pp. 140–141

Knowledge Assessment
Section Assessment, SE, pp. 127, 132, 139
Assessment, TWE, pp. 129, 134
Problem-Solving Lab, TWE, p. 138
GeoLab, TWE, pp. 140–141

Skill Assessment
Assessment, TWE, pp. 127, 139
MiniLab, TWE, p. 126

Be sure to check the Earth Science Web Site for links to chapter material: earthgeu.com

GLENCOE'S ASSESSMENT ADVANTAGE

Sedimentary and Metamorphic Rocks

Introducing the Chapter

Hold up a rice cake and a sample of coarse sandstone. Ask students how they are the same and how they are different. Point out that the most common type of sedimentary rock, clastic rock, is composed of cemented particles.

Interpreting the Photo

Situated between Ribbon Creek Valley and the Kananaskis River, Mt. Kidd stands 2958 m high. It was named for Stuart Kidd, an outfitter who moved to the area in 1907 and supplied expeditions in the Kananaskis Valley.

Chapter Themes

The following themes from the National Science Content Standards are covered in this chapter. Refer to page 8T of the Teacher Guide for an explanation of the correlations.
Systems, order, and organization (UCP.1); Change, constancy, and measurement (UCP.3); Form and function (UCP.5)

0:00 *Out of Time?*

If time does not permit teaching the entire chapter, use the Chapter Summary on page 143 and the GeoDigest found at the end of the unit as an overview.

NY Core Curriculum Standards

Page 120: St 4 KI 1.2j & 3.1c
Page 121: St 1 Science KI 1, 2, & 3, St 6 KI 5

What You'll Learn

- How sedimentary rocks are formed.
- How metamorphic rocks are formed.
- How rocks continuously change from one type to another in the rock cycle.

Why It's Important

Sedimentary rocks provide information about surface conditions and organisms that existed in Earth's past. In addition, mineral resources are found in sedimentary and metamorphic rocks. The rock cycle further provides evidence that Earth is a dynamic planet, constantly evolving and changing.

Earth Science Online

To find out more about sedimentary and metamorphic rocks, visit the Earth Science Web Site at earthgeu.com

Mount Kidd, Alberta, Canada

Sedimentary and Metamorphic Rocks

Discovery Lab

Process Skills

observe and infer, draw a conclusion

Safety Precautions 🥽

Do not use soil that contains rocks large enough to break the jar during shaking.

Procedure

Troubleshooting

The best layering occurs when the sediment settles through as much water as possible. Have students hesitate momentarily with the jar upside down before tipping it upright for the last time.

- Explain to students that smaller, lighter grains fall more slowly as a result of the friction and viscosity of water.

- Prepare a demonstration settlement column ahead of time for students to observe if they fail to obtain the expected results.

Observe

The coarsest sediment will settle out first. The topmost layers will be composed of clay, silt, and organic particles. Sedimentary rocks that have been

Discovery Lab   Model Sediment Layering

Sedimentary rocks are usually found in layers. How do these layers form? In this activity, you will investigate how layers form from particles that settle in water.

1. Obtain 100 mL of soil from a location specified by your teacher. Place the soil in a tall, narrow, jar.

2. Add water to the jar until it is three-fourths full. Put the lid on the jar so that it is tightly sealed.

3. Pick up the jar with both hands and turn it upside down several times to mix the water and soil.

4. Quickly turn the jar upright and set it on a flat surface.

Observe In your science journal, draw a diagram of what you observe. What type of particles settled out first? What type of particles form the topmost layers? How is this activity related to the layering that occurs in sedimentary rocks?

Section 6.1

Prepare

Section Background

For section content background, refer to **Turbidites** on page 120C.

Preplanning

Refer to the Chapter Organizer on pages 120A–B

1 Focus

Section Focus

Before presenting the lesson, display **Section Focus Transparency 14** on the overhead projector. L1 ELL

Tying to Previous Knowledge

Refer students to Bowen's reaction series in Chapter 5. Tell students that minerals that crystallize early are more susceptible to chemical weathering than those that crystallize later. Ask students which type of mineral grain they would expect to be most common in a clastic sedimentary rock. the most resistant minerals, such as quartz and feldspar

---

SECTION 6.1
Formation of Sedimentary Rocks

OBJECTIVES

- **Sequence** *the formation of sedimentary rocks.*
- **Explain** *the formation and classification of clastic sediments.*
- **Describe** *features of sedimentary rocks.*

VOCABULARY

sediment
clastic
deposition
lithification
cementation

bedding
graded
  bedding
cross-bedding

You learned in Chapter 5 that igneous rocks are the most common rocks in Earth's crust, yet when you look at the ground, you may not see igneous rocks. In fact, you usually don't see any solid rock at all. Why is this? Much of Earth's surface is covered with sediments. **Sediments** are pieces of solid material that have been deposited on Earth's surface by wind, water, ice, gravity, or chemical precipitation. When sediments become cemented together, they form sedimentary rocks. The formation of sedimentary rocks begins when weathering and erosion produce sediments.

WEATHERING

Wherever Earth's crust is exposed at the surface, it is continuously being worn away by weathering, a set of physical and chemical processes that break rock into smaller pieces. Chemical weathering occurs when the minerals in a rock are dissolved or otherwise

6.1 *Formation of Sedimentary Rocks* **121**

---

deposited by water can be sorted into layers of similar grain size.

Portfolio Most sedimentary rock layers do not contain all the different grain sizes. Ask students to diagram and describe how layers of only coarse sand and gravel might be formed. The water may be carrying only sand and gravel or the sediments were deposited in moving water with enough energy to prevent the finer particles from settling out.

Study Guide for Content Mastery, pp. 33–34 L2

Section Focus Transparency 14 L1 ELL

Teaching Transparency 13 L2 ELL

121

Tying to Previous Knowledge

Refer students to mineral characteristics in Chapter 4. Ask students which mineral characteristics have the greatest effect on the shape of grains after erosion and transport. Hardness and cleavage; the grains of hard minerals take a long time to become smooth and round, and minerals with strong cleavage have a tendency to be angular.

Discussion

Ask students how weathering differs from erosion. Weathering loosens particles; erosion transports particles.

Using Scientific Terms

Ask students what words they can think of that are similar to sediment and how they might be related. sedimentation, sedate, and sedative Sedimentation is another form of the noun, sediment. Sedative and sedate are not related.

NATIONAL GEOGRAPHIC

CD-ROM
Geology PictureShow
Rocks and Minerals

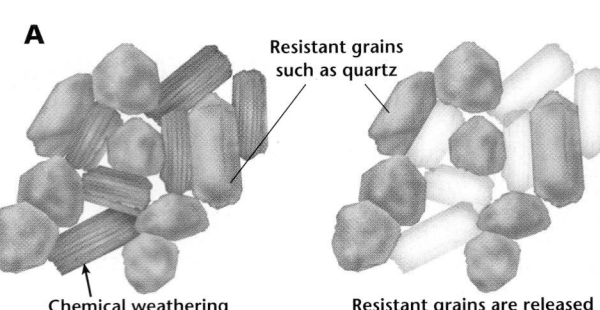

A

Resistant grains such as quartz

Chemical weathering attacks less resistant minerals

Resistant grains are released as weaker grains break down

B

Figure 6-1 The process of chemical weathering is illustrated in **(A)**. Granite breaks apart easily under the effects of chemical weathering **(B)**.

chemically changed. Study *Figure 6-1*. What happens to more-resistant minerals during weathering? While the less-stable minerals are chemically broken down, the more-resistant grains are broken off of the rock as smaller grains. During physical weathering, on the other hand, minerals remain chemically unchanged. Rock fragments simply break off of the solid rock along fractures or grain boundaries.

Weathering produces rock and mineral fragments known as **clastic** sediments. The word *clastic* comes from the Greek word *klastos*, meaning "broken." Clastic sediments range in size from huge boulders to microscopic particles. *Table 6-1* summarizes the classification of clastic sediments based on size. Clastic sediment particles usually have worn surfaces and rounded corners caused by physical abrasion during erosion and transport.

EROSION AND TRANSPORT

After rock fragments have been weathered out of outcrops, they are transported to new locations. The removal and movement of surface materials from one location to another is called erosion.

Table 6-1 Classification of Clastic Sediments		
Particle Size	**Sediment**	**Rock**
> 256 mm 256–64 mm 64–2 mm	Gravel } Boulder Cobble Pebble	Conglomerate
2–0.062 mm	Sand	Sandstone
0.062–0.0039 mm	Silt	Siltstone
<0.0039 mm	Clay	Mudstone or shale

122 CHAPTER 6 *Sedimentary and Metamorphic Rocks*

Cultural Diversity

Ayers Rock—Uluru In Kata Tjuta National Park, south-west of Alice Springs in the Northern Territory of Australia, a huge sandstone monolith rises 345 m above the desert. It is 2 km wide and semi-oval in shape. It is called Ayers Rock, or Uluru, as the Aboriginals (native Australians) named it. Uluru is a sacred site for the Aboriginal people. They believe that there is an energy source emanating from the rock and that the area around it is inhabited by ancestral beings. The rock seems to change color from blue to red, depending on the time of day and the quality of light. Uluru bears many carvings and paintings made by the Aboriginals who conduct sacred rites there. The Australian government restored ownership of Uluru and the Kata Tjuta National Park to the Aboriginals in 1985. The Aboriginal people received a UNESCO Picasso Gold Medal Award for superior management of the park. The Uluru-Kata Tjuta National Park and the Australian Nature Conservation Agency and UNESCO presented this award.

Figure 6-2 shows the four main agents of erosion: wind, moving water, gravity, and glaciers. Visible signs of erosion are all around you. For example, water in streams becomes muddy after a storm because silt and clay particles have been added to it. The dust that collects on shelves in your home is another indication of erosion. Where do you think this dust comes from? How is it carried and how does it eventually settle on the shelves?

Eroded materials are almost always carried downhill. Although wind can sometimes carry fine sand and dust to higher elevations, particles transported by water are almost always moved downward. Eventually, even wind-blown dust and fine sand are pulled downhill by gravity. You will learn more about this in the next chapter.

Deposition When sediments are laid down on the ground or sink to the bottoms of bodies of water **deposition** occurs. During the *Discovery Lab* at the beginning of this chapter, what happened when you stopped moving the jar full of sediment and water? The sediment sank to the bottom and was deposited. Similarly, in nature, sediments are

Figure 6-2 Winds blow sand into dunes on the Navajo Indian Reservation in Arizona **(A)**. The river Lethe cuts through the Valley of Ten Thousand Smokes in Katmai National Park, Alaska **(B)**. This landslide in Papua, New Guinea, carried the entire hillside 300 m into the canyon **(C)**. This terminal moraine was built up by the Athabasca Glacier in Jasper National Park, Alberta, Canada **(D)**.

B

A

C

D

6.1 *Formation of Sedimentary Rocks* **123**

In-Text Questions

Page 123 Where do you think this dust comes from? How is it carried and how does it eventually settle on the shelves? Dust on shelves is carried by air currents and is an example of erosion by wind. A sunbeam coming through a window will illuminate the dust particles in the air.

Activity

Logical-Mathematical Have students use magnifying glasses and microscopes to observe dust samples from windowsills or elsewhere. Have students list the types of particles that they can identify. Ask students to predict what percentage of the particles are silt and clay grains. **L2** **ELL**

Interpreting the Photos

Figure 6-2 Ask students which of the four mechanisms of erosion moved the largest particles. Also ask students in which environment shown they would expect to find well-sorted sediments. Landslides and glaciers moved the largest particles. The sand dunes contain well-sorted sand grains.

Across the Curriculum

Biology Ask students how their respiratory systems deal with air-borne dust. Nasal hairs filter out dust; fluid on the lining of lungs traps particles.

Differentiated Instruction

Visually Impaired Have students with visual impairments feel different types of sediment, including gravel, sand, silt, and soil, to differentiate them based on texture.

NY Core Curriculum Standards

Page 122: St 4 KI 3.1a & 3.1c, St 6 KI 5
Page 123: St 1 Science KI 3, St 6 KI 5

Students may think that deposition of sediments occurs only when transport stops.

Uncover the Misconception
Have students make a list of different environments where they would expect sedimentation to occur. Have students write explanations of why the sediments are deposited in each environment.

Demonstrate the Concept
Explain to students that deposition more commonly occurs as transport slows, not stops. For example, as water velocity slows down, the larger particles can be deposited even while the finer particles are still being carried away.

Assess New Knowledge
Have students explain how a well-sorted gravel bar may form in the middle of a river transporting sand and gravel. Students should be able to explain that if water velocity slows down, the gravel can be deposited in a bar while the sand is carried farther downstream. Therefore, a decrease in velocity causes a decrease in the size of particles and the amount of sediment transported.

Enrichment

Winter storm waves commonly have higher levels of energy than summer storm waves do. Ask students to predict how beach sediments deposited in winter might be different from those deposited in summer. The higher-energy winter waves deposit coarser particles on the beach than summer waves do.

Figure 6-3 This large sand dune **(A)** in Algeria, Africa, is made up of fine sand such as this from Kalahari, South Africa **(B)**.

deposited when transport stops. Perhaps the wind stops blowing or a river enters a quiet lake or the ocean. In each case, the particles being carried will settle out, forming layers of sediment. You observed this when you completed the *Discovery Lab* at the beginning of this chapter, that the sediment formed layers as it settled to the bottom of the jar. The sediment formed a layered deposit with the largest, grains at the bottom and the smallest particles at the top. As the water in the jar slowed down, the largest particles settled out first. Why? Faster-moving water can transport larger particles. As water slows down, the largest particles settle out first, then the next-largest, and so on, so that different-sized particles are sorted into layers. Such deposits are characteristic of sediment transported by water and wind. Wind, however, can move only small grains. For this reason, sand dunes, such as the ones shown in *Figure 6-3A,* are commonly made of fine, well-sorted sand like the sand in *Figure 6-3B.*

Not all sediment deposits are sorted. Glaciers, for example, move all materials with equal ease. Large boulders, sand, and mud are all carried along by the ice and dumped in an unsorted pile at the end of the glacier. Landslides create similar deposits when sediment moves downhill in a jumbled mass.

Burial Most sediments are ultimately deposited on Earth in depressions called sedimentary basins. These basins may contain layers of sediment that together are more than 8 km thick. As more and more sediment is deposited in an area, the bottom layers are subjected to increasing pressure and temperature. These conditions cause **lithification,** the physical and chemical processes that transform sediments into sedimentary rocks. *Lithify* comes from the Greek word *lithos,* which means "stone."

124 CHAPTER 6 *Sedimentary and Metamorphic Rocks*

Environmental Connection

Floods are not all bad. When a river floods, quiet water spreads horizontally a great distance from the riverbanks. These floodwaters deposit a layer of fine silt, clay, and organic material that improves the fertility of the soil. The dams on the Nile River in Egypt have interrupted this cycle, and soil fertility along the river is declining.

Using Scientific Terms

Have students find other words that have the Greek prefix *lithos. lithograph, lithography, lithosphere, lithology,* and *lithophyte*

LITHIFICATION

Lithification begins with compaction. The weight of overlying sediments forces the sediment grains closer together, causing the physical changes shown in *Figure 6-4*. Layers of mud may contain up to 60 percent water, and these shrink as excess water is squeezed out. Sand, however, is usually well compacted during deposition, and resists additional compaction during burial. Grain-to-grain contacts in sand form a supporting framework that helps maintain open spaces between the grains. Groundwater, oil, and natural gas are commonly found in these spaces in sedimentary rocks.

The temperature in Earth's crust increases with depth by about 30°C per kilometer. Sediments that are buried 3 to 4 km deep experience temperatures that are high enough to start the chemical and mineral changes that cause cementation. **Cementation** occurs when mineral growth cements sediment grains together into solid rock. There are two common types of cementation. The first type occurs when a new mineral, such as calcite ($CaCO_3$) or iron oxide (Fe_2O_3) grows between sediment grains as dissolved minerals precipitate out of groundwater. The second type occurs when existing mineral grains grow larger as more of the same mineral precipitates from groundwater and crystallizes around them. These two types of cementation are shown in *Figure 6-5*.

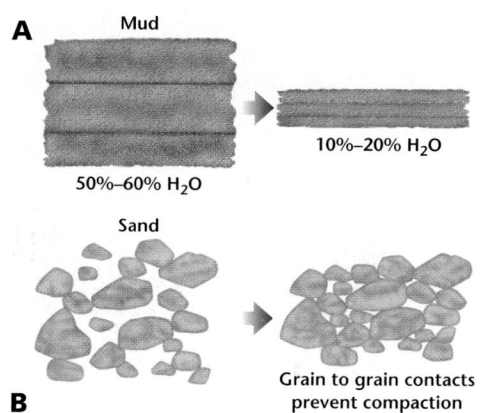

Figure 6-4 Pressure and weight from overlying sediments causes flat clay particles to compact **(A)**. The irregular shape of sand grains prevents similar amounts of compaction **(B)**.

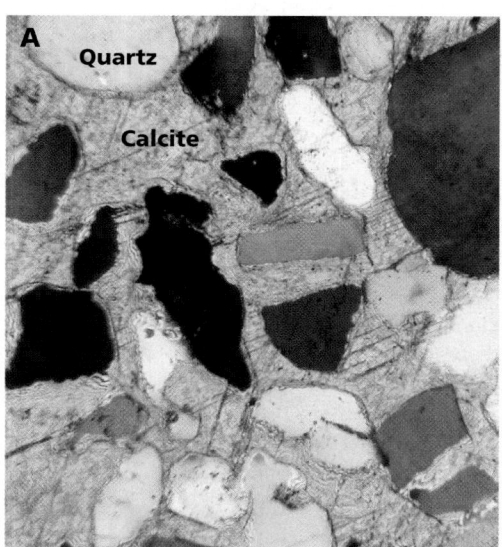

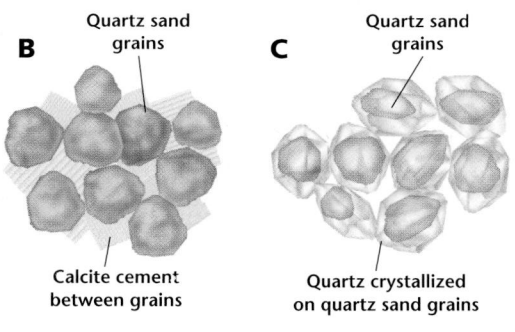

Figure 6-5 Cementation occurs in one of two ways. Either a new mineral, such as the calcite shown in **A,** grows between the grains **(B)** or, the same mineral grows between and over the grains in a process called overgrowth **(C)**.

6.1 *Formation of Sedimentary Rocks* **125**

Demo

Put some coarse gravel in a clear container to demonstrate grain-to-grain contacts and pore spaces. Tell students that magnified sand grains would look the same.

Using an Analogy

Ask students which of the two types of cementation is found in marshmallow-and-cereal treats. The marshmallow cement is equivalent to a new mineral forming between existing grains.

Tying to Previous Knowledge

Refer students to mineral characteristics in Chapter 4. Ask students how they might distinguish between calcite-cemented sandstone and quartz-cemented sandstone. Dilute HCl would fizz when applied to calcite-cemented sandstone.

Tying to Previous Knowledge

Review Bowen's reaction series from Chapter 5. Ask students why quartz is a common cement for sedimentary rocks, while other minerals, such as pyroxene, are not. Quartz often precipitates from the final hydrothermal solutions, while pyroxene crystallizes from molten rock. Quartz-rich hydrothermal solutions can penetrate the pore spaces between sediments and form cement. **L3**

Project

Interpersonal Have groups of students design an experiment to measure the amount of pore space in a sample of coarse sand. **L2** **COOP LEARN**

NY Core Curriculum Standards

Page 124: St 4 KI 2.1u, St 6 KI 5
Page 125: St 4 KI 3.1b, St 6 KI 5

MiniLab

Purpose

Students will interpret animal behavior from fossil footprint patterns and draw a pattern of footprints that show animal activity.

Process Skills

interpret scientific illustrations, sequence, draw a conclusion

Materials

photographs or drawings of sets of dinosaur or reptile footprints

Teaching Strategies

Have students focus on the obvious first. For example, they should determine the number of tracks and the direction of travel before attempting to interpret more complex interactions.

Expected Results

Students will describe a single set of footprints that appear to represent an animal's randomly walking about. Students may suggest that the animal was looking for food.

Analyze and Conclude

1. one
2. types of animals, direction of travel, relative stride lengths and weights of the animals, number of toes, which tracks were made first, and so on
3. Diagrams will likely have multiple interpretations because different animal interactions may leave similar types of tracks.

✔ Assessment

Skill Have students list the types of information that cannot be determined from fossilized footprints. Fossilized footprints do not contain any information about what the animal actually looked like: no bones, no skeletal structures, and no evidence of any part of the animal that did not touch the ground.

MiniLab

What happened here?

Interpret animal activity from patterns of fossil footprints.

Procedure

1. Study the photograph of a set of footprints that has been preserved in sedimentary rocks.
2. Write a description of how these tracks might have been made.
3. Draw your own diagram of a set of fossilized footprints that record the interactions of organisms in the environment.
4. Give your diagram to another student and have them interpret what happened.

Analyze and Conclude

1. How many animals made the tracks shown?
2. What types of information can be inferred from a set of fossil footprints?
3. Did other students interpret your diagram the same way? What might have caused any differences?

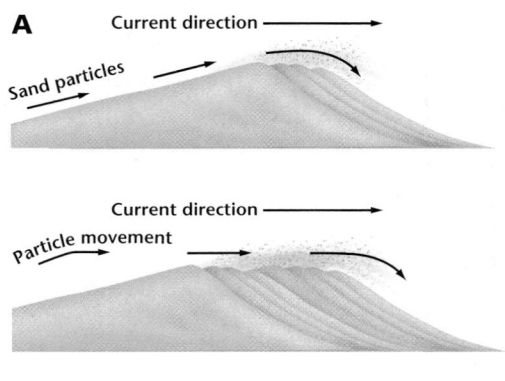

A

Current direction →

Sand particles

Current direction →

Particle movement

FEATURES OF SEDIMENTARY ROCKS

The primary feature of sedimentary rocks is horizontal layering, called **bedding.** Bedding can range from a millimeter-thick layer of shale to sandstone deposits several meters thick. The type of bedding depends upon the method of transport, while the size of the grains and the material within the bedding depend upon many factors.

Bedding in which the particle sizes become progressively heavier and coarser towards the bottom layers is called **graded bedding.** Graded bedding is often observed in marine sedimentary rocks that were deposited by underwater landslides. As the sliding material slowly came to rest underwater, the largest and heaviest material settled out first and was followed by progressively finer material.

Another characteristic feature of sedimentary rocks is cross-bedding. As you can see in *Figure 6-6A,* **cross-bedding** is formed as inclined layers of sediment move forward across a horizontal surface. Small-scale cross-bedding can be observed at sandy beaches and along sandbars in streams and rivers. Most large-scale cross-bedding, such as that shown in *Figure 6-6B,* is formed by migrating sand dunes. Small sedimentary features, such as the ripple marks shown

Figure 6-6 Cross-bedding is formed as sediment is carried forward across a layer of sediment, and cascades down the front face of the layer **(A).** Large-scale cross-bedded sandstones are common in Zion National Park **(B).**

B

Resource Manager

Laboratory Manual, pp. 41–44 L2
GeoLab and MiniLab Worksheets, p. 23 L2

Figure 6-7 Given the right sedimentary conditions, these modern sand ripples **(A)** could become preserved like these ripple marks in Capitol Reef National Park, Utah **(B)**.

in *Figure 6-7,* are also preserved in sedimentary rocks. Ripple marks form when sediment is moved into small ridges by wind or wave action, or by a river current. The back-and-forth movement of waves creates ripples that are symmetrical, while a current flowing in one direction, such as in a river or stream, produces asymmetrical ripples. If a rippled surface is buried gently by more sediment without being disturbed, it might later be preserved in solid rock.

Evidence of Past Life Probably the best-known features of sedimentary rocks are fossils. Fossils are the preserved remains, impressions, or any other evidence of once-living organisms. When an organism dies, it may be buried before it decomposes. If its remains are further buried without being disturbed, it might be preserved as a fossil. During lithification, parts of the organism can be replaced by minerals and turned into rock, such as fossilized shells. Fossils are of great interest to Earth scientists because fossils provide evidence of the types of organisms that lived in the distant past, the environments that existed in the past, and how organisms have changed over time. You will learn more about fossils and how they form in Chapter 21. By doing the *MiniLab* on the previous page, you can learn first-hand how fossils can be used to interpret past events.

SECTION ASSESSMENT

1. How are clastic sediments formed, and how do scientists classify them?

2. Why do sediment deposits tend to form layers?

3. As sediments are buried, what two factors increase with depth? How do these factors cause lithification?

4. Compare and contrast graded bedding and cross-bedding.

5. **Thinking Critically** Is it possible for a layer of cross-bedded strata to show graded bedding as well? Explain.

SKILL REVIEW

6. **Sequencing** Sequence the processes by which a sedimentary rock is formed from clastic sediments. For more help, refer to the *Skill Handbook.*

earthgeu.com/self_check_quiz

6.1 *Formation of Sedimentary Rocks* **127**

---

3 Assess

Check for Understanding

Discussion

Ask students how the type of transport and deposition affects how sediment is sorted. Sediment deposited by water is usually well sorted, sediment deposited by wind is well sorted, and sediment deposited by ice or by landslides is not sorted.

Reteach

Linguistic Have students use the headings and vocabulary terms to outline the major concepts of this section. L2

✓Assessment

Skill Have students review the processes of erosion and deposition. Ask students to explain why some types of fossils are uncommon. Erosion and transport can destroy fragile organic material; deposition and burial must occur before decomposition and must occur quickly.

SECTION ASSESSMENT

1. They are formed from rock and mineral fragments through weathering and erosion. They are classified by size.
2. Sediment deposits form layers because the particles settle as a result of gravity when transport slows or stops.
3. temperature and pressure; these cause lithification by compaction and mineral growth, and particles are cemented together.
4. Both are depositional features. Graded bedding consists of horizontal layers with grain size fining upward. Cross-bedding consists of parallel layers that are inclined to the horizontal.
5. Yes. Each cross-bedded layer represents a depositional event. It is possible that each layer will show an upward-fining sequence. Also, if cross-bedding is being formed while water velocity is decreasing, the grain size may decrease from one cross-bed to another.
6. weathering and erosion, transport, deposition, burial, increased pressure and temperature, compaction, and lithification.

NY Core Curriculum Standards

Page 126: St 1 Science KI 2 & 3, St 4 KI 1.2i, St 6 KI 2
Page 127: St 1 Science KI 2, St 4 KI 1.2i & 1.2j, St 6 KI 5

127

Section Background

For section content background, refer to **Karst Topography** on page 120C.

Preplanning

Refer to the Chapter Organizer on pages 120A–B

1 Focus

Section Focus

Before presenting the lesson, display **Section Focus Transparency 15** on the overhead projector.
L1 ELL

Demo

Visual-Spatial Display clear containers of materials that represent the three main groups of sedimentary rocks: a sand-gravel mix (clastic), a shell-plant mix (organic), and rock salt (evaporite).

SECTION 6.2 *Types of Sedimentary Rocks*

OBJECTIVES

- **Describe** *the types of clastic sedimentary rocks.*
- **Explain** *how chemical sedimentary rocks form.*
- **Describe** *organic sedimentary rocks.*
- **Recognize** *the importance of sedimentary rocks.*

VOCABULARY

clastic sedimentary rock
porosity
evaporite

The classification of sedimentary rocks is based on how they were formed. There are three main groups of sedimentary rocks: clastic, chemical, and organic. *Table 6-2* summarizes the classification system for sedimentary rocks.

CLASTIC SEDIMENTARY ROCKS

The most common type of sedimentary rocks, **clastic sedimentary rocks,** are formed from the abundant deposits of loose sediments found on Earth's surface. Clastic sedimentary rocks are further classified according to the sizes of their particles. This classification system was shown in *Table 6-1* on page 122.

Coarse-Grained Clastics Sedimentary rocks consisting of gravel-sized rock and mineral fragments are classified as coarse-grained clastics, as shown in *Figure 6-8.* What differences between these two rocks do you notice? Conglomerates are coarse-grained sedimentary rocks that have rounded particles, whereas breccias contain angular fragments. How are these different-shaped particles formed? Because of its relatively large mass, gravel is transported by high-energy flows of water, such as those generated by mountain streams, flooding rivers, some ocean waves, and glacial meltwater. During transport, gravel becomes abraded and rounded as the particles scrape against one another. This is why beach and river gravels are often well rounded. Conglomerates provide evidence that this type of transport occurred in the past. In contrast, the angularity of

Table 6-2 Classification of Sedimentary Rocks		
Rock Type	**Rock Name**	**Method of Formation**
Clastic		
Coarse-grained	Conglomerate or breccia	Lithification of
Medium-grained	Sandstone	clastic sediments
Fine-grained	Shale	
Chemical	Limestone	
Calcite	Rock salt	Precipitation of
Halite	Rock gypsum	dissolved minerals
Gypsum		from water
Organic		
Calcium carbonate–shells	Limestone	Accumulation and lithification of remains
plant matter	Coal	of living things

Resource Manager

Laboratory Manual, pp. 45–48 L2
Study Guide for Content Mastery, p. 35 L2
Section Focus Transparency 15 L1 ELL
Teaching Transparency 14 L2 ELL

particles in breccias indicates that the sediments from which they formed did not have time to become rounded. This suggests that the particles were transported only a short distance and deposited close to their source. Under what kinds of circumstances might this type of transport occur?

Medium-Grained Clastics In what types of environments is sand found? Stream and river channels, beaches, and deserts often contain abundant sand-sized sediments. Sedimentary rocks that contain sand-sized rock and mineral fragments are classified as medium-grained clastic rocks. When these medium-sized sediments are buried and lithified, sandstone is formed. Sandstone usually contains several features of interest to scientists. For example, because ripple marks and cross-bedding indicate the direction of current flow, geologists find sandstone layers particularly useful in mapping old stream and river channels.

Another important feature of sandstone is its relatively high porosity. **Porosity** is the percentage of open spaces between grains in a rock. Loose sand can have a porosity of up to 40 percent; some of its open spaces are maintained during the formation of sandstone. The incomplete cementation of mineral grains can result in porosities as high as 30 percent. When pore spaces are connected to one another, fluids can move through sandstone. This feature makes sandstone layers valuable as underground reservoirs of oil, natural gas, and groundwater.

Fine-Grained Clastics Sedimentary rocks consisting of silt and mud are called siltstone and mudstone. Siltstone is mostly composed of silt-sized grains, while shale is composed mostly of silt and clay-sized particles. Shale often breaks along thin layers, as shown in *Figure 6-9.* Unlike sandstone, this fine-grained sedimentary rock has very low porosity. It often forms barriers that hinder the movement of groundwater and oil.

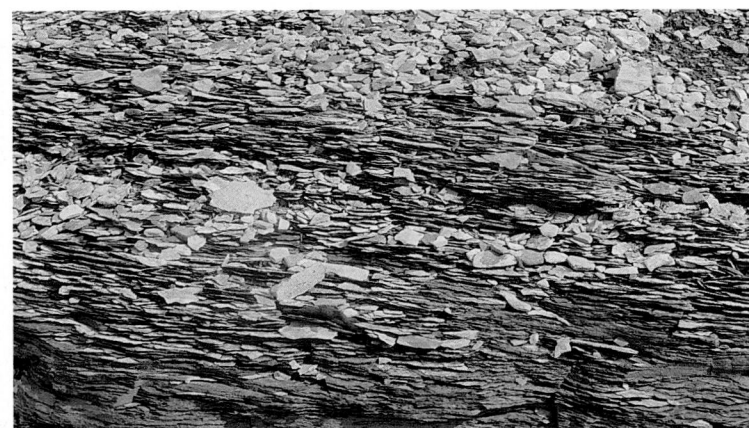

Figure 6-8 This coarse-grained breccia **(A)** has angular fragments, and the conglomerate **(B)** has rounded fragments.

Using Math

Using Percentages Assume that the volume of a layer of mud will decrease by 35 percent during burial and compaction. If the original sediment layer is 30 cm thick, what will be the thickness of the shale layer after compaction and lithification?

Figure 6-9 The thin bedding that is characteristic of shale is clearly seen in this outcrop from Ontario, Canada.

129

CHEMICAL SEDIMENTARY ROCKS

What happens when you allow a glass of saltwater to evaporate? Eventually, the water disappears and a layer of salt accumulates on the bottom of the glass. A similar process occurs in nature when chemical sedimentary rocks are formed. During chemical weathering, minerals can be dissolved and carried into lakes and oceans. As water evaporates from the lakes and oceans, the dissolved minerals are left behind. In arid regions, high evaporation rates can increase the concentration of dissolved minerals in bodies of water. The Great Salt Lake, shown in *Figure 6-10A,* is a well-known example of a lake that has high concentrations of dissolved minerals.

Rocks Formed from Evaporation When the concentration of dissolved minerals in a body of water reaches saturation, which is the point at which no more minerals can be dissolved in the water, crystal grains precipitate out of solution and settle to the bottom. The layers of chemical sedimentary rocks that form as a result are called **evaporites**. Evaporites most commonly form in arid regions, in oceans and in drainage basins on continents that have low water flow. Because little freshwater flows into these areas, the concentration of dissolved minerals remains high.

As more dissolved minerals are carried into the basins, evaporation continues to remove freshwater and maintain high mineral concentrations. Over time, thick layers of evaporite minerals can accumulate on the basin floor, as illustrated in *Figure 6-10B.*

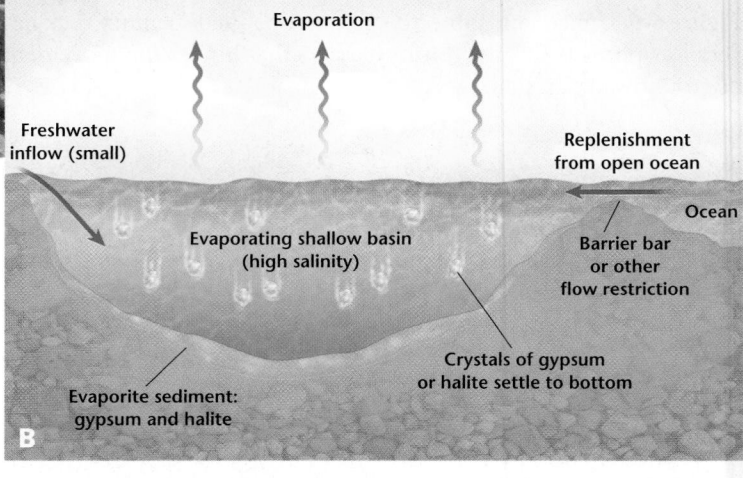

Figure 6-10 Evaporation of water from the Great Salt Lake, Utah, has resulted in salt precipitation on these boulders **(A).** The process of evaporite formation is illustrated in **B.**

130 CHAPTER 6 *Sedimentary and Metamorphic Rocks*

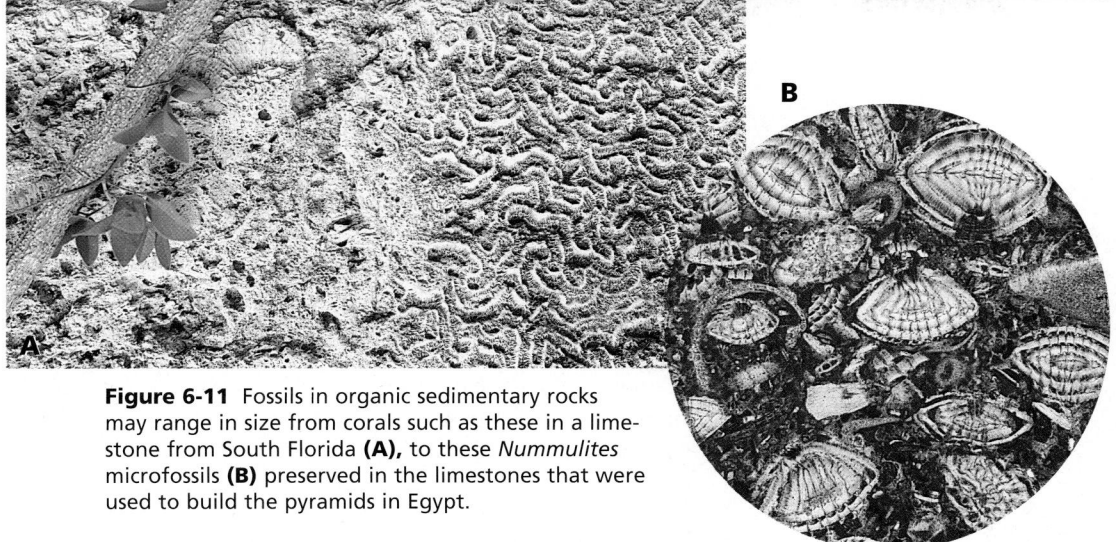

Figure 6-11 Fossils in organic sedimentary rocks may range in size from corals such as these in a limestone from South Florida **(A)**, to these *Nummulites* microfossils **(B)** preserved in the limestones that were used to build the pyramids in Egypt.

Magnification: 12×

The three most common evaporite minerals are calcite ($CaCO_3$), halite (NaCl), and gypsum ($CaSO_4$). Layers of these minerals are often mined for their chemical content.

Organic Sedimentary Rocks Organic sedimentary rocks are formed from the remains of once-living things. The most abundant organic sedimentary rock is limestone, which is composed primarily of calcite. Some organisms that live in the ocean use the calcium carbonate dissolved in seawater to make their shells. When these organisms die, their shells settle to the bottom of the ocean and can form thick layers of carbonate sediment. During burial and lithification, calcium carbonate precipitates out of the water, crystallizes between the grains of carbonate sediment, and forms limestone. Limestone is common in shallow water environments such as those in the Bahamas, where coral reefs thrive in 15 to 20 m of water just offshore. The skeleton and shell materials that are currently accumulating there will someday become limestone as well. Many types of limestone contain evidence of their biologic origin in the form of abundant fossils. As shown in *Figure 6-11,* these fossils range from large corals to microscopic unicellular organisms. Other organisms use silica to make their shells. These shells form sediment that is often referred to as siliceous ooze because it is rich in silica.

Another type of organic sedimentary rock, coal, forms from the remains of plant material. Over long periods of time, thick layers of vegetation slowly accumulate in swamps and coastal areas. When these layers are buried and compressed, they are slowly lithified into coal. Coal is composed almost entirely of carbon and can be burned for fuel. You will learn more about coal as an energy source in Chapter 25.

Earth Science Online

Topic: Coral Reefs
For an online update of coral reefs in the Bahamas, visit the Earth Science Web Site at earthgeu.com

Activity: Discuss the cause and significance of the major bleaching event of 1997-1998 in coral reefs around the world.

Check for Understanding

Reinforcement
Ask students the following question: If a sedimentary rock provides a "snapshot" of past surface conditions, how might a scientist obtain a "video" of past surface conditions? A thick sequence of sediments represents changing depositional conditions over time.

Reteach

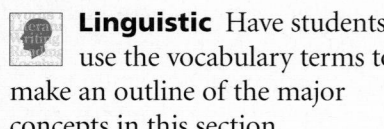 **Linguistic** Have students use the vocabulary terms to make an outline of the major concepts in this section.

Performance Have students make a data table that lists the importance of sedimentary rocks from both a scientific point of view and an economical point of view. Use the Performance Task Assessment List for Data Table in **PASC,** p. 37.

IMPORTANCE OF SEDIMENTARY ROCKS

The characteristic textures and features of sedimentary rocks, such as cross-bedding, ripple marks, layering, and fossils, provide a geologic "snapshot" of surface conditions in Earth's past. Fossils, for example, provide information about animals and plants that existed in the past. Other sedimentary features indicate the location and direction of flow of ancient rivers, the wave or wind direction over lakes and deserts, and ancient shoreline positions. Rock fragments found in conglomerates and breccias are large enough to easily identify what types of bedrock they were eroded from. By considering all of this information, geologists can reconstruct the nature of Earth's surface at various times in the past. Thus, they can better understand how geologic changes occur over time.

ENVIRONMENTAL CONNECTION

Energy Resources The study of sedimentary rocks provides information about Earth's past, but it also has great practical value. Many of the natural resources used by humans come from sedimentary rocks. For example oil, natural gas, and coal are found in sedimentary rocks. Uranium, which is used for nuclear power, is often mined from sandstone. Large deposits of phosphate, which is used for fertilizer, and iron, which is used to make steel, are also found in sedimentary rocks. Limestone is processed to make cement for the construction industry. Sandstone and limestone are often cut into blocks for use in walls and buildings. Were any sedimentary rocks used to construct your school? What sedimentary rocks were used in the construction of your home?

SECTION ASSESSMENT

1. Compare and contrast the main types of clastic sedimentary rocks.

2. Why do chemical sedimentary rocks form primarily in areas that have high rates of evaporation?

3. Why is coal an organic sedimentary rock?

4. What are some of the commercial values of sedimentary rocks?

5. **Thinking Critically** The original concentration of dissolved minerals in a restricted ocean basin was enough to form only a thin evaporite layer. How, then, is it possible that thick evaporite layers formed there?

SKILL REVIEW

6. **Comparing and Contrasting** Make a data table to compare and contrast the formation of the three types of sedimentary rock. For more help, refer to the *Skill Handbook.*

earthgeu.com/self_check_quiz

SECTION ASSESSMENT

1. conglomerate—coarse-grained rounded particles; breccia—coarse-grained, angular particles; sandstone—medium-grained particles, many depositional features; siltstone and mudstone—fine-grained particles, thin layers

2. Evaporation removes freshwater and maintains high concentrations of minerals in the remaining water.

3. organic, because coal is formed from plant material; sedimentary rock, because the organic material is deposited, buried, and lithified

4. Sedimentary rocks are reservoirs for oil, gas, and groundwater, and they contain ore deposits of iron, phosphate, and uranium; cement is made from limestone; limestone and sandstone blocks are used as construction materials.

5. New water entering the basin replenished the dissolved minerals and maintained a high concentration of these minerals and nearly continuous precipitation.

6. Clastic and organic rocks are formed by the accumulation and lithification of sediments that were formed primarily by mechanical processes. Clastic sediments are rock and mineral fragments, while organic sediments are derived from the remains of once-living things. Chemical sedimentary rocks are formed by the precipitation of dissolved minerals from water.

You have learned that increasing pressure and temperature during burial cause recrystallization and cementation of sediments. What happens when rocks are buried at even greater depths?

CAUSES OF METAMORPHISM

Pressure and temperature increase with depth. When temperature or pressure becomes high enough, rocks melt and form magma. But what happens if the rocks do not quite reach the melting point? When high temperature and pressure combine to alter the texture, mineralogy, or chemical composition of a rock without melting it, a metamorphic rock forms. The word *metamorphism* is derived from the Greek words *meta,* meaning "change," and *morphē* meaning "form." During metamorphism, a rock changes form while remaining solid.

The high temperatures required for metamorphism ultimately are derived from Earth's internal heat, either through deep burial or from nearby igneous intrusions. The high pressures required for metamorphism can be generated in two ways: from vertical pressure caused by the weight of overlying rock, or from the compressive forces generated as rocks are deformed during mountain building.

TYPES OF METAMORPHISM

Different combinations of temperature and pressure result in different types of metamorphism, shown in *Figure 6-12.* Each combination produces a different group of metamorphic minerals and

OBJECTIVES

- **Compare** *and* **Contrast** *the different types and causes of metamorphism.*
- **Distinguish** *among metamorphic textures.*
- **Explain** *how mineral and compositional changes occur during metamorphism.*
- **Understand** *how rocks continuously change from one type to another in the rock cycle.*

VOCABULARY

regional metamorphism
contact metamorphism
hydrothermal metamorphism
foliated
nonfoliated
porphyroblast
rock cycle

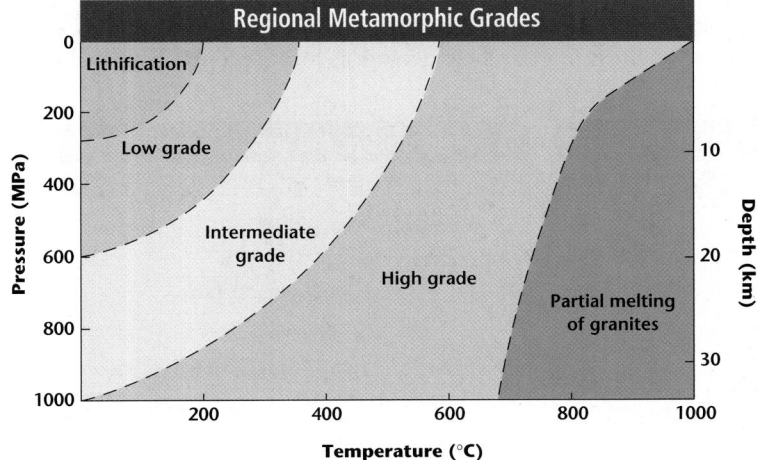

Figure 6-12 The grade of metamorphism, whether it is low, medium or high, is dependent upon the pressure on the rocks, the temperature and the depth below the surface.

Section 6.3

Prepare

Section Background

For section content background, refer to **Skarn Deposits** on page 120D.

Preplanning

Refer to the Chapter Organizer on pages 120A–B.

1 Focus

Section Focus

Before presenting the lesson, display **Section Focus Transparency 16** on the overhead projector.
L1 ELL

Section Focus Transparency 16 L1 ELL
Study Guide for Content Mastery,
pp. 36–38 L2

Tying to Previous Knowledge

Have students review how rocks melt in Chapter 5. Ask students the following question: As rocks reach high-grade metamorphism and are close to melting, which minerals will be most affected? the minerals that crystallize last, such as quartz, orthoclase, and Na-plagioclase.

NY Core Curriculum Standards

Page 132: St 1 Science KI 1, St 4 KI 1.2i, 1.2j, 3.1a, 3.1b, & 3.1c
Page 133: St 4 KI 1.2j & 3.1b, St 6 KI 5

Content Background

Most people think of garnet as being a gemstone. However, very few garnets are of gem quality. The vast majority of metamorphic garnets are used as abrasives. Garnet is a very hard mineral that breaks with an irregular fracture. This makes it especially useful in sandpaper. The light-orange sandpaper found in hardware stores is often called garnet paper because it is made from crushed garnets.

Discussion

Ask students what grade of regional metamorphism they would expect to see in the eroded roots of mountain ranges. Because these regions were buried at great depth, they will show evidence of high-grade metamorphism.

Using an Analogy

Tell students that baking a loaf of bread is similar to metamorphism. The texture and composition change as a result of the heat, but the materials do not melt.

Figure 6-13 The northeast portion of North America has undergone several episodes of regional metamorphism. The results can be seen in the distribution of metamorphic rocks.

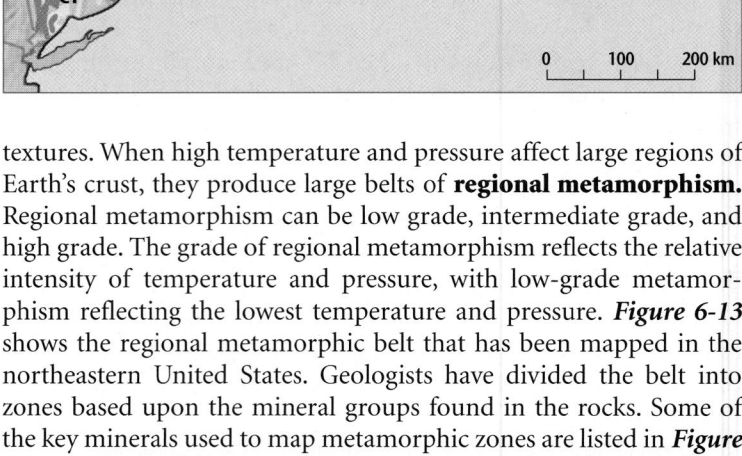

Figure 6-14 Mineral changes in shale **(A)** and basalt **(B)**, as a result of metamorphism follow a specific path. The grade of metamorphism (low, intermediate, or high) determines which minerals will form.

textures. When high temperature and pressure affect large regions of Earth's crust, they produce large belts of **regional metamorphism.** Regional metamorphism can be low grade, intermediate grade, and high grade. The grade of regional metamorphism reflects the relative intensity of temperature and pressure, with low-grade metamorphism reflecting the lowest temperature and pressure. *Figure 6-13* shows the regional metamorphic belt that has been mapped in the northeastern United States. Geologists have divided the belt into zones based upon the mineral groups found in the rocks. Some of the key minerals used to map metamorphic zones are listed in *Figure 6-14.* Knowing the temperatures that certain areas experienced when rocks were forming can help geologists locate economically valuable

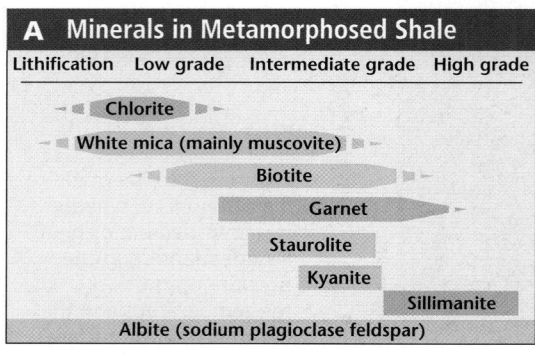

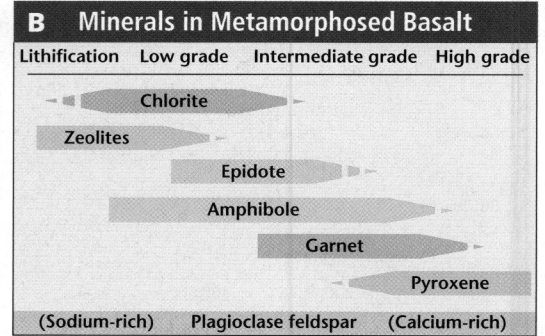

✔Assessment

Knowledge Ask students the following question. Which of the following groups of minerals would you expect to find in basalt that has been subjected to intermediate-grade metamorphism?
a. chlorite, zeolite, and pyroxene
b. epidote, amphibole, and garnet
c. pyroxene, garnet, and chlorite
d. zeolites, garnets, and calcium-rich plagioclase
The answer is b.

Interpreting the Illustration

Figure 6-13 Ask students to study the diagram and explain the approximate circular pattern made by the metamorphic zones. If a single igneous intrusion caused this metamorphism, it was most likely in the center of the orange or Sillimanite zone. The heat spread out around the intrusion.

metamorphic minerals such as garnet and talc. An interesting connection between talc and asbestos, another metamorphic mineral, is described in the *Science in the News* feature at the end of this chapter.

When molten rocks, such as those in an igneous intrusion, come in contact with solid rock, a local effect called **contact metamorphism** occurs. High temperature and moderate-to-low pressure form the mineral assemblages that are characteristic of contact metamorphism. *Figure 6-15* shows zones of different minerals surrounding an intrusion. Why do you think these zones occur? Because temperature decreases with distance from an intrusion, metamorphic effects also decrease with distance. Recall from Chapter 4 that minerals crystallize at specific temperatures. Minerals that crystallize at high temperatures are found closest to the intrusion, where it is hottest. Contact metamorphism from extrusive igneous rocks is limited to thin zones. Normally, lava cools too quickly for the heat to penetrate very far into surface rocks.

When very hot water reacts with rock and alters its chemistry and mineralogy **hydrothermal metamorphism** occurs. The word *hydrothermal* is derived from the Greek words *hydro,* meaning "water," and *thermal,* meaning "heat." Hydrothermal fluids can dissolve some minerals, break down others, and deposit new minerals. These types of changes caused the yellow color of the cliffs shown in *Figure 6-16.* Hydrothermal metamorphism is common around igneous intrusions and near active volcanoes.

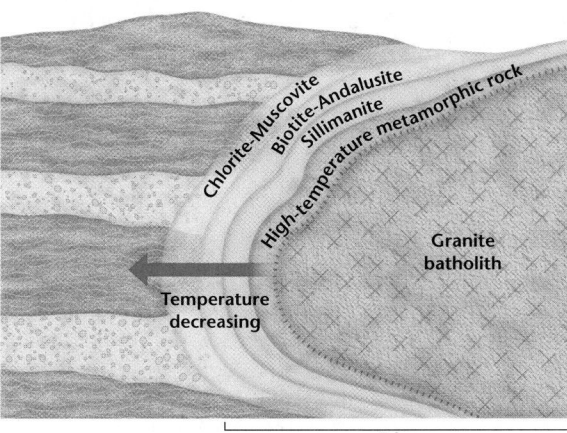

Figure 6-15 Contact metamorphism results in large-scale mineral changes with little deformation. Geologists can follow the occurrence of metamorphic minerals to locate the igneous intrusion.

Figure 6-16 Yellowstone National Park's name comes from the hydrothermally changed rocks of the area. These rocks are beautifully exposed in the Grand Canyon of the Yellowstone, Wyoming.

6.3 *Metamorphic Rocks* **135**

135

Modeling

Kinesthetic Have students model the effect of pressure on grain orientation. Have students mix rice grains into a ball of clay, then cut open the ball with a plastic knife and draw the orientation of the grains. Have students re-form the ball and then flatten it down on a desk. When they cut open the clay again, students should observe that most of the rice grains are oriented with their long axes perpendicular to the direction of pressure. **L2**

Concept Development

In the past, roads were sometimes paved with rock. Ask students which type of metamorphic rock would make the best street paver, quartzite, gneiss, schist, or marble? Why? Quartzite would make the best street paver. It is composed of quartz, a very hard and stable mineral at surface temperatures. Marble is composed of calcite, and thus it is very soft. The foliation in gneiss and schist create planes of weakness along the foliations.

Using an Analogy

Tell students that mineral grains in a nonfoliated rock make a pattern like the pieces of a jigsaw puzzle. The mineral grains in a foliated rock are more like a pile of playing cards scattered on a table.

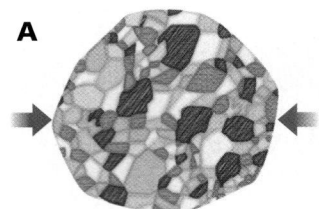
A

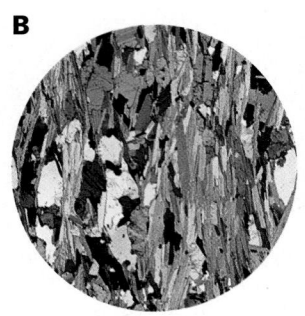
B

Magnification: 7×

Figure 6-17 Compressional pressure causes elongate minerals to line up perpendicular to the pressure direction **(A).** This photomicrograph of a mica schist **(B)** shows the resulting foliation.

Figure 6-18 These common foliated rocks are arranged in order of increasing metamorphic grade: slate **(A),** phyllite **(B),** gneiss **(C),** and schist **(D).**

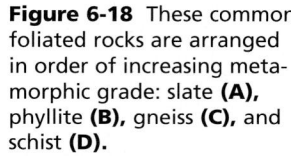

A

B

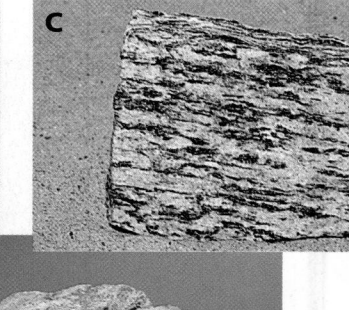
C

D

METAMORPHIC TEXTURES

Metamorphic rocks are classified into two textural groups: foliated and nonfoliated. Wavy layers and bands of minerals characterize **foliated** metamorphic rocks. High pressure during metamorphism causes minerals with flat or needlelike crystals to form with their long axes perpendicular to the pressure, as shown in *Figure 6-17.* This parallel alignment of minerals creates the layers observed in foliated metamorphic rocks. The two most common types of foliated metamorphic rock are schist, which is derived from shale, and gneiss, which is derived from granite. Some common foliated metamorphic rocks are compared in *Figure 6-18.*

Unlike foliated rocks, **nonfoliated** metamorphic rocks lack mineral grains with long axes in one direction. Nonfoliated rocks are composed mainly of minerals that form with blocky crystal shapes. Two common examples of nonfoliated rocks, shown in *Figure 6-19,* are quartzite and marble. Quartzite is a hard, light-colored rock formed by the metamorphism of quartz-rich sandstone. Marble is formed by the metamorphism of limestone. Some marbles have very smooth textures that are formed by interlocking grains of calcite. Such marbles are sought by artists for sculptures.

Porphyroblasts Under certain conditions, new metamorphic minerals can grow quite large while the surrounding minerals remain small. The large crystals, which can range in size from a few millimeters to a few centimeters, are called **porphyroblasts.** Porphyroblasts are found in areas of both contact and regional metamorphism. These crystals resemble the very large crystals found in porphyritic igneous rocks but form not from magma but

Project

Visual-Spatial Have groups of students make posters showing one of the types of metamorphism. The posters should include the expected minerals, the different zones, and the expected temperature and pressure conditions. **L2** **P**

Content Background

Some old, historic buildings have roofs covered with pieces of slate. Blocks of slate were quarried from outcrops, then the tiles were separated along the slaty cleavage. Although these tiles are heavy and brittle, they are nearly indestructible to weathering and are completely fireproof. A few slate tile quarries are still in operation to meet a limited demand stemming from restoration work on historic buildings.

in solid rock by the reorganization of atoms during metamorphism. Garnet, shown in *Figure 6-20,* is a mineral that commonly forms porphyroblasts.

MINERAL CHANGES

How do minerals change without melting? Think back to the concept of fractional crystallization, discussed in Chapter 5. Minerals are stable at certain temperatures and crystallize from magma at different temperatures. Scientists have discovered that these stability ranges also apply to minerals in solid rock. During metamorphism, the minerals in a rock change into new minerals that are stable under the new temperature and pressure conditions. Minerals that change in this way are said to undergo solid-state alterations. Scientists have conducted experiments to identify the metamorphic conditions that create specific minerals. When these same minerals are found in rocks, scientists are able to interpret the conditions inside the crust during the rocks' metamorphism. Recall from page 134 that these conditions are temperature- and pressure-related, with low temperatures and pressures resulting in low-grade metamorphism. You will compare the changes in mineralogy as a result of high- and low-grade metamorphism in the *Problem-Solving Lab* on the next page.

COMPOSITIONAL CHANGES

Most metamorphic rocks reflect the original chemical composition of the parent rock. Gneiss, for example, has the same general chemical composition as granite. In some instances, however, the chemistry of a rock can be altered along with its minerals and texture. This occurs because hot fluids migrate in and out of the rock during metamorphism, which can change the original composition of the rock. Chemical changes are especially common during contact metamorphism near igneous intrusions. Hydrothermal fluids invade the surrounding rocks and change their mineralogy, textures, and chemistry. Valuable ore deposits of gold, copper, zinc, tungsten, and lead are formed in this manner.

Figure 6-20 This garnet mica schist comes from an exposure in Roxbury Falls, Connecticut.

Content Background

The coarse, light and dark banding observed in gneiss is formed during metamorphism. The original rock, such as granite, had randomly distributed mineral grains. Under conditions of high-grade metamorphism, new mineral assemblages formed that were dominated by quartz, feldspar, micas, and amphiboles. These new minerals have a tendency to segregate themselves into light and dark colored bands.

Discussion

Have students carefully observe the schist layers around the garnet porphyroblast shown in **Figure 6-20**. The layers have deformed around the garnet. This shows that the growing garnet formed between the matrix crystals and pushed them aside instead of replacing them. This is evidence of the migration of atoms and fluids during metamorphism.

Tying to Previous Knowledge

Have students refer to the plagioclase continuous reaction series in Chapter 5. Have them explain how this is an example of a solid-state alteration. The solid plagioclase crystals react with the surrounding liquid and continuously change their chemical composition without melting.

Enrichment

Have students research how bricks are made. What type of metamorphism is this process most similar to? This is a high-temperature, low-pressure process, so it is most similar to contact metamorphism. What determines the characteristics of the final brick? The temperature, the duration of firing, and the type of clay used are factors that affect the bricks' characteristics.

Purpose

Students compare metamorphic mineral assemblages formed under different conditions from different parent rocks.

Process Skills

interpret scientific illustrations, compare and contrast, think critically

Teaching Strategies

Explain to students how to read the charts. Each horizontal band represents the stability range of a single mineral. A vertical line from each metamorphic grade will intersect the minerals that will form the characteristic mineral assemblage for those conditions.

Analysis

1. Chlorite is the main mineral, but albite, a sodium-rich plagioclase, can also be present.
2. sillimanite

Thinking Critically

3. shale—muscovite, biotite, garnet, staurolite, kyanite, albite; basalt— chlorite, epidote, amphibole, garnet, plagioclase; limestone— calcite
4. Shale has a higher Al and Si content, while basalt has more Fe and Mg. Aluminum-silicate minerals such as staurolite, kyanite, and sillimanite form from shale, while more Fe- and Mg-rich minerals such as amphiboles and pyroxenes form from basalt.
5. Limestones contain few elements other than Ca, C, and O, so minerals other than calcite cannot form. Also, calcite is very stable over a wide range of temperatures and pressures.

Assessment

Knowledge Ask students the following questions. If a high-grade metamorphic rock was subjected to low-grade conditions, would you expect any mineral changes? What if a low-grade metamorphic rock was exposed to high-grade metamorphic conditions? Accept any student response that is supported by good

reasoning. There is no clear answer. The high temperature and pressure of high-grade metamorphic conditions would cause mineral changes in a low-grade rock. However, when high-grade mineral assemblages are subjected to low-grade conditions, the minerals are also out of equilibrium and will possibly break down into low-grade forms. The reactions may be much slower than those at high-grade conditions.

THE ROCK CYCLE

Metamorphic rocks are formed by the changing of other rocks. What types of rocks can metamorphic rocks be changed into? The three types of rock—igneous, sedimentary, and metamorphic—are grouped according to how they form. Igneous rocks crystallize from magma; sedimentary rocks form from cemented sediments; and metamorphic rocks form by changes in temperature and pressure. Once a rock forms, does it remain the same type of rock forever? Maybe, but probably not. Heat and pressure may change an igneous rock into a metamorphic rock. A metamorphic rock may be changed into another metamorphic rock or melted to form an igneous rock. Or, the metamorphic rock may be weathered and eroded into sediments that may become cemented into a sedimentary rock. In fact, any rock can be changed into any other type of rock. This continuous changing and remaking of rocks is called the **rock cycle.** The rock cycle is summarized in *Figure 6-21.* The arrows represent the different processes that change rocks into different types. Essentially, rocks are recycled into different rock types much like glass is recycled into different types of jars and bottles. You will learn more about the similarities and differences between rock types when you complete the *GeoLab* at the end of this chapter.

Interpreting Scientific Illustrations

Determine which metamorphic minerals will form The types of minerals found in metamorphic rocks depends on metamorphic grade and composition of the original rock. In this activity, you will compare how these factors affect metamorphic minerals.

Analysis

1. Study *Figure 6-14* on page 134, showing the different mineral groups that are created under different metamorphic conditions. What mineral is formed when shale and basalt are exposed to low-grade metamorphism?
2. What mineral is formed when shale is exposed to high-grade metamorphism

that is not found in basalts under the same conditions?

Thinking Critically

3. Compare the mineral groups you would expect to form from intermediate metamorphism of shale, basalt and limestone.
4. What are the major compositional differences between shale and basalt? How are these differences reflected in the minerals formed during metamorphism?
5. When limestones are metamorphosed, there is very little change in mineralogy, and calcite is still the dominant mineral. Explain why this happens.

OTHER POSSIBLE PATHS

There is more than one path in the rock cycle. Sandstone might just as easily become uplifted and weathered back into sediments, thereby bypassing the metamorphic and igneous stages. Another possibility is that sandstone could become intruded by magma and melted, thereby directly becoming an igneous rock and bypassing metamorphism. Can you think of other possible paths? How might a metamorphic rock become a sedimentary rock?

The rocks of Earth's crust are constantly being recycled from one type to another. At any given time, magma is crystallizing, sediments are being cemented, and deeply buried rocks are metamorphosing. These processes take place underground, where they cannot be easily observed. However, as you have learned, not all phases of the rock cycle occur beneath Earth's surface. The processes that help shape Earth's landscapes are also part of the rock cycle. You will learn more about these surface processes in the next few chapters.

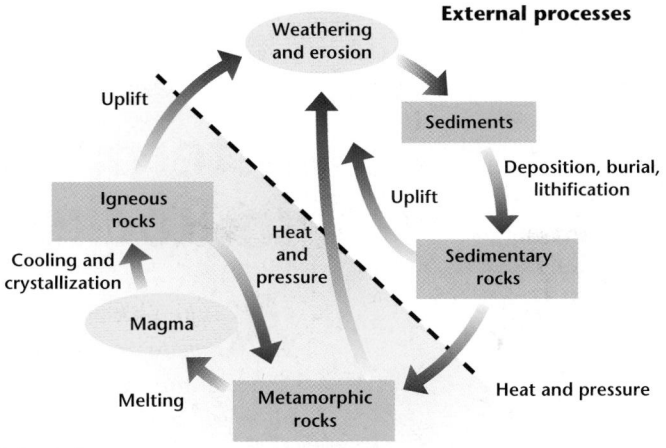

Figure 6-21 The rocks of Earth, whether at the surface or below the crust, are always positioned somewhere on the rock cycle.

SECTION ASSESSMENT

1. How can the chemical composition of a rock be changed during metamorphism?

2. What are the three main types of metamorphism? Compare and contrast the factors that cause each type.

3. How does quartzite differ from schist?

4. What causes foliated metamorphic textures?

5. How are the three types of rocks classified?

6. What parts of the rock cycle occur deep in Earth's crust?

7. **Thinking Critically** Which would you

expect to cause the greatest amount of contact metamorphism: an intrusion of basaltic magma or an intrusion of rhyolitic magma?

SKILL REVIEW

8. **Interpreting Photos** Study *Figure 6-18C*. If this sample is in the exact position it was when it formed, from which direction did the compressional forces originate? What group of metamorphic minerals would you expect during high-grade metamorphism of shale? For more help, refer to the *Skill Handbook*.

earthgeu.com/self_check_quiz

Check for Understanding

Activity
Have each student draw a temperature-versus-pressure-diagram similar to the one shown in **Figure 6-12.** On the diagram, have students label regions representing all three grades of regional metamorphism, contact metamorphism, and hydrothermal metamorphism.

Reteach

Have each student make a data table listing the characteristics of the three types of metamorphism.

✔Assessment

Skill Have each student make a list in which they compare and contrast the rock-cycle processes. They should divide their lists into two categories: those processes that occur at Earth's surface and those processes that occur at depth. Ask students to identify those processes that can occur in both places. Some examples include the following: chemical weathering can occur at Earth's surface but also at depth from hydrothermal alteration; igneous rocks form both at depth and at Earth's surface; and sediments can be cemented at Earth's surface—they do not have to be buried.

SECTION ASSESSMENT

1. It is an open system. Atoms can move in and out of the rock during metamorphism.

2. regional metamorphism—temperature and pressure affect large areas of Earth's crust; contact metamorphism—local effects caused by the heat from nearby igneous intrusions; hydrothermal metamorphism—alteration of rocks as a result of reactions with very hot water.

3. There are both compositional and textural differences. Schist is foliated; quartzite is

not. Schist contains plate- and needle-shaped minerals such as mica and hornblende, while quartzite is composed primarily of blocky crystals of quartz.

4. High pressure causes minerals with flat or linear crystal forms to grow with a preferred orientation.

5. They are classified by their mode of formation.

6. melting, heat and pressure, cooling and crystallization

7. The basaltic intrusion is at a much higher temperature and will probably cause greater contact metamorphism. However, the rhyolitic magma has a higher water content and may cause greater hydrothermal metamorphism.

8. The compressional forces came from the top and the bottom.

139

Time Allotment

1–2 hours, depending on the number of rock samples

Process Skills

compare and contrast, measure and use numbers, observe and infer

Preparation

If supplies are short, organize the samples in sets, with each set being a sedimentary–metamorphic series, for example, siltstone, shale, slate, and schist. Have student groups work on one set at a time instead of all at once.

Procedure

Teaching Strategies

- After students have made their plans for determining volume, remind them of the proper techniques for water displacement to avoid splashing or breakage.
- Ask students to think about how immersing sandstone samples may affect their density.

Data and Observations

Data tables should include the following headings: Rock Name, Rock Type, Mass, Volume, Density, and Special Characteristics

NY Core Curriculum Standards

Page 140: St 1 Science KI 1, 2, & 3, St 4 KI 3.1a, 3.1b, & 3.1c, St 6 KI 1 & 5

Page 141: St 1 Math KI 3, Science KI 1, 2, & 3, St 4 KI 3.1a & 3.1c, St 6 KI 1 & 5

GeoLab | Interpreting Changes in Rocks

As the rock cycle continues, and rocks change from one type to another, more changes occur than meet the eye. Color, grain size, texture and mineral composition are easily observed and described visually. Yet, with mineral changes come changes in crystal structure and density. How can these be accounted for and described? Studying pairs of sedimentary and metamorphic rocks can show you how.

Preparation

Problem

How do the characteristics of sedimentary and metamorphic rocks compare?

Materials

samples of sedimentary rocks and their metamorphic equivalents
magnifying glass or hand lens
paper
pencil
beam balance
100-mL graduated cylinder or beaker large enough to hold the rock samples
water

Objectives

In this GeoLab, you will:

- **Describe** the characteristics of sedimentary and metamorphic rocks.
- **Determine** the density of different rock types.
- **Infer** how metamorphism changes the structure of rocks.

Safety Precautions

Always wear safety goggles and an apron in the lab.

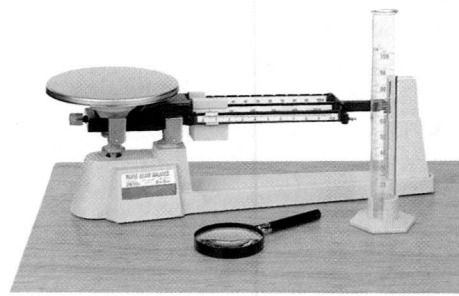

Resource Manager

GeoLab and MiniLab Worksheets, pp. 24–25 **L2**

Procedure

1. Prepare a data table similar to the one shown below.
2. Observe each rock sample. Record your observations in the data table.
3. Recall that density = mass/volume. Make a plan that will allow you to measure the mass and volume of a rock sample.
4. Determine the density of each rock sample and record this information in the data table.

Analyze

1. Compare and contrast a shale and a sandstone.
2. How does the grain size of a sandstone change during metamorphism?
3. What textural differences do you observe between a shale and a slate?
4. Compare the densities you calculated with other students. Does everybody have the same answer? What are some of the reasons that answers may vary?

Conclude & Apply

1. Why does the color of a sedimentary rock change during metamorphism?
2. Compare the density of a slate and a quartzite. Which rock has a greater density? Explain.
3. Compare the densities of shale and slate, sandstone and quartzite, and limestone and marble. Does density always change in the same way? Explain the results that you observed.

Sample number	Rock Type	Specific characteristics	Mass	Volume	Density
DATA TABLE					
1					
2					
3					
4					

GeoLab **141**

✓Assessment

Knowledge Have students predict which would have a greater overall density, calcite-cemented, iron-oxide-cemented, or quartz-cemented sandstone. Ask students to explain their reasoning. Assuming that the sand grains are the same, the rock with the highest-density cement would have the greatest overall density. Iron oxide is the most-dense, quartz is the next-dense, and calcite is the least-dense mineral.

Analyze

1. shale—darker color, finer grained, thin layers; sandstone—lighter color, medium grained, thicker layers or massive.
2. The grains become larger as they grow together.
3. Slate has thinner foliated layers and may have a smoother feel and shinier luster because of the presence of metamorphic mica minerals.
4. The calculated densities will be variable. Possible sources of error are mathematical mistakes, mass differences between wet and dry samples, lack of precision in volume measurements, and slight differences between samples.

Conclude & Apply

1. The grain size is changing and new minerals are growing.
2. Depending upon samples used, the densities may be close. Slate will usually have a greater density than quartzite. Quartzite will have a density very close to quartz—2.6 g/cm^3. The mica minerals in slate often have a greater density than quartz does.
3. The slate will be more dense than the shale because denser minerals have grown. Quartzite is denser than sandstone because silica has grown into the pore spaces which had previously been filled with air or water. Marble is more dense than limestone because the calcite has recrystallized into a denser, interlocking structure.

Science in the News

Purpose

Students will learn that inhaling asbestos fibers leads to fatal lung diseases. Students will also realize that talc, a commercially valuable metamorphic mineral, is similar to asbestos.

Content Background

It is difficult for testers to distinguish talc fibers from asbestos fibers in products that contain talc.

Asbestos has been clearly linked to lung disease. Asbestosis is linked to asbestos exposure by itself. The risk of developing lung cancer and mesothelioma is greatly increased by smoking cigarettes. Much asbestos-related illness would be eliminated if people exposed to asbestos did not smoke.

Asbestos-related diseases are expected to crest in the next 20 years, and then taper off as the effects of the ban on the use of asbestos begin to show. Most people were exposed to asbestos in the 1950s and 1960s.

Teaching Strategies

- Ask students to raise their hands if they have heard of the danger posed by asbestos. Select one or two students to share their knowledge with the class.
- Ask students to discuss why children are supposedly safe from talc fibers in crayons. The amount of asbestos fibers in crayons is very low, and because they are embedded in wax, the asbestos fibers are not likely to become airborne and be inhaled.

Science in the News

Good News—Crayons Safe

The Consumer Products Safety Commission, after extensive testing, declared that crayons are safe for children to use. Although trace amounts of asbestos and asbestos-related fibers were found in many of the crayons tested, the amounts were not considered to be dangerous. No recall was issued, but crayon manufacturers were urged to create a new "recipe" for crayons to exclude the asbestos fibers.

What do crayons have to do with rocks? A metamorphic mineral—talc—is used in the manufacture of crayons. In fact, it's the properties of talc that led to the asbestos scare.

Talc and Asbestos

Talc is a soft white mineral with a hardness of 1. It is used in many cosmetics and art supplies. Talc is often found in association with serpentine, which is the parent rock of asbestos. Asbestos comes from the mineral chrysotile, which breaks into tiny, hairlike fibers. Asbestos has been used in insulation and in fireproof fabrics and building products. However, in the 1960s and 1970s, it was discovered that inhaling asbestos fibers leads to lung cancer, asbestosis, and mesothelioma—each of which can be fatal. Beginning in the 1980s, virtually all uses of asbestos were banned in the United States and much of Europe.

Blue, green, and asbestos?

Ground up talc is used as a hardener in crayons, which are basically a mixture of pigments, hardeners, and wax. Without talc, crayons would get too sticky to handle. However, when talc is ground, fibers that resemble asbestos are created. Testers aren't sure whether the tiny amount of asbestos found in crayons comes from these asbestos-like fibers, from chrysotile contamination of the talc, or from both. They

point out, though, that if the talc fibers look so much like asbestos fibers, they are likely to have the same affect in the lungs.

The risk to children from the asbestos and asbestos-like fibers in crayons is extremely small. The amount of fibers present is very low, and, because the talc is embedded in wax, there is little likelihood that the fibers will be inhaled. The Consumer Product Safety Commission did a test that simulated one half-hour of hard coloring and found no airborne fibers. Still, crayon manufacturers understand that, when it comes to children, any slight risk is too much. All of the major crayon makers have decided to change their crayon formulas to eliminate all use of talc. The use of talc in children's chalk, clay, and sand is also being investigated. The use of asbestos was phased out in the United States in 2001.

Activity

Research the use of talc in other products. Why is talcum powder no longer recommended for infants? Does the use of talc in make-up expose teens to the same asbestos risk that crayons posed for younger children? Present your findings in a written report.

Activity

Student reports will vary. There is a slightly increased risk whenever a powdered talc product is used. If the make-up is a powder or a cream that dries, there is more risk from airborne fibers than from wax crayons. Students should be aware that the fibers must be inhaled to be dangerous.

Summary

SECTION 6.1

Formation of Sedimentary Rocks

Main Ideas

- The processes of weathering, erosion, deposition, burial, and lithification form sedimentary rocks.
- Clastic sediments are rock and mineral fragments produced by weathering and erosion. They are classified based on particle size.
- Sediments are lithified into rock by the processes of compaction and cementation.
- Sedimentary rocks can contain depositional features such as horizontal bedding, cross-bedding, and ripple marks.
- Fossils are the remains or other evidence of once-living things that are preserved in sedimentary rocks.

Vocabulary

bedding (p. 126)
cementation (p. 125)
clastic (p. 122)
cross-bedding (p. 126)
deposition (p. 123)
graded bedding (p. 126)
lithification (p. 124)
sediment (p. 121)

SECTION 6.2

Types of Sedimentary Rocks

Main Ideas

- There are three main classes of sedimentary rocks: clastic, which are formed from clastic sediments; chemical, which are formed from minerals precipitated from water; and organic, which are formed from the remains of once-living things.
- Clastic sedimentary rocks are classified by particle size and shape.
- Evaporites are chemical sedimentary rocks that form primarily in restricted ocean basins in regions with high evaporation rates.
- Limestone, composed primarily of calcite, is the most abundant organic sedimentary rock. Coal is another organic sedimentary rock.
- Sedimentary rocks provide geologists with information about surface conditions that existed in Earth's past.

Vocabulary

clastic sedimentary rock (p. 128)
evaporite (p. 130)
porosity (p. 129)

SECTION 6.3

Metamorphic Rocks

Main Ideas

- Metamorphic rocks are formed when existing rocks are subjected to high temperature and pressure, which cause changes in the rocks' textures, mineralogy, and composition.
- The three main types of metamorphism are regional, contact, and hydrothermal.
- Metamorphic rocks are divided into two textural groups: foliated and nonfoliated.
- During metamorphism, minerals change into new minerals that are stable under the conditions of temperature and pressure at which they formed.
- The rock cycle is the set of processes whereby rocks continuously change into other types of rock.

Vocabulary

contact metamorphism (p. 135)
foliated (p. 136)
hydrothermal metamorphism (p. 135)
nonfoliated (p. 136)
porphyroblast (p. 136)
regional metamorphism (p. 134)
rock cycle (p. 138)

earthgeu.com/vocabulary_puzzlemaker

Study Guide **143**

Main Ideas

Summary statements can be used by students to review the major concepts of the chapter.

VOCABULARY PuzzleMaker

For additional help with vocabulary, have students access the Vocabulary Puzzlemaker online.

earthgeu.com/ vocabulary_puzzlemaker

⏱ 0:00 *Out of Time?*

If time does not permit teaching the entire chapter, use the GeoDigest at the end of the unit as an overview.

Earth Science Online

Be sure to check the Earth Science Web Site for links to chapter material:
earthgeu.com

GLENCOE *Technology*

Videotape/DVD
MindJogger Videoquizzes
Chapter 6: *Sedimentary and Metamorphic Rocks*
Have students work in groups as they play the videoquiz game to review key chapter concepts.

Resource Manager

Chapter Assessment, pp. 31–36
MindJogger Videoquizzes DVD/VHS
ExamView® Pro CD-ROM
Performance Assessment in Earth Science

NY Core Curriculum Standards

Page 142: St 1 Science KI 3, St 4 KI 3.1a, St 7 KI 1
Page 143: St 4 KI 1.2i, 3.1a, 3.1b, & 3.1c, St 6 KI 1 & 5

Understanding Main Ideas

1. b
2. c
3. d
4. d
5. c
6. a
7. a
8. b
9. b
10. compaction and cementation
11. They are formed from particles broken from solid rock; and *clastic* is derived from the Greek word *klastos*, meaning "broken."
12. As dissolved minerals precipitate out of groundwater, two types of cementation occur: growth of new minerals between sediment grains and enlargement of existing mineral grains by overgrowths of the same mineral.
13. The three types of sedimentary rock are classified by how the particles formed.
14. igneous rocks—weathering, erosion, deposition, burial, cementation; sedimentary rocks—heat and temperature, recrystallization; metamorphic rocks—melting, crystallization
15. schist and gneiss
16. Porphyroblasts are large metamorphic crystals surrounded by finer-grained crystals. They form in solid rock by the reorganization of atoms during metamorphism.
17. weathering, erosion, deposition, some types of cementation, and solidification of extrusive igneous rocks

---

Understanding Main Ideas

1. What are solid particles that have been deposited on Earth's surface called?
   a. porphyroblasts
   b. sediments
   c. schists
   d. quartzites

2. What process breaks solid rock into smaller pieces?
   a. deposition
   b. cementation
   c. weathering
   d. metamorphism

3. What agent of erosion can usually move only sand-sized or smaller particles?
   a. landslides
   b. glaciers
   c. water
   d. wind

4. Which of the following is an example of a medium-grained clastic sedimentary rock?
   a. conglomerate
   b. breccia
   c. evaporite
   d. sandstone

5. Which of the following are formed by the chemical precipitation of minerals from water?
   a. sandstones
   b. coal beds
   c. salt beds
   d. shale

6. Which of the following would you expect to have the greatest porosity?
   a. sandstone
   b. gneiss
   c. shale
   d. quartzite

7. Which of the following is a common mineral found in both organic and chemical sedimentary rocks?
   a. calcite
   b. quartz
   c. garnet
   d. biotite

8. By what process are surface materials removed and transported from one location to another?
   a. weathering
   b. erosion
   c. deposition
   d. cementation

9. What mineral commonly forms porphyroblasts?
   a. quartz
   b. garnet
   c. talc
   d. calcite

---

10. What are the two primary causes of lithification?
11. Why is the term *clastic* appropriate for particles weathered from solid rock?
12. Describe the two main types of cementation.
13. How are the three types of sedimentary rocks classified?
14. Rearrange the terms below to create a concept map of the rock cycle.

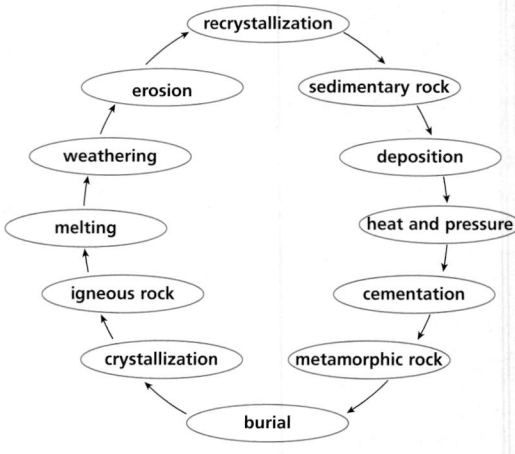

15. What are the two most common types of foliated metamorphic rocks?
16. What are porphyroblasts, and how do they form?
17. What parts of the rock cycle occur at Earth's surface?

Test-Taking Tip

WORDS ARE EASY TO LEARN Whenever you hear or read a word that you cannot define, jot it down on an index card. Then look it up in the dictionary and write the definition on the back of the card. Try to write a sentence or draw a picture using the word, too. Practice saying the word aloud until you are comfortable with it.

earthgeu.com/chapter_test

Applying Main Ideas

18. Chemical weathering can weaken mineral grains along boundaries and fractures.
19. Glacial ice has an extremely high viscosity, allowing it to carry all sizes of particles with equal effort.
20. As sediment transport slows, the coarser material settles out first.
21. The ripple marks were formed as the mud was deposited by water. The mud cracks formed when the water receded and the mud began to dry out. Later, the mudflat was submerged and gently buried by a layer of sand.
22. Large particle size indicates high-energy transport; angular shape indicates short transport distance.
23. the shells of aquatic organisms
24. a metamorphic; calcite is soft, and thus easily worked; the grain size is uniform; and it is massive, occurring in large blocks with few zones of weakness.

Applying Main Ideas

18. How can chemical weathering assist physical weathering?

19. Glaciers move very slowly, yet they are able to carry large particles with ease. Why?

20. How does graded bedding form?

21. Geologists have uncovered a mudstone layer containing mud cracks and ripple marks. This layer lies beneath a layer of sandstone. Explain how these structures and layers might have formed during the deposition of the sediments.

22. What information about sedimentary environments can be interpreted from a breccia?

23. What is the source of the calcite found in organically formed limestone?

24. What type of rock is marble? What characteristics make it well suited for sculptures?

25. How might a sedimentary rock become another sedimentary rock without first changing into another rock type?

Thinking Critically

26. Why are sand dunes commonly composed of fine, well-sorted sand?

27. Why do muds lose more volume during compaction than sands do?

28. How could you tell the difference between sedimentary rocks formed from an underwater landslide and sedimentary rocks formed from a landslide on Earth's surface?

29. Sand is often found between the larger grains of conglomerates, but large particles are seldom found in sandstone. Why is this?

30. Would you expect foliated metamorphic textures in rocks that have undergone contact metamorphism? Why or why not?

earthgeu.com/standardized_test

Standardized Test Practice

1. What initiates the process that turns sediments into sedimentary rocks?
   a. bedding
   c. cementation
   b. burial
   d. compaction

2. Which sedimentary rock is used to make cement for the construction industry?
   a. shale
   c. phosphate
   b. sandstone
   d. limestone

3. Which of the following are rocks composed of minerals that form with blocky crystal shapes?
   a. foliated
   c. porphyroblasts
   b. nonfoliated
   d. phenocrysts

INTERPRETING SCIENTIFIC ILLUSTRATIONS
Use the illustration below to answer question 4.

4. Which rocks are most likely to metamorphose from a lava flow?
   a. only the rocks in the crater of the volcano, where the lava is hottest
   b. rocks in the crater and rocks along the top half of the mountain
   c. all the rocks on the mountain
   d. all the rocks reached by the lava flow

Assessment **145**

25. The rock is uplifted back to the surface and recycled into sediments without encountering metamorphic or igneous conditions underground.

Thinking Critically

26. Sand dunes are formed by wind-blown particles and only particles of a certain size are moved by the wind. Coarser sand is left behind, and finer silt grains are carried away.

27. Muds contain more water, which is squeezed out during compaction. Also, grain-to-grain contacts in sand help support the grains and resist compaction.

28. A terrestrial landslide would be unsorted. An aquatic landslide would show graded bedding as the different-sized particles settled out of the water.

29. When sand is deposited, the transport energy is too low to move large particles; they have been deposited somewhere else. When a conglomerate is deposited, sand is also being carried, and these grains filter down and become trapped between the coarser particles.

30. No, contact metamorphism is characterized by low pressure and high temperature. Foliated textures are caused by high pressure.

EXAMVIEW® PRO

Use ExamView® Pro Testmaker CD-ROM to:

• Create **multiple versions** of tests.
• Create **modified** tests with one mouse click for struggling students.
• **Edit** existing questions and add your own questions.
• **Build** tests based on national curriculum standards.

Standardized Test Practice

1. b
2. d
3. b
4. b

NY Core Curriculum Standards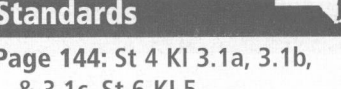

Page 144: St 4 KI 3.1a, 3.1b, & 3.1c, St 6 KI 5
Page 145: St 4 KI 1.2j, 3.1a, 3.1b, & 3.1c, St 6 KI 1 & 5

Prepare

Purpose

This GeoDigest can be used as an overview of Earth's composition. If time is limited, you may wish to use this unit summary to teach these concepts in place of the chapters in Unit 2.

Key Concepts

Students are introduced to the composition of Earth. They learn about atoms, elements, minerals, and sedimentary, igneous, and metamorphic rocks.

1 Focus

Section Focus

Visual-Spatial Before beginning the lesson, have students examine an assortment of quartz, plagioclase feldspar, orthoclase feldspar, biotite mica, hornblende, and a few large pieces of granite. Ask students to distinguish between the minerals and the rocks. Ask what granite is made of and what quartz is made of. Point out that granite is made of a mixture of the minerals, and that each mineral is identifiable in the granite. Ask students to find each of these minerals in the granite, and to define a mineral and a rock. Then, ask students to define elements and atoms.

0:00 Out of Time?

If time does not permit teaching the entire unit, use this GeoDigest as an overview.

For a **preview** of Earth's composition, study this GeoDigest before you read the chapters. After you have studied the chapters, you can use the GeoDigest to **review** the unit.

Composition of Earth

Matter and Atomic Structure

Elements Atoms are the basic building blocks of matter. They are made of protons, which have positive electrical charges; electrons, which have negative electrical charges; and neutrons, which are neutral. Protons and neutrons make up the nucleus of an atom; electrons surround the nucleus in energy levels. An element is a substance consisting of atoms with a specific number of protons in their nuclei. Examples of elements include hydrogen, neon, gold, carbon, and uranium. Isotopes of an element differ by the number of neutrons in their nuclei. All elements are mixtures of isotopes. The number of electrons in the outermost energy levels of atoms determines their chemical behavior. Elements with the same number of electrons in their outermost energy levels have similar chemical properties.

How Atoms Combine Atoms of different elements combine to form compounds. Molecular compounds are formed when atoms are held together by the sharing of electrons in covalent bonds. Atoms also combine ionically. Ions are electrically charged atoms or groups of atoms. Positive and negative ions attract each other and form ionic compounds. Acids are solutions containing hydrogen ions. Bases are solutions containing hydroxide ions. Acids and bases can neutralize each other. A mixture is a combination of components that retain their identities and can still be distinguished. A solution is a mixture in which the components can no longer be distinguished as separate. Solutions can be liquid, solid, or gaseous.

States of Matter On Earth, matter exists in three physical states: solid, liquid, and gas. The universe also contains a fourth state of matter: plasma. Most solids have crystalline structures. Atoms, ions, or molecules in crystals are arranged in regular geometric patterns. Most rocks are polycrystalline materials. Liquids are densely packed arrangements of mobile particles. Gases are widely separated, individual particles. Plasmas are hot, highly ionized, electrically conductive gases. Changes of state involve thermal energy. Melting and evaporation absorb thermal energy, whereas freezing and condensation release thermal energy.

Minerals

A mineral is a naturally occurring, inorganic solid with a specific chemical composition and a definite crystalline structure. There are at least 3000 known minerals in Earth's crust. Minerals form from

Sodium and chlorine reaction

Multiple Learning Styles

Visual-Spatial Section Focus, p. 146, Activity, p. 149

Logical-Mathematical Activity, p. 147

Linguistic Reteach, p. 149

magma or from solution. Most minerals are formed from the eight most common elements in Earth's crust. Oxygen readily combines with other elements to form a diverse group of minerals, including silicates, carbonates, and oxides. Minerals are virtually everywhere. Your body needs many of the elements found in minerals to survive, such as iron, calcium, and sodium. Some minerals are found as ores. A mineral is an ore if it contains a useful substance that can be mined at a profit. Ores from deep within Earth are removed by underground mining. Ores close to Earth's surface are obtained from open-pit mines. If responsible procedures are not followed, mining can cause environmental damage. Gems, such as diamonds and rubies, are valuable minerals that are prized for their rarity and beauty. The presence of trace elements can make one variety of a mineral more colorful and thus more prized than other varieties of the same mineral. For example, amethyst which contains traces of manganese, is a gem form of quartz.

Identifying Minerals
Minerals can be identified based on their physical and chemical properties. The most reliable way to identify a mineral is to use a combination of tests of color, hardness, and density, among other characteristics. A mineral's color is generally the result of trace elements within the mineral. Texture describes how a mineral feels. Luster describes how a mineral reflects light. Cleavage and fracture describe how a mineral breaks. A mineral's streak, its color in powdered form, its hardness, and its density are also methods of identification. Special properties of minerals, such as magnetism, can also be used for identification purposes.

Igneous Rocks
Formation and Types Igneous rocks, formed by the cooling and crystallization of magma, may be intrusive or extrusive. Intrusive rocks form inside

Earth's crust; extrusive rocks form at or near Earth's surface. Minerals crystallize from magma in a sequential pattern known as Bowen's reaction series. Different minerals melt and crystallize at different temperatures in the processes of partial melting and fractional crystallization. Igneous rocks are classified as felsic, intermediate, mafic, and ultramafic, depending upon their mineral compositions. Igneous groups are further identified by crystal size, also called texture. For example, extrusive rocks, which cool more rapidly than intrusive rocks, are generally more fine grained meaning they have small crystals. Early forming minerals may have well-shaped crystals, while later-forming minerals have irregular shapes. Porphyritic textures contain both large and small crystals.

Igneous Rock Resources Igneous rocks are often used as building materials because of their strength, durability, and beauty. Valuable ore deposits and gem crystals are often associated with igneous intrusions. For example, diamonds are found in rare types of igneous intrusions known as kimberlite pipes.

Dioptase on panchéite

Vital Statistics

Top Ten Diamond-Mining Countries

Country	Mine Production (in carats)
Botswana	15 000 000
Australia	13 400 000
Russia	11 500 000
South Africa	4 000 000
Kinshasa	3 500 000
Canada	2 000 000
Namibia	1 990 000
Angola	1 080 000
Ghana	649 000
Liberia	600 000

2 Teach

Activity

Logical-Mathematical Give students copies of Mohs Scale of Hardness and a table that lists the hardness of common objects (e.g., fingernail = 2.5, copper penny = 3.5). Explain how to use an object's known hardness to determine the relative hardness of an unknown mineral. Have students determine the hardnesses of unknown mineral samples.

Content Background
In biological and chemical reactions, atoms are never created, destroyed, or changed. They are only rearranged to form different molecules and compounds. This is known as the law of conservation of matter. A metamorphic rock is altered as a result of increased heat or pressure. During the metamorphic process, parent rock can undergo chemical changes to form new minerals from the existing elements. The elements are simply rearranged, not lost or destroyed.

Demo
Demonstrate the relationship of metamorphic rocks to their precursors using visual aids. Suggested examples include quartz sandstone and quartzite; limestone and marble; and shale and slate. Show the progression of metamorphic grade using samples of slate, phyllite, schist, and gneiss. Ask students to put these four samples in order from low to high metamorphic grade. Tell students that the precursor is shale, and tell them which samples have undergone the least and the most physical and chemical changes.

GeoDigest

GeoDigest

Using Scientific Terms

Matter is defined as anything that occupies space and has mass, which includes solids, liquids, and gases. *Mass* is a measure of the quantity of matter a body contains and is not dependent on gravity. *Weight* is the force on a body resulting from the pull of gravity. An astronaut in space has the same mass as on Earth, but weighs less than on Earth.

Content Background

Oxygen is the most abundant element in Earth's crust followed by silicon. Silica is oxygen combined with silicon. Pure silica is the mineral quartz (SiO_2). Most minerals contain silica and are known as silicates. The oxygen and silicon combine in a 4-to-1 ratio in the shape of a tetrahedron (SiO_4^{-4}). The silica tetrahedron is known as the basic building block of silicate crystals. The classification of silicate minerals is based on the arrangement of the tetrahedra which also influences the physical characteristics of the minerals. These arrangements include isolated tetrahedra, single-chain, double-chain, sheet, and framework structures. For example, mica is a flat, flaky mineral because it has a sheet silicate structure. Quartz is a very hard mineral because it has a framework silicate structure.

✔ *Assessment*

Skill Give students an assortment of minerals, igneous rocks, metamorphic rocks, and sedimentary rocks. Ask student to separate the minerals from the rocks and the rocks into the three different types. Ask students to describe the characteristics of each group.

Metamorphic rock, Ontario, Canada

Sedimentary and Metamorphic Rocks

Formation and Types Sedimentary rocks are formed by weathering, erosion, deposition, burial, and lithification. Clastic sediments are rock and mineral fragments produced by weathering and erosion. Lithification occurs through the processes of compaction and cementation. Sedimentary rocks can be identified by depositional features such as horizontal bedding, cross-bedding, and ripple marks. Sedimentary rocks often contain the remains or evidence of once-living things: fossils. Sedimentary rocks also provide geologists with information about surface conditions that existed in Earth's past. Clastic sedimentary rocks form from sediments and are classified by particle size and shape. Chemical sedimentary rocks are formed from minerals precipitated from water. Such rocks include evaporites, which form primarily in restricted ocean basins in regions of high evaporation. Organic sedimentary rocks are formed from the remains of once-living things. Limestone and coal are organic sedimentary rocks.

Metamorphism and the Rock Cycle

Metamorphic rocks are formed when existing rocks are subjected to high temperature and pressure, which cause changes in the rocks' texture, mineralogy, and composition. The three main types of metamorphism are regional, contact, and hydrothermal. The two textural groups of metamorphic rocks are foliated and nonfoliated. During metamorphism, minerals change into new minerals that are stable for the temperature and pressure conditions under which they formed. Geologists use the stability ranges for these minerals to infer the history of Earth's crust. Metamorphism is part of the rock cycle, whereby rocks continuously change into other types of rock. Any type of rock can be changed into any other type of rock.

FOCUS ON CAREERS

Sculptor
Sculptors use rocks, minerals, and other Earth materials to create works of art. Many sculptors cast in bronze, an alloy of copper and tin. Others carve the metamorphic rock marble. Sculptors usually refine their talents in art schools or in the art departments of universities. A good understanding of the materials used is critical to creating a sculpture. The sculptor must know which tools to use on rocks of different hardnesses, how a material will fracture, and how a material in an outdoor sculpture will hold up in weather.

Differentiated Instruction

Gifted In addition to mineral hardness, ask students to identify more physical properties of the same mineral samples. These properties can include streak, color, cleavage, luster, striation, reaction to acid, magnetism, and specific gravity. **L3**

ASSESSMENT

Understanding Main Ideas

1. How are atoms best described?
   a. negatively charged
   b. the building blocks of matter
   c. isotopes
   d. energy levels surrounded by nuclei

2. Hydrogen, neon, gold, carbon, and uranium are examples of what?
   a. elements   **c.** protons
   b. energy levels   **d.** nuclei

3. What is a combination of components that retain their identities called?
   a. an ionic solution   **c.** hydroxide ions
   b. acids and bases   **d.** a mixture

4. How are atoms, ions, or molecules in crystals arranged?
   a. as widely separated particles
   b. as densely packed mobile particles
   c. in regular geometric patterns
   d. in solution

5. What is a useful substance that can be mined at a profit called?
   a. calcium   **c.** an ore
   b. hematite   **d.** a mineral

Model of a water molecule

6. Which of the following tests is the most reliable means of identifying a mineral?
   a. hardness
   b. streak
   c. density
   d. a combination of tests

7. Where do intrusive igneous rocks form?
   a. on Earth's surface
   b. inside Earth's crust
   c. in the ocean
   d. in Bowen's reaction series

8. What is a kimberlite pipe?
   a. an igneous intrusion
   b. an igneous extrusion
   c. a durable gem
   d. an extrusive igneous rock

9. How are clastic sedimentary rocks classified?
   a. by particle color
   b. by ripple marks
   c. by the presence of fossils
   d. by particle size and shape

10. What is the process whereby rocks continuously change into other types of rocks?
   a. the rock cycle
   b. metamorphism
   c. porphyry
   d. erosion

Thinking Critically

1. Why would a tossed salad be classified as a mixture?
2. Compare and contrast texture and luster.
3. Describe how clastic sedimentary rocks are formed.

3 Assess

Check for Understanding

Activity

Visual-Spatial Show students photographs of local or famous buildings and ask them to determine what type of rock the buildings are made of. Ask students to describe the uses of ores and rocks in your school.

Reteach

Linguistic Have students each write an essay that describes the different types of sedimentary rocks and how they are formed.

 **Assessment**

Portfolio Have students research the bedrock of their city or town. Ask students to determine what type of rock the bedrock is and how it was formed. Is the local bedrock mined, and, if so, what is it used for? Have students report their findings in a one-to-two page essay.

ASSESSMENT

Understanding Main Ideas

1. b   **3.** d   **5.** c   **7.** b   **9.** d
2. a   **4.** c   **6.** d   **8.** a   **10.** a

Thinking Critically

1. The salad is a combination of components, such as lettuce, tomatoes, and cucumbers, that retain their identities and can still be distinguished from one another.

2. Texture describes how a mineral feels. Luster describes how a mineral reflects light. Both help to identify minerals.

3. Sedimentary rocks are formed by weathering, erosion, deposition, burial, and lithification. Weathering and erosion produce rock and mineral fragments called clastic sediments. Lithification occurs through the processes of compaction and cementation.

NY Core Curriculum Standards

Page 146: St 4 KI 3.1a, 3.1b, & 3.1c
Page 147: St 4 KI 3.1a, 3.1b, & 3.1c
Page 148: St 4 KI 2.1l
Page 149: St 4 KI 3.1b, St 6 KI 2

Surface Processes on Earth

Unit Overview

Earth Processes In Unit 3, students are introduced to the external processes on Earth, such as landslides, wind, glaciers, and surface water, that alter Earth's landscapes and impact human populations. U-shaped valleys, sand dunes, underground caves, and the formation of soil all result from these processes, which are driven by gravity.

Chapter Breakdown Chapter 7 introduces the processes of weathering and erosion, as well as the formation of soil. Glaciers, wind erosion, and mass movements are covered in Chapter 8. Chapter 9 discusses many landscape features on Earth that are produced and changed by surface water. Groundwater, the largest source of freshwater available for human use, is discussed in Chapter 10.

0:00 Out of Time?

If time does not permit teaching the entire unit, use the GeoDigest at the end of the unit as an overview.

Surface Processes on Earth

Earth has a system of external processes that shape its surface. For example, weathering and erosion change landforms and form soil, an important natural resource. Other external processes such as landslides, glaciers, and avalanches change the landscape. Earth's external processes also have impacts on human populations. Every year, flooding and mudflows, as well as landslides and avalanches cause the loss of life and property in many regions in the world. The photo shows the Emerald Pools in Zion Canyon in Zion National Park in Utah.

Unit Contents

7 Weathering, Erosion, and Soil

8 Mass Movements, Wind, and Glaciers

9 Surface Water

10 Groundwater

NATIONAL GEOGRAPHIC

Go to the National Geographic Expedition on page 870 to learn more about topics that are connected to this unit.

150

NATIONAL GEOGRAPHIC

eXpeditions!

The Remaking of a River Some topics of Earth science deserve more attention than others because they're unusual, informative, or just plain interesting. National Geographic Society has created visually exciting multipage *Expeditions!* features that inform, excite, and motivate your students.

Expeditions! Features are relevant to the Earth science content of the student edition. Assign them as a lead-in to special research projects and in-depth studies for extra credit. Use them as a basis for colorful visual displays and bulletin boards.

Introducing the Unit

Preconceptions The picture shows Emerald Pools in Zion National Park in Utah. The pool is beneath a high cliff of sandstone in Zion Canyon. For 4 million years, Zion's Virgin River has been cutting down the canyon's sandstone cliffs and carrying away tons and tons of rock and sand. What reactions and images do rivers bring up in the students' minds? Ask for specific examples of how rivers can change Earth's landscape. Ask students who have lived near a river to describe a river's environment.

Historical Examples During the summer of 1993, the upper Mississippi River basin experienced severe flooding that caused an unprecedented amount of destruction to many communities, homes, businesses, and natural ecosystems. Thirty locations along the river in Iowa set new flood records. In this unit, students will explore how Earth's landscape features are changed by water, wind, and glaciers and how these processes affect human populations.

A System of External Processes Collect and display a variety of photographs from periodicals and newspapers that show landslides, avalanches, caves, rivers, and streams. Stress how external forces such as mass movement, surface water, groundwater, wind, and glaciers are constructive, as well as destructive. How are some lakes formed by glacial activity? Why are humans still vulnerable to dangerous floods, mudslides, and avalanches? All of these processes are connected.

Earth Science Online

Note Internet addresses that you find useful in the space below for quick reference.

_____

_____

_____

_____

_____

For Internet tips, see Glencoe's **Using the Internet in the Science Classroom.**

Chapter 7

Weathering, Erosion, and Soil

Refer to pages 8T–9T of the Teacher Guide for an explanation of the National Science Content Standards correlations.

Section	Objectives	National Science Content Standards	State/Local Standards
SECTION 7.1 **Weathering** 🕐 1 session 📦 ½ block	1. **Distinguish** between weathering and erosion. 2. **Identify** variables that affect the rate of weathering.	UCP.1, UCP.2, UCP.3, UCP.4, UCP.5; A.1, A.2; B.4; D.1, D.2, D.3; F.3, F.4; G.3	St 1 Math KI 2, Science KI 1, 2, & 3, St 4 KI 2.1a, 2.1r, 2.1s, 2.1t, 3.1a, & 3.1c, St 6 KI 1, 2, 4, & 5
SECTION 7.2 **Erosion and Deposition** 🕐 1 session 📦 ½ block	3. **Analyze** the impact of living and nonliving things on the processes of weathering and erosion. 4. **Describe** the relationship of gravity to all agents of erosion.	UCP.1, UCP.2, UCP.3, UCP.4; A.1, A.2; B.4; D.1, D.2, D.3; F.6	St 1 Science KI 1, 2, 3, & Engin KI 1, St 4 KI 2.1t, 2.1u, St 6 KI 1, 2, 4, & 5
SECTION 7.3 **Formation of Soil** 🕐 3 sessions 📦 2 blocks	5. **Describe** how soil forms. 6. **Explain** the relationship between the organic and inorganic components of soil. 7. **Identify** soil characteristics. 8. **Recognize** soil horizons in a soil profile.	UCP.1, UCP.2, UCP.3, UCP.4, UCP.5; A.1, A.2; B.4; D.1, D.2, D.3; E.2; F.3, F.4, F.6; G.3	St 1 Math KI 1, 2, 3, Science KI 1, 2, & 3, St 4 KI 2.1r, 2.1s, 2.1t, 2.1u, & 3.1a, St 6 KI 1, 2, 3, 4, 5, & 6, St 7 KI 1

A complete Planning Guide is provided on pages 30T–32T.

🕐 The number of recommended single-period sessions

📦 The number of recommended blocks

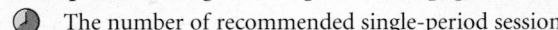

Activity Materials

Discovery Lab *page 153*
250-mL beakers (2), sugar cube, granulated sugar (5 g), stirring rods (2), watch or timer, water

GeoLab *pages 174–175*
plastic jar with lid, halite chips (100 g), balance, timer, paper towels, water

MiniLab *page 163*
bar of soap, toothpick, catch basin, metric ruler, water, paper, pencil

Demo *page 155*
foam board, paring knife

page 170
aquarium, assorted soil types, labels

page 173
sand, clay, silt, water, balance, tube, watch or timer

Need materials? Contact Science Kit at 1-800-828-7777 or at www.sciencekit.com on the Internet. For alternate materials, see the activity on the listed page.

Key to Teaching Strategies

L1 Level 1 activities should be appropriate for students with learning difficulties.

L2 Level 2 activities should be within the ability range of all students.

L3 Level 3 activities are designed for above-average students.

ELL ELL activities should be within the ability range of English-language learners.

COOP LEARN Cooperative learning activities are designed for small-group work.

P These strategies represent student products that can be placed in a best-work portfolio.

📦 These strategies are useful in a block-scheduling format.

Chapter Organizer

Glencoe Exclusive!
TeacherWorks™
All-In-One Planner and Resource Center

Activities/Features	Reproducible Masters	Transparencies
Discovery Lab: Model Interfaces, p. 153 **Using Math:** Using Numbers, p. 155	**Exploring Environmental Problems,** pp. 25–28 L3 **Laboratory Manual,** pp. 49–52 L2 **Study Guide for Content Mastery,** pp. 41–42 L2	**Section Focus Transparency 17** L1 ELL **Teaching Transparency 16** L2 ELL
MiniLab: How do rocks weather? p. 163	**Exploring Environmental Problems,** pp. 33–36 L3 **GeoLab and MiniLab Worksheets,** p. 27 L2 **Study Guide for Content Mastery,** pp. 43–44 L2	**Section Focus Transparency 18** L1 ELL **Teaching Transparency 17** L2 ELL
Problem-Solving Lab: Interpreting Data in a Table, p. 172 **GeoLab:** Effects of Weathering, pp. 174–175 **Science & the Environment:** Shifting Sands, p. 176	**GeoLab and MiniLab Worksheets,** pp. 28–30 L2 **Laboratory Manual,** pp. 53–56 L2 **Study Guide for Content Mastery,** pp. 45–46 L2	**Section Focus Transparency 19** L1 ELL **Teaching Transparency 18** L2 ELL

✔Assessment

Chapter Assessment, pp. 37–42
Performance Assessment in the Science Classroom (PASC)
MindJogger Videoquiz DVD/VHS
Performance Assessment in Earth Science
ExamView® Pro CD-ROM
5 Days to the Regents Exam

GLENCOE'S ASSESSMENT ADVANTAGE

Additional Resources

Guided Reading Audio Program **ELL**
Cooperative Learning in the Science Classroom **COOP LEARN**
Lesson Plans
Block Scheduling
earthgeu.com
NY Lesson Plans
NY Block Scheduling
Review Handbook for Regents Earth Science Exam

☐ NATIONAL GEOGRAPHIC

Teacher's Corner

Products Available from National Geographic Society
To order the following products, call the National Geographic Society at 1-800-368-2728:
Curriculum Kit
GeoKit: *Rocks and Minerals*
CD-ROM
111 years of National Geographic Magazine

Video
Living on Our Changing Planet
Book
National Geographic Desk Reference

Content Background

Weathering
Section 7.1

The processes of weathering, erosion, and formation of soil are closely interrelated, as are many processes on Earth. Weathering includes both the disintegration and decomposition of surface or near-surface rock material. Disintegration is the physical or mechanical breakdown of Earth materials, and decomposition is the chemical altering of the composition of Earth materials. A change in location or exposure to changing atmospheric conditions can affect the rate of weathering of Earth materials. Weathering is an unending process that plays an important role in the rock cycle. The results of weathering change Earth's landscapes and reveal resources that help to meet humans' energy demands.

Erosion and Deposition
Section 7.2

In Earth science, perhaps no other two words are more closely related than *erosion* and *deposition*. The processes are dependent on one another. Distinguishing one from the other is a means to enhance understanding and to emphasize the importance of all aspects of this Earth cycle. Erosion and deposition are primarily responsible for the changing of Earth's surface features. Various erosional agents pick up Earth materials, carry them to other locations, and deposit the relocated materials in a variety of settings or environments.

The depositional environment of a sedimentary rock provides geologists with valuable clues to the geologic history of an area. Determining the depositional environment is also a crucial step in the exploration for petroleum and other geological commodities.

Erosion is a destructive process that wears down Earth's surface, while deposition is a constructive process that builds up Earth's surface. Together, they help maintain the dynamic equilibrium of Earth's surface features.

Formation of Soil
Section 7.3

Soil is the product of a series of complex processes that begin with the weathering

Multiple Learning Styles

- **Kinesthetic** Modeling, p. 169
- **Visual-Spatial** Reinforcement, p. 158, Activity, p. 167, Collaborative Learning, p. 171
- **Interpersonal** Project, p. 157
- **Intrapersonal** Applying Earth Science, p. 156
- **Linguistic** Earth Science Journal, p. 164, Earth Science Journal, p. 169
- **Logical-Mathematical** Across the Curriculum, p. 154

GLENCOE
Technology

The following multimedia resources are available from Glencoe.

Geology PictureShow
Weathering and Erosion

The Infinite Voyage Series
The Future of the Past
Living with Disaster

Vocabulary Puzzlemaker

TeacherWorks™ CD-ROM

MindJogger Videoquizzes DVD/VHS

ExamView® Pro CD-ROM

Interactive Chalkboard CD-ROM

Chapter Organizer

of Earth materials. The rate of soil formation is controlled by interdependent environmental conditions. The weathering and erosion of rock and mineral fragments that are found on Earth's surface, called regolith, begin the process. Of all the major factors that influence the rate of soil formation, including parent material and climatic conditions, time is one of the most crucial. Other factors that influence soil formation

include the topography and the types of organisms present—including plants, animals, and microorganisms. Mature soil consists of identifiable horizons, A, B, and C, which become further defined with time. These horizons can be further subdivided based on their characteristics, such as texture and fertility. Soil often includes material from both the A and B horizons, which, together, constitute what is called the solum.

Identifying Misconceptions

Some students are likely to think that the only importance of soil to humans is as a substance in which to grow plants. Ask students leading questions to help them identify common benefits of soil and materials gained either directly or indirectly from soil. For example, ask students what the role of soil is in producing a piece of wooden furniture. Other examples include wood for homes and other buildings, cotton and silk for clothing, pigments for paint, medicinal products, and so on.

✓Assessment

Portfolio Assessment
  Assessment, TWE, p. 161

Performance Assessment
  Discovery Lab, SE, p. 153
  MiniLab, SE, p. 163
  MiniLab, TWE, p. 163
  GeoLab, SE, pp. 174–175

Knowledge Assessment
  Discovery Lab, TWE, p. 153
  Section Assessment, SE, pp. 161, 166, 173
  Assessment, TWE, pp. 162, 166, 168
  Problem-Solving Lab, TWE, p. 172

GeoLab, TWE, pp. 174–175
Chapter Assessment, SE, pp. 178–179

Skill Assessment
  Assessment, TWE, pp. 171, 173

Be sure to check the Earth Science Web Site for links to chapter material: <u>earthgeu.com</u>

Chapter 7

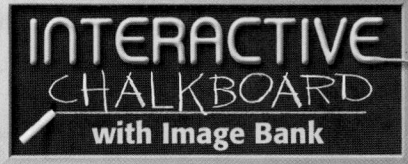

Weathering, Erosion, and Soil

Introducing the Chapter

Ask students to each bring an item to the front of the classroom. Pick up one item at a time and ask students to write in their science journals what they think the connection is between the item and what they are about to learn in this chapter.

Interpreting the Photo

Bryce Canyon, Utah, is located in an area that was uplifted during the formation of the Rocky Mountains. The limestones, sandstones, and shales of the canyon were deposited in the Late Jurassic and Early Cretaceous. In the Tertiary, iron-rich sediments were deposited in this area; they give the rocks their red color. The shapes that we see today are a result of erosion.

INTERACTIVE CHALKBOARD with Image Bank

PowerPoint® Presentations

This CD is an editable Microsoft® PowerPoint® presentation that includes:

- Section presentations
- Section checks
- Image bank
- Links to Earth Science Online
- All transparencies
- Animations
- Audio

Chapter 7 Weathering, Erosion, and Soil

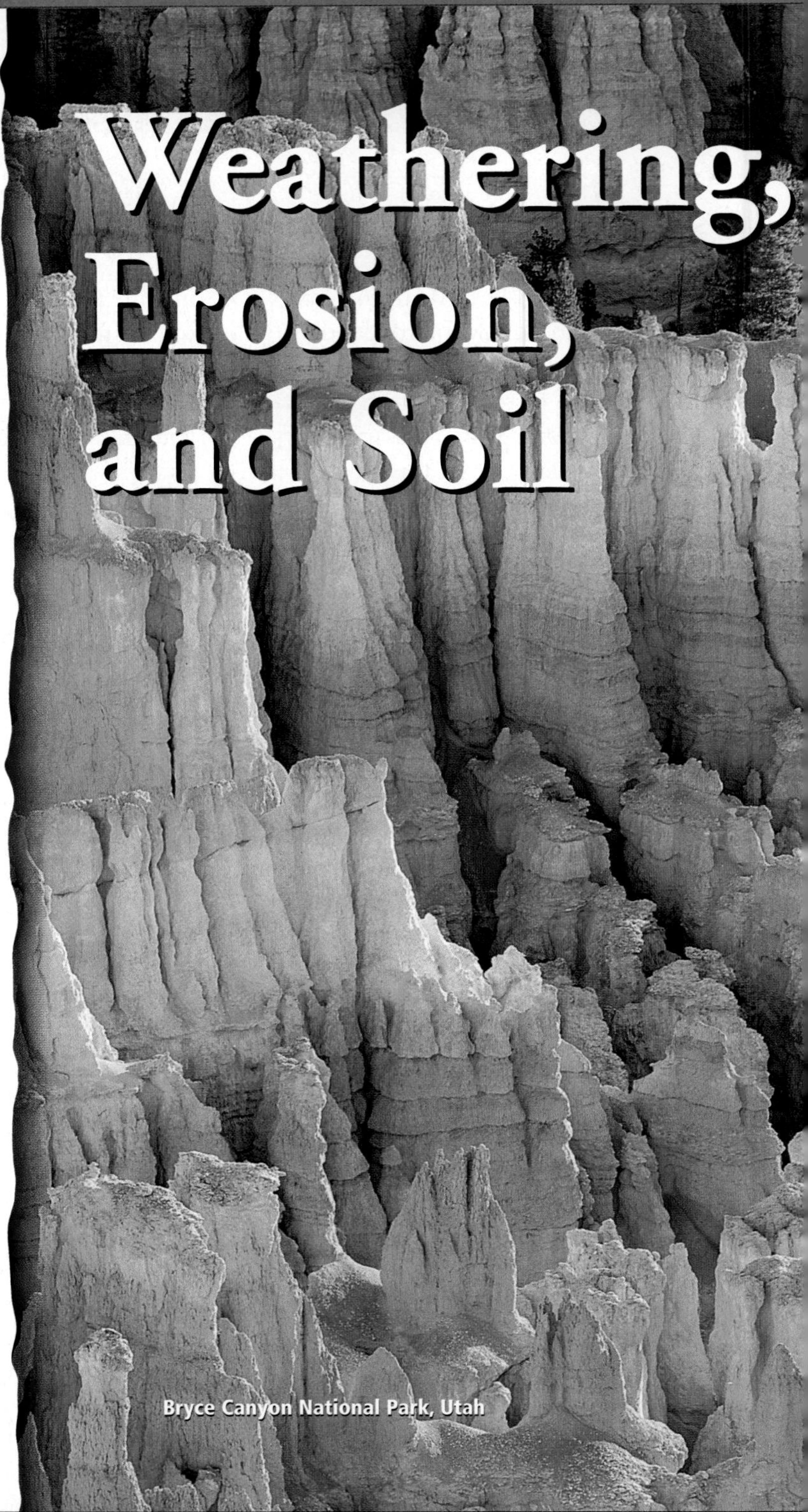

What You'll Learn

- How the process of weathering breaks down rocks and how erosion transports weathered materials from one place to another.
- How soil is formed and why soil is an important natural resource.

Why It's Important

The processes of weathering and erosion change Earth's landforms and form soil, an important natural resource.

Earth Science Online

To find out more about weathering, erosion, and soil, visit the Earth Science Web Site at earthgeu.com

Bryce Canyon National Park, Utah

152

Discovery Lab

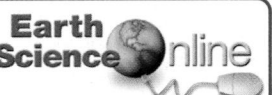

Process Skills

observe and infer, recognize cause and effect, communicate, model, predict, measure, use numbers

Safety Precautions

Remind students not to put any material used in the lab in their mouths, including the sugar.

Procedure

Have students record time to the nearest second.

Troubleshooting

If warm water is used, the granulated sugar may dissolve faster than students can measure. Make sure that the mass of the sugar cube and the mass of the loose sugar are the same.

Observe

Students will readily see that granulated sugar dissolves much faster than sugar cubes. Students should recognize that breaking a cube of sugar into

Discovery Lab

Model Interfaces

Changes can take place at the interface between substances. An interface is where a substance comes in contact with another substance or condition. For example, the surface of a rock is the interface where the rock comes in contact with its environment. The more surface area that is exposed to environmental conditions, the more changes that can take place.

1. Fill two 250-mL beakers with water at room temperature.

2. Drop a sugar cube in one beaker and 5 mL of granulated sugar in the other beaker at the same time. Record the time.

3. Slowly and continuously stir the solution in each beaker. Use

caution in stirring so as not to crack or break the beaker.

4. Observe the sugar in both beakers. Record the amount of time it takes for the sugar to completely dissolve in each beaker of water.

 *CAUTION: Always wear safety goggles and an apron in the lab.*

Observe In your science journal, describe what happened to the sugar cube and the granulated sugar. Explain why one form of sugar dissolved faster than the other. Infer how you could decrease the time required to dissolve the other form of sugar.

SECTION 7.1

Weathering

OBJECTIVES

- **Distinguish** *between weathering and erosion.*

- **Identify** *variables that affect the rate of weathering.*

VOCABULARY

weathering	exfoliation
erosion	chemical
mechanical	weathering
weathering	hydrolysis
frost	oxidation
wedging	

In 1880, an impressive granite monument, Cleopatra's Needle, was moved from Egypt to Central Park, in New York City. Although the monument had existed in Egypt for more than 3500 years, in less than 75 years in New York City's climate, the monument had become dramatically worn and damaged. Today, markings on the surface can barely be read.

Why do you think this has happened? Changes occur every day to Earth's rocks and surface features. Just as the granite of Cleopatra's Needle has undergone changes, so, too, does granite in Earth's crust. The process by which rocks on or near Earth's surface break down and change is called **weathering.** The removal and transport of weathered material from one location to another is known as **erosion.** The processes of weathering and erosion have been going on since the crust of Earth formed, billions of years ago.

7.1 Weathering **153**

---

smaller pieces and thereby increasing its total surface area would reduce the time it takes for the sugar to dissolve.

✓Assessment

Knowledge Have students answer the following question. Which size of hard candy will dissolve most quickly?

a. 5 cm^3 **b.** 15 cm^3 **c.** 25 cm^3 **d.** 10.3 cm^3

The answer is a.

Resource Manager

Section Focus Transparency 17 L1 ELL

Study Guide for Content Mastery, pp. 41–42 L2

Exploring Environment Problems, pp. 25–28 L3

Section Focus

Before presenting the lesson, display **Section Focus Transparency 17** on the overhead projector.
L1 ELL

Chapter Themes

The following themes from the National Science Content Standards are covered in this chapter. Refer to page 8T of the Teacher Guide for an explanation of the correlations.
Systems, order, and organization (UCP.1); Evidence, models, and explanation (UCP.2); Change, constancy, and measurement (UCP.3); Evolution and equilibrium (UCP.4); Form and function (UCP.5)

0:00 *Out of Time?*

If time does not permit teaching the entire chapter, use the Chapter Summary on page 177 and the GeoDigest found at the end of the unit as an overview.

NY Core Curriculum Standards

Page 152: St 4 KI 2.1s & 2.1t, St 6 KI 4 & 5

Page 153: St 1 Science KI 1, 2, & 3, St 4 KI 2.1s & 2.1t, St 6 KI 4 & 5

Identifying Misconceptions

Students may confuse the term *weathering* with *weather.*

Uncover the Misconception
Ask students to give the definitions of *weather* and *weathering.*

Demonstrate the Concept
Explain to students that *weather* is the condition of the atmosphere at a given time and includes such variables as temperature, humidity, wind direction, etc. Then explain *weathering* as the breakdown of Earth's solid crust. Explain that the elements of weather play an important role in the weathering process, but other conditions that are not weather related can also affect the weathering process.

Assess New Knowledge
Ask students which of the following statements is true:
1. Weather can affect weathering.
   true
2. Weathering can affect weather.
   false

Content Background

The weathered, outermost portion of a rock specimen, which can be easily observed once the rock is split open, is called the weathering rind. Some scientists use the thickness of a rock's weathering rind to determine the relative age of the rock compared to other rocks in similar environments.

Figure 7-1 This 3600-year-old monument, Cleopatra's Needle was moved from Egypt to Central Park, New York City. After many years in New York City's climate, some markings on the monument have all but disappeared as a result of weathering.

Figure 7-2 The mechanical weathering of these rocks occurred in Monument Valley in Arizona. *How do you know that these formations occurred as a result of weathering?*

MECHANICAL WEATHERING

Before the agents of erosion can pick up and transport Earth materials, these materials must undergo some form of weathering. Weathering caused the result seen in *Figure 7-1.* Mechanical and chemical weathering are the two processes that can wear down rocks and minerals. Both types of weathering occur at the same time on Earth's landforms.

The process by which rocks and minerals break down into smaller pieces is **mechanical weathering,** also called physical weathering. Mechanical weathering does not involve any change in a rock's composition, only changes in the size and sometimes the shape of the rock, as shown in *Figure 7-2.* A variety of factors are involved in mechanical weathering.

Temperature Temperature plays a significant role in mechanical weathering. When water freezes, it expands and increases in volume by approximately nine percent. Thus, ice takes up approximately nine percent more space than liquid water does. You have observed this increase in volume if you have ever made ice in an ice-cube tray in a freezer. In many places on Earth's surface, water collects in the cracks of rocks and rock layers. If the temperature drops to the freezing point of water, it freezes, expands, exerts pressure on the rocks, and may cause them to split, as shown in *Figure 7-3A.* When the temperature then increases, the ice in the cracks of rocks and rock layers melts. The repeated thawing and freezing of water in the cracks of rocks is called **frost wedging.** Frost wedging is also responsible for the formation of potholes in many roads in the northern United States in early spring, as shown in *Figure 7-3B.*

Pressure Pressure is another factor in mechanical weathering. Bedrock at great depths is under pressure from the overlying rock layers. When the overlying rock layers are removed, the pressure on the bedrock below is reduced. The bedrock surface, formerly

Figure Caption Question

Figure 7-2 How do you know that these formations occurred as a result of weathering?
There was no change in their chemical composition; they changed only in shape and size.

Math Have students mark the height of water on a container before freezing it, then measure the height of the marks indicating the liquid water and the ice. Then have students subtract one from the other, divide the difference by the height of the liquid water, and multiply the result by 100 to obtain a percentage.

Figure 7-3 Frost wedging has split this granite boulder in the Sierra Nevada, California **(A).** Frost wedging also causes potholes to develop in early spring in Washington State **(B).** This boulder in Baja, California, is undergoing the process of exfoliation **(C).** This birch tree is growing out of a crack in bedrock in New Jersey **(D).**

buried, is then able to expand, and long, curved cracks can form. These cracks, also known as joints, occur parallel to the surface of the rock. Reduction of pressure also allows existing cracks in the bedrock to widen.

Over time, the outer layers of rock are stripped away in succession, similar to an onion's layers being peeled off one by one. The process by which outer rock layers are stripped away is called **exfoliation,** shown in *Figure 7-3C.* Exfoliation often results in dome-shaped formations such as Liberty Cap and Half Dome in Yosemite National Park and Stone Mountain in Georgia. Sometimes, the effects of reduced pressure on rock layers are dramatic. For example, when several layers of overlying rocks are removed from a deep mine, the sudden decrease of pressure can cause large pieces of rock to explode off the walls of the mine tunnels.

The roots of trees and other plants can wedge themselves into cracks in rocks. As the roots grow and expand, they can exert pressure on the rocks to split, as shown in *Figure 7-3D.*

CHEMICAL WEATHERING

The process by which rocks and minerals undergo changes in their composition as the result of chemical reactions is called **chemical weathering.** Significant agents of chemical weathering include water, oxygen, carbon dioxide, and acids. Chemical reactions between rocks and water result in the formation of new minerals and the release of dissolved substances. The new minerals have different properties from those of the original rocks. For example, rust on an iron chain has a different chemical composition from that of the iron on which it formed. To some extent, the composition of rocks determines the effects that chemical weathering will have on them.

Using Math

Using Numbers
When water freezes, it expands and increases in volume by nine percent. What is the volume of ice that will form from 100 cm³ of water?

7.1 *Weathering* **155**

Using Math

The volume of ice that will form from 100 cm³ of water is 109 cm³.

Demo
Cut a piece of foam board into large, irregular pieces. Keep the pieces in place with the pressure of your hands using a desk or table as a base. Have students observe that the model stays together in one piece. Then, release the pressure of your hands so that the pieces separate and fall away from one another. This is similar to the pressure unloading that occurs when pressure on joints is reduced above and around bedrock.

Resource Manager

Laboratory Manual, pp. 49–52
L2

Differentiated Instruction

Learning Disabled To demonstrate frost wedging, drill a series of holes two centimeters deep across the middle of a brick. Keep the brick in the freezer. Each day for a week, remove the brick and cover the top with water, making sure the holes are filled; then return the brick to the freezer until the next class session. Have students observe the size of the holes and the condition and strength of the brick each day. Have them relate this demonstration to how potholes form.

Discussion

Discuss with students the amazing power of roots to break apart hard rocks. Roots first enter cracks and crevasses in rocks when they are very small and slowly exert more pressure as they grow until the rocks break apart. The processes associated with root growth may also release chemicals that help to break down rocks and weaken them.

NY Core Curriculum Standards

Page 154: St 4 KI 2.1a & 2.1s, St 6 KI 4 & 5
Page 155: St 4 KI 2.1s & 3.1c, St 6 KI 4 & 5

Enrichment

A water molecule is composed of one oxygen atom and two hydrogen atoms. They are arranged so that the two hydrogen atoms are attached on one end of the molecule and the oxygen atom is on the opposite end of the molecule. One end of the water molecule has a positive charge and the opposite end has a negative charge. This polarity of the water molecule is responsible for water's ability to dissolve substances.

Applying Earth Science

Intrapersonal Ask students what items they have seen that have rusted. Answers likely will include such items as cars, bicycles, fences, and so on. Then ask students what they could do to such objects to prevent or reduce rusting. Answers will likely include painting the objects. Students should recognize that painting will prevent oxygen from coming in contact with the metal.

Figure 7-4 The surface of this limestone rock was chemically weathered by the activities of water. The rock is located in Slickhorn Canyon, Glen Canyon National Recreation Area, in Arizona.

Figure 7-5 This limestone cave in Guatemala was formed when carbonic acid dissolved the calcite in the limestone rock.

Some minerals, such as calcite, may dissolve completely. Rocks that contain calcite, such as limestone and marble, are also greatly affected by chemical weathering. Buildings and monuments made of these rocks readily show signs of wear resulting from weathering.

Temperature is another significant factor in chemical weathering because it influences the rate at which chemical reactions occur. Usually, chemical reaction rates increase as temperature increases. With all other factors being equal, the rate of chemical weathering reactions doubles with each 10°C increase in temperature.

Water Water is an important agent in chemical weathering because it can dissolve many kinds of minerals and rocks, as shown in *Figure 7-4.* Water has an active role in some reactions, while it simply serves as a medium through which other reactions occur. The reaction of water with other substances is known as **hydrolysis.** Hydrolysis occurs in the decomposition of silicate minerals, such as the decomposition of potassium feldspar into kaolinite, a fine-grained clay mineral common in soils.

Oxygen Like water, oxygen can combine with other substances. The chemical reaction of oxygen with other substances is called **oxidation.** Approximately 21 percent of Earth's atmosphere is oxygen gas. Iron in rocks and minerals readily combines with this atmospheric oxygen to form minerals with the oxidized form of iron as shown in the following reaction.

$$2Fe_3O_4 \ + \ \frac{1}{2}O_2 \ \rightarrow \ 3Fe_2O_3$$

magnetite   hematite

Common minerals that contain the reduced form of iron include magnetite, hornblende, biotite, and pyrite.

Across the Curriculum

Math Ask students to calculate the increase in the rate of chemical weathering for a substance whose temperature increases 50°C. ten times faster

Using Scientific Terms

Hydrolysis, oxidation, and *carbonation* are terms that students will encounter in chemistry. It might be wise to talk with the chemistry teacher at your school to make sure that his or her descriptions of these processes are consistent with yours. Students who readily learn the chemical aspects of this chapter should be encouraged to continue on in the sciences and take chemistry.

Carbon Dioxide Another atmospheric gas that contributes to the chemical weathering process is carbon dioxide, which is produced by living organisms during the process of respiration. When carbon dioxide combines with water in the atmosphere, it forms a weak carbonic acid that falls to Earth's surface as precipitation. The formation of carbonic acid is shown in the following reaction.

$$H_2O + CO_2 \rightarrow H_2CO_3$$
$$\text{water} \quad \text{carbon dioxide} \quad \text{carbonic acid}$$

Carbonic acid reacts with minerals such as calcite in limestone and marble to dissolve rocks. For example, limestone caverns, as shown in *Figure 7-5,* can form when carbonic acid dissolves the calcite in limestone rocks. Carbonic acid can also affect silicate minerals such as mica, and feldspar by reacting with elements in the minerals, such as magnesium and calcium. This chemical weathering process results in the formation of clay minerals. High concentrations of carbonic acid accumulate in soil, where decaying organic matter and plant respiration produce high levels of carbon dioxide. When water from precipitation seeps into the ground and combines with carbon dioxide, large amounts of carbonic acid become available for the process of chemical weathering.

Acid Precipitation Another agent of chemical weathering is acid precipitation, which is caused mainly by the oxidation of sulfur dioxide and nitrogen oxides that are released into the atmosphere by human activities. Sulfur dioxide forms from the industrial burning of fossil fuels, while nitrogen oxides are emitted from motor-vehicle exhausts. These two gases combine with oxygen and water in the atmosphere to form sulfuric and nitric acids.

We describe how acidic a solution is by using the pH scale. *Figure 7-6* illustrates the pH scale. The lower the pH number, the greater the acidity of a substance. Acid precipitation is precipitation that has a

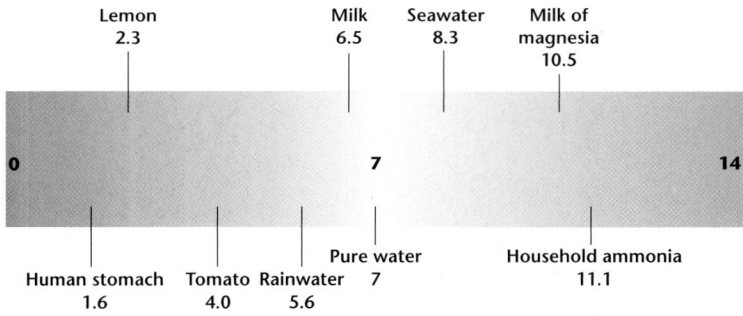

Lemon 2.3 — Milk 6.5 — Seawater 8.3 — Milk of magnesia 10.5

0 — 7 — 14

Human stomach 1.6 — Tomato 4.0 — Rainwater 5.6 — Pure water 7 — Household ammonia 11.1

Figure 7-6 The pH scale is used to determine the acidity of substances.

Topic: Weathering
To find out more about weathering, visit the Earth Science Web Site at earthgeu.com

Activity: Identify an example of weathering in your state. Is it the result of mechanical weathering, chemical weathering, or both?

ENVIRONMENTAL CONNECTION

Across the Curriculum

Chemistry Acids and bases are standard topics in the study of chemistry. Acids have pH values less than 7 and bases have pH values greater than 7. A pH of 7 is neutral. Some plants and animals may thrive only within specific pH ranges.

Resource Manager

Teaching Transparency 16 L2 ELL

Project

Interpersonal Have students work in groups of three or four to determine the pH levels of common materials found at home. Ask each student to bring in one common household item, such as vinegar, milk, orange juice, apple juice, or shampoo, to test. Make sure students do not bring in hazardous chemicals such as bleach, ammonia, or lye. Have students put on safety goggles and then use litmus paper to determine the pH levels of the items. Then, compile the data on the chalkboard for students to record in their science journals. **L1** **COOP LEARN**

Collaborative Learning

Ask students to bring in samples of water from their homes or other places within the community. Have students work in groups of three or four to test the pH levels of the water samples. Then, on the chalkboard, list the pH values of all water samples. Have the class determine the range of pH levels of the water samples. Once the list is complete, ask students to record the data in their science journals. Provide a large map of the community on which students can record the locations and pH values of all the water samples collected by the class. Ask for a volunteer to draw isolines on the map. Then, ask each group to draw conclusions from the data and map. List these conclusions on the overhead projector or chalkboard and discuss them with the class. **COOP LEARN**

NY Core Curriculum Standards

Page 156: St 4 KI 2.1s & 3.1a, St 6 KI 4 & 5
Page 157: St 4 KI 2.1s & 3.1a, St 6 KI 4 & 5

Environmental Connection

The effects of acid precipitation on people are different from its effects on the aquatic species shown in **Table 7-1.** Swimming in an acidic lake may not harm a human, but it will harm a frog or a fish. However, the gases in the atmosphere that cause acid precipitation are harmful to humans. These gases, sulfur dioxide and nitrogen oxides, irritate and damage people's lungs.

Activity

Take the class on a field trip to a cemetery. Have students work in groups of three to four. Each group will need to bring a notebook, pencil, paper with which to make tombstone rubbings, metric ruler, camera, and compass. Make sure students take care to avoid poisonous plants such as poison ivy. Each group will collect information and make a report that includes the following:

1. the average rate of weathering of at least ten tombstones (based on tombstone dates)
2. a map of the cemetery with the locations of the tombstones noted and a legend with a directional component
3. photographs and accompanying rubbings of the tombstones studied
4. a group report that includes the purpose of the investigation, the procedures followed, data, and conclusions

pH value below 5.6, the pH of normal rainfall. Because acids can be harmful to many organisms and destructive to nonliving things, acid precipitation creates problems. It adversely affects fish and aquatic plant populations in lakes. Most freshwater lakes have a natural pH in the range of 6 to 8. These lakes can support many kinds of amphibians, aquatic invertebrates, and fish. However, when the lake water becomes too acidic, the species diversity decreases as shown in **Table 7-1.** The table indicates which organisms can survive at a particular pH. As you can see, wood frogs are able to survive at a lower pH than other species.

WHAT AFFECTS THE RATE OF WEATHERING?

The natural weathering of Earth materials occurs very slowly. For example, it may take 2000 years to weather 1 cm of limestone, and yet most rocks weather at even slower rates. Certain conditions and interactions can accelerate or slow the weathering process as demonstrated in the *GeoLab* at the end of the chapter.

Climate The climate of an area is a major influence on the rate of chemical weathering of Earth materials. Variables of climate include precipitation, temperature, and evaporation. The interaction between temperature and precipitation has the greatest effect on a region's rate of weathering. Chemical weathering occurs readily in

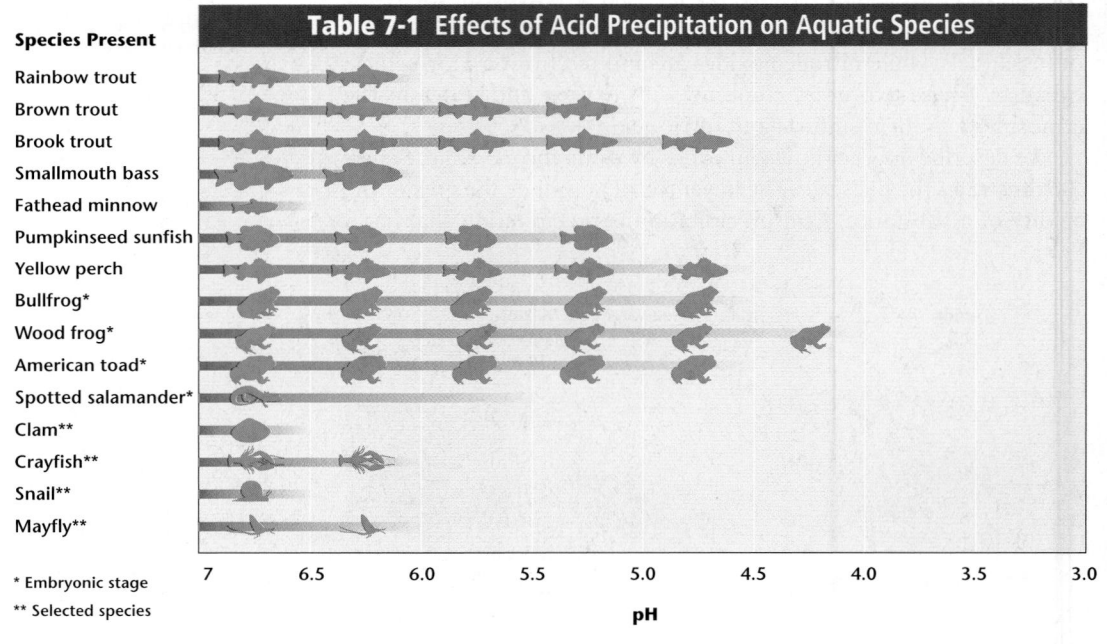

Table 7-1 Effects of Acid Precipitation on Aquatic Species

Species Present: Rainbow trout, Brown trout, Brook trout, Smallmouth bass, Fathead minnow, Pumpkinseed sunfish, Yellow perch, Bullfrog*, Wood frog*, American toad*, Spotted salamander*, Clam**, Crayfish**, Snail**, Mayfly**

pH: 7, 6.5, 6.0, 5.5, 5.0, 4.5, 4.0, 3.5, 3.0

* Embryonic stage
** Selected species

Reinforcement

Visual-Spatial Assign students to take photographs within the community that show the effects of weathering on natural and human-made structures. Have each student present his or her photographs in an album format complete with captions for each photo. Captions should each include a title, the location, date, and a description of the photo. **ELL** **P**

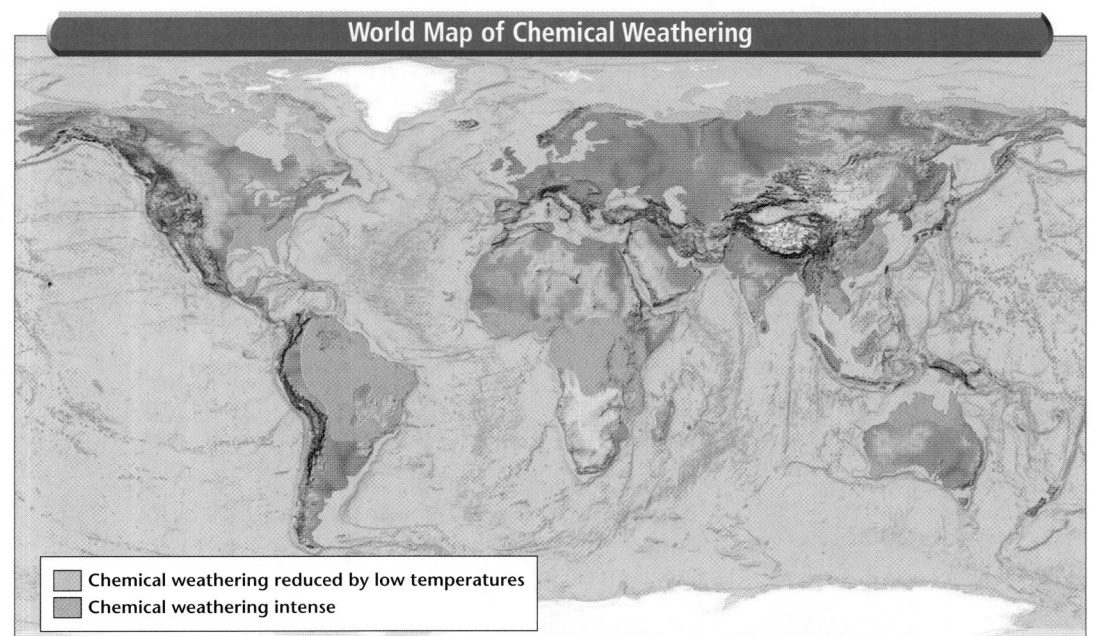

World Map of Chemical Weathering

◻ Chemical weathering reduced by low temperatures
◼ Chemical weathering intense

Figure 7-7 This world map shows areas where chemical weathering occurs. *What areas in the world are subject to the most intense chemical weathering?*

climates with warm temperatures, abundant rainfall, and lush vegetation. These climatic conditions produce thick soils that are rich in organic matter. When water from heavy rainfalls combines with the carbon dioxide in this organic matter to produce high levels of carbonic acid, the weathering process is accelerated. Chemical weathering is evident in tropical Central America, Southeast Asia and other areas as shown in *Figure 7-7.*

Conversely, physical weathering occurs readily in cool, dry climates. Physical weathering rates are highest in areas where water undergoes repeated freezing and thawing. Conditions in such climates do not favor chemical weathering because cool temperatures slow or inhibit chemical reactions. Little or no chemical weathering occurs in areas that are frigid year-round.

The different rates of weathering caused by different climatic conditions can be illustrated by a comparison of Asheville, North Carolina, and Phoenix, Arizona. Phoenix has dry, warm, conditions; temperatures do not drop below the freezing point of water, and humidity is low. In Asheville, temperatures sometimes drop below the freezing point during the colder months. Asheville has more monthly rainfall and higher levels of humidity than Phoenix does, as

Concept Development

In addition to the effects of climate, the rates of weathering are affected by the type and structure of rock. For example, rocks composed of quartz are more resistant to weathering than rocks made of less resistant minerals, such as feldspars. Rocks of high porosity (void spaces) and high permeability (ease with which fluid moves through) are readily weathered. Fractures and bedding planes in rocks act as natural passageways for water, which accelerates weathering processes. They also increase the surface area exposed to weathering. Therefore, sedimentary and highly fractured rocks weather more rapidly than equivalent nonfractured rocks.

Figure Caption Question

Figure 7-7 What areas in the world are subject to the most intense chemical weathering?
Central America and Southeast Asia

NY Core Curriculum Standards

Page 158: St 4 KI 2.1r, 2.1s, & 3.1a, St 6 KI 4 & 5
Page 159: St 4 KI 2.1r, 2.1s, & 3.1a, St 6 KI 4 & 5

According to Koeppen's climatic classification system, Phoenix is classified as a dry climate—more specifically, as a cool and dry, arid desert. The mean annual temperature of this climate region is below 18°C (64°F). In a region with a dry climate, rates of evaporation and transpiration exceed rates of precipitation. Often, rain evaporates into the air before reaching the ground. Asheville, North Carolina, is classified as a moist climate with mild winters—more specifically, a humid subtropical climate. The summers are long and hot, with average temperatures in the warmest months above 22°C (72°F). Humid subtropical climates experience rainfall year-round, in addition to receiving precipitation from coastal storms.

Figure Caption Question

Figure 7-9 What do you think caused the rocks to form in this way? The sandstone is more resistant to erosion than the softer coal.

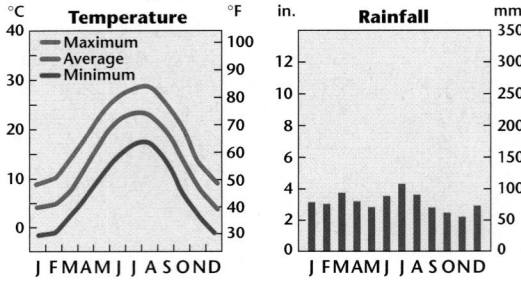

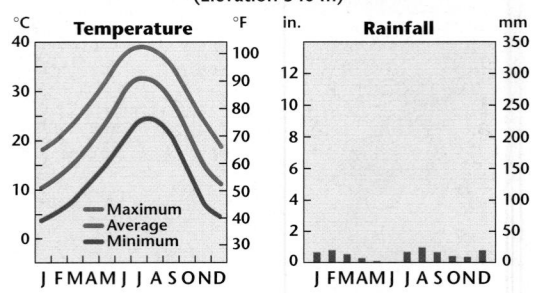

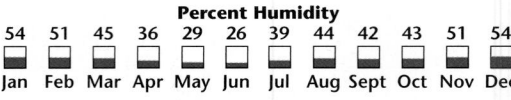

Figure 7-8 These graphs show a comparison of climatic conditions in Asheville and Phoenix.

shown in *Figure 7-8.* Because of these differences in their climates, rocks and minerals in Asheville experience a higher rate of mechanical and chemical weathering than those in Phoenix do.

Rock Type and Composition A wide variety of rocks and minerals cover Earth's surface. The characteristics of rocks, including how hard or resistant they are to being broken down, depend on their type and composition. In general, sedimentary rocks are more easily weathered than harder igneous and metamorphic rocks. The dramatic landscape in the Bisti Badlands of New Mexico exhibits rock layers with different degrees of resistance to weathering, as illustrated in *Figure 7-9.*

Figure 7-9 In the Bisti Badlands in New Mexico, these formations of resistant sandstone are situated on top of softer coal layers. *What do you think caused the rocks to form in this way?*

160 CHAPTER 7

Across the Curriculum

Biology Many children are told to chew their food thoroughly before swallowing. The purpose of chewing food is to break it down into smaller pieces. The smaller the pieces, the greater the surface area and thus the greater the contact area for chemical digestive processes to take place. The same concept applies to the rate of weathering.

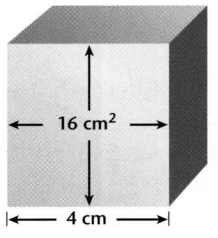

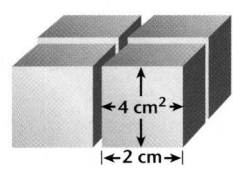

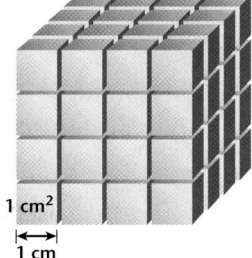

16 cm² 4 cm Surface: 96 cm²

4 cm² 2 cm Surface: 192 cm²

Volume constant: 64 cm³

1 cm² 1 cm Surface: 384 cm²

Figure 7-10 In this example, the original object has a surface area of 96 cm². When the same object is broken up into two pieces or more, the surface area increases.

Surface Area Mechanical weathering breaks up rocks into smaller pieces. As the pieces get smaller, their surface area increases, as illustrated in *Figure 7-10.* This means that more total surface area is available for chemical weathering. Thus, the greater the total surface area, the more weathering that occurs, as you learned in the *Discovery Lab.*

Topography and Other Variables Earth materials cover the surfaces of slopes and level areas. Materials on level areas are likely to remain in place as they undergo changes, whereas materials on slopes have a greater tendency to move as a result of gravity. As material moves down a slope, it exposes underlying rock surfaces and thus provides more opportunities for weathering to occur. As you learned earlier, organisms also affect the rate of weathering. Decaying organic matter and living plant roots release carbon dioxide, which combines with water to produce acid, which in turn increases the weathering rate.

SECTION ASSESSMENT

1. Distinguish between weathering and erosion.
2. List several variables that affect the rate of weathering.
3. What two climatic factors are most important in the weathering process?
4. **Thinking Critically** Describe how one variable may affect another variable in the weathering process.

SKILL REVIEW

5. **Making Graphs** Make a graph of the relationship between the rate of weathering and the surface area of a material. Plot the weathering rate on the *y*-axis and the surface area on the *x*-axis. For more help, refer to the *Skill Handbook.*

earthgeu.com/self_check_quiz

7.1 *Weathering* **161**

SECTION ASSESSMENT

1. Weathering is the breakdown of Earth materials, and erosion is the transport of weathered Earth materials to other locations on Earth's surface.
2. climate (temperature and humidity), rock type and composition, surface area, topography, and type of vegetation
3. temperature and rainfall
4. As the surface area increases as a result of mechanical weathering, it will have an increased effect on the material's rate of chemical weathering.
5. Graphs should reflect an increase in the rate of weathering with an increase in surface area. The *x* and *y* axes should be labeled *surface area* and *weathering rate,* respectively.

161

Section Background

For section content background, refer to **Erosion and Deposition** on page 152C.

Preplanning

Refer to the Chapter Organizer on pages 152A–B.

1 Focus

Section Focus

Before presenting the lesson, display **Section Focus Transparency 18** on the overhead projector.
L1 **ELL**

Section Focus Transparency **18** **SOIL EROSION**
Use with Chapter 7, Section 7.2

❶ What could have caused this area to become like this?
❷ What can be done to keep this problem from getting worse?

Section Focus Transparency   Earth Science: Geology, the Environment, and the Universe

NY Core Curriculum Standards

Page 162: St 4 KI 2.1t, St 6 KI 4 & 5

Page 163: St 1 Science KI 1, 2, & 3, St 4 KI 2.1t & 2.1u, St 6 KI 4 & 5

SECTION 7.2 *Erosion and Deposition*

OBJECTIVES

- **Analyze** the impact of living and nonliving things on the processes of weathering and erosion.
- **Describe** the relationship of gravity to all agents of erosion.

VOCABULARY

deposition
rill erosion
gully erosion

As you have learned, erosion is the process that transports Earth materials from one place to another. A number of different agents transport weathered materials on Earth. Running water in streams and rivers, glaciers, wind, and ocean currents and waves all pick up and carry materials. Humans, plants, and animals also play a role in the erosional process. Erosion can result from the loss of plant cover, as shown in *Figure 7-11.* The land becomes barren as increasing amounts of soil are lost to wind and water erosion. At some point, the movement of transported materials will slow down. When this happens, the materials are dropped in another location in a process known as **deposition,** the final stage of the erosional process.

GRAVITY'S ROLE IN EROSION

Gravity is associated with many erosional agents, because the force of gravity tends to pull all materials downslope. Without gravity, glaciers would not move downslope and streams would not flow. Gravity is also an agent of mass movements such as landslides, mudflows, and avalanches, which you will learn about in Chapter 8.

EROSION BY RUNNING WATER

With the exception of the extremely strong winds associated with tornadoes and hurricanes, water has more power to move large particles of weathered material than wind does. As you might expect, stream erosion is greatest when a large volume of water is moving rapidly, such as during spring thaws and torrential downpours. Water flowing down steep slopes also has greater potential to erode Earth materials, because the steeper the slope, the faster the water flows. Not only does swiftly flowing water have greater erosional power than wind, but it can also carry more material along with it and over a greater distance.

162

Figure 7-11 Major erosion can occur on steep slopes as a result of the loss of plant cover due to the clearcutting of a forest.

Resource Manager

Section Focus Transparency 18 **L1** **ELL**
Study Guide for Content Mastery, pp. 43–44 **L2**
Exploring Environmental Problems, pp. 33–36 **L3**
GeoLab and MiniLab Worksheets, p. 27 **L2**

✓Assessment

Knowledge Ask students the following question. Which of the following features are erosional features and which are depositional features?

- **a.** cliffs
- **b.** arches
- **c.** sandbars
- **d.** sand dunes

a and b are erosional features and c and d are depositional features

Running water moves along Earth's surface from higher to lower elevations. Small streams at high elevations flow down to join larger streams at lower elevations. Such a network of streams drains an area called a watershed as the water works its way down toward the ocean.

The erosion by running water in small channels, on the side of a slope is called **rill erosion,** shown in *Figure 7-12A*. Rills commonly form on a slope. When a channel becomes deep and wide, it can evolve into **gully erosion,** as shown in *Figure 7-12B*. Gullies can be more than 3 m deep. They can be a major problem in farming and grazing areas.

Coastal Deposition and Erosion

Rocks exposed to their surrounding environment are slowly weathered away, as modeled in the *MiniLab* on this page. Each year, streams and rivers carry billions of metric tons of sediments and weathered materials to coastal areas. The Mississippi River alone carries 750 million metric tons of eroded material off the continent and into the Gulf of Mexico annually. When a

Figure 7-12 Rill erosion has occurred on these rocks in Badlands National Park **(A).** The removal of too much vegetation caused gully erosion in this farming area **(B).**

MiniLab

How do rocks weather?

Model how rocks are exposed to their surrounding environment and slowly weather away.

Procedure

1. Carve your name deeply into a bar of soap with a toothpick. Weigh the soap.
2. Measure and record the depth of the letters carved into the soap.
3. Place the bar of soap on its edge in a catch basin.
4. Sprinkle water over the bar of soap until a noticeable change occurs in the depth of the carved letters.
5. Measure and record the depth of the carved letters.

Analyze and Conclude

1. How did the depth of the letters carved into the bar of soap change?
2. Did the shape, size, or weight of the bar of soap change?
3. Where did the missing soap go?
4. What additional procedure could you follow to determine whether any soap wore away?

MiniLab

Purpose

Students will demonstrate how a model of a rock erodes when exposed to environmental conditions.

Process Skills

model, recognize cause and effect, communicate, interpret data, observe and infer, measure in SI

Materials

bar of soap, toothpick, catch basin, container of water, metric ruler marked in millimeters

Teaching Strategies

Some soaps are softer than others and will "weather" more quickly. Pretest the brand of soap you plan to use.

Safety Precautions

Remind students to always wear safety goggles in the laboratory. Care should be taken with toothpicks to avoid puncturing skin or eyes.

Expected Results

Results should indicate a decrease in the depth of the letters with the continued flow of water.

Analyze and Conclude

1. The depth of the letters carved in the soap decreased as more water was poured over it.
2. The shape of the bar of soap became more rounded and the bar of soap became smaller. The soap might also have lost mass.
3. The missing soap dissolved in the water and eventually was carried away in the drain.
4. Measure the mass of the soap before and after water is added.

Assessment

Performance Have students design and conduct an experiment to compare weathering rates of different brands of soap and present their data in a chart and graph format. Ask students to correlate their results to specific rocks. Use the Performance Task Assessment List for Designing an Experiment in **PASC**, p. 23.

Differentiated Instruction

Learning Disabled Have students create a daily diary for a small pebble or a grain of sand as it is moved from one location to another by one of the processes of erosion. Have students note the type of erosion, the speed of movement, and points of deposition. If students have difficulty writing a diary, let them record their diary using a tape recorder.

Tying to Previous Knowledge

Bring in a sample of quartz sand. Ask students to look at the individual grains of sand with a microscope or hand lens. Ask students why most of the grains are quartz.

Content Background

Erosion can occur only after other Earth processes such as weathering have broken down solid Earth material. Energy from the movement of agents of erosion dislodges, carries, and transports the particles. Hence, the sizes and masses of the particles being moved are limited by the amount of energy and force associated with each erosional agent. The erosional-depositional process is an energy system in which energy cycles between potential and kinetic energy.

Applying Earth Science

Areas prone to wind erosion generally are not heavily populated. To help students make real-world connections to the power of wind to move small particles, provide examples, such as dirt on a baseball diamond being picked up by wind, the snow blowing during a winter storm, and the dirt from a newly plowed field being picked up and carried away.

Figure 7-13 This photograph, taken aboard the space shuttle, shows the huge amount of sediment deposited at the Nile Delta.

Figure 7-14 A barrier island such as the Queens Atlantic Beach in New York was formed from the buildup of sandbars.

Figure 7-15 Groins at Cape May, New Jersey, are used to protect the beaches from wave erosion. Groins are vertical walls of rock placed perpendicular to the shore to trap sand from ocean currents.

river enters a large body of water, such as the ocean, the water slows down and deposits large amounts of sediments. The build-up of sediments forms deltas, such as the Nile Delta, shown in *Figure 7-13.* The volume of river flow and the action of tides determine the shapes of deltas, most of which contain fertile soil. Coastal areas also undergo erosion by ocean waves and wind. You will learn more about coastal erosion in the *Science & the Environment* feature at the end of this chapter.

In the ocean, weathering and erosional processes continue. The work of ocean currents, waves, and tides carves out cliffs, arches, and other features along the continents' edges. In addition, sand particles accumulate on shorelines and form dunes and beaches. Erosion of materials also occurs along the ocean floor and at continental and island shorelines. The constant movement of water and the availability of accumulated weathered material result in a continuous erosional process, especially along ocean shorelines. Sand along a shoreline is repeatedly picked up, moved, and deposited by ocean currents. In this way, sandbars form from offshore sand deposits. If the sandbars continue to be built up with sediments, they can become barrier islands. Many barrier islands, as shown in *Figure 7-14,* have formed along the Gulf and Atlantic Coasts of the United States.

164 CHAPTER 7

Astronomy Wind erosion is a major influence on the formation of surface features on Mars. Mars has been known to have dust storms that have lasted for months at a time. Photographs from the Mariner and Viking space missions have provided evidence of Mars's hostile, desert environment.

Earth Science
Journal

Linguistic Assign students to write essays in their science journals about the positive effects of past glacial activity on civilization today. Student essays might include landscape beauty, enjoyable and useful lakes, outstanding skiing and mountain-climbing opportunities, and transport of sediments that become fertile soils from one location to another.

Figure 7-16 This rock in Yosemite National Park, California, was polished by the activity of a glacier.

Erosion also occurs on islands, where the constant movement of water wears away at the shorelines. Changing tides and conditions associated with coastal storms can have a great impact on coastal erosion as well. Human development and population growth along shorelines have led to attempts to control the ocean's movements of sand. However, efforts to keep the sand on one beachfront disrupt the natural migration of sand along the shore, thereby depleting sand from another area. *Figure 7-15* shows one method used to help prevent beach erosion. You will learn more about ocean and shoreline features in Chapters 15 and 16.

GLACIAL EROSION

Although glaciers currently cover less than ten percent of Earth's surface, their erosional effects are large-scale and dramatic. Glaciers scrape and gouge out large sections of Earth's landscape. Because they are so dense, glaciers have the capacity to carry huge rocks and piles of debris over great distances. Glacial movements scratch and grind some surfaces, while they polish others, as shown in *Figure 7-16.* The landscape features left in the wake of glacial movements include valleys with majestic waterfalls, lakes, and variously shaped deposits of sediment. Such features are common in New England. The erosional effects of glaciers also include deposition. For example, soils in the northern sections of the United States are deposits of material once carried by glaciers. In these and other ways, glaciers continue to affect erosional processes on Earth, even though the time of the most recent ice age is long past. You will learn more about glaciers in the next chapter.

WIND EROSION

Wind is a major erosional agent in areas on Earth that experience both limited precipitation and high temperatures. Such areas typically have little vegetative cover to hold soil in place. Wind can easily pick up and move these fine, dry particles. When conditions become ideal for wind erosion, the effects can be dramatic and devastating. The abrasive action of wind-blown particles can damage both natural features and human-made structures. Wind erosion is common in Death Valley. *Figure 7-17* is in Death Valley. Shore areas also experience wind erosion. Even though winds can blow against the force

Figure 7-17 The plant's roots have protected the soil from the wind erosion that has eroded the surrounding area in Death Valley, California.

Concept Development

The last glacial period occurred so recently in geologic time in North America, South America, and Eurasia that other erosional processes such as weathering and erosion have not had time to significantly change the landscape formed by glacial activity during that time. As a result, what is observable on Earth's surface today, aside from the cover of vegetation, remains very much as it was formed by the most recent glacial activity. Thus, scientists are able to reconstruct the shapes of glaciers and infer their movements.

Reinforcement

When a glacier moves over Earth's crust, it can change landscape features by scraping the land like a plow, scratching and grinding the surface like a file, and carrying sediment along with it like a conveyor belt as it plows its way downslope.

Enrichment

Evidence obtained through the study of old documents indicates that during the sixteenth and seventeenth centuries, there was a so-called little ice age. The expansion of glaciers over small villages in the Alps, and generally cooler climates have also been documented from the mid-thirteenth century through the mid-nineteenth century. Thus, small-scale ice ages between major ice ages appear to be a natural phenomenon.

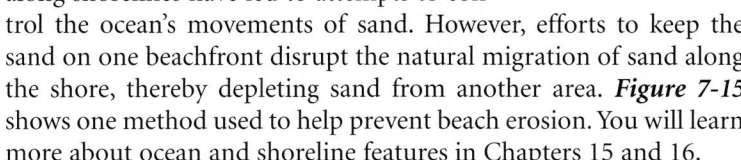

Resource Manager

Teaching Transparency 17 L2 ELL

Time Line

Have students work in small groups to research an east coast area. Have students find dated documentation of changes to the coastline over time. They can make a visual time line by using illustrations or copied photos of the coastal area over time.

NY Core Curriculum Standards

Page 164: St 4 KI 2.1u, St 6 KI 4 & 5
Page 165: St 4 KI 2.1u, St 6 KI 1, 4, & 5

Check for Understanding

Discussion

Lead a class discussion in which erosion on Earth and on the Moon are compared. As you proceed with the discussion, develop a data table on the chalkboard entitled "A Comparison of Erosion." Subdivide the table into one column for Earth and another for the Moon. Use the following row headings: Gravity's Influence on Erosion, Running Water, Glaciers, Wind, and Plants and Animals. The discussion should lead students to see that the lack of erosion on the Moon is a result of its relatively weak gravitation force and its lack of an atmosphere, water, and life.

Reteach

Have students outline the main points of this section in their science journals. Ask students to find pictures in magazines to paste into their science journals in appropriate places to serve as examples.

✔Assessment

Knowledge Ask students to describe the similarities and differences among erosion caused by water, wind, and glaciers. How are these agents of erosion similar to and different from erosion caused by plants, animals, and humans?

Figure 7-18 The construction of a new highway in Ohio requires the removal of large amounts of soil.

ENVIRONMENTAL CONNECTION

of gravity and easily move materials uphill, wind erosion is relatively insignificant when compared to the erosion accomplished by running water and glacial activity.

Wind Barriers One farming method that reduces the effects of wind erosion is the planting of wind barriers, also called windbreaks. Wind barriers are trees or other vegetation planted perpendicular to the direction of the wind. In many cases, a wind barrier may be simply a row of trees along the edge of a field. In addition to reducing soil erosion, wind barriers can trap blowing snow, conserve moisture, and protect crops from the effects of the wind.

EROSION BY PLANTS, ANIMALS, AND HUMANS

Plants and animals living on the surface of Earth also play a role in erosion. As plants and animals carry on their life processes, they move Earth's surface materials from one place to another. For example, Earth materials are relocated as animals burrow into soil and shovel it to another place. Humans also excavate areas and move soil from one location to another. Planting a garden, developing a new athletic field, and building a highway, shown in *Figure 7-18,* are all examples of human activities that result in the moving of Earth materials from one place to another. The effects of erosion by the activities of plants, animals, and humans, however, are minimal in comparison to the erosional effects of water, wind, and glaciers.

SECTION ASSESSMENT

1. In the erosional process, what is gravity's role in relationship to the other agents of erosion?

2. Describe the agents of erosion and how they affect Earth's landforms.

3. What is the difference between rill erosion and gully erosion? Which is the most damaging?

4. **Thinking Critically** In what ways do the activities of humans affect the processes of erosion and weathering?

SKILL REVIEW

5. **Making and Using Tables** Make a data table that compares the various agents of erosion. In your table, rate each agent's overall ability to erode and list any conditions necessary for each type of erosion to occur. Note which erosional agent is most powerful and which is most dominant on Earth. For more help, refer to the *Skill Handbook.*

earthgeu.com/self_check_quiz

SECTION ASSESSMENT

1. Gravity is the force that moves other agents of erosion. Gravity itself is an agent of erosion.
2. Streams and rivers, glaciers, wind, and ocean currents and waves all pick up and carry Earth material from one place to another and continuously change the landscape.
3. Erosion by water running downslope in small channels is rill erosion. Gully erosion can cause more damage than rill erosion because of the larger volume of water involved.
4. Humans excavate the land for buildings, roads,

and bridges. When more rocks are exposed at Earth's surface, weathering increases.
5. Column heads: Agent of Erosion; Ability to Erode; Necessary Condition
- Glacier; Most powerful; In glaciated areas
- Running water; Powerful; In stream areas
- Wind; Less powerful; In areas with loose, fine particles
- Gravity; Force behind all others; Slope; Distance from lowest level of Earth
- Plants/animals; Minor; Where they live

Soil is an important natural resource because it is essential to life on Earth. It would be difficult to imagine a world without soil. Humans and other organisms are dependent on plants, which grow in soil, for food and other basic needs. If you were to make a list of all the things that humans obtain directly and indirectly from soil, you might be surprised by the number of items on your list. In addition to wood from trees, such things as oxygen from plants, food from plants, and meat from animals that are dependent on plants are all products of soil. Soil even helps to filter pollutants.

DEVELOPMENT OF SOIL

Except for some steep mountain slopes and extremely cold regions, soil is found almost everywhere on Earth's surface. But what is soil? Weathered rock alone is not soil. **Soil** is the loose covering of broken rock particles and decaying organic matter, called humus, overlying the bedrock of Earth's surface. Soil is the result of chemical and mechanical weathering and biological activity over long periods of time. The soil-forming process begins when weathering breaks solid bedrock into smaller pieces. These pieces of rock continue to undergo weathering and break down into smaller and smaller pieces. Many organisms, such as bacteria, fungi, and insects, begin to live in these weathered materials. Over time, the organisms die, decay, and add nutrients to the weathered materials to form soil, which, in turn, supports a variety of life forms, as shown in *Figure 7-19.*

The process of continual breakdown of organic materials is thus begun. Nutrients continue to be added to the soil, soil texture improves, and the soil's capacity to hold water increases. While all

OBJECTIVES

• **Describe** *how soil forms.*

• **Explain** *the relationship between the organic and inorganic components of soil.*

• **Identify** *soil characteristics.*

• **Recognize** *soil horizons in a soil profile.*

VOCABULARY

soil
residual soil
transported soil
soil profile
soil horizon

Figure 7-19 Burrowing animals, insects, bacteria, and fungi help add organic matter to soil.

7.3 *Formation of Soil* **167**

Resource Manager

Section Focus Transparency 19 L1 ELL
Study Guide for Content Mastery,
  pp. 45–46 L2

Section 7.3

Prepare

Section Background

For section content background, refer to **Formation of Soil** on page 152C–D.

Preplanning

Refer to the Chapter Organizer on pages 152A–B.

1 Focus

Section Focus

Before presenting the lesson, display **Section Focus Transparency 19** on the overhead projector.
L1 ELL

Activity

Visual-Spatial Have students each bring in a plastic bag full of soil. Each bag should have a label identifying the student's name, the date, and a description of the location it was taken from (for example, along a stream bank or on a hillside). Set up a display in the classroom. Have students note similarities and differences among the soil samples. ELL

167

Content Background

Soil types can be classified according to different systems. One method of classifying soils is based on the soils' compositions. With this method, most soil types belong in one of three broad categories: pedalfers, pedocals, or laterites. The term *pedalfer* is a combination of *ped,* meaning "soil," *al,* meaning "aluminum," and *fe,* meaning "iron." Pedalfers are common in humid, midlatitude, temperate regions. Most soluble materials leach out of pedalfer soils, leaving accumulations of aluminum-rich clays and iron oxides. Pedalfers support the growth of forests and are common in the eastern portion of the United States, which experiences annual rainfall greater than 50–60 cm. The term *pedocal* is a combination of *ped,* meaning "soil" and *cal,* meaning "calcite" (calcium carbonate). Pedocal soils are found in the dry, temperate regions in the western portion of the United States, which experiences annual rainfall of less than 50–60 cm. Pedocals have accumulations of calcium carbonate and support the growth of grasses and bushes. Laterites are wet, tropical soils resulting from intense weathering and high bacterial activity, which leaves soil with very little humus. This soil type has had much of its calcite and silica leached out and is often left with high concentrations of iron and aluminum, which often result in a reddish color and poor growth conditions.

Figure 7-20 This freshly plowed field in southwestern Georgia has a residual soil that is red.

soils contain some organic matter in various states of decay, the amount of such matter varies widely among different types of soil. For example, forest soils contain a much higher percentage of organic matter than desert soils do.

SOIL COMPOSITION

During the process of its development, soil forms in layers. The solid bedrock from which weathered pieces of rock first break off is known as the parent rock. As these pieces of weathered bedrock break off, they rest on top of the parent rock layer. The pieces of rock continue to weather, and the smaller pieces form a layer that rests on top of the larger pieces. Thus, the smallest pieces of weathered rock, along with living and dead organisms, remain in the very top layer. Rainwater seeps through this top layer of materials, dissolves soluble minerals, and carries them into the lower layers of the soil.

Soil located above its parent material is called **residual soil.** Kentucky's bluegrass soil is an example of residual soil, as are the red soils in Georgia, shown in *Figure 7-20.* In contrast, **transported soil** has been moved to a location away from its parent bedrock. Agents of erosion, such as running water, wind, and glaciers, may transport soil from its place of origin to new locations. For example, glaciers have transported sediments to form soil from other places to the northern regions of the United States. Streams and rivers, especially during times of flooding, also transport and deposit great amounts of soil on floodplains along their banks at downstream locations. Winds carry and deposit very fine material to new locations as well.

While the parent bedrock determines what kinds of minerals a soil contains, the proportion of minerals in a soil and in the parent bedrock may not be the same. Differences may occur as the result of chemical weathering. The length of time it takes for soil to form also depends on the type of parent rock, as well as the climatic conditions of an area. In general, however, the process of soil formation occurs over a very long period of time; it can take hundreds of years for only a centimeter of soil to form.

SOIL PROFILES

Digging a deep hole in the ground will expose a soil profile, as when heavy machinery digs out soil in the process of building roads or highways. A **soil profile** is the vertical sequence of soil layers, as illustrated in *Figure 7-21A.* Some soils have more distinct layers than

✔Assessment

Knowledge Ask students the following question. Soil is composed of which of the following?
a. weathered rock
b. living organisms
c. dead organisms
d. moisture
e. atmospheric gases
f. all of the above
The answer is F.

Cultural Diversity

Pedro Sanchez (1940–) Pedro Sanchez is a Cuban-born soil scientist. He is a full professor of soil science at North Carolina State University. He is best known for his soil management research program in Yurimaguas, a tiny, remote town in Peru. This is a long-term project to help farmers increase their rice production and create sustainable agricultural practices based on renewable resources. Sanchez is now working on a similar project in Kenya.

A

B

Figure 7-21 A soil profile is the vertical sequence of soil layers **(A)**. A gardener is growing plants in rich, black soil **(B)**.

others. For example, poorly developed soils show little distinction between layers. A distinct layer, or zone, within a soil profile is called a **soil horizon.** There are three major soil horizons: A, B, and C. High concentrations of organic matter and humus are found in A horizons. Soils rich in humus are usually dark colored; they range from gray to black. *Figure 7-21B* shows black soils. Horizons B and C, the layers under horizon A, are less-developed soil. Horizon B contains subsoils that are enriched with clay minerals. Many subsoils have a zone of accumulation consisting of soluble minerals that have been leached, or washed out, from the topsoil. Subsoils may be red or brown in color as a result of the presence of iron oxides. Accumulations of clay in the B horizon can cause the formation of a hard material, commonly called hardpan, which may be so dense that it allows little or no water to pass through it. Horizon C, below horizon B and directly above solid bedrock, contains weathered parent material. Horizons A, B, and C are distinct and well developed in mature soils. However, all horizons may not be present in a given soil.

Topography The topography of a region affects the thickness of developing soil. In sloped areas, where runoff readily occurs, the coarser particles of soil remain on the slopes, while the smaller particles move downslope. As a result, soils on slopes tend to be thin, coarse, and infertile, whereas soils formed in lower areas, such as in valleys, are thick and fertile. Because south-facing slopes receive the most direct sunlight, they have somewhat more vegetation and therefore thicker soils than slopes facing in other directions.

Reinforcement

Have students make concept maps with the following terms: *thick soil, steep slopes, low runoff, coarse soil, high runoff, infertile soil, fertile soil, valleys, thin soil.*

Modeling

Kinesthetic Have students draw, label, and color a model of the vertical layers of a soil profile. Take students out to the schoolyard so they can compare their models with an actual soil profile. Use a garden trowel to dig a narrow but deep pit (about 10 cm). Pull the soil away from the pit so students can see the different layers. While they are outdoors, have students sketch a real soil profile. They should record observations about organic material, texture, size of particles, and color. Take a small sample back to the classroom and classify the soil type.

Earth Science

Journal

Linguistic Ask students to each write a letter in their science journals from the point of view of a farmer who lives on a hill. The letter is to be addressed to another farmer (one who lives in the valley) and should discuss the problems that the farmer who lives on the hill is having with soil, including soil thickness, fertility, and erosional problems.

Differentiated Instruction

Visually Impaired Have students who are visually impaired construct soil profiles in plastic shoeboxes or other containers. Make sure they note the textures and moisture content of each horizon in the profiles.

NY Core Curriculum Standards

Page 168: St 4 KI 2.1s, 2.1t, & 2.1u, St 6 KI 1, 4, & 5
Page 169: St 6 KI 1, 4, & 5

Using an Analogy

Parent bedrock weathers into rock pieces that eventually form soil. The characteristics of a soil are dependent on the characteristics of the parent bedrock. An analogy can be drawn between parent bedrock and soil and children and their parents. Characteristics that children have are often similar to those of their parents. A child with black hair is likely to have at least one parent with black hair. A tall child usually has a tall parent. As is the case with children, soils have characteristics similar to those of their parent bedrock.

Using Scientific Terms

There are many terms associated with the study of soil. The terms *caliche, calcrete, hardpan,* and *silcrete* are terms associated with some temperate soils. Caliche, also called calcrete, is a soil in which carbonates are dominant, and silcrete is a soil in which silica is dominant. Hardpan refers to soil that contains a large amount of clay. Clay soils usually do not allow water to filtrate readily through them.

Figure Caption Question

Figure 7-22 What soil types are found in the United States? The continental United States has temperate, desert, tropical, and mixed soils. Alaska has polar soils.

The development of mature soil with distinct horizons takes a very long time. Only over time can vegetation grow and mature in a soil and increase the rate of soil development. Vegetation contributes to the buildup of humus and supplies acids that further promote the weathering process.

SOIL TYPES

A soil's appearance, rate of formation, and productivity are determined to a great extent by climate. Because soils form from different parent bedrock material and undergo different climatic conditions, soils vary greatly from one place to another. Other factors contribute to the development of soil, including the types of plants and animals living in the soil, the topography of the area, and the length of time that the soil has been forming. However, because climatic conditions are the main influence on soil development, soils are often classified based on the climates in which they form. The four major types of soil, are polar, temperate, desert, and tropical. *Figure 7-22* shows a map of major soil types.

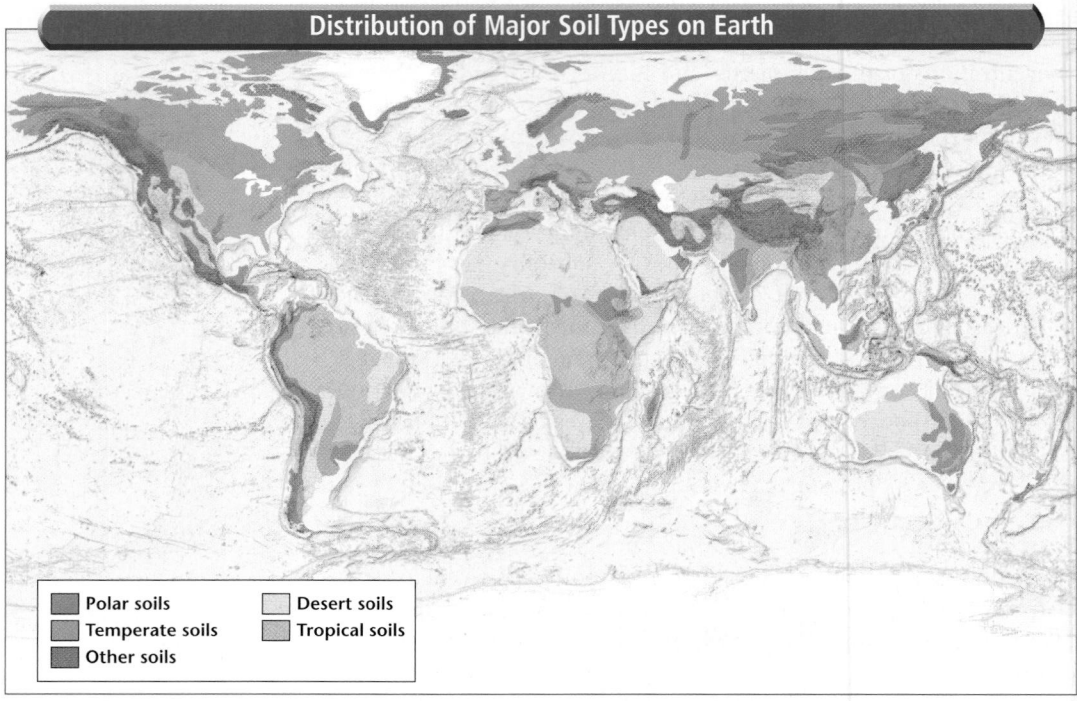

Distribution of Major Soil Types on Earth

- Polar soils
- Temperate soils
- Other soils
- Desert soils
- Tropical soils

Figure 7-22 The major soil types include polar soils, temperate soils, desert soils, and tropical soils. Some climate regions have a variety of different soil types. They are identified on the map as "other." *What soil types are found in the United States?*

Demo

Use an old aquarium to show a model of a soil profile. Each side of the aquarium can be labeled as a different soil type and exhibit the particular horizons of that soil type. Once the model is set up, it can be left in the classroom for student reference and review. You can either make the model yourself and display it, or have students construct it as a class demonstration as the topic is being presented.

Resource Manager

Teaching Transparency 18 L2 ELL
Laboratory Manual, pp. 53–56 L2

Polar Soils Polar soils form at high latitudes and high elevations in places such as Greenland, Canada, and Antarctica. These soils have good drainage but no distinct horizons because they are very shallow, sometimes only a few centimeters deep. Permanently frozen ground, called permafrost, is often present under thin polar soils.

Temperate Soils Temperate soils vary greatly and are able to support such diverse environments as forests, grasslands, and prairies. While the temperate zone in general experiences annual rainfall greater than 50–60 cm, the specific amount of rainfall in an area determines the type of vegetation that will grow in temperate soils. Grasslands, which have an abundance of humus, are characterized by rich, fertile, soils, whereas forest soils are characterized by less deep and less fertile soils that contain aluminum-rich clays and iron oxides, such as those commonly found in the eastern portion of the United States. Soils in the drier, temperate prairies of the western United States support the growth of grasses and bushes. These areas experience annual rainfall of less than 50–60 cm.

Desert Soils Deserts receive low levels of precipitation—less than 25 cm per year. As a result, desert soils often have a high level of accumulated salts and can support only a limited amount of vegetation. Desert soils have little or no organic matter and a very thin A horizon. However, deserts often have abundant nutrients. During periods of precipitation deserts are able to support many plants that are adapted to survival during long periods of drought. Desert soils are also light-colored, coarse, and may contain salts and gypsum.

Tropical Soils Tropical areas experience high temperatures and heavy rainfall. These conditions lead to the development of intensely weathered and often infertile soil, such as that shown in *Figure 7-23*. The intense weathering combined with a high degree of bacterial activity leave tropical soils with very little humus and very few nutrients. These soils experience much leaching of soluble materials, such as calcite and silica, but they have high concentrations of iron and aluminum. The characteristic red color of tropical soils is the result of the oxidation of iron. While these soils provide poor growth conditions, high-grade iron ore is mined from Brazilian, Australian, and Jamaican tropical soils.

Figure 7-23 In the rain forests of Malaysia, the tropical soils are intensely weathered and contain very few nutrients.

7.3 Formation of Soil **171**

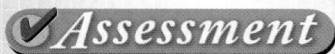
Students will use a soil-textural triangle to determine the relative percentages of sand, silt, and clay in soil samples.

Process Skills

use numbers, observe and infer, think critically, make and use tables, interpret scientific illustrations, recognize cause and effect

Materials

soil-textural triangle, paper, pencil

Teaching Strategies

Go through examples with the class as a whole and in small groups to be sure that students can use the soil-textural triangle.

Analysis

1. sample 2 has 50% sand—sandy clay-loam texture; sample 3 has 70% silt—silt-loam texture; sample 4 has 60% clay—clay texture
2. Sample 4 consists mostly of clay.
3. Sample 2 has a sandy clay-loam texture.

Thinking Critically

4. All the percentages for a given sample add up to 100. This is because each is a percentage of the whole sample, and together they make up the whole sample.
5. ability to compact

✔Assessment

Knowledge Ask students what particle sizes fertile soil contains and why. Fertile soil has a combination of all particle sizes to provide good water retention and drainage.

NY Core Curriculum Standards

Page 172: St 1 Math KI 1, 2, & 3, St 6 KI 1, 2, 4, & 5
Page 173: St 4 KI 2.1r & 2.1s, St 6 KI 1, 4, & 5

Table 7-2 Soil Textures	
Soil Particles	**Size**
Very coarse sand	2–1 mm
Coarse sand	1–0.5 mm
Medium sand	0.5–0.25 mm
Fine sand	0.25–0.10 mm
Very fine sand	0.10–0.05 mm
Silt	0.05–0.002 mm
Clay	< 0.002 mm

SOIL TEXTURES

Particles of soil are classified according to size as being clay, silt, or sand, with clay being the smallest and sand being the largest, as shown in *Table 7-2*. The relative proportions of these particle sizes determine a soil's texture, as you will discover in the *Problem-Solving Lab* on this page. The proportions of different-sized particles present in a soil sample can be determined by first placing the sample along with water in a clear jar, shaking the jar, and allowing the particles to settle. With ample water, sediments will sort as they settle, and the percentage of settled clay, silt, and sand can then be estimated. This information, along with a soil textural triangle, shown in *Figure 7-24,* is used to determine a soil's texture. The texture of a soil affects its capacity to retain moisture and therefore its ability to support plant growth.

SOIL FERTILITY

Soil fertility is the measure of how well a soil can support the growth of plants. Factors that affect soil fertility include the availability of minerals and nutrients, the number of microorganisms present, the amount of precipitation available, topography, and the level of acidity. Conditions necessary for growth vary with plant species. Farmers use

Problem-Solving Lab

Interpreting Data in a Table

Classify soils by texture Soils can be classified with the use of a soil textural triangle. Soil texture is determined by the relative proportions of particle sizes that make up the soil. The smallest particles are clay, and the largest are sand.

Analysis

1. Use the soil textural triangle shown in *Figure 7-24* to complete the data table. Record the percentages of particle sizes in the soil samples and the names of their textures.
2. Infer from the data table which soil sample has the greatest percentage of the smallest-sized particles.
3. Which soil sample has a sandy clay loam texture?

Soil Classification				
Soil Sample	**Percent Sand**	**Percent Silt**	**Percent Clay**	**Texture**
1	50	40	10	Loam
2	50	20	30	sandy clay loam
3	20	70	10	silt loam
4	20	20	60	clay

Thinking Critically

4. What can you conclude about the total of the percentages of sand, silt, and clay for each sample? Explain.
5. Name one characteristic of soil other than water-holding capacity that is determined by the soil's particle sizes.

Across the Curriculum

Math Millimeters can be converted to centimeters by moving the decimal point one place to the left. Meters can be converted to millimeters by moving the decimal point three places to the right. Meters can be converted to kilometers by moving the decimal point three places to the left. When a number is being converted from small units to larger units, the decimal moves to the left. When a number is being converted from larger units to smaller units, the decimal moves to the right. Have students convert the following numbers to units of meters, centimeters, and millimeters: 1 m, 2 cm, and 3 mm.

= 1 m, 0.02 m, and 0.003 m
= 100 cm, 2 cm, and 0.3 cm
= 1000 mm, 20 mm, and 3 mm

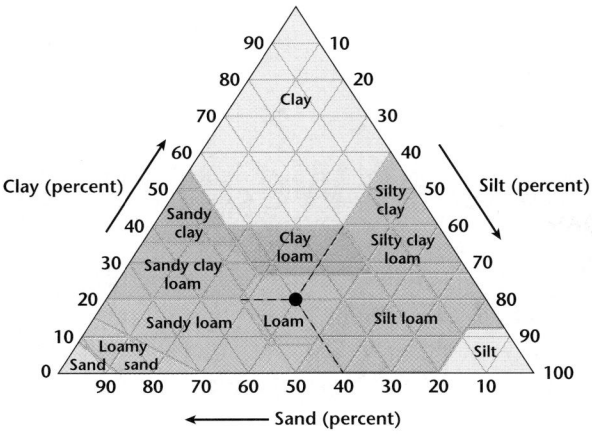

Figure 7-24 A soil textural triangle is used to determine a soil's texture. *To determine the texture of a soil sample, find its percent for sand, silt and clay. Follow the percent lines for all three soils. The texture for the sample, will be where all three lines intersect. As an example, a soil sample of 40 percent silt, 40 percent sand, and 20 percent clay is the texture of loam.*

natural and commercially produced fertilizers to replace minerals and maintain soil fertility. Commercial fertilizers add nitrate, potassium, and phosphorus to soil. The planting of legumes, such as peas, beans, and clover, allows bacteria to grow on plant roots and replace nitrates in the soil. Pulverized limestone is often added to soil to reduce acidity and enhance crop growth. The addition of compost, organic mulch, and peat moss to soil also helps to maintain its fertility.

Soil Color A soil's composition and the climate in which it develops are the main factors that determine a soil's color. Topsoil is usually dark-colored because it is rich in humus. However, color alone is unreliable as an indicator of soil fertility. Red and yellow soils may be the result of oxidation of iron minerals. However, yellow soils are usually poorly drained and are often associated with environmental problems. Grayish or bluish soils are common in poorly drained regions where soils are constantly wet and lack oxygen.

SECTION ASSESSMENT

1. Explain the stages involved in the formation of soil.

2. Describe three characteristics of soil.

3. Explain the difference between temperate soils and tropical soils.

4. **Thinking Critically** How do the horizons in a typical soil profile differ from one another?

SKILL REVIEW

5. **Inferring** Infer what type of soil exists in your area and describe how you would determine whether your inference is correct. For more help, refer to the *Skill Handbook*.

earthgeu.com/self_check_quiz

7.3 *Formation of Soil* **173**

SECTION ASSESSMENT

1. Stages involved in soil formation: 1. Bedrock begins to break into large pieces. 2. Rock pieces get smaller as a result of weathering. 3. Organisms begin to live in the weathered rock. 4. When organisms die, organic material and minerals are added. 5. Rainwater moves minerals from the upper levels to the lower levels of soil. 6. The process continues for many years.

2. rock and mineral composition—what the soil is made up of; texture—the relative amounts of sand, silt, and clay that give soil its "feel"; fertility—the ability of soil to grow plants; color—from composition and interaction with environment

3. Temperate soils are fertile, vary greatly, contain much humus; tropical soils are intensely weathered, often infertile, contain little humus.

4. The soil horizons increase in moisture and humus as you move upward from C to A. They increase in parent material as you move downward from A to C.

5. Types of soil classified according to climate include polar, temperate, and desert soils. Types according to topography include soils found on slopes or flat areas. Answers may suggest digging out an area to draw the soil profile with its horizons, close examination of the type of material, measurement of depth, and procedures to determine soil texture.

173

GeoLab

GeoLab

Effects of Weathering

Time Allotment

45 minutes

Process Skills

acquire and analyze information, make and use graphs, make and use tables, measure and use numbers, observe and infer, predict, recognize cause and effect, think critically

Safety Precautions

Remind students to always wear safety goggles when conducting laboratory investigations.

Disposal

Remaining soaked chips can be dried and reused in the future. The water used can be drained into a sink after the rock pieces have been separated.

Preparation

Soak the rock chips before using them to reduce water absorption during the activity.

Alternative Materials

Different rock chips may be used if their dissolving rate can be accomplished within the time frame of a class period.

Procedure

Many factors affect the rate of weathering of Earth materials. Two major factors that affect the rate at which a rock weathers include the length of time it is exposed to a weathering agent and the composition of the rock.

Preparation

Problem

Investigate the relationship between time and the rate of weathering of halite chips.

Materials

plastic jar with lid   balance
water (300 mL)   timer
halite chips (100 g)   paper towels

Objectives

In this Geolab, you will:

• **Determine** the relationship between the length of time that rocks are exposed to running water and the degree of weathering of the rocks.
• **Describe** the appearance of weathered rocks.
• **Infer** what other factors may influence the rate of weathering.
• **Apply** your results to a real-world situation.

Safety Precautions

Wear splash-resistant safety goggles and an apron while you do this activity. Do not ingest the halite chips.

174 CHAPTER 7 *Weathering, Erosion, and Soil*

Teaching Strategies

• Having students work in small groups will allow them to develop an appreciation of the importance of teamwork in scientific investigations.
• Remind students to make sure the lid is tightly sealed before shaking.

• Drying rocks thoroughly before weighing them is important to avoid sources of error.
• Shaking in a uniform manner helps to provide some level of control for the investigation.
• Use halite chips made for water softeners so that the chips do not dissolve completely.

Data and Observations

Data should reflect decreases in weight with increases in shaking time.

1. Soaking in water is important so that the chips have already absorbed all the water they can. Absorption of water during the lab would lead to inconsistencies in data.
2. Overall weight decreased with an increase in shaking time.
3. The rock chips became more rounded and smooth.
4. degree of accuracy, care in not losing pieces of rock chips, not shaking in a similar manner in each lab group

Conclude & Apply

1. rocks moving in a stream
2. Acid precipitation would speed up the rate of weathering by making the water more acidic.
3. The pieces of quartz would not wear away in the time allotted for this investigation.

✔ Assessment

Knowledge Have students each write a conclusion for this investigation. A possible conclusion might be: More pieces of the rocks wear away the longer they are carried in water. The rocks become smoother and rounder the longer they are carried by water.

WEATHERING DATA	
Average Shaking Time in Minutes	**Weight of Chips (g)**
3	_____
6	_____
9	Answers will vary.
12	_____

Procedure

1. Soak 100 g of halite chips in water overnight.
2. As a class, decide on a uniform method of shaking the jars.
3. Pour off the water and place the halite chips in the plastic jar.
4. Add 300 mL of water to the jar.
5. Secure the lid on the jar.
6. Shake the jar for the assigned period of time.
7. Remove the water from the jar.
8. Use paper towels to dry the halite chips.
9. Use a balance to weigh the chips. Record your measurement in a data table similar to the one provided.

Analyze

1. Why did you need to soak the chips before conducting the investigation?
2. How did the mass of the rocks change with the length of time they were shaken?
3. How did the shape of the rocks change as a result of being shaken in a jar with water?
4. What factors could have affected a team's results?

Conclude & Apply

1. What real-world process did you model in this investigation?
2. How would acid precipitation affect this process in the real world?
3. How would the results of your investigation be affected if you used pieces of quartz instead of halite?

GeoLab **175**

Troubleshooting

Presoaking the rock chips and thoroughly drying the chips before weighing them is necessary to ensure the accuracy of results. Make sure the balances are zero-balanced before using them.

Resource Manager

GeoLab and MiniLab Worksheets, pp. 28–30 L2

NY Core Curriculum Standards

Page 174: St 1 Science KI 1, 2, & 3, St 4 KI 2.1s & 3.1a, St 6 KI 1, 3, 4, & 5

Page 175: St 1 Science KI 1, 2, & 3, St 4 KI 2.1s & 3.1a, St 6 KI 1, 3, 4, & 5

Science & the Environment

Purpose

This feature discusses the rescue of Cape Hatteras lighthouse and examines the causes of barrier island migration, as well as some methods and the associated costs of protecting coastal structures.

Content Background

Barrier islands are coastal features which migrate continuously as they are battered by wind, waves, and storms. Erosion moves the sand on which these islands are built, sometimes resulting in damage to structures built along the shoreline.

Teaching Strategies

Have students focus on the following as they read the feature:

- Why was moving the Cape Hatteras lighthouse an enormous engineering feat?
- Why are lighthouses often found on barrier islands?
- What is a barrier island? How were barrier islands formed?
- What role do barrier islands play in coastal ecology?
- Why are Atlantic barrier islands migrating to the southwest?
- Encourage students to express their opinions in verbal and/or written form. Prior to the debate, have students view a detailed animation of the process used to relocate the lighthouse at the Earth Science Web Site at earthgeu.com.

Shifting Sands

On June 17, 1999, thousands of people gathered on an island off North Carolina to witness an historic event. As the 4800 ton, 65-m tall Cape Hatteras lighthouse began its half-mile journey away from the sea to safety, people cheered. Engineers had scored a victory, however temporary, against the battering of the Atlantic Ocean on a beloved piece of American history.

Cape Hatteras lighthouse is the tallest brick lighthouse in the world. When the lighthouse was built in 1870, it was 500 m from the ocean. The strong beacon helped sailors navigate a coastline so dangerous that it was known as "The Graveyard of the Atlantic." By 1987, this famous light was only 50 m from the sea, and in danger of destruction.

Barrier Islands

The lighthouse is one of several found on barrier islands off the coast of North Carolina. These long, narrow islands of sand running parallel to the coast are relatively young, formed as rising global temperatures caused glaciers to begin melting 15 000 years ago. Sea level rise caused massive coastal flooding, separating dunes and beaches from the mainland and forming the barrier islands. These islands move constantly as wind, waves, and storms shift the unstable sand on which they are built.

Barrier islands are important. The islands absorb the first onslaught of waves and wind coming ashore from the Atlantic, sheltering the mainland from hurricanes and other storms.

Sea Level On the Rise

Earth has continued to warm and glaciers to melt since the last ice age ended, making sea level 100 m higher today than it was 15 000

years ago. The impact on barrier islands is enormous. Erosion on east-facing shorelines and sand accumulation on southwest-facing shorelines has resulted in southwest migration of North Carolina's barrier islands. Hatteras Island is moving, but it is not taking Cape Hatteras lighthouse with it.

Protecting structures built in coastal areas comes at great financial cost. The projected cost in the United States alone is at least $270 billion per 1 m rise in sea level. Various methods are used to protect property, including constructing bulkheads and levees, and pumping sand onto beaches to replace that lost to erosion. Moving Cape Hatteras lighthouse was a controversial method of saving the structure. The expenditure of nearly 12 million dollars on this project was questioned by many as a temporary fix for the permanent problem of barrier island erosion and migration.

Activity

A recent study projects a cost to U.S. taxpayers of between 270 and 450 billion dollars to protect coastal structures from destruction by a 1 meter sea level rise. Is this a wise expenditure of money? Debate this issue with other students in your class.

Activity

Comments made during the debate will vary. It is expensive to protect coastal structures, but it is also expensive to replace these structures further inland if they are claimed by the ocean. The loss of homes and other property is not a pleasant situation to envision. Conversely, some students will feel that money of this magnitude could be better spent in other ways.

Summary

SECTION 7.1

Weathering

Main Ideas
- The process of weathering breaks down Earth materials. Chemical weathering results in a change in the composition of a rock, whereas mechanical weathering results only in a change in a rock's size and shape.
- Temperature and pressure are major factors in the process of mechanical weathering. Changes in temperature can cause rocks to split.
- In chemical weathering, chemical reactions between rocks and water result in the formation of new minerals and the release of dissolved substances. The new minerals have different properties from those of the original rocks.

Vocabulary
chemical weathering (p. 155)
erosion (p. 153)
exfoliation (p. 155)
frost wedging (p. 154)
hydrolysis (p. 156)
mechanical weathering (p. 154)
oxidation (p. 156)
weathering (p. 153)

SECTION 7.2

Erosion and Deposition

Main Ideas
- Erosion is the process that moves weathered pieces of rock to new locations.
- Agents of erosion include moving water in streams and oceans, glaciers, wind, and gravity. Gravity is the driving force behind most agents of erosion.

Vocabulary
deposition (p. 162)
gully erosion (p. 163)
rill erosion (p. 163)

SECTION 7.3

Formation of Soil

Main Ideas
- Soil consists of weathered rock and humus, which is decayed organic matter in soil.
- Soil is residual or transported. Residual soil remains on top of its parent bedrock. Transported soil is moved to a location away from its parent bedrock by water, wind, or a glacier.
- A soil profile has horizons A, B, and C. Topsoil is located in horizon A, subsoil is in horizon B, and horizon C contains weathered rock from the bedrock.
- Characteristics of soil include texture, fertility, and color. Parent rock and environmental conditions determine a soil's composition.

Vocabulary
residual soil (p. 168)
soil (p .167)
soil horizon (p. 169)
soil profile (p. 168)
transported soil (p. 168)

earthgeu.com/vocabulary_puzzlemaker

Main Ideas

Summary statements can be used by students to review the major concepts of the chapter.

VOCABULARY PuzzleMaker

For additional help with vocabulary, have students access the Vocabulary Puzzlemaker online.

earthgeu.com/ vocabulary puzzlemaker

0:00 Out of Time?

If time does not permit teaching the entire chapter, use the GeoDigest at the end of the unit as an overview.

Earth Science Online

Be sure to check the Earth Science Web Site for links to chapter material:
earthgeu.com

GLENCOE
Technology

Videotape/DVD
MindJogger Videoquizzes
Chapter 7: *Weathering, Erosion, and Soil*
Have students work in groups as they play the videoquiz game to review key chapter concepts.

Resource Manager

Chapter Assessment, pp. 37–42
MindJogger Videoquizzes DVD/VHS
ExamView® Pro CD-ROM
Performance Assessment in Earth Science

NY Core Curriculum Standards

Page 176: St 4 KI 2.1t & 2.1u, St 6 KI 5 & 6, St 7 KI 1
Page 177: St 4 KI 2.1s, 2.1t, 2.1u, & 3.1a, St 6 KI 1, 4, & 5

177

Understanding Main Ideas

1. a
2. b
3. d
4. a
5. c
6. b
7. b
8. a
9. a
10. a

Applying Main Ideas

11. The smaller the pieces of rock, the greater the surface area of the total volume of the rock. The greater the surface area, the faster the rate of weathering.

12. Human activities can increase the rate of weathering by breaking down the rocks at the surface as land is moved to allow for construction of buildings, highways, bridges, and so on.

13. The beaches wear away an average of 2–7 m per year, and a vacation home may be in the water within a given number of years depending on how far it is from the shoreline.

14. Both are forms of chemical weathering and result in a change in the composition of the rock material undergoing weathering.

15. Acid precipitation increases the pH level of precipitation and consequently increases the pH of water on Earth's surface and in the ground. Water with higher pH levels can more effectively wear away Earth materials.

Understanding Main Ideas

1. What erosional agent accounts for most of the erosion on Earth's surface?
   a. water   c. glaciers
   b. wind   d. living things

2. What is the underlying force of all agents of erosion?
   a. magnetism   c. friction
   b. gravity   d. light

3. The variables that most affect the weathering process are rock composition and what?
   a. topography   c. living things
   b. surface area   d. climate

4. Humus is found in which horizon?
   a. A   c. C
   b. B   d. D

5. What is the chemical reaction of oxygen with other substances called?
   a. precipitation c. oxidation
   b. hydrolysis   d. humidity

6. What type of soil has the most humus?
   a. polar   c. tropical
   b. temperate   d. desert

7. On which side of a mountain slope is the greatest amount of vegetation likely to grow?
   a. north   c. east
   b. south   d. west

8. In which area is the topsoil most likely to be thickest?
   a. on level land c. on a mountain slope
   b. on a hillside d. in a river bed

9. Deep, rich soils are found in which regions?
   a. temperate   c. polar
   b. desert   d. tropical

10. What is the name of the soil type that is from a location that experiences high temperatures and high precipitation?
    a. tropical   c. desert
    b. polar   d. temperate

Applying Main Ideas

11. How does the size of an exposed rock affect its rate of weathering?

12. Describe how human activities can affect the rate of weathering.

13. What erosional process might convince a person not to purchase a home built on an ocean shore?

14. What do oxidation and hydrolysis have in common in relation to the weathering process?

15. What role does acid precipitation play in the weathering process?

16. How does the use of a wind barrier reduce erosion on a farm?

17. How do glaciers both remove and build up Earth's surface?

18. What unique feature does water exhibit in response to temperature changes?

earthgeu.com/chapter_test

16. The wind barrier is placed on a field perpendicular to the direction of the wind. The barrier reduces the wind's force over the land surface and decreases wind erosion.

17. Glaciers gouge out pieces of Earth's crust from one location and drop off the material at another location. Thus, glaciers lower the landscape in one area and build up the landscape in another.

18. Water expands when it changes to ice and contracts when it melts. Usually, materials expand when they are heated and contract when they are cooled.

Thinking Critically

19. Name one reason why precipitation today is more acidic than precipitation in the 1800s.

20. If no water existed on Earth, how would erosional processes be affected?

21. Compare the rate of soil formation to the average human lifespan.

22. Describe how carbonic acid is formed.

23. In the blank circle below, divide and label the areas for each of the following components of a soil sample.
- 60% mineral matter
- 2% organic matter
- 30% air
- 8% water

24. Make a bar graph of the data in question 23.

25. Use the following terms to construct a concept map to organize the major ideas in Section 7.2, Erosion and Deposition. For more help, refer to the *Skill Handbook*.

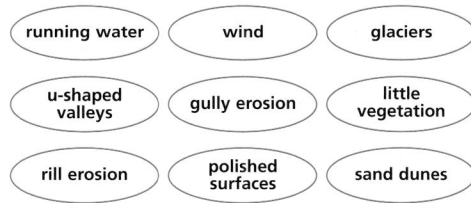

running water | wind | glaciers
u-shaped valleys | gully erosion | little vegetation
rill erosion | polished surfaces | sand dunes

Standardized Test Practice

1. Which is NOT an agent of chemical weathering?
- **a.** water
- **b.** oxygen
- **c.** carbon dioxide
- **d.** wind

INTERPRETING DATA Use the diagrams below to answer questions 2–4.

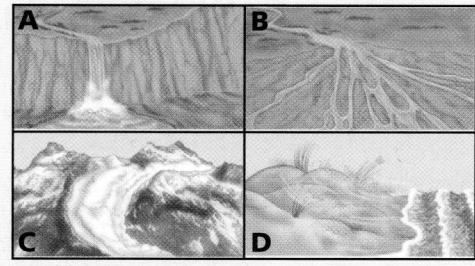

A B C D

2. Which picture shows the erosional agent that was responsible for leaving behind U-shaped valleys, hanging valleys, lakes, and deposits of sediment in New England and New York State?
- **a.** A
- **b.** B
- **c.** C
- **d.** D

3. Which picture shows the erosional agent responsible for dunes formed along the Gulf and Atlantic coasts of the U.S.?
- **a.** A
- **b.** B
- **c.** C
- **d.** D

4. What common factor is responsible for three of the four erosional processes pictured?
- **a.** wind
- **b.** heat
- **c.** human intervention
- **d.** gravity

5. Which farming method is used to reduce wind erosion?
- **a.** planting different crops
- **b.** planting wind barriers
- **c.** building earth mounds
- **d.** building stone walls

Thinking Critically

19. Precipitation today is more acidic than precipitation in the 1800s because there are more acid-producing materials being added to the atmosphere from the industrial burning of fossil fuels and from automobile exhausts.

20. There would be no erosion by glaciers or running water.

21. The average life span is less than 100 years, and the time for one centimeter of soil to form may be hundreds of years. Soil lost by erosion therefore cannot be replaced in a human lifetime.

22. Carbonic acid can be formed when carbon dioxide combines with water in the atmosphere and falls to the ground with precipitation.

23. Answers should have correct percentages indicated and labels provided on circle.

24. Answers should have bar lines corresponding to percentages given in question 23. One axis should be labeled with names and the other axis should be labeled 0-100%. The graph should be titled.

25. running water, rill erosion, gully erosion; glaciers, polished surfaces, U-shaped valleys; little vegetation, wind, sand dunes

EXAM*VIEW*® PRO

Use Exam*View*® Pro Testmaker CD-ROM to:
- Create **multiple versions** of tests.
- Create **modified** tests with one mouse click for struggling students.
- **Edit** existing questions and add your own questions.
- **Build** tests based on national curriculum standards.

Standardized Test Practice

1. d
2. c
3. d
4. d
5. b

NY Core Curriculum Standards

Page 178: St 4 KI 2.1r, 2.1s, 2.1t, & 2.1u, St 6 KI 1, 5, & 6, St 7 KI 1

Page 179: St 4 KI 2.1r, 2.1s, 2.1t, & 2.1u, St 6 KI 1, 2, 5, & 6, St 7 KI 1

Chapter 8

Mass Movements, Wind, and Glaciers

Refer to pages 8T–9T of the Teacher Guide for an explanation of the National Science Content Standards correlations.

Section	Objectives	National Science Content Standards	State/Local Standards
SECTION 8.1 **Mass Movements At Earth's Surface** 🕐 2 sessions 📦 1 block	1. **Identify** factors that affect mass movements. 2. **Relate** how mass movements affect people. 3. **Analyze** the relationship between gravity and mass movements.	UCP.1, UCP.2, UCP.3, UCP.4; A.1, A.2; B.4; D.1, D.3; F.5, F.6	St 1 Science KI 1, 2, & 3, St 4 KI 2.1t & 2.1u, St 6 KI 1, 2, 4, & 5, St 7 KI 1
SECTION 8.2 **Wind** 🕐 1 session 📦 ½ block	4. **Describe** conditions that contribute to the likelihood that an area will experience wind erosion. 5. **Identify** wind-formed landscape features. 6. **Describe** how dunes form and migrate. 7. **Explain** the effects of wind erosion on human activities.	UCP.1, UCP.2, UCP.3, UCP.4, UCP.5; A.1, A.2; B.4; D.1, D.3; F.5; G.3	St 4 KI 2.1r, 2.1t, & 2.1u, St 6 KI 1, 2, 4, 5, & 6
SECTION 8.3 **Glaciers** 🕐 2 sessions 📦 1 block	8. **Explain** how glaciers form. 9. **Compare** and **contrast** the conditions that produce valley glaciers and those that produce continental glaciers. 10. **Describe** how glaciers modify the landscape. 11. **Recognize** glacial landscape features.	UCP.1, UCP.2, UCP.3, UCP.4, UCP.5; A.1, A.2; B.4; D.1, D.3; E.1, E.2; F.5, F.6; G.3	St 1 Math KI 1, 2, 3, Science KI 1, 2, & 3, St 2 KI 1, 2, & 3, St 4 KI 2.1t, 2.1u, & 2.1v, St 6 KI 1, 2, 3, 4, 5, & 6, St 7 KI 1

A complete Planning Guide is provided on pages 30T–32T.

🕐   The number of recommended single-period sessions

📦   The number of recommended blocks

Activity Materials

Discovery Lab *page 181*
aluminum pie plates (3), 250-mL graduated cylinder, dry sand, cardboard, water, safety goggles

GeoLab *pages 204-205*
ruler, paper, pencil

MiniLab *page 194*
wind-erosion map (Figure 8-12), paper, pencil

Demo *page 182*
wooden board, books, cork, water

page 187
round rocks, flat rocks, rocks of various shapes

page 192
tray, soil, sod, sand, electric fan with fan guard

page 201
flour, water, board, toothpicks

page 202
plastic bag, water, soil, large tray, freezer

Key to Teaching Strategies

L1   Level 1 activities should be appropriate for students with learning difficulties.

L2   Level 2 activities should be within the ability range of all students.

L3   Level 3 activities are designed for above-average students.

ELL   ELL activities should be within the ability range of English-language learners.

COOP LEARN   Cooperative learning activities are designed for small-group work.

P   These strategies represent student products that can be placed in a best-work portfolio.

📦   These strategies are useful in a block-scheduling format.

Need materials? Contact Science Kit at 1-800-828-7777 or at 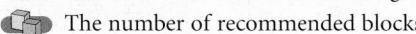www.sciencekit.com on the Internet. For alternate materials, see the activity on the listed page.

Chapter Organizer

Activities/Features	Reproducible Masters	Transparencies
Discovery Lab: Model Sand-Slope Activity, p. 181	**Study Guide for Content Mastery,** pp. 47–48 **L2**	**Section Focus Transparency 20** **L1** **ELL** **Teaching Transparency 19** **L2** **ELL**
MiniLab: Where does wind erosion occur?, p. 194	**Study Guide for Content Mastery,** pp. 49–50 **L2** **Laboratory Manual,** pp. 57–60 **L2** **GeoLab and MiniLab Worksheets,** p. 31 **L2**	**Section Focus Transparency 21** **L1** **ELL** **Teaching Transparency 20** **L2** **ELL**
Problem-Solving Lab: Using Graphs, p. 200 **GeoLab:** Mapping a Landslide, pp. 204–205 **Science & Math:** Rates of Glacial Movement, p. 206	**Study Guide for Content Mastery,** pp. 51–52 **L2** **Laboratory Manual,** pp. 61–64 **L2** **Exploring Environmental Problems,** pp. 13–16 **L3** **GeoLab and MiniLab Worksheets,** pp. 32–34 **L2**	**Section Focus Transparency 22** **L1** **ELL** **Teaching Transparency 21** **L2** **ELL**

✓ Assessment

Chapter Assessment,
pp. 43–48
Performance Assessment in the Science Classroom (PASC)
MindJogger Videoquiz DVD/VHS
Performance Assessment in Earth Science
ExamView® Pro CD-ROM
5 Days to the Regents Exam

Additional Resources

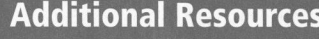

Guided Reading Audio Program **ELL**
Cooperative Learning in the Science Classroom
COOP LEARN
Lesson Plans
Block Scheduling
earthgeu.com
NY Lesson Plans
NY Block Scheduling
Review Handbook for Regents Earth Science Exam

NATIONAL GEOGRAPHIC

Teacher's Corner

Products Available from National Geographic Society
To order the following products, call the National Geographic Society at 1-800-368-2728:
CD-ROM
111 Years of National Geographic Magazine

Videos
Glaciers: Ice on the Move
Book
National Geographic Desk Reference

Content Background

Mass Movements At Earth's Surface
Section 8.1

Earth's surface continually experiences forces that are both constructive (building up) and destructive (wearing down). This is because Earth material is continuously being transported from one location to another. Movement of Earth material is influenced by environmental factors such as wind and water. The force of gravity pulls Earth material downward. The downward movement of Earth material is referred to as mass movement and can take many forms.

The slope of a surface and the amount of water present greatly affect the stability of Earth material. Steep slopes and great amounts of water allow the force of gravity to easily move material downslope. The presence of vegetation can hinder downslope movement and reduce mass movements.

Most mass movements are natural, spontaneous occurrences. However, human activities can instigate and accelerate mass movements in isolated situations. Mass movements may occur on a massive or small scale. An understanding of the factors that affect mass movements can help save lives and property.

Wind
Section 8.2

The uneven heating of Earth's surface that results in the movement of air from one place to another is called wind. Winds may be local or global. Local winds are affected by terrain and vegetation, and global winds are influenced by major air masses and Earth's rotation. Large continental areas experience greater temperature variations over short time periods than do expansive oceanic areas. As a result, although winds may be more sustained over the ocean, they are more changeable over continental areas.

The ability of wind to pick up and move surface material is directly related to its speed. Some geographic areas are prone to steady winds, especially along coastal areas. Expansive ocean areas provide large fetches, which sustain wind. Flat continental areas, such as plains regions, allow for greater wind speeds than do areas of uneven topography. Weather conditions may cause wind to change on a daily basis, and severe storms can produce winds capable of major destruction of both natural features and human-made structures.

Fine, loose, dry particles are most easily moved by wind. The presence of water and vegetation can dramatically reduce the ability of wind to move Earth particles. Particles moved by wind can form distinctive shapes that indicate the direction and speed of the wind.

Multiple Learning Styles

Kinesthetic Modeling, pp. 183, 202, Project, p. 199, Modeling, p. 202

Visual-Spatial Demo, p. 187, Project, p. 189, Reteach, p. 203

Interpersonal Collaborative Learning, pp. 184, 188, 193 Discussion, p. 185, Reteach, p. 197

Intrapersonal Applying Earth Science, p. 186

Linguistic Earth Science Journal, p. 186

Naturalist Environmental Connection, p. 189

GLENCOE Technology

The following multimedia resources are available from Glencoe.

Dynamic Earth PictureShow
Forces of Change

Vocabulary Puzzlemaker

TeacherWorks™ CD-ROM

MindJogger Videoquizzes DVD/VHS

ExamView® Pro CD-ROM

Interactive Chalkboard CD-ROM

Chapter Organizer

Glaciers
Section 8.3

Most of Earth's freshwater supply is locked up in the form of glaciers. Glaciers are found in areas where climatic conditions can sustain their formation and preservation year-round. Today, most of the glaciers on Earth exist in Greenland and Antarctica, but they also can be found at high elevations on most continents.

Earth has experienced ice ages for approximately 20–30 percent of its history. The most recent ice age occurred during the Pleistocene Epoch and ended approximately 10 000 years ago. Since then, Earth has been experiencing an interglacial period with temperatures approximately 15°C warmer, resulting in the melting of most of the glaciers formed during that time. Glacial melting has raised sea level. There currently is concern that global warming may affect climatic conditions and speed up the melting of glaciers and the rising of sea level.

Glaciers can shape Earth's surface through the processes of erosion and deposition. Of all agents of erosion, glaciers are the most powerful because of their ability to carve large areas from the landscape. Many of Earth's current surface features were formed by ancient glaciers.

Identifying Misconceptions

Students may think that Earth's surface generally stays the same in most places. Show the class some evidence of change in examples such as the following: an old photograph of a familiar place where change is evident, a rock with striations on it, and samples of soil and rocks. Explain that all these examples provide evidence that change is a constant occurrence on Earth's crust.

✓Assessment

Portfolio Assessment
Assessment, TWE, p. 184
Problem-Solving Lab, TWE, p. 200

Performance Assessment
Discovery Lab, SE, p. 181
Discovery Lab, TWE, p. 181
Assessment, TWE, pp. 190, 197
MiniLab, SE, p. 194
GeoLab, SE, pp. 204–205

Knowledge Assessment
Assessment, TWE, pp. 185, 189, 194, 199, 201
Section Assessment, SE, pp. 190, 197, 203

MiniLab, TWE p. 194
GeoLab, TWE, pp. 204–205
Chapter Assessment, SE, pp. 208–209

Skill Assessment
Assessment, TWE, p. 183, 195, 203

Be sure to check the Earth Science Web Site for links to chapter material: earthgeu.com

Mass Movements, Wind, and Glaciers

Introducing the Chapter

Divide the class into groups of four. Ask each group to bring in both old and recent photographs of the same area of the local landscape. Give students at least a week before beginning the chapter to allow time for them to search through family photographs and public records. Check students' progress daily to help them find appropriate photographs. Have each group share its photographs with the class, then display the photographs on a bulletin board.

Interpreting the Photo

A young man is digging out of a devastating mudflow in northern Venezuela. It occurred in December, 1999.

INTERACTIVE CHALKBOARD
with Image Bank

PowerPoint® Presentations

This CD is an editable Microsoft® PowerPoint® presentation that includes:
- Section presentations
- Section checks
- Image bank
- Links to Earth Science Online
- All transparencies
- Animations
- Audio

What You'll Learn
- How the processes of mass movements, wind, and glaciation change landscape features.
- What external features on Earth's surface are caused by mass movements, wind, and glaciers.

Why It's Important
Earth's external processes shape its surface. Some of the processes, such as landslides and avalanches, represent hazards. Mass movements, wind, and glaciers change the landscape and have an impact on human populations in many regions.

Earth Science Online

To find out more about mass movements, wind, and glaciers, visit the Earth Science Web Site at earthgeu.com

180

Mass Movements, Wind, and Glaciers

Discovery Lab

Process Skills

measure, observe and infer, recognize cause and effect, communicate, model, predict **L1** **ELL**

Procedure
Troubleshooting
- Be sure to use clean sand to avoid unpleasant odors from the sand-water mixture. Make sure safety goggles are worn.
- Very fine or very coarse sand may require a modi-

fication of the amount of water added. To ensure student success, do the lab first yourself with the sand that will be used.

- Some students may try to make shapes that are too complex. It is best for them to stick with simple models such as pyramid or mountain shapes.

Observe
Some water is necessary to help the sand hold its molded shape. However, if too much water is added, the sand will not retain its molded shape. When there is a large amount of water between the sand particles, the force of gravity causes the particles to slide downslope over one another.

Discovery Lab

Model Sand-Slope Activity

Water affects sediment grains on slopes. If there is too little water, the sediments may not hold together, and as a result, they may move downslope. In this activity, you will demonstrate how the addition of water affects how sediments are held together.

1. Place 225 mL of sand in each of three separate containers, such as aluminum pie plates.

2. To the first container of sand, add 20 mL of water and mix well. To the second container of sand, add 100 mL of water and mix well. To the third container of sand, add 200 mL of water and mix well.

3. Empty the three mixtures of sand and water onto a tray or piece of cardboard. Keep each mixture separate.

4. Test each mixture for its ability to be molded and retain its shape. Compare your results for the three samples.

CAUTION: Always wear safety goggles and an apron in the lab.

Observe In your science journal, describe how the addition of water affected the sand's ability to be molded in the three samples.

Section Focus

Before presenting the lesson, display **Section Focus Transparency 20** on the overhead projector.
L1 ELL

Chapter Themes

The following themes from the National Science Content Standards are covered in this chapter. Refer to page 8T of the Teacher Guide for an explanation of the correlations.
Systems, order, and organization (UCP.1); Evidence, models, and explanation (UCP.2); Change, constancy, and measurement (UCP.3); Evolution and equilibrium (UCP. 4); Form and function (UCP.5)

0:00 *Out of Time?*

If time does not permit teaching the entire chapter, use the Chapter Summary on page 207 and the GeoDigest found at the end of the unit as an overview.

SECTION 8.1

Mass Movements at Earth's Surface

OBJECTIVES

• **Identify** *factors that affect mass movements.*

• **Relate** *how mass movements affect people.*

• **Analyze** *the relationship between gravity and mass movements.*

VOCABULARY

mass movement
creep
mudflow
landslide
slump
avalanche

Every day, the landscape around us undergoes changes. If you compared old and new photographs of the landscape around your home, you might have to look very closely to notice some of the subtle differences. Other changes, such as landslides, occur quickly and have very noticeable, immediate effects.

MASS MOVEMENTS

How do landforms such as mountains, hills, and plateaus wear down and change? Landforms can change through processes involving wind, ice, and water, and sometimes through the force of gravity alone. The downslope movement of loose sediments and weathered rock resulting from the force of gravity is called **mass movement.** In the development of most of Earth's landforms, erosion is the step that follows weathering. After weathering processes weaken and break rock into smaller and smaller pieces, mass movements may

8.1 Mass Movements at Earth's Surface **181**

✔Assessment

Performance Ask students which of the sand and water mixtures held its molded shape best. Ask them to explain the results that they obtained. Use the Performance Task Assessment List for Making Observations and Inferences in **PASC,** p. 17.

Resource Manager

Study Guide for Content Mastery, pp. 47–48 L2

Section Focus Transparency 20 L1 ELL

NY Core Curriculum Standards

Page 180: St 4 KI 2.1u, St 6 KI 4 & 5

Page 181: St 1 Science KI 1, 2, & 3, St 4 KI 2.1t & 2.1u, St 6 KI 4 & 5

Tying to Previous Knowledge

Students learned in Chapter 2 that maps are models of Earth's surface. Maps can be used to highlight areas of high risk. For example, the USGS and the Colorado Geological Survey have recently worked together to make detailed digital maps of 36 areas in western Colorado. These maps are important because of the number of active landslides in this rapidly developing area.

2 Teach

Content Background

The internal strength of Earth materials is usually able to maintain the materials in their relative positions on Earth's surface even though the materials are always experiencing the downward pull of the force of gravity. Particles of Earth material move downslope, even along imperceptible slopes, when the force of gravity exceeds the opposing forces of cohesion and friction between the surfaces of the particles. The presence of water in and around the particles reduces the contact between them and therefore reduces the amount of friction that must be overcome for movement to occur.

Figure Caption Question

Figure 8-1 How are they alike? How are they different? All are downslope movements affected by gravity and water. They differ in whether the mass moves as a whole (slide); moves as a mass of mixed particles (flow); or is a free fall of material.

---

occur and carry the debris downslope. Because climate has a major effect on the vegetation and the weathering activities that occur in a particular area, climatic conditions determine which materials and how much of each will be made available for mass movement.

All mass movements occur on slopes. Because very few places on Earth are completely flat, almost all of Earth's surface undergoes mass movement. Mass movements range from extremely slow motions to sudden slides, falls, and flows. The Earth materials that are moved range from fine mud to large boulders.

VARIABLES THAT INFLUENCE MASS MOVEMENTS

Several variables influence the mass movements of Earth's material. One variable is the material's weight resulting from gravity, which works to pull the material down a slope. A second variable is the material's resistance to sliding or flowing. A third variable can be a trigger, such as an earthquake, that works to shake material loose from a slope, as shown in *Figure 8-1A.* Mass movement occurs when the forces working to pull material down a slope are stronger than the material's resistance to sliding, flowing, or falling. Some common types of mass movement are illustrated in *Figure 8-1B.*

A

Figure 8-1 Sudden mass movements can be started by a trigger, such as an earth-quake, which caused this landslide in Gallatin National Forest, Montana **(A)**. There are three common types of mass movement. *How are they alike? How are they different?* **(B)**

B

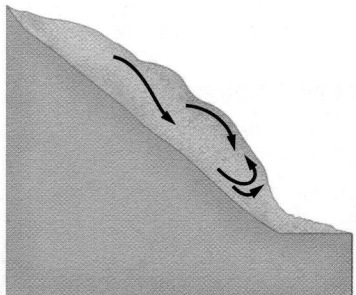

Slide
Moves as block of Earth material

Flow
Movement involves mixing of particles within moving mass

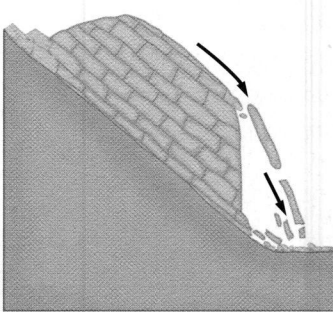

Fall
Free fall of Earth material

Differentiated Instruction

Learning Disabled Have students make ice cream sundaes to demonstrate the variables that influence mass movement. Have them cover ice cream with sprinkles and crushed peanuts and note that the peanuts, which weigh more, fall first. Shake the sundae dish to observe how "tremors" affect the movement of the toppings. Conclude the activity by allowing students to consume their mass movements. NOTE: Make sure you have sugar-free ice cream or frozen yogurt available for students with diabetes.

Demo

Place a wooden board on an incline by propping up one side with a few textbooks. On the board, place a small object such as a cork. Have students note that the cork stays in its position. Then, slowly run some water down the board. The cork should move downslope. This demonstration will show students how water reduces the friction that keeps particles in one place. **L1** **ELL**

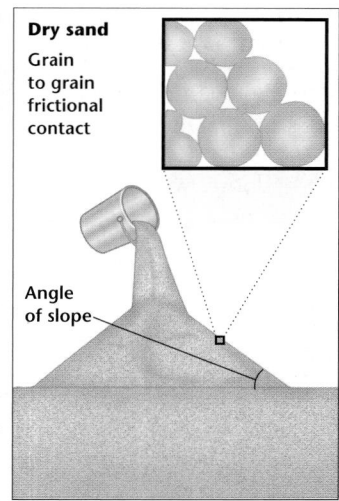

Dry sand

Grain to grain frictional contact

Angle of slope

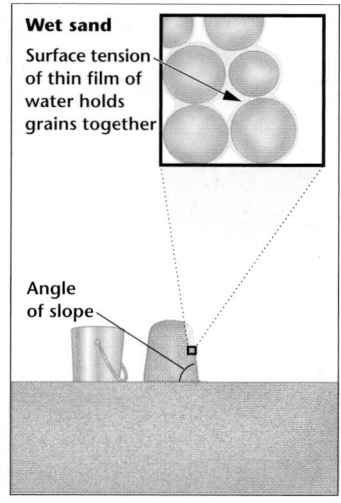

Wet sand

Surface tension of thin film of water holds grains together

Angle of slope

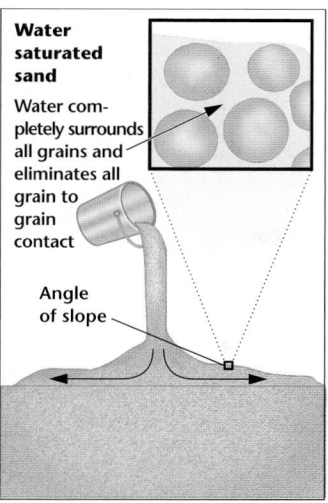

Water saturated sand

Water completely surrounds all grains and eliminates all grain to grain contact

Angle of slope

Figure 8-2 Water plays a key role in mass movements. Water acts as a lubricant between grains of sand to reduce friction between them.

Erosion and the undermining of soil at the foot of a slope increase the potential of Earth materials to move downhill, as does the increased weight from torrential rainfall. An important force that determines a material's resistance to downhill movement is friction between the material and the slope.

Water Water is a fourth variable that influences mass movements, as illustrated in *Figure 8-2.* On a slope, too little water may prevent sediment grains from holding together at all, thereby increasing the material's potential for movement. You could demonstrate this concept by trying to form dry, loose soil into a ball. It would be difficult to get the particles to hold together. However, if you added small amounts of water, the particles of soil would cling together and remain in the shape in which you formed them. Similarly, the addition of water to sediments on a slope helps to hold the grains together and makes the material more stable. On the other hand, too much water can make a slope unstable. Saturation by water greatly increases the weight of soils and sediments. In addition, as the water fills the tiny open spaces between grains, it may act as a lubricant between the grains to reduce the friction between them. Thus, the force of gravity is more likely to pull the saturated material downhill. While water is very important to the process of mass movement, it is important to note that water is not involved as a transport agent. In mass movements, water moves along with Earth materials. This is in contrast to stream transport, in which sediment moves along with the water.

Across the Curriculum

Physics To help students understand the concept of forces, provide a definition similar to one they will use when studying physics. A force is a push or a pull on an object. On Earth, the force of gravity pulls objects, Earth material, and water toward Earth's center. This means that material is pulled down to the lowest level possible on Earth's surface.

Science Field Book

Earth Science
Journal

Ask students to write in their Earth science journals about a situation in which they experienced a reduction in friction as they walked along a surface. Students might write about such situations as slipping on wet grass or on ice. Some situations may be humorous, but others might have resulted in injury or property damage. **L1**

P

Skill Ask students to identify the variables that influence mass movement of Earth material. The material's weight resulting from gravity, the material's resistance to sliding and flowing, and a trigger, such as an earthquake.

Tying to Previous Knowledge

The movement of Earth particles in wet conditions is similar to a student's ability to run and slide more easily on a wet surface than on a dry one. It also is easier to slide on ice than on a dry surface because there is less friction.

Modeling

Kinesthetic Have small groups of students each make a clay model that demonstrates a form of mass movement. Once the models have been completed, have the groups rotate to the different models and identify the form of mass movement exhibited by each model. Models can then be left on display for review and reinforcement. **L2** **ELL**

Teaching Transparency 19 **L2** **ELL**

NY Core Curriculum Standards

Page 182: St 4 KI 2.1t & 2.1u, St 6 KI 4 & 5
Page 183: St 4 KI 2.1u, St 6 KI 4 & 5

Interpersonal Have students work in groups to plan a demonstration to show how triggers suddenly start mass movements. Each group can demonstrate for the class how its trigger model works. Students may experiment with sound, tremors, or objects moving over Earth's surface. Factors that affect a material's susceptibility to triggers might also be included in more-advanced student models, as well as an acknowledgment that a trigger in one situation is not necessarily a trigger in other situations. **ELL** **COOP LEARN**

Using an Analogy

Compare the movement of creep with what would happen to a person standing on a rug if the rug were pulled out from under his or her feet. Although the rug would be pulled at a much faster rate than creep, have students imagine taking a video of the action and playing it back frame by frame. Just as a person's body would begin to fall backward as the rug was pulled, fences and gravestones tilt backward as soil at the base of the structure moves downslope.

Figure Caption Question

Figure 8-3 Is there any evidence of creep in your area? Answers will vary. Students should look for evidence such as tilting of objects on slopes.

NY Core Curriculum Standards

Page 184: St 4 KI 2.1u, St 6 KI 1, 4, & 5

Page 185: St 4 KI 2.1t & 2.1u, St 6 KI 1, 4, & 5

TYPES OF MASS MOVEMENTS

Mass movements are classified as creep, flows, slides, and falls. Mass movements can move different types of materials in various ways. Let's investigate the different types of mass movement.

Creep The slow, steady, downhill flow of loose, weathered Earth materials, especially soils, is called **creep.** Because movement may be as little as a few centimeters per year, the effects of creep usually are noticeable only over long periods of time. One way to tell whether creep has occurred is to observe the positions of structures and objects. As illustrated in *Figure 8-3,* creep can cause the tilting of once-vertical utility poles, fences, and gravestones, the bending of trees, the cracking of walls, and the breaking of underground pipelines. Loose materials on almost all slopes, even the very gentlest, undergo creep. Soil creep moves huge amounts of surface material each year.

The slow, downhill movement of loose, water-logged materials that occurs in regions of permafrost is called solifluction. The material moved in solifluction is a mudlike liquid that is produced when water is released from melting permafrost during the warm season. The water saturates the surface layer of soil and is unable to move downward through the underlying permafrost. As a result, the surface layer can slide slowly down a slope. Solifluction may also occur in humid regions where the ground remains saturated year-round.

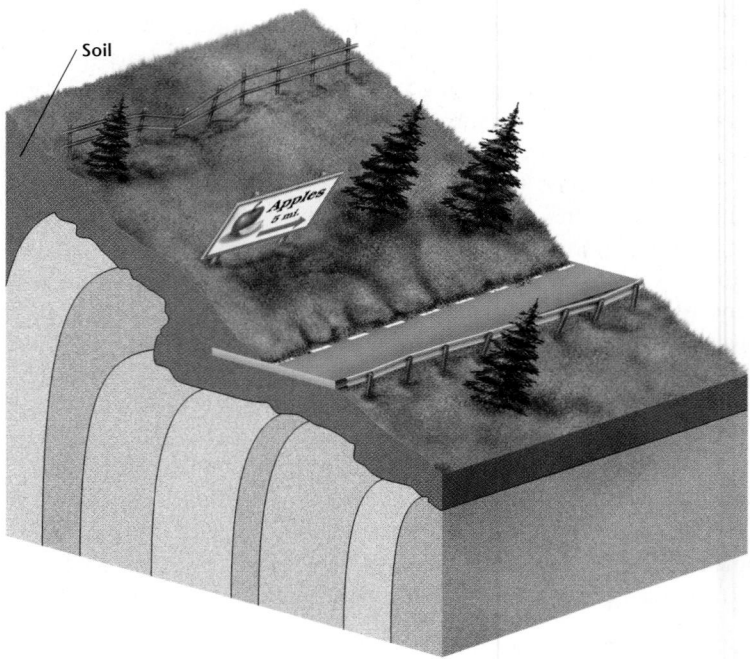

Figure 8-3 Creep can cause the slow tilting of various objects on slopes. *Is there any evidence of creep in your area?*

✓Assessment

Portfolio Have students research well-documented mass movements, such as mud-flows and avalanches, that were set off by a trigger. Information can be presented in poster format and displayed in the classroom or hall-way. **L2** **P**

Figure 8-4 Major mudflows occurred after the eruption of Mount St. Helens in 1980 **(A)**. In 1998, a mudflow in Sarno, Italy, caused the deaths of 135 people and the destruction of many buildings **(B)**.

Flows In some mass movements, Earth materials flow as if they were a thick liquid. The materials can move as slowly as a few centimeters per year or as rapidly as hundreds of kilometers per hour. Earth flows are moderately slow movements of soils, whereas **mudflows** are swiftly moving mixtures of mud and water. Mudflows can be triggered by earthquakes or similar vibrations and are common in volcanic regions where the heat from a volcano melts snow on nearby slopes that have fine sediment and little vegetation. The meltwater fills the spaces between the small particles of sediment and allows them to slide readily over one another and move down the slope. As shown in *Figure 8-4A,* when Mount St. Helens erupted in 1980, it triggered mudflows that traveled downhill at speeds of over 30 km/h. Although the area was sparsely populated, the mudflows damaged or destroyed more than 200 homes. In 1998, a mudflow in Italy caused many deaths and much destruction, as shown in *Figure 8-4B.*

Mudflows are also common in sloped, semi-arid regions that experience intense, short-lived rainstorms. The Los Angeles Basin in southern California is an example of an area where mudflows are common. In such areas, periods of drought and forest fires can leave the slopes with little protective vegetation. When heavy rains eventually fall in these areas, they can cause massive, destructive mudflows. Mudflows are destructive in areas where urban development has spread to the bases of mountainous areas.

8.1 *Mass Movements at Earth's Surface* **185**

185

Figure 8-5 A landslide occurs when a sheet of loose Earth materials separates from the bedrock and moves quickly downslope **(A)**. In March of 1998, a landslide caused about 120,000 m³ of dirt and debris to flow into the Blackfoot River in Ovando, Montana. The river became well known after its portrayal in the movie *A River Runs Through It* **(B)**.

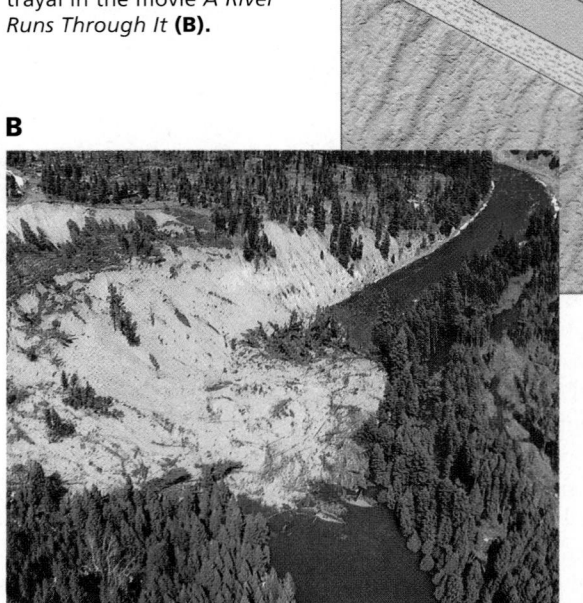

Slides A rapid, downslope movement of Earth materials that occurs when a relatively thin block of loose soil, rock, and debris separates from the underlying bedrock is called a **landslide,** illustrated in *Figure 8-5A.* The material rapidly slides downslope as one block, with little internal mixing. Some landslides may reach speeds of 200 km/h. As shown in *Figure 8-5B,* a landslide mass eventually stops and becomes a pile of debris at the bottom of a slope, sometimes damming rivers and causing flooding. Landslides are common on steep slopes, especially when soils and weathered bedrock are fully saturated by water. This destructive form of mass movement causes almost $2 billion in damage and several deaths per year in the United States alone. You will explore the movement of a landslide in the *Mapping GeoLab* at the end of this chapter.

A rock slide is a type of landslide that occurs when a sheet of rock moves downhill on a sliding surface. During a rock slide, relatively thin blocks of rock are broken into smaller blocks as they move downslope. Often triggered by earthquakes, rock slides can move large amounts of material.

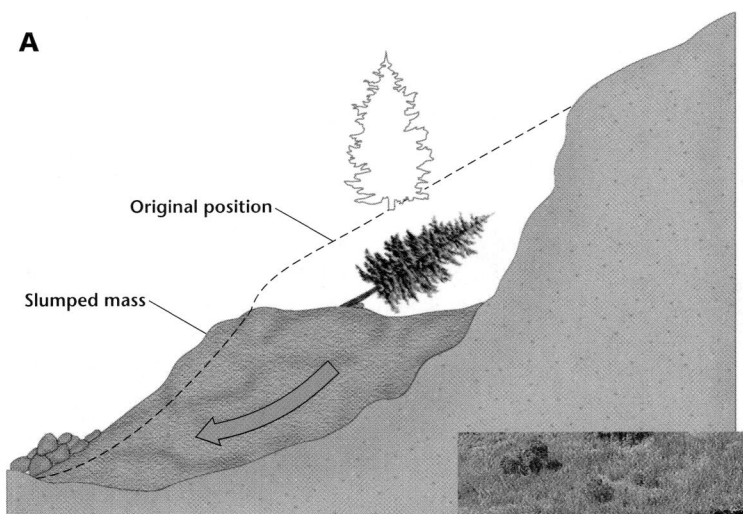

A

Original position

Slumped mass

B

Slumps As illustrated in *Figure 8-6A,* when the mass of material in a landslide rotates and slides along a curved surface, a **slump** results. Slumps, such as the one shown in *Figure 8-6B,* may occur in areas that have thick soils on moderate-to-steep slopes. Sometimes, slumps occur along highways where the slopes of soils are extremely steep. Slumps are common after rains, when water reduces the frictional contact between grains of soil and acts as a lubricant between surface materials and underlying layers. The weight of the additional water pulls material downhill. As with other types of mass movement, slumps can be triggered by earthquakes. Slumps leave crescent-shaped scars on slopes.

Avalanches Landslides that occur in mountainous areas with thick accumulations of snow are called **avalanches.** Avalanches usually occur on slopes of at least 35°. About 10 000 avalanches occur each year in the mountains of the western United States alone. Radiation from the Sun can melt surface snow, which then refreezes at night into an icy crust. Snow that falls on top of this crust can eventually build up, become heavy, slip off, and slide down a slope as an avalanche.

8.1 Mass Movements at Earth's Surface **187**

Demo

Visual-Spatial Make three piles of rocks on a desk or table. Make one pile out of rocks that have different sizes and shapes. In another pile, place rocks that are all round. In the third pile, use flat rocks. Then, bump the table. Have students observe which pile of rocks is most stable and which is least stable. Rock piles composed of round rocks are least stable, and those composed of flat rocks are most stable. Ask students what measures can be taken to stabilize hillsides covered with loose rocks. Hillsides can be stabilized with human-made abutments and vegetation. **L1** **ELL**

Across the Curriculum

English Some words have more than one meaning or are used in different contexts. Have students think of how the word *slump* is used in science and write in their science journals one other meaning of the word *slump.* Students are likely to mention the use of *slump* to mean "slouch," as in "Don't slump in your seat." In both cases, *slump* refers to a curved movement or a sliding motion.

Figure 8-7 In February of 1999, a deadly avalanche occurred in Switzerland. Several people were killed and many homes were destroyed. The damage was estimated at $100 million.

Another type of weak snow layer forms in early winter as the ground, which is still warm, melts the overlying snow. The snow then refreezes into a layer of jagged, slippery snow crystals. A vibrating trigger, even from a single skier, can send such an unstable layer sliding down a mountainside at speeds of up to 300 km/h. As shown in *Figure 8-7,* avalanches pose particular risks in places such as Switzerland, where more than 50 percent of the population lives in avalanche terrain. In the 1998–1999 season, for example, hundreds of major avalanches swept down the Swiss Alps.

Rock Falls Rock falls commonly occur at high elevations, in steep road cuts, and on rocky shorelines. On high cliffs, rocks are loosened by physical weathering processes, such as freezing and thawing, and by plant growth. As rocks break up and fall directly downward, they may bounce and roll, ultimately producing a cone-shaped pile of coarse debris, called talus, at the base of the slope. On human-made rock walls, such as road cuts, rock falls are particularly common. "Falling Rock" warning signs can often be seen along highways that run through steep, rocky areas, as shown in *Figure 8-8.* Rock falls are less likely to occur in humid regions, where the rock is typically covered by a thick layer of soil, vegetation, and loose materials.

Figure 8-8 These rocks on a highway in Colorado were deposited by a rock fall. In areas where rock falls are common, signs are posted to warn motorists.

188 CHAPTER 8 *Mass Movements, Wind, and Glaciers*

MASS MOVEMENTS AFFECT PEOPLE

While mass movements are natural processes, human activities often contribute to the factors that cause mass movements. Activities such as constructing heavy buildings, roads, and other structures can make slope materials unstable. In addition, poor maintenance of septic systems, which often leak, can trigger slides.

Dangerous Mudflows Human lives are in danger when people live on steep terrain or in the path of unstable slope materials. For example, in December of 1999, northern Venezuela experienced the heaviest rains that had fallen there in 100 years. Within several days, between 30 to 48 cm of unseasonal rainfall occurred in this area. The sudden saturation of sediments, combined with the area's steep topography and widespread deforestation, resulted in severe mudflows and landslides, as shown in *Figure 8-9.* Tens of thousands of people died, more than 114 000 people were left homeless, and 23 000 homes were destroyed. Entire villages were buried in mud, rock, and debris. The widespread loss of human life was primarily a result of the location of villages both high up in steep terrain and at the foot of unstable, saturated slopes.

REDUCING THE RISKS

Catastrophic mass movements are most common on slopes greater than 25° that experience annual rainfall of over 90 cm. The best way to minimize the destruction caused by mass movements is to avoid building structures on such steep and unstable slopes.

Figure 8-9 Deadly mudflows that occurred in Venezuela in 1999 caused extensive damage in Los Corales.

ENVIRONMENTAL CONNECTION

Enrichment

Ask students just how steep a slope they think is too steep to live on. Many planning regulations discourage development on slopes greater than 10%. Have students engage in a study of slopes and the difficulty of climbing slopes with a bicycle. This activity will help students develop a physical understanding of the steepness of slopes.

✓Assessment

Knowledge Ask students the following question. Which of the following can be changed by physical weathering?
a. the shapes of Earth materials and surfaces
b. the size of rocks
c. rock composition
a and b

Project

Visual-Spatial Have small groups of students each make a photographic journal of common activities that result in mass movement. Have the groups review one another's photographic journals. You may want to have students use digital or instant photos to reduce the cost and time involved. **COOP LEARN** P

Environmental Connection

Naturalist Ask students to describe in their science journals how humans can change environmental conditions in the region in which they live. Students may mention increases in population and urbanization, agriculture, transportation, lifestyles, and technological advances. Have students share their ideas in class.

NY Core Curriculum Standards

Page 188: St 4 KI 2.1t & 2.1u, St 6 KI 1, 4, & 5
Page 189: St 4 KI 2.1t & 2.1u, St 6 KI 4 & 5, St 7 KI 1

Check for Understanding

Discussion

Ask students what they think will have happened to Earth's surface in their community when their grandchildren are in high school, keeping in mind the types of changes discussed in this section. Student answers should all reflect that some changes will occur, some will be more noticeable than others, and some will be more of a threat to humans.

Reteach

Students can listen to an audio-tape of the section to review the material covered. After students listen to the tape, ask them if they heard anything on the tape that they do not remember being covered in class. If so, check their level of understanding of the particular concept.

✔Assessment

Performance Have students make models of their community with locations of possible mass movements and escape routes labeled. Use the Performance Task Assessment List for Model in PASC, p. 51. **L2** **COOP LEARN**

Figure 8-10 This steel net was installed along Route 101 near Quilcene, Washington, to protect motorists from rockslides **(A)**. In Wolf Creek Pass, Colorado, a fence was built along this highway to protect motorists from rock slides **(B)**.

Preventive Actions Although preventing mass-movement disasters is not an easy task, some actions can help to avoid the potential hazards. For example, a series of trenches can be dug to divert running water around a slope and control its drainage. Other approaches to controlling landslides include covering steep slopes with materials such as steel nets, and constructing protective fences along highways in areas where rock slides are common, as shown in *Figure 8-10.* Still other approaches involve the installation of retaining walls to support the bases of weakened slopes and prevent them from falling. Most of these efforts at slope stabilization and prevention of mass movements, however, are generally successful only in the short run. The best way to reduce the number of disasters related to mass movements is to educate people about the problems of building on steep slopes. 🍃

SECTION ASSESSMENT

1. Identify and describe one type of rapid mass movement and one type of slow mass movement.

2. Describe the underlying force behind all forms of mass movement and explain its role in the process of mass movement.

3. How does water affect the process of mass movement?

4. What precautions can humans take to avoid the dangers associated with mass movements?

5. **Thinking Critically** Explain how one particular human activity can increase the risk of mass movement and suggest a solution to the problem.

SKILL REVIEW

6. **Making Tables** Design a data table that shows the similarities and differences among the forms of mass movement discussed in this section. For more help, refer to the *Skill Handbook.*

earthgeu.com/self_check_quiz

SECTION ASSESSMENT

1. A rapid movement is a landslide, which occurs when Earth material moves rapidly downslope. A slow movement is creep. Creep occurs when very fine sediment becomes saturated with water and slowly moves downslope.

2. Gravity is the underlying force behind all mass movements and pulls all material to the lowest level on Earth's surface.

3. Water contributes to the process of mass movement by adding weight and filling the spaces between sediment particles, thereby allowing the particles to more easily slide over one another as they move downslope.

4. Structures built in areas where mass movements are known to occur should be designed and built with features that provide extra strength.

5. Leveling an area along a slope may undermine it and risk future mass movements.

Solution: select a location not at the base of the slope.

6.

Name	Rapid/Slow	Type of Material	Danger to Humans
landslide	R	any type/size	little to much
avalanche	R	any type/size	little to much
mudflow	R	usually fine grained	little to much
creep	S	usually soil mixtures	usually little

Moving air can pick up and transport Earth materials in the process of erosion. Unlike water, wind can transport sediments uphill as well as downhill. As an erosional agent, wind can modify and change landscapes in arid and coastal areas.

WIND EROSION AND TRANSPORT

A current of rapidly moving air can pick up and carry sediments in the same way that water does. However, except for the extreme winds of hurricanes, tornadoes, and other strong storms, winds generally cannot carry particles as large as those transported by moving water. Thus, the relative ability of wind to erode materials is less than that of other erosional agents, such as water and ice.

Winds transport materials by causing their particles to move in different ways. For example, wind can move sand on the ground in a rolling motion. A method of transport by which strong winds cause particles to stay airborne for long distances, as shown in *Figure 8-11A,* is called suspension. Another method of wind transport, called saltation, causes a bouncing motion of particles. Saltation accounts for most sand transport by wind. Both suspension and saltation are shown in *Figure 8-11B.* Most areas where wind transport and erosion occur experience limited amounts of precipitation, which helps to hold down sediments and allows plants to grow.

OBJECTIVES

- **Describe** *conditions that contribute to the likelihood that an area will experience wind erosion.*
- **Identify** *wind-formed landscape features.*
- **Describe** *how dunes form and migrate.*
- **Explain** *the effects of wind erosion on human activities.*

VOCABULARY

deflation
abrasion
ventifact
dune
loess

A

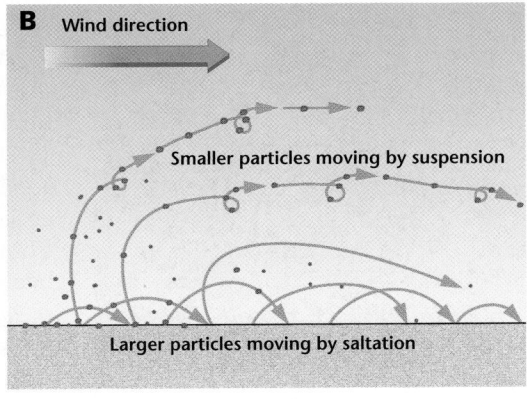

B Wind direction

Smaller particles moving by suspension

Larger particles moving by saltation

Figure 8-11 Dust storms, caused by suspension, are common in the Arizona desert **(A).** Strong winds can transport sediments by suspension and saltation **(B).**

8.2 *Wind* **191**

Section 8.2

Prepare

Section Background

For section content background, refer to **Wind** on page 180C

Preplanning

Refer to the Chapter Organizer on pages 180A–B.

1 Focus

Section Focus

Before presenting the lesson, display **Section Focus Transparency 21** on the overhead projector. **L1** **ELL**

Resource Manager

Study Guide for Content Mastery, pp. 49–50 **L2**

Section Focus Transparency 21 **L1** **ELL**

Project

Have students make an anemometer. Materials should include 5 small soda cups, 2 soda straws, a paper punch, a straight pin, and a stapler. Instruct students to exercise caution with the straight pin, as it may puncture the skin. Students can measure the rate of revolutions per minute. Use the circumference of the anemometer to determine the velocity in meters/minute (number of revolutions × circumference). Complete instructions can be found at earthgeu.com.

NY Core Curriculum Standards

Page 190: St 4 KI 2.1t, St 6 KI 1, 2, 4, & 5, St 7 KI 1
Page 191: St 4 KI 2.1t & 2.1u, St 6 KI 4 & 5

Content Background

Wind is described in terms of both speed and direction. The wind vane, an old yet still commonly used weather tool, points in the direction from which the wind is coming. Winds are named according to the direction from which they are blowing. Forces that affect wind include gravity, the Coriolis effect, centrifugal force, and friction. In addition, the landscape over which wind moves can influence both its speed and direction.

Demo

In a tray, place a layer of soil. Place a piece of sod on top of the soil in half of the tray. On the other half, put a layer of dry sand over the layer of soil. Sprinkle some dry sand on the sod. Have all students put on safety goggles. Turn a fan on low speed, making sure to face the fan away from all students before turning it on. Allow the fan to blow air evenly across the tray. Ask students to observe which conditions cause more wind erosion. Students should notice that the sand in the sod does not move as readily with the wind as does the sand in the other half of the tray. Students should recognize from the demonstration the importance of vegetation in reducing wind erosion.

Figure Caption Question

Figure 8-12 What areas in the United States are subject to wind erosion? Why is wind erosion a problem in those areas? Much of the wind erosion in the United States takes place in the west and along the eastern coast. Dryness in the west and steady winds along the coast contribute to wind erosion.

Figure 8-12 *What areas in the United States are subject to wind erosion? Why is wind erosion a problem in those areas?*

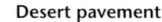

Wind Erosion in the United States

☐ Wind erosion areas

Figure 8-13 Desert pavement is the coarse sediment found on a desert floor **(A).** This desert pavement is located near the Gila River in New Mexico and Arizona **(B).**

A

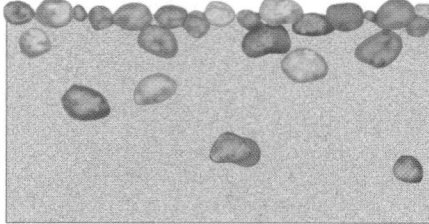

Desert pavement

B

Thus, wind transport and erosion primarily occur in areas with little vegetative cover, such as deserts, semi-arid areas, seashores, and some lakeshores. As shown in **Figure 8-12,** wind erosion is a problem in many parts of the United States. You will learn more about wind erosion in the *MiniLab* later in this section.

The lowering of the land surface that results from the wind's removal of surface particles is called **deflation.** The particles removed may be composed of any material. In areas of intense wind erosion, coarse gravel and pebbles are usually left behind as the finer surface material is removed by winds. The coarse surface left behind is called desert pavement, shown in **Figures 8-13A and 8-13B.** Deflation is a major problem in many agricultural areas of the world.

During the 1930s, portions of the Great Plains region, which stretches from Montana to Texas, experienced severe drought. The area was already suffering from the effects of poor agricultural practices, in which huge areas of natural vegetation were removed to clear the land for farming. Strong winds readily picked up the dry surface particles, which lacked any protective vegetation. Such severe dust storms resulted that daytime

192 CHAPTER 8 *Mass Movements, Wind, and Glaciers*

Resource Manager

Laboratory Manual, pp. 57–60 L2

skies were often darkened and the region became known as the Dust Bowl. Today, the Great Plains are characterized by thousands of shallow depressions known as deflation blowouts. They are the result of the removal of surface sediment by wind erosion during the 1930s. The depressions range in size from a few meters to hundreds of meters in diameter.

Another process of erosion, called **abrasion,** occurs when particles such as sand rub against the surface of rocks or other materials. Abrasion occurs as part of the erosional activities of winds, streams, and glaciers. In wind abrasion, wind picks up materials such as sand particles and blows them against rocks and other objects. Because sand is often made of quartz, a very hard mineral, wind abrasion can be a very effective agent of erosion; windblown sand particles eventually wear away rocks, as shown in *Figure 8-14.* Structures such as telephone poles also may be worn away or undermined by wind abrasion, and paint and glass on homes and vehicles may be damaged by windblown sand. Materials that are exposed to wind abrasion show unique characteristics. For example, windblown sand causes rocks to become pitted and grooved. With continued abrasion, rocks become polished on the windward side and develop smooth surfaces with sharp edges, as shown in *Figure 8-15A.* In areas of shifting winds, abrasion patterns correspond to wind shifts, and different sides of rocks become polished and smooth. Rocks shaped by wind-blown sediments, such as those shown in *Figure 8-15B,* are called **ventifacts.**

Figure 8-14 The forces of abrasion carved this conglomerate rock called the Baja Mushroom, located at Puerto Ballandra, near La Paz, Baja, Mexico.

Figure 8-15 Rocks that are exposed to windblown sand become pitted and grooved **(A).** These ventifacts are located in Bull Pass, Antarctica **(B).**

A

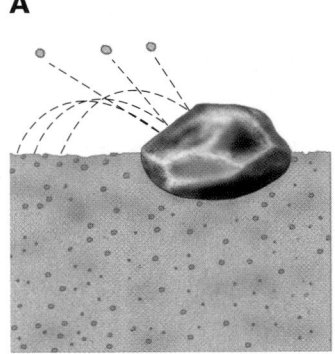
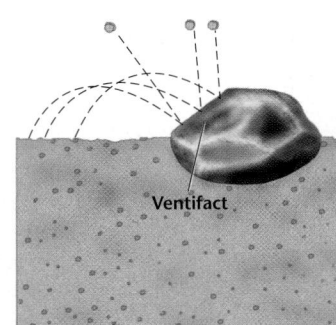

Ventifact

B

8.2 *Wind* **193**

MiniLab

Purpose

Students will interpret a wind-erosion map to identify areas of the United States that are subject to wind erosion.

Process Skills

interpret maps and data, recognize cause and effect, observe and infer, communicate

Materials

Figure 8-12, paper, pen

Teaching Strategies

Have students work in small groups to analyze and discuss the wind erosion map.

Expected Results

Students will recognize that wind erosion occurs in some regions of the United States but not in others. Students should conclude that areas with dry conditions and areas along seashores are more likely to experience wind erosion.

Analyze and Conclude

1. Wind erosion occurs in the Great Plains area and along the eastern and southern shorelines.
2. The largest area of wind erosion is the Great Plains, and the second largest is along the eastern and southern shorelines.
3. the mid-Atlantic and southern shorelines and shorelines along the northern and western portions of the Gulf of Mexico

✔Assessment

Knowledge Ask students how irrigation would affect the areas prone to wind erosion. Students should recognize that irrigation would allow more vegetation to grow and therefore more loose particles would be held in place. However, the use of irrigation is not without problems, so the diversion of water for irrigation purposes must be carefully planned.

MiniLab

Where does wind erosion occur?

Interpret a wind erosion map to find out what parts of the United States are subject to wind erosion.

Procedure

Refer to the wind erosion map shown in *Figure 8-12* to answer the following questions.

Analyze and Conclude

1. Which areas of the United States experience wind erosion?
2. Where is the largest area of wind erosion? The second largest?
3. What coastal areas are subject to wind erosion?

Figure 8-16 The wind is lifting sand particles from the top of this sand dune in the Namibia Desert in Namibia, a country located on the west coast of Africa.

✔Assessment

Knowledge Ask students the following question. Which of the following provides evidence of wind erosion?
a. rounded particles
b. rocks with scratches in them
c. unusually-shaped mountains
d. angular, polished boulders
The answer is d.

WIND DEPOSITION

Wind deposition occurs in areas where there are changes in wind velocity. As wind velocity decreases, some of the wind-blown sand and other materials can no longer stay airborne, and they drop out of the air stream to form a deposit on the ground.

Formation of Dunes In wind-blown environments, sand particles tend to accumulate where an object, such as a rock, landform, or piece of vegetation, blocks the particles' forward movement. Sand continues to be deposited as winds blow in one general direction. Over time, the pile of wind-blown sand develops into a **dune,** as shown in *Figure 8-16.* The conditions under which a dune forms determine its particular shape. These conditions include the availability of sand, wind velocity, wind direction, and the amount of vegetation present. All dunes have a characteristic profile. The gentler slope of a dune is located on the side from which the wind blows, the windward side. The steeper slope is on the side protected from the wind, called the leeward side.

The velocity of the wind above the ground surface determines the height of a dune. The heights of dunes are usually in the range of 12 to 25 m. The maximum height is variable, but the world's tallest dunes, in Saudi Arabia, measure more than 100 m in height.

Although quartz sand is the most common component of dunes, any dry, granular material can be formed into a dune, as long as winds continue to blow in a consistent direction and at a speed great enough to transport particles. Gypsum dunes are found at the White Sands National Monument in New Mexico, for example, and there are calcite dunes in Bermuda and areas in the Caribbean.

Resource Manager

GeoLab and MiniLab Worksheets, p. 31

Table 8-1 Types of Sand Dunes

Type	Shape	Size	Area of formation
Barchan	(illustration, labeled "Wind")	Maximum size: 30 m high, 300 m point to point.	The most common dunes. Generally form in areas of constant wind direction. Migrate 8–15 m per year.
Transverse	(illustration)	Maximum height: 25 m.	Form in areas with strong winds and abundant sand.
Parabolic	(illustration)	Maximum height: 30 m.	Form in areas with moderate winds and some vegetation. Include extremely curved types called hairpin dunes. Common on seacoasts.
Longitudinal	(illustration)	Maximum height: 90 m. Can be 100 km long. Average dimensions are 8 m in height and 60 m in length.	Form in areas with high, somewhat variable winds and little sand.

Types of Dunes Dunes are classified according to their shapes, as shown in *Table 8-1*. Barchan dunes are solitary, crescent-shaped dunes that form in flat areas where there is little sand or vegetation. Transverse dunes are formed where there is plenty of sand, little or no vegetation, and strong, steady, prevailing winds. Transverse dunes form in a series of long ridges that are perpendicular to the direction of the wind. In humid areas, U-shaped dunes, called parabolic dunes, form between clumps of plants. Where there is limited sand available, strong prevailing winds shape longitudinal dunes, which are parallel to the wind direction.

On offshore islands and on lakeshores, dunes are formed by winds blowing off the water toward the shore. Coastal dunes protect against beach and coastal erosion by reducing the direct action of wind on beach sand. They also act as buffers against the action of waves and provide shelter for vegetation. Once dune vegetation is established, it helps to anchor coastal dunes.

Content Background

Parabolic dunes are also referred to as U-shaped, hairpin, or blowout dunes. Parabolic dunes have elongated arms that follow the dune as a result of the vegetation holding some of the sand in place. The longest trailing arms recorded are 12 km long.

Enrichment

In New Mexico, at the northern end of the Chihuahuan Desert, the brilliant white gypsum dunes of the Tularosa Basin formed from a shallow sea that covered the area 250 million years ago. The Tularosa Basin is surrounded by mountain ranges, including the San Andres and Sacramento Mountains. Because there was no river to carry dissolved gypsum to the ocean, gypsum became trapped in the basin and settled there.

✓Assessment

Skill Have students take out a sheet of paper, divide it into fourths, and label each fourth 1–4. As you orally describe how each of the four types of sand dunes form, have students draw the dune type. Testing orally helps students to develop listening skills and drawing answers helps students apply concepts. **L2**

Across the Curriculum

English Provide students the opportunity to use the topic of wind for a poem or other creative writing piece. Read a poem about wind to provide an example for students.

NY Core Curriculum Standards

Page 194: St 4 KI 2.1u, St 6 KI 2, 4, & 5
Page 195: St 4 KI 2.1u, St 6 KI 1, 4, & 5

Content Background

Dunes can migrate great distances. With less sand to be moved, small dunes can migrate farther and faster than large dunes. Coastal dunes can move out to sea and extend the coastline. A German freighter that became stranded off Africa's southwestern coast in the early 1900s is now landlocked by migrating coastal dunes more than a kilometer from the shoreline.

Discussion

Ask students whether they have ever been to a beach along an ocean and noticed any attempts to protect sand dunes. Were people staying off of the dunes? Have students share any problems that they think might be involved in protecting shoreline dunes. Enforcement, importance of tourism, the local economy, and costs may be some issues brought up by students.

Figure 8-17 This sign was posted to make people aware that dunes are being restored in Okaloosa County, Florida.

Earth Science Online

Topic: Wind Erosion
To find out more about wind erosion, visit the Earth Science Web Site at earthgeu.com

Activity: Research a dune restoration project. Write a newspaper article describing the project.

Human activities, such as building in coastal-dune areas and removing dune vegetation, have disrupted dune growth and damaged dunes in many coastal areas of the United States. The destruction of dunes has led to increased beach erosion and nearshore flooding in these locations. Dune restoration areas, as shown in *Figure 8-17*, seek to restore and protect dunes in coastal areas.

As shown in *Figure 8-18*, dune migration is caused when prevailing winds continue to move sand from the windward side of a dune to its leeward side, thereby causing the dune to move slowly over time. As long as winds continue to blow, dunes continue to migrate and cover anything in their paths. Migrating dunes can block highways and cover farmland. Large dunes can even bury houses and other structures.

Loess Wind can carry fine, lightweight particles such as silt and clay in great quantities and for long distances. Many parts of Earth's surface are covered by thick layers of windblown silt, which are thought to have accumulated as a result of thousands of years of

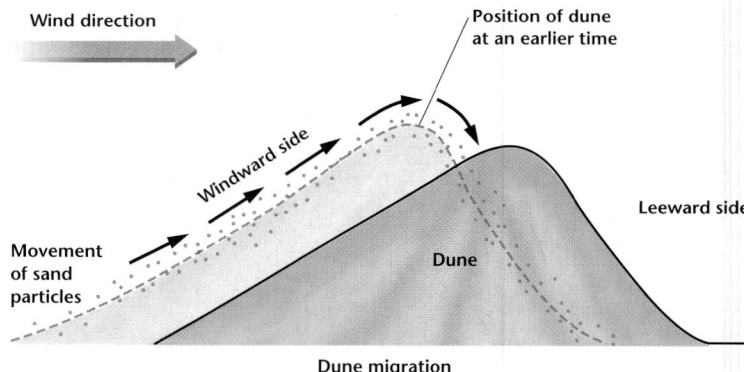

Wind direction

Position of dune at an earlier time

Windward side

Leeward side

Movement of sand particles

Dune

Dune migration

Figure 8-18 As dunes migrate, sand is moved from the windward side to the leeward side over a period of time.

Earth Science Journal

 **Linguistic** In their science journals, have students write a scenario about the development of a sand dune, beginning with the solid granite in Earth's crust. Ask students to include in their writing where each event occurs.

L2 **P**

Across the Curriculum

History Have students write a brief research report on the importance of wind to the economy of a region. In particular, direct their attention to the economic importance of loess soils in the United States and China. Ask students to include in their reports their opinions about how the agricultural history of the region might have been different if wind erosion and deposition had been absent.

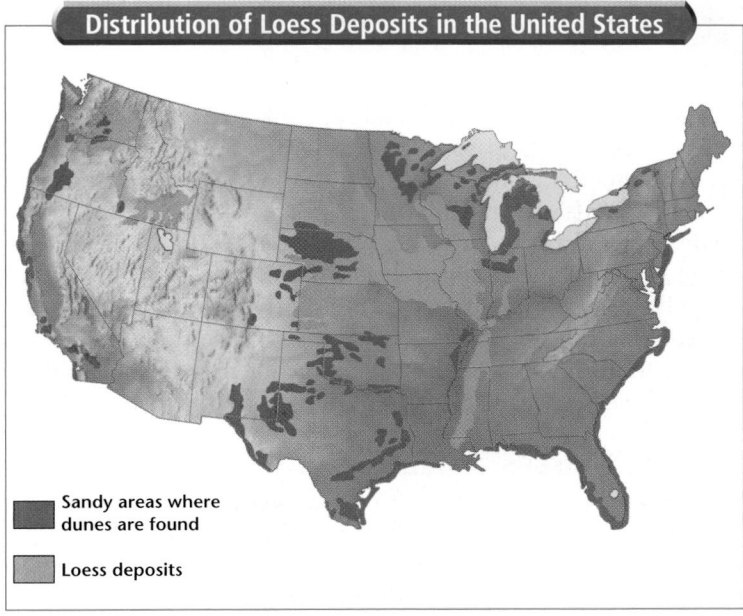

Distribution of Loess Deposits in the United States

Sandy areas where dunes are found

Loess deposits

Figure 8-19 This map shows the distribution of loess soil in the United States. *Where is the largest deposit of loess soil?*

dust storms. The source of these silt deposits may have been the fine sediments that were exposed when glaciers melted after the last ice age, more than 10 000 years ago. These thick, wind-blown silt deposits are known as **loess.** As shown in *Figure 8-19,* loess deposits are located in Illinois, Iowa, Missouri, South Dakota, Nebraska, Kansas, and Idaho. Where precipitation is adequate, loess soils are some of the most fertile soils on Earth because they contain abundant minerals and nutrients.

SECTION ASSESSMENT

1. What climatic conditions are most likely to produce wind erosion?

2. How does the vegetation growing in an area affect the wind's ability to modify the surface of Earth?

3. Draw a diagram showing how deflation occurs in wind erosion.

4. Why is wind abrasion such an effective agent of erosion?

5. How do dunes form?

6. **Thinking Critically** How can wind erosion directly affect human activities?

SKILL REVIEW

7. **Inferring** Describe the differences in appearance of wind-worn particles and water-worn particles. For more help, refer to the *Skill Handbook.*

earthgeu.com/self_check_quiz

SECTION ASSESSMENT

1. Dry conditions in areas supporting little or no protective vegetative cover are most likely to produce wind erosion.

2. Vegetation holds soil particles together and makes it more difficult for them to be picked up.

3. Students should be able to diagram how wind deflation occurs. Diagrams should indicate a lowering of the land surface as particles are removed by wind.

4. Wind abrasion is an effective agent of erosion because the particles being carried provide a constant abrading action. In addition, the abrading particles are often hard, resistant materials, such as quartz.

5. when wind-blown sand collects behind an object such as a rock or clump of vegetation

6. Wind directly affects human activities when dunes cover roadways and structures.

7. Wind-worn particles are pitted and commonly have angularly faceted surfaces, while water-worn particles are rounded and smooth.

Figure Caption Question

Figure 8-19 Where is the largest deposit of loess soil?
The largest loess deposit covers parts of Illinois, Iowa, Missouri, South Dakota, Nebraska, and Kansas.

3 Assess

Check for Understanding
Project
Use a video camera to record how particles of sand move when they are exposed to wind. Shoot the video against a black background so that the movement of the particles is readily observable. Use the camera's zoom capabilities, and play back the movement of the particles in slow motion or stop-frame fashion. Have students identify the skip-hop motion, the rolling, and the suspension of the sand particles. You might want to expand this project to show dune development. You might also print and display still photographs of key frames and use them for testing purposes.

Reteach

Interpersonal Have students debate the issue of restrictions on the use and development of sand dunes.

Performance Have students work in small groups to develop a bulletin board highlighting dune types, formation of dunes, locations of particular interest, and environmental issues associated with this section. Use the Performance Task Assessment List for Bulletin Board in **PASC,** p. 59.
L1 ELL COOP LEARN

197

Prepare

Section Background

For section content background, refer to **Glaciers** on page 180D.

Preplanning

Refer to the Chapter Organizer on pages 180A–B.

1 Focus

Section Focus

Before presenting the lesson, display **Section Focus Transparency 22** on the overhead projector.
L1 **ELL**

Figure Caption Question

Figure 8-20 Are all glaciers located only in polar regions? No; many are found at high altitudes in other regions.

NY Core Curriculum Standards

Page 198: St 4 KI 2.1u, St 6 KI 4 & 5

Page 199: St 4 KI 2.1u, St 6 KI 1, 4, & 5

198 CHAPTER 8

SECTION 8.3 *Glaciers*

OBJECTIVES

- **Explain** *how glaciers form.*
- **Compare** *and* **contrast** *the conditions that produce valley glaciers and those that produce continental glaciers.*
- **Describe** *how glaciers modify the landscape.*
- **Recognize** *glacial landscape features.*

VOCABULARY

glacier
valley glacier
continental glacier
cirque
moraine
outwash plain
drumlin
esker

Glaciers formed much of the landscape that exists presently in the northern United States and elsewhere in the world. Glaciers shape the landscape by eroding, transporting, and depositing huge volumes of rocks and sediments. Today, scientists measure the movements of glaciers and changes in their sizes to track climatic changes. Air bubbles trapped deep in glacial ice can provide data about the composition of Earth's atmosphere at the time when these ancient ice layers were formed. Scientists can also study ice cores in glaciers to learn about Earth's environmental past, as shown in the *Problem-Solving Lab* in this section.

MOVING MASSES OF ICE

A large, moving mass of ice is called a **glacier.** Glaciers form near Earth's poles and in mountainous areas at high elevations. They currently cover only about 10 percent of Earth's surface, as shown in *Figure 8-20.* Even in the past, when glaciers were much more widespread than they are today, many areas of the world did not experience glacial activity. For example, during the last ice age, which began about 1.6 million years ago and ended over 10 000 years ago, ice probably covered only about 30 percent of Earth.

Areas of high latitude, such as Greenland and Antarctica, and areas of high elevation, such as the Alps, have cold temperatures year-round. Cold temperatures keep fallen snow from completely melting, and each year, the snow that has not melted accumulates in

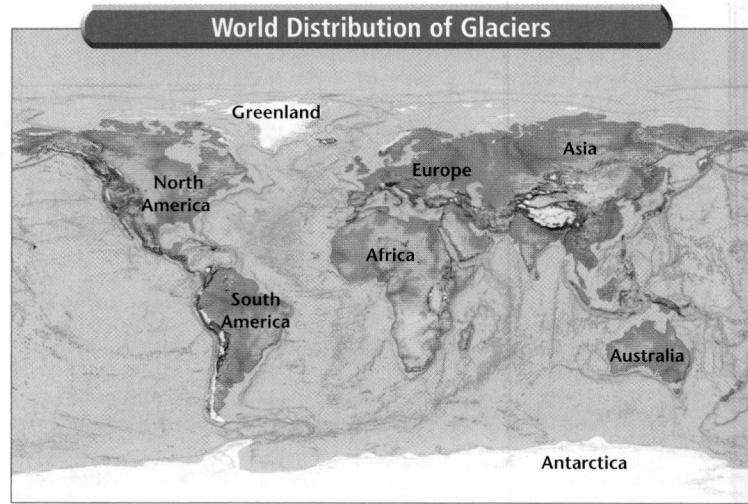

Figure 8-20 This map shows glacial distribution throughout the world. *Locate the glacial areas in white. Are all glaciers located only in the polar regions?*

198 CHAPTER 8 *Mass Movements, Wind, and Glaciers*

Resource Manager

Study Guide for Content Mastery, pp. 51–52 **L2**

Section Focus Transparency 22 **L1** **ELL**

Tying to Previous Knowledge

Show students large, color photos of a valley glacier and a continental glacier. Ask students to list observations of each type on the board. Ask students to also list how these two types of glaciers might change the landscapes they move across. Ask them if there is evidence of glaciers once occupying their region of the country.

an area called a snowfield. Thus, the total thickness of the snow layer increases as the years pass, and a glacier begins to form. The weight of the top layers of snow eventually exerts enough downward pressure to force the accumulated snow below to recrystallize into ice. This recrystallization is familiar to you if you have ever made a snowball: firmly compacting the snowball in your hands causes it to recrystallize, or partially melt to form ice. A glacier can develop in any location that provides the necessary conditions. For example, small glaciers form even in mountainous tropical areas along the equator, such as in Chile.

Valley Glaciers Glaciers can be classified as one of two types: valley glaciers or continental glaciers as shown in *Figures 8-21* and *8-22.* Glaciers that form in valleys in high, mountainous areas are called **valley glaciers.** A valley glacier is shown in *Figure 8-21.* The movement of a valley glacier occurs when the growing ice mass

Figure 8-22 This continental glacier is located on Antarctic Peninsula.

8.3 *Glaciers* **199**

2 Teach

Content Background

Glaciers form when more snow falls annually than melts or evaporates. Freshly fallen snow has a low density; generally, its volume consists of as much as 90 percent air. However, the snow quickly settles and compacts to the point at which air may comprise 50 percent or less of its volume. As the snow becomes packed, along with some melting and refreezing, the snow becomes even more compact. The accumulation of snow over the years leads to the formation of large snowfields. The pressure of overlying snow results in the recrystallization of the snow into ice and thus the formation of a glacier. Close inspection of glacial ice has revealed a crystal pattern similar to the patterns of coarse-grained rocks such as granite.

Enrichment

The crystalline pattern of ice can be observed by placing a sheet of paper on a piece of ice, holding a pencil sideways, and rubbing the pencil across the surface of the paper to make a print.

Project

Kinesthetic Obtain snow or ice shavings by mixing ice in a blender or using a snow-cone machine. Have students compress a handful of the snow or ice shavings into a compact form to simulate a glacier. Ask students to compare the properties of the material before and after it was compressed. **L1** **ELL**

Collaborative Learning

Divide the class into two groups. After giving the groups ample time to prepare, have them participate in a debate entitled: "Are we headed toward the next ice age?" **L3**

✓Assessment

Knowledge Ask students the following question. Which statements are true?
a. Glaciers experience cycles of expansion and recession.
b. There are more glaciers today than there were ten years ago.
c. Glaciers can be found in polar, temperate, and tropical latitudes.
d. Glaciers flow in a manner similar to a river.
The answers are a, c, and d.

Purpose

Students will observe how ice cores record Earth's history.

Process Skills

observe and infer, recognize cause and effect, think critically, use graphs

Materials

paper, pencil, graph (provided)

Teaching Strategies

Ask students whether they know of any method used to determine what Earth's climates were like hundreds of years ago.

Analysis

1. The highest amount was between 410–425 cm. The lowest was between 115–150 cm.
2. Radioactivity levels dropped in the ice cores.
3. The amount of radioactivity in the ice cores probably decreased unless there were other nuclear accidents.

Thinking Critically

4. Ice cores contain whatever material was in the atmosphere and indicate human activities such as nuclear testing and natural activities such as volcanic eruptions.

✔Assessment

Portfolio Have each student draw and label a picture of a glaciated landscape. Have students include depositional and erosional features. Students should number the glacial features and include a key with text that describes how the features formed.

---

becomes too heavy to maintain its rigid shape and begins to flow, much like a thick liquid. For most valley glaciers, flow begins when the accumulation of snow and ice exceeds 20 m in thickness. As a valley glacier moves, deep cracks in the surface of the ice, called crevasses, can form.

The speed of a valley glacier's movement is affected by the slope of the valley floor, the temperature and thickness of the ice, and the shape of the valley walls. The sides and bottom of a valley glacier move more slowly than the middle because friction slows down the sides and bottom, where the glacier comes in contact with the ground. Movement downslope is usually very slow, less than a few millimeters per day. You will learn more about the rates of glacial movement in the *Science & Math* feature at the end of this chapter. As valley glaciers flow downslope, their powerful carving action widens V-shaped stream valleys into U-shaped glacial valleys.

Continental Glaciers Glaciers that cover broad, continent-sized areas, such as the one shown in *Figure 8-22,* are called **continental glaciers.** They form under the same climatic conditions as valley glaciers, but they move in a different way. A continental glacier is

■ NATIONAL GEOGRAPHIC

To learn more about glaciers, go to the National Geographic Expedition on page 874.

Problem-Solving Lab

Using Graphs

Observe how ice cores record history Scientists drill ice cores from glaciers and study them to learn about the past. Ice cores taken from the arctic region, for example, have been found to contain preserved radioactive fallout. Data collected from the study of these ice cores have been plotted on the graph. Use the graph to answer the following questions.

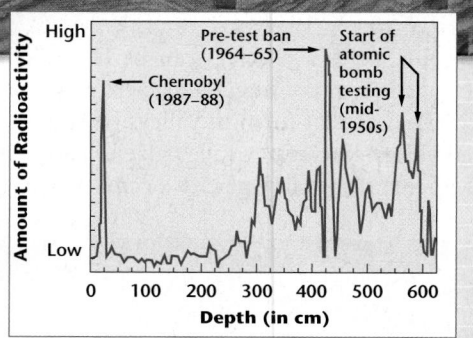

Analysis

1. At what depth in the ice cores was the highest amount of radioactivity found? At what depth was the lowest amount found?
2. Describe what happened to the amount of radioactivity in the ice cores between the pre-test ban and Chernobyl.
3. Infer what happened to the amount of radioactivity in the ice cores after Chernobyl.

Thinking Critically

4. What information or material other than radioactive fallout do you think ice cores might preserve within them?

Cultural Diversity

Preserved in the Glacial Ice He might have been a traveling salesman, a sheepherder, or a hunter; what is fairly certain is that he lived around 2000 B.C. This Copper Age "Ice Man," discovered in 1991 by a group of hikers in the Alps on the border of Italy and Austria, is one of the oldest, most complete, and best-preserved mummified bodies ever found. His tool kit and fragments of his clothing, including a leather boot stuffed with grass, were found to be amazingly intact. Scientists theorize that the body was naturally preserved in an airtight pocket of glacial ice. The remains are kept in a bulletproof refrigerated case in a northern Italian town. Hundreds of tourists visit every year to wonder about the identity, the cultural origins, and the tragic fate of the mysterious Ice Man.

thickest at its center. The weight of this thicker central region forces the rest of the glacier to flatten out in all directions. Continental glaciers, also called ice sheets, are much larger than valley glaciers. During periods in the past, when Earth experienced colder average temperatures than it does today, continental glaciers covered huge portions of Earth's surface. Today's continental glaciers cover much smaller areas, and they are confined to Greenland, northern Canada, and Antarctica.

GLACIAL EROSION

Of all the erosional agents, glaciers are the most powerful because of their great size, weight, and density. When a valley glacier moves, it breaks off pieces of rock through a process called plucking. Fallen rocks also accumulate along the edges of glaciers and give the sides a striped appearance. When glaciers with embedded rocks move over bedrock valley walls, they act like the grains on a piece of sandpaper, grinding out parallel scratches into the bedrock, as shown in *Figure 8-23*. Small scratches are called striations, and the larger ones are called grooves. Scratches and grooves provide evidence of a glacier's history and establish its direction of movement.

Glacial erosion can create certain features, as shown in *Figure 8-24*. In addition to carving U-shaped valleys, valley glaciers also scoop out deep depressions, called **cirques.** Where two cirques on opposite sides of a valley meet, they form a sharp, steep ridge called an arete. Where

Figure 8-23 Glacial striations are found on quartzite rocks located in Blue Mounds State Park in Minnesota.

Figure 8-24 Glacial features include hanging valleys, cirques, waterfalls, U-shaped valleys, horns, and aretes.

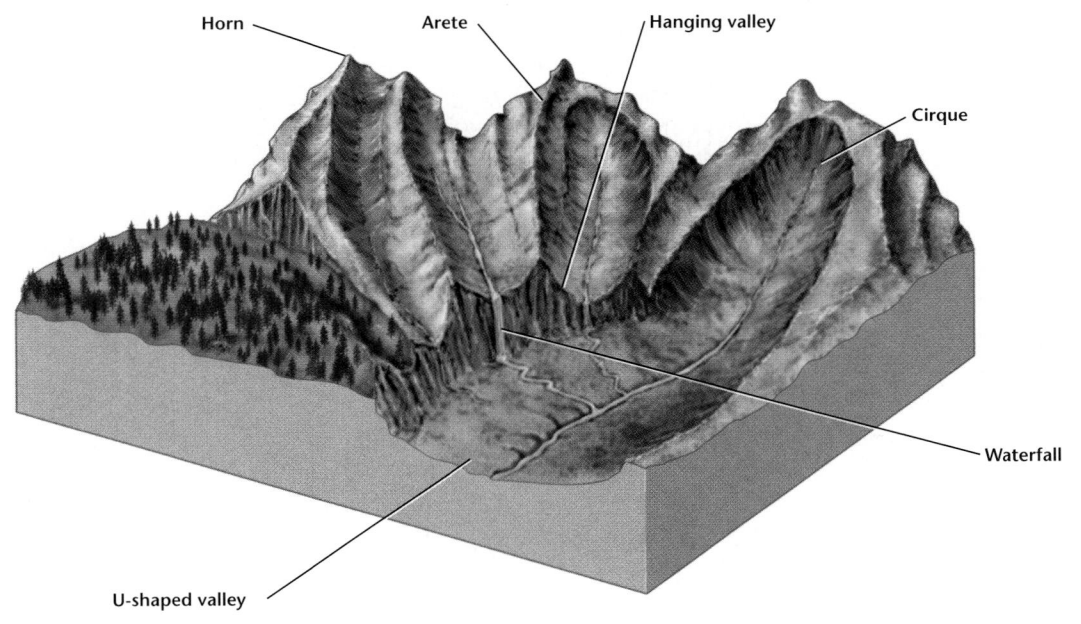

Horn — Arete — Hanging valley

Cirque

Waterfall

U-shaped valley

Concept Development

Glaciers other than those in Antarctica and Greenland comprise only approximately 6 percent of all glaciers on Earth. However, meltwater from these other glaciers results in water being recycled more quickly than the water in glaciers in Greenland and Antarctica, and therefore these glaciers have a more rapid effect on sea level.

Discussion

Some scientific terms are words that are used in everyday language. Knowing the common meanings of such words can help students understand their use in a scientific context. For example, the word *lateral* means "side" and the word *medial* means "in the middle." When either of these words is used with the word *moraine*, it indicates where the moraine formed in relation to the glacier.

✓Assessment

Knowledge Ask students which of the following glacial features are the result of erosion and which are the result of deposition: moraines, cirques, striations, till, and horns. Erosional features include cirques, horns, and striations. Depositional features include moraines and till.

Resource Manager

Teaching Transparency 21
L2 ELL

Laboratory Manual, pp. 61–64
L2

Across the Curriculum

Art Have students each draw or paint a landscape that includes glacial features. The glacial features should be labeled.

Demo

Mix flour with a little water to make a thick, doughlike mixture. Place the dough on an inclined board and have students check the position of the dough several times during the class period. The mixture will slowly flow down the slope. To help students determine which areas are moving fastest, place toothpicks in different locations on the dough so that students can observe changes in the position of the toothpicks.

Discussion

Share with students the fact that investigators at NASA have used satellite imagery, airborne laser altimeter flights, and the Global Positioning System to determine that Greenland's ice sheets are experiencing an increase in the rate of melting. Ask students to share their thoughts about the reason for the apparent increase in melting rate. Responses might include global warming and El Niño. Students may wish to know what information is available about coastline changes resulting from the increase in melting rates. Effects on shorelines have been negligible, but if the melting rate continues to increase, changes in coastlines will occur.

Modeling

 **Kinesthetic** Have students use clay to model glacial landscapes. List the features that students should include in their models, such as moraines, drumlins, eskers, glacial lakes, and flood plains. **L1** **ELL**

Resource Manager

Exploring Environmental Problems, pp. 13–16 **L3**

NY Core Curriculum Standards

Page 202: St 4 KI 2.1t, 2.1u, & 2.1v, St 6 KI 4 & 5
Page 203: St 4 KI 2.1t & 2.1u, St 6 KI 1, 2, 4, & 5

Figure 8-25 This terminal moraine was formed on Exit Glacier in Kenai Fjords National Park, in Alaska.

there are glaciers on three or more sides of a mountaintop, a steep, pyramid-shaped peak forms. This is known as a horn. The most famous example of this feature is Switzerland's Matterhorn. A tributary valley that enters a U-shaped valley from high up a mountain side is called a hanging valley.

GLACIAL DEPOSITION

Glacial till is the mixed debris that glaciers carry embedded in their ice and on their tops, sides, and front edges. When a glacier melts, glacial till is left behind. Ridges consisting of till deposited by glaciers are called **moraines.** Those at the foot of a large glacier are called terminal moraines, shown in *Figure 8-25,* and those at its sides are called lateral moraines. Where two glaciers join together, their lateral moraines combine to form a medial moraine.

Outwash When a glacier melts and begins to recede, meltwater floods the valley below. Meltwater contains gravel, sand, and fine silt formed from the grinding action of the glacier on underlying rock. When this sediment is deposited by meltwater, it is called outwash. The area at the leading edge of the glacier, where the meltwater streams flow and deposit outwash, is called an **outwash plain.**

Drumlins and Eskers Glaciers that move over older moraines form the material into elongated landforms called **drumlins.** A drumlin's steeper slope faces the direction from which the glacier came. Drumlin fields are found in Wisconsin, Massachusetts, and New York State. Long, winding ridges of layered sediments that are deposited by streams flowing under a melting glacier are called **eskers.**

202 CHAPTER 8 *Mass Movements, Wind, and Glaciers*

Differentiated Instruction

Learning Disabled Have students create their own moraines by pushing a block of ice through a mixture of sand, soil, and pebbles on a slightly slanted board. They should identify the terminal and lateral moraines. As the ice melts, discuss outwash and have students identify where an outwash plain may occur.

Demo

Place a plastic bag full of water in a freezer. Once it is frozen, remove the ice from the plastic bag and place it on a large tray that has soil evenly spread over it. Slightly incline the tray by placing a book under one end. Sprinkle dirt randomly on the block of ice. Have students monitor the changes in the block of ice. Allow the block of ice to melt, and then have students compare the patterns of runoff and deposition to those of a glacial landscape.

A

B

Figure 8-26 This kettle lake, which was formed in glacial till, is located in Glacial Lakes State Park, Minnesota **(A)**. This cirque lake is located in the western Cascade Mountains, in the state of Washington **(B)**.

Glacial Lakes Sometimes, a large block of ice breaks off a glacier and is later covered by sediment. When the ice block melts, it leaves behind a depression called a kettle hole. After the ice block melts, the kettle hole fills with water from precipitation and runoff to form a kettle lake. Kettle lakes, such as the one shown in *Figure 8-26A,* are common in New England, New York State, and Wisconsin. As shown in *Figure 8-26B,* cirques also can fill with water, and they become cirque lakes. When a terminal moraine blocks off a valley, the valley fills with water to form a lake. Moraine-dammed lakes include the Great Lakes and the Finger Lakes of northern New York State which are long and narrow.

Mass movements, wind, and glaciers all contribute to the changing of Earth's surface. These processes constantly wear down landforms, and in many ways, they also impact human populations and activities.

SECTION ASSESSMENT

1. Explain how valley glaciers and continental glaciers form.

2. Draw a glacial landscape and label the glacial features.

3. How can a valley glacier modify the mountainous area where it forms? What glacial features form in mountainous areas?

4. How is a kettle lake formed?

5. **Thinking Critically** What evidence of past glaciers can be found on Earth today?

SKILL REVIEW

6. **Comparing and Contrasting** Make a data table that compares and contrasts the characteristics of valley glaciers and continental glaciers. For more help, refer to the *Skill Handbook.*

3 Assess

Check for Understanding
Reinforcement
Have each student develop five review questions. Collect all questions and randomly select questions for members of two opposing teams to answer.

Reteach
Visual-Spatial Show a video about glaciers that will review the features covered in the section. Provide students with a list of features to check off as they view the video.

✓Assessment

Skill Have students each develop a concept map using the following terms and phrases: *valley glacier, continental glacier, V-shaped valley, U-shaped valley, cirque, more snow falls than melts each year, high elevations, large broad areas,* and *till.* more snow falls than melts each year→1) high elevations → valley glacier → cirque → V-shaped valley → U-shaped valley → till; 2) large broad areas → continental glaciers → till

SECTION ASSESSMENT

1. Glaciers form where more snow falls than melts each year in a continuing pattern. Snow that accumulates at higher altitudes in mountainous regions forms valley glaciers. Snow that accumulates on broad continental areas forms continental glaciers.

2. Diagrams may include the following: hanging valley, cirque, arête, horn, till, moraine, drumlin, esker, kettle lake, outwash plain, and moraine-dammed lake.

3. Valley glaciers move downslope and carve out valleys in the mountainside. The basin that a valley glacier forms during this process on a mountain slope is called a cirque, which can fill with water and become a cirque lake. The higher remaining divisions of the land between cirques are called arêtes. A series of cirques and arêtes around a mountaintop form a horn.

4. A kettle lake is formed when an ice block melts and leaves a depression that fills up with runoff and precipitation.

5. drumlins, moraines, kettle lakes, glacial lakes, and U-shaped valleys in New York and New England

6.

Comparing Factor	Continental Glaciers	Valley Glaciers
Size	very large	much smaller
Location	broad land area	in mountains
Where found today	Greenland, Antarctica	Alaska, the Alps

203

Mapping GeoLab

Mapping a Landslide

Around midday on April 27, 1993, in a normally quiet, rural area of New York State, the landscape dramatically changed. Unexpectedly, almost 1 million m³ of earth debris slid over 300 m down the lower slope of Bare Mountain and into Tully Valley. The debris flowed over the road and buried nearby homes. The people who lived there had no knowledge of any prior landslides occurring in the area, yet this landslide was the largest to occur in New York State in more than 75 years. What caused this large mass of earth material to move so suddenly?

Time Allotment

45 minutes

Process Skills

communicate, observe and infer, interpret scientific illustrations, measure and use numbers, recognize cause and effect, sequence, draw a conclusion

Preparation

Review the use of compass directions on maps.

Procedure

Teaching Strategies

- To increase student proficiency in using SI, have students give their answers in both English units and SI units.
- Measurements should be to the nearest tenth.
- Team students with visual impairments with students who can easily discern small print.
- Encourage student partners to discuss their work as they proceed to help each other with comprehension and understanding of content and procedures.

Data and Observations

Students will measure distances, interpret map symbols, determine direction of flow, and analyze the map and topography to determine the cause of the flow and draw conclusions.

Preparation

Problem
How can you use a drawing based on a topographic map to infer how the Tully Valley Landslide occurred?

Materials
metric ruler
pencil

Procedure

1. Use the map to answer the following questions. Be sure to check the map's scale.

2. Measure the length and width of the Tully Valley in kilometers. Double-check your results.

Analyze

1. What does the shape of the valley tell you about how it formed?

2. In what direction did the landslide flow?

3. In what direction does the Onondaga Creek flow?

4. Infer from the map, which side of Tully Valley has the steepest valley walls.

5. What conditions must have been present for the landslide to occur?

6. At the time of the Tully Valley Landslide, the trees were bare. How could this have affected the conditions that caused the landslide?

Conclude & Apply

1. Why do you think the Tully Valley Landslide occurred?

2. If you planned to move into an area prone to mass movements, such as landslides, what information would you gather beforehand?

204 CHAPTER 8 *Mass Movements, Wind, and Glaciers*

Resource Manager

GeoLab and MiniLab Worksheets,
pp. 32–34 L2

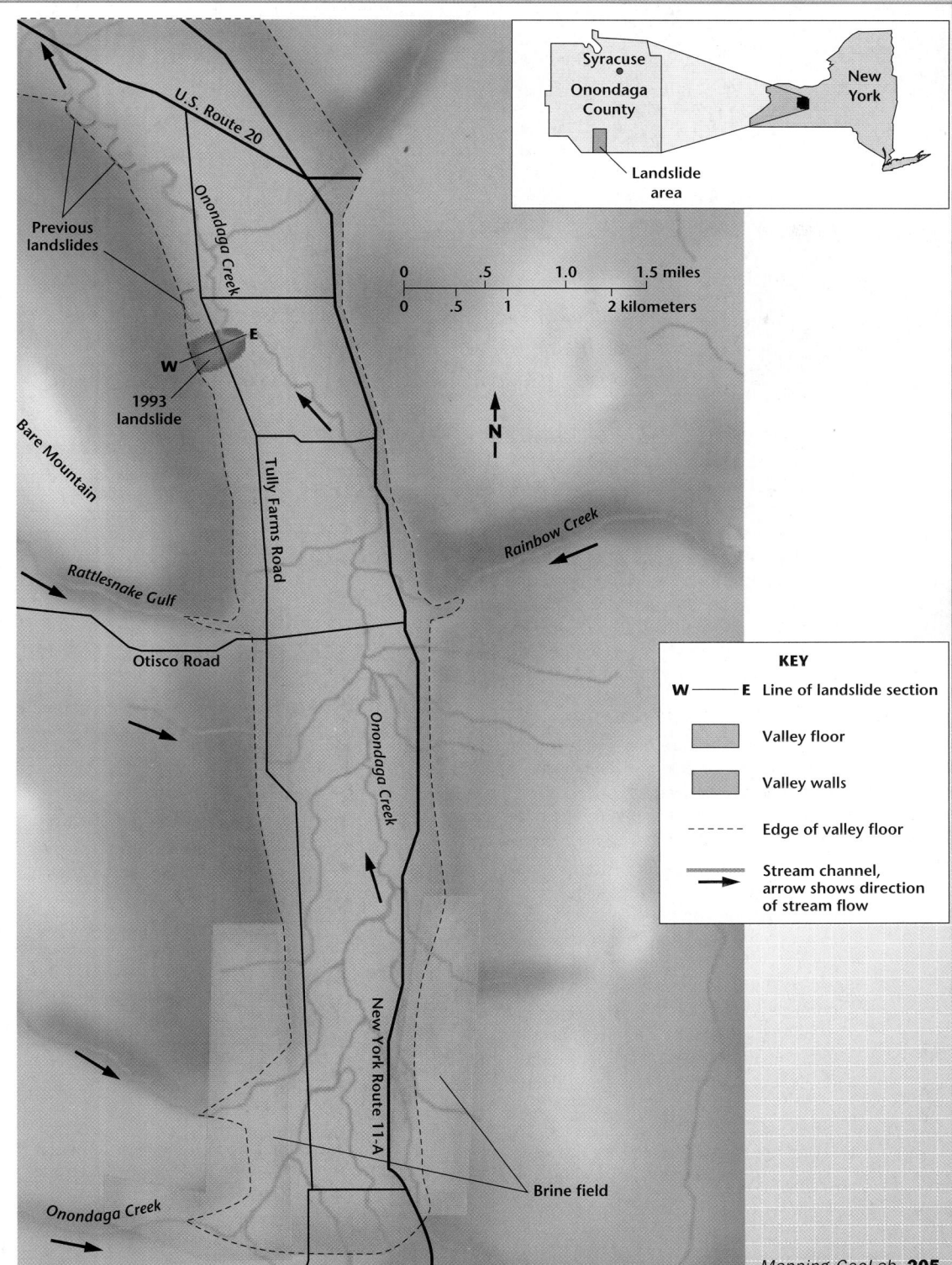

Syracuse
Onondaga County

New York

Landslide area

U.S. Route 20

Onondaga Creek

Previous landslides

E
W
1993 landslide

Bare Mountain

Rattlesnake Gulf

Tully Farms Road

Otisco Road

Onondaga Creek

Rainbow Creek

N

Brine field

New York Route 11-A

Onondaga Creek

0   .5   1.0   1.5 miles
0   .5   1   2 kilometers

KEY

W ——— E Line of landslide section

Valley floor

Valley walls

- - - - - Edge of valley floor

Stream channel, arrow shows direction of stream flow

Mapping GeoLab **205**

Analyze

1. The shape of the valley indicates that it was formed by glacial activity.
2. west to east
3. north
4. Students should infer from the map that the western side has experienced landslides in the past and is steepest.
5. The ground had to be saturated with water.
6. Trees with leaves would have soaked up more of the water in the ground and the landslide may not have occurred.

Conclude & Apply

1. The fine particles that made up the sediments in the valley were saturated with water. The water reduced friction between the particles and allowed the rock material to slide downslope.
2. Check with local planning boards and other governmental agencies and groups to determine the past history of the area; scout the area out and look for possible signs of previous slumping, erosion, and so on; and do not purchase or build in geologically questionable sites such as at the base of a steep mountain.

✔ Assessment

Knowledge Ask students to determine why the mass movement event examined in the GeoLab is classified as a landslide. Ask students how a landslide differs from creep, slump, flow, an avalanche, and a rock fall.

NY Core Curriculum Standards

Page 204: St 1 Math KI 2, 3, & Science KI 1, St 4 KI 2.1t & 2.1u, St 6 KI 1, 2, 3, 4, 5, & 6, St 7 KI 1

Page 205: St 1 Math KI 2, 3, & Science KI 1, St 4 KI 2.1t & 2.1u, St 6 KI 1, 2, 3, 4, 5, & 6, St 7 KI 1

Purpose

Students will learn about the movement of glaciers and how to determine their movement rates.

Content Background

Different parts of glaciers move at different rates. There is no way to measure all the rates within a glacier, so an average rate is taken to determine the overall rate of movement.

Teaching Strategies

- Review the concept of rates with students.
- You may wish to explain further that the depth is measured from the reference point of the surface of the glacier. Because the surface represents zero, distances measured below the surface are negative.

NY Core Curriculum Standards

Page 206: St 1 Math KI 1, 2, & 3, St 2 KI 3, St 4 KI 2.1u, St 6 KI 5, St 7 KI 1
Page 207: St 4 KI 2.1t & 2.1u, St 6 KI 1, 4, 5, & 6

Science & Math

Rates of Glacial Movement

Rates are commonly used in everyday life. An example of a rate is the number of kilometers that a car travels per hour. A rate is a ratio of measurements, where one measurement is time. The most commonly used rate is distance per unit of time, also called speed.

Scientists who want to measure how fast a glacier moves typically refer to the overall speed of the glacier's movement. However, this is only an average, because a glacier moves at many different rates. A glacier is similar to a river in that the outside edges of a glacier move more slowly than the middle as a result of friction with the banks. A cross section of a glacier from top to bottom shows how different horizontal levels of the glacier move. The top surface of a glacier may move more quickly than the bottom surface.

Making the Measurements

To measure the rate of a glacier moving at various speeds, scientists calculate the glacier's average speed. The average speed of a glacier is the sum of the different speeds within the glacier divided by the total number of measurements.

Scientists can measure the difference in speed from the top surface of a glacier to the bottom by drilling into the glacier and placing a rod through the hole. After a period of time, the rod leans in the direction of the glacier's movement. The table at right shows data obtained from a rod placed in the Worthington Glacier in Alaska after 66 days. The distance the glacier moved at different depths is given in the table. The depths were measured from the surface of the glacier.

Procedure

1. Using the rod data, calculate the speed at which the glacier moved at each depth.

Rod Data from Worthington Glacier		
Depth (m)	Distance (m)	Average Speed = Distance/Time
0	13.1	0.198 m/day
20	13.1	0.198 m/day
60	12.8	0.194 m/day
100	12.2	0.185 m/day
140	11.2	0.170 m/day
180	9.57	0.145 m/day
Average Speed of Glacier		0.182 m/day

2. After you compute the speed calculations for all depths, average them together to find the average speed of the glacier.

Challenge

1. Note that the top surface of the glacier did not move as quickly as the portion of the glacier 20 m deep. What are some possible reasons for this?

2. Graph the average speed of the glacier at each depth. Do you notice a trend? If scientists drilled another 40 m, what would the speed of the glacier's movement be at that depth?

Earth Science Online

To find out more about the rates of glacial movement, visit the Earth Science Web Site at earthgeu.com

Challenge

1. The movement depends on the bed of the glacier. If the bed is frozen to the ground and there is a lot of friction, then the friction lessens in each layer going towards the top. If the bed of the glacier can move easily due to water, then the distribution of speeds is lessened, and the glacier tends to move at the same rate throughout the layers.

2.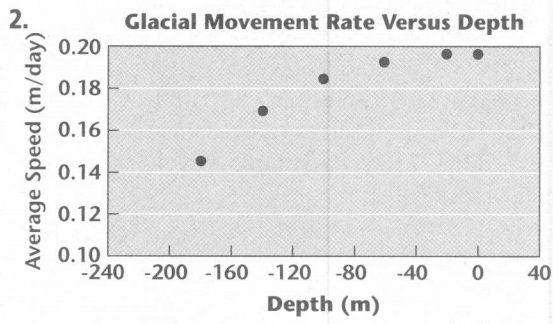

At 220 m, speed would be about 0.11 m/day

Summary

SECTION 8.1

Mass Movements at Earth's Surface

Main Ideas

- Mass movement is the movement of Earth materials downslope as the result of the force of gravity. Almost all of Earth's surface undergoes mass movement.
- Mass movements may occur very slowly and become noticeable only over long periods of time. Creep is a form of slow mass movement. Rapid mass movements are noticeable.
- Variables involved in the mass movement of Earth materials include the material's weight, its resistance to sliding, and sometimes a trigger such as an earthquake. Water is important to the process of mass movement.
- Mass movements can cause great damage and loss of lives. Human activities may increase the potential for the occurrence of mass movements.

Vocabulary

avalanche (p. 187)
creep (p. 184)
landslide (p. 186)
mass movement (p. 181)
mudflow (p. 185)
slump (p. 187)

SECTION 8.2

Wind

Main Ideas

- Arid, semi-arid, and seashore environments are likely to experience wind erosion. Limited amounts of precipitation and protective vegetation commonly contribute to wind erosion in an area.
- Wind-carried sediments can cause abrasive action. Rocks exposed to continual wind abrasion often exhibit angular shapes with polished, smooth sides on the windward side. Features formed in wind-affected areas include deflation blowouts, dunes, and desert pavement. Dunes are classified by shape.
- The transport of Earth materials by wind can create problems for humans. Migrating dunes can block highways and cover structures.
- Loess soils deposited by wind are fertile soils because they contain minerals and nutrients.

Vocabulary

abrasion (p. 193)
deflation (p. 192)
dune (p. 194)
loess (p. 197)
ventifact (p. 193)

SECTION 8.3

Glaciers

Main Ideas

- Glaciers are large, moving masses of ice that form near Earth's poles and in mountainous areas at high elevations.
- Valley glaciers are formed in mountains, and continental glaciers are formed over broad regions of land. Valley glaciers move down mountainsides and form unique glacial features. Continental glaciers usually spread out from their centers.
- Features formed by glaciers include U-shaped valleys, hanging valleys and waterfalls in the mountains, moraines, drumlins, kettle holes along outwash plains, and several types of lakes.

Vocabulary

cirque (p. 201)
continental glacier (p. 200)
drumlin (p. 202)
esker (p. 202)
glacier (p. 198)
moraine (p. 202)
outwash plain (p. 202)
valley glacier (p. 199)

earthgeu.com/vocabulary_puzzlemaker

Study Guide **207**

Main Ideas

Summary statements can be used by students to review the major concepts of the chapter.

VOCABULARY PuzzleMaker

For additional help with vocabulary, have students access the Vocabulary Puzzlemaker online.

earthgeu.com/ vocabulary puzzlemaker

0:00 Out of Time?

If time does not permit teaching the entire chapter, use the GeoDigest at the end of the unit as an overview.

Earth Science Online

Be sure to check the Earth Science Web Site for links to chapter material:
earthgeu.com

GLENCOE
Technology

Videotape/DVD
MindJogger Videoquizzes
Chapter 8: *Mass Movements, Wind, and Glaciers*
Have students work in groups as they play the videoquiz game to review key chapter concepts.

Resource Manager

Chapter Assessment, pp. 43–48
MindJogger Videoquizzes DVD/VHS
ExamView® Pro CD-ROM
Performance Assessment in Earth Science

Understanding Main Ideas

1. b
2. c
3. d
4. d
5. b
6. d
7. d
8. c
9. c

Applying Main Ideas

10. extensive farming
11. earth flows and mudflows
12. Diagrams of barchan, transverse, parabolic, and longitudinal sand dunes should look similar to *Table 8-1* on page 195.
13. Loess soils are fertile because they contain abundant minerals and nutrients from the silt from which they formed.
14. Wind-eroded particles are pitted, with angular, faceted surfaces, while water-eroded particles are smooth and round.
15. drumlins, eskers, and glacial lakes
16. Removing the "toe" of a slope, or undermining it, can result in landslides.
17. Unsorted sediments were dropped directly by the glacier, whereas sorted sediments were carried by meltwater and deposited in a sorted manner as a result of the slowing down of the water.
18. Conditions are favorable for glacial formation at high elevations in the mountains of the tropical latitudes.

Understanding Main Ideas

1. What underlying force causes all forms of mass movement?
   a. friction
   c. magnetism
   b. gravity
   d. the Coriolis effect

2. Which of the following is an example of a slow mass movement?
   a. a mudflow
   c. creep
   b. a landslide
   d. an avalanche

3. Which of the following has the greatest erosional power?
   a. wind
   c. an avalanche
   b. a landslide
   d. a glacier

4. What is the movement of dunes called?
   a. ablation
   c. deflation
   b. abrasion
   d. migration

5. What percentage of Earth's surface is covered by glaciers?
   a. 5 percent
   c. 15 percent
   b. 10 percent
   d. 20 percent

6. Which feature is NOT formed by glaciers?
   a. moraines
   c. kettle holes
   b. drumlins
   d. dunes

7. Which state is most likely to experience wind erosion?
   a. Louisiana
   c. Connecticut
   b. Kentucky
   d. Utah

8. Which of the following has the fastest movement?
   a. solifluction
   c. mudflow
   b. creep
   d. earth flow

9. Which particles can wind move most easily?
   a. sand
   c. silt
   b. pebbles
   d. gravel

Applying Main Ideas

10. What human activity contributed to the dust storms in the Great Plains in the 1930s?
11. What mass movements are dependent on the addition of water?
12. Draw a simple diagram of the four major types of sand dunes. Then draw an arrow to show the direction of wind movement across each of the dunes.
13. Why is loess soil usually fertile?
14. How do particles eroded by wind differ from particles eroded by water?
15. What features on Earth's surface are characteristic of an outwash plain?
16. Give an example of one type of mass movement that could be caused by human activity.
17. Why do some glacial depositions have sorted sediments, while others do not?
18. How is it possible that glaciers exist at the equator?
19. How do valley glaciers form?
20. Why are some glacial lakes long and narrow, while others are round?
21. Why is wind abrasion such an effective agent of erosion?
22. What is one way to reduce the number of disasters related to mass movements?

Test-Taking Tip

USE THE BUDDY SYSTEM Study in groups. A small gathering of people works well because it allows you to draw from a broader base of skills and expertise. However, keep the group small and keep on target.

Standardized Test Practice

1. a
2. a
3. c
4. b
5. c

Thinking Critically

Use the following information and diagram to answer questions 23 and 24.

A person studying glaciers placed flags on tall rods across a valley glacier, as shown in diagram A. When the person returned to the site the following year, the flag rods were in the positions shown in diagram B.

A 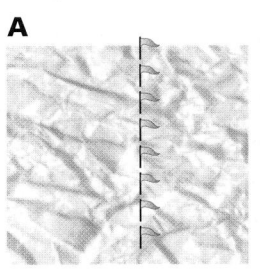   **B**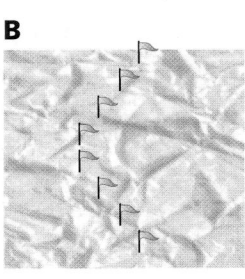

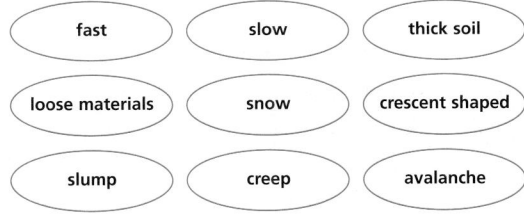

West ⟶

23. Based on the change in the positions of the flag rods, in which direction is the glacier moving?
    a. north   **b.** south   **c.** east   **d.** west

24. What can you tell about the rate of speed of different parts of the glacier?

25. **Concept Mapping** Use the following terms to construct a concept map of mass movements. For more help, refer to the *Skill Handbook*.

(fast)   (slow)   (thick soil)

(loose materials)   (snow)   (crescent shaped)

(slump)   (creep)   (avalanche)

earthgeu.com/standardized_test

Standardized Test Practice

INTERPRETING DATA Use the table below to answer questions 1-2.

Region	Characteristics
A	semi-arid; experiences intense but brief rainstorms
B	permafrost; much loose, water-logged material
C	mountainous; thick accumulations of snow
D	thick soils on semi-steep and steep slopes; occasional earthquake activity
E	arid; high cliffs and rocky shorelines

1. Which mass movement is most likely to occur in Region A?
   a. mudflow   **c.** slump
   b. avalanche   **d.** rock fall

2. Which mass movement is most likely to occur in Region B?
   a. solifluction   **c.** avalanche
   b. mudflow   **d.** slump

3. What are dunes a result of?
   a. wind erosion   **c.** wind deposition
   b. deflation   **d.** abrasion

4. Which of the following is NOT a feature of valley glaciers?
   a. cirques   **c.** moraines
   b. loess   **d.** arete

5. What is it called when wind transports materials by causing a bouncing motion of particles?
   a. suspension   **c.** saltation
   b. deflation   **d.** abrasion

Assessment **209**

19. A valley glacier forms when the growing ice mass at high elevations in a mountainous area becomes too heavy to maintain its shape and begins to flow.

20. Long, narrow lakes likely formed from valley glaciers sliding down a slope and forming a valley or depression that later filled in with water. Round lakes (kettle lakes) formed from blocks of ice left in the outwash plain that later melted and formed basins that filled with water.

21. Wind abrasion, which can polish and smooth different kinds of rocks and can wear away the base of telephone poles and remove paint on homes, constantly bombards structures with wind-borne particles of hard substances such as quartz.

22. warning people to avoid building structures on slopes that are too steep

Thinking Critically

23. **The answer is d,** west.
24. It moves very slowly overall but faster in the middle than on the sides.
25. avalanche, fast, snow; creep, slow, loose materials; slump, thick soil, crescent shaped

---

NY Core Curriculum Standards

Page 208: St 4 KI 2.1t & 2.1u, St 6 KI 1, 2, 4, 5, & 6
Page 209: St 6 KI 2, 4, & 5

Chapter 9

Surface Water

Refer to pages 8T–9T of the Teacher Guide for an explanation of the National Science Content Standards correlations.

Section	Objectives	National Science Content Standards	State/Local Standards
SECTION 9.1 **Surface Water Movement** 🕐 2 sessions 📦 1 block	1. **Explain** how surface water can move weathered materials. 2. **Explain** how a stream carries its load. 3. **Describe** how a floodplain develops.	UCP.1, UCP.2, UCP.3; A.1, A.2; B.2, B.4; D.1; F.3, F.5, F.6	St 1 Math KI 1, 2, 3, Science KI 1, 2, & 3, St 2 KI 3, St 4 KI 1.2g, 2.1i, 2.1r, 2.1t, 2.1u, & 2.1v, St 6 KI 1, 2, & 5
SECTION 9.2 **Stream Development** 🕐 1½ sessions 📦 1 block	4. **Describe** some of the physical features of stream development. 5. **Explain** the process of rejuvenation in stream development.	UCP.2, UCP.3, UCP.4, UCP.5; B.4; D.1	St 1 Math KI 1, 2, & 3, St 4 KI 2.1r, 2.1u, & 2.1v, St 6 KI 1, 2, 4, & 5
SECTION 9.3 **Lakes and Freshwater Wetlands** 🕐 2½ sessions 📦 1½ blocks	6. **Explain** the formation of freshwater lakes and wetlands. 7. **Describe** the process of eutrophication. 8. **Recognize** the effects of human activity on lake development.	UCP.1, UCP.2, UCP.3, UCP.4, UCP.5; A.1, A.2; B.4; C.4; D.1, D.3; F.4, F.5, F.6; G.3	St 1 Math KI 2, Science KI 1, 2, & 3, St 2 KI 3, St 4 KI 1.2g, 2.1r, 2.1u, 2.1v, & 2.1w, St 6 KI 1, 2, 4, 5, & 6, St 7 KI 2

**A complete Planning Guide is provided on pages 30T–32T.*

🕐 The number of recommended single-period sessions

📦 The number of recommended blocks

Activity Materials

Discovery Lab *page 211*
clear plastic shoe boxes (2), window screens (2), stopwatch, sod clump, soil clump, water

GeoLab *pages 232-233*
vinyl gutter tape (1 m), ring stand with clamp, stopwatch, grease pen, meter-stick, paper, hole punch, protractor with plumb bob, water source with hose, sink or large basin

MiniLab *page 229*
clear plastic shoe boxes (3), clay, sand, gravel, water

Demo *page 213*
soil, large clear containers (2), water

page 217
soil, water, hand lens, safety goggles

page 222
large tray, soil, cup or beaker, book, water

page 226
shallow container, soil, water

Need materials? Contact Science Kit at 1-800-828-7777 or at <u>www.sciencekit.com</u> on the Internet. For alternate materials, see the activity on the listed page.

Key to Teaching Strategies

L1 Level 1 activities should be appropriate for students with learning difficulties.

L2 Level 2 activities should be within the ability range of all students.

L3 Level 3 activities are designed for above-average students.

ELL ELL activities should be within the ability range of English-language learners.

COOP LEARN Cooperative learning activities are designed for small-group work.

P These strategies represent student products that can be placed in a best-work portfolio.

📦 These strategies are useful in a block-scheduling format.

Chapter Organizer

Activities/Features	Reproducible Masters	Transparencies
Discovery Lab: Modeling Water Movement, p. 211 **Problem-Solving Lab:** Using Graphs, p. 217	**Study Guide for Content Mastery,** pp. 53–54 L2 **Exploring Environmental Problems,** pp. 1–4 L3 **Laboratory Manual,** pp. 69–72 L2	**Section Focus Transparency 23** L1 ELL **Teaching Transparency 22** L2 ELL
Using Math: Using Numbers, p. 226	**Study Guide for Content Mastery,** pp. 55–56 L2 **Laboratory Manual,** pp. 65–68 L2	**Section Focus Transparency 24** L1 ELL **Teaching Transparency 23** L2 ELL
MiniLab: Surface Materials Determine Where a Lake Can Form, p. 229 **GeoLab:** Modeling Stream Velocity and Slope, pp. 232–233 **Science & the Environment:** The Jewel of Siberia, p. 234	**Study Guide for Content Mastery,** pp. 57–58 L2 **GeoLab and MiniLab Worksheets,** p. 35 L2 **GeoLab and MiniLab Worksheets,** pp. 36–38 L2	**Section Focus Transparency 25** L1 ELL **Teaching Transparency 24** L2 ELL

✔ Assessment

Chapter Assessment, pp. 49–54
Performance Assessment in the Science Classroom (PASC)
MindJogger Videoquiz DVD/VHS
Performance Assessment in Earth Science
ExamView® Pro CD-ROM
5 Days to the Regents Exam

Additional Resources

Guided Reading Audio Program ELL
Cooperative Learning in the Science Classroom
COOP LEARN
Lesson Plans
Block Scheduling
earthgeu.com
NY Lesson Plans
NY Block Scheduling
Review Handbook for Regents Earth Science Exam

NATIONAL GEOGRAPHIC

Teacher's Corner

Products Available from National Geographic Society
To order the following products, call the National Geographic Society at 1-800-368-2728:
CD-ROM
111 Years of National Geographic Magazine

Video
Water: A Celebration
Book
National Geographic Desk Reference

Content Background

Surface Water Movement
Section 9.1

The competence and capacity of a stream determine how much load the stream can carry. The maximum size of the particles that a stream can carry is referred to as its competence. The larger the particles a stream can carry, the greater the stream's competence. The competence of a stream is determined by the stream's velocity. The faster the water is moving, the more power it has to carry larger and larger particles. In general, the competence of a stream increases as the square of the stream's velocity. For example, if a stream's velocity doubles, the competence will increase fourfold, and if the velocity triples, the competence will increase nine times. The total load that can be carried by a stream is its capacity, which is related to the stream's discharge. The greater the volume of water that a stream is moving, the greater the stream's capacity. During times of flooding, an increase in both the velocity and volume of water occurs, and as a result, both the competence and capacity of a stream increase. Hence, floodwaters gain a tremendous amount of destructive and erosive power.

Stream Development
Section 9.2

A stream is part of a larger system called a drainage basin. A drainage basin consists of all the interconnecting streams that drain runoff into a particular river. The high areas between drainage basins are called divides. Divides may occur on a small or large scale. The Rocky Mountains are an example of a large divide. On the western side of the Rocky Mountains, runoff drains into the Pacific Ocean, while on the eastern side, runoff flows into the Gulf of Mexico. Drainage systems are often a network of streams. The patterns that streams make as they flow into one another depend on the bedrock over which the water is flowing. If the bedrock is generally uniform, the stream pattern is similar to tree branches. This pattern, called a dendritic pattern, is the most common. If the bedrock has a series of parallel joints and faults, a rectangular stream pattern forms, while if the bedrock has alternating parallel bands of rocks with varying degrees of resistance, a trellis pattern forms.

Multiple Learning Styles

- **Kinesthetic** Modeling, pp. 214, 225, Collaborative Learning, p. 215, Activity, p. 220
- **Visual-Spatial** Project, p. 213, Demo, p. 217
- **Interpersonal** Project, pp. 223, 226, 227, Modeling, p. 231
- **Intrapersonal** Applying Earth Science, p. 230
- **Linguistic** Earth Science Journal, pp. 214, 223, Reteach, p. 221
- **Logical-Mathematical** Project, p. 218

GLENCOE Technology

The following multimedia resources are available from Glencoe.

Vocabulary Puzzlemaker

TeacherWorks™ CD-ROM

MindJogger Videoquizzes DVD/VHS

ExamView® Pro CD-ROM

Interactive Chalkboard CD-ROM

Chapter Organizer

Lakes and Freshwater Wetlands
Section 9.3

All lakes consist of water and the materials contained within the water. If a lake bottom is porous, water will leach out of the depression. The depression will contain water only during times of heavy rain or excessive runoff from spring thaws. A depression that receives more water than it loses from leaching, evaporation, or use by people will remain as a lake for a long period of time. From a geological perspective, lakes are temporary water-holding areas.

Water on Earth's surface consists of living and nonliving components as well as water molecules. A lake is an ecosystem that contains organic and inorganic components, such as dissolved oxygen. Living organisms in the water use oxygen from and add waste products to the water. In addition, the decay of dead organisms depletes oxygen supplies in the water. The amount of dissolved oxygen (DO) and the biochemical oxygen demand (DOB) are two of the major factors that determine the quality of water for living things.

Identifying Misconceptions

Students often underestimate the power of moving water. However, moving water that is only a few centimeters deep can often easily move large objects. Students who have experienced the force of the moving water associated with waves along an ocean shore may need to be reminded of the strength of the force they felt at the time; perhaps they were even knocked off their feet. Students may not relate these experiences to the danger of driving through a flooded street or to the possibility of being swept away by floodwater, which can rise quickly. Refer students to *Figure 9-9,* which shows cars stranded during flood conditions. Also point out that water slamming against the shores of a lake during a storm not only poses a threat to humans, but also can damage or destroy buildings, docks, and boats.

Assessment

Portfolio Assessment
Assessment, TWE, p. 221

Performance Assessment
Discovery Lab, SE, p. 211
Assessment, TWE, p. 218
MiniLab, SE, p. 229
GeoLab, SE, pp. 232–233

Knowledge Assessment
Discovery Lab, TWE, p. 211
Assessment, TWE, pp. 216, 219, 224, 230, 231
Problem-Solving Lab, TWE, p. 217
Section Assessment, SE, pp. 221, 227, 231

MiniLab, TWE, p. 229
Chapter Assessment, SE, pp. 236–237

Skill Assessment
Assessment, TWE, pp. 223, 227
GeoLab, TWE, p. 232–233

Be sure to check the Earth Science Web Site for links to chapter material: <u>earthgeu.com</u>

GLENCOE'S
ASSESSMENT
ADVANTAGE

Introducing the Chapter

Have students describe the ways in which they use water. Compile students' responses on the chalkboard. The list can then be categorized by uses, such as essential uses, recreational uses, and so on. Pose the following question for students to answer: Can you live without water? Having students recognize the importance of water will prepare them for the study of Earth's surface water.

Interpreting the Photo

This is a photo of a woman sea kayaking in Alaska. Water is essential to human beings, because we need water to live. Ask students to list ways surface water is important to us.

INTERACTIVE CHALKBOARD
with Image Bank

PowerPoint® Presentations

This CD is an editable Microsoft® PowerPoint® presentation that includes:
• Section presentations
• Section checks
• Image bank
• Links to Earth Science Online
• All transparencies
• Animations
• Audio

Chapter 9

What You'll Learn

• What landscape features on Earth are formed and changed by surface water.

• How surface water moves materials and impacts humans.

Why It's Important

Landscape features formed by surface water are among the most numerous and visible features on Earth. Running water has the greatest impact on humans because we depend on streams for drinking-water supplies and irrigation. Humans also experience the negative effects of floods.

Earth Science Online

To find out more about surface water, visit the Earth Science Web Site at earthgeu.com

210

Surface Water

Discovery Lab

Process Skills

observe and infer, recognize cause and effect, communicate, model, measure, use numbers **L1** **ELL**

Safety Precaution

Make sure that students wear safety goggles.

Disposal

Provide a bucket for muddy water to be collected and discarded outside the school building onto a grassy area.

Preparation

Materials needed for this lab include two window screens big enough to lay over the plastic boxes, an 8 cm × 16 cm clump of sod or a mat of grass, and an 8 cm × 16 cm clump of barren soil. Make sure the plastic boxes do not leak.

Procedure

Have students measure the water to the nearest millimeter.

Discovery Lab

Modeling Water Movement

When water seeps into the ground, it moves at various rates through the different materials that make up Earth's surface. These Earth materials are comprised of different particle sizes. In this activity, you will investigate the movement of water as it seeps through two different kinds of Earth materials.

1. Place a small window screen on each of two clear plastic shoe boxes.

2. Place an 8 cm × 16 cm clump of grass or sod on one screen.

3. Place an 8 cm × 16 cm clump of barren soil on the other screen.

4. Lightly sprinkle 500 mL of water on each clump.

🔧 **CAUTION:** *Always wear an apron in the lab.*

Observe In your science journal, describe what happens to the water after five minutes. Measure how much water passes through each clump and collects in the plastic shoe box. Explain any differences in the amount of water collected in each plastic shoe box.

SECTION 9.1 *Surface Water Movement*

OBJECTIVES

- **Explain** *how surface water can move weathered materials.*

- **Explain** *how a stream carries its load.*

- **Describe** *how a floodplain develops.*

VOCABULARY

runoff	bed load
watershed	discharge
divide	flood
solution	floodplain
suspension	

Earth's water supply is recycled in a continuous process called the water cycle. Water molecules move continuously through the water cycle following many pathways: they evaporate from a body of water or the surface of Earth, condense into cloud droplets, fall as precipitation back to Earth's surface, and soak into the ground. As part of a continuous cycle, the water eventually evaporates back into the atmosphere, again forms clouds, again falls as precipitation, and so on. Understanding the mechanics of the water cycle helps to explain the reasons for variations in the amount of water that is available throughout the world.

Often, a water molecule's pathway involves time spent within a living organism or as part of a snowfield, glacier, lake, or ocean. Although water molecules may follow a number of different pathways, the overall process is one of repeated evaporation and condensation powered by the Sun's energy. What happens once water reaches Earth's surface? Does all the water sink into the ground or evaporate?

9.1 Surface Water Movement **211**

Observe
Students will readily see that the sod holds more water than the barren soil. The amount of water that collects in the plastic box below the soil should be significantly greater than the water in the box below the sod.

✔ Assessment

Knowledge Ask students which will hold more water from precipitation, a surface with or without vegetation. The surface with vegetation holds more water than the surface without vegetation.

Resource Manager

Study Guide for Content Mastery, pp. 53–54 ⏹ L2

Section Focus Transparency 23 L1 ELL

Section 9.1

1 Focus

Section Focus

Before presenting the lesson, display **Section Focus Transparency 23** on the overhead projector.
L1 ELL

Chapter Themes

The following themes from the National Science Content Standards are covered in this chapter. Refer to page 8T of the Teacher Guide for an explanation of the correlations.
Systems, order, and organization (UCP.1); Evidence, models, and explanation (UCP.2); Change, constancy, and measurement (UCP.3)

 **Out of Time?**

If time does not permit teaching the entire chapter, use the Chapter Summary on page 235 and the GeoDigest found at the end of the unit as an overview.

NY Core Curriculum Standards

Page 210: St 4 KI 1.2g, St 6 KI 1
Page 211: St 1 Science KI 1, 2, & 3, St 4 KI 1.2g, St 6 KI 1 & 5

211

Identifying Misconceptions

Most students think that clouds are made up of water vapor.

Uncover the Misconception
Ask students what clouds are made of. Students usually respond that clouds are made up of water vapor and air.

Demonstrate the Concept
Tell students that cloud droplets form when air becomes saturated with water vapor and the water vapor condenses on small, solid particles called condensation nuclei, such as dust, pollen, or salt. Explain that condensation is the changing of a gas to a liquid (when water vapor condenses into the solid water particles). Tell students that these liquid drops are suspended in the atmosphere and that when they occur in concentrations large enough to block out varying degrees of sunlight so that they can be recognized as a mass in themselves, the aggregate of droplets is referred to as a cloud. Hence, clouds are composed of liquid drops of water, not water vapor.

Assess New Knowledge
Ask students to answer the following question. Which of the following is a true statement?
a. Clouds are made up of concentrated water vapor.
b. Clouds are made up of liquid drops of water.
c. Clouds are made up of atmospheric gases and water vapor.
d. Clouds are made up of dust particles floating in air.
The answer is B.

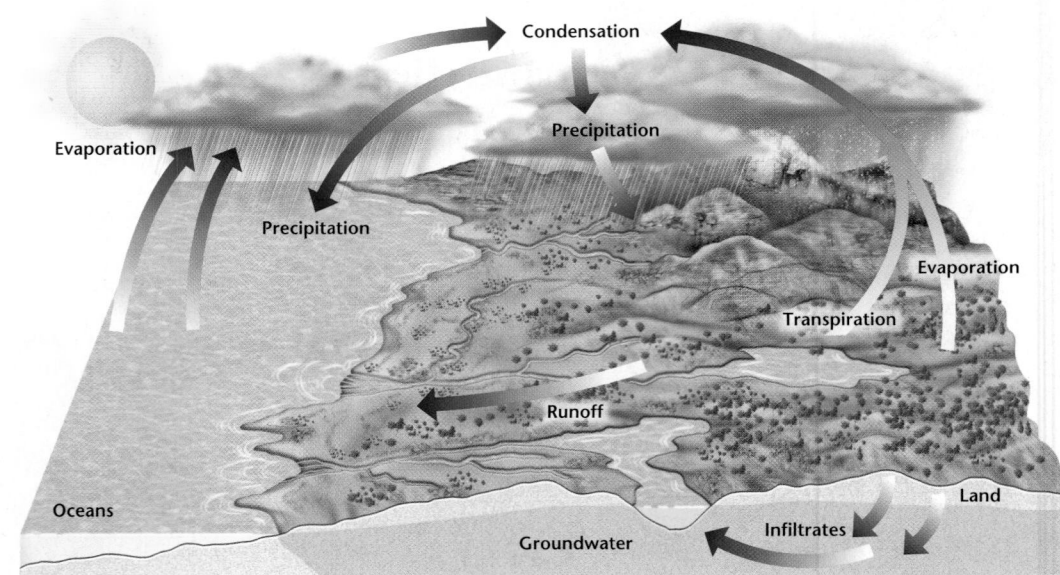

Figure 9-1 The water cycle, also referred to as the hydrologic cycle, is a never-ending, natural circulation of water through Earth's systems. The Sun provides the energy for the water cycle. Radiation from the Sun causes water to change to a gas called water vapor. The process of water vapor changing to a fluid is called condensation.

RUNOFF

As shown in *Figure 9-1,* precipitation falls to Earth's surface in the form of rain, snow, sleet, or hail. In most instances, solid forms of precipitation, such as snow, sleet, and hail, may eventually melt. Or they can also be incorporated into the mass of a glacier. Once water reaches Earth's surface, it can evaporate into the atmosphere, soak into the ground, or flow down slopes on Earth's surface. Water flowing downslope along Earth's surface is called **runoff.** Runoff may reach a stream, river, or lake, may evaporate, or it may accumulate as puddles in low-lying small depressions and eventually seep into the ground. During and after heavy rains, you can observe these processes occurring in your own yard or local park. Water that seeps into Earth's surface becomes groundwater.

A number of conditions determine whether water on Earth's surface will seep into the ground or become runoff. For water to enter the ground, there must be large enough pores or spaces in the ground's surface materials to accommodate the water's volume, as in the loose soil illustrated in *Figure 9-2A.* If the pores already contain water, the newly fallen precipitation will either remain standing on top of the ground or, if the area has a slope, run downhill. Water standing on the surface of Earth eventually evaporates or flows away.

Content Background
Runoff that consolidates in long, narrow depressions produces channel or stream flows. Runoff that flows downslope in generally broad sheets is called overland flow. There are different types of overland flows. When runoff flows over smooth surfaces in continuous, thin sheets, it is called sheet flow. Runoff that flows over steep slopes of bare soil or less resistant bedrock flows in long, slender channels called shoestring rills.

Tying to Previous Knowledge
Ask students what they notice when a glass of ice water sits on a table during the summer. The glass seems to sweat and water appears around the glass. Explain to students that what happens to the glass is part of the water cycle. The cooled container of water cools the air and causes water vapor in the air to condense and form water on the outside of the glass of ice water.

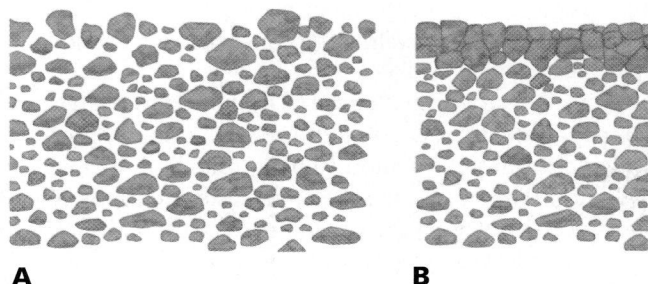

A   **B**

Figure 9-2 Soil that has open surface pores or spaces between particles allows water to infiltrate **(A).** Soil that has few or no pores or spaces can restrict water's ability to seep in **(B).**

Vegetation Soils that contain grasses or other vegetation allow more water to enter the ground than do soils with no vegetation. Precipitation falling on vegetation slowly flows down leaves and branches, and it eventually drops gently to the ground. In contrast, precipitation falls with far more force onto barren land. In such areas, soil particles clump together and form dense aggregates with few pores or spaces between them. The force of falling rain may then push the soil clumps together, thereby closing pores and allowing less water to enter, as illustrated in *Figure 9-2B.* This is why gardeners do not pack the soil around their plants. Compacting the soil reduces the spaces between the particles that are available for water to seep in, thus reducing the amount of water that is available to the plants' roots.

Rate of Precipitation Light, gentle precipitation infiltrates the dry ground. However, the rate of precipitation may temporarily exceed the rate of infiltration. For example, during heavy precipitation, water falls too quickly to soak into the ground and becomes runoff. Thus, a gentle, long-lasting rainfall is more beneficial to plants and causes less erosion by runoff than a torrential downpour. If you have a garden, remember that more water will enter the ground if you water your plants slowly and gently.

Soil Composition The physical and chemical composition of soil also affects its water-holding capacity. Soil consists of decayed organic matter, called humus, and minerals. Humus creates pores in the soil, thereby increasing a soil's ability to retain water. The minerals in soil have different particle sizes, which are classified as sand, silt, or clay. As you learned in Chapter 7, the percentages of particles of each size vary from soil to soil. Soil with a high percentage of coarse particles, such as sand, has relatively large pores between its particles that allow water to enter and pass through the soil quickly. In contrast, soil with a high percentage of fine particles, such as clay, clumps together and has few or no spaces between the particles.

9.1 *Surface Water Movement* **213**

Demo

Pack soil into a large, clear container. Fill another clear container loosely with soil. Sprinkle equal amounts of water into both containers of soil. Ask students to note which container of soil allows the most water to penetrate. The loosely packed soil allows more water to penetrate because it has spaces available for the water. The packed soil has few or no spaces for the water to enter.

Project

Visual-Spatial Have students each devise an experiment that compares the water-holding capacity of soils with different percentages of humus. Students can begin with soil samples that have little humus and can then use mixtures of this soil and a given percentage of partially decayed organic matter, such as leaves. Possible ratios of original soil samples to organic matter include 25:75, 50:50, and 75:25. Students can use graduated cylinders to measure how much water can be added to the soil mixtures before they become saturated. The data can then be compiled in table format and graphed. Ask students to draw conclusions from their data. Also ask students what possible sources of error may exist for their setups. **L2**

Differentiated Instruction

Learning Disabled Prepare several cardboard boxes with approximately 15 centimeters of various types of soil in each. You may use packed clay, sand, topsoil, and gravel. Have students slowly pour 40 milliliters of water into each box and place the boxes on separate cookie sheets. Have students check the bottoms of the boxes at one-minute intervals for signs that moisture has begun to leak through. Have students discuss their observations.

NY Core Curriculum Standards

Page 212: St 4 KI 1.2g, St 6 KI 1 & 5
Page 213: St 4 KI 1.2g, St 6 KI 1 & 5

Modeling

Kinesthetic Have students work in groups of four to make a model of a stream system. This can be done using a stream table or a large tray with a mound of dirt placed at one end. Have students sprinkle water from a hose or watering can over the mass of dirt and allow the water to form rills and gullies. Larger streams will naturally form with tributaries and meanders. The moving water within the stream system will carry and deposit different particle sizes in the same manner as a stream does when it flows over Earth's surface. The erosional and depositional features of stream action will also be evident in the student models. Make sure that students carefully watch during the setup to avoid water overflows onto the classroom floor. **L1** **ELL**

Using Scientific Terms

The words *stream* and *river* can be used interchangeably in Earth science for the most part. Although the word *river* generally indicates a large stream, water moves in the same manner in both small and large bodies of moving water. As a result, the word *stream* is commonly used to refer to moving bodies of water of various sizes.

In-Text Question

Page 214 If there are any brooks or streams near your home, can you locate where they feed into other streams or lakes? Encourage students to consult maps of their area to discover the routes of local streams.

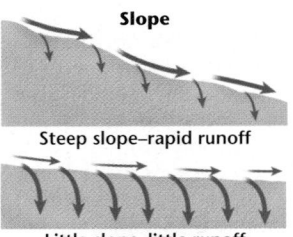

Figure 9-3 The angle of a slope is one variable that influences the movement of surface water on a slope.

NATIONAL GEOGRAPHIC

To learn more about rivers, go to the National Geographic Expedition on page 870.

Figure 9-4 Numerous tributaries flow into several stream systems that drain into the Salton Sea in California.

Such small pores restrict both the amount of water that can enter the ground and the ease of movement of water through the soil.

Slope As you have learned, the slope of a land area plays a large role in determining the ability of water to enter the ground, as shown in *Figure 9-3*. Water from precipitation falling on slopes flows to areas of lower elevation. The steeper the slope, the faster the water flows. There is also greater potential for erosion on steep slopes. In areas with steep slopes, little water seeps into the ground before it runs off.

STREAM SYSTEMS

Precipitation that does not enter the ground usually runs off the surface quickly. Some surface water flows in thin sheets and eventually collects in small channels. As the amount of runoff increases, the channels widen, deepen, and become longer. Although it is common for these small channels to dry up shortly after precipitation stops, the channels again fill with water each time it rains and become larger and longer. If a sufficient supply of water develops, the water begins to flow more permanently in a channel and can become a stream.

All streams flow downslope in a watery path to lower elevations. However, the path of a stream can vary considerably, depending on the slope of the land and the type of material through which the stream flows. Some streams flow into lakes, while others flow directly into the ocean. Still others, called tributaries, flow into other streams, as shown in *Figure 9-4.* Each tributary increases the size of the stream it is joining and adds water to it. A large stream is called a river, and all its tributaries make up a stream, or river system. Small streams are called brooks and creeks. If there are any brooks or streams near your home, can you locate where they feed into other streams or lakes?

Earth Science
Journal

Science Field Book

Linguistic Have students write a story in their science journals that is centered around a stream. Ask students to write their stories so that a reader can visualize features of the stream, including size, velocity, shape, source, and surroundings. Have each student add to the finished story a cover page portraying some aspect of the story involving the stream. **P**

WATERSHEDS AND DIVIDES

All of the land area whose water drains into a stream system is called the system's **watershed,** or drainage basin. Watersheds can be relatively small or extremely large in area. A **divide** is a high land area that separates one watershed from another. Each tributary in a stream system has its own watershed and divides, but they are all part of the larger stream system to which the tributary belongs. The watershed of the Mississippi River, shown in *Figure 9-5,* is the largest in North America.

STREAM LOAD

All the materials that the water in a stream carries is known as the stream's load. The living components of water include microscopic life-forms as well as larger plants and animals. The nonliving components of surface water include sediments, dissolved solids, and dissolved atmospheric gases, such as oxygen. There are three ways in which a stream carries its load.

Solution Material is carried in **solution** after it becomes dissolved in a stream's water. How much of a stream's load is carried in solution depends on the material through which the stream's water has passed. When water runs through or over rocks containing soluble

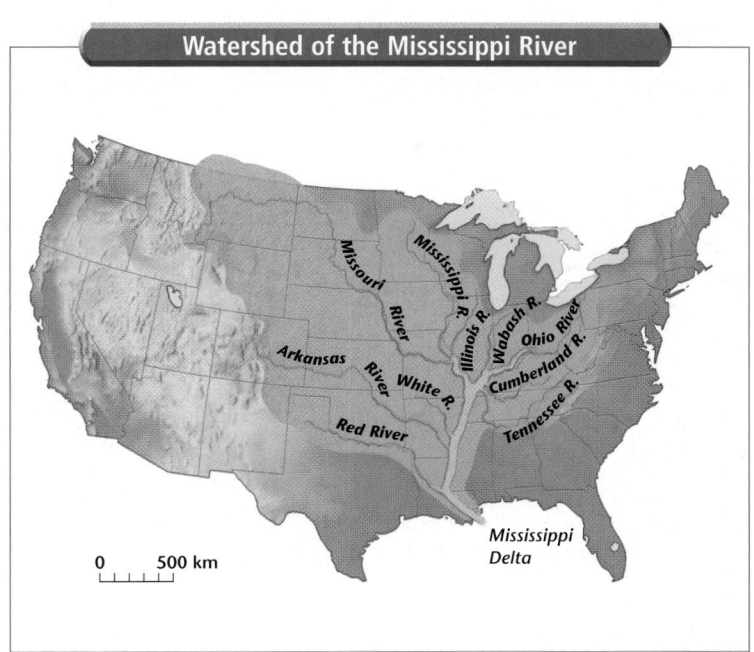

Watershed of the Mississippi River

0   500 km

Missouri River

Mississippi R.

Illinois R.

Wabash R.

Ohio River

Cumberland R.

Arkansas River

White R.

Tennessee R.

Red River

Mississippi Delta

Figure 9-5 The watershed of the Mississippi River includes a large stream system. *How many major rivers are part of the Mississippi watershed?*

9.1 *Surface Water Movement* **215**

215

Environmental Connection

The quality of a stream's water is often determined based on the concentration, in parts per million, of various chemicals. Environmental conditions affect what and how much of a substance is dissolved in a stream and added to its dissolved load. Environmental conditions can be natural or influenced by humans. Monitoring concentrations at various stream locations can indicate whether harmful material is being added to the water from various sources. Volunteers often act as watchdog groups to bring information about harmful additives in water to the public's attention.

Discussion

Ask students why groundwater adds most of a stream's dissolved load, while runoff adds only a small amount. Groundwater, in general, moves over and through rocks for a longer period of time than runoff moves over Earth's surface. As a result, groundwater has more opportunity to come in contact with the minerals in rocks and dissolve them. Runoff, on the other hand, not only spends less time moving over Earth's surface, but it also may not flow directly on the rocks themselves but may instead flow over vegetation.

minerals, it dissolves small amounts of the minerals and carries them away in solution. Water may readily dissolve calcium carbonate from limestone and marble, for example. Streams also commonly carry soluble magnesium compounds. Groundwater adds most of the dissolved load to stream water, while runoff adds only a very small amount.

The amount of dissolved material that water carries is often expressed in parts per million, or ppm, as shown in *Table 9-1.* For example, a measurement of 10 ppm means that there are 10 parts of dissolved material for every 1 million parts of water. The total concentration of materials in solution in streams averages 115–120 ppm, although some streams carry as little dissolved materials as 10 ppm. Values greater than 10 000 ppm have been observed for streams draining desert basins. Measuring the amount of material in solution helps scientists monitor water quality.

Suspension All particles small enough to be held up by the turbulence of a stream's moving water are carried in **suspension.** Particles, such as silt, clay, and sand, that are carried in suspension are part of a stream's suspended load. The amount of material in suspension varies with the volume and velocity of the stream water. Rapidly moving water can carry larger particles in suspension than slowly moving water can. As the velocity of water decreases, the heavier particles settle to the bottom, as you can see by doing the *Problem-Solving Lab* on the next page.

Table 9-1 Concentrations of Some Materials Dissolved in River Water and Seawater

Materials	Concentration (ppm)			
	Amazon River	Mississippi River	World Average (est.)	Average Seawater
Silica (SiO$_2$)	7.0	6.7	13.0	6.4
Calcium (Ca^{2+})	4.3	42.0	15.0	400.0
Sodium (Na$^+$)	1.8	25.0	6.3	10 500.0
Potassium (K$^+$)	—	2.9	2.3	380.0
Magnesium (Mg^{2+})	1.1	12.0	4.1	1350.0
Chloride (Cl$^-$)	1.9	30.0	7.8	19 000.0
Fluoride (F$^-$)	0.2	0.2	—	1.3
Sulfate (SO$_4^{2-}$)	3.0	56.0	11.0	2700.0
Bicarbonate (HCO$_3^-$)	19.0	132.0	58.0	142.0
Nitrate (NO$_3^-$)	0.1	2.4	1.0	0.5

Source: J. D. Hem, *Study and Interpretation of the Chemical Characteristics of Natural Water,* U.S. Geological Survey Water-Supply Paper 1473, 1970, pp. 11, 12, and 50.

216 CHAPTER 9 *Surface Water*

✓ Assessment

Knowledge Ask students the following question. Sand, silt, and clay are present in streams in what state?
a. in solution
b. in suspension
c. in parts per million
d. in a dissolved state
The answer is B.

Bed Load Sediments that are too large or heavy to be held up by turbulent water are transported by streams in another manner. A stream's **bed load** consists of sand, pebbles, and cobbles that the stream's water can roll or push along the bed of the stream. The faster the water moves, the larger the particles it can carry both in suspension and as part of its bed load. As the particles move, they rub, scrape, and grind against one another or against the solid rock of the streambed in a process called abrasion, the wearing away of solid Earth material. This action contributes to the physical weathering of the stream's bottom and sides, and it provides an additional source of material to be eroded by the stream, either in solution or as part of the suspended load.

As gravity pulls stream water to lower elevations, the stream's load moves along with the water. The moving water continuously tosses and tumbles the weathered material, whose pieces become smooth and rounded over time, as shown in *Figure 9-6.* Most pebbles along the bottoms and sides of streams are round and polished as a result of this process.

Bed load sediments not only wear away one another, but they also abrade the surface of the streambed. Potholes may form on the bottoms of streams where pebbles have continued to swirl around in

Figure 9-6 The rounded shapes and smooth pebbles were caused by the stream erosion of the Snake River in Grand Teton National Park, Wyoming.

Problem-Solving Lab

Using Graphs

Predict how sediments move in a stream The velocity of water affects the transport of different-sized particles.

Analysis
1. Study the graph at right.
2. At what velocity would flowing water pick up a pebble?
3. Over what range of velocities would flowing water carry a pebble?

Thinking Critically
4. Infer which of the following objects would not fall into the same size range as a pebble: a large chicken egg, a baseball, a golf ball, a table-tennis ball, a volleyball, and a pea. How would you test your conclusions?

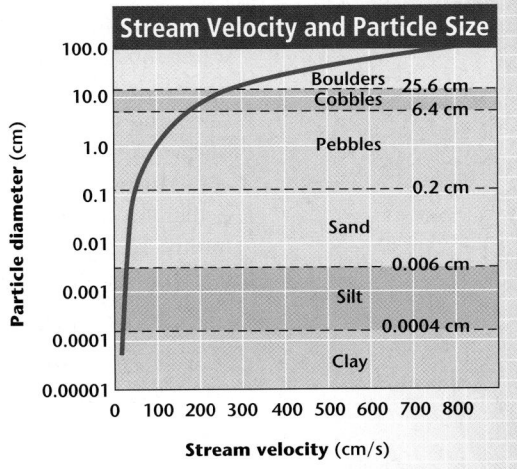

Stream Velocity and Particle Size

Particle diameter (cm) — vertical axis: 100.0, 10.0, 1.0, 0.1, 0.01, 0.001, 0.0001, 0.00001

Boulders 25.6 cm
Cobbles 6.4 cm
Pebbles
0.2 cm
Sand
0.006 cm
Silt
0.0004 cm
Clay

Stream velocity (cm/s) — horizontal axis: 0, 100, 200, 300, 400, 500, 600, 700, 800

Problem-Solving Lab

Purpose
Students will apply the concept of how the velocity of water affects the transport of different-sized sediments by reading and interpreting a graph.

Process Skills
use graphs, use numbers

Materials
paper, pencil

Teaching Strategies
• Ask students whether they have ever dropped something into a stream and had it carried away by the stream. Did some objects simply fall to the bottom of the stream, or did they move along with the stream? Have students share their experiences.
• Review with students the function of the *x*-axis and the *y*-axis on the graph.

Analysis
1. Give students time to study the graph.
2. at 50 cm/s
3. 50 cm/s

Thinking Critically
4. Baseball and volleyball; measure the objects to see if they fall between 0.2 and 6.4 cm.

✓ Assessment

Knowledge Ask students whether they can imagine a situation that would prevent the results from falling into the ranges given. If the particles had varied shapes, they could become caught in grooves and niches along stream channels, or if the particles were made of very dense or very light material, they might produce results outside of the given ranges.

Demo

Visual-Spatial Run water over a mound of soil and have students observe the bed load with a hand lens. **CAUTION:** *Have students wear safety goggles during their observation period.* Ask them to describe how the sediment particles are moving. They should observe that the rounder sediments roll and the flatter sediments slide in the water. The smaller sediments may be suspended in the water, while the heavier sediments will roll along the bottom.

Figure 9-7 The potholes in this Wisconsin River streambed were scoured out by the abrasive action of the stream's bed load. The river is located at Grandfather Falls, Wisconsin.

Project

Logical-Mathematical
Have students collect and label water samples from several streams and then allow the sediment in the water samples to settle. Have students separate the sediments by particle size. Ask students to describe each of the groups of sediments that they have separated. Ask students to use the data that they have collected to estimate the speed (slow or swiftly moving) and depth (shallow or deep) of the body of water from which each sample was taken. Students should then write a report in which they compare their estimations to the actual conditions of the stream from which each sample was taken. Student reports should include any problems encountered and possible explanations for any discrepancies between their data and actual conditions.

L2 **COOP LEARN**

✓Assessment

Performance Have students sketch different shapes and sizes of streambeds. Sketches should also show the slopes of the stream channels. Ask students to predict in which conditions the stream would move most quickly or slowly. Streams with steep slopes are more likely to move quickly. Water moving in streambeds offering the least resistance are most likely to move quickly. Use the Performance Task Assessment List for Scientific Drawing in **PASC,** p. 55.

one area and have slowly worn holes into solid rock. For example, potholes more than 3 m deep have formed near Little Falls, New York, in the Mohawk River Valley. Potholes can be found even in streambeds composed of very hard, exposed bedrock. The huge depressions in the streambed of the Wisconsin River, shown in *Figure 9-7,* were scoured out of granite. Large streambed potholes dramatically illustrate the powerful abrasive action caused by a stream's bed load.

STREAM VELOCITY AND CARRYING CAPACITY

The ability of a stream to transport material, referred to as its carrying capacity, depends on both the velocity and the amount of water moving in the stream. Study *Figure 9-8* as you read. The channel's slope, depth, and width all affect the speed and direction in which water moves within it. A stream's water moves more quickly where there is less friction; consequently, smooth-sided channels with great slope and depth allow water to move most rapidly. The total volume of moving water also affects a stream's carrying capacity. **Discharge** is the measure of the volume of stream water that flows over a particular location within a given period of time. Discharge is commonly expressed in cubic meters per second (m^3/s). The following formula is used to calculate the discharge of a stream:

$$\text{discharge} = \text{width} \times \text{depth} \times \text{velocity}$$
$$(m^3/s) \qquad (m) \qquad (m) \qquad (m/s)$$

The largest river in North America, the Mississippi, has a huge average discharge of 173 600 m^3/s. However, the Amazon River, the largest in the world, has an incredible discharge ten times that amount. The discharge from the Amazon River over a 24-hour period would supply New York City's water needs for nine years!

Across the Curriculum

History Have students each write a report about how streams have affected the history of a country. Students may write about the role that a stream played in a battle, a fight for water rights, the use of a stream as a boundary, or the problems associated with the need to cross streams.

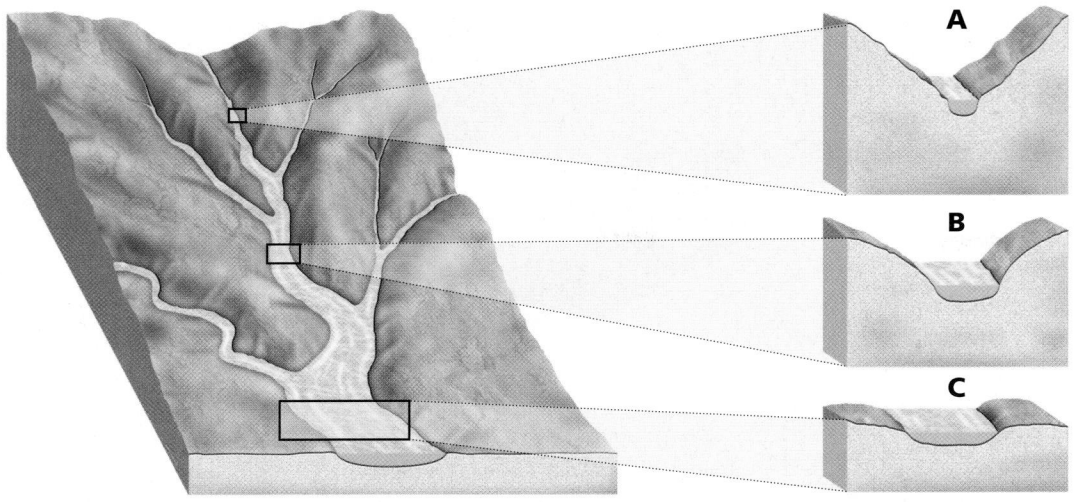

Figure 9-8 Describe the changes in the downstream direction of the stream's channel as the water flows from section A to section C.

As a stream's discharge increases, the stream's carrying capacity increases as well. The increased discharge results in a stream with greater carrying capacity as modeled in the *GeoLab* at the end of the chapter. Both water velocity and volume increase during times of heavy precipitation, rapid melting of snow, and flooding. In addition to increasing a stream's carrying capacity, these conditions heighten a stream's ability to erode the land over which it passes. As a result of an increase in erosional power, a streambed can widen and deepen, thereby increasing the stream slope and further adding to the stream's carrying capacity. As shown in *Figure 9-9,* the extraordinary power of water during such times can be especially hazardous for people who do not anticipate the dangers associated with flooding.

FLOODPLAINS

The amount of water being transported in a particular stream at any given time varies with weather conditions. Sometimes, more water pours into a stream than the banks of the stream channel can hold. A **flood** occurs when water spills over the sides of a stream's banks onto the adjacent land. The broad, flat area that extends out from a stream's bank and is covered by excess water during times of flooding is known as the stream's **floodplain.** Floodwater carries along with it a great amount of sediment eroded from Earth's surface and the sides of the stream channel. As floodwater recedes and its volume and speed decrease, the water drops its sediment load onto the stream's floodplain.

Figure 9-9 Several days of heavy rains in Buenos Aires, Argentina caused flood waters to strand traffic in the city.

9.1 *Surface Water Movement* **219**

Resource Manager

Laboratory Manual, pp. 69–72 L2

Figure 9-10 Floodplain
deposits contain fertile soils.

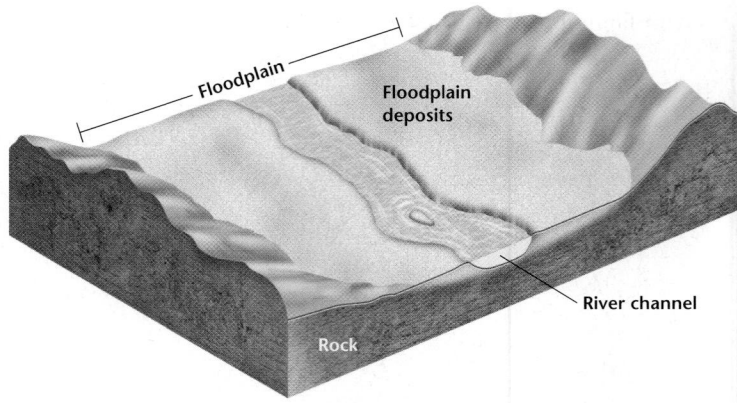

Activity

Kinesthetic Students will need water, a spray bottle, 2 dry sponges, and a dishpan for this activity. Have students place one dry sponge in a tilted dishpan. They should spray the sponge for exactly one minute on the spray nozzle setting, and then repeat with the other dry sponge and the mist setting. Ask students to record their observations. How do the two different nozzle settings relate to the natural environment? **ELL**

Applying Earth Science

Show students a FEMA flood insurance rate map (FIRM) or the equivalent digital Q3 map. Ask students to make observations about the flood zones and compare the FIRM map with a topographic map of the same area. Explain what the flood lines mean. FEMA FIRMs can be obtained by phone, fax, or mail for your area: Map Service Center, P.O. Box 1038, Jessup, MD 20794-1038, Tel: (800) 358-9616, Fax: (800) 358-9620.

Earth Science Online

Topic: Floods
To find out more about floods and flood prevention, visit the Earth Science Web Site at earthgeu.com

Activity: Write a brief report to compare and contrast the flooding of the Yellow River in China, the Nile River in Egypt, and the Mississippi River in the United States.

Figure 9-11 Davenport, Iowa was just one of many areas that was flooded by the Mississippi River in 1993.

Figure 9-10 illustrates a floodplain after a river overflows its channel. Floodplains develop highly fertile soils as more sediment is deposited with each subsequent flood. These fertile soils have historically enticed farmers to use the land for crop production, even at the risk of losing homes and crops to subsequent flooding.

FLOODS

Floods are a natural occurrence. When a stream reaches its flood stage, a flood can occur, as shown in ***Figure 9-11.*** Flood stage is the level at which a stream overflows its banks and the crest of the stream is the maximum height. Because it takes time for runoff to collect in streams, the water continues to rise and may reach its crest days after precipitation ends. The resulting flooding may occur over localized, small areas or across large regions. The flooding of a small area is known as an upstream flood. Sudden rainstorms that drop large amounts of rain within a short period of time cause upstream floods,

NY Core Curriculum Standards

Page 220: St 4 KI 1.2g, 2.1i, & 2.1r, St 6 KI 1 & 5
Page 221: St 2 KI 3, St 4 KI 1.2g, 2.1i, & 2.1t, St 6 KI 1, 2, & 5

as do dam failures. Although they are localized, upstream floods can do a great deal of damage within a very short period of time.

Heavy accumulations of excess water from large regional drainage systems result in downstream floods. Such floods occur during or after long-lasting, intense storms or spring thaws of large snowpacks. The tremendous volumes of water involved in a downstream flood can result in extensive damage. For example, the devastating floods in 1993 along the Mississippi River, which frequently causes downstream flooding, left landscape scars that are still visible today.

FLOOD MONITORING AND WARNING SYSTEMS

In an attempt to provide warnings for people at risk, government agencies monitor potential flood conditions. The National Weather Service monitors changing weather conditions. Earth-orbiting weather satellites photograph Earth and collect and transmit information about weather conditions, storms, and streams. In addition, the U.S. Geological Survey (USGS) has established gauging stations, as shown in *Figure 9-12,* on approximately 4400 streams in the United States. The gauging stations provide a continuous record of the water level in each stream. Technological advances have made it possible for anyone with Internet access to obtain real-time data on streams through government-sponsored Web sites.

In areas that are prone to severe flooding, warning systems are the first step in implementing emergency management plans. Flood warnings and emergency plans often allow people to safely evacuate an area in advance of a flood.

Figure 9-12 This USGS stream gauging station is located in the northwest section of Washington State.

ENVIRONMENTAL CONNECTION

SECTION ASSESSMENT

1. Describe ways in which moving water can carve a landscape.

2. Explain the three ways in which a stream carries its load.

3. What is the relationship between the carrying capacity of a stream and its discharge and velocity?

4. Explain why little water from runoff seeps into the ground in areas of steep slopes.

5. Discuss how a floodplain forms and why people live on floodplains.

6. **Thinking Critically** Under what conditions might a stream's volume increase, and under what conditions might it decrease? How would the size of the sediment particles in the stream's load differ in the two situations?

SKILL REVIEW

7. **Making Tables** Design a data table that compares how silt, clay, sand, and large pebbles settle to the bottom of a stream as the velocity of water decreases. For more help, refer to the *Skill Handbook.*

earthgeu.com/self_check_quiz

9.1 *Surface Water Movement* **221**

Section Background

For section content background, refer to **Stream Development** on page 210C.

Preplanning

Refer to the Chapter Organizer on pages 210A–B.

1 Focus

Section Focus

Before presenting the lesson, display **Section Focus Transparency 24** on the overhead projector.
L1 **ELL**

Demo

Spread soil evenly over the bottom of a large tray. Prop up one side of the tray by placing a thin book under one side. Pour water from a cup or beaker onto the higher side of the tray. Have students note what happens to the water. After the water has moved toward the lower end of the tray, ask students to examine the source, channel, and banks of the temporary stream.

Stream Development

OBJECTIVES

- **Describe** *some of the physical features of stream development.*
- **Explain** *the process of rejuvenation in stream development.*

VOCABULARY

stream channel
stream bank
meander
delta
rejuvenation

As a stream develops, it changes in shape, width, and size, as well as the landscapes over which it flows. Stream flow is part of a dynamic system that is greatly influenced by the varying environmental conditions of the stream's surroundings.

MOVING WATER CARVES A PATH

The first and foremost condition necessary for stream formation is an adequate supply of water. Precipitation provides the water for the beginnings of stream formation. In areas where precipitation falls infrequently, stream development and flow are also infrequent. For example, in some desert areas, where years pass between rainfalls, the streams that form are short-lived. However, most parts of the temperate and tropical regions on Earth experience precipitation on a regular basis.

The region where water first accumulates to supply a stream is called the headwaters. It is common for a stream's headwaters to be high in the mountains. Falling precipitation accumulates in small gullies at these higher elevations and forms briskly moving streams. As surface water first begins its flow, its path may not be well defined. In time, however, the moving water carves a narrow pathway into the sediment or rock called a **stream channel.** The channel widens and deepens as more and more water accumulates and cuts into Earth's surface. As shown in *Figure 9-13,* the moving water is held within the confines of the stream channel by the **stream banks,** the ground bordering the stream on each side. If you have ever fished in a stream, you might have sat on a stream bank to do so.

Figure 9-13 The river banks confine the water of the San Pedro River in the San Pedro Riparian National Conservation Area in Arizona.

222 CHAPTER 9 *Surface Water*

Resource Manager

Study Guide for Content Mastery,
pp. 55–56 **L2**

Section Focus Transparency 24 **L1** **ELL**

Across the Curriculum

Math Give students topographic maps of two types of streams and ask them to compare the stream gradients of each. The gradient is determined by the change in elevation, in feet, divided by the change in distance, in miles [(elevation A – elevation B) / (total distance between point A and B)]. This is easily remembered by the phrase "rise over run."

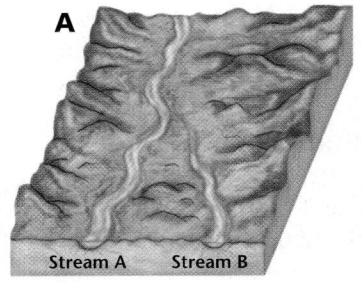

A

Stream A Stream B

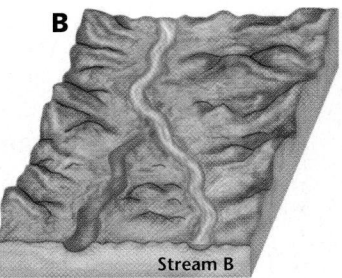

B

Stream B

Figure 9-14 The headward erosion of stream B cuts into stream A and draws away its waters into one stream.

The process by which small streams erode away the rock or soil at the head of a stream is known as headward erosion. Headward erosion involves lengthening the stream. Streams at this point in their development are relatively small and narrow. These streams move swiftly over the rough terrain, and they often form waterfalls and rapids as they flow over steep inclines.

Sometimes, a stream erodes its way through the high area separating two drainage basins, joins another stream, and then draws away its water. This process is called stream capture, or stream piracy. As shown in *Figure 9-14,* the lower portion of the captured stream loses its water source, while the invading stream gains an additional source of water.

FORMATION OF STREAM VALLEYS

As a stream actively erodes its path through the sediment or rock, a V-shaped channel develops. V-shaped channels have steep sides and sometimes form canyons or gorges. The Grand Canyon is perhaps the best-known example of a V-shaped valley carved by a stream, the Colorado River. Ausable Chasm, in New York State, is another impressive, but very narrow, deep gorge carved by a stream. *Figure 9-15* shows the classic V-shaped valley created by the Yellowstone River.

A stream continues to erode until it reaches its base level, the elevation at which it enters another stream or body of water. The lowest base level possible for any stream is sea level, the point at which the stream enters the ocean. As a stream continues to erode its channel toward its base level, erosion will continue along the sides of the

Figure 9-15 A V-shaped valley was formed on the Lower Falls of the Yellowstone River in Wyoming.

9.2 Stream Development **223**

2 Teach

Content Background

When sediments are carried in greater amounts than a stream can hold, the sediments are deposited along the bottom of the stream's channel. This process is called aggradation. The contrasting process, in which the stream is capable of carrying more load than it currently is carrying and results in downcutting, is called degradation. Aggradated streams are likely to have shallow, broad stream channels that often are characterized by the deposition of long bars of gravel or sand that develop into braided streams.

Project

Interpersonal Have students collect information about the Grand Canyon. Much information can be collected by writing to the National Park Service. As information is collected, have groups of students be in charge of posting the information on a bulletin board. Add to the bulletin board a topographic map that shows the Grand Canyon area. **COOP LEARN**

✔ *Assessment*

Skill Ask students to list sources of water that may enter a stream. Sources include precipitation of all forms, springs, and overflows from lakes and human-made drainage systems for discharge of excess water.

Earth Science

Science Field Book

Journal

Linguistic Ask students to each write a story in the form of a camper's log about a camping trip to the Grand Canyon. Each story should be written in a notebook with additional material taped or pasted next to journal entries so that it is interesting for others to look through. A good source of colorful additions is cutouts from travel brochures. **P**

Differentiated Instruction

Learning Disabled Pack two-meter sections of aluminum gutter with soil, gravel, sand, clay, and other materials to simulate areas where a stream may form. Tip the gutter into a sink containing a large bucket. Use a hose to send a stream of water down the gutter. Have students note the shape of the stream channel that forms and areas where the stream changes direction. Also have students note the types and sizes of sediments that are washed into the bucket. Have students sketch their observations.

NY Core Curriculum Standards

Page 222: St 4 KI 2.1r & 2.1u, St 6 KI 1, 4, & 5
Page 223: St 4 KI 2.1r & 2.1u, St 6 KI 1, 4, & 5

Figure 9-16 The Delaware Water Gap in Pennsylvania has been eroded into a wider, broader valley.

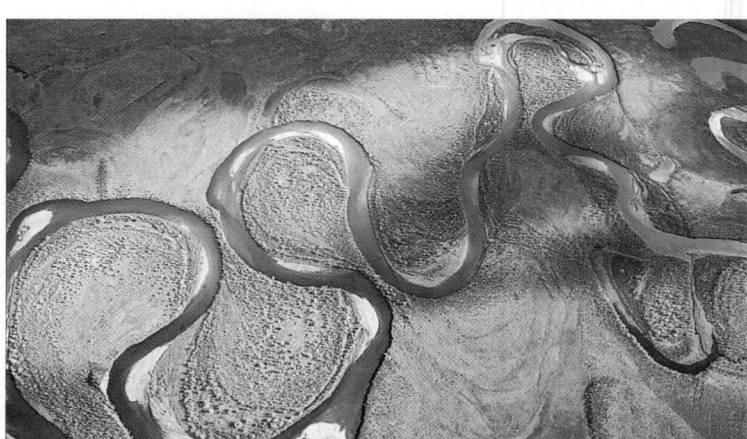

Figure 9-17 Several meanders are formed in the Tundra River in Yukon, Canada.

V-shaped channel. As shown in **Figure 9-16,** in time, a V-shaped valley will be eroded into a broader valley that has gentle slopes.

MEANDERING STREAMS

As stream channels develop into U-shaped valleys, the volume of water and sediment that they are able to carry increases. In addition, a stream's slope, or gradient, decreases as it nears its base level, and as a result the channel gets wider. The decrease in gradient causes water to build up within the stream channel. Sometimes, the water begins to erode the sides of the channel in such a way that the overall path of the stream starts to bend or wind. As shown in **Figure 9-17,** a bend or curve in a stream channel caused by moving water is called a **meander.**

Water in the straight parts of a stream flows at different velocities, depending on the location of the water in the channel. In a straight length of a stream, water in the center of the channel is flowing at the maximum velocity. Water along the bottom and sides of the channel flows more slowly because it experiences friction as it moves against the land. In contrast, the water moving along the outside of a meander curve experiences the greatest rate of flow within the meander. The water that flows along this outside part of the curve continues to erode away the sides of the streambed, thus making the meander larger. Along the inside of the meander, the water moves more slowly and deposition is dominant. These differences in the rate of water flow within meanders cause the meanders to become more accentuated over time. **Figure 9-18** illustrates the processes of erosion and

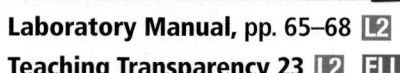

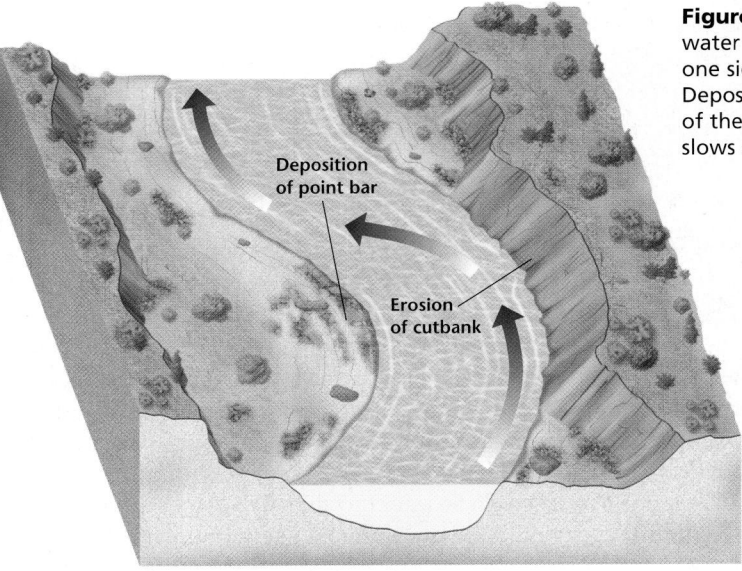

Figure 9-18 The high velocity of water in a meandering stream erodes one side of the stream's bank. Deposition occurs when the velocity of the water in a meandering stream slows down.

Deposition of point bar

Erosion of cutbank

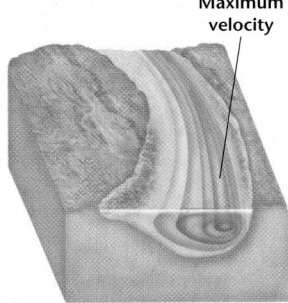

Maximum velocity

Maximum velocity

Figure 9-19 The maximum velocity of water in a stream will change its direction as the stream meanders.

deposition along a meander, and *Figure 9-19* shows the points of maximum water velocity within a meander and within a straight part of a stream. Stream meanders continue to develop and become larger and wider over time. After some degree of winding, however, it is common for a stream to cut off a meander and once again flow along a straighter path. The stream then deposits material along the adjoining meander and eventually blocks off its water supply, as shown in *Figure 9-20.* The blocked-off meander becomes an oxbow lake, which eventually dries up.

As a stream approaches a larger body of water or its ultimate end point, the ocean, the streambed's gradient flattens out and its channel becomes very wide. The area of the stream that leads into the ocean or another large body of water is called the mouth. The mouth of the Mississippi River is extremely wide.

Figure 9-20 The Devil's Elbow is an oxbow lake along the Congaree River in Congaree Swamp National Monument in South Carolina.

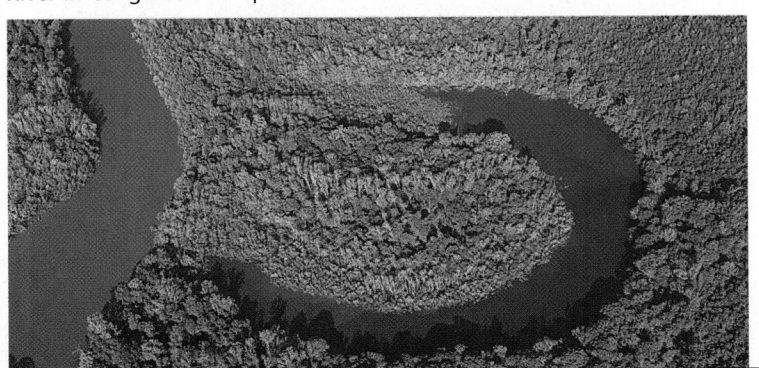

9.2 *Stream Development* **225**

Demo

In a leakproof, shallow container, make a mound of soil to represent a mountain. Slowly pour water on the top of the mound and let the water flow down one side of it. As the water flows down the mound, it will pick up sediment and carry it down the slope. As the water loses its velocity at the bottom of the hill, it will drop the sediment it has picked up along its journey in the shape of a fan. This is a model of the formation of an alluvial fan. You can also model the formation of a delta by allowing water-carrying sediment to enter a larger body of water and slow down. Both alluvial fans and deltas form very readily on artificial models.

Project

 **Interpersonal** Have students work in small groups to make diagrams of hypothetical islands with varied topographies. Have students indicate on their diagrams where they believe streams, deltas, and alluvial fans would be found. If students wish to test their ideas, they can make models of their hypothetical islands and test them accordingly.

COOP LEARN

NY Core Curriculum Standards

Page 226: St 1 Math KI 1, 2, & 3, St 4 KI 2.1v, St 6 KI 1, 4, & 5

Page 227: St 4 KI 2.1r & 2.1u, St 6 KI 1, 2, 4, & 5

Figure 9-21 An alluvial fan was formed at Mormon Point beneath Black Mountain in Death Valley National Park in California.

Using Math

Using Numbers If a stream's average velocity is 5 m/s, its width is 30 m, and its average depth is 10 m, what is the amount of the stream's discharge?

Figure 9-22 This photo shows a portion of the Mississippi River Delta. The delta consists of silt, sand, and clay deposits.

DEPOSITION OF SEDIMENT

Streams that lose velocity also lose their ability to carry sediment. A stream's velocity lessens and its sediment load drops when its gradient abruptly decreases. In dry regions, where mountain streams commonly flow down narrow valleys onto broad, flat, valley floors, a stream's gradient may suddenly decrease causing the stream to drop its sediment as a fan-shaped deposit called an *alluvial fan*. Alluvial fans are sloping depositional features formed at the bases of slopes and composed mostly of sand and gravel. They are found worldwide but are most common in dry, mountainous regions such as Death Valley, California, shown in *Figure 9-21*.

Streams also lose velocity and the ability to carry sediment when they join larger bodies of quiet water. The triangular deposit that forms where a stream enters a large body of water is called a **delta**, named for the triangle-shaped Greek letter *delta* (Δ). Delta deposits usually consist of silt and clay particles. As a delta develops, sediments build up and slow the stream water, sometimes even blocking its movement. Smaller distributary streams then form to carry the stream water through the developing delta. The Mississippi River Delta, shown in *Figure 9-22*, began forming millions of years ago. Today, the city of New Orleans, Louisiana is located on that delta, an area that was under seawater only 5000 years ago.

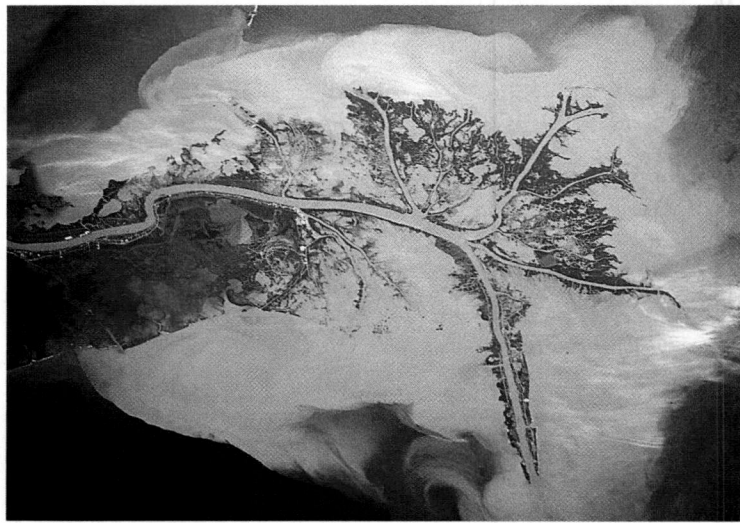

Cultural Diversity

Ancient Riverworks Artificial rivers have been discovered beneath the Sahara and in Turkey, Iran, Afghanistan, parts of Russia, and sections of China. These human-made rivers are called *foggara* in Arabic, *qanat* in Turkish, and *quarez* in Persian. No one knows exactly who made these ancient riverworks and aqueducts, but Iranian people still build similar structures today. Two or three "rivers" supply all the water necessary to support a village. Modern surveyors dig shafts and trenches through which groundwater runs. Scientists theorize that the ancient aqueducts were built similarly. Some qanats are several thousand years old.

REJUVENATION

During the process of stream formation, downcutting, or the wearing away of the streambed, is a major erosional process until the stream reaches its base level, when downcutting stops. However, if the land over which the stream is flowing uplifts or if the base level lowers, the stream undergoes rejuvenation. *Rejuvenation* means "to make young again." During **rejuvenation,** the stream actively resumes the process of downcutting toward its base level. This causes an increase in the stream's rate of flow, and the stream's channel once again becomes V-shaped. If rejuvenation occurs in an area where there are meanders, deep sided canyons are formed. This effect is evident in Utah's Escalante River, shown in *Figure 9-23.*

SECTION ASSESSMENT

1. Describe the formation of an oxbow lake.

2. Compare the rate of water flow on the inside of a meander curve with that on the outside of the curve.

3. Describe four changes that a stream undergoes as it works its way toward the ocean.

4. What are the differences between an alluvial fan and a delta?

5. **Thinking Critically** How does the type of bedrock over which a stream flows affect the time it takes for the stream to reach its base level?

SKILL REVIEW

6. **Making Graphs** Make a line graph that plots the direction of change in a hypothetical stream's rate of flow at the stream's headwaters, at midstream, and at its mouth. For more help, refer to the *Skill Handbook.*

---

3 Assess

Check for Understanding
Project

Interpersonal Ask students in small groups to develop methods to measure the speed at which water in a stream is flowing. Take the groups to a nearby stream to test their plans. Upon returning to the classroom, have the various groups critique their own setups and make suggestions for improvements.
COOP LEARN

Reteach
Assign small groups of students the task of creating a game with a game board that represents the water flowing on Earth's surface. Students must use facts from the chapter that will help them review terms and concepts. Once the games are completed, they can be rotated from one group to another for students to play and test the games.

Skill Ask each student to develop a question about the material in this section and to write the question on an index card with the answer on the reverse side. Collect the cards and use them in a whole-class review.

SECTION ASSESSMENT

1. An oxbow lake begins when a stream's meander becomes cut off by the stream. The stream deposits sediment where it was formerly joined to the stream, and the oxbow lake becomes separated from the stream. The water in the oxbow lake eventually dries up.

2. Water moves more quickly on the outside of a curve than it does on the inside.

3. (a) the amount of water in the stream increases; (b) the velocity of the stream's water decreases; (c) the stream channel becomes wider; (d) the stream channel becomes deeper

4. An alluvial fan forms at the base of a hill or mountain, is composed mainly of sand and gravel, is sloped, and flows onto dry land. A delta forms where a stream enters a quiet body of water, has deposits which consist mainly of silt and clay in fairly flat formations and forms under water.

5. Rocks that are resistant to weathering will wear away slowly and it will take longer for the stream to reach its base level. Less-resistant rocks will wear away quickly as water moves over them and the stream will reach its base level in less time.

6. Graphs should have *Rate of Flow* on the *y*-axis and the terms *Headwaters*, *Midstream*, and *Mouth* on the *x*-axis. Graphs should show a decreasing rate of flow from headwaters to midstream to mouth.

Section Background

For section content background, refer to **Lakes and Freshwater Wetlands** on page 210D.

Preplanning

Refer to the Chapter Organizer on pages 210A–B.

1 Focus

Section Focus

Before presenting the lesson, display **Section Focus Transparency 25** on the overhead projector. L1 ELL

Section Focus Transparency 25
A CHANGING LAKE
Use with Chapter 9, Section 9.3

❶ How has this lake changed from the sparkling clear body of water it once was?
❷ What could have caused this lake to change?

Section Focus Transparency — Earth Science: Geology, the Environment, and the Universe

NY Core Curriculum Standards

Page 228: St 4 KI 2.1r, St 6 KI 1 & 5
Page 229: St 1 Science KI 1, 2, & 3, St 4 KI 2.1r, St 6 KI 1, 2, & 5

SECTION 9.3

Lakes and Freshwater Wetlands

OBJECTIVES

- **Explain** *the formation of freshwater lakes and wetlands.*
- **Describe** *the process of eutrophication.*
- **Recognize** *the effects of human activity on lake development.*

VOCABULARY

lake
eutrophication
wetland

You have probably swum in, fished in, or gazed at the beauty of a lake. But, did you ever think about how lakes form? A **lake** is a depression in the surface materials of a landscape that collects and holds water. As shown in the *MiniLab* on the following page, surface materials determine where a lake can form. Lakes sometimes accumulate water from streams and runoff that flow into them. Lakes also receive water from local precipitation, springs, and other sources. Most lakes have outlets from which water flows to rivers and to the ocean. People sometimes build small lakes called ponds to serve as sources of water for livestock, to maintain fish supplies, to attract wildlife, or for their natural beauty. Reservoirs are lakes made for the primary purpose of storing water for a community's use.

ORIGINS OF LAKES

Natural lakes form in different ways in surface depressions and in low areas. As you have learned, oxbow lakes form when streams cut off meanders and leave isolated channels of water. Lakes can also form when stream flow becomes blocked by sediment from landslides. Other lakes, such as Utah's Great Salt Lake, shown in *Figure 9-24*, are remnants of prehistoric lakes that have receded to lower-lying areas.

Still other lakes have glacial origins, as you learned in Chapter 8. The basins of these lakes formed as glaciers gouged out the land during the ice ages. Most of the lakes in Europe and North America are in recently glaciated areas. Glacial moraines originally dammed some of these depressions and restricted the outward flow of water. The lakes that formed as a result are known as moraine-dammed lakes, shown in *Figure 9-25*. In another process, cirques carved high in the mountains by valley glaciers filled with water to form cirque lakes. Other lakes

Figure 9-24 The Great Salt Lake in northern Utah has a much greater salinity than the oceans.

Resource Manager

Study Guide for Content Mastery, pp. 57–58 L2

Section Focus Transparency 25 L1 ELL

Activity

Divide the class into teams of 4 to 5 people. Ask each team to write down as many uses of lakes as it can. After a given amount of time, ask each team to report one use on its list. Give a point for each use that was not thought of by the other teams. This will encourage students to come up with as many different uses as possible and get them ready to learn about lakes.

formed as blocks of ice left on the outwash plain ahead of melting glaciers eventually melted and left depressions called kettles. When these depressions filled with water, they formed kettle lakes.

Many lakes are found in areas where limestone is the dominant bedrock. As groundwater percolating through limestone bedrock slowly dissolves calcium carbonate, it leaves holes in the limestone and forms caverns. In some places, the ceilings of these caverns become so thin and weak that they collapse, which leaves depressions that may fill with water in time.

LAKES UNDERGO CHANGE

Water from precipitation, runoff, and underground sources can maintain a lake's water supply. Some lakes contain water only during times of heavy rain or excessive runoff from spring thaws. A depression that receives more water than it loses to evaporation or use by humans will exist as a lake for a long period of time. However, lakes are temporary water-holding areas; over hundreds of thousands of years, lakes usually fill in with sediment and become part of a new landscape.

Eutrophication Through the process of photosynthesis, plants add oxygen and waste products to lake water. Animals that live in a lake use the water's oxygen and add waste products to the water as they conduct their life processes. The decay process that occurs after plants and animals die also uses up dissolved oxygen supplies. The amount of dissolved oxygen helps determine the quality of lake water and its ability to support life.

Figure 9-25 The moraine-dammed lakes in Banff National Park in Alberta, Canada were formed from glacial activity.

MiniLab

Surface materials determine where a lake can form.

Model how different Earth materials may allow lakes to form. Lakes form when depressions or low areas fill with water.

Procedure 🥽 👕 **CAUTION: Always wear safety goggles and an apron in the lab.**

1. Use three clear, plastic shoe boxes. Half fill each one with Earth materials: clay, sand, and gravel.
2. Slightly compress the material in each shoe box. Then make a shallow depression in each surface.
3. Slowly pour 500 mL of water into each of the depressions.

Analyze and Conclude

1. Describe what happened to the 500 mL of water that was added to each shoe box.
2. How is this activity similar to what actually happens on Earth's surface when a lake forms?
3. What can you infer about the Earth materials in which lakes most commonly form?

9.3 *Lakes and Freshwater Wetlands* **229**

Tying to Previous Knowledge

Ask students to write the name of a lake they know about or have visited in their science journals. Ask students to write about how the lake formed and give some details, such as location, size, use by humans, and life-forms that it contains. Tell students that during this section of the chapter, they should be collecting information about this lake for a future assignment.

MiniLab

Purpose 📦
Students will demonstrate how different types of material found on Earth's surface determine where a lake can form.

Process Skills
model, recognize cause and effect, communicate, interpret data, observe and infer, measure in SI

Materials
three clear plastic shoe boxes, clay, sand, gravel, supply of water, graduated cylinder, beaker

Alternate Materials
Any type of clear plastic container can be used in place of the boxes and beaker as long as a graduated cylinder is used to measure the amount of water.

Teaching Strategies
Have students work in pairs to share in the development of ideas, in noting observations, and in cleaning up.

Expected Results
Students will observe that gravel allows water to penetrate through it most easily and clay least easily. Hence, clay is a better material to contain water in a depression.

Analyze and Conclude
1. The water should quickly flow through the gravel. The water will flow through the sand less quickly. The water will remain on the top of the clay the longest.
2. When water collects in an area where the spaces between the particles of surface material are small, the water is more likely to form a lake.
3. Surface materials that lead to the formation of lakes usually do not allow water to easily pass through them.

✓ Assessment

Knowledge Ask students to describe the characteristics of a material that does not easily allow water to pass through it. The material is likely composed of small particles with few spaces between them.

229

Content Background

Lakes may form in desert regions following rare but heavy rainstorms. Such lakes are usually temporary, and when they dry up, they leave a dry lake bed on the desert called a playa. *Playa* is a Spanish word meaning "beach." Repeated filling and drying of these lakes lead to the significant buildup of evaporite minerals that can be used for industrial purposes.

Enrichment

Allow students who wish to extend themselves the opportunity to work in small groups to research a nearby wetland area. Encourage students to visit the wetland, under the supervision of an adult, and to make a video or take photographs and a sampling of the vegetation. Remind students that they will need permission from the property owner. The group can report back to the class and show the video or photographs.

✓Assessment

Knowledge Ask students which of the following statements about wetlands are true.
a. They are damp places on Earth's surface.
b. They help clean surface water.
c. They have unique plants growing in them.
d. They are home to many birds and other wildlife.
e. They are overprotected.
f. They waste a large part of the land.
The true statements are a, b, c, and d.

Figure 9-26 The aquatic species of this pond will change over the years because of the effects of eutrophication.

The process by which lakes become rich in nutrients from the surrounding watershed, thereby resulting in a change in the kinds of organisms in the lake, is called **eutrophication**. *Figure 9-26* shows a pond undergoing eutrophication. Although eutrophication is a natural process, it can be sped up with the addition of nutrients, such as fertilizers, that contain nitrogen and phosphorus. When this happens, the animal and plant communities in the lake can change rapidly. Algae growing in the water may suddenly multiply very quickly. The excessive algae growth in a lake or pond appears as green scum. Other organisms that eat the algae can multiply in numbers as well. The resulting overpopulation and decay of a large number of plants and animals depletes the water's oxygen supply. Fish and other sensitive organisms may die as a result of the lack of oxygen in the water.

Other major sources of nutrients that concentrate in lakes are animal wastes and phosphate detergents. Lakes can also suffer from the release of toxins from nearby industries and untreated sewage, as shown in the *Science & the Environment* feature at the end of the chapter.

Freshwater Wetlands A **wetland** is a land area that is covered with water for a large part of the year. Wetlands include environments commonly known as bogs, marshes, and swamps. They have certain soil types and support specific plant species.

A bog, shown in *Figure 9-27,* is an interesting wetland that deserves a closer look. Bogs are not stream-fed, but instead receive their water from precipitation. The waterlogged soil tends to be rich in *Sphagnum,* also called peat moss. The breakdown of peat moss produces acids, thereby contributing to the soil's acidity. The waterlogged, acidic soil supports unusual plant species, including insect-eating pitcher plants, sundew, and Venus' flytrap.

Figure 9-27 This bog in Norway has acid-rich soil that supports a variety of organisms.

Applying Earth Science

Intrapersonal Ask students to each make a list of the detergents used both at home and in the school. Along with the name of each detergent, have students list the detergent's ingredients to determine which, if any, contain phosphate or other materials that may be harmful to the environment. Have students decide on an approved course of action if they do indeed find that cleaning materials that are harmful to the environment are being used.

Freshwater marshes frequently form along the mouths of streams and in areas with extensive deltas. The constant supply of water allows for the lush growth of marsh grasses. The shallow roots of the grasses anchor deposits of silt and mud on the delta, thereby slowing the water and expanding the marsh area. Grasses, reeds, sedges, and rushes, along with abundant wildlife, are common in marsh areas.

Swamps are low-lying areas often located near streams. Swamps may develop from marshes that have filled in sufficiently to support the growth of shrubs and trees. As these larger plants grow and begin to shade the marsh plants, the marsh plants die. Swamps that existed 250 million years ago developed into present-day coal reserves that are common in Pennsylvania and many other locations in the United States and around the world.

Wetlands play a valuable role in improving water quality. They serve as a filtering system that traps pollutants, sediments, and pathogenic bacteria contained in water sources. Wetlands also provide vital habitats for migratory waterbirds and homes for an abundance of other wildlife, as shown in *Figure 9-28*. Unfortunately, people's desire for land often conflicts with the need to preserve wetlands. In the past, it was common for wetland areas to be filled in to create more land on which to build. Government data reveal that from the late 1700s to the mid-1980s, the continental United States lost 50 percent of its wetlands. By 1985, it was estimated that 50 percent of the wetlands in Europe were drained. Now, however, the preservation of wetland areas has become a global concern.

Figure 9-28 The wetlands in Bosque del Apache National Wildlife Refuge in New Mexico are home to migrating snow geese.

SECTION ASSESSMENT

1. Describe the process of eutrophication.
2. What human activities affect the process of eutrophication?
3. What conditions are necessary for the formation of a natural lake?
4. **Thinking Critically** Describe a situation in which protection of wetlands may conflict with human plans for land use.

SKILL REVIEW

5. **Making Tables** Design a data table that compares the various types of lakes, their origins, and their characteristics. For more help, refer to the *Skill Handbook*.

earthgeu.com/self_check_quiz

9.3 *Lakes and Freshwater Wetlands* **231**

SECTION ASSESSMENT

1. Eutrophication is the natural process by which lake water becomes rich in decayed organic material. The nutrients from the decayed material cause a further increase in algal growth and the lake becomes depleted of oxygen.
2. agriculture, pesticides, detergents, sewage
3. source of water, depression to catch the water, bottom of lake has to be able to hold water for a given period of time
4. A person owns land that he or she would like to sell for a profit, but the land is a wetland and development is prohibited.

5.

Type of Lake	Where It Forms	Size	Special Characteristics
oxbow	floodplains	varies	curved shape, dries up
cirque	mountains	varies	basin-shaped, glacial origin
kettle	fields	small	round, glacial origin
glacial	varies	varies	long, glacial origin

3 Assess

Check for Understanding
Modeling

Interpersonal Have students work in small groups to develop dioramas that depict the stages of change that a lake may undergo. Instruct students to include the lake's formation and possible scenarios that may have resulted in the eutrophication of the lake. The dioramas can be clay or papier-mâché models, or shadow boxes. Each diorama will require the development of an explanatory script that is recorded on audiotape. Once the dioramas are set up around the room, they can serve as learning and review stations for students.
L2 **ELL** **COOP LEARN**

Reteach

Have students each develop a list of vocabulary words to define in their science journals. Review the terms as a class and have students add to their lists words that other students have contributed.

✓ Assessment

Knowledge Show the class slides or photographs that represent particular stages of development or eutrophication of lakes. Ask students to relate each photograph to concepts covered in this section. Have students develop one question for each photograph that they can answer using what they have learned in this section.

NY Core Curriculum Standards

Page 230: St 6 KI 1 & 5
Page 231: St 4 KI 2.1w, St 6 KI 1, 2, & 5

231

GeoLab

GeoLab

Time Allotment

45 minutes

Process Skills

observe and infer, interpret data, make a model, analyze data, interpret scientific illustrations, communicate, recognize cause and effect, compare and contrast

Safety Precautions

Make sure that students wear safety goggles and aprons during this lab.

Preparation

This investigation works best with students working in groups of four. One student can be in charge of maintaining water flow. One student can drop the floating marker. A third student can be in charge of water drainage, and the fourth can time the rate of flow. It may be helpful to have student groups make their protractors with plumb bobs ahead of time.

Procedure

Teaching Strategies

- Caution students to make sure that the clamps are securely attached to the gutter pipe and that the hose is securely attached to the faucet.
- Instruct students to slowly turn on the water to avoid spurts and excessive water spills.
- Caution students to watch for twists in the water hose that may temporarily impede water flow.

Modeling Stream Velocity and Slope

Water in streams flows from areas of higher elevation to areas of lower elevation. The rate of stream flow varies from one stream to another and also in different areas of the same stream.

Preparation

Problem

Determine how slope may affect stream-flow velocity.

Materials

1-m length of vinyl gutter pipe
ring stand and clamp
water source with long hose
protractor with plumb bob
sink or container to catch water
stopwatch
grease pencil
meterstick
paper
hole punch

Objectives

In this GeoLab, you will:

- **Measure** the time it takes for water to flow down a channel at different slopes and depths.
- **Organize** your data in a table.
- **Plot** the data on a graph to show how stream velocity is directly proportional to the stream channel's slope and depth.
- **Describe** the relationship between slope and rate of stream flow.

Safety Precautions

Always wear safety goggles in the lab.

Troubleshooting

Students may need help measuring the angle of the slope.

Data and Observations

Students' data will show that the rate of water flow increases with an increase in slope.

Procedure

1. Use the hole punch to make 10 to 15 paper circles to be used as floating markers.
2. Use the illustration below as a guide to set up the protractor with the plumb bob.

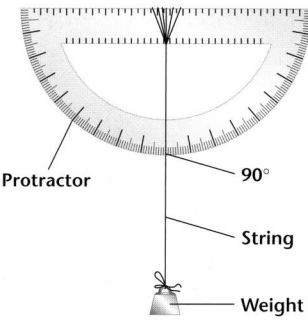

Protractor   90°

String

Weight

3. Use the grease pencil to mark two lines across the inside of the gutter pipe at a distance of 40 cm apart.
4. Use the ring stand and clamp to hold the gutter pipe at an angle of 10°. Place the end of the pipe in a sink or basin to collect the discharged flow of water.
5. Attach a long hose to a water faucet in the sink.
6. Keep the hose in the sink until you are ready to use it. Then turn on the water and adjust the flow until the water is moving quickly enough to provide a steady flow.
7. Bend the hose temporarily to block the water flow until the hose is positioned at least 5 cm above the top line marked on the pipe.
8. Keep the water moving at the same rate of flow for all slope angles being investigated.
9. Drop a floating marker approximately 4 cm above the top line on the pipe and into the flowing water. Measure the time it takes for the floating marker to move from the top line to the bottom line. Record the time in your science journal.
10. Repeat step 9 two more times.
11. Repeat steps 9 and 10 but change the slope to 20°, then 30°, and then 40°.
12. Make a line graph of the average stream-flow velocity.

Analyze

1. Why is it important to keep the water flow constant in this activity?
2. Which variables had to be controlled to avoid errors in your data?
3. Using your graph, predict the velocity of water flow for a 35° slope.

Conclude & Apply

1. What is the relationship between the rate of water flow and the angle of the slope?
2. Describe one reason why a stream's slope might change.
3. Where would you expect to find streams with the highest water-flow velocity?

Analyze

1. A change in water flow would result in either a higher or lower reading. If there were a change in water flow, the data collected would reflect the change in water volume instead of only the change in slope.
2. the rate of water flow from the hose and the volume of water from the hose
3. Answers will vary depending on student data.

Conclude & Apply

1. There is a direct relationship between the rate of flow and the angle of the slope. Velocity increases as the angle of the slope increases.
2. As a stream erodes its base, the stream's slope is reduced.
3. at higher elevations

✓ Assessment

Skill Have four students each draw a profile view of a stream on the chalkboard. Number the stream profiles 1 through 4. Ask the class to list the stream profiles in order of increasing rate of flow. Answers should reflect the streams in order from those having the least slope to the greatest slope.

GeoLab **233**

Resource Manager

GeoLab and MiniLab Worksheets,
   pp. 36–38 L2

NY Core Curriculum Standards

Page 232: St 1 Science KI 1, 2, & 3, St 4 KI 2.1u, St 6 KI 2 & 5
Page 233: St 1 Science KI 1, 2, & 3, St 4 KI 2.1u, St 6 KI 2 & 5

Purpose

To understand the ramifications of surface water pollution and the effects it has on nature as a whole.

Content Background

- Scientists discovered the first known freshwater hydrothermal vent in Lake Baikal. Found near the vent were sponges, which are not typically found near similar vents in the ocean, bacteria, and shrimp. Studies indicate that the vent may be young in comparison to its counterparts in the oceans.
- The lake has become a natural laboratory. The life forms in Lake Baikal are the focus of studies of the evolution of organisms. The many life forms found in the area also allow scientists to study the different species in their natural habitat.
- Lake Baikal is not only of ecological importance, but it is also of cultural importance, holding many clues about the region's historic past. For example, rock drawings and what appear to be settlements are believed to be remnants from the Buryats and Evenks—early people who lived in the area. Many groups have fought to protect the area, calling it a cultural landmark.

Science & the Environment

The Jewel of Siberia

Pollution is threatening the ecosystems of Lake Baikal, the oldest, largest, and deepest freshwater lake on Earth. What is causing the problems? Are there any solutions for saving the lake?

A Natural Paradise

Known as the "Jewel of Siberia," Lake Baikal is the oldest and largest freshwater lake on Earth. Estimated to be 25 million years old, Lake Baikal contains 20% of Earth's unfrozen freshwater, that is, one-fifth of the world's fresh surface water. The lake contains approximately 80% of the former Soviet Union's freshwater supply and covers approximately 31 500 km^2. It reaches a maximum depth of approximately 1637 m making it the deepest lake in the world.

Fed by 330 tributaries, and surrounded by forests and mountain ranges, it is home to a wide variety of plant and animal species. The area is home to everything from microscopic organisms to large mammals including elk, moose, deer, and the brown bear.

One animal found only in this area is the Nerpa or Baikal seal. The Nerpa is the only known species of freshwater seal. It is believed that the seal may have migrated to the area in search of food while the lake was being formed thousands of years ago.

Threatened

Pollution has begun to slowly take its toll on animal and plant species in the region. Studies have reported that the fish population is dying out and thousands of the Baikal seals have died. High toxin levels from a nearby pulp and paper factory may be the cause. According to other studies, DDT and other pesticides have entered the waters via aerial spraying, and have been found in the lake's sediment.

Attempts to restrict the release of toxins into the freshwater lake have failed due to concern over the loss of industry and jobs. For example, if a lakeside pulp and paper factory were forced to close, many people would be left unemployed.

Many organizations have banded together in Russia to attempt to preserve the Lake Baikal area. There is even cooperation between groups in the United States and Russia who have been working together to come up with solutions to the problems facing the industry and the environment. Their activities range from efforts to save the Baikal seal to promoting tourism as a more attractive form of economic stability in the area.

Activity

Form small groups to research and discuss possible solutions to the problems threatening the ecosystems of Lake Baikal. How can the lake and its inhabitants be preserved without having to totally remove industry from the area? Visit the Earth Science Web Site at **earthgeu.com** to learn more about the struggle to save Lake Baikal and its many inhabitants.

234 CHAPTER 9 *Surface Water*

Teaching Strategies

- Have students discuss how surface water affects their everyday lives. How would pollution of these waters affect them?
- Have students explore incidents of water pollution within their own communities. Are there streams, lakes, or ponds nearby that could possibly be polluted by nearby factories? What can students do to help prevent pollution of their freshwater supply?

Activity

Some argue that by closing down the factories near Lake Baikal, Siberia's economy would be seriously endangered. Others argue that by closing down the factories that pollute the surface water and saving the natural habitat, tourism could be used to regain economic stability. Culturally, it is argued that the region needs to be protected from industry and pollution to preserve the many artifacts that contain keys to the region's heritage.

Summary

SECTION 9.1
Surface Water Movement

Main Ideas

- Water on Earth may follow a variety of pathways as it is recycled through the processes of evaporation and condensation.
- Infiltration of water into the ground depends on the number of open pores or spaces in Earth materials and on the presence of unsaturated pores in the ground.
- All the land area that drains into a stream system is the system's watershed, or drainage basin. Elevated land areas called divides separate one watershed from another.
- A stream's load is all the material the stream carries, including material in solution, in suspension, and as bed load.
- A floodplain is a broad, flat area that extends out from a stream's bank during times of flooding.
- Flooding occurs in small, localized areas as upstream floods or in large, downstream floods. Damage from flooding can be devastating.

Vocabulary
bed load (p. 217)
discharge (p. 218)
divide (p. 215)
flood (p. 219)
floodplain (p. 219)
runoff (p. 212)
solution (p. 215)
suspension (p. 216)
watershed (p. 215)

SECTION 9.2
Stream Development

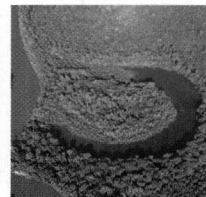

Main Ideas

- Water from precipitation gathers in gullies at a stream's source area, or headwaters. The stream's water flows in channels confined by the stream's banks.
- Alluvial fans and deltas form when stream velocity decreases and sediment is deposited. Alluvial fans are fan shaped, and they form where water flows down steep slopes onto flat plains. Deltas are triangular, and they form when streams enter large, relatively quiet bodies of water.

Vocabulary
delta (p. 226)
meander (p. 224)
rejuvenation (p. 227)
stream bank (p. 222)
stream channel (p. 222)

SECTION 9.3
Lakes and Freshwater Wetlands

Main Ideas

- Lakes form in a variety of ways when depressions on land fill with water. Lakes may be natural or human-made.
- Eutrophication is a natural nutrient enrichment process that may be sped up when nutrients from fertilizers, detergents, or sewage are added.
- Wetlands are low-lying areas that are periodically saturated with water and support specific plant species. Wetlands include bogs, marshes, and swamps.

Vocabulary
eutrophication (p. 230)
lake (p. 228)
wetland (p. 230)

Main Ideas

Summary statements can be used by students to review the major concepts of the chapter.

VOCABULARY PuzzleMaker

 For additional help with vocabulary, have students access the Vocabulary Puzzlemaker online.

earthgeu.com/ vocabulary puzzlemaker

0:00 Out of Time?

If time does not permit teaching the entire chapter, use the GeoDigest at the end of the unit as an overview.

Earth Science Online

Be sure to check the Earth Science Web Site for links to chapter material: **earthgeu.com**

GLENCOE
Technology

Videotape/DVD
MindJogger Videoquizzes
Chapter 9: *Surface Water*
Have students work in groups as they play the videoquiz game to review key chapter concepts.

Resource Manager

Chapter Assessment, pp. 49–54
MindJogger Videoquizzes DVD/VHS
ExamView® Pro CD-ROM
Performance Assessment in Earth Science

NY Core Curriculum Standards

Page 234: St 4 KI 1.2g, St 6 KI 5 & 6, St 7 KI 2
Page 235: St 4 KI 1.2g, 2.1r, 2.1u, & 2.1v, St 6 KI 1, 4, & 5

Understanding Main Ideas

1. d
2. c
3. c
4. b
5. b
6. a
7. d
8. a
9. d

Applying Main Ideas

10. Both deltas and alluvial fans are depositional features that form as water slows and loses its carrying capacity. Deltas form where a stream enters a large, quiet body of water, and alluvial fans form at the bases of mountains and hills. Deltas form in the water, while alluvial fans form on land. Alluvial fans are primarily composed of sand and gravel, and deltas are primarily composed of silt and clay.

11. Wetlands improve water quality by trapping pollutants, sediments, and pathogenic bacteria. They also provide habitats for living things.

12. Technology has helped humans to develop weather stations, satellites, stream-monitoring instrumentation, computers, and communication systems. Currently, monitoring takes place continuously from local and remote sensing units. People are aware of potential problems and are warned of danger in time to evacuate areas.

13. c
14. a

Understanding Main Ideas

1. Which factor least affects the rate of runoff?
   a. slope
   b. vegetation
   c. volume of runoff
   d. nearness to water

2. What areas are most likely to contain fertile soils?
   a. watersheds
   b. dried-up streambeds
   c. floodplains
   d. mountainous areas

3. Which substance is most likely to be carried by a stream in solution?
   a. quartz
   b. sand
   c. calcite
   d. silt

4. What material plays a major role in the eutrophication of lakes?
   a. iron
   b. phosphate
   c. ozone
   d. salt

5. During the process of eutrophication, what happens to the oxygen present in a lake?
   a. It increases.
   b. It decreases.
   c. It stays the same.
   d. It evaporates.

6. What kind of streams form V-shaped valleys?
   a. streams that are first forming
   b. streams that carry much sediment
   c. streams that move slowly
   d. streams that have meanders

7. Where does water move most rapidly in the straight length of a stream?
   a. along the bottom
   b. along the sides
   c. near the surface
   d. in the center

8. If a stream is carrying sand, silt, clay, and small pebbles, which one is deposited last as the stream begins to slow down?
   a. clay
   b. silt
   c. sand
   d. small pebbles

9. Where do alluvial fans form?
   a. on the outside of meanders
   b. where streams enter the ocean
   c. near lakes
   d. along the bases of mountains

Applying Main Ideas

10. In what ways are a delta and an alluvial fan similar, and in what ways are they different?

11. Why is it important to preserve wetlands?

12. What means do governments use to try to prevent the loss of life and property in flood-prone areas?

Use the following aerial view of a stream to answer questions 13–15.

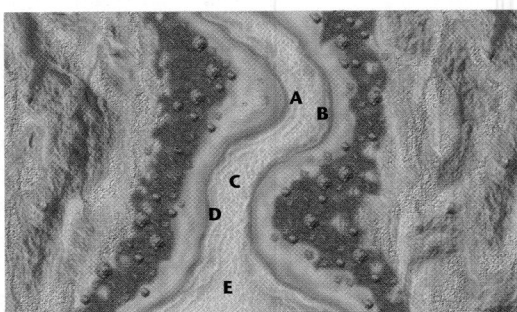

Test-Taking Tip

BEAT THE CLOCK—AND THEN GO BACK As you take a practice test, pace yourself to finish each section just a few minutes early so you can go back and check over your work. You will sometimes find a mistake or two.

earthgeu.com/chapter_test

15. b
16. 22 500 m^3/s

Thinking Critically

17. Clay is a smaller particle and the spaces between clay particles are therefore smaller. As a result, water cannot easily pass through the spaces between clay particles.

Standardized Test Practice

1. b
2. c
3. a
4. c
5. d

13. At which location in the aerial view does the stream's water have the greatest velocity?

14. At which location is deposition most actively occurring?

15. At which location is erosion most actively occurring?

16. What is the discharge of a stream that has a velocity of 300 m/s and is 25-m wide and 3-m deep?

Thinking Critically

17. Why is a lake with a clay bottom able to hold more water than a lake with a sand bottom?

18. One morning, there was a torrential thunderstorm. In the afternoon, the skies cleared and a gardener decided to plant a tree. After digging in the ground only a short distance down, the gardener found that the ground was very dry. How could the ground be dry despite the heavy rains earlier in the day?

19. If floodplains are such hazardous areas to live in, why have so many people settled in these potential flood zones?

20. Use the following terms to construct a concept map to organize the major ideas in Section 9.1. For more help, refer to the *Skill Handbook*.

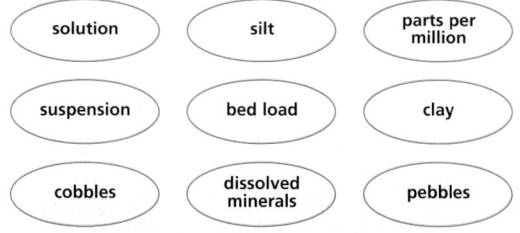

solution · silt · parts per million · suspension · bed load · clay · cobbles · dissolved minerals · pebbles

Standardized Test Practice

1. Which condition would create the most runoff?
   a. land covered with vegetation
   b. plants in densely packed soil
   c. light precipitation
   d. soil with a high percentage of sand

2. In which part of a meander does the water travel the fastest?
   a. the water that moves along the inside curve of the meander
   b. the water that moves along the bottom of the meander
   c. the water that moves along the outside curve of a meander
   d. all water flows at the same rate

3. Which of the following is NOT a value of wetlands?
   a. feeding lakes and deltas with nutrient- and oxygen-rich water
   b. filtering water by trapping pollutants, sediments, and pathogenic bacteria
   c. providing habitats for migratory birds and other wildlife
   d. preserving fossils due to the anaerobic and acidic conditions

4. As the velocity of a stream decreases, which transported particle size would settle to the stream's bottom first?
   a. clay   **c.** pebble
   b. silt   **d.** sand

5. Which condition helps determine the quality of lake water?
   a. the amount of nitrogen
   b. the amount of dissolved calcium carbonate
   c. the amount of potassium
   d. the amount of dissolved oxygen

18. The downpour may have pushed the soil aggregates together, thereby closing off the openings through which water could have entered the ground. As a result, the excess water flowed downslope, away from the area where the gardener was planting the tree.

19. Many settlements were established a long time ago, before the threat of flooding to the area was known. At the time of settlement, the need to be close to water outweighed the potential for flooding. Over time, settlements grew and developed, and put more people and property at risk. In addition, many years may pass between periods of severe flooding. The flat, fertile land of floodplains produces good crops and offers scenic beauty and recreational facilities. Rivers also provided a means of transportation and power for manufacturing activities.

20. solution—dissolved minerals—parts per million; suspension—clay, silt; bedload—pebbles, cobbles

EXAM*VIEW*® PRO

Use Exam*View*® Pro Testmaker CD-ROM to:

- Create **multiple versions** of tests.
- Create **modified** tests with one mouse click for struggling students.
- **Edit** existing questions and add your own questions.
- **Build** tests based on national curriculum standards.

NY Core Curriculum Standards

Page 236: St 2 KI 3, St 4 KI 1.2g, 2.1r, 2.1u, & 2.1v, St 6 KI 1, 4, & 5
Page 237: St 1 Math KI 2, St 2 KI 3, St 4 KI 1.2g, 2.1r, 2.1u, & 2.1v, St 6 KI 1, 2, 4, 5, & 6

237

Chapter 10

Groundwater

Refer to pages 8T–9T of the Teacher Guide for an explanation of the National Science Content Standards correlations.

Section	Objectives	National Science Content Standards	State/Local Standards
SECTION 10.1 **Movement and Storage of Groundwater** 🕐 2 sessions 🧊 1¼ blocks	1. **Describe** how groundwater is stored and moves underground. 2. **Explain** what an aquifer is.	UCP.1, UCP.2, UCP.3, UCP.4; A.1, A.2; B.4; D.1, D.2, D.3; F.3, F.5	St 1 Math KI 1, 2, 3, Science KI 1, 2, 3, & Engin KI 1, St 4 KI 1.2g, 2.1f, & 2.1h, St 6 KI 1, 2, & 5
SECTION 10.2 **Groundwater Erosion and Deposition** 🕐 1½ sessions 🧊 1 block	3. **Explain** how groundwater dissolves and deposits rocks and minerals. 4. **Describe** how caves form and how karst topography develops on Earth's surface.	UCP.1, UCP.2, UCP.3; D.1, D.2	St 1 Math KI 1, 2, & 3, St 4 KI 1.2g, St 6 KI 1, 2, & 5
SECTION 10.3 **Groundwater Systems** 🕐 1½ sessions 🧊 ¾ block	5. **Relate** the different types of springs to common systems of aquifers. 6. **Explain** how groundwater is withdrawn from aquifer systems by wells. 7. **Describe** the major problems that threaten groundwater supplies.	UCP.1, UCP.2, UCP.3, UCP.5; A.1, A.2; D.1, D.2; E.1, E.2; F.3, F.4, F.5, F.6	St 1 Math KI 1, 2, 3, Science KI 1, 2, 3, & Engin KI 1, St 4 KI 1.2g, St 6 KI 1, 2, 5, & 6, St 7 KI 1 & 2

A complete Planning Guide is provided on pages 30T–32T.

🕐 The number of recommended single-period sessions

🧊 The number of recommended blocks

Activity Materials

Discovery Lab *page 239*
250-mL graduated cylinders (2), sand, water, safety goggles

GeoLab *pages 258–259*
tracing paper, graph paper, ruler, calculator, USGS 7.5 minute quadrangle or topographic map of Forest City, Florida

MiniLab *page 254*
plastic shoe box, book, sand, clay, water, clear plastic drinking straws (3),

safety goggles

Demo *page 245*
sandstone, granite, limestone, HCl (1*M* hydrochloric acid), dropper

page 250
rubber tubing, water

page 251
aquarium, sand, water, food coloring, rubber tubing

page 252
cylindrical plastic container, water

Key to Teaching Strategies

L1 Level 1 activities should be appropriate for students with learning difficulties.

L2 Level 2 activities should be within the ability range of all students.

L3 Level 3 activities are designed for above-average students.

ELL ELL activities should be within the ability range of English-language learners.

COOP LEARN Cooperative learning activities are designed for small-group work.

P These strategies represent student products that can be placed in a best-work portfolio.

🧊 These strategies are useful in a block-scheduling format.

Need materials? Contact Science Kit at 1-800-828-7777 or at www.sciencekit.com on the Internet. For alternate materials, see the activity on the listed page.

Chapter Organizer

Activities/Features	Reproducible Masters	Transparencies
Discovery Lab: Model Underground Water Storage, p. 239	**Study Guide for Content Mastery,** pp. 59–60 L2 **Laboratory Manual,** pp. 73–76 L2	**Section Focus Transparency 26** L1 ELL **Teaching Transparency 25** L2 ELL
Using Math: Using Numbers, p. 247	**Study Guide for Content Mastery,** pp. 61–62 L2	**Section Focus Transparency 27** L1 ELL **Teaching Transparency 26** L2 ELL
Problem-Solving Lab: Using Tables and Making Graphs, p. 253 **MiniLab:** How does an artesian well work? p. 254 **GeoLab:** Mapping Pollution, pp. 258–259 **Science & the Environment:** The High Plains Aquifer, p. 260	**Study Guide for Content Mastery,** pp. 63–64 L2 **Laboratory Manual,** pp. 77–80 L2 **GeoLab and MiniLab Worksheets,** p. 39 L2 **GeoLab and MiniLab Worksheets,** pp. 40–42 L2	**Section Focus Transparency 28** L1 ELL **Teaching Transparency 27** L2 ELL

Assessment

Chapter Assessment, pp. 55–60
Performance Assessment in the Science Classroom (PASC)
MindJogger Videoquiz DVD/VHS
Performance Assessment in Earth Science
ExamView® Pro CD-ROM
5 Days to the Regents Exam

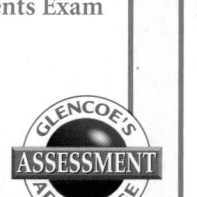

Additional Resources

Guided Reading Audio Program ELL
Cooperative Learning in the Science Classroom COOP LEARN
Lesson Plans
Block Scheduling
earthgeu.com
NY Lesson Plans
NY Block Scheduling
Review Handbook for Regents Earth Science Exam

NATIONAL GEOGRAPHIC

Teacher's Corner

Products Available from National Geographic Society
To order the following products, call the National Geographic Society at 1-800-368-2728:
Video
Telling the Weather
Atmosphere: On the Air
Water: A Precious Resource

Transparency Set
NGS PicturePack: *Water*
Book
National Geographic Desk Reference

Content Background

Movement and Storage of Groundwater
Section 10.1

Groundwater is the subsurface water below the water table. Nowhere is the water table completely horizontal, so groundwater moves gradually downslope under the pull of gravity. The flow paths of the moving water are not parallel to the water table, but are concave upward between the points of recharge and discharge. The speed of groundwater motion is given by Darcy's law: $V = k(h/L)$, where V is the hypothetical flow velocity, k is the hydraulic conductivity, and h/L is the average slope of the water table (h is the rise; L is the run) between the two points connecting the flow path. The flow velocity, therefore, is proportional to the slope of the water table; high slopes produce higher flow velocities than low slopes, as might be expected. The hydraulic conductivity, k, is related to the permeability of the subsurface material and ranges over many orders of magnitude for different geological materials. Some representative values for k are 400 m/day for gravel, 12 m/day for sand, 3 m/day for sandstone, 0.1 m/day for silt, and 0.0002 m/day for clay. This means that coarse-grained, permeable materials such as sand and gravel permit higher flow velocities than do impermeable materials such as silt and clay, no matter what their slope.

Groundwater Erosion and Deposition
Section 10.2

Most of the geologic activity of groundwater involves the dissolution and precipitation of calcium carbonate. The dissolution of calcium carbonate produces caves and karst topography in limestone regions. The precipitation of calcium carbonate forms stalactites and stalagmites in caves, as well as the cements of many sedimentary rocks. Groundwater that is acidic dissolves calcium carbonate. The most common acid in groundwater is carbonic acid, which forms from carbon dioxide dissolved in groundwater through the reaction $CO_2 + H_2O \leftrightarrows H_2CO_3$.

The double arrow indicates that all three molecules (CO_2, H_2O, and H_2CO_3) are present in groundwater, and that, under equilibrium conditions, the rate of formation of H_2CO_3 molecules by the forward reaction (arrow to the right) equals the rate of dissociation into CO_2 and H_2O molecules by the reverse reaction (arrow to the left). Some of the H_2CO_3 molecules dissociate further into hydrogen ions (protons) and bicarbonate ions by the reaction $H_2CO_3 \leftrightarrows H^+ + HCO_3^-$.

Again, under equilibrium conditions, the forward reaction rate equals the reverse reaction rate. If acidic groundwater is in contact with limestone, the

Multiple Learning Styles

- **Kinesthetic** Collaborative Learning, p. 246, Modeling, p. 250
- **Visual-Spatial** Modeling, p. 240, Demo, p. 250
- **Interpersonal** Project, p. 252, Reteach, p. 257
- **Intrapersonal** Earth Science Journal, p. 255
- **Linguistic** Reteach, pp. 243, 248
- **Logical-Mathematical** Activity, p. 241
- **Naturalist** Earth Science Journal, p. 256

GLENCOE
Technology

The following multimedia resources are available from Glencoe.

Vocabulary Puzzlemaker

TeacherWorks™ CD-ROM

MindJogger Videoquizzes DVD/VHS

ExamView® Pro CD-ROM

Interactive Chalkboard CD-ROM

water dissolves calcium carbonate through the reaction $CaCO_3 + H^+ \leftrightarrows Ca^{2+} + HCO_3^-$. This equation describes both the dissolution (forward reaction) and precipitation (reverse reaction) of limestone. Stalactites and stalagmites form by the reverse process. When the solution containing dissolved limestone drips from the ceiling, some of the CO_2 comes out of the solution and goes back into the atmosphere. H_2CO_3 molecules dissociate into H_2O and CO_2 to replace the lost CO_2, H^+ and HCO_3^- ions recombine to replace the lost H_2CO_3, and $CaCO_3$ precipitates through the reaction $Ca^{2+} + HCO_3^- \rightarrow CaCO_3 + H^+$.

Groundwater Systems
Section 10.3

In coastal areas and on islands, fresh groundwater floats in hydrostatic equilibrium on top of denser salt water within the zone of saturation. Seawater has a density of about 1.025 g/cm³, while freshwater has a density of 1.000 g/cm³

or less. This means that a 40-m column of seawater weighs as much as a 41-m column of lower-density freshwater. Therefore, if the freshwater thickness in a coastal water-table aquifer is 41 m, the water table must be 1 m above sea level. In general, the water table elevation above sea level is roughly 1/40 of the freshwater thickness. If a coastal freshwater well is pumped excessively, the water table is lowered relatively little, but the salt water/freshwater interface rises significantly. Theoretically, for every meter of freshwater removed, the salt water rises 97.5 cm and the water table drops 2.5 cm. In this way, the freshwater withdrawn from a coastal well is gradually replaced by rising salt water at depth until the well becomes brackish or salty.

Identifying Misconceptions

Many people are under the erroneous impression that groundwater is confined to underground rivers or natural conduits, and that wells must be drilled into specific conduits. While this may be partially true in areas where there are substantial deposits of limestone or bodies of crystalline rock, explain to students that groundwater is present everywhere beneath the water table, and that all materials below the water table are completely saturated with water. As long as a well is drilled into a permeable material below the water table, it will produce water.

✓ Assessment

Portfolio Assessment
Assessment, TWE, p. 257

Performance Assessment
Discovery Lab, SE, p. 239
Assessment, TWE, p. 243
MiniLab, SE, p. 254
GeoLab, SE, pp. 258–259

Knowledge Assessment
Assessment, TWE, pp. 240, 251
Section Assessment, SE, pp. 243, 248, 257
Problem-Solving Lab, TWE, p. 253
MiniLab, TWE, p. 254

GeoLab, TWE, pp. 258–259
Chapter Assessment, SE, pp. 262–263

Skill Assessment
Discovery Lab, TWE, p. 239
Assessment, TWE, p. 248

Be sure to check the Earth Science Web Site for links to chapter material: earthgeu.com

Introducing the Chapter

Ask students how they think caves form. Point out that caves form in limestone and that limestone consists of calcium carbonate. Remind students that calcium carbonate fizzes and dissolves when it comes in contact with acid. Ask students what they know about groundwater. List their responses on the chalkboard and discuss them with the class.

Interpreting the Photo

This photo was taken inside Lechuguilla Cave, New Mexico. Lechuguilla Cave is the deepest limestone cave in the United States, with a measured depth of 500 meters. Since 1984, cavers have mapped over 160 kilometers of passages, which makes Lechuguilla the fifth longest cave in the world. Scientists have found rare chemolithoautotrophic bacteria inside the cave, which feed on sulfur, iron, and manganese.

INTERACTIVE CHALKBOARD
with Image Bank

PowerPoint® Presentations

This CD is an editable Microsoft® PowerPoint® presentation that includes:

- Section presentations
- Section checks
- Image bank
- Links to Earth Science Online
- All transparencies
- Animations
- Audio

Chapter 10

Groundwater

What You'll Learn

- How large amounts of water are stored underground.
- How groundwater dissolves limestone and forms caves and other natural features.
- How groundwater is removed from the ground by humans and what problems endanger our groundwater supply.

Why It's Important

Groundwater provides drinking water for half of the world's population and is a major source of the water used by agriculture and industry. However, groundwater supplies are threatened by overuse and pollution.

Earth Science Online

To find out more about groundwater, visit the Earth Science Web Site at earthgeu.com

238

Lechuguilla Cave, New Mexico

Discovery Lab

Process Skills

acquire and analyze information, compare and contrast, measure and use numbers, observe and infer, predict, communicate

Safety Precautions

Make sure that students wear safety goggles.

Procedure

Troubleshooting

It may be difficult for students to see the water level within the sand column. If so, students should overfill the first cylinder and pour the excess water back into the second cylinder. If water is spilled, students should make an estimated correction to the amount of water left in the second cylinder. Have students dispose of excess water in the sink and return all sand-filled cylinders to you.

Observe

The volume of water in the sand cylinder equals the

Discovery Lab

Model Underground Water Storage

Beneath your feet, there are vast amounts of water. This water fills in the pore spaces of sediments and rocks deep in the ground. In this activity, you will discover how much water can be stored in sand.

1. Fill a 250-mL graduated cylinder with dry sand.

2. Fill another 250-mL graduated cylinder with water.

3. Pour water from the second cylinder into the sand-filled cylinder until the water level is flush with the surface of the sand. Measure

and record the volume of saturated sand in the cylinder.

4. Measure and record how much water is left in the second cylinder.

🥽 🧪 *CAUTION: Always wear safety goggles and an apron in the lab.*

Observe In your science journal, describe how much water is present in the saturated sand. Calculate the ratio of water volume to the volume of sand. Infer how many liters of water could be stored in a cubic meter of sand.

SECTION 10.1

Movement and Storage of Groundwater

OBJECTIVES

• **Describe** how groundwater is stored and moves underground.

• **Explain** what an aquifer is.

VOCABULARY

infiltration
porosity
zone of saturation
water table
permeability
aquifer

If you drill a deep enough hole anywhere on Earth, it will partially fill with groundwater, even in the desert! Groundwater is present everywhere beneath the surface of the land, but nevertheless is a small fraction of all the water on Earth.

THE HYDROSPHERE

The water on and in Earth's crust makes up the hydrosphere, named after *hydros*, the Greek word for "water." About 97 percent of the hydrosphere is contained in the oceans. The water contained by landmasses—nearly all of it freshwater—makes up only about 3 percent of the hydrosphere.

Freshwater is one of Earth's most abundant and important renewable resources. However, of all the freshwater, more than 90 percent is in the form of polar ice caps and glaciers. You may be surprised to

10.1 Movement and Storage of Groundwater **239**

---

original volume in the second cylinder minus the volume remaining in the second cylinder. To determine the volume of water in one m³ of sand, it is best for students to use ratios, based on the fact that 1 m³ = 1000 L.

✔ Assessment

Skill Ask students to calculate which contains more water: a large swimming pool with a volume of 1 million L or a saturated cube of sand 10 m on each side. the swimming pool; the sand cube is not 100 percent water.

Resource Manager

Study Guide for Content Mastery, pp. 59–60 L2

Section Focus Transparency 26 L1 ELL

Section Focus

Before presenting the lesson, display **Section Focus Transparency 26** on the overhead projector.
L1 ELL

Chapter Themes

The following themes from the National Science Content Standards are covered in this chapter. Refer to page 8T of the Teacher Guide for an explanation of the correlations.
Systems, order, and organization (UCP.1); Evolution and equilibrium (UCP.4); Form and function (UCP.5)

⏲ Out of Time?

If time does not permit teaching the entire chapter, use the Study Guide on page 261 and the GeoDigest at the end of the unit as an overview.

NY Core Curriculum Standards

Page 238: St 4 KI 1.2g, St 6 KI 1 & 5
Page 239: St 1 Math KI 1, 2, 3, Science KI 1, 2, & 3, St 4 KI 1.2g, St 6 KI 1 & 5

239

Content Background

Groundwater is present only in the upper part of Earth's crust, because the pressure of the overlying rocks gradually compresses the pore spaces. Below a depth of about 10 km, all pore spaces are essentially closed, and rocks contain only traces of water. The deeper groundwater (below the top 1-2 km) is always salty, because most of it represents ancient seawater trapped in the marine sediments that later became continental sedimentary rocks through tectonic processes.

Modeling

Visual-Spatial Have students draw a hypothetical cross-sectional view of the ground that includes the following: soil moisture zone, zone of aeration, water table, and the zone of saturation. Ask students to draw a second cross section of the same hypothetical location shortly after it has rained. What happens to the thickness of the zone of aeration and the zone of saturation? What happens to the position of the water table?

✓Assessment

Knowledge Ask your students whether precipitation, such as rain or snow, is freshwater or salt water. freshwater Ask what the ultimate source of the water in the atmosphere is. the oceans Then ask how the water got into the atmosphere. by evaporation of seawater Ask students to explain how the evaporation of salt water produces freshwater. Only water molecules evaporate. The salt ions remain in the ocean.

Table 10-1 World's Water Supply				
Location	Surface Area (km²)	Water Volume (km³)	Percentage of Total Water	Estimated Average Residence Time of Water
Oceans	361 000 000	1 230 000 000	97.2	Thousands of years
Atmosphere	510 000 000	12 700	0.001	Nine days
Rivers and streams	—	1200	0.0001	Two weeks
Groundwater: shallow, to a depth of 0.8 km	130 000 000	4 000 000	0.31	Hundreds to many thousands of years
Lakes (freshwater)	855 000	123 000	0.009	Tens of years
Ice caps and glaciers	28 200 000	28 600 000	2.15	Tens of thousands of years and longer

learn that most of the remaining freshwater is groundwater. All the rivers, streams, and lakes on Earth represent only a small fraction of Earth's liquid freshwater, as shown in *Table 10-1*.

PRECIPITATION AND GROUNDWATER

The ultimate source of all water on land is the oceans. Evaporation of seawater introduces water into the atmosphere in the form of invisible water vapor and visible clouds. Winds and weather systems move this atmospheric moisture all over Earth, much of it over the continents. Precipitation brings atmospheric moisture back to Earth's surface, mostly in the form of rain and snow. Some of this precipitation falls directly into the oceans, and some falls on land.

Much of the precipitation that falls on land enters the ground through the process of **infiltration** and becomes groundwater. Only a small portion of precipitation becomes runoff and is returned directly to the oceans through streams and rivers. Solid precipitation, such as snow, may cover the ground for long periods of time before it melts and becomes runoff or infiltrates to become groundwater. Groundwater slowly moves through the ground, eventually returns to the surface through springs, and then flows back to the oceans.

GROUNDWATER STORAGE

Puddles of water that are left after a rain quickly disappear, partly by evaporating and partly by percolating into the ground. On sandy soils, rain soaks into the ground almost immediately. Where does that water go? Subsurface Earth materials are not totally solid, but instead contain countless small openings, or pores, which make up a large portion of some of these materials, as you see in *Figure 10-1.*

Resource Manager

Teaching Transparency 25 L2 ELL

Across the Curriculum

Physics The residence time is the average length of time that a substance spends in a reservoir. For instance, if water is exchanged (added and removed) in a bathtub holding 600 L at a rate of 0.5 L/s, then the residence time (or exchange time) of that water is 600/0.5 s, or 1200 s (20 min). Have students calculate the residence time in years of Earth's groundwater, given that the total amount of groundwater is 4 000 000 km³, and the infiltration (replacement) rate is 2000 km³/y. 2000 y

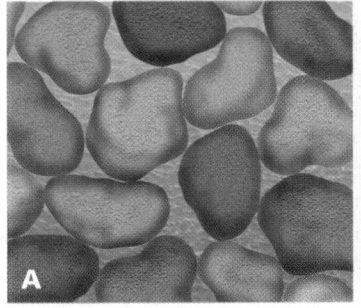
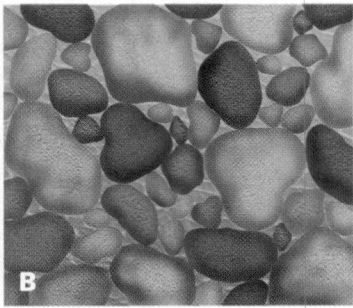

The percentage of pore space in a material is called its **porosity.** Subsurface materials have porosities ranging from 2 or 3 percent to more than 50 percent. For example, the porosity of well-sorted sand is typically around 30 percent. In poorly sorted sediments, however, smaller particles of sediment occupy some of the pore spaces and reduce the overall porosity of these sediments. Similarly, the cement that binds the grains of sedimentary rocks together reduces the rocks' porosity. Nevertheless, enormous quantities of groundwater are stored in the pore spaces of rocks and sediments.

THE ZONE OF SATURATION

The depth below Earth's surface at which groundwater completely fills all the pores of a material is called the **zone of saturation.** The upper boundary of the zone of saturation is the **water table,** as shown in *Figure 10-2.* Strictly speaking, only the water in the zone of saturation is called groundwater. In the zone of aeration, which

Figure 10-2 Groundwater flows toward valleys where the water table is close to the surface. During dry periods the level of the water table falls.

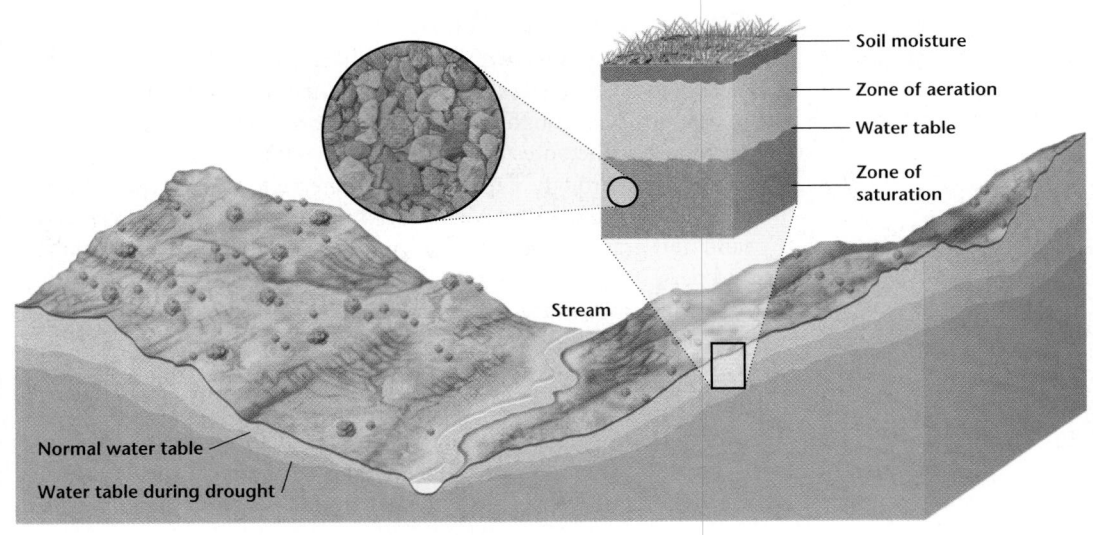

Soil moisture
Zone of aeration
Water table
Zone of saturation
Stream
Normal water table
Water table during drought

Activity

Logical-Mathematical
Porosity is the fraction of a material occupied by void spaces. It can be expressed as a percentage or as a decimal, for example, 30% = 0.3. Poorly sorted sediments have a lower porosity than well-sorted sediments. Have students work in groups to compare and contrast the porosity of well-sorted and poorly sorted materials by completing the following exercise. Assume that the porosity of well-sorted sand and well-sorted gravel is the same: 30 percent (0.3). Determine the porosity of a mixture of sand and gravel, assuming that fine sand with a porosity of 30 percent fills all the pore spaces of the gravel (30 percent of the gravel). In other words, what is 30 percent of 30 percent? 9 percent

This exercise can be done mathematically (0.3 × 0.3 = 0.09), or graphically, using columns to represent 100 percent. The empty spaces in the gravel are represented by a column divided vertically into a solid section 70 units long and a void section 30 units long. The sand-filled gravel column should have a solid gravel section 70 units long, a solid sand section 21 units long (70 percent of the original void section), and a void section 9 units long. Demonstrate this concept on the chalkboard using 50 percent of 50 percent (= 25 percent). **L2** **COOP LEARN**

Enrichment

Have students calculate the maximum porosity of a sediment consisting of spherical grains of equal size, packed in a perfect cubic arrangement. The volume of the spherical grains is $4/3\pi r^3$, where r is the radius. The volume of void space around each grain is equal to the volume of the cube (with an edge length of $2r$) minus the volume of the grain. The porosity is equal to the volume of void space divided by the volume of the cube, $8r^3$.
0.476 or 47.6 percent

NY Core Curriculum Standards

Page 240: St 4 KI 1.2g, 2.1f, & 2.1h, St 6 KI 1 & 5
Page 241: St 4 KI 1.2g, St 6 KI 1

Discussion

Ask students to estimate the United States groundwater usage per year. In 1995, the U.S. withdrew an average of 77 billion gallons of water per day. Ask students to think about the major uses of groundwater. In 1995, approximately 66.7% of groundwater used was for irrigation purposes, 18.7% for public use, 8% for industrial uses and 6.6% for rural use. Show students a graph of groundwater usage. The graph can be used to discuss the changes and trends of groundwater use over time.

Interpreting the Illustration

Figure 10-3 Point out that **Figure 10-3B** is magnified ten times more than **Figure 10-3A** and that the grains shown in **Figure 10-3B** are therefore much smaller. The thickness of the water sheaths around the grains is the same in both illustrations.

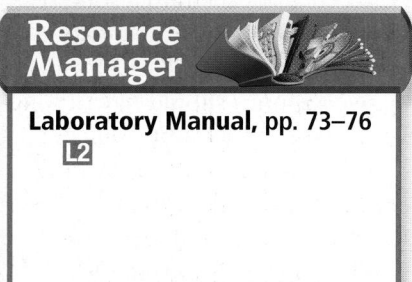
Figure 10-3 In a saturated material, all grains are coated with a thin film of motionless water. In coarse-grained material like sand **(A)** this film occupies a relatively small fraction of the pore space, and moving water can pass freely through the pores. In fine-grained material like silt **(B)** this film occupies most of the pore space and blocks the movement of water. As a result, sand has a much higher permeability than silt.

A

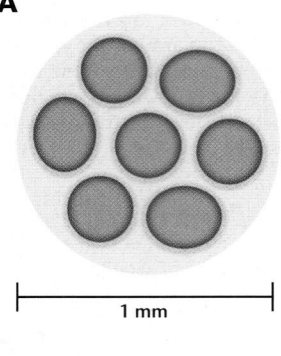

1 mm

B

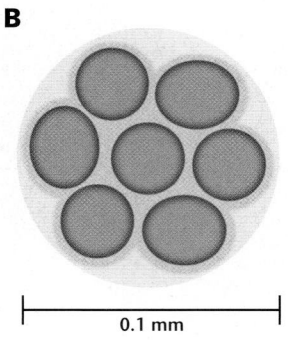

0.1 mm

is above the water table, materials are moist, but the pores contain mostly air. Water in the zone of saturation can be classified as either gravitational water or capillary water. Gravitational water is water that trickles downward as a result of gravity. Capillary water is water that is drawn upward from the water table and is held in the pore spaces of rocks and sediments as a result of surface tension. Materials that are directly above the water table, especially fine-grained materials, are nearly saturated with capillary water. Capillary action is similar to the action of water that is drawn upward through the pore spaces of a paper towel when the end of it is dipped into water.

The Water Table The depth of the water table varies depending on local conditions. For example, in stream valleys, groundwater is close to Earth's surface, and thus the water table is a few meters deep at most. In swampy areas, the water table is almost at Earth's surface, whereas on hilltops or in arid regions, the water table can be tens to hundreds of meters or more beneath the surface. As shown in *Figure 10-2,* the topography of the water table follows the topography of the land above it. For example, the water table slopes toward valleys and forms hills under topographic hills. Water table topography forms in this way because water underground moves slowly and conforms to surface contours.

Because of its dependence on precipitation, the water table fluctuates with seasonal and other weather conditions. It rises during wet seasons, usually in spring, and drops during dry seasons, often in late summer.

GROUNDWATER MOVEMENT

Groundwater flows downhill in the direction of the slope of the water table. In most cases, this downhill movement is slow because the water has to squeeze through numerous tiny pores in the subsurface material. In fact, if the pores are small, not even individual water molecules can squeeze through. The ability of a material to let water pass through it is called **permeability.** Materials with large, connected pores, such as sand and gravel, as shown in *Figure 10-3A,* have high permeabilities and permit relatively high flow velocities, up to 1 m/h or more. Other permeable subsurface materials include sandstone, limestone, and all highly fractured bedrock.

Fine-grained materials typically have low permeabilities because their pores are so tiny, as shown in *Figure 10-3B.* These materials are said to be impermeable. Flow velocities in impermeable materials are so low that they are often measured in meters per year. Some examples of impermeable materials are silt, clay, and shale. Clay is so

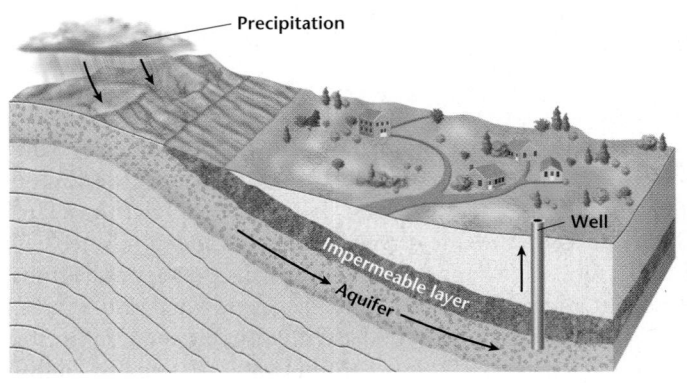

Figure 10-4 The aquifer is located in a permeable sandstone layer that is sealed beneath a capping layer of impermeable rock.

impermeable that a clay-lined depression will hold water. For this reason, clay is often used to line artificial ponds and landfills.

The flow velocity of groundwater primarily depends on the slope of the water table, because the force of gravity pulling the water downward is greater when the slope of the water table surface is steeper. You have experienced a similar effect if you have ever ridden a bicycle down a steep street and a gently sloping street. Although the flow velocity of groundwater is proportional to both the slope of the water table and the permeability of the material through which the water flows, permeability is the major factor. Thus, flow velocities through permeable materials are always higher than those through impermeable materials, regardless of the slope of the water table. Most groundwater flow takes place through permeable layers, called **aquifers,** such as the one shown in *Figure 10-4.* Impermeable layers, called aquicludes, are barriers to groundwater flow. In the next section, you'll discover what happens when groundwater moves slowly through materials.

SECTION ASSESSMENT

1. What is the greatest source of freshwater on Earth?

2. Where is the water table closest to Earth's surface: in the floodplain of a river, in a swamp, or on a hilltop?

3. What two factors determine the flow velocity of groundwater?

4. What is an aquifer?

5. **Thinking Critically** What is the difference between porosity and permeability in subsurface materials?

SKILL REVIEW

6. **Making and Using Tables** Design a data table that compares and contrasts the porosity and permeability of sand and a mixture of sand and gravel. Which material has the greater porosity? The greater permeability? For more help, refer to the *Skill Handbook*.

earthgeu.com/self_check_quiz

SECTION ASSESSMENT

1. The greatest source of freshwater is the polar ice caps and glaciers. However, this water is unavailable for human use.

2. The water table is closest to the surface in a swamp.

3. The flow velocity depends on the slope of the water table and the permeability of the material.

4. An aquifer is a permeable layer that allows groundwater to flow through it.

5. Porosity is the percentage of pore spaces in a material. Permeability is the ability of a material to let water pass through it.

6.

	Porosity	Permeability
Sand	High	Medium
Gravel	High	High
Mixture	Low	Less than sand

3 Assess

Check for Understanding
Discussion
Ask students what happens to rainwater that infiltrates the ground. Infiltrating water trickles through the zone of aeration to the water table, enters the zone of saturation, and slowly moves downslope through aquifers until it is discharged through springs to the surface and flows back to the ocean.

Reteach
Linguistic Explain the hydrologic cycle and the motion of groundwater. Have students look up the following terms in a dictionary, compare the dictionary definitions with those in the glossary in the back of the text, and list their meanings in their science journals: *groundwater, water table, porosity, saturation, permeability,* and *aquifer.*

✓Assessment

Performance Have students compare and contrast porosity and permeability, and how grain size, grain shape, cementation, and sorting influence these two properties. Have students record their analyses in their science journals. Porosity is independent of grain size, decreases with grain angularity, decreases with cementation, and increases with sorting. Permeability increases with grain size, decreases with grain angularity, decreases with cementation, and increases with sorting. Use the Performance Task Assessment List for Science Journal in **PASC,** p. 103.

243

Groundwater Erosion and Deposition

Section Background

For section content background, refer to **Groundwater Erosion and Deposition** on pages 238C–D.

Preplanning

Refer to the Chapter Organizer on pages 238A–B.

1 Focus

Section Focus

Before presenting the lesson, display **Section Focus Transparency 27** on the overhead projector.
L1 ELL

Tying to Previous Knowledge

An understanding of the dissolution and precipitation of calcium carbonate by groundwater requires some familiarity with chemical equations. Revisit and review those equations with students.

OBJECTIVES

- **Explain** *how groundwater dissolves and deposits rocks and minerals.*
- **Describe** *how caves form and how karst topography develops on Earth's surface.*

VOCABULARY

cave
sinkhole
karst topography
stalactite
stalagmite
travertine

In Chapter 3, you learned about the corrosive properties of acids. Acids are solutions that contain hydrogen ions. Most groundwater contains some acid, in most cases carbonic acid. Carbonic acid forms when carbon dioxide dissolves in water and combines with water molecules. This happens when rain falls through the atmosphere and interacts with carbon-dioxide gas or when groundwater percolates through carbon-rich, decaying organic material in soil. As a result of these processes, groundwater is usually slightly acidic and attacks carbonate rocks, especially limestone. Limestone consists mostly of calcium carbonate ($CaCO_3$), which dissolves readily in any kind of acid, the results of which are shown in *Figure 10-5.*

DISSOLUTION BY GROUNDWATER

The process by which carbonic acid forms and dissolves calcium carbonate can be described by three simple chemical equations.

In the first process, carbon dioxide and water combine to form carbonic acid, as represented by the following equation.

$$CO_2 + H_2O \longrightarrow H_2CO_3$$

In the second process, the carbonic acid (H_2CO_3) molecules in the water split into hydrogen ions (H^+) and bicarbonate ions (HCO_3^-). This process is represented by the following equation.

$$H_2CO_3 \longrightarrow H^+ + HCO_3^-$$

In the third process, the hydrogen ions react with calcium carbonate and dissolve it, as represented by the following equation.

$$CaCO_3 + H^+ \longrightarrow Ca^{2+} + HCO_3^-$$

Figure 10-5 A viewing pagoda is standing among the massive limestone pillars of the stone forest in China. Carbonic acid is slowly dissolving the calcium carbonate in the limestone pillars.

For every carbon dioxide molecule dissolved in groundwater, one hydrogen ion is produced and one calcium carbonate molecule is dissolved. The resulting calcium (Ca^{2+}) and bicarbonate (HCO_3^-) ions are then flushed away by the groundwater. Eventually, they precipitate out somewhere else. Precipitation of calcium carbonate occurs when the groundwater evaporates or when the gas carbon dioxide diffuses out of the water. Both the dissolution and formation of calcium carbonate play a major role in the formation of limestone caves.

Interpreting the Photo

Figure 10-5 The corrosion shown in the limestone pillars was caused by acids in rainwater. In addition to carbonic acid, atmospheric moisture typically contains other acids, such as nitric and sulfuric acids, as a result of pollutants that are emitted by automobiles and coal-burning power plants. These additional acids rapidly dissolve calcium carbonate. Groundwater also contains acid and also dissolves calcium carbonate, albeit at a much slower rate.

Resource Manager

Study Guide for Content Mastery,
  pp. 61–62 L2
Section Focus Transparency 27 L1 ELL

Figure 10-6 In Mammoth Cave, Kentucky, there are a series of underground passages that extend to a length of more than 500 km.

Caves A natural underground opening with a connection to Earth's surface is called a **cave.** Some caves form three-dimensional mazes of passages, shafts, and great chambers that stretch for many kilometers. Many caves have structures that hang from the caves' ceilings. Some caves are dry, while others contain underground streams or lakes. Still others are totally flooded and can be explored only by cave divers. One of the most spectacular caves is the recently discovered Lechuguilla Cave of New Mexico, shown in the photograph at the beginning of this chapter. Another cave system in New Mexico, Carlsbad Caverns, includes a huge subterranean chamber over 1 km long and 100 m high. Mammoth Cave, in Kentucky, as shown in *Figure 10-6,* is composed of a series of connected underground passages.

Practically all caves of significant size are formed when groundwater dissolves limestone. Most caves develop in the zone of saturation just below the water table. As groundwater percolates through the cracks and joints of limestone formations, it gradually dissolves the adjacent rock and enlarges these passages to form an interconnected network of openings. Thus, the limestone formation becomes more permeable. The resulting increased downhill flow of groundwater gradually lowers the water table until much of the cave system is filled with air. New caves then form beneath the lowered water table. If the water table continues to drop, the thick limestone formations eventually become honeycombed with caves and caverns. This is a common occurrence in limestone regions that have been uplifted by tectonic forces.

10.2 *Groundwater Erosion and Deposition* **245**

Demo

This demonstration requires several pieces of sandstone (quartz-cemented), limestone, and granite; a small bottle of acid (HCl); and a dropper. Drop some of the acid on each rock sample. Point out that only the acid dropped on limestone fizzes, that limestone is mostly calcium carbonate, and that the fizzing gas bubbles are carbon dioxide released during the dissolution of calcium carbonate. Explain again that groundwater is slightly acidic and slowly dissolves limestone.

Content Background

Not all caves are composed of limestone. Caves can also develop in other sedimentary rocks if they contain soluble cements, such as sandstone that contains calcium-carbonate cement. Some sizable caves were formed from lava tubes in volcanic rocks after the lava drained out of them. Examples of large lava-tube caves exist in Hawaii. In addition, differential erosion of coastal rocks by surf action often produces sea caves. Nevertheless, the vast majority of caves are produced by the dissolution of limestone.

245

Content Background

Water and carbon dioxide can be thought of as agents of change in an area of limestone bedrock. Areas of the country with limestone bedrock exhibit morphologies associated with the processes of $CaCO_3$ dissolution and precipitation. Caves and sinkholes are a result of the process of dissolution. Often found inside caves, large pillars made of $CaCO_3$ are a result of the deposition of $CaCO_3$.

Collaborative Learning

Kinesthetic Have students act out the chemical reactions on page 244. You will need 11 volunteers to represent two hydrogen atoms, six oxygen atoms, two carbon atoms, and one calcium atom, identified by appropriate name tags such as H (hydrogen), O (oxygen), C (carbon), and Ca (calcium). Have students form the following three molecules by linking arms: carbon dioxide (CO_2), water (H_2O), and calcium carbonate ($CaCO_3$). Next, have students simulate the three reactions: the CO_2 molecule holds hands with the H_2O molecule to form a H_2CO_3 molecule; an H atom breaks away from the H_2CO_3 molecule, leaving a bicarbonate ion; and the single H atom attacks the $CaCO_3$ molecule, pulls away the Ca atom, and takes its place, forming another bicarbonate ion. **ELL**

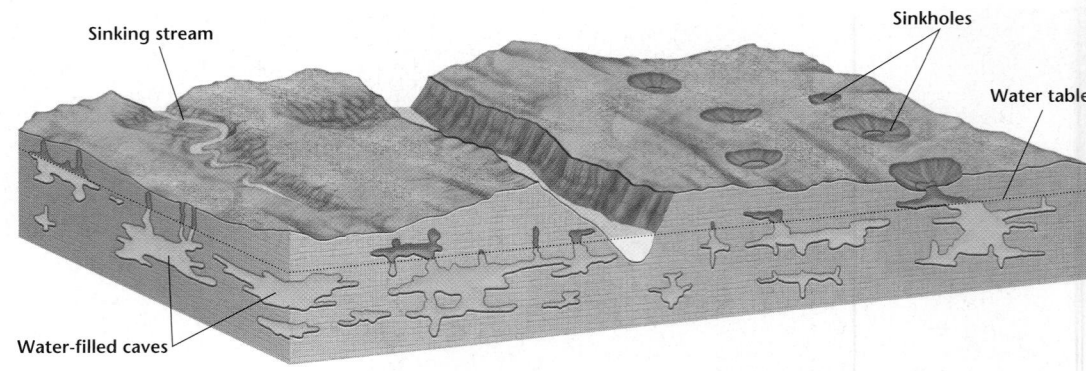

Figure 10-7 In the development of karst topography, caves form near or below the water table. Streams deepen their valleys. The water table drops and new caves form below the water table. Collapsing caves or dissolution of bedrock at the surface produce sinkholes.

Karst Topography *Figure 10-7* shows some of the characteristic surface features produced by the dissolution of limestone. The main feature is a **sinkhole,** as shown in *Figure 10-8.* A sinkhole is a depression in the ground caused by the collapse of a cave or by the direct dissolution of bedrock by acidic rain or moist soil. Another type of feature forms when a surface stream drains into a cave system, continues underground, and leaves a dry valley above. Such a stream, called a sinking stream, sometimes reemerges abruptly on Earth's surface as a karst spring.

Limestone regions that have sinkholes, sinks, and sinking streams are said to have **karst topography.** The word *karst* comes from the name of a limestone region in Croatia where these features are

Figure 10-8 Sinkholes developed near Roswell, New Mexico.

Earth Science Journal

Science Field Book

Have students research and report on the cave systems of one of the National Parks listed below using the Earth Science Web Site at earthgeu.com and other available sources. Students should include both tourist and geological information in their reports. Have students select their caves from the following sites: Carlsbad Caverns National Park, NM; Great Basin National Park, NV; Jewel Cave National Monument, SD; Mammoth Cave National Park, KY; Oregon Caves National Monument, OR; Ozark National Scenic Riverways, MO; Russell Cave National Monument, AL; Sequoia National Park, CA; Timpanogos Cave National Monument, UT; and Wind Cave National Park, SD.

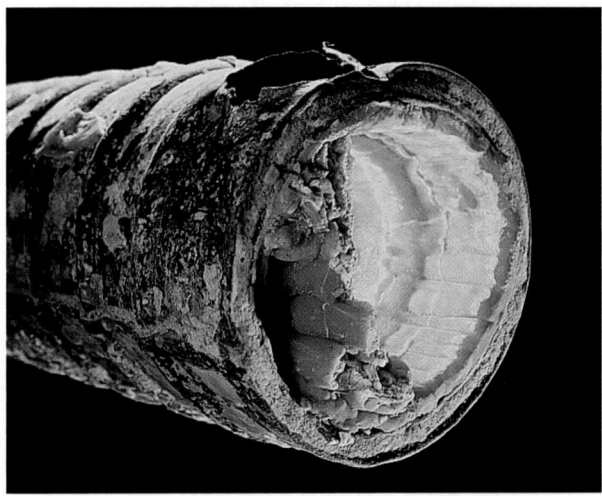

especially well developed. Prominent karst regions in the United States are located in Kentucky. The Mammoth Cave region in Kentucky has karst topography that contains tens of thousands of sinkholes. Most of the lakes in Central Florida are sinkholes.

GROUNDWATER DEPOSITS
You are probably aware that your tap water contains various dissolved materials. Some water contains sulfur compounds, and some contains dissolved iron compounds. Water that contains iron compounds typically leaves brownish or red stains on kitchen and bathroom fixtures.

Hard Water Water that contains high concentrations of calcium, magnesium, or iron is called hard water. Hard water is common in limestone areas where the groundwater is nearly saturated with calcium carbonate. Household use of hard water usually can cause a problem: deposits of calcium bicarbonate eventually clog water pipes, as shown in *Figure 10-9.* These problems can be controlled with a water softener, which removes dissolved ions from hard water. Water that contains few dissolved ions is called soft water.

Natural Deposits The most remarkable deposits produced by groundwater are the dripstone formations that decorate many caves above the water table. As their name indicates, these formations are built slowly as water drips through caves. Each drop of water hanging on the ceiling of a cave loses some of its carbon dioxide and deposits a tiny amount of calcium carbonate. Over many years, these deposits gradually form cone-shaped or cylindrical structures called

Using Numbers
Each drop of water deposits a 1-nm-thick layer of calcium carbonate at the tip of a stalactite growing in a cave. Given that $1 \text{ nm} = 10^{-9}$ m, if a drop falls every 30 seconds, what length, in centimeters, will the stalactite be in 100 years? How many years will it take for the stalactite to reach a length of 5 m?

3 Assess

Check for Understanding

Discussion

Ask students to explain the formation of caves. Caves form through the dissolution of limestone by groundwater.

Reteach

Linguistic Explain the formation of caves in general terms, and have students read an article of their choice about caves in *National Geographic* magazine. Have students write brief summaries of the articles they read in their science journals.

✓Assessment

Skill Have students explain how a geologist is able to identify a limestone region, such as Central Florida, from the air or from a satellite image. Have them list and describe at least two possible indicators. Karst regions are identified by sinkholes, which are closed depressions formed by bedrock dissolution or the collapse of a cave; disappearing streams, which are drained off into a cave system; dry valleys left by disappearing streams; karst springs, which are large streams emerging from a cave; and generally irregular topography with disrupted drainage. Caves themselves are generally not visible from the air.

Figure 10-10 Stalactites, stalagmites, and dripstone columns are found in the Carlsbad Caverns of New Mexico.

stalactites that hang from the cave's ceiling like icicles. As the water drops splash to the floor of the cave, they gradually build mound-shaped dripstone deposits, called **stalagmites,** underneath the stalactites. In time, stalactites and stalagmites may grow together to form dripstone columns, such as the ones shown in *Figure 10-10.* These and other types of dripstone formations are composed of a type of limestone called **travertine.**

SECTION ASSESSMENT

1. What acid is most commonly present in groundwater?
2. How do caves form?
3. Compare the formation of stalactites and stalagmites.
4. What is karst topography?
5. **Thinking Critically** If you visited a region that consisted mostly of igneous rocks, would you expect to find karst topography? Explain.

SKILL REVIEW

6. **Concept Mapping** Use the following terms to construct a concept map to organize the major ideas in this section. For more help, refer to the *Skill Handbook.*

clogged water pipes   stalagmites   sinkholes   karst topography

calcium carbonate   hard water   Croatia

stalactites   caves

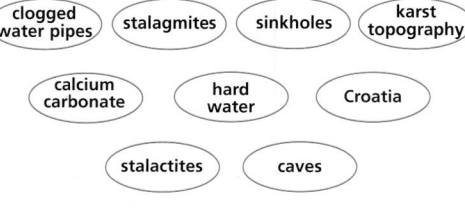

earthgeu.com/self_check_quiz

SECTION ASSESSMENT

1. Carbonic acid is the most common acid in groundwater. Carbonic acid dissolves the calcium carbonate in limestone.
2. Most caves form by the dissolution of limestone by groundwater.
3. Stalactites form from calcium carbonate deposited by drops of water hanging on the roof of a cave; stalagmites are calcium-carbonate deposits on a cave floor formed by dripping water.
4. Karst topography is irregular topography formed by the dissolution of limestone by groundwater.
5. Areas that are subject to karst topography would have limestone formations, not igneous rock.
6. clogged water pipes, hard water, calcium carbonate; caves, stalagmites, stalactites; karst topography, sinkholes, Croatia

SECTION 10.3 *Groundwater Systems*

The average length of time that groundwater remains underground is several hundred years. Groundwater moves slowly but continuously through aquifers and eventually returns to Earth's surface. You may wonder how this can happen. Can groundwater flow upward against gravity? In some cases, it can, as you will learn in this section. In most cases, however, groundwater emerges wherever the water table intersects Earth's surface. Such intersections commonly occur in areas that have sloping surface topography. The exact places where groundwater emerges depend on the arrangement of aquifers and aquicludes in an area.

SPRINGS

You have learned that aquifers are permeable underground layers through which groundwater moves with relative ease, while aquicludes are impermeable layers. Aquifers are commonly composed of layers of sand and gravel, sandstone, and limestone. Because of its many solution cavities, limestone is usually highly permeable and permits high flow velocities. Underground streams in cavernous limestone formations may transport groundwater at a rate of several kilometers per day. In contrast, aquicludes, such as layers of clay or shale, block groundwater movement. As a result, groundwater tends to discharge at Earth's surface where an aquifer and an aquiclude come in contact, as shown in *Figure 10-11.* These natural discharges of groundwater are called **springs.**

Figure 10-11 A spring occurs where an aquifer and an aquiclude come in contact at Earth's surface. At this point, the water flows out of the rock.

OBJECTIVES

- **Relate** *the different types of springs to common systems of aquifers.*
- **Explain** *how groundwater is withdrawn from aquifer systems by wells.*
- **Describe** *the major problems that threaten groundwater supplies.*

VOCABULARY

spring
hot spring
geyser
well
drawdown
recharge
artesian well

Content Background

In a hydrologic system at least as many units of water are moving downward as are moving upward. The upward-moving water is pushed by hydrostatic pressure, which is produced by gravity. Ask students to consider a U-shaped tube with a removable barrier at its lowest point. If the water level is higher on one side, the water pressure on that side will be higher. If the barrier is removed, water will flow toward the side with lower pressure and rise until the water levels are equal.

Resource Manager

Study Guide for Content Mastery, pp. 63–64 L2

Section Focus Transparency 28 L1 ELL

Section 10.3

ENVIRONMENTAL CONNECTION

Prepare

Section Background

For section content background, refer to **Groundwater Systems** on page 238D.

Preplanning

Refer to the Chapter Organizer on pages 238A–B.

1 Focus

Section Focus

Before presenting the lesson, display **Section Focus Transparency 28** on the overhead projector.
L1 ELL

Section Focus Transparency 28 WILD WATER
Use with Chapter 10, Section 10.3

❶ What is this feature called?
❷ What do you think causes water to behave this way?

NY Core Curriculum Standards

Page 248: St 4 KI 1.2g, St 6 KI 1, 2, & 5
Page 249: St 4 KI 1.2g, St 6 KI 1

Modeling

Kinesthetic Have the class build a model of a perched water table in the form of a hill made of fine-grained sand, with a flat foam board representing an aquiclude inserted horizontally part way up, such that the aquiclude intersects the surface of the hill all the way around. Have a volunteer slowly pour water onto the apex of the hill until "springs" appear at points of contact between the foam board and the sand. Have students each sketch a cross section of the model, indicating and describing its pertinent features, including the aquifers, aquiclude, perched water table, zone of saturation, spring horizon, and upper and lower zones of aeration. **L1** **ELL**

Applying Earth Science

Central Florida is underlain by a thick limestone formation and has many karst features, including copious karst springs. Many of Central Florida's lakes are flooded sinkholes, which are fed by karst springs. These karst springs are indicated on maps, and some can be identified by a sizable stream emerging from a lake with no comparable stream flowing into the lake. Have the class scrutinize the streams and lakes of Central Florida on a map and identify some lakes that must be fed by karst springs. Examples include Orange Lake, Lake George, Crescent Lake, Lake Harris, Lake Griffin, Lake Apopka, Lake Dora, Lake Hancock, and Lake Arbuckle.

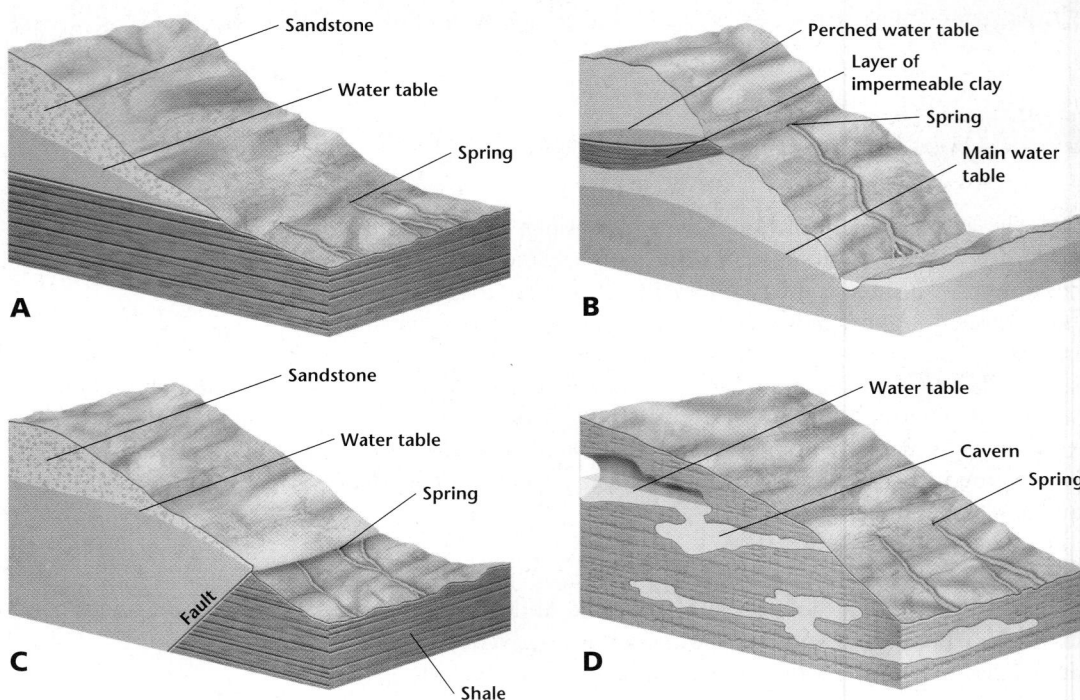

Figure 10-12 Springs occur in various places, such as at the sides of valleys and at the edges of perched water tables. The volume of water varies from the flow of a small spring to the rush of a large river.

Emergence of Springs The volume of water that is discharged by a spring may be a mere trickle, or, in karst regions, an entire river may emerge from the ground. Such a superspring is called a karst spring. Many of Florida's lakes are flooded sinkholes that are fed by karst springs whose discharge causes full-sized rivers to flow out of these lakes. In regions of near-horizontal sedimentary rocks, springs often emerge on the sides of valleys at about the same elevation, at the bases of aquifers, as shown in *Figure 10-12A.* Springs may also emerge at the edges of perched water tables. A perched water table, as shown in *Figure 10-12B,* is a zone of saturation that overlies an aquiclude that separates it from the main water table below. Other areas where springs tend to emerge are along faults, which are huge fractures that offset rock formations and sometimes block aquifers, as shown in *Figure 10-12C.* In limestone regions, springs discharge water from underground pathways, as shown in *Figure 10-12D.*

Temperature of Springs Spring water is usually thought of as being cool and refreshing. Actually, the temperature of groundwater that is discharged through a spring is generally the average annual temperature of the region in which it is located. Thus, springs in New

250 CHAPTER 10 *Groundwater*

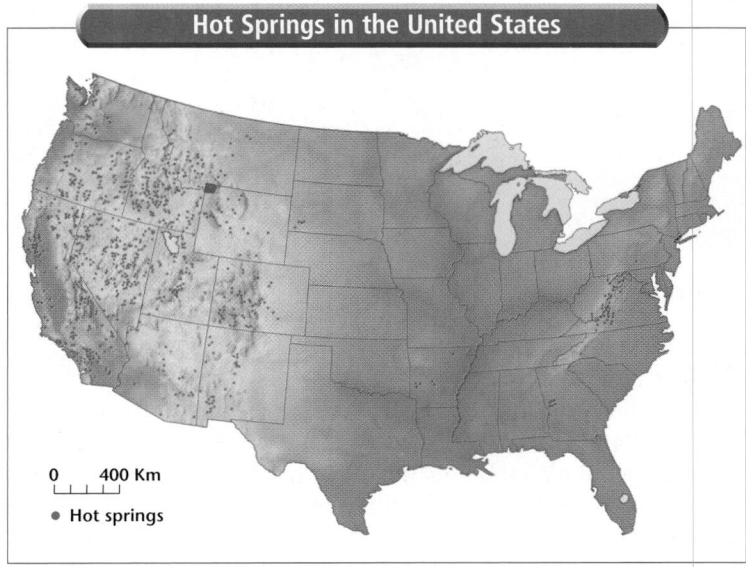

Hot Springs in the United States

0   400 Km

● Hot springs

Figure 10-13 Hot springs occur in many areas of the United States.

England have year-round temperatures of about 10°C, while those in the Gulf states have temperatures of about 20°C.

Compared to air temperatures, groundwater is colder in the summer and warmer in the winter. However, in some regions of the United States, certain springs discharge water that is much warmer than the average annual temperature. These springs are called warm springs or hot springs, depending on their temperatures. **Hot springs** have temperatures higher than that of the human body. There are thousands of hot springs in the United States alone, as shown in *Figure 10-13.* Most of these are located in the western United States in areas where the subsurface is still quite hot from relatively recent igneous activity. A number of hot springs also occur in some eastern states. These eastern hot springs emerge from aquifers that descend to great depths in Earth's crust and allow deep, hot water to rise. The underground water is hot because temperatures in Earth's crust increase with depth by about 25°C for every kilometer. Among the most spectacular features produced by Earth's underground heat in volcanic regions are geysers, as shown in *Figure 10-14.* **Geysers** are explosive hot springs that erupt at regular intervals. One of the world's most famous geysers, Old Faithful, is located in Yellowstone National Park, Wyoming. Old Faithful erupts approximately every hour with a 40-m high column of boiling water and steam.

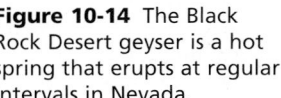

Figure 10-14 The Black Rock Desert geyser is a hot spring that erupts at regular intervals in Nevada.

10.3 *Groundwater Systems* **251**

Demo

To demonstrate a cone of depression, obtain a Plexiglas box or a large aquarium tank. Fill the box or aquarium with very fine sand and water that has been colored with food coloring such that the water table is a few centimeters below the level sand surface. Rapidly withdraw water from a simulated well at the center of the box or near the center of one of the long aquarium walls using a tube with one end stuck in the sand below the water table and the other end at a lower elevation than the box or aquarium. Point out to students the resulting drawdown and cone of depression in the water table. Then, return or recharge the water and have students observe the recovery of the water table.

✓Assessment

Knowledge Ask students to compare and contrast the distribution of hot springs and geysers in the eastern and western United States. Most hot springs and all geysers in the United States are located in the western states because there has been more recent volcanic activity in that part of the country.

Resource Manager

Laboratory Manual, pp. 77–80
L2

NY Core Curriculum Standards

Page 250: St 4 KI 1.2g, St 6 KI 1
Page 251: St 4 KI 1.2g, St 6 KI 1

Project

👥 **Interpersonal** There are many features associated with thermal activity that can be found at Yellowstone National Park, Wyoming, and in other parts of the world. To study these features, divide the class into 5 groups and assign each group one of the following thermal features: geysers, hot springs, mud pots, fumaroles, and travertine terraces. These five features are all found at Yellowstone National Park, Wyoming. Ask each group to draw a large diagram of its feature and research how the system works. Each group should present its findings to the class.

COOP LEARN 📦

Interpreting the Illustration

Figure 10-16 The artesian aquifer shown in the figure can be compared to the way in which a water tower supplies water to a community. On the chalkboard, draw a water tower surrounded by buildings of different heights, some lower and some higher than the water tower. Show the water level in the water tower and draw a horizontal line at that level through the buildings. The water tower represents the recharge area, the water level in the tower represents the water table in the recharge area, and the horizontal line represents the piezometric (pressure) surface. Point out that water supplied by the tower can be raised only to a corresponding level in the buildings. Explain that pressure from the elevated recharge area causes a similar pressure surface to which artesian groundwater can rise.

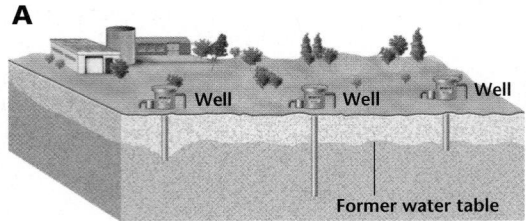

A Before heavy pumping

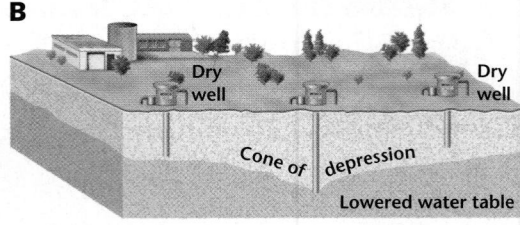

B After heavy pumping

Figure 10-15 Wells must be drilled far enough below the water table so that they are not affected by seasonal water table fluctuations **(A)**. Overpumping of wells causes a lowering of the entire water table **(B)**.

WELLS

Wells are holes dug or drilled deep into the ground to reach a reservoir of groundwater. To produce water, a well must tap into an aquifer. The simplest wells are those that are dug or drilled below the water table, into the zone of saturation, and into what is called a water-table aquifer, as shown in *Figure 10-15A*. Initially, the water level in such a well is the same as the level of the water table. However, overpumping of the well lowers the water level in it and produces a cone of depression in the water table around the well, as shown in *Figure 10-15B*. The difference between the original water-table level and the water level in the pumped well is called the **drawdown**. If many wells withdraw water from a water-table aquifer, their cones of depression may overlap and cause an overall lowering of the water table, which can cause shallow wells to go dry. Water from precipitation and runoff is added back to the zone of saturation in the process of **recharge.** Groundwater recharge from precipitation and runoff sometimes replenishes the water withdrawn from wells. However, if recharge does not keep pace with groundwater withdrawal, the water table continues to drop until all wells in the area go dry.

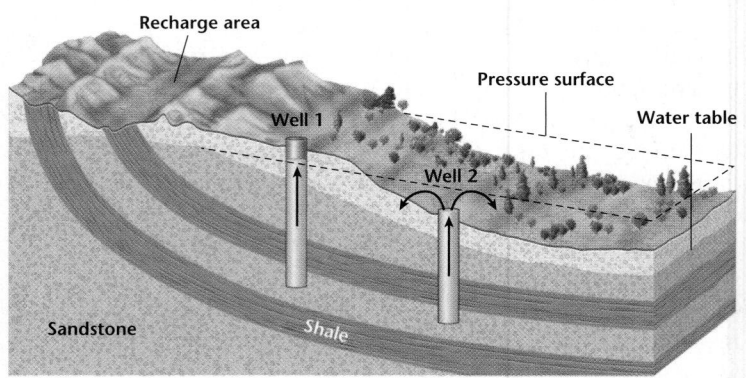

Figure 10-16 The level to which the water in an artesian well can rise is called the pressure surface.

Demo

The following experiment can be used to demonstrate both the nature of hydrostatic pressure and the concept that hydrostatic pressure depends only on water depth, not on the geometry of the container. Drill two or three pinholes, one above the other, into a long, slender, cylindrical plastic container, then fill the container with water. Water will spurt out of all the holes, but the water from the lowest hole will squirt the farthest because it is under the highest hydrostatic pressure. Next, tilt the container to one side so that the water no longer covers the bottom of the container or the pinholes. Add water so that the water surface is at the same distance from the bottom of the container as before. The water should spurt out of the pinholes with a similar force as before. Any change will be a result of the small change in elevation of the pinholes. Explain to the class that as long as a pinhole is at the same depth below the water level, it will discharge water at the same rate, no matter where the actual water surface is.

CONFINED AQUIFERS

Water-table aquifers are unconfined and unprotected, and thus, they are easily polluted. Surface spills of pollutants often reach the water table and spread throughout aquifers. More reliable and less easily polluted water supplies can be found in deeper aquifers, called confined aquifers, which are generally sandwiched between aquicludes. The aquicludes form barriers that prevent pollutants from reaching such aquifers.

Artesian Wells Because the area of recharge is usually at a higher elevation than the rest of an aquifer, a confined aquifer contains water under pressure, as you can see by doing the *Problem-Solving Lab* on this page. The aquifer is called an artesian aquifer. When the rate of recharge is high enough, the pressurized water in a well drilled into a confined aquifer may spurt above the land surface in the form of a fountain called an **artesian well,** as shown in *Figure 10-16.* Similarly, a spring that discharges pressurized water is called an artesian spring.

Problem-Solving Lab

Using Tables and Making Graphs

Make inferences about the water levels of an artesian aquifer Artesian aquifers contain water under pressure. The table provides the following data about an artesian aquifer for three sites, spaced 100 m apart, along a survey line: elevations of the land surface, the water table, and the upper surface of the aquiclude on top of the artesian aquifer; and the artesian pressure surface, which is the level to which the artesian water can rise.

Site	Surface Elevation	Water Table Elevation	Aquiclude Elevation	Pressure Surface
1	396 m	392 m	388 m	394 m
2	394	390	386	393
3	390	388	381	392

2. A well has been drilled at each site. The wells at sites 1 and 3 are 7 m deep. The well at site 2 was drilled into the artesian aquifer at a depth of 14 m. Sketch the wells at their proper depths on your cross section.

Thinking Critically

3. At what depth below the ground surface are the water levels in the three wells before they are pumped?
4. What would happen if a well was drilled into the confined aquifer at site 3?
5. At what sites could there be an artesian spring?

Analysis

1. Plot the elevation data on a graph with the sites on the *x*-axis and the elevations on the *y*-axis. Make a cross section of the survey line from site 1 to site 3. Use a heavy line to indicate the land surface.

Problem-Solving Lab

Purpose
Students' understanding of artesian aquifers will be enhanced.

Process Skills
make and use graphs, measure and use numbers, apply concepts, compare and contrast, predict, think critically

Materials
pencil, paper, metric ruler

Alternate Materials
graph paper

Teaching Strategies
• Review artesian springs and wells with the class.
• Show students how to plot a similar cross section on the chalkboard using fictitious numbers.

Analysis
1.–2. Student cross sections should reflect the elevations in the data table.

Thinking Critically
3. well 1: 4 m, well 2: 4 m, well 3: 2 m
4. The water would rise above the surface by 2 m at site 3.
5. at site 3

✓ Assessment

Knowledge Ask students what would happen to the water levels in the three wells if they were pumped regularly, but not excessively. The water levels in wells 1 and 3 would drop, and a cone of depression would develop. The water level in well 2 would be unaffected.

Using an Analogy

Ask students what would happen if they drilled a small hole into the bottom of a boat. The water would spurt about as high as the water level outside the boat; this level is the invisible pressure surface inside the boat. The level of the lake is analogous to the water table in a recharge area, the bottom of the boat to the upper aquiclude, the water under the boat to an artesian aquifer, and the hole to an artesian spring.

NY Core Curriculum Standards

Page 252: St 4 KI 1.2g, St 6 KI 1
Page 253: St 1 Math KI 1, 2, & 3, St 4 KI 1.2g, St 6 KI 1, 2, & 5

Purpose

Students will demonstrate the nature of artesian wells.

Process Skills

acquire and analyze information, compare and contrast, observe and infer, recognize cause and effect, draw a conclusion, hypothesize, predict

Materials

several large containers, sand, water, silicone putty, soda straws, safety goggles

Teaching Strategies

- Review artesian aquifers and piezometric (pressure) surfaces prior to the lab.
- Use a latex-based putty to avoid high levels of volatile organic compounds.

Expected Results

After the box is tilted, the water levels in the straws should be highest at the low end of the container and lowest at the high end.

Analyze and Conclude

1. highest in the lowest straw, lowest in the highest straw
2. below the silicone putty
3. at low end of container because of the hydrostatic pressure produced by the weight of the water above that level
4. Both the water table in the sand and the pressure surface will be lowered.

✔Assessment

Knowledge Ask students where the water pressure is greater: at the bottom of a lake 10 m below the water surface or in an artesian limestone aquifer 10 m below the water table in the recharge area. The pressures should be equal. Frictional loss of pressure in a cavernous limestone aquifer should be negligible.

MiniLab

How does an artesian well work?

Model the changes that an artesian aquifer undergoes when a well is dug into it. What causes the water to rise above the ground surface?

Procedure 🥽 🧤 *CAUTION: Always wear safety goggles and an apron in the lab.*

1. Half-fill a plastic shoe box or other container with sand. Add enough water to saturate the sand. Cover the sand completely with a 1-or 2-cm layer of clay or a similar impermeable material.
2. Tilt the box at an angle of about 10°. Use a book for a prop.
3. Punch three holes through the clay, one each near the low end, the middle, and the high end of the box. Insert a clear straw through each hole into the sand below. Seal the holes around the straws.

Analyze and Conclude

1. Observe the water levels in the straws. Where is the water level the highest? The lowest?
2. Where is the water table in the box?
3. Where is the water under greatest pressure? Explain.
4. Predict what will happen to the water table and the surface if the water flows from one of the straws.

Figure 10-17 In the United States, the greatest amount of water usage is for agricultural activities, mostly for irrigation.

Resource Manager

GeoLab and MiniLab Worksheets,
p. 39 L2

The name *artesian* is derived from the French province of Artois, where such wells were first drilled almost 900 years ago. To discover how an artesian well works, refer to the *MiniLab* on this page.

An important artesian aquifer in the United States is the Ogallala Aquifer, which is located in the Great Plains. This aquifer delivers water to a huge area stretching from South Dakota to Texas. The recharge areas of the Ogallala Aquifer are located in the Black Hills and the Rocky Mountains.

THREATS TO OUR WATER SUPPLY

Freshwater is Earth's most precious natural resource. Think about it! You can survive without gasoline, without electricity, and without most of the other materials that may seem to be essential, but you can't live without water. Human demands for freshwater are enormous. Not only is water used in households, but it is also used extensively in agriculture and industry, as shown in *Figure 10-17.* Groundwater supplies much of this water.

U.S. Water Use

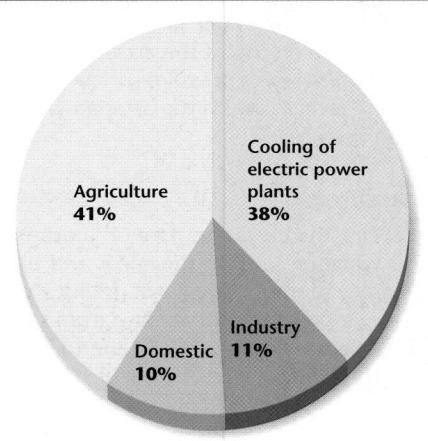

- Agriculture 41%
- Cooling of electric power plants 38%
- Industry 11%
- Domestic 10%

Overuse Groundwater supplies can be depleted. If groundwater is pumped out at a rate greater than the recharge rate, the groundwater supply will inevitably decrease, and the water table will drop. This is what is happening to the Ogallala Aquifer. Its water, used mostly for irrigation, is being withdrawn at a rate much higher than the recharge rate. You will learn more about the Ogallala Aquifer in the *Science & Environment* feature at the end of the chapter.

Subsidence Another problem caused by the excessive withdrawal of groundwater is ground subsidence, the sinking of land. The weight of the material overlying an aquifer is partly borne by water pressure. If that pressure is reduced, the weight of the overlying material is increasingly transferred to the aquifer's mineral grains, which then squeeze together more tightly. As a result, the land surface above the aquifer sinks.

Pollution in Groundwater In general, the most easily polluted groundwater reservoirs are water-table unconfined aquifers. Confined aquifers are affected less frequently by local pollution because they are protected by impermeable barriers. When the recharge areas of confined aquifers are polluted, however, those aquifers become contaminated as well.

The most common sources of groundwater pollution are sewage, industrial waste, landfills, and agricultural chemicals. These pollutants enter the ground above the water table, but they are eventually flushed downward by infiltrating precipitation and become mixed with the groundwater. Most sewage enters groundwater from sources such as faulty septic tanks. In highly permeable aquifers, all pollutants, including raw sewage, can spread quickly, as shown in *Figure 10-18.*

Figure 10-18 Pollutants from sewage are traveling through a coarse-grained aquifer that will contaminate downslope wells.

Earth Science
Journal

Science Field Book

Intrapersonal Lead a discussion with students about how people can conserve groundwater. Ask students to write one-page essays in their science journals about the ways they can reduce usage of water in their homes and why it is important.

Content Background

It doesn't take much contamination by seawater to make well water undrinkable. According to World Health Organization standards, the maximum allowable concentration of total dissolved solids (TDS) in drinking water is 1500 ppm. Water exceeding this limit is considered to be brackish. The average salinity of seawater is 35 000 ppm. If nine parts of distilled water are mixed with one part seawater, the resulting mixture will have a salinity of 3500 ppm, well above the allowable limit. A mixture containing 4 percent seawater would have a salinity of 1400 ppm. However, most fresh groundwater already contains several hundred ppm of dissolved ions. If, for instance, groundwater containing 500 ppm of dissolved ions is mixed with seawater, then a mixture containing less than 3 percent seawater would exceed the allowable limit of 1500 ppm. As a result, many wells in coastal areas contain brackish water.

Across the Curriculum

Chemistry Among the pollutants found in groundwater are various organic and inorganic chemicals. Inorganic chemicals dissolved in groundwater include acids, salts, nitrates and phosphates from fertilizers, and compounds of toxic metals such as mercury and lead. Organic chemicals include hydrocarbons such as oil and gasoline, and synthetic chemicals in paint products, pesticides, solvents, and detergents, among others.

Differentiated Instruction

Behaviorally Disordered Have students with behavioral disorders use the Earth Science Web Site at earth.geu.com to find Web sites containing information relevant to groundwater pollution problems. Have students discuss the Web sites with the class.

NY Core Curriculum Standards

Page 254: St 1 Science KI 1, 2, & 3, St 4 KI 1.2g, St 6 KI 1, 2, & 5

Page 255: St 4 KI 1.2g, St 6 KI 1

Environmental Connection

One of the most popular poisons in murder mysteries is arsenic. Surprise your students by informing them that they drink arsenic every day: drinking water contains arsenic. Minute concentrations of arsenic are present in groundwater everywhere. Some of it is introduced by industrial waste and mining activities, but most of it occurs naturally, having been leached from arsenic-bearing rocks and minerals underground. Concentrations of arsenic in groundwater typically are several parts per billion (ppb). Arsenic concentrations tend to be higher in the western states than in the eastern and southern states, but in all states, arsenic concentrations are much too small to cause poisoning. However, recent studies have linked high arsenic concentrations in drinking water to lung and bladder cancer. Proposed EPA guidelines limit concentrations in drinking water to 5 ppb, a value exceeded by at least some groundwater systems.

Before pumping

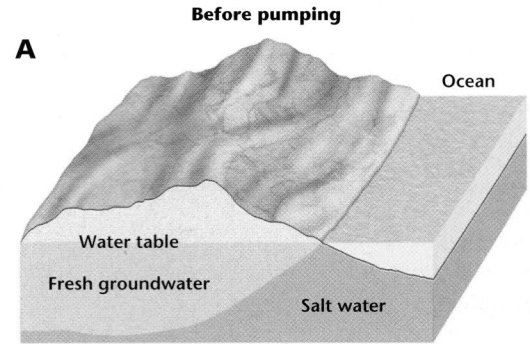

After pumping

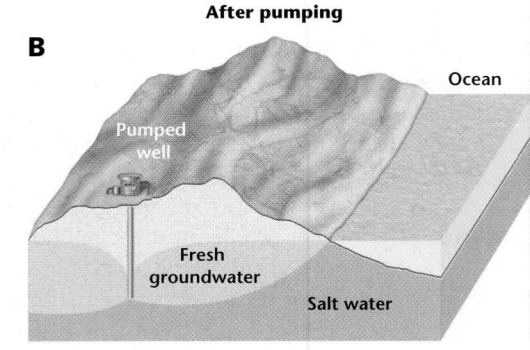

Figure 10-19 Saltwater incursion into groundwater can occur in coastal areas **(A)**. Freshwater floats on top of denser seawater within the aquifer **(B)**. Overpumping of wells draws the underlying saltwater into the wells and the freshwater zone.

Earth Science Online

Topic: Groundwater
To find out more about the ways to protect groundwater, visit the Earth Science Web Site at earthgeu.com
Activity: Write a TV ad describing measures being taken in your community to protect the groundwater.

Chemicals Chemicals dissolved or transported with groundwater are in the form of ions and molecules, so they cannot be filtered out in fine-grained sediments. For this reason, chemicals such as arsenic can contaminate any type of aquifer. They generally move downslope from a source in the form of a pollution plume, a mass of contaminants that spreads through the environment. Once chemical contaminants have entered groundwater, they cannot be easily removed.

Salt Not all pollutants are toxic or unhealthful in and of themselves. For example, ordinary table salt is widely used to season food. However, water is undrinkable when its salt content is too high. In fact, salt pollution is one of the major threats to groundwater supplies. In many coastal areas, the contamination of freshwater by salt water is the major problem. In such areas, the fresh groundwater near Earth's surface is underlain by denser, salty seawater as shown in *Figure 10-19A*. The overpumping of wells can cause the underlying salt water to rise into the wells and contaminate the freshwater aquifer, as shown in *Figure 10-19B*.

Radon Another source of natural pollution is radioactive radon gas, which is one of the leading causes of cancer in the United States. This form of radon is generated by the radioactive decay of uranium in rocks and sediments, and it usually occurs in very low concentrations in all groundwater. However, some rocks, especially granite and shale, contain more uranium than others. The groundwater in areas where these rocks are present therefore contains more radioactive radon than normal. Some of this radon may seep into houses, and, because it is heavier than air, it can accumulate in poorly ventilated basements. The U. S. Environmental Protection Agency (EPA) advises homeowners in radon-prone regions to regularly have their homes tested for radon gas.

Earth Science Journal

Naturalist Have each student compile a report about problems that affect groundwater supplies. Have students use the Web sites provided for students in the Meeting Individual Needs activity on the Earth Science Web Site at earthgeu.com or use library resources. Have them present their reports to the class. L2

Resource Manager

Teaching Transparency 27 L2 ELL

Table 10-2 Groundwater Pollution Sources

Accidental spills from vehicles

Leaks from storage tanks

Seepage from acid mine drainage

Seepage from faulty septic systems

Saltwater intrusion into aquifers near shorelines

Leaks from waste disposal sites

PROTECTING OUR WATER SUPPLY

There are a number of ways in which groundwater resources can be protected and restored. First, all major pollution sources, which are listed in *Table 10-2,* need to be identified and eliminated. Pollution plumes that are already in the ground can be monitored with observation wells and other techniques. You will learn more about pollution plumes in the *Mapping GeoLab* at the end of this chapter. Most pollution plumes spread slowly. Thus, there is often time for alternate water supplies to be found. In some cases, pollution plumes can be stopped by the building of impermeable underground barriers. Polluted groundwater can be pumped out for chemical treatment on the surface.

While these measures can have limited success, they alone cannot save Earth's water supply. An important part of the solution is for humans to become more aware of how their activities impact the groundwater system.

SECTION ASSESSMENT

1. How are springs related to the water table?

2. What is the basic characteristic of an artesian well?

3. List four common sources of groundwater pollution.

4. Why are chemical contaminants a serious pollution problem in groundwater?

5. Artesian aquifers contain water under pressure. Explain why.

6. **Thinking Critically** What can you do to conserve and protect groundwater so that there will be safe and abundant water supplies in the future?

SKILL REVIEW

7. **Comparing and Contrasting** Compare and contrast different uses of water in the United States. For more help, refer to the *Skill Handbook.*

earthgeu.com/self_check_quiz

10.3 *Groundwater Systems* **257**

Mapping GeoLab

Mapping Pollution

You can use a map to estimate the direction of groundwater flow and the movement of a pollution plume from its source, such as a leaking underground gasoline storage tank.

Time Allotment

one class period

Process Skills

collect and interpret data, measure, use numbers, make and use graphs, apply concepts, draw a conclusion, predict

Preparation

Run through the entire activity prior to class so that you can anticipate potential problems.

Procedure

Teaching Strategies

- Review map scales and contour lines with the class.
- Have students work in groups of three or four. If possible, each group should include a gifted student.
- Make sure that students follow the instructions step by step.

Troubleshooting

- Some students may have trouble locating all the lakes in the data table. Be prepared for questions.
- Some lake elevations are not given. These can be estimated from the topographic map contours.
- The water-table contours are not well defined everywhere by data points. Be sure that students produce reasonable contour maps.

Preparation

Problem
A major gasoline spill occurred at Jim's Gas Station near Riverside Acres, Florida. How can you determine the movement of the resulting pollution plume?

Materials
USGS topographic map of Forest City, Florida
transparent paper   ruler
graph paper   calculator

Procedure

1. Identify the lakes and swamps in the southeast corner of this map, and list their names or numbers and elevations in a data table. Note: The elevations are given or can be estimated from the contour lines.
2. Place the transparent paper over the southeast part of the map and trace the approximate outlines of these lakes or swamps, as well as the major roads. Enter lake or swamp elevations on your overlay, and indicate the location of Jim's gas station on Forest City Rd., about 1400 feet north of the Seminole County line (at the 96 foot elevation mark).
3. Add contour lines to your overlay using a contour interval of 10 feet.
4. Construct a cross section of the surface topography and the water table from Lake Lotus to Lake Lucien (through Jim's Gas Station).

Analyze

1. What is the slope of the water table at Jim's Gas Station?
2. What is the approximate direction of the water table slope at Jim's Gas Station?
3. In which direction will the pollution plume move?
4. Which settlements or houses are threatened by this pollution plume?

Conclude & Apply

1. How far below the surface is the water table in the highest area?
2. What is the relationship of the water table to the surface topography?

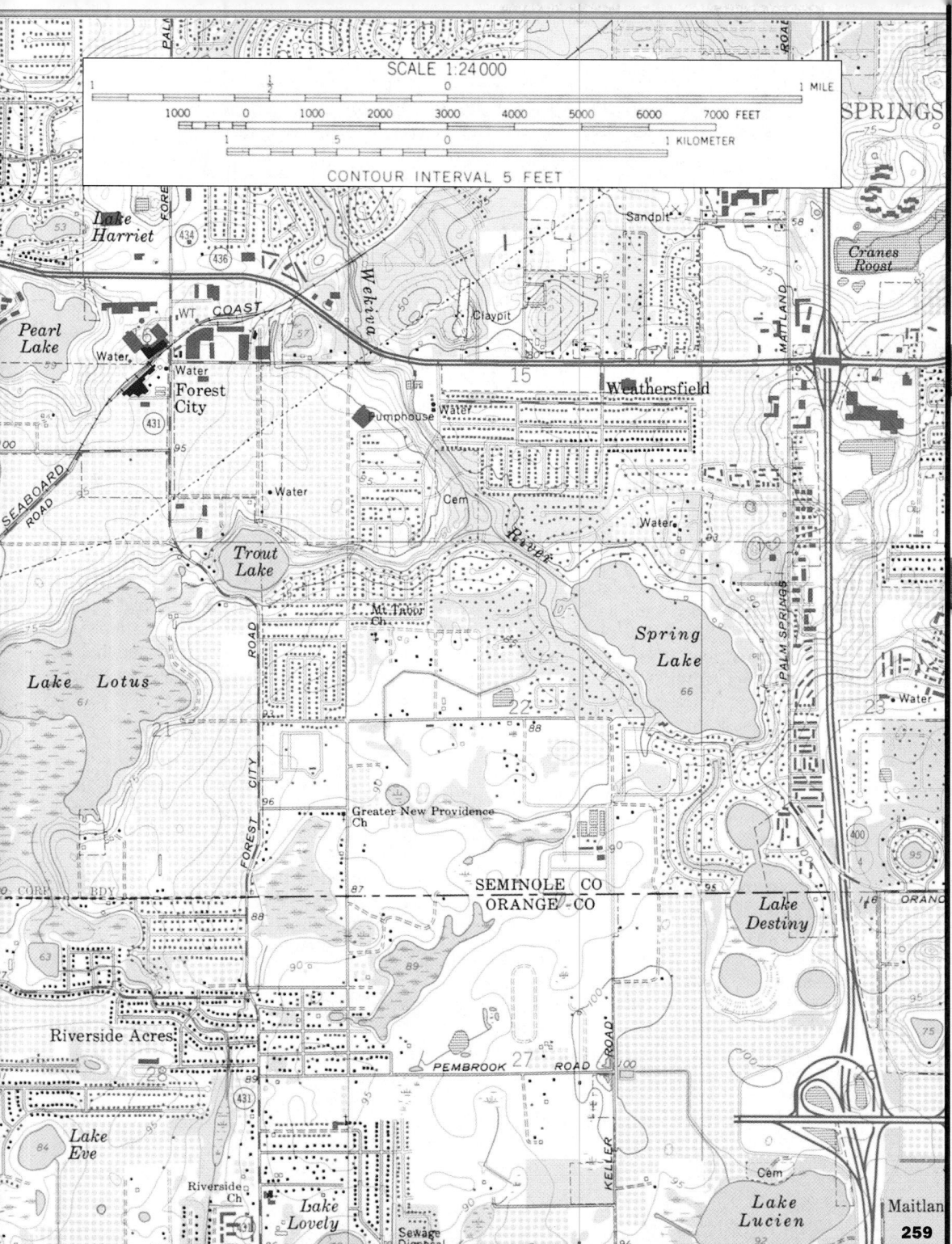

SCALE 1:24 000

1000   0   1000   2000   3000   4000   5000   6000   7000 FEET

1   5   0   1 KILOMETER

CONTOUR INTERVAL 5 FEET

259

Data and Observations

Data Table:

Lake elevations (in feet):
Eve, 84; Lotus, 61; Unnamed 1, 63; Trout, 59; Unnamed 2, 57; Pearl, 59; Harriet, 53; Cranes Roost, 49; Spring, 66; Destiny, 89; Unnamed 4, 95; Lucien, 92; Unnamed 5, 89

Analyze

1. at most, 1/100 (10'/1000')
2. northwest
3. northwest
4. none

Conclude & Apply

1. about 5 feet
2. The water table generally follows the surface topography.

Assessment

Knowledge If a deep well was drilled and pumped east of Jim's Gas Station, what might happen to the pollution plume? Explain. The pollution plume might flow to the east because the drawdown of the water table east of Jim's Gas Station might reverse the slope of the water table.

Resource Manager

GeoLab and MiniLab Worksheets,
   pp. 40–42 L2

NY Core Curriculum Standards

Page 258: St 4 KI 1.2g, St 6 KI 1 & 6, St 7 KI 1 & 2
Page 259: St 4 KI 1.2g, St 6 KI 1 & 6, St 7 KI 1 & 2

Science & the Environment

Purpose

Students will learn about the significance of the High Plains Aquifer and how its use affects the Great Plains region of the United States.

Content Background

The Ogallala Aquifer is believed to supply approximately one third of the nation's fresh groundwater. Since World War II and the development of improved pumping technology, farmers have converted an extremely dry area into one of the best farming regions in the United States. As a result, the water levels under the region have steadily dropped. The amount of precipitation in the area is not enough to replace the amount of groundwater that is drawn out.

Regulations have been put in place, but because so many states are involved these regulations have not been completely successful. Not only is the level of the water contained in the aquifer a concern, but so is the contamination of the groundwater supply. The same farmers who have come to depend on the water to nourish their crops have also polluted portions of the aquifer through the use of pesticides to protect crops from insects. Measures have been taken to protect the groundwater supply from such contamination.

The High Plains Aquifer

*T*he High Plains Aquifer, also known as the Ogallala Aquifer, is located beneath parts of Colorado, Kansas, Nebraska, New Mexico, South Dakota, Texas, Oklahoma, and Wyoming. Environmentalists are concerned about the future of this source of fresh groundwater.

Long Term Effects of Water Use

Buried beneath 106 250 km² of sand and rock lies the largest groundwater system in the United States, the High Plains Aquifer, also known as the Ogallala Aquifer. The High Plains Aquifer, which contains the Ogallala Formation, is made of clay, gravel, sand, and silt. The result of deposition from an ancient snow melt in the Rocky Mountains region, the formation is divided into two sections. The upper section is known as the unsaturated zone. The lower section contains the Ogallala Aquifer, the water-bearing area. The Ogallala makes up approximately 80 percent of the High Plains Aquifer.

The aquifer's freshwater supply has been used for many years. Shortly after World War I, farmers began tapping into the groundwater reserves in Texas. By 1940, the aquifer had become a widely used source of irrigation in the Great Plains region as more and more farmers began to pump water from the aquifer.

By 1980, it was estimated that parts of the aquifer's water level were down as much as 30 meters. Because of concern about the decline in water levels, the U.S. Geological Survey began a monitoring program in 1988. The program revealed that from 1980 to 1994, water levels continued to decline in certain areas of the Texas High Plains, the Oklahoma Panhandle, and southwestern Kansas. In the eastern High Plains of Nebraska, higher than normal amounts of rainfall since 1980 have caused either a rise in the water level or a slower decline.

Demand placed upon the water supply over the years increased rapidly as more wells were drilled. In 1950, an estimated 8.6 trillion L of water were pumped from the aquifer. By 1980, the estimated amount had increased to 24 trillion L. The amount of water currently being pumped from the aquifer far exceeds the amount of water naturally replenished. Presently, 89 percent of the aquifer's water supply is still available despite the 170 000 wells drawing water. However, it has been predicted that by the year 2020, 25 percent of the water supply could be exhausted.

What Needs to be Done

While scientists cannot be sure that the aquifer will ever be completely depleted, there is reason to be concerned about the continuous lowering of water levels in the region. Wells in some areas overlying the aquifer have gone dry. Concerns about the depletion of the water supply have prompted several states to develop regulatory policies to protect this natural resource, which has often been taken for granted.

> ### Activity
>
> Research and construct a 3-dimensional model of the Ogallala Aquifer. Include the states that are part of the groundwater system. Label the aquifer's zone of saturation and water table.

Teaching Strategies

- If you suddenly found that the water you have used and taken for granted all of your life was suddenly unavailable, how might your life change? possible water rationing, bottled water, etc.
- Where does the water supply in your community come from? Have you ever had to limit your water usage? If so, how did it change the way you used water?

Activity

Go to the Earth Science Web Site at earthgeu.com for information to assist students with the models. The models should have labels similar to those on *Figure 10-2.*

Summary

SECTION 10.1

Movement and Storage of Groundwater

Main Ideas
- Some precipitation infiltrates the ground to become groundwater.
- Groundwater is stored below the water table in the pore spaces of rocks and moves through permeable layers called aquifers. Impermeable layers are called aquicludes.

Vocabulary
aquifer (p. 243)
infiltration (p. 240)
permeability (p. 242)
porosity (p. 241)
water table (p. 241)
zone of saturation (p. 241)

SECTION 10.2

Groundwater Erosion and Deposition

Main Ideas
- Groundwater dissolves limestone and forms underground caverns. Sinkholes form at Earth's surface when bedrock is dissolved or when caves collapse. Irregular topography caused by groundwater dissolution is called karst topography.
- The precipitation of dissolved calcium carbonate forms stalactites, stalagmites, and travertine deposits, including dripstone columns, in caves.

Vocabulary
cave (p. 245)
karst topography (p. 246)
sinkhole (p. 246)
stalactite (p. 248)
stalagmite (p. 248)
travertine (p. 248)

SECTION 10.3

Groundwater Systems

Main Ideas
- The natural discharge of groundwater takes place through springs. Springs emerge where the water table intersects Earth's surface.
- Wells are drilled into the zone of saturation to provide water for human needs. The pumping of shallow wells produces cones of depression in the water table. Artesian wells tap deep, confined aquifers that contain water under pressure.
- In many regions, groundwater withdrawal exceeds groundwater recharge and causes considerable lowering of the water table as well as ground subsidence.
- The most common sources of groundwater pollution are sewage, industrial waste, landfills, and agricultural chemicals.

Vocabulary
artesian well (p. 253)
drawdown (p. 252)
geyser (p. 251)
hot spring (p. 251)
recharge (p. 252)
spring (p. 249)
well (p. 252)

earthgeu.com/vocabulary_puzzlemaker

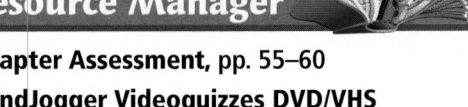

GLENCOE
Technology

Videotape/DVD
MindJogger Videoquizzes
Chapter 10: *Groundwater*
Have students work in groups as they play the videoquiz game to review key chapter concepts.

Resource Manager
Chapter Assessment, pp. 55–60
MindJogger Videoquizzes DVD/VHS
ExamView® Pro CD-ROM
Performance Assessment in Earth Science

CHAPTER 10
Study Guide

Main Ideas

Summary statements can be used by students to review the major concepts of the chapter.

VOCABULARY PuzzleMaker ONLINE SCIENCE

For additional help with vocabulary, have students access the Vocabulary Puzzlemaker online.

earthgeu.com/ vocabulary puzzlemaker

0:00 *Out of Time?*

If time does not permit teaching the entire chapter, use the GeoDigest at the end of the unit as an overview.

Earth Science online

Be sure to check the Earth Science Web Site for links to chapter material:
earthgeu.com

NY Core Curriculum Standards

Page 260: St 1 Engin KI 1, St 6 KI 2 & 5
Page 261: St 4 KI 1.2g, St 6 KI 1 & 5

Understanding Main Ideas

1. c
2. c
3. a
4. a
5. a
6. a
7. b
8. c
9. d
10. c
11. a
12. d
13. b
14. a

Applying Main Ideas

15. Soft water contains few dissolved ions, while hard water contains high concentrations of calcium, magnesium, or iron.
16. limestone
17. 60°C
18. iron oxides
19. Caves form by the dissolution of calcium carbonate by acidic groundwater.
20. The water table in the recharge area drops, and the pressure in the aquifer decreases. Shallow wells may dry up.

Understanding Main Ideas

1. Where is most freshwater found on Earth?
   a. the oceans
   b. the atmosphere
   c. polar ice caps and glaciers
   d. lakes and rivers

2. What is a major source of freshwater in the United States?
   a. the Rocky Mountain snowpack
   b. the Mississippi River
   c. groundwater
   d. the Great Lakes

3. What happens to most of the precipitation that falls on land?
   a. It evaporates.   c. It seeps into the ground.
   b. It becomes runoff. d. It becomes glacial ice.

4. What source usually replenishes groundwater?
   a. precipitation   c. underground streams
   b. surface water   d. municipal wastewater

5. Of the following materials, which is the most porous?
   a. a well-sorted sand   c. sandstone
   b. a poorly sorted sand d. granite

6. Of the following materials, which is the most permeable?
   a. sandstone   c. silt
   b. shale   d. clay

7. What is the main characteristic of an aquifer?
   a. surface topography   c. subsidence
   b. permeability   d. dissolution

8. Which rock type is most easily dissolved by groundwater?
   a. sandstone   c. limestone
   b. granite   d. shale

9. What are the cone-shaped dripstone deposits that are found on the floor of caves?
   a. icicles   c. stalactites
   b. rocksicles   d. stalagmites

10. Which of the following are typical features of karst topography?
    a. moraines   c. sinkholes
    b. dunes   d. landslides

11. Where is groundwater closest to Earth's surface?
    a. in stream valleys
    b. on hilltops
    c. on mountaintops
    d. in arid regions

12. What does hard water usually contain?
    a. fluorine   c. carbonic acid
    b. chloride   d. calcium

13. What do artesian aquifers always contain?
    a. hot water   c. salt water
    b. water under pressure d. steam

14. Which of the following is a common groundwater problem in coastal areas?
    a. saltwater contamination
    b. contamination by crude oil
    c. high sulfur content
    d. excessive recharge

Test-Taking Tip

BREATHE Oxygen helps to calm the anxiety associated with test-taking. When you start to feel your stomach lurch, take a deep breath and exhale slowly.

Applying Main Ideas

15. What is the difference between soft water and hard water?

16. What type of bedrock most likely exists in an area that has numerous sinkholes?

17. Subsurface temperatures increase with depth by about 25°C/km. What is the subsurface temperature 2 km below the surface in a region where the average annual surface temperature is 10°C?

18. A dripping water faucet in your home has produced brownish-red stains in the sink. What could have caused these stains?

19. Describe the processes involved in the formation of caves.

20. If the withdrawal of groundwater from an artesian aquifer exceeds the groundwater recharge, what consequence can be expected?

Thinking Critically

21. A well drilled into a water-table aquifer produces water only during springtime. Why?

Use the diagram below to answer question 22.

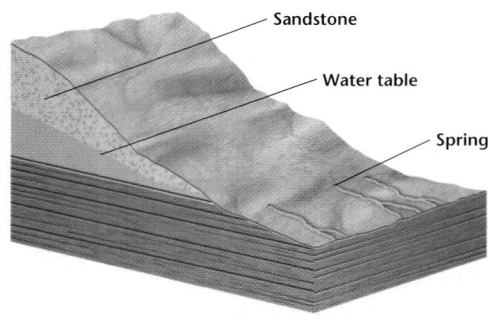

Sandstone

Water table

Spring

22. Make an inference on what can happen to the spring if the water table drops.

Standardized Test Practice

1. Which of the following materials would be best suited for lining a pond?
   a. gravel   **c.** clay
   b. limestone   **d.** sand

2. What are natural structures hanging from a cave's ceiling?
   a. geyserites   **c.** stalagmites
   b. travertines   **d.** stalactites

3. Which of the following usually describes the temperature of groundwater flowing through a natural spring?
   a. hotter than the region's average temperature
   b. cooler than the region's average temperature
   c. the same temperature no matter where the spring is located
   d. the same temperature as the region's average temperature

4. Which of the following water sources are the most easily polluted?
   a. water-table aquifers   **c.** artesian wells
   b. confined aquifers   **d.** hot springs

5. What is the composition of dripstone formations?
   a. carbonic acid
   b. carbon dioxide
   c. iron oxide
   d. calcium carbonate

Thinking Critically

21. There is a higher rate of recharge and a higher water table in the spring.

22. The spring will dry up if the water table drops below its present level.

EXAM*VIEW*® PRO

Use Exam*View*® Pro Testmaker CD-ROM to:

- Create **multiple versions** of tests.
- Create **modified** tests with one mouse click for struggling students.
- **Edit** existing questions and add your own questions.
- **Build** tests based on national curriculum standards.

Standardized Test Practice

1. c
2. d
3. d
4. a
5. d

NY Core Curriculum Standards

Page 262: St 4 KI 1.2g, St 6 KI 1 & 5
Page 263: St 1 Math KI 2 & 3, St 4 KI 1.2g, St 6 KI 1 & 5

For a **preview** of Earth's surface processes, study this GeoDigest before you read the chapters. After you have studied the chapters, you can use the GeoDigest to **review** the unit.

Prepare

Purpose

This GeoDigest can be used as an overview of the processes that occur at Earth's surface. If time is limited, you may use this unit summary to teach these concepts in place of the chapters in Unit 3.

Key Concepts

Students are introduced to natural processes that change Earth's surface. They learn about changes to Earth's surface that result from the forces involved in the weathering and erosional processes, the formation of soil, mass movements, wind, glaciers, and the movement of water along the surface and infiltrating crustal surfaces.

1 Focus

Section Focus

Kinesthetic Provide samples of three different soils. Ask students to touch and observe the soil samples and write a description of each in their science journals. Place a given amount of one soil sample in a clear plastic jar that is 2/3 full of water. The soil should fill 1/3 of the jar. Repeat this procedure for each of the other soil samples. Securely place a leak-proof cover on each jar, shake them thoroughly, and allow the material to settle. Have students note the different sizes of particles that settle and the amount of the different sized particles in each of the soil samples.

Surface Processes on Earth

Weathering, Erosion, and Soil

Chemical and mechanical weathering break down Earth materials. Chemical weathering causes a change in the composition of a rock. Agents of chemical weathering include hydrolysis, oxidation, acids from decaying organic matter, and acid precipitation. Each of these processes or substances combines with Earth materials, resulting in new combinations of minerals or in other substances. Mechanical weathering causes a change only in a rock's size and shape. Temperature and pressure are the major factors in mechanical weathering. Temperature changes can cause rocks to split. Pressure changes can cause rocks to crack or break apart.

Yosemite National Park, California

Erosion and Deposition Gravity is the driving force behind all agents of erosion, the process by which weathered pieces of rock are moved to new locations. Other agents of erosion include moving water, wind, and glaciers. Deposition occurs when the movement of transported materials slows down and they are dropped in a new location.

Formation of Soil Soils vary with climate and are classified as polar, temperate, desert, or tropical. A single centimeter of soil takes hundred of years to develop, but can erode away in just seconds. Soil is made of weathered rock and decayed organic matter called humus. Residual soil remains on top of its parent bedrock. Transported soil is moved away from its parent bedrock by weathering agents. A cross section of layers of soil is called a soil profile. The top layer, called horizon A, is topsoil.

Horizons B and C are subsoil. Below horizon C is solid bedrock. Parent rock and environmental conditions determine a soil's composition. Soil texture is determined by the relative amounts of clay, sand, and silt the soil contains. Soil fertility is a soil's ability to grow crops. Farmers conserve soil through methods that include wind barriers.

Mass Movements, Wind, and Glaciers

The landscape is changed by mass movements, wind, and glaciation. Mass movement refers to the movement of Earth materials downslope as a result of gravity. Almost all of Earth's surface undergoes mass movements, which may be slow, as in creep, or rapid, as in landslides, mudflows, rock slides, rock falls, and avalanches. Mass movements are affected by the weight of the material involved, its level of

Multiple Learning Styles

Kinesthetic Section Focus, p. 264

Visual-Spatial Activity, p. 265, Modeling, p. 266

Logical-Mathematical Enrichment, p. 265

Linguistic Earth Science Journal, p. 266

Intrapersonal Activity, p. 267

saturation, its resistance to sliding, and sometimes, a trigger such as an earthquake. Mass movements can cause great damage and loss of life.

Wind Limited precipitation and scarce vegetation, conditions common to arid, semi-arid, and seashore environments, contribute to wind erosion. Wind-carried sediment causes abrasive action which wears down or polishes the sides of rocks that face the wind. Wind-formed Earth features include deflation blowouts, desert pavement, and sand dunes. Dunes are classified by shape as barchan, transverse, longitudinal, or parabolic. Wind-deposited soils called loess contain minerals and nutrients and are highly fertile.

Glaciers Large, moving masses of ice called glaciers form near Earth's poles and high in mountains, where cold temperatures keep fallen snow from completely melting. Over time, the weight of the snow exerts enough downward pressure to cause the accumulated snow to recrystallize into ice. Glacial features include U-shaped valleys, hanging valleys, and waterfalls in the mountains; moraines, drumlins, and kettles in outwash plains; and a variety of glacially formed lakes. Valley glaciers

Sand overwhelms building, Namibia

form in mountains and move downslope. Valley glaciers are much smaller than continental glaciers, which form over broad regions and spread out from their centers.

Surface Water

Many landscape features on Earth are produced and changed by surface water. The amount of water in the ground depends on the number and sizes of pores in a particular Earth material and the amount of vegetation. A watershed or drainage basin is the land area drained by a stream system. Divides, which are raised areas of land, separate watersheds. All of the material carried by the stream, including material in solution, in suspension, and as bed load, is called the stream's load. Throughout history, humans built communities near water sources for survival and economic reasons. However, this practice has left humans vulnerable to dangerous floods. Weather and stream monitoring provides warnings of flooding.

Stream Development At a stream's source, or headwaters, water from precipitation begins its flow in channels confined by the stream's banks. Mountain streams have rapidly flowing water and often form waterfalls. When stream velocity

Tahquamenon River, Michigan

---

2 Teach

Activity

Visual-Spatial Have students stack closed plastic containers to build as tall a structure as possible. Once the structure is done, have a student jump on the floor or clap hands to make it topple without touching it. If this does not topple the structure, have students try blowing on it. Once they succeed in toppling the structure ask which of the mass movements this model most closely represents. Students will be quick to recognize the relationship to landslides. **L1** **ELL**

Enrichment

Logical-Mathematical Ask students to modify the activity above using the same plastic containers. Students may add weight to each of the containers by filling them with sand or tape them together to build strength. Ask students how their changed model may compare to techniques currently used in areas with unstable landscape features.

> **0:00** **Out of Time?**
>
> If time does not permit teaching the entire unit, use this GeoDigest as an overview.

✔Assessment

Knowledge Assessment
GeoDigest Assessment, SE, p 267

Skill Assessment
Assessment, TWE p. 267

Resource Manager

Study Guide for Content Mastery, pp. 65–66 **L2**

> **NY Core Curriculum Standards**
>
> **Page 264:** St 4 KI 2.1s, 2.1t, 2.1u, & 2.1v
> **Page 265:** St 4 KI 1.2g, 2.1t, & 2.1u

Modeling

 Visual-Spatial Have students model a watershed area by pouring water down a small slope in the schoolyard or in the classroom. Ask students to observe how the water moves and what features determine the path the water takes. Ask students to draw diagrams of their models and label any apparent stream features. **L1** **ELL**

Demo

Pour muddy water through a strainer holding a handful of mixed aggregates into a container and have students describe the appearance of the water. Repeat the process running muddy water through a tall, screen-bottomed bucket of mixed aggregates. Ask students how the two samples of collected water compare and have them account for any differences noted. Students will notice that the muddy water that flows through more aggregates will end up cleaner. This is the same way water is cleaned by running through Earth materials.

decreases, the stream's load is deposited in triangle-shaped alluvial fans or deltas. Alluvial fans form when streams flow out onto plains. Deltas form when streams enter large bodies of water. Uplifting of the land or lowering of the base level causes a stream to undergo rejuvenation and again begin to cut a V-shaped valley.

Lakes and Freshwater Wetlands Lakes form when depressions on land fill with water. Some lakes are human-made. When nutrients from fertilizers, detergents, or sewage enter a lake, eutrophication may be accelerated. The nutrients lead to an overabundance of some organisms and then a depletion of oxygen. Wetlands such as bogs, marshes, and swamps are low areas that regularly fill with water and support specific plants. Wetlands filter and clean water and are protected by law.

Groundwater

Groundwater is the largest source of freshwater available for human use. Groundwater is the portion of precipitation that infiltrates into the ground and is stored below the water table in the pore spaces of rocks. Groundwater moves through permeable layers called aquifers. Most groundwater contains carbonic acid which attacks carbonate

rocks such as limestone which consists of calcium carbonate. The dissolution and precipitation of calcium carbonate plays a role in the formation of limestone caves. Caverns, sinkholes, karst topography, and travertine deposits are formed from groundwater action.

Groundwater Systems Springs, which are natural discharges of groundwater, emerge where the water table intersects Earth's surface. Wells drilled into the zone of saturation provide water for humans, but pumping of these wells may cause cones of depression in the water table. Artesian wells contain water under pressure from confined aquifers. When groundwater withdrawal exceeds groundwater recharge, it causes considerable lowering of the water table and ground subsidence. Pollution of aquifers may come from sewage, industrial waste, agricultural chemicals, and landfills.

Vital Statistics

Earth's Eight Longest Rivers

Nile (Africa)	6650 km
Amazon (South America)	6400 km
Yangtze (Asia)	6300 km
Mississippi-Missouri (North America)	5971 km
Yenisey (Asia)	5540 km
Ob-Irtysh (Asia)	5410 km
Paraná (South America)	4880 km
Congo (Africa)	4700 km

FOCUS ON CAREERS

Landscaper
A landscaper makes a plan for outdoor scenery in an area and then follows the plan by planting the gardens and grounds. In addition to knowing about plants, a landscaper needs to know the soil characteristics and water drainage patterns in the area. Landscape architects have college degrees, but many others in the field start out with a high school degree and then gather the training they need on the job.

NATIONAL GEOGRAPHIC

CD-ROM

Dynamic Earth PictureShow
Forces of Change
Geology PictureShow
Weathering and Erosion

Across the Curriculum

Math The term *delta* is used in math as well as in science. *Delta* in math refers to a change. It is represented by the Greek letter *delta*, which is shaped like a triangle. A Δx value would mean the change in x.

Earth Science Journal

Science Field Book

Linguistic Have students make lists of careers related to this unit. For each career listed, have students write one advantage and disadvantage of the career from their point of view. **L2**

GeoDigest

ASSESSMENT

Understanding Main Ideas

1. What is the most powerful agent of erosion?
  a. water
  b. wind
  c. glaciers
  d. living things

2. What material makes up horizon B in a soil profile?
  a. topsoil
  b. loess
  c. subsoil
  d. bedrock

3. What is the underlying force of all agents of erosion?
  a. suspension
  b. friction
  c. magnetism
  d. gravity

4. Which of the following types of mass movement is not rapid?
  a. a landslide
  b. a mudflow
  c. an avalanche
  d. creep

5. What erosional agent causes deflation blowouts, desert pavement, and dunes?
  a. wind
  b. water
  c. earthquakes
  d. groundwater

6. Which of the following is a characteristic of valley glaciers?
  a. They form over broad regions.
  b. They move downslope.
  c. They are larger than continental glaciers.
  d. They completely melt each summer.

7. Which of the following occurs when a stream's velocity decreases?
  a. The stream load increases.
  b. The stream cuts a V-shaped valley.
  c. Deposition occurs.
  d. A drainage basin is formed.

8. Where do alluvial fans mostly occur?
  a. near lakes
  b. along the bases of mountains
  c. on the outside of meanders
  d. where streams enter the ocean

9. Of the following materials, which one is most permeable?
  a. mud
  b. clay
  c. silt
  d. gravel

10. What is the largest source of freshwater on Earth?
  a. lakes
  b. groundwater
  c. oceans
  d. glaciers

Thinking Critically

1. Describe the agents of erosion involved in chemical weathering.
2. Explain how groundwater works to form sedimentary rock.
3. How would you describe a soil's texture?
4. Discuss at least two factors that affect mass movement.
5. List at least two reasons why wetlands should be protected.

Himalayas

GeoDigest **267**

3 Assess

Check for Understanding
Activity

Intrapersonal Have students write a letter to their state legislators explaining their concern about protection of the groundwater in their community. Ask students to provide supportive material to back up their arguments.

Reteach

Have students make crossword puzzles using the terms and definitions in this unit. Have students exchange puzzles as a review.

✓Assessment

Skill Wear latex gloves and safety goggles during this activity. Place a drop of dilute hydrochloric acid on a rock specimen containing calcite, labeled specimen A. Repeat the procedure with another specimen that does not contain calcite or carbonate material and label that specimen B. Ask the students what conclusions they could make regarding specimens A and B. Students should recognize that specimen A contains calcite and specimen B does not.

ASSESSMENT

Understanding Main Ideas
1. c **3.** d **5.** a **7.** c **9.** d
2. c **4.** d **6.** b **8.** b **10.** d

Thinking Critically
1. hydrolysis, oxidation, acids from decaying organic matter, and acid precipitation; each of these processes or substances combines with Earth materials to result in new combinations of minerals or other substances

2. Dissolved minerals in the groundwater precipitate as cements in the pores of sediments. The cements harden, converting the sediments to sedimentary rock.

3. State the relative amounts of clay, sand, and silt it contains.

4. angle of the slope, amount of water in sediments, amount of vegetation, triggers

5. Wetlands provide wildlife and plant habitats and improve water quality.

NY Core Curriculum Standards

Page 266: St 4 KI 1.2g
Page 267: St 4 KI 1.2g, 2.1s, 2.1t, & 2.1u

The Atmosphere and the Oceans

Unit Overview

The Play Between Air and Water In Unit 4, students are introduced to the structure and composition of Earth's atmosphere and oceans. Students will learn how the atmosphere and the oceans interact to produce weather patterns, climates, and ocean currents. Hurricanes, for instance, are fueled by warm tropical oceans, while ocean surface currents are driven by winds.

Chapter Breakdown Chapter 11 describes the composition, structure, and properties of Earth's atmosphere. In Chapter 12, students are introduced to meteorology, which is the study of atmospheric phenomena. Chapter 13 explores various types of severe weather, such as hurricanes and tornadoes. The focus of Chapter 14 is climate—specifically, why different types of climates occur and how they are classified. Chapter 15 introduces the study of the oceans, known as oceanography. This topic is expanded upon in Chapter 16, which explores the formation of ocean-floor features such as trenches and ridges.

0:00 Out of Time?

If time does not permit teaching the entire unit, use the GeoDigest at the end of the unit as an overview.

The Atmosphere and the Oceans

Off the Na Pali coast in Hawaii, clouds stretch toward the horizon. In this unit, you'll learn how the atmosphere and the oceans interact to produce clouds and crashing waves. You'll come away from your studies with a deeper understanding of the common characteristics shared by Earth's oceans and its atmosphere.

Unit Contents

11 Atmosphere

12 Meteorology

13 The Nature of Storms

14 Climate

15 Physical Oceanography

16 The Marine Environment

NATIONAL GEOGRAPHIC

Go to the **National Geographic Expedition** on page 880 to learn more about topics that are connected to this unit.

268

NATIONAL GEOGRAPHIC

e**X**peditions!

Plunging into History Some topics of Earth science deserve more attention than others because they're unusual, informative, or just plain interesting. The National Geographic Society has created visually exciting, multipage *Expeditions!* features that inform, excite, and motivate your students.

Expeditions! features are relevant to the Earth science content of the student edition. Assign them as a lead-in to special research projects and in-depth studies for extra credit. Use them as a basis for colorful visual displays and bulletin boards.

Kauai, Hawaii

269

Introducing the Unit

Preconceptions Tsunamis are large, destructive ocean waves generated by earthquakes in ocean basins or by underwater landslides. They are often mistakenly called "tidal waves" in the press and popular literature. Tidal waves, however, usually are relatively small, calm bulges of water generated by the gravitational attraction of the Sun and the Moon. These bulges of water, commonly known as tides, break against the shores as waves, as shown in the photograph of the Na Pali Coast in Kauai, Hawaii. Tell students that tsunamis and tidal waves have some similarities —both travel through the ocean as shallow-water waves. In a tsunami, however, the wavelength, or horizontal distance between the highest points of two successive waves, may be hundreds of kilometers long. Tidal waves have wavelengths that are thousands of kilometers long.

Ocean-Air Interactions Ask students whether they have ever been to the ocean. Have those students who answer in the affirmative share their experiences. Encourage students to describe the movement of the breaking waves on the shore. Also, have them describe the weather conditions. Was there a cool ocean breeze? Generally, the weather along coastal areas is cooler than that of areas farther inland. Tell students that the ocean often affects weather and vice versa. In this unit, students will learn about the factors that affect Earth's atmosphere and oceans.

Earth Science Online

Note Internet addresses that you find useful in the space below for quick reference.

_____

_____

_____

_____

_____

_____

For Internet tips, see Glencoe's **Using the Internet in the Science Classroom.**

Chapter

11

Atmosphere

Refer to pages 8T–9T of the Teacher Guide for an explanation of the National Science Content Standards correlations.

Section	Objectives	National Science Content Standards	State/Local Standards
SECTION 11.1 **Atmospheric Basics** 🕐 1 session 📦 ½ block	1. **Describe** the composition of the atmosphere. 2. **Compare** and **contrast** the various layers of the atmosphere. 3. **Identify** three methods of transferring energy throughout the atmosphere.	UCP.1, UCP.2, UCP.3, UCP.5; A.1, A.2; B.6; D.1; F.3, F.4, F.5, F.6; G.3	St 1 Science KI 2 & 3, St 4 KI 1.2g, 2.2a, 2.2b, & 2.2c, St 6 KI 1
SECTION 11.2 **State of the Atmosphere** 🕐 1 session 📦 ½ block	4. **Describe** the various properties of the atmosphere and how they interact. 5. **Explain** why atmospheric properties change with changes in altitude.	UCP.1, UCP.2, UCP.3; A.1, A.2; B.6; D.1	St 1 Math KI 1, 2, 3, Science KI 1, 2, & Engin KI 1, St 4 KI 2.1a, 2.1b, 2.1c, 2.1e & 2.1f, St 7 KI 1 & 2
SECTION 11.3 **Moisture in the Atmosphere** 🕐 2 sessions 📦 1 block	6. **Explain** how clouds are formed. 7. **Identify** the basic characteristics of different cloud groups. 8. **Describe** the water cycle.	UCP.1, UCP.2, UCP.3, UCP.5; A.1, A.2; B.3, B.4, B.6; D.1; F.3, F.4, F.5, F.6	St 1 Science KI 1, 2, & 3, St 4 KI 1.2g, 2.1a, 2.1b, 2.1c, 2.1e, 2.1f, 2.1i, 2.2a, 2.2b, & 2.2c, St 6 KI 1, 2, & 5, St 7 KI 1

A complete Planning Guide is provided on pages 30T–32T.

🕐 The number of recommended single-period sessions

📦 The number of recommended blocks

Activity Materials

Discovery Lab *page 271*
drinking glass, ice cubes, alcohol thermometer, water

GeoLab *pages 292–293*
clean, clear, plastic 2-L bottle with cap; plastic straws; scissors; liquid-crystal temperature strip; tape; watch

MiniLab *page 290*
clear, plastic bowl; water; self-sealing plastic bag; ice cubes; tape; plastic wrap

Demo *page 279*
CoCl₂, paintbrush, white paper, water

page 281
dark colored cotton shirt

page 288
board, waxed paper, water

Need materials? Contact Science Kit at 1-800-828-7777 or at www.sciencekit.com on the Internet. For alternate materials, see the activity on the listed page.

Key to Teaching Strategies

L1 Level 1 activities should be appropriate for students with learning difficulties.

L2 Level 2 activities should be within the ability range of all students.

L3 Level 3 activities are designed for above-average students.

ELL ELL activities should be within the ability range of English-language learners.

COOP LEARN Cooperative learning activities are designed for small-group work.

P These strategies represent student products that can be placed in a best-work portfolio.

 These strategies are useful in a block-scheduling format.

Chapter Organizer

Glencoe Exclusive!
TeacherWorks™
All-In-One Planner and Resource Center

Activities/Features	Reproducible Masters	Transparencies
Discovery Lab: Dew Formation, p. 271	**Study Guide for Content Mastery,** pp. 67–68 **L2** **Laboratory Manual,** pp. 81–84 **L2** **Exploring Environmental Problems,** pp. 9–12 **L3**	**Section Focus Transparency 29** **L1** **ELL** **Teaching Transparency 28** **L2** **ELL**
Using Math: Using Numbers, p. 283 **Problem-Solving Lab:** Interpreting Graphs, p. 283	**Study Guide for Content Mastery,** pp. 69–70 **L2** **Laboratory Manual,** pp. 85–88 **L2**	**Section Focus Transparency 30** **L1** **ELL** **Teaching Transparency 29** **L2** **ELL**
MiniLab: What affects the formation of clouds and precipitation?, p. 290 **GeoLab:** Interpreting Pressure-Temperature Relationships, pp. 292–293 **Science in the News:** The Ozone "Hole," p. 294	**Study Guide for Content Mastery,** p. 71–72 **L2** **GeoLab and MiniLab Worksheets,** p. 43 **L2** **GeoLab and MiniLab Worksheets,** pp. 44–45 **L2**	**Section Focus Transparency 31** **L1** **ELL** **Teaching Transparency 30** **L2** **ELL**

Assessment

Chapter Assessment, pp. 61–66
Performance Assessment in the Science Classroom (PASC)
MindJogger Videoquiz DVD/VHS
Performance Assessment in Earth Science
ExamView® Pro CD-ROM
5 Days to the Regents Exam

GLENCOE'S **ASSESSMENT** ADVANTAGE

Additional Resources

Guided Reading Audio Program **ELL**
Cooperative Learning in the Science Classroom **COOP LEARN**
Lesson Plans
Block Scheduling
earthgeu.com
NY Lesson Plans
NY Block Scheduling
Review Handbook for Regents Earth Science Exam

▢ NATIONAL GEOGRAPHIC

Teacher's Corner

Products Available from National Geographic Society
To order the following products, call the National Geographic Society at 1-800-368-2728:
Curriculum Kit
GeoKit: *Weather*

CD-ROM
111 Years of National Geographic Magazine
Transparency
PicturePack: *Water*
PicturePack: *Introduction to Weather*

Content Background

Earth's Primitive Atmosphere
Section 11.1

Earth's original atmosphere was probably composed mainly of methane and ammonia. In the first billion years after Earth formed, its surface was much more volcanically active than it is today. Thus, its primitive atmosphere changed over geologic time as erupting volcanoes emitted gases such as water vapor, chlorine, carbon dioxide, hydrogen, and nitrogen. Over millions of years, as the young planet cooled, the water vapor condensed and absorbed most of the carbon dioxide. Storm clouds formed and torrential rains began to fall. Scientists hypothesize that this water filled low basins on Earth's surface and ultimately formed the planet's first oceans. Oxygen was probably formed from the dissociation of water molecules and by photosynthesis of primitive cyanobacteria.

Smog
Section 11.1

In addition to gases and microscopic solids, the atmosphere contains smog, a form of pollution. Exhaust from cars and other vehicles expels nitrogen oxides and unburned hydrocarbons into the air. These pollutants mix with oxygen and other chemicals in the presence of sunlight to form photochemical smog, a type of brown smog common in Los Angeles and Mexico City. Sulfur oxides from burning fossil fuels such as coal and oil produce a gray smog known as sulfurous smog. The burning of fossil fuels releases sulfur compounds, dust, and smoke particles into the air. Sulfurous smog forms when these substances collect in areas where there's little or no wind. In such a case, a blanket of gray smog may hang over a city for several days.

The Transfer of Energy
Section 11.1

The transfer of energy by radiation does not involve matter. In theory, the transfer of energy by convection distributes energy until equilibrium is reached. On Earth, however, equilibrium is never attained. The tropics always receive more radiant energy than the rest of Earth. Therefore, energy transfer is always occurring in the atmosphere.

Multiple Learning Styles

 Kinesthetic Demo, p. 272

 Visual-Spatial Activity, p. 275; Modeling, p. 276; Demo, pp. 279, 288

 Linguistic Reteach, p. 277; Earth Science Journal, p. 280; Applying Earth Science, p. 283

 Interpersonal Activity, p. 285; Collaborative Learning, p. 289

GLENCOE Technology

The following multimedia resources are available from Glencoe.

The Infinite Voyage Series
Crisis in the Atmosphere
Secrets from a Frozen World

Vocabulary Puzzlemaker

TeacherWorks™ CD-ROM

MindJogger Videoquizzes DVD/VHS

ExamView® Pro CD-ROM

Interactive Chalkboard CD-ROM

Chapter Organizer

Properties of Air
Section 11.2

Because air is composed of matter, it has many properties. Air can absorb and retain heat, move, hold moisture, and exert pressure. The main source of atmospheric heat is Earth's surface. Thus, the air near the surface is usually warmest, and temperature usually decreases with height through the troposphere. The moisture that air holds can be present in varying amounts and in all three states of matter. The density of air varies, depending on how many molecules of air are present in a certain space. The weight of a parcel of air is dependent on its density and temperature, so changes in these properties affect how much pressure air exerts.

The Water Cycle
Section 11.3

Worldwide each year, about 500 000 km^3 of water evaporates. About 110 000 km^3 of this water eventually falls on land as precipitation; the rest falls as rain, snow, or sleet into the oceans. Some of the water that falls on land is absorbed by plants, filters into the soil, fills lakes, or becomes runoff that eventually flows to the oceans. During evaporation, heat energy causes the water molecules to move apart. The water then changes from a liquid to a gas. During condensation, water molecules lose energy and move closer together. The water changes from a gas to a liquid.

Identifying Misconceptions

Because air cannot, for the most part, be readily detected by our senses, it is natural for students to believe that Earth's atmosphere is composed of basically nothing. Help them to understand that air is matter, and thus it is made up of different substances with distinct physical and chemical properties. Explain that even though we can't readily detect air, it has physical and chemical properties, many of which can be measured. Have students compare the weights of an inflated balloon and a noninflated balloon to demonstrate that air has mass.

Assessment

Portfolio Assessment
Assessment, TWE, pp. 277, 291

Performance Assessment
Discovery Lab, SE, p. 271
Discovery Lab, TWE, p. 271
MiniLab, SE, p. 290
GeoLab, SE, pp. 292–293

Knowledge Assessment
Assessment, TWE, pp. 276, 281, 284, 289
Problem-Solving Lab, TWE, p. 283
GeoLab, TWE, pp. 292–293
Section Assessment, SE, pp. 277, 284, 291
Chapter Assessment, SE, pp. 296–297

Skill Assessment
MiniLab, TWE, p. 290

Be sure to check the Earth Science Web Site for links to chapter material: earthgeu.com

Atmosphere

Introducing the Chapter

Have the class monitor weather reports on television, in the newspaper, or on the Earth Science Web Site for the same location each day for ten days. Have the class record daily measurements of temperature, air pressure, relative humidity, and wind direction and speed.

Interpreting the Photo

This spectacular sand dune is located on the Skeleton Coast in Namibia, part of the southwestern coast of Africa. The arid climate is caused in part by atmospheric factors such as the moisture content of the air and air temperature. Tell students that they will learn about the atmospheric factors that affect an area's climate.

Chapter Themes

The following themes from the National Science Content Standards are covered in this chapter. Refer to page 8T of the Teacher Guide for an explanation of the correlations.
Systems, order, and organization (UCP.1); Evidence, models, and explanation (UCP.2); Change, constancy, and measurement (UCP.3)

(0:00) Out of Time?

If time does not permit teaching the entire chapter, use the Chapter Summary on page 295 and the GeoDigest found at the end of the unit as an overview.

Atmosphere

What You'll Learn

- The composition, structure, and properties that make up Earth's atmosphere.
- How solar energy, which fuels weather and climate, is distributed throughout the atmosphere.
- How water continually moves between Earth's surface and the atmosphere in the water cycle.

Why It's Important

Understanding Earth's atmosphere and its interactions with solar energy is the key to understanding weather and climate, which control so many different aspects of our lives.

Earth Science Online

To find out more about the atmosphere, visit the Earth Science Web Site at earthgeu.com

---

Discovery Lab

Process Skills

observe and infer, recognize cause and effect, communicate, model, interpret data, measure in SI **L1** **ELL**

Procedure

Troubleshooting

This activity works best when there is a large difference between the inside relative humidity and the outside relative humidity, such as during hot weather when an air conditioner is used indoors, or during cold weather when a building is heated.

Observe

The ice water cooled the glass and, in turn, the air in contact with the outside of the glass. As the air cooled, it condensed into moisture on the outside of the glass. In a similar way, dew forms when moist air near the ground cools and condenses. Graphs and experimental results will vary, depending upon location.

Discovery Lab
Dew Formation

Dew forms when moist air near the ground cools and the water vapor in the air changes into water droplets. In this activity, you will model the formation of dew.

1. Fill a glass about two-thirds full of water. Record the temperature of the room and the water.

2. Add ice cubes until the glass is full. Record the temperature of the water at 10-second intervals.

3. Observe the outside of the glass. Note the time and the temperature at which changes occurred on the outside of the glass.

4. Repeat the experiment outside. Record the temperature of the water and the air outside.

Observe In your science journal, describe what happened to the outside of the glass in step 3 and step 4. Relate your observations to the formation of dew. Graph the temperature of the water during both experiments. Did the results vary with location? Explain.

SECTION 11.1
Atmospheric Basics

OBJECTIVES

- **Describe** *the composition of the atmosphere.*
- **Compare** *and* **contrast** *the various layers of the atmosphere.*
- **Identify** *three methods of transferring energy throughout the atmosphere.*

VOCABULARY

ozone	*exosphere*
troposphere	*radiation*
stratosphere	*conduction*
mesosphere	*convection*
thermosphere	

Imagine living in the blazing heat of the Sahara desert, near the equator. Then imagine living in the frozen vastness above the arctic circle. Why are these places so different? The answer lies in how solar energy interacts with the atmosphere, and how the interactions combine to produce weather and climate.

ATMOSPHERIC COMPOSITION

The ancient Greeks thought that air was one of the fundamental elements that could not be broken down into anything else. Today, we know that air is a combination of many gases, each with its own unique characteristics. Together, these gases form Earth's atmosphere, which extends from Earth's surface to outer space.

About 99 percent of the atmosphere is composed of nitrogen and oxygen, with the remaining one percent consisting of small amounts of argon, hydrogen, carbon dioxide, water vapor, and other gases. The percentages of the main components, nitrogen and oxygen, are critical to life on Earth. If either were to change significantly, life as we know it could not exist. Among the lesser-percentage gases, however,

11.1 *Atmospheric Basics* **271**

Content Background

The gases of Earth's atmosphere are selective absorbers of energy from the Sun. The type of energy absorbed by the atmosphere depends on the kinds of gases that are present in a particular part of the atmosphere. Ozone, for instance, is found mainly in the stratosphere and absorbs ultraviolet rays. Thus, temperatures in the stratosphere increase with height. The gases in the troposphere do not absorb as much ultraviolet radiation as the gases in the stratosphere. Thus, temperatures in the troposphere decrease with height. In general, temperature trends throughout the atmosphere are largely caused by differences in chemical composition among atmospheric layers and variations in energy absorption as a result of those differences.

Demo

Kinesthetic Tell students to reach out and grab a handful of air. Explain that they are holding a handful of matter, including elements such as argon, oxygen, and nitrogen, and compound gases such as water vapor and carbon dioxide. They are also holding minute amounts of atmospheric dust and salt. Ask students why these substances aren't visible. Students should realize that the reason is because the substances are present in the gaseous state, or are present in concentrations so small that they can't be detected by the human eye.

Figure 11-1 Nitrogen makes up 78 percent of the gases in Earth's atmosphere. Oxygen makes up 21 percent. The remaining one percent consists of small amounts of various other gases.

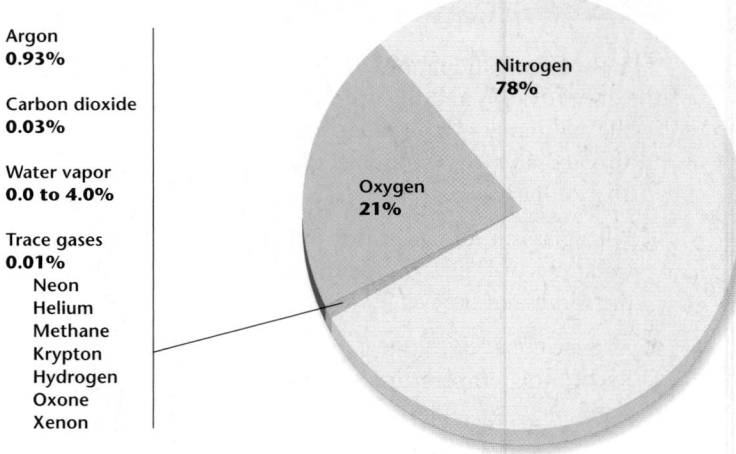

Percentages of Gases That Make Up Earth's Atmosphere

Argon
0.93%

Carbon dioxide
0.03%

Water vapor
0.0 to 4.0%

Trace gases
0.01%
Neon
Helium
Methane
Krypton
Hydrogen
Oxone
Xenon

Nitrogen
78%

Oxygen
21%

there is some variability, particularly in water vapor and carbon dioxide. **Figure 11-1** shows the composition of the atmosphere.

Key Atmospheric Gases The amount of water vapor in the atmosphere at any given time or place changes constantly. It can be as much as four percent of the atmosphere or as little as almost zero. The percentage varies with the seasons, with the altitude of a particular mass of air, and with the surface features beneath the air. Air over deserts, for instance, is drier than air over oceans. Carbon dioxide, another variable gas, makes up under one percent of the atmosphere. Why is it necessary to even mention these seemingly insignificant gases?

The level of both carbon dioxide and water vapor are critical because they play an important role in regulating the amount of energy the atmosphere absorbs. Water vapor, the gaseous form of water, is the source of clouds, rain, and snow. In addition, water is the only substance in the atmosphere that exists in three states: solid, liquid, and gas. This is important because when water changes from one state to another, heat is either absorbed or released, and this heat greatly affects the atmospheric motions that create weather and climate.

The atmosphere also contains solids in the form of tiny particles of dust and salt. Dust is carried into the atmosphere by wind. Salt is picked up from ocean spray. Dust and salt play a role in cloud formation, as you'll learn later. Ice is the third solid found in the atmo-

272 CHAPTER 11 *Atmosphere*

Differentiated Instruction

Learning Disabled Use a hot plate to heat a cup of water until it boils. **CAUTION:** *Boiling water can burn exposed skin. Be careful when handling the cup.* Pour some tap water into a glass, and put a few ice cubes on a plate. Place the cup of steaming water, the water in the glass, and the plate with ice cubes on a table. Have students with learning disabilities observe water as a solid, a liquid, and a gas. Encourage them to describe differences among liquid water, ice, and water vapor. Be sure students do not put their hands near the steam. Relate student observations to water in the atmosphere. Tell them that water occurs as a solid when it falls as snow or hail, it occurs as a gas in clouds, and it occurs as a liquid when it falls as rain. **L1**

sphere, usually in the form of hail and snow.

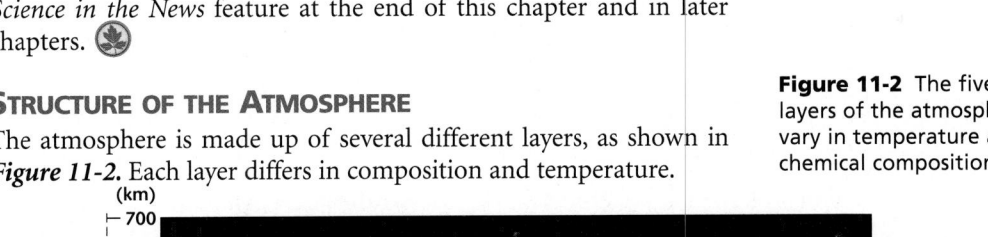 **Ozone** Another component of the atmosphere, **ozone** (O_3), is a gas formed by the addition of a third oxygen atom to an oxygen molecule (O_2). Ozone exists in small quantities mainly in a layer well above Earth's surface. It is important because it absorbs ultraviolet radiation from the Sun. If ozone did not control the amount of ultraviolet radiation reaching Earth's surface, our fragile skin could not tolerate exposure to the Sun for long. Evidence indicates that the ozone layer is thinning. You'll learn more about this issue in the *Science in the News* feature at the end of this chapter and in later chapters.

STRUCTURE OF THE ATMOSPHERE

The atmosphere is made up of several different layers, as shown in *Figure 11-2.* Each layer differs in composition and temperature.

ENVIRONMENTAL CONNECTION

Figure 11-2 The five main layers of the atmosphere vary in temperature and chemical composition.

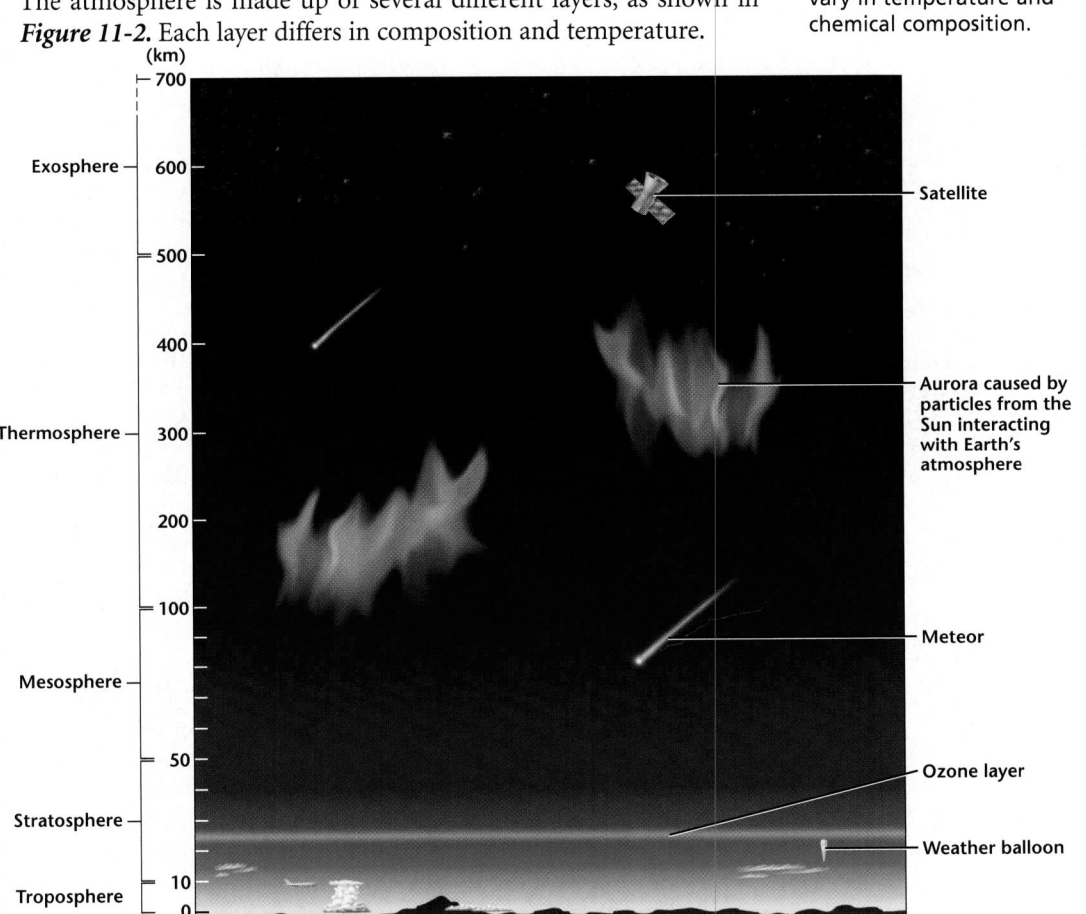

11.1 *Atmospheric Basics* **273**

Environmental Connection

Evidence suggests that compounds called chlorofluorocarbons (CFCs), which were used in hair sprays, spray paints, and refrigerants, have damaged the ozone layer above Antarctica. CFCs are very destructive to atmospheric ozone. In the upper atmosphere, CFCs are broken down by ultraviolet light into their components, one of which is chlorine. A chlorine atom alone, or in combination with an oxygen atom as chlorine monoxide, breaks down ozone molecules. It is estimated that just one chlorine atom can destroy as many as 100 000 ozone molecules. It is also estimated that CFCs remain in the atmosphere, capable of destroying ozone, for as long as 75 years.

Although the damage caused by CFCs is often referred to as a "hole" by the media, it is more properly called a thinning of the ozone layer. This thinning of stratospheric ozone could eventually be responsible for widespread health problems. Have students research ways to stop or reduce the damage to the ozone layer.

Resource Manager

Laboratory Manual, pp. 81–84 [L2]
Exploring Environmental Problems, pp. 9–12 [L3]

Across the Curriculum

Biology Tell students that the primary danger resulting from the thinning of the ozone layer is the increase in ultraviolet radiation that reaches Earth's surface. Ask students to research which parts of their bodies would most likely be directly affected by this increased radiation. Answers should include damage to the skin, possibly causing skin cancer, and damage to the eyes, possibly causing cataracts or blindness.

NY Core Curriculum Standards

Page 270: St 4 KI 1.2g & 2.2a
Page 271: St 1 Science KI 2 & 3, St 4 KI 2.2a & 2.2c, St 6 KI 1
Page 272: St 4 KI 2.2b
Page 273: St 6 KI 1

Identifying Misconceptions

Students should have no trouble understanding horizontal temperature changes on Earth's surface. However, it may be harder for them to understand that vertical temperature changes also occur in Earth's atmosphere. Students may believe that if a thermometer reads 20°C, it is 20°C throughout the atmosphere. They may even believe that the atmosphere gets warmer with height because of increased nearness to the Sun.

Uncover the Misconception
Tell students that the temperature outside is about −30°C. They will likely disagree. But, technically, this is true. This is the probable temperature at about 6000 m above Earth's surface. Do not share this point with students yet.

Demonstrate the Concept
Instead, ask students whether they have ever been to the top of a mountain. Ask those students who answer in the affirmative to describe what they noticed about the temperature. Students should note that the temperature was much cooler at the top of the mountain than it was at the bottom, regardless of the season. This demonstrates that the atmosphere cools with altitude.

Assess New Knowledge
Tell students again that the temperature outside is −30°C. Have them infer how this can be the case. Based on the understanding that temperature decreases with height, students should now realize that you are referring to a vertical change in temperature.

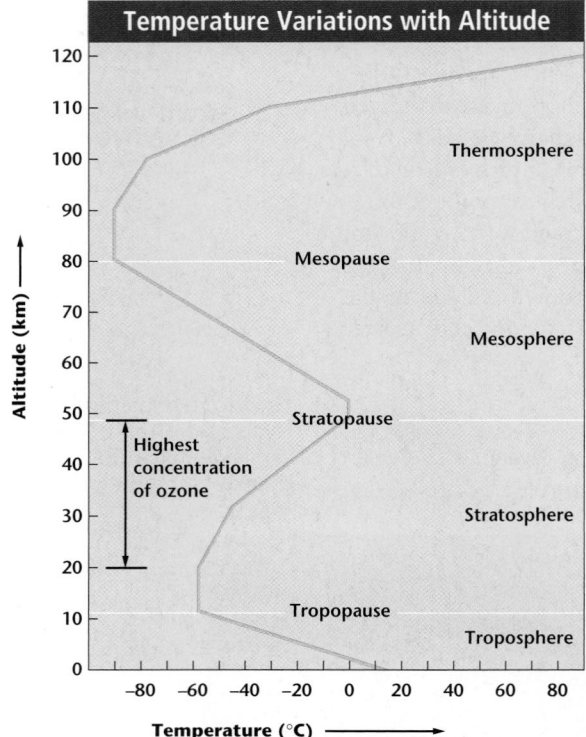

Figure 11-3 Differences in chemical composition cause air temperatures to vary throughout the atmosphere.

Lower Atmospheric Layers The layer closest to Earth's surface, the **troposphere,** contains most of the mass of the atmosphere, including water vapor. This is the layer in which most weather takes place and most air pollution collects. The troposphere is characterized by a general decrease in temperature from bottom to top. The upper limit of the troposphere, called the tropopause, varies in height. It's about 16 km above Earth's surface in the tropics and about 9 km or less at the poles. The tropopause is where the gradual decrease in temperature stops.

Above the tropopause is the **stratosphere,** a layer made up primarily of concentrated ozone. Ozone absorbs more ultraviolet radiation than does air in the troposphere. As a result, the stratosphere is heated, and air gradually increases in temperature to the top of the layer, called the stratopause, located about 50 km above Earth's surface.

Upper Atmospheric Layers Above the stratopause is the **mesosphere.** There is no concentrated ozone in the mesosphere, so the temperature decreases once again, as shown in *Figure 11-3.* The top of this layer, the mesopause, is the boundary between the mesosphere and the next layer, the thermosphere. The **thermosphere** contains only a minute portion of the atmosphere's mass. What air does exist in this layer increases in temperature once again, this time to more than 1000°C. In the thermosphere, however, the molecules that make up air are so sparse and widely spaced that, despite the high temperature, this layer would not seem warm to a human passing through it.

The ionosphere is part of the thermosphere. It is made up of electrically charged particles and layers of progressively lighter gases. The **exosphere** is the outermost layer of Earth's atmosphere. Light gases such as helium and hydrogen are found in this layer. Above the exosphere lies outer space. There is no clear boundary between the atmosphere and space. There are simply fewer and fewer molecules with increasing altitude until, for all practical purposes, you have entered outer space.

SOLAR FUNDAMENTALS

The Sun is the source of all energy in the atmosphere. This energy is transferred to Earth and throughout the atmosphere in three ways.

Radiation The Sun is shining on, and therefore warming, some portion of Earth's surface at all times. This method of energy transfer is called radiation. **Radiation** is the transfer of energy through space by visible light, ultraviolet radiation, and other forms of electromagnetic waves. All substances that have temperatures above absolute zero emit radiation. The higher the temperature of a substance, the shorter the wavelength it emits.

While Earth is absorbing solar radiation, it is also continuously sending energy back into space. As you can see from *Figure 11-4,* about 35 percent of incoming solar radiation is reflected into space by Earth's surface, the atmosphere, or clouds. Another 15 percent is absorbed by the atmosphere itself. This means that only about 50 percent of incoming solar radiation is absorbed directly or indirectly by Earth's surface. The rate of absorption for any particular area varies depending on the physical characteristics of the area and the amount of solar radiation it receives. Different areas absorb energy and heat up at different rates. For example, water heats up and cools down more slowly than land. And, as a general rule, darker objects absorb energy faster than lighter ones.

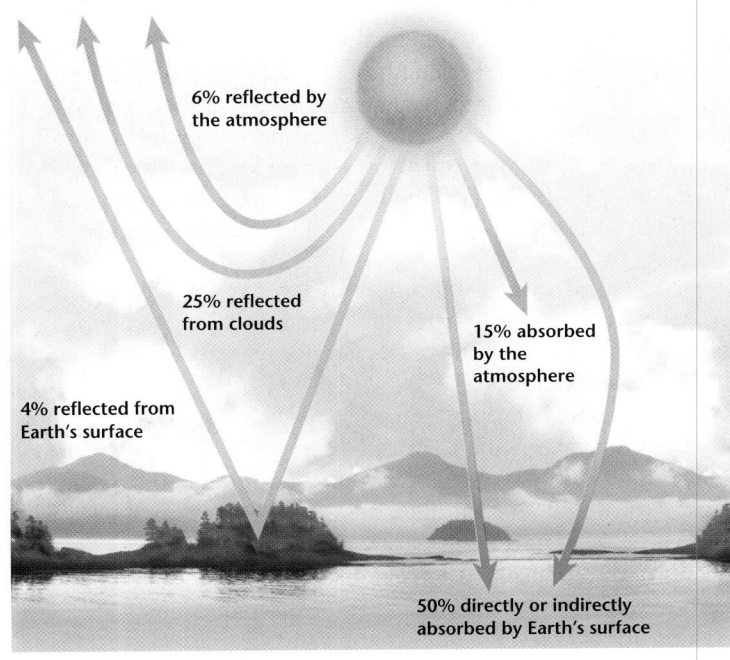

6% reflected by the atmosphere

25% reflected from clouds

4% reflected from Earth's surface

15% absorbed by the atmosphere

50% directly or indirectly absorbed by Earth's surface

Figure 11-4 Over the course of a year, Earth sends back into space just about as much energy as it receives from the Sun. This is fortunate: if Earth sent back too much, it would gradually cool off, while if it sent back too little, it would warm up to potentially dangerous levels.

Concept Development

The exosphere, which begins at a height of around 500 km, marks the transition of Earth's atmosphere to extremely sparse interplanetary gas. In the exosphere, light molecules of hydrogen and helium absorb solar radiation. This radiant energy increases the movement of the molecules, and they escape from Earth's gravitational field. Thus, there is a constant seepage of atmospheric gases into outer space.

Activity

Visual-Spatial Do the following activity to help students understand that different surfaces absorb the Sun's energy at different rates. On a warm, sunny afternoon, have students record air temperatures over an asphalt parking lot at heights ranging from a couple of centimeters to several meters. Have students graph the temperature changes with height. Repeat the procedure over a grassy area. Have students explain any differences in temperature trends between the two locations.

Interpreting the Illustration

Figure 11-3 Have students discuss why life flourishes in only a small layer of the atmosphere near Earth's surface, and why life as we know it is unlikely to exist in any layer except the troposphere. Possible reasons include harsh temperatures, lower amounts of oxygen, and the presence or absence of ozone.

NY Core Curriculum Standards

Page 274: St 6 KI 1
Page 275: St 4 KI 2.2a, 2.2b, & 2.2c, St 6 KI 1

Using an Analogy

Ask students the following question: Why does the inside of a closed, parked car heat up, while the windows stay cool? The windows are much like the atmosphere—they allow incoming radiation to pass through without much absorption. The inside of the car, though, is like Earth's surface—it absorbs the incoming energy and turns it into heat. This heat, however, cannot pass back through the windows and thus the inside of the car warms up.

Modeling

Visual-Spatial Have groups of students model what happens to incoming solar radiation. Have them use a flashlight to model solar radiation, a pan of water to demonstrate how energy is reflected back to space, a sheet of dark construction paper to simulate absorption of energy by Earth's surface, and a white sheet of paper held between the dark sheet of paper and the flashlight to demonstrate both the absorptive and reflective characteristics of clouds. Have students describe each element in the model. Have them also describe what effects could not be modeled, such as re-radiation by clouds and absorption of energy by the atmosphere itself. Explain that all of these processes are critical to the distribution of solar energy on Earth. **L1** **ELL**

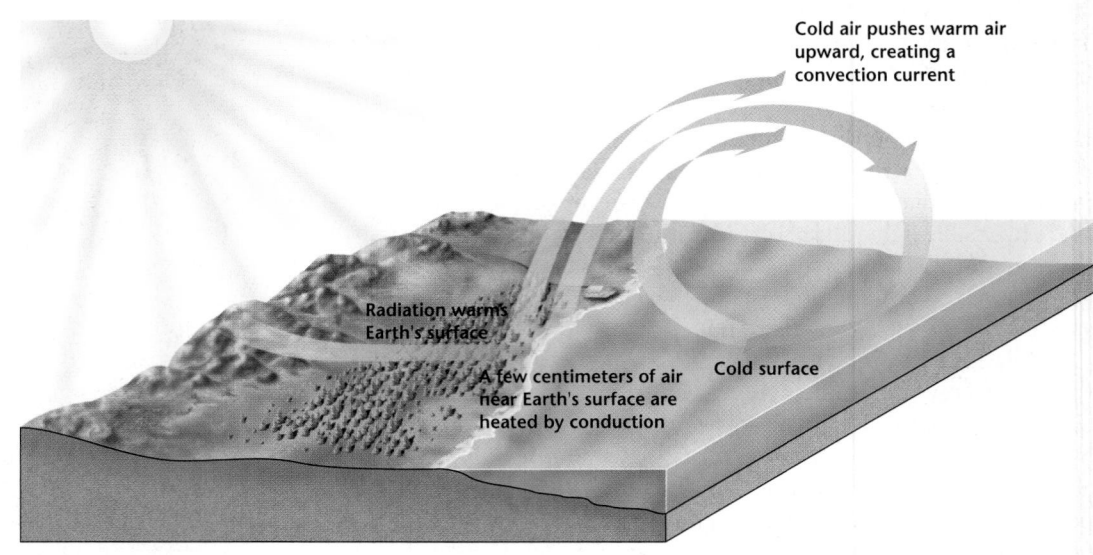

Cold air pushes warm air upward, creating a convection current

Radiation warms Earth's surface

A few centimeters of air near Earth's surface are heated by conduction

Cold surface

Figure 11-5 Energy is transferred throughout the atmosphere by the processes of conduction, convection, and radiation.

For the most part, solar radiation does not heat air directly. How, then, does air become warm? Most of the solar radiation that travels through the atmosphere does so at short wavelengths. The atmosphere does not easily absorb short wavelengths, so much of the solar radiation passes through the atmosphere and is absorbed by Earth's surface. The surface then radiates energy, but the radiation it gives off has a longer wavelength than the energy coming from the Sun. The energy radiated by Earth's surface does not pass back through the atmosphere. Rather, it is absorbed by the atmosphere and warms air through the processes of conduction and convection, which, along with radiation, make up the three methods of energy transfer illustrated in *Figure 11-5.*

Conduction To understand how the energy radiated by Earth's surface warms the atmosphere, think about what happens when you turn on a burner on the stove. The hot burner radiates energy much like Earth's surface does.

Now, imagine that you place a pot of water on the burner. Through **conduction,** which is the transfer of energy that occurs when molecules collide, energy is transferred from the bottom of the pot into the lowest part of the water. In the same way, energy is transferred from the particles of air near Earth's surface to the particles of air in the lowest layer of the atmosphere. For conduction to occur, substances must be in contact with one another. That's why conduction affects only a very thin atmospheric layer near Earth's surface.

Teaching Transparency 28 **L2** **ELL**

✓Assessment

Knowledge Ask students how conduction is related to cold air temperatures at the poles, which are covered with ice and snow. Because ice and snow absorb and retain little heat, they cannot conduct much heat into the atmosphere, so the air in those areas does not warm up nearly as much as in areas that more effectively absorb heat.

Convection Once the energy has made its way into the lower part of the atmosphere, can it ever move higher? Recall the pot of water. Energy has been transferred by conduction to the lowest layer of water molecules. This heated water expands, becomes less dense, and forms bubbles that rise. The rising bubbles bring the warm water to the top. The water at the top then cools, causing pockets of cool water to sink and become reheated when they come into contact with the bottom of the pot. This process is known as **convection,** the transfer of energy by the flow of a heated substance—in this case, the water. A similar process takes place in the atmosphere. Pockets of air near Earth's surface are heated, become less dense than the surrounding air, and rise. As the warm air rises, it expands and starts to cool. When it cools below the temperature of the surrounding air, it increases in density and sinks. As it sinks, it warms again and the process starts anew. Convection currents, as these movements of air are called, are among the main mechanisms responsible for the vertical motions of air, which in turn cause the different types of weather shown in *Figure 11-6.*

Figure 11-6 Many different factors, including convection currents, cause the different types of weather shown here.

SECTION ASSESSMENT

1. Describe the importance of water vapor in the atmosphere.

2. Why does temperature increase with height through the stratosphere?

3. Rank the main atmospheric gases in the troposphere in order from most abundant to least abundant. Do not include trace gases.

4. **Thinking Critically** Based on what you know about radiation and conduction, what conclusion might you make about

summer temperatures in a large city compared with those in the surrounding countryside?

SKILL REVIEW

5. **Predicting** Of the three main processes of energy transfer throughout the atmosphere, which do you think plays the greatest role in warming the upper troposphere? Why? For more help, refer to the *Skill Handbook.*

SECTION ASSESSMENT

1. It can exist as a solid, liquid, or gas, and it is the main ingredient in the formation of clouds and precipitation.

2. The stratosphere contains a large amount of concentrated ozone, which easily absorbs ultraviolet radiation and thus causes the layer to warm.

3. nitrogen, oxygen, argon, carbon dioxide, water vapor (The amount of water vapor varies; students may correctly rank it after oxygen.)

4. They would likely be warmer, as large areas of dark pavement would absorb heat more rapidly than grass in the countryside would.

5. Convection; radiation does not directly heat the atmosphere, and conduction affects only the lowest layer of the atmosphere, while convection currents transport heat up through the troposphere.

---

3 Assess

Check for Understanding
Discussion
Have students describe the three methods by which solar energy that reaches Earth is transferred. It is transferred through space by radiation, then absorbed by Earth's surface. The energy is then transferred to the lower atmosphere through conduction, and it is moved throughout the atmosphere through convection.

Reteach

Linguistic Have students outline the main points of this section in their science journals. Ask them to include specific examples in support of each point.

✓Assessment

Portfolio Have students develop posters showing the different layers of the atmosphere and the different characteristics of each layer. Posters should also show how solar energy is transferred throughout the atmosphere. **L1** **ELL** **COOP LEARN** **P**

NY Core Curriculum Standards

Page 276: St 4 KI 2.2a, 2.2b, & 2.2c

Page 277: St 4 KI 2.2a, 2.2b, & 2.2c, St 6 KI 5

277

Section Background

For section content background, refer to **Properties of Air** on page 270D.

Preplanning

Refer to the Chapter Organizer on pages 270A–B.

1 Focus

Section Focus

Before presenting the lesson, display **Section Focus Transparency 30** on the overhead projector. L1 ELL

Tying to Previous Knowledge

Students know that different surfaces absorb heat at different rates. Make sure students understand that different surfaces lose heat at different rates as well. For instance, materials such as grass lose heat very quickly at night. The condensation temperature, in turn, is reached quickly, and dew forms on these materials.

OBJECTIVES

• **Describe** *the various properties of the atmosphere and how they interact.*

• **Explain** *why atmospheric properties change with changes in altitude.*

VOCABULARY

temperature
heat
dew point
condensation
lifted condensation level
temperature inversion
humidity
relative humidity

When people talk about the weather by saying that it's sunny or cloudy or cold, they're describing the current state of the atmosphere. Scientists describe the atmosphere, too, using words such as *temperature, air pressure, wind speed,* and *the amount of moisture in the air.* These are atmospheric properties that describe weather conditions. We'll examine each in turn, beginning with temperature.

TEMPERATURE VERSUS HEAT

Most of us tend to think of heat and temperature as being essentially the same thing. They are, in fact, two different concepts. **Temperature** is a measurement of how rapidly or slowly molecules move around. More molecules or faster-moving molecules in a given space generate a higher temperature. Fewer molecules or slower-moving molecules generate a lower temperature and cause a substance—air, for instance—to cool. **Heat,** on the other hand, is the transfer of energy that occurs because of a difference in temperature between substances. The direction of heat flow depends on temperature. Heat flows from an object of higher temperature to an object of lower temperature. How does this relate to the atmosphere? Heat is the transfer of energy that fuels atmospheric processes, while temperature is used to measure and interpret that energy.

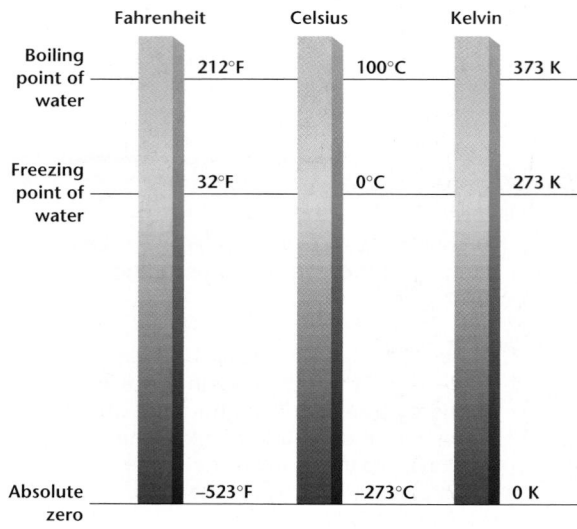

Figure 11-7 The Kelvin scale starts at 0 K, which corresponds to −273°C and −523°F.

278 CHAPTER 11 *Atmosphere*

Measuring Temperature Temperature can be measured in degrees Fahrenheit (°F), in degrees Celsius (°C), or in kelvins (K). Fahrenheit is the scale most commonly used in the United States. Celsius, the scale used in this book, is convenient because the difference between its freezing and boiling points is exactly 100 degrees. The kelvin is the SI unit of temperature. The Kelvin scale measures the number of kelvins above absolute zero, which corresponds to approximately −273°C and −523°F. This scale is a more direct measure of molecular activity, because at absolute zero, molecular motion theoretically stops. Because nothing can be colder than absolute zero, there are no negative numbers on the Kelvin scale. *Figure 11-7* compares the different temperature scales.

Resource Manager

Section Focus Transparency 30 L1 ELL

Study Guide for Content Mastery, pp. 69–70 L2

Teaching Transparency 29 L2 ELL

Dew Point Another atmospheric measurement is the dew point. The **dew point** is the temperature to which air must be cooled at constant pressure to reach saturation. Saturation is the point at which the air holds as much water vapor as it possibly can. The dew point is important because until air is saturated, condensation cannot occur. **Condensation** occurs when matter changes state from a gas to a liquid. In this case, water vapor changes into liquid water and eventually falls as rain. Given its role in this process, the dew point is often called the condensation temperature.

VERTICAL TEMPERATURE CHANGES

The temperature on a mountaintop is cooler than at lower elevations because the temperature of the lower atmosphere decreases with increasing distance from its heat source—Earth's surface. Individual masses of air moving upward through the atmosphere experience a change in temperature, too. An air mass that does not exchange heat with its surroundings will cool off by about 10°C for every 1000-m increase in altitude. This is called the dry adiabatic lapse rate—the rate at which unsaturated air to which no heat is added or removed will cool. If the air is able to continue rising, eventually it will cool to its condensation temperature. The height at which condensation occurs is called the **lifted condensation level** (LCL). As shown in *Figure 11-8,* clouds form when water vapor condenses into water droplets, so the height of the LCL often corresponds to the base of clouds. Above the LCL, air becomes saturated and cools more slowly. The rate at which saturated air cools is called the moist adiabatic lapse rate. This rate ranges from about 4°C/1000 m in very warm air to almost 9°C/1000 m in very cold air.

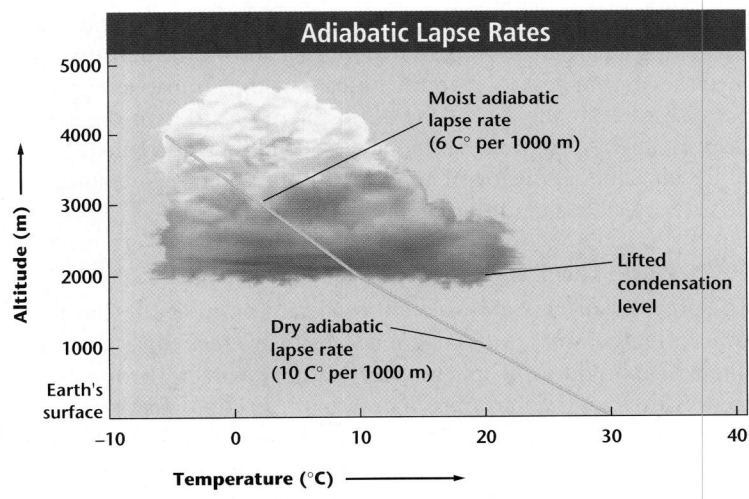

Figure 11-8 Condensation occurs at the lifted condensation level (LCL). Air above the LCL is saturated and thus cools more slowly than air below the LCL.

Content Background

One of the most important concepts for students to understand is that while the troposphere as a whole cools with height, an individual parcel of air moving through the troposphere can be either warmer or cooler, and wetter or drier, than the air around it at any given time. For instance, the air over a parking lot might be heated more than surrounding air and start to rise. On a larger scale, an air mass covering thousands of square kilometers may have a higher moisture content than the air surrounding it. The interactions of these parcels of air with the atmosphere through which they are moving influence weather.

Demo

Visual-Spatial Use cobalt chloride test paper to show moisture in the air. Place pieces of the test paper in different areas inside and outside the school. Have students record the color of each piece of paper. Pink indicates high relative humidity; blue indicates low relative humidity.

Across the Curriculum

Biology Many organisms that live in the Namib Desert, shown in the chapter-opener photograph, depend on dew as their only source of water. The dew comes from the small amount of moisture in the air and in plants. Plant transpiration releases water into the air and onto plant surfaces. Nocturnal organisms collect the water at night by licking the wet plant surfaces.

NY Core Curriculum Standards

Page 278: St 1 Math KI 1 & 2, St 4 KI 2.1a, 2.1b, & 2.1c
Page 279: St 1 Math KI 2 & 3, St 4 KI 2.1c & 2.1f

Applying Earth Science

Tell students that a parcel of dry air on a hot summer afternoon had a temperature of 30°C. It rose 1500 m until it became saturated. It then rose an additional 3500 m. Have students calculate the temperature of the air at 1500 m and 5000 m. The air initially rose according to the dry adiabatic lapse rate of 10°C/1000 m. Thus, at 1500 m, its temperature would have been 15°C. The then-saturated air would have cooled at the moist adiabatic lapse rate. Because it was a hot summer afternoon, the moist adiabatic lapse rate would have likely been about 4°C/1000 m. By the time the air reached 5000 m, it would have cooled an additional 14°C, giving it a temperature of 1°C.

Reinforcement

Ask students to explain what happens to temperature with height through the atmosphere. Then ask the same question as it relates to pressure. Make sure students understand that as long as density remains constant, as temperature increases or decreases, pressure does, too, and vice versa.

NY Core Curriculum Standards

Page 280: St 1 Math KI 2 & 3, St 4 KI 2.1c & 2.1f
Page 281: St 4 KI 2.1e & 2.1f, St 7 KI 1

Table 11-1 Density Changes With Altitude			
Altitude km	Density g/L	Altitude km	Density g/L
0	1.23	30	0.018
2	1.01	40	0.004
4	0.82	50	0.001
6	0.66	60	0.0003
8	0.53	70	0.00009
10	0.41	80	0.00002
15	0.19	90	0.000003
20	0.09	100	0.0000005

AIR PRESSURE AND DENSITY

Just like water in the ocean, air has mass and constantly exerts pressure on our bodies. Why? The gravitational attraction between Earth and atmospheric gases causes particles of gas to be pulled toward the center of Earth. You don't notice this pressure because you have spent your whole life under it and are accustomed to it. A fish living deep in the ocean exists under pressure that would crush our bodies, but the fish survives because its body is adapted to such pressure. Just as water pressure increases with depth in the ocean, pressure increases as you near the bottom of the atmosphere because of the greater mass of the atmosphere above you. Conversely, atmospheric pressure decreases with height because there are fewer and fewer gas particles exerting pressure.

The density of air is proportional to the number of particles of air occupying a particular space. As **Table 11-1** shows, the density of air increases as you get closer to the bottom of the atmosphere. This is because gases at the top of the atmosphere press down on the air below, thereby compressing the particles and increasing the density of the air. Thus, at the top of a mountain, temperature, pressure, and density are all less than they are at lower elevations.

PRESSURE-TEMPERATURE-DENSITY RELATIONSHIP

The previous discussion raises an important point about the atmosphere: temperature, pressure, and density are related, as shown in **Table 11-2.** In the atmosphere, temperature is directly proportional to pressure. So, if an air mass maintains a certain density—that is, the number of gas particles in a fixed volume remains the same—as temperature increases or decreases, pressure does, too. By the

Table 11-2 Atmospheric Relationships
As T ↑, P ↑
As T ↓, P ↓
As T ↓, D ↑
As T ↑, D ↓
T = Temperature
P = Pressure
D = Density
↑ = Increases
↓ = Decreases

Earth Science Journal

Science Field Book

Linguistic Have students use the relationship between temperature and density to explain why smoke rises from a chimney. Chimneys vent excess heat. That heat warms the air inside the chimney, which causes the density of the heated air to decrease. Because the air is then less dense than the air around it, it rises. **P**

same token, as pressure increases or decreases, temperature does, too. You will further explore this relationship in the *GeoLab* at the end of this chapter.

The relationship between temperature and density, on the other hand, is inversely proportional. So, if an air mass maintains a certain pressure, as temperature increases, density decreases, and as temperature decreases, density increases. This is why air rises when its temperature increases—it becomes less dense.

In most atmospheric interactions, however, neither density nor pressure remains unchanged, and this muddles the relationship among temperature, pressure, and density. Earlier, for example, we noted that both temperature and density decrease with increasing altitude in the troposphere. If density decreases with height, how can temperature decrease as well if it is inversely proportional to density? The answer lies in the fact that temperature varies with changes in both pressure and density. In this case, temperature is proportional to the ratio of pressure to density, which decreases with increasing altitude.

Temperature Inversions In the atmosphere, the relationship between temperature and pressure is not always fixed. Although temperature and pressure in the overall troposphere decrease with height, there is an exception to this rule known as a temperature inversion. A **temperature inversion** is an increase in temperature with height in an atmospheric layer. It's called a temperature inversion because the temperature-altitude relationship is inverted, or turned upside down. This can happen in several ways. We'll consider one that involves the rapid cooling of land on a cold, clear, winter night when the wind is calm. Under these circumstances, the lower layers of the atmosphere are not receiving heat from Earth's surface—they're losing heat. As a result, the lower layers of air become cooler than the air above them, so that temperature increases with height and forms a temperature inversion. In some cities, such as the one shown in *Figure 11-9,* a temperature inversion can worsen air-pollution problems by acting like a lid to trap pollution under the inversion layer. In all cases, the presence or absence of inversions can have a profound effect on weather conditions, as you'll learn in the next chapter.

Figure 11-9 A temperature inversion in Long Beach, California, traps air pollution above the city.

11.2 *State of the Atmosphere* **281**

Using Scientific Terms

A wind blowing down the slope of a mountain is known as a katabatic wind. If the wind warms during its downhill journey, it is called a foehn (foen). The Santa Anas of Southern California are foehn winds. They often cause grass fires and forest fires to spread rapidly. Another type of foehn is the chinook, which blows down the eastern slopes of the Rocky Mountains. Chinooks can raise air temperature as much as 30°C in as little as 15 minutes.

In-Text Question

Page 282 Would you expect the wind to blow more strongly over the ocean or across the dunes?
over the ocean

Using Math

6 g ÷ 17 g = 0.35 or 35 percent

Activity

Because solar energy feels warm on our skin, students may suppose that it heats the atmosphere in a similar fashion. In reality, air is heated indirectly by energy emitted by Earth's surface. Have students draw diagrams showing the path of energy from the Sun. Diagrams should show how much energy is absorbed and reflected by clouds, how much is absorbed directly by the atmosphere, and how much reaches Earth's surface.

NY Core Curriculum Standards

Page 282: St 1 Math KI 1, St 4 KI 2.1c & 2.1e, St 7 KI 1
Page 283: St 1 Math KI 1, 2, & 3, St 4 KI 2.1c & 2.1e, St 7 KI 1 & 2

Figure 11-10 When wind blows over these sand dunes in Namibia, it encounters more friction than when it blows over water.

WIND

You may have entered a large, air-conditioned building on a hot summer day. As you opened the door, a sudden rush of cool air greeted you. This happened because the air conditioner created an imbalance between the warm, less-dense air outside the building and the cool, more-dense air inside. The cool air, being denser, had settled toward the bottom of the building. When the door opened, the cool, dense air rushed out to try to relieve the imbalance. The rush of air that you experienced is commonly known as wind.

In essence, the atmosphere works much like an air-conditioned building. Cool air, being more dense, sinks and forces warm, less-dense air upward. In the lower atmosphere, air generally moves from areas of high density to areas of low density. The air moves in response to density imbalances created by the unequal heating and cooling of Earth's surface. These imbalances, in turn, create areas of high and low pressure. In its simplest form, wind can be thought of as air moving from an area of high pressure to an area of low pressure. Wind is usually measured in miles per hour or kilometers per hour. Ships at sea usually measure wind in knots. One knot is equal to 1.85 km/h.

Like temperature and pressure, wind changes with height in the atmosphere. Why? Near Earth's surface, wind is constantly disrupted by the friction that results from its contact with trees, buildings, and hills—even the surface of water affects air motion. Farther up from Earth's surface, air encounters less friction, and wind speeds increase. Look at *Figure 11-10.* Would you expect the wind to blow more strongly over the ocean or across the dunes?

RELATIVE HUMIDITY

Just for fun, reach out and grab a handful of air. You may not know it, but you also grabbed some water vapor. Air in the lower portion of the atmosphere always contains at least some water vapor, even though that amount may be very small. The amount of water vapor in air is referred to as **humidity.**

Imagine now that you take your handful of air—and its water vapor—into a room full of dry air and let it go. Would that roomful of air have the same humidity as your handful? No, because the water vapor in that handful would be very small relative to how much water vapor that roomful of air could actually hold. The ratio of water vapor in a volume of air relative to how much water vapor that volume of air is capable of holding is called **relative humidity.** As the graph in the *Problem-Solving Lab* shows, relative humidity varies with temperature. Warm air is capable of holding more moisture than cool air. Thus, if the temperature of a room increased, the air in

Using Math

Using Numbers At 20°C, a cubic meter of air can hold a total of 17 g of water vapor. What is the air's relative humidity if it holds only 6 g of water vapor?

Problem-Solving Lab

Interpreting Graphs

Determine relative humidity

Relative humidity is the ratio of water vapor in a given volume of air compared with how much water vapor that volume of air can actually hold. Use the graph at the right to answer the following questions.

Analysis

1. How much water vapor can a cubic meter of air hold at 25°C?
2. How much water vapor can the same volume of air hold at 15°C?

Thinking Critically

3. Why do the values in questions 1 and 2 differ?
4. If the relative humidity of the air in question 1 was 50 percent, how much water vapor would it hold?
5. If you wanted to decrease the relative humidity of a room, would you increase or decrease its temperature? Explain your answer.

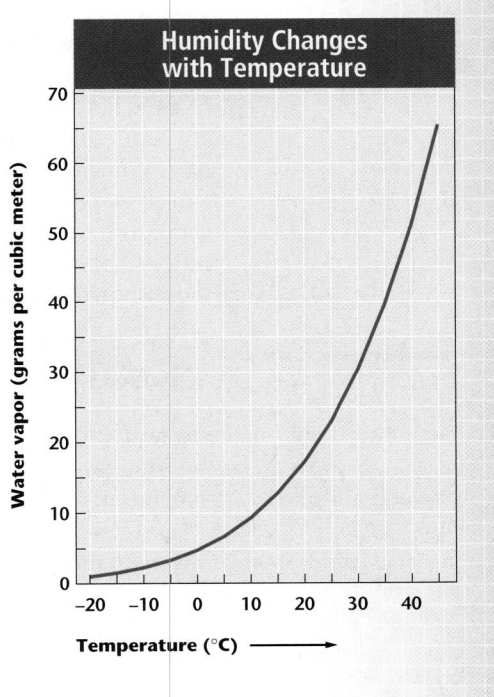

Humidity Changes with Temperature

Water vapor (grams per cubic meter) vs *Temperature (°C)*

11.2 *State of the Atmosphere* **283**

Check for Understanding

Reinforcement

Have students restate the relationship between temperature and pressure, and between temperature and density. Temperature is directly proportional to pressure and inversely proportional to density.

Reteach

Have students use the relative humidity table in Appendix F to determine whether two areas with the same relative humidity also have the same temperature. Have students explain their answers. No, they do not. Relative humidity in the table is based on the difference in temperature between the dry-bulb thermometer and the wet-bulb thermometer.

✓Assessment

Knowledge Ask students to imagine a parcel of hot air rising from Earth's surface. Ask them to answer the following questions about how properties of the parcel of air would change.
a. Would the rising parcel of air warm up or cool down? cool down
b. Would air pressure around the parcel increase or decrease? decrease
c. Would the relative humidity of the parcel increase or decrease? increase

NY Core Curriculum Standards

Page 284: St 1 Math KI 2, 3, Science KI 1, 2, & Engin KI 1, St 4 KI 2.1c & 2.1e, St 7 KI 1
Page 285: St 4 KI 2.1e & 2.1f, St 6 KI 1 & 5

Figure 11-11 Clouds form when a mass of rising air becomes saturated and condenses its water vapor into large groups of water droplets.

the room would be capable of holding more moisture. If no additional water vapor was added to the air, its relative humidity would decrease. Conversely, if more water vapor was added to the air, its relative humidity would increase. Do the *Problem-Solving Lab* on the previous page to learn more about relative humidity.

Relative humidity is expressed as a percentage. If a certain volume of air is holding as much water vapor as it possibly can, then its relative humidity is 100 percent. If that same volume of air is holding half as much water vapor as it can, its relative humidity is 50 percent, and so on. Recall that air is saturated when it holds as much water vapor as it possibly can. As you'll see next, this has important implications for the development of precipitation and clouds such as those shown in *Figure 11-11.*

SECTION ASSESSMENT

1. How is dew point related to saturation?
2. What is the relationship between temperature and altitude in a temperature inversion?
3. How does atmospheric pressure change with height in the atmosphere? Why does it change?
4. Compare and contrast humidity and relative humidity.

5. **Thinking Critically** Which would melt more ice—a pot of hot water or a tub of warm water? Explain your answer.

SKILL REVIEW

6. **Designing an Experiment** Design an experiment that shows how average wind speeds change over different types of surfaces. For more help, refer to the *Skill Handbook.*

SECTION ASSESSMENT

1. Dew point is the temperature to which air must be cooled for saturation to occur.
2. In a temperature inversion, temperature increases with height.
3. Air pressure decreases with height because there are fewer and fewer particles of gas exerting pressure in the upper atmosphere.
4. Humidity is the total amount of moisture in a parcel of air. Relative humidity is the ratio of that moisture to the amount of moisture the parcel is capable of holding.

5. The tub of warm water has a larger volume and therefore more total energy. Thus, it would be able to melt more ice, even though the water in the pot has a higher temperature.
6. Experiments will differ. Students may use a fan to compare and contrast wind speeds over a grassy area and a paved area. Accept all reasonable experimental designs.

Would you like to be able to predict the weather? To do so, you'll probably need to learn more about clouds. Certain types of clouds are associated with certain types of weather. Before learning about cloud types, however, you need to understand how clouds form.

CLOUD FORMATION

You know that air generally contains some amount of water vapor and that warm, less-dense air rises, while cool, more-dense air sinks. This tendency to rise or sink as a result of differences in density is called buoyancy. As you can see in *Figure 11-12,* clouds form when warm, moist air rises, expands, and cools in a convection current. As the air reaches its dew point, the water vapor in the air condenses around condensation nuclei. **Condensation nuclei** are small particles in the atmosphere around which cloud droplets can form. They come from a variety of sources, including sea salt and dust. When millions of these droplets collect, a cloud forms.

Clouds can also form when wind encounters a mountain and the air has no place to go but up. The effect is the same as with any rising air—it expands and cools. This method of cloud formation, shown in *Figure 11-13A* on the next page, is called **orographic lifting.** Another method of cloud formation involves the collision of air masses of different temperatures, as shown in *Figure 11-13B* on the next page. Recall that cold, more-dense air is heavier than warm, less-dense air, so it tends to collect near Earth's surface. As warmer air moves into the area, some of it will warm up the cold air, but the bulk of it will be forced to rise over the more-dense, cold air. As the warm air cools, the water vapor in it condenses and forms a cloud.

OBJECTIVES

- **Explain** how clouds are formed.
- **Identify** the basic characteristics of different cloud groups.
- **Describe** the water cycle.

VOCABULARY

condensation nuclei
orographic lifting
stability
latent heat
coalescence
precipitation
water cycle
evaporation

Figure 11-12 Clouds form when warm air is forced up in a convection current.

11.3 *Moisture in the Atmosphere* **285**

Content Background

In addition to the processes of thermal and orographic lifting, there is another way for air to be lifted. In fact, it is one of the more common methods. Called dynamical lifting, it occurs because of the large-scale rising and sinking of air associated with large-scale weather systems, such as cyclones, anticyclones, and fronts.

Resource Manager

Section Focus Transparency 31 L1 ELL
Study Guide for Content Mastery,
    pp. 71–72 L2

Section 11.3

Prepare

Section Background

For section content background, refer to **The Water Cycle** on page 270D.

Preplanning

Refer to the Chapter Organizer on pages 270A–B.

1 Focus

Section Focus

Before presenting the lesson, display **Section Focus Transparency 31** on the overhead projector.
L1 ELL

Activity

Interpersonal To prepare students for the discussion of clouds, have them describe what happens to air that is warmer than the surrounding air. Tell students that once the rising air is saturated, the water vapor in the air condenses into water droplets. These droplets coalesce, and a cloud is born.
COOP LEARN

285

Discussion

By now, students should understand that a parcel of air will rise if it is warmer than the surrounding air. Conversely, a parcel of air will sink if it is cooler than the surrounding air. Students also should realize that air cools as it rises—eventually, it will reach the same temperature as the surrounding air and stop rising. It's common, however, for air to rise well above the point where it should have cooled to the temperature of the surrounding air. Challenge students to infer why. Help them to understand that other processes, such as the release of latent heat, cause the parcel of air to continue rising. This will prepare students for the discussion on latent heat.

Using an Analogy

To keep a hot-air balloon aloft, a pilot must periodically supply more heat to the balloon. This is because the air inside the balloon interacts with the air outside the balloon and cools through conduction. A rising parcel of warm air follows the same principle. It cools through conduction and needs a catalyst to continue rising. Often, the atmospheric equivalent of the pilot firing a burner is the release of latent heat when condensation occurs.

Stability Regardless of how a cloud forms, all rising air expands and cools. How rapidly any given mass of air cools determines its stability. **Stability** is the ability of an air mass to resist rising. Imagine an air mass that is warmer than the surface beneath it. Heat flows from the warmer air to the colder surface. The lower layer of the air mass thus loses heat and cools. The cooling air resists rising—it is stable. The rate at which an air mass cools depends in part on the temperature of the surface beneath the air. The temperature of surrounding air masses and the temperature of the air mass itself also play a role in determining the cooling rate.

Air can become unstable if it is cooler than the surface beneath it. In this case, heat flows from the warmer surface to the cooler air. The air warms and becomes less dense than the surrounding air. The less-dense air mass rises. If temperature conditions are right and the air mass rises rapidly, it can produce the type of clouds associated with thunderstorms.

Latent Heat As water vapor in the air condenses, heat is released. Where does this heat come from? It takes energy to change liquid water into a gaseous state. The energy that is transferred to the gas doesn't just go away; it is stored in the water vapor and will not be released into the air until condensation occurs. The stored energy is called **latent heat.** Until condensation occurs, latent heat is not available to warm the atmosphere.

When condensation takes place, latent heat is released and warms the air. At any given time, the amount of water vapor present in the atmosphere is a significant source of energy because of the latent heat it contains. When condensation occurs, this latent heat can provide energy to a weather system, thereby increasing its intensity.

Figure 11-13 Clouds form when warm moist air is forced to rise over a mountain **(A)** and when two air masses of different temperatures meet **(B).**

Across the Curriculum

Physics An object in motion will not immediately stop when the force that set it in motion is removed because the object has momentum. Air that rises through the atmosphere has momentum. Thus, it won't stop rising immediately after cooling to the surrounding air temperature. Rather, it will rise a short distance farther. In the atmosphere, that short distance is critical because it allows condensation to continue to the point that enough latent heat is released to keep the air rising on its own.

Differentiated Instruction

Gifted There are three main cloud classifications, grouped according to the heights at which their bases form. However, each of these three groups is further subdivided into nine subgroups. Have students research these subgroups and then create data tables detailing the main cloud classifications and their subgroups. Have them write descriptions of each category, along with illustrations or photos. Students should share their results with the class. L3 P

TYPES OF CLOUDS

When a mass of rising air reaches its lifted condensation level or LCL, water vapor condenses into droplets of liquid water or ice, depending on the temperature. If the density of these droplets is great enough, they become visible in the form of a cloud. While this is the basic principle behind the formation of all clouds, this process can take place at many different altitudes—sometimes even in contact with Earth's surface, in which case it is known as fog. In addition to forming at different heights, clouds form in different shapes, depending on the factors involved in their formation.

Clouds are generally classified according to a system originally developed by English naturalist Luke Howard in 1803. As shown in *Table 11-3,* the modern system groups clouds by the altitude at which they form and by their shape. Low clouds typically form below 2000 m. Middle clouds form mainly between 2000 m to 6000 m. High clouds composed of ice crystals form above 6000 m. The final group of clouds includes those that spread throughout all altitudes—at the same time, no less. These are vertical development clouds.

Earth Science Online

Topic: Clouds
To find out more about clouds, visit the Earth Science Web Site at earthgeu.com

Activity: Make a poster or media presentation showing the types of clouds you observed during a one-week period.

Table 11-3 Cloud Classification

Height		Shape	
Prefix		**Prefix**	
Cirro Describes high clouds with bases starting above 6000 m.		**Cirrus** Latin meaning: "hair." Describes wispy, stringy clouds.	
		Cumulus Latin meaning: "pile or heap." Describes puffy, lumpy-looking clouds.	
Alto Describes middle clouds with bases between 2000 m to 6000 m.		**Stratus** Latin meaning: "layer." Describes featureless sheets of clouds.	
Strato Refers to low clouds below 2000 m.		**Nimbus** Latin meaning: "cloud." Describes low, gray rain clouds.	

11.3 Moisture in the Atmosphere **287**

Concept Development

Students now know that as a rising parcel of air is heated near Earth's surface and reaches its LCL, a visible cloud can form if sufficient moisture is present. How, though, does this explain the development of clouds that are usually well above the LCL, such as middle altocumulus clouds and cirriform clouds made of ice crystals? Large-scale weather disturbances cause air to rise at many levels of the atmosphere, and over very large areas. Regardless of the level, if enough lift exists to cool the air to its saturation temperature, condensation can occur and clouds can form.

Interpreting the Illustration

Table 11-3 Show students photographs of different types of clouds and have students classify the clouds according to the information provided in **Table 11-3**.

NY Core Curriculum Standards

Page 286: St 4 KI 2.1e & 2.1f, St 6 KI 1
Page 287: St 4 KI 2.1c & 2.1e, St 6 KI 1

Demo

Visual-Spatial Lay a piece of waxed paper on a board. Next, sprinkle some water on the waxed paper. **CAUTION:** *Wipe up spills immediately to avoid accidents.* Incline the board slightly. At this point, the water droplets should not move. Gently manipulate the waxed paper so that the droplets start to move around and touch each other. Eventually, the drops will coalesce and become large enough to roll down the incline and fall off the paper. Have students relate this process to cloud formation and precipitation. Small water droplets coalesce to form large drops. These drops may eventually become too large to be held aloft by rising air, and they will fall to the ground as precipitation.

Using Scientific Terms

Sometimes, rain or snow falls through a layer of air so dry that the precipitation evaporates. The precipitation can actually be seen falling from the base of the cloud, but it disappears into filmy wisps as it evaporates. This is known as virga, a type of precipitation that falls but doesn't reach the ground. Virga is most often observed in the United States in the Great Plains, the Rocky Mountain region, and the deserts of the Southwest. In these places, layers of very dry air are more common than in coastal regions.

NY Core Curriculum Standards

Page 288: St 4 KI 2.1b, 2.1c, 2.1e, & 2.1f, St 6 KI 1
Page 289: St 4 KI 2.1c, 2.1e, & 2.1f, St 6 KI 1

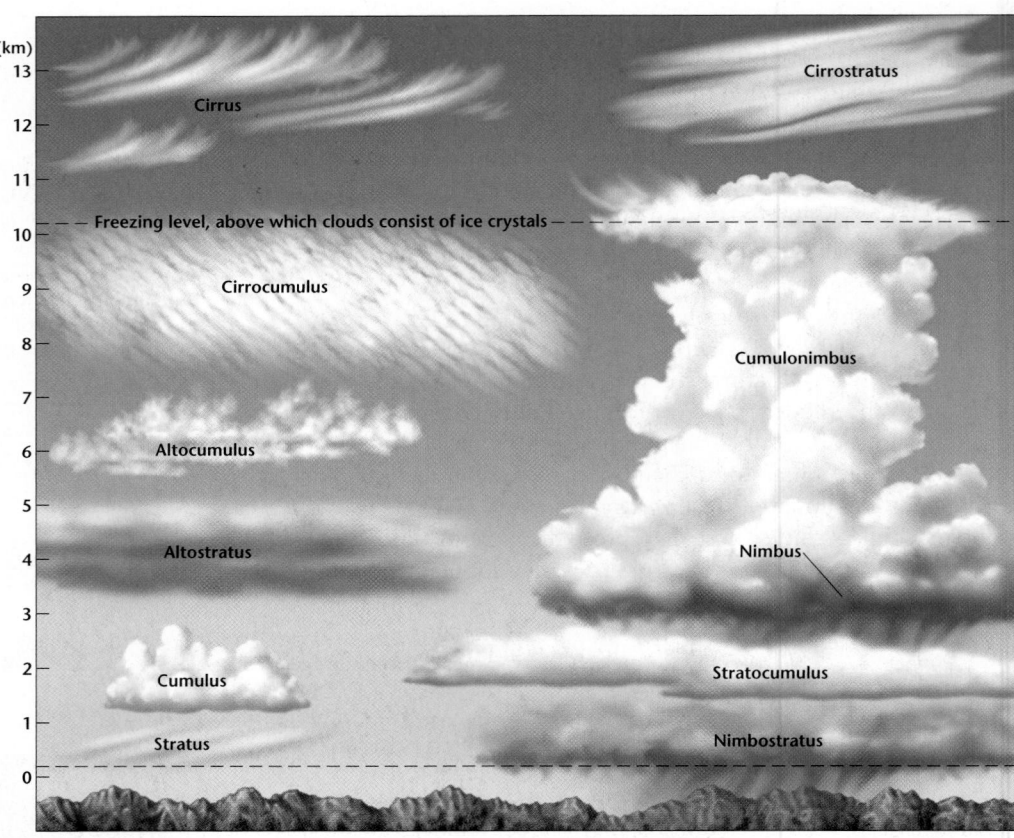

Figure 11-14 Clouds form at different heights and in different shapes. **Compare and contrast cirrus and stratus clouds.**

Low Clouds Imagine a warm, summer afternoon. The Sun is beating down, heating Earth's surface. In areas where the heating is particularly intense, such as fields with dark soil, conduction causes air above the surface to become warmer than the surrounding air. As the temperature rises, the air expands. Its density becomes lower than that of surrounding air and it begins to rise and cool by further expansion. When it reaches its LCL, it becomes saturated, and the water vapor it contains condenses into water droplets. These droplets eventually become numerous enough to form a visible cloud. If the air stays warmer than the surrounding air, the cloud will continue to grow. If the air does not stay warmer than the surrounding air, the cloud will flatten out and winds will spread it horizontally into stratocumulus or layered cumulus clouds. Another type of low cloud that forms at heights below 2000 m is a stratus, a layered cloud that covers much or all of the sky in a given area. Stratus clouds often form when fog lifts away from Earth's surface. *Figure 11-14* shows these and other types of clouds.

Concept Development

Make sure students understand that the release of latent heat allows a cumulus cloud to continue to grow until it reaches the cumulonimbus stage. Also, reinforce that this growth is largely dependent upon the amount of moisture that the cloud is able to draw into itself to continue the condensation process necessary for the release of latent heat.

Middle Clouds Altocumulus and altostratus clouds, which form at heights between 2000 m and 6000 m, can be either all liquid or a mixture of liquid and ice crystals. This is due to the cooler temperatures generally present at the heights at which these clouds form. Middle clouds are usually layered. Altocumulus clouds often resemble white fish scales. Altostratus clouds are dark but thin veils of clouds that sometimes produce mild precipitation.

High Clouds Because they form above heights of 6000 m, where temperatures are below freezing, high clouds are made up of ice crystals. Thus, some, such as cirrus clouds, often have a wispy, indistinct appearance. Another type of cirriform cloud, called a cirrostratus, forms as a continuous layer that sometimes covers the sky. Cirrostratus clouds can vary in thickness from being almost transparent to being dense enough to block out the Sun or Moon.

Clouds of Vertical Development If the air that makes up a cumulus cloud is unstable enough, the cloud will be warmer than the surface or surrounding air and will continue to grow. As it rises, water vapor condenses, and the air receives additional warmth from the release of latent heat. The cloud can grow through middle altitudes as a towering cumulus; if conditions are right, it can reach nearly 18 000 m. Its top is then composed of ice crystals. Strong winds can spread it into a familiar anvil shape. A puffy, white cumulus cloud can thus develop into a full-fledged cumulonimbus, as shown in *Figure 11-15.* What began as a small mass of moist air is now an atmospheric giant, capable of producing the torrential rains and strong winds that are characteristic of thunderstorms.

Figure 11-15 Cumulonimbus clouds, such as this one, in Arizona, are associated with thunderstorms.

PRECIPITATION

When cloud droplets collide, they join together to form a larger droplet in a process called **coalescence.** As the process continues, the droplet eventually becomes too heavy to be held aloft. At this point, gravity takes over and the droplet falls to Earth as precipitation. **Precipitation** includes all forms of water, both liquid and solid, that fall from clouds. Rain, snow, sleet, and hail are the four main types of precipitation. Coalescence is the primary process responsible for the formation of precipitation from warm clouds. Precipitation from cold clouds generally involves the interaction of ice and

Collaborative Learning

Interpersonal Have groups of students research all the things that might happen to water when it falls to Earth as precipitation. One group might examine how surface runoff makes its way through various waterways to the oceans. Another group could research what happens to water absorbed by Earth's surface. Yet another group could focus on annual variations in the amount of water stored in ice fields near the poles. Groups should share their results with the class. **L2** **COOP LEARN**

✓Assessment

Knowledge Ask students the following question: Of the following, which describes a layered cloud that is dense enough to block out the Sun and is composed entirely of ice crystals?
a. stratus
b. cirrostratus
c. altostratus
d. clouds of vertical development
Statement b is correct. Stratus and altostratus clouds are layered and dense, but they are not high enough to be composed entirely of ice crystals. Clouds of vertical development are not layered.

Applying Earth Science

Cloud seeding can cause a developing or ongoing storm to produce more rain. This is done by seeding clouds with microscopic particles that act as condensation nuclei. Cloud seeding allows more raindrops to form, and the storm releases all the moisture it can. Ask students to identify the main drawback of cloud seeding. Cloud seeding enhances rainfall in an area where rain is already falling, but it can't make rain.

MiniLab

Purpose

Students will model the water cycle.

Process Skills

model, recognize cause and effect, observe and infer, predict

Materials

clear plastic bowl, warm water, plastic wrap, self-sealing plastic bag, ice cubes, tape

Teaching Strategies

Divide students into groups of four. One student should prepare the bowl of warm water; another should prepare the ice. The third student should be responsible for observing the changes that occur, and the fourth should record observations in his or her science journal.

Expected Results

As warmer air rises from the surface of the water, it is cooled because of the ice and condenses on the underside of the wrap. These droplets coalesce until they are big enough to drop back into the water.

Analyze and Conclude

1. Water droplets formed as rising, warm air condensed near the ice.
2. The rising, warm air models evaporation, the water droplets model condensation, and the falling droplets model precipitation.
3. More precipitation would have formed more rapidly. The air would have risen more quickly, which in turn would have caused a faster rate of condensation.

✔Assessment

Skill Have students modify the experiment by extending the distance between the water surface and the plastic wrap or by using different water temperatures. Have students suggest processes in the atmosphere that might cause similar differences in results. Use the Performance Task Assessment List for Assessing a Whole Experiment and Planning the Next Experiment in **PASC**, p. 33. L2 ELL

MiniLab

What affects the formation of clouds and precipitation?

Model the water cycle.

Procedure 🥽 👕

1. Pour about 125 mL of warm water into a clear, plastic bowl.
2. Loosely cover the top of the bowl with plastic wrap. Overlap the edges by about 5 cm.
3. Fill a self-sealing plastic bag with ice cubes, seal it, and place it in the center of the plastic wrap on top of the bowl. Push the bag of ice down so that the plastic wrap sags in the center, but doesn't touch the surface of the water.
4. Use tape to seal the plastic wrap around the bowl.
5. Observe the surface of the plastic wrap directly under the ice cubes every 10 minutes for one-half hour, or until the ice melts.

Analyze and Conclude

1. What formed on the underside of the wrap? Infer why this happened.
2. Relate your observations to processes in the atmosphere.
3. Predict what would happen if you repeated this activity with hotter water.

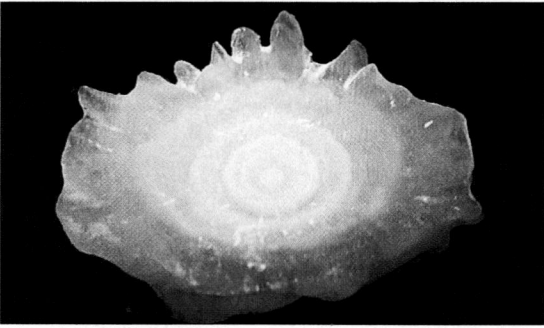

---

water molecules in the clouds. Do the *MiniLab* on this page to model the formation of clouds and precipitation.

Why are there so many variations in precipitation? When precipitation forms at cold temperatures, it takes the form of ice crystals or snow. Sometimes, convective currents carry the droplets up and down through freezing and nonfreezing air, thereby forming ice pellets or sleet. If that up-and-down motion is especially strong and takes place over large stretches of the atmosphere, it can form very large ice pellets known as hail. *Figure 11-16* shows a sample of hail.

THE WATER CYCLE

The total amount of water on Earth is constant, and probably has been for millions of years. More than 97 percent of Earth's water is salt water found in oceans. Only three percent is freshwater, and two-thirds of this is frozen in ice caps at the poles. At any one time, only a small percentage of water is present in the atmosphere. Still, this water is vitally important because as it continually moves between the atmosphere and Earth's surface, it nourishes living things. The constant movement of water between the atmosphere and Earth's surface is known as the **water cycle.**

The water cycle, shown in *Figure 11-17,* receives its energy from the Sun. Radiation from the Sun causes liquid water to change into a gas. The process of water changing from a liquid to a gas is called **evaporation.** This is the first step in the water cycle. Water evaporates from lakes, streams, and oceans

Figure 11-16 Note the distinctive layers in the cross-section of the hailstone. *Infer how the layers formed.*

Earth Science
Journal

Technology for estimating the amount of precipitation that falls ranges from simple rain gauges to sophisticated satellite systems. Information obtained from these sources is used in part to forecast floods. Have students research and write brief reports about the different types of equipment used to measure rainfall. P 📦

Resource Manager

GeoLab and MiniLab Worksheets, p. 43 L2
Teaching Transparency 30 L2 ELL

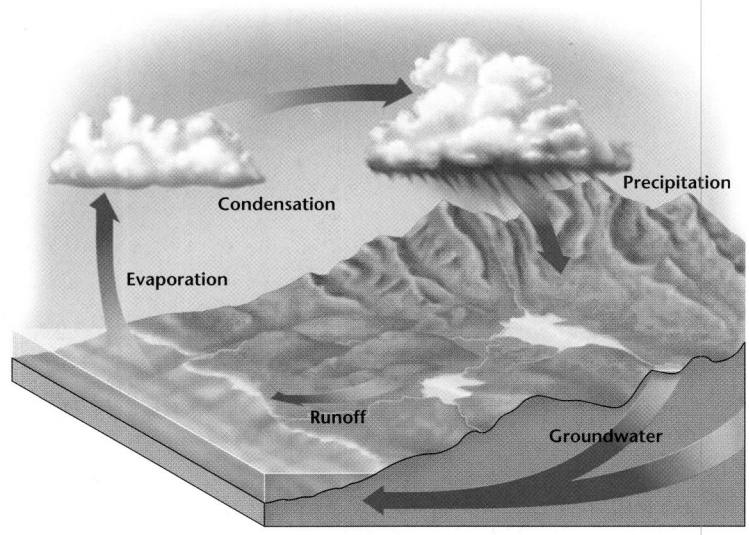

Condensation

Precipitation

Evaporation

Runoff

Groundwater

and rises into Earth's atmosphere. As water vapor rises, it cools and changes back into a liquid. This process, as you have learned, is called condensation, the second step of the water cycle. When water vapor condenses, it forms clouds.

In the third step of the water cycle, water droplets combine to form larger drops that fall to Earth as precipitation. This water soaks into the ground and enters lakes, streams, and oceans, or it falls directly into these bodies of water and eventually evaporates, and the water cycle continues.

SECTION ASSESSMENT

1. Explain why a cumulonimbus cloud is not considered to be a low, middle, or high cloud.

2. Describe the process that causes a water droplet to fall to Earth as precipitation.

3. What determines whether precipitation will fall as rain or snow?

4. **Thinking Critically** Based on what you have learned about latent heat, explain why the lapse rate of moist air is less than that of dry air.

SKILL REVIEW

5. **Concept Mapping** Use the following terms to construct a concept map that describes the processes of the water cycle. For more help, refer to the *Skill Handbook.*

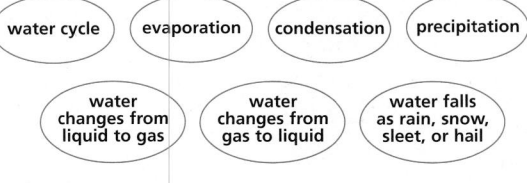

water cycle   evaporation   condensation   precipitation

water changes from liquid to gas   water changes from gas to liquid   water falls as rain, snow, sleet, or hail

earthgeu.com/self_check_quiz

SECTION ASSESSMENT

1. A cumulonimbus cloud extends vertically through the atmosphere. Because it exists in all three layers of cloud development, it cannot be classified as forming in any one layer.

2. Through coalescence, a water droplet grows until it finally becomes too heavy to withstand the force of gravity and falls to Earth.

3. Snowflakes form only when the entire formation process takes place at temperatures below the freezing point of water.

4. Once air is saturated, it releases latent heat. This slows the cooling process as the air continues to rise, causing the air to have a lower lapse rate.

5. Concept maps should be constructed in the following order. The first level is water cycle. In the next levels, in any order, evaporation should be linked to water changes from liquid to gas; condensation should be linked to water changes from gas to liquid; precipitation should be linked to water falls as rain, snow, sleet, or hail.

3 Assess

Check for Understanding
Reinforcement
Ask students to identify the major cloud groups and at least two subcategories of each major group. Have them identify the probable heights at which the cloud bases form, whether the clouds are composed of liquid water or ice crystals, and whether they are likely to produce precipitation.

Reteach
Ask students to construct concept maps showing the life cycle of a water droplet. Concept maps should include evaporation of water from the ocean surface; lifting of the warm, less-dense, moist air; cooling of the air to its LCL; saturation; condensation; coalescence; precipitation; and finally, the return of the water droplet to the ocean through a waterway. L2

Assessment

Portfolio Have students observe the sky during class for a few minutes each day for two weeks. Have them note the types of clouds they observe, as well as the weather that is occurring at the time. Also ask students to look for patterns. Was any one type of cloud observed more often than the others? Students should use their observed patterns to describe the relationship between clouds and weather. L1 P

NY Core Curriculum Standards
Page 290: St 1 Science KI 2 & 3, St 4 KI 1.2g, 2.1e & 2.1f, St 6 KI 1 & 2
Page 291: St 4 KI 1.2g, 2.1c, 2.1e, & 2.1f, St 6 KI 1 & 2

GeoLab

Time Allotment

30–45 minutes

Process Skills

observe and infer, interpret and analyze data, recognize cause and effect, interpret scientific illustrations, compare and contrast, model

Safety Precautions

Advise students to be careful when using scissors.

Preparation

Make sure that bottles are clean and dry.

Procedure

Teaching Strategies

Inform students that their activities here will simulate the changes in temperature that take place when atmospheric pressure increases or decreases.

Troubleshooting

- Bottles and temperature strips should not be handled any more than necessary to avoid transfer of body heat. Once the strips are placed inside the bottles and the bottles are capped, students should leave the bottles undisturbed for about five minutes to allow the temperature inside to stabilize.
- Students may want to take turns pressing down on the bottle.

Interpreting Pressure-Temperature Relationships

A s you go up a mountain, both temperature and air pressure decrease. These effects are easily explained. Temperature decreases as you get farther away from the atmosphere's heat source, Earth's surface. Pressure decreases as you ascend the mountain because there are fewer and fewer particles of air above you. Pressure and temperature, however, are also related through the expansion and compression of air, regardless of height. In this activity, you will demonstrate that relationship.

Preparation

Problem
Demonstrate the relationship between temperature and pressure.

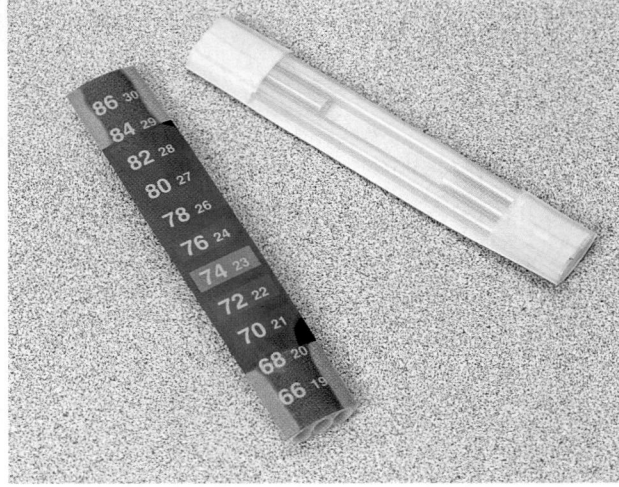

Objectives
In this GeoLab, you will:
- **Model** the temperature and pressure changes that take place as a result of the expansion and compression of air.
- **Relate** the changes to processes in the atmosphere.

Materials
clean, clear, plastic 2-L bottle with cap
plastic straws
scissors
thin, liquid-crystal temperature strip
tape
watch or timer

Safety Precautions
Always wear safety goggles and an apron in the lab.

Data and Observations

Students will model the relationship between temperature and air pressure. Students will note a slight temperature increase as pressure is applied to the bottle and a slight decrease when pressure is released.

Procedure

1. Cut two pieces of straw, each the length of the temperature strip. Then cut two 2-cm pieces of straw. Lay the two long pieces on a table. Place the two shorter pieces within the space created by the longer pieces so that the four pieces form a supportive structure for the temperature strip, as shown in the photograph on the previous page.
2. Tape the four pieces of straw together. Place the temperature strip lengthwise upon the straws. Tape the strip to the straws.
3. Slide the temperature strip-straw assembly into the clean, dry bottle. Screw the cap on tightly.
4. Place the sealed bottle on the table so that the temperature strip faces you and is easy to read. Do not handle the bottle any more than is necessary so that the temperature inside will not be affected by the warmth of your hands.
5. Record the temperature of the air inside the bottle as indicated by the temperature strip.
6. Next, position the bottle so that about half its length extends beyond the edge of the table. Placing one hand on each end of the bottle, push down on both ends so that the bottle bends in the middle. Hold the bottle this way for two minutes. During this time, your partner should record the temperature every 15 seconds.
7. Release the pressure on the bottle. Observe and record the temperature every 15 seconds for the next two minutes.

Analyze

1. What was the average temperature of the air inside the bottle as you applied pressure to the bottle? How did this differ from the average temperature of the bottled air when you released the pressure on the bottle?
2. Make a graph of the temperature changes you recorded throughout the experiment.
3. Explain how these temperature changes are related to changes in pressure.

Conclude & Apply

1. Predict how the experiment would change if you took the cap off the bottle.
2. Given your observations and what you know about the behavior of warm air, would you expect the air over an equatorial desert at midday to be characterized by high or low pressure?

Resource Manager

GeoLab and MiniLab Worksheets, pp. 44–45 L2

Analyze

1. Average temperatures will differ. However, in all cases, temperature should have decreased when pressure was released.
2. Graphs will vary, but all should show that temperature increased when pressure was applied and decreased when pressure was released.
3. As pressure increases, the molecules that make up air are packed more tightly together. This creates more collisions and produces more heat.

Conclude & Apply

1. Air would escape when pressure was applied on the bottle. There would be no change in pressure and thus no change in temperature.
2. Low pressure; in the atmosphere, the hot desert air would be less dense than the air around it and therefore would rise. When air rises, it pushes down with less force, which lowers atmospheric pressure.

✓ Assessment

Knowledge Ask students to explain what happens to the molecules in a parcel of air when the air cools. Students should realize that the molecular motions are slowing down. Thus, there are less collisions, and less heat is produced.

NY Core Curriculum Standards

Page 292: St 1 Science KI 1, St 4 KI 2.1e & 2.1f, St 6 KI 1
Page 293: St 1 Science KI 1, 2, & 3, St 6 KI 1, 2, & 5

Science in the News

Purpose

Students will learn about the effects of CFCs on atmospheric ozone. The feature also discusses international measures to limit the use of CFCs.

Content Background

In addition to their use as a chemical propellant, CFCs are used for medical purposes. The chemical compounds have been used in metered-dose inhalers (MDIs) for the treatment of breathing disorders such as asthma. These inhalers are used to disperse the medication that opens the inflamed bronchial tissue inside the lungs of a patient.

Researchers have been able to create two alternatives to CFCs for medical purposes. Hydro-fluoroalkanes (HFAs) and hydro-fluorocarbons (HFCs) are composed of carbon, hydrogen, and fluorine. Because they contain no chlorine, they should not damage the ozone layer.

Teaching Strategies

Discuss the items used on a regular basis that have had to be changed to comply with regulations established to slow ozone depletion. Possible items include hair spray, spray paint, pesticides, and refrigerants. Have students weigh the pros and cons of banning chemicals such as CFCs, including higher prices for certain items. Encourage students to realize that in the long run, such bans are far more beneficial to humans than any relatively small inconveniences the bans may cause.

The Montreal Protocol and the Ozone Layer

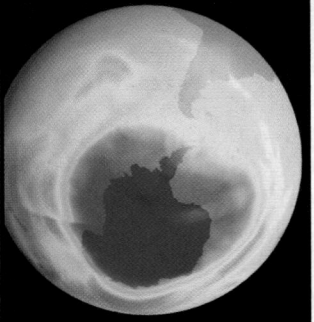

In 2002, scientists reported that the amount of ozone-destroying chemicals in the atmosphere, particularly chlorine, was decreasing. This decrease is largely due to the efforts of the countries that have signed the Montreal Protocol, an international treaty which set restrictions on the global production and use of chlorofluorocarbons (CFCs) and other ozone-destroying chemicals that can reach the atmosphere.

The ozone layer, located in the stratosphere, absorbs up to 99 percent of incoming ultraviolet radiation. Overexposure to ultraviolet radiation can lead to the development of skin cancer and cataracts.

Chemical Reactions

Once they enter the atmosphere, CFCs, chemicals that were used in refrigerators and air conditioners, and halons, used in fire extinguishers, are broken down by ultraviolet light. The products of these breakdowns include highly reactive chlorine and bromine. The chlorine and bromine atoms destroy ozone molecules during chemical reactions. A single chlorine or bromine atom can destroy hundreds of ozone molecules before it reacts with another gas, thus ending the destruction. Because of all this, a small amount of reactive chlorine or bromine can have a large impact on the ozone layer.

International Effort

After the discovery of the "hole" in the ozone layer, an international effort began to stop the destruction of the ozone layer. At its inception in 1987, 24 countries signed the Montreal Protocol. The Montreal Protocol called for a phase-out in the production and use of most ozone-destroying chemicals by developed countries by the year 2005. Developing countries around the world are working to achieve the same goal by 2015. By 2003, 186 countries had signed and were abiding by the restrictions of the Montreal Protocol.

Future Outlooks

Recent studies indicate that actions taken as a result of the Montreal Protocol restrictions have an effect on levels of chlorine in the atmosphere, which are decreasing each year. Scientists warn that even complete compliance with the Montreal Protocol will still leave the ozone layer vulnerable for the next decade. However, based on current trends in data, a return to pre-1980 ozone amounts over Antarctica is expected by the middle of this century.

Activity

Research the latest information about the Montreal Protocol. What amendments were added in 1999? What has occurred since 1999? Write a short report explaining the latest goals of and changes to the Montreal Protocol.

Activity

The Montreal Protocol called for a 50-percent reduction in CFCs by 1999. In 1997, the agreement was amended to speed up the phasing-out process of CFCs. For example, the initial deadline for phasing out the use of methyl bromide was 2010. In 1997, this deadline was changed to 2005.

Summary

SECTION 11.1

Atmospheric Basics

Main Ideas

- Earth's atmosphere is made of a combination of several gases, primarily nitrogen and oxygen. It also contains small amounts of water vapor, carbon dioxide, ozone, and dust, which play key roles in the production of weather and climate.
- The atmosphere consists of several layers characterized by differences in temperature. The most important for weather is the lowest layer, the troposphere, where most of the mass of the atmosphere is found.
- The Sun is the source of energy in Earth's atmosphere. Solar energy absorbed by Earth's surface is transferred throughout the atmosphere by the processes of radiation, conduction, and convection.

Vocabulary

conduction (p. 276)
convection (p. 277)
exosphere (p. 274)
mesosphere (p. 274)
ozone (p. 273)
radiation (p. 275)
stratosphere (p. 274)
thermosphere (p. 274)
troposphere (p. 274)

SECTION 11.2

State of the Atmosphere

Main Ideas

- Heat is the transfer of energy that occurs because of a difference in temperature between substances. Temperature is the measure of how rapidly or slowly molecules move around. Atmospheric temperature generally decreases with altitude.
- Air has mass and exerts a force called atmospheric pressure. Because there are fewer molecules of gas in the upper atmosphere, atmospheric pressure decreases with increasing altitude.
- Wind is the movement of air that results from differences in pressure. Wind speed is affected by friction; mountains, forests, and buildings slow wind down.

Vocabulary

condensation (p. 279)
dew point (p. 279)
heat (p. 278)
humidity (p. 283)
lifted condensation level (p. 279)
relative humidity (p. 283)
temperature (p. 278)
temperature inversion (p. 281)

SECTION 11.3

Moisture in the Atmosphere

Main Ideas

- Clouds are formed as warm, moist air is forced upward, expands, and cools. Orographic lifting is a method of cloud formation that involves air moving up the side of a mountain. Clouds may also form when air masses of different temperatures collide.
- Clouds are generally classified according to the altitudes at which they form and their shapes.
- As cloud droplets collide, they coalesce into larger droplets, which may fall to Earth as precipitation. The four main types of precipitation are rain, snow, sleet, and hail.
- In the water cycle, water continually moves between Earth's surface and the atmosphere through the processes of evaporation, condensation, and precipitation.

Vocabulary

coalescence (p. 289)
condensation nuclei (p. 285)
evaporation (p. 290)
latent heat (p. 286)
orographic lifting (p. 285)
precipitation (p. 289)
stability (p. 286)
water cycle (p. 290)

 earthgeu.com/vocabulary_puzzlemaker

---

CHAPTER 11
Study Guide

Main Ideas

Summary statements can be used by students to review the major concepts of the chapter.

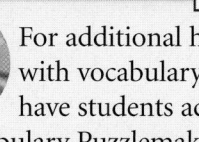

VOCABULARY PuzzleMaker ONLINE SCIENCE

For additional help with vocabulary, have students access the Vocabulary Puzzlemaker online.

earthgeu.com/ vocabulary puzzlemaker

0:00 ⏱ **Out of Time?**

If time does not permit teaching the entire chapter, use the GeoDigest at the end of the unit as an overview.

Earth Science Online

Be sure to check the Earth Science Web Site for links to chapter material:
earthgeu.com

GLENCOE
Technology

Videotape/DVD
MindJogger Videoquizzes
Chapter 11: *Atmosphere*
Have students work in groups as they play the videoquiz game to review key chapter concepts.

 **Resource Manager**

Chapter Assessment, pp. 61–66
MindJogger Videoquizzes DVD/VHS
ExamView® Pro CD-ROM
Performance Assessment in Earth Science

NY Core Curriculum Standards

Page 294: St 2 KI 1, St 4 KI 2.1i, St 7 KI 1
Page 295: St 4 KI 2.1a, 2.1b, 2.1c, 2.1e, 2.1f, 2.2a, 2.2b, & 2.2c

295

Understanding Main Ideas

1. b
2. a
3. b
4. b
5. b
6. b
7. a
8. b
9. d
10. a
11. differences in density, temperature, or pressure
12. a layer in which temperature rises with height instead of falling
13. Latent heat is heat released from water vapor as it condenses into liquid water.
14. Condensation around a nucleus forms a water droplet. These droplets gather and become a cloud. Clouds are classified by shape and height.
15. Water evaporates. Water vapor then rises, cools, and condenses. The water droplets combine and fall as precipitation.

Applying Main Ideas

16. Earth's surface absorbs solar energy, transforms it into heat, warms the air near the surface through conduction, and distributes the heat vertically through convection.
17. Nitrogen and oxygen make up most of the atmosphere. Other important gases include argon, hydrogen, carbon dioxide, and water vapor.
18. See concept map on this page.

Understanding Main Ideas

1. What process describes the change of state of water from a liquid to a gas?
   - **a.** condensation
   - **b.** evaporation
   - **c.** melting
   - **d.** drying

2. Condensation nuclei are involved in the formation of which of the following?
   - **a.** cloud droplets
   - **b.** ozone
   - **c.** dry ice
   - **d.** carbon dioxide

3. Which atmospheric layer contains most of the mass of Earth's atmosphere?
   - **a.** tropopause
   - **b.** troposphere
   - **c.** stratosphere
   - **d.** mesosphere

4. Which object would heat up most rapidly?
   - **a.** water
   - **b.** asphalt
   - **c.** grass
   - **d.** cement

5. What percentage of incoming solar radiation does Earth's atmosphere absorb?
   - **a.** 100 percent
   - **b.** 15 percent
   - **c.** 50 percent
   - **d.** 35 percent

Use this diagram to answer questions 6–8.

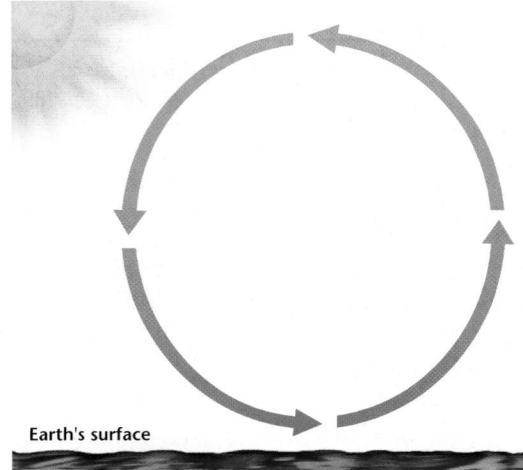

Earth's surface

6. What type of energy transfer is shown in the diagram on this page?
   - **a.** radiation
   - **b.** convection
   - **c.** conduction
   - **d.** vaporization

7. In the diagram, what type of air is rising?
   - **a.** warm
   - **b.** cool
   - **c.** dry
   - **d.** cold

8. Which statement describes the rising air in the diagram in relation to the surrounding air?
   - **a.** The rising air is more dense.
   - **b.** The rising air is less dense.
   - **c.** The rising air is cooler.
   - **d.** The rising air is thicker.

9. What do we call the temperature at which air becomes saturated?
   - **a.** humidity
   - **b.** the lapse rate
   - **c.** the LCL
   - **d.** the dew point

10. What type of cloud is a stratus cloud?
   - **a.** low
   - **b.** vertical development
   - **c.** high
   - **d.** middle

11. What causes wind?
12. Describe a temperature inversion.
13. What is latent heat?
14. How do clouds form? How are they classified?
15. Explain the three main processes involved in the water cycle.

Test-Taking Tip

QUIET ZONE It's best to study in a similar environment to the one in which you'll be tested. Thus, try to study in a quiet, disturbance-free, well-lit place. Avoid blaring stereos, video games, chatty friends, and television screens.

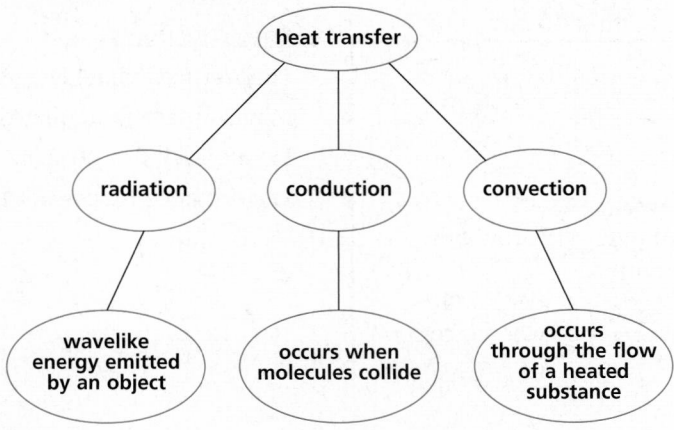

Applying Main Ideas

16. If clouds absorb only a small amount of solar radiation, how is Earth's atmosphere heated?

17. Which two gases make up most of Earth's atmosphere? List other important atmospheric gases.

18. Use the following terms to construct a concept map that shows the three methods of energy transfer in the atmosphere.

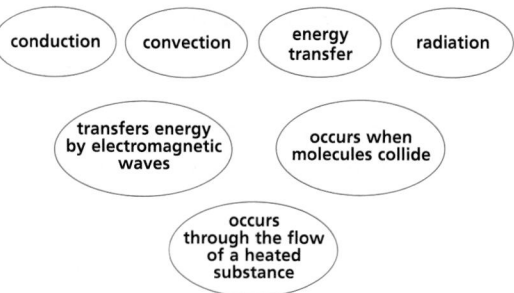

19. What type of cloud might produce the most intense precipitation? Explain your answer.

Thinking Critically

20. A summer rain could begin as a snowstorm in the clouds overhead. How is this possible?

21. Given that air cannot rise through a stable inversion layer, predict the effects of a temperature inversion on a heavily populated, highly industrial city located beneath the inversion.

22. Given the varying depths of the troposphere, why do holes in the ozone layer tend to appear mainly in the polar regions?

23. A spoon that sits in a bowl of hot soup feels hot when touched. How was energy transferred to the spoon?

Standardized Test Practice

INTERPRETING DATA Use the diagram below to answer questions 1 and 2.

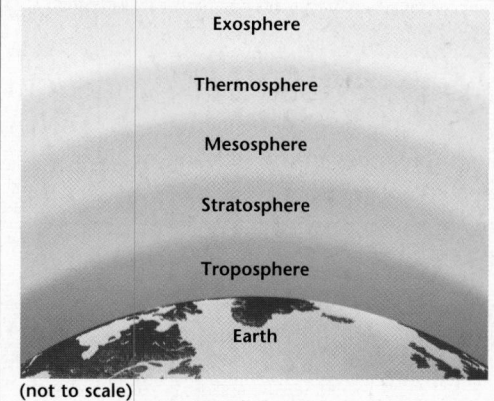
(not to scale)

1. In which layer of Earth's atmosphere is air most likely warmed by conduction?
 a. troposphere   **c.** thermosphere
 b. stratosphere   **d.** exosphere

2. Which of the following is NOT true of ozone?
 a. It absorbs ultraviolet radiation.
 b. Its concentration is decreasing or thinning.
 c. It is concentrated in the atmospheric layer called the mesosphere.
 d. It is a gas formed by the addition of one oxygen atom to an oxygen molecule.

3. Which of the following is most likely to cause orographic lifting?
 a. a sandy beach   **c.** a rocky mountain
 b. a flowing river   **d.** a sand dune

4. Which clouds are most likely to form when fog lifts away from Earth's surface?
 a. cumulus   **c.** stratus
 b. cirrostratus   **d.** altocumulus

earthgeu.com/standardized_test

Assessment **297**

19. A cumulonimbus cloud has the greatest height and the greatest vertical motion. Thus, it has the greatest potential to condense water vapor into precipitation.

Thinking Critically

20. The layer through which the precipitation formed could have been cold enough for snow to form. The snow then melted as it fell through the warmer air below, and it reached the ground as rain.

21. Because the pollution cannot rise, it remains trapped near the ground, causing a severe pollution problem.

22. The troposphere is shallower at the poles than at other places on Earth. Thus, all atmospheric layers, including the stratosphere, which contains the bulk of concentrated ozone, are closest to Earth's surface at the poles. This makes it easier for ozone-destroying chemicals to reach the stratosphere.

23. conduction

Standardized Test Practice

1. c
2. d
3. c
4. c

NY Core Curriculum Standards

Page 296: St 4 KI 2.1b, 2.1e, 2.1f, 2.2a, & 2.2b, St 6 KI 1
Page 297: St 4 KI 2.1b, 2.1e, 2.1f, 2.1i, 2.2b, & 2.2c, St 6 KI 1 & 5

Chapter 12

Meteorology

Refer to pages 8T–9T of the Teacher Guide for an explanation of the National Science Content Standards correlations.

Section	Objectives	National Science Content Standards	State/Local Standards
SECTION 12.1 **The Causes of Weather** ⏱ 1 session 🔲 ½ block	1. **Compare** and **contrast** weather and climate. 2. **Analyze** how imbalances in the heating of Earth's surface create weather. 3. **Describe** how and where air masses form.	UCP.1, UCP.2, UCP.3; A.1, A.2; D.1; F.4, F.6; G.3	St 1 Math KI 1, Science KI 1, 2, & 3, St 4 KI 2.1a–2.1c, 2.1g–2.1i, 2.2a, 2.2b, & 2.2c, St 6 KI 1, 2, 4, & 5, St 7 KI 2
SECTION 12.2 **Weather Systems** ⏱ 2 sessions 🔲 1 block	4. **Describe** how the rotation of Earth affects the movement of air. 5. **Compare** and **contrast** wind systems. 6. **Identify** the various types of fronts.	UCP.1, UCP.2, UCP.3; D.1	St 1 Math KI 1 & 2, St 2 KI 1, St 4 KI 2.1c, 2.1e, 2.1f, 2.1g, & 2.2b, St 6 KI 1 & 2, St 7 KI 1
SECTION 12.3 **Gathering Weather Data** ⏱ ½ session 🔲 ½ block	7. **Recognize** the importance of accurate weather data. 8. **Describe** the technology used to collect weather data. 9. **Analyze** the strengths and weaknesses of weather observation systems.	UCP.1, UCP.2, UCP.3; B.6; D.1; E.1, E.2; F.6; G.1	St 1 Engin KI 1, St 2 KI 1, 2, & 3, St 4 KI 2.1c, 2.1d, & 2.1g, St 6 KI 1 & 2, St 7 KI 1 & 2
SECTION 12.4 **Weather Analysis** ⏱ 1½ sessions 🔲 1 block	10. **Analyze** a basic surface weather chart. 11. **Distinguish** between analog and digital forecasting. 12. **Describe** problems with long-term forecasts.	UCP.1, UCP.2, UCP.3; D.1; E.1, E.2; F.5, F.6	St 1 Math KI 1, 2, 3, & Engin KI 1, St 2 KI 1, 2, & 3, St 4 KI 2.1c–2.1i, 2.2b, 2.2c, & 2.2d, St 6 KI 1–5, St 7 KI 1 & 2

A complete Planning Guide is provided on pages 30T–32T.

⏱ The number of recommended single-period sessions

🔲 The number of recommended blocks

Activity Materials

Discovery Lab *page 299*
2 liquid-crystal temperature strips, ice cubes in ice-cube tray, 2 pencils

GeoLab *pages 322–323*
pencil, ruler

MiniLab *page 302*
flashlight, pencil, dark colored construction paper

Demo *page 305*
loose soil

page 309
shovel, soil

page 314
weather radar image

Need materials? Contact Science Kit at 1-800-828-7777 or at www.sciencekit.com on the Internet. For alternate materials, see the activity on the listed page.

Key to Teaching Strategies

L1 Level 1 activities should be appropriate for students with learning difficulties.

L2 Level 2 activities should be within the ability range of all students.

L3 Level 3 activities are designed for above-average students.

ELL ELL activities should be within the ability range of English-language learners.

COOP LEARN Cooperative learning activities are designed for small-group work.

P These strategies represent student products that can be placed in a best-work portfolio.

🔲 These strategies are useful in a block-scheduling format.

Chapter Organizer

Glencoe Exclusive!
Teacher Works™
All-In-One Planner and Resource Center

Activities/Features	Reproducible Masters	Transparencies
Discovery Lab: Model a Cold Air Mass, p. 299 **MiniLab:** How does the angle of the Sun's rays differ? p. 302	**Study Guide for Content Mastery,** p. 73 L2 **GeoLab and MiniLab Worksheets,** p. 47 L2	**Section Focus Transparency 32** L1 ELL **Teaching Transparency 31** L2 ELL
Using Math: Using Numbers, p. 310	**Study Guide for Content Mastery,** pp. 74–75 L2 **Laboratory Manual,** pp. 89–92 L2	**Section Focus Transparency 33** L1 ELL **Teaching Transparency 32** L2 ELL
	Study Guide for Content Mastery, p. 76 L2	**Section Focus Transparency 34** L1 ELL **Teaching Transparency 33** L2 ELL
Problem-Solving Lab: p. 318 **GeoLab:** pp. 322–323 **Science & Technology:** p. 324	**Study Guide for Content Mastery,** pp. 77–78 L2 **GeoLab and MiniLab Worksheets,** pp. 48–50 L2 **Laboratory Manual,** pp. 93–96 L2	**Section Focus Transparency 35** L1 ELL **Teaching Transparency 34** L2 ELL

✔Assessment

Chapter Assessment, pp. 67–72
Performance Assessment in the Science Classroom (PASC)
MindJogger Videoquiz DVD/VHS
Performance Assessment in Earth Science
ExamView® Pro CD-ROM
5 Days to the Regents Exam

GLENCOE'S ASSESSMENT ADVANTAGE

Additional Resources

Guided Reading Audio Program ELL
Cooperative Learning in the Science Classroom COOP LEARN
Lesson Plans
Block Scheduling
earthgeu.com
NY Lesson Plans
NY Block Scheduling
Review Handbook for Regents Earth Science Exam

NATIONAL GEOGRAPHIC

Teacher's Corner

Products Available from National Geographic Society
To order the following products, call the National Geographic Society at 1-800-368-2728:
Curriculum Kits
GeoKit: *Weather*

CD-ROM
111 Years of National Geographic Magazine
Transparency Set
PicturePack: *Water*
PicturePack: *Introduction to Weather*

Content Background

Air Masses
Section 12.1

The study of meteorology is basically a study of Earth's heat balance. One of the ways in which Earth's heat remains in balance is through the development and movement of air masses. Air masses develop as air over different parts of the world acquires the characteristics of the surface below it. For example, air masses that form over oceans are more moist than those that form over landmasses, and those that form over the tropics are warmer than those that develop in polar regions. Most air masses have two defining characteristics: average temperature and average humidity. As air masses move away from their source regions, they become modified by the new surfaces that they travel over.

Monsoons
Section 12.2

Monsoons are seasonal winds that occur in tropical areas because of temperature and pressure differences between land and oceans. During the summer, when the air above the heated land is warm and less dense than the air above the cooler oceans, winds blow from the ocean toward the land. When these winds are strong, they transport vast amounts of moisture inland and can trigger torrential rains and floods. During the winter, when the air over the land is cooler and drier than the air over the oceans, the winds reverse. Winter is the dry season for these tropical areas.

Rawinsonde Observation
Section 12.3

The ground-based instrument that tracks a radiosonde also computes the radiosonde's range and angle on a minute-by-minute basis. This process, known as rawinsonde observation, can be used to determine wind speed and direction at different atmospheric levels because the position of the radiosonde relative to the ground station is known at each minute. This allows for the development of a triangle, with the three vertices representing the ground station, the location of the radiosonde at the previous minute, and the location of the radiosonde at the current minute. The use of trigonometry allows the computation of the direction of movement and the distance from minute to minute. Because the only thing that could be moving the instrument is the wind, wind speed and direction for each minute are thus computed.

Multiple Learning Styles

 **Visual-Spatial** Project, p. 314

Interpersonal Collaborative Learning, p. 308

Intrapersonal Modeling, p. 303

Linguistic Applying Earth Science, p. 307, Activity, p. 310, Reteach, pp. 316, 321

GLENCOE
Technology

The following multimedia resources are available from Glencoe.

The Infinite Voyage Series
Living with Disaster

Newton's Apple
Physical Science

Vocabulary Puzzlemaker

TeacherWorks™ CD-ROM

MindJogger Videoquizzes DVD/VHS

ExamView® Pro CD-ROM

Interactive Chalkboard CD-ROM

Chapter Organizer

Weather Forecasts
Section 12.4

The weather forecasts on television use computer imaging and sleight of hand with cameras to project images of weather maps onto television screens. Using a process called chroma key, a weather forecaster stands in front of a special, single-color backdrop. There are no maps or graphics on this backdrop. Instead, weather-related information is shown on TV monitors located on either side of the backdrop. The monitors show the same weather maps that audiences at home see on their television screens. The forecaster looks at these TV monitors to see where to point on the backdrop. Skilled forecasters make it appear as though they are pointing to changing information on the backdrop itself.

Weather Analysis
Section 12.4

Once the current state of the atmosphere has been measured, the physical laws that govern atmospheric motion can be applied to predict how the atmosphere will change over time. This process, known as weather forecasting, is rife with inaccuracies because meteorologists cannot possibly measure the state of the atmosphere over the entire world throughout all levels of the atmosphere.

Identifying Misconceptions

Students may believe that weather forms in the lowest portion of the troposphere. In reality, the weather we experience at Earth's surface is largely a result of changes taking place thousands of meters into the atmosphere. Ask students what part of the troposphere weather forms in. Most will probably indicate the part closest to Earth's surface. Remind students that clouds form at many different heights and move in different directions. Clouds are concrete evidence that weather-related processes take place at different levels of the troposphere. Tell students that the weather we experience at Earth's surface is affected by processes that operate at all levels of the troposphere.

✓Assessment

Portfolio Assessment
Assessment, TWE, p. 316

Performance Assessment
Discovery Lab, SE, p. 299
Discovery Lab, TWE, p. 299
MiniLab, SE, p. 302
MiniLab, TWE, p. 302
GeoLab, SE, pp. 322–323

Knowledge Assessment
Assessment, TWE, pp. 303, 304, 309
Section Assessment, SE, pp. 304, 311, 316, 321
Chapter Assessment, SE, pp. 326–327

Skill Assessment
Assessment, TWE, pp. 311, 321
Problem-Solving Lab, TWE, p. 318
GeoLab, TWE, pp. 322–323

Earth Science Online

Be sure to check the Earth Science Web Site for links to chapter material: earthgeu.com

GLENCOE'S ASSESSMENT ADVANTAGE

Chapter 12

Meteorology

Introducing the Chapter

Have the class monitor daily weather forecasts on television and the Internet for one week. Students should record high and low temperatures, and levels of precipitation. Students should also record actual weather conditions throughout the week. At the end of the week, have students present their findings to the class.

Interpreting the Photo

The rainbow shown here occurred over the Lamar River Valley in Yellowstone National Park, Wyoming. Tell students that rainbows are types of atmospheric phenomena formed when moisture in the air refracts and reflects sunlight. Other types of atmospheric phenomena include clouds, snowflakes, and fog.

PowerPoint® Presentations

This CD is an editable Microsoft® PowerPoint® presentation that includes:
- Section presentations
- Section checks
- Image bank
- Links to Earth Science Online
- All transparencies
- Animations
- Audio

Chapter 12 — Meteorology

What You'll Learn
- What determines global weather patterns.
- How air masses move and change.
- How the strengths and weaknesses of weather forecasts differ.
- How to create a weather chart.

Why It's Important

Few aspects of the environment have as much impact on our everyday decisions as weather does. A basic knowledge of weather processes can make those decisions easier and sometimes far safer.

Earth Science Online

To find out more about meteorology, visit the Earth Science Web Site at earthgeu.com

---

Discovery Lab

Process Skills

observe and infer, recognize cause and effect, communicate, model **L1** **ELL**

Safety Precautions

Students may spill water when filling the ice-cube trays. Wipe up spills immediately to prevent accidents.

Procedure

Troubleshooting

For best results, have students use plastic or wooden pencils, not metal or mechanical types. Also, be sure to tell students that the ice cubes should not touch either of the temperature strips.

Observe

Through conduction, the ice cubes cooled the air immediately around them. This caused the temperature of the air above and beneath the ice-cube tray to drop. The temperature of the strip beneath the tray dropped more because the cooled air, being dense, settled to the surface of the table. This sinking

Discovery Lab

Model a Cold Air Mass

An air mass is a large body of air that takes on the characteristics of the area over which it forms. You can demonstrate the formation of a cold air mass using simple materials.

1. Place a tray full of ice cubes on a table with a pencil underneath each end of the tray so that the tray is slightly elevated.

2. Slide a liquid-crystal temperature strip underneath the ice-cube tray.

3. Rest another temperature strip on two pencils on top of the tray.

4. Record the temperature of each strip at one-minute intervals for about five minutes.

⚠ **CAUTION: Always wear protective clothing in the lab.**

Observe In your science journal, make a graph showing the temperature changes for each temperature strip. What happened to the temperature of the air beneath the tray and the air above the tray? Explain how this model represents a cold air mass.

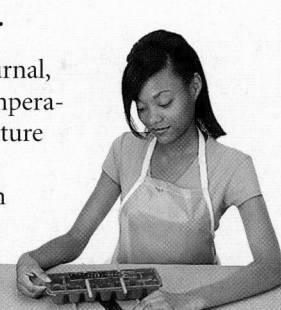

Section Focus

Before presenting the lesson, display **Section Focus Transparency 32** on the overhead projector.
L1 ELL

Chapter Themes

The following themes from the National Science Content Standards are covered in this chapter. Refer to page 8T of the Teacher Guide for an explanation of the correlations.
Systems, order, and organizations (UCP.1); Evidence, models, and explanation; (UCP.2); Change, constancy, and measurement (UCP.3); Evolution and equilibrium (UCP.4)

0:00 Out of Time?

If time does not permit teaching the entire chapter, use the Chapter Summary on page 325 and the GeoDigest found at the end of the unit as an overview.

SECTION 12.1 *The Causes of Weather*

OBJECTIVES

- **Compare** and **contrast** *weather and climate.*

- **Analyze** *how imbalances in the heating of Earth's surface create weather.*

- **Describe** *how and where air masses form.*

VOCABULARY

meteorology
weather
climate
air mass
air mass modification

Have you ever sat back and watched the sky on a lazy summer afternoon? You might have noticed clouds of different shapes, or felt the warmth of the sun against your face or an occasional puff of wind as it cooled your skin. All of these phenomena are part of a highly organized sequence of events with specific causes. Those events and the factors that cause them are all part of meteorology. **Meteorology** is the study of atmospheric phenomena. The root of the word *meteorology—meteor—*is the name given in modern times to a flaming rock falling through space. But the ancient Greek meaning of *meteor* was "high in the air," and it is this meaning that pertains to meteorology.

Clouds, raindrops, snowflakes, fog, dust, and rainbows are all types of atmospheric "meteors." The primary types are cloud droplets and forms of precipitation that contain water in any phase; they are known as hydrometeors. Smoke, haze, dust, and other condensation nuclei are called lithometeors. Thunder and lightning are examples of electrometeors, which are visible or audible manifestations of atmospheric electricity. These various phenomena are the objects and events that meteorologists study.

12.1 *The Causes of Weather* **299**

---

of cold air is a key component in the formation of cold air masses.

✔Assessment

Performance Ask students to infer what happened to the temperature of the air 2 cm above and below the ice-cube tray. Then have students repeat the experiment to find out whether their inferences were supported. Use the Performance Task Assessment List for Making Observations and Inferences in **PASC,** p. 17.

Resource Manager

Section Focus Transparency 32 L1 ELL
Study Guide for Content Mastery, p. 73 L2

Content Background

Many meteorological processes entail basic atmospheric motions, such as convection, on many different time and spatial scales. For instance, a warm air current rising from the ground on a summer afternoon and the growth of a powerful thunderstorm are both the result of the rising and sinking of air over space and time. Basic atmospheric motions also are evident in the formation of air masses and wind systems. Point out these common processes throughout the chapter to demonstrate how seemingly unrelated events share the same underlying processes.

Concept Development

Different surfaces absorb solar energy at different rates. Dark, moist soil absorbs solar energy very efficiently, while ice and snow reflect a great deal of solar radiation. Have students discuss where different surfaces are found in their area and consider how the surfaces affect energy absorption.

WEATHER AND CLIMATE

Atmospheric phenomena, shown in *Figure 12-1,* interact to affect the environment and life on Earth. This is basically what we call weather. **Weather** is the current state of the atmosphere. When we speak of weather, we are referring mainly to short-term variations in the atmosphere. These variations can take place over minutes, hours, days, weeks, or months. Long-term variations in weather for a particular area make up the **climate** of that area. Climate is usually averaged over the course of 30 years or more. You'll learn more about climate in Chapter 14. For now, simply recognize that meteorology, weather, and climate are related. Meteorology is the study of the atmosphere; weather is the current state of the atmosphere, including short-term variations that affect our lives; and climate describes the average weather over a long period of time.

A QUESTION OF BALANCE

As you've learned, the Sun heats the surface of Earth, and Earth radiates back to space about as much energy as it receives over the course of a year. In meteorology, a crucial question is how that radiation is distributed around the planet. You know that the Sun feels hotter during the afternoon, when its rays strike Earth more directly, than it does in the early morning or evening, when its rays strike Earth at a low angle. The Sun's rays are more spread out when they strike Earth at a low angle, as you'll see in the *MiniLab* later in this chapter. The same amount of energy is spread over a larger area. As shown in *Figure 12-2,* the solar radiation reaching Earth's surface at the poles is therefore less intense. This explains, in part, why the tropics are warmer than the poles. But why don't the tropics become steadily warmer if the Sun is always directly overhead? How do regions manage to maintain fairly constant average temperatures?

Figure 12-1 Snowflakes **(A),** lightning **(B),** and fog **(C)** are types of atmospheric phenomena.

Across the Curriculum

Biology, Geology Point out that balances are very common in nature. In biology, for instance, balances develop between predators and prey. In geology, the shifting of tectonic plates and the relieving of stress created by earthquakes are ways in which the forces acting on Earth's crust are balanced. The movement toward the establishment of balance is a recurring theme throughout nature and is evident in meteorology.

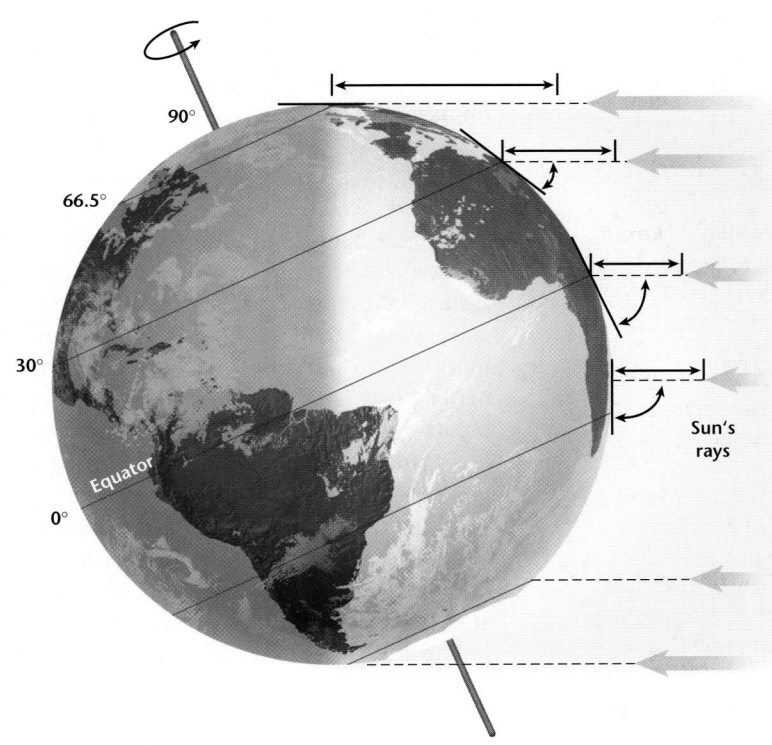

Figure 12-2 The Sun's rays strike Earth more directly at the tropics than they do at the poles. At the poles, the same amount of solar radiation is spread over a larger area than at the equator. Therefore, polar regions are never very warm.

Balancing the Budget The tropics and other places maintain fairly constant average temperatures because heat energy is redistributed around the world. The continual motion of air and water reallocates heat energy among Earth's surface, oceans, and atmosphere and brings it into balance. Virtually everything that we consider to be weather—every atmospheric motion from the tiniest convection current to thunderstorms to large-scale weather systems—is part of this constant redistribution of Earth's heat energy.

AIR MASSES

In Chapter 11, you learned that when air over a warm surface, such as a parking lot, becomes warmer than the surrounding air because of conduction, the warm air rises. Now, imagine this same process taking place over thousands of square kilometers. Imagine that the warm air remains over this same area for days or weeks. The result is the formation of an air mass. An **air mass** is a large body of air that takes on the characteristics of the area over which it forms. Meteorologists call the region over which an air mass forms the source region. Air masses form over land or water. Those that form

12.1 *The Causes of Weather* **301**

Interpreting the Illustration

Figure 12-2 Have students contrast the angle at which the Sun's rays strike the equator and the poles. The Sun's rays strike the equator more directly than they strike the poles.

MiniLab

Purpose

Students will demonstrate how differences in the angle of the Sun affect the amount of solar energy received in the tropics and the polar regions.

Process Skills

model, recognize cause and effect, observe and infer

Materials

flashlight, pencil, dark construction paper

Teaching Strategies

Students should work in groups of three: one student to hold the flashlight, one to verify its angle and distance from the paper, and one to trace the outline of the light on the paper.

Expected Results

As the angle of the flashlight changes, the light is spread over a wider area. Solar energy also is spread over a wider area as the angle of latitude increases.

Analyze and Conclude

1. The outline of the light was larger in step 3. It changed because the light covered a larger area.
2. The amount of light received at any one place decreases when the light covers a larger area.
3. Solar energy is spread over a large area at the poles; thus, polar regions receive less solar radiation than do areas near the equator.

✔Assessment

Performance Challenge students to model the angle at which the Sun's rays strike the poles during winter. Students should increase the angle of the flashlight until the light is almost parallel to the paper. Use the Performance Task Assessment List for Model in **PASC,** p. 51.

MiniLab

How does the angle of the Sun's rays differ?

Model the angle at which sunlight reaches Earth's surface. This angle greatly affects the intensity of solar energy received in any one place.

Procedure

1. Hold a flashlight several centimeters above a piece of paper and point the flashlight straight down.
2. Use a pencil to trace the outline of the light on the paper. The outline models how the Sun's rays strike the equator.
3. Keeping the flashlight at the same distance above the paper, tilt the top of the flashlight to roughly a 30° angle.
4. Trace the new outline of the light. This is similar to how the Sun's rays are received at the poles.

Analyze and Conclude

1. Describe how the outline of the light differed between step 1 and step 3. Explain why it differed.
2. How do you think the change in area covered by the light affects the intensity of light received at any one place?
3. The flashlight models solar radiation striking the surface of Earth. Knowing this, compare how much heat energy is absorbed near the equator and near the poles.

---

over land have less exposure to large amounts of moisture, so they are drier than those that form over water. Air masses take on the temperature of the source region, too.

Classifying Air Masses Air masses are classified exactly as we have already described them: according to their source regions. The main types of air masses, shown in *Figure 12-3,* are warm and dry continental tropical (cT), warm and humid maritime tropical (mT), cold and dry continental polar (cP), cold and humid maritime polar (mP), and arctic (A). An arctic air mass is basically the same as a continental polar air mass, but much colder. It's the type you may have heard most about because it brings the most frigid outbreaks of winter. Extremely cold arctic air masses are usually associated with very high pressure as a result of the massive sinking of cold air over a large area.

Source Regions All five main types of air masses can be found in North America because of the continent's proximity to the source regions associated with each air mass. Maritime polar air forms over the cold waters of the North Atlantic and North Pacific. It primarily affects the West Coast, bringing occasionally heavy rains in winter. Continental polar air forms over the interior of Canada and Alaska and can be quite frigid in the winter, when nights are long. In the summer, however, cP air can bring pleasant relief from heat and humidity because of its cool and relatively dry composition.

The origins of maritime tropical air are tropical and subtropical oceans, such as the Caribbean Sea and the Gulf of Mexico. In the summer, mT air brings hot, oppressively humid weather to the eastern two-thirds of the United States and Canada. The desert Southwest and Mexico are the source regions

---

Differentiated Instruction

Learning Disabled On a warm day, have students place a pan of water in a sunny window sill and a piece of dark construction paper next to the pan. After the Sun has been shining on the pan and paper for about 30 minutes, have students touch both to observe which is warmer. Have groups of students repeat the process with different types of materials such as soil, rock, and ice.

Have the groups relate the experiment to different types of air masses forming over different surfaces. Students can present reports on the type of air masses that they modeled. This is a quick and easy demonstration of how land heats up more quickly than water, which is an important concept in the development of air masses. L1 ELL

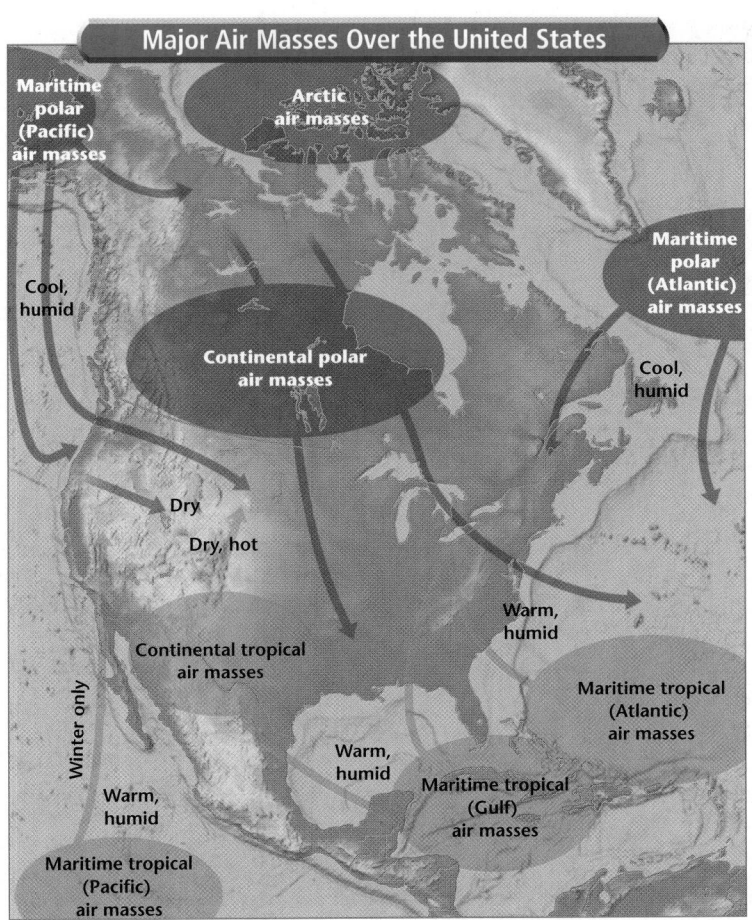

Major Air Masses Over the United States

Maritime polar (Pacific) air masses

Arctic air masses

Cool, humid

Continental polar air masses

Maritime polar (Atlantic) air masses

Cool, humid

Dry

Dry, hot

Warm, humid

Continental tropical air masses

Maritime tropical (Atlantic) air masses

Winter only

Warm, humid

Warm, humid

Maritime tropical (Gulf) air masses

Warm, humid

Maritime tropical (Pacific) air masses

Figure 12-3 Each of the major air masses that affects weather in the United States has a similar temperature and moisture content as the area over which it formed.

of continental tropical air, which is hot and dry, especially in summer. Arctic air develops over latitudes above 60°N in the ice- and snow-covered regions of Siberia and the Arctic Basin. During the winter, this area receives almost no solar radiation but continues to radiate heat out to space, so it can get very cold indeed. In addition to temperature and humidity, another important characteristic of an air mass is its stability. The stability of air is an important factor in its ability to produce clouds and precipitation.

Air Mass Modification Like the warm air over a large city during a summer afternoon, air masses do not stay in one place indefinitely. Eventually, they move, transferring heat from one area to another and thus establishing the heat balance discussed earlier. As an air mass moves, it may travel over land or water that has different

Modeling

Intrapersonal Have students describe what happens when they take a hot shower in a closed room. Tell them that this scenario represents a model of a maritime tropical (mT) air mass, in which very warm air combines with abundant moisture, as happens over tropical oceans. The combination of warm temperatures and moisture produces air masses with high values of relative humidity. Have students brainstorm other scenarios that represent different types of air masses.

Reinforcement

Have students review the two basic variables that are involved in air-mass formation: average temperature and average moisture content. These variables produce four basic types of air masses: warm and dry, warm and wet, cool and dry, and cool and wet. The other air-mass subtypes are simply variations of these four basic combinations.

Resource Manager

GeoLab and MiniLab Worksheets, p. 47 L2

✔Assessment

Knowledge Ask students the following question. A cool, wet air mass that brings cloudy, rainy weather to the Pacific Northwest is an example of what type of air mass?
a. continental tropical
b. maritime polar
c. continental polar
d. maritime tropical
The answer is b, maritime polar.

NY Core Curriculum Standards

Page 302: St 1 Math KI 1, Science KI 1, 2, & 3, St 4 KI 2.1h & 2.1i, St 6 KI 1 & 2
Page 303: St 1 Math KI 1, St 4 KI 2.1a, 2.1h, 2.1i, 2.2a, & 2.2b

Check for Understanding

Collaborative Learning

Have students form four groups, and assign each group a different air mass to research from among the following: mT, cT, cP, and mP. Groups should describe how their air masses are modified as they move over areas with different characteristics. **COOP LEARN**

Reteach

Have students make data tables showing the different types of air masses in the northern hemisphere, their origins, their characteristics, and the areas that they affect. **L2** **P**

✔Assessment

Knowledge Have students match the main air mass types with places in the United States that are influenced by those air masses. Example: arctic–Alaska; cT–Arizona.

Table 12-1 Air Mass Characteristics

Air Mass Type	Source Region Stability		Characteristics	
	Winter	Summer	Winter	Summer
A	Stable		Bitter cold, dry	
cP	Stable	Stable	Very cold, dry	Cool, dry
cT	Unstable	Unstable	Warm, dry	Hot, dry
mP (Pacific)	Unstable	Unstable	Mild, humid	Mild, humid
mP (Atlantic)	Unstable	Stable	Cold, humid	Cool, humid
mT (Pacific)	Stable	Stable	Warm, humid	Warm, humid
mT (Atlantic)	Unstable	Unstable	Warm, humid	Warm, humid

characteristics from those of its source region. The air mass then starts to acquire some of the characteristics of the new surface beneath it. When this happens, it is said to undergo **air mass modification,** which is the exchange of heat or moisture with the surface over which an air mass travels. *Table 12-1* summarizes the characteristics of the main types of air masses before modification.

All air masses become modified to some extent as they move away from their source regions. Eventually, an air mass becomes modified to such a degree that its characteristics are almost the same as the new surface over which it is traveling. At this point, the air mass has lost its original identity and is now simply part of the air over the new source region it has encountered.

SECTION ASSESSMENT

1. What is the difference between weather and climate? How do both relate to the science of meteorology?

2. What must happen to keep the poles from steadily cooling off and the tropics from heating up over time?

3. What method of heat transfer plays the primary role in the formation of an air mass?

4. Describe how the moisture in a maritime polar (mP) air mass that formed over the North Pacific Ocean would modify as it moved inland over the western coast of North America.

5. **Thinking Critically** Explain why an arctic air mass is usually more stable than a maritime tropical air mass. In other words, why does the arctic air resist rising more than the tropical air does?

SKILL REVIEW

6. **Predicting** Which type of air mass would you expect to become modified more quickly: an arctic air mass moving over the Gulf of Mexico in winter or a maritime tropical air mass moving into the southeastern United States in summer? For more help, refer to the *Skill Handbook.*

earthgeu.com/self_check_quiz

SECTION ASSESSMENT

1. Weather describes changes in the atmosphere over short time periods. Climate is the average weather of an area over a long period of time. Both weather and climate are based on the study of atmospheric phenomena, which is the definition of meteorology.

2. Some mechanism must exist to transfer excess heat from the tropics to the poles.

3. Conduction; through conduction, the air near the surface takes on the characteristics of the surface below it.

4. It would mix with dry continental air and gradually take on the characteristics of the continental air mass.

5. An arctic air mass consists of cold, dense air near Earth's surface. Being more dense than the air above it, an arctic air mass cannot rise, and thus, it is stable.

6. The arctic air mass; the waters of the Gulf of Mexico would be very warm compared to the arctic air. The warm water would rapidly modify the cold air. The mT air would move over warm land, and thus it would be modified less quickly.

NY Core Curriculum Standards

Page 304: St 4 KI 2.1b, 2.1c, 2.1h, 2.1i, 2.2a, 2.2b, & 2.2c, St 6 KI 1, 4, & 5

Page 305: St 1 Math KI 1, St 4 KI 2.1h, 2.1i, 2.2a, 2.2b, & 2.2c, St 6 KI 1

If Earth were either all land or all water and did not rotate on its axis, a large convection cell would form in each hemisphere with the colder and denser air at the poles sinking to the surface and flowing toward the tropics. There, it would force the warm air already at the equator to rise, and then it would cool and flow back toward the poles. The problem with this proposal is that Earth does rotate from west to east. This rotation causes the **Coriolis effect,** wherein moving particles such as air are deflected to the right in the northern hemisphere and to the left in the southern hemisphere. The Coriolis effect, illustrated in *Figure 12-4A,* combines with the heat imbalance found on Earth to create distinct global wind systems that transport colder air to warmer areas and warmer air to colder areas. The end result is the balancing of heat energy on Earth.

GLOBAL WIND SYSTEMS

There are three basic zones, or wind systems, in each hemisphere, as shown in *Figure 12-4B.* The first, known as the **trade winds,** occurs at 30° north and south latitude. There, air sinks, warms, and moves toward the equator in a westerly direction. When the air reaches the equator, it rises again and moves back toward latitude 30°, where it sinks and the process starts anew. The circulation pattern for the trade

OBJECTIVES

• **Describe** *how the rotation of Earth affects the movement of air.*

• **Compare** *and* **contrast** *wind systems.*

• **Identify** *the various types of fronts.*

VOCABULARY

Coriolis effect
trade winds
prevailing westerlies
polar easterlies
jet stream
front

Figure 12-4 The rotation of Earth causes the Coriolis effect **(A)**, which, along with the heat imbalance on Earth, creates the three major global wind systems **(B)**. The convection cells show the movement of air in each zone.

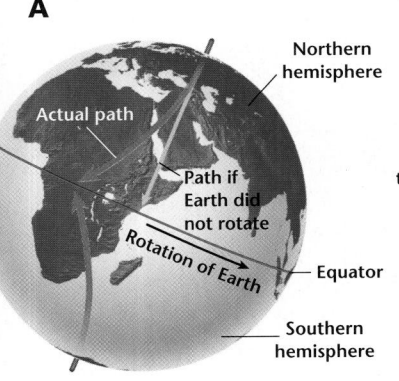

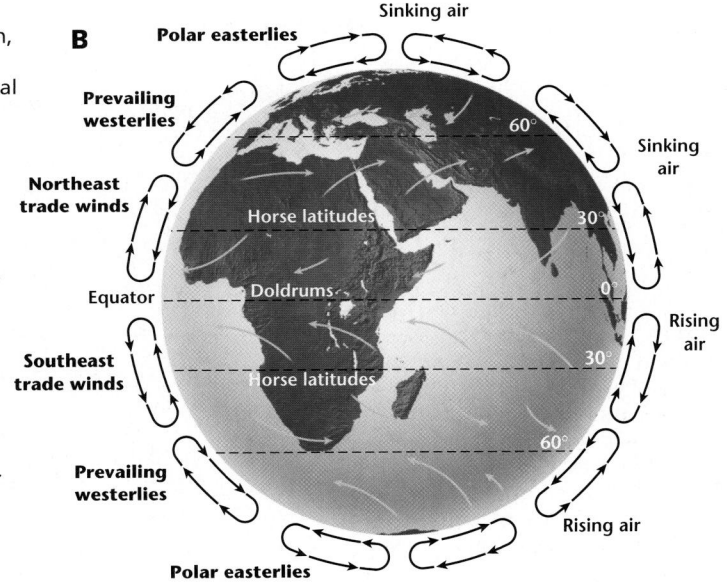

12.2 *Weather Systems* **305**

Resource Manager

Section Focus Transparency 33 L1 ELL
Study Guide for Content Mastery,
  pp. 74–75 L2

Interpreting the Illustration

Figure 12-4 Have students use a computer graphics program to make models of the three main global wind systems. Students should label each wind system and show in which general direction it moves.

Section 12.2

Prepare

Section Background

For section content background, refer to **Monsoons** on page 298C.

Preplanning

Refer to the Chapter Organizer on pages 298A–B.

1 Focus

Section Focus

Before presenting the lesson, display **Section Focus Transparency 33** on the overhead projector. L1 ELL

Demo

To show how air converges along the Intertropical Convergence Zone, take two handfuls of loose soil and place them side by side on a flat table. Then, move these piles together so that they form one large pile. Tell students that the two piles represent two different air masses that converged into one mass.

Tying to Previous Knowledge

The three convection cells in each hemisphere are basically large versions of the convection cells that form the basis of cumulus clouds. These large cells have both horizontal and vertical movements of wind.

Concept Development

As the boundary between the tropical wind systems of the northern and southern hemispheres, the Intertropical Convergence Zone serves as the "meteorological equator," the zone where the two hemispheric wind systems meet. Students will learn that this large mass of rising air contributes to cloudy conditions and periodic thunderstorms. In addition, it can contain tropical disturbances, which can grow into tropical cyclones, as will be discussed in more detail in Chapter 13.

winds closely fits a model proposed by English scientist George Hadley in 1735; thus, this zone is sometimes known as the Hadley cell.

Around 30° latitude, the sinking air associated with the trade winds creates a belt of high pressure that in turn causes generally weak surface winds. Spanish sailors called this belt the horse latitudes because their ships became stranded in these waters as a result of the near-calm winds. According to legend, they could no longer feed or water their horses and were forced to throw them overboard.

Near the equator, the trade winds from both hemispheres move together from two different directions, as shown in *Figure 12-4.* The air converges, is forced upward, and creates an area of low pressure. This process, called convergence, can occur on a small or large scale. Near the equator, it occurs over a large area called the intertropical convergence zone (ITCZ). As *Figure 12-5* shows, the ITCZ migrates south and north of the equator as the seasons change. In essence, it follows the path of the Sun's rays, which are directly over the equator in September and March. Because the ITCZ is a region of rising air, it is characterized by a band of cloudiness and occasional showers that help provide the moisture for many of the world's tropical rain forests. Note that the ITCZ is also called the doldrums. As in the horse latitudes, sailing ships were often stranded in this belt of light winds.

Other Wind Zones The second wind system, the **prevailing westerlies,** flows between 30° and 60° north and south latitude in a circulation pattern opposite that of the trade winds. In this zone, surface winds move toward the poles in a generally easterly direction, as shown in *Figure 12-4.* Note that wind is named for the direction

Figure 12-5 The mean position of the ITCZ basically follows the path of the Sun's rays throughout the year. The two paths don't match exactly because the ITCZ responds gradually to changes in the Sun's position, and thus lags behind the Sun.

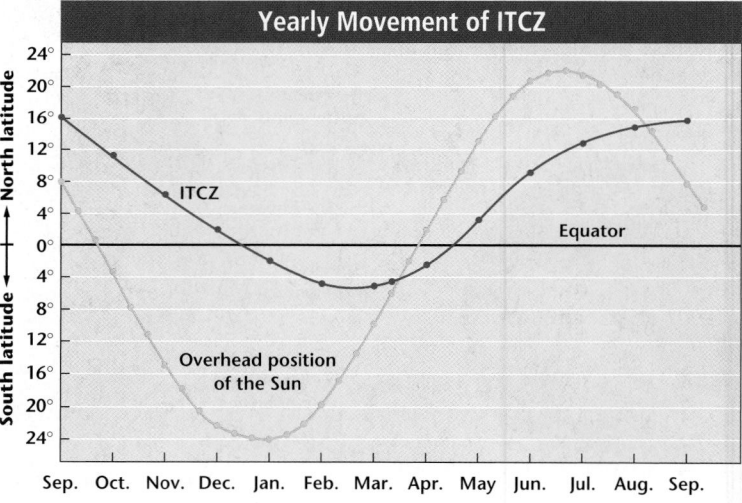

Yearly Movement of ITCZ

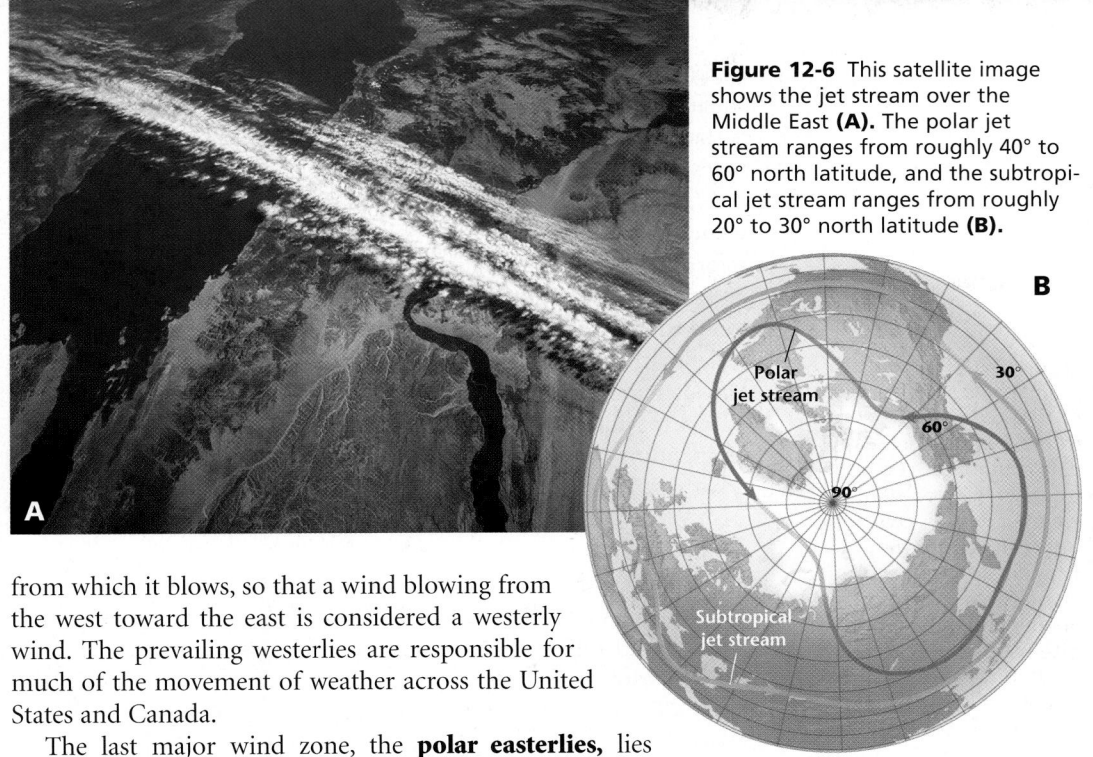

Figure 12-6 This satellite image shows the jet stream over the Middle East **(A)**. The polar jet stream ranges from roughly 40° to 60° north latitude, and the subtropical jet stream ranges from roughly 20° to 30° north latitude **(B)**.

from which it blows, so that a wind blowing from the west toward the east is considered a westerly wind. The prevailing westerlies are responsible for much of the movement of weather across the United States and Canada.

The last major wind zone, the **polar easterlies,** lies between 60° latitude and the poles. Similar to the trade winds, the polar easterlies flow from the northeast to the southwest in the northern hemisphere. Note that global wind direction reverses in the southern hemisphere. South of the equator, for instance, the polar easterlies flow from the southeast to the northwest. In both hemispheres, the polar easterlies are characterized by cold air.

JET STREAMS

Earth's weather is strongly influenced by atmospheric conditions and events that occur at the boundaries between wind zones. On either side of these imaginary boundaries, both surface and upper-level air differs greatly in temperature and pressure. Remember that wind, temperature, and pressure are related. Differences in temperature and pressure cause wind. Therefore, a large temperature gradient in upper-level air should result in strong westerly winds, and indeed, this is what happens. Narrow bands of fast, high-altitude, westerly winds called **jet streams** flow at speeds up to 185 km/h at elevations of 10.7 km to 12.2 km. Jet streams, shown in *Figure 12-6,* are so named because they resemble jets of water. The most significant one, the polar jet stream, separates the polar easterlies from the prevailing westerlies. A second version, the subtropical jet stream, is located where the trade winds meet the prevailing westerlies.

Applying Earth Science

Linguistic The strength and position of jet streams have significant effects on the aviation industry. Because jet streams often attain speeds in excess of 320 km/h, they can provide either very favorable tailwinds or extremely strong headwinds. Tailwinds result in the savings of hundreds of thousands of dollars in fuel costs. Conversely, headwinds increase fuel costs. Have students make a list of airline routes across the country and identify how travel along these routes might be impacted by the presence of a strong jet stream. **L3**

NATIONAL GEOGRAPHIC

CD-ROM
Introduction to Weather PictureShow
What is Weather?

Earth Science

Journal

Science Field Book

Many countries in tropical regions have agricultural economies that depend on monsoon rainfall. Recent discoveries have led to more accurate predictions of the arrival and strength of monsoons. Have students research how variations in the strength of monsoons in any given year have affected the economies of tropical nations. Ask students to also research modern methods of predicting the strength of monsoons. Students should explain how these predictions can benefit those economies.

Content Background

While the railroad track analogy is helpful in understanding how the jet stream steers weather systems, students should not lose sight of the fact that traveling weather systems and the jet streams associated with them are interrelated. The motion and intensity of a weather system are directly connected to changes that are taking place in the jet stream itself. In other words, unlike a real railroad track, this atmospheric "track" can speed up or slow down, change positions, and sometimes disappear altogether.

Collaborative Learning

Interpersonal Have students form four teams, and assign each team a different kind of front. Have each team research the kinds of hazardous weather that its fronts might be expected to bring to your area. Students should also research during which times of year the fronts are strongest and most frequent. Have students combine their results with those of other groups to produce a chart detailing the relative frequency of the different kinds of fronts in your area and the kinds of hazardous weather associated with each front. **L2**

COOP LEARN P 🗂

Figure 12-7 These diagrams show the structures of the four main types of fronts. Symbols below each diagram indicate how the fronts are represented on a weather map. A cold front often moves quickly. Thunderstorms may form along the front **(A)**. In a warm front, precipitation often occurs over a wide band. High-altitude cirrus clouds may form as water vapor condenses **(B)**. Light wind and precipitation are sometimes associated with a stationary front **(C)**. Strong winds and heavy precipitation may occur along an occluded front **(D)**.

Large-Scale Weather Systems Disturbances form along jet streams and give rise to large-scale weather systems that transport surface cold air toward the tropics and surface warm air toward the poles. Keep in mind that the position of the jet stream varies. It can dive almost directly south or north, instead of following its normal westerly direction. It can also split into different branches and later reform into a single stream. Whatever form or position it takes, the jet stream represents the strongest core of westerly winds. Together, these winds form a sort of atmospheric railroad track, with large-scale weather systems serving as the atmospheric trains. Weather systems generally follow the path of these winds. The jet stream also affects the intensity of weather systems by moving air of different temperatures from one region to another. Thus, despite its altitude, it has a significant impact on weather.

FRONTS

The different temperatures and pressures of air masses have other consequences apart from the jet stream. In the middle latitudes, air masses with different characteristics sometimes collide, forming a front. A **front** is the narrow region separating two air masses of different densities. The density differences are caused by differences in temperature, pressure, and humidity. Fronts can stretch over thousands of kilometers across Earth's surface. The interaction between the colliding air masses can bring dramatic changes in weather. As shown in **Figure 12-7,** there are four main types of fronts: cold fronts, warm fronts, stationary fronts, and occluded fronts.

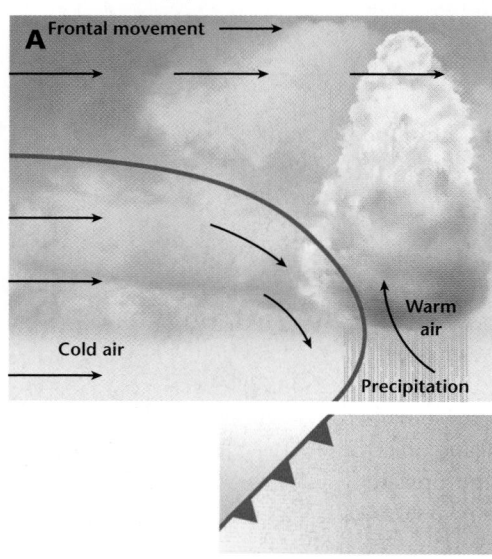

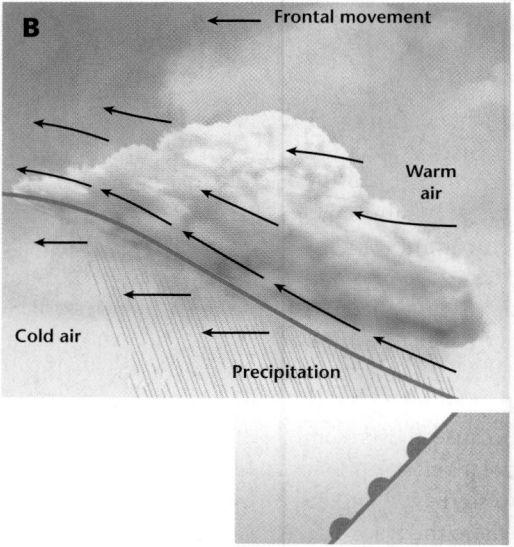

308 CHAPTER 12 *Meteorology*

NY Core Curriculum Standards

Page 308: St 4 KI 2.1e & 2.1h, St 6 KI 1
Page 309: St 4 KI 2.1e, 2.1g, & 2.1h, St 6 KI 1

Cold Fronts In a cold front, shown in *Figure 12-7A,* cold, dense air displaces warm air and forces the warm air up along a steep front. As the warm air rises, it cools and condenses. Clouds, showers, and sometimes thunderstorms are associated with cold fronts. A cold front is represented on a weather map as a solid blue line with blue triangles that point in the direction of the front's motion.

Warm Fronts In a warm front, advancing warm air displaces cold air, as shown in *Figure 12-7B.* Because the air ahead of a warm front moves more slowly than does an advancing cold air mass, the warm air encounters less friction with the ground and thus develops a gradual frontal slope rather than a steep boundary. A warm front is characterized by extensive cloudiness and precipitation. On a weather chart, a warm front appears as a solid red line with regularly spaced, solid red semicircles pointing in the direction of the front's motion.

Stationary Fronts Sometimes, two air masses meet and neither advances into the other's territory. In this case, the boundary between the air masses stalls. This type of front, called a stationary front, frequently occurs when two air masses have become so modified in their travels that the temperature and pressure gradients between them are small. Stationary fronts seldom have extensive cloud and heavy precipitation patterns; any patterns that do occur are somewhat similar to those of a warm front. A stationary front is represented on a weather map by a combination of short segments of cold- and warm-front symbols as shown in *Figure 12-7C.*

Earth Science Online

Topic: Weather
To find out more about weather fronts, visit the Earth Science Web Site at earthgeu.com

Activity: Obtain a weather map showing today's weather. Label the weather fronts.

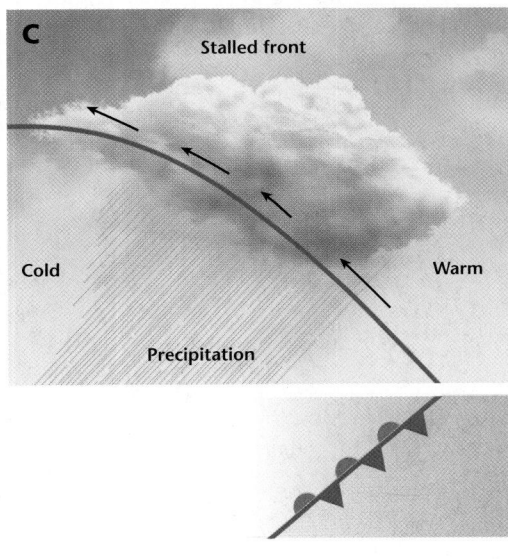

C
Stalled front
Cold   Warm
Precipitation

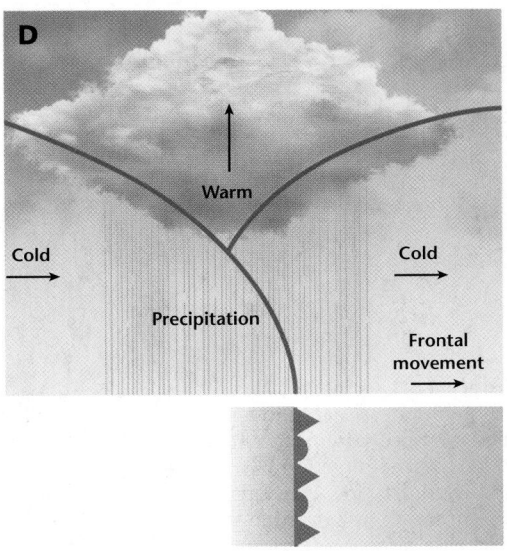

D
Warm
Cold   Cold
Precipitation
Frontal movement

12.2 *Weather Systems* **309**

Demo

Use a shovel and some soil to model how a cold front forces air to rise. Sprinkle the soil on the ground. Then invert the shovel and put the blade edge flat against the ground. Next, push the inverted shovel into the soil. The soil will pile up and rise against the shovel blade. Tell students that a cold front is similar in that cold air forces warm air to rise. As the warm air rises and cools, it becomes saturated, causing clouds and precipitation to form.

Activity

Linguistic Have students research several different types of cyclones, or low-pressure systems, that occur around the world, including blizzards, tropical cyclones, hurricanes, typhoons, tornadoes, waterspouts, dust devils, and wave cyclones. Students should provide brief descriptions of each system, including its average size, intensity, and potential for causing damage or loss of life. Have students identify which of these cyclonic storms affect their area.
L2

Using Math

Using Numbers
Most weather occurs in the troposphere between the surface of Earth and an altitude of 11 km. Suppose the temperature in an area drops about 7°C for each kilometer of increase in altitude. If the surface temperature is 15°C, what is the temperature at an altitude of 3 km?

Occluded Fronts Sometimes, a cold air mass moves so rapidly that it overtakes a warm front. The advancing cold air wedges the warm air upward, as shown in *Figure 12-7D* on page 309. Recall that a warm front involves warm air gliding over a cold air mass. When the warm air is lifted, this cold air mass collides with the advancing cold front. The warm air is thus squeezed upward between the two cold air masses. This is called an occluded front and is represented on a weather map by a line with alternating purple triangles and semi-circles that point toward the direction of motion. Precipitation is common on both sides of an occluded front.

PRESSURE SYSTEMS

You have learned that at Earth's surface, rising air is associated with low pressure and sinking air is associated with high pressure. Rising or sinking air, combined with the Coriolis effect, results in the formation of rotating low- and high-pressure systems in the atmosphere. Air in these systems moves in a general circular motion around either a high- or low-pressure center.

High-Pressure Systems In a surface high-pressure system, air sinks, so that when it reaches Earth's surface, it spreads away from the center. The deflection of air to the right caused by the Coriolis effect makes the overall circulation around a high-pressure center move in a clockwise direction in the northern hemisphere, as shown in *Figure 12-8A.* Keep in mind that the Coriolis effect is reversed in the southern hemisphere; there, high-pressure systems rotate in a counterclockwise direction. Some high-pressure systems are associated with cold air masses that move and modify; others, such as subtropical high-pressure systems, are more stationary.

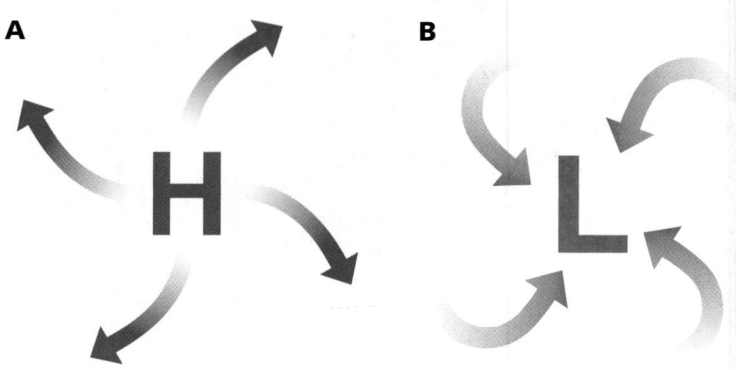

Figure 12-8 In the northern hemisphere, winds in a high-pressure system rotate in a clockwise direction **(A),** and winds in a low-pressure system rotate in a counter-clockwise direction **(B).**

Differentiated Instruction

Visually Impaired To help students with visual impairments understand the concepts of fronts and air masses, place a bowl of ice on a table. Place a fan near the bowl so that the fan blows cold air from the ice on the students. Explain that the sudden rush of cold air is similar to how a cold front moves through an area, and that the cool air that remains behind is the equivalent of a cool air mass that moves in behind a front.

Low-Pressure Systems In surface low-pressure systems, air rises. The rising air must be replaced by air from outside the system, so the net flow is inward toward the center and then upward. In contrast to air in a high-pressure system, air in a low-pressure system in the northern hemisphere moves in a counterclockwise direction, as shown in *Figure 12-8B*. This movement is reversed in the southern hemisphere.

Recall from Chapter 11 that it's difficult for clouds to form when air is sinking, as it does in high-pressure systems. Thus, high-pressure systems are usually associated with fair weather, while low-pressure systems are associated with clouds and precipitation. In fact, most of Earth's subtropical oceans are dominated by large high-pressure systems with generally pleasant conditions. One of the main producers of inclement weather in the middle latitudes, meanwhile, is a specific type of low-pressure system called a wave cyclone. A wave cyclone usually begins along a stationary front. Some imbalance in temperature, pressure, or density causes part of the front to move south as a cold front and another part of the front to move north as a warm front. This sets up a counterclockwise or cyclonic circulation, as shown in *Figure 12-9*. Eventually, if upper-level conditions are favorable, a fully developed low-pressure system forms. Pushed by the prevailing westerlies, this system may travel thousands of kilometers affecting large areas in the middle latitudes.

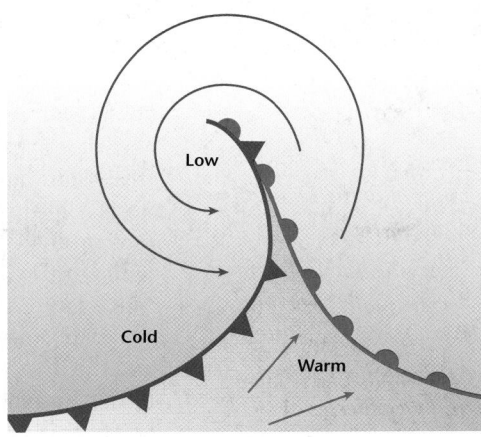

Figure 12-9 The counterclockwise circulation is characteristic of a wave cyclone.

Check for Understanding

Discussion
Tell students that clashes between different air masses cause tornadoes. Ask students to use this information to explain why tornadoes are more common in the U.S. Central Plains than in Puerto Rico. Puerto Rico is located in a tropical ocean dominated by only one type of air mass, mT. The Central Plains frequently experience different types of air masses, and the clashes between them spawn tornadoes.

Reteach

Have students make data tables listing the various types of fronts, and the types of air masses and weather that are associated with each. L2 P

✓Assessment

Skill Have students diagram why precipitation occurs along different types of fronts. Diagrams should show air rising over frontal boundaries, air cooling as it rises, air saturating, water vapor condensing into clouds, and precipitation.

SECTION ASSESSMENT

1. Describe the main global wind systems. Give characteristics of each.

2. Explain why most tropical rain forests are located near the equator.

3. How does the jet stream affect the movement of air masses?

4. What is the Coriolis effect? How does it affect air in the northern and southern hemispheres?

5. Compare and contrast a low-pressure system and a high-pressure system.

6. **Thinking Critically** Based on what you know about the three major zones of global air circulation, form a hypothesis about why most of the world's deserts are located between 10° and 30° north and south latitudes.

SKILL REVIEW

7. **Interpreting Scientific Illustrations** Refer to the illustrations of the four types of fronts shown in *Figure 12-7*. Sketch the fronts in your science journal or use a computer graphics program to make a model of them. Label the warm and cold air masses. Indicate the direction of their movement and describe the type of weather associated with each front. For more help, refer to the *Skill Handbook*.

SECTION ASSESSMENT

1. Trade winds; surface air sinks near 30° north and south latitude and moves toward the tropics in a westerly direction. Prevailing westerlies; surface air moves mainly from west to east. Polar easterlies; surface air moves in a westerly direction from the poles toward the zone of prevailing westerlies.

2. The ITCZ is near the equator and is characterized by rising air over a large area, which creates clouds and abundant precipitation.

3. Surface weather systems that move air masses travel along the jet stream, and the intensity of these systems depends on the strength of the jet stream.

4. The motion imparted to a moving mass as a result of Earth's rotation; it causes moving air to be deflected to the right in the northern hemisphere and to the left in the southern hemisphere.

5. A low-pressure system consists of air moving inward and in a counterclockwise direction in the northern hemisphere. It is characterized by rising air, cloudy weather, and precipitation. A high-pressure system consists of air moving outward and in a clockwise direction in the northern hemisphere. It is characterized by sinking air and fair weather.

6. Air sinks, dries, and warms by compression in these areas, creating hot and dry conditions over large portions of landmasses.

7. Student sketches will vary.

Prepare

Section Background

For section content background, refer to **Rawinsonde Observation** on page 298C.

Preplanning

Refer to the Chapter Organizer on pages 298A–B.

1 Focus

Section Focus

Before presenting the lesson, display **Section Focus Transparency 34** on the overhead projector. **L1** **ELL**

Project

Have students research the number of surface-observation sites and upper-air observation sites in the United States. surface-observation sites: roughly 1000; upper-air observation sites: roughly 100 Lead students to understand that without accurate and thorough measurements of upper-atmospheric conditions, weather forecasts are likely to contain inaccuracies.

OBJECTIVES

- **Recognize** *the importance of accurate weather data.*
- **Describe** *the technology used to collect weather data.*
- **Analyze** *the strengths and weaknesses of weather observation systems.*

VOCABULARY

thermometer
barometer
anemometer
hygrometer
ceilometer
radiosonde
Doppler effect

When you visit a doctor, she or he first measures your temperature and blood pressure to make an accurate diagnosis and prescribe treatment. If the doctor's data are incomplete or inaccurate, the diagnosis is likely to be inaccurate as well. The same principle applies to meteorology. Meteorologists measure the atmospheric variables of temperature, air pressure, wind, and relative humidity to make accurate weather forecasts. The quality of the data is critical. In fact, two of the most important factors in weather forecasting are the accuracy and the density of the data—density in this case refers to the amount of data available. Just as a doctor uses several different instruments to assess your health, meteorologists use several types of technology to gather information about the atmosphere.

SURFACE DATA

One of the most common weather instruments is a **thermometer,** a device used to measure temperature. Usually, thermometers contain liquids such as mercury or alcohol, which expand when heated. The height of the liquid column indicates temperature. Another common weather instrument, the barometer, also uses mercury to obtain weather data. **Barometers** measure air pressure. In a mercury barometer, changes in air pressure are indicated by changes in the height of a column of mercury. An aneroid barometer contains a vacuum

Figure 12-10 A thermometer **(A)**, barometer **(B)**, anemometer **(C)**, and hygrometer **(D)** are commonly used weather instruments.

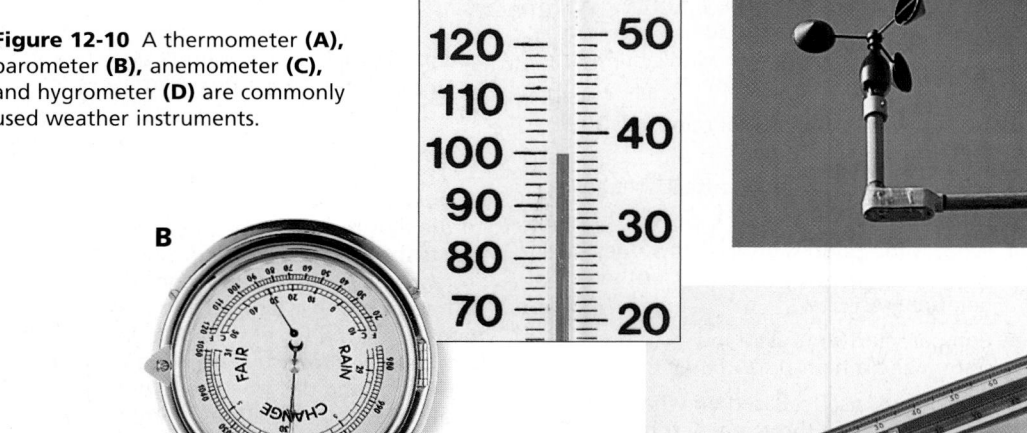

Differentiated Instruction

Visually Impaired Allow students with visual impairments to carefully handle different types of weather instruments such as thermometers and barometers. Take care that mercury thermometers and barometers do not break. **L1** **ELL**

Resource Manager

Section Focus Transparency 34 **L1** **ELL**
Study Guide for Content Mastery, p. 76 **L2**

inside a metal chamber. The chamber contracts or expands with changes in air pressure. A thermometer and a mercury barometer are shown in *Figures 12-10A* and *12-10B*.

Other Surface Instruments An **anemometer,** shown in *Figure 12-10C,* is used to measure wind speed. The simplest type of anemometer has cupped arms that rotate as the wind blows. A **hygrometer** measures relative humidity. One type of hygrometer, shown in *Figure 12-10D,* uses wet- and dry-bulb thermometers. As water evaporates from the wet bulb, the bulb cools, creating a temperature difference between the wet bulb and the dry bulb. This temperature difference is used in conjunction with a relative humidity chart to determine relative humidity. See *Appendix F* for an example of a relative humidity chart.

Automated Surface Observing System To make weather forecasts, meteorologists analyze and interpret data gathered from weather instruments. In this regard, timing is crucial. Data must be gathered at the same time at many different locations. Why? It would do no good to analyze how temperature and air pressure are interacting in the atmosphere if the two variables were measured at different times. Meteorologists need an accurate "snapshot" of the atmosphere at a particular moment in time to develop a reliable forecast. Thus, the National Weather Service in the United States has established a surface observation network across the country. Made up of some 1700 official sites, the network gathers data in a consistent manner at regular intervals—usually a minimum of once an hour. Most of these data are collected by the Automated Surface Observing System (ASOS), shown in *Figure 12-11.* In addition to the weather instruments already discussed, the ASOS uses a rain gauge for measuring rainfall, as well as a **ceilometer,** which measures the height of cloud layers and estimates the amount of sky covered by clouds. You'll learn more about the ASOS in this chapter's *Science & Technology* feature.

UPPER-LEVEL DATA

While surface weather data are important, the weather that we experience is largely the result of changes that take place high in the troposphere. To make accurate forecasts, meteorologists must gather atmospheric data at heights of up to 30 000 m. This is a more formidable task than gathering surface data, and therefore it requires more sophisticated technology.

Figure 12-11 This automated weather system measures surface data.

12.3 *Gathering Weather Data* **313**

Figure 12-12 Radiosondes are used to gather upper-level weather data.

At present, the instrument of choice for gathering upper-level data is a balloon-borne package of sensors called a **radiosonde,** shown in *Figure 12-12.* The sensors on a radiosonde measure temperature, air pressure, and humidity. These readings are constantly sent back by radio signal to a ground station that tracks the movements of the radiosonde. Tracking is a crucial component of upper-level observations—meteorologists can determine wind speed and direction by tracking how fast and in what direction the radiosonde is moving. The various data are plotted on a chart, giving meteorologists a profile of the temperature, pressure, humidity, wind speed, and wind direction of a particular part of the troposphere. Such charts are used to forecast atmospheric changes that affect surface weather. While radiosondes provide accurate snapshots of atmospheric conditions, they are quite expensive. It is hoped that in the future, data from satellites will replace or greatly supplement radiosonde observations.

WEATHER RADAR

There are thousands of surface observation sites and 100 upper-level observation sites across the United States. Yet the data from these sites cannot pinpoint where rain is falling at any given moment. For that purpose, a weather radar system is needed. The term *radar* stands for "radio detecting and ranging." A radar system is made of several parts. A transmitter generates electromagnetic waves, which leave the transmitter through antennae. In weather radar systems, the waves are programmed to ignore small cloud droplets and to bounce off large raindrops. The large raindrops scatter some of the radio waves. These scattered waves, or echoes as they are often called, are received by other antennae. An amplifier increases the wave signals of the scattered waves. A computer then processes the signals and displays them on a screen. From this, meteorologists can compute the distance to the raindrops and the location of the rain relative to the receiving antennae. The radar system rotates in a circle, allowing meteorologists to gauge where rain is falling within the radar's range—usually an area with a diameter of about 400 km.

314 CHAPTER 12 *Meteorology*

Across the Curriculum

Physics The Doppler effect is used in astronomy as evidence that the universe is expanding. In 1924, Edwin Hubble used a spectrograph to study light from other galaxies. He noticed a redshift in the light from galaxies beyond the Local Group, which is the cluster that includes the Milky Way. The Doppler effect in light causes redshifts, or the lengthening of the wavelengths of light from galaxies that are moving away from Earth. Galaxies that are approaching Earth demonstrate blueshifts, or the shortening of their wavelengths of light. Because all galaxies outside of the Local Group show redshifts in their spectra, the galaxies are moving away from Earth—evidence that the universe is expanding.

Doppler Radar Many advanced weather radar systems take advantage of a phenomenon called the Doppler effect. The **Doppler effect** is the change in wave frequency that occurs in energy, such as sound or light, as that energy moves toward or away from an observer. You've probably noticed that sounds produced by a horn from an approaching train change once the train has passed. Look at *Figure 12-13.* As the train approaches, the frequency and pitch of the sound coming from the horn are high. As the train passes, the frequency and pitch lower. This is the Doppler effect in action. Meteorologists use Doppler radar, which is based on the Doppler effect, to plot the speed at which raindrops move toward or away from a radar station. Because the motion of the moving raindrops is caused by wind, Doppler radar provides a good estimation of the wind speeds associated with precipitation areas, including those that are experiencing severe weather such as thunderstorms and tornados. The ability to measure wind speeds gives Doppler radar a distinct advantage over conventional weather radar systems.

WEATHER SATELLITES

In addition to communications, one of the main uses of satellites in orbit around Earth is to observe weather. Cameras mounted aboard a weather satellite take photos of Earth at regular intervals. These photos are beamed back to ground stations and their data are plotted on maps. Unlike weather radar, which tracks precipitation but not clouds, satellites track clouds but not necessarily precipitation. By combining data from the two types of technology, meteorologists can determine where both clouds and precipitation are occurring.

Figure 12-13 As the train approaches, the sound waves ahead of it are compressed. These short waves have a high frequency, so the horn sounds high. Behind the train, the sound waves are stretched out. These longer waves have a lower frequency, so the horn sounds lower.

12.3 *Gathering Weather Data* **315**

Resource Manager

Teaching Transparency 33 L2 ELL

Collaborative Learning

Doppler radar measures the motion of atmospheric particles toward and away from a radar receiver. Have students explain how Doppler radar can detect a tornado within a developing thunderstorm. When atmospheric particles moving both toward and away from the radar show up on the radar immediately next to each other, they indicate the presence of the tight wind circulation characteristic of a tornado.

Using an Analogy

To demonstrate the need for infrared satellite imagery, have students imagine trying to take a photograph in a dark closet. The photo would not turn out because of the lack of light. Meteorologists face the same problem when they try to photograph the dark side of Earth. The technology of infrared imagery was developed in part to obtain images of all parts of Earth's surface during day and night.

Interpreting the Illustration

Figure 12-13 Have students brainstorm other examples of the Doppler effect. For instance, students may note that the frequency and pitch of an ambulance siren also change when the ambulance approaches or passes an observer.

NY Core Curriculum Standards

Page 314: St 2 KI 1, 2, & 3, St 4 KI 2.1c, 2.1d, & 2.1g
Page 315: St 2 KI 1, 2, & 3, St 4 KI 2.1c, 2.1d, & 2.1g, St 7 KI 2

Check for Understanding

Enrichment

Have students use what they have learned in this section to describe in their science journals the equipment they would need to set up a fully functioning weather observatory. The observatory should be capable of monitoring surface and upper-air data, as well as large-scale cloud and precipitation patterns.

Reteach

Linguistic Ask students to each make a data table listing the various weather instruments that they learned about in this section and what the instruments are used to measure.

✓Assessment

Portfolio On a partly cloudy day, have students take photographs or draw sketches of the sky once every 5 minutes for about 30 minutes. Students should take each photo or draw each sketch from the same spot and the same angle. Have students create a time-lapse view of how the sky changes over the course of 30 minutes. Students should relate this project to the use of satellite imagery to detect the motion of large-scale weather systems. **L2** **ELL** **P**

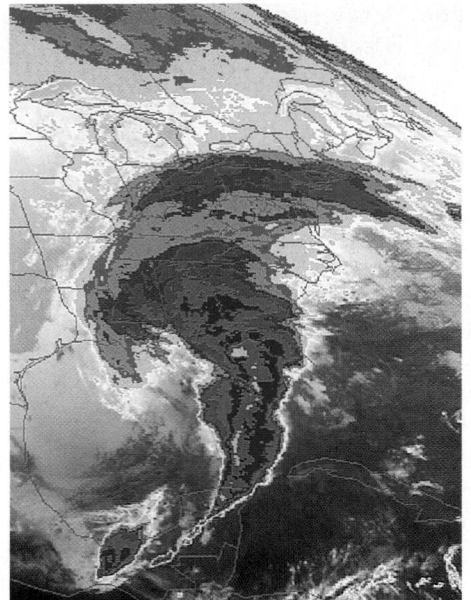

Figure 12-14 This infrared image shows a huge storm system over the eastern United States.

Infrared Imagery Weather satellites use both visible light and invisible radiation to observe the atmosphere. The satellites discussed thus far use cameras that need visible light to take photos. When such a satellite is observing a portion of Earth that is in darkness, however, its cameras are useless. Thus, some satellites are designed to use infrared imagery. Infrared imagery detects differences in thermal energy, which are used to map either cloud cover or surface temperatures. In an infrared image, such as the one shown in *Figure 12-14,* objects that radiate warmth at slightly different frequencies show up as different colors. As you learned in Chapter 11, different types of clouds form at different levels of the atmosphere, which are characterized by different temperatures. Infrared images allow meteorologists to determine the temperature of a cloud. From this, they can infer what type it is and estimate its height. Infrared imagery is especially useful in detecting strong thunderstorms that extend to great heights in the atmosphere and consequently show up as very cold areas on an infrared image. Because the strength of a thunderstorm is related to its height, infrared imagery can be used to establish a storm's potential to produce severe weather.

SECTION ASSESSMENT

1. If your goal was to vastly improve the density of weather data in the United States, would you focus on gathering more surface data or more upper-level data? Explain.

2. What is the main advantage of Doppler radar over conventional weather radar?

3. Compare and contrast infrared imagery and visible-light imagery.

4. What is the main disadvantage of radiosondes?

5. **Thinking Critically** All else being equal, would you expect weather forecasts to be more accurate for the state of Kansas or a Caribbean island? Why?

SKILL REVIEW

6. **Concept Mapping** Use the following terms to construct a concept map about instruments that gather surface weather data. For more help, refer to the *Skill Handbook.*

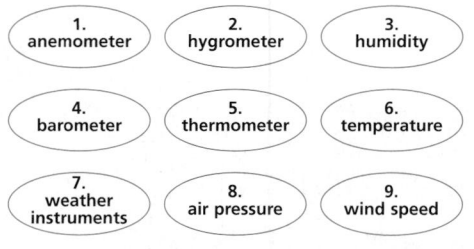

earthgeu.com/self_check_quiz

SECTION ASSESSMENT

1. Upper air data; there are already many more surface-observation sites than upper-air sites. More upper-air sites are needed to make a sufficient network.
2. Doppler radar can detect wind speeds.
3. Infrared imagery detects differences in thermal energy and thus can be used to take images of the dark side of Earth. Visible light imagery requires light. The photographs show clouds and other features as humans would see them.

4. They are expensive.
5. Kansas; it is in the middle of a country with a well-established weather-observation network.
6. top layer of concept map: 7; second layer: 1, 2, 4, and 5 in any order; third layer: 1 should be connected to 9, 2 should be connected to 3, 4 should be connected to 8, and 5 should be connected to 6

SECTION 12.4 *Weather Analysis*

After weather observations are gathered, meteorologists plot the data on a map, using station models for individual cities or towns. A **station model** is a record of weather data for a particular site at a particular time. Meteorological symbols, such as the ones shown in *Figure 12-15,* are used to represent weather data in a station model. (For a more complete list of the symbols that meteorologists use to represent weather data, see *Appendix E.*) A station model allows meteorologists to fit a large amount of data into a small space. It also gives meteorologists a uniform way of communicating weather data. You'll use station models and weather maps to forecast the weather in the *Mapping GeoLab* at the end of this chapter.

SURFACE ANALYSIS

Station models provide information for individual sites. To plot data nationwide or globally, meteorologists use **isopleths,** which are lines that connect points of equal or constant values. The values represent different weather variables, such as pressure or temperature. Lines of equal pressure, for example, are called isobars; lines of equal temperature are called isotherms. The lines themselves are similar to the contour lines—lines of equal elevation—that you studied in Chapter 2. Just as you can make inferences about elevation by studying contour intervals on a map, you can also make inferences about weather by studying isobars or isotherms on a map. For instance, you can tell how fast wind is blowing in an area by noting how closely isobars are spaced. Isobars that are close together indicate a large

OBJECTIVES

- **Analyze** *a basic surface weather chart.*
- **Distinguish** *between analog and digital forecasting.*
- **Describe** *problems with long-term forecasts.*

VOCABULARY

station model
isopleth
digital forecast
analog forecast

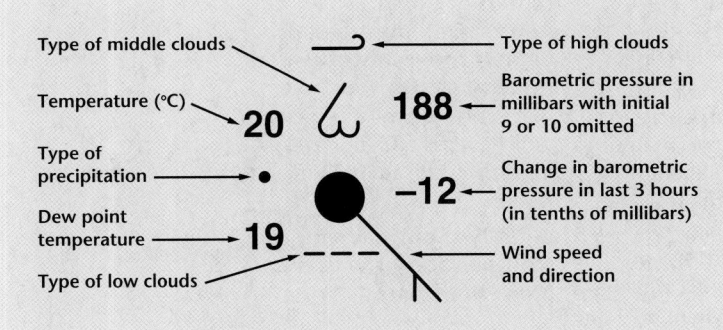

Figure 12-15 A station model shows weather data for a particular area at a particular time.

12.4 *Weather Analysis* **317**

Section 12.4
ENVIRONMENTAL CONNECTION

Prepare

Section Background

For section content background, refer to **Weather Forecasts** and **Weather Analysis** on page 298D.

Preplanning

Refer to the Chapter Organizer on pages 298A–B.

1 Focus

Section Focus

Before presenting the lesson, display **Section Focus Transparency 35** on the overhead projector. **L1** **ELL**

Tying to Previous Knowledge

Have students review the concept of map legends from Chapter 2. Tell students that station models are basically map legends that show weather variables in symbolic forms.

Problem-Solving Lab

Purpose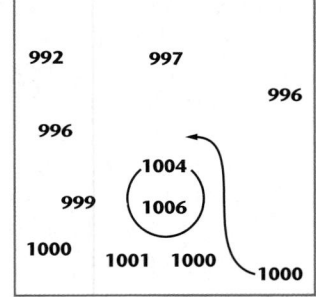
Students will analyze pressure data on a surface weather map.

Process Skills
interpret scientific illustrations, analyze data, predict

Teaching Strategies
Review topographic maps and contour lines, which students learned about in Chapter 2. Tell students that isobars are similar to contour lines in that they connect points of equal values.

Analysis
1 & 2. Isobars on diagrams should connect points of equal air pressure.

Thinking Critically
3. 4 mb
4. A blue H should be drawn inside the 1004 isobar.
5. The H is a high-pressure system normally associated with fair weather.

✓Assessment

Skill Have students draw arrows to show wind direction around the low- and high-pressure centers in their diagrams. Tell students that the diagrams should represent an area in the northern hemisphere. Wind flows counterclockwise and inward around a low-pressure center and clockwise and outward around a high-pressure center. ⓛ2 🔲

pressure difference over a small area. A large pressure difference causes strong winds. Conversely, isobars that are spread far apart indicate a small difference in pressure. Winds in these areas would be light. As shown in *Figure 12-16*, isobars also indicate the locations of high- and low-pressure systems. This information is especially useful when combined with isotherms, which identify temperature gradients and, consequently, frontal systems. Using isobars, isotherms, and station-model data, meteorologists can analyze current weather conditions for a particular time and place. This is crucial information—meteorologists must understand current weather conditions before they can move on to forecasting the weather. You'll learn more about isobars in the *Problem-Solving Lab* on this page.

SHORT-TERM FORECASTS

In the early days of weather forecasting, meteorologists simply observed current weather conditions, compared these conditions to those that had occurred a day or two before, and then extrapolated the changes a day or two into the future. The resulting positions of

Problem-Solving Lab

Interpreting Scientific Illustrations

Create and analyze isobars on a weather map Areas of high and low pressure can be indicated on a weather map by lines of approximately equal pressure called isobars.

Analysis

1. On a blank piece of paper, trace the diagram shown here, along with the pressure values at various locations, which are given in millibars (mb).

2. A 1004-mb isobar that encircles one location on this map has been drawn and labeled. Complete and label the 1000-mb isobar that has been started. Finally, draw a 996-mb isobar and a 992-mb isobar. The isobars may not

completely encircle a location in a map of this scale.

Thinking Critically

3. What is the contour interval of the isobars on this map?

4. A blue letter *H* and a red letter *L* in the centers of closed isobars mark the areas of highest and lowest pressure, respectively. On your map, place a blue *H* or a red *L*—whichever is appropriate—inside the closed 1004-mb isobar.

5. What type of weather is commonly associated with this pressure system?

991	994	992
992	997	
		996
996		
	1004	
999	1006	
1000	1001 1000	1000

Resource Manager

Teaching Transparency 34 ⓛ2 ELL
Laboratory Manual, pp. 93–96 ⓛ2

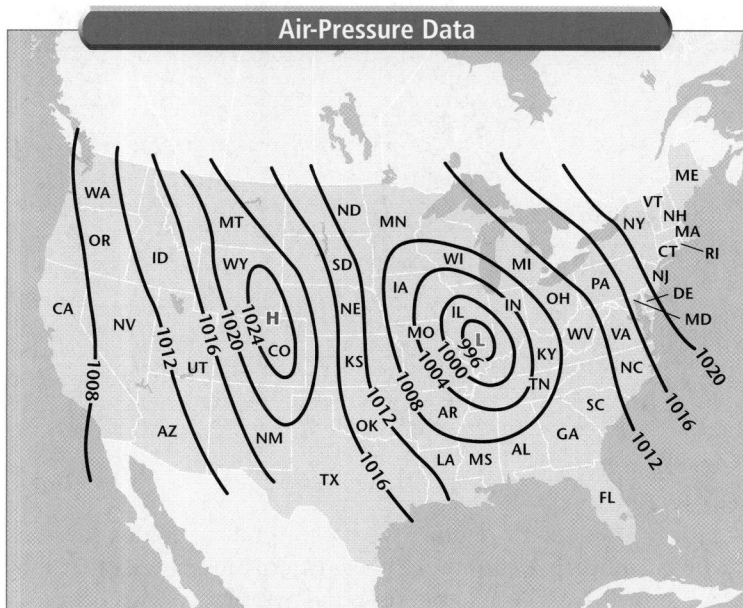

Air-Pressure Data

Figure 12-16 This map shows air-pressure data for the United States. *Where would you expect light winds?*

the weather systems served as the basis for their forecasts. Weather forecasting, however, is too complicated to rely on extrapolating the past movements of weather systems. Weather systems change directions, speed, and intensity with time. These changes take place in response to changes in the upper atmosphere, so a reliable forecast must analyze data from different levels in the atmosphere.

Digital Forecasts The key to unlocking the forecast puzzle lies in the fact that the atmosphere behaves much like a fluid. Thus, we can apply many of the same principles to the atmosphere and its variables, such as temperature, pressure, density, and so on, that we can apply to a fluid. Furthermore, these principles can be expressed in mathematical equations to determine how atmospheric variables change with time. For meteorologists to solve these equations on a global or national level would take an impossibly large amount of time. Fortunately, high-speed computers can do the job. A forecast such as this that relies on numerical data is known as a **digital forecast.** Digital forecasting is the main method used by modern meteorologists, such as the one shown in *Figure 12-17.* It is highly dependent on the density of the data available—basically, the more data, the more accurate the forecast.

Figure 12-17 This meteorologist is preparing a weather forecast.

12.4 *Weather Analysis* **319**

Using an Analogy

Have students imagine heating alphabet soup in a pot until it boils, then trying to predict where each of the letters will be a minute later. This is similar to weather forecasting in that meteorologists must attempt to predict how all the variables in the atmosphere at various levels will change with time.

Activity

Challenge students to count to 1 million. After they have reached 100 or 200 and realized how tedious this task is, tell them that weather forecasting on a national or global level involves numerous weather variables for thousands of places. The interactions of these weather variables can be expressed as mathematical equations, but the task of mentally calculating the equations would take an extremely long time. That's why high-speed computers are used in digital forecasting, a type of weather forecasting that students will learn about in this section.

NATIONAL GEOGRAPHIC

CD-ROM
Introduction to Weather

Interpreting the Illustration

Figure 12-16 Where would you expect light winds? Light winds are likely occurring where isobars are spread far apart. On the map, these places include Nevada, Arizona, Texas, and Georgia, among others.

NY Core Curriculum Standards

Page 318: St 1 Math KI 2 & 3, St 4 KI 2.1c & 2.1g, St 6 KI 1, 2, & 5

Page 319: St 1 Math KI 1, St 2 KI 1, 2, & 3, St 4 KI 2.1c & 2.1g, St 6 KI 5, St 7 KI 1

319

Digital methods have been applied to different models of Earth's climate to analyze the effects of global warming, the greenhouse effect, volcanic eruptions, and changes in climate caused by variations in Earth's orbit and rotation.

Discussion

Have students describe which type of air mass would most likely move into an area after a cold front passes. Also ask them what types of air masses might be on either side of a stationary front. Lead students to understand that a front is simply the boundary between two air masses, and not the warm or cold air mass itself.

Interpreting the Illustration

Figure 12-18 Have students infer the benefits of short-term and long-term forecasts. What might these forecasts be used for? Answers will vary. Students may say that short-term forecasts are used to issue weather warnings and alerts. Long-term forecasts are used for agricultural purposes. Accept all reasonable answers.

Figure 12-18 This graph shows that forecast uncertainty increases with time.

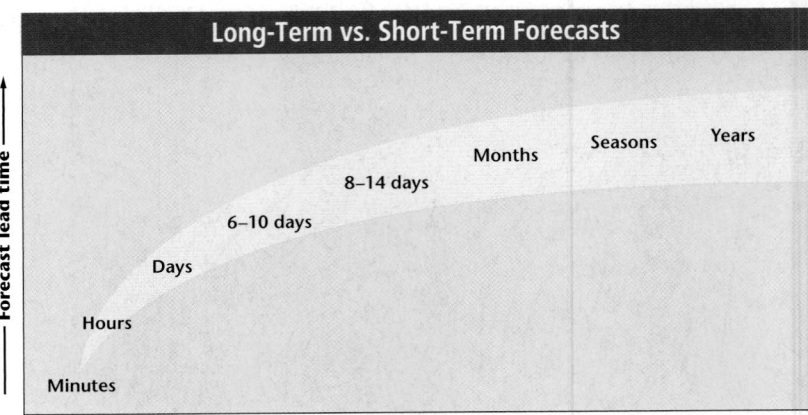

Analog Forecasts Another type of forecast, an **analog forecast,** involves comparing current weather patterns to patterns that took place in the past. The assumption is that weather systems behave in a similar fashion. Analog forecasting is so called because meteorologists look for a pattern from the past that is analogous, or similar to, a current pattern. To ensure an accurate analog forecast, meteorologists must find a past event that is similar to a current event through all levels of the atmosphere, and also over a large area. This is the main drawback of analog forecasting. Still, analog forecasting is useful for conducting monthly or seasonal forecasts, which are based mainly on the past behavior of cyclic weather patterns. Let's explore the strengths and weaknesses of long-term forecasts.

LONG-TERM FORECASTS

Regardless of the forecasting method used, all forecasts become less reliable when they attempt to predict long-term changes in the weather. Why? Even high-tech computers cannot model every factor that affects the weather. Recall that mountains, valleys, rivers, lakes, cities, and countless other features on Earth's surface affect the amount of heat absorbed in a particular location. This, in turn, affects the pressure and therefore the wind of that area, which in turn affects cloud formation and virtually all other aspects of the weather. Over time, all these factors interact to create progressively more complicated scenarios.

The most accurate and detailed forecasts are short-term in nature, as shown in *Figure 12-18.* For hourly forecasts, extrapolation is a reliable forecasting method because the current weather is dominated by small-scale weather features that are readily observable by radar and satellite. Forecasts in the one- to three-day range, however, are no longer based on the movement of observed clouds and precipitation, which change by the hour. These forecasts are dependent on the behavior of larger surface and upper-level features, such as low-pressure systems. A one- to three-day forecast can somewhat accurately predict whether the day will be rainy or dry, and, if rainy, when the precipitation will occur. At this range, however, the forecast will not be able to pinpoint an exact temperature or sky condition at a specific time.

Accuracy Declines with Time At the four- to seven-day range, forecasts must attempt to predict changes in surface weather systems based on circulation patterns throughout the troposphere and lower stratosphere. Meteorologists can estimate each day's weather but can offer little detail as to when or what exact weather conditions will occur. At the one- to two-week range, forecasts are based on changes in large-scale circulation patterns. Thus, these forecasts are vague and based mainly on analogous conditions.

Long-term forecasts involving months and seasons are based largely on patterns or cycles. Several of these cycles, such as the one shown in *Figure 12-19*, involve changes in the atmosphere, ocean currents, and solar activity, all of which might be occurring at the same time. The key to future improvement in weather forecasts lies in identifying the many influences involved, understanding these influences and how they interact, and finally, determining their ultimate effect on weather over progressively longer periods of time. 🍃

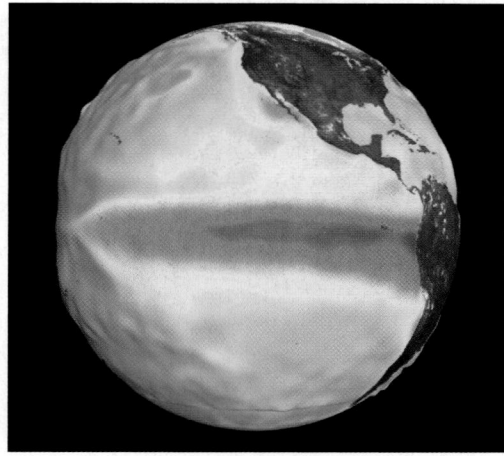

Figure 12-19 Changes in ocean-surface temperatures can trigger changes in weather patterns. This satellite image shows a cyclic event known as El Niño wherein the Pacific Ocean warms along the equator and triggers short-term climatic changes.

SECTION ASSESSMENT

1. Find an example of a station model in your local newspaper and describe the symbols on the model.

2. Compare and contrast analog and digital forecasting.

3. Explain why long-term forecasts aren't always accurate.

4. **Thinking Critically** Based on what you have learned about digital forecasting, what single improvement do you think would be necessary to increase the reliability of this type of forecasting?

SKILL REVIEW

5. **Forming a Hypothesis** For a time period of three days or less, hypothesize which would be more accurate: digital forecasting or analog forecasting. Explain your hypothesis. For more help, refer to the *Skill Handbook*.

earthgeu.com/self_check_quiz

SECTION ASSESSMENT

1. Descriptions should correspond to the weather map symbols in Appendix E.

2. Analog forecasting compares the current positions and strengths of weather systems with similar, or analogous, past weather events. Digital forecasting relies on principles of physics and mathematics to predict how atmospheric variables will change with time.

3. Long-term forecasts must analyze all the factors that will affect forecasts. Often, changes in these factors cannot be predicted with any degree of accuracy beyond a three-day range.

4. Digital forecasts are highly dependent on the density of the data. Thus, improving the data network would likely improve the accuracy of digital forecasts.

5. The analog method may work well during the first day. However, it could not accurately predict further changes in the size, intensity, and movement of a weather system. The digital method would be most accurate over a three-day period.

Check for Understanding

Discussion
Tell students that new satellite technology enables better moisture-level measurements to be made throughout the atmosphere. Ask students how this might help meteorologists to produce digital weather forecasts. Additional moisture data would result in more accurate digital forecasts because the density of the data would be improved.

Reteach

Linguistic Have students each make a data table that lists the three main types of weather forecasts and includes the strengths and weaknesses of each forecast method. Students should also include which method would be most accurate for short-term and long-term forecasts. **L2**

✔Assessment

Skill For three consecutive days, have students obtain a weather map from a newspaper or the Internet. On the fourth day, students should use the extrapolation method to predict the location of high- and low-pressure systems and fronts. Also, students should predict the weather for their area, then compare their predictions to actual weather conditions.

Mapping GeoLab

Mapping GeoLab

Interpreting a Weather Map

It's time to put your knowledge of meteorology into action. The surface weather map on the following page shows actual weather data for the United States. In this activity, you will use the station models, isobars, and pressure systems on the map to forecast the weather.

Time Allotment

one class period

Process Skills

analyze data, communicate, interpret data, predict, interpret scientific illustrations

Preparation

Special Instructions

Review the weather symbols for high- and low-pressure systems and fronts. Be sure that students have completed the Problem-Solving Lab on page 318. Refer students to Appendix E, which shows station-model symbols. Students will need this appendix to answer the Analyze questions.

Procedure

Teaching Strategies

To increase student proficiency in using SI, have students give their answers in both English units and SI units when appropriate.

Troubleshooting

Team students with visual impairments with students who can easily discern small print.

Data and Observations

Students will measure distances, interpret map symbols, and apply meteorological principles to make conclusions and predictions.

Preparation

Problem
How can you use a surface weather map to interpret information about current weather and to forecast future weather?

Materials
pencil
ruler

Procedure

1. The map scale is given in nautical miles. Refer to the scale when calculating distances.
2. The unit for isobars is millibars (mb). In station models, pressure readings are abbreviated. For example, 1021.9 mb is plotted on a station model as 219 but read as 1021.9.
3. Wind shafts point in the direction from which the wind is blowing.

Analyze

1. What is the contour interval of the isobars?
2. What are the highest and lowest isobars? Where are they located?
3. In which direction are the winds blowing across Texas and Louisiana?
4. What and where are the coldest and warmest temperatures that you can find in the continental United States?

Conclude & Apply

1. Would you expect the weather in Georgia and Florida to be clear or rainy? Why?
2. Both of the low-pressure systems in eastern Canada and off the Oregon coast are moving toward the east at about 15 mph. What kind of weather would you predict for Oregon and for northern New York for the next few hours? Explain.

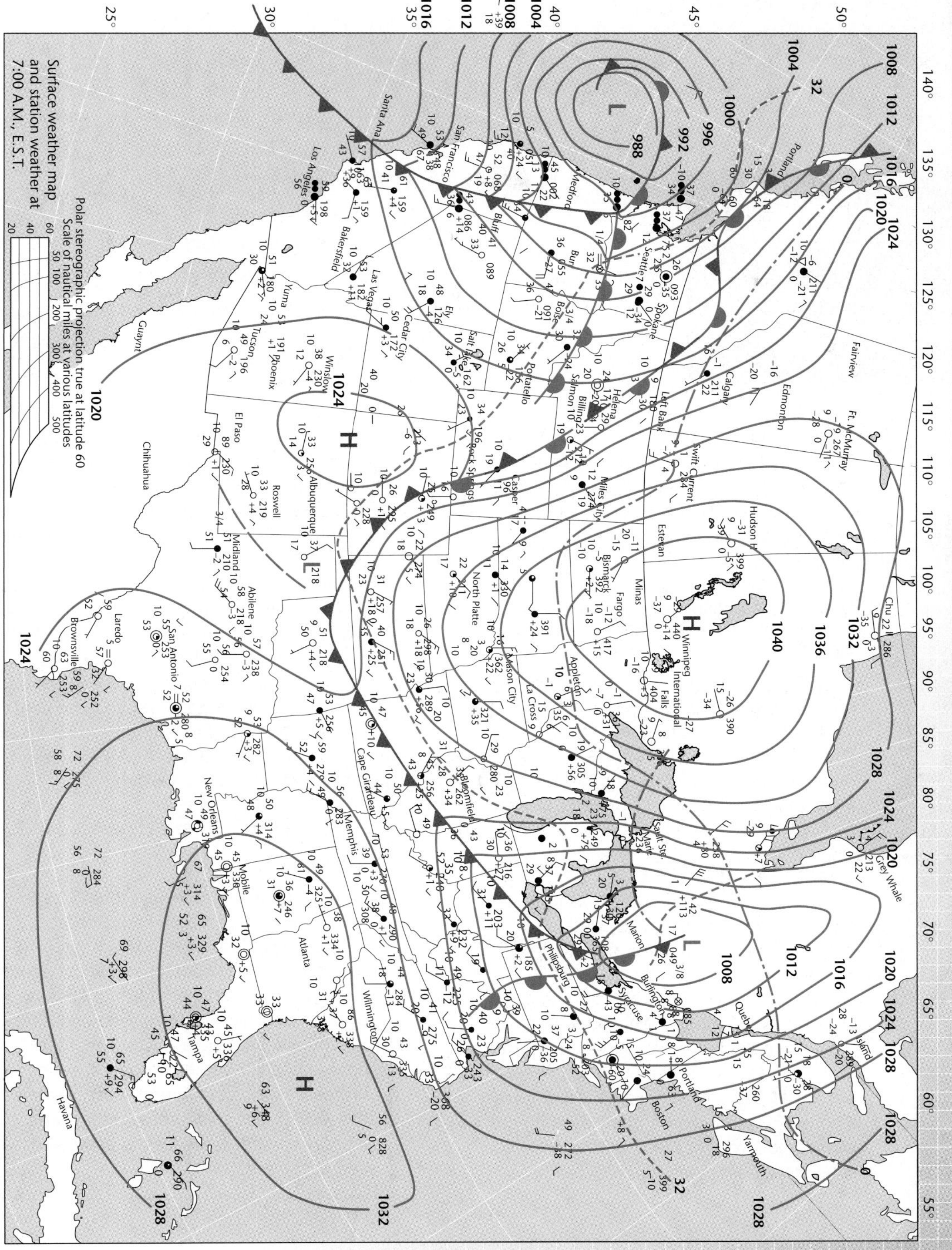

The weather map occupies the left portion of the page. Map labels include the map title and legend:

Surface weather map and station weather at 7:00 A.M., E.S.T.

Polar stereographic projection true at latitude 60

Scale of nautical miles at various latitudes
20 40 60
100 200 300 400 500

Analyze

1. 4 mb
2. The highest isobar is 1040 mb and is around the high-pressure center in South-Central Canada. The lowest isobar is 988 mb and is around the low-pressure center off the coast of Oregon.
3. They are blowing mainly from the south or southeast.
4. The coldest is −12°F at Fargo, North Dakota. The warmest is 65°F at both Miami and Key West, Florida.

Conclude & Apply

1. It would probably be clear because the high-pressure system along the coast would cause air to sink and dry out.
2. The low-pressure systems would cause air to rise and produce clouds and rain.

✓Assessment

Skill Have students find your area on the map. Based on the data shown in the map, students should use the extrapolation method to forecast the next day's weather for your location. **L2**

P

Mapping GeoLab **323**

Resource Manager

GeoLab and MiniLab Worksheets, pp. 48–50 **L2**

NY Core Curriculum Standards

Page 322: St 4 KI 2.1g, St 6 KI 1, 2, & 5

Page 323: St 4 KI 2.1g, St 6 KI 1, 2, & 5

Purpose

This feature describes the latest weather-observation technology and explores some of the controversy surrounding its use.

Content Background

Lowered visibility is not the only weather-related danger that aircraft face as they attempt to land or take off. Strong winds called microbursts have caused planes to crash on the runway. Microbursts are associated with severe thunderstorms. These powerful winds are brief in duration and thus hard to detect. Their strong downward force can create sudden headwinds and tailwinds that can drive a plane into the ground.

Teaching Strategies

Have students research the ASOS system using information available from the National Weather Service, the Federal Aviation Administration, or the National Air Traffic Controllers Association. Students should each make a diagram of the system and label its parts.

Tracking Atmospheric Change

On July 16, 1999, John F. Kennedy Jr. piloted a small private plane bound for Martha's Vineyard. The plane never reached its destination. Searchers determined that the plane crashed into the Atlantic Ocean, killing all three people on board. While no one will know exactly what happened, the dense fog may have been a factor in the crash.

Safety is a priority in the aviation industry. Pilots must be aware of weather conditions to avoid crashing when landing or taking off. Prior to 1990, National Weather Service personnel were responsible for gathering and communicating weather data to pilots. These professionals collected data on air pressure, wind speed, temperature, cloud cover, and precipitation.

ASOS

Concern about possible human errors prompted scientists to develop a more efficient system for transmitting weather data to pilots. The resulting computerized system, called the Automated Surface Observing System (ASOS), is now the cornerstone of weather forecasting and communication in this country.

The Pros and Cons

Today, more than 1000 ASOS units are in operation at major airports, continuously recording air pressure, temperature, wind speed and direction, runway visibility, cloud ceiling, and precipitation intensity. Data are automatically updated every minute. While human observations are based on what can be seen from a given vantage point, computerized observations are not affected by varying light and terrain conditions. For this reason, many aviation professionals believe that ASOS data are more consistent than manually collected data.

Some aviation professionals, however, disagree. The National Air Traffic Controllers Association believes that human observers were replaced by machines primarily to save money, and that the loss of trained weather observers is detrimental to aviation safety. On the evening that Kennedy's plane went down, the ASOS indicated that visibility was 13 to 16 km. In actuality, visibility was reported to be so poor by other pilots that the lights of Martha's Vineyard could not be seen from the air. The National Weather Service admits that the ASOS needs to be refined and continues to implement upgrades. Still, this group insists that widespread use of the ASOS will reduce weather-related aviation accidents.

Activity

Does your local airport use the ASOS? Go to the Earth Science Web Site at earthgeu.com to research which airports use the ASOS, or contact your local airport. Write to airport officials for statistics on aviation accidents both prior to and after the installation of the ASOS. Has there been a change in the number of aviation accidents since the airport implemented the ASOS? Use this information to write a short opinion piece on the continued use of the ASOS.

324 CHAPTER 12 *Meteorology*

Activity

Reports will vary depending on information gathered by students. Students should back up their opinions with scientific facts.

NY Core Curriculum Standards

Page 324: St 2 KI 1, 2, & 3, St 7 KI 2

Page 325: St 4 KI 2.1c, 2.1d, 2.1e, 2.1f, 2.1g, 2.1h, 2.1i, & 2.2c, St 6 KI 1 & 2

Summary

SECTION 12.1

The Causes of Weather

Main Ideas
- Meteorology is the study of the atmosphere. Weather is the current state of the atmosphere, and climate is the average weather over a long period of time.
- An air mass is a large body of air that takes on the characteristics of the area over which it forms.

Vocabulary
air mass (p. 301)
air mass modification (p. 304)
climate (p. 300)
meteorology (p. 299)
weather (p. 300)

SECTION 12.2

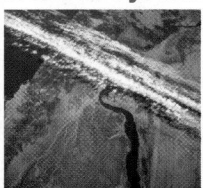

Weather Systems

Main Ideas
- The Coriolis effect deflects air to the right in the northern hemisphere and to the left in the southern hemisphere. The Coriolis effect combines with the heat imbalance found on Earth to form the trade winds, prevailing westerlies, and polar easterlies.
- Weather in the middle latitudes is strongly influenced by fast-moving, high-altitude jet streams.
- A front is the boundary between two air masses of different densities. The four types of fronts are cold fronts, warm fronts, occluded fronts, and stationary fronts.

Vocabulary
Coriolis effect (p. 305)
front (p. 308)
jet stream (p. 307)
polar easterlies (p. 307)
prevailing westerlies (p. 306)
trade winds (p. 305)

SECTION 12.3

Gathering Weather Data

Main Ideas
- Two of the most important factors in weather forecasting are the accuracy and the density of the data. Surface data are easier to gather than upper-level data.
- The most common instrument for collecting upper-level data is a balloon-borne radiosonde. Radiosondes measure temperature, pressure, humidity, wind speed, and wind direction.
- Weather radar pinpoints exactly where precipitation occurs. Weather satellites use both visible-light imagery and infrared imagery to observe weather conditions on Earth.

Vocabulary
anemometer (p. 313)
barometer (p. 312)
ceilometer (p. 313)
Doppler effect (p. 315)
hygrometer (p. 313)
radiosonde (p. 314)
thermometer (p. 312)

SECTION 12.4

Weather Analysis

Main Ideas
- A station model is a record of weather data for a particular site at a particular time. On a weather map, lines of equal pressure are called isobars and lines of equal temperature are called isotherms.
- Digital forecasting uses numerical data. Analog forecasting compares current weather patterns to patterns that took place in the past. All forecasts become less reliable when they attempt to predict long-term changes in the weather.

Vocabulary
analog forecast (p. 320)
digital forecast (p. 319)
isopleth (p. 317)
station model (p. 317)

earthgeu.com/vocabulary_puzzlemaker

Main Ideas

Summary statements can be used by students to review the major concepts of the chapter.

VOCABULARY PuzzleMaker

For additional help with vocabulary, have students access the Vocabulary Puzzlemaker online.

earthgeu.com/ vocabulary_puzzlemaker

0:00 *Out of Time?*

If time does not permit teaching the entire chapter, use the GeoDigest at the end of the unit as an overview.

Earth Science Online

Be sure to check the Earth Science Web Site for links to chapter material:
earthgeu.com

GLENCOE *Technology*

Videotape/DVD
MindJogger Videoquizzes
Chapter 12: *Meteorology*
Have students work in groups as they play the videoquiz game to review key chapter concepts.

Resource Manager

Chapter Assessment, pp. 67–72
MindJogger Videoquizzes DVD/VHS
ExamView® Pro CD-ROM
Performance Assessment in Earth Science

Understanding Main Ideas

1. b
2. b
3. b
4. c
5. b
6. c
7. b
8. d
9. a
10. c
11. Meteorology is the study of atmospheric phenomena, weather describes the current state of the atmosphere, and climate describes long-term averages of weather.
12. point C
13. Point B may experience thunderstorms as the cold front passes. Point B should also experience colder temperatures as the cold front passes.

Applying Main Ideas

14. It is much easier to position data-gathering equipment on land than over the open ocean.
15. Doppler radar is technology based on the Doppler effect; it plots the speed at which raindrops are moving toward or away from a radar station.
16. It takes on the characteristics of the surface it is traveling over.

Understanding Main Ideas

1. Which term best describes a snowflake?
   a. hydrosphere
   c. lithometeor
   b. hydrometeor
   d. electrometeor

2. What winds blow between 30° and 60° north and south latitude?
   a. trade winds
   c. polar easterlies
   b. prevailing westerlies
   d. jet streams

3. What would be the most likely classification for an air mass originating over Alaska and Canada?
   a. mT
   c. cT
   b. cP
   d. mP

4. What would be the most likely dominant air mass over the eastern United States in summer?
   a. cT
   c. mT
   b. cP
   d. mP

5. What instrument is used to measure the heights of the bases of clouds?
   a. radiosonde
   c. hygrometer
   b. ceilometer
   d. barometer

6. Which term describes changes in air motion resulting from Earth's rotation?
   a. jet stream
   c. Coriolis effect
   b. convergence
   d. Hadley cell

7. What forecast method is best for researching past weather events?
   a. digital
   c. extrapolation
   b. analog
   d. numerical

8. Which of the following is NOT characteristic of a high-pressure system?
   a. sinking air
   c. fair weather
   b. dense air
   d. thunderstorms

9. Which of the following would NOT be included in a station model?
   a. humidity
   c. pressure
   b. wind
   d. temperature

10. What does an anemometer measure?
    a. humidity
    c. wind speed
    b. air pressure
    d. wind direction

11. Describe the relationship among meteorology, weather, and climate.

Use the surface weather chart below to answer questions 12 and 13.

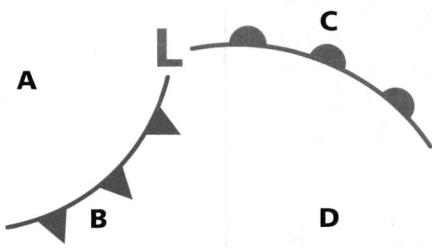

12. What location will soon experience a warm front?

13. At what location would you forecast the greatest probability of thunderstorms? At what location would you forecast the weather to turn colder over the next day?

Standardized Test Practice

1. d
2. c
3. c
4. a
5. b

Applying Main Ideas

14. Is meteorological data easier to gather on land or on water? Explain your answer.

15. What is Doppler radar?

16. What happens to an air mass as it moves away from its source region?

17. Why are rain showers common near the ITCZ?

18. In your own words, describe the global wind systems.

19. Construct a station model using the following data: temperature: –5°F; dew point: –12°F; wind: north, 20 knots; barometric pressure: 1038.5 mb; sky: clear.

Thinking Critically

20. Forecast the weather for the next 24 hours for an area experiencing the same conditions as those included in the station model you constructed in question 19.

21. Like the north pole, the south pole receives little solar radiation during the winter. Unlike the north pole, however, the south pole does not send outbreaks of extremely frigid air as far as the subtropics. Why? (Hint: You may want to study a world map to answer this question.)

22. You hear on a news report that an area has received nearly twice its normal snowfall during the winter. What can you infer about the position of the jet stream from this report?

23. Review *Figure 12-4* on page 305, which shows global wind systems, then note the relative positions of North America and Europe on a world map. Hypothesize why the winds that blow between 30° north and south latitude and the equator are called the trade winds.

earthgeu.com/standardized_test

Standardized Test Practice

1. Which of the following types of air masses are most likely to form over land near the equator?
a. mP **c.** cP
b. mT **d.** cT

2. Which wind system flows between 30° and 60° latitude north and south of the equator in an easterly direction toward the poles?
a. trade winds **c.** prevailing westerlies
b. Coriolis effect **d.** polar easterlies

INTERPRETING DATA Use the photo to answer question 3.

3. Meteorologists use many different instruments to gather atmospheric information. What is the instrument shown here called?

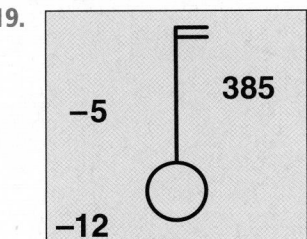

a. a hygrometer **c.** a radiosonde
b. a ceilometer **d.** radar

4. What does Doppler radar monitor?
a. the motion of moving raindrops
b. atmospheric pressure
c. temperature, air pressure, and humidity
d. the height of cloud layers

5. The data gathered by Doppler radar can be used to make a type of forecast that relies on numerical data. What is this type of forecast called?
a. an analog forecast **c.** an isopleth
b. a digital forecast **d.** ASOS

17. The ITCZ is characterized by rising, moist air, which is the basic ingredient for thunderstorms.

18. The trade winds occur between 30° north latitude and 30° south latitude, and blow in a westerly direction; the prevailing westerlies are located between 30° and 60° north latitude and between 30° and 60° south latitude, and flow in an easterly direction; the polar easterlies are located between 60° north and south latitude and the poles, and flow in a westerly direction.

19.

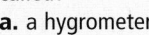

Thinking Critically

20. Clear, windy, and cold

21. Much of the southern hemisphere is covered by water, which retains heat longer than land does. Polar air is therefore more quickly modified as it moves away from the south pole.

22. It has been very close to that area. Low-pressure systems follow the jet stream—these systems produce the most precipitation.

23. These are the winds that trade ships used to sail between Europe and North America during the early colonization of the New World.

Chapter 13

The Nature of Storms

Refer to pages 8T–9T of the Teacher Guide for an explanation of the National Science Content Standards correlations.

Section	Objectives	National Science Content Standards	State/Local Standards
SECTION 13.1 **Thunderstorms** ⏱ 1 session ▱ ½ block	1. **Identify** the processes that form thunderstorms. 2. **Compare** and **contrast** different types of thunderstorms. 3. **Describe** the life cycle of a thunderstorm.	UCP.1, UCP.2, UCP.3; A.1, A.2; D.1; F.5, F.6	St 1 Math KI 2, Science KI 1, & 3, St 4 KI 2.1b, 2.1c, 2.1e, 2.1f, 2.1h, 2.1i, & 2.2b, St 6 KI 1, 2, 4, & 5
SECTION 13.2 **Severe Weather** ⏱ 1 session ▱ ½ block	4. **Explain** why some thunderstorms are more severe than others. 5. **Recognize** the dangers of severe thunderstorms, including lightning, hail, high winds, and floods. 6. **Describe** how tornadoes form.	UCP.1, UCP.3; B.6; D.1; F.5, F.6	St 2 KI 3, St 4 KI 2.1c, 2.1e, 2.1f, 2.1h, 2.1i, & 2.2b, St 6 KI 1, 4, & 5, St 7 KI 1
SECTION 13.3 **Tropical Storms** ⏱ 1 session ▱ ½ block	7. **Identify** where tropical cyclones originate. 8. **Describe** the life cycle of a tropical cyclone. 9. **Recognize** the dangers of hurricanes.	UCP.1, UCP.3; D.1; F.5, F.6	St 1 Math KI 1, 2, & 3, St 2 KI 3, St 4 KI 2.1b, 2.1c, 2.1h, 2.1i, 2.2a, 2.2b, 2.2c, & 2.2d, St 6 KI 1 & 5, St 7 KI 1
SECTION 13.4 **Recurring Weather** ⏱ 2 sessions ▱ 1 block	10. **Describe** recurring weather patterns and the problems they create. 11. **Identify** atmospheric events that cause recurring weather patterns.	UCP.1, UCP.2, UCP.3; A.1, A.2; D.1; E.1, E.2; F.5, F.6; G.3	St 1 Math KI 1, 2, 3, Science KI 1, 2, & 3, St 2 KI 1, 2, & 3, St 4 KI 2.1c, 2.1e, 2.1f, 2.1g, 2.1h, 2.1i, 2.2a, 2.2b, 2.2c, & 2.2d, St 6 KI 1, 4, & 5, St 7 KI 1 & 2

A complete Planning Guide is provided on pages 30T–32T.

⏱ The number of recommended single-period sessions

▱ The number of recommended blocks

Activity Materials

Discovery Lab *page 329*
brown paper lunch bag

GeoLab *pages 352-353*
hurricane-tracking chart, pencil

MiniLab *page 348*
ice-cube tray; clean, plastic dishwashing-detergent bottle; water; large sink or tub; metric ruler

Demo *page 335*
books

page 341
oval platter, pencil, paper

Need materials? Contact Science Kit at 1-800-828-7777 or at www.sciencekit.com on the Internet. For alternate materials, see the activity on the listed page.

Key to Teaching Strategies

L1 Level 1 activities should be appropriate for students with learning difficulties.

L2 Level 2 activities should be within the ability range of all students.

L3 Level 3 activities are designed for above-average students.

ELL ELL activities should be within the ability range of English-language learners.

COOP LEARN Cooperative Learning activities are designed for small-group work.

P These strategies represent student products that can be placed in a best-work portfolio.

▱ These strategies are useful in a block-scheduling format.

Chapter Organizer

Glencoe Exclusive!
TeacherWorks™
All-In-One Planner and Resource Center

Activities/Features	Reproducible Masters	Transparencies
Discovery Lab: Model Thunder, p. 329	**Study Guide to Content Mastery,** pp. 79–80 L2	**Section Focus Transparency 36** L1 ELL **Teaching Transparency 35** L2 ELL
	Study Guide to Content Mastery, pp. 81–82 L2 **Laboratory Manual,** pp. 97–100 L2	**Section Focus Transparency 37** L1 ELL **Teaching Transparency 36** L2 ELL
Using Math: Using Numbers, p. 344 **Internet GeoLab:** Tracking a Hurricane, pp. 352–353	**Study Guide to Content Mastery,** p. 83 L2 **Laboratory Manual,** pp. 101–104 L2	**Section Focus Transparency 38** L1 ELL **Teaching Transparency 37** L2 ELL
MiniLab: How can mild rains cause floods?, p. 348 **Problem-Solving Lab:** Making and Using Graphs, p. 350 **Science & Technology:** Taming Lightning, p. 354	**Study Guide for Content Mastery,** p. 84 L2 **GeoLab and MiniLab Worksheets,** p. 51 L2 **GeoLab and MiniLab Worksheets,** pp. 52–54 L2	**Section Focus Transparency 39** L1 ELL **Teaching Transparency 38** L2 ELL

✔Assessment

Chapter Assessment, pp. 73–78
Performance Assessment in the Science Classroom (PASC)
MindJogger Videoquiz DVD/VHS
Performance Assessment in Earth Science
ExamView® Pro CD-ROM
5 Days to the Regents Exam

GLENCOE'S
ASSESSMENT
ADVANTAGE

Additional Resources

Guided Reading Audio Program ELL
Cooperative Learning in the Science Classroom  COOP LEARN
Lesson Plans
Block Scheduling
earthgeu.com
NY Lesson Plans
NY Block Scheduling
Review Handbook for Regents Earth Science Exam

◻ NATIONAL GEOGRAPHIC — Teacher's Corner

Products Available from National Geographic Society
To order the following products, call the National Geographic Society at 1-800-368-2728:
Curriculum Kit
GeoKit: *Weather*

Videos
Weather: Come Rain Come Shine
After the Hurricane
Can't Drown This Town
Natural Disasters
Where Storms Begin

Content Background

Thunderstorm Distribution
Section 13.1

While thunderstorms are a common phenomenon throughout the world, they are most numerous in the United States, particularly in the Southeast and in the Great Plains states. The unique combination of heat, moisture, and lift provided by the clash of air masses makes the United States the thunderstorm capital of the world. Thunderstorms occur in many sizes and intensities. Some are isolated rainshowers with a few claps of thunder. Others are squall lines extending for hundreds of kilometers.

Supercells
Section 13.2

Most thunderstorms are characterized by heavy rain, thunder, lightning, and gusty winds. Under the right conditions, these storms can grow into raging tempests known as supercells. The transformation takes place as a result of various mechanisms that act to enhance the convective currents that power a storm. These currents can be strengthened by the addition of heat to the lower portions of the storm or by the cooling of the upper layers—any mechanism, in fact, that increases the vertical temperature differences in the storm's environment and therefore decreases the stability of the air that fuels the storm.

Meso-Lows
Section 13.2

The supercell concept was proposed by the late Dr. Theodore Fujita. His studies revealed that, in extreme convection cells, updrafts lift enough air to lower surface pressure and create a so-called meso-low at Earth's surface. This low, being cyclonic, acquires a counterclockwise rotation in the northern hemisphere; thus, the thunderstorm itself exhibits rotation in the updrafts. The resulting violent updrafts can produce severe weather because their ability to hold large ice pellets aloft facilitates the formation of hail, and also because they are a crucial component in the development of tornadoes.

Multiple Learning Styles

- **Linguistic** Enrichment, p. 331, Reteach, p. 340, Project, p. 342, Earth Science Journal, p. 345
- **Visual-Spatial** Reteach, p. 333
- **Interpersonal** Project, p. 334, Reteach, p. 346
- **Kinesthetic** Project, p. 336, Modeling, p. 345
- **Logical-Mathematical** Project, p. 349
- **Intrapersonal** Reteach, p. 351

GLENCOE Technology

The following multimedia resources are available from Glencoe.

The Infinite Voyage Series
Living with Disaster
Vocabulary Puzzlemaker
TeacherWorks™ CD-ROM
MindJogger Videoquizzes DVD/VHS
ExamView® Pro CD-ROM
Interactive Chalkboard CD-ROM

Chapter Organizer

Cyclone Safety
Section 13.3

People often seek to escape the harsh winters of northern climates by settling along the coasts in warmer latitudes. Unfortunately, these areas are frequently hit by violent tropical cyclones. The increasing population along coastal areas presents a problem for emergency planners. The evacuation of large groups of people can be a logistical nightmare. Safety measures have become increasingly dependent on a greater understanding of the nature of tropical cyclones and the dangers associated with them.

Repercussions of Recurring Weather
Section 13.4

In recent years, there have been increasing environmental problems caused by recurring weather, which includes floods, droughts, cold waves, and heat waves. These events cause billions of dollars of damage and economic ruin in many farming areas. Such problems are worsened by an increasing human population vying for limited land. Heat waves and cold waves also impact natural resources by causing increased demand for energy to fuel heaters and air conditioners. In ways such as these, recurring weather events can impact humans as much as the most violent tornadoes and hurricanes do.

Identifying Misconceptions

Students may think of thunderstorms, blizzards, tornadoes, and hurricanes as very different types of storms. However, these storms are quite similar in many ways. All are basically caused by intense low-pressure systems characterized by strong convection cells with violent updrafts, heavy precipitation, and violent winds. In general, blizzards and thunderstorms originate in temperate latitudes, while hurricanes form in tropical latitudes. Tornadoes can be produced by both thunderstorms and hurricanes.

✔Assessment

Portfolio Assessment
Assessment, TWE, pp. 340, 351

Performance Assessment
Discovery Lab, SE, p. 329
Assessment, TWE, p. 346
MiniLab, SE, p. 348
GeoLab, SE, pp. 352–353
GeoLab, TWE, pp. 352–353

Knowledge Assessment
Assessment, TWE, p. 333
Section Assessment, SE, pp. 333, 340, 346, 351
MiniLab. TWE, p. 348
Problem-Solving Lab, TWE, p. 350
Chapter Assessment, SE, pp. 356–357

Skill Assessment
Discovery Lab, TWE, p. 329

GLENCOE'S
ASSESSMENT
ADVANTAGE

Be sure to check the Earth Science Web Site for links to chapter material: earthgeu.com

The Nature of Storms

Introducing the Chapter

On any given day, a portion of the United States is likely experiencing some sort of inclement weather. Have students monitor weather reports for one week. Students should list different types of severe weather occurring around the country, as well as any weather-related injuries and property damage.

Interpreting the Photo

In this photograph of a thunderstorm over Arizona, the great mass of the cumulonimbus cloud is clearly visible, as is the lightning associated with thunderstorms. Tell students that they will learn more about the development of thunderstorms and other types of severe weather in this chapter.

PowerPoint® Presentations

This CD is an editable Microsoft® PowerPoint® presentation that includes:
• Section presentations
• Section checks
• Image bank
• Links to Earth Science Online
• All transparencies
• Animations
• Audio

The Nature of Storms

What You'll Learn

• How thunderstorms, tornadoes, and hurricanes form.

• What the effects of severe weather are.

• How repetitive weather patterns can cause droughts, floods, and other hazards.

Why It's Important

Severe weather can result in extensive property damage and loss of life. To implement safety measures and make other preparations for severe weather, it's necessary to understand when and where severe weather is likely to occur.

To find out more about severe weather, visit the Earth Science Web site at earthgeu.com

328

Discovery Lab

Process Skills

observe and infer, recognize cause and effect, model

L2 ELL

Procedure

Troubleshooting
Make sure that the lunch bags have no holes, and that their bottoms are properly sealed to hold air.

Observe

The air inside the bag makes a noise when the bag bursts because of the sudden contraction of the air when the bag is struck. This is similar to what takes place when a lightning bolt instantaneously heats air, causing the air to contract. The thunderstorm is moving away.

<table>
<tr><td>

Discovery Lab

Model Thunder

Did you know that lightning causes thunder? During a thunderstorm, lightning can reach temperatures of 30 000°C. This extreme heat causes the air around the lightning to expand rapidly, then quickly cool and contract. The rapid expansion of air generates sound waves heard as thunder. You can model thunder using a paper bag.

1. Blow into a brown paper lunch bag until it is full of air.

2. Hold the top of the bag firmly in one hand and twist it so that the air inside is trapped. Take care not to tear the bag.

3. Strike the bag sharply with your other hand so that the bag breaks.

 **CAUTION: Always wear safety goggles in the lab.**

Observe What did you hear when the bag broke? How is this similar to the thunder produced by a lightning bolt? Light moves much faster than sound. Knowing this, what can you infer about the movement of a thunderstorm if the amount of time between when you see the lightning and hear the thunder increases between each lightning flash?

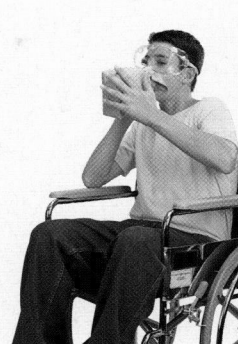

</td></tr>
</table>

Section Focus

Before presenting the lesson, display **Section Focus Transparency 36** on the overhead projector. L1 ELL

SECTION 13.1 *Thunderstorms*

OBJECTIVES

- **Identify** *the processes that form thunderstorms.*
- **Compare** *and* **contrast** *different types of thunderstorms.*
- **Describe** *the life cycle of a thunderstorm.*

VOCABULARY

air-mass thunderstorm
sea-breeze thunderstorm
frontal thunderstorm

At any given moment, nearly 2000 thunderstorms are occurring around the world. Most do little more than provide welcome relief on a muggy summer afternoon. Some, however, grow into atmospheric monsters capable of producing hail the size of baseballs, swirling tornadoes, and surface winds of more than 160 km/h. These severe thunderstorms can also provide the energy for nature's most destructive storms: hurricanes. All thunderstorms, regardless of intensity, have certain characteristics in common.

HOW THUNDERSTORMS FORM

In Chapter 11, you learned that under the right conditions, convection can cause a cumulus cloud to grow into a cumulonimbus cloud. You also learned that cumulonimbus clouds produce thunderstorms. What conditions are necessary for this to happen? For a thunderstorm to form, three conditions must exist. First, there must be an abundant source of moisture in the lower levels of the atmosphere.

13.1 *Thunderstorms* **329**

Chapter Themes

The following themes from the National Science Content Standards are covered in this chapter. Refer to page 8T of the Teacher Guide for an explanation of the correlations.
Systems, order, and organizations (UCP.1); Evidence, models, and explanation (UCP.2); Change, constancy, and measurement (UCP.3); Evolution and equilibrium (UCP.4)

0:00 Out of Time?

If time does not permit teaching the entire chapter, use the Chapter Summary on page 355 and the GeoDigest found at the end of the unit as an overview.

✓Assessment

Skill Ask students to infer what would happen if they compressed the bag slowly. Would the bag still make a sound when it broke? Have students test their inferences by repeating the experiment but compressing the bag slowly. Use the Performance Task Assessment List for Making Observations and Inferences in **PASC,** p. 17.

Resource Manager

Section Focus Transparency 36 L1 ELL
Study Guide for Content Mastery, pp. 79–80 L2

Content Background

Much of what we know about thunderstorms comes from information obtained during the U.S. Thunderstorm Project, a joint experiment that took place among the former U.S. Weather Bureau and several other agencies between 1946 and 1949. This project first defined a thunderstorm as a collection of convection cells characterized by vigorous columns of rising and descending air. The project also was responsible for identifying the different stages in the life cycle of a thunderstorm: the cumulus stage, the mature stage, and the dissipation stage.

Concept Development

A key factor in the development of clouds and thunderstorms is the environment surrounding the convection cell. If the environment is unstable, the cell will likely continue to grow. If the environment is stable, the cell will have a short lifetime. In unstable conditions, rising air continues to encounter cooler air, and the rising air therefore remains buoyant. In stable conditions, rising air quickly encounters warm air, and the rising air is unable to rise any farther.

As this moisture condenses, it releases latent heat. The release of latent heat keeps the cloud warmer than the air around it, which is crucial in maintaining the upward motion of the cloud. Second, some mechanism must lift the air so that the moisture can condense and release latent heat. You'll read about these mechanisms on the next page. Last, the portion of the atmosphere through which the cloud grows must be unstable. In other words, the air must continue to cool with increasing altitude for the growing cloud to stay warmer than the surrounding air. Recall that air can rise only if it's warmer than the air around it. If an air mass is stable, even the release of latent heat will not keep that air warmer than the air around it. The upward motion and growth of the cloud will stop.

Limits to Growth If the three conditions just described are met, the air will keep rising, causing more moisture to condense and creating more latent heat. This process will continue until the rising air meets a layer of stable air that it cannot overcome, or until the rate of condensation, which diminishes with height, is insufficient to generate enough latent heat to keep the cloud warmer than the surrounding air. This second factor limits most cumulonimbus clouds to a height of around 18 000 m. Because of factors which you'll learn about later in this section, typical thunderstorms last only about 30 minutes, and individual storms are only about 24 km in diameter. *Figure 13-1* shows which areas of the United States experience the most thunderstorms annually.

Figure 13-1 Geography and the movement of air masses both play roles in making thunderstorms most common in the southeastern United States.

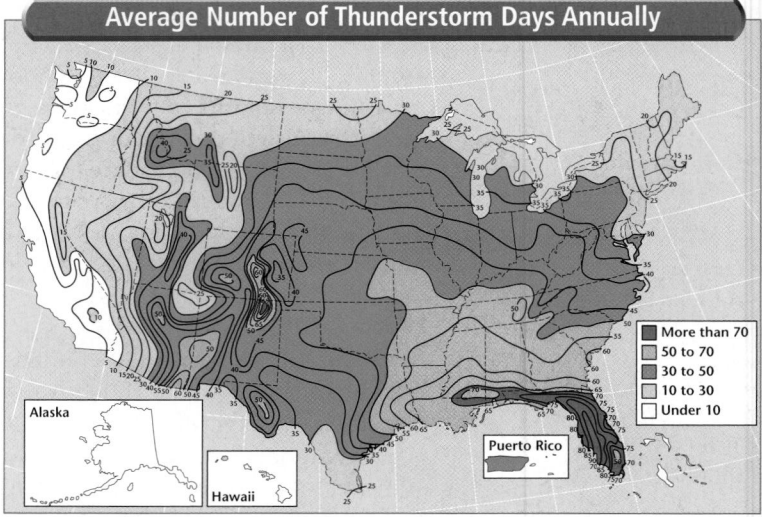

Average Number of Thunderstorm Days Annually

More than 70
50 to 70
30 to 50
10 to 30
Under 10

Alaska

Hawaii

Puerto Rico

Source: National Climatic Data Center, NOAA

Interpreting the Illustration

Figure 13-1 Once students have studied thunderstorm development and types, have them identify the areas on the map where different types of thunderstorms are most likely to occur. Students should find that most storms occur near the air masses that contain the most moisture, namely those found by the Atlantic and Gulf Coasts.

AIR-MASS THUNDERSTORMS

Earlier you learned that some mechanism must lift air through a growing cloud so that its moisture can condense and release latent heat. Thunderstorms are often classified according to the mechanism that caused the air to rise. If the air rose because of unequal heating of Earth's surface within one air mass, the thunderstorm is called an **air-mass thunderstorm.** The unequal heating of Earth's surface reaches its maximum during mid-afternoon. Thus, air-mass thunderstorms are most common then.

There are two common types of air-mass thunderstorms. Mountain thunderstorms occur when an air mass rises as a result of orographic lifting, which, as you learned in Chapter 11, involves air moving up the side of a mountain. Sea-breeze thunderstorms are common along coastal areas during the summer, especially in the tropics and subtropics. **Sea-breeze thunderstorms** are local air-mass thunderstorms caused in part by extreme temperature differences between the air over land and the air over water, as shown in *Figure 13-2.*

FRONTAL THUNDERSTORMS

The second main classification of thunderstorms is **frontal thunderstorms,** which are produced by advancing cold fronts and, more rarely, warm fronts. In a cold front, cold air pushes warm air rapidly up the steep cold-front boundary. This rapid upward motion can produce a line of thunderstorms, sometimes hundreds of kilometers long, along the leading edge of the cold front. Cold-front thunderstorms get their initial lift from the push of the cold air. Because they are not dependent on daytime heating for their initial lift, cold-front thunderstorms can persist long into the night.

Less frequently, thunderstorms can develop along the advancing edge of a warm front. In a warm front, a warm air mass slides up and over a cold air mass. The boundary between the two air masses is not steep; thus, the air rises gradually. However, if the warm air behind the warm front is unstable and moisture levels are sufficiently high, a relatively mild thunderstorm can develop.

STAGES OF DEVELOPMENT

A thunderstorm usually has three stages: the cumulus stage, the mature stage, and the dissipation stage. The stages are classified according to the direction in which the air is moving.

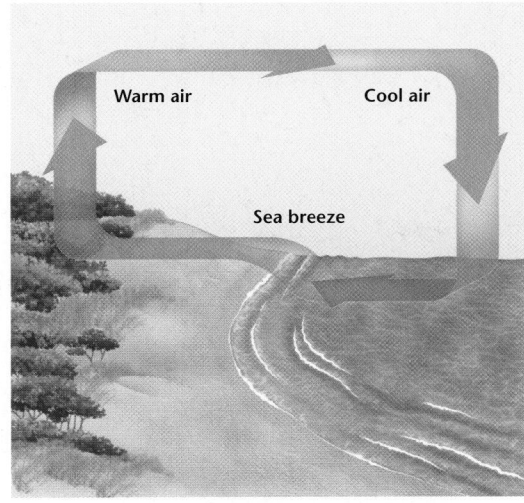

Figure 13-2 During the day, cool air over the ocean moves inland and creates a sea breeze. The cool air forces warm air over the land to rise. The rising air cools and sinks, creating a convection cell. These conditions can produce strong updrafts that result in thunderstorms.

13.1 *Thunderstorms* **331**

Enrichment

Linguistic Weather radar images typically depict precipitation as a series of colors that correspond to the intensity of rainfall rather than the overall strength of a storm. Usually, blue or green represent light precipitation, and yellow, red, and orange represent heavy precipitation. Have interested students each research and write a report on weather radar images. Students should include several radar images in their reports and share their results with the class. **L2 P**

Reinforcement

Remind students that air will continue to rise only if it is warmer than the surrounding air. The atmosphere cools with height, which severely limits how high air can rise before it cools to a temperature below that of the surrounding air. This is why the release of latent heat and an abundant supply of moisture are so crucial to rising air. As more moisture is condensed, more latent heat is released, which allows the air to remain warm and continue to rise for a longer period of time.

Resource Manager

Teaching Transparency 35 L2 ELL

Differentiated Instruction

Gifted Thunderstorms occur most often near moist air masses. Ask students to explain why more thunderstorms don't occur along the Pacific Coast. Prevailing winds at lower latitudes along the Pacific Coast during summer transport moist, maritime air offshore, rather than inland. **L3**

NY Core Curriculum Standards

Page 330: St 4 KI 2.1c, 2.1e, 2.1h, & 2.2b, St 6 KI 1 & 4
Page 331: St 4 KI 2.1b, 2.1c, 2.1e, & 2.1h, St 6 KI 1 & 5

In Chapter 12, students learned that cold fronts move forward and spread cold air under warmer, less-dense air, thereby forcing the warm air to rise. This process, which produces thunderstorms, is similar to the formation of storms by sea breezes. As the cooler air moves inland, it displaces the warmer air, thereby producing clouds and usually precipitation.

Discussion

Ask students what happens when the updrafts in a thunderstorm cease. Make sure students understand that the storm has entered the dissipation stage, but it is not yet dead and may continue to produce rain for several hours. Tell students that it takes time for the upward momentum within the storm cell to fade completely, and thus the coalescence of already formed water droplets can take some time to cease. Even when the lower levels of the storm no longer produce updrafts, the remaining middle levels can still produce light rainfall.

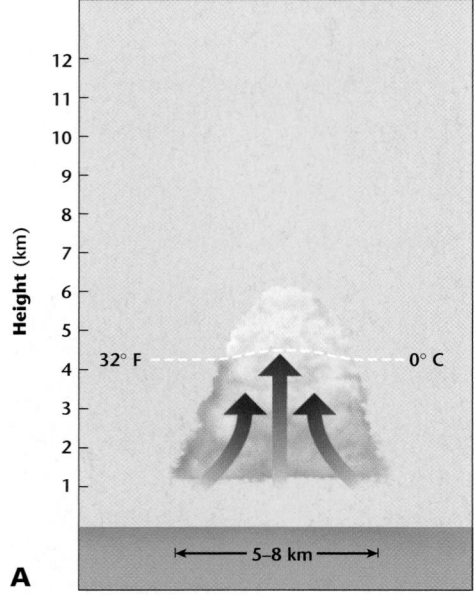

A

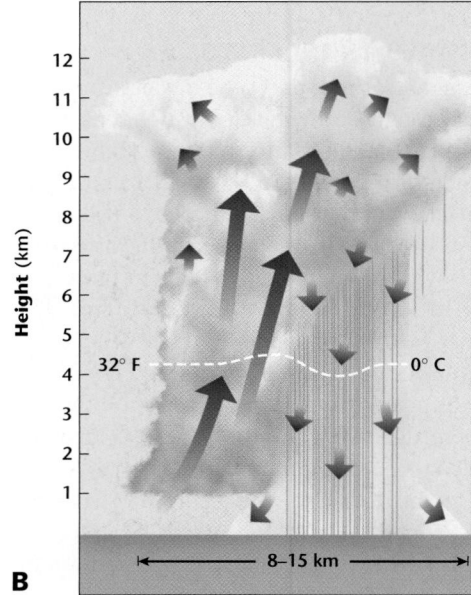

B

Figure 13-3 The cumulus stage of a thunderstorm is characterized mainly by updrafts **(A).** The mature stage is characterized by strong updrafts and downdrafts **(B).** The storm loses energy in the dissipation stage **(C).**

Cumulus Stage In the cumulus stage, air starts to rise nearly vertically upward, as shown in *Figure 13-3A.* This creates updrafts, which transport moisture to the upper reaches of the cloud. The moisture condenses into visible cloud droplets and releases latent heat. As the cloud droplets coalesce, they form larger and larger droplets, which eventually fall to Earth as precipitation. This begins the mature stage of a thunderstorm.

Mature Stage Precipitation in a thunderstorm is composed of water droplets that formed at high, cool levels of the atmosphere. As the precipitation falls, it cools the air around it. The newly cooled air is more dense than the surrounding air, so it sinks rapidly to the ground along with the precipitation. This creates downdrafts. As *Figure 13-3B* shows, the updrafts and downdrafts form a convection cell that produces the gusty surface winds associated with thunderstorms. In the mature stage, nearly equal amounts of updrafts and downdrafts exist side by side in the cumulonimbus cloud.

Dissipation Stage The production of downdrafts is ultimately the thunderstorm's undoing. The convection cell can exist only if there is a steady supply of warm, moist air at Earth's surface. Once that supply runs out, the updrafts slow and eventually stop. In a thunderstorm, shown in the photo on the next page, the supply of warm, moist air runs out because the cool downdrafts spread in all directions when they reach Earth's surface. This cools the areas from which the storm

Across the Curriculum

Chemistry In many ways, the life cycle of a thunderstorm is similar to a chemical reaction. When chemicals mix, a reaction begins, much like the cumulus stage of a thunderstorm when heat and moisture form a convection cell. Just as a chemical reaction has a point of peak efficiency, a thunderstorm intensifies at the point at which it most efficiently utilizes heat and moisture. Just as a chemical reaction eventually slows, a thunderstorm dissipates when it runs out of heat or moisture.

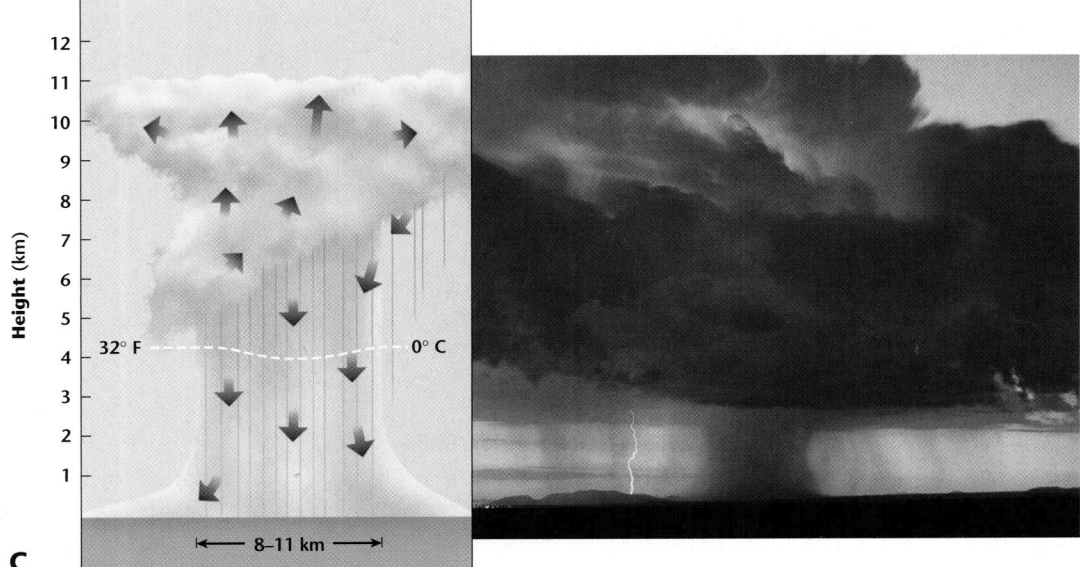

C

draws its energy. Without the warm air, the updrafts cease and precipitation can no longer form. The storm is then in the dissipation stage, as shown in *Figure 13-3C.* This stage, which is characterized primarily by lingering downdrafts, will last until the cloud runs out of previously formed raindrops. Next, you'll explore the destructive forces that can be unleashed when a severe thunderstorm strikes.

SECTION ASSESSMENT

1. It's 2:00 A.M. in the northeastern United States. A thunderstorm rumbles on the horizon. What type is it most likely to be? Why?

2. What conditions must be present for a thunderstorm to form?

3. Explain why a cold-front thunderstorm is usually more severe than a warm-front thunderstorm.

4. **Thinking Critically** In the tropics, where the tropopause is higher than in other areas, cumulonimbus clouds commonly reach towering heights of 15 000 m. Why is the height of the tropopause a factor in how tall a cumulonimbus cloud can grow?

SKILL REVIEW

5. **Concept Mapping** Use the following phrases to complete an events-chain concept map about the life cycle of a thunderstorm. For more help, refer to the *Skill Handbook.*

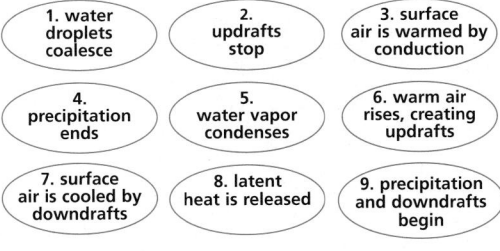

1. water droplets coalesce	2. updrafts stop	3. surface air is warmed by conduction
4. precipitation ends	5. water vapor condenses	6. warm air rises, creating updrafts
7. surface air is cooled by downdrafts	8. latent heat is released	9. precipitation and downdrafts begin

earthgeu.com/self_check_quiz

13.1 *Thunderstorms* **333**

---

3 Assess

Check for Understanding
Discussion
Ask students to compare and contrast different types of thunderstorms.

Reteach
Visual-Spatial Have students divide a map of the United States into several regions. Then, have them develop a thunderstorm profile for each region. The profiles should include the relative frequency of thunderstorms, the probable season of occurrence, and the probable types of thunderstorms that occur in each particular region. L2

✓*Assessment*

Knowledge Have students outline the three stages in the development of a thunderstorm.

SECTION ASSESSMENT

1. a frontal thunderstorm; this type is more likely to occur at night because its lift does not depend on the unequal heating of Earth's surface by the Sun

2. an abundant source of moisture, a mechanism to lift the air, and an unstable environment to allow the air to keep rising

3. Because the slope of a cold front is much steeper than that of a warm front, the air is forced upwards much more quickly, which creates stronger convection cells.

4. Above the tropopause, air no longer cools with height. Thus, the air becomes stable and resists further upward motion.

5. Concept maps should be in the following order: surface air warmed by conduction; warm air rises, creating updrafts; water vapor condenses; latent heat is released; water droplets coalesce; precipitation and downdrafts begin; surface air is cooled by downdrafts; updrafts stop; precipitation ends.

NY Core Curriculum Standards

Page 332: St 4 KI 2.1b, 2.1c, 2.1e, 2.1f, & 2.1h, St 6 KI 1
Page 333: St 4 KI 2.1c, 2.1e, 2.1f, 2.1h, & 2.2b, St 6 KI 1 & 5

333

Section Background

For section content background, refer to **Supercells** and **Meso-Lows** on page 328C.

Preplanning

Refer to the Chapter Organizer on pages 328A–B.

1 Focus

Section Focus

Before presenting the lesson, display **Section Focus Transparency 37** on the overhead projector. L1 ELL

Project

Interpersonal There are many types of lightning, including cloud-to-ground, cloud-to-cloud, sheet, and ball lightning. Have students research the different types of lightning and then make presentations based on their research. Students should include labeled photos of different types of lightning. L2

SECTION 13.2 *Severe Weather*

OBJECTIVES

- **Explain** *why some thunderstorms are more severe than others.*
- **Recognize** *the dangers of severe thunderstorms, including lightning, hail, high winds, and floods.*
- **Describe** *how tornadoes form.*

VOCABULARY

supercell
downburst
tornado
Fujita tornado intensity scale

Figure 13-4 An anvil-shaped cumulonimbus cloud is characteristic of many severe thunderstorms **(A)**. The most severe thunderstorms are supercells **(B)**.

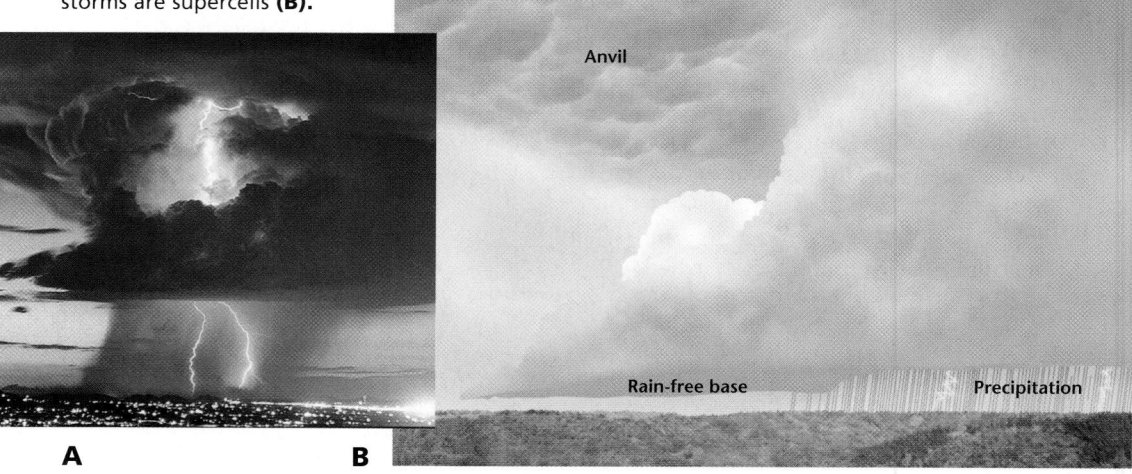

A   B

334 CHAPTER 13 *The Nature of Storms*

All thunderstorms are not created equal. Some die out within minutes, while others flash and thunder throughout the night. What makes one thunderstorm more severe than another? Occasionally, weather events come together in such a way that there is a continuous supply of surface moisture. This happens along a cold front that moves into warmer territory and can lift and condense a continuous supply of warm air. In this case, a line of thunderstorms can last for hours or even days as they continually regenerate themselves with the new, warm air that is introduced into the updrafts.

SEVERE THUNDERSTORMS

Other factors also play a role in causing some storms to be more severe than others. Cold fronts are usually accompanied by upper-level, low-pressure systems that are marked by pools of cold air. This cold, high air increases the temperature difference between the upper and lower parts of the storm, which causes the air to become more unstable. As the instability of the air increases, the strength of the storm's updrafts and downdrafts intensifies. The storm is then considered to be severe. Severe thunderstorms can produce some of the most violent weather conditions on Earth. They may develop into self-sustaining, extremely powerful storms called **supercells,** which are characterized by intense, rotating updrafts. *Figure 13-4B* shows an illustration of a supercell. These furious storms can last for several hours and can have updrafts as strong as 240 km/h.

Resource Manager

Section Focus Transparency 37 L1 ELL
Study Guide for Content Mastery, pp. 81–82 L2

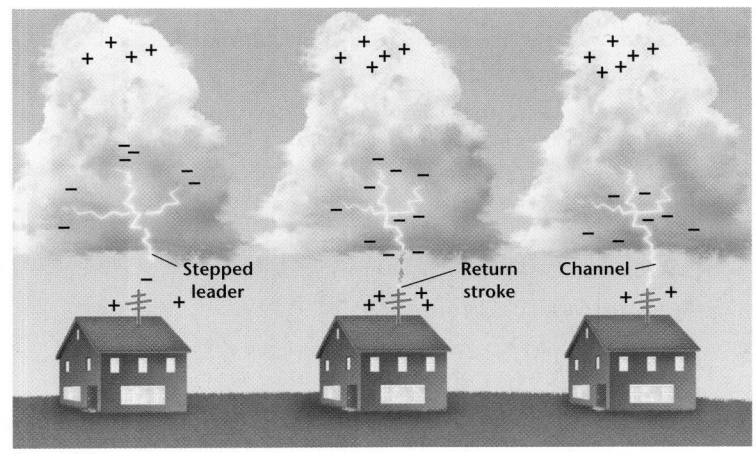

Figure 13-5 When a stepped leader nears an object on the ground, a powerful surge of electricity from the ground moves upward to the cloud, and lightning is produced.

Of the estimated 100 000 thunderstorms that occur each year in the United States, only about ten percent are considered to be severe, and fewer still reach classic supercell proportions. But when certain atmospheric conditions come together in the right way, the results can be spectacular and sometimes deadly, as you'll learn next.

Lightning

Have you ever touched a metal object on a dry winter day and been zapped by a spark of electricity? If so, you were, in a sense, playing with lightning. Lightning is electricity caused by the rapid rush of air in a cumulonimbus cloud. A lightning bolt forms when friction between the updrafts and downdrafts within a cumulonimbus cloud separates electrons from some of their atoms either in the cloud or near the ground. The atoms that lose electrons become positively charged ions. Other atoms receive the extra electrons and become negatively charged ions. As *Figure 13-5* shows, this creates regions of air with opposite charges. To relieve the electrical imbalance, an invisible channel of negatively charged air, called a stepped leader, moves from the cloud toward the ground. When the stepped leader nears the ground, a channel of positively charged ions, called the return stroke, rushes upward to meet it. The return stroke surges from the ground to the cloud, illuminating the channel with about 100 million V of electricity. That illumination is lightning. You'll learn more about lightning in the *Science & Technology* feature at the end of this chapter.

The Power of Lightning A lightning bolt heats the surrounding air to about 30 000°C. That's about five times hotter than the surface of the Sun! The thunder you hear is the sound produced as this superheated air rapidly expands and contracts. Because sound waves travel

2 Teach

Collaborative Learning

Have students debate whether lightning starts from the cloud down or from the ground up. Technically, both answers are correct because a stepped leader and a return stroke are both required to discharge the lightning bolt. The return stroke from the ground, however, causes the illumination and discharge called lightning.

Demo

Ask a volunteer to hold his or her arms straight out at chest level. Carefully load books onto the student's arms. **CAUTION:** *The student should not be wearing open-toed sandals.* Eventually, the load of books will become so heavy that the student will drop them. Relate this to the development of a downburst. Updrafts continually pump air upward into a storm, until eventually, the mass of air becomes too great for the updrafts to keep aloft. At that point, the entire mass of air is released at once, and it plummets to Earth as a downdraft.

Cultural Diversity

Weather Expert Sulochana Gadgil is an atmospheric scientist from India best known for her studies on monsoons, winds that bring severe storms to Asia. She has investigated the climatic changes, the effects on Asia's agriculture, and the rainfall patterns associated with these violent winds. Gadgil earned her Ph.D. in mathematics from Harvard University, but later changed her focus of study to meteorology. In 1971, she returned to her birthplace to teach at the Indian Institute of Science in Bangalore. Gadgil has also served as chair of the Center for Atmospheric Sciences at the Indian Institute since 1989. She is the author of more than 40 scientific articles on climatology, atmospheric and oceanic circulation, and monsoon research.

NY Core Curriculum Standards

Page 334: St 4 KI 2.1c, 2.1e, 2.1h, & 2.1i, St 6 KI 1 & 4
Page 335: St 4 KI 2.1c, 2.1e, 2.1f, & 2.1h, St 6 KI 1 & 4

Enrichment

While wind damage is frequently attributed to tornadoes, downbursts are often the real cause of damage. Remind students that downbursts are straight-line winds, and that tornadoes rotate. Then, ask students to propose ways to distinguish downburst damage from tornado damage. Students can use the Earth Science Web Site or other resources for information. They should realize that wind damage caused by a downburst is usually in a straight line in one direction, while wind damage caused by a tornado usually spreads out in several directions.

Project

Kinesthetic Have students demonstrate how torrential rainfall can cause flooding. Fill a small pan with dirt and a glass salt shaker with water. Sprinkle the water slowly onto the dirt. It will be absorbed, with little change to the surface of the dirt. Next, repeat the process, only this time take off the top of the shaker and pour the water onto the dirt. The dirt will be washed away in one area—the equivalent of a flood in a torrential downpour. **L1** **ELL**

Table 13-1 Thunderstorm and Lightning Safety

When Thunderstorms Approach . . .

- Remember: If you can hear thunder, you are close enough to the storm to be struck by lightning. Go to a safe shelter immediately.

- Move to a sturdy building or car. Do not take shelter in small sheds, under isolated trees, or in convertible automobiles.

- If lightning is occurring and a sturdy shelter is not available, get inside a hard-topped automobile and keep the windows up.

- Get out of boats and away from water.

- Telephone lines and metal pipes can conduct electricity. Unplug appliances not necessary for obtaining weather information. Avoid using any electrical appliances. Use phones ONLY in an emergency.

If You Are Caught Outdoors and No Shelter Is Nearby . . .

- Find a low spot away from trees, fences, and poles. Make sure the place you choose is not subject to flooding.

- If you are in the woods, take shelter under the shorter trees.

- If you feel your skin tingle or your hair stand on end, squat low to the ground on the balls of your feet. Place your hands on your knees with your head between them. Make yourself the smallest target possible, and minimize your contact with the ground.

Source: NOAA

more slowly than light waves, you may see lightning well before you hear thunder, even though they are generated at the same time.

Each year in the United States, lightning accounts for about 7500 forest fires, which result in the loss of millions of acres of forest. In addition, lightning strikes in the United States cause a yearly average of 300 injuries and 93 deaths to humans. *Table 13-1* lists safety tips to follow to avoid property damage and loss of life from lightning strikes.

THE FURY OF THE WIND

Recall that rain-cooled downdrafts descend to Earth's surface during a thunderstorm and spread out as they reach the ground. Sometimes, however, instead of dispersing that downward energy over a large area underneath the storm, the energy becomes concentrated in a local area. The resulting winds are exceptionally strong, with speeds of more than 160 km/h. Violent downdrafts that are concentrated in a local area are called **downbursts.**

Based on the size of the area they affect, downbursts are further classified as either macrobursts or microbursts. Macrobursts can cause a path of destruction up to 5 km wide. They have wind speeds of more than 200 km/h and can last up to 30 minutes. Smaller in size, though

---

Differentiated Instruction

Gifted The National Weather Service issues Severe Thunderstorm Warnings for high winds and hail but not for lightning, which actually kills more people. Ask students to infer why. Warnings for lightning would have to be issued for every thunderstorm that develops because a thunderstorm, by definition, exhibits lightning.

Figure 13-6 This car was damaged by large hailstones similar to the one shown here.

deadlier in force, microbursts affect areas of less than 3 km but can have winds exceeding 250 km/h. Despite lasting less than 10 minutes on average, a microburst is especially deadly because its smaller size makes it extremely difficult to detect and thus prepare for.

HAIL

Each year in the United States, almost $1 billion in damage is caused by another danger associated with thunderstorms: hail. Hail is precipitation in the form of balls or lumps of ice. It can do tremendous damage to crops, particularly in the Central United States, where hail occurs most frequently. Hail is most common during the spring growing season. *Figure 13-6* shows the damage that hail can cause.

Hail forms because of two characteristics common to thunderstorms. First, water droplets exist in the liquid state in the parts of a cumulonimbus cloud where the temperature is actually below freezing. When these supercooled water droplets encounter ice pellets, the water droplets freeze on contact and cause the ice pellets to grow larger. The second characteristic that allows hail to form is an abundance of strong updrafts and downdrafts existing side by side within a cloud. The growing ice pellets are caught alternately in the updrafts and downdrafts, so that they are constantly encountering more supercooled water droplets. The ice pellets keep growing until they are too heavy for even the strongest updrafts to keep aloft, and they finally fall to Earth as hail.

FLOODS

Sometimes, the wind currents in the upper atmosphere that cause weather systems to move are weak, and the weather systems and resulting storms move slowly. When this happens, a storm may dump its rain over a limited location, rather than spreading it over a large area. Floods such as the one in *Figure 13-7* can occur. The situation can worsen if there is abundant moisture available not just at Earth's surface, but also throughout the atmosphere. This makes the whole process of condensation, coalescence, and precipitation much more

Using Scientific Terms

The term *flash flood* is frequently used to describe floods, but it actually applies only to hilly or mountainous areas. A flash flood occurs when a normally dry or nearly dry riverbed receives torrential rainfall in the area of its headwaters. In places with somewhat steep terrains, the water quickly drains into the riverbed and rapidly moves downstream, gathering more water on its way. As it travels downstream, the water become a raging torrent that is capable of washing away people, cars, roads, and even buildings. The flooding that occurs in urban areas as a result of poor drainage is not flash flooding. Technically, it is a "ponding" of water, but it can still be dangerous.

Figure 13-7 This rural community was devastated by a flood in Arizona.

Applying Earth Science

Flood-related deaths often occur when people drive their automobiles into moving water. Swiftly moving water contains tremendous force—it can be lower than a vehicle's hubcaps but still sweep the vehicle downstream. Tell students that one of the most important safety rules during heavy rainfall is to never venture into moving water—on foot or in a car—without knowing the water's depth.

Resource Manager

Laboratory Manual, pp. 97–100 L2

NY Core Curriculum Standards

Page 336: St 4 KI 2.1c, 2.1e, & 2.1h, St 6 KI 1

Page 337: St 4 KI 2.1c, 2.1e, 2.1f, & 2.1h, St 6 KI 1 & 4

Interpreting the Illustration

Figure 13-8 Wind shear is a sudden change in wind direction or speed that can occur either vertically or horizontally. In regard to the formation of a tornado, the vertical change in direction is most important because it leads to the development of the horizontal tube, or vortex. As this vortex is incorporated into the parent thunderstorm's strong updrafts, it tilts in a vertical direction and creates a funnel-shaped tornado.

Using Scientific Terms

Sometimes, the developing stages of a tornado take place well above the ground, and the funnel never reaches the ground. When this happens, the swirling vortex is called a funnel cloud. A funnel cloud becomes a tornado if it reaches the ground. Tell students that a tornado can be identified by the presence of swirling dust or debris on the ground at the end of the funnel. If such a swirl is not visible, the vortex is most likely a funnel cloud rather than a fully developed tornado.

Figure 13-8 A change in wind direction and speed creates a horizontal rotation in the lower atmosphere **(A)**. Strong updrafts tilt the rotating air from a horizontal to a vertical position **(B)**. A tornado forms within the rotating winds **(C)**.

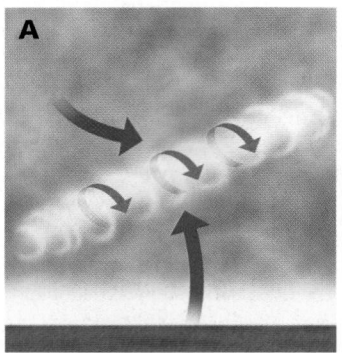 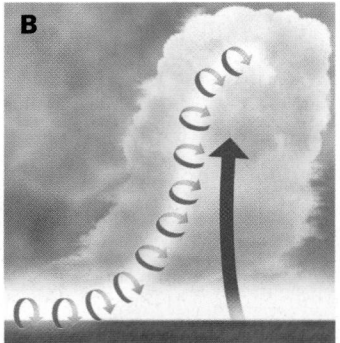 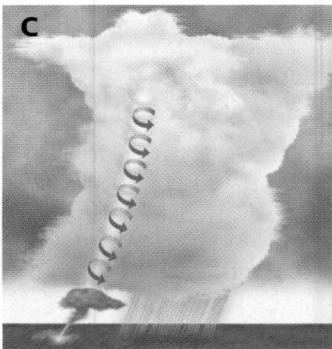

efficient and thus produces more rainfall. If the rain falls faster than the ground can absorb it, or faster than streams and rivers can transport it out of the area, flooding can occur. Floods are the main cause of thunderstorm-related deaths in the United States each year.

TORNADOES

Of all the dangers associated with thunderstorms, the most impressive by far is a tornado. A **tornado** is a violent, whirling column of air in contact with the ground. Before a tornado reaches the ground, it is called a funnel cloud. Tornadoes are often associated with supercells, the most severe thunderstorms. The air in a tornado is made visible by dust and debris drawn into the swirling column, or by the condensation of water vapor into a visible cloud. Over the area it covers, few storms on Earth can match a tornado's violence.

A tornado forms when wind speed and direction change suddenly with height, a phenomenon known as wind shear. Under the right conditions, this can produce a horizontal rotation near Earth's surface, as shown in *Figure 13-8.* If this rotation takes place close enough to the thunderstorm's updrafts, the twisting column of wind can be tilted from a horizontal to a vertical position. As updrafts accelerate the rotation, air is removed from the center of the column, which in turn lowers air pressure in the center. The extreme pressure gradient between the center and the outer portion of the tornado produces the violent winds associated with tornadoes. Although tornadoes rarely exceed 200 m in diameter and usually last only a few minutes, they can be extremely destructive. In fact, they are classified according to their destructive force.

Tornado Classification Tornadoes can vary greatly in size and intensity. They are classified according to the **Fujita tornado intensity scale,** which ranks tornadoes according to their path of destruction, wind speed, and duration. The Fujita scale was named

Across the Curriculum

Geography While tornadoes are common in the United States, some parts of the country experience very few of these storms. For example, tornadoes virtually never strike Alaska or Hawaii and rarely strike the Pacific Northwest. Ask students to infer why. Conditions aren't right to generate the updrafts needed for tornadoes to develop from thunderstorms.

for Japanese tornado researcher Dr. Theodore Fujita. The scale ranges from F0, which is characterized by winds of up to 118 km/h, to the incredibly violent F5, which can pack winds of more than 500 km/h. Most tornadoes do not exceed the F1 category. In fact, only about one percent ever reach the violent categories of F4 and F5. Those that do, however, can lift entire buildings from their foundations and toss automobiles and trucks around like toys. The Fujita scale is shown in **Table 13-2.**

Tornado Distribution While tornadoes can occur at any time and at any place, there are some times and locations that are more conducive to their formation. Most tornadoes—especially the violent ones—form in the spring during the late afternoon and evening, when the temperature contrasts between polar air, which still has winter characteristics, and tropical air, which is steadily becoming warmer, are the greatest. These large temperature contrasts often spark the development of supercells, which are each capable of producing several strong tornadoes. Large temperature contrasts occur most frequently in the Central United States, where cold continental polar air collides with maritime tropical air moving northward from the Gulf of Mexico. More than 700 tornadoes touch down each year in the United States. Many of these occur in a region called "Tornado Alley," which extends from northern Texas through Oklahoma, Kansas, and Missouri.

Tornado Safety In the United States, an average of 80 deaths and 1500 injuries result from tornadoes each year. In an ongoing effort to reduce tornado-related fatalities, the National Weather Service issues tornado watches and warnings before a tornado actually strikes. These advisories are broadcast on local radio stations when tornadoes are

Table 13-2 Fujita Scale

Weak Tornadoes (F0 and F1)

80% of all tornadoes
Path: up to 3 miles
Wind speed: 60 to 115 mph
Duration: 1–10 minutes +

Strong Tornadoes (F2 and F3)

19% of all tornadoes
Path: 15 miles +
Wind speed: 110 to 205 mph
Duration: 20 minutes +

Violent Tornadoes (F4 and F5)

1% of all tornadoes
Path: 50 miles +
Wind speed: 200 mph +
Duration: 1 hour +

13.2 *Severe Weather* **339**

Discussion

Tornadoes have been the subject of several recent movies. One such movie depicted a couple surviving an F5 tornado by tying themselves to large irrigation pipes in the middle of a field, while the buildings around them were destroyed. Ask students to discuss whether this is a realistic depiction of what might happen during an F5 tornado. This is a far-fetched scenario. Violent winds would toss debris from the buildings and surrounding area that could easily strike and kill the couple. Also, the couple could have been sand-blasted to death by dirt driven at them at speeds in excess of 500 km/h.

Content Background

While F4 and F5 tornadoes account for only a small percentage of the total number of tornadoes, they cause most deaths and tornado-related property damage. More than 90 percent of all tornadoes are classified as F0 or F1, but they account for only a small percentage of total tornado damage. It's hard to issue advance warnings for weak tornadoes because they are small and brief, and therefore they may not be detected by weather radar or they may not be detected in time for advance warnings to be of use. In contrast, violent tornadoes are usually easily detected by weather radar, and warnings can usually be issued in time for people to take protective actions.

Resource Manager

Teaching Transparency 36

NY Core Curriculum Standards

Page 338: St 4 KI 2.1c, 2.1e, & 2.1h, St 6 KI 1 & 5
Page 339: St 2 KI 3, St 4 KI 2.1c, 2.1e, & 2.1h, St 6 KI 1

Check for Understanding

Reinforcement

Have students describe the development of a tornado, beginning with the formation of the parent thunderstorm.

Reteach

Linguistic Have students each make a data table showing the hazards associated with thunderstorms. Student tables should include the types of hazards, their relative severity, and the basic processes that cause them to develop. P

✓Assessment

Portfolio Have students each research a well-known tornado, such as the one that occurred in Xenia, Ohio, in 1974. Allow them to use the Earth Science Web Site, reference books, magazines, and newspapers to gather information. Students should then each develop a multimedia presentation that includes data on the damage path of the tornado; statistics on deaths, injuries, and property damage; and suggestions about what could have been done to mitigate the damage. P

Table 13-3 Tornado Safety

If a Warning Is Issued or If Threatening Weather Approaches . . .

- If you are in a home or building, move to a predesignated shelter, such as a basement.
- If an underground shelter is not available, move to an interior room or hallway on the lowest floor and get under a sturdy piece of furniture.
- Stay away from windows.
- Get out of automobiles.
- Do not try to outdistance a tornado in a car; instead, leave the car immediately.
- If you are caught outside or in a vehicle, lie flat in a nearby ditch or depression.
- Mobile homes, even when tied down, offer little protection from tornadoes and should be abandoned.

Source: NOAA

indicated on weather radar or spotted in the region. During a severe thunderstorm, the presence of dark, greenish skies, a towering wall of clouds, large hailstones, and a loud, roaring noise similar to that of a freight train are signs of an approaching or developing tornado. *Table 13-3* lists safety measures recommended by the National Weather Service in the event of a tornado. The agency stresses that despite advanced tracking systems, some tornadoes develop exceedingly quickly. In these cases, advance warnings may not be possible. However, the threat of tornado-related injury can be substantially decreased when people seek shelter at the first sign of threatening skies. In the next section, you'll learn about another type of severe weather: tropical storms.

SECTION ASSESSMENT

1. Describe two characteristics of thunderstorms that lead to hail formation.
2. Compare and contrast a macroburst and a microburst.
3. What type of front would you expect to be associated with flooding? Why?
4. Why are some thunderstorms more severe than others?
5. If the time between when you see lightning and hear thunder is increasing, a storm is moving away from you. Why is this true?
6. **Thinking Critically** Based on what you know about stepped leaders and return strokes, why are tall objects more likely to be struck by lightning than shorter ones?

SKILL REVIEW

7. **Recognizing Cause and Effect** In the United States, most thunderstorms occur in Florida, yet the central states experience the strongest tornadoes. Why doesn't Florida have more violent tornadoes? For more help, refer to the *Skill Handbook.*

earthgeu.com/self_check_quiz

SECTION ASSESSMENT

1. the presence of supercooled water, and intense updrafts and downdrafts
2. Both are downbursts. The macroburst takes place over a larger area than does the microburst.
3. A stationary front would allow repeated thunderstorms to move across the same area. Thus, large amounts of rain would fall.
4. Some thunderstorms are influenced by mechanisms that destabilize the surrounding air and increase the intensity of the updrafts and downdrafts. This causes the storms to become stronger.
5. Light moves faster than sound, so a greater interval between the flash and the thunder would mean that the distance to the thunderstorm was increasing.
6. It is much easier for return strokes and stepped leaders to connect from tall objects because the distance they have to travel is relatively short.
7. The most violent tornadoes form only with the presence of the most violent updrafts, which normally occur as a result of a collision of very different air masses. Florida generally doesn't experience extreme differences in air masses—cold air is greatly modified by the time it reaches this southern state. The presence of water on three sides of Florida also helps to modify cold air.

If you wanted to search for the origin of the most violent type of storm on Earth, the last place you'd probably look would be the calm, sunny tropics. However, during summer and fall, the sunny tropics are the birthing grounds of large, rotating, low-pressure storms called **tropical cyclones.** The strongest of these cyclonic storms are known in the United States and other parts of the Atlantic Ocean as hurricanes. *Figure 13-9* illustrates the rotating nature of a typical hurricane.

TROPICAL CYCLONES

Unlike midlatitude storms that derive their energy from the contrast between warm and cold air masses, tropical cyclones thrive on the tremendous amount of energy in warm, tropical oceans. As water evaporates from the ocean surface, latent heat is stored. This latent heat is later released when the air begins to rise and water vapor condenses into clouds and rain. The air usually rises because of some sort of existing weather disturbance moving across the tropics. Many such disturbances originate along the Intertropical Convergence Zone (ITCZ), which you learned about in Chapter 12. As these disturbances produce more precipitation, more energy is released. In addition, the rising air creates an area of low pressure at the ocean surface. As more warm air moves toward the low-pressure center to replace the air that has risen, the Coriolis effect causes the moving air to turn counterclockwise in the northern hemisphere. This produces the cyclonic rotation of a tropical cyclone.

As the moving air approaches the center of the growing storm, it rises, rotates faster and faster, and increases in speed as more energy is released through condensation. In the process, air pressure in the center of the system continues to decrease, while surface wind speeds

OBJECTIVES

- **Identify** *where tropical cyclones originate.*
- **Describe** *the life cycle of a tropical cyclone.*
- **Recognize** *the dangers of hurricanes.*

VOCABULARY

tropical cyclone
eye
eyewall
Saffir-Simpson hurricane scale
storm surge

Figure 13-9 The characteristic rotating nature of cyclonic storms is evident in this hurricane that formed over the Atlantic Ocean.

Interpreting the Photo

Figure 13-9 Seen from above, a tropical cyclone is easily identified by its distinct features. A mature tropical cyclone has an eye, which is the calm—and at times, nearly clear —circular center of the storm. Also, a tropical cyclone doesn't exhibit a long front of clouds, as do other storms. This is because a tropical cyclone derives it energy from warm ocean waters, not from the energy generated by clashing air masses.

Resource Manager

Section Focus Transparency 38 L1 ELL
Study Guide for Content Mastery, p. 83 L2

Prepare

Section Background

For section content background, refer to **Cyclone Safety** on page 328D.

Preplanning

Refer to the Chapter Organizer on pages 328A–B.

1 Focus

Section Focus

Before presenting the lesson, display **Section Focus Transparency 38** on the overhead projector.
L1 ELL

Demo

Trace the edge of an oval platter in a clockwise direction, starting with a long, curved edge closest to you to model how a tropical cyclone moves in the northern hemisphere. Tell students that the platter represents the Bermuda High, and the traced line represents the path of a tropical cyclone. The Bermuda High steers storms around it, much like the platter steered the pencil.

Content Background

Why are hurricanes more common in some years than others? One reason is the amount of wind shear present in the tropics. When wind shear in the tropics is large —that is, there is a large change in wind direction or speed with height—the small tropical disturbances that can potentially grow into hurricanes become tilted with height and cannot develop into a vertical column through which condensation—and the heat it releases—can be sustained. This prohibits further growth of the disturbance.

Project

Linguistic Studies have shown that when the phenomenon known as El Niño occurs in the Pacific Ocean, there are fewer hurricanes than normal in the Atlantic, Caribbean, and Gulf of Mexico basins. Have students research the effects of El Niño and report on why El Niño causes fewer tropical cyclones to occur in these basins. The presence of El Niño increases wind shear across these basins and thus prevents small tropical disturbances from developing into hurricanes. **L2**

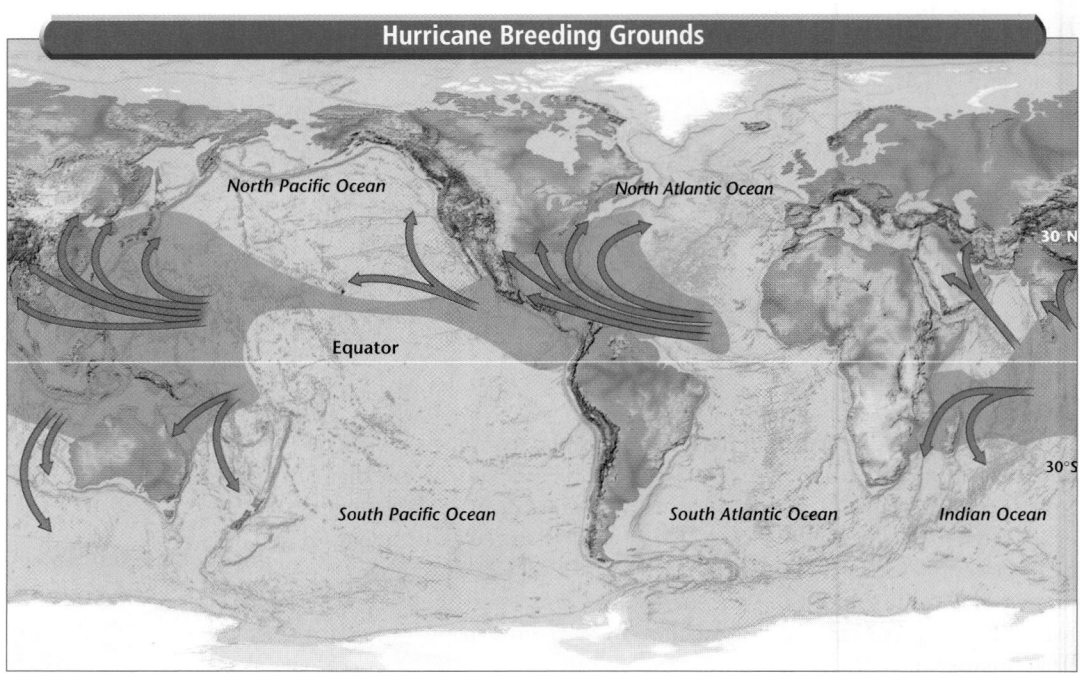

Hurricane Breeding Grounds

North Pacific Ocean
North Atlantic Ocean
30° N
Equator
30° S
South Pacific Ocean
South Atlantic Ocean
Indian Ocean

Figure 13-10 Hurricanes form in all of Earth's tropical oceans except in the relatively cool waters of the South Pacific and South Atlantic Oceans.

increase—sometimes in excess of 240 km/h. This process will continue as long as atmospheric conditions allow warm air to be fed into the system at the surface and to be removed from the system in the upper atmosphere.

Formation of Tropical Cyclones Tropical cyclones require two basic conditions to form: an abundant supply of very warm ocean water and some sort of disturbance to lift warm air and keep it rising. These conditions exist in all tropical oceans except the South Atlantic Ocean and the Pacific Ocean west of the South American Coast. Ocean waters in these areas are somewhat cooler. In addition, the ITCZ is positioned farther north. As a consequence, tropical cyclones do not occur in these areas. They do occur in the large expanse of warm waters in the western Pacific Ocean, where they are known as typhoons. To people living near the Indian Ocean, they are known as cyclones. Near the Atlantic Ocean, the Caribbean Sea, the Gulf of Mexico, and along the western coast of Mexico, they are called hurricanes. The map in *Figure 13-10* shows where hurricanes generally form. They occur most frequently in the late summer and early fall, when Earth's oceans contain their greatest amount of stored heat energy.

Differentiated Instruction

Gifted Some tropical cyclones have altered the course of history, usually by interfering with naval fleets. Have interested students each research one such occurrence and provide details about the location of the event, the estimated strength of the tropical cyclone, the damage it caused, and how it affected historical events.

Movement of Tropical Cyclones Like all large-scale storms, tropical cyclones move according to the wind currents that steer them. Recall that many of the world's oceans are home to subtropical high-pressure systems that are present to some extent throughout the year. In the deep tropics, tropical cyclones are often caught up in the circulation of these high-pressure systems. They move steadily toward the west, then eventually turn poleward when they reach the far edges of the high-pressure systems. There, they are guided by prevailing westerlies and begin to interact with midlatitude systems. At this point, the interaction of the various wind and weather systems makes the movement of the storms unpredictable.

Stages of Tropical Cyclones A traveling tropical disturbance, which can cause air in a developing tropical cyclone to rise, is the first stage of a tropical cyclone. Disturbances can originate either from the ITCZ or as weak, low-pressure systems called tropical waves. These disturbances are common during the summer and early fall. Sometimes, midlatitude weather disturbances can move into the tropics, become stranded there, and gradually acquire tropical characteristics. Whatever their origin, only a small percentage of tropical disturbances ever develop into full-fledged hurricanes. This is because conditions throughout the atmosphere must be such that rising air can be dispersed into the upper atmosphere. *Figure 13-11* shows a cross section of a hurricane.

Figure 13-11 In this hurricane cross section, the rising, moist air—indicated by small red arrows—forms clouds in bands around the eye. The photo shows the eye of a hurricane that formed over the Pacific Ocean in 1991.

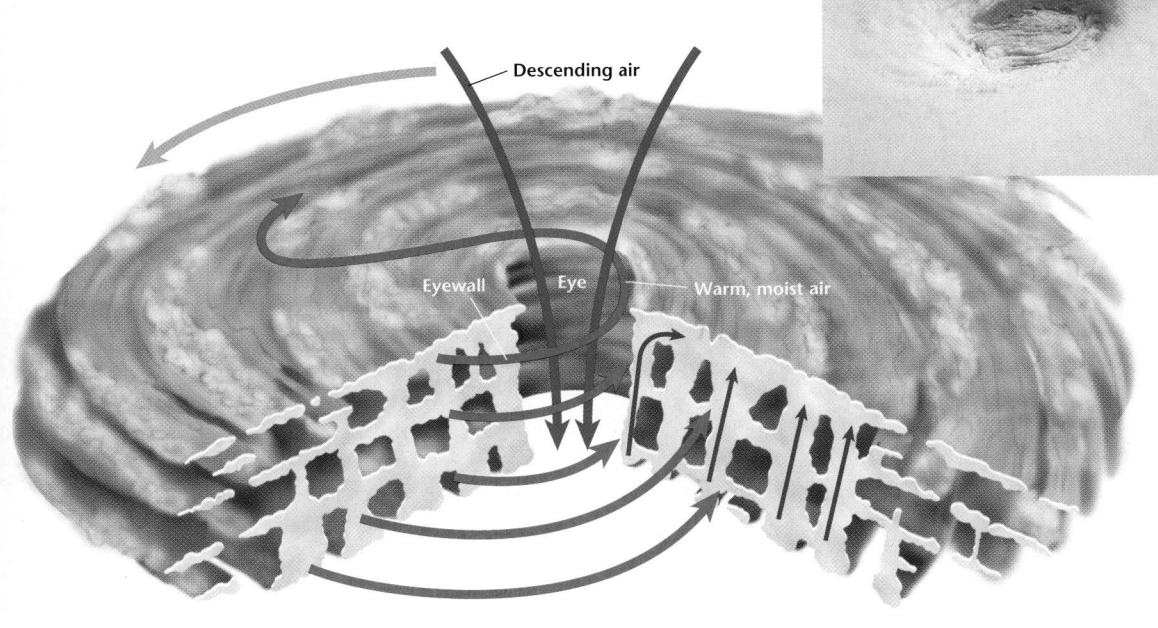

Descending air

Eyewall Eye Warm, moist air

Content Background

In the 1960s and early 1970s, the U.S. government initiated a program to weaken hurricanes. Called Project Stormfury, the experiment involved seeding a tropical cyclone with silver iodide. Massive amounts of condensation nuclei—in this case, silver iodide—were infused into the storm so that it would expend its energy through rainfall instead of wind. The results of the experiment were inconclusive.

Tying to Previous Knowledge

In Chapter 12, students were introduced to the concept of heat balance on Earth, which requires the transfer of energy from the tropics to the poles. In this section, students are introduced to one of the more dramatic methods by which this transfer takes place: the tropical cyclone. Fueled almost entirely by energy drawn from warm tropical waters, these massive storms play an important part in transporting energy from the warm tropics to the colder polar regions.

Concept Development

Like any other moving body on Earth's surface, a tropical cyclone is subject to the Coriolis effect. Thus, it will always try to move to the right of the direction in which it is traveling. This is why a storm moving westward across the tropical waters of the northern hemisphere eventually turns northward. Initially, its path is usually blocked by the large high-pressure systems that dominate these ocean areas. Once the storm reaches the edge of those systems, it is able to turn right and follow a recurring path, providing that no stronger weather systems interfere.

Using Math

2900 km ÷ 25 km/h = 116 h or 4.8 days

Identifying Misconceptions

Given the destructive power of hurricanes, many people wonder why these storms cannot be stopped while they are still weak.

Uncover the Misconception
Ask students to consider how much damage hurricanes can do, and whether it is a good idea to try to destroy them before they grow strong enough to be a problem. Several students likely will say that this is a good idea.

Demonstrate the Concept
Point out that even a weak tropical cyclone is so huge that not even an atomic device could destroy it. Next, point out that hurricanes play an important role in maintaining Earth's heat balance. The consequences could be severe if hurricanes were not allowed to fulfill this role. For instance, nature might well find another way to balance heat—one that could make hurricanes seem tame.

Assess New Knowledge
Help students realize that better preparation rather than destruction is the key to dealing effectively with hurricanes. Encourage students to suggest safety measures that can be taken before and during a hurricane. Also, have them discuss problems related to overdevelopment in hurricane-prone regions.

Using Math

Using Numbers
Suppose that a hurricane has been spotted at 25°N, 50°W, which is roughly 2900 km from Miami, Florida. The hurricane is moving west at 25 km/h. How long will it take the hurricane to reach Miami?

Table 13-4 Saffir-Simpson Hurricane Scale			
Scale Number (Category)	Sustained Winds (mph)	Damage	Examples of Hurricanes and the States Affected
1	74–95	Minimal	Florence, 1988 (LA) Charley, 1988 (NC)
2	96–110	Moderate	Kate, 1985 (FL Panhandle) Bob, 1991 (RI)
3	111–130	Extensive	Alicia, 1983 (N. TX) Emily, 1993 (NC Outer Banks)
4	131–155	Extreme	Andrew, 1992 (S. FL) Hugo, 1989 (SC)
5	> 155	Catastrophic	Camille, 1969 (LA/MS) Labor Day Hurricane, 1935 (FL Keys)

Source: National Weather Service

When a disturbance over a tropical ocean acquires a cyclonic circulation around a center of low pressure, it has reached the next developmental stage, which is known as a tropical depression. When wind speeds around the low-pressure center of a tropical depression exceed 65 km/h, the system is called a tropical storm. If air pressure continues to fall and winds around the center reach at least 120 km/h, the storm is officially classified as a hurricane. Once winds reach these speeds, another phenomenon takes place—the development of a calm center of the storm called an **eye.** The strongest winds in a hurricane are usually concentrated in a band immediately surrounding the eye called the **eyewall.**

CLASSIFYING HURRICANES
The **Saffir-Simpson hurricane scale** classifies hurricanes according to wind speed, air pressure in the center, and potential for property damage. As shown in *Table 13-4,* the Saffir-Simpson hurricane scale ranges from Category 1 hurricanes, which have minimum wind speeds of 74 mph (120 km/h), to the monstrous Category 5 storms, which can have winds in excess of 155 mph (250 km/h). Once a hurricane reaches Category 3 status, it is considered to be a major hurricane, with good reason. Most of the deadliest hurricanes that strike the United States were classified as major hurricanes.

Running Out of Energy A hurricane will last until it can no longer produce enough energy to sustain itself. This usually happens when the storm moves over land and no longer has access to the warm ocean surface from which it draws its energy, or when the

344 CHAPTER 13 *The Nature of Storms*

Resource Manager

Teaching Transparency 37 L2 ELL
Laboratory Manual, pp. 101–104 L2

344 CHAPTER 13

storm moves over colder water. During its life cycle, a hurricane can undergo several fluctuations in intensity as it interacts with other atmospheric systems.

HURRICANE HAZARDS

Hurricanes can cause a lot of damage, particularly along coastal areas where human populations have increased. Much of this damage is associated with violent winds. The strongest winds in a hurricane are usually confined to the eyewall, the band about 40 to 80 km wide that surrounds the calm eye. Outside of the eyewall, winds taper off with distance from the center, although winds of more than 60 km/h can extend as far as 400 km from the center of a hurricane.

Storm Surges Strong winds moving onshore in coastal areas are partly responsible for another major hurricane threat: storm surges. A **storm surge** occurs when hurricane-force winds drive a mound of ocean water toward coastal areas, where it washes over the land. Storm surges can sometimes reach 6 m above normal sea level, as shown in *Figure 13-12.* When this occurs during high tide, the surge can cause enormous damage. In the northern hemisphere, a storm surge occurs primarily on the right side of a storm relative to its eye, where the strongest onshore winds occur.

The heat released through the condensation of vast amounts of water vapor fuels hurricanes. This condensation also produces great amounts of rain. Thus, floods are an additional hurricane hazard, particularly if the storm moves over mountainous areas, where orographic lifting enhances the upward motion of air.

Figure 13-12 Storm surges can sometimes reach 6 m above normal sea level and cause enormous damage **(A).** This storm surge in the Florida Keys was caused by Hurricane Irene **(B).**

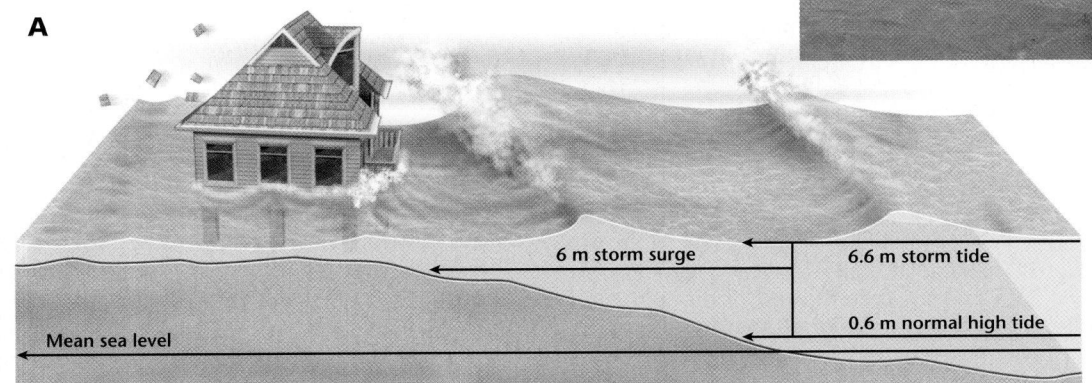

6 m storm surge
6.6 m storm tide
0.6 m normal high tide
Mean sea level

Modeling

Kinesthetic A storm surge occurs mainly because extreme winds blowing onshore in coastal areas pile up water, although the low pressure at the center of the storm also makes a contribution by allowing a small rise in sea level. Have students model a storm surge by filling a small pan of water nearly to the top and then blowing hard on the water. **CAUTION:** *Wipe up spills immediately to avoid accidents.* Make sure students blow outward from the center of the pan toward the edge. The water should pile up along the edge of the pan and overflow, simulating a storm surge. **L1** **ELL**

Using an Analogy

Tell students that a weakening hurricane is similar to a car that has run out of fuel. Just as the car's forward speed slows when it runs out of gas, a tropical cyclone's wind speed weakens when it runs out of the warm water from which it derives its energy.

Earth Science
Journal

Linguistic Have students each choose a coastal location in the hurricane belt that is as near as possible to their location. Students should research how past tropical cyclones have affected that location. Have students record in their science journals the names of the storms; when they struck land; their strength; and the damage they inflicted. **L2**

Check for Understanding

Discussion

Tell students that some of the strongest hurricanes on record have moved through the very warm waters of the western Caribbean Sea. Challenge students to explain why this area produces such strong storms. This very warm water contains a tremendous amount of energy for hurricanes to utilize.

Reteach

Interpersonal Have students work in groups to develop a chart that shows the path of an imaginary hurricane that strikes the Atlantic Coast of the United States. Students should show the developmental stages of the storm as it moves from the ocean to land and finally weakens. Students' hurricane charts should reflect knowledge of the content in this chapter. **L2**

✓Assessment

Performance Have students work in groups to prepare evacuation plans for residents of an area along the coast that will soon be struck by a hypothetical hurricane. Tell students that they have two days to set the plans in action. Have them use maps to show the areas that will be evacuated and the evacuation routes. Student groups can present their plans in booklets or pamphlets. Use the Performance Task Assessment List for Management Plan in **PASC,** p. 101.

Table 13-5 Hurricane Safety

- Turn the refrigerator to the maximum cold setting and open it only when necessary.
- Turn off utilities if told to do so by authorities.
- Unplug small appliances.
- Turn off propane tanks.
- Fill bathtubs and large containers with water for sanitary purposes.

If Winds Become Strong . . .

- Stay away from windows and doors even if they are covered. Take refuge in a small interior room, closet, or hallway.
- Close all interior doors. Secure and brace external doors.
- If you are in a two-story house, go to an interior first-floor room, such as a bathroom or closet.
- If you are in a multiple-story building and away from water, go to the first or second floor and take refuge in a hall or other interior room away from windows.
- Lie on the floor under a table or other sturdy object.

Source: NOAA

Hurricane Advisories The National Hurricane Center, which is responsible for tracking and forecasting the intensity and motion of tropical cyclones in the western hemisphere, issues a hurricane warning at least 24 hours before a hurricane strikes. The center also issues regular advisories that indicate a storm's position, strength, and movement. Using this information, people can then track a storm on a hurricane-tracking chart, such as the one you'll use in the *Internet GeoLab* at the end of this chapter. This type of awareness, combined with proper safety precautions such as those listed in *Table 13-5,* has greatly reduced death tolls associated with hurricanes in recent years.

SECTION ASSESSMENT

1. Identify the four main stages of a tropical cyclone.

2. Describe the changing wind systems that guide a tropical cyclone as it moves from the tropics to the midlatitudes.

3. Why don't tropical cyclones form in the South Atlantic Ocean or off the western coast of South America?

4. What two conditions must exist for a tropical cyclone to form?

5. **Thinking Critically** Suppose that you live on the eastern coast of the United States and are advised that the center of a hurricane is moving inland 70 km north of your location. Would you predict that a storm surge will be a major problem in your area? Why or why not?

SKILL REVIEW

6. **Making and Using Tables** Research at least ten hurricanes that have occurred throughout the world since 1980. Based on the Saffir-Simpson scale, make a data table showing wind speed, air pressure in the center, and property damage associated with each hurricane. For more help, refer to the *Skill Handbook.*

SECTION ASSESSMENT

1. tropical disturbance, tropical depression, tropical storm, and hurricane

2. In the deep tropics, the storm is steered by subtropical high-pressure systems. As the storm enters the midlatitudes, it is influenced by weather systems that move with the prevailing westerlies.

3. Sea-surface temperatures in these regions are lower than those in other tropical oceans, and the position of the ITCZ is farther north.

4. warm ocean temperatures and an already existing weather disturbance

5. No; because of the counterclockwise rotation of the storm in the northern hemisphere, the center of a hurricane moving north of a given location would create offshore winds. A storm surge is greatest where winds are onshore.

6. Tables will vary depending on which hurricanes students research. All tables should include information on wind speed, air pressure in the center of the hurricane, and property damage associated with each hurricane.

SECTION 13.4 *Recurring Weather*

On a hot, summer day, a sudden thunderstorm is a welcome event. Such rains are not so welcome, however, when they continue for hours or even days. Persistent or repetitive weather can negatively affect agriculture, transportation, and recreation.

FLOODS AND DROUGHTS

An individual thunderstorm can unleash enough rain to produce floods, and hurricanes are notorious for their torrential downpours. Floods can also occur, however, when weather patterns cause even mild storms to persist over the same area. For example, a storm with a rainfall rate of 1.5 cm/h is not much of a problem—providing that it lasts only an hour or two. If this same storm were to remain over one spot for 18 hours, however, total rainfall would be 27 cm, which is more than enough to create flooding in most areas. You will learn more about floods in the *MiniLab* on the following page.

On the other hand, too much dry weather can create nearly as much havoc as too much rainfall. **Droughts** are extended periods of well-below-normal rainfall. One of the most extreme droughts occurred during the 1930s in the Central United States. *Figure 13-13* shows a dust storm that occurred in the Dust Bowl, which was the name given to the affected states. This extended drought put countless farmers out of business, as rainfall for several seasons was inadequate to grow crops.

OBJECTIVES

- **Describe** *recurring weather patterns and the problems they create.*
- **Identify** *atmospheric events that cause recurring weather patterns.*

VOCABULARY

drought
heat wave
cold wave
wind-chill factor

Figure 13-13 The dust blowing over this highway was caused by a severe drought in the Central United States during the 1930s.

13.4 *Recurring Weather* **347**

Content Background

Tell students that of all weather events, flooding probably causes the most problems for humans. Flooding can be caused by a stationary jet stream, which allows a succession of stormy weather systems to affect the same general area for days. Floods also can develop from a single, slow-moving thunderstorm or a violent tropical cyclone.

Resource Manager

Section Focus Transparency 39 L1 ELL
Study Guide for Content Mastery, p. 84 L2

Prepare

Section Background

For section content background, refer to **Repercussions of Recurring Weather** on page 328D.

Preplanning

Refer to the Chapter Organizer on pages 328A–B.

1 Focus

Section Focus

Before presenting the lesson, display **Section Focus Transparency 39** on the overhead projector.
L1 ELL

Tying to Previous Knowledge

Students have learned how the jet stream changes positions and steers weather systems. Sometimes, however, the position of the jet stream does not change appreciably with time. This can result in recurring weather patterns.

MiniLab

Purpose
Students will demonstrate how slow-moving weather systems can cause floods.

Process Skills
model, observe and infer, analyze

Materials
large sink or tub; ice-cube tray; clean, dishwashing-detergent bottle with pull cap; metric ruler; water

Troubleshooting
- Wipe up spills immediately to avoid accidents.
- Let students practice maintaining a steady flow of water prior to conducting the MiniLab.

Expected Results
Moving the bottle slowly will produce a greater depth of water in the tray than does moving the bottle quickly.

Analyze and Conclude
1. The average depth decreased in step 5 because the water fell over each compartment in a shorter amount of time.
2. Storms that move slowly can release more rain over any one place than can storms that move quickly.
3. speed up or slow down the motion of the water bottle; open or close the twist top slightly to simulate heavier or lighter rainfall

✔ Assessment

Knowledge Tell students that the ability of the ground to absorb water has a major effect on flooding. Ask them to infer which would cause more flooding: saturated ground or dry ground. Saturated ground would cause more flooding than dry ground, which would absorb some of the rain. **L2**

MiniLab

How can mild rains cause floods?

Model the effects of repeated, slow-moving storms that drop rain over the same area for a long period of time.

Procedure 🔧 🥽
1. Place an ice-cube tray on the bottom of a large sink or tub.
2. Pour water into a clean, plastic dishwashing-detergent bottle until it is two-thirds full. Replace the cap on the bottle.
3. Hold the bottle upside down with the cap open about 8 cm above one end of the ice-cube tray. Gently squeeze the bottle to maintain a constant flow of water into the tray. Slowly move the bottle from one end of the tray to the other over the course of 30 seconds. Try to put approximately equal amounts of water in each ice-cube compartment.
4. Measure the depth of water in each compartment. Calculate the average depth.
5. Repeat steps 1–4, but move the bottle across the ice-cube tray in 15 seconds.

Analyze and Conclude
1. How did the average depth of the water differ in steps 4 and 5? How might you account for the difference?
2. Based on these results, infer how the speed of a moving storm affects the amount of rain received in any one area.
3. How could you alter the experiment to simulate different rates of rainfall?

Droughts are usually the result of shifts in global wind patterns that allow large high-pressure systems to persist for weeks or months over continental areas. Under a dome of high pressure, air sinks on a large scale. Because the sinking air will resist any attempt to lift moisture through it, condensation cannot occur, and drought will set in until global patterns shift enough to move the high-pressure system out of the way.

Heat Waves An unpleasant side effect of droughts often comes in the form of **heat waves,** which are extended periods of above-normal temperatures. Heat waves can be formed by the same high-pressure systems that cause droughts. As the air under a large high-pressure system sinks, it warms by compression and causes above-normal temperatures. The high-pressure system also blocks cooler air masses from moving into the area, so there is little relief from the heat. Because it is difficult for condensation to occur under the sinking air of the high-pressure system, there are few, if any, clouds to block the blazing sunshine. To make matters worse, the jet stream, or "atmospheric railway," that weather systems follow is farther north and weaker during the summer. Thus, the upper-air currents that might guide the high-pressure system are so weak that the system scarcely moves.

Even increasing humidity does not ease the discomfort of a heat wave. Human bodies cool by evaporating moisture from the surface of the skin. In the process, heat is removed from the body. If air is humid, the rate of evaporation is reduced, which diminishes the body's ability to regulate internal temperature. In heat waves, this can lead to serious health problems such as heatstroke, sunstroke, and even death.

Applying Earth Science

Floods and droughts affect food prices. When these weather events occur in agricultural areas, they can wipe out entire crops over large areas. This creates a shortage of the affected crops, which in turn drives up food prices. Food prices also increase because farmers must offset their losses, and thus they charge more for whatever portion of the crops they are able to salvage.

Resource Manager

GeoLab and MiniLab Worksheets, p. 51 **L2**

Relative Humidity (%)	Air Temperature (°F)										
	70	75	80	85	90	95	100	105	110	115	120
	Apparent Temperature (°F)										
0	64	69	73	78	83	87	91	95	99	103	107
10	65	70	75	80	85	90	95	100	105	111	116
20	66	72	77	82	87	93	99	105	112	120	130
30	67	73	78	84	90	96	104	113	123	135	148
40	68	74	79	86	93	101	110	123	137	151	
50	69	75	81	88	96	107	120	135	150		
60	70	76	82	90	100	114	132	149			
70	70	77	85	93	106	124	144				
80	71	78	86	97	113	136					
90	71	79	88	102	122						
100	72	80	91	108							

Table 13-6 The Heat Index

Source: National Weather Service, NOAA

Because of the extreme dangers posed by the lethal combination of heat and humidity, the National Weather Service routinely reports the heat index, shown in *Table 13-6.* Note that the National Weather Service uses the Fahrenheit scale in the heat index because most U.S. citizens are most familiar with this scale. The heat index assesses the effect of the body's increasing difficulty in regulating its internal temperature as relative humidity rises. For example, an air temperature of 85°F (29°C) combined with relative humidity of 80 percent would require the body to cool itself at the same rate as if the air temperature were 97°F (36°C). Do the *Problem-Solving Lab* on the following page to learn more about heat waves.

COLD WAVES

The flip side of a heat wave is a **cold wave,** which is an extended period of below-normal temperatures. Interestingly, cold waves are also brought on by large, high-pressure systems. However, cold waves are caused by systems of continental polar or arctic origin. During the arctic winter, little sunlight is available to provide warmth. At the same time, the snow-covered surface is constantly radiating its limited heat back to space. The combined effect of these two factors is the development of large pools of extremely cold air over polar continental areas. Because cold air sinks, the pressure near the surface increases, creating a strong high-pressure system.

13.4 Recurring Weather **349**

Environmental Connection

Drought and heat waves often occur together because the same sinking air that blocks precipitation also causes warming by air compression. This combination significantly impacts ecosystems. As streams, creeks, and ponds dry up, oxygen levels in the water decrease and aquatic life suffers.

Project

Logical-Mathematical Heat-index values are classified according to their threat to health and safety. Values between 80° and 90°F are in the "Caution" range; those between 90° and 105°F are in the "Extreme Caution" range, those between 105° and 120°F are in the "Danger" range, and those above 120°F fall into the "Extreme Danger" range. Have students research average summer temperatures and humidity levels for their location. Students can use the heat index to determine the classification of summer temperatures and humidity levels in their area. **L2** **P**

NY Core Curriculum Standards

Page 348: St 1 Math KI 2, 3, Science 1, 2, & 3, St 4 KI 2.1e, 2.1h, & 2.1i, St 6 KI 1, St 7 KI 1
Page 349: St 2 KI 3, St 4 KI 2.1e, 2.1h, & 2.1i, St 6 KI 1

Purpose

Students will graph and analyze the progress of a heat wave.

Process Skills

make and use graphs, use numbers, make and use tables, infer, predict

Materials

graph paper, pencil, ruler

Teaching Strategies

Ask students whether they have ever experienced a severe heat wave. Those students who answer in the affirmative can share their experiences with the class.

Analysis

1. See annos on the student page.
2. & 3. Graphs should reflect lab data.

Thinking Critically

4. The heat wave began on day 3 and lasted until day 7.
5. The average temperature during the heat wave was 85.8°F. The average temperature of the remaining days was 83°F.
6. wear loose-fitting clothing, drink water, stay out of sunlight

✔Assessment

Knowledge Cold waves are the result of masses of very cold air that spread southward across land.
Ask students the following question. Which of the following types of air masses would most likely be associated with cold waves?
a. continental polar
b. maritime polar
c. arctic
d. continental tropical
The answer is a and c.

NY Core Curriculum Standards

Page 350: St 1 Math KI 1, 2, & 3, St 2 KI 3, St 4 KI 2.1e, 2.1h, & 2.1i, St 6 KI 1, St 7 KI 1 & 2
Page 351: St 2 KI 3, St 4 KI 2.1e, 2.1h, & 2.1i, St 6 KI 1 & 5, St 7 KI 1 & 2

Because of the location and the time of year in which they occur, winter high-pressure systems are much more influenced by the jet stream than are summer high-pressure systems. Moved along by the jet stream, these high-pressure systems rarely linger in any area. However, the winter location of the jet stream may remain essentially unchanged for days or even weeks. This means that several polar high-pressure systems can follow the same path and subject the same areas to bout after bout of numbing cold. *Figure 13-14* shows some effects of prolonged periods of cold weather.

Because wind transports heat away from the body, the effects of cold air are worsened by wind. This phenomenon is known as the **wind-chill factor.** The wind-chill factor is measured by the wind-chill index, which estimates the heat loss from human skin caused by the combination of cold air and wind. This index estimates how cold the air actually feels to the human body. As with the heat index, the National Weather Service records the wind-chill index in U.S. units

Problem-Solving Lab

Making and Using Graphs

Charting a heat wave The following data represent the daily maximum and minimum temperatures for ten consecutive summer days in a major city.

Daily Temperatures			
Day	Maximum	Minimum	Average
1	92	76	84
2	91	75	83
3	94	78	86
4	95	75	85
5	93	77	85
6	96	76	86
7	94	80	87
8	96	72	84
9	92	74	83
10	94	68	81

Analysis

1. Copy the data table in your science journal. Calculate the average temperature for each day, then include those temperatures in your data table.

2. Plot the daily maximum temperatures on a graph with the days on the x-axis and the maximum temperatures on the y-axis. Connect the data points to show how the maximum temperature changed over the ten-day period.

3. Repeat step 2 for the minimum and average temperatures.

Thinking Critically

4. A heat wave is defined as two or more consecutive days with an average temperature of 85°F or higher. On what day did the city begin its heat wave? How long did the heat wave last?

5. Calculate the average temperature for the days of the heat wave only. Compare this to the average temperature of the remaining days.

6. What safety measures could residents of the city take to minimize the effects of a heat wave?

Interpreting the Photo

Figure 13-14 Have students study the photographs and describe the impacts of cold waves on human activities. Students may mention that a severe cold wave can pose a hazard to health, temporarily halt all forms of transportation and recreation, and close down businesses and schools.

Resource Manager

Teaching Transparency 38 L2 ELL

Figure 13-14 An ice storm in 1990 damaged utility lines in Watertown, New York **(A)**. Nearly 2.3 m of snow fell near Lake Ontario in 1996 **(B)**.

for the sake of convenience. While the wind-chill index is helpful, it does not account for individual variations in sensitivity to cold, the effects of physical activity, or humidity. Some scientists, noting that this system has been in place since the 1940s, are calling for the development of new methods that more accurately estimate the effects of cold weather on the human body.

SECTION ASSESSMENT

1. Why are droughts usually associated with high-pressure systems?

2. Describe a situation wherein a relatively light rain could cause flooding.

3. Compare and contrast a cold wave and a heat wave.

4. What is the wind-chill factor? What does the wind-chill index measure?

5. Using *Table 13-6,* estimate the heat index for air with a temperature of 80°F and relative humidity of 90 percent.

6. Extreme floods occur more often in summer than any other time of the year. Use your knowledge of the jet stream to explain why this is true.

7. **Thinking Critically** Air in a summer high-pressure system warms by compression. Based on what you know about molecular motion, explain why air in a winter high-pressure system doesn't warm by compression, too.

SKILL REVIEW

8. **Forming a Hypothesis** A key requirement for the formation of snow is cold air. Yet some parts of the United States have more annual snowfall than Canada, which is farther north and should therefore be colder. Form a hypothesis to explain the apparent discrepancy. For more help, refer to the *Skill Handbook.*

Check for Understanding

Reinforcement

Ask students to identify various recurring weather events and to explain some dangers associated with these events.

Reteach

Intrapersonal Ask several students to each state a safety rule for floods, heat waves, or cold waves. Students should defend their safety rules with scientific reasoning. **L1**

✓Assessment

Portfolio Have students research a heat wave or cold wave that occurred in their area. For information, they can contact the local branch of the National Weather Service. Students also can use the Earth Science Web Site, newspaper articles, and interviews of local residents. **L2** **P**

SECTION ASSESSMENT

1. High-pressure systems cause air to sink and thus block the upward vertical motion necessary for clouds and precipitation to form.

2. If light rain was to fall for a prolonged period of time, it could cause flooding, particularly if the soil was already saturated and the terrain was hilly.

3. A heat wave develops when a strong, subtropical high-pressure system stalls over an area for an extended period of time, causing dry weather and heating the lower atmosphere through compression. A cold wave takes place when a high-pressure system of arctic origin sweeps into an area; a cold wave usually moves on within a few days.

4. The wind-chill factor describes the effects of cold air and wind on the human body. The wind-chill index measures heat loss from human skin.

5. 88°F

6. Because the jet stream is weak during the summer, cold fronts tend to become stationary, which can lead to heavy rains.

7. Cold temperatures slow molecular motion. The increase in motion of molecules of air caused by compression cannot overcome this pronounced slowing.

8. A sample hypothesis might be, "More moisture must be available in those areas of the United States that have more snow than Canada."

351

Internet GeoLab

Tracking a Hurricane

Hurricanes are violent storms. That's why it's important to have plenty of advance warning before they hit land. By tracking the changing position of a storm on a chart and connecting these positions with a line, you can determine a hurricane's path.

Time Allotment

two to three hours for data collection on the Internet or at the library; an hour and a half for the procedure

Process Skills

make and use tables, communicate, collect data, interpret data, observe and infer, interpret scientific illustrations, predict

Preparation

Special Instructions

If you do not have access to the Internet, use historical data available from the library or from the local National Weather Service office.

Possible Hypotheses

Hypotheses will vary depending on the hurricane chosen. Most students should hypothesize that damage increases with proximity to a storm, especially in areas on the right side of the storm center in relation to the storm's direction of motion. This is where onshore winds occur.

Plan the Experiment

Teaching Strategies

- This lab can be done in groups of three or as an individual project. If students are working in groups, one student can obtain data, another can develop the data table, and a third can plot the hurricane's track. Students can trade roles for each hurricane they research.

Preparation

Problem

What information can you obtain by studying the path of a hurricane?

Hypothesis

Gather information about the path of a hurricane. **Form a hypothesis** about how the hurricane's path can be used to predict the strength of the storm and where most damage might be inflicted.

Objectives

- **Gather** and **communicate** data about hurricanes.
- **Plot** data on a hurricane-tracking chart.
- **Predict** where storm-inflicted damage might occur.

Data Sources

Go to the Earth Science Web site at earthgeu.com to find links to hurricane data, or use information provided by your teacher. Make copies of the hurricane-tracking chart in this lab or download a chart from the Web site.

Plan the Experiment

1. Find a resource that lists major hurricanes that have occurred within the past five years. The Earth Science Web site provides a list of sites that have information about hurricanes.
2. Choose a hurricane to research. Some recent major hurricanes include Hurricane Claudette, Hurricane Isabel, and Hurricane Floyd.
3. Gather data about the hurricane from the links on the Earth Science Web site or the library.

Procedure

1. Incorporate your research into a data table. Add any additional information that you think is important.
2. Go to the Earth Science Web site at earthgeu.com to post your data.
3. Visit sites listed on the Earth Science Web site for information on other major hurricanes.

- Obtain hurricane charts of historical hurricanes so that students can observe storm paths.
- Review the concepts of latitude and longitude before proceeding with this lab.

Possible Procedures

Students will gather data from Internet sites, which can be accessed through the Earth Science Web Site. Based on the data gathered, students will prepare tables and plot information on their hurricane-tracking charts. Conclude & Apply questions should reflect information in students' tables and tracking charts.

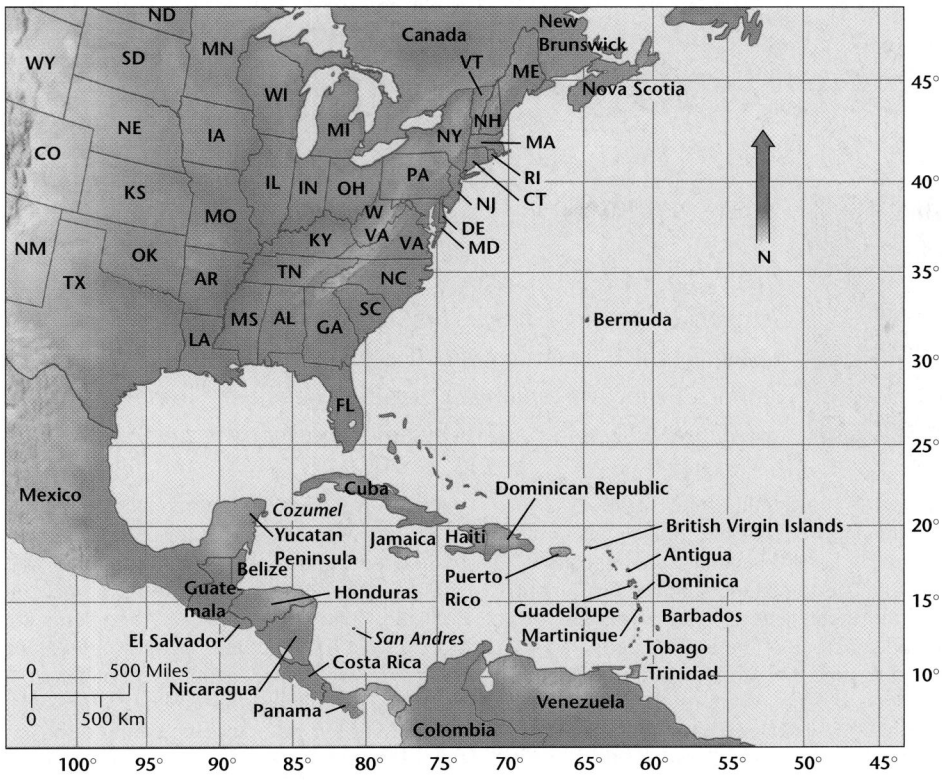

Data and Observations

Data tables should include six hourly latitude and longitude positions, maximum wind speeds, and minimum central pressures. Tracking charts should show the six hourly positions connected by a straight line to form a track.

Conclude & Apply

1–5. Answers will vary depending on which hurricane students researched.

6. The storm surge would be strongest on the side of the storm where onshore winds developed as the storm center moved inland.

7. Wind speeds decrease rapidly when a storm center moves inland because the storm becomes cut off from its energy source and weakens.

Sharing Your Data

Post your students' data on the Earth Science Web Site. Compare your students' findings with those of other classrooms around the country.

Conclude & Apply

Sharing Your Data Find this *Internet GeoLab* on the Earth Science Web site at earthgeu.com. Post your data in the table provided for this activity. Use the additional data from other students to complete your chart and answer the Conclude & Apply questions.

1. Plot the position, air pressure, wind speed, and stage of the hurricane at six-hour intervals throughout its existence.
2. Plot the changing position of the hurricane on your hurricane-tracking chart.
3. What was the maximum wind speed in knots that the hurricane reached?

4. Multiply the value from question 3 by 1.15 to find the wind speed in miles per hour. Based on this value, how would the hurricane be classified on the Saffir-Simpson scale?
5. Using your completed hurricane-tracking chart, list the landmasses over which the hurricane passed.
6. Where would you expect the storm surge to have been greatest? Explain. Compare your answer to the information you gathered on the damage inflicted by the storm. Was your answer correct?
7. How was the hurricane's strength affected when its center passed over land?

Internet GeoLab **353**

✓Assessment

Performance Have students mount their data tables and tracking charts on poster-board. Display them around the room. Provide time for each student or group to present its findings to the class. Use the Performance Task Assessment List for Poster in **PASC,** p. 73.

Resource Manager

GeoLab and MiniLab Worksheets, pp. 52–54 L2

NY Core Curriculum Standards

Page 352: St 1 Science KI 3, St 2 KI 1, 2, & 3, St 4 KI 2.1c & 2.1g
Page 353: St 1 Math KI 2 & Science KI 3, St 2 KI 1, 2, & 3, St 4 KI 2.1c & 2.1g

Purpose

Students will learn about laser-triggered lightning, which has been successfully tested outdoors by scientists in Japan.

Content Background

Lightning occurs when the charges in a thundercloud become separated. The bottom of the cloud becomes negatively charged and the top becomes positively charged. The mechanism of this separation is not wholly understood. It is generally hypothesized that large raindrops and hail become charged by friction as they fall through the cloud. The negative cloud bottom attracts positive charges to Earth's surface. When there are enough charges, the air, which is normally an insulator, becomes a conductor, and charges flow between a cloud and Earth. The charges surge upward from the ground at an amazing speed of 129 000 000 m/s. Lightning may also take place within a cloud or between two clouds.

Teaching Strategies

Ask students to sequence the events leading up to an afternoon thunderstorm. Have them list each stage on the chalkboard. Very warm, humid air is rapidly forced up by cooler air. Strong convection currents form. The rising warm air cools to its dew point and cumulonimbus clouds form. Water droplets stick together, and rain and hail start to fall.

Science & Technology

Taming Lightning

In a high-voltage laboratory in Canada, scientists experiment with lightning on a regular basis. Their goal is to one day work outside, triggering lightning bolts and directing them safely away from people and property. They are among a group of scientists worldwide who are developing new and better ways to tame lightning before it strikes.

Each year in the United States, lightning accounts for 7500 forest fires, roughly 93 deaths, several hundred injuries, and millions of dollars in damage to communications equipment, buildings, electrical systems, and power lines. To guard against loss of life and property, most homes and commercial structures are equipped with lightning-protection systems. These systems use lightning rods—slender metal rods placed upon rooftops—to gather positive charges from the ground. The positive charges attract the negative charges in the base of a thundercloud and neutralize them split seconds before they coalesce into a lightning strike. Aluminum or copper cables act as conducters, connecting the lightning rods to ground terminators, which are metal rods buried beneath the soil. The function of these rods is to guide the electrical current harmlessly into the ground.

Lightning-protection systems such as these have been around since Benjamin Franklin flew his kite in a storm some 200 years ago, demonstrating conclusively that lightning is indeed electricity. Today, one of the most promising areas of lightning-protection research involves something that Benjamin Franklin never had at his disposal—laser beams.

Home-Grown Lightning

Let's return to the high-voltage lab in Canada. There, scientists use two huge, circular elec-

trodes to re-create the natural conditions that result in a shocking bolt of lightning. One electrode is suspended about 6 m above the other. The top electrode represents the base of a thundercloud. The bottom electrode represents the ground. Just as in nature, negative charges flow down from the "thundercloud" and positive charges flow up from the "ground." The wave of current that surges upward to meet the downward discharge results in the bright, jagged flash known as lightning.

The goal of these scientists, however, is not simply to model lightning. They want to learn how to harness lightning—to trigger controlled strikes and guide them to safe locations. To do this, the scientists aim a laser beam through a hole in the center of the bottom electrode. The beam displaces electrons from charged particles in the air, simultaneously provoking a lightning strike and providing a guided path for the discharge to follow. Instead of a jagged bolt of lightning, the controlled strike is as straight as a laser beam.

Activity

Where's the safest place to be during a thunderstorm? If you're caught outside in the open, what should you do? Research lightning safety tips, then develop a safety brochure for distribution at your school.

Activity

Students should realize that the safest place to be during a thunderstorm is inside a building or car. If they are caught outside, they should avoid standing under trees because lightning seeks the shortest path to the ground, and trees provide that path. Student brochures should be scientifically accurate.

Summary

SECTION 13.1
Thunderstorms

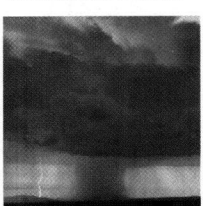

Main Ideas
- For a thunderstorm to occur, there must be abundant moisture in the lower levels of the atmosphere and a mechanism to lift the moisture so it can condense. In addition, the air must be unstable so that the growing cloud will continue to rise.
- Thunderstorms are classified according to the mechanism that caused the air to rise. In an air-mass thunderstorm, the cloud rises because of unequal heating of Earth's surface within one air mass. In a frontal thunderstorm, the air rises because it is pushed up by an advancing air mass.

Vocabulary
air-mass thunder-storm (p. 331)
frontal thunderstorm (p. 331)
sea-breeze thunder-storm (p. 331)

SECTION 13.2
Severe Weather

Main Ideas
- Lightning is produced when an advancing stepped leader unites with an upward-moving return stroke. Thunder is the sound made by the rapid expansion of air around the lightning bolt as a result of extreme heating of the lightning channel.
- Thunderstorms can damage property and cause loss of life. The hazards of thunderstorms include lightning, violent winds, hail, floods, and tornadoes.
- The Fujita tornado intensity scale classifies tornadoes according to wind speed, path of destruction, and duration.

Vocabulary
downburst (p. 336)
Fujita tornado inten-sity scale (p. 338)
supercell (p. 334)
tornado (p. 338)

SECTION 13.3
Tropical Storms

Main Ideas
- Tropical cyclones derive their energy from the evaporation of warm ocean water and the release of heat.
- The Saffir-Simpson hurricane scale classifies hurricanes according to intensity.
- Hurricane hazards include violent winds, floods, and storm surges. The National Hurricane Center tracks hurricanes and issues advance warnings to help reduce loss of life.

Vocabulary
eye (p. 344)
eyewall (p. 344)
Saffir-Simpson hurricane scale (p. 344)
storm surge (p. 345)
tropical cyclone (p. 341)

SECTION 13.4
Recurring Weather

Main Ideas
- Examples of persistent weather events include floods, droughts, cold waves, and heat waves.
- The heat index assesses the impact of humidity combined with excessive heat on the human body. The wind-chill index esti-mates the heat loss from human skin caused by a combination of cold air and wind.

Vocabulary
cold wave (p. 349)
drought (p. 347)
heat wave (p. 348)
wind-chill factor (p. 350)

Main Ideas

Summary statements can be used by students to review the major concepts of the chapter.

VOCABULARY PuzzleMaker

 For additional help with vocabulary, have students access the Vocabulary Puzzlemaker online.

earthgeu.com/ vocabulary puzzlemaker

0:00 *Out of Time?*

If time does not permit teaching the entire chapter, use the GeoDigest at the end of the unit as an overview.

Earth Science Online

Be sure to check the Earth Science Web Site for links to chapter material:
earthgeu.com

GLENCOE
Technology

Videotape/DVD
MindJogger Videoquizzes
Chapter 13: *The Nature of Storms*
Have students work in groups as they play the videoquiz game to review key chapter concepts.

Resource Manager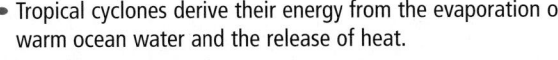

Chapter Assessment, pp. 73–78
MindJogger Videoquizzes DVD/VHS
ExamView® Pro CD-ROM
Performance Assessment in Earth Science

NY Core Curriculum Standards

Page 354: St 1 Science KI 3, St 2 KI 1, St 4 KI 2.1c
Page 355: St 4 KI 2.1c, 2.1e, 2.1h, 2.1i, & 2.2a, St 6 KI 1 & 4

355

CHAPTER 13
Assessment

Understanding Main Ideas

1. b
2. c
3. a
4. c
5. b
6. c
7. a
8. b
9. a
10. b
11. b
12. d
13. b
14. Tornadoes are small, intense, low-pressure systems that derive their energy from the clash of air masses. Tornadoes form when wind shear creates a horizontal circulation that is tilted into a vertical position by intense updrafts. Hurricanes are large, strong, low-pressure systems that derive their energy from warm ocean waters. Hurricanes produce strong winds, heavy rainfall, and storm surges.
15. The boundary along a cold front is much steeper than the boundary along a warm front. This causes the air in a cold front to rise more rapidly and produces the strong updrafts that cause the storm to become severe.

Understanding Main Ideas

1. Which of the following would work against the development of a thunderstorm?
   a. rising air   c. moisture
   b. stable air   d. unstable air

2. Which of the following does NOT describe a type of damaging thunderstorm wind?
   a. downburst   c. land breeze
   b. microburst   d. macroburst

3. Flooding is most likely to take place because of rains associated with what type of front?
   a. stationary front   c. cold front
   b. occluded front   d. warm front

4. During what stage of a tropical cyclone does an eyewall develop?
   a. tropical depression c. hurricane
   b. tropical storm   d. tropical wave

5. What is the first stage of a lightning bolt?
   a. return stroke   c. positive charge
   b. stepped leader   d. downdraft

6. Which of the following does NOT play a key role in the development of hail?
   a. supercooled water   c. warm ocean water
   b. strong downdrafts   d. strong updrafts

7. Heat waves involve high-pressure systems that cause air to sink and warm by which of the following processes?
   a. compression   c. evaporation
   b. conduction   d. condensation

8. Which of the following weather hazards involves lack of moisture?
   a. hail   c. storm surge
   b. drought   d. flood

9. What percentage of tornadoes are classified as F4 or F5 on the Fujita tornado intensity scale?
   a. one percent   c. 50 percent
   b. ten percent   d. 75 percent

10. Which of the following factors, if increased, would make a thunderstorm severe?
    a. temperature   c. duration
    b. surface moisture   d. conduction

11. Which way do hurricanes rotate in the southern hemisphere?
    a. south   c. counterclockwise
    b. clockwise   d. north

12. In which ocean would you NOT expect to experience a tropical cyclone?
    a. West Pacific   c. North Atlantic
    b. Indian   d. South Atlantic

13. What weather events are cold waves most often associated with?
    a. floods
    b. polar high-pressure systems
    c. tropical high-pressure systems
    d. droughts

14. Compare and contrast tornadoes and hurricanes.

15. Why are cold fronts more likely to produce severe thunderstorms than warm fronts?

earthgeu.com/chapter_test

Applying Main Ideas

16. 100°F
17. Category 3
18. point A; in the northern hemisphere, the storm surge is greatest on the right side of the hurricane in relation to its direction of motion
19. Seek shelter in a sturdy dwelling, preferably in a basement or an interior room away from windows. Cover your face and head. Understand the difference between a tornado watch and a tornado warning. Be ready to take quick action if a warning is issued for your area.
20. the South Atlantic Ocean and the Pacific Ocean west of the South American Coast; ocean waters are cooler and the ITCZ is positioned farther north

Applying Main Ideas

16. Using *Table 13-6,* determine the heat index if the temperature is 90°F and relative humidity is 60 percent.

17. Using *Table 13-4,* classify a hurricane with a maximum wind speed of 120 mph.

Use the illustration of a hurricane in the northern hemisphere to answer question 18.

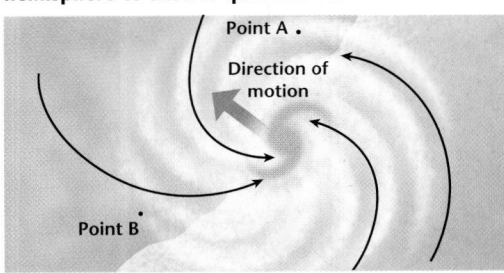

18. Would a storm surge be more likely to occur at point A or point B? Why?

19. How might you prepare for a tornado? What safety measures would you recommend?

20. In which oceans would you NOT expect to experience a tropical cyclone? Why?

Thinking Critically

21. Extreme cold waves are more common in the northern hemisphere than in the southern hemisphere. Why?

22. Tropical cyclones are never observed within about 5° north and south latitudes. What do you think might account for this?

23. Supercells that produce tornadoes often produce large hailstones as well. Explain.

24. Why are boats on lakes or on the ocean especially vulnerable to lightning strikes?

earthgeu.com/standardized_test

Standardized Test Practice

INTERPRETING SCIENTIFIC ILLUSTRATIONS
Use the illustration below to answer questions 1 and 2.

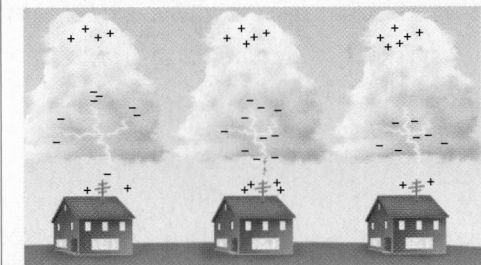

1. Which type of cloud is lightning associated with?
- **a.** altocumulus
- **b.** stratocumulus
- **c.** cirrus
- **d.** cumulonimbus

2. Lightning is the illumination that occurs when an invisible channel of negatively charged air descends to the ground and a channel of positively charged ions rushes upward to meet it. What is the channel of positively charged ions called?
- **a.** return stroke
- **b.** stepped leader
- **c.** ground stroke
- **d.** electronic leader

3. What occurs when winds of at least 120 km/h drive a mound of ocean water toward coastal areas?
- **a.** downburst
- **b.** cold wave
- **c.** storm surge
- **d.** tornado

4. Which factor is NOT associated with a heat wave?
- **a.** a high-pressure system
- **b.** a weakened jet stream
- **c.** above-normal temperatures
- **d.** increased cloud cover

Thinking Critically

21. More of the southern hemisphere is covered by water; water retains more heat than land, which makes it more difficult for large pools of cold air to develop without being quickly modified by the ocean water.

22. This area is too close to the equator for the Coriolis effect —which does not exist at the equator—to deflect winds, which allows wind rotation to occur.

23. Both large hail and tornadoes are the result of the very intense updrafts that are common in supercells.

24. The return strokes that are necessary to complete a lightning channel are more likely to come from objects that are relatively tall. On the open water, there are no trees, hills, or buildings—boats are the tallest objects around.

EXAMVIEW® PRO

Use ExamView® Pro Testmaker CD-ROM to:

- Create **multiple versions** of tests.
- Create **modified** tests with one mouse click for struggling students.
- **Edit** existing questions and add your own questions.
- **Build** tests based on national curriculum standards.

Standardized Test Practice

1. d
2. a
3. c
4. d

NY Core Curriculum Standards

Page 356: St 4 KI 2.1e, 2.1f, 2.1h, 2.1i, 2.2b, & 2.2c, St 6 KI 1, 4, & 5
Page 357: St 1 Math KI 1, 2, & 3, St 4 KI 2.1e, 2.1f, 2.1h, 2.1i, 2.2a, 2.2b, & 2.2c, St 6 KI 1, 4, & 5

Chapter 14 Climate

Refer to pages 8T–9T of the Teacher Guide for an explanation of the National Science Content Standards correlations.

Section	Objectives	National Science Content Standards	State/Local Standards
SECTION 14.1 **What is climate?** 🕐 ½ session 🧊 ¼ block	1. **Describe** different types of climate data. 2. **Recognize** limits associated with the use of normals. 3. **Explain** why climates vary.	UCP.1, UCP.2, UCP.3; A.1, A.2; D.1; F.4, F.6; G.3	St 1 Math KI 1, 2, 3, Science KI 1, 2, & 3, St 4 KI 1.1f, 2.1c, 2.1h, 2.1i, 2.2a, 2.2b, 2.2c, & 2.2d, St 6 KI 5, St 7 KI 1
SECTION 14.2 **Climate Classification** 🕐 ½ session 🧊 ¼ block	4. **Describe** the criteria used to classify climates. 5. **Compare** and **contrast** different climates.	UCP.1, UCP.2, UCP.3; D.1; F.5, F.6	St 1 Math KI 2 & 3, St 4 KI 2.1f, 2.1i, 2.2a, 2.2b, & 2.2c, St 6 KI 1 & 2
SECTION 14.3 **Climatic Changes** 🕐 1½ sessions 🧊 1 block	6. **Distinguish** among different types of climatic changes. 7. **Recognize** why climatic changes occur.	UCP.1, UCP.2, UCP.3; D.1, D.2, D.3; F.6; G.3	St 4 KI 1.1f, 1.2j, 2.1c, 2.1i, 2.2a, 2.2b, 2.2c, & 2.2d, St 6 KI 1, 2, & 5
SECTION 14.4 **The Human Factor** 🕐 2½ sessions 🧊 1½ blocks	8. **Compare** and **contrast** the greenhouse effect and global warming. 9. **Identify** how humans impact climate.	UCP.1, UCP.2, UCP.3; A.1, A.2; D.1, D.3; F.3, F.4, F.5, F.6; G3	St 1 Science KI 1, 2, 3, & Engin KI 1, St 4 KI 2.1c, 2.1d, 2.1f, 2.1i, 2.2a, 2.2b, 2.2c, & 2.2d, St 6 KI 1, 2 & 5

A complete Planning Guide is provided on pages 30T–32T.

🕐 The number of recommended single-period sessions

🧊 The number of recommended blocks

Activity Materials

Discovery Lab *page 359*
2 rocks, umbrella, 2 sheets dark colored construction paper

GeoLab *pages 378–379*
thermometer, psychrometer, windsock or strip of paper, meterstick, relative humidity chart (Appendix F)

MiniLab *page 376*
cardboard box, 2 thermometers, glass jar, graph paper, pencil

Demo *page 367*
lamp, piece of concrete, leaves

Need materials? Contact Science Kit at 1-800-828-7777 or at 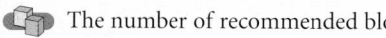www.sciencekit.com on the Internet. For alternate materials, see the activity on the listed page.

Key to Teaching Strategies

L1 Level 1 activities should be appropriate for students with learning difficulties.

L2 Level 2 activities should be within the ability range of all students.

L3 Level 3 activities are designed for above-average students.

ELL ELL activities should be within the ability range of English-language learners.

COOP LEARN Cooperative learning activities are designed for small-group work.

P These strategies represent student products that can be placed in a best-work portfolio.

🧊 These strategies are useful in a block-scheduling format.

Chapter Organizer

Glencoe Exclusive!
TeacherWorks™
All-In-One Planner and Resource Center

Activities/Features	Reproducible Masters	Transparencies
Discovery Lab: Model Cloud Cover, p. 359 **Problem-Solving Lab:** Making and Using Tables, p. 360	**Study Guide for Content Mastery,** p. 85 L2 **Laboratory Manual,** pp. 109–112 L2	**Section Focus Transparency 40** L1 ELL **Teaching Transparency 39** L2 ELL
Using Math: Estimating, p. 365	**Study Guide for Content Mastery,** p. 86 L2 **Laboratory Manual,** pp. 105–108 L2	**Section Focus Transparency 41** L1 ELL **Teaching Transparency 40** L2 ELL
	Study Guide for Content Mastery, pp. 87–88 L2	**Section Focus Transparency 42** L1 ELL **Teaching Transparency 41** L2 ELL
MiniLab: How does the atmosphere affect the transfer of energy?, p. 376 **Design Your Own GeoLab:** Microclimates, pp. 378–379 **Science & Math:** Global Warming, p. 380	**Study Guide for Content Mastery,** pp. 89–90 L2 **GeoLab and MiniLab Worksheets,** p. 55 L2 **GeoLab and MiniLab Worksheets,** pp. 56–58 L2 **Exploring Environmental Problems,** pp. 13–16 L3	**Section Focus Transparency 43** L1 ELL **Teaching Transparency 42** L2 ELL

Assessment

Chapter Assessment, pp. 79–84
Performance Assessment in the Science Classroom (PASC)
MindJogger Videoquiz DVD/VHS
Performance Assessment in Earth Science
ExamView® Pro CD-ROM
5 Days to the Regents Exam

GLENCOE'S
ASSESSMENT
ADVANTAGE

Additional Resources

Guided Reading Audio Program ELL
Cooperative Learning in the Science Classroom COOP LEARN

Lesson Plans
Block Scheduling
earthgeu.com
NY Lesson Plans
NY Block Scheduling
Review Handbook for Regents Earth Science Exam

NATIONAL GEOGRAPHIC
Teacher's Corner

Products Available from National Geographic Society
To order the following products, call the National Geographic Society at 1-800-368-2728:
Curriculum Kit
GeoKit: *Weather*
CD-ROM
111 Years of National Geographic Magazine

Videos
Telling the Weather
Weather: Come Rain, Come Shine
Atmosphere: On the Air

Content Background

Climate or Weather?
Section 14.1

Climate is the average weather of an area over a long period of time. Average weather, however, is based on values that can vary widely. For example, a climate with an average annual temperature of 18°C could easily experience temperatures as high as 38° C or as low as –5°C during a given year. A change in long-term average annual temperature of just 2°C over a period of 30 years, however, would be considered a massive climatic change. Climate, then, involves the time scale over which changes take place, while weather reflects the impacts of short-term changes.

Lake-Effect Snow
Section 14.2

Lake-effect snow is a type of microclimate that occurs when cold waves interact with large bodies of water to produce heavy snows. The phenomenon is called *lake-effect snow* because it occurs most frequently over areas just downwind from the Great Lakes. When extremely cold air moves over a large, relatively warm body of water, the water warms the air immediately above it by conduction. The cold air then is underlain by a layer of much warmer air. The air mass becomes unstable and the warm air rises. The rising air contains water evaporated off the water's surface and is nearly saturated. If the wind moves the air over land, the air is forced to rise when it reaches the higher elevation of a land-

mass. Also, friction between the wind and the land slows down the wind, and as a result, parcels of air pile up much like a traffic jam. Both these factors cause the air to rise even further. The resulting clouds dump their moisture in the form of precipitation. Because the overall air mass is cold, the precipitation falls as snow. This type of snowfall can be extremely heavy. It will persist as long as the wind flow and the temperature contrast between the air mass and the water surface remain basically unchanged.

La Niña
Section 14.3

During El Niño, the South Pacific high-pressure system becomes reestablished and El Niño eventually weakens. Warm water moves back across the Pacific Ocean, and conditions along the South American coast cool off. Sometimes, however, there is too much of a rebound, and the ocean and air off the South

Multiple Learning Styles

 Visual-Spatial Reteach, p. 368, Modeling, p. 373

 Interpersonal Reteach, p. 363, Project, p. 364, Collaborative Learning, p. 366

 Linguistic Earth Science Journal, p. 360

GLENCOE
Technology

The following multimedia resources are available from Glencoe.

The Infinite Voyage Series
Secrets from a Frozen World
Crisis in the Atmosphere

Vocabulary Puzzlemaker

TeacherWorks™ CD-ROM

MindJogger Videoquizzes DVD/VHS

ExamView® Pro CD-ROM

Interactive Chalkboard CD-ROM

Chapter Organizer

American coast turn colder than normal. This condition, called La Niña, has effects of its own, one of the more unpleasant ones being a marked increase in hurricane activity in the Atlantic Ocean.

El Niño and La Niña cause the warm waters of the tropical Pacific Ocean to "slosh" back and forth across the ocean. In this ocean cycle, El Niño is the warm phase and La Niña is the cold phase. On average, El Niño reappears every two to seven years, but during the latter part of the twentieth century, it often appeared more frequently. Some scientists theorize that this change was the result of large-scale interactions between the ocean and the atmosphere. Meteorologists and climatologists are just beginning to identify and understand this complex cycle.

Analyzing Climatic Change
Section 14.4

By analyzing air bubbles trapped in glaciers, scientists have determined that the amount of carbon dioxide in the atmosphere has increased from approximately 280 parts per million (ppm) in 1750 to around 350 ppm in 1995. The cause of this increase is still hotly debated; however, human activities such as burning fossil fuels have undoubtedly contributed to the increase in atmospheric carbon dioxide.

To analyze the air trapped in glacial samples, scientists drill long cores of ice from ice sheets. They then cut the cores into small pieces. Each piece is placed in a vacuum chamber and crushed by needles. During this process, air is released from the ice and sucked out of the sealed chamber into a tube. A laser beam of infrared light then shoots through the tube; this beam measures the amount of carbon dioxide in the sample of air.

Identifying Misconceptions

Many people mistakenly believe that individual climates don't vary, apart from minor monthly or yearly deviations. In reality, however, Earth's climates have continually undergone major changes throughout geologic time as a result of many different processes. Such changes continue to occur. Humans don't notice many of these changes because most take place over the course of many human lifetimes.

✓ Assessment

Portfolio Assessment
Assessment, TWE, p. 368

Performance Assessment
Discovery Lab, SE, p. 359
Assessment, TWE, p. 374
MiniLab, SE, p. 376
GeoLab, SE, pp. 378–379
GeoLab, TWE, pp. 378–379

Knowledge Assessment
Discovery Lab, TWE, p. 359
Assessment, TWE, pp. 363, 373, 377
Section Assessment, SE, pp. 363, 368, 374, 377
MiniLab, TWE, p. 376
Chapter Assessment, SE, pp. 382–383

Skill Assessment
Problem-Solving Lab, TWE, p. 360

Be sure to check the Earth Science Web Site for links to chapter material: earthgeu.com

GLENCOE'S ASSESSMENT ADVANTAGE

Climate

Introducing the Chapter

No one sitting in the middle of a raging blizzard would be likely to mistake his or her location for a beach in sunny Florida or Southern California. This is because we know that different parts of the world have distinctive types of weather. Tell students that climate can be thought of as the study of why these differences in weather occur.

Interpreting the Photo

This rain forest in southern Australia is characterized by ample precipitation and mild temperatures year-round. It is an example of a marine climate and is heavily influenced by the ocean. Tell students that this chapter describes tropical and temperate rain forests, as well as savannas, icy polar regions, and deserts.

INTERACTIVE CHALKBOARD
with Image Bank

PowerPoint® Presentations

This CD is an editable Microsoft® PowerPoint® presentation that includes:
- Section presentations
- Section checks
- Image bank
- Links to Earth Science Online
- All transparencies
- Animations
- Audio

Chapter 14

Climate

What You'll Learn
- What causes different climates.
- How climates are classified.
- How climates change as a result of natural events and human activities.

Why It's Important
This rain forest is one example of the wide variety of plants found in different climates. Climate affects where we live, what we wear, and what we eat. Changes in climate can have far-reaching effects on agriculture, industry, transportation, and recreation.

Earth Science Online

To find out more about climate, visit the Earth Science Web Site at **earthgeu.com**

358

Temperate rain forest, Australia

Discovery Lab

Process Skills

observe and infer, recognize cause and effect, model
 L1 ELL

Safety Precaution

Caution students to be careful when handling the umbrella; its pointed tip can cause injuries.

Preparation

Monitor weather forecasts to identify the best night to conduct this lab. The lab must be completed on a calm, clear night.

Procedure
Troubleshooting
Tell students to be sure that the umbrella completely covers the construction paper.

Observe
Students should observe that no dew or frost forms on the paper under the umbrella, while the paper

Model Cloud Cover

Some areas are generally more cloudy than others. This affects both the temperature and the amount of precipitation that these areas receive. In this activity, which should be done only when the weather forecast calls for clear, calm skies overnight, you'll model the effect of cloud cover on local temperatures.

1. On a calm, clear afternoon, lay two sheets of dark construction paper on the grass in an open area. Place a rock on each sheet of paper to prevent them from blowing away.

2. Open an umbrella and prop it on the ground over one of the sheets of paper.

3. The next morning, observe what has happened to the sheets of paper.

Observe In your science journal, describe any differences in dew formation that you observed. How is the umbrella in this activity similar to clouds in the atmosphere? Based on your observations, infer how temperatures during the night might differ between climates with extensive cloud cover and climates with fewer clouds.

SECTION 14.1

What is climate?

OBJECTIVES

• **Describe** *different types of climate data.*

• **Recognize** *limits associated with the use of normals.*

• **Explain** *why climates vary.*

VOCABULARY

climatology   tropics
climate   temperate zone
normal   polar zone

Fifty thousand years ago, the United States had much different weather patterns than those that exist today. The average temperature was several degrees cooler, and the jet stream was probably farther south. Understanding and predicting such climatic changes are the basic goals of climatology. **Climatology** is the study of Earth's climate and the factors that affect past, present, and future climatic changes.

CLIMATE: MORE THAN JUST AVERAGE WEATHER

Climate, as you'll recall from Chapter 12, describes the long-term weather patterns of an area. These patterns include much more than average weather conditions. Climate also describes annual variations of temperature, precipitation, wind, and other weather variables. Studies of climate show extreme fluctuations of these variables over time. For example, climatic data can indicate the warmest and coldest temperatures ever recorded for a location. This type of information, combined with comparisons between recent conditions and

exposed to the open sky collects dew or frost. The umbrella models cloud cover by trapping surface heat. On cloudy nights, clouds trap heat from Earth's surface and temperatures increase.

✔Assessment

Knowledge Ask students to infer what might be the best place to pitch a tent on a camping trip to avoid having a wet tent in the morning. The best place to pitch a tent would be under a tree, or some other location that offers cover.

Resource Manager

Section Focus Transparency 40 L1 ELL
Study Guide for Content Mastery,
    p. 85 L2

Section 14.1

1 Focus

Section Focus

Before presenting the lesson, display **Section Focus Transparency 40** on the overhead projector.
L1 ELL

Chapter Themes

The following themes from the National Science Content Standards are covered in this chapter. Refer to page 8T of the Teacher Guide for an explanation of the correlations.
Systems, order, and organization (UCP.1); Evidence, models, and explanation (UCP.2); Change, constancy, and measurement (UCP.3); Evolution and equilibrium (UCP.4)

0:00 Out of Time?

If time does not permit teaching the entire chapter, use the Chapter Summary on page 381 and the GeoDigest found at the end of the unit as an overview.

Problem-Solving Lab

Purpose
Students will become familiar with the use of climatological data.

Process Skills
use numbers, make and use tables, make and use graphs, predict, infer

Materials
graph paper, pencil, calculator

Teaching Strategies
Ask students whether they have ever heard weather forecasters say that temperature or precipitation is above or below normal. Explain that the forecasters are comparing current data to a set of established long-term averages, or normals, and that changes in these values can be used to determine climatic trends.

Analysis
1. July and August
2. warmest: 105° F in July 1942; coldest: 7°F in January 1985

Thinking Critically
3. Graphs should be plotted according to the data provided in the table of normals. The average daily maximum temperature is 78.9°F.
4. April, May, June, July, August, September, and October were warmer; November, December, January, February, and March were colder.

✓Assessment

Skill Ask students to examine the highest daily maximum temperatures and the lowest daily minimum temperatures. Have students describe any trends that they notice.
L1 **COOP LEARN**

---

long-term averages, can be used by companies to decide where to locate new facilities and by people who have medical conditions that require them to live in certain climates.

NORMALS

The data used to describe an area's climate are compiled from meteorological records, which are continuously gathered at thousands of locations around the world. These data include daily high and low temperatures, amounts of rainfall, wind speed and direction, humidity, and air pressure. Once the data are gathered, they are averaged on a monthly or annual basis for a period of at least 30 years to determine the **normals,** or standard values, for a location. The *Problem-Solving Lab* below lists some normals for Jacksonville, Florida.

Problem-Solving Lab

Making and Using Tables

Infer climatic conditions from normals Normals offer a comprehensive look at local weather conditions over relatively long periods of time. Use the data provided in the table to answer the following questions about the climate of Jacksonville, Florida.

Analysis
1. According to normal daily maximum temperatures, during what months would you expect the temperature to reach at least 90°F?
2. What were the highest and lowest temperatures ever recorded in this city, and in what month and year?

Thinking Critically
3. Use graph paper to plot the monthly values for normal daily maximum temperatures which cover the 30-year time period from 1966 through 1996. Next, use the monthly values to calculate the average daily maximum temperature for the 30-year period.
4. Which months were warmer than the average daily maximum temperature of the 30-year period? Which months were colder?

Normals for Jacksonville, Florida													
Temperature F°	Time Period (Years)	Jan	Feb	Mar	Apr	May	Jun	Jul	Aug	Sep	Oct	Nov	Dec
Normal Daily Maximum	30	64.2	67.0	73.0	79.1	84.7	89.3	91.4	90.7	87.2	80.2	73.6	66.8
Highest Daily Maximum	55	85	88	91	95	100	103	105	102	100	96	88	84
Year of Occurrence		1947	1962	1974	1968	1967	1954	1942	1954	1944	1951	1986	1994
Normal Daily Minimum	30	40.5	43.3	49.2	54.9	62.1	69.1	71.9	71.8	69.0	59.3	50.2	43.4
Lowest Daily Minimum	55	7	19	23	34	45	47	61	63	48	36	21	11
Year of Occurrence		1985	1996	1980	1987	1992	1984	1972	1984	1981	1989	1970	1983

Earth Science
Journal
Science Field Book

Linguistic Tell students that a degree day is defined as the difference between the actual daily average temperature and an arbitrary daily average value—usually 65°F. Ask students to research and write reports in their science journals that describe cooling- and heating-degree days, and their uses. A cooling-degree day occurs when the actual average daily temperature is warmer than 65°F; the day is classified as a cooling-degree day because temperatures must cool off to reach 65°F. A heating-degree day occurs when the actual average daily temperature is colder than 65°F. Degree days are particularly useful for energy and utility companies that must plan for increases in consumer energy demands.

While normals offer valuable information, they must be used with caution. Weather conditions on any given day might differ widely from normals. For instance, the average high temperature in January for a city might be 0°C. However, it's possible that no one day in January had a high of exactly 0°C. Normals are not intended to describe usual weather conditions. They are simply the average values over a long period of time.

Another issue complicates the use of normals. While climate describes the average weather conditions for a region, normals apply only to the specific place where the meteorological data were collected. Most meteorological data are gathered at airports, which cannot operate without up-to-date, accurate weather information. Do you know anyone who lives at an airport? Probably not. In fact, many airports are located well outside city limits because of the noise and traffic that they generate. When climatic normals are based on airport data, they may differ quite a lot from actual weather conditions in nearby cities. Why? Changes in elevation and other factors such as proximity to large bodies of water can cause climates to vary, as you'll learn next.

WHAT CAUSES CLIMATES?

One glance at the map shown in *Figure 14-1* shows that climates around the country vary greatly. For example, average daily temperatures are much warmer in Dallas, Texas, than in Minneapolis,

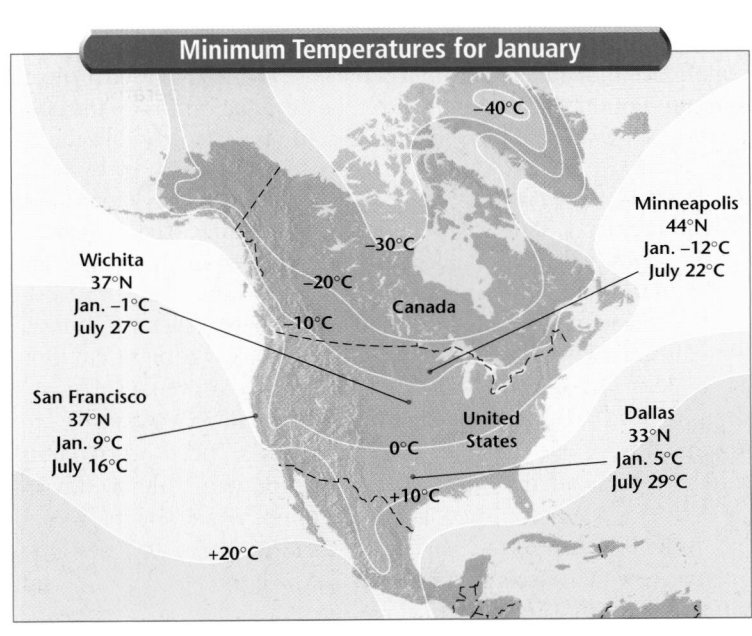

Figure 14-1 This map shows daily minimum temperature in January across the United States. The latitudes of the cities are shown because, as you'll learn on the next page, latitude greatly affects climate.

14.1 *What is climate?* **361**

Content Background

The first nucleus of a climatological network in the United States began on May 2, 1814, when the current Army Surgeon General, Dr. J. Tilton, ordered hospital surgeons to "keep a diary of the Weather." The resulting reports were first published in 1826 by Surgeon General Dr. J. Lovell. In 1842, another young surgeon, Dr. S. Forry, produced the first scientific climatological study of the United States, titled "The Climate of the United States and Its Endemic Influence."

Project

Climatological data are recorded for most large cities by the National Climatic Data Center and are available on the Internet through links provided at National Weather Service Web sites. Have students each select a large city and search Web sites for that city's climatological data. Students should record maximum and minimum temperatures, monthly average temperatures, and average annual precipitation and snowfall. Have students compare their data with those of other students. **L2**

Collaborative Learning

Most temperature and precipitation normals are calculated over a period of 30 years. Ask students to discuss why such a long period is used. Annual temperatures can fluctuate greatly from year to year. A period of 30 years or more is necessary to filter out short-term changes and to identify only those changes that truly represent long-term trends.

NY Core Curriculum Standards

Page 358: St 4 KI 2.2a, 2.2c, & 2.2d, St 7 KI 1

Page 359: St 1 Science KI 1, 2, & 3, St 4 KI 2.1c, 2.1h, & 2.1i, St 6 KI 5

Page 360: St 1 Math KI 2 & 3, St 4 KI 2.1c, 2.1h, & 2.1i, St 6 KI 5

Page 361: St 4 KI 2.1c & 2.2c

Interpreting the Illustration

Figure 14-2 Students learned in Chapter 11 that the tropics are the source of warm air masses and that the poles are the source of cold air masses. Tell students that climates follow a similar pattern. Average temperatures in polar regions are generally quite cold, while those in the tropics are quite warm. Based on what students know about air masses in the middle latitudes and about prevailing westerlies, ask students to infer the probable climate of those latitudes. Midlatitudes exhibit characteristics of both the tropics and the poles because warm, tropical air masses and cold, polar air masses often invade the region. For this same reason, midlatitudes also have the greatest contrast in temperatures.

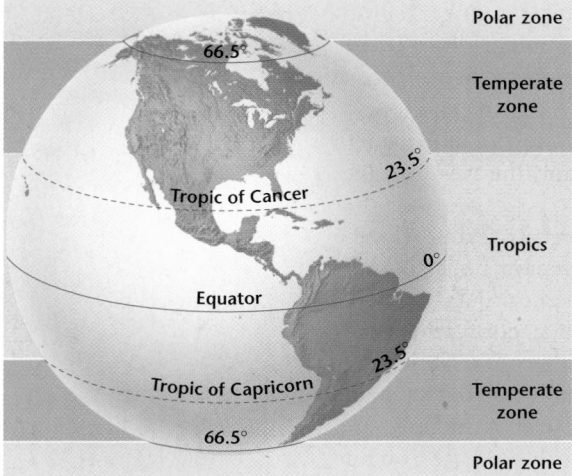

Figure 14-2 Latitude has a great effect on climate. The amount of solar radiation received on Earth decreases in intensity from the equator to the poles.

Earth Science Online

Topic: Tropics
To find out more about the tropics, visit the Earth Science Web Site at earthgeu.com

Activity: Design a Venn diagram to compare and contrast the three major types of tropical climates.

Minnesota. There are several reasons for such climatic variations, including latitude, topography, closeness of lakes and oceans, availability of moisture, global wind patterns, ocean currents, and air masses.

Latitude Recall that different parts of Earth receive different amounts of solar radiation. The amount of solar radiation received by any one place varies because Earth is tilted on its axis, and this affects how the Sun's rays strike Earth's surface. As *Figure 14-2* shows, the area between 23.5° south of the equator and 23.5° north of the equator, known as the **tropics,** receives the most solar radiation because the Sun's rays strike that area from almost directly overhead. As you might expect, temperatures in the tropics are generally warm year-round. The **temperate zones** lie between 23.5° and 66.5° north and south of the equator. As their name implies, temperatures in these regions are moderate. The **polar zones** are located from 66.5° north and south of the equator to the poles. Solar radiation strikes the polar zones at a low angle. Thus, polar temperatures are nearly always cold.

Topographic Effects Water heats up and cools down more slowly than land. Thus, large bodies of water affect the climates of coastal areas. Many coastal regions are warmer in the winter and cooler in the summer than inland areas of similar latitude.

Also, temperatures in the lower atmosphere generally decrease with altitude. Thus, mountain climates are usually cooler than those at sea level. In addition, climates often differ on either side of a mountain. Air rises up one side of a mountain as a result of orographic lifting. The rising air cools, condenses, and drops its moisture. The climate on this side of the mountain—the windward side—is usually wet and cool. On the opposite side of the mountain—the leeward side—the air is dry, and it warms as it descends. For this reason, deserts are common on the leeward sides of mountains, as shown in *Figure 14-3*.

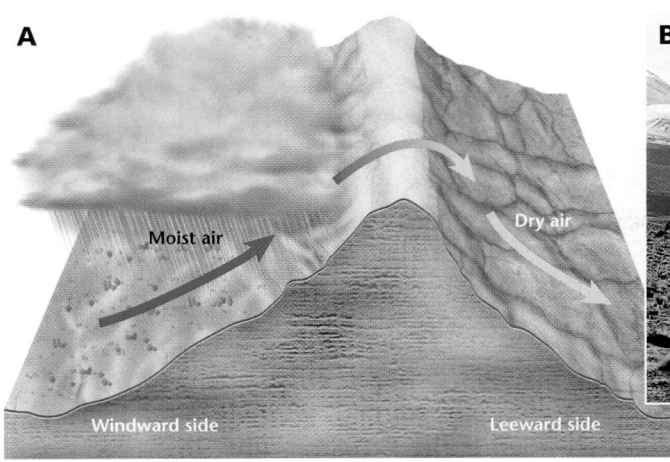

A

B

Figure 14-3 On the windward side of a mountain, moist air is forced upward, cools, condenses, and drops its moisture **(A)**. The air and the climate on the leeward side of the mountain are dry. Deserts such as the Atacama in Chile are common on leeward sides of mountains **(B)**.

Air Masses Two of the main causes of weather are the movement and interaction of air masses. Air masses affect climate, too. They have distinct regions of origin, caused primarily by differences in the amount of solar radiation. The properties of air masses are also dependent on whether they formed over land or water.

Average weather conditions in and near regions of air-mass formation are fairly similar to those exhibited by the air masses themselves. For example, consider an island in the tropical Atlantic Ocean. Because this island is located in an area where maritime tropical (mT) air masses dominate the weather, the island's average weather conditions, or climate, have maritime tropical characteristics.

3 Assess

Check for Understanding
Reinforcement
Ask students to identify three different factors that can influence climate. variations in latitude, proximity to large bodies of water, and mountains

Reteach

Interpersonal Divide students into three groups. Have each group research the climate of a different location in the tropics, the temperate zones, and the polar regions. Ask each group of students to develop a sample set of monthly average temperatures for their location. Student groups should share their data with other groups. **L2**
COOP LEARN

✔Assessment

Knowledge Ask students to explain why climatological normals do not necessarily describe normal weather conditions. Normals represent standard averages rather than any one actual value.

SECTION ASSESSMENT

1. Compare and contrast temperatures in the tropics, temperate zones, and polar zones.

2. Infer how climate data can be used by farmers.

3. What are some limits associated with the use of normals?

4. Describe two topographic features that cause variations in climate.

5. **Thinking Critically** Average daily temperatures for one city, located at 15° south latitude, are 5°C cooler than average daily temperatures for a second city, located at 30° south latitude. What might account for the cooler temperatures in the first city, which lies so near the equator?

SKILL REVIEW

6. **Forming a Hypothesis** Suppose that meteorological data for an area are normally gathered at an airport located 10 km from a large lake. Hypothesize how normals for the area might change if the data were gathered from the edge of the lake. For more help, refer to the *Skill Handbook.*

SECTION ASSESSMENT

1. Temperatures in the tropics are generally warm. In temperate zones, temperatures are moderate. The poles are nearly always cold.

2. They can be used to determine average temperatures and rates of precipitation, as well as the length of the growing season.

3. Actual weather conditions may vary widely from normals. Also, normals apply only to the specific place where the data were collected.

4. Students may mention large bodies of water and mountains.

5. Answers may vary. Students may say that the city at 15° south latitude is at a higher elevation than the city at 30° south latitude. Accept all reasonable answers.

6. Daily high temperatures might be slightly lower; overnight low temperatures might be slightly higher. There would be fewer extreme variations in temperature because of the presence of the lake.

NY Core Curriculum Standards

Page 362: St 4 KI 1.1f, 2.1c, 2.2a, 2.2b, & 2.2c
Page 363: St 1 Math KI 1, 2, & 3, St 4 KI 2.1h, 2.2a, & 2.2c, St 6 KI 5

Section Background

For section content background, refer to **Lake-Effect Snow** on page 358C.

Preplanning

Refer to the Chapter Organizer on pages 358A–B.

1 Focus

Section Focus

Before presenting the lesson, display **Section Focus Transparency 41** on the overhead projector.
L1 **ELL**

Project

Interpersonal Divide the class into seven groups, and assign each group a continent. As students study this section, have each group keep an ongoing record of the various climates of its continent. After the section is completed, student groups should present reports about the climates of their continents. **L2**
COOP LEARN

OBJECTIVES

- **Describe** *the criteria used to classify climates.*
- **Compare** *and* **contrast** *different climates.*

VOCABULARY

Koeppen classification system
microclimate
heat island

Picture a parched desert with wind-blown dunes stretching toward the horizon. Now, imagine a glistening iceberg floating amid a polar sea. These images represent vastly different climates. What criteria would you use to classify them? Temperature is an obvious choice, as is amount of precipitation. The **Koeppen classification system,** a widely used classification system for climates, uses both of these criteria. Developed by Russian-born German climatologist Wladimir Koeppen (1846–1940), the system is based on the average monthly values of temperature and precipitation. It also takes into account the distinct vegetation found in different climates.

Figure 14-4 Koeppen's classification system, shown here in a modified version, is made up of six main divisions.

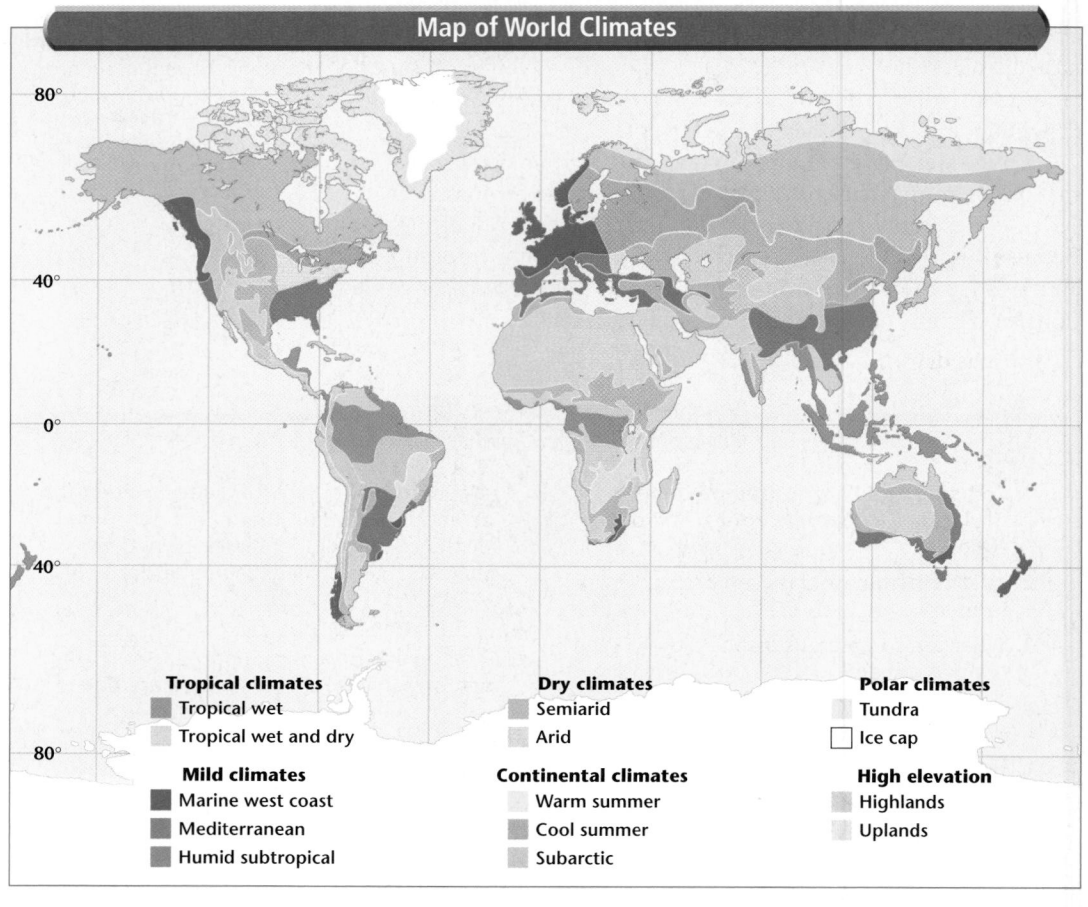

Map of World Climates

Tropical climates
- Tropical wet
- Tropical wet and dry

Mild climates
- Marine west coast
- Mediterranean
- Humid subtropical

Dry climates
- Semiarid
- Arid

Continental climates
- Warm summer
- Cool summer
- Subarctic

Polar climates
- Tundra
- Ice cap

High elevation
- Highlands
- Uplands

364 CHAPTER 14 *Climate*

Differentiated Instruction

Learning Disabled Give students about a dozen beads of different sizes and colors and have them develop a classification system for the beads. This strategy will help students realize that subgroups are part of a common whole and in this way will further their understanding of climate classification. After the activity, tell students that climates are classified, too, but according to average weather conditions over long periods of time.

Resource Manager

Section Focus Transparency 41 **L1** **ELL**
Teaching Transparency 40 **L2** **ELL**
Study Guide for Content Mastery, p. 86 **L2**
Laboratory Manual, pp. 105–108 **L2**

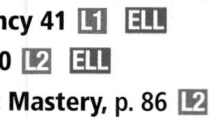

KOEPPEN CLASSIFICATION SYSTEM

Koeppen decided that a good way to distinguish among different climatic zones was by natural vegetation. Palm trees, for instance, are not located in polar regions; they are largely limited to tropical and subtropical regions. Koeppen later realized that quantitative values would make his system more objective and therefore more scientific. Thus, he revised his system to include the numerical values of temperature and precipitation. A map of global climates according to a modified version of Koeppen's classification system is shown in **Figure 14-4.**

Tropical Climates Constant high temperatures characterize tropical climates. In some tropical areas, the heat is accompanied by up to 600 cm of rain each year. The combination of heat and rain produces tropical rain forests, which contain some of the most dramatic vegetation on Earth. You saw an example of a tropical rain forest in the photograph at the beginning of this chapter. Tropical regions are almost constantly under the influence of maritime tropical air. The transition zones that border the rainy tropics north and south of the equator, known as tropical wet and dry zones, have distinct dry winter seasons as a result of the occasional influx of dry continental air masses. Tropical wet and dry zones include savannas, as shown in **Figure 14-5.** These tropical grasslands are found in Africa, among other places.

Dry Climates Dry climates, which cover about 30 percent of Earth's land area, make up the largest climatic zone. Most of the world's deserts, such as the Sahara, the Gobi, and the Australian, are classified as dry climates. In these climates, continental tropical (cT) air dominates, precipitation is low, and vegetation is scarce. Many of these areas are located near the tropics. Thus, intense amounts of solar radiation result in high rates of evaporation and few clouds. Overall, evaporation rates exceed precipitation rates. The resulting moisture deficit gives this zone its name. Within this classification, there are two subtypes: arid regions or deserts, and semi-arid regions or steppes. Steppes are more humid than deserts; they generally separate arid regions from bordering wet climates.

Using Math

Estimating Use the map in **Figure 14-4** to determine the approximate percentage of land covered by tropical wet climates.

Figure 14-5 This watering hole in Botswana is found in a savanna.

Content Background

One of the most distinguishing characteristics of tropical climates is the lack of variability in temperatures from month to month. Cold air masses rarely penetrate the deep tropics. In addition, the Sun's rays strike the tropics from almost directly overhead throughout the year. Thus, the lengths of days and nights remain nearly the same, a factor that helps to maintain constant temperatures.

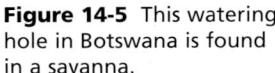

Using Math

The correct answer is 6 percent. However, student answers will be based on estimates and thus will likely vary. Answers between five to ten percent are acceptable.

Across the Curriculum

History Ancient Greeks developed one of the first known climate classification systems. They divided each hemisphere into three zones: torrid, temperate, and frigid. This simple scheme was based on Earth-Sun relationships. The boundaries were the four astronomically important parallels: the Tropic of Cancer, the Tropic of Capricorn, the arctic circle, and the antarctic circle.

Interpreting the Illustration

Figure 14-4 This illustration shows the six main climate types according to a modified version of the Koeppen classification system. Ask students to infer why the greatest variation in climate type occurs in the midlatitudes. The combined influence of the polar, tropical, moist, and dry air masses that move through midlatitudes causes climates to vary widely.

NY Core Curriculum Standards

Page 364: St 4 KI 2.2c, St 6 KI 1
Page 365: St 1 Math KI 2 & 3, St 4 KI 2.1i & 2.2c, St 6 KI 1

Interpersonal A common fallacy about deserts is that they are lifeless. Have students work in groups to research desert plants and some plant adaptations. Desert plants are highly resistant to drought. Many have waxy leaves, stems, or branches, or thickened outer layers to reduce water loss. Others have extensive root systems that tap moisture deep in the ground. Often, plant stems are thickened by a spongy tissue that stores water. **COOP LEARN**

Discussion

Ask students to explain why the polar climates are cold. Very little solar radiation is received during polar winters. Even during the long days of summer, the angle of the Sun's rays is so low that solar radiation is dispersed over a wide area and thus does not warm these regions.

Concept Development

Polar climates can be divided into two subtypes: ice caps and tundra. The boundary of the tundra marks the limit of tree growth; vegetation is mainly grasses, sedges, mosses, and lichens. Temperatures in the ice-cap climate are below freezing year-round. The surface is covered by permanent ice and snow.

Figure 14-6 The Golden Gate Bridge in San Francisco, California, is nearly hidden beneath a dense layer of fog. Fog is characteristic of marine west coast climates.

Mild Climates Mild climates can be classified into three subtypes: humid subtropical climates, marine west coast climates, and mediterranean climates. Humid subtropical climates are influenced by the subtropical high-pressure systems that are normally found over oceans in the summer. The southeastern United States has this type of climate. There, warm, muggy weather prevails during the warmer months and dry, cool conditions predominate during the winter. The marine west coast climates are dominated by the constant inland flow of air off the ocean, which creates mild winters and cool summers, with abundant precipitation throughout the year. An example of this type of climate is shown in *Figure 14-6.* Mediterranean climates, found in Italy and parts of Spain, among other places, are influenced by the Mediterranean Sea. Summers in these climates are generally warm because the lack of cool ocean currents in the Mediterranean Sea results in relatively warm water temperatures.

Continental Climates Continental climates are also classified into three subtypes: warm summer climates, cool summer climates, and subarctic climates. Located in the zone dominated by the polar front, continental climates are battlegrounds for clashing tropical and polar air masses. Thus, these zones experience rapid and sometimes violent changes in weather. Both summer and winter temperatures can be extreme because the influence of polar air masses is strong in winter, while warm tropical air dominates in summer. The presence of warm, moist air causes summers to be generally wetter than winters, especially in latitudes that are relatively close to the tropics.

Polar Climates To the north of continental climates lie the polar climates, the coldest regions on Earth. Just as the tropics are known for their year-round warmth, polar climates are known for their constant cold—the mean temperature of the warmest month is less than 10°C. Precipitation is generally low because cold air holds less moisture than warm air. Also, the amount of heat radiated by Earth's surface is too low to produce the strong convection currents needed to release heavy precipitation. *Figure 14-7A* shows an ice-cap polar climate.

A variation of the polar climate is found at high elevations. This type of climate includes parts of the Andes Mountains of South America, shown in *Figure 14-7B,* which lie near the equator. The intense solar radiation found near such equatorial regions is offset by the decrease in temperature that occurs with altitude.

NY Core Curriculum Standards

Page 366: St 4 KI 2.1i, 2.2b, & 2.2c, St 6 KI 1
Page 367: St 4 KI 2.2a, 2.2b, & 2.2c, St 6 KI 1

A

B

Figure 14-7 Penguins are one of the few species that can survive in Antarctica's ice-cap polar climate **(A)**. Llamas are common in the high-elevation climates of the Andes Mountains **(B)**.

MICROCLIMATES

Sometimes, the climate of a small area can be much different from that of the larger area surrounding it. A localized climate that differs from the main regional climate is called a **microclimate.** If you climb to the top of a mountain, you can experience a type of microclimate; the climate becomes cooler with increasing elevation. You'll learn more about microclimates in the *Design Your Own GeoLab* at the end of this chapter. *Figure 14-8* shows a microclimate in a city.

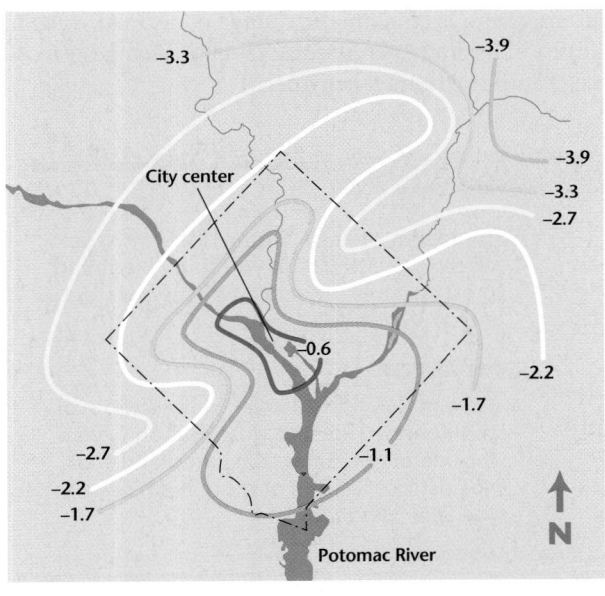

Figure 14-8 This diagram shows winter temperatures in Washington, D.C. The buildings and paved surfaces of the city create a microclimate. The temperature in the center of the city is –0.6°C, nearly 3°C warmer than temperatures in some parts of the surrounding area.

Demo

The heat-island effect can be demonstrated using a lamp, a small chunk of concrete, and some leaves or grass. **CAUTION:** *The lamp will get hot.* Position the light just above both the concrete and the vegetation for at least 30 minutes, then have students touch both surfaces. The concrete will be noticeably warmer showing that areas covered by asphalt and concrete absorb heat more efficiently than the surrounding countryside does.

Enrichment

Have students who wish to further explore the subject of microclimates examine the microclimate that exists just above Earth's surface. The air directly above Earth's surface experiences greater extremes in temperature than the air several meters above the ground. Ask students to infer why. Because air is heated by conduction, it is warmest in the area just above Earth's surface.

Environmental Connection

The development of heat islands is an excellent example of the effects that humans have on climate. Heat islands impact more than temperature and precipitation levels. The heat combines with industrial pollution to worsen smog problems. Ask students to brainstorm other effects that heat islands have on climate.

Check for Understanding

Reinforcement

Have students compare and contrast the main climate types in the Koeppen classification system. L2

Reteach

Visual-Spatial Have students make posters that illustrate the main characteristics of the climatic zone of their state. If the state is made up of several different climatic zones, divide students into groups and have each group make a poster illustrating the different climatic zones. L2 P

✓Assessment

Portfolio Have students research a major urban area to determine whether a heat-island effect is apparent in the city's climatological data. Students can do this by comparing the city's data with those of surrounding rural areas. Tell students to use the Internet, reference books, magazines, and newspapers to gather information about the cities of their choice. Have students present their results to the class. Encourage students to use a variety of media in their presentations. L2 P

NY Core Curriculum Standards

Page 368: St 4 KI 2.1f, 2.2a, 2.2b, & 2.2c, St 6 KI 1 & 2

Page 369: St 4 KI 1.2j, 2.1i, 2.2a, 2.2b, 2.2c, & 2.2d, St 6 KI 1 & 5

368 CHAPTER 14

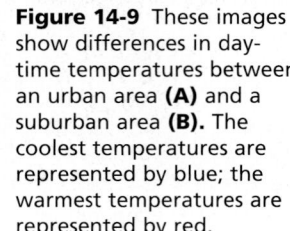

Figure 14-9 These images show differences in daytime temperatures between an urban area **(A)** and a suburban area **(B)**. The coolest temperatures are represented by blue; the warmest temperatures are represented by red.

Heat Islands The mere presence of a building can create microclimates in the area immediately surrounding it. How? The building casts shadows that lower air temperature. The presence of many concrete buildings and large expanses of asphalt can create **heat islands,** wherein the climate is warmer than in surrounding rural areas. This effect was recognized as long ago as the early nineteenth century, when Londoners noticed that the temperature in their city was noticeably warmer than in the surrounding countryside.

The heat-island effect occurs because large areas of asphalt and concrete radiate far more heat into the air than do grasslands, wooded areas, and bodies of water. This causes mean temperatures in large cities to be significantly warmer than in surrounding areas, as shown in *Figure 14-9.* The heat-island effect also causes greater changes in temperature with altitude, which sparks strong convection currents. This in turn produces increased cloudiness and up to 15 percent more total precipitation in cities.

Heat islands are examples of climatic change on a small scale. In the next sections, we'll examine large-scale climatic changes caused by both natural events and human activities.

SECTION ASSESSMENT

1. Compare and contrast the five main climate types.

2. What criteria is the Koeppen climate classification system based on?

3. What are microclimates? What climatic effects do heat islands have on large cities?

4. Describe the climate of your area. Which zone do you live in? What type of air masses generally affect your climate?

5. **Thinking Critically** Of the different types of climates, which do you think would be most strongly influenced by the polar jet stream? Why?

SKILL REVIEW

6. **Making and Using Tables** Make a table of the Koeppen climate classification system. Include major zones, subzones, and characteristics of each. For more help, refer to the *Skill Handbook.*

earthgeu.com/self_check_quiz

SECTION ASSESSMENT

1. Tropical climates have high temperatures; some are characterized by abundant rainfall. Dry climates have low precipitation and scarce vegetation. Mild climates have generally warm winters and cool summers. Continental climates have extreme temperatures in summer and winter. Polar climates are cold year-round.

2. vegetation, temperature, and precipitation

3. Microclimates are localized climates that differ from the main regional climate. Heat islands cause more heat to be absorbed in cities.

4. Answers will vary depending on students' location.

5. The mild or continental climates; they are found well north of the tropics and south of the poles —regions where the polar jet stream is most active.

6. Student tables should include the main characteristics of each climate type and subtype discussed in this section.

Some years may be warmer, cooler, wetter, or drier than others, but during the average human lifetime, climates do not appear to change significantly. However, a study of Earth's history over hundreds of thousands of years shows that climates always have been, and currently are, in a constant state of change. These changes usually take place over extremely long time periods. Geologic records show that in the past, Earth was sometimes much colder or warmer than it is today.

ICE AGES

A good example of climatic change involves glaciers, which have alternatively advanced and retreated over the past 2 million years. At times, much of Earth's surface was covered by vast sheets of ice. During these periods of extensive glacial coverage, called **ice ages,** average global temperatures decreased by an estimated 5°C. Although this may not seem like a large decrease, global climates became generally colder and snowfall increased, which sparked the advance of existing ice sheets. Ice ages alternate with warm periods called interglacial intervals—we are currently experiencing such an interval. The most recent ice age ended only about 10 000 years ago. In North America, glaciers spread from the east coast to the west coast and as far south as Indiana, as shown in *Figure 14-10.* The results of this glacial period are apparent in the Great Lakes and the Finger Lakes of central New York, which were scoured out as the glaciers retreated.

Figure 14-10 The last ice age covered large portions of North America, Europe, and Asia. Average global temperatures were roughly 5°C lower than normal.

Section 14.3

Prepare

Section Background

For section content background, refer to **La Niña** on pages 358C–D.

Preplanning

Refer to the Chapter Organizer on pages 358A–B.

1 Focus

Section Focus

Before presenting the lesson, display **Section Focus Transparency 42** on the overhead projector. L1 ELL

Project

The last sunspot maximum was in the year 2000. Have students identify the three previous maxima and then research local climate records to see whether temperature or precipitation were significantly above or below normal.

Resource Manager

Section Focus Transparency 42 L1 ELL
Study Guide for Content Mastery, pp. 87–88 L2

Interpreting the Illustration

Figure 14-10 Tell students that ice ages not only affected ice-covered regions, but they also affected the climates of areas not covered by ice. The reflection of solar radiation by ice and snow, as well as the inability of ice to effectively absorb and retain solar radiation, caused lowered temperatures around the world.

369

Enrichment

The solstices, which are the times of year when solar radiation is at its maximum and minimum, occur around June 21 and December 21, respectively. However, these dates are merely the beginning of astronomical summer and winter, respectively, and thus they may not be the warmest or coldest times of the year. The warmest and coldest temperatures usually occur about one to two months after the solstices. Ask students to infer why. Earth's land-ocean-atmosphere system takes time to respond to changes in the amount of solar energy received on Earth. Thus, a so-called seasonal lag occurs between the dates of the solstices and the dates of deepest summer and winter.

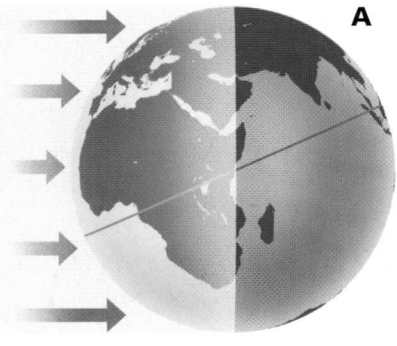

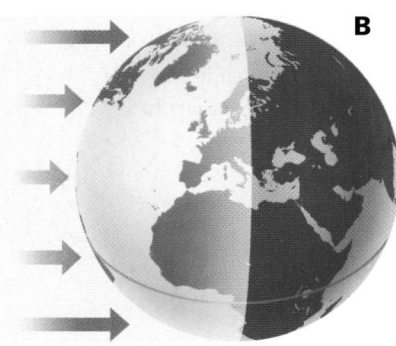

Figure 14-11 When the north pole is pointed toward the Sun, the northern hemisphere experiences summer and the southern hemisphere experiences winter **(A)**. During spring and fall, neither pole points toward the Sun **(B)**.

SHORT-TERM CLIMATIC CHANGES

While ice ages take place over many thousands of years, other climatic changes take place in much shorter time periods. The most obvious of these are **seasons,** which are short-term periods of climatic change caused by regular variations in daylight, temperature, and weather patterns. These variations are the result of changes in the amount of solar radiation an area receives. As *Figure 14-11* shows, the tilt of Earth on its axis as it revolves around the Sun causes different areas of Earth to receive different amounts of solar radiation. During summer in the northern hemisphere, the north pole is tilted toward the Sun, and this hemisphere experiences long hours of daylight and warm temperatures. At the same time, it is winter in the southern hemisphere. The south pole is tilted away from the Sun, and the southern hemisphere experiences long hours of darkness and cold temperatures. Throughout the year, the seasons are reversed in the north and south hemispheres.

El Niño Other short-term climatic changes are caused by **El Niño,** a warm ocean current that occasionally develops off the western coast of South America. In the Southeast Pacific Ocean, atmospheric and ocean currents along the coast of South America normally move north, transporting cold water from the Antarctic region. Meanwhile, the trade winds and ocean currents move westward across the tropics, keeping warm water in the western Pacific. This circulation, driven by a semipermanent high-pressure system, creates a cool, dry climate along much of the northwestern coast of South America.

Occasionally, however, for reasons that are not fully understood, this high-pressure system and its attendant trade winds weaken drastically, which allows the warm water from the western Pacific to surge eastward toward the South American coast. The sudden presence of this warm water heats the air near the surface of the water. Convection currents strengthen, and the normally cool and dry northwestern coast of South America becomes much warmer and wetter. The increased precipitation pumps large amounts of heat and moisture into the upper atmosphere, where upper-level winds transport the hot, moist air eastward across the tropics. This hot, moist air in the upper atmosphere is responsible for dramatic climatic changes. Sharp temperature differences in the upper air allow the jet stream to shift farther south. This causes weather systems to take a more southerly track, bringing violent storms to California and the Gulf Coast, which are usually south of the storm tracks.

Cultural Diversity

El Niño and the Fishing Industry The fishing industries in Peru and Ecuador have recognized the existence of El Niño for more than 100 years. In fact, these fishing crews called the phenomenon El Niño, which means "the child" in Spanish, because it usually occurred around Christmas. These crews also noticed that El Niño disrupts marine feeding patterns. In normal years, cold, deep waters move westward, carrying rich nutrients from organisms that sank to the ocean floor and decayed. Upwelling occurs near the coast, and the nutrients rise to the surface and feed countless fish. During El Niño, however, the current becomes warmer and the fish migrate to colder waters. NASA is working with fisheries in Peru and Ecuador to help them prepare for El Niño.

Figure 14-12 During El Niño, some areas of the world experience extreme droughts while other areas are ravaged by heavy floods.

The effects of hot, moist upper air spread farther east, bringing stormy weather to areas that are normally dry and drought conditions to areas that are normally wet. The end result is extensive property damage and untold human suffering. This is especially true in tropical regions, where the effects of El Niño are most pronounced. El Niño does have one positive effect—the strong upper winds it produces keep tropical disturbances from increasing to hurricane-strength storms in the Atlantic Ocean. This results in fewer hurricanes in that region for the duration of El Niño. Eventually, the South Pacific high-pressure system becomes reestablished and El Niño weakens, but not before it causes the climatic effects shown in *Figure 14-12.* The warm water moves back across the Pacific Ocean, and conditions along the South American coast cool off.

CHANGE CAN BE NATURAL

Much discussion has taken place in recent years about whether Earth's climate is changing as a result of human activities. We'll discuss this in the next section. For now, it's important to note that climatic changes occurred long before humans came on the scene. Studies of tree rings, ice-core samples, fossils, and radiocarbon samples provide evidence of past climatic changes. These changes in Earth's climate were caused by natural events such as variations in solar activity, changes in Earth's tilt and orbit, and volcanic eruptions.

14.3 *Climatic Changes* **371**

Project

Beyond El Niño's effects on weather and climate, the sudden presence of warm water off the western coast of South America also has profound effects on marine ecosystems. Have students research and report on the impact of El Niño on the food chains of this coastal area. Students should share their results with the class. **L2**

Concept Development

Increased understanding of El Niño and its effects has greatly improved the reliability of seasonal weather forecasting. In addition to its well-known inhibiting influence on Atlantic tropical cyclones, El Niño also enhances the westerly component of the jet stream and prevailing westerlies across North America. This results in more air masses moving across the continent from west to east, and fewer moving from north to south. These eastward-moving systems mainly have their origin over the comparatively mild Pacific Ocean, as opposed to the bitter cold arctic air masses that move down from the north. As a result, a forecast of a mild winter during El Niño will usually meet with a reasonable degree of accuracy.

Much is heard in the media about the many ways in which humans negatively impact the environment. However, it is a misconception to blame all climatic changes on human activities.

Uncover the Misconception
Ask students to infer what causes climatic changes, such as global warming. Most will probably mention human activities that cause increased levels of pollution.

Demonstrate the Concept
Tell students that Earth goes through various cycles and that these cycles can have profound effects on Earth's climate. For instance, many scientists hypothesize that we are now in an interglacial period, which affects sea level and global temperatures. Point out that there likely are other natural cycles that have not yet been identified.

Assess New Knowledge
After students have completed this section, ask them whether all climatic changes are caused by human activities. Most students will realize that many factors affect climatic change.

Using Scientific Terms

The term given to the change in inclination of Earth's axis is called *precession*. While *wobble* is often used to describe this motion, this term suggests a random movement of Earth's axis, which is not accurate. Earth's axis actually rotates in a circular motion.

Figure 14-13 Very few sunspots occurred during the Maunder minimum, and temperatures were lower than normal. Thus, scientists theorize solar activity may be linked to climatic changes.

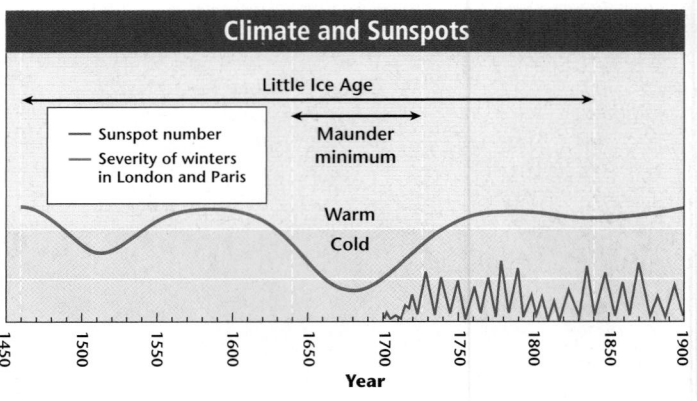

Figure 14-14 Scientists theorize that a more elliptical orbit around the Sun could produce significant changes in Earth's climate.

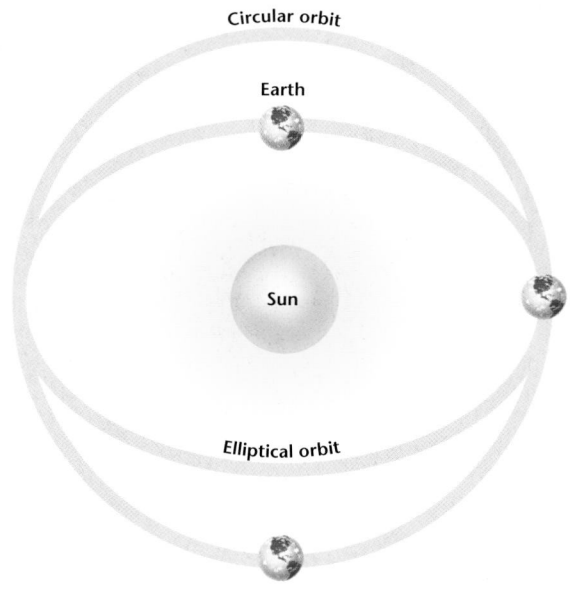

Solar Activity Evidence of a possible link between solar activity and Earth's climate was provided by English astronomer E. W. Maunder in 1893. The existence of sunspot cycles lasting approximately 11 years had been recognized since the days of Galileo. However, Maunder found that from 1645 to 1716, sunspot activity was scarce to nonexistent. This period of very low sunspot activity, called the **Maunder minimum,** closely corresponds to an unusually cold climatic episode called the "Little Ice Age." During this time, much of Europe experienced bitterly cold winters and below-normal temperatures year-round. Residents of London are said to have ice-skated on the Thames River in June. The relationship between climate and periods of low sunspot activity is illustrated in *Figure 14-13.* Studies indicate that increased solar activity coincides with warmer-than-normal climates, while periods of low solar activity, such as the Maunder minimum, coincide with cold climatic conditions.

Earth's Orbit Climatic changes may also be triggered by changes in Earth's axis and orbit. The shape of Earth's elliptical orbit appears to change, becoming more elliptical, then more circular, over the course of a 100 000-year cycle. As *Figure 14-14* shows, when the orbit elongates, Earth passes closer to the Sun, and temperatures become warmer than normal. When the orbit is more circular, Earth is farther from the Sun and temperatures dip below average. The amount of radiation

372 CHAPTER 14 *Climate*

Across the Curriculum

Astronomy Sunspots are just one of several types of solar disturbances that have been identified. Have students research the other types, including solar flares and prominences. These disturbances also have significant effects on Earth and its atmosphere, beyond changes in climate. Students should identify these effects and explain the relationship among flares, prominences, and sunspots.

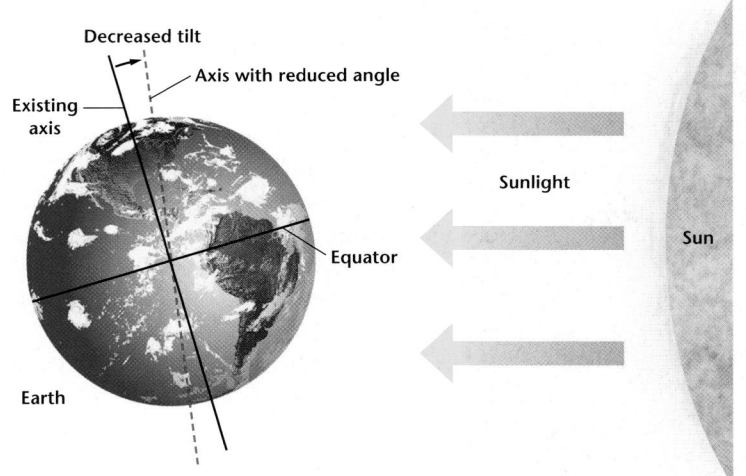

Figure 14-15 If the angle of tilt of Earth's axis decreased, there would be less temperature contrast between summer and winter.

Earth receives when its orbit elongates is much higher than when its orbit is more circular.

As you know, seasons are caused by the tilt of Earth's axis. At present, the angle of the tilt is 23.5°. However, the angle of tilt varies from a minimum of 22.1° to a maximum of 24.5° every 41 000 years. Scientists theorize that these changes in angle cause seasons to become more severe. For example, a decrease in the angle of the tilted axis, as shown in *Figure 14-15,* might cause a decrease in the temperature difference between winter and summer. Winters would be warmer and wetter, and summers would be cooler. The additional snow in latitudes near the poles would not melt in summer because temperatures would be cooler than average. This could result in expanded glacial coverage. In fact, some scientists hypothesize that changes in the angle of Earth's tilted axis cause ice ages.

Earth's Wobble Another movement of Earth may be responsible for climatic changes. Over a period of about 26 000 years, Earth wobbles as it spins on its axis. Currently, the axis points toward the North Star, Polaris, as shown in *Figure 14-16.* Because of Earth's wobbling, however, the axis will tilt toward another star, Vega, by about the year 14 000. Currently, winter occurs in the northern hemisphere when Earth is closest to the Sun, and summer occurs when Earth is farthest from the Sun. When the axis tilts toward Vega, however, winter will occur in the northern hemisphere when Earth is farthest from the Sun, and summer will occur when Earth is closest to the Sun. This will cause warmer summers and colder winters than those that we now experience.

Figure 14-16 By about the year 14 000, Earth's axis will point toward the star, Vega. Winter will then occur in the northern hemisphere when Earth is farthest from the Sun, causing winters to be colder.

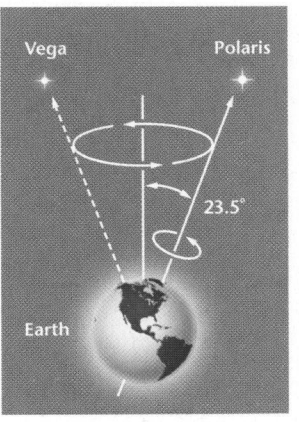

14.3 *Climatic Changes* **373**

Content Background

Sunspots, which are associated with the Sun's ejection of huge masses of magnetic particles, recently have been linked to changes in climatic cycles and to individual seasonal events. Research has shown some correlation between the sunspot cycle and periods of drought in the Great Plains, as well as the number of tropical cyclones that occur during any given year. No widely accepted theory has yet been developed to explain exactly how solar variations cause climatic changes.

NY Core Curriculum Standards

Page 372: St 4 KI 2.1i, 2.2a, 2.2b, 2.2c, & 2.2d, St 6 KI 1 & 5

Page 373: St 4 KI 1.1f, 2.1i, 2.2a, 2.2b, 2.2c, & 2.2d, St 6 KI 1 & 5

Page 374: St 4 KI 1.1f, 2.1c, 2.1i, 2.2a, 2.2b, 2.2c, & 2.2d, St 6 KI 1, 2, & 5

Page 375: St 4 KI 2.2a, 2.2b, & 2.2d

Discussion

Ask students to explain the difference between short-term and long-term climatic changes and to give examples of each type. Ask students to classify these changes according to whether they are largely astronomical phenomena or Earth-based processes.

Reteach

Ask students the following questions. Which areas does El Niño affect least? El Niño affects polar regions the least. Conversely, which areas does El Niño affect most? It affects equatorial regions the most.

✔Assessment

Performance Have students use their knowledge of prevailing winds to describe how volcanic ash from an imaginary eruption would spread around the world. What types of climatic changes could be expected? What areas would be most severely affected? Use the Performance Task Assessment List for Making Observations and Inferences in **PASC,** p. 17.

Figure 14-17 The dust and gases released by this volcanic eruption in New Guinea blocked incoming solar radiation and affected global climates.

Volcanic Activity Climatic changes can also be triggered by the immense quantities of dust released into the atmosphere during major volcanic eruptions, shown in *Figure 14-17.* Volcanic dust can remain suspended in the atmosphere for several years, blocking incoming solar radiation and thus lowering global temperatures. Some scientists theorize that periods of high volcanic activity cause cool climatic periods. This theory is supported by records over the past century because several large eruptions have been followed by below-normal global temperatures. For instance, the ash released during the 1991 eruption of Mt. Pinatubo in the Philippines resulted in slightly cooler temperatures around the world the following year. Generally, volcanic eruptions appear to have only short-term effects on climate. These effects, as well as the others you've read about thus far, are a result of natural causes. In the next section, you'll learn about climatic changes caused by human activities.

SECTION ASSESSMENT

1. What three changes in Earth's movement in space might result in long-term climatic changes?

2. What are seasons? What causes them?

3. Explain how El Niño might affect weather in California and along the Gulf Coast.

4. Why are the greatest effects of El Niño experienced mainly in the tropics?

5. How does volcanic activity affect climate? Are these effects examples of short-term or long-term climatic change?

6. **Thinking Critically** What might be the effect on seasons if Earth's orbit became more elliptical and, at the same time, the angle of the tilt of Earth's axis increased?

SKILL REVIEW

7. **Concept Mapping** Use the following phrases to complete a concept map of the effects of El Niño. For more help, refer to the *Skill Handbook.*

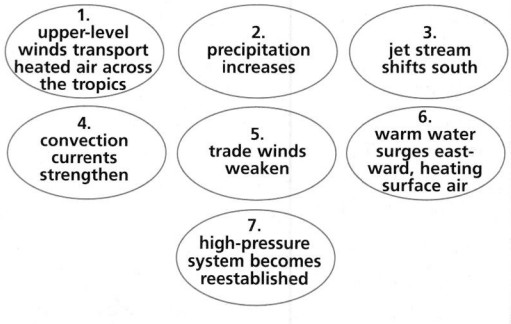

- 1. upper-level winds transport heated air across the tropics
- 2. precipitation increases
- 3. jet stream shifts south
- 4. convection currents strengthen
- 5. trade winds weaken
- 6. warm water surges eastward, heating surface air
- 7. high-pressure system becomes reestablished

earthgeu.com/self_check_quiz

SECTION ASSESSMENT

1. changes in Earth's orbit, changes in the tilt of Earth's axis in relation to the Sun, and the wobbling of Earth's axis

2. Seasons refer to short-term periods of climatic change caused by regular variations in daylight, temperature, and weather patterns. These changes are caused by changes in the amount of solar radiation received in a given location during a year.

3. The additional heat in the upper atmosphere causes the jet stream, which steers storms systems, to shift farther south. Thus, these areas would experience more storms.

4. El Niño is caused by ocean-temperature changes that occur in the tropics. The heat added to the atmosphere occurs mainly in the tropics and is transported eastward across the tropical latitudes.

5. Volcanic dust from eruptions blocks incoming solar radiation and lowers global temperatures; it is an example of a short-term change.

6. These combined factors would likely produce greater seasonal contrasts in temperature. Thus, there would be more extreme differences in temperatures between summer and winter.

7. Concept maps should be in the following order: 5, 6, 4, 2, 1, 3, 7.

SECTION 14.4 *The Human Factor*

One of the most significant influences on Earth's climate is the atmosphere. As you learned in Chapter 11, solar radiation that is not reflected by clouds passes freely through the atmosphere. It's then absorbed by Earth's surface and released as long-wavelength radiation. This radiation is absorbed by atmospheric gases such as water vapor, methane, and carbon dioxide. The atmospheric gases then reradiate the stored energy, so that Earth receives energy from two sources: the Sun and the atmosphere.

THE GREENHOUSE EFFECT

The retention of heat by the atmosphere results in the **greenhouse effect,** which is the natural heating of Earth's surface caused by certain atmospheric gases called greenhouse gases. Without the greenhouse effect, which is illustrated in *Figure 14-18,* life as we know it could not exist on Earth. Our planet would be cold, like Mars, which has an extremely thin atmosphere and surface temperatures that dip to −90°C. On the other hand, a marked increase in the greenhouse effect might cause our planet to be hot, like Venus, which, because of

OBJECTIVES

- **Compare** *and* **contrast** *the greenhouse effect and global warming.*
- **Identify** *how humans impact climate.*

VOCABULARY

greenhouse effect
global warming

Figure 14-18 Solar radiation reaches Earth's surface and is reradiated as long-wavelength radiation. This radiation cannot escape through the atmosphere, and is absorbed and re-released by atmospheric gases. This process is called the greenhouse effect because it is similar to the way that heat is trapped and released in a greenhouse.

14.4 *The Human Factor* **375**

Interpreting the Illustration

Figure 14-18 Recent satellite data indicate that increases in greenhouse gases such as carbon dioxide may be contributing to warmer ocean temperatures in the northern hemisphere. Ocean temperatures in the southern hemisphere are decreasing slightly. Have students infer why. Fewer people live in the southern hemisphere; thus, less greenhouse gases are generated there.

Resource Manager

Section Focus Transparency 43 L1 ELL
Teaching Transparency 42 L2 ELL
Study Guide for Content Mastery, pp. 89–90 L2
GeoLab and MiniLab Worksheets, p. 55 L2
Exploring Environmental Problems, pp. 13–16 L3

Section 14.4
ENVIRONMENTAL CONNECTION

Prepare

Section Background

For section content background, refer to **Analyzing Climatic Change** on page 358D.

Preplanning

Refer to the Chapter Organizer on pages 358A–B.

1 Focus

Section Focus

Before presenting the lesson, display **Section Focus Transparency 43** on the overhead projector.
L1 ELL

Tying to Previous Knowledge

Tell students that the causes and effects of global warming are hotly debated. This is a good opportunity to reinforce the idea that many scientific topics are not fully understood, and that the body of scientific knowledge is continually refined as new insights are acquired.

MiniLab

Purpose 📦
Students will model the greenhouse effect.

Process Skills
make a model, observe and infer, analyze, graph

Safety Precautions
Students should notify you if any breakage occurs.

Materials
cardboard box, two alcohol thermometers, glass jar, graph paper, pencil

Teaching Strategies
Tell students that the glass jar represents greenhouse gases in the atmosphere that trap sunlight. Make sure students understand that this is a simplistic model, and that other factors help maintain Earth's surface temperatures.

Expected Results
The air inside the jar warms more quickly than does the air outside the jar.

Analyze and Conclude
1. Graphs will vary depending on student measurements.
2. The thermometer in the jar should show higher readings than does the uncovered thermometer. The air was trapped inside the jar.
3. In the atmosphere, greenhouse gases absorb and trap solar radiation, much like the glass jar absorbed and trapped energy from the Sun.

✔Assessment

Knowledge Ask students to infer how this activity would change if they used a jar made of thicker glass. They would likely record higher temperatures. Have students relate the thicker glass to increasing levels of atmospheric greenhouse gases.

MiniLab

How does the atmosphere affect the transfer of energy?
Model the greenhouse effect.

Procedure
1. On a clear day, place a cardboard box outside in a shaded area. Prop two thermometers against the box. Make sure the thermometers are not in direct sun.
2. Cover one thermometer with a clean glass jar.
3. Observe and record the temperature changes of each thermometer every two minutes over a 30-minute period.

Analyze and Conclude
1. Make a graph showing how the temperatures of the two thermometers changed over time.
2. Based on your graph, which thermometer experienced the greatest increase in temperature? Why?
3. Relate your observations to the greenhouse effect in the atmosphere.

---

its thick atmosphere, has surface temperatures of 470°C. You'll model the greenhouse effect in the *MiniLab* on this page.

Scientists theorize that it is possible to increase or decrease the greenhouse effect by changing the amount of atmospheric greenhouse gases, particularly carbon dioxide (CO_2). Any increase in the amount of these gases would theoretically result in the increased absorption of radiation. Levels of atmospheric carbon dioxide are increasing. This in turn can lead to a rise in global temperatures, known as **global warming.**

GLOBAL WARMING
Temperatures worldwide have indeed shown an upward trend over the past 200 years, with several of the warmest years on record having occurred within the last two decades. If the trend continues, polar ice caps might melt, sea level might rise and flood coastal cities, deserts could spread into fertile regions, and the frequency and severity of storms could increase.

Based on available evidence, many scientists agree that global warming is occurring. They disagree, however, about what is causing this warming. As you've learned, natural cycles of Earth and the Sun can affect climate. Some scientists hypothesize that these natural changes adequately explain the increased temperatures. Mounting evidence indicates, however, that the warming trend is a result of increases in atmospheric carbon dioxide. Global warming remains a controversial issue. Neither viewpoint can be proven or disproven conclusively; it might very well be that there are several factors involved. However, if increased carbon dioxide is responsible, two logical questions follow: What is causing the increase? Can anything be done to stop it?

Differentiated Instruction

Gifted Tell students that there is another side to the global warming debate. Namely, the increased heat would cause increased atmospheric convection, which in turn would cause more clouds. Ask students to infer how this might affect atmospheric processes. The increased cloud cover would reflect more solar radiation back to space, which could actually result in atmospheric cooling. This is just one question in the global warming debate that has yet to be answered with any certainty.

Content Background

Although the impact of human activities on global warming is debated, most scientists agree that human activities have led to the thinning of the ozone layer. Tell students that this problem can be controlled by limiting the use of CFCs.

IMPACT OF HUMAN ACTIVITIES

To find a possible cause for rising levels of atmospheric carbon dioxide, we need look no further than our driveways. Automobile exhaust is a prime source of atmospheric CO_2, as are industrial emissions. In fact, almost any process that involves the burning of fossil fuels results in the release of carbon dioxide and other gases into the atmosphere. In addition, deforestation, the mass removal of trees, plays a role in increasing levels of atmospheric CO_2. During photosynthesis, vegetation removes carbon dioxide from the atmosphere. When trees such as the ones shown in *Figure 14-19A* are cut down, rates of photosynthesis are reduced and more carbon dioxide remains in the atmosphere. Many scientists hypothesize that deforestation intensifies global warming trends.

ENVIRONMENTAL EFFORTS

Because global warming appears to be linked to human activities that cause pollution or widespread deforestation, we must closely examine those activities and work to reduce their environmental impact. Individuals can combat global warming by conserving energy, which in turn reduces the consumption of fossil fuels. Some easy ways to conserve energy include turning off appliances and lights when a room is not in use, turning down thermostats in the winter, and recycling. An additional option is shown in *Figure 14-19B.* You'll learn more about global warming in the *Science & Math* feature at the end of this chapter.

Figure 14-19 Deforestation in places such as Guatemala may increase global warming **(A).** Automobile exhaust may also increase global warming; thus, riding bikes is one way to help the environment **(B).**

SECTION ASSESSMENT

1. Why do some scientists theorize that global warming might not be the result of increases in atmospheric carbon dioxide?

2. What are some possible consequences of global warming?

3. Describe some human activities that may have an impact on Earth's climate. List several actions you can take to reduce this impact.

4. Compare and contrast global warming and the greenhouse effect.

5. **Thinking Critically** Based on what you have learned in this section, explain why tropical rain forests are often called the "lungs" of our planet.

SKILL REVIEW

6. **Designing an Experiment** When green plants photosynthesize, they take carbon dioxide out of the atmosphere. Design an experiment in which you could use green plants and glass jars to study the effects of carbon dioxide on global warming. For more help, refer to the *Skill Handbook.*

earthgeu.com/self_check_quiz

Time Allotment

three hours

Process Skills

communicate, make and use graphs, collect data, interpret data, observe and infer

Safety Precaution

The use of mercury thermometers is discouraged. If you must use them, extreme caution is advised.

Preparation

Possible Hypotheses

Hypotheses will vary but should mention that darker and denser objects will likely exhibit greater differences in temperature with increasing height above Earth's surface than will lighter and less dense objects. Students might also hypothesize that the greatest change in variables will occur in the first few centimeters above the ground, and that relative humidity and wind will be lower near Earth's surface, while temperatures will be higher.

Plan the Experiment

Teaching Strategies

- This lab works best on a warm, sunny day with little cloud cover.
- This lab is best done as a group project. Assign one student to collect data at each location. Another student can map the data, and a third can graph the data. The group as a whole should complete the Conclude & Apply questions.

DESIGN YOUR OWN GeoLab

Microclimates

Microclimates can be caused by tall buildings, large bodies of water, and mountains, among other things. In this activity, you'll observe different microclimates and then attempt to determine which factors strengthen microclimates and how these factors change with distance from Earth's surface.

Preparation

Problem
Which type of surface creates the most pronounced microclimate?

Possible Materials
thermometer
psychrometer
paper strip or wind sock
meterstick
relative humidity chart *(Appendix F)*

Hypothesis
Hypothesize how different areas of Earth's surface, such as grassy lawns, asphalt parking lots, and bodies of water, affect local climates. Consider also whether distance from the ground might affect temperature, relative humidity, and wind speed.

Objectives
In this GeoLab, you will:
- **Design** and **carry out** an experiment to study microclimates both at Earth's surface and above its surface.
- **Observe** and **record** temperature, relative humidity, and wind speed.
- **Infer** how different surfaces and changes in height above these surfaces affect microclimates.

Safety Precautions
Be careful when you handle glass thermometers, especially those that contain mercury. If the thermometer breaks, do not touch it. Have your teacher properly dispose of the glass and the mercury.

Possible Procedures

Preselect a list of locations from which students can choose. The list should include locations that have different surfaces, such as asphalt, concrete, bare ground, grassy areas, and water. This will allow students to observe a wide range of microclimates.

Data and Observations

Data should be based on observations at several different locations and at several different heights above the ground. At a minimum, data should include temperature and relative humidity, and, ideally, wind speed and direction.

Plan the Experiment

1. As a group, agree upon and write out your hypothesis. List the steps needed to test your hypothesis. Include in your plan how you will use your equipment to measure temperature, relative humidity, and wind speed at different surfaces and at various heights above these surfaces.
2. Select your sites. Possible sites include a grassy playground area, a paved parking lot, and a swimming pool.
3. Be sure to control variables. For instance, different members of your group should make observations at each site at the same time each day. You'll also need to record weather variables at several different distances above each surface. Possible distances include 5 cm, 1 m, and 2 m.
4. Make a map of your test sites. Design and construct data tables for recording your observations. You'll need separate data tables for each site.
5. Read over your entire plan to make certain all steps are in logical order. Identify constants and variables in your plan.
6. Make sure your teacher approves your plan before you proceed with your experiment.
7. Carry out your plan.

Analyze

1. **Comparing and Contrasting** Map your data. Color code the areas on your map to show which surfaces had the highest and lowest temperatures, the highest and lowest relative humidity, and the greatest and least wind speed. On your map, include data for surface areas only.
2. **Making and Using Graphs** Graph your data for each site, showing differences in temperature with height. Plot temperature on the *x*-axis and height on the *y*-axis. Repeat this step for relative humidity and wind speed.
3. **Interpreting Scientific Illustrations** Analyze your maps, graphs, and data to find patterns. Which surfaces had the most pronounced microclimates? Did height above the surface affect your data? Infer why or why not.
4. **Thinking Critically** Analyze your hypothesis and the results of your experiment. Was your hypothesis supported? Explain.

Conclude & Apply

1. Why did some areas have more pronounced microclimates than others? Which factors seemed to contribute most to the development of microclimates?
2. Which variable changed most with height: temperature, relative humidity, or wind speed? Which variable changed least? Infer why some variables changed more than others with height.

Design Your Own GeoLab **379**

Analyze

1. Student maps will vary. Generally, the larger the scale of the map, the easier the data are to plot and read.
2. Graphs will vary but should reflect collected data.
3. Students should find that darker and denser surfaces are generally warmer and less humid than are lighter and less dense surfaces. With increasing height, temperature should decrease, and humidity and wind speed should increase.
4. Answers will vary depending on individual results. If the weather variables showed appropriate changes with different heights and surfaces, student hypotheses were likely supported.

Conclude & Apply

1. Darker and denser surfaces absorb more sunlight and therefore warm up faster. This higher rate of absorption also affects relative humidity. Areas protected from the wind likely experienced the most variation.
2. Answers will vary depending on the exposure of individual locations. Any of the variables might show the most change, but normally, temperature varies most. Wind is least likely to change, but again, this depends on the exposure of the location.

Assessment

Performance Have students mount their data tables and maps on posterboard to be displayed around the room. Provide time for individuals or groups to present their findings to the class. Use the Performance Task Assessment List for Poster in **PASC,** p. 73.

Resource Manager

GeoLab and MiniLab Worksheets,
   pp. 56–58 **L2**

NY Core Curriculum Standards

Page 378: St 1 Science KI 1, 2, & 3, St 4 KI 2.1c, 2.1d, & 2.2c, St 6 KI 2 & 5
Page 379: St 1 Science KI 1, 2, & 3, St 4 KI 2.1c, 2.1d, & 2.2c, St 6 KI 2 & 5

Purpose

Carbon-dioxide levels have increased by 25 percent over the last 150 years. This feature describes the deforestation of tropical rain forests and how it contributes to increasing carbon emissions. Students will use global atmospheric data to create and analyze a graph of increasing carbon-dioxide concentration from 1745 to 1994.

Content Background

Remind students that the greenhouse effect is a natural phenomenon that helps maintain surface temperatures on Earth. Also, while temperatures were warmer in the last half of the twentieth century, global warming alone did not cause these increases.

Teaching Strategies

- Ask students to describe what the climate in their area would be like if average temperatures increased by several degrees. Make sure students understand that even slight increases in average temperatures can result in massive climatic changes.
- Have students do additional research on the endangered plant and animal species that inhabit tropical rain forests. Students should each write a brief report that explains the importance of maintaining biodiversity.

Science & Math

Global Warming

According to the National Academy of Scientists, Earth's surface temperature has risen about one degree Fahrenheit in the past 100 years. This increase in temperature can be correlated to an increase in the concentration of carbon dioxide and other greenhouse gases in the atmosphere. How might this increase in temperature affect Earth's climate?

Carbon dioxide is one of the greenhouse gases that helps keep temperatures on Earth warm enough to support life. However, a build-up of carbon dioxide and other greenhouse gases such as methane and nitrous oxide can lead to global warming, an increase in Earth's average surface temperature. Since the industrial revolution in the 1800s, atmospheric concentrations of carbon dioxide have increased by almost 30 percent, methane concentrations have more than doubled, and nitrous oxide concentrations have increased approximately 15 percent. Scientists attribute these increases to the burning of fossil fuels for automobiles, industry, and electricity, as well as deforestation, increased agriculture, landfills, and mining.

Impact on Climate

Based on current data, scientists estimate that Earth's average surface temperature could rise between 1 and 4.5 degrees Fahrenheit in the next 50 years. As the temperature increases, evaporation rates increase, which can lead to increased precipitation. With increased evaporation rates, soil may become drier and intense rainstorms more frequent. Some scientists estimate that sea levels may rise as much as two feet along most of the U.S. coast.

Procedure

1. Create a line graph which displays the information shown in the data table below.

Challenge

1. During which time period did Earth's atmosphere experience a slow, steady increase in carbon dioxide? Describe the carbon dioxide increase in the last 50 years.
2. Assuming that carbon dioxide levels continue to increase at the current rate, predict the global atmospheric CO_2 concentration in parts per million in the year 2015.

Global Levels of Atmospheric CO_2			
Year	Global Atmospheric CO_2 Concentration (parts per million)	Year	Global Atmospheric CO_2 Concentration (parts per million)
1745	279	1949	311
1791	279.7	1958	312
1816	283.8	1965	318
1843	287.4	1974	330.1
1854	288.2	1984	344.3
1874	289.5	1994	358.8
1894	297	1995	361
1909	299.2	1996	363
1921	301.6	1997	364
1935	306.6	1998	367

Procedure

Data and Observations
The table in the features provides data on levels of atmospheric carbon dioxide in parts per million.

Sources of Error
The years in the table are not consecutive. Remind students to take this into account when creating their graphs.

Challenge

1. There was a slow, steady increase in levels of carbon dioxide until the late 1950s. There has been a sharper increase in CO_2 levels in the last 50 years.
2. If the current trend continues, carbon-dioxide levels could reach 385 to 390 ppm by 2015.

Summary

SECTION 14.1

What is climate?

Main Ideas
- Climate describes the long-term weather patterns of a region. Climatological data include annual variations of temperature, precipitation, wind, and other weather variables, as well as extreme fluctuations in these variables.
- The factors that influence climate include latitude, topography, closeness of lakes and oceans, availability of moisture, global wind patterns, ocean currents, and air masses.

Vocabulary
climate (p. 359)
climatology (p. 359)
normal (p. 360)
polar zone (p. 362)
temperate zone (p. 362)
tropics (p. 362)

SECTION 14.2

Climate Classification

Main Ideas
- The Koeppen classification system divides climates into five basic types according to temperature, rainfall, and vegetation.
- A microclimate is a localized climate that differs from the surrounding regional climate. In cities, the numerous concrete buildings and large expanses of asphalt can create heat islands, wherein the climate is warmer than in surrounding rural areas.

Vocabulary
heat island (p. 368)
Koeppen classification system (p. 364)
microclimate (p. 367)

SECTION 14.3

Climatic Changes

Main Ideas
- Earth's climate is in a constant state of change. These changes usually take place over extremely long time periods. Fossils, ice cores, and other geologic records show that Earth was sometimes much colder or warmer than it is today.
- Periods of extensive glacial coverage, called ice ages, are examples of long-term climatic changes. Examples of short-term climatic changes include the seasons and the effects of El Niño.
- Some changes in Earth's climate may be caused by a combination of numerous natural cycles involving solar activity, changes in the tilt of Earth's axis and its orbit, and volcanic eruptions.

Vocabulary
El Niño (p. 370)
ice age (p. 369)
Maunder minimum (p. 372)
season (p. 370)

SECTION 14.4

The Human Factor

Main Ideas
- The greenhouse effect is the retention of heat by atmospheric gases that helps to keep Earth warm enough to sustain life. An increase in greenhouse gases may lead to global warming.
- Some scientists theorize that human activities such as the burning of fossil fuels and deforestation cause global warming.

Vocabulary
global warming (p. 376)
greenhouse effect (p. 375)

earthgeu.com/vocabulary_puzzlemaker

Study Guide **381**

Main Ideas

Summary statements can be used by students to review the major concepts of the chapter.

VOCABULARY PuzzleMaker

For additional help with vocabulary, have students access the Vocabulary Puzzlemaker online.

earthgeu.com/ vocabulary puzzlemaker

0:00 Out of Time?

If time does not permit teaching the entire chapter, use the GeoDigest at the end of the unit as an overview.

Earth Science Online

Be sure to check the Earth Science Web Site for links to chapter material:
earthgeu.com

GLENCOE
Technology

Videotape/DVD
MindJogger Videoquizzes

Chapter 14: *Climate*
Have students work in groups as they play the videoquiz game to review key chapter concepts.

Resource Manager

Chapter Assessment, pp. 79–84
MindJogger Videoquizzes DVD/VHS
Performance Assessment in Earth Science
ExamView® Pro CD-ROM

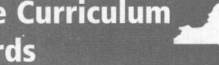
NY Core Curriculum Standards

Page 380: St 4 KI 2.2d, St 6 KI 2 & 5
Page 381: St 4 KI 2.1c, 2.1i, 2.2a, 2.2b, 2.2c, & 2.2d, St 6 KI 1 & 5

Understanding Main Ideas

1. b
2. b
3. c
4. b
5. d
6. a
7. a
8. c
9. c
10. a
11. b
12. b
13. An ice age is a period of extensive glacial coverage. The last ice age ended 10 000 years ago.
14. Deforestation is the mass removal of trees. It increases greenhouse gases because fewer trees are available to fulfill their function of removing carbon dioxide from the atmosphere.
15. A desert would most likely form on the leeward side of a mountain because the air would have dropped its moisture on the windward side and thus descended on the leeward side as a dry air mass.
16. A savanna is a type of tropical climate characterized by grasslands. A steppe is a type of dry climate that generally separates deserts from bordering wet climates.
17. When the orbit elongates, Earth passes closer to the Sun. At that time, temperatures become warmer than normal.

Understanding Main Ideas

1. Which of the following does NOT influence climate?
   a. latitude
   c. mountains
   b. satellites
   d. large bodies of water

2. A heat island is an example of what type of climate?
   a. tropical climate
   c. dry climate
   b. microclimate
   d. polar climate

3. Which of the following is NOT a factor used to classify climates in the Koeppen classification system?
   a. temperature
   c. wind
   b. moisture
   d. vegetation

4. Which of the following is an example of a long-term climatic change?
   a. fall
   c. summer
   b. ice ages
   d. El Niño

5. What is El Niño?
   a. a warm wind
   c. a cool wind
   b. a cool ocean current
   d. a warm ocean current

6. Which of the following would normals best describe?
   a. a specific location
   c. an ocean
   b. a land mass
   d. a mountain

7. What is the Maunder minimum?
   a. a period of low sunspot activity
   b. an ice age
   c. a volcanic eruption
   d. a cycle of Earth's orbit

8. Which of the following would NOT be likely to produce a microclimate?
   a. an ocean shoreline
   c. a flat prairie
   b. a valley
   d. a large city

9. Which greenhouse gas is most associated with global warming?
   a. methane
   c. carbon dioxide
   b. ozone
   d. carbon monoxide

10. If it's winter in the northern hemisphere, what season is it in the southern hemisphere?
    a. summer
    c. winter
    b. fall
    d. spring

11. El Niño develops because of a weakening of what?
    a. the polar front
    b. the trade winds
    c. the prevailing westerlies
    d. the jet stream

12. Which of the following is not a natural cause of long-term climatic change?
    a. solar activity
    b. industrialization
    c. changes in the tilt of Earth's axis
    d. changes in Earth's rotation

13. What is an ice age? When did the last ice age end?

14. What is deforestation? How is it linked to global warming?

15. On which side of a mountain would a desert most likely form? Why?

16. Compare and contrast a steppe and a savanna.

17. When Earth's orbit elongates, are temperatures warmer or cooler than normal? Explain.

Test-Taking Tip

PLAN AHEAD Find out where and when your test will take place. If the location is unfamiliar, go there ahead of time to be sure you can find your way. Find out if you will need identification or other items on the day of the test.

earthgeu.com/chapter_test

Standardized Test Practice

1. c
2. b
3. d
4. c

Applying Main Ideas

18. The graph on this page shows sunspot activity from 1860 to 1995. Predict when the next maximum will occur.

Use this graph to answer question 18.

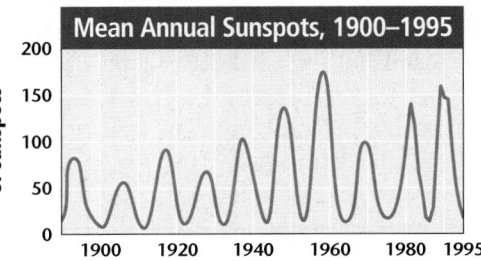

Mean Annual Sunspots, 1900–1995

19. Based on the data shown in the *Problem-Solving Lab* on page 360, what months are good for planting crops that cannot survive frosts?

20. Use a world map and *Figure 14-4* to determine the climate classifications of the following cities: Paris, France; Athens, Greece; London, England; and Sydney, Australia.

Thinking Critically

21. Which would El Niño affect more: Anchorage, Alaska, or Los Angeles, California? Why?

22. How might a mountain valley produce a microclimate?

23. Based on the results of the *Discovery Lab* that you performed at the beginning of this chapter, would you expect temperatures during the night to drop more sharply in marine climates or continental climates? Why?

24. A large, three-story shopping mall is built near a town. Would you expect temperatures in the immediate region to increase, decrease, or remain the same? Explain.

earthgeu.com/standardized_test

Standardized Test Practice

INTERPRETING DATA Use the table below to answer questions 1 and 2.

Location	Climate Description
New Caledonia, South Pacific	Constant high temperatures, plenty of rain
Southern Israel	Humid in summer, dry in winter
Gobi Desert, Mongolia	Continental tropical air, low precipitation, scarce vegetation
Bogotá, Colombia	Mild winters, cool summers, abundant precipitation
Yukon, Canada	Year-round cold, low precipitation

1. According to the modified Koeppen classification system, Southern Israel has what kind of climate?
- **a.** tropical
- **b.** dry
- **c.** humid subtropical
- **d.** continental

2. Where is a steppe most likely to be found?
- **a.** New Caledonia
- **b.** Gobi Desert
- **c.** Bogotá
- **d.** Yukon

3. Where is a heat island most likely to be found?
- **a.** a farm
- **b.** a beach
- **c.** a mountaintop
- **d.** an inner city

4. Why is deforestation often linked to global warming?
- **a.** It increases the amount of dry land on Earth's surface.
- **b.** It releases toxic gases and pollutants into the atmosphere.
- **c.** It increases the amount of CO_2 released into the atmosphere.
- **d.** It decreases the amount of CO_2 released into the atmosphere.

Applying Main Ideas

18. 2011–2012
19. April through October
20. Paris: marine west coast; Athens: Mediterranean; London: marine west coast; Sydney: marine west coast

Thinking Critically

21. Los Angeles; it is closer to the tropics where the effects of El Niño are most pronounced.
22. Cooler air would sink and settle in a mountain valley, and once there, it would be unlikely to be modified because warm air would tend to pass above it. That warmer air also would create extra lift. Thus, the overall effect might be a cloudy and cool microclimate.
23. Continental climates; land loses heat more quickly than water does. Also, the air over coastal regions has many of the same characteristics as an ocean climate.
24. Temperatures would probably increase slightly. The presence of so much added concrete and asphalt would create a heat island and cause the immediate region to absorb more heat.

EXAMVIEW® PRO

Use ExamView® Pro Testmaker CD-ROM to:

- Create **multiple versions** of tests.
- Create **modified** tests with one mouse click for struggling students.
- **Edit** existing questions and add your own questions.
- **Build** tests based on national curriculum standards.

NY Core Curriculum Standards

Page 382: St 4 KI 2.1f, 2.1i, 2.2a, 2.2b, 2.2c, & 2.2d, St 6 KI 1 & 5
Page 383: St 4 KI 2.1f, 2.1i, 2.2a, 2.2b, 2.2c, & 2.2d, St 6 KI 1, 2, & 5

Physical Oceanography

Refer to pages 8T–9T of the Teacher Guide for an explanation of the National Science Content Standards correlations.

Section	Objectives	National Science Content Standards	State/Local Standards
SECTION 15.1 **The Oceans** 🕐 1½ sessions 🧊 1 block	1. **Identify** methods used by scientists to study Earth's oceans. 2. **Discuss** the origin and composition of the oceans. 3. **Describe** the distribution of oceans and major seas.	UCP.1, UCP.2, UCP.3, UCP.4, UCP.5; A.1, A.2; B.2; D.1, D.2, D.3; E.1, E.2; G.1, G.3	St 1 Math KI 1, 2, 3, Science KI 1, 2, & 3, St 2 KI 1, 2, & 3, St 4 KI 1.1a, 1.1i, 1.2c, 1.2d, 1.2e, 1.2f, 1.2g, & 1.2j, St 6 KI 1, 2, 3, 4, & 5, St 7 KI 1
SECTION 15.2 **Seawater** 🕐 1½ sessions 🧊 1 block	4. **Compare** and **contrast** the physical and chemical properties of seawater. 5. **Explain** ocean layering. 6. **Describe** the formation of deep-water masses.	UCP.1, UCP.2, UCP.3, UCP.4, UCP.5; A.1, A.2; B.2; D.2, D.3	St 1 Math KI 1, 2, 3, Science KI 3, St 2 KI 1, 2, & 3, St 4 KI 1.2g & 3.1a, St 6 KI 4 & 5, St 7 KI 1
SECTION 15.3 **Ocean Movements** 🕐 3 sessions 🧊 1½ blocks	7. **Describe** the physical properties of waves. 8. **Explain** how tides form. 9. **Compare** and **contrast** various ocean currents.	UCP.1, UCP.2, UCP.3, UCP.4, UCP.5; A.1, A.2; B.2, B.4; D.1, D.2, D.3; E.1, E.2; F.6; G.1, G.3	St 1 Math KI 1, 2, Science KI 1, 2, & 3, St 2 KI 1, St 4 KI 1.1a, 1.1e, 1.1i, 2.1i, 2.2b, & 2.2c, St 6 KI 1, 2, & 5, St 7 KI 1 & 2

A complete Planning Guide is provided on pages 30T–32T.

🕐 The number of recommended single-period sessions

🧊 The number of recommended blocks

Activity Materials

Discovery Lab *page 385*
globe, ruler, string, blue marker

GeoLab *page 406–407*
laboratory scale, 500-mL graduated cylinder, 4 100-mL beakers, food coloring, NaCl, thermometer, dropper, graph paper, ruler, pencil, calculator, water

MiniLab *page 394*
1-L beaker, 1-L graduated cylinder, 7 100-mL beakers, 7 small bottles, NaCl, $MgCl_2$, Na_2SO_4, $CaCl_2$, KCl, $NaHCO_3$, KBr, stirring rod, distilled water, laboratory scale

Demo *page 388*
stopwatch

page 400
1-L graduated cylinder, wooden stick, water

Need materials? Contact Science Kit at 1-800-828-7777 or at www.sciencekit.com on the Internet. For alternate materials, see the activity on the listed page.

Key to Teaching Strategies

L1 Level 1 activities should be appropriate for students with learning difficulties.

L2 Level 2 activities should be within the ability range of all students.

L3 Level 3 activities are designed for above-average students.

ELL ELL activities should be within the ability range of English-language learners.

COOP LEARN Cooperative Learning activities are designed for small-group work.

P These strategies represent student products that can be placed in a best-work portfolio.

🧊 These strategies are useful in a block-scheduling format.

Chapter Organizer

Glencoe Exclusive!
TeacherWorks™
All-In-One Planner and Resource Center

Activities/Features	Reproducible Masters	Transparencies
Discovery Lab: Measure Earth's Land and Water, p. 385	**Study Guide for Content Mastery,** pp. 91–92 **L2**	**Section Focus Transparency 44** **L1** **ELL** **Teaching Transparency 43** **L2** **ELL**
MiniLab: What is the chemical composition of seawater? p. 394 **Using Math:** Using Numbers, p. 395	**Study Guide for Content Mastery,** pp. 93–94 **L2** **GeoLab and MiniLab Worksheets,** p. 59 **L2** **Laboratory Manual,** pp. 113–116 **L2**	**Section Focus Transparency 45** **L1** **ELL** **Teaching Transparency 44** **L2** **ELL**
Problem-Solving Lab: Making and Using Graphs, p. 401 **GeoLab:** Modeling Water Masses, pp. 406–407 **Science in the News:** Caught in the Current, p. 408	**Study Guide for Content Mastery,** pp. 95–96 **L2** **GeoLab and MiniLab Worksheets,** pp. 60–62 **L2** **Laboratory Manual,** pp. 117–120 **L2**	**Section Focus Transparency 46** **L1** **ELL** **Teaching Transparency 45** **L2** **ELL**

✔Assessment

Chapter Assessment, pp. 85–90
Performance Assessment in the Science Classroom (PASC)
MindJogger Videoquiz DVD/VHS
Performance Assessment in Earth Science
ExamView® Pro CD-ROM
5 Days to the Regents Exam

GLENCOE'S
ASSESSMENT
ADVANTAGE

Additional Resources

Guided Reading Audio Program **ELL**
Cooperative Learning in the Science Classroom **COOP LEARN**
Lesson Plans
Block Scheduling
earthgeu.com
NY Lesson Plans
NY Block Scheduling
Review Handbook for Regents Earth Science Exam

▨ NATIONAL GEOGRAPHIC

Teacher's Corner

Products Available from National Geographic Society
To order the following products, call the National Geographic Society at 1-800-368-2728:
Curriculum Kit
GeoKit: *Oceans*

CD-ROM
111 years of National Geographic Magazine
Videos
Oceans in Motion
Water: A Precious Resource

Content Background

Brief History of Oceanography
Section 15.1

The ancient Egyptians were the first to build seafaring ships, around 4000 B.C. Later, the Phoenicians explored the Mediterranean Sea and beyond. The ancient Greeks had relatively accurate, detailed maps of the Mediterranean Sea and surrounding regions, and some knowledge of nearby oceans. Between the ninth and twelfth centuries, Viking seafarers discovered Iceland, Greenland, and parts of North America. Columbus rediscovered America in 1492 and helped launch the great European age of exploration. Magellan circumnavigated Earth between 1519 and 1522, sailing mostly in the southern hemisphere. Between 1768 and 1779, James Cook undertook three voyages through the major oceans, gathered extensive scientific data, and discovered New Zealand, Australia, and the Pacific coasts of America, Hawaii, and Alaska. The epic scientific journey of Charles Darwin on the HMS *Beagle* took place between 1831 and 1836. Sir James Ross found the last unknown landmass on Earth, Antarctica, in 1839. The Arctic Ocean was explored by Sir John Ross and Fridjof Nansen in 1888 and 1893, respectively. Other noteworthy developments in physical oceanography were the determination of Earth's circumference and the use of latitude and longitude by the ancient Greeks, the recognition of the water cycle by the ancient Romans, the explanation of tides by Leonhard Euler in 1740, and the charting of major ocean currents by Benjamin Franklin in 1769 and Matthew Maury in 1855.

Density of Water
Section 15.2

Density is defined as mass per volume, and it is usually expressed in grams per cubic centimeter (g/cm^3) or grams per milliliter (g/mL). Note that 1 g/cm^3 is equal to 1000 kg/m^3. The density of water depends on its temperature and salinity. Freshwater reaches its maximum density of 1 g/cm^3 at 4°C. At higher temperatures, thermal expansion causes a decrease in the density of freshwater. At lower temperatures, more hydrogen bonds form, and the cold water has a molecular structure similar to ice. At 0°C, the density of freshwater is 0.9998 g/cm^3, and that of pure ice is 0.918 g/cm^3. Dissolved salt ions increase the density of water. As a result, the density of seawater ranges from about 1.02 g/cm^3 to 1.03 g/cm^3, depending on salinity and temperature. Dissolved salts interfere with the formation of hydrogen bonds and decrease the freezing point of

Multiple Learning Styles

Kinesthetic Modeling, p. 386

Logical-Mathematical Demo, p. 388, Reteach, p. 391, Activity, p. 403

Interpersonal Collaborative Learning, p. 393

Visual-Spatial Modeling, p. 396

Linguistic Reteach, p. 405

GLENCOE *Technology*

The following multimedia resources are available from Glencoe.

Vocabulary Puzzlemaker

TeacherWorks™ CD-ROM

MindJogger Videoquizzes DVD/VHS

ExamView® Pro CD-ROM

Interactive Chalkboard CD-ROM

seawater to about –2°C. Because of the relative scarcity of hydrogen bonds, the maximum density of seawater corresponds to its freezing point of –2°C. Accordingly, the densest seawater has a temperature of –2°C and high salinity. Water density also increases with pressure, but this relationship does not affect the movement of water masses and thus is usually ignored by oceanographers.

Tidal Forces
Section 15.3

Tides exist because gravitational forces decrease with distance. The force per unit of mass, g, exerted by a gravitating body of mass, m, at a distance, d, is found using the equation $g = Gm/d^2$, where G is the universal gravitational constant. Consider the gravitational attraction of the Moon at points A and B on Earth's surface:

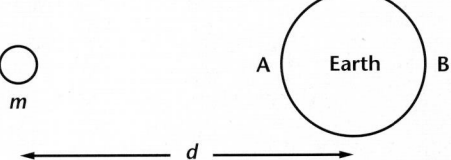

If Earth's radius is r, and the separation of the centers of Earth and the Moon is d, then the lunar gravitational attraction caused by the Moon's mass, m, at the center of Earth is $g_C = Gm/d^2$. At point A, this attraction is $g_A = Gm/(d - r)^2$, and at point B it is $g_B = Gm/(d + r)^2$. Clearly, the gravitational force on point A, which is closer to the Moon, is stronger than that at point B. This difference in lunar attraction generates a stretching force that acts on Earth along the Earth-Moon line. This stretching force is the lunar tidal force. Because both points A and B are pulled away from Earth's center by this force, the tidal force can be calculated by subtracting the Moon's attraction at Earth's center from the lunar attraction at either point A or B.

Identifying Misconceptions

We can usually see through the water in a glass, sink, bucket, or bathtub. Thus, many people have the erroneous impression that water is transparent. In reality, however, all water absorbs light. In fact, a layer of ocean water 100 m thick absorbs more than 99 percent of incident light. This means that the oceans are essentially dark below a depth of 100 m. Even in clear, tropical waters, the seafloor cannot be seen from the surface in waters deeper than about 50 m.

✔*Assessment*

Portfolio Assessment
  Assessment, TWE, p. 391

Performance Assessment
  Discovery Lab, SE, p. 385
  MiniLab, SE, p. 394
  Assessment, TWE, p. 398
  GeoLab, SE, pp. 406–407

Knowledge Assessment
  Assessment, TWE, pp. 386, 397, 405
  Section Assessment, SE, pp. 391, 398, 405
  Chapter Assessment, SE, pp. 410–411

Skill Assessment
  Discovery Lab, TWE, p. 385
  MiniLab, TWE, p. 394
  Problem-Solving Lab, TWE, p. 401
  GeoLab, TWE, pp. 406–407

Be sure to check the Earth Science Web Site for links to chapter material: earthgeu.com

Physical Oceanography

Introducing the Chapter

Use a globe to emphasize that most of Earth's surface is covered by water. Point out to students that this is true regardless of the direction from which Earth is viewed.

Interpreting the Photo

The humpback whale in this photograph is swimming in Paradise Bay, off the coast of Antarctica. Have students locate Paradise Bay on a map or globe. Then have them describe the position of the Antarctic Ocean relative to the Atlantic Ocean. Emphasize that there are no borders between the major oceans. Use the map to show students that all oceans are connected, and that the continents are huge islands within the global ocean.

INTERACTIVE CHALKBOARD
with Image Bank

PowerPoint® Presentations

This CD is an editable Microsoft® PowerPoint® presentation that includes:
- Section presentations
- Section checks
- Image bank
- Links to Earth Science Online
- All transparencies
- Animations
- Audio

What You'll Learn

- How scientists study oceans, how the oceans formed, and where they are located.

- How the physical and chemical properties of seawater differ from those of freshwater.

- What causes tides, waves, and ocean currents.

Why It's Important

More than 71 percent of Earth's surface is covered by oceans. These vast bodies of water affect weather, climate, food supplies, recreation, global trade, and marine life, such as this humpback whale in Paradise Bay, Antarctica.

Earth Science Online

To learn more about oceanography, visit the Earth Science Web Site at earthgeu.com

---

Physical Oceanography

Discovery Lab

Process Skills

analyze data, compare and contrast, measure in SI, use numbers, observe and infer, communicate **L1** **ELL**

Preparation

Procure three to four globes, if possible, with diameters of about 30 cm and several water-soluble, blue markers. Cut several pieces of string about 1 m in length or long enough to fit around the globes' equators. Run through the entire activity prior to class.

Procedure
Teaching Strategies

- Divide the class into several groups. Give each group a piece of string and a blue marker.

- Review how to convert fractions to percentages.

Troubleshooting

Caution students to be precise and to be careful not to mark up the globe when coloring the string.

Discovery Lab

Measure Earth's Land and Water

Earth is often referred to as the "blue planet" because so much of its surface is made up of water. If you study a globe or a photograph of Earth taken from space, you can clearly see that oceans cover much more of Earth than landmasses do. This activity will help you to quantify the amount of water on Earth's surface.

1. Stretch a piece of string about 1 m in length around the equator of a globe.

2. Use a blue marker to color the sections of the string that cross the oceans.

3. Measure the length of the globe's equator, then measure the length of each blue section on the string. Add the lengths of the blue sections.

4. Divide the total length of the blue sections by the length of the globe's equator.

Observe What percentage of the globe's equator is made up of oceans? What percentage of the globe's equator is made up of land? Study the globe again. Are the oceans separate bodies of water, or do they interconnect? Describe your observations in your science journal.

The Oceans

OBJECTIVES

- **Identify** *methods used by scientists to study Earth's oceans.*

- **Discuss** *the origin and composition of the oceans.*

- **Describe** *the distribution of oceans and major seas.*

VOCABULARY

oceanography
side-scan sonar
sea level

Since prehistoric times, people have used Earth's oceans for travel and recreation and to obtain food. Early Polynesians and Phoenicians were accomplished sailors who discovered new lands and sea routes for commerce. These seafarers acquired considerable knowledge of the oceans, but they lacked the technology to explore the ocean depths. Such exploration had to wait until the late 1800s, when the British *Challenger* expedition became the first research ship to use relatively sophisticated measuring devices to study the oceans. *Challenger* also was the first expedition devoted exclusively to the scientific study of Earth's oceans, known as **oceanography.** The discipline of oceanography is usually considered to have started with the *Challenger.*

MODERN OCEANOGRAPHY

The *Challenger* expedition investigated ocean currents, water temperature and chemical composition, seafloor sediments and topography,

15.1 The Oceans **385**

Section Focus

Before presenting the lesson, display **Section Focus Transparency 44** on the overhead projector.
L1 ELL

Chapter Themes

The following themes from the National Science Content Standards are covered in this chapter. Refer to page 8T of the Teacher Guide for an explanation of the correlations.
Systems, order, and organization (UCP.1); Evidence, models, and explanation (UCP.2); Change, constancy, and measurement (UCP.3)

0:00 Out of Time?

If time does not permit teaching the entire chapter, use the Chapter Summary on page 409 and the GeoDigest found at the end of the unit as an overview.

Observe

About 80 percent of the equator crosses oceans, and 20 percent crosses landmasses. All oceans are interconnected.

Assessment

Skill Ask students to answer the following questions in terms of latitude. Which area of Earth's surface is covered by more land than water? between about 45°N and 70°N Between which latitudes is there no land at all? between about 55°S and 65°S

Resource Manager

Section Focus Transparency 44 L1 ELL
Study Guide for Content Mastery, pp. 91–92 L2

Kinesthetic Before the development of echo sounding and sonar, ocean depths were determined by wire-line soundings. Perform the following exercise to model wire-line sounding. Place two or three objects on the bottom of a large cooler, then fill the cooler with muddy water that completely obscures the bottom. Have students use a small weight attached to a line to measure the depth to the bottom at various points. Students should then produce a contour plot of the bottom topography and compare it to actual bottom features after the cooler has been drained. **L1** **ELL**

✓Assessment

Knowledge A knowledge of latitude and longitude is crucial to understanding oceanography. To review these concepts, have students examine a globe or atlas to determine the approximate latitude and longitude of the following locations.
1. their school Answers will vary.
2. Washington, DC 39°N, 77°W
3. the northernmost point in the United States Barrow, Alaska, 71°N, 157°W
4. the southernmost point in the United States the island of Hawaii, 19°N, 156°W

and marine life. The expedition used nets, bottom dredges, and other tools to gather enough research to fill 50 thick volumes. Later expeditions, such as that of the German research ship *Meteor* in the 1920s, used sonar for the first time to map the seafloor features of the South Atlantic Ocean, including the Mid-Atlantic Ridge. *Sonar* stands for *so*und *na*vigation and *r*anging. It uses the return time of an echo and the known velocity of sound in water to determine water depth. The velocity of sound in water is 1500 m/s. To determine ocean depth in a particular place, scientists send a sonar signal to the ocean floor and time its return, or echo. They multiply the time by 1500 m/s, then divide by 2 to calculate the distance to the ocean floor. *Figure 15-1* has more information about sonar.

Advanced Technology Recent technological advances such as the one shown in *Figure 15-2* have tremendously expanded scientific knowledge of the oceans. Satellites such as the *Topex/Poseidon* continually monitor the ocean's surface temperatures, currents, and wave conditions. Submersibles, or underwater vessels, investigate the deepest ocean trenches. Large portions of the seafloor have been mapped using **side-scan sonar,** a technique that directs sound waves to the seafloor at an angle, so that the sides of underwater hills and other topographic features can be mapped. You'll

Figure 15-1 A ship equipped with sonar can gather data about deep-lake and ocean-floor features **(A)**. Computers use the resulting data to make maps of underwater features such as this color-enhanced map of Lake Tahoe in Nevada **(B)**.

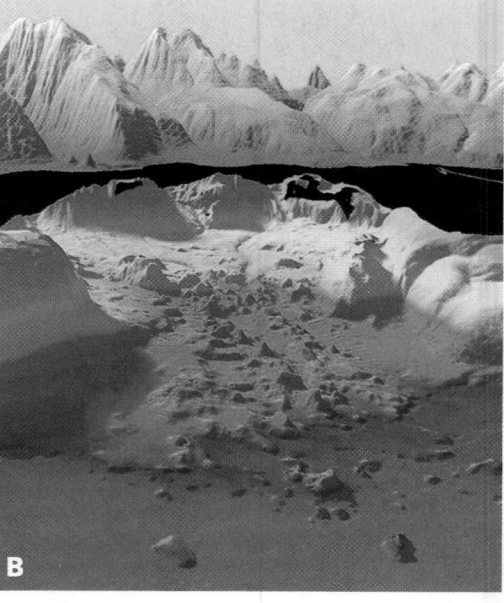

Resource Manager

Teaching Transparency 43 **L2** **ELL**

Figure 15-2 The *Topex/Poseidon* satellite orbits 1331 km above Earth, gathering data about the oceans.

learn more about seafloor topography in the next chapter. For now, let's examine what all the various oceanography studies have taught us about the ocean's origin and composition.

ORIGIN OF THE OCEANS

Have you ever wondered whether Earth has always had oceans? Several geological clues indicate that oceans have existed almost since the beginning of geologic history. Studies of radioactive isotopes indicate that Earth is about 4.6 billion years old. Scientists have found rocks nearly as old that formed from sediments deposited in water. Ancient lava flows are another clue—some of these lava flows have glassy crusts that form only when molten lava is chilled rapidly under water. Radioactive studies and lava flows offer evidence that there has been abundant water throughout Earth's geologic history.

Where did the water come from? Scientists hypothesize that Earth's water could have originated from two sources. Comets, such as the one shown in *Figure 15-3,* travel throughout the solar system and occasionally collide with Earth. These impacts release water, possibly enough to have filled the ocean basins over geologic time. In addition, studies of meteorites, which are composed of the same material that may have formed the early planets, indicate that meteorites contain up to 0.5 percent water. If the early Earth contained the same percentage of water, it would have been more than sufficient to form the early oceans. However, some mechanism must have existed to allow the water to rise from deep in Earth's interior to its surface. Scientists theorize that that mechanism was volcanism.

Figure 15-3 Comets such as Hyakutake are composed of dust and rock particles mixed with frozen water and gases. Early in Earth's geologic history, collisions with comets may have released water that, over an extremely long period of time, formed the first oceans.

Interpreting the Photo

Figure 15-3 Comets have been compared to dirty snowballs. They consist of a mixture of frozen gases and dust, and have diameters averaging a few kilometers. The frozen gases are mostly water vapor, methane, and ammonia. Most known comets travel in highly eccentric orbits. As they approach the Sun, the gases vaporize and generate large, visible tails.

Content Background

Water pressure is caused by the weight of the overlying water column pressing down on the water below. A column of water 10 m tall exerts a pressure of 1 standard atmosphere (atm). The pressure at sea level is 1 atm. At a depth of 10 m, it is 2 atm, and at a depth of 100 m, it is 11 atm. The water pressure on the seafloor in the abyssal plains, which are 5 km deep, is approximately 500 atm. In deep-sea trenches, water pressure is as high as 1000 atm.

CD-ROM
Oceans PictureShow
Journeys

NY Core Curriculum Standards

Page 384: St 4 KI 1.1a, & 1.2f
Page 385: St 1 Math KI 2, Science KI 1, 2, & 3, St 2 KI 1, 2, & 3, St 4 KI 1.1i, St 6 KI 2 & 3
Page 386: St 1 Math KI 1, St 2 KI 1, 2, & 3, St 7 KI 1
Page 387: St 4 KI 1.2c, 1.2d, & 1.2j, St 7 KI 1

Logical-Mathematical

Sonar or echo sounding involves timing the return of an echo, multiplying that time by the velocity of sound, and dividing the resulting distance by 2. To demonstrate how sonar works, take the class outside and have students stand at least 50 m away from the school. Have a student volunteer shout or clap his or her hands. Time the interval between the initial sound and the echo with a stopwatch, and have the class record that time. Repeat the demonstration with students standing farther away from the school. In class, tell students that the speed of sound in air is 334 m/s, and have them calculate how far they stood from the school in both demonstrations.

In-Text Question

Page 388 What do you think would happen over geologic time if they didn't? The amount of water on Earth would increase if ultraviolet radiation decreased. Or, the amount of water on Earth would decrease if ultraviolet radiation increased.

Figure 15-4 In addition to comets, water for Earth's early oceans may have come from volcanic eruptions. An intense period of volcanism occurred shortly after the planet formed. This volcanism released large quantities of water vapor and other gases into the atmosphere. The water vapor eventually condensed into oceans.

Carbon dioxide
Hydrogen
Chlorine   Water vapor
Nitrogen

Volcanism During volcanic eruptions, significant quantities of gases are emitted. These volcanic gases consist mostly of water vapor and carbon dioxide. Shortly after the formation of Earth, when the young planet was much hotter than it is today, an episode of massive, violent volcanism took place over the course of perhaps several hundred million years. As shown in *Figure 15-4,* this volcanism released huge amounts of water vapor, carbon dioxide, and other gases, which combined to form Earth's early atmosphere. As Earth's crust cooled, the water vapor gradually condensed into oceans. By the time the oldest known crustal rock formed some 4 billion years ago, Earth's oceans may have been close to their present size. Water is still being added to the hydrosphere by volcanism, but some water molecules in the atmosphere are continually being destroyed by ultraviolet radiation from the Sun. These two processes balance each other. What do you think would happen over geologic time if they didn't?

DISTRIBUTION OF EARTH'S WATER

The oceans contain 97 percent of the water found on Earth. Another 3 percent is freshwater located in the frozen ice caps of Greenland and Antarctica and in rivers, lakes, and underground sources. The percentage of ice on Earth has varied over geologic time from near zero to perhaps as much as 10 percent of the hydrosphere. Thus, global **sea level,** which is the level of the oceans' surfaces, has risen and fallen by hundreds of meters in response to melting ice during warm periods and expanding glaciers during ice ages. Other processes that affect sea level are tectonic forces that lift or lower portions of the seafloor. A rising seafloor causes a rise in sea level, while

Across the Curriculum

Chemistry Ultraviolet radiation dissociates water molecules into hydrogen and oxygen atoms. Oxygen atoms are about 16 times more massive than hydrogen atoms. At any given temperature, the atoms and molecules in the atmosphere have the same average kinetic energy, but because of the differences in their masses, their velocities differ. Hydrogen atoms move, on average, four times faster than oxygen atoms move. Because of their high velocities, hydrogen atoms can escape from Earth's gravitational field and leak into space. Thus, water molecules gradually disappear as their hydrogen atoms escape into space. Scientists theorize that the planet Mars, which has a weak gravitational field, lost most of its water this way.

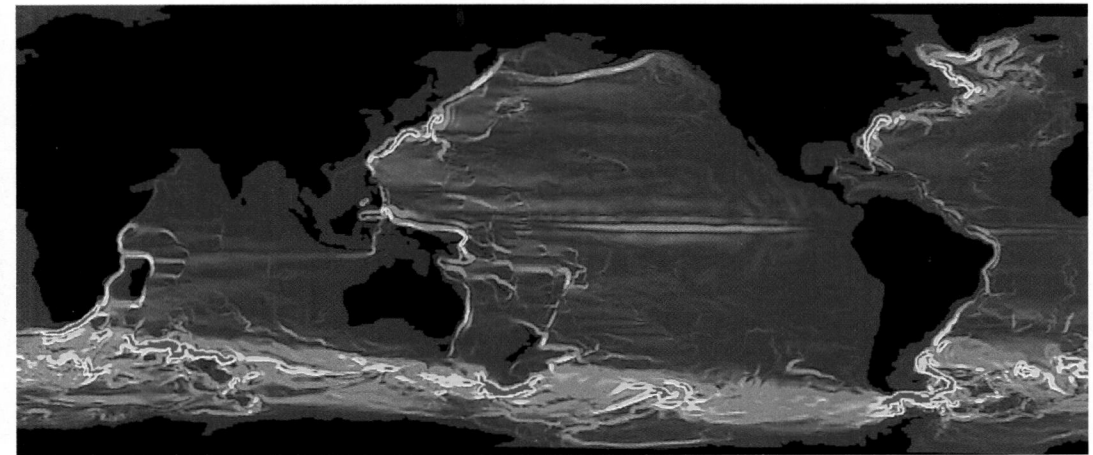

a sinking seafloor causes sea level to drop. At present, average global sea level is slowly rising at a rate of 1 to 2 mm per year in response to melting glaciers.

The Blue Planet As shown in the image of Earth in *Figure 15-5,* Earth is known as the "blue planet" for good reason—approximately 71 percent of its surface is covered by oceans. The average depth of these oceans is 3800 m. Earth's landmasses are like huge islands, almost entirely surrounded by water. Because most landmasses are in the northern hemisphere, oceans cover only 61 percent of the surface there. However, 81 percent of the southern hemisphere is covered by water. *Figure 15-6* shows the distribution of water in the northern and southern hemispheres. Note that all the oceans are really one vast, interconnected body of water. They have been divided into specific oceans and seas largely because of historic and geographic considerations.

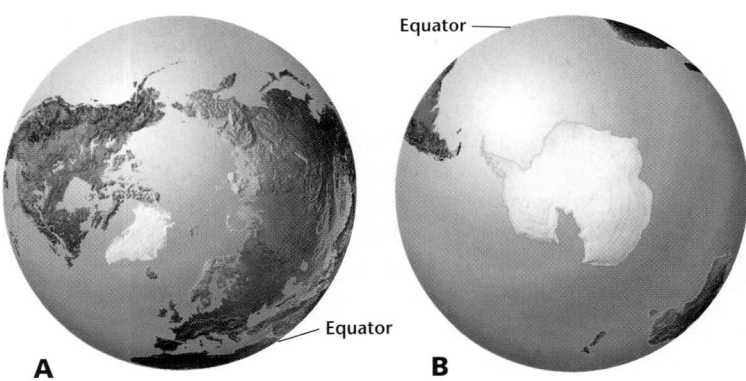

Equator

Equator

A

B

Figure 15-6 The northern hemisphere is covered by slightly more water than land **(A).** The southern hemisphere, however, is covered mainly by water **(B).**

15.1 *The Oceans* **389**

As students learned in Chapter 2, Earth's circumference is about 40 000 km. Because Earth is a sphere, it can be divided into 360 degrees. The distance of a degree of latitude is equal to 40 000 divided by 360°, or 111 km. The Atlantic Ocean covers about 180 degrees of latitude, or about 20 000 km, from Siberia to Antarctica.

Remind students that lines of longitude converge at the poles. Thus, the distance of a degree of longitude varies with location. At the equator, a degree of longitude equals 111 km. At the poles, it equals zero.

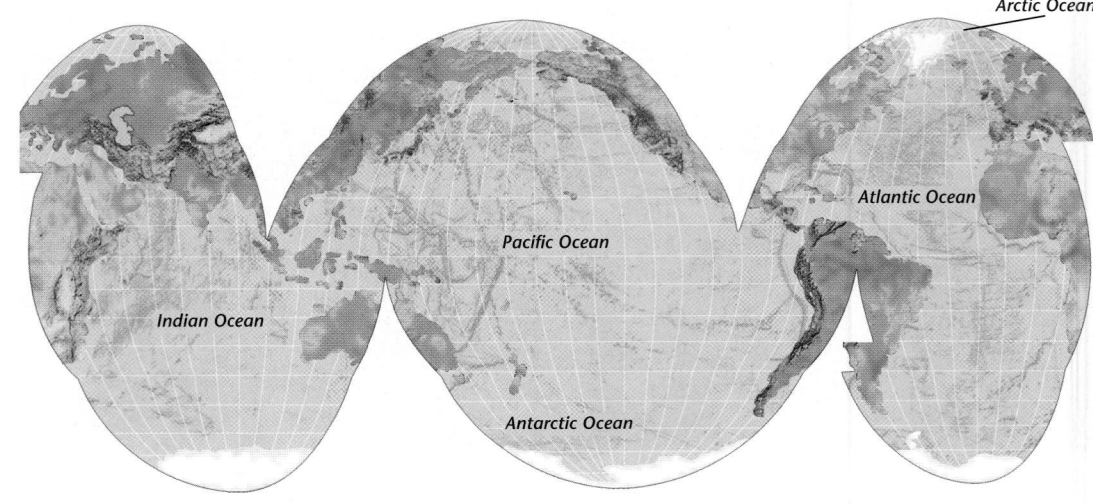

Figure 15-7 The Pacific, Atlantic, and Indian Oceans stretch from Antarctica to the north. The smaller Arctic and Antarctic Oceans are located near the north and south poles, respectively.

Major Oceans As *Figure 15-7* shows, there are three major oceans: the Pacific, the Atlantic, and the Indian. The Pacific Ocean is the largest. Containing roughly half of Earth's seawater, it is larger than all of Earth's landmasses combined. The second-largest ocean, the Atlantic, extends for more than 20 000 km from Antarctica to the arctic circle. North of the arctic circle, the Atlantic Ocean is often referred to as the Arctic Ocean. The third-largest ocean, the Indian, is located mainly in the southern hemisphere. The storm-lashed region surrounding Antarctica, south of 50° south latitude, is known as the Antarctic Ocean.

Figure 15-8 Ice is present in this polar sea year round.

Sea Ice The Arctic and Antarctic Oceans are covered by vast expanses of sea ice, particularly during the winter. In summer, the ice breaks up somewhat, as shown in *Figure 15-8.* Ice is less dense than water, so it floats. When sea-ice crystals first form, a sort of ice-crystal slush develops at the surface of the water. The thickening ice eventually solidifies into individual round pieces called pancake ice. Eventually, these pieces of pancake ice thicken and freeze into a continuous ice cover called pack ice. In the coldest parts of the Arctic and Antarctic Oceans, there is no summer thaw, and the pack ice is generally several meters thick. In the winter, the pack-ice cover may be more than 1000 km wide.

Differentiated Instruction

English-Language Learners Ask students with international backgrounds to translate the names of major oceans and seas into their native languages. Students can share these names with the class as they point out major bodies of water on a world map. **ELL**

NY Core Curriculum Standards

Page 390: St 1 Math KI 1, St 4 KI 1.1i
Page 391: St 1 Math KI 1, 2, & 3, St 4 KI 1.1i & 1.2f, St 6 KI 1

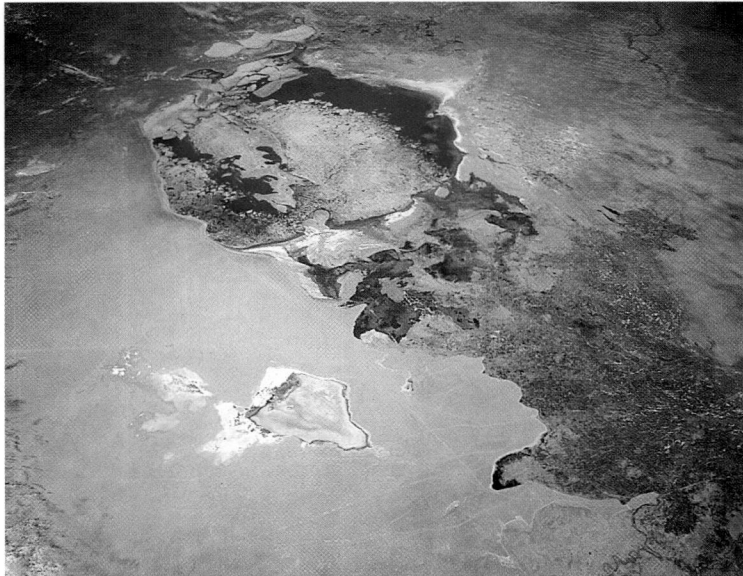

Figure 15-9 The Aral Sea, located in Asia, is an example of a land-locked body of water.

Seas Seas are smaller than oceans and are partly or mostly land-locked. A prominent example, the Aral Sea, is shown in *Figure 15-9.* Another example, the Mediterranean Sea, is located between Africa and Europe. It was the first sea to be explored and mapped by ancient peoples such as the Egyptians, Phoenicians, Greeks, and Romans. Notable seas in the northern hemisphere include the Gulf of Mexico, the Caribbean Sea, and the Bering Sea, which is located between Alaska and Siberia. Keep in mind that all seas and oceans belong to one global ocean whose waters are thoroughly mixed. As a result, ocean water everywhere contains nearly identical proportions of dissolved salts, as you'll learn in the next section.

SECTION ASSESSMENT

1. What is oceanography? What was learned from the *Challenger* expedition?

2. What is sonar? Which research vessel first used sonar to map the Mid-Atlantic Ridge?

3. What evidence indicates that oceans formed early in Earth's geologic history?

4. Where did the water in Earth's early oceans come from?

5. **Thinking Critically** The Great Lakes contain as much water as some seas. Why aren't they considered to be seas?

SKILL REVIEW

6. **Measuring in SI** Calculate the distance to the ocean floor if a sonar signal takes six seconds to return to a ship's receiver. For more help, refer to the *Skill Handbook.*

3 Assess

Check for Understanding

Reinforcement
Ask students to describe how sonar is used to calculate ocean depth. To determine ocean depth using sonar, multiply the speed of sound by the travel time of the echo, then divide by 2.

Reteach

Logical-Mathematical Have students calculate the travel times of an echo received from depths of 4 km and 1 km below sea level. Remind students that the speed of sound in sea-water is 1500 m/s.
4000 m ÷ 1500 m/s × 2 = 5.4 s;
1000 m ÷ 1500 m/s × 2 = 1.34 s

✓Assessment

Portfolio Have students research selected aspects of the history of oceanography, such as the voyages of the early explorers, the development of sonar, or the exploration of polar seas. Students can use the Earth Science Web Site and other sources to prepare scientific reports to share with the class. The reports should have illustrations and proper citations of sources. **L2 P**

SECTION ASSESSMENT

1. Oceanography is the study of the oceans. The *Challenger* expedition investigated ocean currents, the composition and temperatures of seawater, seafloor topography and sediments, and marine life.

2. Sonar is a technique that uses the return time of an echo and the known velocity of sound in water to determine water depth. It was first used by the German research ship *Meteor* to map the Mid-Atlantic Ridge.

3. radioactive studies of ancient rocks and lava flows

4. Water in the oceans came from impacting comets and from Earth's interior through volcanism.

5. The Great Lakes contain freshwater and aren't connected to the ocean.

6. The velocity of sound in seawater is 1500 m/s. Depth is equal to velocity multiplied by travel time divided by 2, or 1500 × 6 ÷ 2 = 4500 m.

Section Background

For section content background, refer to **Density of Water** on pages 384C–D.

Preplanning

Refer to the Chapter Organizer on pages 384A–B.

1 Focus

Section Focus

Before presenting the lesson, display **Section Focus Transparency 45** on the overhead projector.
[L1] [ELL]

Tying to Previous Knowledge

In Chapter 11, students learned about Earth's water cycle, wherein water is continually recycled from the atmosphere to Earth's surface through the processes of evaporation, precipitation, and condensation. Review these processes, and emphasize that the ocean is an integral part of the water cycle.

SECTION 15.2 *Seawater*

OBJECTIVES

- **Compare** *and* **contrast** *the physical and chemical properties of seawater.*
- **Explain** *ocean layering.*
- **Describe** *the formation of deep-water masses.*

VOCABULARY

salinity
temperature profile
thermocline

Have you ever accidentally swallowed a gulp of seawater? If so, you've noticed its salty taste. Seawater is a solution of about 96.5 percent water and 3.5 percent dissolved salts. The most abundant salt in seawater is sodium chloride (NaCl). Other salts present in seawater are chlorides and sulfates of magnesium, potassium, and calcium. In fact, most elements on Earth are present in seawater. Because these substances are dissolved, they are in the form of ions. *Table 15-1* shows the concentrations of the most important ions in the oceans.

CHEMICAL PROPERTIES OF SEAWATER

Salinity is a measure of the amount of dissolved salts in seawater. Oceanographers express salinity as grams of salt per kilogram of water, or parts per thousand (ppt). The total salt content of seawater is, on average, 35 ppt, or 3.5 percent. In addition to salt ions, seawater contains dissolved gases and nutrients. The dissolved gases are mostly oxygen, nitrogen, and carbon dioxide, and the dissolved nutrients are commonly nitrates, phosphates, and silicates. As you might guess, the nutrients and dissolved gases in seawater greatly affect life in the oceans.

Sodium chloride crystals

Table 15-1 Major Ions in Seawater		
Ion	Chemical Symbol	ppt in seawater
Chloride	Cl^-	19.35
Sodium	Na^+	10.76
Sulfate	SO_4^{2-}	2.71
Magnesium	Mg^{2+}	1.29
Calcium	Ca^{2+}	0.41
Potassium	K^+	0.39
Bicarbonate	HCO_3^-	0.14
Bromide	Br^-	0.067
Strontium	Sr^{2+}	0.008
Boron	B^{3+}	0.004
Fluoride	F^-	0.001
Total		~35.00

Content Background

The presence of ions in seawater is normally described in terms of weight. However, it can also be described in terms of number of ions. The six most common ions in seawater in terms of number are Cl^- (48.6 percent), Na^+ (41.6 percent), Mg^{2+} (4.8 percent), SO_4^{2-} (2.5 percent), Ca^{2+} (0.9 percent), and K^+ (0.9 percent).

Resource Manager

Section Focus Transparency 45 [L1] [ELL]
Study Guide for Content Mastery, pp. 93–94 [L2]

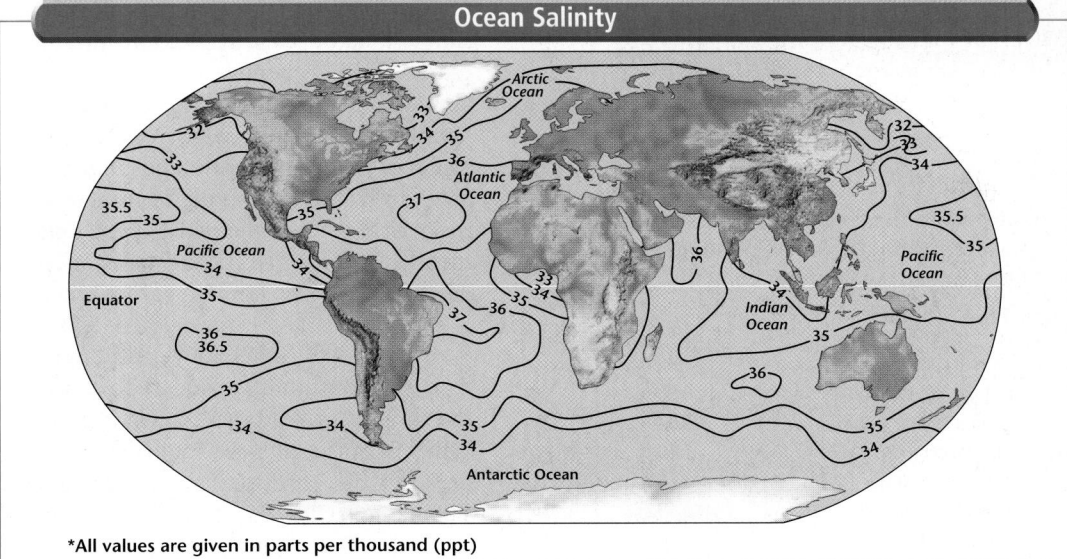

Ocean Salinity

*All values are given in parts per thousand (ppt)

Variations in Salinity Although the average salinity of the oceans is 35 ppt, actual salinities vary from place to place, as shown in *Figure 15-10.* In subtropical regions where rates of evaporation exceed those of precipitation, salt ions left behind by the evaporation of water molecules accumulate in the surface layers of the ocean. There, salinities may be as high as 37 ppt. In equatorial regions where precipitation is abundant, salinities are lower. Even lower salinities of 32 or 33 ppt occur in polar regions where seawater is diluted by melting sea ice. The lowest salinities often occur where large rivers empty into the oceans. Even though salinities vary, the relative proportion of major sea salts is always constant because all ocean water continually intermingles and is thoroughly mixed. Do the *MiniLab* on the following page to further analyze the salinity of seawater.

Sources of Sea Salt Geological evidence indicates that the salinity of ancient seas was not much different from that of today's oceans. One line of evidence is based on the proportion of magnesium in the calcium-carbonate shells of some marine organisms. That proportion depends on the overall salinity of the water in which the shells form. Present-day shells, such as the one shown in *Figure 15-11,* contain about the same proportion of magnesium as similar shells throughout geologic time.

Just as the proportion of sea salts has remained the same over time, so too have the sources of sea salts. In addition to water vapor, volcanic gases contain chlorine and sulfur dioxide. These gases

Figure 15-10 Ocean salinities vary from place to place. High salinities are common in areas with high rates of evaporation. Low salinities often occur where rivers empty into oceans.

Figure 15-11 By comparing the proportion of magnesium in present-day shells, such as this nautilus, with those of ancient shells, scientists have determined that the salinity of Earth's oceans has remained nearly the same over geologic time.

15.2 Seawater **393**

2 Teach

Collaborative Learning

Interpersonal This exercise will demonstrate how the ions in seawater are related to the ionic compounds listed in the MiniLab on page 394. Tell students that they will model salt ions in a microscopic drop of seawater. The seawater contains the following 21 ions: ten chlorine ions, eight sodium ions, two magnesium ions, and one sulfate ion. Write the names of the ions individually on name tags, and give one name tag each to 21 students. Students should put on the name tags, then walk around the room to "mix the seawater." Tell students that the water is evaporating, and that they must link up by holding hands with oppositely charged ions to form electrically neutral molecules. On the chalkboard, record the molecules formed by the links. Possible outcomes include eight molecules of $NaCl$, one molecule of $MgCl_2$, and one molecule of $MgSO_4$, or six molecules of $NaCl$, two molecules of $MgCl_2$, and one molecule of Na_2SO_4. **COOP LEARN**

Differentiated Instruction

Gifted Have interested students calculate the percentages of the ions in the Collaborative Learning exercise both by number of ions and by weight. Give students the atomic weights of chlorine (35.45), sodium (23.0), sulfur (32.1), oxygen (16.0), and magnesium (24.3). The molecular weight of the sulfate ion is 96.1. by number of ions: $Cl^- = 10/21 = 47.6$ percent, $Na^+ = 8/21 = 38.1$ percent, $Mg^{2+} = 2/21 = 9.5$ percent, and $SO_4^{2-} = 1/21 = 4.8$ percent by weight: $Cl^- = 10 \times 35.45 = 354.5$, $Na^+ = 8 \times 23.0 = 184$, $Mg^{2+} = 2 \times 24.3 = 48.6$, and $SO_4^{2-} = 96.1$; total weight = 683.2 atomic mass units; percentage weight: $Cl^- = 354.5/683.2 = 51.9$ percent, $Na^+ = 184/683.2 = 26.9$ percent, $Mg^{2+} = 48.6/683.2 = 7.1$ percent, and $SO_4^{2-} = 96.1/683.2 = 14.1$ percent

NY Core Curriculum Standards

Page 392: St 1 Math KI 1, 2, & 3
Page 393: St 4 KI 3.1a,
St 6 KI 4 & 5

MiniLab

Purpose

Students will enhance their understanding of salinity and units of measurement.

Process Skills

measure in SI, use numbers, apply concepts, compare and contrast, classify, observe and infer

Materials

1-L beaker, 1-L graduated cylinder, seven small beakers or cups, scale, seven labeled salt containers containing the salts listed on the student page, stirrers, distilled water

Teaching Strategies

- Have the class calculate the volume of 965.57 g of distilled water at room temperature. They should use a density value of 0.998 g/cm^3. 965.57 ÷ 0.998 = 967.5 g/cm^3
- Be sure that students stir the salt until it dissolves.

Safety Precautions

Students should wear safety goggles and protective clothing while doing this lab. Also, students should not handle the chemicals with their bare hands. Have students wash their hands after completing this lab. Dilute the solutions with water before disposing of them.

Expected Results

The water level in the 1-L beaker should rise slightly after each addition of salt. The final volume of salt-water should be around 975 cm^3. This can be verified by pouring the saltwater into the cylinder.

Analyze and Conclude

1. 34.43 g of salt + 965.57 g of water = 1000 g of saltwater 34.43 g ÷ 1000 g = 0.03443 or 3.443 percent
2. 3.443 percent = 34.43 ppt
3. Cl$^-$, Na$^+$, SO$_4^{2-}$, Mg^{2+}, Ca^{2+}, K$^+$, HCO$_3^-$, Br$^-$
4. The solution doesn't contain the trace elements and nutrients dissolved in seawater.

MiniLab

What is the chemical composition of seawater?

Determine the chemical composition of seawater using the following ingredients. The salinity of seawater is commonly measured in parts per thousand (ppt).

sodium chloride (NaCl)	23.48 g
magnesium chloride (MgCl$_2$)	4.98 g
sodium sulfate (Na$_2$SO$_4$)	3.92 g
calcium chloride (CaCl$_2$)	1.10 g
potassium chloride (KCl)	0.66 g
sodium bicarbonate (NaHCO$_3$)	0.19 g
potassium bromide (KBr)	0.10 g

Procedure

1. Carefully measure the ingredients and put them all in a large beaker.
2. Add 965.57 g of distilled water and mix.

Analyze and Conclude

1. How many grams of solution do you have? What percentage of this solution is made up of salts?
2. Given that 1 percent is equal to 10 ppt, what is the salinity of your solution in parts per thousand?
3. Identify the ions in your solution.
4. Infer how your solution differs from actual seawater.

Figure 15-12 Salts that have precipitated from seawater form deposits along the coast of Baja, Mexico.

dissolve in water and form the chlorine and sulfate ions of seawater. The weathering of crustal rocks generates most of the other abundant ions in seawater. Sodium, calcium, and potassium come from the weathering of feldspars. Iron and magnesium come from the weathering of minerals and rocks rich in these elements. These ions are then flushed into rivers and transported to oceans.

Removal of Sea Salts Although salt ions are continuously added to seawater, the salinity of seawater does not increase. Why? Because salts are removed from the ocean at the same rate as they are added. The removal of sea salts involves several processes. Some precipitate from seawater near arid, coastal regions such as the one shown in *Figure 15-12.* This process removes immense quantities of sodium chloride, calcium sulfate, and other sea salts. In addition, small salty spray droplets from breaking waves are picked up by winds and deposited inland. Marine organisms also remove ions from seawater to build their shells, bones, and teeth. As these organisms die, their solid parts accumulate on the seafloor and become incorporated into the bottom sediments. All these

✔Assessment

Skill Ask students to determine the salinity of a solution of 34.43 g of salt in 1 L of distilled water. The density of the distilled water is 0.998 g/cm^3. 0.998 g/cm^3 × 1000 cm^3 = 998 g of water, 998 g of water + 34.43 g of salt = 1032.43 g of saltwater, 34.43 ÷ 1032.43 = 0.03335 = 3.335 % = 33.35 ppt

Resource Manager

GeoLab and MiniLab Worksheets, p. 59

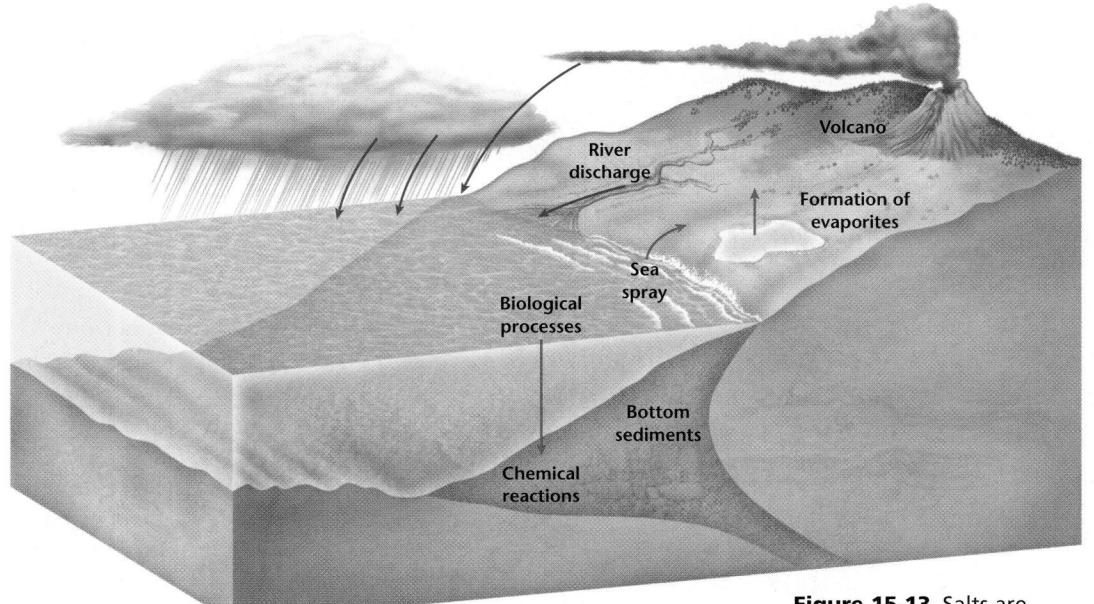

Discussion

Many people do not realize that all the oceans are connected and thus form one global ocean. Ask students whether the Atlantic and Pacific Oceans are connected naturally. Students should not consider canals. Also, ask students whether these two oceans have the same sea level. Then show the class a map of the world and point out the Drake Passage, which is located between South America and Antarctica, and the Bering Strait, which is located between Siberia and Alaska. Explain that all connected bodies of water have the same mean water level.

Interpreting the Illustration

Fig. 15-13 Have students study the illustration, then describe in their own words the processes that add salts to seawater and the processes that remove salts from seawater. Challenge students to infer how marine life might be affected if this balance changed.

processes remove immense quantities of salt ions from the ocean. Thus, the existing salinity of seawater represents a balance between the processes that remove salts and those that add them, as shown in *Figure 15-13.*

Figure 15-13 Salts are added to seawater by volcanic eruptions and by the weathering and erosion of rocks. Salts are removed from seawater by the formation of evaporites and biological processes. Salty droplets also are deposited inland by winds.

PHYSICAL PROPERTIES OF SEAWATER

The presence of various salts causes the physical properties of seawater to be quite different from those of freshwater. Freshwater has a maximum density of 1.00 g/cm³. Because salt ions are heavier than water molecules, they increase the density of water. Seawater is therefore denser than freshwater, and its density varies, depending on its salinity. Temperature also affects density—cold water is denser than warm water. Because of salinity and temperature variations, the density of seawater ranges from about 1.02 g/cm³ to 1.03 g/cm³. These variations may seem small, but they are significant. They affect many oceanic processes, which you'll learn about in the next chapter. Variations in salinity also cause the freezing point of seawater to be somewhat lower than that of freshwater. Freshwater freezes at 0°C. Because salt ions interfere with the formation of hydrogen bonds, the freezing point of seawater is –2°C.

Absorption of Light If you've ever swum in a lake, you may have noticed that the intensity of light decreases with depth. The water may be clear, but if the lake is deep, the bottom waters will be dark.

Using Math

Using Numbers If the density of a sample of seawater is 1.02716 g/mL, calculate the mass of 4.00 mL of the sample.

Cultural Diversity

Desalinization Desalinization is a process whereby salt is extracted from seawater. Many coastal communities have found this system to be an ecologically beneficial means to obtain freshwater. Aruba, an island in the southern Caribbean off the coast of Venezuela, has the purest water in the Caribbean and the second-purest water in the world. This 30-km island has seven desalination plants. The seawater is boiled at an extremely high temperature to kill all bacteria until the water vaporizes and then condenses into a distillate. The leftover salt is then returned to the ocean. The Aruban desalination plants supply water to 28 000 households and provide an example of how desalination can be an ecologically sound solution to a water shortage.

NY Core Curriculum Standards

Page 394: St 1 Math KI 1, 2, 3, & Science KI 3, St 4 KI 3.1a, St 6 KI 4 & 5

Page 395: St 1 Math KI 1, 2, & 3, St 4 KI 1.2g

Modeling

Visual-Spatial Different colors penetrate to different depths in water. In clear water, blue light penetrates to the greatest depth. In turbid water, all colors penetrate less, and the greatest penetration takes place in the green or yellow part of the spectrum. Light penetration at different wavelengths can be demonstrated using Secchi disks of different colors. Blue light, for instance, will penetrate to twice the depth at which a blue-colored disk can be seen from the water's surface. To demonstrate light penetration, fill an aquarium with muddy water so that a white disk at the bottom of the aquarium is barely visible. Then submerge red, orange, yellow, green, and blue disks. Have student volunteers use metric rulers to measure the depths at which the different disks can no longer be seen.

Content Background

Most midlatitude lakes are stratified like the ocean with warm surface water on top, cold water at the bottom, and a thermocline in between. This stratification is caused by density differences; dense, cold water sinks to the bottom, and less-dense, warm water floats on top. Because the densest freshwater has a temperature of 4°C, the temperature of deep lake waters is 4°C year-round. In summer, surface waters are very warm, and a strong thermocline prevents them from mixing with deep waters. In fall, surface waters cool and eventually reach 4°C. At that point, the thermocline disappears, and top and bottom waters become well mixed. In winter, the surface waters become colder than the deep water, and ice may form. In spring, the surface waters warm again to 4°C, and the mixing of surface and deep waters resumes.

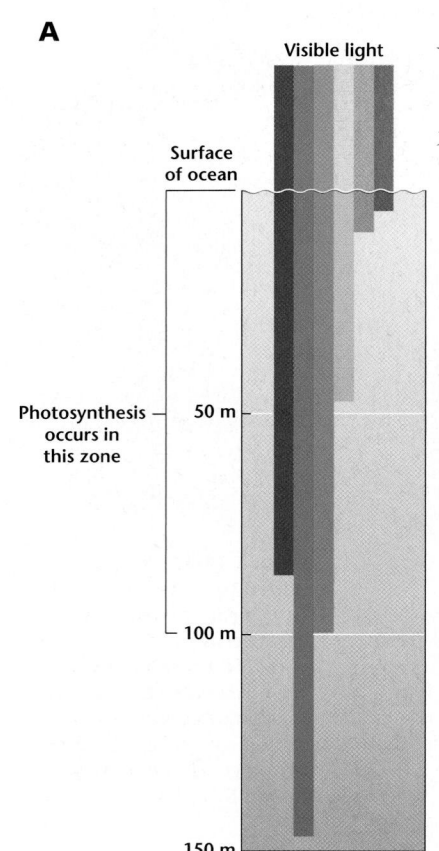

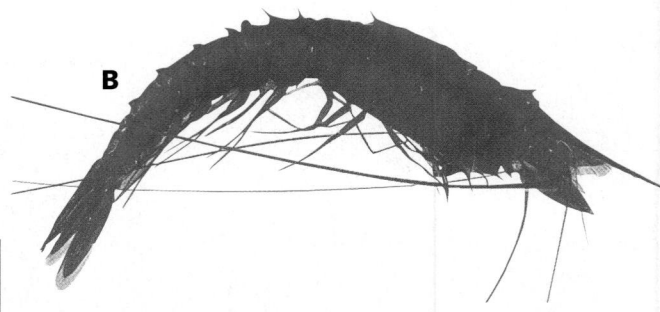

Figure 15-14 Red light does not penetrate as far as blue light in the ocean **(A)**. Thus, red marine organisms such as this deep-sea shrimp **(B)** appear black below a depth of 10 m. This helps them escape predators.

Water absorbs light, which gives rise to another physical property of oceans—they are dark. In general, light penetrates only the upper 100 m of seawater. Below that depth, all is darkness. *Figure 15-14* illustrates how light penetrates ocean water. Notice that red light penetrates less than blue light. Red objects appear black below the depth of penetration of red light, and other reflecting objects in the water appear green or blue. Although some fading blue light may reach depths of a few hundred meters, light sufficient for photosynthesis exists only in the top 100 m of the ocean.

OCEAN LAYERING

Ocean surface temperatures range from –2°C in polar waters to 30°C in equatorial regions, with the average surface temperature being 15°C. Ocean water temperatures, however, decrease significantly with depth. Thus, deep ocean water is always cold, even in tropical oceans. *Figure 15-15* shows a typical ocean **temperature profile,** which plots changing water temperatures with depth. Such profiles vary, depending on location and season. In the temperature profile shown here, beneath roughly 100 m, temperatures decrease continuously with depth to around 4°C at 1 km. The dark waters below 1 km have fairly uniform temperatures of less than 4°C. Based on temperature variations, the ocean can be divided into three layers, as shown in *Figure 15-16.* The first is a relatively warm, sunlit, surface layer some 100 m thick. Under this is a transitional layer known as the **thermocline,** which is characterized by rapidly decreasing temperatures with depth. The bottom layer is cold and dark with temperatures near freezing. Both the thermocline and the warm surface layer are absent in polar seas, where water temperatures are cold from top to bottom. In general, ocean layering is caused by density differences. Because cold water is more dense than warm water, cold water sinks to the bottom, while less-dense, warm water is found near the ocean's surface.

Resource Manager

Teaching Transparency 44 L2 ELL
Laboratory Manual, pp. 113–116 L2

Interpreting the Illustration

Figure 15-14 Tell students that plant life in oceans is restricted to the photic zone, the depth to which photosynthesis can occur. In clear waters, the photic zone can reach a depth of 200 m. On average, however, photosynthesis is limited to the top 100 m of oceans.

WATER MASSES

The temperature of the bottom layer of ocean water is near freezing even in tropical oceans, where surface temperatures are warm. Where does all this cold water come from? The source is Earth's polar seas. Recall that high salinity and cold temperatures cause seawater to become more dense. When seawater freezes during the arctic or antarctic winter, sea ice forms. However, salt ions aren't incorporated into the growing ice crystals and accumulate beneath the ice. Consequently, the cold water beneath the ice becomes saltier and denser than the surrounding seawater, and this saltier water sinks. This salty water then migrates toward the equator as a cold, deep water mass along the ocean floor. Other cold, deep water masses form when surface currents in the ocean bring relatively salty midlatitude or subtropical waters into polar regions. In winter, these waters become colder and denser than the surrounding polar surface waters, and thus, they sink.

Three water masses account for most of the deep water in the Atlantic Ocean. Antarctic Bottom Water forms when antarctic seas freeze during the winter. With temperatures below 0°C, this water

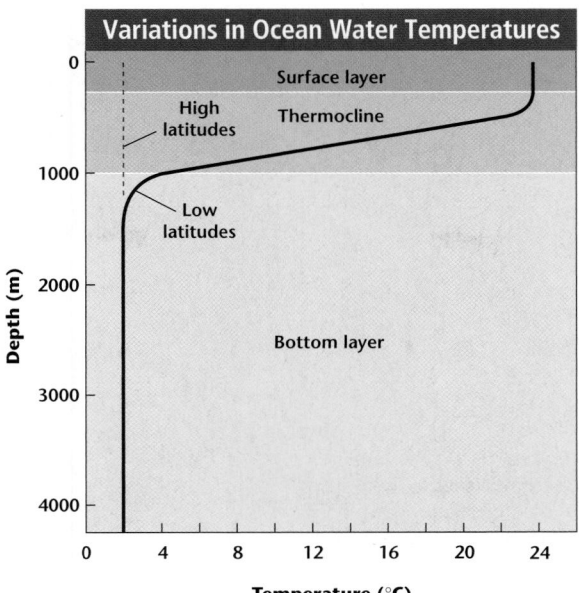

Figure 15-15 Ocean water temperatures decrease with depth. Areas near the equator have warmer ocean surface temperatures than do midlatitudes or areas near the poles.

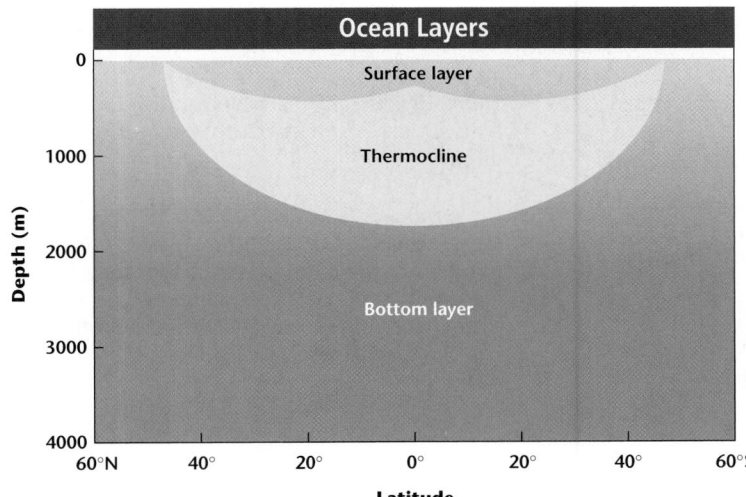

Figure 15-16 Based on water temperatures, the ocean can be divided into three layers: the relatively warm surface layer, the transitional thermocline, and the cold bottom layer.

15.2 *Seawater* **397**

Environmental Connection

On many small islands and in some coastal areas, freshwater is in short supply. In these areas, freshwater can be obtained by the desalination of seawater. One common desalination technique is the distillation of seawater; seawater is heated and evaporates, and the salts are left behind. The resulting water vapor is cooled and condenses as freshwater. Another technique involves the freezing of seawater. Sea ice is freshwater ice containing pockets of brine. The brine can be flushed from an ice-brine mix. The most economic desalination method is reverse osmosis; seawater is pressed through a semipermeable membrane that allows water molecules, but not salt ions, to pass through. This method is used in most modern desalination plants to produce freshwater.

✓Assessment

Knowledge Ask students the following questions.

1. Which deep-water mass has temperatures below 0°C? Antarctic Bottom Water

2. Which deep-water mass is the least dense? Antarctic Intermediate Water

3. Which deep-water mass forms off the shore of Greenland? North Atlantic Deep Water

NY Core Curriculum Standards

Page 396: St 1 Math KI 1 & 2, St 6 KI 5
Page 397: St 6 KI 5

Check for Understanding

Discussion

Ask students to explain why deep water in all oceans—even tropical ones—is always cold. Cold, dense water from polar regions moves along the seafloor and displaces warmer, less-dense water.

Reteach

Have students each design an experiment that models the movement of Antarctic Bottom Water to the equator and beyond. **L2**

✓Assessment

Performance Place students in groups of four. Provide several water samples with various salinities to each group. Have the groups use test kits to analyze the chemistry of the samples. Students should display their results in data tables. Use the Performance Task Assessment List for Carrying Out a Strategy and Collecting Data in **PASC,** p. 25.

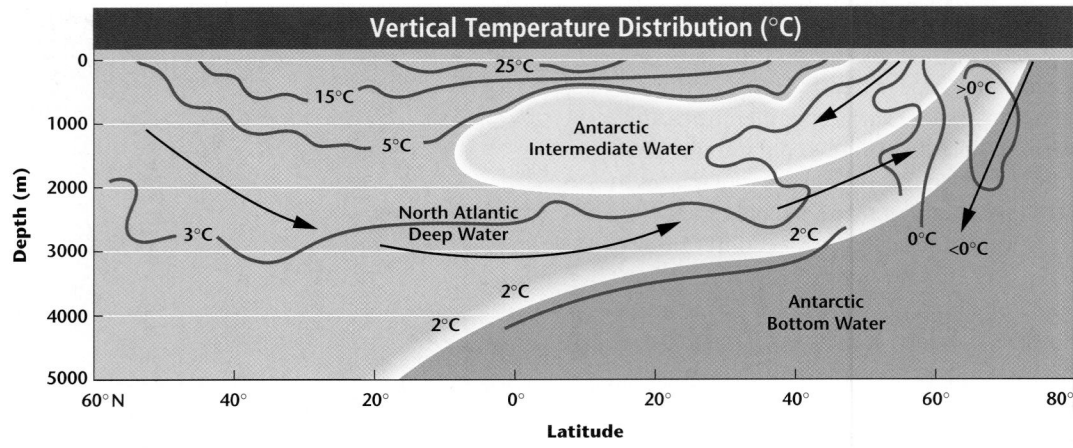

Figure 15-17 Antarctic Bottom Water is the densest and coldest deep water mass. It is overridden by the slightly warmer and less dense North Atlantic Deep Water. Antarctic Intermediate Water is still warmer and less dense, and thus it overrides the other two deep water masses.

mass is the coldest and densest in all the oceans, as shown in *Figure 15-17.* North Atlantic Deep Water forms in a similar manner offshore from Greenland. It is warmer and less dense than Antarctic Bottom Water and thus overrides it. Antarctic Intermediate Water forms when the relatively salty waters of the Antarctic Ocean decrease in temperature during winter and sink. Being slightly warmer and less dense than North Atlantic Deep Water, Antarctic Intermediate Water overrides the other two water masses. While the Atlantic Ocean contains all three major deep-water masses, the Indian and Pacific Oceans contain only the two deep antarctic water masses. You'll model water masses in the *GeoLab* at the end of this chapter. In the next section, you'll learn about other water movements in the ocean.

SECTION ASSESSMENT

1. What is the most abundant salt in seawater? How do salts enter the ocean?

2. How does the salinity of seawater affect its density?

3. The salinity of seawater is higher in subtropical regions than at the equator. Why?

4. Explain why North Atlantic Deep Water and Antarctic Intermediate Water override Antarctic Bottom Water.

5. Which is more dense, cold freshwater or warm seawater? Explain.

6. **Thinking Critically** Why do red fish look black at ocean water depths greater than about 10 m?

SKILL REVIEW

7. **Recognizing Cause and Effect** Based on what you have learned about the freezing point of seawater, explain why salt is often used to de-ice roads in the winter. For more help, refer to the *Skill Handbook.*

earthgeu.com/self_check_quiz

SECTION ASSESSMENT

1. The most abundant salt in seawater is NaCl. Salts enter the ocean through volcanism and the weathering of crustal rocks.
2. Seawater density increases with salinity.
3. In subtropical regions, water molecules evaporate and the salt ions remain in the ocean; this increases the water's salinity. In equatorial regions, rates of precipitation may exceed rates of evaporation; thus, the seawater is diluted by rainwater.

4. Antarctic Bottom Water is colder and denser than North Atlantic Deep Water or Antarctic Intermediate Water.
5. Seawater is always denser than freshwater because of its high salinity.
6. Red light cannot penetrate below an ocean depth of 10 m. The red light is absorbed by the seawater.
7. The freezing point of water decreases with increasing salt content. Thus, ice will melt if salt is added to it.

NY Core Curriculum Standards

Page 398: St 6 KI 5, St 7 KI 1
Page 399: St 1 Math KI 1 & 2, St 6 KI 1 & 5

SECTION 15.3 Ocean Movements

Oceans are never completely motionless. Their most obvious movement is the constant motion of the waves. A **wave** is a rhythmic movement that carries energy through space or matter—in this case, ocean water. Ocean waves are generated mainly by wind flowing over the water's surface. As an ocean wave passes, the water moves up and down in a circular pattern and returns to its original position, as shown in *Figure 15-18A.* Only the energy moves steadily forward. The water itself moves in circles until the energy passes, but it does not move forward.

WAVE CHARACTERISTICS

In the open ocean, a typical wave has the characteristics shown in *Figure 15-18B.* The highest point of a wave is the **crest,** and the lowest point is the **trough.** The vertical distance between crest and trough is the wave height; the horizontal crest-to-crest distance is the wavelength. The wavelength determines the depth to which the wave disturbs the water. That depth, called the wave base, is equal to half the wavelength. The wavelength also determines the speed with which waves move through deep water. Wave speed increases with wavelength.

OBJECTIVES

- **Describe** the physical properties of waves.
- **Explain** how tides form.
- **Compare** and **contrast** various ocean currents.

VOCABULARY

wave	tide
crest	density current
trough	surface current
breaker	upwelling

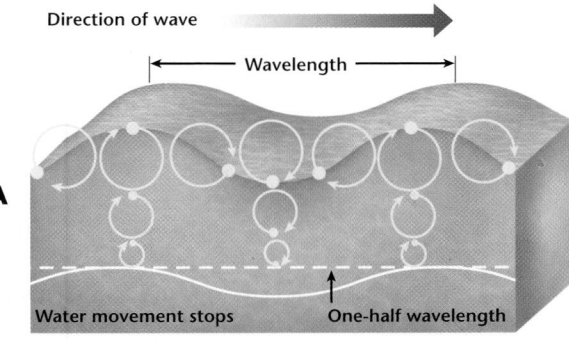

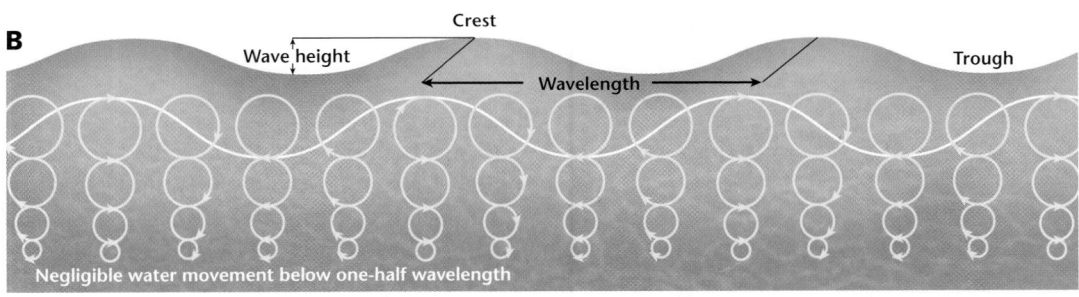

Figure 15-18 In a wave, water moves in circles that decrease in size with depth. At a depth equal to half the wavelength, water movement stops **(A).** Wave characteristics include wave height, wavelength, crest, and trough **(B).**

Direction of wave

Wavelength

A

Water movement stops · One-half wavelength

B

Crest

Wave height · Wavelength · Trough

Negligible water movement below one-half wavelength

15.3 Ocean Movements **399**

Content Background

In deep water, where the seafloor is below the wave base, the speed of waves is proportional to the square root of the wavelength. Long, deep-water waves always travel faster than shorter ones. If the water depth is less than the wave base, friction with the bottom dissipates energy and lowers the wave speed. For very shallow water, wave speed depends only on water depth and is independent of wavelength.

Resource Manager

Section Focus Transparency 46 L1 ELL
Laboratory Manual, pp. 117–120 L2
Study Guide for Content Mastery, pp. 95–96 L2

Section 15.3

Prepare

Section Background

For section content background, refer to **Tidal Forces** on page 384D.

Preplanning

Refer to the Chapter Organizer on pages 384A–B.

1 Focus

Section Focus

Before presenting the lesson, display **Section Focus Transparency 46** on the overhead projector. L1 ELL

Tying to Previous Knowledge

Ask students whether they have ever seen a wave performed at a sporting event. Point out that the wave moves around the stadium, but that the people in the wave stay in the same seats. In a similar way, the water in a wave moves up and down, but it does not move forward. Only the energy in the wave moves forward.

399

Content Background

Fetch is the unobstructed expanse of water over which the wind can blow and build waves. Small bodies of water, such as lakes, have limited fetches, and can produce only small storm waves. In the ocean, however, fetch is limited only by the size of the storm generating the waves. Large storms can produce huge ocean waves if the wind is strong for a long period of time. As a general rule, maximum wave height is roughly equal to wind speed in knots. For example, wind speeds in hurricanes exceed 64 knots and are capable of raising waves in excess of 10 m. In order to do so, however, the wind must blow at 64 knots for several days in the same direction. Because hurricanes are relatively small, fast-moving systems, they rarely generate waves higher than 10 m. The largest ocean waves are produced by huge, slow-moving, long-lasting winter storms in the North Atlantic, North Pacific, and Antarctic Oceans.

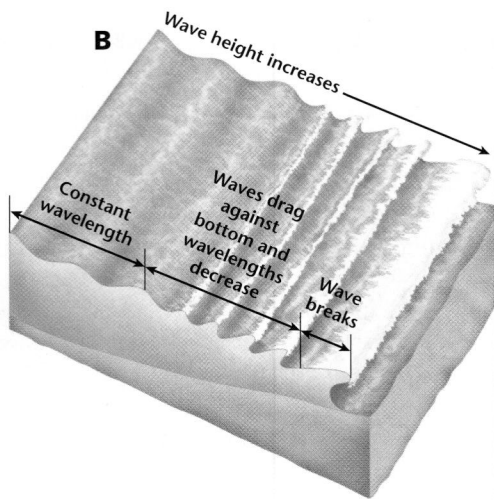

Figure 15-19 A breaker **(A)** forms when wavelength decreases and wave height increases as the wave nears the shore **(B)**.

Earth Science Online

Topic: High Tides
To learn more about tides, visit the Earth Science Web Site at earthgeu.com

Activity: Research the best places on Earth to observe high tides. Note these places on a map of the world.

Wave Height Wave heights depend upon three factors: wind speed, wind duration, and fetch. Fetch refers to the expanse of water that the wind blows across. Large storm waves can be much higher than average. For instance, hurricanes can generate waves more than 10 m high. The greatest wave height ever recorded was more than 30 m. This monstrous wave occurred in the North Pacific.

Breaking Waves As ocean waves reach the shallow water near shorelines, they begin to lose energy because of friction with the ocean bottom. This causes the waves to slow down. As the water becomes shallower, incoming wave crests gradually catch up with the slower wave crests ahead. As a result, the crest-to-crest wavelength decreases. The incoming waves become higher, steeper, and unstable, and their crests collapse forward. Collapsing waves, such as those shown in *Figure 15-19,* are called **breakers.** The formation of breakers is also influenced by the motion of wave crests, which are less affected by friction than wave troughs and thus overrun the troughs. The collapsing crests of breakers moving at high speeds toward shore play a major role in shaping shorelines. You'll learn more about breakers and shoreline processes in the next chapter.

TIDES

Tides are the periodic rise and fall of sea level. The highest level to which water rises is known as high tide, and the lowest level is called low tide. Because of differences in topography and latitude, the tidal range—the difference between high tide and low tide—varies from place to place. In the Gulf of Mexico, the tidal range is less than 1 m. In New England, it can be as high as 6 m. The greatest tidal range

Demo

Place a wooden stick in a water-filled, graduated cylinder. Have a student volunteer mark the flotation level of the stick. Next, depress the stick to the water surface and release it. The stick will rise, overshoot the equilibrium point, and oscillate a few times before coming to rest at the previous flotation level. Explain to the class that if the ocean surface is depressed at a particular point, it will move in a similar manner and create waves of oscillation. Specifically, a ring of elevated water will appear around a point of depression. As the depression rebounds, the ring becomes a depressed moat, which generates a second ring. In this way, successive rings (crests) and moats (troughs) spread out from the center of a disturbance.

NY Core Curriculum Standards

Page 400: St 4 KI 1.1i & 2.1i, St 6 KI 1 & 5
Page 401: St 4 KI 1.1i, St 6 KI 1, 2, & 5

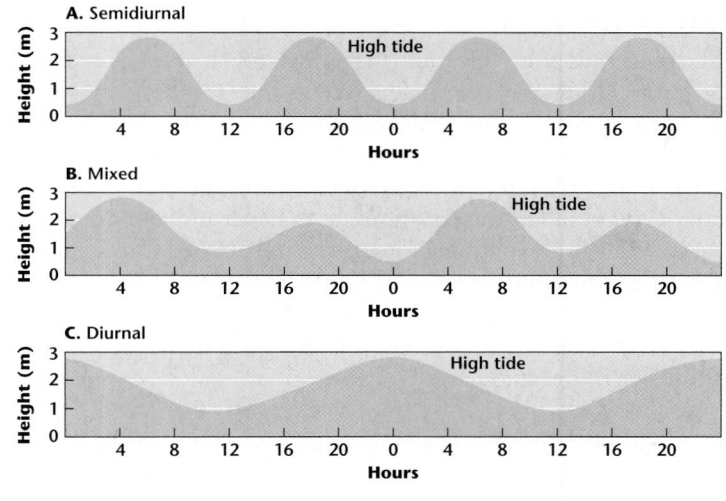

A. Semidiurnal

High tide

B. Mixed

High tide

C. Diurnal

High tide

Figure 15-20 Differences in topography and latitude cause three different daily tide cycles. Areas with semidiurnal cycles experience two high tides per day. Areas with mixed cycles have one pronounced and one smaller high tide each day. Areas with diurnal cycles have one high tide per day.

occurs in the Bay of Fundy between New Brunswick and Nova Scotia, Canada, where it is as high as 15 m. Generally, a daily cycle of high and low tides takes 24 hours and 50 minutes. As shown in *Figure 15-20,* the daily cycle can follow three distinct patterns. You'll learn about tides in the *Problem-Solving Lab* on this page.

Problem-Solving Lab

Making and Using Graphs

Analyze a tidal record The water levels shown in the data table were measured over a 24-hour period.

Analysis

1. Plot these values on graph paper with time on the *x*-axis and water level on the *y*-axis.
2. Estimate the approximate times and water levels of high tides and low tides.

Thinking Critically

3. Refer to *Figure 15-20* to determine the tidal pattern shown in your graph.
4. What is the tidal range for this area?

5. Predict the water level at the next high tide. Estimate when that high tide will occur.

Tidal Record			
Time (h)	Water Level (m)	Time (h)	Water Level (m)
00:00	3.08	13:00	2.78
01:00	3.35	14:00	2.81
02:00	3.33	15:00	2.59
03:00	3.03	16:00	2.16
04:00	2.53	17:00	1.64
05:00	1.95	18:00	1.15
06:00	1.44	19:00	0.84
07:00	1.10	20:00	0.78
08:00	1.02	21:00	1.00
09:00	1.21	22:00	1.46
10:00	1.59	23:00	2.07
11:00	2.07	24:00	2.67
12:00	2.51		

Across the Curriculum

Astronomy Earth's tidal bulges are always aligned with the Moon. Because of the orbital motion of the Moon, Earth's rotational period relative to the Moon—the so-called tidal day— is 24 hours and 50 minutes. This means that the tidal pattern observed at a given location repeats every 24 hours and 50 minutes, and that specific tidal phases, such as high tide, occur 50 minutes later on the following day.

Concept Development

Observed tides are usually not perfectly aligned with the Moon's motion. For instance, high tide doesn't usually occur when the Moon is overhead or at its highest altitude. The reason for this difference between theoretical and observed tides is the dynamic response of the ocean to tidal forces. The ocean is broken up by continents. Tidal bulges must go around these continents in complicated patterns. The motion of tidal bulges is further complicated by the fact that they have a wavelength of 20 000 km—half of Earth's circumference—and behave like shallow-water waves. In a part of the ocean that is 5 km deep, the velocity of tidal bulges can be no more than about 800 km/h. Earth's rotational speed at the equator is 1610 km/h. Therefore, even if Earth had no continents, tidal bulges couldn't keep up with Earth's rotation except in high latitudes.

CAUSES OF TIDES

The basic causes of tides are the gravitational attraction among Earth, the Moon and the Sun, as well as the fact that gravitational attraction decreases with distance. Consider the Earth-Moon system. As shown in *Figure 15-21,* the Moon does not actually orbit Earth. Rather, both Earth and the Moon orbit around a common center of gravity. As a result of their motions, both Earth and the Moon experience differing gravitational forces. The unbalanced forces generate tidal bulges on opposite sides of Earth. The gravitational effect on Earth's oceans is similar to what happens to the liquid in a coffee cup inside a car as the car goes around a curve. The liquid sloshes toward the outside of the curve.

The Sun's Influence The gravitational attraction of the Sun and Earth's orbital motion around the Sun also generate tides. However, even though the Moon is much smaller than the Sun, lunar tides are more than twice as high as those caused by the Sun because the Moon is much closer to Earth. Consequently, Earth's tidal bulges are always aligned with the Moon. Although the Sun's tidal effect is smaller than that of the Moon, it is still significant because of the Sun's great mass. Depending on the phases of the Moon, solar tides can either enhance or diminish lunar tides, as illustrated in *Figure 15-22.* Notice that large tidal ranges, called spring tides, occur when the Moon is either full or new. These phases of the Moon occur when the Sun, the Moon, and Earth are aligned. During spring tides, high tides are higher than normal and low tides are lower than normal. Small tidal ranges, called neap tides, occur when there is a first- or third-quarter Moon. During these times, the Sun, the Moon, and

Figure 15-21 The Moon and Earth revolve around a common center of gravity and experience unbalanced gravitational and centrifugal forces. These forces cause tidal bulges on opposite sides of Earth.

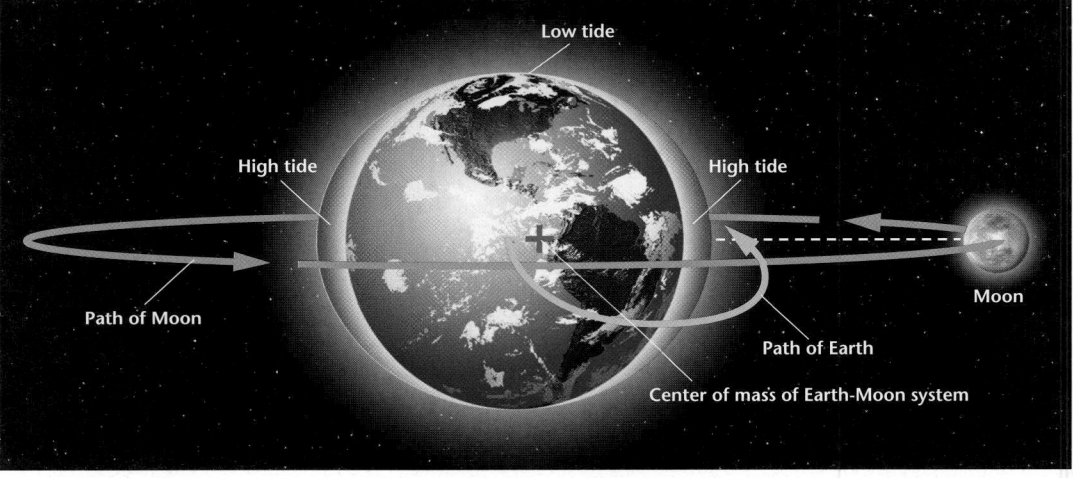

Resource Manager

Teaching Transparency 45 L2 ELL

Differentiated Instruction

Learning Disabled Reinforce the concepts of sea level, tides, and tidal ranges with students with learning disabilities. Have these students determine how far above mean sea level the tide will rise if the tidal range is 2 m. 1 m

NY Core Curriculum Standards

Page 402: St 4 KI 1.1a, & 1.1i, St 6 KI 1 & 5
Page 403: St 4 KI 1.1a, 1.1f, 1.1i, & 2.2b, St 6 KI 1 & 5

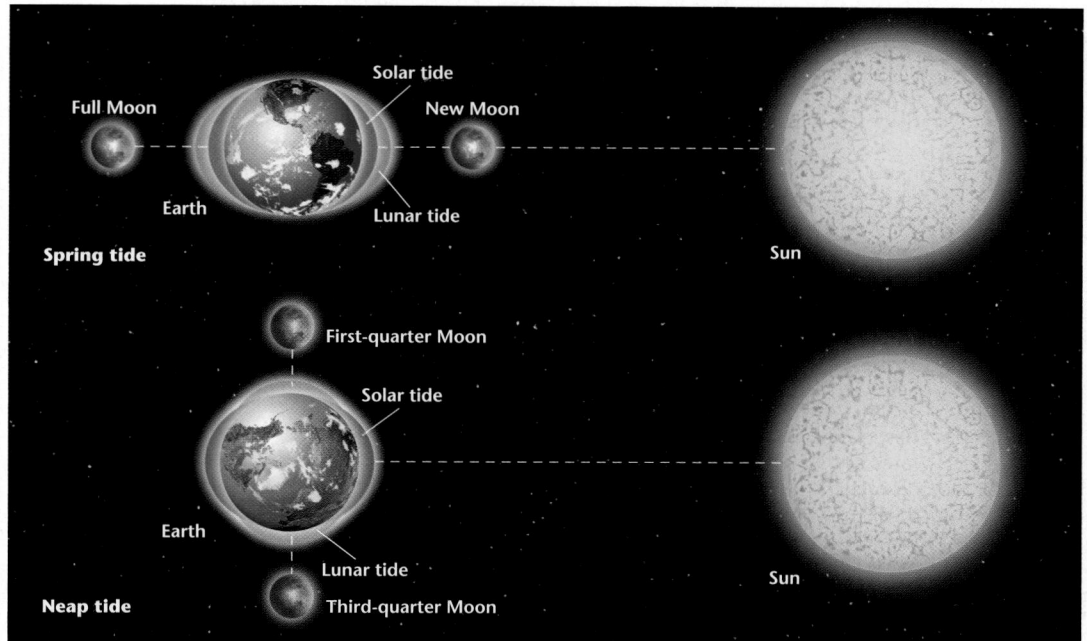

Figure 15-22 Spring tides occur when the Sun, the Moon, and Earth are aligned **(A)**. Neap tides occur when the Sun, the Moon, and Earth form a right angle **(B)**.

Logical-Mathematical
Divide the class into groups. Have each group use graph paper to determine the effect of tidal fluctuations on a beach. Tell students that the beach has a slope of 1/10, its average width is 30 m, and it rises to 3 m above mean sea level. Tell them to assume an average tidal range of 2 m. Have students draw the beach as a sloping line on the graph paper. Students should draw lines showing mean sea level and the water level of average high and low tides. **L3**
COOP LEARN

Content Background

Tidal forces decrease with the cube of the distance from the Moon and the Sun. Because of this, lunar tides are larger than those produced by the much more massive Sun. The Sun's mass is 333 000 times Earth's mass, while the lunar mass is only 0.0123 percent of Earth's mass. However, the Sun's mean distance from Earth is almost 150 million km, while the lunar distance averages only 384 000 km. The solar and lunar tidal forces are given by $2GMr/D^3$ and $2Gmr/d^3$, respectively, where r is Earth's radius, M is the solar mass, m is the lunar mass, D is the solar distance, and d is the lunar distance. The ratio of solar to lunar tidal forces is therefore $M/m \times (d/D)^3$. Substituting the appropriate numbers, this ratio works out to 0.46, or 46 percent. Thus, solar tides are less than half as strong as lunar tides.

Earth form a right angle. During neap tides, high tides are lower and low tides are higher than normal. Spring and neap tides alternate every two weeks. On average, spring tides are three times higher than neap tides.

OCEAN CURRENTS

Recall the discussion of Antarctic Bottom Water in the previous section. The movement of Antarctic Bottom Water is an example of an ocean current. In this case, the current is called a **density current** because it is caused by differences in the temperature and salinity of ocean water, which in turn affect density. Density currents move slowly in deep ocean waters.

More noticeable than underwater density currents are wind-driven surface currents. **Surface currents** affect mainly the upper few hundred meters of the ocean, and they can move as fast as 100 km per day. Driven by Earth's global wind systems, surface currents follow predictable patterns. In the northern hemisphere, tropical trade winds blow from east to west. The resulting tropical ocean currents also flow from east to west. In northern midlatitudes, the prevailing westerlies and resulting ocean currents move from west to east. In northern polar regions, polar easterly winds push surface waters from east to west.

Interpreting the Illustration

Figure 15-22 Have students describe the positions of the Sun, Earth, and the Moon during spring tides and neap tides. During spring tides, the Sun, Earth, and the Moon are aligned. During neap tides, the Sun, Earth, and the Moon form a right angle.

Across the Curriculum

Biology Sea turtles lay their eggs on beaches above the high-water level of the spring tide so that the eggs can incubate in the dry, sun-warmed sand. The hatchlings emerge during a subsequent spring tide. The high-water level ensures that the hatchlings have a relatively short dash to the safety of the ocean and thus increases their chances for survival.

Interpreting the Illustration

Figure 15-23 Floating objects drift with the surface currents of an ocean. Tell students to use this figure and the speeds 1 m/s for warm currents and 0.5 m/s for cold currents to estimate the travel path, travel time, and possible landing sites of bottles with messages that were thrown into the ocean at the following three locations: Miami, FL, possible landing sites and times: New England, 31 days; Newfoundland, 52 days; Europe, 3 months San Francisco, CA, possible landing sites and times: Japan, 7 months; Alaska, 10 months and Puerto Rico. possible landing sites and times: Cuba, 12 days; Florida, 22 days; New England, 53 days

Figure 15-23 The Coriolis effect deflects water and other free-moving objects to the right north of the equator and to the left south of the equator. Thus, gyres in the northern hemisphere circulate in a clockwise direction. The motion is reversed in the southern hemisphere.

Gyres If Earth had no landmasses, the global ocean would have simple belts of easterly and westerly surface currents. But the continents deflect ocean currents to the north and south so that closed circular current systems, called gyres, develop. As shown in *Figure 15-23,* there are five major gyres: the North Pacific, the North Atlantic, the South Pacific, the South Atlantic, and the Indian Ocean. Because of the Coriolis effect, which you learned about in Chapter 12, the gyres of the northern hemisphere circulate in a clockwise direction, and those of the southern hemisphere circulate in a counterclockwise direction. The parts of all gyres closest to the equator move towards the west as equatorial currents. When these currents encounter a landmass, they are deflected toward the poles. These poleward-flowing waters carry warm, tropical water into higher, colder latitudes. A well-known example of a warm current is the Kuroshio, or Japan Current in the western North Pacific.

After these warm waters enter polar regions, they gradually cool and, deflected by landmasses, move back toward the equator. The resulting currents then bring cold water from higher latitudes into tropical regions. An example of such cold ocean currents is the California Current in the eastern North Pacific. You'll learn more about currents in the *Science in the News* feature at the end of this chapter.

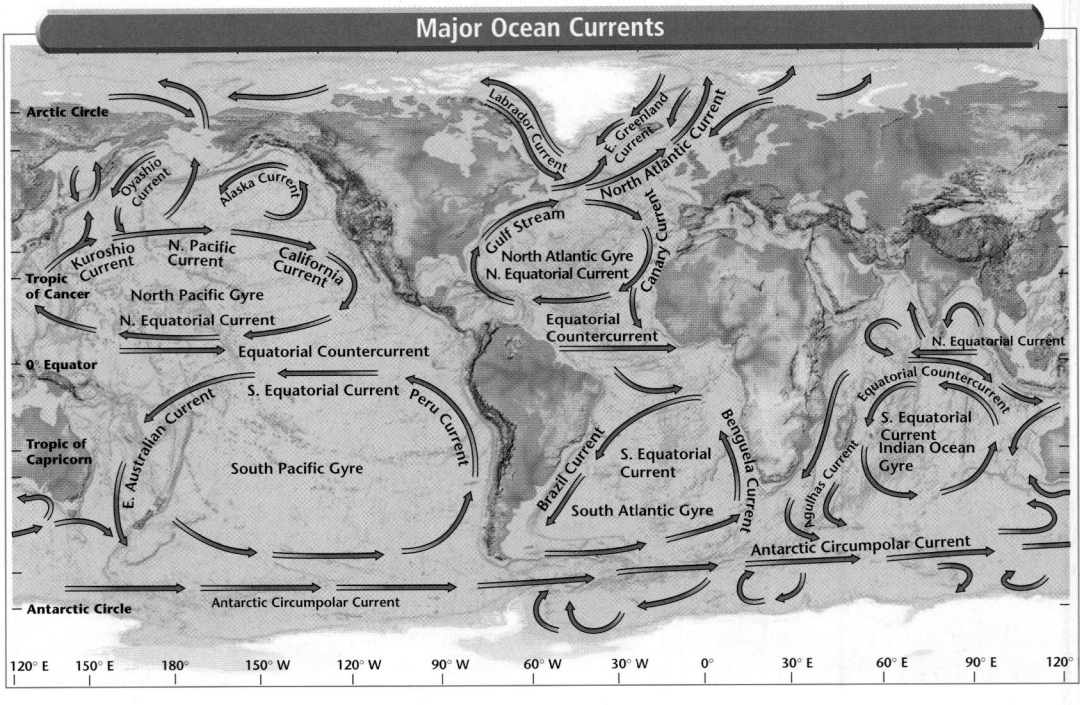

Major Ocean Currents

NY Core Curriculum Standards

Page 404: St 4 KI 1.1e & 2.2b, St 6 KI 1 & 5
Page 405: St 4 KI 1.1a, 1.1i, 2.1i, & 2.2b, St 6 KI 1 & 5

Science Field Book

Earth Science
Journal

To familiarize students with the circulation patterns of Earth's oceans, have them research the ten major cold and warm ocean currents associated with the Atlantic, Pacific, and Indian Oceans. Students should create data tables in their science journals listing the name, location, speed, direction of motion, and temperature of each current. L2 P

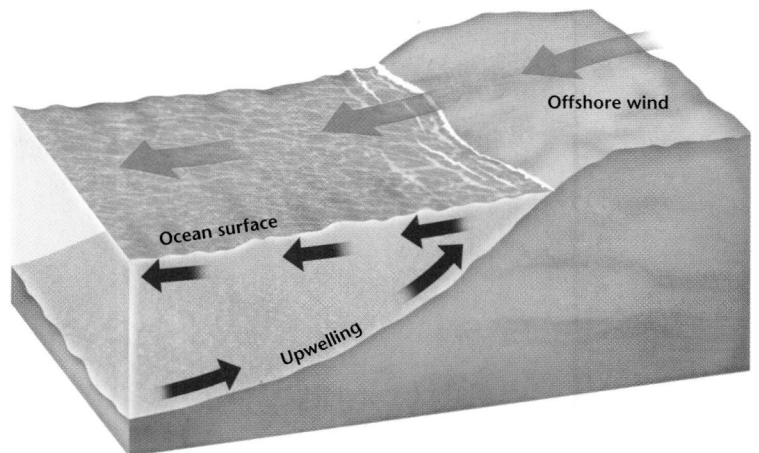

UPWELLING

In addition to moving horizontally, ocean water moves vertically. The upward motion of ocean water is called **upwelling.** Upwelling waters originate from the bottom of the ocean and thus are cold. Areas of upwelling exist mainly off the western coasts of continents in the trade-wind belts. As *Figure 15-24* shows, the trade winds blow surface water offshore, and the surface water is replaced by upwelling deep water. Upwelling waters are rich in nutrients, which support abundant populations of marine life. Consequently, some of the world's richest fishing grounds are found off the coasts of Peru and California.

SECTION ASSESSMENT

1. Describe how water moves as a wave passes.

2. What three factors determine the height of a wave?

3. What causes tides? Compare and contrast a spring tide and a neap tide.

4. Why are upwelling waters always cold?

5. **Thinking Critically** Upwelling currents are rich in nutrients. Predict the effects on marine ecosystems if these currents stopped.

SKILL REVIEW

6. **Concept Mapping** Use the following phrases to complete a concept map of wave characteristics. For more help, refer to the *Skill Handbook.*

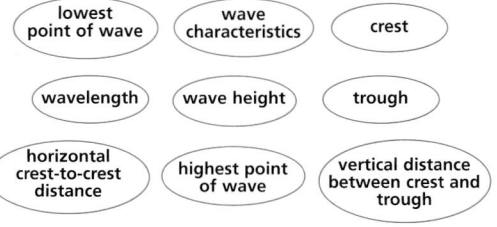

lowest point of wave | wave characteristics | crest
wavelength | wave height | trough
horizontal crest-to-crest distance | highest point of wave | vertical distance between crest and trough

Check for Understanding
Reinforcement
Ask students to compare and contrast the Gulf Stream and the California Current in terms of movement and temperature. The warm Gulf Stream flows north and transports warm, tropical water to higher latitudes. The cold California Current flows south and brings cold, North Pacific water to lower latitudes.

Reteach
Linguistic Have students each draw a northern-hemisphere gyre and indicate its circulation pattern. Have them describe the gyre's pattern and temperature in their science journals. **L2**

✓*Assessment*

Knowledge Have students use the Coriolis effect to explain the movement of gyres in the southern hemisphere. The Coriolis effect deflects all free-moving objects to the left in the southern hemisphere. This causes gyres in the southern hemisphere to move in a counterclockwise direction.

SECTION ASSESSMENT

1. The water moves in a circle: backward in the trough, upward in the wave front, forward in the crest, and downward in the back of the wave.

2. Wave height depends on wind velocity, wind duration, and fetch.

3. Tides are caused mainly by the gravitational attraction of the Sun and the Moon. Spring tides are unusually high tides that occur when the Sun, Earth, and the Moon are aligned. Neap tides are unusually low tides that occur when the Moon and the Sun are at right angles relative to Earth.

4. because they originate from the bottom of the ocean

5. Marine ecosystems would be disrupted if their supply of nutrient-rich deep waters was eliminated.

6. First level of concept map: wave characteristics; second level, in any order: crest, wavelength, wave height, trough; third level: lowest point of wave should connect to trough, horizontal crest-to-crest distance should connect to wavelength, highest point of wave should connect to crest, and vertical distance between crest and trough should connect to wave height.

Time Allotment

one class period

Process Skills

analyze data, observe and infer, compare and contrast, recognize cause and effect, make and use graphs, predict, interpret data

Safety Precautions

Make sure that students wear safety goggles and lab aprons.

Disposal

After the lab is complete, dispose of the solutions in the sink.

Preparation

The warm water should be at room temperature or about 20°C; the refrigerated water should be colder than 5°C.

Procedure

Teaching Strategies

Review the concepts of salinity and units of measurement (fractions, g/kg, percent, ppt). Students also should review the Problem-Solving Lab.

NY Core Curriculum Standards

Page 406: St 1 Science KI 1, 2, & 3, St 6 KI 1, 2, & 5
Page 407: St 1 Science KI 1, 2, & 3, St 6 KI 1, 2, & 5, St 7 KI 1

GeoLab Modeling Water Masses

The water in the oceans is layered because water masses with higher densities sink below those with lower densities. The density of seawater depends on its temperature and salinity. In this activity, you'll model different types of water masses to observe the effects of density firsthand.

Preparation

Problem
Determine how changes in salinity and temperature affect water density.

Materials
scale
graduated 500-mL cylinder
100-mL glass beakers (4)
water
red, yellow, and blue food coloring
salt
thermometer
eyedropper
graph paper
pencil
ruler
calculator

Objectives
In this GeoLab you will:
- **Compare** and **contrast** the movement of different water samples.
- **Determine** the relative densities of the water samples.

- **Predict** the arrangement of layers in a body of water.
- **Construct** and **interpret** a temperature profile.

Safety Precautions
Always wear safety goggles and an apron in the lab. Wash your hands after completing the lab.

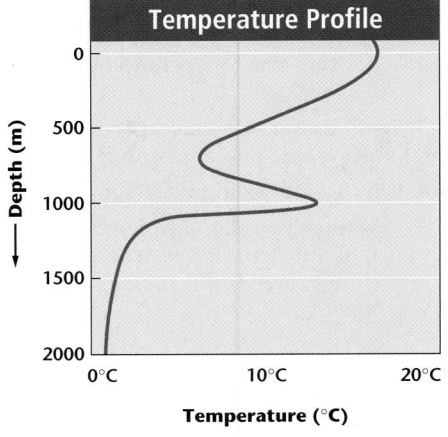

Troubleshooting

If the experiment isn't done quickly, the temperature and density differences may be too small to allow observable sinking motions. Also, the temperature of the droppers should be about the same as that of the cold-water samples.

Data and Observations

The cold, red saltwater will sink in the warm, yellow saltwater; the cold, blue freshwater will sink in the warm, clear freshwater; and the cold, blue freshwater will float on the warm, yellow saltwater.

Procedure

1. Mix 200 mL of water and 7.5 g of salt in the graduated cylinder. Pour equal amounts of the salt solution into two beakers. Fill each of the two other beakers with 100 mL of freshwater.
2. Put a few drops of red food coloring in one of the salt solutions. Put a few drops of yellow food coloring in the other salt solution. Put a few drops of blue food coloring in one of the beakers of freshwater. Do not add food coloring to the other beaker of freshwater.
3. Place the beakers with the red salt solution and the blue freshwater in the refrigerator. Refrigerate them for 30 minutes.
4. Measure and record the temperature of the water in all four beakers.
5. Put several drops of the cold, red saltwater into the beaker with the warm, yellow saltwater and observe what happens. Record your observations.
6. Put several drops of the cold, blue freshwater into the beaker with the warm, clear freshwater and observe what happens. Record your observations.
7. Put several drops of the cold, blue freshwater into the beaker with the warm, yellow saltwater and observe what happens. Record your observations.

Analyze

1. In your science journal, describe the movement of the cold, red saltwater in step 5. Compare this to the movement of the cold, blue freshwater in step 7. What accounts for the differences you observed?
2. Based on your observations, list the water samples by color in order of increasing density.
3. If you poured the four water samples into the graduated cylinder, how would they arrange themselves into layers by color, from top to bottom?

Conclude & Apply

1. Assume that four water masses in a large body of water have the same characteristics as the water in the four beakers. The warm water layers are 100 m thick, and the cold layers are 1000 m thick. Graph the temperature profile of the large body of water.
2. What is the salinity in parts per thousand of the combined saline solutions? (Hint: ppt equals grams of salt per kilogram of solution. Assume that 200 mL of water has a mass of 200 g. Be sure to include the mass of the salt in the total mass of the solution.)
3. The temperature profile on the opposite page was constructed from measurements taken in the Atlantic Ocean off the coast of Spain. Study the profile, then infer why a high-temperature layer exists beneath the thermocline. Is this layer denser than the colder water above? Explain.

GeoLab **407**

Resource Manager

GeoLab and MiniLab Worksheets,
  pp. 60–62 ☐2

Analyze

1. Cold saltwater sinks in warm saltwater; cold freshwater floats in warm saltwater. Cold saltwater is denser than warm saltwater; cold freshwater is less dense than warm or cold saltwater. The amount of salinity in the water accounts for the differences observed.
2. clear, blue, yellow, red
3. clear, blue, yellow, red

Conclude & Apply

1. Student graphs should show that the first layer extends to a depth of 100 m and has a temperature of 20°C. The second layer extends to 1100 m and has a temperature of 5°C. The third layer extends to 1200 m and has a temperature of 20°C. The fourth layer extends to 2200 m and has a temperature of 5°C.
2. mass of solution: 207.5 g salinity = 7.5 g/207.5 g = 0.036 = 36 ppt
3. The high-temperature layer is saltier than the colder thermocline above it. It is therefore denser than the thermocline because salinity causes an increase in density.

✔Assessment

Skill Give students the following data and have them list the data in a table. water mass A: density: 0.998 g/cm³, salinity: 500 ppm, temperature: 20°C; water mass B: density: 1.000 g/cm³, salinity: 500 ppm, temperature 5°C; water mass C: density: 1.025 g/cm³, salinity: 35 000 ppm, temperature: 20°C; and water mass D: density: 1.026 g/cm³, salinity: 35 000 ppm, temperature 5°C

Purpose

Students will build an understanding of how ocean currents affect navigation.

Content Background

- Caroline Alexander's research was sponsored by the American Museum of Natural History, which in 1999 sponsored a comprehensive exhibit related to the journey of the *Endurance*. Information about this exhibit can be accessed at the Earth Science Web Site.
- Ernest Shackleton was an inspired leader. He managed his crew with care, neutralizing troublemakers and keeping careful watch on morale. He believed that pessimism was more dangerous than any of the other conditions that the crew faced. When the crew camped on the ice after the ship broke up, Shackleton took the most difficult members of the crew into his own tent so that they would not disrupt the morale of the remaining crew.

Teaching Strategies

- Discuss the coldest conditions that students have ever encountered. Have students share how they coped with the cold and whether their measures were effective.
- Have students research currents that have played a major role in world affairs, such as the Gulf Stream. All reports, whether oral or written, should be accompanied by maps.

Science in the News

Caught in the Current

*"**T**he gale was still blowing from the northeast on January 21, drifting snow from the continental ice shelf...Held fast in the ice, the* Endurance *was being carried with the rest of the pack by the Weddell Sea's current; soon she would be moving away from land."—from* The Endurance: Shackleton's Legendary Antarctic Expedition, *by Caroline Alexander (Knopf, 1999).*

Alexander's book tells the story of the *Endurance* and the 28 men who sailed in the ship to Antarctica in 1914. The explorers on board planned the first overland crossing of the Antarctic continent. The ship left South Georgia Island in the South Atlantic in December 1914. During the next two years, the expedition suffered both horrible misfortune and incredible luck.

Frozen Solid

In mid-December, the *Endurance* neared the coast of Antarctica. The pack ice that year was especially dense, and by January 1915, the ship had frozen solidly into the ice just 126 km from its destination—126 km of solid ice. The ship and its crew could only drift aimlessly with the ice.

In this part of the sea a clockwise current churns the ice pack in endless circles. The ice crunches against the Antarctic Peninsula, generating massive waves of pressure. The *Endurance*, still frozen in the ice, was carried by the current farther and farther from land. In November 1915, the pressure of the ice pack crushed the ship to pieces. The crew escaped but was forced to camp on the drifting ice in sub-zero temperatures with thin tents as their only shelter. They managed to salvage some supplies and three small boats.

As the Current Turns

The crew hoped that the ice would carry them toward land. However, the ice carried them into the open waters of the South Atlantic. Desperate, they launched their boats into the ocean. They stayed awake for days, battling rough waves and towering icebergs that threatened to crush the small boats to pieces. In April 1916, they finally reached a small barren island. The largest of the boats continued on a perilous journey to South Georgia Island for help. The boat was crewed by Shackleton and five others. These men faced an almost impossible task: to travel in a tiny boat more than a thousand kilometers across the roughest expanse of sea in the world.

Despite the odds, Shackleton and his crew did reach South Georgia Island. By this time, winter was approaching and it was several months before they could rescue the shipwrecked members of the *Endurance's* crew. All 28 men survived the adventure. They failed in their mission to cross Antarctica, but their survival remains a tale of great glory.

Activity

Plot a course for a journey by boat from the coast nearest you to Antarctica. Use the map of ocean currents in *Figure 15-23* to identify the currents you would use and those you would avoid.

Activity

Courses will vary, depending in part on the school's location. All plotted courses, however, should be scientifically valid. For instance, students should not plot a course that runs counter to prevailing currents.

Summary

SECTION 15.1
The Oceans

Main Ideas
- Oceanography is the scientific study of Earth's oceans. Oceanographers use sonar, satellites, and submersibles, among other tools, to explore the ocean.
- Earth's first oceans likely formed more than 4 billion years ago. Some water may have come from impacting comets or from deep within Earth's interior. Scientists theorize that water from within Earth's interior was released by volcanism.
- Approximately 71 percent of Earth's surface is covered by oceans. The major oceans are the Pacific, Atlantic, Indian, Arctic, and Antarctic.

Vocabulary
oceanography (p. 385)
sea level (p. 388)
side-scan sonar (p. 386)

SECTION 15.2
Seawater

Main Ideas
- Seawater contains 96.5 percent water and 3.5 percent dissolved salts. The average salinity of seawater is 35 ppt. The salinity of the ocean remains constant because salts are removed from the ocean at the same rate as they are added.
- Ocean surface temperatures range from −2°C in polar waters to 30°C in equatorial waters. Seawater density changes with changes in salinity and temperature.
- Ocean water temperatures decrease with depth. The ocean can be divided into three layers: the surface layer, the transitional thermocline, and the bottom layer.

Vocabulary
salinity (p. 392)
temperature profile (p. 396)
thermocline (p. 396)

SECTION 15.3
Ocean Movements

Main Ideas
- Ocean waves are generated by wind. Water in a wave moves in a circular motion but does not move forward. When waves reach shallow water, friction with the ocean bottom slows them, and they become breakers.
- Tides are caused by the gravitational attraction among Earth, the Moon, and the Sun. Lunar tides are twice as high as solar tides.
- Density currents are deep currents generated by salinity and temperature differences. Wind-driven surface currents affect the upper few hundred meters of the ocean. Upwelling occurs when winds push surface water aside and the surface water is replaced by cold, deep water.

Vocabulary
breaker (p. 400)
crest (p. 399)
density current (p. 403)
surface current (p. 403)
tide (p. 400)
trough (p. 399)
upwelling (p. 405)
wave (p. 399)

 earthgeu.com/vocabulary_puzzlemaker

---

Main Ideas

Summary statements can be used by students to review the major concepts of the chapter.

VOCABULARY PuzzleMaker

 For additional help with vocabulary, have students access the Vocabulary Puzzlemaker online.

earthgeu.com/vocabulary_puzzlemaker

0:00 *Out of Time?*

If time does not permit teaching the entire chapter, use the GeoDigest at the end of the unit as an overview.

Earth Science Online

Be sure to check the Earth Science Web Site for links to chapter material:
earthgeu.com

GLENCOE *Technology*

Videotape/DVD
MindJogger Videoquizzes
Chapter 15: *Physical Oceanography*
Have students work in groups as they play the videoquiz game to review key chapter concepts.

Resource Manager

Chapter Assessment, pp. 85–90
MindJogger Videoquizzes DVD/VHS
ExamView® Pro CD-ROM
Performance Assessment in Earth Science

NY Core Curriculum Standards

Page 408: St 4 KI 2.1i & 2.2b, St 6 KI 1 & 5, St 7 KI 2
Page 409: St 4 KI 1.1a, 1.1i, 2.1i, & 2.2b

Understanding Main Ideas

1. c
2. c
3. c
4. c
5. c
6. d
7. a
8. d
9. c
10. a
11. c
12. a
13. The Moon is much closer to Earth than the Sun is.
14. Seas are smaller than oceans and are partly or completely landlocked.
15. The highest salinity values occur in subtropical oceans, where evaporation exceeds precipitation. Evaporation causes a buildup of salts in seawater.
16. 100 m
17. The North Pacific; all northern-hemisphere gyres move in clockwise directions.

NY Core Curriculum Standards

Page 410: St 2 KI 1, St 4 KI 1.1a, 1.1e, 1.1i, & 2.2b, St 6 KI 1 & 5
Page 411: St 4 KI 2.1i, 2.2b, & 2.2c, St 6 KI 1, 2, & 5

Understanding Main Ideas

1. Which of the following is used to measure ocean depth?
   a. bottom dredges   c. sonar
   b. nets   d. tidal patterns

2. Which of the following are the most common gases emitted by volcanoes?
   a. hydrogen and helium
   b. oxygen and nitrogen
   c. water vapor and carbon dioxide
   d. chlorine and hydrogen

3. What is the average depth of the oceans?
   a. 380 m   c. 3800 m
   b. 38 m   d. 3 km

4. What is the average salinity of seawater?
   a. 100 ppt   c. 35 ppt
   b. 50 ppt   d. 3.5 ppt

5. What is the average temperature of deep water below the thermocline?
   a. 15°C   c. less than 4°C
   b. more than 4°C   d. 0°C

6. What basic motion does water follow during the passage of a wave?
   a. forward   c. up and down
   b. backward   d. circular

7. Which of the following does not affect wave height in deep water?
   a. wavelength   c. wind speed
   b. wind duration   d. fetch

8. Which type of seawater has the greatest density?
   a. warm, with low salinity
   b. warm, with high salinity
   c. cold, with low salinity
   d. cold, with high salinity

9. To what average depth does light penetrate in the ocean?
   a. 1 m   c. 100 m
   b. 10 m   d. 1000 m

10. What type of high tides occur during a full Moon?
    a. spring tides   c. tidal ranges
    b. neap tides   d. tidal cycles

11. What is the the densest water mass in the Atlantic Ocean?
    a. North Atlantic Deep Water
    b. surface water
    c. Antarctic Bottom Water
    d. Antarctic Intermediate Water

12. The Arctic Ocean is the northern part of which body of water?
    a. Atlantic Ocean   c. Bering Sea
    b. Pacific Ocean   d. Indian Ocean

13. Explain why the Moon exerts a greater tidal influence than the Sun.

14. What distinguishes a sea from an ocean?

15. Where in the oceans are the highest values of salinity found? Explain.

16. What would be the wave base for a wave that is 200 m long?

17. Which gyre would have clockwise circulation: the North Pacific, the South Pacific, the South Atlantic, or the Indian Ocean? Explain.

Test-Taking Tip

MAXIMIZE YOUR SCORE If possible, find out how your standardized test will be scored. In order to do your best, you need to know if there is a penalty for guessing, and if so, how much of one. If there is no random-guessing penalty, you should always fill in an answer.

Standardized Test Practice

1. d
2. b
3. b
4. a
5. c

18. Why does a wave break?

19. Copy the illustration on this page. Then use the following terms to label the characteristics of an ocean wave: *crest, trough, wave height,* and *wavelength.*

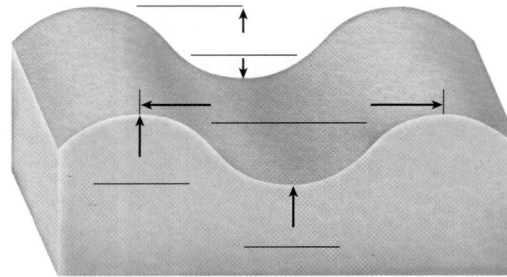

20. Cold water masses are generally denser than warm water masses, yet warm water from the Mediterranean Sea sinks to a depth of more than 1000 m when it flows into the Atlantic Ocean. Why?

Thinking Critically

21. One of the effects of El Niño, which you learned about in the previous chapter, is that the trade winds reverse direction. Predict how this might affect upwelling off the coast of Peru.

22. Based on what you have learned about water density, describe the movement of freshwater from a river as it flows into the sea.

23. Surface currents can affect coastal climates. Would the Gulf Stream and the Peru Current, both of which are surface currents, have the same effect on coastal climate? Explain.

24. Use your knowledge of global warming to hypothesize why sea level is rising.

earthgeu.com/standardized_test

Standardized Test Practice

1. Which sea was the first to be mapped?
   a. the Bering Sea
   b. the Caribbean Sea
   c. the Gulf of Mexico
   d. the Mediterranean Sea

2. Which region's seawater is most likely to have the highest concentration of dissolved salts?
   a. an equatorial region
   b. a subtropical region
   c. a polar region
   d. a delta where rivers empty into oceans

INTERPRETING SCIENTIFIC ILLUSTRATIONS
Use the illustration below to answer questions 3 and 4.

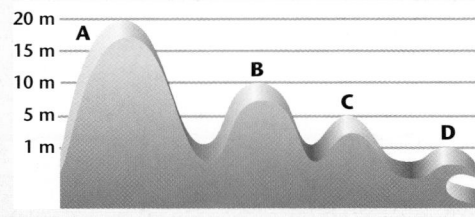

3. Which wave is most likely caused by a strong hurricane?
   a. A   **c.** C
   b. B   **d.** D

4. Why is Wave D most likely collapsing?
   a. friction from the ocean floor
   b. storm activity
   c. increased crest-to-crest wavelength
   d. opposing tidal movement

5. Which ocean movement is slow-moving and occurs in deep waters?
   a. surface currents   **c.** density currents
   b. upwelling   **d.** gyres

Assessment **411**

Applying Main Ideas

18. As waves near the shore, the water becomes shallower. The waves begin to lose energy because of friction with the ocean bottom. Incoming wave crests gradually catch up with slower wave crests ahead. The crest-to-crest wavelength decreases. The incoming waves become higher, steeper, and unstable, and their crests collapse forward.

19. See student page for answers.

20. Seawater density depends on both temperature and salinity. Warm Mediterranean water is saltier and therefore denser than the colder water above it.

Thinking Critically

21. The trade winds move surface water off the shore of Peru. This water is replaced by upwelling. Reversal of the trade winds stops both the offshore movement of surface water and upwelling.

22. River water is less salty and therefore less dense than seawater. Fresh river water would float on top of ocean water.

23. The Gulf Stream is a warm ocean current, and the Peru Current is a cold ocean current. Thus, the Gulf Stream has a warming effect on coastal climates, and the Peru Current has a cooling effect.

24. Sea level is rising because higher temperatures cause an expansion of seawater in the oceans, and the water from melting glaciers is increasing the amount of water in the oceans.

Chapter 16

The Marine Environment

Refer to pages 8T–9T of the Teacher Guide for an explanation of the National Science Content Standards correlations.

Section	Objectives	National Science Content Standards	State/Local Standards
SECTION 16.1 **Shoreline Features** 🕐 1 session 📦 ½ block	1. **Explain** how shoreline features are formed and modified by marine processes. 2. **Describe** the major erosional and depositional shoreline features.	B.4; D.1, D.2, D.3; F.5	St 1 Math KI 1 & Science KI 3, St 4 KI 1.1i, 1.2g, 2.1a, 2.1c, & 2.1p, 2.1t, 2.1u, & 2.1v
SECTION 16.2 **The Seafloor** 🕐 3 sessions 📦 2 blocks	3. **Explain** the reason for the existence of continents and ocean basins. 4. **Compare** the major geologic features of continental margins and ocean basins. 5. **Describe** the different types of marine sediments and their origin.	UCP.2, UCP.3; A.1, A.2; C.4, C.6; D.1, D.2, D.3	St 1 Math KI 3, Science KI 1, 2, & 3, St 4 KI 1.2f, 2.1k, 2.1l, 2.1m, 2.1n, 2.1o, 2.1p, 2.1t, 2.1u, 2.1v, 2.1w, & 3.1b, St 6 KI 2, 3, & 5

*A complete Planning Guide is provided on pages 30T–32T.

🕐 The number of recommended single-period sessions

📦 The number of recommended blocks

Activity Materials

Discovery Lab *page 413*
pieces of natural chalk, mortar and pestle, microscope slide, coverslip, microscope, paper, pencil

GeoLab *pages 430–431*
topographic map, metric ruler, drafting compass, pencil, graph paper, calculator

MiniLab *page 428*
five round pebbles and sand grains, set

of sieves, 250-mL graduated cylinder, cooking oil, clock or stopwatch, pencil, paper

Demo *page 415*
250-mL beaker, sand, mud, stirring rod, water

page 422
transparency of seafloor features, overhead projector

Need materials? Contact Science Kit at 1-800-828-7777 or at 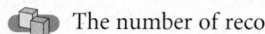www.sciencekit.com on the Internet. For alternate materials, see the activity on the listed page.

Key to Teaching Strategies

L1 Level 1 activities should be appropriate for students with learning difficulties.

L2 Level 2 activities should be within the ability range of all students.

L3 Level 3 activities are designed for above-average students.

ELL ELL activities should be within the ability range of English-language learners.

COOP LEARN Cooperative learning activities are designed for small-group work.

P These strategies represent student products that can be placed in a best-work portfolio.

📦 These strategies are useful in a block-scheduling format.

Chapter Organizer

Glencoe Exclusive!
Teacher Works™
All-In-One Planner and Resource Center

Activities/Features	Reproducible Masters	Transparencies
Discovery Lab: Composition of Chalk, p. 413 **Using Math:** Using Numbers, p. 420	**Exploring Environmental Problems,** pp. 13–16 L2 **Study Guide for Content Mastery,** pp. 97–99 L2 **Laboratory Manual,** pp. 125–128 L2	**Section Focus Transparency 47** L1 ELL **Teaching Transparency 46** L2 ELL
Problem-Solving Lab: Interpreting Graphs, p. 423 **MiniLab:** How fast do sediment grains sink?, p. 428 **GeoLab:** Identifying Coastal Landforms, pp. 430–431 **Science & the Environment:** Deep Sea Dangler, p. 432	**Study Guide for Content Mastery,** pp. 100–102 L2 **Laboratory Manual,** pp. 121–124 L2 **GeoLab and MiniLab Worksheets,** p. 63 L2 **GeoLab and MiniLab Worksheets,** pp. 64–66 L2	**Section Focus Transparency 48** L1 ELL **Teaching Transparency 47** L2 ELL

 **Assessment**

Chapter Assessment, pp. 91–96
Performance Assessment in the Science Classroom (PASC)
MindJogger Videoquiz DVD/VHS
Performance Assessment in Earth Science
ExamView® Pro CD-ROM
5 Days to the Regents Exam

ASSESSMENT ADVANTAGE

Additional Resources

Guided Reading Audio Program ELL
Cooperative Learning in the Science Classroom COOP LEARN
Lesson Plans
Block Scheduling
earthgeu.com
NY Lesson Plans
NY Block Scheduling
Review Handbook for Regents Earth Science Exam

 **NATIONAL GEOGRAPHIC**

Teacher's Corner

Products Available from National Geographic Society
To order the following products, call the National Geographic Society at 1-800-368-2728:
Videos
Living on Our Changing Planet
Fossils: Clues to the Past
Oceans in Motion

Water: A Precious Resource
Sun, Earth, Moon
Curriculum Kit
GeoKit: *Earth's Crust*

Content Background

Beaches and Longshore Transport
Section 16.1

Moving water transports sediments. The largest particle size that can be transported by a current is called its competency, and the maximum amount of material that a current can move is its capacity. Most beaches consist of loose sediments spread from their source along the shore by longshore transport. The strength of the longshore current depends on the size of the waves driving it. Large waves are associated with fast-moving longshore currents and effective longshore transport, which is characterized by high capacity and high competency. The resulting beaches are relatively coarse grained. Because of this, coasts that are subjected to frequent storms generally have pebble, shingle, or cobble beaches, which are characterized by steep beach faces. Another factor that affects the grain size of beaches is transport distance. Beaches close to rocky source areas tend to have larger particles than those further away. Beaches with fine sand are generally far from rocky source areas and experience relatively small waves. No matter their grain size, beach sediments are usually very well sorted by the action of the waves.

Settling of Sediment Grains
Section 16.2

Sediment grains settling through water are subject to two opposing forces: the downward pull of gravity and the frictional resistance of the water. The gravitational force is the effective weight of the particle, which depends on the cube of the particle's diameter. The frictional force is proportional to the viscosity of the water and the particle's cross section or diameter, depending on whether the particle is larger than about 1 mm or smaller than about 0.1 mm. In either case, the weight or downward force increases much more with increasing diameter than the frictional drag; as a result, larger particles sink faster than smaller ones. Theoretical sinking velocities for small, spherical quartz grains are obtained, approximately, by $V = 40 \times d^2$, where V is the velocity in centimeters per second and d is the grain diameter in millimeters. This equation predicts a settling velocity of 40 cm/s for 1-mm sand grains; 0.4 cm/s for 0.1-mm sand grains; and 0.004 cm/s for 0.01-mm silt grains. For grains larger than 1 mm, water turbulence becomes a factor, and the approximate theoretical relationship is $V = 40 \times \sqrt{d}$. This predicts a settling velocity of 126 cm/s for a 10-mm pebble. The results of the MiniLab will vary from these theoretical values because the grain sizes are intermediate, and thus they are not adequately covered by either relationship.

Multiple Learning Styles

- **Kinesthetic** Modeling, p. 427
- **Visual-Spatial** Reinforcement, p. 418
- **Interpersonal** Project, p. 424
- **Linguistic** Collaborative Learning, p. 426

GLENCOE
Technology

The following multimedia resources are available from Glencoe.

The Infinite Voyage Series
Living with Disaster

Vocabulary Puzzlemaker

TeacherWorks™ CD-ROM

MindJogger Videoquizzes DVD/VHS

ExamView® Pro CD-ROM

Interactive Chalkboard CD-ROM

Chapter Organizer

Marine Habitats
Section 16.2

Ecologists classify marine habitats based on location and water depth. Habitats are classified either as *pelagic*, which are open water habitats, or as *benthic*, which are habitats on the seafloor. Pelagic habitats are divided into *neritic habitats*, which are those in shallow water, and *oceanic habitats*, which are those in water deeper than 200 m and away from the continental shelf, that is, the open ocean. Benthic habitats are divided into *intertidal habitats*, which are those in the beach area between the high and low tide lines, and into *sublittoral*, *abyssal*, and *hadal habitats*. Organisms that live in marine ecosystems can be identified by the areas in which they spend most of their lives.

Each type of marine environment has a different community of organisms. Most marine organisms are found in the *photic zone*, the top layer of the ocean to a depth of 100 m to 200 m, the area where sunlight penetrates. The amount of sunlight needed for photosynthesis to occur generally extends to a depth of just 100 m, but sunlight may penetrate beyond 200 m in waters that are very clear. Organisms also are found in the benthic zone at nearly all depths. For the most part, the middle depths of the ocean below the photic zone are empty of life, except for the marine organisms that move through the oceanic zone on their way to feeding or mating grounds.

The most productive ecosystems in the ocean, coral reefs, are located in the benthic zone in the shallow water of the continental margin. Most reefs are found in tropical seas where currents and waves bring nutrients and carry away wastes. Sponges, algae, sea urchins, sea stars, and fishes also live on or around coral reefs. Coral reefs usually occur as one of three distinct types: fringing reefs, barrier reefs, or atolls. A fringing reef hugs the shoreline, a barrier reef is separated from the shore by a shallow lagoon, and an atoll is a ring of reefs and limestone islands surrounding a lagoon. The formation of an atoll follows a pattern that includes all three reef types as a result of coral growth around sinking volcanic islands.

Identifying Misconceptions

Many people think that all beaches consist of sand. This may be because most people who visit seashores only go to places that have wide, sandy beaches. In fact, beaches consist of various types of loose sediment, depending on the local sediment source and the strength of the waves. Beaches may consist of sand, pebbles, gravel, or cobbles. The sediment on most beaches is sorted by size by the action of the waves. Sandy beaches are the most common because of the abundance of sand-sized sediment.

✔Assessment

Portfolio Assessment
Assessment, TWE, p. 420

Performance Assessment
Problem-Solving Lab, TWE, p. 423
GeoLab, SE, pp. 430–431
MiniLab, SE, p. 428
Discovery Lab, SE, p. 413

Knowledge Assessment
Section Assessment, SE, pp. 421, 429
Chapter Assessment, SE, pp. 434–435
Assessment, TWE, pp. 415, 421
MiniLab, TWE, p. 428
Discovery Lab, TWE, p. 413

Skill Assessment
Assessment, TWE, p. 429
GeoLab, TWE, pp. 430–431

Earth Science Online

Be sure to check the Earth Science Web Site for links to chapter material: earthgeu.com

GLENCOE'S
ASSESSMENT
ADVANTAGE

The Marine Environment

Introducing the Chapter

Have the class look at a world map that shows continental elevations in different shades of green, yellow, and brown, and ocean depths in different shades of blue. Ask students where the real edges of the continents are. Inform them that the continents extend under the coastal oceans and include the light-blue, shallow-water regions adjacent to the continents, and point out the deep-water ocean basins beyond.

Interpreting the Photo

Waves crashing along a rocky shore cause erosion, and the eroded materials end up in the bays that form between rocky headlands. Over time, the shoreline becomes straight.

INTERACTIVE CHALKBOARD
with Image Bank

PowerPoint® Presentations

This CD is an editable Microsoft® PowerPoint® presentation that includes:
- Section presentations
- Section checks
- Image bank
- Links to Earth Science Online
- All transparencies
- Animations
- Audio

The Marine Environment

What You'll Learn

- How wave action affects shorelines and produces erosional and depositional coastal features.

- What major features and sediments are found on the ocean floor.

Why It's Important

The oceans cover 71 percent of Earth's surface and have a major impact on weather and climate. Shoreline features provide recreational opportunities as well as protection from major storms along coastlines.

Earth Science Online

To learn more about the marine environment, visit the Earth Science Web Site at earthgeu.com

412

Discovery Lab

Process Skills

observe and infer, analyze, draw a conclusion, think critically, communicate **L1** **ELL**

Safety Precautions

Caution students to wear safety goggles and to be careful with glass slides.

Procedure

- Divide the class into several groups. Provide a microscope, chalk, and glass slides for each group. Make sure every member of the group participates.

Troubleshooting

- Classroom chalk may be synthetic; be sure to use natural chalk.

Discovery Lab

Composition of Chalk

Although you may not live anywhere near a coast, parts of your environment were shaped by the ocean. For example, you may be just a few meters away from former seafloor deposits that are now part of the bedrock underground. One such seafloor deposit is chalk. How can you tell that chalk formed on the seafloor?

1. Grind up a small piece of natural chalk into a powder. Make a slide of the powdered chalk.

2. Observe the chalk powder through a microscope. Describe the powder. Are the grains irregular in shape or

size? Do some of the grains have patterns?

3. Analyze the powder and hypothesize the origin of the chalk.

 **CAUTION: Always wear safety goggles and an apron in the lab. Use caution to prevent chalk dust from becoming airborne.**

Observe In your science journal, describe the composition of the powdered chalk. What is the origin of the chalk? On what evidence do you base your conclusion?

SECTION 16.1 — *Shoreline Features*

OBJECTIVES

• **Explain** how shoreline features are formed and modified by marine processes.

• **Describe** the major erosional and depositional shoreline features.

VOCABULARY

wave refraction
beach
estuary
longshore bar
longshore current
barrier island

Some of the most interesting places on our planet are the seashores, the places where the land meets the sea. They are places of continuous, often dramatic geologic activity, places where you can see geological changes occurring almost daily. Shorelines are shaped by the action of waves, tides, and currents. As waves erode some coastlines, they create some of the most impressive rock formations on Earth. In other areas, waves deposit loose material and build wide, sandy beaches. To understand how waves act in different areas of the coast, let's reexamine the behavior of breakers.

EROSIONAL LANDFORMS

You learned in Chapter 15 that waves increase in height and become breakers as they approach a shoreline. Large breakers can hurl thousands of metric tons of water, together with suspended rock fragments, against a shore with such destructive force that they are capable of eroding even solid rock. This destructive action of breakers is most evident at rocky headlands, which are points of land sticking out into the ocean.

16.1 *Shoreline Features* **413**

Section Focus

Before presenting the lesson, display **Section Focus Transparency 47** on the overhead projector. L1 ELL

Chapter Themes

The following themes from the National Science Content Standards are covered in this chapter. Refer to page 8T of the Teacher Guide for an explanation of the correlations.
Systems, order, and organization (UCP.1); Evidence, models, and explanation (UCP.2); Change, constancy, and measurement (UCP.3)

Observe

Grain size varies, but many grains have regular shapes and surface patterns. Students should be able to observe fragments of shells of marine organisms and hypothesize that chalk is derived from sedimentary deposits of organic matter.

 **Assessment**

Knowledge Ask students what specific type of rock chalk is. limestone Ask them what the chemical composition of chalk is. calcium carbonate

Resource Manager

Study Guide for Content Mastery, pp. 97–99 L2

Section Focus Transparency 47 L1 ELL

0:00 *Out of Time?*

If time does not permit teaching the entire chapter, use the Summary on page 433 and the GeoDigest found at the end of the unit as an overview.

Activity

Line up about eight student volunteers in a straight line (6 to 7 m long), at a distance from a wall so that they make an angle of about 30° with the wall. Inform the class that these students represent a wave crest approaching a straight shoreline. Tell the volunteers to hold hands, slowly walk towards the wall, and slow down when they get to within 0.25 m of the wall. When two students have reached the wall, say "Stop!" The line of students should then be bent towards the wall. Ask students what caused the bend in the line. Point out that wave crests approaching a shoreline bend in a similar way. Ask what would happen to a similar line of students if they encountered an obstacle (a headland) in the middle of the line.

Content Background

The speed of waves in shallow water is nearly proportional to the square root of the water depth: approximately 10 m/s in water 10-m deep, 6 m/s in water 4-m deep, and 3 m/s in water 1-m deep. Consequently, incoming waves progressively slow down, and successive wave crests crowd closer together as they approach the shore.

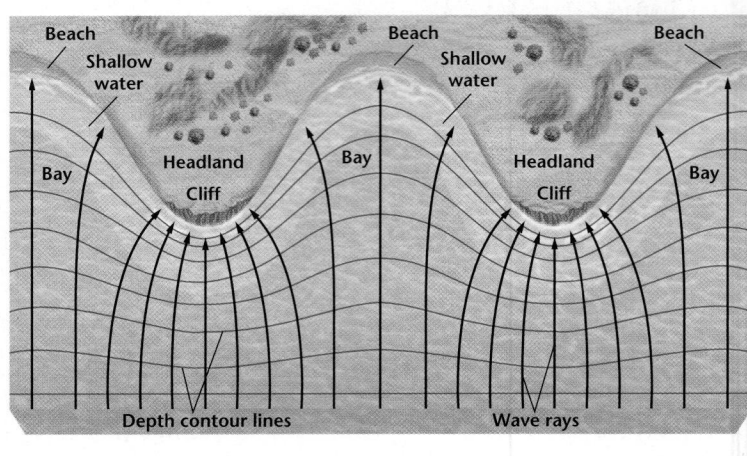

Figure 16-1 Wave crests advance toward the shoreline and slow down when they encounter shallow water. This causes the wave crests to bend toward the headlands and move in the direction of the arrows. Wave rays, drawn perpendicular to the wave crests, show the direction of wave travel and bending of wave crests.

Waves move faster in deep water than in shallow water. This difference in wave speed causes initially straight wave crests to bend when part of the crest moves into shallow water, a process known as **wave refraction,** illustrated in *Figure 16-1.* Along an irregular coast with headlands and bays, the wave crests bend towards the headlands. As a result, most of the breaker energy is concentrated along the relatively short section of the shore around the tips of the headlands, while the remaining wave energy is spread out along the much longer shoreline of the bays. The headlands thus undergo severe erosion. The material eroded from the headlands is swept into the bays, where it is deposited in the form of crescent-shaped beaches. Can you guess what the long-term effect of this process is? The headlands are worn back and the bays are filled in until the shoreline straightens. Given enough time, irregular shorelines are straightened by wave action.

Figure 16-2 A headland can be modified by wave erosion. The dotted lines indicate the original shape of the headland.

Landforms of Rocky Headlands Many headlands have spectacular rock formations. Generally, as a headland is gradually worn away, a flat erosional surface called a wave-cut platform is formed. The wave-cut platform terminates against a steep wave-cut cliff, as illustrated in *Figure 16-2.* Differential erosion, the removal of weaker rocks or rocks near sea level, produces many of the other characteristic landforms of rocky headlands. As shown in *Figure 16-3,* sea stacks are isolated rock towers or similar erosional remnants left on wave-cut platforms, and sea arches are formed as stronger rocks are undercut by wave erosion. Sea caves are tubelike passages

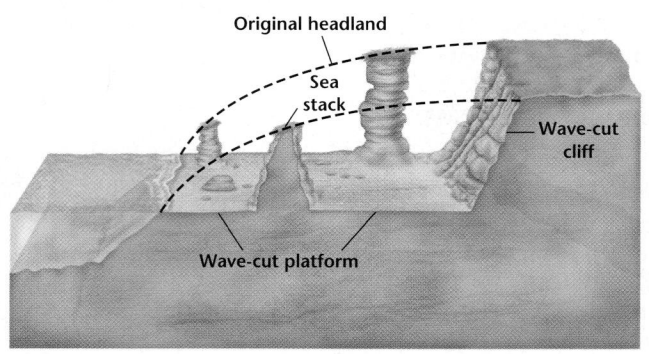

blasted into the headland at sea level by the never-ending assault of the breakers.

BEACHES

Have you ever visited any of the beaches along the coastline of the United States? Long stretches of our coastlines are lined with wide, sandy beaches. A **beach** is a sloping band of sand, pebbles, gravel, or mud at the edge of the sea. Beaches are composed of loose sediments deposited and moved about by waves along the shoreline. The size of sediment particles depends on the energy of the waves striking the coast and on the source of the sediment. Beaches pounded by large waves or formed on rocky coasts usually consist of coarse materials such as pebbles and cobbles.

The composition of beach material also depends upon the source of the material. Some Hawaiian beaches consist of black sand, tiny grains of minerals derived from the volcanic rocks that make up most of the Hawaiian Islands. The white and pink sand that form the beaches of southern Florida and the Bahamas has the consistency of cornmeal; these beaches are composed mostly of small fragments of local corals and seashells. Beaches near the mouths of large rivers are composed of the sandy sediments that are washed in by river water and made up of small grains of quartz and feldspar.

ESTUARIES

If you look at the map of the eastern coast of the United States shown in *Figure 16-4,* you will see rivers and streams entering the ocean. The area where the lower end of a freshwater river or stream enters the ocean is an **estuary.**

Figure 16-4 Estuaries provide an abundant supply of food and shelter to the young of commercially-important marine organisms. Sea grasses in estuaries also trap sediment and help filter out some water pollutants.

Figure 16-3 These sea stacks and sea arches along the rugged coastline of Washington State were formed by wave refraction at a rocky headland.

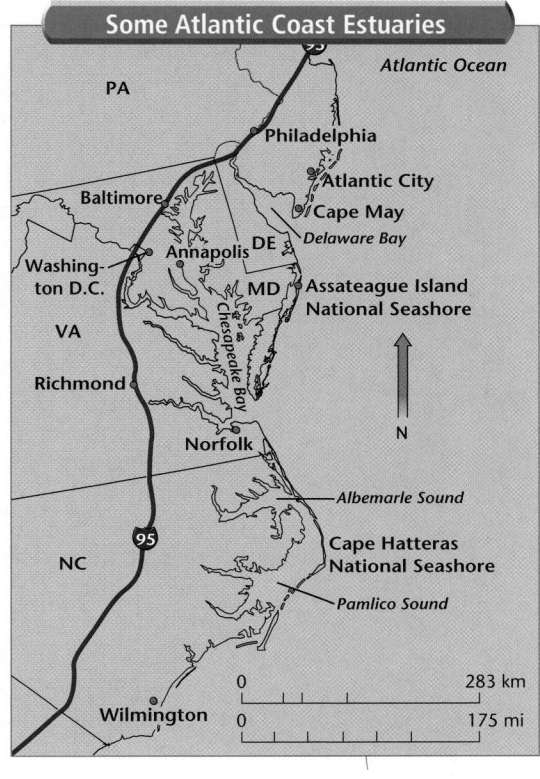

Some Atlantic Coast Estuaries

16.1 *Shoreline Features* **415**

Demo

Wear safety or splash goggles for this demonstration. Beach material is usually well sorted because of the action of the breaking waves. This action can be demonstrated as follows. Place a few cubic centimeters of a mixture of sand and mud in a beaker filled halfway with water. Stir the mixture. Hold the beaker under a faucet and turn on a small stream of water. Move the beaker around so that the water stream stirs all the sediment on the bottom. Let the beaker overflow until the water is clear. Turn off the faucet. Show the class that the remaining sediment is a mixture of fine and coarse sand, and explain that the turbulence flushed out all the smaller grains. Then repeat the experiment with a stronger stream of water. This should flush out the fine sand and leave only coarse sand and pebbles behind. Explain that the more turbulent the waves, the larger the grain size of beach sediment.

✓Assessment

Knowledge Ask students to name an estuary other than Chesapeake Bay or Pamlico Sound that is shown in **Figure 16-4.** Delaware Bay

NY Core Curriculum Standards

Page 412: St 4 KI 1.1i & 2.1c
Page 413: St 1 Math KI 1 & Science KI 3
Page 414: St 4 KI 2.1p, 2.1t, & 2.1u
Page 415: St 4 KI 2.1u, & 2.1v

Content Background

In regions with seasonal climates, many beaches undergo an annual cycle. During summer, beaches are wider and contain finer sediment than in winter. This is because of the annual meteorological cycle. Winds are stronger and storms are more frequent in winter than in summer. The more powerful surf during the winter months erodes beach material, which is deposited offshore in the form of submerged sandbars. During the summer months, the beaches are replenished by longshore transport and the on-shore movement of previously eroded, finer material.

Environmental Connection

Many beaches are enriched with sediments washed into the ocean by rivers. When a river is dammed, the sediment load previously transported downstream to the ocean is deposited behind the dam in the reservoir. Such reservoirs have to be dredged regularly to remove the accumulated sediment. This sediment is no longer available to replenish the beaches, and beach erosion results. Ask students what would happen if all rivers were dammed near coasts. Many beaches would disappear.

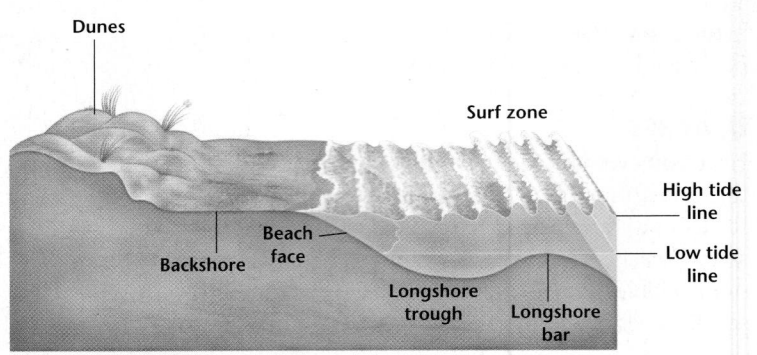

Figure 16-5 The sloping beach face is shaped by daily wave action, while the dunes behind the beach are affected only by large storm waves. Coastal dunes form from beach sand blown inland. The submerged longshore bar is located in the surf zone.

The water in estuaries is brackish, a mixture of freshwater and salt water. Estuaries are nurseries to the young of many different species, including ocean fishes. *Figure 16-4* reveals many large estuaries, such as Chesapeake Bay and Pamlico Sound.

LONGSHORE CURRENTS

Suppose you stood on a beach at the edge of the water and began to walk out into the ocean. As you walked, the water would get deeper for a while, but then it would become shallow again. The shallow water offshore lies above a sand bar, called the **longshore bar,** that forms in front of most beaches, as illustrated in *Figure 16-5.* Waves break on the longshore bar in the area known as the surf zone. The deeper water closer to shore than the longshore bar is called the longshore trough. The waves striking the beach are almost parallel to the shoreline, although the waves seaward of the longshore bar are generally not parallel to the shore. This is another case of wave refraction. The slowing of the waves in shallow water causes the wave crests to bend towards the shore. As water from incoming breakers spills over the longshore bar, a current flowing parallel to the shore, called the **longshore current,** is produced. This current varies in strength and direction from day to day. Over the course of a year, because of prevailing winds and wave patterns, one direction usually dominates.

Movement of Sediments Longshore currents move large amounts of sediments along the shore. Fine-grained material such as sand is suspended in the turbulent, moving water, and larger particles are pushed along the bottom by the current. Additional sediment is moved back and forth on the beach face by incoming and retreating waves. Incoming waves also move sediment at an angle to the shoreline in the direction of wave motion. Overall, the transport of sediment is in the direction of the longshore current. On both the Atlantic and Pacific Coasts of the United States, longshore transport is generally to the south.

Cultural Diversity

Marie Tharp (1920–) Marie Tharp is an American geologist and oceanic cartographer; she creates maps of the ocean floor. Tharp became interested in this subject when very little was known about the ocean floor and its geology. She earned a master's degree in geology from the University of Michigan in 1944. After graduation, she worked for an oil company. At the time, women were not allowed to do field work, so instead, she worked on the maps for the field crews. She and her partner, Bruce Heezen, gathered data from echo-sounding equipment about the seafloor. Tharp discovered a valley that divides the Mid-Atlantic Ridge and found that new seafloor was being formed at these ridges. This discovery confirmed the theory of seafloor spreading and led to the acceptance of plate tectonics, which students will learn more about in the next chapter. In 1978, Tharp and Heezen won the Hubbard medal. The physiographic maps of the seafloor in this chapter are based on Tharp and Heezen's original work. Tharp now does consulting work for oceanographers.

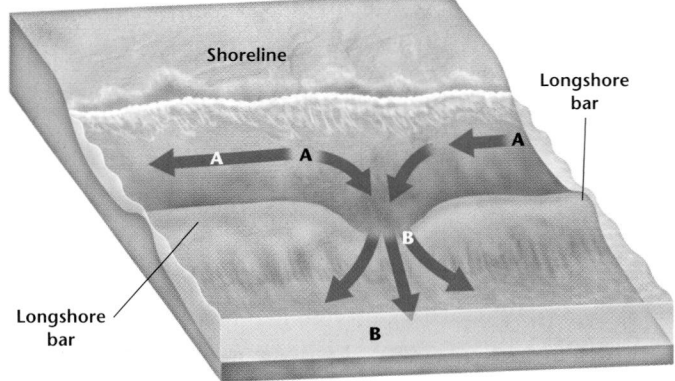

Figure 16-6 Longshore currents **(A)** are driven by incoming waves. Rip currents **(B)** return water through gaps in the longshore bar out to sea. Rip currents spread out and weaken beyond the longshore bar.

Shoreline

Longshore bar

Longshore bar

Rip Currents Wave action also produces rip currents, which flow out to sea through gaps in the longshore bar. Rip currents return the water spilled into the longshore trough to the open ocean. These dangerous currents can reach speeds of several kilometers per hour. If you are ever caught in a rip current, you should not try to swim against it, but rather swim parallel to the shore to get out of it. *Figure 16-6* illustrates both longshore and rip currents.

DEPOSITIONAL FEATURES OF SEASHORES

As a result of wave erosion, longshore transport, and sediment deposition, most seashores are in a constant state of change. Sediments are eroded by large storm waves and deposited wherever waves and currents slow down. Sediments moved and deposited by longshore currents build various characteristic coastal landforms, such as spits and barrier islands, illustrated in *Figure 16-7*. A narrow bank of sand that projects into the water from a bend in the coastline is called a spit. A spit, which forms where a shoreline changes direction, is protected from wave action. When a growing spit crosses a bay, a baymouth bar forms.

Figure 16-7 Depositional features of coastlines include spits, baymouth bars, lagoons, and barrier islands.

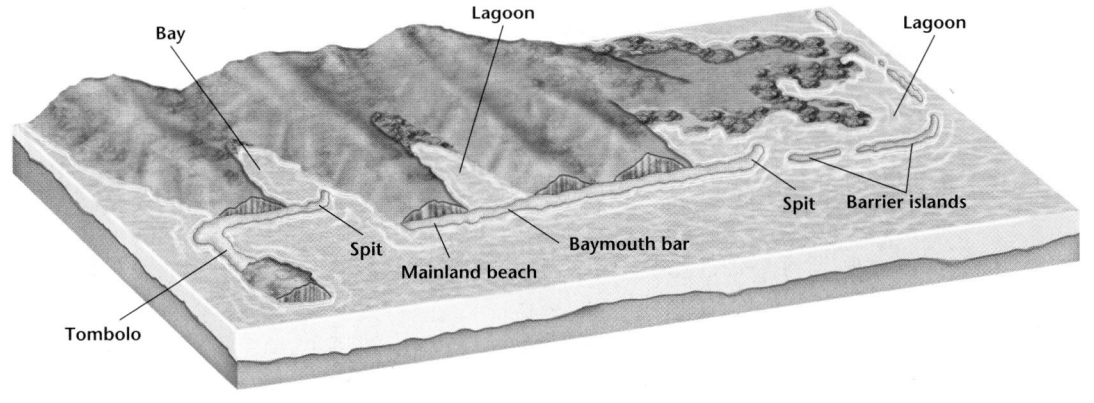

Bay
Lagoon
Lagoon
Spit
Barrier islands
Spit
Baymouth bar
Mainland beach
Tombolo

16.1 *Shoreline Features* **417**

Barrier islands are long ridges of sand or other sediment, deposited or shaped by the longshore current, that are separated from the mainland. Barrier islands can be several kilometers wide and tens of kilometers long. Most of the Gulf Coast and the eastern coast south of New England are lined with an almost continuous chain of barrier islands. The shallow, protected bodies of water behind baymouth bars and barrier islands are called *lagoons,* which essentially are saltwater coastal lakes that are connected to the open sea by shallow, restricted outlets. Another, somewhat peculiar coastal landform is a tombolo, a ridge of sand that forms between the mainland and an island and connects the island to the mainland. When this happens, the island is no longer an island, but the tip of a peninsula.

All of these depositional coastal landforms, including large barrier islands, are unstable and temporary. Occasionally, major storms sweep away entire sections of barrier islands and redeposit the material elsewhere. Even in the absence of storms, however, changing wave conditions can slowly erode beaches and rearrange entire shorelines. For example, the shoreline of Cape Cod, Massachusetts, is retreating by as much as 1 m per year. *Figure 16-8* shows some results of retreating shorelines.

You may wonder how longshore transport can build coastal features that rise well above sea level. Several factors play a role in this. At high tide, a longshore current can deposit sediment on a beach so that it extends in the direction of the longshore current. In addition, storm waves can pile up submerged sediments to heights well above the level of the highest tides. Wherever sediments are exposed at low tide, winds pick up dry sand and build sand dunes.

Figure 16-8 Shore erosion during a storm undermined the cliffs on which these houses were built, along the coast of Pacifica, California **(A).** The ocean has eroded the beach near Galveston, Texas, to the extent that the bases of telephone poles along a beach road now are under water **(B).**

Resource Manager

Teaching Transparency 46 L2 ELL

PROTECTIVE STRUCTURES

In many coastal areas, protective structures such as seawalls, groins, jetties, and breakwaters are built in an attempt to prevent beach erosion and destruction of oceanfront properties. *Figure 16-9* illustrates the effects of building structures in areas of longshore transport. These artificial structures interfere with natural shoreline processes and can have unexpected negative effects. For example, seawalls built along the shore to protect beachfront properties from powerful storm waves reflect the energy of such waves back towards the beach, where they worsen beach erosion. Eventually, seawalls are undercut and have to be rebuilt larger and stronger than before. Groins are wall-like structures built into the water perpendicular to the shoreline for the purpose of trapping beach sand. Groins interrupt natural longshore transport and deprive beaches down the coast of sand. The result is aggravated beach erosion down the coast from groins. Similar effects are caused by jetties, which are walls of concrete built to protect a harbor entrance from drifting sand. Jetties trap sand upshore from a harbor and prevent sand from reaching the beaches downshore. Eventually, sand drifts around the jetty and closes the harbor entrance anyway, unless it is removed periodically by dredging. Breakwaters are built in the water parallel to straight shorelines to provide anchorages for small boats.

Breakwaters affect the longshore current in much the same way as offshore islands do. The current slows down behind the breakwater and is no longer able to move its load of sediment, which is then deposited behind the breakwater. If the accumulating sediment is left alone, it will eventually fill the anchorage. To prevent this, all such anchorages have to be dredged regularly at great expense. In general, protective structures cause an overall loss of the sediments that maintain beaches.

Figure 16-9 The entrance to Channel Island Harbor in Oxnard, California, is protected by jetties and a breakwater **(A).** Jetties deprive downshore beaches of sand **(B).** Breakwaters cause beach sand to accumulate and eventually close the anchorage **(C).**

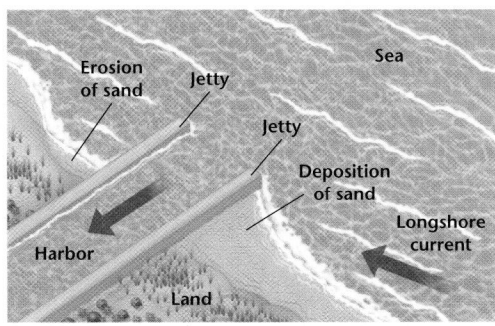

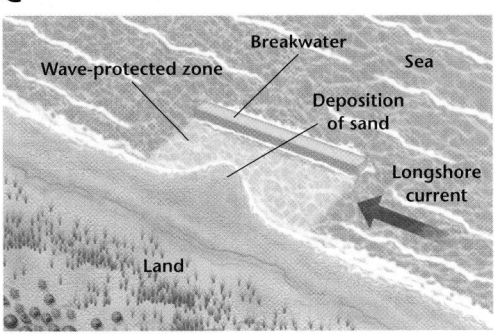

Applying Earth Science

Many shorelines have coastal sand dunes. Ask students to determine where this sand comes from and which way the dunes are moving: towards the sea, parallel to the shore, or inland. The sand in dunes is beach sand blown inland, and the dunes tend to move inland unless they are anchored by vegetation.

Earth Science
Journal

Science Field Book

Have students study maps of the coasts of the United States. Ask students to compare and contrast the coastal features on the East and West Coasts. Ask students the following questions: What are the major differences between the two coasts? Which coast is emergent? Which is submergent? Have students list and describe these features in their science journals. **L2**

Environmental Connection

A recent study released by the Federal Emergency Management Agency suggests that beach erosion is a significant threat on all U.S. coasts. According to the study, the worst beach erosion, approximately 2 m/y, occurs along the Gulf Coast. Beach erosion along the Atlantic Coast averages 1 m/y. The least amount of erosion occurs along the Pacific Coast and the shores of the Great Lakes, where it averages about 0.3 m/y or less. It is estimated that, nationwide, some 1500 coastal structures will be destroyed annually by the sea. If the current rise in sea level of about 15 cm per century continues, a total of 87 000 buildings, representing about one quarter of all beachhouses, will be lost over the next 60 years. This figure could be significantly higher if the rise in sea level accelerates as a result of global warming.

Discussion

Breakwaters, jetties, and groins interfere with longshore transport and affect the width and shape of beaches. Discuss with students what effect, if any, a fishing pier built perpendicular to a beach would have on the beach. Some accumulation of sand would result from a reduction in wave energy by the pilings, but the effect would be small. Ask students what would be the effect of an offshore wreck on the longshore bar. It would eventually create a tombolo connecting it to the shore.

Using Math

Using Numbers The highest point in the state of Florida is Walton County, at an elevation of just 105 m above sea level. If the sea level continues to rise at the highest estimated rate of 3.9 mm/y, in how many years will all of Florida be under water?

Figure 16-10 Fjords are flooded U-shaped valleys carved by glaciers. Fjords may be up to 1200 m deep.

420

CHANGES IN SEA LEVEL

At the height of the last ice age, approximately 10 000 years ago, the global sea level was about 130 m lower than it is at present. Since that time, the melting of most of the ice-age glaciers has raised the ocean to its present level. In the last 100 years, the global sea level has risen 10 to 15 cm. It continues to rise slowly; estimates suggest a rise in sea level of 1.5 to 3.9 mm/year. Many scientists contend that this continuing rise in sea level is the result of global warming. Over the last century, Earth's average surface temperature has increased by approximately 0.5°C. As Earth's surface temperature rises, seawater warms up and as it warms, it also expands, which adds to the total volume of the seas. In addition, higher temperatures on Earth's surface cause glaciers to melt, and the meltwater flowing into the oceans increases their volume. Scientists predict that global sea levels could rise another 30 cm in the next 70 years.

Effects of Sea Level Changes If Earth's remaining polar ice sheets, in Greenland and Antarctica, melted completely, their meltwaters would raise sea level by another 70 m. This rise would totally flood some countries, such as the Netherlands, along with some coastal cities in the United States, such as New York City, and low-lying states such as Florida and Louisiana. Fortunately, this isn't likely to happen anytime soon. However, if Earth's surface temperature continues to rise, an unstable part of the Antarctic ice sheet eventually could melt and cause a rise in sea level of about 6 m. Many of the barrier islands of the Atlantic and Gulf Coasts may be former coastal dunes that were drowned by rising sea levels. Other features produced by rising sea levels are the fjords of Norway, shown in *Figure 16-10.* Fjords are deep coastal valleys that were scooped out by glaciers during the ice age and later flooded when these glaciers melted.

✓ Assessment

Portfolio Have students copy a topographic map of the U.S. and indicate on the map where the shoreline would be if sea level rose 70 m. Have them estimate how far away the nearest dry land would be from Charleston (100 km), New Orleans (100 km), Miami (800 km), and other coastal cities. [L1] [ELL]

Resource Manager

Laboratory Manual, pp. 125–128 [L2]
Exploring Environmental Problems, pp. 13–16 [L2]

Figure 16-11 This series of elevated marine terraces can be found on San Clemente Island in California.

Effects of Tectonic Forces Other processes that affect local sea levels are tectonic uplift and sinking. If a coastline sinks, there is a relative rise in sea level along that coast. A rising coastline, on the other hand, produces a relative drop in sea level. As a result of tectonic forces in the western United States, much of the West Coast is being pushed up much more quickly than the sea level is rising. Because much of the West Coast was formerly under water, it is called an emergent coast. Emergent coasts tend to be relatively straight because the exposed seafloor topography is much smoother than typical land surfaces with hills and valleys. Other signs of an emergent coast are former shoreline features such as sandy beach ridges located far inland. Among the most interesting of these features are elevated marine terraces, former wave-cut platforms that are now high and dry, well above current sea level. *Figure 16-11* shows striking examples of such platforms. Some old wave-cut platforms in southern California are hundreds of meters above current sea level. You will identify an emergent coast in the *Mapping GeoLab* at the end of this chapter.

SECTION ASSESSMENT

1. Irregular shorelines have headlands and bays. Which of these experiences the most severe erosion by breakers? Why?

2. What are sea stacks, and how are they formed?

3. What effect does a seawall have on a beach?

4. If a coast has elevated marine terraces, is it rising or sinking? Explain.

5. **Thinking Critically** Resort communities such as Ocean City, Maryland, are built on barrier islands. These communities spend thousands of dollars each year to add sand to the beaches along the shoreline. Explain why this is necessary.

SKILL REVIEW

6. **Predicting** Are rip currents most dangerous on calm days, on stormy days with winds blowing from the land, or on stormy days with winds blowing from the ocean? Explain. For more help, refer to the *Skill Handbook*.

SECTION ASSESSMENT

1. Headlands experience the most severe erosion because wave refraction bends breakers towards the headlands.

2. Sea stacks are rocky, towerlike erosional remnants of former headlands left on the wave-cut platform as a result of differential erosion.

3. Seawalls cause beach erosion by reflecting storm waves back onto the beach.

4. Elevated marine terraces are former wave-cut platforms lifted above sea level by a rising coast.

5. Barrier islands continually change shape in response to changing wind and wave conditions. In addition, most barrier islands undergo beach erosion because of rising sea levels.

6. Rip currents return water, spilled by breakers into the longshore trough, back to sea. Both breakers and rip currents are most powerful on stormy days with winds blowing from the ocean.

3 Assess

Check for Understanding
Reinforcement
The Great Lakes experience coastal processes similar to those that the seashores experience. The prevailing winds on Lake Erie are from the west. Have students study a map of the Great Lakes and answer the following questions: What is the direction of the longshore current along Lake Erie's north and south shores? west to east What is the direction of the breakers striking the U.S. shore when there is a west wind? from the northwest as a result of wave refraction Name an example of a spit on Lake Erie's shore. Presque Isle, Point Pele, Long Point

Reteach
Explain that wave refraction turns incoming waves towards the shore, that water spilled by breakers at an angle to the shore produces a longshore current parallel to the shore (downwind in the absence of ocean swells), and that longshore transport builds spits such as those on Lake Erie.

✓Assessment

Knowledge Have students look for evidence of longshore transport along New York's Long Island shoreline and identify the pertinent coastal features. spits and barrier islands built by east-to-west longshore transport

421

Prepare

Section Background

For section content background, refer to **Settling of Sediment Grains** on page 412C and **Marine Habitats** on page 412D.

Preplanning

Refer to the Chapter Organizer on pages 412A–B.

1 Focus

Section Focus

Before presenting the lesson, display **Section Focus Transparency 48** on the overhead projector. [L1] [ELL]

Demo

Use an overhead transparency of a global map of seafloor features. Point out the continental margins. Also point out deep-sea trenches, mid-ocean ridges, fracture zones, and other seafloor features, including the Hawaii-Emperor Seamount chain. Explain that much of the ocean floor is rugged, but different from continental landscapes.

SECTION 16.2 *The Seafloor*

OBJECTIVES

- **Explain** the reason for the existence of continents and ocean basins.
- **Compare** the major geologic features of continental margins and ocean basins.
- **Describe** the different types of marine sediments and their origin.

VOCABULARY

continental margin
continental shelf
continental slope
turbidity current
continental rise
abyssal plain
deep-sea trench
mid-ocean ridge
seamount

If you were asked to draw a map of the seafloor, what kind of topographic features would you include? Until recently, most people had little knowledge of the features of the ocean floor. However, modern oceanographic techniques, including satellite imagery, reveal that the topography of the ocean bottom is as varied as that of the continents. *Appendix C* on pages 912–913 shows the major features of the seafloor that have been revealed by modern scientific methods.

OCEANIC AND CONTINENTAL CRUST

The topography of the seafloor is surprisingly rough and irregular, with numerous high mountains and deep depressions. The deepest place on the seafloor, the Marianas Trench in the Pacific Ocean, is just over 11 km deep. This is deeper than the height of Mount Everest, the tallest mountain on Earth.

Recall that Earth has two types of crust: continental crust, with an average thickness of 40 km; and thin oceanic crust, with an average thickness of 6 or 7 km. Crustal elevation depends on crustal thickness, and thus the thick continental crust is always associated with higher elevations on land, and the thin oceanic crust is always associated with the deep ocean basins. You will find out more about surface elevations on Earth in the *Problem-Solving Lab* on the next page. Note that part of the continental section is actually below sea level and that the ocean covers parts of the continents. These submerged parts of continents are called **continental margins.** They represent the shallowest parts of the ocean. As shown in *Figure 16-12,* a continental margin includes

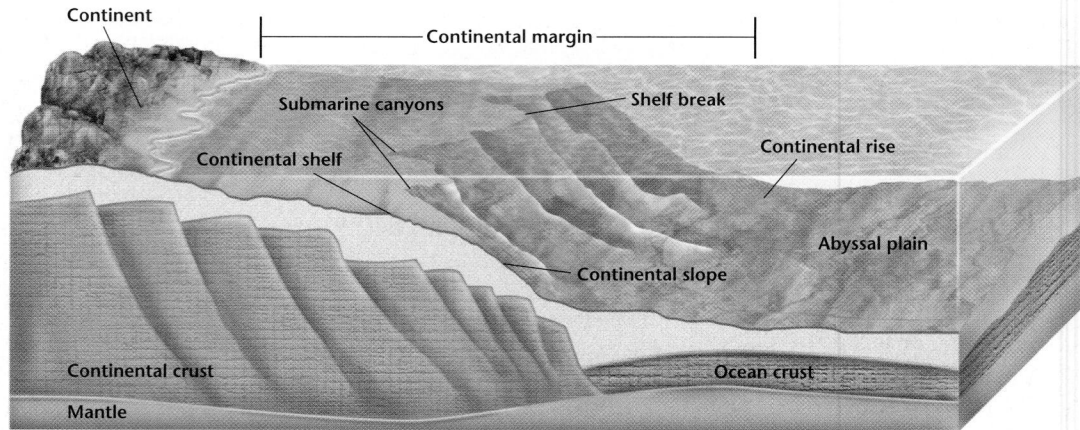

Figure 16-12 The major features of the continental margin are illustrated in this diagram.

Resource Manager

Teaching Transparency 47 [L2] [ELL]
Section Focus Transparency 48 [L1] [ELL]
Study Guide for Content Mastery, pp. 100–102 [L2]

the continental shelf, the continental slope, and the continental rise. Study *Figure 16-12* as you read about the features in this section.

CONTINENTAL SHELVES

The continental margins are the areas where the edges of continents meet the ocean. The shallowest part of a continental margin extending seaward from the shore is the **continental shelf.** Although continental shelves vary greatly in width, the average width is 60 km. On the Pacific Coast of the United States, the continental shelf is only

Problem-Solving Lab

Interpreting Graphs

Compare surface elevations A useful comparison of the heights of the continents to the depths of the oceans is given by the curve in the graph below. Note that the curve has two relatively flat sections, one near sea level, and another at a depth of about 5 km. The flat section near sea level represents the continents; the lower flat section represents the ocean basins.

Analysis

1. How tall is the highest mountain on Earth's surface in km approximately?
2. At about what depth would you begin to find trenches on the ocean floor?

3. What percentage of Earth's surface is above current sea level?
4. What percentage of Earth's surface is represented by the continental margin?

Thinking Critically

5. The oceanic crust is that part of the crust that is at a depth of 2 km or more below sea level. What percentage of Earth's surface lies above the oceanic crust?
6. What is the total average difference in surface elevations on Earth?

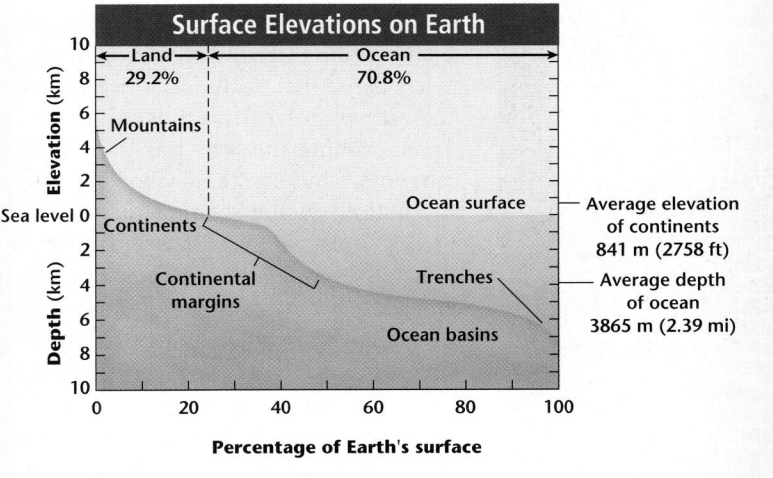

16.2 *The Seafloor* **423**

Problem-Solving Lab

Purpose
Students will interpret a hypsographic curve.

Process Skills
use numbers, interpret data, predict

Materials
none

Teaching Strategies
Ask students why Mount Everest is considered to be the highest mountain on Earth. because heights on Earth's surface are measured from sea level
Please note that while Mount Everest and the Mariana Trench are almost 9 km and 11 km respectively, because they comprise such a small portion of the graph they are not indicated.

Analysis
1. 5 km high
2. at about 6 km in depth
3. approximately 23 percent
4. about 21 percent

Thinking Critically
5. about 60 percent
6. 841 m + 3865 m = 4705 m

✓ Assessment

Performance The hypsographic curve can be used to estimate the relative proportion of Earth's surface occupied by various marine provinces. Have interested students determine the approximate percentage of Earth's surface taken up by the continental margins (having elevations between sea level and 4 km depth), the deep ocean floor (with elevations between 4 km and 6 km depth), and deep-sea trenches (with depths greater than 6 km). Ask students which of the preceding answers is fundamentally flawed, and why. 52% − 29% = 23%; 93% − 52% = 41%; 100% − 93% = 7%; the answer to the first question, because it includes the mid-ocean ridges Use the Performance Task Assessment List for Making Observations and Inferences in **PASC**, p. 7.

423

Project

Content Background

Crustal elevations are high where the crust is thick because Earth's crust has a lower density than the underlying mantle rocks. Crustal rocks have densities averaging around 2.8 g/cm³; mantle rocks have densities generally greater than 3.3 g/cm³. In a sense, Earth's crust floats on Earth's mantle in a way similar to how ice floats on water. The density of ice is about 0.9 g/cm³, and that of water is 1.0 g/cm³. As a result, floating ice has a freeboard approximately equal to one tenth of its thickness. Consequently, a 1-m thick ice raft has a freeboard of about 10 cm, a 2-m thick ice raft has a 20-cm freeboard, and so on. In other words, the thicker the ice raft, the higher its elevation. For the same reason, crustal elevations are roughly proportional to crustal thickness. Thus, thin oceanic crust has the lowest elevation (the lowest freeboard above the mantle) and forms the ocean basins.

---

a few kilometers wide, whereas the continental shelf of the Atlantic Coast is hundreds of kilometers across. The average depth of the water above continental shelves is about 130 m. Recall that sea level during the last ice age was some 130 m lower than at present; therefore, most of the world's continental shelves must have been above sea level at that time. As a result, present day coastlines are radically different from the way they were during the last ice age. At that time, Siberia was attached to North America by the Bering land bridge, Great Britain was attached to Europe, and a large land mass existed where today there are only the widely scattered islands of the Bahamas. When Earth's surface began to warm after the last ice age, and the continental ice sheets began to melt, the sea gradually covered up the continental shelves. Beaches, river valleys, and other coastal landforms from that time are now submerged and located far beyond the present shoreline. Large numbers of commercially valuable fishes now inhabit the shallow, nutrient-rich waters of the continental shelves. In addition, the thick sedimentary deposits on the shelves are significant sources of oil and natural gas.

CONTINENTAL SLOPES

Beyond the continental shelves, the seafloor drops away quickly to depths of several kilometers, with slopes averaging nearly 100 m/km. These sloping regions are the **continental slopes.** To geologists, the continental slope is the true edge of a continent because it generally marks the edge of the continental crust. In many places, this slope is cut by deep submarine canyons, similar to canyons on land, some of which are comparable in size to the Grand Canyon of Arizona. How do you think these canyons formed? On land, canyons like these are cut by rivers. But the sea level never dropped below the edge of the continental shelves, and the water from freshwater rivers flowing into the ocean is less dense than seawater, which means that it floats at the ocean's surface and thus cannot erode the seafloor. These submarine canyons were cut by **turbidity currents,** which are rapidly flowing water currents along the bottom of the sea that carry heavy loads of sediments, similar to mudflows on land. Turbidity currents, illustrated in *Figure 16-13,* may originate as underwater landslides on the continental slope that are triggered by earthquakes, or they may originate from sediment stirred up by large storm waves on the continental shelf. Once formed, a turbidity current can reach speeds exceeding 30 km/h and effectively erode bottom sediments and bedrock. The sediments carried down the

Figure 16-13 Turbidity currents flow along the seafloor because the seawater-sediment mixture of the current is denser than seawater alone.

Across the Curriculum

continental slope by these currents eventually come to rest at the bottom of the slope and beyond. The gently sloping accumulation of deposits from turbidity currents that forms at the base of the continental slope is called a **continental rise.** A continental rise may be several kilometers thick. The rise gradually gets thinner and eventually merges with the sediments of the seafloor beyond the continental margin. In some places, especially around the Pacific Ocean, the continental slope ends in deeper depressions, known as deep-sea trenches, in the seafloor. In such places, there is no continental rise at the foot of the continental margin.

OCEAN BASINS

Beyond the continental margin are ocean basins, which are deeper parts of the seafloor that lie above the thin, basaltic, oceanic crust. Ocean basins represent about 60 percent of Earth's surface and contain some of Earth's most interesting topography. *Figure 16-14* shows the topography of the ocean basin beneath the Atlantic Ocean.

Figure 16-14 Features of the ocean basin can be identified in this physiographic map of the Atlantic Ocean.

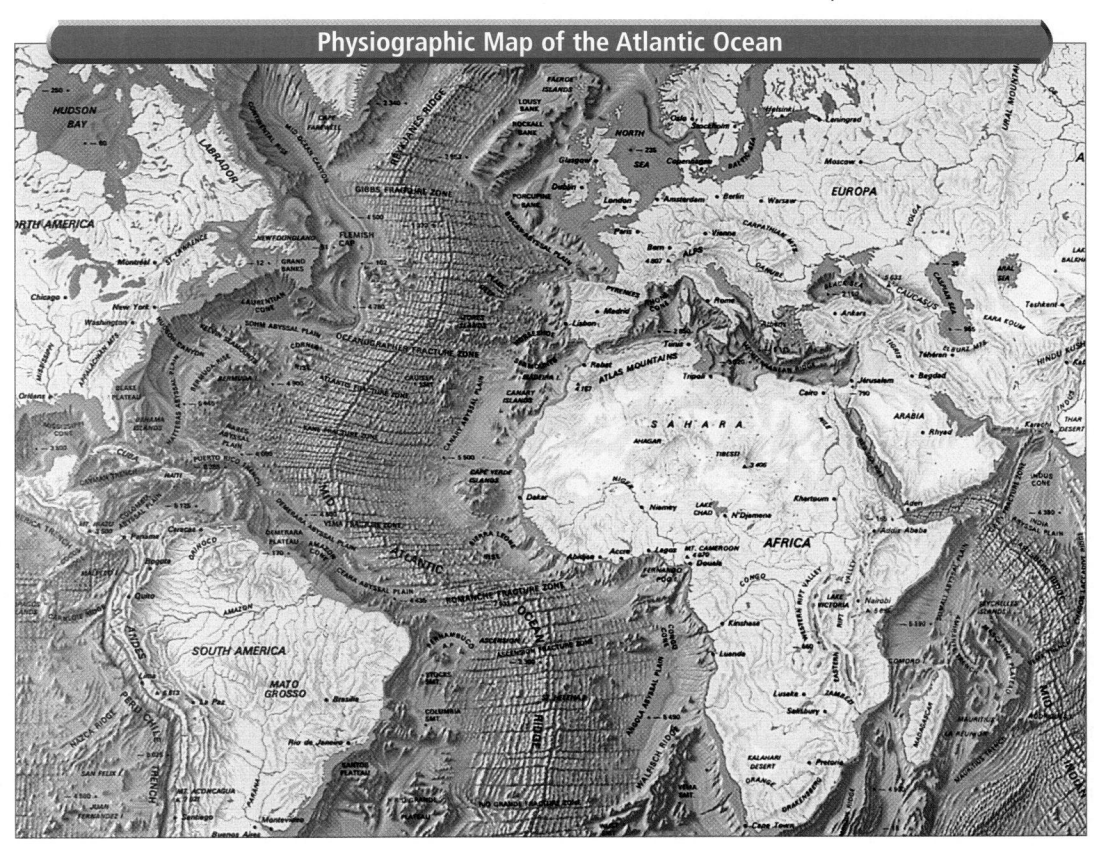

Physiographic Map of the Atlantic Ocean

Figure 16-14 Have students study the illustration and look towards the left side of the map to find the eastern coast of North America. Tell students that the eastern coast of the U.S. and other Atlantic coasts have passive continental margins. The margin of the eastern coast of the U. S. formed when the supercontinent Pangaea broke apart some 180 million years ago. The initial stage of this breakup was a continental rift, characterized by normal faults on both sides of the rift valley. These ancient faults are still present underneath a thick cover of sediments, now mostly converted to sedimentary rocks, that have accumulated since the breakup. Sediment thicknesses are on the order of 10 km on top of both the continental shelf and the continental rise. Note that the other half of the ancient rift is now on the other side of the Atlantic Ocean.

Content Background

Ocean waves move the water column to a depth equal to one half the wavelength. This depth is called the wave base. Large storm waves and swells have wavelengths of several hundred meters with a wave base of well over 100 m. Because the maximum depth of the continental shelves is 130 m, such storm waves or swells can move and stir up the sediment of the entire continental shelf and set in motion a turbidity current.

NY Core Curriculum Standards

Page 422: St 4 KI 2.1l, 2.1m, 2.1n, & 2.1o
Page 423: St 4 KI 2.1n, & 2.1o, St 6 KI 2 & 3
Page 424: St 4 Ki 2.1o & 2.1p
Page 425: St 4 KI 2.1n, 2.1o, & 2.1p

Abyssal Plains The smooth parts of the ocean floor 5 or 6 km below sea level are called abyssal plains. **Abyssal plains** are plains covered with hundreds of meters of fine-grained muddy sediments and sedimentary rocks that were deposited on top of basaltic volcanic rocks. These plains, extending seaward from the continental margins, are probably the flattest surfaces on Earth, and cover large areas of Earth's surface.

Deep-Sea Trenches The deepest parts of the ocean basins are the **deep-sea trenches,** which are elongated, sometimes arc-shaped depressions in the seafloor several kilometers deeper than the adjacent abyssal plains. Many deep-sea trenches lie next to chains of volcanic islands, such as the Aleutian Islands of Alaska, and most of them are located around the margins of the Pacific Ocean, as you can see in *Figure 16-15.* Deep-sea trenches are relatively narrow, about 100 km across, but they may extend for thousands of kilometers. Their significance will be discussed in more detail in Chapter 17.

Figure 16-15 The seafloor of the Pacific is characterized by many deep-sea trenches.

Mid-Ocean Ridges The most prominent features of the ocean basins are the **mid-ocean ridges,** which run through all the ocean basins and have a total length of over 65 000 km, more than Earth's

Physiographic Map of the Pacific Ocean

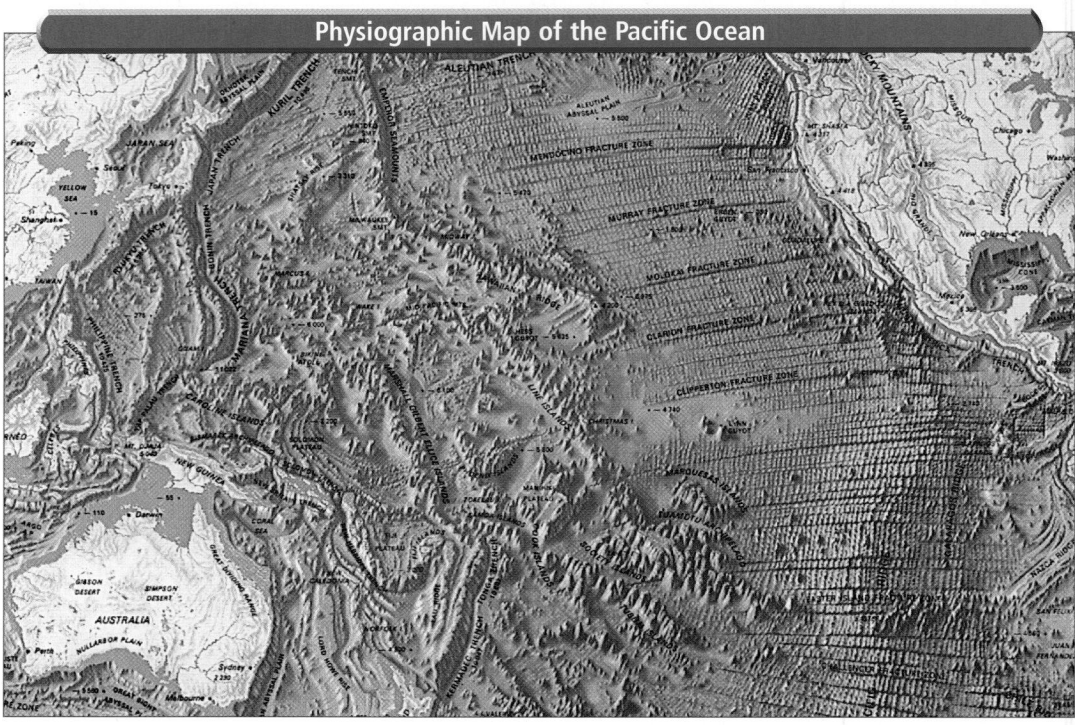

Across the Curriculum

Math Many geological and oceanographic processes involve rates, such as the flow rate of a current, the rate of erosion, the settling rate of sediment particles, and so on. A rate is the change in some quantity, for instance, distance per unit of time, which may be expressed as rate = distance/time. If the rate of a process is known, then distance or time can be calculated as follows: distance = rate × time, or time = distance/rate. For example, if a longshore current moves at 500 m/h, how far will it move in a day? You can find the answer as follows: distance = 500 m/h × 24 h; distance = 12 000 m = 12 km. Or, if polar creep moves 10 m/day, how long will it take to reach the equator, which is 8000 km away? Answer: time = 8000 × 10^3 m/10 m/day; time = 800 000 days = 2190 years. Ask students to calculate how long it will take a silt particle sinking at 20 cm/h to reach the bottom of a continental shelf 130 m deep. Answer: time = 130 m/0.2 m/h; time = 650 h = 27 days.

circumference. Mid-ocean ridges have an average height of 1500 m, but they may be thousands of kilometers wide. The highest peaks in mid-ocean ridges are over 6 km tall and emerge from the ocean as volcanic islands. Mid-ocean ridges are sites of frequent volcanic eruptions and earthquake activity. The crests of these ridges often have valleys called rifts running through their centers. Rifts may be up to 2 km deep.

Mid-ocean ridges do not form continuous lines. The mid-ocean ridges break into a series of shorter, stepped sections, which run at right angles across each mid-ocean ridge. The areas where these breaks occurs are called fracture zones. Fracture zones are about 60 km wide, and they curve gently across the seafloor, sometimes for thousands of kilometers. Volcanic and earthquake activity occurs frequently in fracture zones. Some volcanic islands, such as the Azores in the Atlantic Ocean and the Galápagos Islands in the Pacific Ocean, lie along fracture zones.

Hydrothermal Vents Have you ever heard of hydrothermal vents on the seafloor? A hydrothermal vent is a hole in the seafloor through which fluid heated by magma erupts. Most hydrothermal vents are located along the bottom of the rifts in mid-ocean ridges. When the heated fluid that erupts from these vents contains metal oxides and sulfides, they immediately precipitate out of the fluid and produce thick, black, smokelike plumes. This type of hydrothermal vent, known as a black smoker, ejects superheated water with temperatures of up to 350°C. *Figure 16-16* illustrates the black smokers found in the rift valley of a mid-ocean ridge. A second type of vent, known as a white smoker, ejects warm water. Smokers are caused by seawater circulating through the hot crustal rocks in the centers of mid-ocean ridges. The fundamental cause of mid-ocean ridges and the volcanic activity associated with them is plate tectonics, which will be discussed in Chapter 17.

SEAFLOOR VOLCANOES

Satellite radar imagery has revealed that the ocean floor is dotted with tens of thousands of solitary mountains. These mountains are not located near areas of active volcanism. How, then, did they form? You have learned that the ocean basins are volcanically active at mid-ocean ridges and fracture zones. The almost total absence of earthquakes in most other areas of the seafloor suggests that volcanism in those areas must have ceased a long time ago. Thus, most of the mountains on the

Figure 16-16 Unique communities of organisms can be found around black smokers.

Earth Science Online

Topic: Organisms
To learn more about hydrothermal vent communities, visit the Earth Science Web Site at earthgeu.com

Activity: Research the types of organisms found near hydrothermal vents. List four types of organisms found in these communities.

16.2 *The Seafloor* **427**

Demo

Show the class examples of marine sediments, including well-sorted beach sand and brown or red deep-sea mud, and marine sedimentary rocks such as well-sorted sandstone, red shale, chalk (fossil ooze), coquina (fossil shell hash), and poorly sorted, coarse-grained sandstone (turbidite).

Modeling

Kinesthetic Collect a variety of materials that could substitute for marine sediments, such as sugar for beach sand, brownie or cake mix for brown or red deep-sea mud, and broken walnuts, crushed granola cereal, or crushed hard candies for fossil marine sediments. Have students draw a profile of the seafloor, from the continental shelf to the abyssal plains, on a piece of posterboard. Then, have students glue the substitute marine sediments on the posterboard at the places where they would expect to find each type of sediment. Ask them to label the seafloor features and the sediment type found there.

Differentiated Instruction

Gifted Have students research the implications of the theoretical sinking velocity of small grains, given by $V = 40 \times d^2$, where V is the velocity in centimeters per second, and d is the grain diameter in millimeters. Have students create a data table with the headings Particle Type (coarse sand, fine sand, silt, and clay), Grain Size (1 mm, 0.1 mm, 0.01 mm, and 0.001 mm), Velocity, and Time to Bottom, and calculate all pertinent entries, assuming a water depth of 5 km. Have students speculate what grain sizes dominate continental shelf and deep-sea deposits, and compare their data with actual marine sediment patterns. coarse sand, 1 mm, 40 cm/s, 3.5 h; fine sand, 0.1 mm, 0.4 cm/s, 14.5 days; silt, 0.01 mm, 0.004 cm/s, almost 4 y; clay, 0.001 mm, 0.00004 cm/s, 396 y **L3** **P**

NY Core Curriculum Standards

Page 426: St 4 KI 2.1n & 2.1o
Page 427: St 4 KI 2.1k, 2.1m, & 2.1n

MiniLab

Purpose

Students will determine the effect of grain size on settling speed.

Process Skills

interpret data, compare and contrast, classify, draw a conclusion, predict

Materials

sand grains and small pebbles, set of sieves, 250-mL graduated cylinder, cooking oil, stopwatch, pocket calculator, pencil, paper

Teaching Strategies

- Divide the class into groups of three or four students.
- Have each student in a group do a specific task, such as selecting and measuring grains.
- Each student should calculate settling speeds and plot a graph.

Safety Precautions

Have students wear safety goggles and aprons. If oil is spilled, make sure it is cleaned up immediately to prevent accidents.

Expected Results

Grain Size	Settling Speed (cm/s)
0.5 mm	0.3
1.0 mm	1.1
2.0 mm	4.0
5.0 mm	12
10 mm	30

Analyze and Conclude

1. Settling speeds decrease with decreasing size.
2. A 10-mm particle sinks almost 30 times as fast as a 1-mm particle.
5. A 1-mm sand particle would take 8.7 h (31 250 s) to settle 5 km. A 0.001-mm particle would take 26.7 y (31 250 s $\times$ 30^3). Note: Students' results will vary.

✔Assessment

Knowledge Ask students which of the following sediments settles the fastest—sand, silt, or clay. Which settles the slowest? Why? Sand settles the fastest because it has the largest grain size. Clay settles the slowest because it has the smallest grain size.

MiniLab

How fast do sediment grains sink?

Investigate how grain size affects settling speed.

Procedure 🌊 👥 *CAUTION: Always wear safety goggles and an apron in the lab.*

1. Obtain five round pebbles and sand grains with approximate diameters of 0.5 mm, 1 mm, 2 mm, 5 mm, and 10 mm.
2. Draw a data table in your science journal with these headings: Type of Particle, Diameter (mm), Distance (cm), Time (sec), Settling Speed (cm/s).
3. Measure the diameters of each specimen using a set of sieves. Record these measurements in your data table.
4. Fill a 250-mL graduated cylinder with cooking oil.
5. Drop the largest specimen into the oil. Measure the time it takes for the specimen to sink to the bottom of the cylinder. If the specimen doesn't fall quickly, measure the time it takes to fall a given distance. Record this time in your data table.
6. Repeat step 5 for the remaining specimens.
7. Calculate the settling speed for each specimen and fill in your data table.
8. Plot the settling speed (cm/s) against particle diameter (mm) on a graph.

Analyze and Conclude

1. How do settling speeds change as particle sizes decrease?
2. How much faster does a 10-mm particle sink compared to a 1-mm particle?
3. How long would it take a 1-mm sand grain and a 0.001-mm clay particle to settle to the bottom of the ocean at a depth of 5 km?

---

seafloor probably are extinct volcanoes. Investigations of individual volcanoes on the seafloor have revealed that there are two types: seamounts and guyots. **Seamounts** are submerged basaltic volcanoes more than 1 km high. Many linear chains of seamounts are stretched out across the Pacific Ocean Basin in roughly the same direction. Guyots, also called tablemounts, are large, extinct, basaltic volcanoes with flat, submerged tops.

While extinct volcanoes on land erode within a few million years, this doesn't happen on the deep seafloor, because currents are generally too weak to erode solid rock and no other mechanisms of erosion exist. Once they are formed, seafloor structures persist practically forever. The only process that modifies them after they are formed is sedimentation; the oldest seamounts are covered with thick marine sediments.

MARINE SEDIMENTS

The sediments that cover the ocean floor come from a variety of sources, but most come from the continents. Land-derived sediments include mud and sand washed into the oceans by rivers, as well as dust and volcanic ash blown over the ocean by winds. Much of the coarser material supplied by rivers settles out near shorelines or on beaches, but fine-grained material such as silt and clay settles so slowly through water that some tiny particles take centuries to reach the bottom. You will examine how quickly sediment settles in the *MiniLab* on this page.

Ocean currents disperse fine silt, clay, and volcanic ash throughout the ocean basins, and thus the dominant type of sediment on the deep ocean floor is fine-grained, deep-sea mud. Deep-sea mud usually has a reddish color because the iron present in some of the sediment grains becomes oxidized during their journey to the ocean bottom. Closer to

---

Content Background

When particles settle through water, the sinking behavior of small grains (smaller than 0.1 mm in diameter) is dominated by the molecular viscosity of the water. Their sinking velocity increases with the square of their diameter. For larger grains (with diameters greater than 1 mm), sinking velocity increases only with the square root of their diameter.

land, the sediments become mixed with coarser materials such as sand, but some sandy sediments occasionally reach the abyssal plains in particularly strong turbidity currents.

Ooze Another major source of deep-sea sediments is the shells and hard parts of marine organisms. You can find out more about one marine organism in the *Science & the Environment* feature at the end of this chapter. When these organisms die, their shells rain down on the ocean floor and accumulate there. Sediments containing a large percentage of particles derived from once-living organisms are called oozes. Most of these particles are small and consist of either calcium carbonate or silica.

The oozes and deep-sea muds of the deep ocean typically accumulate at a rate of only a few millimeters per thousand years. Although the wreck of the *Titanic* has been resting on the ocean bottom since 1912, it has acquired a fine dusting of sediments barely a fraction of a millimeter thick.

Manganese Nodules Another type of sediment, manganese nodules consist of oxides of manganese, iron, copper, and other valuable metals that precipitated directly from seawater. Their growth rates are incredibly slow, and thus they are measured in millimeters per million years. Manganese nodules usually resemble potatoes of variable sizes, as shown in *Figure 16-17,* and cover huge areas of the seafloor.

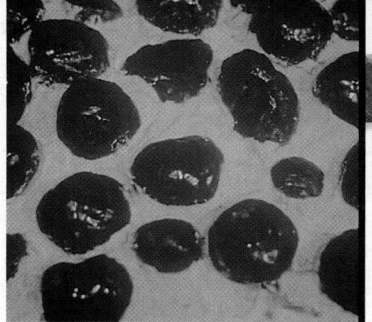

Figure 16-17 Scientists estimate that manganese nodules such as these cover 20 to 50 percent of the Pacific seafloor.

NATIONAL GEOGRAPHIC

To learn more about the *Titanic,* go to the National Geographic Expedition on page 880.

SECTION ASSESSMENT

1. What is the relationship between crustal thickness and surface elevation?

2. How are submarine canyons formed?

3. Which sediment grains sink faster, pebbles or sand grains?

4. What is the difference in origin between deep-sea muds and oozes?

5. **Thinking Critically** If there is little volcanic activity on abyssal plains, yet they are dotted with thousands of seamounts, where did these extinct volcanoes come from?

SKILL REVIEW

6. **Concept Mapping** Use the following terms to complete the concept map below: the continental shelf, the continental rise, turbidity currents, submarine canyons. For more help, refer to the *Skill Handbook.*

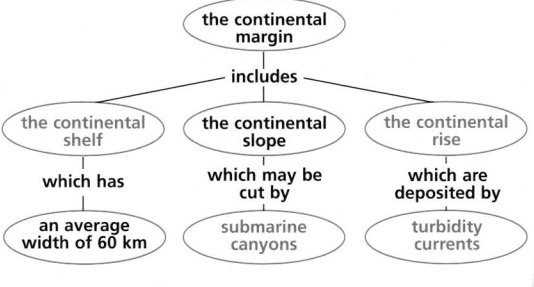

The continental margin — includes — the continental shelf / the continental slope / the continental rise
which has → an average width of 60 km
which may be cut by → submarine canyons
which are deposited by → turbidity currents

SECTION ASSESSMENT

1. Surface elevations are high where the crust is thick.
2. Submarine canyons are usually formed by turbidity currents.
3. Pebbles sink faster than sand grains.
4. Oozes are the remains of marine organisms, whereas deep-sea muds are silt and clay that have settled out of the ocean waters.

5. The seamounts must have formed earlier in time when the crust on which they are located was near volcanic activity along the ridges.
6. See the annotations on the student page.

Identifying Coastal Landforms

Topographic maps of coastal areas show a two-dimensional representation of coastal landforms. You can identify an emergent coast by the landforms along the coastline as well as landforms found inland.

Time Allotment
one class period

Process Skills
measure and use numbers, classify, compare and contrast, draw a conclusion, recognize cause and effect, predict, hypothesize

Safety Precautions
Remind students to be careful with their drafting compasses. Compasses have sharp points that can puncture skin.

Preparation

Special Instructions
It is best for you to follow the procedures first so that you can anticipate any problems students may have with this activity.

Procedure

Teaching Strategies
- Explain map scales prior to the lab. Point out that 1:24 000 means 1 in. on the map = 2000 ft.
- Have students work in small groups.
- Make sure each group includes a gifted student.
- Teachers who wish to order the actual map may request USGS 7.5 minute quadrangle Morro Bay South, California map through the USGS web site. Go to **earthgeu.com** and follow the links.

NY Core Curriculum Standards
Page 430: St 1 Science KI 1, St 6 KI 2 & 3
Page 431: St 6 KI 2

Preparation

Problem
How can you identify and describe the coastal landforms of an emergent coast on a topographic map?

Materials
metric ruler   graph paper
drafting compass   calculator
pencil

Procedure

1. Determine the map scale and the contour interval.
2. On the inset map, plot a west-east cross section of the coast just north of Islay Creek from the 60 ft depth contour to a point 5000 feet inland. Use a scale of 1:24 000 and a vertical exaggeration of 4.
3. Use both maps to answer the following questions.

Analyze

1. What kind of coastal landform is the Morro Rock Peninsula?
2. What kind of feature is Pillar Rock, and how was it formed?
3. On what coastal feature is Morro Bay State Park located? How was the feature formed?
4. What are the irregular sand hills in Morro Bay State Park?
5. What is the direction of the longshore transport along Morro Bay? Explain.
6. Your west-east cross section shows an elevated flat area next to the shoreline. What kind of coastal landform is this? How was it formed?
7. If sea level dropped 10 m, how would the shoreline change? How far would it move seaward? Would it become more regular or irregular? What would happen to Morro Bay?
8. If sea level rose 6 m, how would the coastal region change? Name three major changes.

Conclude & Apply

1. Is this portion of the California coast emergent or submergent? What features of this coastline provide evidence for your answer?

Troubleshooting
- Many students may not understand the concept of vertical exaggeration. Explain the concept and draw an example on the chalkboard if necessary.
- Islay Creek is identified only as "Islay" on the map.

Data and Observations
1. Map scale: 1:24 000; contour interval, 40 ft (solid) and 20 ft (dotted).
2. Plot prior to lab.
3. See answers on page 431.

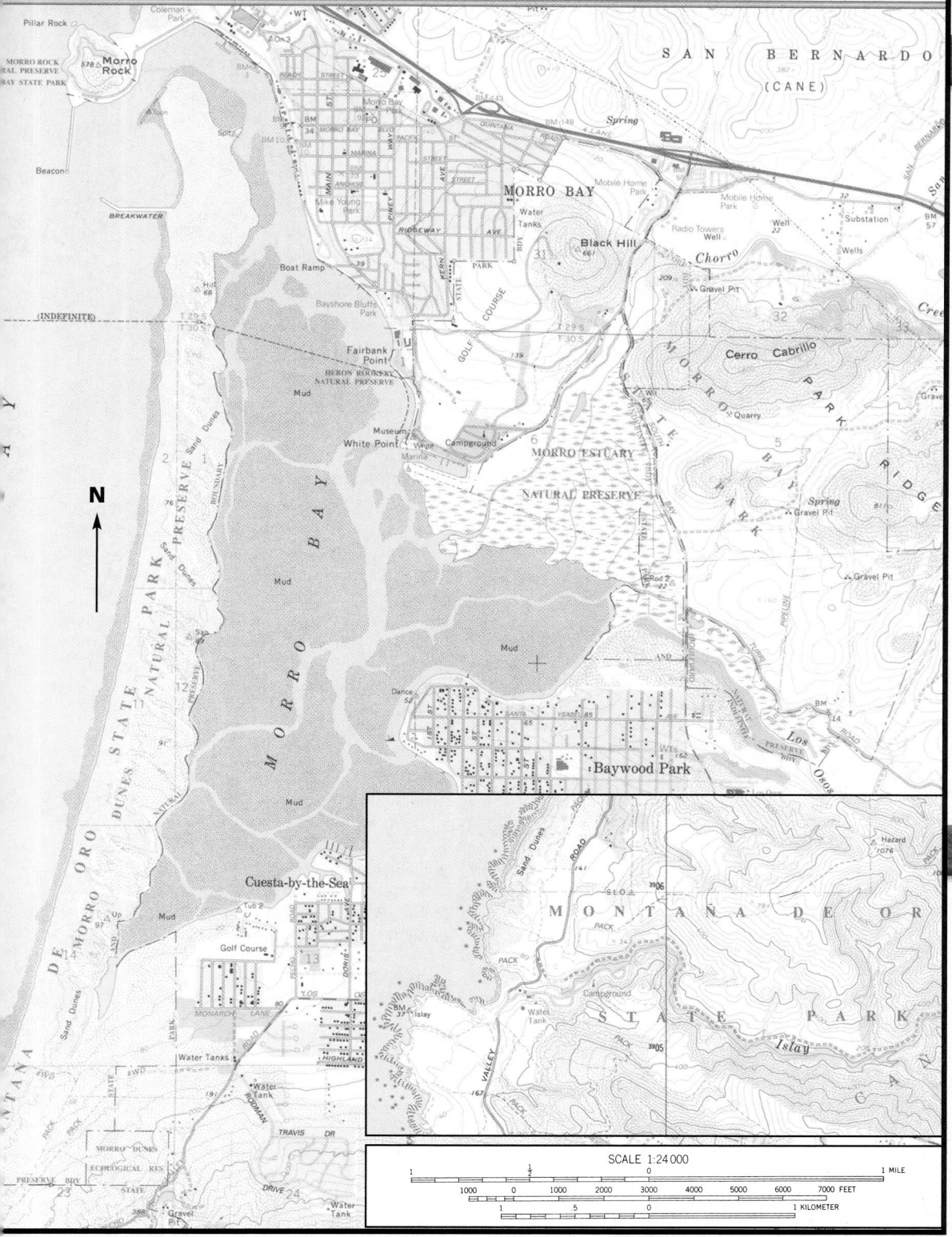

SCALE 1:24 000

Resource Manager

GeoLab and MiniLab Worksheets,
  pp. 64–66 **L2**

GeoLab and MiniLab Worksheets,
  p. 63 **L2**

Analyze

1. tombolo
2. sea stack; formed by differential erosion
3. baymouth bar; formed when a spit crosses a bay
4. sand dunes
5. to the north; sand is piling up on the south side of the breakwater
6. an elevated marine terrace; formed by uplifting of a wavecut platform
7. The shoreline would move 2000 ft seaward and become more regular. Morro Bay would dry up.
8. Morro Rock would become an island, most of the coastal communities would be flooded, the coastline would become more irregular, and Morro Bay would become a large, branching estuary extending almost 2 mi further inland.

Conclude & Apply

1. this coast is emergent; elevated marine terraces, fairly straight shoreline

✔ Assessment

Skill Have students compare and contrast this coastal section with a section of the Texas coast between Corpus Christi and Galveston. Ask them the following questions: Which coastal features are similar? Which are different? The Gulf Coast is dominated by low topography, large barrier islands, large lagoons and estuaries, and baymouth bars. There are no rocky headlands with sea stacks or elevated marine terraces. Is the Gulf coast emergent or submergent? It is a submergent coast.

Science & the Environment

Purpose

Students will explore the habits and habitat of the deep-sea anglerfish.

Content Background

- In bioluminescence, four substances react chemically to produce light. Two of these substances, oxygen and ATP, are always present in glowing organisms. Luciferin is a substance that is used up in the glowing reaction. Luciferase is a substance that causes the reactions but is not used up. Every glowing organism has unique luciferin and luciferase.

- The weight of the water at 900 m below the surface, where the anglerfish live, is so heavy that 100 kg of pressure presses on every square centimeter. A human would be crushed at this pressure. Scientists use remote-controlled robotic submersibles at this depth to collect specimens for study.

Teaching Strategies

- Review the different types of organisms that live in each of the ocean's zones. Have students discuss the similarities and differences of organisms within and across zones.

- Have students explore the roles of scavengers and decomposers in marine ecosystems.

Deep Sea Dangler

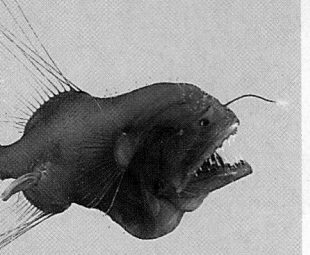

Imagine the darkest darkness, the coldest cold, the heaviest pressure. Off in the distance, there is a light, a tiny pinprick of white. It acts as a beacon, drawing you forward. You approach the light with curiosity, when—suddenly—you are pulled forward into the belly of a giant beast. That is the experience of a tiny fish being eaten by a bigger fish deep beneath the ocean's surface.

The animal luring its prey out of the dark with its own light is an anglerfish. Light from the Sun only penetrates to a depth of about 200 m. Below that depth, organisms such as the anglerfish often create their own light.

A Fishing Fish

Like a human angler with a fishing rod, an anglerfish dangles bait in the water from a fin on its back that sticks out in front of the fish. The tip of the fin glows—which is an exciting sight in the darkness. Curious fishes are attracted to the light. Slowly, the anglerfish pulls the bait—and its dinner—closer and closer to its mouth. When it opens its huge jaws, water rushes into its mouth. The prey animal is caught up in the current and ends up in the anglerfish's stomach.

Food is scarce in the deep ocean, so fishes can't afford to let any food go by, even food that seems too big. Deep-sea fishes may have mouths lined with teeth that slant backwards so dinner can't get out once it is caught. Many of these fish also have expandable stomachs. Some deep-sea fishes scavenge for food near the surface at night, but spend the day in the ocean depths. These fishes are eaten by predators like the anglerfish, which stay below 900 m in depth all the time.

Anglerfish Life Cycle

Anglerfish lay eggs in the deep ocean. The eggs float to the ocean surface, where they hatch. The young drift downward until, by maturity, they are submerged in darkness. Male anglerfish are tiny; they attach to the side of the female. In the darkness, this is a way for these fish to make sure that they find a mate. The female is the only one that glows; thus, she does all the fishing and eating for both of them. The male gets food from her bloodstream.

Glowing From Within

Below 1800 m, every swimming animal glows in some way. Living things that glow are bioluminescent. Bioluminescence is a cold light produced by living things. Many bioluminescent fishes get their light from glowing bacteria that live in the fishes. In this symbiotic association, the bacteria get food from the fish, and the bacteria lure food for the fish.

Activity

Use library resources or go to earthgeu.com to research food chains that end with a deep-sea predator such as the anglerfish. Make a diagram of one of these food chains.

Activity

Food chains vary, but all student diagrams should begin with the Sun's energy and move to planktonic organisms in the upper portion of the ocean. As an extension of this activity, have students work in groups to construct three-dimensional food webs.

Resource Manager

Laboratory Manual, pp. 121–124 L2

CHAPTER 16
Study Guide

Summary

SECTION 16.1

Shoreline Features

Main Ideas

- Wave erosion of headlands produces wave-cut platforms and cliffs, sea stacks, sea arches, and sea caves. Wave refraction concentrates breaker action on headlands.
- Beaches consist of loose sediment deposited along the shoreline. Wave action and longshore currents move sediment along the shore and build barrier islands and other depositional features. Artificial protective structures interfere with longshore transport.
- Sea levels in the past were 130 m lower than at present. When the land is rising, coasts are emergent and relatively straight.

Vocabulary

barrier island (p. 418)
beach (p. 415)
estuary (p. 415)
longshore bar (p. 416)
longshore current (p. 416)
wave refraction (p. 414)

SECTION 16.2

The Seafloor

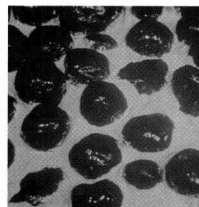

Main Ideas

- The oceans cover the thin oceanic crust and the lower parts of the thicker continental crust. The submerged part of a continent is the continental margin, the shallowest part of the ocean.
- A continental margin consists of the continental shelf, the continental slope, and the continental rise. Turbidity currents cut submarine canyons in the continental slopes and deposit their sediments in the form of continental rises.
- The flat part of the seafloor is the abyssal plain. Most deep-sea trenches are in the Pacific Ocean. Mid-ocean ridges extend through all ocean basins. Countless active and extinct volcanoes are on the mid-ocean ridges and deep seafloor.
- Most deep-sea sediments are fine-grained and accumulate slowly. Sediments may be derived from land or living organisms, or they may precipitate from seawater. Oozes are rich in sediment derived from organisms. Deep-sea muds are mostly derived from the land. Manganese nodules are precipitated from seawater.

Vocabulary

abyssal plain (p. 426)
continental margin (p. 422)
continental rise (p. 425)
continental shelf (p. 423)
continental slope (p. 424)
deep-sea trench (p. 426)
mid-ocean ridge (p. 426)
seamount (p. 428)
turbidity current (p. 424)

CHAPTER 16
Study Guide

Main Ideas

Summary statements can be used by students to review the major concepts of the chapter.

VOCABULARY PuzzleMaker ONLINE SCIENCE

For additional help with vocabulary, have students access the Vocabulary Puzzlemaker online.

earthgeu.com/ vocabulary puzzlemaker

0:00 Out of Time?

If time does not permit teaching the entire chapter, use the GeoDigest at the end of the unit as an overview.

Earth Science Online

Be sure to check the Earth Science Web Site for links to chapter material:
earthgeu.com

GLENCOE
Technology

Videotape/DVD
MindJogger Videoquizzes
Chapter 16: *The Marine Environment*
Have students work in groups as they play the videoquiz game to review key chapter concepts.

Resource Manager

Chapter Assessment, pp. 91–96
MindJogger Videoquizzes DVD/VHS
ExamView® Pro CD-ROM
Performance Assessment in Earth Science

NY Core Curriculum Standards

Page 432: St 4 KI 1.2f
Page 433: St 4 KI 2.1n, 2.1o, 2.1p, 2.1t, & 2.1u

Understanding Main Ideas

1. d
2. d
3. d
4. d
5. c
6. b
7. c
8. d
9. c
10. b
11. b
12. a
13. c
14. b
15. b

Applying Main Ideas

16. Incoming wave crests are bent towards the shore.

17. The longshore current is produced as water from incoming breakers spills over the longshore bar.

18. Sea level is currently rising. During the last ice age, sea level was 130 m lower than it is now because more water was frozen in the glaciers.

19. Oozes are sediments formed from the hard parts of marine organisms. Chalk is a sedimentary rock formed from oozes.

Understanding Main Ideas

1. Which coastal features are usually found in the bays along irregular coasts with headlands?
   a. sea stacks
   b. wave-cut cliffs
   c. wave-cut platforms
   d. beaches

2. Which of the following coastal landforms is NOT produced by longshore transport?
   a. a barrier island
   b. a sand spit
   c. a baymouth bar
   d. an estuary

3. What percentage of Earth's surface is below sea level?
   a. 10 percent
   b. 30 percent
   c. 50 percent
   d. 70 percent

4. What do the sediments of the abyssal plains mostly consist of?
   a. sand and gravel
   b. oozes
   c. seashells
   d. mud

5. Where are most deep-sea trenches located?
   a. in the Atlantic Ocean
   b. in the Indian Ocean
   c. in the Pacific Ocean
   d. in the Arctic Ocean

6. Which is the longest mountain system on Earth?
   a. the Hawaii-Emperor seamount chain
   b. the mid-ocean ridge system
   c. the Himalayas
   d. the Rocky Mountains

Use the map below to answer questions 7 and 8.

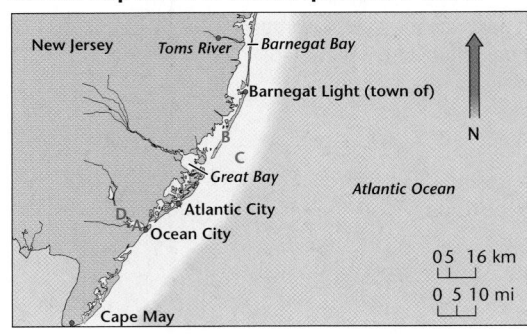

7. Which letter indicates the continental shelf?
   a. A
   b. B
   c. C
   d. D

8. Which feature is indicated by the letter A?
   a. a guyot
   b. a continental slope
   c. a continental rise
   d. an estuary

9. Under which circumstances do waves move faster?
   a. in shallow water
   b. over the longshore bar
   c. in deep water
   d. behind breakwaters

10. Which features are not caused by differential erosion?
    a. wave-cut platforms
    b. barrier islands
    c. sea stacks
    d. sea arches

11. Which marks the true edge of a continent?
    a. submarine canyon
    b. continental slope
    c. continental shelf
    d. abyssal plain

12. Which seafloor feature can be found along rifts in the mid-ocean ridges?
    a. hydrothermal vents
    b. manganese nodules
    c. deep sea trenches
    d. seamounts

Test-Taking Tip

PROCESS OF ELIMINATION On any multiple-choice test, there are two ways to find the correct answer to each question. You can either choose the right answer immediately or you can eliminate the answers that you know are wrong. It may be easier to find wrong answers than right ones. Find the ones you know are wrong and cross them out. You may be surprised at how few choices are left!

earthgeu.com/chapter_test

NY Core Curriculum Standards

Page 434: St 4 KI 2.1l, 2.1n, 2.1o, 2.1p, 2.1t, & 2.1u
Page 435: St 4 KI 2.1l, 2.1n, 2.1o, 2.1p, 2.1t, & 2.1u

13. Which represents the flattest part of Earth's surface?
- **a.** deep-sea trenches
- **c.** abyssal plains
- **b.** continental margins
- **d.** mid-ocean ridges

14. Which features of the seafloor are cut by turbidity currents?
- **a.** longshore bars
- **c.** abyssal plains
- **b.** submarine canyons
- **d.** baymouth bars

15. Which is not associated with mid-ocean ridges?
- **a.** black smokers
- **c.** fracture zones
- **b.** guyots
- **d.** hydrothermal vents

Applying Main Ideas

16. Describe the effect that wave refraction has on incoming wave crests that approach the shore of a straight coast at an angle.

17. Explain how incoming waves along a shoreline create the longshore current.

18. Is global sea level currently rising, falling, or staying the same? During the last ice age, was the sea level higher, lower, or the same as at present? Explain.

19. Explain the relationship between oozes and the sedimentary rock known as chalk.

20. Why are the continental shelves considered part of the continents when they are presently covered by the oceans?

Thinking Critically

21. Is it possible to have submergent coasts when global sea level is falling? Explain your reasoning.

22. Why are submergent coasts more irregular than emergent coasts?

23. Why do geologists think that seamounts are extinct volcanoes?

Standardized Test Practice

INTERPRETING SCIENTIFIC ILLUSTRATIONS
Use the illustration below to answer questions 1–5.

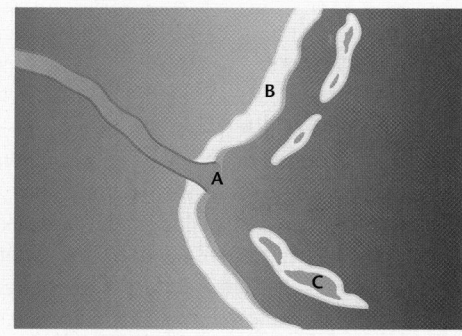

1. What shoreline feature is indicated by letter A?
- **a.** a barrier island
- **c.** an estuary
- **b.** a spit
- **d.** a bay

2. What type of water typically would be found in the area indicated by letter A?
- **a.** freshwater
- **c.** brackish water
- **b.** salt water
- **d.** very cold water

3. What shoreline feature is indicated by letter B?
- **a.** a tombolo
- **c.** a lagoon
- **b.** a spit
- **d.** a beach

4. What shoreline feature is indicated by letter C?
- **a.** a barrier island
- **c.** an estuary
- **b.** the longshore bar
- **d.** a beach

5. Which of these forms the area indicated by letter C?
- **a.** large storm waves
- **b.** gaps in the longshore bar
- **c.** the longshore current
- **d.** a rip current

20. The continental shelves are low parts of the continents that are presently covered by water. The true edges of continents are the places where the continental shelves break and fall rapidly through the continental slope to the ocean floor.

Thinking Critically

21. A coast can be submergent if the land is sinking faster than sea level is dropping.

22. Land surfaces have a more irregular topography than the seafloor. Flooding of an irregular topography produces an irregular shoreline.

23. The seafloor is dotted with thousands of solitary mountains that are not located near present sites of volcanic activity. Scientists hypothesize that these seamounts represent extinct volcanoes because no other forces on the seafloor could have formed these mountains.

EXAM*VIEW*® PRO

Use Exam*View*® Pro Testmaker CD-ROM to:

- Create **multiple versions** of tests.
- Create **modified** tests with one mouse click for struggling students.
- **Edit** existing questions and add your own questions.
- **Build** tests based on national curriculum standards.

Standardized Test Practice

1. c		**4.** a
2. c		**5.** c
3. d		

UNIT 4
GeoDigest

Prepare

Purpose

This GeoDigest can be used as an overview of the concepts of weather, climate, and physical characteristics of the oceans. If time is limited, you may wish to use this unit summary to teach these concepts in place of the chapters in Unit 4.

Key Concepts

Students are introduced to the relationship between solar energy and Earth's weather and climates. Students will learn how various aspects of weather are measured and how severe weather forms. They will also discover how weather differs from climate, and how Earth's oceans play an important role in both.

1 Focus

Section Focus

Logical-Mathematical
Before beginning the lesson, list weather- and climate-related terms on the chalkboard and ask students to determine whether each term is more closely related to weather or climate. Ask them to infer what effects oceans might have on weather and how oceanic changes might lead to changes in the atmosphere. Have students also infer what other changes might account for changes in Earth's weather and climates.

⏲ *Out of Time?*

If time does not permit teaching the entire unit, use this GeoDigest as an overview.

For a **preview** of Earth's atmosphere and oceans, study this GeoDigest before you read the chapters. After you have studied these chapters, you can use the GeoDigest to **review** the unit.

The Atmosphere and the Oceans

Atmosphere

Atmospheric Basics
Earth's atmosphere is made up primarily of nitrogen and oxygen. The atmosphere consists of several layers of different temperatures. The lowest layer, the troposphere, is the most important for weather. In this layer, temperatures generally decrease with altitude. Solar energy absorbed by Earth's surface is transferred through the atmosphere by radiation, conduction, and convection. The weight of air exerts a force called atmospheric pressure. In the troposphere, atmospheric pressure generally decreases with increasing altitude. Wind is the movement of air resulting from differences in pressure. Wind speed is affected by friction. Clouds form when warm, moist air is forced upward, expands, and cools. Clouds are classified according to the altitudes at which they form and according to their shapes. Precipitation such as rain, snow, sleet, and hail occurs when cloud droplets collide to form larger droplets. The water cycle is the continual movement of water between Earth's surface and the atmosphere through the processes of evaporation, condensation, and precipitation.

Meteorology

Weather Basics
Meteorology is the study of the atmosphere. Weather is the current state of the atmosphere. Climate is the average of weather patterns of an area over a long period of time. Differing amounts of solar radiation received by different parts of Earth lead to uneven heating; the motion of water and air balances this heat. The

Lightning

Coriolis effect deflects air and, with the heat imbalance, creates global wind systems. An air mass is a body of air that takes on the same characteristics as the land over which it formed. A front is the boundary between two air masses. High-pressure systems cause fair weather. Low-pressure systems cause precipitation and clouds.

Weather Analysis
Accuracy and density of data are important in forecasting weather. Balloon-borne instruments called radiosondes collect data about temperature, pressure, humidity, wind speed, and wind direction from high in the atmosphere. Weather radar locates precipitation, while Doppler radar measures wind speed. Weather satellites use visible light and infrared imagery to record weather. Symbols are used with station models to record weather for a given place and time. Isobars and isotherms are used on weather maps to connect lines of equal pressure and equal temperature, respectively.

436 UNIT 4

Multiple Learning Styles

Visual-Spatial Enrichment, p. 438

Linguistic Reteach, p. 439

Logical-Mathematical Section Focus, p. 436

GeoDigest

Most modern forecasts use digital forecasting methods. Analog forecasting compares current and past weather patterns.

The Nature of Storms

Severe Weather Abundant moisture in the lower atmosphere, a mechanism to lift the moisture, and unstable air are necessary for a thunderstorm to form. The way in which the air rises—whether by the unequal heating of Earth's surface or by the push of an advancing front—determines the type of storm that develops. The three stages of a thunderstorm are the cumulus stage, the mature stage, and the dissipation stage. Thunderstorm hazards include lightning, violent winds, hail, floods, and tornadoes. The Fujita tornado intensity scale classifies tornadoes. The Saffir-Simpson hurricane scale rates hurricane intensity.

Climate

Climatic Basics Climate is the long-term weather pattern of a region and includes annual variations of temperature, precipitation, and wind. Data covering at least 30 years are averaged on a monthly or yearly basis to determine a region's normals. Latitude, topography, bodies of water, moisture, wind patterns, ocean currents, and air masses are factors that influence climate. The tropical latitudes are always warm. The temperate zones have moderate climates. Polar zones are always cold.

Time lapse photo of a hurricane

Climatic Changes Climatic changes are indicated by fossils, ice cores, and other evidence. Ice ages, or periods of extensive glacial coverage, are examples of long-term climatic changes. Seasons are examples of short-term climatic changes. Climatic changes may be caused by changes in solar activity, the tilt of Earth's axis, Earth's orbit, and volcanic eruptions. Some human activities may cause climatic change. Global warming may be caused by a rise in atmospheric carbon dioxide. The burning of fossil fuels and deforestation may contribute to global warming, but scientists are still investigating its causes.

Vital Statistics

Deadliest Hurricanes of the Twentieth Century (Western Hemisphere)

Location	Year	Lives Lost
Hurricane Mitch, Central America	1998	11 000
Galveston, Texas	1900	8000
Hurricane Fifi, Honduras	1974	8000
Dominican Republic	1930	8000
Hurricane Flora, Haiti and Cuba	1963	7200

GeoDigest **437**

Assessment

Knowledge Assessment
Assessment, TWE, p. 439
GeoDigest Assessment, SE, p. 439

Resource Manager

Study Guide for Content Mastery,
pp. 103–104

2 Teach

Interpreting the Photo

The photo on this page is a time-lapse photograph of Hurricane Andrew as it approached the shoreline of the southeastern United States. Have students observe the changes in the hurricane over the time period captured in the photograph.

Concept Development

Most students are familiar with the concept that the weather in the tropics is warmer than that at the poles. Demonstrate Earth's tilt relative to the Sun and how it varies over the year, and ask students to infer how that tilt might have an effect on Earth's weather and climates. Help students realize that the Sun's rays are more direct at the equator (the tropics) than they are at the poles, and as a result, more solar energy is received near the equator than at the poles. The forces that correct this global imbalance of solar energy, and the Coriolis effect produced by Earth's rotation, are the underlying causes of most of Earth's weather.

Content Background

Wladimir Koeppen, a Russian-born German climatologist, introduced the climate classification method used today. Koeppen distinguished between different climatic divisions, or zones, based on the predominant natural vegetation they contain. His system includes five principle divisions: tropical, dry, subtropical, temperate, and polar climates. High-elevation climates are a form of polar climate because their vegetation types are similar.

GeoDigest

GLENCOE
Technology

CD-ROM
Earth's Climate
PictureShow
What Is Climate?
How Does Climate Change?
Oceans PictureShow
Journeys

Videodisc
The Infinite Voyage:
Living with Disaster
Chapter 4: *Save the Beaches:*
Soil Erosion from Barrier-Reef
Islands 6:00

Reinforcement

When powerful hurricane winds are blowing onshore, they pile up water near the shore. Because oceans become shallower near shores, the strong winds will not allow the water to return to the oceans. Thus, this piled-up water has nowhere to go but onto the shores. This effect is greatest where the onshore winds are strongest and is known as the hurricane storm surge.

Enrichment

Visual-Spatial Have students examine a map or globe that shows Earth's main oceanic currents. Then, have students examine a chart that shows average prevailing winds. Students should notice that in many areas, the ocean currents follow the same general direction as the prevailing winds. This is an example of how the atmosphere and oceans are dependent on one another.

British Virgin Islands

Physical Oceanography

The Oceans The first oceans probably formed more than 4 billion years ago. The water may have come from impacting comets or from volcanic eruptions which released water from Earth's interior. About 71 percent of Earth's surface is covered by oceans. Seawater is 96.5 percent water and 3.5 percent dissolved salts, which are added and removed from the ocean at the same rate. Seawater density changes with temperature and salinity. Water temperature decreases with depth, forming three layers. Ocean waves are generated by wind. Water in a wave moves in a circular motion but does not move forward. When waves reach shallow water they become breakers. Tides are caused by the gravitational attraction of the Sun and the Moon. Density currents are deep currents caused by differences in temperature and salinity. Upwelling occurs when winds push surface water aside and it is replaced by cold, deep water.

The Marine Environment

Shoreline and Seafloor Wave erosion and refraction shape shorelines. Beaches are made of loose sediment deposited along shorelines. Longshore currents move sediment along the shore, building barrier islands and other depositional features. Sea level has changed over time. The submerged part of a continent is the continental margin. The oceans cover thinner, oceanic crust. The flat part of the seafloor is the abyssal plains. Deep-sea trenches are found mainly in the Pacific Ocean. Mid-ocean ridges extend through all ocean basins. Active and inactive volcanoes are found on mid-ocean ridges and the seafloor. Deep-sea sediments are fine-grained and accumulate slowly. They may be derived from land or living organisms or may precipitate out of seawater.

FOCUS ON CAREERS

Mariculturist
Mariculturists farm marine organisms such as salmon, oysters, mussels, clams, scallops, shrimp, crayfish, prawns, and seaweed. Marine organisms may be sold as food or they may be raised for research purposes. Many mariculturists have a degree in fisheries. Some mariculturists receive advanced training in field techniques and biology of the species that they plan to raise.

Across the Curriculum

Physics Explain to students that one way in which weather, climate, and the oceans are related is by the physical laws that apply to them. The atmosphere is actually a solution composed of different elements and gases. Thus, the atmosphere follows roughly the same physical laws as liquid solutions do. This is important, because liquid motions are much easier to model, observe, and measure in a laboratory than the motions of gaseous solutions are. The motions of the atmosphere are used, in conjunction with observed data, as the basis for atmospheric forecast models, called numerical forecasts.

GeoDigest

ASSESSMENT

Understanding Main Ideas

1. What forms when warm, moist air is forced upward, expands, and cools?
- **a.** clouds
- **b.** density currents
- **c.** atmospheric pressure
- **d.** altitude

2. What happens to atmospheric pressure in the troposphere with increasing altitude?
- **a.** It gets thicker.
- **b.** It gets warmer.
- **c.** It increases.
- **d.** It decreases.

3. What do we call the average weather patterns for an area over a long period of time?
- **a.** the Coriolis effect
- **b.** meteorology
- **c.** climate
- **d.** pressure systems

4. What kind of imagery do satellites use to record weather from space?
- **a.** analog
- **b.** infrared
- **c.** symbolic
- **d.** directional

5. What helps shape the shoreline?
- **a.** waves
- **b.** reflection
- **c.** atmospheric pressure
- **d.** solar energy

6. Which scale is used to classify tornadoes?
- **a.** the Fujita intensity scale
- **b.** the Saffir-Simpson scale
- **c.** the Richter scale
- **d.** the heat index

7. How many years of weather are usually averaged together to determine a region's normals?
- **a.** 3
- **b.** 30
- **c.** 300
- **d.** 3000

8. Which of the following provides evidence of climatic change?
- **a.** deforestation
- **b.** fossil fuels
- **c.** tilt of Earth's orbit
- **d.** ice cores

9. What percentage of Earth is covered by water?
- **a.** 3.5 percent
- **b.** 7.1 percent
- **c.** 35 percent
- **d.** 71 percent

10. What is the flat part of the seafloor called?
- **a.** abyssal plain
- **b.** deep-sea trench
- **c.** continental margin
- **d.** mid-ocean ridge

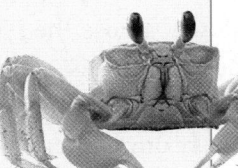

Fiddler crab

Thinking Critically

1. If a meteorologist wanted to know how fast a storm was moving, would he or she use traditional weather radar or Doppler radar? Why?

2. You watch a wave approach the shore. Is the water that breaks onshore the same water that you observed offshore? Explain your answer.

3. Suppose you collected a sample of deep-sea sediments. How could you determine the derivation of these sediments?

Foraminifera

GeoDigest **439**

3 Assess

Check for Understanding

Activity
Ask students to identify whether each of the following is more closely related to weather, climate, the oceans, or a combination. continental margin oceans El Niño combination thunderstorm weather season climate

Reteach

Linguistic Have students each write an essay in which they describe the formation of barrier islands as a result of deposition of sediments by longshore currents. **L2**

Assessment

Knowledge Have students research the organisms that live near hydrothermal vents. Have each student choose one organism and research its feeding habits, relationships to other organisms in the environment, and basic biology. Have students prepare reports on their organisms and present them to the class.

ASSESSMENT

Understanding Main Ideas

1. a
2. d
3. c
4. a
5. a
6. a
7. b
8. d
9. d
10. a

Thinking Critically

1. The meteorologist would use Doppler radar because it indicates wind speed.

2. No, because the water itself doesn't move.

3. by examining the sediments under a microscope and measuring the grains

NY Core Curriculum Standards

Page 436: St 4 2.1a, 2.1c, 2.1d, 2.1e, 2.1f, 2.1g, 2.1h, 2.2a, & 2.2b

Page 437: St 4 KI 2.2a, 2.2c, & 2.2d

Page 438: St 4 KI 1.1i, 1.2i, & 1.2g

Page 439: St 2 KI 1, St 4 KI 1.1i, 2.1c, 2.1g, 2.1h, & 2.2c

The Dynamic Earth

Unit Overview

Tectonism In Unit 5, students are introduced to the theory of plate tectonics and how interactions among tectonic plates are responsible for most of Earth's volcanoes, mountain ranges, and earthquakes. The relationships between tectonic plate movements and convection currents in Earth's mantle are also discussed.

Chapter Breakdown Chapter 17 provides a detailed discussion of one of the unifying theories of geology, plate tectonics, and the evidence that led to its proposal. Chapter 18 builds on this information by introducing the concept of igneous activity, both deep within Earth and at its surface. Chapter 19 provides a brief but concise overview of seismology. Chapter 20 is an introduction to the various processes that have led to the formation of Earth's mountain peaks and ranges.

⏲ Out of Time?

If time does not permit teaching the entire unit, use the GeoDigest at the end of the unit as an overview.

Unit 5

The Dynamic Earth

The mountain shown in the photograph is Mount Fuji, an inactive volcano in Japan that towers above the surrounding landscape. Its snow-covered peak rises more than 3700 m above sea level to overlook five, interconnected lakes. How did this magnificent structure form? Earth's outermost layers are broken into enormous slabs that shift slowly across the planet's surface. The movements, which occur at rates of only a few centimeters per year, cause mountains to form, volcanoes to erupt, and earthquakes to shake our planet. In this unit, you will explore how and why these slabs of rock move to change Earth.

Unit Contents

17 Plate Tectonics   **19** Earthquakes

18 Volcanic Activity   **20** Mountain Building

NATIONAL GEOGRAPHIC

Go to the National Geographic Expedition on page 886 to learn more about topics that are connected to this unit.

440

NATIONAL GEOGRAPHIC   eXpeditions!

One Hot Topic Some topics of Earth science deserve more attention than others because they're unusual, informative, or just plain interesting. The National Geographic Society has created visually exciting, multipage *Expeditions!* features that will inform, excite, and motivate your students.

Expeditions! features are relevant to the content of the student edition. Assign them as lead-ins to special research projects and in-depth studies for extra credit. Use them as a basis for colorful, visual displays and bulletin boards.

Mount Fuji, Japan

441

Introducing the Unit

Volcanoes—One Result of Tectonism The volcano shown in the photograph is Mount Fuji, a dormant volcano southwest of Tokyo, Japan, that rises 3776 m above sea level. Mount Fuji is the highest mountain in this Asian country. The mountain formed during the Tertiary Period, which began about 66 million years ago. The last eruption of Mount Fuji occurred in 1707. Five interconnecting lakes, which formed as the result of ancient volcanic activity, ring the base of the volcano. Ask students to name some other volcanoes with which they are familiar, such as Mount St. Helens, Mount Etna, Mauna Loa, and Mount Kilimanjaro.

Volcanoes and Earthquakes Have students speculate about what causes volcanoes to form and what makes them erupt. Also ask students what they think causes earthquakes. Tell students that they will discover the answers to these and other questions in this unit.

Tectonism and Landforms Keep a physiographic world map displayed in the classroom so that students can refer to it as you teach the unit. Take time to identify the relationships between the various tectonic processes discussed in the text and landforms on the map. Stress that many of the features of Earth's surface are the results of processes and forces at work deep within the planet.

Earth Science Online Note Internet addresses that you find useful in the space below for quick reference.

_____
_____
_____
_____
_____

For Internet tips, see Glencoe's **Using the Internet in the Science Classroom.**

441

Plate Tectonics

Refer to pages 8T–9T of the Teacher Guide for an explanation of the National Science Content Standards correlations.

Section	Objectives	National Science Content Standards	State/Local Standards
SECTION 17.1 **Drifting Continents** 🕐 1 session 📦 ½ block	1. **Describe** one piece of early evidence that led people to suggest that Earth's continents may have once been joined. 2. **Discuss** evidence of continental drift. 3. **Explain** why continental drift was not accepted when it was first proposed.	UCP.2, UCP.4; B.4; D.1, D.3; G.1, G.3	St 1 Science KI 1, St 4 KI 1.2j, 2.1l, 2.1n, & 2.1o, St 6 KI 3
SECTION 17.2 **Seafloor Spreading** 🕐 1½ sessions 📦 1 block	4. **Summarize** the evidence that led to the discovery of seafloor spreading. 5. **Explain** the significance of magnetic patterns on the seafloor. 6. **Explain** the process of seafloor spreading.	UCP.2; D.1, D.2; E.1, E.2	St 4 KI 2.1l, 2.1m, 2.1n, & 3.1a
SECTION 17.3 **Theory of Plate Tectonics** 🕐 1½ sessions 📦 1 block	7. **Explain** the theory of plate tectonics. 8. **Compare** and **contrast** the three types of plate boundaries and the features associated with each.	UCP.2; D.1, D.2, D.3	St 4 KI 2.1l, 2.1n, & 2.1o, St 6 KI 2 & 3
SECTION 17.4 **Cause of Plate Motions** 🕐 2 sessions 📦 1 block	9. **Explain** the process of convection. 10. **Summarize** how convection in the mantle is related to the movements of tectonic plates. 11. **Compare** and **contrast** the processes of ridge push and slab pull.	UCP.2; A.1, A.2; B.4; D.1, D.2, D.3; E.1, E.2; G.2, G.3	St 1 Math KI 1, 2, & 3, St 2 KI 1, St 4 KI 2.1j, 2.1k, 2.1l, 2.1m, 2.1n, 2.1o, & 2.2b, St 6 KI 2 & 3, St 7 KI 1

A complete Planning Guide is provided on pages 30T–32T.

🕐 The number of recommended single-period sessions

📦 The number of recommended blocks

Activity Materials

Discovery Lab *page 443*
ruler, pencil, paper

GeoLab *pages 464–465*
tracing paper, No. 2 pencil, colored pencils, ruler

MiniLab *page 456*
world map, pencil, ruler, scissors, paper

Demo *page 451*
bar magnet, iron filings, transparency, overhead projector

page 460
1-L beaker, water, candle, ring stand with ring, food coloring, ice cube, water

Need materials? Contact Science Kit at 1-800-828-7777 or at www.sciencekit.com on the Internet. For alternate materials, see the activity on the listed page.

Key to Teaching Strategies

L1 Level 1 activities should be appropriate for students with learning difficulties.

L2 Level 2 activities should be within the ability range of all students.

L3 Level 3 activities are designed for above-average students.

ELL ELL activities should be within the ability range of English-language learners.

COOP LEARN Cooperative Learning activities are designed for small-group work.

P These strategies represent student products that can be placed in a best-work portfolio.

📦 These strategies are useful in a block-scheduling format.

Chapter Organizer

Glencoe Exclusive!
Teacher Works™
All-In-One Planner and Resource Center

Activities/Features	Reproducible Masters	Transparencies
Discovery Lab: Coming Apart at the Seams? p. 443	**Study Guide for Content Mastery,** p. 105 L2	**Section Focus Transparency 49** L1 ELL
Using Math: Using Numbers, p. 452	**Study Guide for Content Mastery,** pp. 106–107 L2 **Laboratory Manual,** pp. 133–136 L2	**Section Focus Transparency 50** L1 ELL **Teaching Transparency 48** L2 ELL
MiniLab: Model Ocean–Basin Formation, p. 456 **Problem-Solving Lab:** Interpreting Scientific Illustrations, p. 458	**Study Guide for Content Mastery,** pp. 108–109 L2 **GeoLab and MiniLab Worksheets,** p. 67 L2 **Laboratory Manual,** pp. 129–132 L2	**Section Focus Transparency 51** L1 ELL **Teaching Transparencies 49 and 50** L2 ELL
Mapping GeoLab: Making a Paleomagnetic Map, pp. 464–465 **Science & Technology:** The Global Positioning System, p. 466	**Study Guide for Content Mastery,** p. 110 L2 **GeoLab and MiniLab Worksheets,** pp. 68–70 L2	**Section Focus Transparency 52** L1 ELL

✓ Assessment

Chapter Assessment, pp. 97–102
Performance Assessment in the Science Classroom (PASC)
MindJogger Videoquiz DVD/VHS
Performance Assessment in Earth Science
ExamView® Pro CD-ROM
5 Days to the Regents Exam

GLENCOE'S
ASSESSMENT
ADVANTAGE

Additional Resources

Guided Reading Audio Program ELL
Cooperative Learning in the Science Classroom COOP LEARN
Lesson Plans
Block Scheduling
earthgeu.com
NY Lesson Plans
NY Block Scheduling
Review Handbook for Regents Earth Science Exam

▢ NATIONAL GEOGRAPHIC

Teacher's Corner

Products Available from National Geographic Society
To order the following products, call the National Geographic Society at 1-800-368-2728:

Video
Our Dynamic Earth

Content Background

Continental Drift
Section 17.1

When Alfred Wegener proposed his hypothesis of continental drift, there were two competing hypotheses about Earth's ancient geography. Biologists and paleontologists had looked at the distribution of both living and fossil species and proposed that Earth's continents were once connected by land bridges that later sank beneath the oceans. Geophysicists, on the other hand, stated that isostatic principles made it impossible for land bridges to sink into oceanic crust. Both groups of scientists firmly believed in the theory of permanence, which stated that the ocean basins and continents were permanent, unchanging features. Wegener attempted to solve the controversy by reasoning that the biological data were solid evidence that couldn't be ignored. He also agreed with geophysicists that large land bridges were improbable. This reasoning led Wegener to propose that the biological and geophysical evidence would agree if Earth's continents had changed positions over time.

Earth's Magnetic Field
Section 17.2

Earth's magnetic field is caused primarily by internal sources. The most widely accepted hypothesis is that a geomagnetic dynamo is operating in the core, which is thought to be composed of the conducting elements Ni and Fe. It is hypothesized that fluid motion in the core generates an electric field, which, in turn, creates the magnetic field detected at the surface. The fluid motion is caused by thermal heating, which is caused by both radioactive decay and the release of heat that occurs when the liquid outer core freezes against the solid inner core. As convection currents rise, they twist as a result of the Coriolis effect to give rise to the magnetic field.

Subduction Zones
Section 17.3

Early evidence that subduction zones were sites of plate destruction included ocean-floor trenches, the relatively young age of ocean crust, and the existence of island arcs. Other evidence that supports the concept of subduction is the less-than-normal heat flow from the ocean

Multiple Learning Styles

Kinesthetic Modeling, p. 452, Enrichment, p. 462

Visual-Spatial Demo, pp. 443, 451, 460

Interpersonal Project, p. 445, Collaborative Learning, p. 446, Modeling, p. 446

Linguistic Using Scientific Terms, p. 452

Naturalist Environmental Connection, p. 446

GLENCOE *Technology*

The following multimedia resources are available from Glencoe.

Vocabulary Puzzlemaker

TeacherWorks™ CD-ROM

MindJogger Videoquizzes DVD/VHS

ExamView® Pro CD-ROM

Interactive Chalkboard CD-ROM

floor, which is thought to be the result of the lower temperature of the subducted slab. Also, the gravitational field over a subduction zone is slightly less than expected because there is extra crust where the two plates overlap. Deep-focus earthquakes, however, provide the strongest evidence of subduction. Earthquakes originating nearly 700 km beneath Earth's surface have been detected near deep-sea trenches. At this depth, the mantle is not rigid enough to break and therefore cause earthquakes. Thus, these deep-focus quakes must be originating in the still cool and solid portions of the subducted plate.

Tectonic Forces

Section 17.4

The forces involved in plate movements are thought to be concentrated along plate boundaries. There are four major forces acting on plates. The slab pull force acts on the subducting plate and is the result of the negative buoyancy of the cooler, sinking slab. The subduction suction force, which is also called the trench suction force, pulls on the edge of the overlying plate. These two subduction-zone forces create tension in the lithosphere. The ridge push force acts at ocean ridges and is the result of the hotter, less-dense material that makes up the ridge. This force causes lateral compression in the oceanic plates near the ridge. The mantle drag force is a force that acts on the base of a moving plate. Because of the low viscosity of the asthenosphere, this force is relatively small when compared to the other forces.

Identifying Misconceptions

Some students may think that continental movement is too slow to measure and that this movement has not actually been measured. Ask a few volunteers to draw a line that shows how much a continent might move in a year. Inform students that continents move at rates from about 1 to 10 cm/y. Have students calculate and measure the distance a continent would move in 50 years at a rate of 3 cm/y. 150 cm or 1.5 m

✔*Assessment*

Portfolio Assessment
GeoLab, TWE, pp. 464–465

Performance Assessment
Discovery Lab, SE, p. 443
MiniLab, SE, p. 456
MiniLab, TWE, p. 456
Assessment, TWE, p. 459
GeoLab, SE, pp. 464–465

Knowledge Assessment
Assessment, TWE, pp. 450, 454, 461, 463
Section Assessment, SE, pp. 447, 454, 459, 463
Problem-Solving Lab, TWE, p. 458
Chapter Assessment, SE, pp. 468–469

Skill Assessment
Discovery Lab, TWE, p. 443
Assessment, TWE, p. 447

Earth Science Online

Be sure to check the Earth Science Web Site for links to chapter material: earthgeu.com

GLENCOE'S ASSESSMENT ADVANTAGE

Plate Tectonics

Introducing the Chapter

Give small groups of students simple outlines of each continent. Allow students about a minute to connect the continents to form a single landmass. Compare and contrast the results. Have each group compare its landmass to Pangaea, the supercontinent that began to fragment about 200 M.Y.B.P., shown in **Figure 17-1.**

Interpreting the Photo

Iceland's Eldfell Volcano, shown here, began to form in January of 1973. Within five months, the volcano was 235 m high. Like the majority of volcanism on Earth, volcanism in Iceland is associated with tectonic plate boundaries. Iceland sits atop the Mid-Atlantic Ridge, a divergent plate boundary.

with Image Bank

PowerPoint® Presentations

This CD is an editable Microsoft® PowerPoint® presentation that includes:
- Section presentations
- Section checks
- Image bank
- Links to Earth Science Online
- All transparencies
- Animations
- Audio

What You'll Learn

- Why continental drift was not accepted when it was first proposed and what kinds of evidence led to its acceptance.

- How Earth's tectonic plates interact.

- What causes tectonic plates to move.

Why It's Important

Understanding the theory of plate tectonics is important because interactions between the enormous slabs of Earth's crust and rigid upper mantle result in the formation of many of Earth's surface features, including volcanoes and some mountain ranges. Many earthquakes are also caused by plate movements.

To learn more about plate tectonics, visit the Earth Science Web Site at **earthgeu.com**

442

Plate Tectonics

Eldfell Volcano, Iceland

Discovery Lab

Process Skills

measure in SI, predict, infer, communicate

L1   ELL

Procedure

Troubleshooting

- Because the map scale is much smaller than the distance being measured, students may have trouble accurately measuring the distance. By using the map scale to mark a series of distances along a piece of paper, students can make a map-scale ruler.

- If students have trouble with their conversions, remind them that there are 100 000 centimeters in a kilometer.

Answer to Question

The actual distance between San Francisco and Los Angeles is about 600 km. At a rate of 5 cm/y, it will take 12 million years (600 km × 100 000 cm/km ÷ 5 cm/y = 12 000 000 y) for the two cities to meet. Of course, neither city will exist after that amount of time has passed.

Discovery Lab

Coming Apart at the Seams?

Southwestern California is separated from the rest of the state by a system of cracks along which movement takes place. These cracks are called faults. One of these cracks, as you may already know, is the San Andreas Fault. Movement along this fault is sending southwestern California to the northwest in relation to the rest of North America at a rate of about 5 cm/y.

1. Use a metric ruler and the map scale to determine the actual distance between San Francisco and Los Angeles.

2. At the current rate of movement, when will these two cities be next-door neighbors?

Infer Infer what might be causing these large pieces of land to move. Describe your inference in your science journal.

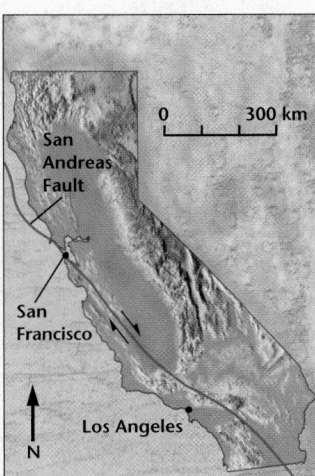

SECTION 17.1 *Drifting Continents*

OBJECTIVES

- **Describe** *one piece of early evidence that led people to suggest that Earth's continents may have once been joined.*

- **Discuss** *evidence of continental drift.*

- **Explain** *why continental drift was not accepted when it was first proposed.*

VOCABULARY

continental drift
Pangaea

With the exception of events such as earthquakes, volcanic eruptions, and landslides, Earth's surface appears to remain relatively unchanged during the course of an average human lifetime. On the geologic time scale, however, Earth's surface is changing at rates almost too great to imagine! South America is moving away from Africa at a rate of 2 to 3 cm/y. The volcanic islands that make up Hawaii are migrating toward the northwest at a rate of 8 to 9 cm/y. And Mt. Everest, Earth's highest point, is slowly rising. What could be causing such enormous pieces of land to move?

EARLY OBSERVATIONS

Some of the first people to consider the idea of moving landmasses were early mapmakers. In the late 1500s, Abraham Ortelius, a Dutch mapmaker, noticed the apparent fit of continents on either side of the Atlantic Ocean. He (incorrectly) proposed that North and South America had been separated from Europe and Africa by earthquakes and floods. Over the next 300 years, many people noticed and

17.1 *Drifting Continents* **443**

Infer

Students will infer various causes for this movement; those with prior knowledge may discuss mantle movements as being the driving force behind plate motions.

✓ Assessment

Skill Ask students to compute how far apart the cities will be after 15 million years. 750 km

Resource Manager

Section Focus Transparency 49 L1 ELL
Study Guide for Content Mastery, p. 105 L2

Section 17.1

1 Focus

Section Focus

Before presenting the lesson, display **Section Focus Transparency 49** on the overhead projector.
L1 ELL

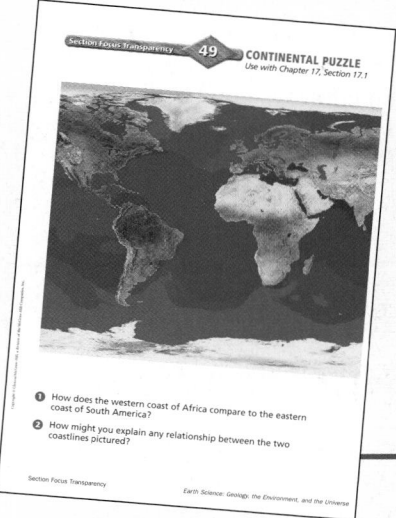

Chapter Themes

The following themes from the National Science Content Standards are covered in this chapter. Refer to page 8T of the Teacher Guide for an explanation of the correlations.
Systems, order, and organization (UCP.1); Evidence, models, and explanation (UCP.2); Change, constancy, and measurement (UCP.3)

0:00 **Out of Time?**

If time does not permit teaching the entire chapter, use the Chapter Summary on page 467 and the GeoDigest found at the end of the unit as an overview.

Content Background

Alfred Wegener's education and experience were primarily in meteorology, but he also studied geology, geophysics, and geography. In 1915, he published the first edition of *The Origins of Continents and Oceans*. The book was rewritten four times between 1915 and 1929; each edition contained new data and material in an effort to combat the criticism Wegener received about his hypothesis from the scientific community.

Identifying Misconceptions

Some students might think that the basic shapes of continental coastlines have remained unchanged since the breakup of Pangaea.

Uncover the Misconception
Have students make a sketch of what they think North America looked like when the Atlantic Ocean started to open, about 200 M.Y.B.P.

Demonstrate the Concept
If necessary, help students identify North America in the series of sketches in **Figure 17-1.** Have students compare their sketches with those in the figure.

Assess New Knowledge
Have students make a series of sketches of North America using **Figure 17-1.** Ask students to sequence the sketches from oldest to most recent and write three or four sentences that describe how the overall shape of the continent has changed over the past 200 million years.

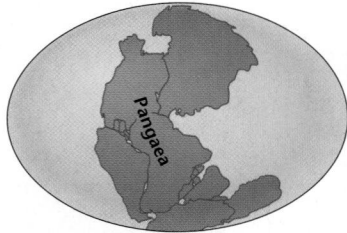

200 million years ago

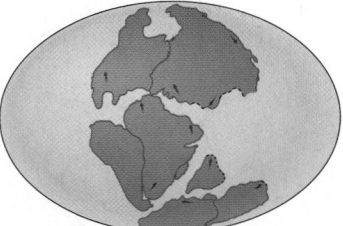

180 million years ago

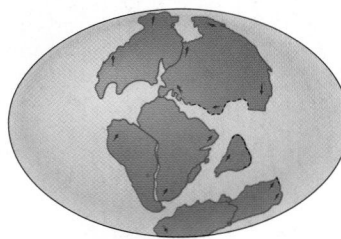

135 million years ago

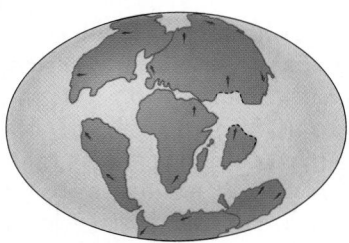

65 million years ago

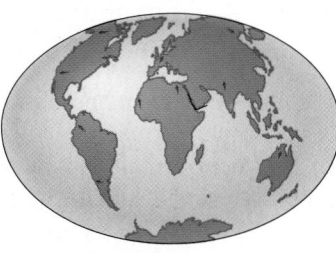

Present

commented on the matching coastlines. In the late 1800s, Eduard Suess, an Austrian geologist, hypothesized that the present southern continents had once been joined as a single landmass that he named Gondwanaland. The first time that the idea of moving continents was proposed as a serious scientific hypothesis, however, occurred in the early 1900s. In 1912, a German scientist named Alfred Wegener presented his ideas about continental movement to the scientific community.

CONTINENTAL DRIFT

Wegener called his hypothesis **continental drift,** which proposed that Earth's continents had once been joined as a single landmass. He called this supercontinent **Pangaea,** a Greek word that means "all the earth." Wegener proposed that Pangaea began to break apart about 200 million years ago. Since that time, he reasoned, the continents had continued to slowly move to their present positions, as shown in *Figure 17-1.*

Wegener was one of the first supporters of the concept of drifting continents to base his hypothesis on more than just the puzzlelike fit of continental coastlines on either side of the Atlantic Ocean. For Wegener, these gigantic puzzle pieces were just the beginning. He also collected and organized rock, fossil, and climatic data to support his hypothesis.

Evidence from Rock Formations Wegener reasoned that when Pangaea began to break apart, large geologic structures, such as mountain ranges, would have fractured as the continents separated. Using this reasoning, Wegener hypothesized that there should be areas of similar rock types on opposite sides of the Atlantic Ocean. He observed that some of the rocks of the Appalachian Mountains in the United States shared similar features with rocks in Greenland and Europe. These similar groups of rocks, all older than 200 million years, supported Wegener's idea that the continents had once been joined. What other groups of rocks shown in *Figure 17-2* suggest the existence of a single landmass in the past?

Figure 17-1 Pangaea was an ancient landmass that was made up of Earth's continents. Pangaea began to break apart about 200 million years ago.

Interpreting the Illustration

Figure 17-1 Have students determine which continental piece has moved the farthest and which has moved the least. Asia has moved the farthest; Antarctica the least.

Evidence from Fossils Wegener also gathered evidence of the existence of Pangaea from fossils. Similar fossils of several different animals and plants that once lived on land had been found on widely separated continents, as shown in *Figure 17-2.* Wegener reasoned that the land-dwelling animals, such as *Kannemeyerid* and *Labyrinthodont,* could not have swum the great distances that now exist between continents. Wegener also argued that because fossils of *Mesosaurus,* an aquatic reptile, had been found only in freshwater rocks, it was unlikely that this species could have crossed the oceans. The ages of these different fossils also predated Wegener's time frame for the breakup of Pangaea, which gave him the confidence he needed to move forward with his hypothesis.

Another fossil that Wegener used to support his hypothesis of continental drift was *Glossopteris,* a seed fern that resembled low shrubs. Fossils of this plant had been found on many continents, which today have very different climates. Because he had a strong background in meteorology, Wegener was able to reason that the area separating these fossil finds was too large to have had a single climate. This led him to conclude that the rocks containing these fossil ferns had once been joined. Wegener also argued that because *Glossopteris* grew in temperate climates, the places where these fossils had been found were once closer to the equator.

Figure 17-2 Alfred Wegener used fossils and the similarity of rock formations on opposite sides of the Atlantic Ocean as evidence that Earth's continents were once joined.

Some Evidence of Continental Drift

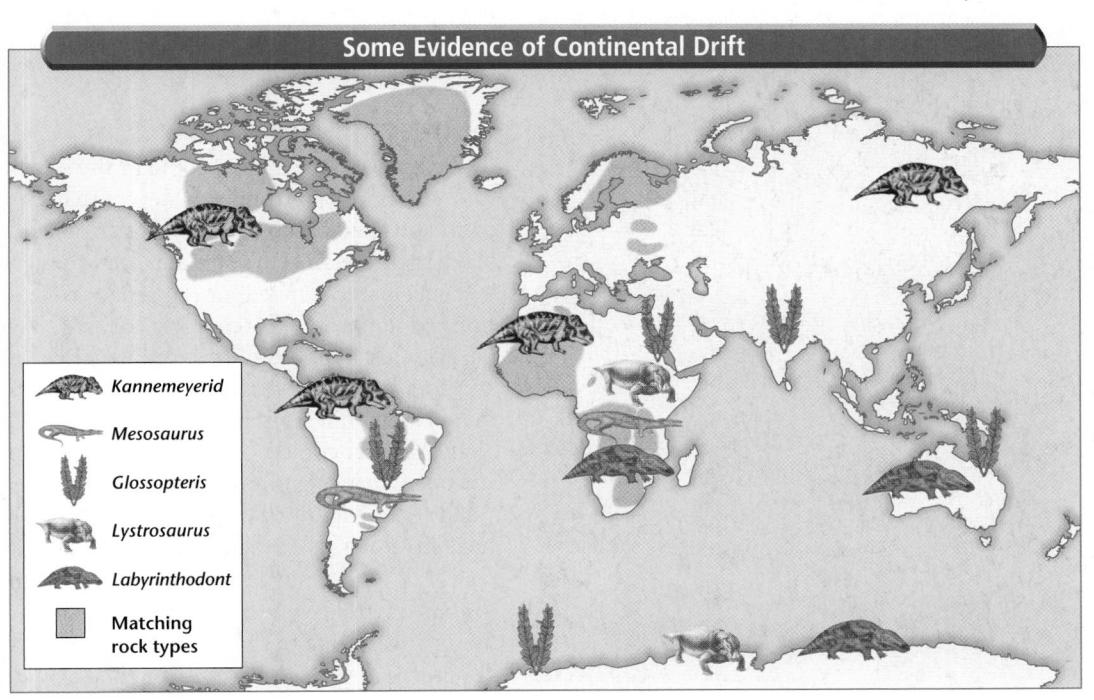

Kannemeyerid

Mesosaurus

Glossopteris

Lystrosaurus

Labyrinthodont

Matching rock types

17.1 *Drifting Continents* **445**

In-Text Question

Page 444 What other groups of rocks shown in **Figure 17-2** suggest the existence of a single landmass in the past? Groups of rocks in South America and Africa are evidence that Earth's continents were once joined as a single landmass.

Project

Interpersonal Have pairs of students do research to find out whether there are any 200-million-year-old fossils in your state. Challenge students to also find out about the climate that existed in your part of the country during this time. Have student pairs each prepare a visual display of their findings. **L2** **COOP LEARN**

Interpreting the Illustration

Figure 17-2 Have students study this map as well as the maps shown in **Figure 17-1.** Pose this question: Why do you think there are no *Glossopteris* fossils in North America or Europe? It was probably too cold for this fern to have existed in these areas.

Across the Curriculum

Biology *Glossopteris* fossils were used by Wegener to support his hypothesis of continental drift. Have students find out when ferns first appeared on Earth. Challenge students to describe how these ancient ferns differed from their modern-day relatives. Ask a volunteer to explain the life cycle of a fern to the rest of the class.

Differentiated Instruction

Learning Disabled Enlarge and copy **Figure 17-2** onto stiff paper. Have students cut out each continent, or assist them with this task, and guide them to reconstruct Pangaea using the rock and fossil evidence shown on the map.

NY Core Curriculum Standards

Page 442: St 4 KI 2.1l & 2.1o
Page 443: St 1 Science KI 1, St 4 KI 2.1l, St 6 KI 3
Page 444: St 4 KI 1.2j, 2.1l, & 2.1n
Page 445: St 4 KI 1.2j

Interpersonal Ask students how they would feel if their peers rejected their ideas and work. Have students role-play a scenario in which Wegener is trying to convince other scientists of the validity of his ideas.
COOP LEARN

Modeling

Interpersonal Wegener proposed that Earth's continents were plowing through the seafloor. Physicists, however, argued that the crust was too brittle to withstand this type of motion. To demonstrate why the crust is considered brittle on a geologic scale, have students draw a scale cross section of a piece of crust 6000 km long and 20 km thick. This will demonstrate how thin the crust actually is when compared to other dimensions of Earth.

Environmental Connection

Naturalist Have interested students find out how burning coal pollutes the air and contributes to global warming.

Ancient Climatic Evidence Recall from Chapter 6 that sedimentary rocks provide clues to past environments and climates. By studying various sedimentary rocks, Wegener found evidence of vast climatic changes on some continents. Coal deposits, for example, had been found in Antarctica. Coal forms from dead swamp plants. Swamps are areas of wet, spongy land often covered by water. The existence of coal beds in Antarctica, then, indicated that this frozen land once had a temperate, rainy climate. Wegener used this evidence to conclude that Antarctica must have been closer to the equator sometime in the geologic past.

Another piece of climatic evidence came from glacial deposits found in Africa, India, Australia, and South America. The presence of these 290-million-year-old deposits, some of which are shown in *Figure 17-3,* suggested to Wegener that these areas had once been covered by thick ice caps. Because continental glaciers do not presently exist on these continents, Wegener proposed that they once were located near the south pole, as shown in *Figure 17-4,* before Pangaea began to fracture. Furthermore, because the south pole is not presently located near Africa or India, Wegener suggested two possibilities to explain the glacial deposits. The first was that the pole had shifted its position, and the second was that these landmasses had drifted away from the pole. Wegener argued that it was more likely that the landmasses drifted away from the south pole than that Earth changed its axis of rotation.

Figure 17-3 These glacial deposits in Africa helped support Wegener's hypothesis of continental drift.

A REJECTED HYPOTHESIS

In the early 1900s, many people in the scientific community strongly believed that the continents and ocean basins were permanent, fixed features of Earth's surface. Even though Wegener had compiled an impressive collection of data, most scientists of his day rejected his hypothesis of continental drift. Wegener's hypothesis had two major flaws that prevented it from being widely accepted. First, Wegener could not satisfactorily explain what was causing the continents to move. What force could be strong enough to move such large masses of rock over such great distances? Wegener suggested that the rotation of Earth could be responsible. Physicists, though, were able to show that this force was not great enough to move continents.

Across the Curriculum

Chemistry Have students find out about the physical and chemical changes that result in the formation of coal. Suggest to students that they display their findings as posters. P

Scientists also had questions about how the continents were moving. Wegener had proposed that the continents were plowing through a stationary ocean floor. His peers, however, argued that continents could not push through the ocean floor without fracturing, because crustal rock is too brittle. Also, because no evidence for such fracturing had been found, geologists argued that the continents could not be moving as Wegener had proposed. These two unanswered questions—what forces could move continents and how continents could move without shattering—were the main reasons that the hypothesis of continental drift was rejected when it was first proposed.

Alfred Wegener did not give up when his hypothesis was not accepted by most other scientists of his time. He continued to search for evidence to support his hypothesis of continental drift. Wegener died in 1930 on an expedition to Greenland, but the controversy over his hypothesis remained alive for several decades after his death. It wasn't until the early 1960s that new evidence revealed a process that could explain why and how the continents move. This evidence, which was found on the seafloor, will be discussed in the next section.

Figure 17-4 Glacial deposits nearly 300 million years old on several continents led Wegener to propose that these landmasses may have once been joined and covered with ice. The extent of the ice is shown by the dashed line.

SECTION ASSESSMENT

1. What early evidence suggested that Earth's continents might be moving?

2. How do ancient glacial deposits in Africa, India, Australia, and South America support the idea of continental drift?

3. How did Alfred Wegener use rock and fossil evidence to support his hypothesis?

4. Why was Wegener's hypothesis rejected by most scientists of the early 1900s?

5. **Thinking Critically** Oil deposits approximately 200 million years old have been discovered in Brazil. Where might geologists find oil deposits of a similar age? Explain.

SKILL REVIEW

6. **Comparing and Contrasting** Compare and contrast the different types of evidence used by Wegener to support his idea of continental drift. Which type do you think provides the strongest support for his hypothesis? Why? For more help, refer to the *Skill Handbook*.

Check for Understanding
Discussion
A hypothesis that competed with Wegener's idea of continental drift was that Earth's continents were connected by land bridges. Ask students the following question: Which evidence used by Wegener is consistent with the possibility of land bridges and which is not? The biological data, the fossils, support the possibility of land bridges. Climatic and rock data do not support the hypothesis that there were land bridges.

Reteach
Have students refer to **Figures 17-2** and **17-4** as you summarize the types of evidence—rock, fossil, and climatic—used by Wegener to support his hypothesis of continental drift.

✓Assessment

Skill Have students each make a table that summarizes the different types of evidence that Wegener used to support his hypothesis of continental drift.

SECTION ASSESSMENT

1. The matching coastlines of continents on either side of the Atlantic Ocean suggested that Earth's landmasses might have once been joined and have moved to their present positions.

2. The deposits indicate that these continents were once located much closer to the south pole.

3. Rocks with similar features on continents now separated by oceans were used to support the hypothesis of continental drift. Fossils of land animals that could not have crossed the oceans and plant fossils indicative of climates different from those of today also provided evidence that Earth's continents were once joined.

4. Wegener could not explain what forces could cause a continent to move without shattering.

5. Correlative deposits are found in Africa. Such deposits formed under the same conditions when the continents were still joined.

6. Evidence for continental drift includes coastline shapes, matching rock formations, similar fossils on separate continents, and climatic data. Students' choices for the strongest evidence will vary. Accept any answer that can be logically justified.

SECTION 17.2
Seafloor Spreading

Prepare

Section Background

For section content background, refer to **Earth's Magnetic Field** on page 442C.

Preplanning

Refer to the Chapter Organizer on pages 442A–B.

1 Focus

Section Focus

Before presenting the lesson, display **Section Focus Transparency 50** on the overhead projector. **L1 ELL**

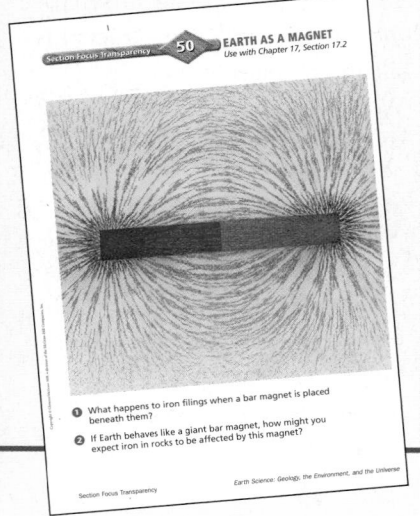

Tying to Previous Knowledge

Review ocean-floor topography from Chapter 15. Explain that features such as trenches, seamounts, and ocean ridges all provide evidence of seafloor spreading.

OBJECTIVES

- **Summarize** *the evidence that led to the discovery of seafloor spreading.*
- **Explain** *the significance of magnetic patterns on the seafloor.*
- **Explain** *the process of seafloor spreading.*

VOCABULARY

magnetometer
paleomagnetism
magnetic reversal
isochron
seafloor spreading

Until the mid-1900s, most people, including many scientists, thought that the ocean floor, unlike the continents, was essentially flat. Many people also had the misconceptions that oceanic crust was unchanging and was much older than continental crust. Advances in technology during the 1940s and 1950s, however, proved all of these widely accepted ideas to be wrong.

HELP FROM TECHNOLOGY

One advance that allowed scientists to study the ocean floor in great detail was the development of echo-sounding methods. One type of echo sounding is sonar, which uses sound waves to measure water depth. As shown in *Figure 17-5*, regular pulses of sound are sent out from a device aboard a ship. The sound waves travel through the water and are reflected from the ocean floor. The time it takes for these waves to travel from the device and back to a receiver can be used to calculate the distance from the sonar device to the ocean floor. Look again at *Figure 17-5.* How would the travel times of waves differ at various points along this hypothetical ocean bottom?

Another technological advance that was used to study the ocean floor was the magnetometer. A **magnetometer** is a device that can detect small changes in magnetic fields. Magnetometers towed by ships record the magnetic field strength in the rocks that make up the ocean floor. The measurements are then used to construct magnetic maps of the seafloor. You'll learn more about magnetism and how it supports the hypothesis of continental drift later in this section.

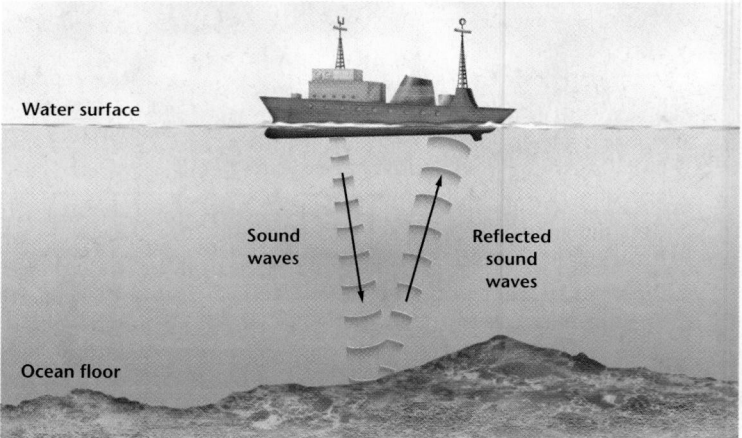

Figure 17-5 Sonar is an echo-sounding technique that has been used to map ocean-floor topography. The travel times of the sound waves can be used to calculate the distance to the ocean floor.

448 CHAPTER 17 *Plate Tectonics*

In-Text Question

Page 448 How would the travel times of waves differ at various points along this hypothetical ocean bottom? Travel times to topographic lows in the seafloor would be longer than travel times to topographic highs.

Resource Manager

Section Focus Transparency 50 **L1** **ELL**
Study Guide for Content Mastery, pp. 106–107 **L2**

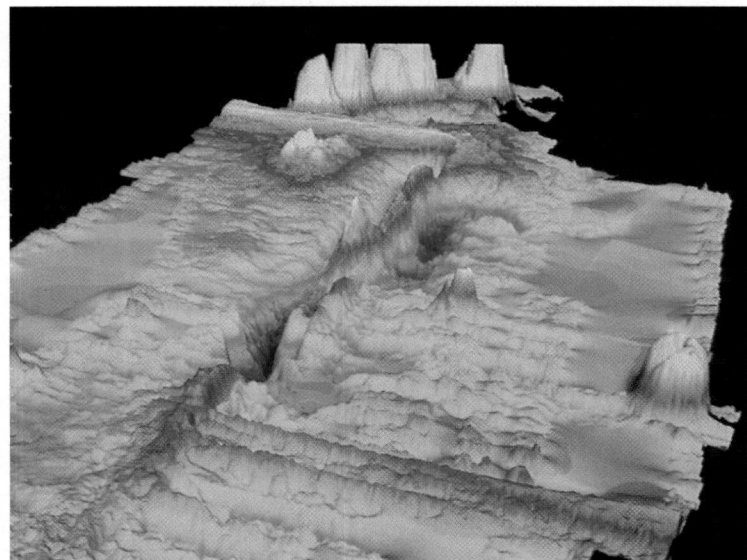

OCEAN FLOOR TOPOGRAPHY

The maps made from the data collected by sonar and magnetometers surprised many scientists. Vast, underwater mountain chains called ocean ridges were discovered. These features of the ocean floor form the longest continuous mountain range on Earth. When they were first discovered, these ridges generated much discussion simply because of their size. Later, scientists discovered that earthquakes and volcanism are common along the ridges. A false-color photo of part of the East Pacific Rise, which is a ridge in the Pacific Ocean, is shown in *Figure 17-6.*

Maps generated with sonar data also revealed that these underwater mountain chains had counterparts called deep-sea trenches. Recall from Chapter 16 that a deep-sea trench is a narrow, elongated depression in the seafloor with very steep sides. Trenches can be thousand of kilometers long and are extremely deep. The deepest trench is in the Pacific Ocean. This chasm, called the Mariana Trench, is just over 11 km deep!

These two topographic features of the ocean floor—deep-sea trenches and ocean ridges—puzzled geologists for over a decade after their discovery. What could have formed an underwater mountain range that extended around Earth? What is the source of the volcanism that is associated with these mountains? What kinds of forces could depress Earth's crust far enough to create trenches nearly six times as deep as the Grand Canyon? You'll find out the answers to these questions later in this chapter.

Across the Curriculum

Math Have students imagine that they are on the seafloor near the Mariana Trench and one student drops a rock into the trench. Ask students to compute how long it will take for the rock to reach the bottom of the trench if the rock falls through water at 3 m/s. about an hour Some submersibles can descend at a rate of 15 m/min. Have students calculate how long it would take such a submersible to reach the bottom of the trench.

about 12 h

2 Teach

Content Background

Strangely enough, the concepts of seafloor spreading and plate tectonics are connected to WWII submarine warfare. Unfortunately, the demands of war often promote periods of rapid technological advance. Fortunately, scientists are often quick to utilize military technology for more peaceful projects. During WWII, sonar technology was improved because submarine pilots needed detailed maps and a way to navigate under water.

Magnetometers that could be towed behind ships were originally developed to detect the magnetic fields generated by the steel hulls of submarines. Scientists modified these magnetometers to measure the magnetic field strength of ocean-floor rocks. The magnetic patterns that were discovered provided key support for the theory of seafloor spreading.

Interpreting the Illustration

Figure 17-6 Inform students that this is a false-color, three-dimensional image of a part of the East Pacific Rise, an ocean ridge located west of Central America. The rise itself is shown in red. The Clipperton Transform Fault, which offsets the ridge by about 85 km, is shown in blue. Tell students that they will learn about transform faults in Section 17.3.

NY Core Curriculum Standards

Page 448: St 4 KI 2.1l
Page 449: St 4 KI 2.1n

OCEAN ROCKS AND SEDIMENTS

In addition to making maps, scientists collected samples of deep-sea sediments and the underlying crust to try to better understand Earth's ocean floors. Analysis of the rocks and sediments produced two important discoveries. First, the ages of the rocks that make up the seafloor vary in different places, and these variations change in a predictable way. Rock samples taken from areas near ocean ridges were younger than samples taken from areas near deep-sea trenches. Detailed analysis showed that the age of oceanic crust consistently increases with distance from a ridge, shown in *Figure 17-7.* Scientists also discovered from the rock samples that the oldest part of the seafloor is geologically young at about 180 million years old. Why are ocean-floor rocks so young compared to continental rocks, some of which are 3.8 billion years old? Geologists knew that oceans had existed for more than 180 million years. Where, then, they wondered, is the ocean crust from those earlier oceans?

The second discovery involved the sediments that are deposited on the ocean floor. Measurements showed that the thickness of ocean-floor sediment is, in general, much less than expected. Ocean-floor sediments are typically a few hundred meters thick. Large areas of continents, on the other hand, are blanketed with sedimentary rocks from a few kilometers to about 20 kilometers thick. Scientists knew that erosion and deposition were at work in Earth's oceans. Why, then, they asked, aren't seafloor sediments as thick as their continental counterparts? Could the relatively thin blanket of ocean sediments be a result of the age of the ocean crust? Careful observations of ocean-floor sediments also revealed that the thickness of the sediments increases with distance from an ocean ridge, as shown in *Figure 17-7.*

Topic: Ocean Floor Depths
To learn more about Earth's ocean floors, visit the Earth Science Web Site at earthgeu.com

Activity: Research the deepest places in the ocean. Draw a graph comparing the five deepest places on the ocean floor.

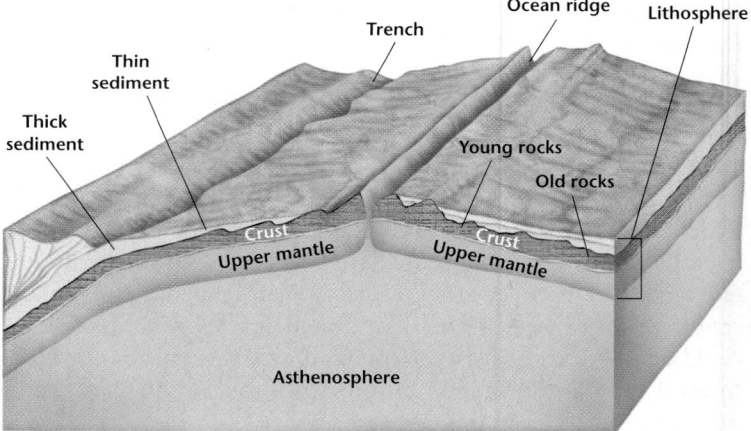

Figure 17-7 The ages of ocean crust and the thicknesses of ocean-floor sediments increase with distance from an ocean ridge.

MAGNETISM

Prior to their studies of the seafloor, scientists knew that rocks containing iron-bearing minerals provided a record of Earth's magnetic field. The study of this magnetic record is called **paleomagnetism.** Basalt, because it is rich in iron-bearing minerals, provides an accurate record of ancient magnetism. As basaltic lava cools, the iron-bearing minerals become oriented parallel to Earth's magnetic field. These minerals are, in effect, compass needles. When the lava hardens, the magnetic orientation is locked in place and provides a record of Earth's magnetic field at that time.

The Geomagnetic Time Scale Studies of continental basalt flows in the early 1960s revealed a pattern of magnetic reversals over geologic time. A **magnetic reversal** is a change in Earth's magnetic field. A magnetic field that has the same orientation as Earth's present field is said to have normal polarity. A magnetic field that is opposite to the present field has reversed polarity. The data gathered from continental basalt flows allowed scientists to construct the geomagnetic time scale, shown in *Figure 17-8.*

To find out how the continental basalt-flow data compared with the basalts that make up the ocean floor, scientists proposed that magnetometers be towed behind ships to measure the magnetic field of the ocean floor. A very interesting pattern emerged. In some places, the magnetic field strength was greater than normal. In other places, the field strength was lower than normal. In places where the magnetic readings of the ocean floor matched Earth's present field, the two fields combined. This produced a stronger-than-normal reading (+). In places where the magnetic data were reversed in relation to Earth's present magnetic field, the two fields partially cancelled one another. In these cases, a lower-than-normal reading (−) was recorded, as shown in *Figure 17-9.*

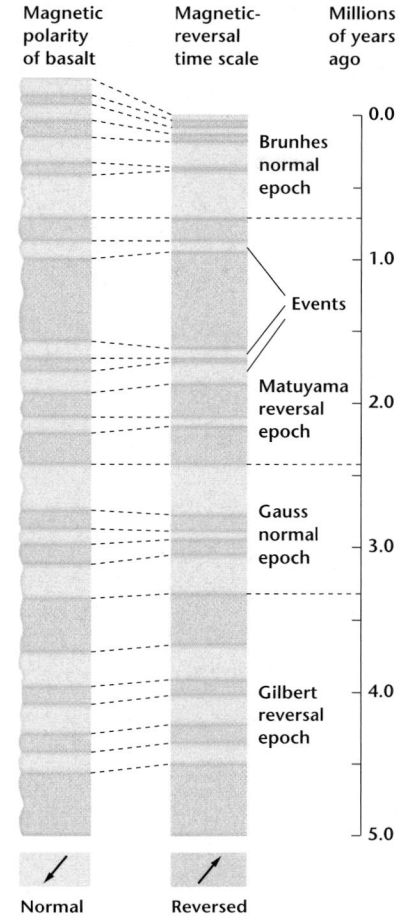

Figure 17-8 Continental basalt flows were used to construct the geomagnetic time scale. Long term changes in Earth's magnetic field are called epochs. Short term changes are called events.

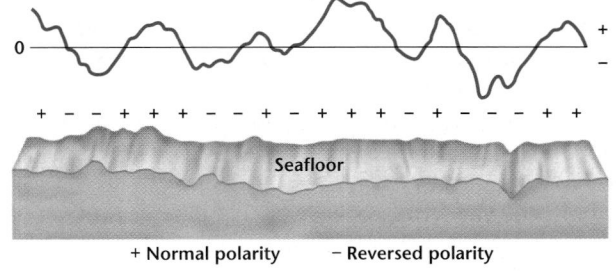

Figure 17-9 A stronger-than-normal magnetic reading (+) indicates a normal field. A weaker-than-usual reading (−) indicates a field with reversed polarity.

Differentiated Instruction

Gifted Challenge students to find out the answers to the following questions. Is the location of Earth's north magnetic pole in the same place as the geographic north pole? How does this affect the accuracy of compasses near the north pole? Have students draw a diagram to show the orientation of a compass arrow when the compass is at the geographic north pole. **L3**

Demo

Visual-Spatial Use a bar magnet, iron filings, and an overhead projector and transparency to model the field lines set up by Earth's magnetic field. **CAUTION:** *Wear safety goggles during this entire demonstration and have students do the same.* Place the magnet under the transparency. Carefully sprinkle the filings onto the transparency. Have students observe and describe the lines of magnetic force. Explain that the lines of force of Earth's magnetic field are similar to the lines around the magnet. Point out that the filings cluster around the poles of the magnet, where the magnetic field is strongest. Once you have completed this demonstration, carefully return the filings to their original container and thoroughly wash your hands.

Using Scientific Terms

Have students use a dictionary to find the meaning of the word part *paleo-*. Ask students to use the meaning of this word part to define the term *paleomagnetism* in their own words.

Interpreting the Illustration

Figure 17-8 Have students use the figure to answer the following questions. What is the current epoch? the Brunhes normal epoch How many times did Earth's magnetic field change polarity during the Gilbert reversal epoch? four times

NY Core Curriculum Standards

Page 450: St 4 KI 1.2j & 2.1n
Page 451: St 4 KI 2.1m & 3.1a

Using Math

Using Numbers The average time between reversals is a little over 1 million years. Over the past 4.5 million years, Earth's magnetic field has had reversed polarity for about 3 million years and normal polarity for just over 2 million years. Thus, Earth's magnetic field has been reversed about 66 percent of the time and normal about 44 percent of the time over the past 4.5 million years.

Using Scientific Terms

Linguistic Have students each make a list of other scientific terms that contain the word part *iso-*. Terms might include *isobar, isopach, isotope,* and *isostatic,* among others. Ask students to write a brief definition next to each term.

Modeling

Kinesthetic Have students use long paper strips, books, two desks, and the following procedure to model seafloor spreading and the magnetic patterns of ocean-floor rocks. Push two desks together and partially pull two paper strips up between the desks. Lay the exposed portions of the strips on the desks and secure them with the books. Slide the books apart so that they pull the paper up between the desks and out onto the surface. Stop every few centimeters and color a band on both sides of the central gap. The colored bands represent the magnetic pattern of ocean-floor rocks. The bands closest to the "ridge axis" are the youngest rocks. **L1** **ELL**

Figure 17-10 Reversals in the polarity of Earth's magnetic field are recorded in the rocks that make up the ocean floor. *What is the polarity of the rocks closest to the ridge?*

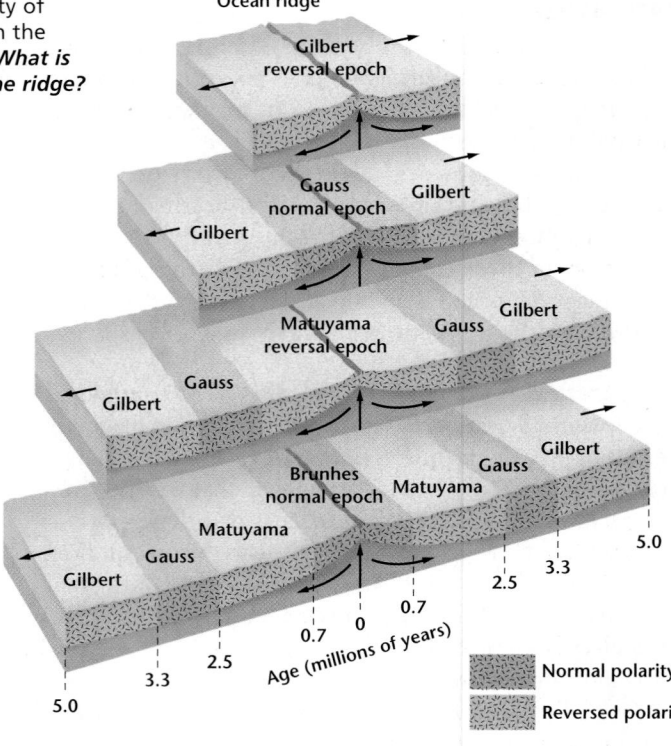

Using Math

Using Numbers Refer to *Figure 17-8.* What is the average time interval between reversals? Over the last 4.5 million years, how many years has the field experienced reversed polarity? Normal polarity? What is the percentage of the total time spent in each orientation?

Magnetic Symmetry As more data were collected, scientists noticed that the positive and negative areas formed a series of stripes that were parallel to ocean ridges. Compare the magnetic pattern on opposite sides of the ocean ridge shown in *Figure 17-10.* How would you describe this pattern? The magnetic pattern on one side of the ridge is a mirror image of the pattern on the other side of the ridge.

As scientists sought to explain these parallel stripes, they made another important discovery. The magnetic data collected from the ocean floor, shown in *Figure 17-10,* matched the pattern of magnetic reversals that had been found in basalt flows on land, which is shown in *Figure 17-8.* By matching the patterns on the seafloor with the known pattern of reversals on land, scientists were able to determine the age of the ocean floor from a magnetic recording. This method enabled scientists to quickly create isochron maps of the ocean floor. An **isochron** is a line on a map that connects points that have the same age. In the isochron map shown in *Figure 17-11,* note that relatively young ocean-floor crust is near ocean ridges, while older ocean crust is found along deep-sea trenches. You will generate and analyze an isochron map of a part of the seafloor in the *Mapping GeoLab* at the end of this chapter.

452 CHAPTER 17 *Plate Tectonics*

Resource Manager

Laboratory Manual, pp. 133–136 **L2**

Interpreting the Illustration

Figure 17-10 If necessary, have students refer to **Figure 17-8** to help them answer the question posed in the figure caption. What is the polarity of the rocks closest to the ridge? Rocks closest to the ridge have normal polarity.

SEAFLOOR SPREADING

Once scientists had compiled all the topographic, sedimentary, age, and magnetic data from the seafloor, an American scientist named Harry Hess proposed a theory that could explain their observations. This theory, called **seafloor spreading,** states that new ocean crust is formed at ocean ridges and destroyed at deep-sea trenches. What actually happens during seafloor spreading? Magma, because it is hotter and less dense than surrounding mantle material, is forced toward the crust along an ocean ridge and fills the gap that is created as shown in *Figure 17-12A,* on page 454. When the magma hardens, a small amount of new ocean floor is added to Earth's surface, as illustrated in *Figure 17-12B.* As spreading along a ridge continues, more magma is forced upward and hardens. Each cycle of spreading and the intrusion of magma results in the formation of another small section of ocean floor, which slowly moves away from the ridge, as shown in *Figure 17-12C.*

Figure 17-11 Each colored band on this isochron map of the ocean floor represents the age of that strip of the crust. *What pattern do you observe?*

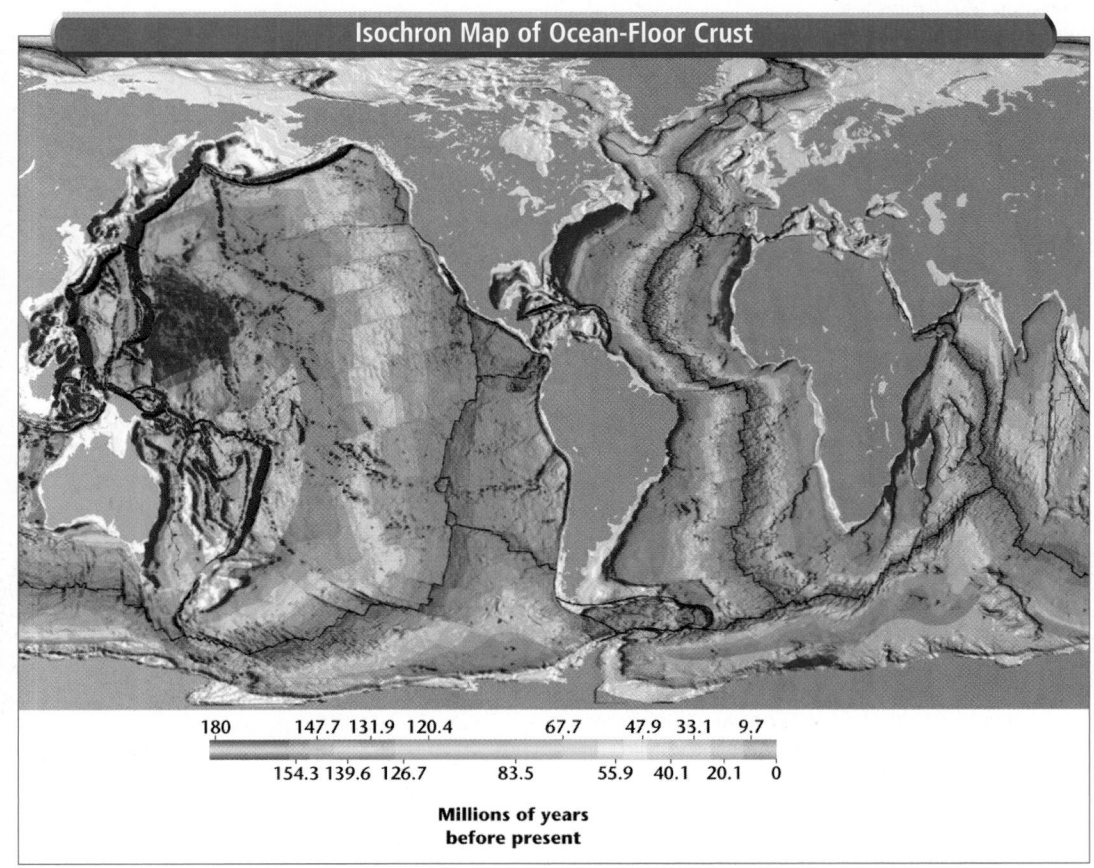

Isochron Map of Ocean-Floor Crust

| 180 | 147.7 | 131.9 | 120.4 | | 67.7 | | 47.9 | 33.1 | 9.7 | |
| 154.3 | 139.6 | 126.7 | | 83.5 | | 55.9 | | 40.1 | 20.1 | 0 |

Millions of years before present

Interpreting the Illustration

Figure 17-11 Have students use this map to answer the following questions. Where is the oldest portion of ocean crust on this map? in the northwestern Pacific Ocean Which ocean basin formed most recently? the Red Sea Why is the seafloor relatively young west of South America even though it is near the Peru-Chile Trench? The ocean crust west of South America is relatively young because the Peru-Chile Trench is not far from an ocean ridge.

Figure Caption Question

Figure 17-11 What pattern do you observe? Students should observe that the youngest crust is closest to ocean ridges and that the same age pattern exists on either side of the same ridge.

Differentiated Instruction

Visually Impaired Provide enlarged, color photocopies of **Figure 17-11** to students with visual impairments to help them understand the pattern of correlative magnetic stripes on either side of an ocean ridge. Adding black lines to delineate the different ages of the crust will also make the diagram more effective for these students. **L1** **ELL**

Resource Manager

Teaching Transparency 48 **L2** **ELL**

NY Core Curriculum Standards

Page 452: St 4 KI 2.1n & 3.1a
Page 453: St 4 KI 2.1n

Check for Understanding

Reinforcement

Have students each use the headings in this section to make a concept map that summarizes the ideas presented in the section. As an alternative, provide students with the headings and relevant information and have each student organize the text as a concept map. L2

Reteach

Explain that the process of seafloor spreading is analogous to the movement of a conveyor belt at a supermarket checkout counter.

✓Assessment

Knowledge Ask students to imagine that they are oceanographers studying core samples of the ocean floor. Sample 1 was taken near a trench. Sample 2 was taken near an ocean ridge. Have students describe the differences they could expect to observe in the two core samples.

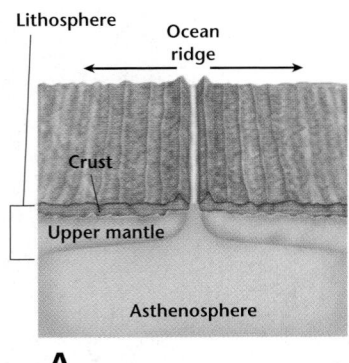
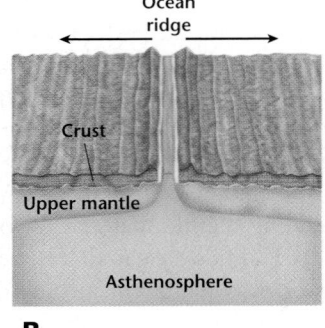
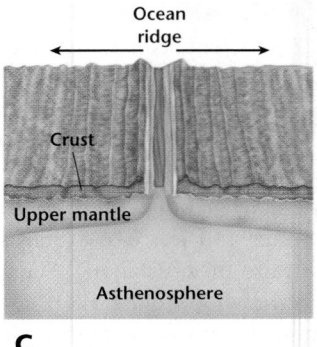

A   **B**   **C**

Figure 17-12
Magma that forms in the asthenosphere intrudes into the ocean floor along a ridge and fills the gap that is created **(A)**. When the molten material solidifies, new ocean crust is formed **(B)**. This continuous intrusion and consequent spreading results in the addition of more crust to the ocean floor **(C)**.

The Missing Link Seafloor spreading was the missing link needed by Wegener to complete his model of continental drift. Recall that while Wegener compiled many data to support his idea that the continents are drifting across Earth's surface, he could not explain what caused the landmasses to move or how they moved. Seafloor spreading provides the answer to the *how* question. Continents are not pushing through ocean crust, as Wegener proposed; they are merely passengers that ride with ocean crust as it slowly moves away from ocean ridges. In the next section, you will learn what causes slabs of Earth's crust and rigid upper mantle to move.

SECTION ASSESSMENT

1. How do ocean ridges and deep-sea trenches support the theory of seafloor spreading?

2. Explain how ocean-floor rocks and sediments are evidence of seafloor spreading.

3. Compare and contrast normal magnetic polarity and reversed magnetic polarity.

4. Explain how an isochron map of the ocean floor supports the theory of seafloor spreading.

5. **Thinking Critically** Refer to *Figure 17-11.* Why are the magnetic bands in the eastern Pacific Ocean so far apart compared to the magnetic bands along the Mid-Atlantic Ridge?

SKILL REVIEW

6. **Concept Mapping** Make an events-chain concept map to show the sequence of steps involved in seafloor spreading. For more help, refer to the *Skill Handbook.*

> **Initiating event:**
> Magma forms.
> ↓ **Event 1:**
>
> ↓ **Event 2:**
>
> ↓ **Event 3:**

SECTION ASSESSMENT

1. The theory of seafloor spreading states that ocean ridges are places where new ocean crust is formed; trenches are places where it is destroyed.

2. Both sediment thickness and the ages of ocean-floor rocks increase with distance from a ridge. These data are consistent with new crust forming at ridges and being destroyed at trenches.

3. Both are orientations of Earth's magnetic field. Normal fields have the same polarity as today's field. Reversed fields have the opposite polarity as today's field.

4. An isochron map of the ocean floor shows that the age of ocean-floor crust increases with distance from the ridge at which it formed. The map also shows that the age of the ocean crust is symmetrical in relation to the ridge.

5. Magnetic bands in the eastern Pacific Ocean are farther apart than bands along the Mid-Atlantic Ridge because the rates of spreading in the Pacific Ocean are faster than those in the Atlantic Ocean.

6. See the student page for one possible map.

SECTION 17.3 — *Theory of Plate Tectonics*

Have you ever wondered why some regions of Earth are dotted with many active volcanoes while other regions have none? Or why earthquakes occur more frequently in certain areas than in others? The answers to these and many other questions are explained by the **theory of plate tectonics,** which states that Earth's crust and rigid upper mantle are broken into enormous slabs called plates. There are a dozen or so major plates and several smaller ones, as shown in *Figure 17-13.* Refer to this figure as you read about tectonic plates. Tectonic plates move in different directions and at different rates over Earth's surface. Rates of movement have been measured with the use of a sophisticated system of receivers and satellites that you'll learn about in the *Science & Technology* feature at the end of this chapter.

PLATE BOUNDARIES

Tectonic plates interact at places called plate boundaries. At some boundaries, plates come together, or converge. At others, plates move away from one another, or diverge. At the third type of boundary, plates move horizontally past one another. Each type of boundary has certain geologic characteristics and processes associated with it.

OBJECTIVES

- **Explain** *the theory of plate tectonics.*
- **Compare and contrast** *the three types of plate boundaries and the features associated with each.*

VOCABULARY

theory of plate tectonics
divergent boundary
rift valley
convergent boundary
subduction
transform boundary

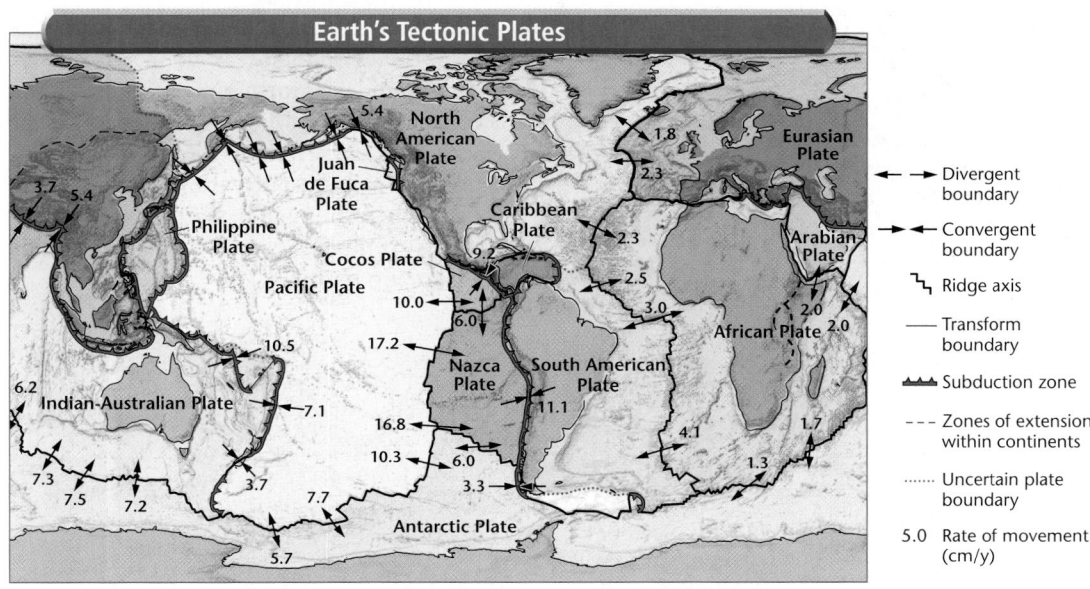

Earth's Tectonic Plates

Divergent boundary
Convergent boundary
Ridge axis
Transform boundary
Subduction zone
Zones of extension within continents
Uncertain plate boundary
5.0   Rate of movement (cm/y)

Figure 17-13 Earth's crust and rigid upper mantle are broken into enormous slabs called tectonic plates that interact at places called boundaries.

Interpreting the Illustration

Figure 17-13 Ask the following questions. What types of plate boundaries are found along the edges of the North American Plate? transform and convergent along the western edge; a divergent boundary is found along the eastern edge Does every plate involve all three types of boundaries? Explain. Yes; Earth is not getting larger. Crust formed at ocean ridges is destroyed at subduction zones.

Resource Manager

Section Focus Transparency 51 L1 ELL
Teaching Transparency 49 L1 ELL
Study Guide for Content Mastery, pp. 108–109 L2

Section 17.3

Prepare

Section Background

For section content background, refer to **Subduction Zones** on pages 442C–D.

Preplanning

Refer to the Chapter Organizer on pages 442A–B.

1 Focus

Section Focus

Before presenting the lesson, display **Section Focus Transparency 51** on the overhead projector. L1 ELL

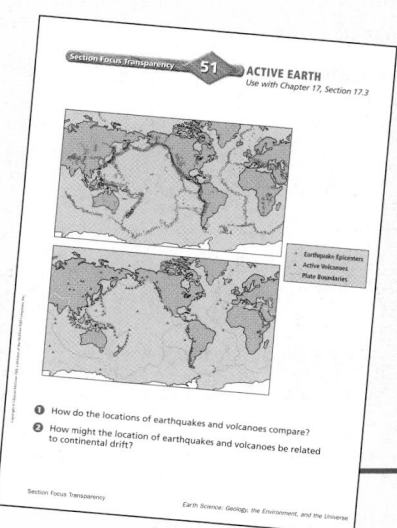

Tying to Previous Knowledge

Ask the following question to stress the link between the theories of seafloor spreading and plate tectonics. According to the theory of seafloor spreading, how are tectonic plates moving at an ocean ridge? An ocean ridge is a boundary where plates are moving apart.

455

MiniLab

Purpose 🎲
Students will model the formation of the South Atlantic Ocean over the last 150 million years.

Process Skills
model, measure in SI

Materials
world map, paper, pencil, scissors, metric ruler

Safety Precaution
Remind students to handle the scissors with care.

Teaching Strategies
If time is limited, provide students with templates of South America and Africa.

Expected Results
The distance increases by 1200 km every 30 million years; and 1200 km = 2.4 cm on the maps. The width of the ocean in the model should be about 12 cm.

Analyze and Conclude
1. The model's width of 6000 km is greater than the actual width of the Atlantic Ocean, which is between 4500 and 5500 km.
2. The spreading rate used in the model is faster than the actual spreading rate.

✔Assessment

Performance Have each student create a map of the South Atlantic Ocean 50 million years from now. Use the Performance Task Assessment List for Poster in **PASC,** p. 73.

In-Text Questions

Page 456 How does this compare to the rate used in the *MiniLab* on this page? Can you explain the difference between the actual size of the Atlantic Ocean Basin and the size of the basin in your model? The rate used in the MiniLab is higher than the actual rate of spreading, which explains the difference in size between the model and the actual basin.

MiniLab

Model ocean-basin formation

Model the formation of the South Atlantic Ocean.

Procedure
1. Use a world map to create paper templates of South America and Africa.
2. Place the two continental templates in the center of a piece of 11" × 17" paper and fit them together along their Atlantic coastlines.
3. Carefully trace around the templates with a pencil. Remove the templates and label the diagram "150 million years ago."
4. Use an average spreading rate of 4 cm/y and a map scale of 1 cm = 500 km to create a series of maps that accurately show the development of the Atlantic Ocean at 30-million-year intervals, beginning 150 million years ago.

Analyze and Conclude
1. Compare your last map with a world map. Is the actual width of the South Atlantic Ocean the same on both maps?
2. What might have caused any difference between the width in your model and the actual width of the present South Atlantic Ocean?

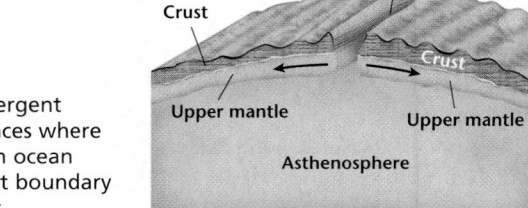

Figure 17-14 Divergent boundaries are places where plates separate. An ocean ridge is a divergent boundary on the ocean floor.

Divergent Boundaries Places where two tectonic plates are moving apart are called **divergent boundaries.** Most divergent boundaries are found on the seafloor, where they form ocean ridges, as shown in *Figure 17-14.* The actual plate boundary is located in a rift, or fault-bounded valley, which forms along the axis of a ridge. It is in this central rift that the process of seafloor spreading begins. The formation of new ocean crust at most divergent boundaries accounts for the high heat flow, volcanism, and earthquakes associated with these boundaries.

Over millions of years, the process of seafloor spreading along a divergent boundary may cause an ocean basin to grow wider. Scientists have measured the rate of growth of the Atlantic Ocean at about 2 to 3 cm/y. How does this compare to the rate used in the *MiniLab* on this page? Can you explain the difference between the actual size of the Atlantic Ocean Basin and the size of the basin in your model?

Although most divergent boundaries form ridges on the ocean floor, some divergent boundaries form on continents. When continental crust begins to separate, the stretched crust forms a long, narrow depression called a **rift valley.** A rift valley is currently forming in East Africa. The rifting might eventually lead to the formation of a new ocean basin.

Resource Manager

GeoLab and MiniLab Worksheets, p. 67 L2
Laboratory Manual, pp. 129–132 L2

NATIONAL GEOGRAPHIC

CD-ROM
Dynamic Earth PictureShow
The Earth is Alive

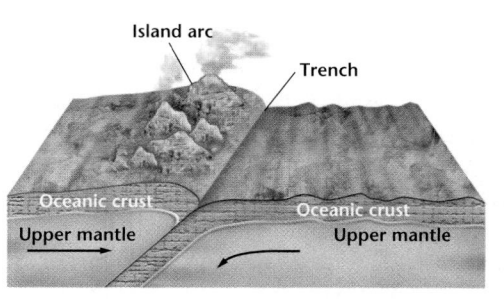

A

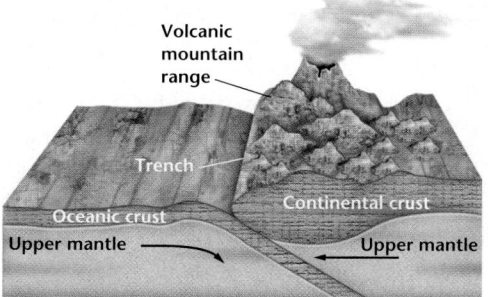

B

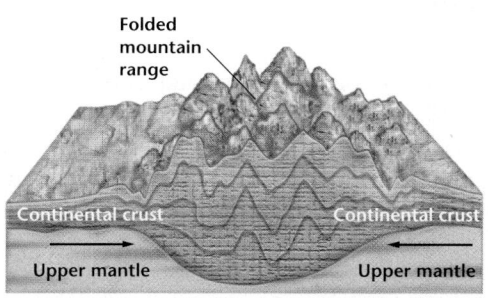

C

Figure 17-15 Convergent plate boundaries are differentiated according to the type of crust involved. There are three types of convergent boundaries: oceanic-oceanic **(A)**, oceanic-continental **(B)**, and continental-continental **(C)**.

Convergent Boundaries Places where two tectonic plates are moving toward each other are **convergent boundaries.** There are three types of convergent boundaries, which are classified according to the type of crust involved. Recall from Chapter 1 that oceanic crust is made mostly of basalt. Continental crust is composed mostly of granite and sedimentary rocks, both of which are less dense than basalt. The three types of convergent boundaries are oceanic crust converging with oceanic crust, oceanic crust converging with continental crust, and continental crust converging and colliding with continental crust. These three types of tectonic boundaries are shown in *Figure 17-15.*

What is happening at the oceanic-oceanic boundary shown in *Figure 17-15A?* One of the two plates is descending beneath the other in a process called **subduction.** A subduction zone forms when one oceanic plate, which has become denser as a result of cooling, descends below another plate. The process of subduction creates a deep-sea trench. The subducted plate descends into the mantle and melts, thereby recycling the oceanic crust formed at the ridge. Some of the magma that forms is forced back to the surface, erupts, and forms an arc of volcanic islands that parallel the trench.

Content Background

Igneous activity is characteristic of subduction zones. Either volcanic island arcs or volcanic-magmatic mountain ranges form as plates converge. The magma that fuels the igneous activity is associated with the subducting plate but is not derived solely from this plate. At depths of 50 to 100 km, some of the basalt and sediments begin to melt, releasing water and other minerals. The ultramafic magma generated slowly changes composition through fractional crystallization and assimilation of crustal rocks during intrusion.

Tying to Previous Knowledge

Ask the following questions to review some of the properties of the two kinds of crust. What are the primary elements found in granite and basalt? silica, iron, and magnesium What is responsible for the differences in density between these two rocks? Basalt has a greater density because it contains minerals with less silica and more iron and magnesium than the minerals in granite.

Differentiated Instruction

Visually Impaired Have students model the three types of convergent boundaries using their hands. Sliding the fingers of the left hand over the backs of the fingers of the right hand models an oceanic-continental boundary. The left fingers should bend upward as they slide to represent the island arc. The right hand represents the subducted plate. Demonstrate the other two types of convergent boundaries in a similar way. **L1** **ELL**

Across the Curriculum

History The Mediterranean Sea is a convergent boundary between Africa and Asia. Have students find out what geologic features have formed as the result of interactions along this boundary and how these features have affected the cultures and history of the region. Earthquakes and volcanoes affected historical events and styles of local architecture, gave rise to myths, and destroyed cities, among other effects.

NY Core Curriculum Standards

Page 454: St 4 KI 2.1n
Page 455: St 4 KI 2.1l & 2.1o
Page 456: St 4 KI 2.1l & 2.1n
Page 457: St 4 KI 2.1n

Figure 17-16 Mt. Cleveland is a volcano in Alaska that formed as the result of convergence along an oceanic-oceanic boundary.

Some examples of trenches and island arcs are the Mariana Trench and Mariana Islands in the West Pacific Ocean and the Aleutian Trench and Aleutian Islands in the North Pacific Ocean. A volcanic peak in the Aleutian Islands is shown in *Figure 17-16.*

Subduction also occurs when an oceanic plate converges with a continental plate, as you can see in *Figure 17-15B.* Note that the denser oceanic plate is subducted. Oceanic-continental convergence also produces a trench and volcanic arc. However, instead of an arc of volcanic islands forming, as in oceanic-oceanic plate convergence, a series of volcanoes erupt along the edge of the continental plate. The result of this type of subduction is a mountain range with many volcanoes. The Peru-Chile Trench and the Andes Mountains, which are located along the western coast of South America, formed in this way.

The third type of convergent boundary forms when two continental plates collide. This convergent boundary forms when an ocean basin between converging oceanic and continental plates is

Problem-Solving Lab

Interpreting Scientific Illustrations

Determine how plate motions change along a transform boundary The figure at right shows the Gibbs Fracture Zone, which is a segment of the Mid-Atlantic Ridge located south of Iceland and west of the British Isles. Copy this figure.

Analysis
1. In what direction is the seafloor moving at each location? Draw arrows on your copy to indicate these directions at each location.
2. Compare the direction of motion for the following pairs of locations: A and D, B and E, and C and F.

Thinking Critically
3. Which locations are on the North American Plate?
4. Which portion of the fracture zone is the boundary between North America and Europe?
5. At which location is the oldest crust located?

Gibbs Fracture Zone

entirely subducted. One continent is pulled into the subduction zone, but it can't be subducted because continental rocks are too buoyant to be forced into the mantle. As a result, the colliding edges of the continents are crumpled and uplifted to form a mountain range, as shown in *Figure 17-15C.* The Himalayas formed in this way.

Transform Boundaries A place where two plates slide horizontally past each other, as shown in *Figure 17-17,* is a **transform boundary.** How does this type of boundary compare to divergent and convergent boundaries? Along divergent boundaries, new crust is formed at ridges, and at convergent boundaries, old crust is destroyed by subduction. At transform boundaries, however, crust is only deformed or fractured. Transform boundaries are characterized by long faults, sometimes hundreds of kilometers in length, and by shallow earthquakes. Most transform boundaries off-set sections of ocean ridges, as you observed in the *Problem-Solving Lab* on the previous page. Rarely do transform boundaries occur on continents. The San Andreas Fault is probably the best-known exception. Recall from the *Discovery Lab* at the beginning of this chapter that the San Andreas Fault system separates southwestern California from the rest of the state. Movements along this transform fault system are responsible for most of the earthquakes that strike California every year.

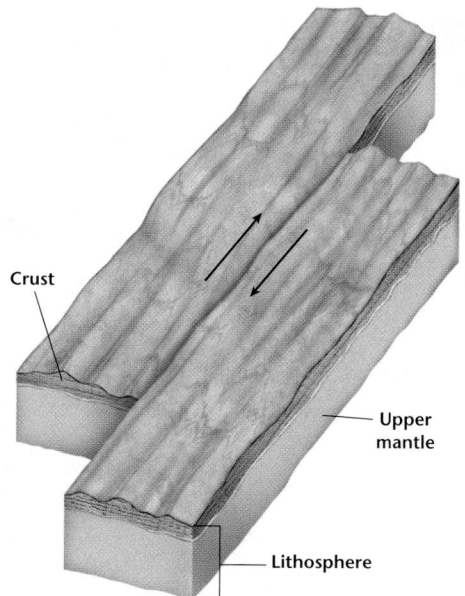

Crust

Upper mantle

Lithosphere

Figure 17-17 Plates move horizontally past each other along a transform plate boundary.

Prepare

Section Background

For section content background, refer to **Tectonic Forces** on page 442D.

Preplanning

Refer to the Chapter Organizer on pages 442A–B.

1 Focus

Section Focus

Before presenting the lesson, display **Section Focus Transparency 52** on the overhead projector.
L1 **ELL**

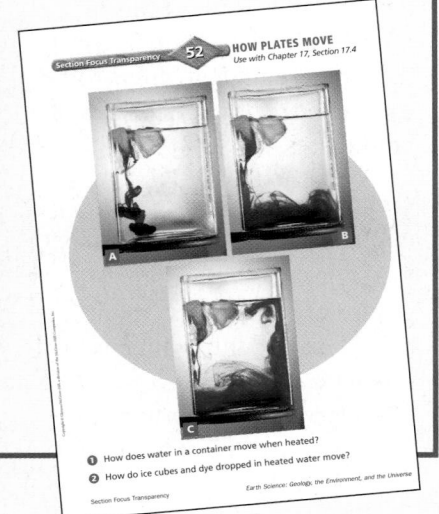

OBJECTIVES

- **Explain** *the process of convection.*
- **Summarize** *how convection in the mantle is related to the movements of tectonic plates.*
- **Compare and contrast** *the processes of ridge push and slab pull.*

VOCABULARY

ridge push
slab pull

Today, plate tectonics is no longer in question. The directions and rates of plate movements have been measured. One of the main questions about the theory of plate tectonics, however, has remained unanswered ever since Alfred Wegener first proposed continental drift. What force or forces cause tectonic plates to move? Even today, what actually causes the plates to move is not well understood. One of the leading hypotheses proposes that large-scale motion in the mantle is the mechanism that drives the movement of tectonic plates.

MANTLE CONVECTION

Recall from Chapter 11 that the transfer of thermal energy by the movement of heated matter is called convection. The heating of matter causes it to expand and to decrease in density. The warmed matter then rises as a result of buoyancy. The cooler part of the matter sinks as a result of gravity. This up-and-down flow produces a pattern of motion called a convection current. Convection currents aid in the transfer of thermal energy from the warmer regions of matter to cooler regions. A convection current can be observed in the series of photographs shown in *Figure 17-18.*

Convection currents in the mantle are thought to be the driving mechanism of plate movements. Recall that even though the mantle is a solid, part of it, the asthenosphere, can flow like a soft, pliable plastic. Convection currents in this part of the mantle are set in motion by the transfer of energy between Earth's hot interior and its cooler exterior. Hot mantle material is less dense than cooler mantle

Figure 17-18 Convection currents transfer thermal energy in unequally heated matter.

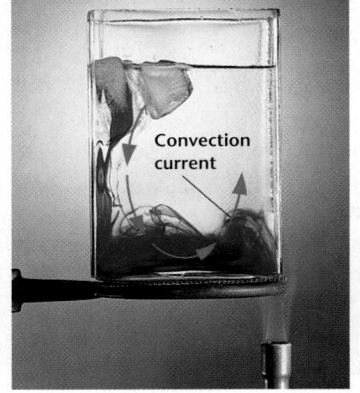
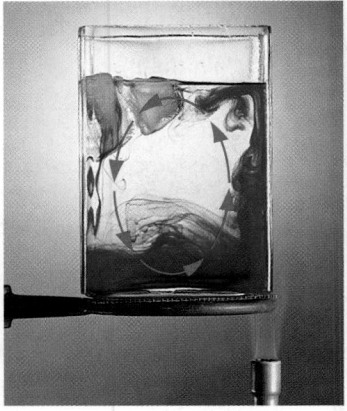

Beaker with H₂O

Ice cube

Drops of blue food coloring

Convection current

Burner

NY Core Curriculum Standards

Page 460: St 4 KI 2.1k, 2.1m, & 2.2b
Page 461: St 4 KI 2.1k, 2.1l, 2.1m, & 2.1n

Demo

Visual-Spatial Use a 1000-mL glass beaker nearly filled with water, a candle, a ring stand, food coloring, and an ice cube to demonstrate how a convection cell forms and moves. **CAUTION:** *Wear safety goggles during this demonstration and insist that students do the same.* Set the candle under one edge of the beaker and put the ice cube in the beaker at the opposite edge. Place a drop of food coloring next to the ice cube. Students will observe the food coloring sink to the bottom of the beaker under the ice cube and then rise in the water above the flame. **L2** **ELL**

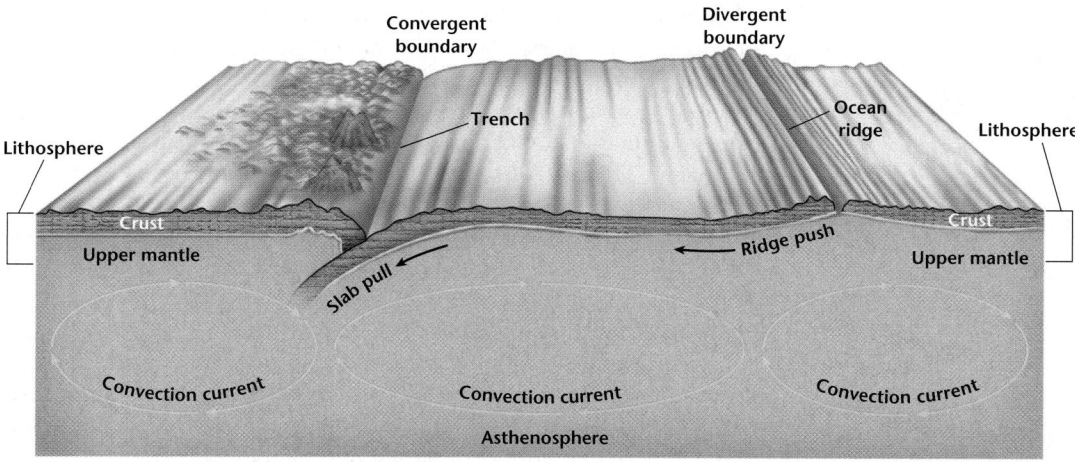

Figure 17-19 Ridge push and slab pull are tectonic processes associated with convection currents in the mantle.

material and, thus, the hot material is slowly forced toward the crust. Cooler parts of this material sink back toward the core. The convection currents that result can be thousands of kilometers across but flow at rates of only a few centimeters per year. Scientists hypothesize that these convection currents are probably set in motion by subducting slabs, thus causing plates to move.

How are convergent and divergent movements related to the flow direction of mantle convection? The rising part of a convection current spreads out as it reaches the upper mantle and causes both upward and lateral forces. These forces lift and split the lithosphere at divergent plate boundaries. As the plates separate, material rising from the mantle supplies the magma that hardens to form new ocean crust. The downward part of a convection current occurs where a sinking force pulls tectonic plates downward at convergent boundaries.

Push and Pull Exactly how is mantle convection related to the movements of tectonic plates? Scientists hypothesize that there are several processes involved. Study *Figure 17-19.* During the formation of an ocean ridge, forces in the mantle cause the asthenosphere to rise. The weight of the uplifted ridge is thought to push an oceanic plate toward the trench formed at the subduction zone in a process called **ridge push** as shown in *Figure 17-19.* In addition to ridge push, the horizontal flow at the top of a convection current could create drag on the lithosphere and thereby contribute to plate motion.

17.4 Causes of Plate Motions **461**

✓Assessment

Knowledge Ask students the following question: What type of mantle convection do you think exists beneath the western coast of South America?
a. downward convection
b. upward convection
c. slab push
d. ridge pull
The correct choice is **a.** Have students refer to **Figure 17-13** again, if necessary.

2 Teach

Identifying Misconceptions

Some students may incorrectly think that buoyancy is caused by an upward, pulling force on the less-dense material rather than a force that pushes from both the sides and below the material.

Uncover the Misconception
Have students each draw a diagram of a block of foam rising through water. Ask students to label the diagram with arrows that show the different forces acting on the foam.

Demonstrate the Concept
Show how water exerts an upward force on a block of polystyrene foam with a bucket half-filled with water. Have a few volunteers attempt to push the block under water. Have them describe the resistance, or upward force, exerted by the water.

Assess New Knowledge
Have students each draw another diagram that correctly shows the forces acting on a material that floats in water.

Interpreting the Illustration

Figure 17-19 Have students use this diagram to answer the following questions. What type of convection is associated with a convergent boundary? downward What type of convection is associated with a divergent boundary? upward

461

Content Background

Refer to **Figure 17-20.** The Farallon Plate is a subducted oceanic plate that has all but disappeared from Earth's surface. The Juan de Fuca Plate, west of Washington State, is a remnant of the Farallon Plate. As the North American Plate began to move west during the breakup of Pangaea, it collided with the Farallon Plate. A subduction zone developed along the entire western edge of North America. Thousands of kilometers of oceanic crust have been subducted to form some of the major geologic features of this region, including the Rocky Mountains, the Basin and Range Province, and the Sierra Nevada.

Interpreting the Illustration

Figure 17-20 Have students use this figure and the text on this page to answer the following questions. How deep does the Farallon Plate extend? It extends to nearly the mantle-core boundary. Is this plate still connected to a surface subduction zone? Yes, the plate is still connected at the surface.

Enrichment

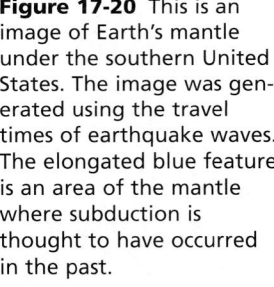 **Kinesthetic** Challenge students to model ridge push and slab pull using old telephone books and the edge of a desk.

A combination of mechanisms may be involved in plate motions at subduction zones as well. A sinking region of a mantle convection current could suck an oceanic plate downward into a subduction zone. The weight of a subducting plate helps pull the trailing lithosphere into the subduction zone in a process called **slab pull,** as shown in *Figure 17-19.*

Unanswered Questions While most scientists agree that convection currents in the mantle are related to the movement of tectonic plates, there are still unanswered questions about how these currents originate and what their actual sizes are. Are mantle convection currents permanent features? Do they shift their positions through geologic time? How does a convection current start? What causes the movement of a convection current to stop? Is convection taking place only in the upper mantle? Or, do these enormous convection currents include the lower mantle? *Figure 17-20* shows an image of the mantle 2700 km below Earth's surface that was generated from earthquake data. This image suggests that the convection currents associated with plate movements might include the lower mantle. Some geologists working in this branch of Earth science have even suggested that subducted slabs, over time, might eventually reach Earth's outer core.

Other remaining questions concern relationships between convection currents and the overlying plates. For example, does downward convection cause a subduction zone, or does the process of subduction create the convection current? Most studies show that the process of slab pull is the most important force driving tectonic plate motions.

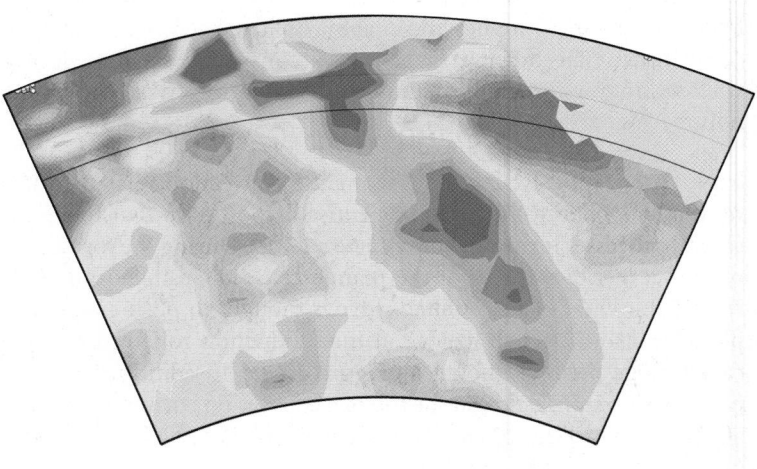

Figure 17-20 This is an image of Earth's mantle under the southern United States. The image was generated using the travel times of earthquake waves. The elongated blue feature is an area of the mantle where subduction is thought to have occurred in the past.

Differentiated Instruction

Gifted Pangaea split in a north-south direction to form the Atlantic Ocean. Challenge students to find the answers to the following questions. What type of convection flow developed beneath Pangaea? How would Earth's present geography be different if the mantle convection had been oriented in an east-west direction? How does the breakup of Pangaea support the hypothesis that mantle convection changes over time? **L3**

 **Earth Science**

Journal

Have students each write a paragraph that discusses why questions about mantle convection have been so difficult for scientists to answer. Students' paragraphs should include that the motion is extremely slow and occurs deep within the planet. Thus, knowledge of this process is based on indirect evidence and observations. **P**

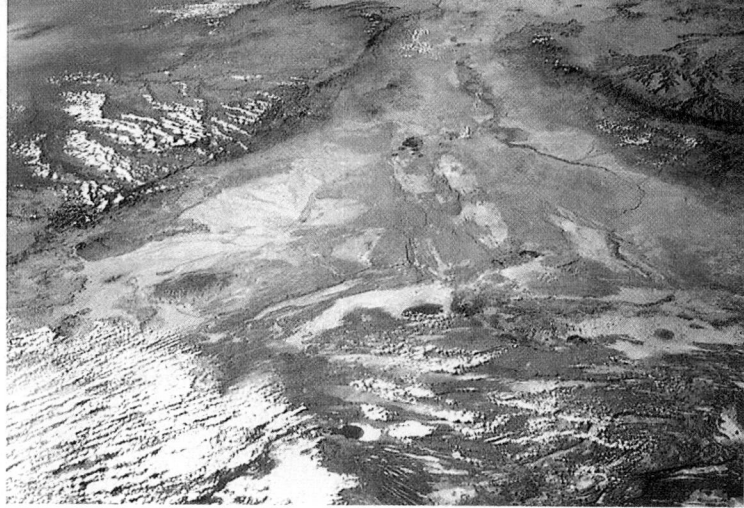

Figure 17-21 Spreading in the Great Rift Valley of East Africa, shown here, is related to convection currents in Earth's mantle.

A similar set of questions surround the formation of divergent plate boundaries. The Great Rift Valley, in Africa, part of which is shown in *Figure 17-21,* is evidence that a divergent boundary can develop on a continent. But what causes an upward convection current to form beneath a continent? One hypothesis is that large continental masses ultimately cause their own breakup by acting as insulating blankets. The underlying mantle then becomes warmer and causes the upward leg of a convection current to develop, which eventually causes the continent to split.

The questions presented here are just some of those that geologists hope to answer in the future. What questions do you have about what causes Earth's crust and rigid upper mantle to slowly but continuously change over geologic time?

SECTION ASSESSMENT

1. Make and label a diagram that explains the process of convection.

2. What are the relationships among mantle convection, ocean ridges, and subduction zones?

3. Hypothesize what might happen to mantle convection currents beneath a continental-continental convergent boundary.

4. How have earthquake data been used to explore the size of convection currents in the mantle?

5. **Thinking Critically** If a subducting slab is pulling the lithosphere into the mantle and a continent is pulled into the subduction zone, what do you think might happen?

SKILL REVIEW

6. **Making Diagrams** Make a diagram that contrasts the tectonic processes of ridge push and slab pull. Include captions in your diagram. For more help, refer to the *Skill Handbook.*

earthgeu.com/self_check_quiz

17.4 *Causes of Plate Motions* **463**

463

Making a Paleomagnetic Map

I ron-bearing minerals in rocks record the orientation of Earth's magnetic field at the time of their formation. These preserved magnetic alignments in ocean-floor rocks can be used to date different parts of the seafloor and to determine rates of spreading along divergent plate margins.

Time Allotment

60 minutes

Process Skills

interpret scientific illustrations, analyze data

Procedure

Teaching Strategies

Trace the base map onto a blank transparency. Copy the magnetic survey data curves onto another transparency. Use the overhead projector to demonstrate how to transfer the data curves to the base map.

Troubleshooting

- Make sure that students use sharp pencils to trace the data curves and that the ocean ridge lines up with the dashed line as they trace.
- Tell students that when drawing the parallel lines, it is best to start at the ridge and work outward. It may be helpful if students carefully shade all the positive magnetic events on each survey line. Remind students that the lines do not cross the transform fault but are offset by the fault.

Data and Observations

The map should show a pattern of colored bands that are parallel and symmetrical with respect to the ridge. The pattern is offset by the transform fault. See the student page.

Preparation

Problem

How can you use paleomagnetic data to interpret information about ocean-floor rocks?

Materials

tracing paper
metric ruler
No. 2 pencil
colored pencils
Figure 17-8

Procedure

1. Use the tracing paper and the No. 2 pencil to carefully copy the base map on the following page. Be sure to include the magnetic survey lines, the map scale, and the location indicated by the letter *X* on your tracing.
2. Transfer the magnetic survey data from PM1 to your tracing by placing the survey line on your map over the PM1 data curve on the following page. Be sure to align the mid-ocean ridge with the dashed line before you begin transferring the line. Label the line.
3. Repeat step 2 for the other four lines.
4. Next, use your ruler to draw a series of parallel lines between PM1 and PM2 to connect the corresponding positive and negative magnetic reversals. Draw the lines past PM2, but stop the lines at the transform boundary.
5. Draw another series of lines between survey lines PM3 and PM4 and between PM4 and PM5. Again, end these lines at the transform boundary.
6. The positive magnetic reading along the mid-ocean ridge represents the Brunhes Magnetic Epoch. The first negative anomaly on either side of the ridge marks the beginning of the Matuyama Magnetic Epoch. Use *Figure 17-8* to identify the magnetic reversals.
7. Assign a color for each magnetic reversal. Then, color the corresponding stripe on each side of the ridge.

Mid-ocean ridge

PM 1
PM 2
✗
PM 3
PM 4
PM 5

50   100 km

Paleomagnetic survey data curves

PM 1
PM 2
PM 3
PM 4
PM 5

Mid-ocean ridge

...vas it necessary to color corre-
...ing stripes on each side of the
...n step 7?

2. Use *Figure 17-8* to determine the age of the seafloor at location *X*.

Conclude & Apply

...might cause an individual mag-
...tripe of ocean-floor crust to
...i width?

2. What is the average spreading rate along this section of the mid-ocean ridge?

Analyze

1. The two stripes originally formed as a single band along the ridge axis. Seafloor spreading split the band in two to form stripes that moved in opposite directions in relation to the ridge.
2. The age of the crust at point X is about 2.8 million years.

Conclude & Apply

1. variable spreading rates along the ridge
2. The average spreading rate is about 5 cm/y. Students can calculate this rate by measuring the distance between location X and the corresponding point on the opposite side of the ridge, which is about 145 km. The age of the crust at point X is 2.8 million years, and 145 km ÷ 2.8 million years = 5.2 cm/y.

✓*Assessment*

Portfolio Have students answer the following question on the backs of their maps and include them in their portfolios. Why is this paleomagnetic map an isochron map? Students should note that the lines drawn between magnetic reversals represent the same instant in time, and therefore they are isochrons. **P**

Resource Manager

GeoLab and MiniLab Worksheets, pp. 68–70 **L2**

NY Core Curriculum Standards

Page 464: St 1 Math KI 1, 2, & 3, St 6 KI 2 & 3, St 7 KI 1
Page 465: St 1 Math KI 1, 2, & 3, St 6 KI 2 & 3, St 7 KI 1

Science & Technology

Purpose

Students will learn how the Global Positioning System (GPS) allows a person to determine the precise location of a point on Earth's surface and how this information can be used.

Teaching Strategies

- Inform students that some car-rental companies have computers that can display a person's location on a map of the city in which the person is located. The system can also suggest routes to a particular destination. Ask students to explain how the GPS might be involved in such a system.
- Have students brainstorm to compile a list of instances in which it might be important to know one's precise location. Answers might include such scenarios as the captains of planes, small boats, and ships needing to know their exact locations to maneuver their crafts or chart their courses.

The Global Positioning System

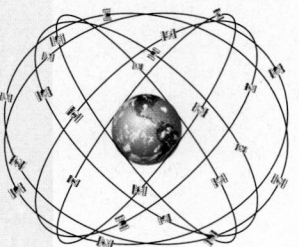

An ambulance driver speeds toward the location of someone having a heart attack. A hiker in unfamiliar territory successfully returns to her campsite. The driver of an armored vehicle transports hundreds of thousands of dollars from businesses to a local bank. What do these people have in common? Each of them is likely to be navigating using a system of satellites currently in orbit around Earth, a system that most people aren't even aware exists.

The Global Positioning System, or GPS, was developed by the United States Department of Defense to track tanks, planes, and ships. Twenty-four satellites, roughly 20 000 km above Earth, are part of this system, each circling on a different orbital path about once every 12 hours. The number of satellites, their distances from Earth, and their orbital periods make the GPS incredibly accurate and essentially give every square meter on our planet a unique address.

How does this system work? A receiver on Earth picks up signals coming from at least three or four satellites in space. The time it takes for the signals to travel from the satellites to the receiver can be used to calculate the latitude, longitude, and elevation of the location of the receiver.

Everyday Uses

The development of the GPS forever changed navigation and mapping. While this system is still operated by the military, there are thousands of civilian users all over the world. Fire, police, and rescue departments, public transportation systems, long-haul trucking companies, taxi services, and fishing fleets all use the GPS to keep drivers and passengers safe, to navigate in unfamiliar territory, and to protect expensive cargo from theft or loss. Hand-held GPS receivers are also used by hikers, hunters, drivers, and boaters.

Scientific Uses

In addition to its everyday uses, the GPS is a valuable tool for collecting information about Earth's surface. Scientists use the GPS to map volcanic regions, where temperature extremes and steep, rocky slopes make it very difficult to use traditional mapping systems. The GPS is also useful in determining sites for nuclear power plants and radioactive waste disposal sites, facilities that must be constructed in areas that are relatively inactive geologically.

The pinpoint accuracy of the GPS has also allowed geophysicists to measure how tectonic plates move in relation to each other over time. For example, the expansion of Iceland, which sits astride the Mid-Atlantic Ridge, is taking place at about 12 mm/year. This rate of movement would have been impossible to measure without the use of the GPS.

Internet

Go to the Earth Science Web Site at **earthgeu.com** to find out how the GPS has been used to help predict earthquakes that occur along the transform boundary called the San Andreas Fault.

Internet

Students should find that scientists have used the GPS to precisely locate markers on either side of a fault. These markers are then used to measure how much stress has built up along the fault. The markers are also used to accurately measure the amount of movement along a fault during an earthquake.

Summary

SECTION 17.1	Main Ideas	Vocabulary
Drifting Continents 	• The matching coastlines of continents on opposite sides of the Atlantic Ocean suggest that the continents were once joined. • Continental drift states that Earth's continents were joined as a single landmass that broke apart and sent the continents adrift. • Wegener supported his hypothesis of continental drift with rock types, fossils, and ancient climatic data. His hypothesis was not accepted at first because he couldn't explain how the continents moved or what caused their motion.	continental drift (p. 444) Pangaea (p. 444)
SECTION 17.2	Main Ideas	Vocabulary
Seafloor Spreading 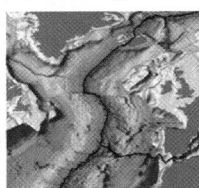	• Sonar and magnetic studies of ocean rocks and sediments led to the proposal of the theory of seafloor spreading. • Magnetic patterns on the seafloor are symmetric in relation to ocean ridges, indicating that ocean crust on either side of the ridge is moving away from the ridge at essentially the same rate. • During seafloor spreading, magma rises and hardens to form new crust, which becomes part of the ocean floor. Each cycle of spreading and intrusion results in the formation of another small section of ocean floor, which slowly moves away from the ridge.	isochron (p. 452) magnetic reversal (p. 451) magnetometer (p. 448) paleomagnetism (p. 451) seafloor spreading (p. 453)
SECTION 17.3	Main Ideas	Vocabulary
Theory of Plate Tectonics 	• Plate tectonics states that Earth's crust and rigid upper mantle are broken into large slabs of rock called plates, which move in different directions and at different rates over Earth's surface. • At divergent plate boundaries, plates move apart. At convergent boundaries, plates come together. At transform boundaries, plates slide horizontally past each other. • High heat flow, volcanism, and earthquakes are associated with divergent boundaries; trenches, island arcs, and folded mountains with convergent boundaries; and faults and earthquakes with transform boundaries.	convergent boundary (p. 457) divergent boundary (p. 456) rift valley (p. 456) subduction (p. 457) theory of plate tectonics (p. 455) transform boundary (p. 459)
SECTION 17.4	Main Ideas	Vocabulary
Causes of Plate Motions 	• Convection is the transfer of energy via the movement of heated matter. Convection currents in the mantle are the result of energy transfer between Earth's hot interior and cooler exterior. • Ridge push occurs when the elevation of a ridge pushes a plate toward a subduction zone. Slab pull occurs as the weight of the subducting plate pulls a plate into a subduction zone.	ridge push (p. 461) slab pull (p. 462)

 earthgeu.com/vocabulary_puzzlemaker

Study Guide **467**

Main Ideas

Summary statements can be used by students to review the major concepts of the chapter.

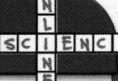
VOCABULARY
PuzzleMaker

 For additional help with vocabulary, have students access the Vocabulary Puzzlemaker online.
earthgeu.com/ vocabulary_puzzlemaker

0:00 *Out of Time?*

If time does not permit teaching the entire chapter, use the GeoDigest at the end of the unit as an overview.

Earth Science Online

Be sure to check the Earth Science Web Site for links to chapter material: **earthgeu.com**

GLENCOE
Technology

Videotape/DVD
MindJogger Videoquizzes
Chapter 17: *Plate Tectonics*
Have students work in groups as they play the videoquiz game to review key chapter concepts.

Resource Manager

Chapter Assessment, pp. 97–102
MindJogger Videoquizzes DVD/VHS
ExamView® Pro CD-ROM
Performance Assessment in Earth Science

NY Core Curriculum Standards

Page 466: St 2 KI 1
Page 467: St 4 KI 2.1k, 2.1l, 2.1m, 2.1n, 2.1o, & 2.2b

Understanding Main Ideas

1. c
2. c
3. a
4. b
5. c
6. Sonar allowed scientists to map Earth's ocean floors. The maps showed highs called ridges and lows called trenches.
7. Sediments are relatively thin close to the ridge and become thicker with distance from the ridge.
8. A magnetic reversal is a change in the orientation of Earth's magnetic field. The orientation of a reversed field is opposite that of today's field. When the magnetic field is the same as the present field, it is a normal field.
9. Movements in the mantle have broken the lithosphere into slabs called plates that move about Earth's surface. Many of Earth's geologic features form as plates interact along their boundaries. Earthquakes are also common along plate boundaries.
10. All three are places where plates come together, or converge. Convergence between oceanic-oceanic boundaries produces island arcs and subduction zones. Convergence of oceanic and continental plates results in subduction zones and mountain ranges that run along the edge of the continent. Continental-continental convergence forms high mountain ranges.

Understanding Main Ideas

1. What was Wegener's hypothesis called?
   a. seafloor spreading
   b. plate tectonics
   c. continental drift
   d. slab pull

2. The fit of the coastlines of which of the following continents led people to suggest that the continents had drifted over time?
   a. North and South America
   b. North America and Africa
   c. South America and Africa
   d. Europe and North America

3. Which of the following evidence was used by Wegener to support his hypothesis that the continents had once been joined?
   a. rock types and ages
   b. plate tectonics
   c. slab pull and ridge push
   d. fossils of ocean plants

4. Which of the following was NOT used by Wegener to support his hypothesis of continental drift?
   a. fossils of land-dwelling animals
   b. paleomagnetic data
   c. coal beds in Antarctica
   d. glacial deposits

5. Why was the hypothesis of continental drift rejected when it was proposed by Wegener?
   a. Wegener thought that the south pole had changed location.
   b. Wegener thought that Earth's rotation was the driving force.
   c. Wegener couldn't explain how or why continents moved.
   d. Wegener died in Greenland in 1930.

6. How did the use of sonar change scientists' ideas about ocean-floor topography?

7. Explain how sediments on the ocean floor vary in relation to an ocean ridge.
8. Differentiate among the following terms: *magnetic reversal*, *reversed field*, and *normal field*.
9. Explain the theory of plate tectonics.
10. Compare and contrast the three types of convergent plate boundaries.

Applying Main Ideas

Use the diagram below to answer questions 11, 12, and 13.

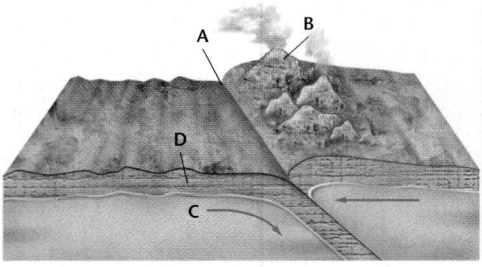

11. What type of boundary is shown?
12. Copy the figure and identify the features labeled A, B, C, and D.
13. Use arrows to label the directions of plate movements.
14. The Andes Mountains are tectonically active. What type of plate boundary is involved in their continued formation?

Test-Taking Tip

READ QUESTIONS CAREFULLY Watch the little words. Underline words like *least, not, except,* and *but* when you see them in test questions. They change the meaning of the question!

earthgeu.com/chapter_test

Applying Main Ideas

11. oceanic-oceanic convergent boundary
12. A—trench, B—volcanic arc, C—asthenosphere or mantle, D—oceanic plate or subducted plate
13. See the student page.
14. a continental-oceanic plate boundary
15. Most divergent boundaries occur on the seafloor, where they form ocean ridges. The actual plate boundary is located in a rift—a fault-bounded valley that forms along the ridge axis.
16. The rising part of a convection cell causes forces that lift and split the lithosphere at a divergent boundary. The downward part of the cell occurs where a sinking force pulls tectonic plates downward at a convergent boundary.
17. an epoch
18. about 900 000 years
19. six; three

15. Explain the relationship among an ocean ridge, a rift, and a divergent plate boundary.

16. Explain how movements at divergent and convergent plate boundaries are related to flow direction of mantle convection currents.

Use *Figure 17-8* on page 451 to answer questions 17, 18, and 19.

17. Which is longer, an event or an epoch?

18. How long did the Gauss Epoch last?

19. How many reversals occurred in the Gilbert Epoch? How many normal events occurred during this epoch?

20. Why did the idea of continental drift become more accepted after seafloor spreading was proposed?

21. Explain what causes the paleomagnetic patterns on the seafloor.

22. Refer to *Figure 17-13* on page 455. Find and identify a place where the Mid-Atlantic Ridge surfaces.

23. Study the rates of plate motions shown in *Figure 17-13* on page 455. How far has the island of Hawaii moved since you were born?

Thinking Critically

24. Locate Africa in *Figure 17-13* on page 455. Identify the major plate boundaries affecting this continent. In which direction is Africa moving in relation to these boundaries?

25. What might cause corresponding magnetic stripes of ocean-floor crust to have different widths?

26. Why do you think earthquakes are common along plate boundaries?

27. Most earthquakes associated with convergent boundaries originate much deeper than earthquakes associated with divergent boundaries. Explain.

earthgeu.com/standardized_test

Standardized Test Practice

1. Which piece of evidence did NOT advance the hypothesis of continental drift?
  a. similar rock types on different continents
  b. crustal rock on the ocean floor
  c. similar fossils on different continents
  d. coal beds in Antarctica

INTERPRETING SCIENTIFIC ILLUSTRATIONS
Use the diagram to answer questions 2–3.

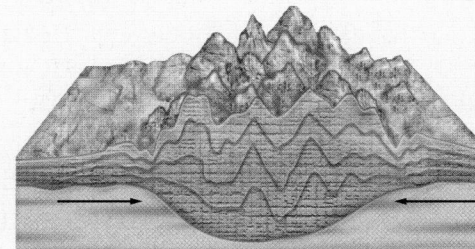

2. What type of plate boundary is shown?
  a. an ocean ridge
  b. a continental-continental boundary
  c. a transform boundary
  d. an oceanic-continental boundary

3. Which of the following features forms along this type of boundary?
  a. subduction zones   **c.** island arcs
  b. oceanic trenches   **d.** folded mountains

4. The weight of a subducting plate helps pull the trailing lithosphere into a subduction zone in which of the following processes?
  a. slab pull   **c.** slab push
  b. ridge pull   **d.** ridge push

Assessment **469**

20. Seafloor spreading explained how continents are being carried along by moving ocean crust.

21. As new ocean crust forms at ridges, it records Earth's magnetic field at the time of its formation. When the magnetic field reverses, the ocean crust forming at this time records the new magnetic polarity.

22. Iceland

23. Hawaii is moving 8–10 cm/y; this equates to about 120–150 cm for a 15-year-old.

Thinking Critically

24. The major plate boundaries are divergent boundaries. Thus, the relative movement is toward the north.

25. different rates of spreading on opposite sides of the ridge

26. Earthquakes are common along plate boundaries because the stresses involved in plate motions cause the rocks to move and break. These motions cause most earthquakes.

27. The forces involved in convergence are much greater than those involved in divergence, and the slab involved in convergence extends deeper into the mantle than the slab involved in divergence.

EXAMVIEW® PRO

Use Exam*View*® Pro Testmaker CD-ROM to:

- Create **multiple versions** of tests.
- Create **modified** tests with one mouse click for struggling students.
- **Edit** existing questions and add your own questions.
- **Build** tests based on national curriculum standards.

Standardized Test Practice

1. b
2. b
3. d
4. a

NY Core Curriculum Standards

Page 468: St 4 KI 2.1l, 2.1n, & 2.1o
Page 469: St 4 KI 2.1l, 2.1n, & 2.1o

Volcanic Activity

Refer to pages 8T–9T of the Teacher Guide for an explanation of the National Science Content Standards correlations.

Section	Objectives	National Science Content Standards	State/Local Standards
SECTION 18.1 **Magma** 🕐 1½ sessions 📦 ½ block	1. **Describe** factors that affect the formation of magma. 2. **Compare** and **contrast** the different types of magma.	UCP.1, UCP.2, UCP.3, UCP.5; A.1, A.2; B.2, B.6; D.1, D.2, D.3; G.3	St 1 Science KI 1, 2, & 3, St 2 KI 1, 2, & 3, St 4 KI 2.1a, 2.1b, 2.1l, 2.1m, & 2.1n, St 6 KI 1, 2, & 5
SECTION 18.2 **Intrusive Activity** 🕐 1½ sessions 📦 ½ block	3. **Explain** how magma affects overlying crustal rocks. 4. **Compare** and **contrast** intrusive igneous rock bodies.	UCP.1, UCP.2, UCP.3, UCP.4, UCP.5; D.1, D.2, D.3	St 4 KI 2.1b, 2.1l, 2.1n, & 3.1b, St 6 KI 1 & 5
SECTION 18.3 **Volcanoes** 🕐 3 sessions 📦 1½ blocks	5. **Describe** the major parts of a volcano. 6. **Compare** and **contrast** shield, cinder-cone, and composite volcanoes. 7. **Contrast** the volcanism that occurs at plate boundaries. 8. **Explain** the relationship between volcanism and hot spots.	UCP.1, UCP.2, UCP.3, UCP.4, UCP.5; A.1, A.2; B.4; D.1, D.2, D.3; F.4, F.5, F.6; G.3	St 1 Math KI 1, 2, 3, & Science KI 1, St 2 KI 1 & 3, St 4 KI 2.1b, 2.1j, 2.1l, 2.1m, 2.1n, 2.1o, & 2.1p, St 6 KI 1, 2, 4, & 5, St 7 KI 2

*A complete Planning Guide is provided on pages 30T–32T.

🕐 The number of recommended single-period sessions

📦 The number of recommended blocks

Activity Materials

Discovery Lab *page 471*
250-mL beaker, 100-mL beaker, ice-cold water, dropper, food coloring, hot water

GeoLab *pages 488–489*
Internet access, pencil, paper

MiniLab *page 474*
NaCl, 250-mL beaker, dishwashing soap, stirring rod, balance

Demo *page 471*
2-L bottle of carbonated water

Need materials? Contact Science Kit at 1-800-828-7777 or at 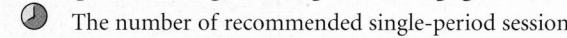www.sciencekit.com on the Internet. For alternate materials, see the activity on the listed page.

Key to Teaching Strategies

L1 Level 1 activities should be appropriate for students with learning difficulties.

L2 Level 2 activities should be within the ability range of all students.

L3 Level 3 activities are designed for above-average students.

ELL ELL activities should be within the ability range of English-language learners.

COOP LEARN Cooperative Learning activities are designed for small-group work.

P These strategies represent student products that can be placed in a best-work portfolio.

📦 These strategies are useful in a block-scheduling format.

Chapter Organizer

Glencoe Exclusive!
TeacherWorks™
All-In-One Planner and Resource Center

Activities/Features	Reproducible Masters	Transparencies
Discovery Lab: Model Magma Movement, p. 471 **MiniLab:** How does silica affect lava flow? p. 474	**Study Guide for Content Mastery,** pp. 111–112 **L2** **GeoLab and MiniLab Worksheets,** p. 71 **L2**	**Section Focus Transparency 53** **L1 ELL** **Teaching Transparencies 51 & 52** **L2 ELL**
	Study Guide for Content Mastery, p. 113 **L2**	**Section Focus Transparency 54** **L1 ELL** **Teaching Transparency 53** **L2 ELL**
Using Math: Using Numbers, p. 486 **Problem-Solving Lab:** Making and Using Graphs, p. 486 **Internet GeoLab:** Ranking Hazardous Volcanoes, pp. 488–489 **Science & the Environment:** The Year Without a Summer, p. 490	**Study Guide for Content Mastery,** pp. 114–116 **L2** **Laboratory Manual,** pp. 137–140, 141–144 **L2** **GeoLab and MiniLab Worksheets,** pp. 72–73 **L2**	**Section Focus Transparency 55** **L1 ELL** **Teaching Transparency 54** **L2 ELL**

 Assessment

Chapter Assessment, pp. 103–108
Performance Assessment in the Science Classroom (PASC)
MindJogger Videoquiz DVD/VHS
Performance Assessment in Earth Science
ExamView® Pro CD-ROM
5 Days to the Regents Exam

GLENCOE'S
ASSESSMENT
ADVANTAGE

Additional Resources

Guided Reading Audio Program ELL
Cooperative Learning in the Science Classroom COOP LEARN
Lesson Plans
Block Scheduling
earthgeu.com
NY Lesson Plans
NY Block Scheduling
Review Handbook for Regents Earth Science Exam

 NATIONAL GEOGRAPHIC

Teacher's Corner

Products Available from National Geographic Society
To order the following products, call the National Geographic Society at 1-800-368-2728:

Videos
Our Dynamic Earth
Curriculum Kits
GeoKit: *Dynamic Earth*

Content Background

Hot Springs and Geysers
Section 18.1

In certain areas of the world, magma chambers lie relatively close to Earth's surface. Surrounding rocks are heated by the magma, which in turn heats the groundwater in the area. Sometimes, this superheated water comes to the surface to form a hot spring. The water may also erupt violently through an opening to form a geyser. Geysers occur when groundwater is heated to extremely high temperatures, which force the water to expand. This expansion, in turn, forces some of the water out of the ground, releasing the pressure on the remaining water. The release of pressure causes the remaining water to boil rapidly. Steam pressure forces the remaining water and steam high into the air. After a geyser erupts, water refills the underground chambers, is reheated, and the geyser erupts again. Geysers are relatively rare; most are found in western parts of the United States, and in Iceland, New Zealand, and Chile.

Columnar Jointing
Section 18.2

Some igneous rock bodies demonstrate a particular type of fracturing known as columnar jointing. Columns range from a few centimeters to 3 m in diameter and can extend vertically to 30 m. Some columns are straight, while others are curved. Most columns have five or six sides, but some can have as few as three or as many as seven sides. Columnar jointing forms as lava cools and lithifies because lava contracts as it cools and causes tensional stresses to build. Eventually, the hardened lava fractures. The fractures propagate at right angles to the outer surfaces of the hardened material. Columnar jointing occurs in lava flows, sills, dikes, ignimbrites, and shallow intrusions. Some well-known examples of columnar jointing are Giant's Causeway in Northern Ireland, Devils Postpile in California, and Devils Tower in Wyoming.

Multiple Learning Styles

Visual-Spatial Modeling, p. 481

Interpersonal Collaborative Learning, p. 482, Project, p. 484

Linguistic Using Scientific Terms, pp. 477, 484

Logical-Mathematical Enrichment, p. 478

GLENCOE
Technology

The following multimedia resources are available from Glencoe.

The Infinite Voyage Series
Living with Disaster

Vocabulary Puzzlemaker

TeacherWorks™ CD-ROM

MindJogger Videoquizzes DVD/VHS

ExamView® Pro CD-ROM

Interactive Chalkboard CD-ROM

Chapter Organizer

The Yellowstone Hot Spot
Section 18.3

Most people don't realize that there is a hot spot located below the North American continent and that this hot spot is the site of what may be the largest volcanic eruption that has ever occurred. As the North American Plate moved westward over the hot spot millions of years ago, various volcanic features formed. The Columbia River flood basalts and the Crater of the Moon National Monument are just two igneous rock bodies that formed as the result of this volcanism. The hot spot is currently located beneath Yellowstone National Park.

Three massive eruptions associated with the Yellowstone hot spot have occurred during the past 2 million years. About 2 million years ago, 2400 km³ of tephra erupted; about 1.3 million years ago, 280 km³ of tephra erupted; and most recently, 600 000 years ago, an estimated 1000 km³ of tephra erupted and left a caldera that is over 80 km in diameter. This caldera is currently buried beneath Yellowstone National Park. The magma chamber beneath the park is still active. Recent uplift, multiple earthquakes, and changes in geyser activity all indicate that the Yellowstone hot spot may erupt again.

Identifying Misconceptions

Some students may have the misconception that all volcanoes are very old and that these dynamic features of Earth form very slowly. Tell students the following story about a volcano called Parícutin. In 1943, a Mexican farmer observed smoke and ash issuing from a crack in his cornfield. Within 24 hours, a 40-m cinder-cone volcano, Parícutin, had formed in the field. Parícutin grew rapidly during the first year, reaching 336 m in height, and eventually it towered 424 m above the field. Parícutin continued to erupt until 1952. The total volume of lava produced by the eruptions was 1.4 km³; it covered over 25 km² of the surrounding land.

✓Assessment

Portfolio Assessment
  Assessment, TWE, p. 479

Performance Assessment
  Discovery Lab, SE, p. 471
  Discovery Lab, TWE, p. 471
  MiniLab, SE, p. 474
  MiniLab, TWE, p. 474
  Assessment, TWE, pp. 475, 487
  GeoLab, SE, pp. 488–489
  GeoLab, TWE, pp. 488–489

Knowledge Assessment
  Assessment, TWE, p. 478
  Section Assessment, SE, pp. 475, 479, 487
  Chapter Assessment, SE, pp. 492–493

Skill Assessment
  Problem-Solving Lab, TWE, p. 486

Earth Science Online

Be sure to check the Earth Science Web Site for links to chapter material: earthgeu.com

GLENCOE'S ASSESSMENT ADVANTAGE

Volcanic Activity

Introducing the Chapter

Lead a discussion to determine what students already know about volcanoes. Pose the following questions. What is a volcano? What types of material erupt from volcanoes? Are all eruptions the same? Can you name at least three volcanoes? Responses will vary. Keep track of inaccurate responses and address these as you teach the chapter.

Interpreting the Photo

The volcano shown here is Pu'uO'o, a small volcanic cone on Kilauea that began to erupt in 1983. The lava shown spewing from this cone is aa—a viscous lava that commonly erupts from Hawaiian volcanoes.

INTERACTIVE CHALKBOARD
with Image Bank

PowerPoint® Presentations

This CD is an editable Microsoft® PowerPoint® presentation that includes:
- Section presentations
- Section checks
- Image bank
- Links to Earth Science Online
- All transparencies
- Animations
- Audio

Volcanic Activity

What You'll Learn
- How magma forms.
- What kinds of features form as the result of igneous activity within Earth.
- How volcanoes form and how they can be classified.

Why It's Important
Many of Earth's internal processes help to shape our planet's surface. Igneous activity deep within Earth and at its surface produce many of the mountains and rock formations on Earth.

Earth Science Online

To learn more about volcanic activity, visit the Earth Science Web Site at earthgeu.com

470

Kilauea, Hawaii

Discovery Lab

Process Skills
observe, infer, model L1 ELL

Safety Precautions
Remind students to carefully handle the beaker containing hot water.

Preparation
- Obtain ice just before you conduct the lab.

- If time is limited, prepare a bucket of ice water and large beakers of hot, colored water ahead of time.

Procedure
Troubleshooting
- This lab works best when the temperature difference between the two volumes of water is great.
- Remind students that the dropper should be inserted and removed very slowly to avoid creating currents in the beaker.

Discovery Lab

Model Magma Movement

Magma is molten rock beneath Earth's surface that rises because it is less dense than the surrounding rock. In this activity, you will model how magma moves within Earth.

1. Fill a 250-mL beaker with 175 mL of ice-cold water.

2. Carefully fill a 100-mL beaker with very hot tap water. Add 2–3 drops of food coloring to the water and stir well.

3. Carefully fill a dropper with the hot, colored water.

4. Slowly insert the full dropper into the 250-mL beaker until the tip of the dropper is 1 cm from the bottom of the beaker. Squeeze the dropper and keep the bulb depressed as you slowly pull the dropper back out of the cold water.

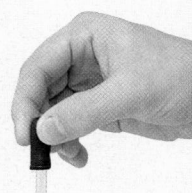 **CAUTION:** *Always wear safety goggles and an apron in the lab.*

Observe In your science journal, describe what happened to the colored water when it entered the beaker. How might this be similar to what happens to magma beneath Earth's surface? Infer what would have happened if you had released the hot water at the surface of the cold water.

Section Focus

Before presenting the lesson, display **Section Focus Transparency 53** on the overhead projector. L1 ELL

Chapter Themes

The following themes from the National Science Content Standards are covered in this chapter. Refer to page 8T of the Teacher Guide for an explanation of the correlations.
Systems, order, and organization (UCP.1); Evidence, models, and explanation (UCP.2); Change, constancy, and measurement (UCP.3); Form and function (UCP.5)

SECTION 18.1 *Magma*

OBJECTIVES

• **Describe** *factors that affect the formation of magma.*

• **Compare** and **contrast** *the different types of magma.*

VOCABULARY

viscosity

Volcanic eruptions are spectacular events. The ash that spews from some volcanoes can form billowy clouds that travel around the world before raining back down to Earth. The red-hot lava that erupts from other volcanoes, such as the Hawaiian volcano Kilauea shown on the facing page, can destroy everything in their paths. In the last 10 000 years, more than 1500 different volcanoes have erupted—providing evidence that Earth is indeed geologically active. Where do ash, lava, and other types of volcanic debris come from?

HOW MAGMA FORMS

All volcanoes are fueled by magma deep beneath Earth's surface. Recall from Chapter 5 that magma is a mixture of molten rock, suspended mineral grains, and dissolved gases deep beneath Earth's surface. Magma forms when temperatures are high enough to melt the rocks involved. Depending on their composition, most rocks begin to melt at temperatures between 800°C and 1200°C. Such

18.1 *Magma* **471**

Observe
The hot water is less dense than the cold water and therefore will rise. Magma rises toward Earth's surface because it is less dense than surrounding rock. If the hot water had been released at the surface of the cold water, it would have merely spread laterally.

 **Assessment**

Performance Have students test their inferences. Use the Performance Task Assessment List for Making Observations and Inferences in **PASC,** p. 17.

 *Out of Time?*

If time does not permit teaching the entire chapter, use the Chapter Summary on page 491 and the GeoDigest found at the end of the unit as an overview.

Content Background

The geothermal gradient is the rate at which temperature increases with depth. Typically, the temperature increases at a rate of about 30°C/km. However, the geothermal gradient varies with location. In active basaltic volcanic regions, the rate can be as high as 60°C/km. Nonvolcanic mountain belts have gradients of about 40°C/km, and stable, continental interiors can have gradients as low as 20°C/km.

Interpreting the Illustration

Figure 18-1 Have students study the graph and answer the questions that follow. What is the relationship between depth and the melting temperature of dry albite? It's a linear relationship; an increase in depth results in an increase in the melting temperature of dry albite. What is the relationship between depth and the melting temperature of wet albite? An increase in depth results in a decrease in the melting temperature of wet albite.

Figure 18-1 Both pressure and the presence of water affect the melting temperature of minerals and thus, rocks.

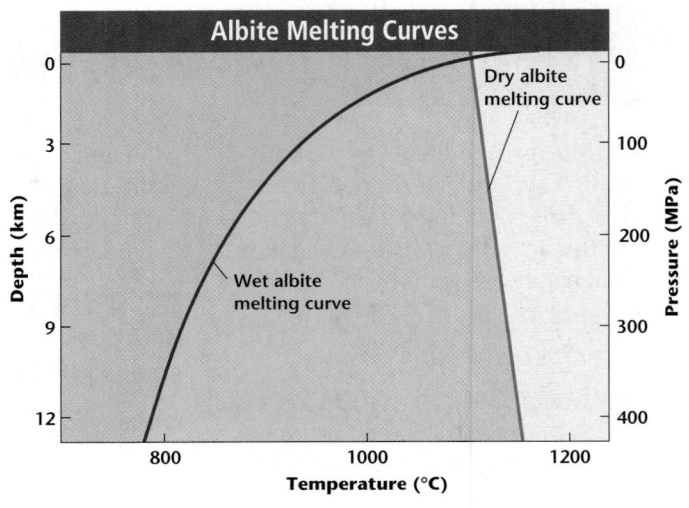

temperatures exist at the base of the lithosphere and in the asthenosphere, the plasticlike portion of the mantle directly beneath the lithosphere. Recall that temperature increases with depth beneath Earth's surface. If rocks melt at temperatures found in the asthenosphere, and temperature increases with depth, then why isn't the entire mantle liquid? What other factors, besides temperature, affect the formation of magma?

Pressure Pressure is one factor that determines whether rocks will melt to form magma. Like temperature, pressure increases with depth because of the weight of overlying rocks. Laboratory experiments have shown that as pressure increases, the temperature at which a substance melts also increases. *Figure 18-1* shows two melting curves for a variety of feldspar called albite. Find the line that represents the dry melting curve. Note that at Earth's surface, dry albite melts at about 1100°C, but at a depth of about 12 km, the melting point of dry albite is about 1150°C. At a depth of about 100 km, the melting point of dry albite increases to 1440°C. The effect of pressure explains why most of the rocks in Earth's lower crust and upper mantle do not melt to form magma, even though the temperatures are high enough.

Water The presence of water also influences whether a rock will melt. Recall that water can be found in the pore spaces of some rocks and can be bound into the crystal structure of some minerals. Even a small amount of water can have a significant effect on a mineral's, and thus a rock's, melting point. At any given pressure, a wet mineral or rock will melt at a lower temperature than the same mineral or rock under dry conditions. Locate the melting curve of wet albite in

Page 470: St 4 KI 2.1m & 2.1n, St 6 KI 1 & 5
Page 471: St 1 Science KI 1, 2, & 3, St 4 KI 2.1a & 2.1m, St 6 KI 2 & 5
Page 472: St 4 KI 2.1a, 2.1l, & 2.1m, St 6 KI 1
Page 473: St 4 KI 2.1b & 2.1m, St 6 KI 1 & 5

Resource Manager

Teaching Transparency 51 L2 ELL

Differentiated Instruction

Gifted When two substances are combined, the melting point of the mixture is significantly lower than the melting points of either of the substances in their pure states. Have students research how mixing substances affects the melting temperature of compounds. L3

Figure 18-1. How does the melting point of wet albite compare to that of dry albite at a depth of 3 km? At a depth of 12 km?

TYPES OF MAGMA

Recall from Chapter 5 that the three major igneous rock types are basalt, andesite, and granite. These rocks form from three major types of magma: basaltic magma, andesitic magma, and rhyolitic magma. The term *rhyolitic* is used to describe the magma that solidifies to form granite because magmas are named after extrusive rocks.

Basaltic magma has the same composition as basalt. Locate the Hawaiian Islands in *Figure 18-2,* which shows some of Earth's active volcanoes. The volcanoes that make up the Hawaiian Islands, which include Kilauea and Mauna Loa, are made of basalt. Surtsey, which formed south of Iceland in 1963, is another basaltic volcano.

Andesitic magma has the same composition as andesite. Mount St. Helens in Washington State and Tambora in Indonesia are two andesitic volcanoes. You will find out more about Tambora in the *Science & the Environment* feature at the end of this chapter. Rhyolitic magma has the same composition as granite. The dormant volcanoes in Yellowstone National Park in the western United States were fueled by rhyolitic magma.

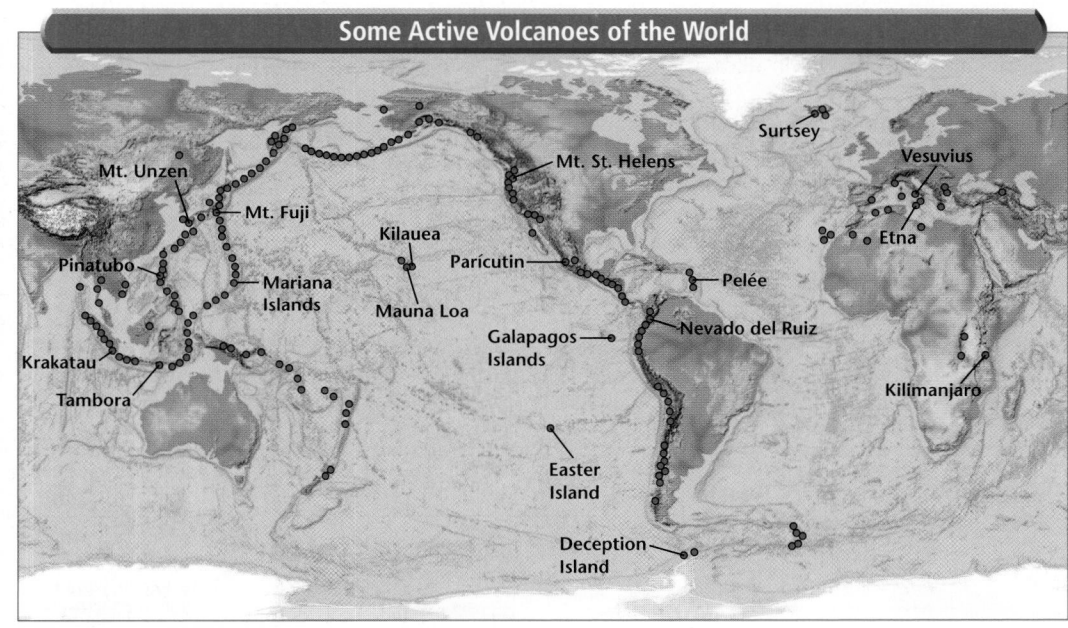

Some Active Volcanoes of the World

Figure 18-2 Compare this map of some of Earth's active volcanoes to the map shown in **Figure 17-13** on page 455. *Where are most active volcanoes located?*

18.1 *Magma* **473**

Page 473 How does the melting point of wet albite compare to that of dry albite at a depth of 3 km? At a depth of 12 km? At a depth of 3 km, wet albite melts at about 900°C and dry albite at about 1150°C. At a depth of 12 km, wet albite melts at about 780°C and dry albite at about 1160°C.

Tying to Previous Knowledge

Have students review, if necessary, the characteristics and compositions of basalt, andesite, and granite from Chapter 5.

Using an Analogy

Explain that magma is under pressure from all directions because it is surrounded by rock. This pressure is called lithostatic pressure. Have students list other examples in which pressure is exerted in all directions on an object. Examples might include air pressure on a balloon afloat above Earth and the hydrostatic pressure exerted on a scuba diver by the surrounding water.

Figure Caption Question

Figure 18-2 Where are most active volcanoes located? Most active volcanoes are located at tectonic plate boundaries.

Resource Manager

Teaching Transparency 52 L2 ELL

Differentiated Instruction

Learning Disabled Have students each make a table to classify the volcanoes shown in **Figure 18-2** by continent. If necessary, list, and identify on a map, Earth's continents.

Across the Curriculum

Math Have students use the geothermal gradient rates given in the Content Background information on page 472 to compute the depth at which the temperature reaches 1000°C in the three different regions named. 16.7 km at 60°C/km; 25 km at 40°C/km; 50 km at 20°C/km

Page 474 What kind of magma has a viscosity similar to that of honey? rhyolitic magma

MiniLab

Purpose
Students will model how the addition of silica affects the viscosity of lava.

Process Skills
model, observe and infer, recognize cause and effect, measure in SI

Materials
dishwashing liquid, NaCl, 250-mL beaker, stirring rod, balance

Expected Results
As more NaCl is added, viscosity increases.

Analyze and Conclude
1. liquid–lava; NaCl–silica
2. As the silica content increases, the viscosity of lava increases.
3. It is low.

✓Assessment

Performance Have students each design an experiment to show the effect of temperature on viscosity. Wax, honey, syrup, or oil can be used to represent the lava. Students should discover that an increase in temperature results in a decrease in viscosity. Use the Performance Task Assessment List for Designing an Experiment in **PASC,** p. 23. 🗌
ELL COOP LEARN

Resource Manager

GeoLab and MiniLab Worksheets, p. 71 🗌

MiniLab

How does silica affect lava flow?

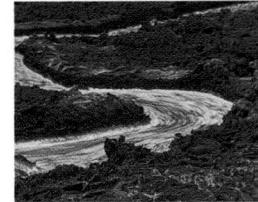

Model the changes in lava viscosity with the addition of silica.

🥽 👕 🧤

CAUTION: Always wear safety goggles and an apron in the lab.

Procedure
1. Pour 120 mL of dishwashing liquid into a 250-mL beaker.
2. Stir the liquid with a stirring rod. Describe the viscosity.
3. Add 30 g of NaCl (table salt) to the liquid. Stir well. Describe what happens.
4. Repeat step 3 three more times.

Analyze and Conclude
1. What do the liquid and NaCl represent?
2. How does an increase in silica affect lava viscosity?
3. Basaltic eruptions are called flows because of the way they move across Earth's surface. What can you infer about the silica content of a basaltic flow?

Magma Composition What accounts for the different types of magma? A number of factors determine the composition of magma, as shown in **Table 18-1.** One of these factors is **viscosity,** the internal resistance to flow. Substances such as honey, liquid soap, and motor oil have a higher viscosity than water, vinegar, and gasoline. Refer to **Table 18-1.** What kind of magma has a viscosity similar to that of honey? You can model the effect of silica content on viscosity in the *MiniLab* on this page.

Basaltic Magma Basaltic magma typically forms when rocks in the upper mantle melt. Most basaltic magma rises relatively rapidly to Earth's surface and reacts very little with crustal rocks because of its low viscosity. Because basaltic magma contains small amounts of dissolved gases and silica, the volcanoes it fuels erupt relatively quietly.

Andesitic Magma Andesitic magma is found along continental margins, where oceanic crust is subducted into Earth's mantle. The source material for this magma can be either oceanic crust or oceanic sediments. As shown in **Table 18-1,** andesitic magma contains about 60 percent silica. This high silica content results in its having an intermediate viscosity. Thus, the volcanoes it fuels are said to have intermediate eruptions.

Table 18-1 Magma Composition and Characteristics

Composition	Source Material	Viscosity	Gas Content	Silica Content	Explosiveness	Location of Magma
Basaltic magma	Upper mantle	Low	1–2%	about 50%	Least	Both oceanic and continental crust
Andesitic magma	Oceanic crust and oceanic sediments	Intermediate	3–4%	about 60%	Intermediate	Continental margins associated with subduction zones
Rhyolitic magma	Continental crust	High	4–6%	about 70%	Greatest	Continental crust

474 CHAPTER 18 *Volcanic Activity*

Environmental Connection
Explain the greenhouse effect and tell students that some volcanic gases are greenhouse gases. List the following volcanic gases on the chalkboard and have students determine which are greenhouse gases: water vapor, carbon dioxide, carbon monoxide, fluorine, chlorine, hydrogen, some sulfur compounds, and nitrogen. Carbon dioxide and water vapor are greenhouse gases.

Rhyolitic Magma Rhyolitic magma forms when molten material rises and mixes with the overlying silica- and water-rich continental crust. The high viscosity of rhyolitic magma inhibits its movement. This resistance to flow, along with the large volume of gas trapped within this magma, makes the volcanoes fueled by rhyolitic magma very explosive.

VISCOSITY

The viscosity of magma and of its surface counterpart, lava, depends on both temperature and composition. The hotter the magma or lava, the lower the viscosity. The temperatures of basaltic lavas are generally between 1000°C and 1250°C. Rhyolitic lava temperatures are usually between 700°C and 900°C. Which type of lava, basaltic or rhyolitic, has a greater viscosity as a result of its temperature? What do you think happens to viscosity as magma or lava cools?

The amount of silica in magma or lava increases the viscosity, as you discovered in the *MiniLab* on the previous page. Thus, magmas and lavas high in silica have higher viscosities than magmas and lavas low in silica. As shown in *Table 18-1,* rhyolitic magmas have the highest silica content, basaltic magmas the lowest, and andesitic magmas have silica contents between these two extremes. Based on composition, which type of lava, basaltic lava or andesitic lava, has a lower viscosity? Basaltic lavas, because of their low silica content, have a lower viscosity than andesitic lavas. The basaltic lava flows that often erupt from Mauna Loa in Hawaii, which is shown in *Figure 18-3,* have been clocked at 16 km/h!

Figure 18-3 Basaltic lava has a low viscosity, and thus, flows relatively quickly from a volcano. The basaltic volcano shown here is Mauna Loa, one of the many volcanoes that make up the Hawaiian Islands.

In-Text Questions

Page 475 Which type of lava, basaltic or rhyolitic, has a greater viscosity as a result of its temperature? rhyolitic What do you think happens to viscosity as magma or lava cools? A decrease in temperature results in an increase in viscosity.

3 Assess

Check for Understanding
Reinforcement
Ask students to identify the factors that determine the composition of magma. composition of the source material, amount of water present, and temperature at which the magma forms

Reteach
Explain, and demonstrate if possible, how an increase in the amount of silica thickens magma in much the same way as flour thickens gravy.

✔Assessment

Performance Have students each research one of the volcanoes labeled in **Figure 18-2.** Have students present their findings as travel brochures or posters. Use the Performance Task Assessment List for Poster in **PASC,** p. 73.

SECTION ASSESSMENT

1. Describe three factors that affect the formation of magma.

2. How does the presence of water affect the melting temperature of a rock?

3. Compare and contrast the properties of the three types of magma.

4. Refer to *Table 18-1.* Where does andesitic magma form? What is the source material of this type of magma?

5. Explain the relationship between the viscosity of a magma and its temperature.

6. **Thinking Critically** A volcano violently erupted in Indonesia in 1883. What can you infer about the composition of the magma that fueled the volcano? If people witnessed the eruption, what do you think they were able to observe about the lava flow?

SKILL REVIEW

7. **Concept Mapping** Use the following terms to construct a concept map to organize the major ideas in this section. For more help, refer to the *Skill Handbook.*

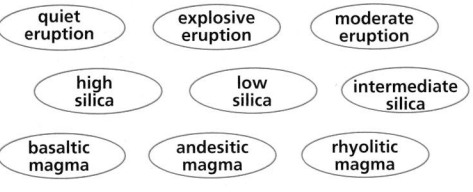

quiet eruption | explosive eruption | moderate eruption
high silica | low silica | intermediate silica
basaltic magma | andesitic magma | rhyolitic magma

SECTION ASSESSMENT

1. temperature, source material, water, pressure
2. Water lowers the melting temperature.
3. basaltic magma: forms from rocks in the upper mantle, low viscosity, low gas and silica content, not explosive, forms beneath oceanic crust; andesitic magma: source is oceanic crust and sediments, intermediate water, silica, and gas content and viscosity; rhyolitic magma: forms from continental crust, high gas and silica content, high viscosity and explosiveness; forms beneath continental crust

4. subduction zones at continental margins; oceanic crust and sediments
5. increasing temperature causes a decrease in viscosity
6. The explosive eruption indicates magma rich in silica and gases. People would have observed very viscous lava flows.
7. rhyolitic magma-high silica-explosive eruption; andesitic magma-intermediate silica-moderate eruption; basaltic magma-low silica-quiet eruption

NY Core Curriculum Standards

Page 474: St 1 Science KI 1, 2, & 3, St 4 KI 2.1m, St 6 KI 1 & 2
Page 475: St 4 KI 2.1m, St 6 KI 1 & 5

SECTION 18.2 *Intrusive Activity*

Prepare

Section Background

For section content background, refer to **Columnar Jointing** on page 470C.

Preplanning

Refer to the Chapter Organizer on pages 470A–B.

1 Focus

Section Focus

Before presenting the lesson, display **Section Focus Transparency 54** on the overhead projector.
[L1] [ELL]

Tying to Previous Knowledge

Have students recall from Chapter 5 how the rate of cooling affects the textures of igneous rocks. The slower the cooling rate, the coarser the texture.

SECTION 18.2 *Intrusive Activity*

OBJECTIVES

- **Explain** *how magma affects overlying crustal rocks.*
- **Compare** *and* **contrast** *intrusive igneous rock bodies.*

VOCABULARY

pluton
batholith
stock
laccolith
sill
dike

Magma, because it is molten, is less dense than surrounding rocks. This density difference, which you modeled in the *Discovery Lab*, forces magma to move upward and eventually come into contact with, or intrude, the overlying crust. Intruding magma can affect the crust in several ways, as shown in *Figure 18-4*. Magma can force the overlying rock apart and enter the newly formed fissures. Magma can also cause blocks of rock to break off and sink into the magma, where the rocks may eventually melt. Finally, magma can melt the rock into which it intrudes. But what happens deep in the magma chamber as the magma slowly cools?

PLUTONS

Recall from Chapter 5 that when magma cools, minerals form. Over a very long period of time, these minerals will combine to form intrusive igneous rock bodies. Some of these rock bodies are thin, ribbonlike features only a few centimeters thick and several hundred meters long. Others are very large, ranging in size from about 1 km^3 to hundreds of cubic kilometers. These intrusive igneous rock bodies, called **plutons,** can be exposed at Earth's surface as a result of uplift and erosion and are classified based on their size, shape, and relationship to surrounding rocks.

Batholiths and Stocks The largest plutons are called **batholiths.** These irregularly shaped masses of coarse-grained igneous rocks cover at least 100 km^2 and take millions of years to form. Batholiths are common in the interiors of major mountain chains. Many batholiths in North America are composed primarily of granite, the

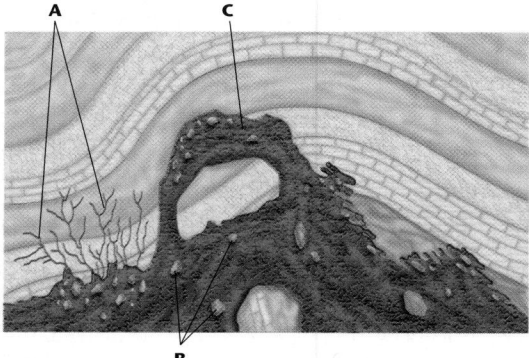

Figure 18-4 Magma can enter fissures in rocks **(A).** Magma can also cause blocks of rock to break off the overlying rock into which the magma intrudes. These blocks of rock become part of the magma body **(B).** Magma can cause the rocks with which it comes in contact to melt **(C).**

476 CHAPTER 18 *Volcanic Activity*

Resource Manager

Study Guide for Content Mastery, p. 113
[L2]

Section Focus Transparency 54 [L1] [ELL]

Teaching Transparency 53 [L2] [ELL]

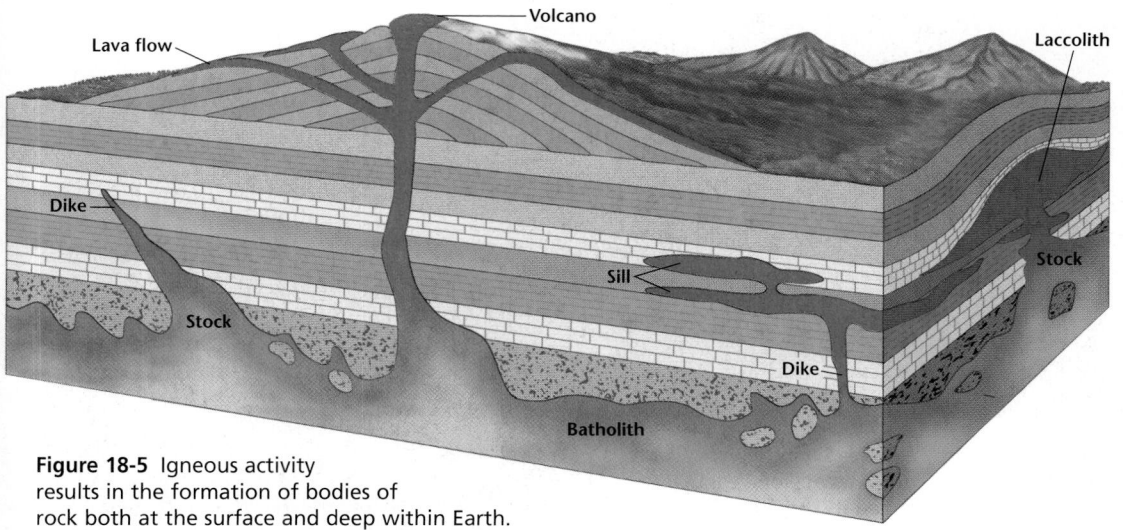

Figure 18-5 Igneous activity results in the formation of bodies of rock both at the surface and deep within Earth.

Labels on figure: Lava flow, Volcano, Laccolith, Dike, Stock, Sill, Stock, Dike, Batholith

most common rock type found in plutons. However, gabbro and diorite, the intrusive equivalents of basalt and andesite, are also found in batholiths. The largest batholith in North America, the Coast Range Batholith in British Columbia, is more than 1500 km long. Irregularly shaped plutons that are similar to batholiths but smaller in size are called **stocks.** Both batholiths and stocks, as shown in *Figure 18-5,* cut across older rocks and generally form 10–30 km beneath Earth's surface.

Laccoliths Sometimes, when magma intrudes into parallel rock layers close to Earth's surface, some of the rocks bow upward as a result of the intense heat and pressure of the magma body. When the magma solidifies, a laccolith forms. As shown in *Figure 18-5,* a **laccolith** is a mushroom-shaped pluton with a round top and flat bottom. Compared to batholiths and stocks, laccoliths are relatively small; they are, at most, up to 16 kilometers wide. Laccoliths exist in the Black Hills of South Dakota, the Henry Mountains of Utah, and the Judith Mountains of Montana, among other places.

Sills and Dikes A **sill** is a pluton that forms when magma intrudes parallel to layers of rock, as shown in *Figure 18-5.* A sill can range from only a few centimeters to hundreds of meters in thickness. The Palisades Sill, which is exposed in the cliffs above the Hudson River near New York City, is about 300 m thick. What effect do you think this sill, shown on the next page, had on the sedimentary rocks into which it intruded?

2 Teach

Interpreting the Illustrations

Figure 18-4 and **Figure 18-5** Ask students to carefully study these two figures as you ask the following question. Which of the mechanisms of intrusion shown in **Figure 18-4** would be involved in the formation of the dikes and sills shown in **Figure 18-5?** magma forcing rocks apart and entering the newly formed fissures

Using Scientific Terms

Linguistic Tell students that sills are concordant plutons, whereas dikes are discordant plutons. Have students use **Figure 18-5** and the information in the text to determine the meanings of these adjectives. *Concordant* means "constant" or "agreeing." *Discordant* means "being at variance" or "disagreeing." Sills agree with or are parallel to the rocks into which they intrude, while dikes disagree with or cut across the rocks into which they intrude. **L1** **ELL**

In-Text Question

Page 477 What effect do you think this sill, shown on the next page, had on the sedimentary rocks into which it intruded? The sill, which was molten during the time of intrusion, caused deformation of the rocks into which it intruded.

Interpreting the Photos

Figure 18-6 and **Figure 18-7**
Have students use their fingers to trace the dike and the sill shown in these two photos.

Knowledge Which of the following statements is false?

a. Batholiths are common in the interiors of mountain chains.
b. Laccoliths have curved bottoms and flat tops.
c. Sills form when magma is forced between rock layers.
d. Most igneous activity occurs deep within Earth.

Choice b is false. Laccoliths have curved tops and flat bottoms.

Content Background

When magma intrudes country rock, large numbers of cracks form in the rock. These numerous channels are often filled by the magma, which upon cooling causes many dikes to form. Thus, dikes rarely are found alone—hundreds or even thousands of them can be found in a region affected by magmatic intrusions.

Enrichment

Logical-Mathematical
The faces of Mount Rushmore were carved into an intrusive igneous rock body that is exposed at Earth's surface. Have interested students research the monument from a technical point of view to answer the following questions. How were the faces carved? How many metric tons of rock were displaced? How long did it take to carve the monument? Why were only the heads of the presidents carved into the rock? **L2**

Figure 18-7 Note that, unlike a sill, this dike, which is in Arizona, cuts across the rocks it intrudes.

Figure 18-6 The Palisades Sill in New York State formed over 200 million years ago when magma forced its way into layers of parallel rock.

Unlike the sill shown in *Figure 18-6,* which is parallel to the rocks it intrudes, a **dike** is a pluton that cuts across preexisting rocks, as shown in *Figure 18-7.* Dikes often form when magma invades cracks in surrounding rock bodies. Most dikes are a few centimeters to several meters wide and up to tens of kilometers long. The Great Dike in Zimbabwe, Africa, however, is an exception: it is about 8 km wide and 500 km long.

While the textures of sills and dikes vary, many of these plutons are coarse grained. Recall from Chapter 5 that grain size is related to the rate of cooling. Coarse-grained sills and dikes are thought to have formed deep in Earth's crust, where the magma cooled relatively slowly to yield large mineral grains.

PLUTONS AND TECTONICS

Many plutons are formed as the result of mountain-building processes. In fact, batholiths are found at the cores of many of Earth's mountain ranges. Where did the enormous volume of magma that cooled to form these igneous bodies come from? Recall from Chapter 17 that many major mountain chains formed along continental-continental convergent plate boundaries. Scientists hypothesize that these collisions might have forced continental crust down into the upper mantle, where it melted, intruded into the overlying rocks, and eventually cooled to form batholiths.

Science Field Book

Earth Science
Journal

Have students answer the following question. Which would cause greater contact metamorphism, a dike intruded at a depth of 10 km or a dike of the same size intruded 1 km beneath Earth's surface? the shallower dike, because minerals at 10 km are in equilibrium at a higher temperature and would not change as much as minerals closer to the surface

Figure 18-8 The granite cliffs that tower over Yosemite National Park in California are parts of the Sierra Nevada batholith that have been exposed at Earth's surface.

Batholiths are also thought to have formed as a result of oceanic-oceanic convergence. Again, recall from Chapter 17 that when two oceanic plates converge, one plate is subducted into the mantle. Parts of this subducted plate melt to form magma. The Sierra Nevada batholith, which has been exposed at Earth's surface as a result of uplift and erosion, formed from at least five episodes of igneous activity beneath what is now California. The famous granite cliffs found in Yosemite National Park, some of which are shown in *Figure 18-8,* are relatively small parts of this extensive batholith.

The plutons that form deep beneath Earth's surface represent the majority of igneous activity on our planet. Nevertheless, most people think of volcanoes when they hear the words *igneous activity.* These often-spectacular examples of igneous activity at Earth's surface are discussed in the next section.

SECTION ASSESSMENT

1. Discuss three ways in which magma affects the crust into which it intrudes.
2. What are plutons, and how are they classified?
3. How are sills and dikes similar? How do they differ? Give an example of each.
4. What is a laccolith?
5. **Thinking Critically** Sometimes, the texture in the same sill varies: finer grains are found along the margins and coarser grains are found toward the middle of the pluton. What might cause this difference in texture?

SKILL REVIEW

6. **Making a Table** Make a table in which you compare and contrast the different types of intrusive igneous bodies. For more help, refer to the *Skill Handbook.*

SECTION ASSESSMENT

1. Rising magma causes rocks to fracture, causes blocks to break off and sink into the magma chamber, where they eventually melt, and causes rocks in contact with the magma to melt.
2. Plutons are intrusive igneous rock bodies that are classified by size, shape, and their relationship to surrounding rocks.
3. Sills and dikes are relatively thin plutons. Sills are parallel to surrounding rock layers. The Palisades Sill in New York State is a sill. Dikes cut across the rocks into which they intrude.

The Great Dike in Zimbabwe is a dike.
4. A laccolith is a mushroom-shaped pluton with a rounded top and a flat bottom.
5. The edges of the sill cooled more quickly than the center part of the intrusion.
6. Students' tables should be arranged in such a way as to show that all plutons are intrusive igneous bodies. Differences among the plutons should include size, shape, and relationship to the rocks into which the plutons intrude.

Section Background

For section content background, refer to **The Yellowstone Hot Spot** on page 470D.

Preplanning

Refer to the Chapter Organizer on pages 470A–B.

1 Focus

Section Focus

Before presenting the lesson, display **Section Focus Transparency 55** on the overhead projector.
L1 ELL

Project

Have students conduct research to find out that volcanoes can be classified as active, dormant, or extinct. Have students differentiate among these terms in their science journals. Challenge students to list at least five examples of each of these volcano types.

SECTION 18.3 Volcanoes

OBJECTIVES

- **Describe** *the major parts of a volcano.*
- **Compare** *and* **contrast** *shield, cinder-cone, and composite volcanoes.*
- **Contrast** *the volcanism that occurs at plate boundaries.*
- **Explain** *the relationship between volcanism and hot spots.*

VOCABULARY

vent
crater
caldera
shield volcano
cinder-cone volcano
composite volcano
tephra
pyroclastic flow
hot spot

What comes to mind when you hear the word *volcano?* Do you picture clouds of ash and jagged rocks being thrown violently into the air? Or do you envision rivers of reddish-orange lava flowing down the slopes of a steep volcanic peak? Both of these represent volcanic activity on Earth's surface. Volcanism produces various features that alter Earth's landscape. In this section, you will examine some of these features, beginning with the one created at the point where magma reaches the surface: the vent.

ANATOMY OF A VOLCANO

At the beginning of this chapter, you learned that magma chambers deep within Earth fuel the volcanoes that erupt at the planet's surface. Also recall that when magma reaches Earth's surface, it is called lava. Lava erupts through an opening in the crust called a **vent.** As lava flows out onto the surface, it cools and solidifies around the vent. Over time, the lava can accumulate to form a mountain known as a volcano. At the top of a volcano, around the vent, is a bowl-shaped depression called a **crater.** The crater is connected to the magma chamber by the vent. Locate the crater of the volcano shown in *Figure 18-9.*

Figure 18-9 A crater is the bowl-shaped depression that surrounds the central vent at a volcano's summit. The volcano shown below is one of many that dot the northern Arizona landscape near Flagstaff.

480

In-Text Question

Page 480 Locate the crater of the volcano shown in **Figure 18-9.** The crater is the bowl-shaped depression at the volcano's summit.

Interpreting the Photo

Figure 18-9 Have students trace the outline of the volcano shown in the photograph. Challenge them to modify the outline into a cross-sectional (cut-away) view of the volcano that includes the magma chamber, the volcanic vent, the crater, and the layers of volcanic debris that accumulated to form the mountain. Students' drawings should resemble the volcano shown in **Figure 18-5.**

Figure 18-10 The caldera now known as Crater Lake is located in Oregon. This caldera formed about 6600 years ago as a result of numerous volcanic eruptions of Mount Mazama.

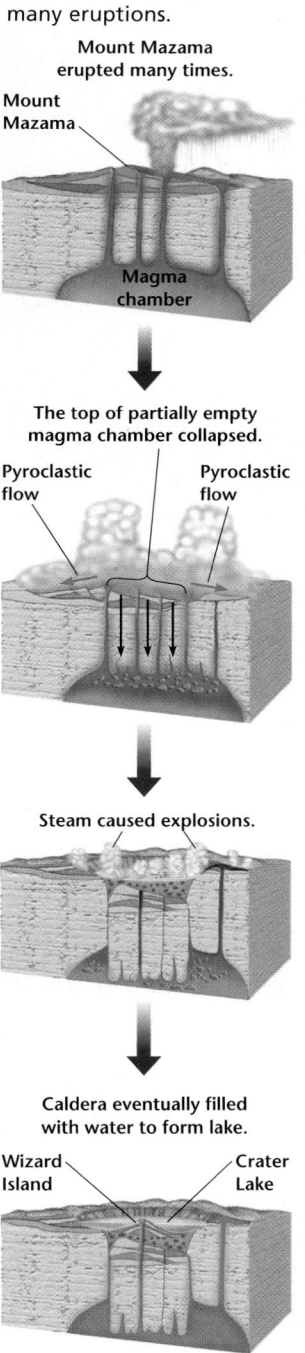

Figure 18-11 Crater Lake formed as the result of many eruptions.

Mount Mazama erupted many times.

Mount Mazama

Magma chamber

The top of partially empty magma chamber collapsed.

Pyroclastic flow

Pyroclastic flow

Steam caused explosions.

Caldera eventually filled with water to form lake.

Wizard Island

Crater Lake

Volcanic craters are usually less than 1 km in diameter. Larger depressions called **calderas,** which can be up to 50 km in diameter, however, can form when the summit or the side of a volcano collapses into the magma chamber that once fueled the volcano. The caldera now known as Crater Lake formed in this way, as shown in *Figure 18-11.* The caldera walls, which are visible in the photograph in *Figure 18-10,* form cliffs that tower nearly 600 m above the water's surface. Wizard Island, which is located in the center of the lake, is actually a small volcanic cone that formed after the caldera collapsed.

TYPES OF VOLCANOES

The appearance of a volcano depends on two factors: the type of material that forms the volcano and the type of eruptions that occur. Based on these two criteria, three major types of volcanoes have been identified: shield volcanoes, cinder-cone volcanoes, and composite volcanoes. Each differs in size, shape, and composition.

Shield Volcanoes A **shield volcano** is a mountain with broad, gently sloping sides and a nearly circular base. Shield volcanoes form when layer upon layer of basaltic lava accumulates during

2 Teach

Content Background
Volcanic eruptions most commonly occur at a volcano's summit, but lava can also be extruded from the flanks of a volcano. Some volcanic eruptions, such as the 1980 eruption of Mount St. Helens, occur laterally as well as vertically. The 1980 eruption of Mount St. Helens, in fact, made many geologists realize that lateral blasts may be more common than was previously thought.

Modeling
Visual-Spatial Have groups of students make models of an erupting volcano. Provide students with modeling clay, baking soda, red food coloring, vinegar, safety goggles, lab aprons, and shallow trays. **CAUTION:** *Make sure that students wear the safety goggles and lab aprons during this entire activity.* Instruct students to use the clay to form a small (no more than 10 cm high) volcano in the shallow tray. Tell students to create a crater 1 cm deep at the summit of the model, and to place a heaping teaspoon of baking soda and a drop of food coloring in the crater. Then, have students add a tablespoon of vinegar to the crater and observe what happens. Have students describe the eruption in their science journals. L1 ELL COOP LEARN

Content Background

The volcanic material that makes up the black sand beaches of Hawaii did not erupt as sand-sized particles. The sand grains formed when basaltic lava flows entered the ocean. The rapid thermal shock, combined with the seawater flashing into steam, caused the lava to explode and shatter into tiny particles. If the beach is young, the particles have very angular shapes.

Collaborative Learning

Interpersonal Have small groups of students use fine-grained sand, coarse-grained sand, and small pieces of angular gravel to determine how particle size and shape affect the angle of repose. **CAUTION:** *Remind students to wear safety goggles during this activity.* The angle of repose is the maximum angle of slope, measured from the horizontal, at which loose materials will come to rest on a pile of similar material. Instruct students to pour one cup of each material slowly onto a desktop to form a pile. Use a protractor to demonstrate how to measure the angle of repose for each material, then have students measure the angle of repose for each of their piles. Have students compare the results of this activity to the small diagrams that accompany the photos on pages 482 and 483.

COOP LEARN

NY Core Curriculum Standards

Page 482: St 4 KI 2.1b, St 6 KI 1
Page 483: St 4 KI 2.1b, St 6 KI 1

Shield cone

Figure 18-12 Mauna Loa, shown in the distance, is a shield volcano in Hawaii. A small cinder-cone volcano on the flank of Mauna Kea is visible in the foreground.

NATIONAL GEOGRAPHIC

To learn more about volcanoes, go to the National Geographic Expedition on page 886.

nonexplosive eruptions. Recall that eruptions involving basaltic lava are less explosive than other eruptions. This is because basaltic lava has a low viscosity as a result of the relatively small amounts of gases and silica it contains. The shield volcanoes that make up the Hawaiian Islands are made of basalt. Mauna Kea, which is shown in *Figure 18-12,* is one such volcano.

Cinder-Cone Volcanoes A **cinder-cone volcano** forms when material ejected high into the air falls back to Earth and piles up around the vent. Cinder-cone volcanoes have steep sides, as shown in *Figure 18-13,* and are generally small; most are less than 500 m high. The magma that fuels cinder-cone volcanoes contains more water and silica than the magma that fuels shield volcanoes. This more viscous magma also contains large volumes of gases, which make cinder-cone volcanoes more explosive in nature than shield volcanoes.

Composite Volcanoes **Composite volcanoes** form when layers of volcanic fragments alternate with lava. As with cinder-cone volcanoes, the magma that forms composite volcanoes commonly contains large amounts of silica, water, and gases. Composite volcanoes are much larger than cinder-cone volcanoes, and, because of their violently explosive nature, they are potentially dangerous to humans and the environment. Two composite volcanoes of the Cascade Range in the western United States, Mount St. Helens and Mount Rainier, are shown in *Figure 18-14.*

Differentiated Instruction

English-Language Learners Have students use dictionaries to look up the definitions of the terms *shield, cinder,* and *composite.* Have students list each term in their science journals. Have students write a sentence next to each term explaining why it is an appropriate adjective for describing that type of volcano. **ELL**

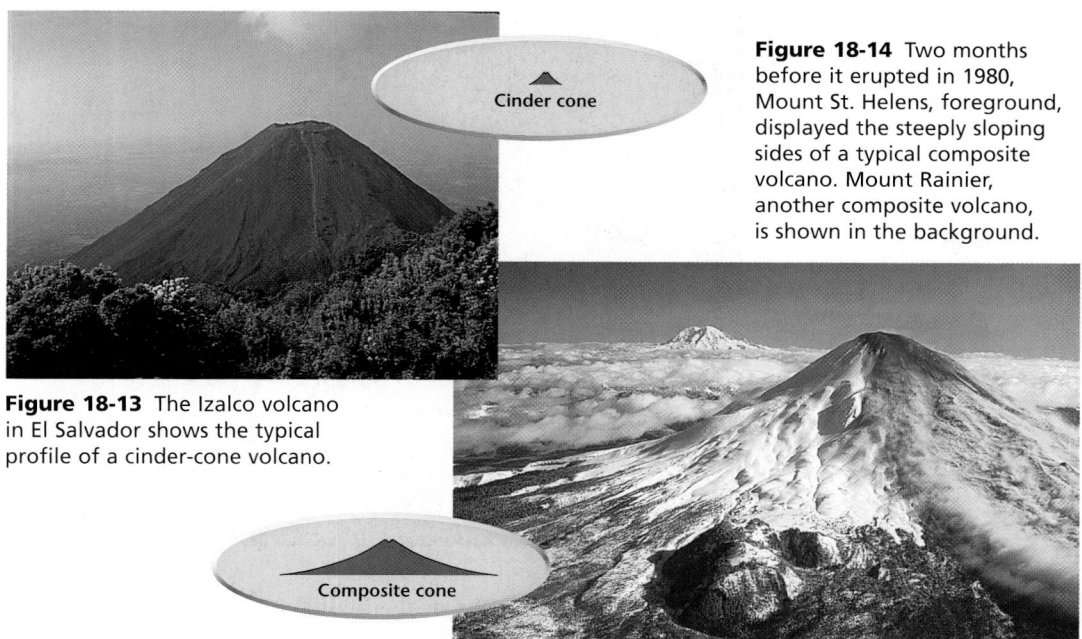

Figure 18-13 The Izalco volcano in El Salvador shows the typical profile of a cinder-cone volcano.

Figure 18-14 Two months before it erupted in 1980, Mount St. Helens, foreground, displayed the steeply sloping sides of a typical composite volcano. Mount Rainier, another composite volcano, is shown in the background.

Size and Slope Look at the small sketches that show the relative sizes of the three types of volcanoes in *Figures 18-12* through *18-14.* These diagrams are drawn to scale. As you can see, shield volcanoes are by far the largest. The smallest volcanoes are cinder-cone volcanoes, which often form on or very near larger volcanoes. Notice, too, that cinder-cone volcanoes have the steepest slopes, while shield volcanoes have the gentlest slopes. The slopes of cinder-cone and composite volcanoes are concave, and the slopes of shield volcanoes are straight. These differences in both size and slope are the result of many factors, including the different kinds of materials that make up each volcano, the vegetation that grows on the volcano's slopes, local climate, and the eruptive history of the volcano.

VOLCANIC MATERIAL

Rock fragments thrown into the air during a volcanic eruption are called **tephra.** Tephra can be newly cooled and hardened lava, mineral grains that started to crystallize prior to the eruption, or pieces of the volcanic cone. Tephra are classified by size. The smallest fragments, called dust, are less than 0.25 mm in diameter. Ash, another kind of tephra, is larger than dust but less than 2 mm in diameter. Somewhat larger fragments of tephra are called lapilli, an Italian word that means "little stones." Lapilli are larger than 2 mm but less than 64 mm in diameter. The largest tephra thrown from a volcano

18.3 *Volcanoes* **483**

NATIONAL GEOGRAPHIC

Video
Our Dynamic Earth

483

Project

Interpersonal Have pairs of students compare and contrast different types of material ejected from volcanoes. Provide students with safety goggles, tephra of different sizes (dust, ash, and lapilli), volcanic beach sand, biologic probes, tweezers, and, if possible, a stereo microscope. Have students separate the tephra into three piles according to size. Then have students compare the size, shape, and texture of the volcanic sand with those of the tephra and record their observations. Encourage students to touch the materials, to sketch the shapes of individual pieces of tephra, and to record all of their observations in their science journals. **CAUTION:** *Remind students to handle the materials carefully, as they can be very abrasive. Have students wash their hands thoroughly after completing this activity.*

Using Scientific Terms

Linguistic Have students research the origin of the word *pyroclastic* and identify several other terms with one of the same roots. *Pyr* is a Greek word that means "fire," and *klastos* is a Greek term that means "broken." *Clastic sediments, funeral pyre,* and *pyromaniac* are a few terms with these roots.

Discussion

Ask students whether it would be possible to outdistance a pyroclastic flow in a car, then ask the following question: If you were 10 km from an advancing pyroclastic flow traveling at 120 km/h, how much time would you have to get away? Even if the road was straight, students would need to drive at 160 kmh (100 mph) to escape, because the flow would travel 10 km in five minutes.

Figure 18-15 More than 29 000 people died as a result of the pyroclastic flow that accompanied the 1902 eruption of Mount Pelée on the island of Martinique. Note that much of the city of St. Pierre was destroyed.

Earth Science Online

Topic: Mt. St. Helens
To learn more about damage caused by volcanoes, visit the Earth Science Web Site at earthgeu.com

Activity: Research the eruption of Mt. St. Helens in 1980. Prepare a brief report or media presentation describing the change in the landscape that occurred.

can be the size of a car or a small building. When these large volcanic fragments are angular, they are called volcanic blocks. Volcanic blocks as large as houses have been ejected more than 10 km into the air during some eruptions. When blobs of lava are forcefully ejected from a volcano, they may cool to form rounded or streamlined tephra called volcanic bombs. Volcanic bombs may harden in the air or they may flatten and solidify after they hit the ground.

Pyroclastic Flows Some tephra cause tremendous damage and kill thousands of people. Violent volcanic eruptions can send clouds of gas, ash, and other tephra down a slope at incredible speeds. This rapidly moving volcanic material, which is called a **pyroclastic flow,** can travel at speeds of nearly 200 km/h and may contain hot, poisonous gases. The temperature at the center of a pyroclastic flow can exceed 700°C. One of the most widely known and deadly pyroclastic flows occurred in 1902 on Mount Pelée, on the island of Martinique in the Caribbean Sea. More than 29 000 people suffocated or were burned to death. What little was left of the town of St. Pierre after the eruption is shown in **Figure 18-15.**

WHERE DO VOLCANOES OCCUR?

The distribution of volcanoes on Earth's surface is not random. Most volcanoes form at plate boundaries. In fact, about 80 percent of all volcanoes are found along convergent boundaries, and about 15 percent are found along divergent boundaries. Only about 5 percent of extrusive igneous activity occurs far from plate boundaries.

Differentiated Instruction

Learning Disabled Provide students with safety goggles and circles drawn on a piece of paper that represent the actual sizes of the different types of tephra. Have students then sort the grains of a small amount (about 1/4 t) of a mixture of coarse sand, fine sand, and gravel according to size. Make sure that students wear the goggles during this entire activity. **L1** **ELL**

Across the Curriculum

Math Approximately 7000 pyroclastic flows occurred on Mount Unzen, in Japan, from 1991 through 1994. Have students calculate the average number of pyroclastic flows that occurred each month during this period of time. 7000 flows ÷ 48 months = 146 flows/month

Convergent Volcanism Recall from Chapter 17 that plates come together along convergent boundaries. Also recall that convergence involving oceanic plates creates subduction zones, places where slabs of oceanic crust descend into the mantle and eventually melt. The magma generated is forced upward through the overlying plate and forms volcanoes when it reaches the surface.

The volcanoes associated with convergent plate boundaries form two major belts, as shown in *Figure 18-16.* The larger belt, the Circum-Pacific Belt, is also called the Pacific Ring of Fire. It stretches along the western coasts of North and South America, across the Aleutian Islands, and down the eastern coast of Asia. Volcanoes in the Cascade Range of the western United States, and Mount Pinatubo in the Philippines are some of the volcanoes in the Circum-Pacific Belt. The smaller belt, which is called the Mediterranean Belt, includes Mount Etna and Mount Vesuvius, two composite volcanoes in Italy.

Divergent Volcanism Volcanic activity is also common along divergent plate boundaries, where two plates are moving apart. Magma is forced upward into the fractures and faults that form as the plates separate. These areas of major faults and fractures are called rift zones. Most of the world's rift volcanism occurs under water along ocean ridges. Recall from Chapter 17 that this type of volcanism results in the formation of new ocean floor during the

Earth Science Online

Update For an online update of recent volcanic eruptions, visit the Earth Science Web Site at earthgeu.com

Figure 18-16 Most of Earth's volcanoes form two distinct volcanic belts: the larger Circum-Pacific Belt and the much smaller Mediterranean Belt.

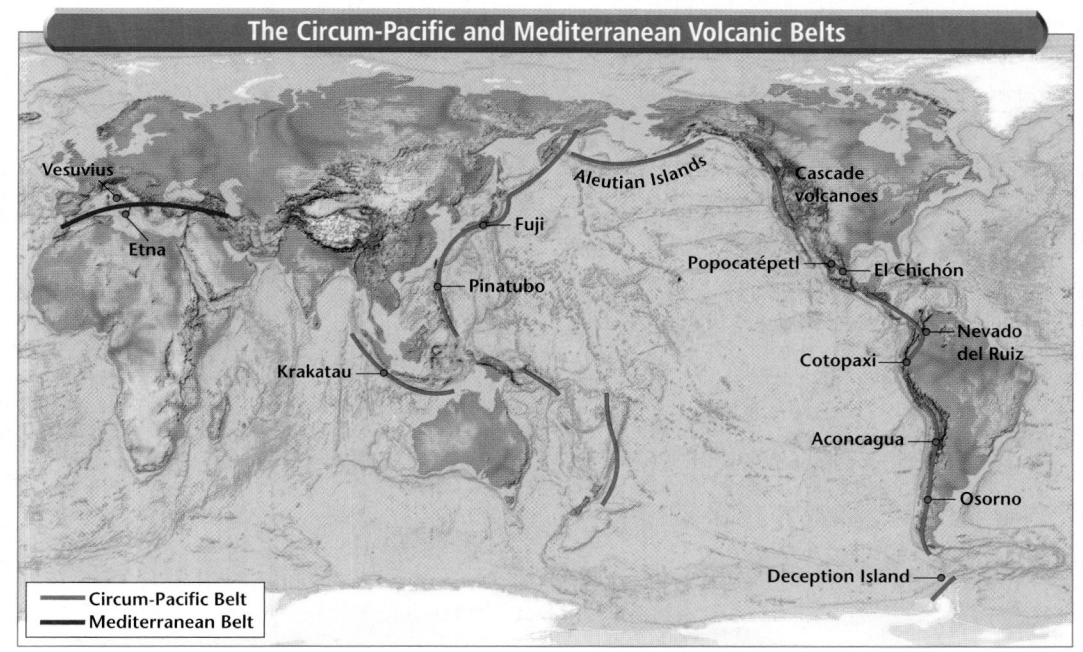

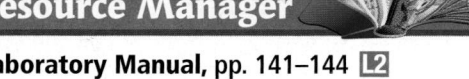
The Circum-Pacific and Mediterranean Volcanic Belts

Vesuvius
Etna
Krakatau
Pinatubo
Fuji
Aleutian Islands
Cascade volcanoes
Popocatépetl
El Chichón
Cotopaxi
Nevado del Ruiz
Aconcagua
Osorno
Deception Island

— Circum-Pacific Belt
— Mediterranean Belt

Tying to Previous Knowledge

Have a volunteer or two summarize the differences between convergent and divergent plate boundaries as discussed in Chapter 17.

Interpreting the Illustration

Figure 18-16 Have students use the map to answer the following questions. Which tectonic plates are associated with the Mediterranean Volcanic Belt? the African, Arabian, and Eurasian Plates When will this belt cease to exist? when the African Plate converges with the Eurasian Plate and subduction stops If students are unable to answer these questions, refer them to **Figure 17-13** on page 455.

Applying Earth Science

Have small groups of students research volcanoes on other planets and their moons. One group might research Mars's Olympus Mons, the largest volcano in the solar system. Another group can find out about Io, a moon of Jupiter and the most volcanically active object in the solar system. The volcanoes of Venus are another possible research topic. Each group should summarize its results on a poster that can be displayed in the classroom.
COOP LEARN **P**

Resource Manager

Laboratory Manual, pp. 141–144 L2
Teaching Transparency 54 L2 ELL

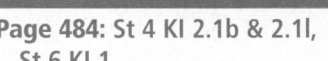
NY Core Curriculum Standards

Page 484: St 4 KI 2.1b & 2.1l, St 6 KI 1
Page 485: St 4 KI 2.1b & 2.1l, St 6 KI 1

Using Math

The Pacific Plate has moved 3500 km in 43 million years. The average speed is 3.5×10^8 cm $\div$ 4.3×10^7 y = 8 cm/y.

Problem-Solving Lab

Purpose
Students will calculate and graph the distance traveled by a lava flow.

Process Skills
make and use tables, make and use graphs, use numbers

Materials
graph paper, pencil, ruler, calculator

Teaching Strategies
The Laki Fissure eruption did not threaten any villages. Ask students what would happen if a similar eruption had occurred near your school.

Analysis
1. The lava flowed at a rate of 4.8 km every 12 hours. Students should calculate the following distances: 12 h, 4.8 km; 24 h, 9.6 km; 36 h, 14.4 km; 48 h, 19.2 km; 60 h, 24 km; 72 h, 28.8 km; 84 h, 33.6 km; 96 h, 38.4 km; 108 h, 43.2 km; 120 h, 48 km.
2. Students' graphs should reflect the values calculated in step 1.

Thinking Critically
3. 45 km $\div$ 0.4 km/h = 112.5 h or about four and a half days
4. 0.4 km/h $\times$ 72 h = 28.8 km

✔Assessment

Skill Inform students that some lavas in Hawaii flow as quickly as 16 km/h. Have students compute how long it would have taken the Laki flow to reach the coastline at this speed.
45 km $\div$ 16 km/h = 2.8 h

Using Math

Using Numbers Look at *Figure 18-17.* Note that the distance from Daikakuji Seamount to Hawaii is about 3500 km. Daikakuji is 43 million years old. What is the average speed of the Pacific Plate?

process of seafloor spreading. One of the few places where rift volcanism can be observed above sea level today is in Iceland. This island is a part of the Mid-Atlantic Ridge, and consequently, several active volcanoes dot the landscape.

Hot Spots Some volcanoes are located far from plate boundaries. These volcanoes form as the result of **hot spots,** which are unusually hot regions of Earth's mantle where high-temperature plumes of mantle material rise toward the surface. Plumes originate deep within the mantle, or perhaps even near the core-mantle boundary. The intense heat of the plumes melts rock, which is then forced upward toward the crust as magma. The magma, in turn, melts through the crust to form volcanoes. While a plume does move vertically, it does not move laterally. As a result, a trail of progressively older volcanoes forms as a plate moves over a hot spot.

Some of Earth's best known volcanoes formed as a result of hot spots under the Pacific Ocean. The Hawaiian Islands, for example, continue to rise above the ocean floor as the Pacific Plate moves slowly over a hot spot. The volcanoes on the oldest island, Kauai, are inactive because the island no longer sits above the hot spot. The world's most active volcano, Kilauea, is on the big island of Hawaii and is currently located over the hot spot. Another volcano, Loihi, is forming on the seafloor east of the big island of Hawaii and may eventually break the ocean surface to form a new island.

Problem-Solving Lab

Making and Using Graphs

Calculate and graph how fast lava flows On June 8, 1783, the Laki fissure zone in Iceland began to erupt in what would become the largest flood basalt in recent history. A flood basalt forms when lava flows from fissures to create a vast plain or plateau. The Laki eruption resulted in a total volume of 14.73 km³ of basalt, which covered 565 km². The lava erupted from fissures located 45 km from the coast, and flowed at speeds averaging 0.4 km/h.

Analysis
1. Design a data table to show the distance traveled by the lava over a five-day period. Calculate the distance every 12 hours.
2. Plot the data on a graph: put time on the *x*-axis and distance on the *y*-axis.

Thinking Critically
3. How long did it take the lava to reach the coast?
4. How many kilometers did the lava travel in three days?

The chains of volcanoes that form over hot spots provide important information about plate motions. The rate and direction of motion can be calculated from the positions of these volcanoes. Even changes in plate motion that occurred in the distant past can be determined. Look at *Figure 18-17.* Note that the Hawaiian Islands are at one end of the 5800-km Hawaiian-Emperor volcanic chain. The oldest seamount, Meiji, is at the other end of the chain and is about 75–80 million years old, which indicates that this hot spot has existed for at least that many years. The bend in the chain at Daikakuji Seamount records a change in the direction of the Pacific Plate that occurred about 43 million years ago.

In addition to seamount chains, hot spots can result in the formation of flood basalts. Flood basalts erupt from fissures rather than a central vent and form flat plains or plateaus rather than volcanic mountains. The volume of basalt in these eruptions can be tremendous. The Columbia River Basalts in the northwestern United States, for example, contain 170 000 km^3 of basalt. The volume of basalt in the Deccan Traps in India is estimated to be 512 000 km^3. The volume of basalt in the Laki eruption in Iceland, which you can analyze in the *Problem-Solving Lab* on page 486, is small by comparison at 14.73 km^3.

Volcanic activity is proof that Earth is a dynamic planet. And, while many volcanic eruptions can be spectacular events, these geologic phenomena can pose risks to humans and their environment. In the *Internet GeoLab* that follows, you will research and rank some of Earth's potentially dangerous volcanoes.

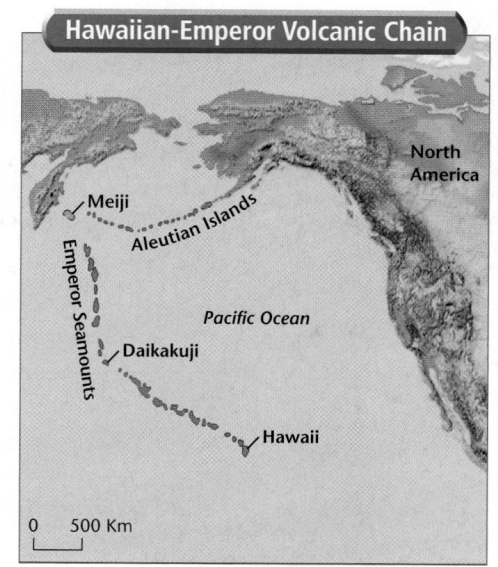

Hawaiian-Emperor Volcanic Chain

North America

Meiji
Aleutian Islands
Emperor Seamounts
Pacific Ocean
Daikakuji
Hawaii

0   500 Km

Figure 18-17 The Emperor Seamounts and the Hawaiian Islands continue to form as the Pacific Plate moves over a stationary hot spot in the mantle.

3 Assess

Check for Understanding
Discussion

Ask the following questions. If a subduction zone developed along the eastern coast of the United States, what type of volcanoes would form? What type of magma would fuel the volcanoes, and what type of eruptions would occur? Composite volcanoes would form, and andesitic magma would erupt explosively.

Reteach

Provide each student with a skeleton of a concept map that summarizes the characteristics of the three types of volcanoes presented in this section. Have students complete the maps and keep them for reference.

Performance Have each student classify each of the volcanoes shown in **Figures 18-2** and **18-16** as a shield volcano, a composite volcano, or a cinder cone. Use the Performance Task Assessment List for Making Observations and Inferences in **PASC,** p. 17.

NY Core Curriculum Standards

Page 486: St 1 Math KI 1, 2, & 3, St 4 KI 2.1b & 2.1n, St 6 KI 1 & 5

Page 487: St 4 KI 2.1b, 2.1j, 2.1l, 2.1n, & 2.1o, St 6 KI 1, 4, & 5

SECTION ASSESSMENT

1. What is a volcanic crater, and how does it differ from a caldera?

2. Describe the different kinds of tephra.

3. Explain why volcanic blocks would be uncommon on shield volcanoes.

4. What is a pyroclastic flow? What are the characteristics of a pyroclastic flow that make them so dangerous?

5. Where are Earth's major volcanic belts located?

6. What are hot spots?

7. **Thinking Critically** The slopes of composite volcanoes are notoriously unstable and prone to landslides. Why?

SKILL REVIEW

8. **Comparing and Contrasting** Compare and contrast the characteristics of the three major types of volcanoes. For more help, refer to the *Skill Handbook.*

SECTION ASSESSMENT

1. A crater is a bowl-shaped depression, less than 1 km in diameter, which forms around the central vent at the summit of a volcano. Calderas are large craters that can be up to 50 km in diameter.

2. dust: less than 0.25 mm in diameter; ash: 0.25–2 mm in diameter; lapilli: 2–64 mm in diameter; blocks and bombs: larger than 64 mm in diameter

3. Volcanic blocks are ejected during explosive eruptions. Shield volcanoes are formed by

quiet eruptions.

4. Pyroclastic flows are clouds of tephra that travel down the flanks of volcanoes. They move at high speeds, are very hot, and contain poisonous gases.

5. Earth's major volcanic belts are located at plate boundaries.

6. Hot spots are high-temperature plumes of material that rise through the mantle to form volcanoes far from plate boundaries.

7. Composite volcanoes are made of alternat-

ing layers of tephra and lava. The tephra are unconsolidated and less stable than the solidified lava.

8. shield: broad, gentle slopes, circular bases, quiet eruptions, usually made of basaltic lava; composite: steep slopes, form high mountains, usually made of andesitic lava; cinder-cone: steep slopes, less than 500-m high, explosive eruptions, made of tephra

Process Skills

collect and interpret data, use references, make and use tables, communicate

Preparation

Special Instructions

If you do not have access to the Internet, use library references about volcanoes. You could also contact the geology department at a local university or your state's geological survey. The U.S. Geological Survey, or USGS, is another source of such information.

Possible Hypotheses

Most students will probably choose an area along the Pacific Ring of Fire as having the most hazardous volcanoes. Iceland or Hawaii might also be chosen.

Planning

Teaching Strategies

- Obtain a world map and have students mark the locations of their volcanoes.
- If computers are limited, have students work in pairs.
- Make several world atlases available so that students can locate cities near their volcanoes.

Possible Procedures

Students should gather data from Internet sites that can be accessed through the Earth Science Web Site. Students will post their data

---

Internet GeoLab — Ranking Hazardous Volcanoes

*S*ome volcanoes can be explosively dangerous. Along with clouds of ash and other volcanic debris that can linger in the air for years after an eruption, pyroclastic flows, landslides, and mudflows are common volcanic hazards. An explosive volcano may not be a hazard to human life and property, however, if it is located in a remote area or erupts infrequently. A number of factors must be taken into account to determine if a particular volcano poses a risk.

Preparation

Problem

Which volcanoes on our planet pose the greatest risk to human life and property?

Mount St. Helens May 18, 1980

Hypothesis

Form a hypothesis about where you think the most hazardous volcanoes are located on Earth. Think about the potential risk to people and property near the volcano when formulating your hypothesis.

Objectives

- **Gather** and **communicate** data about three volcanoes in different parts of the world.
- **Form conclusions** about the hazards posed by the volcanoes based on their location, size, lava type, and eruptive history.

Data Sources

Go to the Earth Science Web Site at <u>earthgeu.com</u> to find links to volcano data on the Internet. You can also use current reference books and scientific magazines to aid in the collection of data.

---

on the site and obtain data from other schools around the country. If students research a volcano that has been previously posted, they should compare their hazard ranking with the previous ranking.

Procedure

Data and Observations

Suppose a student chose Mexico and El Chichon volcano to research. The student

would find that the volcano is located at 17.4°N, 93.2°W, is a composite volcano made of andesite, and is highly explosive. The last eruption of this volcano occurred in 1982, and its eruption interval is unknown. The volcano is 1060 m high, and multiple small villages are located on the volcano itself. The nearby population is estimated to be between 10 000 and 20 000 people. The types of hazards include pyroclastic flows, ash falls, and mudflows. The human hazard ranking is medium because of the long eruption interval.

RANKING OF SOME HAZARDOUS VOLCANOES

Volcano name			
Country			
Location of volcano (latitude and longitude)			
Type of volcano			
Composition of lava/ Explosiveness			
Date of last eruption			
Eruption interval (number of eruptions over a period of time)			
Height of volcano			
Distance to nearest population center			
Approximate number of people living near the volcano			
Type(s) of potential hazards			
Human hazard ranking (high, medium, low)			

Procedure

1. Select a country and find out if there are any volcanoes in that country. If there are no volcanoes, choose another country. If there are a lot of volcanoes in that country, narrow your search.

2. Repeat step 1 for at least two other volcanoes. Copy and complete the data table with the information about each of the volcanoes you selected.

Conclude & Apply

Sharing Your Data Find this Internet GeoLab on the Earth Science Web Site at earthgeu.com. Post your data in the table provided for this activity. Use the additional data from other students to complete your chart and answer the Conclude & Apply questions.

1. Which of the volcanoes you researched threatens the greatest number of people? Where is this volcano located?

2. Analyze the data posted by others at the earthgeu.com site. Which country has the greatest number of potentially dangerous volcanoes? Why?

3. Which country has the greatest total population threatened by volcanoes?

Conclude & Apply

1. Answers will vary; discuss students' results as a class.
2. Students might select Russia or Indonesia. The high number of dangerous volcanoes in these two countries is a result of their proximity to subduction zones.
3. Japan probably has the largest population threatened by dangerous volcanoes because the country is densely populated. Most of Russia's volcanoes are in sparsely populated areas.

Sharing Your Data

Post your students' data on the Earth Science Web Site. Compare your students' findings to those of other classes around the country.

✓Assessment

Performance Have each student display his or her data on a poster. Allow time for all students to present their findings to the class. Ask students to explain how they determined each hazard ranking. Use the Performance Task Assessment List for Poster in **PASC,** p. 73.

Resource Manager

GeoLab and MiniLab Worksheets, pp. 72–73 L2

NY Core Curriculum Standards

Page 488: St 1 Science KI 1, St 2 KI 1 & 3, St 4 KI 2.1l, St 6 KI 5, St 7 KI 2
Page 489: St 1 Science KI 1, St 2 KI 1 & 3, St 4 KI 2.1l, St 6 KI 5, St 7 KI 2

Purpose

Students will learn about the worldwide climatic effects that followed the eruption of Tambora in 1815.

Content Background

- Tambora is a composite volcano on Sumbawa Island and lies about 300 km behind the Sunda Trench. The subduction zone in this region is less than 200 km beneath Tambora. Before its eruption in 1815, Tambora had been dormant for as long as 5000 years.

- The atmospheric effects of volcanic eruptions have received a great deal of attention in the last few decades, particularly in light of global warming. Tambora is not the only volcano that has had global effects on temperature. The Laki eruption in 1783, which students explored in the Problem-Solving Lab, lowered global temperatures an average of 4.8°C. Other volcanic eruptions and their effects on lowering global temperatures include the following: Tambora, 3°C; El Chichon, 0.3°C; Mount St. Helens, 0.1°C; and Pinatubo, 0.5°C. Recent studies have indicated that the amount of tephra erupted is less important than the amount of sulfur gases released. The sulfuric acid droplets that form in the atmosphere cause a greater cooling effect than do dust and ash.

Science & the Environment

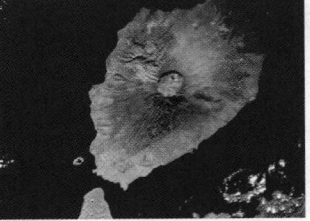
Tambora

The Year Without a Summer

In 1816, Chauncey Jerome, a Connecticut clockmaker, reported that the clothes his wife had hung out to dry the day before had frozen overnight. This would not have been significant, except for the date— it was June 10.

What Jerome and other New Englanders experienced during the cold summer of 1816 was directly linked to an event that had occurred one year earlier and thousands of kilometers away. On April 5, 1815, Mount Tambora, a dormant volcano in Indonesia, came alive in a series of explosive eruptions.

Tambora's Direct Impact

Historic reports attest to Tambora's explosive power. The eruption was heard on Jakarta, which is more than 1200 km away. Over the course of that April week, the volcano ejected an estimated 150 km³ of tephra into the ocean and onto surrounding islands. By contrast, the volume of debris erupted during the 1980 explosion of Mount St. Helens was only 1 km³.

Volcanic ash from Tambora hung thickly in the sky and caused a three-day period of darkness within 600 km of the island. By the time the eruptions stopped, more than a third of the 3900-m mountain had been blown off. Some 12 000 people were killed directly by volcanic fallout, and more than 80 000 died soon after from famine and disease. The disaster, however, was not over. Its global effects would be felt around the world the following year—the year without a summer.

Indirect Consequences

Tambora spewed an immense amount of volcanic dust and gases such as sulfur dioxide into the atmosphere. These particles prevented sun-

light from reaching Earth's surface. In effect, the short wavelengths of incoming sunlight, which are similar in size to particles of dust and gas, collided with the particles and were reflected back into space. The problem was worsened when heat radiated from Earth's surface, which takes the form of longer wavelengths, escaped into space.

The net result was wildly fluctuating weather on a global scale. A snowfall in southern Italy, unusual in itself, caused widespread alarm because the snow was tinted red from the volcanic ash. In New England, summer temperatures dipped and soared from about 2°C to over 31°C within a matter of days. Crops were devastated.

At the time, the cause of the climatic changes was not understood; no one linked the changes to the eruption of Tambora. Today, however, we know that volcanic gases can linger in the atmosphere for years after an eruption and wreak havoc on the weather.

Internet

Not all volcanic eruptions have negative effects. Go to earthgeu.com for links to information on the eruptions that occurred in northern Arizona some 1000 years ago. How did these eruptions affect the Sinagua? What positive impacts did the eruptions have?

490 CHAPTER 18 *Volcanic Activity*

Teaching Strategies

Have students visit the Volcano World and USGS Volcano Web Sites, which contain vast amounts of information on volcanoes and volcanism. The Home page for these sites can be found on the Earth Science Web Site at earthgeu.com.

Internet

Students will find that the volcanic ash enriched the arid soils. Although the Sinagua were forced to move immediately after the eruptions, they later returned to harvest better crops from the enriched soil.

Summary

SECTION 18.1
Magma

Main Ideas
- Temperature, pressure, and the presence of water are factors that affect the formation of magma.
- As pressure increases, the temperature at which a substance melts also increases. At any given pressure, the presence of water will cause a substance to melt at a lower temperature than the same substance under dry conditions.
- There are three major types of magma: basaltic magma, andesitic magma, and rhyolitic magma. These magmas differ in the source rock from which they form, viscosity, silica content, gas content, and explosiveness. Basaltic magma is the least explosive magma; rhyolitic magma is the most explosive.

Vocabulary
viscosity (p. 474)

SECTION 18.2
Intrusive Activity

Main Ideas
- Magmatic intrusions affect the crust in several ways. Magma can force overlying rock apart and enter the newly formed fissures. Magma can also cause blocks of rock to break off and sink into the magma chamber. Magma can melt the rock into which it intrudes.
- Batholiths, stocks, sills, dikes, and laccoliths are plutons that are classified according to their size, shape, and relationship to surrounding rocks. Batholiths are the largest plutons and often form the cores of many of Earth's major mountain chains.

Vocabulary
batholith (p. 476)
dike (p. 478)
laccolith (p. 477)
pluton (p. 476)
sill (p. 477)
stock (p. 477)

SECTION 18.3
Volcanoes

Main Ideas
- Lava flows onto Earth's surface through a vent. Over time, multiple lava flows may accumulate to form a volcano. A crater is a depression that forms around the vent at the summit of a volcano. A caldera is a large crater that forms when a volcano collapses during or after an eruption.
- There are three types of volcanoes: shield volcanoes, cinder-cone volcanoes, and composite volcanoes.
- Rock fragments ejected during eruptions are called tephra.
- Most volcanoes form along convergent and divergent plate boundaries. Volcanoes also form over hot spots, which are unusually hot areas in the mantle that are stationary for long periods of time.
- Flood basalts form when lava flows from fissures to form flat plains or plateaus.

Vocabulary
caldera (p. 481)
cinder-cone volcano (p. 482)
composite volcano (p. 482)
crater (p. 480)
hot spot (p. 486)
pyroclastic flow (p. 484)
shield volcano (p. 481)
tephra (p. 483)
vent (p. 480)

earthgeu.com/vocabulary_puzzlemaker

Study Guide **491**

Main Ideas

Summary statements can be used by students to review the major concepts of the chapter.

VOCABULARY PuzzleMaker

For additional help with vocabulary, have students access the Vocabulary Puzzlemaker online.

earthgeu.com/
vocabulary puzzlemaker

0:00 *Out of Time?*

If time does not permit teaching the entire chapter, use the GeoDigest at the end of the unit as an overview.

Earth Science Online

Be sure to check the Earth Science Web Site for links to chapter material:
earthgeu.com

GLENCOE
Technology

Videotape/DVD
MindJogger Videoquizzes
Chapter 18: *Volcanic Activity*
Have students work in groups as they play the videoquiz game to review key chapter concepts.

Resource Manager

Chapter Assessment, pp. 103–108
MindJogger Videoquizzes DVD/VHS
ExamView® Pro CD-ROM
Performance Assessment in Earth Science

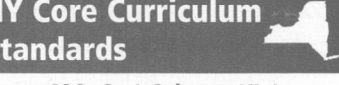
NY Core Curriculum Standards

Page 490: St 1 Science KI 1, St 2 KI 1 & 3, St 4 KI 2.1l & 2.1o, St 6 KI 5, St 7 KI 2
Page 491: St 4 KI 2.1l, 2.1m, & 2.1n, St 6 KI 1 & 5

Understanding Main Ideas

1. d
2. a
3. a
4. b
5. b
6. c
7. b
8. d
9. The Ring of Fire, or Circum-Pacific Belt, is a volcanic belt in the Pacific Ocean. It exists because of the large number of subduction zones around the Pacific Ocean.
10. Hot spots are the cause of most volcanic activity not associated with plate boundaries. Seamount chains, shield volcanoes, and flood basalts are caused by hot spots.
11. $363.9 million
12. $970.7 million
13. ($106.9 million ÷ $970.7 million) × 100% = 11%
14. transportation
15. forestry; ($449.8 million ÷ $970.7 million) × 100% = 46.3%

Applying Main Ideas

16. As pressure decreases, the melting point decreases. However, as water escapes, the melting point increases. The effect of water is greater than that of pressure. Thus, as water is released, the melting point increases and eventually exceeds the temperature of the magma. As a result, the magma solidifies before it reaches Earth's surface.
17. Rising magma causes rocks to fracture. It also causes blocks of rock to break off and sink

---

Understanding Main Ideas

1. Which of the following does NOT play a role in magma formation?
   a. temperature
   c. presence of water
   b. pressure
   d. tephra type

2. Which of the following is true?
   a. An increase in pressure results in a higher melting temperature of a dry substance.
   b. A decrease in pressure increases the temperature at which a dry substance melts.
   c. The addition of water increases the melting temperature of a substance.
   d. An increase in pressure decreases the melting temperature of a dry substance.

3. Which of the following melts to form rhyolitic magma?
   a. continental crust
   c. oceanic sediment
   b. oceanic crust
   d. the upper mantle

4. Which type of pluton is completely parallel to the rock layers into which it intrudes?
   a. dike
   c. laccolith
   b. sill
   d. stock

5. The Hawaiian volcanoes formed as a result of which of the following?
   a. divergence
   c. subduction
   b. a hot spot
   d. subsidence

6. Which of the following is NOT true?
   a. An increase in silica increases the viscosity of a magma.
   b. Andesitic magma has both an intermediate gas content and explosiveness.
   c. An increase in temperature increases a magma's viscosity.
   d. Basaltic magma has a low viscosity and contains little gas.

---

7. What is the largest type of tephra?
   a. ash
   c. dust
   b. volcanic blocks
   d. lapilli

8. Which of the following has broad, gently sloping sides and a circular base?
   a. hot spot
   c. composite cone
   b. cinder-cone volcano
   d. shield volcano

9. What is the Ring of Fire, and why does it exist?
10. Explain the relationship between hot spots and volcanism.

Use the table to answer questions 11–15.

Economic Losses (millions of dollars) from the 1980 Eruption of Mount St. Helens				
Sector	Federal	Private	State	Local
Forestry	168.0	218.1	63.7	——
Clean-up	307.9	9.7	5.0	41.3
Property	43.6	44.8	2.5	16.0
Agriculture	——	39.1	——	——
Income	——	8.9	——	——
Transportation	——	——	——	2.1

11. What was the total economic cost of cleaning up after the eruption?
12. What was the total economic loss from this eruption?
13. What percent of the total loss was caused by property damage?
14. Which sector suffered the smallest loss?
15. Which sector suffered the greatest economic loss? What percent of the total was this?

Test-Taking Tip

STANDARDIZED TEST FORMS Fill in one answer bubble as you answer each question. If you need to skip a question, make sure you skip the corresponding bubble on the answer sheet also.

earthgeu.com/chapter_test

---

into the magma chamber, where they melt. Magma also causes the rocks with which it comes in contact to melt.
18. The lava tubes insulate the lava, which causes the lava to maintain a higher temperature and have a lower viscosity.
19. Batholiths are huge intrusions made of hundreds of kilometers of igneous rock. They form the roots of many mountain ranges, possibly as the result of partial melting of continental crust in the deep roots beneath the mountains.

20. A laccolith is a mushroom-shaped intrusion that forms when magma intrudes into rocks and causes them to bow upward.
21. All three are features of volcanoes. These features differ in size and location. Vents can be located anywhere on a volcano, craters form around a central vent at the summit, and calderas are huge craters that form when a magma chamber collapses.

Applying Main Ideas

16. As rhyolitic magma rises to Earth's surface, pressure decreases and water escapes from the magma. What effect does this have on the melting temperature? How might this cause the magma to solidify before reaching the surface?

17. How does magma affect the rocks into which it intrudes?

18. Hawaiian lava flows can travel great distances through underground passageways called lava tubes. Why would lava flow faster through a lava tube than it would above ground?

19. Describe batholiths and explain where and how they form.

20. What is a laccolith and how does it form?

21. Explain the relationship among a vent, a crater, and a caldera.

Thinking Critically

22. Soils that form from volcanic debris are very productive. What are some reasons for the high fertility of volcanic soils?

23. Pumice, a volcanic glass that contains such a large percentage of holes that it floats in water, is almost never basaltic in composition. Why?

24. Which type of volcano would you expect to produce the largest volume of tephra? Explain.

25. Why do shield volcanoes have gentle slopes and large bases?

26. Geothermal energy associated with magma chambers close to Earth's surface can be used to produce electricity. Name several places in the United States where the use of this energy might be possible.

earthgeu.com/standardized_test

Standardized Test Practice

INTERPRETING DIAGRAMS Use the diagram below to answer the following questions.

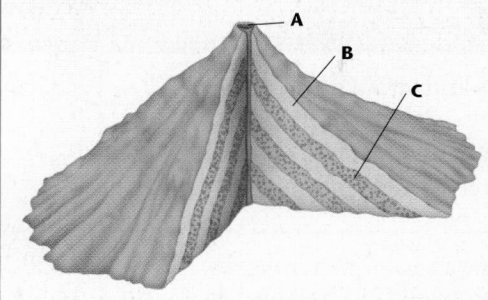

1. What kind of volcano is shown in the diagram?
   a. cinder-cone volcano   c. shield volcano
   b. composite volcano   d. hot-spot volcano

2. What kind of volcanic feature is designated by the letter A?
   a. the vent   c. the crater
   b. the magma chamber   d. the sill

3. What type of material makes up the layer designated by the letter B?
   a. lava   c. tephra
   b. flood basalts   d. volcanic gases

4. What type of material makes up the layer designated by the letter C?
   a. lava   c. tephra
   b. flood basalts   d. volcanic gases

5. Which of the following is NOT true of this type of volcano?
   a. It erupts violently.
   b. The magma that fuels it is rich in silica.
   c. It forms over a hot spot in Earth's mantle.
   d. It has concave slopes.

Thinking Critically

22. Volcanic soils are rich in elements and minerals that make soils fertile. The porous nature of volcanic debris promotes good drainage and enhances the decay of organic material, both of which are important to a soil's fertility.

23. Trapped gases form bubbles in highly viscous rhyolitic lavas; these bubbles cause the holes in pumice. Basaltic magma contains fewer dissolved gases and has a low viscosity.

24. Cinder-cone volcanoes produce the largest volume of tephra because they erupt explosively as a result of the highly viscous magma that fuels them.

25. Shield volcanoes have gentle slopes and broad bases because basaltic lava has low viscosity and flows great distances.

26. California, Nevada, Utah, and Hawaii are among the locations in the United States where the harnessing of geothermal energy is possible because of the volcanism in these areas.

EXAMVIEW® PRO

Use ExamView® Pro Testmaker CD-ROM to:

- Create **multiple versions** of tests.
- Create **modified** tests with one mouse click for struggling students.
- **Edit** existing questions and add your own questions.
- **Build** tests based on national curriculum standards.

Standardized Test Practice

1. b
2. c
3. a
4. c
5. c

NY Core Curriculum Standards

Page 492: St 1 Math KI 1, 2, & 3, St 4 KI 2.1l, 2.1m, & 2.1n, St 6 KI 1 & 5
Page 493: St 4 KI 2.1l, 2.1m, & 2.1n, St 6 KI 1, 2, & 5

Refer to pages 8T–9T of the Teacher Guide for an explanation of the National Science Content Standards correlations.

Section	Objectives	National Science Content Standards	State/Local Standards
SECTION 19.1 **Forces Within Earth** 🕐 1 session 🧊 ½ block	1. **Define** stress and strain as they apply to rocks. 2. **Distinguish** among the three types of faults. 3. **Contrast** three types of seismic waves.	UCP.2; B.4; D.1; F.5	St 1 Science KI 1 & 2, St 4 KI 2.1j, 2.1l, & 2.1n, St 6 KI 2
SECTION 19.2 **Seismic Waves and Earth's Interior** 🕐 1½ sessions 🧊 1 block	4. **Describe** how a seismometer works. 5. **Explain** how seismic waves have been used to determine the structure and composition of Earth's interior.	UCP.2; B.4; D.1, D.3; E.1, E.2; F.6	St 4 KI 2.1j, St 6 KI 2 & 3
SECTION 19.3 **Measuring and Locating Earthquakes** 🕐 1½ sessions 🧊 1 block	6. **Compare** and **contrast** earthquake magnitude and intensity and the scales used to measure each. 7. **Explain** why data from at least three seismic stations are needed to locate an earthquake's epicenter. 8. **Describe** Earth's seismic belts.	UCP.2, UCP.3; D.1; E.1, E.2	St 4 KI 2.1j & 2.1n, St 6 KI 2, 3, & 5
SECTION 19.4 **Earthquakes and Society** 🕐 2 sessions 🧊 1 block	9. **Discuss** factors that affect the amount of damage done by an earthquake. 10. **Explain** some of the factors considered in earthquake probability studies. 11. **Define** seismic gaps.	UCP.2, UCP.3; A.1; B.4; D.1; E.1, E.2; F.5, F.6	St 1 Math KI 1, 3, & Engin KI 1, St 4 KI 2.1j, 2.1l, & 2.1n, St 6 KI 2, 3, & 5

A complete Planning Guide is provided on pages 30T–32T.

🕐 The number of recommended single-period sessions

🧊 The number of recommended blocks

Activity Materials

Discovery Lab *page 495*
wood blocks (2), coarse sandpaper to cover the blocks, thumbtacks

GeoLab *pages 516–517*
tracing paper, pencil, metric ruler, calculator, drafting compass

MiniLab *page 508*
tracing paper, pencil

Demo *page 495*
plastic fork

page 498
coiled-spring toy

page 500
balloon, string, water

page 511
soft drink cans, hammer

Need materials? Contact Science Kit at 1-800-828-7777 or at www.sciencekit.com on the Internet. For alternate materials, see the activity on the listed page.

Key to Teaching Strategies

L1 Level 1 activities should be appropriate for students with learning difficulties.

L2 Level 2 activities should be within the ability range of all students.

L3 Level 3 activities are designed for above-average students.

ELL ELL activities should be within the ability range of English-language learners.

COOP LEARN Cooperative Learning activities are designed for small-group work.

P These strategies represent student products that can be placed in a best-work portfolio.

🧊 These strategies are useful in a block scheduling format.

Chapter Organizer

Glencoe Exclusive!
TeacherWorks™
All-In-One Planner and Resource Center

Activities/Features	Reproducible Masters	Transparencies
Discovery Lab: Model an Earthquake, p. 495	**Study Guide for Content Mastery,** pp. 117–118 **L2**	**Section Focus Transparency 56** **L1** **ELL** **Teaching Transparencies 55 and 56** **L2** **ELL**
Problem-Solving Lab: Making and Using Graphs, p. 502	**Study Guide for Content Mastery,** p. 119 **L2**	**Section Focus Transparency 57** **L1** **ELL**
MiniLab: How is a seismic-intensity map made? p. 508	**Study Guide for Content Mastery,** pp. 120–121 **L2** **Laboratory Manual,** pp. 145–148 **L2** **GeoLab and MiniLab Worksheets,** p. 75 **L2**	**Section Focus Transparency 58** **L1** **ELL** **Teaching Transparency 57** **L2** **ELL**
Using Math: Using Numbers, p. 513 **GeoLab:** Locating an Epicenter, pp. 516–517 **Science in the News:** The Izmit Disaster, p. 518	**Study Guide for Content Mastery,** p. 122 **L2** **Laboratory Manual,** pp. 149–152 **L2** **GeoLab and MiniLab Worksheets,** pp. 76–78 **L2**	**Section Focus Transparency 59** **L1** **ELL** **Teaching Transparency 58** **L2** **ELL**

Assessment

Chapter Assessment, pp. 109–114
Performance Assessment in the Science Classroom (PASC)
MindJogger Videoquiz DVD/VHS
Performance Assessment in Earth Science
ExamView® Pro CD-ROM
5 Days to the Regents Exam

Additional Resources

Guided Reading Audio Program **ELL**
Cooperative Learning in the Science Classroom **COOP LEARN**
Lesson Plans
Block Scheduling
earthgeu.com
NY Lesson Plans
NY Block Scheduling
Review Handbook for Regents Earth Science Exam

NATIONAL GEOGRAPHIC
Teacher's Corner

Products Available from National Geographic Society
To order the following products, call the National Geographic Society at 1-800-368-2728:

Videos
Our Dynamic Earth

Content Background

Faults and Principal Stresses
Section 19.1

The stress state within Earth can be expressed in terms of three principal stresses—P, T, and N—which are at right angles to one other. P is the maximum compressive stress, T the minimum compressive (or tensional) stress, and N is the intermediate stress. When a rock mass fractures, the plane of failure forms a 45° angle with the axis of the maximum compressive stress, P, and the relative motion of the fault is such that the rock mass shortens in the direction of P and expands in the direction of T. There is no motion in the N direction. Consequently, for normal faults, P is vertical and T and N are horizontal. For reverse faults, T is vertical; for strike-slip faults, N is vertical.

Reflection and Refraction of Seismic Waves
Section 19.2

When seismic waves encounter a different medium, they are reflected and refracted at the boundary between the media, as shown in the figure below.

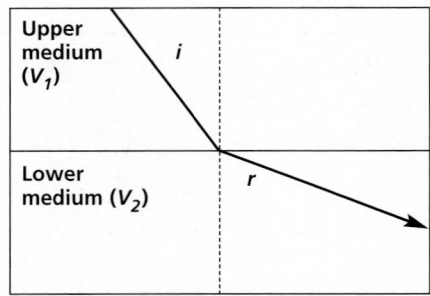

The angle of refraction is determined by Snell's law, which states that $\sin i/V_1 = \sin r/V_2$, where V_1 and V_2 are the seismic velocities in the upper and lower media, respectively. If V_2 is greater than V_1, the refracted ray is bent away from the normal; if V_2 is less than V_1, the ray is bent toward the normal. Because seismic velocities in Earth's mantle increase with depth, seismic ray paths through this part of Earth are concave upward. If the incident angle, i, is such that the angle of refraction, r, is 90°, critical refraction occurs and the refracted ray travels along the boundary in the high-speed medium, generating so-called headwaves along the way that travel back to Earth's surface. This happens along the Moho discontinuity if the earthquake focus is in the crust. From the travel times of the headwaves, crustal thickness can be determined.

Earthquake Magnitude
Section 19.3

Soon after Charles Richter proposed his method of determining earthquake magnitude in 1935, it was learned that the most consistent earthquake

Multiple Learning Styles

Kinesthetic Modeling, p. 501

Visual-Spatial Demo, p. 500

Interpersonal Collaborative Learning, p. 496, Activity, p. 498, Enrichment, p. 506

Intrapersonal Project, p. 514

Linguistic Using Scientific Terms, p. 509

GLENCOE
Technology

The following multimedia resources are available from Glencoe.

The Infinite Voyage Series
Living with Disaster

Vocabulary Puzzlemaker

TeacherWorks™ CD-ROM

MindJogger Videoquizzes DVD/VHS

ExamView® Pro CD-ROM

Interactive Chalkboard CD-ROM

Chapter Organizer

measurements were obtained using surface waves, adjusted for their period (T). This method of determining earthquake magnitude is called the surface-wave magnitude (M_s) method, which is still widely used. Most reported Richter magnitudes are actually surface-wave magnitudes.

Because deep and intermediate earthquakes do not generate large surface waves, a body-wave magnitude (m_b), based on the amplitude and period of the largest P-waves recorded, is used to measure such earthquakes. M_s and m_b values for a given earthquake are different. The relationship between the two magnitudes can be expressed by the following equation: $m_b = 2.94 + 0.56 \times M_s$. Major quakes are often measured using the seismic moment, M_o, of the fault rupture: $M_o = A \times d \times \mu$, where A, d, and μ are the estimated fault area, displacement, and rigidity of the rocks, respectively. This moment-magnitude method is gradually replacing the popular surface-wave magnitude method.

Vibrations and Resonance
Section 19.4

When a guitar string is plucked, it emits a tone with a certain frequency. A nearby guitar string tuned to the same frequency will begin to vibrate by itself in response to the sound waves traveling through the air. This is resonance. Seismic waves can generate the same kind of resonance in structures "tuned" to the same frequency as the seismic waves. All structures have natural frequencies of vibration. Tall buildings sway with a natural period that depends on their heights and other parameters. The higher the building, the longer is its natural period of vibration. Seismic waves with the same period as that of a tall building can cause the building to sway violently and collapse during a quake.

Identifying Misconceptions

Many people have the misconception that major earthquakes in the United States occur only in California. While it is true that parts of California have experienced many destructive earthquakes, large parts of other western states have had comparable seismic activity. Also contrary to popular belief, states in the eastern part of the United States aren't immune to major earthquakes. In 1886, for example, Charleston, South Carolina, was nearly destroyed by a major quake, and the 1811–1812 earthquakes that originated in New Madrid, Missouri, are among the largest earthquakes that have struck the United States.

Assessment

Portfolio Assessment
Assessment, TWE, p. 515

Performance Assessment
Discovery Lab, SE, p. 495
MiniLab, SE, p. 508
GeoLab, SE, pp. 516–517

Knowledge Assessment
Discovery Lab, TWE, p. 495
Assessment, TWE, pp. 499, 501, 507, 510
MiniLab, TWE, p. 508
GeoLab, TWE, pp. 516–517

Section Assessment, SE, pp. 499, 504, 510, 515
Chapter Assessment, SE, pp. 520–521

Skill Assessment
Problem-Solving Lab, TWE, p. 502
Assessment, TWE, p. 504

Be sure to check the Earth Science Web Site for links to chapter material: earthgeu.com

Chapter 19

Earthquakes

Introducing the Chapter

Inform students that earthquakes occur all the time, but only those that cause destruction in populated areas are generally reported. Explain that we live on an active planet and that earthquakes are the effects of ongoing geological adjustments inside Earth.

Interpreting the Photo

The damage shown in the photo resulted from a series of earthquakes and aftershocks that struck Central Taiwan in September, 1999. Earthquakes are common in Taiwan because this country is located along a subduction zone between the Philippine Sea and the Eurasian Plate. The September 1999 quakes occurred as the result of movement along the Chelongpu Fault.

INTERACTIVE CHALKBOARD
with Image Bank

PowerPoint® Presentations

This CD is an editable Microsoft® PowerPoint® presentation that includes:
- Section presentations
- Section checks
- Image bank
- Links to Earth Science Online
- All transparencies
- Animations
- Audio

Chapter 19

Earthquakes

What You'll Learn
- What causes earthquakes and how they affect Earth's surface.
- How earthquakes and the destruction they cause are measured.
- What factors determine seismic risk.

Why It's Important

Earthquakes are natural phenomena that can cause vast amounts of damage as well as many deaths. Understanding what causes earthquakes is essential to our being prepared for these natural disasters.

Earth Science Online

To learn more about earthquakes, visit the Earth Science Web Site at earthgeu.com

Earthquake damage in Taiwan, 1999

Discovery Lab

Process Skills

observe and infer, compare and contrast, communicate L1 ELL

Safety Precautions

Caution students to carefully move the sandpaper-covered blocks so as not to scrape or pinch their fingers. After the lab, have students return the blocks, thumbtacks, and sandpaper to you. Only then should students remove their goggles and aprons.

Procedure
Troubleshooting

Have students use moderate force while moving both sets of blocks.

Observe and Infer

Students should observe that the bare blocks move easily and smoothly against each other. The sandpaper-covered blocks will stick together until increasing shear stress overcomes friction. Then the blocks will slip suddenly, simulating an earthquake.

Discovery Lab — Model An Earthquake

Earthquakes are natural vibrations of the ground. Most quakes are caused by movement along enormous fractures in Earth's crust. In this activity, you will model how movements along these fractures can cause earthquakes.

1. Slide the largest surfaces of two smooth wooden blocks against each other. Describe the movement.

2. Cut two pieces of coarse-grained sandpaper so that they are about 1 cm larger than the largest surface of each block.

3. Place the sandpaper, coarse side up, against the largest surface of each

block. Wrap the paper over the edges of the blocks and secure it with thumbtacks.

4. Slide the sandpaper-covered sides of the blocks against each other. What happens?

Observe and Infer
In your science journal, compare the two movements. Infer which of the two scenarios models what happens during an earthquake.

Section Focus

Before presenting the lesson, display **Section Focus Transparency 56** on the overhead projector.
L1 ELL

Chapter Themes

The following themes from the National Science Content Standards are covered in this chapter. Refer to page 8T of the Teacher Guide for an explanation of the correlations.
Systems, order, and organization (UCP.1); Evidence, models, and explanation; (UCP.2); Change, constancy, and measurement (UCP.3)

SECTION 19.1 — *Forces Within Earth*

OBJECTIVES

- **Define** *stress and strain as they apply to rocks.*
- **Distinguish** *among the three types of faults.*
- **Contrast** *three types of seismic waves.*

VOCABULARY

stress
strain
fault
primary wave
secondary wave
surface wave
focus
epicenter

Earthquakes are natural vibrations of the ground caused by movement along gigantic fractures in Earth's crust, or sometimes, by volcanic eruptions. If you've experienced an earthquake or heard about quakes in the news, you know that they can be extremely destructive. There are some instances in which a single earthquake has killed more than 100 000 people. Earthquakes have even destroyed entire cities. Anyone living in an area prone to earthquakes should be aware of the potential danger posed by these events and how to minimize the damage that they cause.

STRESS AND STRAIN

Most earthquakes occur when rocks fracture, or break, deep within Earth. Fractures form when **stress,** the forces per unit area acting on a material, exceeds the strength of the rocks involved. There are three kinds of stress that act on Earth's rocks: compression, tension, and shear. Compression is stress that decreases the volume of a material, tension is stress that pulls a material apart, and shear is stress that

19.1 *Forces Within Earth* **495**

✓Assessment

Knowledge Ask students to each write a paragraph that summarizes their observations and inferences using the following terms: *bare wood, sandpaper-covered blocks, rough, smooth, small frictional force, large frictional force, continuous motion, sudden failure, earthquake,* and *slow deformation.*

Resource Manager

Study Guide for Content Mastery, pp. 117–118 L2
Section Focus Transparency 56 L1 ELL

0:00 Out of Time?

If time does not permit teaching the entire chapter, use the Study Guide on page 519 and the GeoDigest found at the end of the unit as an overview.

Collaborative Learning

Interpersonal Have small groups of students use flexible, plastic rulers and quarters or heavy metal washers to demonstrate how the flexible plastic reacts to moderate amounts of stress. Give each group two rulers. Instruct one student in each group to position one of the rulers so that about three-fourths of it extends beyond the edge of a desk. Have another student in the group load the overhanging end of the ruler with three or four quarters or washers (adding them one at a time), while the third student in the group measures and records the deflection of the ruler after each quarter or washer is added. Instruct students to unload the ruler in the same way. Have each group use graph paper to plot the load on the ruler against the resulting deflections for both the loading and unloading phases. The graphs should show approximately straight lines. Make sure students note that the ruler returns to its original position when the load is removed. Then have students read the text about elastic deformation on the student page and relate it to this activity. **L1** **ELL** **COOP LEARN**

Figure Caption Question

Figure 19-2 When does failure occur? when stress exceeds the strength of a material

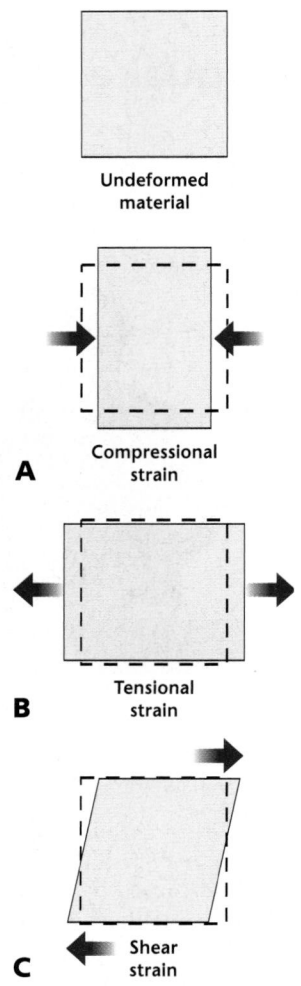

A Undeformed material / Compressional strain

B Tensional strain

C Shear strain

Figure 19-1 Compression causes a material to shorten **(A).** Tension causes a material to lengthen **(B).** Shear causes distortion of a material **(C).**

causes a material to twist. The deformation of materials in response to stress is called **strain.** *Figure 19-1* illustrates the strain caused by compression, tension, and shear.

Laboratory experiments on rock samples show a distinct relationship between stress and strain. When the stress applied to a rock is plotted against strain, a stress-strain curve, like the one shown in *Figure 19-2,* is produced. A stress-strain curve usually has two segments: a straight segment and a curved segment. Low stresses produce the straight segment, which represents the elastic strain of a material. Elastic strain causes a material to bend and stretch, and can be demonstrated by gently applying tension to a rubber band. When this tensional stress is released, the rubber band returns to its original size and shape. In *Figure 19-2,* note that elastic strain is proportional to stress, and thus, if the stress is reduced to zero, the strain, or deformation, disappears.

Ductile Deformation When stress exceeds a certain value, however, a material undergoes ductile deformation, shown by the curved segment of the graph in *Figure 19-2.* Unlike elastic strain, this type of strain produces permanent deformation, which means that the material stays deformed even if the stress is reduced to zero. A rubber band undergoes ductile deformation when it is stretched beyond its elastic limit. This permanent deformation results in an increase in size and produces slight tears or holes in the band. When stress exceeds the strength of a material, the material breaks, or fails, as designated by the X on the graph. From experience, you probably know that exerting too much tension on a rubber band will cause it to snap.

Most materials exhibit both elastic and ductile behavior. Brittle materials, such as glass, certain plastics, and dry wood, fail before much ductile deformation occurs. Ductile materials such as rubber,

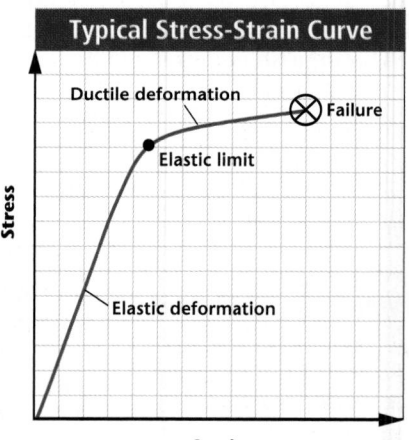

Typical Stress-Strain Curve

Ductile deformation — Failure

Elastic limit

Elastic deformation

Stress / Strain

Figure 19-2 A typical stress–strain curve has two parts. Elastic deformation occurs as a result of low stress; ductile deformation occurs when stress is high. *When does failure occur?*

Interpreting the Illustration

Figure 19-1 Query students to make sure they understand that compressional strain, shown in **Figure 19-1A,** involves a decrease in volume; tensional strain, shown in **Figure 19-1B,** involves an increase in volume; and shear strain, shown in **Figure 19-1C,** involves only a distortion of a material without a change in volume.

Resource Manager

Teaching Transparency 55 **L2** **ELL**

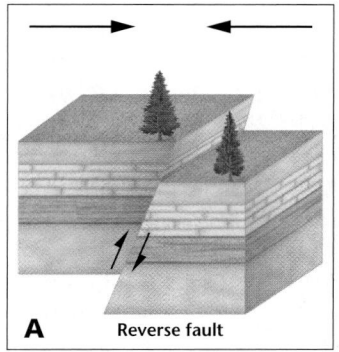

A Reverse fault

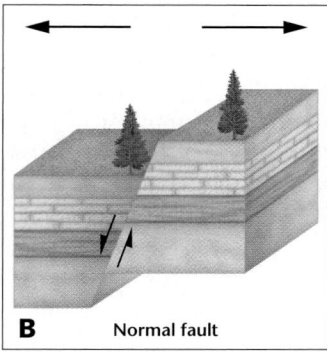

B Normal fault

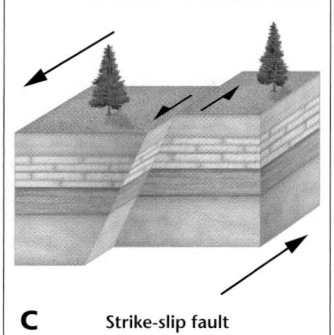

C Strike-slip fault

silicon putty, and metals, on the other hand, can undergo a great deal of ductile deformation before failure occurs, or, they may not fail at all. Most rocks are brittle under the relatively low temperatures that exist in Earth's crust but become ductile at the higher temperatures present at greater depths.

FAULTS

Many kinds of rocks that make up Earth's crust fail when stress is applied too quickly, or when stress is great. The resulting fracture or system of fractures, along which movement occurs, is called a **fault.** The surface along which the movement takes places is called the fault plane. The orientation of the fault plane can vary from nearly horizontal to almost vertical. In diagrams, small arrows along the fault plane indicate the direction of movement of the rocks involved.

Types of Faults There are three basic types of faults, as shown in *Figure 19-3.* Reverse faults are fractures that form as a result of horizontal compression. Note that the compressional force results in a horizontal shortening of the crust involved. What evidence in *Figure 19-3A* indicates this shortening? Normal faults are fractures caused by horizontal tension. Movement along a normal fault is partly horizontal and partly vertical. The horizontal movement along a normal fault occurs in such a way as to extend the crust. Note in *Figure 19-3B* that the two trees separated by the normal fault are farther apart than they were before the faulting.

Strike-slip faults are fractures caused by horizontal shear. The movement along a strike-slip fault is mainly horizontal, as shown in *Figure 19-3C.* The San Andreas Fault, which runs through California, is a strike-slip fault. This fault is one of thousands of faults responsible for many of the state's earthquakes. Motion along this fault has offset features that were originally continuous across the fault, as shown in *Figure 19-4.*

Figure 19-3 Reverse faults form when horizontal stress is exerted on a rock body from opposite sides **(A).** Normal faults form when bodies of rock are pulled from opposite sides **(B).** Strike-slip faults are caused by horizontal shear stress **(C).**

Figure 19-4 The orange trees in the background have moved to the right relative to those in the foreground as the result of the 1940 Imperial Valley earthquake along the San Andreas Fault.

Content Background

There are actually two types of surface waves: Rayleigh waves and Love waves. Rayleigh waves, also called ground roll, cause the ground to move up and down in a rolling motion similar to that of water waves. Love waves are surface shear waves that cause the ground to move horizontally from side to side as the waves pass.

Activity

 **Interpersonal** Based on the results of the Demo below, have a pair of volunteers use the spring toy to demonstrate the movement of surface waves. Use the information in the Content Background above to explain that there are two types of surface waves: Rayleigh waves and Love waves. **COOP LEARN**

Resource Manager

Teaching Transparency 56
L2 **ELL**

EARTHQUAKE WAVES

Most earthquakes are caused by movements along faults. Recall from the *Discovery Lab* that some slippage along faults is relatively smooth. Other movements, modeled by the sandpaper-covered blocks, show that irregular surfaces in rocks can snag and lock. As stress continues to build in these rocks, they reach their elastic limit, break, and produce an earthquake.

Types of Seismic Waves The vibrations of the ground during an earthquake are called seismic waves. Every earthquake generates three types of seismic waves. **Primary waves,** or P-waves, squeeze and pull rocks in the same direction along which the waves are traveling, as shown in *Figure 19-5A*. Note how a volume of rock, which is represented by the small red square, changes shape as a P-wave passes through it. **Secondary waves,** or S-waves, cause rocks to move at right angles in relation to the direction of the waves, as shown in *Figure 19-5B*. **Surface waves** are a third type of seismic wave that move in two directions as they pass through rock. An up-and-down movement similar to that of an ocean wave occurs as a surface wave travels through a rock. A surface wave also causes rocks to move from side to side as it passes, as shown in *Figure 19-5C*.

As you might guess from the name, surface waves travel along Earth's surface. P-waves and S-waves, on the other hand, pass through Earth's interior. For this reason, P-waves and S-waves are also called body waves. The first body waves generated by a quake

Figure 19-5 A P-wave causes rock particles to move back and forth as it passes **(A).** An S-wave causes rock particles to move at right angles to the direction of the wave **(B).** A surface wave causes rock particles to move both up and down and from side to side **(C).**

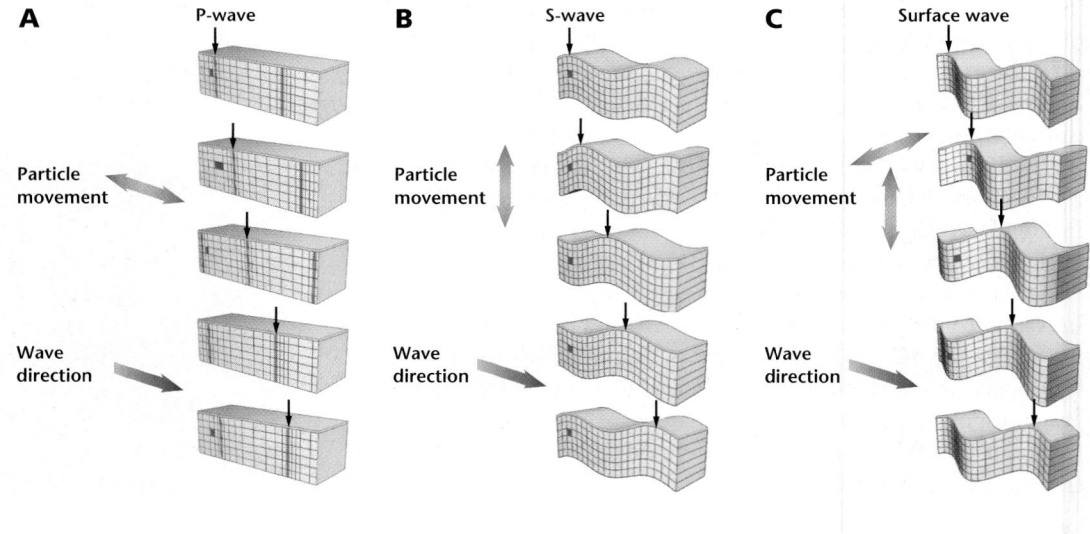

Demo

👓 Have everyone put on safety goggles. Then, use a long, coiled-spring toy and two volunteers to help you demonstrate how P-waves and S-waves travel through rocks. Have the volunteers each hold one end of the coiled-spring toy. Instruct one volunteer to make a quick push-pull motion with his or her hand. Have students describe how the spring reacts. A compressional pulse travels along the spring toward the second volunteer, and particle motion of the coils is longitudinal, which is similar to that of the movement of a P-wave. Instruct the second volunteer to flick his or her wrist to give the spring an up-and-down motion. Have students observe the sine waves produced and relate this movement to the movement of S-waves through rocks.

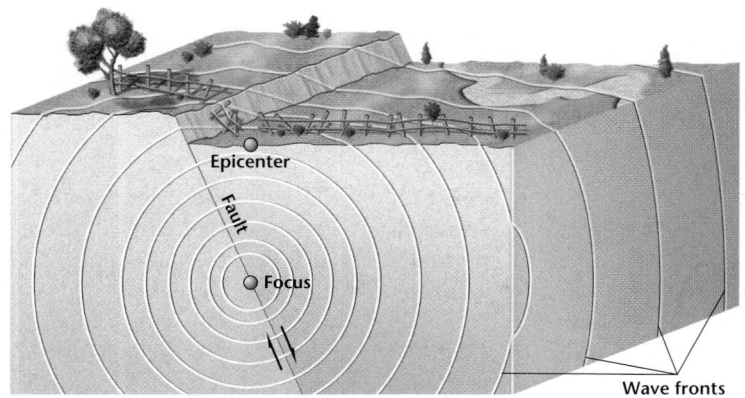

Figure 19-6, The focus of an earthquake is the point of initial fault rupture. The surface point directly above the focus is the epicenter.

spread out from the point of failure of rocks at depth. This point, where an earthquake originates, is the **focus** of the earthquake. The focus is usually at least several kilometers below Earth's surface. The point on Earth's surface directly above the focus is the earthquake's **epicenter.** Locate the focus and the epicenter in the diagram shown in *Figure 19-6.*

You've just learned that Earth's rocks deform when stress is exerted on them. If stress exceeds a certain limit, the rocks fracture to form faults. Movement along faults causes most earthquakes. How are these earth-shattering events measured and what do they tell us about Earth's interior? You'll find out the answer to this question in the next section.

SECTION ASSESSMENT

1. What are stress and strain?

2. Describe a typical stress-strain curve and the relationship between the segments of the curve and stress and strain.

3. Compare and contrast the three types of faults.

4. What causes most earthquakes?

5. **Thinking Critically** Most earthquakes are shallow. Use the concepts of elastic and ductile deformation to explain this fact.

SKILL REVIEW

6. **Concept Mapping** Use the following terms to complete the concept map to organize

some of the major ideas in this section. For more help, refer to the *Skill Handbook.*

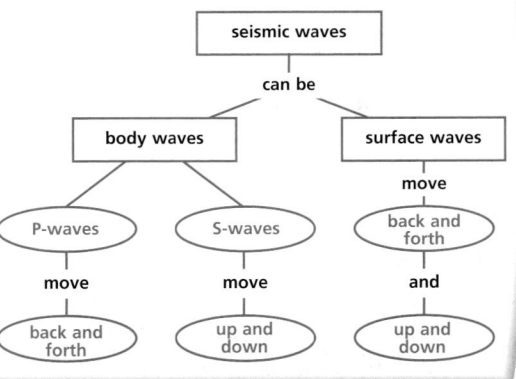

earthgeu.com/self_check_quiz

---

3 Assess

Check for Understanding
Reinforcement
Explain that during many earthquakes, straight rail lines are bent either by surface waves or by fault motion. Pose the following questions. What type of fault or what type of wave motion could produce this kind of deformation? Either a reverse or strike-slip fault, or horizontal ground motion of surface waves could bend rail lines. Is the resulting deformation elastic or ductile? ductile

Reteach
Use your hands to demonstrate the movement along the three types of faults discussed in this section. Have students mimic your movements with their own hands.

✔Assessment

Knowledge Have students construct concept maps using the following terms: *normal fault, reverse fault, strike-slip fault, compression, tension, shear, shortening, extension,* and *horizontal offset.* Students' maps should connect the terms as follows: normal fault–tension–extension; reverse fault–compression–shortening; and strike–slip fault–shear–horizontal offset.

SECTION ASSESSMENT

1. Stress is the forces per unit area acting on a material. Strain is the deformation of a material in response to stress.

2. A typical stress-strain curve has a linear segment representing elastic strain at low stresses, and a curved segment representing ductile deformation at high stresses. The curve ends when the material fails.

3. All faults are fractures along which movement takes place. Normal faults are caused by horizontal tension, reverse faults by horizontal

compression, and strike-slip faults by horizontal shear stresses.

4. Most earthquakes are caused by movements along faults.

5. Temperatures inside Earth increase with depth. Brittle failure occurs only in cold rocks. Hot rocks at depth undergo ductile deformation.

6. See the student page.

NY Core Curriculum Standards
Page 498: St 4 KI 2.1j
Page 499: St 4 KI 2.1j & 2.1n

Section Background

For section content background, refer to **Reflection and Refraction of Seismic Waves** on page 494C.

Preplanning

Refer to the Chapter Organizer on pages 494A–B.

1 Focus

Section Focus

Before presenting the lesson, display **Section Focus Transparency 57** on the overhead projector.
L1 **ELL**

Demo

Visual-Spatial Fill a balloon with water and tie it tightly. Hold the balloon for all students to see and poke it so that it vibrates. Explain that all earthquakes cause the entire Earth to vibrate in a similar manner, but that most vibrations are so small that they can be detected only with sensitive instruments.

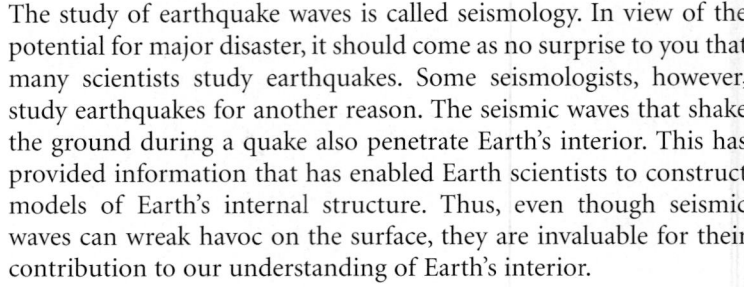

SECTION 19.2 Seismic Waves and Earth's Interior

OBJECTIVES

• **Describe** *how a seismometer works.*

• **Explain** *how seismic waves have been used to determine the structure and composition of Earth's interior.*

VOCABULARY

seismometer
seismogram

The study of earthquake waves is called seismology. In view of the potential for major disaster, it should come as no surprise to you that many scientists study earthquakes. Some seismologists, however, study earthquakes for another reason. The seismic waves that shake the ground during a quake also penetrate Earth's interior. This has provided information that has enabled Earth scientists to construct models of Earth's internal structure. Thus, even though seismic waves can wreak havoc on the surface, they are invaluable for their contribution to our understanding of Earth's interior.

SEISMOMETERS AND SEISMOGRAMS

Vibrations sent out by earthquakes shake the entire globe. Although most of the vibrations can't be felt great distances from a quake's epicenter, they can be detected and recorded by sensitive instruments called seismographs, or **seismometers**. Some seismometers consist of a rotating drum covered with a sheet of paper, a pen or other such recording tool, and a mass. Seismometers vary in design, as shown in *Figure 19-7,* but all include a frame that is anchored to the ground and a mass that is suspended from a spring or wire. Because of inertia, the mass tends to stay at rest as the ground and, consequently, the frame, vibrate during an earthquake. The relative motion of the mass in relation to the frame is then registered on the paper with the recording tool, or is directly recorded onto a computer disk. The record produced by a seismometer is called a **seismogram**, a portion of which is shown in *Figure 19-8.*

Figure 19-7 *Which of these seismometers records horizontal motion during an earthquake? Which detects vertical motion?*

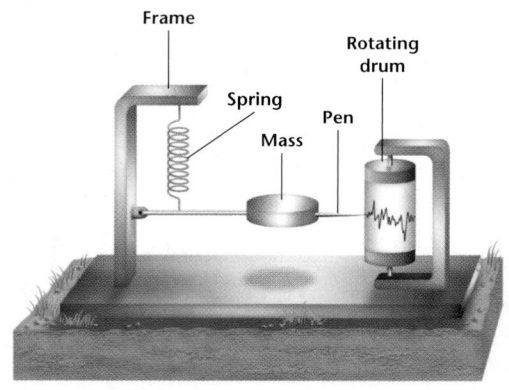
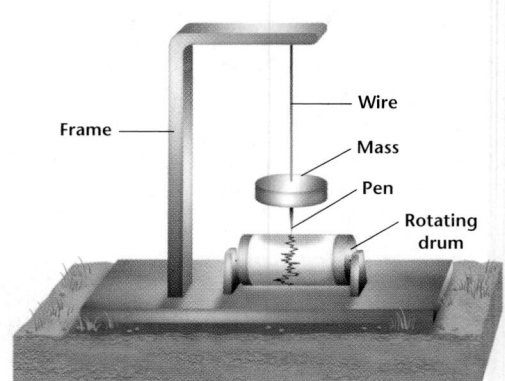

500 CHAPTER 19 *Earthquakes*

Figure Caption Questions

Figure 19-7 Which of these seismometers records horizontal motion during an earthquake? Which detects vertical motion? The seismograph on the right registers horizontal ground motion as the drum moves back and forth horizontally with the ground. The seismograph on the left registers vertical ground motion as the drum moves up and down with the ground.

Resource Manager

Study Guide for Content Mastery, p. 119
L2

Section Focus Transparency 57 **L1** **ELL**

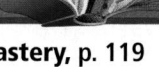

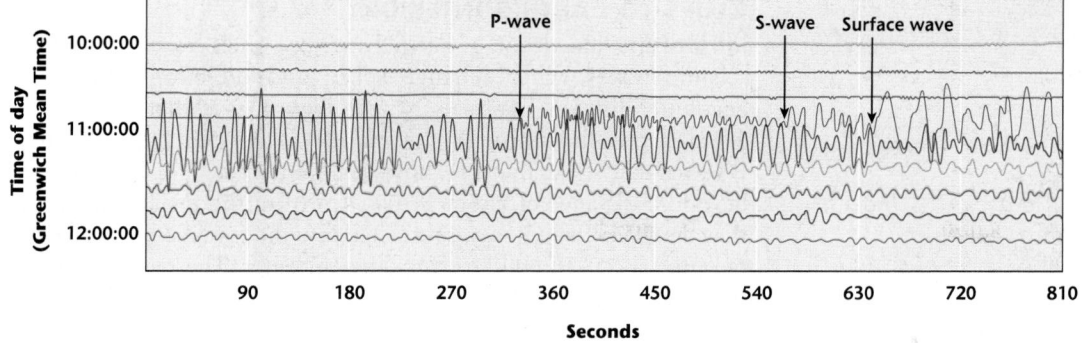

Time of day (Greenwich Mean Time)

10:00:00
11:00:00
12:00:00

P-wave   S-wave   Surface wave

90 180 270 360 450 540 630 720 810

Seconds

Travel-Time Curves Seismic waves that travel from the epicenter of an earthquake are recorded by seismometers housed in distant facilities. Over many years, the arrival times of seismic waves from countless earthquakes at seismic facilities all over the globe have been collected. Using these data, seismologists have been able to construct global travel-time curves for the initial P-waves and S-waves of an earthquake, as shown in *Figure 19-9.* These general curves have provided the average travel times of all seismic waves for different distances, no matter where on Earth an earthquake occurs. You can make and use a travel-time curve by doing the *Problem-Solving Lab* on the next page.

Look at *Figure 19-9.* Note that for any distance from the epicenter, the P-waves always arrive first at a seismic facility. Note, too, that with increasing travel distance, the time separation between the curves for the P-waves and S-waves increases. This means that waves recorded on seismograms from more distant facilities are farther apart than waves recorded on seismograms at stations closer to the epicenter. This separation of seismic waves on seismograms can be used to determine the distance from the epicenter of a quake to the seismic facility that recorded the seismogram. Can you guess how? This method of precisely locating an earthquake's epicenter will be discussed later in this chapter.

Figure 19-8 *Use this section of a seismogram, which contains colored lines to make it easier to read, to determine which of the three types of seismic waves is the fastest. Which type is the slowest?*

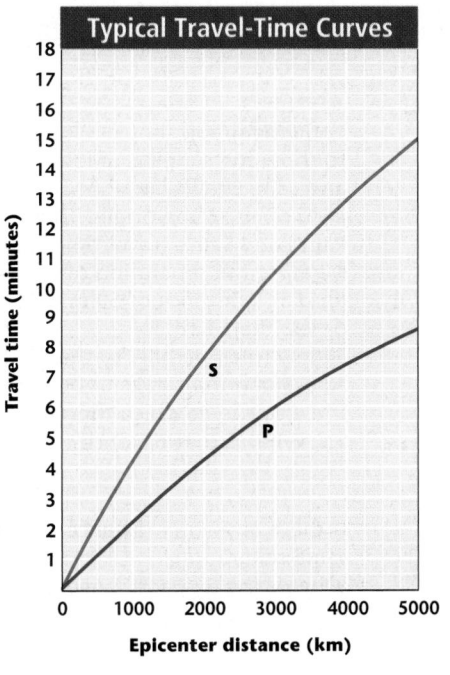

Typical Travel-Time Curves

Travel time (minutes)

18
17
16
15
14
13
12
11
10
9
8
7
6
5
4
3
2
1

S

P

0 1000 2000 3000 4000 5000

Epicenter distance (km)

Figure 19-9 Travel-time curves show the time it takes for P-waves and S-waves to travel to seismic stations located at different distances from an earthquake's epicenter.

19.2 Seismic Waves and Earth's Interior **501**

2 Teach

Modeling

Kinesthetic Use a piece of paper, tape, a lightweight table, and a pencil to model how a seismometer works. Use the tape to attach the piece of paper to the top of the table. Have a student hold a pencil just touching the paper. Have another student slowly pull the table. The resulting line will be straight. Repeat the activity with a third student shaking the table at right angles to the direction in which it is pulled. The resulting line will resemble those shown in **Figure 19-8. COOP LEARN**

Assessment

Knowledge Have students refer to **Figures 19-8** and **19-9** to solve the following problem. A seismic station is 2000 km from the focus of a quake. How long will it take the P- and S-waves to reach that station, and what will the time separation of the P- and S-waves on the seismogram be?
P-wave: 4.2 min; S-wave: 7.7 min; separation is 3.5 min

Interpreting the Illustration

Figure 19-8 Use this section of a seismogram, which contains colored lines to make it easier to read, to determine which of the three types of seismic waves is the fastest. P-waves Which type is the slowest? surface waves

Content Background

Typical P-wave velocities in the upper mantle are 8 km/s or more. P-waves are actually sound waves that can travel through solids, liquids, and gases. Typical S-wave velocities in the upper mantle are 5 km/s or more. S-waves are distortional waves that can travel only through solids. The slowest of the seismic waves are the surface waves, whose typical velocities are 3–4 km/s.

Problem-Solving Lab

Purpose

Students will learn how to use and interpret travel-time curves.

Process Skills

make and use graphs, measure, use numbers, compare and contrast, communicate

Materials

copies of the graph or graph paper, pencil, paper, ruler, calculator

Teaching Strategies

Review graphs and plots of simple functions prior to students' doing this lab.

Answers to Procedures

2. more than 1 s; at 50 m, the travel times are 6 s and 7.25 s, respectively, with a separation of 1.25 s

3. 40 m

Analysis

4. no

5. Pam's average speed is 100 m/12 s = 8.33 m/s; Sam's is 100 m/14.5 s = 6.89 m/s.

Thinking Critically

6. Pam—40 m/8.33 m/s = 4.8 s; Sam—40 m/6.89 m/s = 5.8 s. The difference is 1 s.

7. Pam represents a P-wave, and Sam, an S-wave. Seismic travel-time curves have different slopes because seismic waves travel much faster than the runners. The slopes of seismic travel-time curves decrease with distance because seismic body waves traveling greater distances penetrate deeper into Earth's mantle and have higher velocities than those with shallower penetration. The separation between P- and S-waves on an actual travel-time curve is greater because the difference in P- and S-wave velocities is greater.

✔Assessment

Skill Have students do the same activity for homework but with Pam and Sam running 100 m in 10 s and 12.5 s, respectively.

CLUES TO EARTH'S INTERIOR

Most of the knowledge of Earth's interior comes from the study of seismic waves, which change speed and direction when they encounter different materials. Note in *Figure 19-10* that P-waves and S-waves traveling through the mantle follow fairly direct paths. P-waves that strike the core, however, are refracted, or bent, so that beyond a distance of about 11 000 km from the quake's epicenter, they disappear. The P-waves refracted into the core reemerge at a distance of about 16 000 km from the epicenter. The region between these two distances doesn't receive direct P-waves and is known as the P-wave shadow zone.

What happens to the S-waves generated by an earthquake? S-waves do not enter Earth's core because they cannot travel through liquids. Thus, like P-waves, they also do not reappear beyond the

---

Problem-Solving Lab

Making and Using Graphs

Model seismic-wave travel times
Seismic waves can be compared to runners. Suppose that Pam and Sam are running the 100-m dash. Pam runs the 100 m in 12 s, and Sam runs it in 14.5 s.

Procedure

1. Copy the graph shown. Plot two points to show the running times for Pam and Sam. Draw a straight line from each point to the origin. These are Pam's and Sam's travel-time curves.
2. Measure the separation of the two lines at a distance of 50 m. Is it more or less than 1 s?
3. Slide a ruler, parallel to the vertical axis, along the curves until you find the distance at which the separation is 1 s. What is that distance?

Analysis

4. Is there any other distance with the same separation?
5. What is the average speed, in m/s, of each runner?

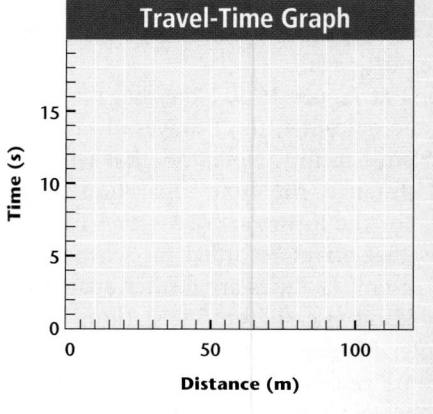

Thinking Critically

6. Double-check your answer by dividing the distance in step 3 by each runner's speed to get each runner's time to that point. Do these times differ by 1 s?
7. What do Pam and Sam represent in terms of seismic waves? Discuss some ways in which a seismic travel-time curve differs from yours.

Cultural Diversity

Coda Waves Keith Aki was born in Japan and received a Ph.D. in seismology from the University of Tokyo. He went to the United States to join the faculty of MIT. Perhaps his most important contribution to seismology is the concept of coda waves. The amplitudes of coda waves remain consistent while traveling through similar geological structures and dissipate at a uniform rate. The study of coda waves reveals important information about sources of earthquakes.

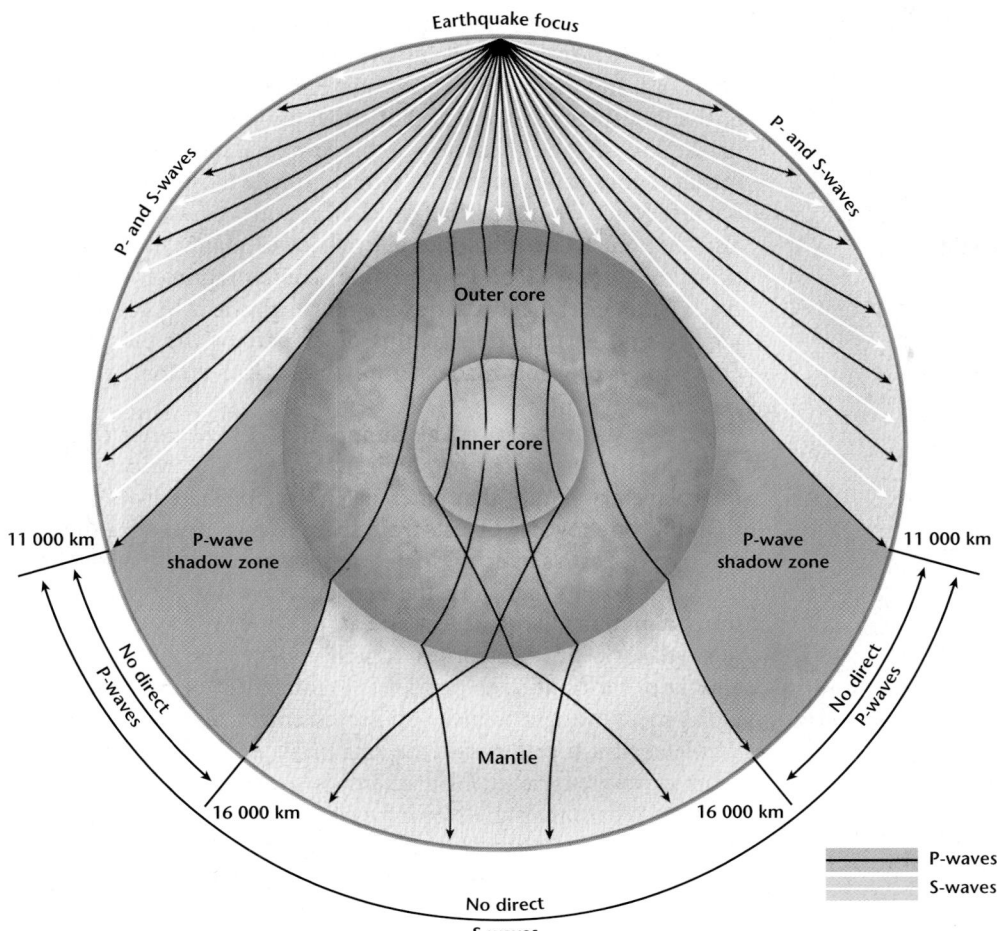

Earthquake focus

P- and S-waves

P- and S-waves

P- and S-waves

Outer core

Inner core

11 000 km

P-wave
shadow zone

P-wave
shadow zone

11 000 km

No direct
P-waves

No direct
P-waves

Mantle

16 000 km

16 000 km

No direct
S-waves

P-waves
S-waves

Figure 19–10 Refraction of P-waves into the outer core generates a P-wave shadow zone on Earth's surface where no direct P-waves appear on seismograms. Other P-waves are reflected and refracted by the inner core. S-waves cannot travel through liquids, and thus, don't reappear beyond the P-wave shadow zone.

11 000-km distance. This disappearance of S-waves has allowed seismologists to reason that Earth's outer core must be liquid. Detailed studies of how other seismic waves reflect deep within Earth show that Earth's inner core is solid.

Earth's Internal Structure The travel times and behavior of seismic waves provide a detailed picture of Earth's internal structure. These waves also provide clues about the composition of the various parts of Earth. By studying seismic-wave travel times, scientists have

Content Background

Dividing Earth's mass by its volume yields Earth's mean density, 5.5 g/cm^3. This value is much higher than the density of any known rock type, and therefore indicates that much of Earth's interior must consist of metal. Earth's moment-of-inertia, known from the precessional period of Earth's rotational axis in response to lunar and solar torques, indicates that Earth's density increases greatly with depth. Earth's crust and much of its mantle have densities much less than 5.5 g/cm^3. Therefore, Earth's core must have a density of at least 10.0 g/cm^{3}and consist of metal. Because the most abundant metal in meteorites and in the solar system is an iron-nickel alloy, Earth's core is thought to consist of an iron-nickel mixture as well. Because the nonmetallic components of meteorites are mostly olivine and pyroxene, Earth's mantle is thought to consist of rocks with a similar composition. Earth's crust represents a thin shell of low-density rocks derived from the mantle.

Differentiated Instruction

Gifted Have students calculate the mass of a sphere consisting of a core with a radius of 3450 km and a density of 12 500 kg/m^3, surrounded by a mantle with an outer radius of 6371 km and a density of 4200 kg/m^3. The mass of a shell with an inner radius r, outer radius R, and density d is
$$m = 4/3 \times (R^3 - r^3)d.$$

core: $m = 4/3 \ (6371m \times 10^3)^3 \times 12\ 500\ \text{kg}/m^3$ $= 2.15 \times 10^{24}$ kg; mantle: $m = 4/3 \ [(6371m \times 10^3)^3 - (3450 \times 10^3)^3] \times 4200\ \text{kg}/m^3 = 3.83 \times 10^{24}$ kg; total: $(2.15 \times 10^{24} + 3.83 \times 10^{24})\text{kg} = 5.98 \times 10^{24}$ kg

Point out that this sphere is a model of Earth. **L3**

503

Check for Understanding

Reinforcement

Ask the following question to check students' understanding of the major concepts presented in this section. How have scientists determined the structure and dimensions of Earth's interior? Earthquake waves and meteorites have been used to determine the structure and composition of Earth's interior. The absence of S-waves in the outer core indicates that it is molten. P-waves reflected from the inner core indicate that it is solid. The velocities of seismic waves inside Earth confirm the composition of the mantle and core. Meteorites have compositions similar to that of Earth; they consist mostly of rocks rich in iron and magnesium, and of an iron-nickel alloy.

Reteach

Draw a two-dimensional model of Earth's interior on the chalkboard. Have volunteers use different colors of chalk to indicate how both P- and S-waves travel from an earthquake's focus. Have a third volunteer mark the extent of the P-wave shadow zone on the drawing.

✔Assessment

Skill Have students each draw a cross section of Earth to scale in their science journals. On their models, have students indicate the composition and state of the crust, the mantle, and the inner and outer cores.

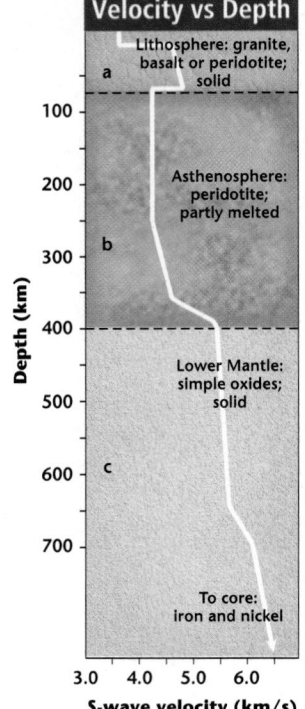

Velocity vs Depth

- a — Lithosphere: granite, basalt or peridotite; solid
- b — Asthenosphere: peridotite; partly melted
- Lower Mantle: simple oxides; solid
- c
- To core: iron and nickel

Figure 19-11 Observations of seismic wave velocities have enabled scientists to subdivide Earth's interior into various layers.

determined that the lithosphere, which includes the crust and the top of the upper mantle, is made up primarily of the igneous rocks granite, basalt, and peridotite as shown in *Figure 19-11.* The crustal part of the lithosphere is composed of either granite or basalt. The mantle section of the lithosphere is made of a dense, coarse-grained, intrusive rock called peridotite, which is made mostly of the mineral olivine. Much of the partially melted mantle, or asthenosphere, is also thought to be peridotite. Earth's lower mantle is solid and is probably composed of simple oxides containing iron, silicon, and magnesium. Seismic waves traveling through the core, together with gravity studies, indicate that this inner part of the planet is very dense and is probably made of a mixture of iron and nickel.

Earth's Composition The composition data obtained from seismic waves is supported by studies of meteorites, which are solid, interplanetary bodies that enter Earth's atmosphere. You might be thinking, but how can objects from space help to determine the composition of Earth's interior? Meteorites are pieces of asteroids, which are rocky bodies that orbit the Sun. Asteroids are thought to have formed in much the same way and at the same time as the planets in our solar system. Meteorites consist mostly of iron, nickel, and chunks of rock similar to peridotite in roughly the same proportions as the rocks thought to make up Earth's core and mantle.

Meteorites, together with the data provided by the travel times of seismic waves, have enabled scientists to indirectly probe Earth's interior. What other kinds of information can these waves provide? As you'll find out in the next section, seismic waves are used to determine the strength of an earthquake as well as the precise location of its epicenter.

SECTION ASSESSMENT

1. Explain how a seismometer works.
2. What is a seismogram?
3. What is a seismic travel-time curve, and how is it used to study earthquakes?
4. What is the P-wave shadow zone, and what causes it?
5. How have scientists determined the composition of Earth's mantle and core?

6. **Thinking Critically** As shown in *Figure 19-8,* on page 501, surface waves are the last to arrive at a seismic station. Why then do they cause so much damage?

SKILL REVIEW

7. **Recognizing Cause and Effect** Is there any way for P-waves to appear in the shadow zone? Explain. For more help, refer to the *Skill Handbook.*

earthgeu.com/self_check_quiz

SECTION ASSESSMENT

1. An inertial mass suspended by a spring remains stationary, while a rotating drum attached to the ground vibrates with the earthquake. The relative motion between the ground and inertial mass is recorded on paper attached to the drum.
2. a record of ground vibrations
3. A travel-time curve is a plot of travel time versus distance of earthquake waves. It is used to determine the distance of a seismic station from a quake's epicenter.

4. It is the zone between 11 000 and 16 000 km from a quake's epicenter in which no direct P-waves or S-waves are recorded. This zone is caused by the refraction of P-waves into Earth's outer core.
5. using velocities of seismic waves and the composition of meteorites
6. They have the largest amplitudes of all seismic waves and cause motion in two directions.
7. P-waves that have been reflected from the outer and inner core can appear in the shadow zone.

SECTION 19.3 Measuring and Locating Earthquakes

How many earthquakes do you suppose occur each year? If you were to rely only on news accounts of these events, you might guess a dozen or so, at most. It may surprise you to learn that more than one million earthquakes occur each year! However, more than 90 percent of these are not felt and cause little, if any, damage. The earthquakes that make the news are major seismic events that cause much damage, such as the one that occurred in Bam, Iran in December 2003.

EARTHQUAKE MAGNITUDE AND INTENSITY

The amount of energy released during an earthquake is measured by its **magnitude.** Many news accounts describe the magnitude of an earthquake on a numerical scale called the Richter scale, which was devised by an American seismologist named Charles Richter. An earthquake's rating on the **Richter scale** is based on the size of the largest seismic waves generated by the quake. Each successive number in the scale represents an increase in seismic-wave size, or amplitude, of a factor of 10. For example, the seismic waves of a magnitude-8 earthquake on the Richter scale are ten times larger than those of a magnitude-7 earthquake, and 100 times larger than those of a magnitude-6 earthquake. The differences in the amounts of energy released by earthquakes are even greater than the differences between the amplitudes of their waves. Each increase in magnitude corresponds to about a 32-fold increase in seismic energy. Thus, an earthquake of magnitude-8 releases about 32 times the energy of a magnitude-7 earthquake, and over 1000 times the energy of a magnitude-6 earthquake. Some of the damage caused by a quake measuring 8.6 on the Richter scale is shown in *Figure 19-12.*

OBJECTIVES

- **Compare** *and* **contrast** *earthquake magnitude and intensity and the scales used to measure each.*
- **Explain** *why data from at least three seismic stations are needed to locate an earthquake's epicenter.*
- **Describe** *Earth's seismic belts.*

VOCABULARY

magnitude
Richter scale
moment magnitude scale
modified Mercalli scale

Figure 19-12 The damage shown here was caused by an 8.6-magnitude earthquake that struck Anchorage, Alaska in 1964.

505

Section 19.3

Prepare

Section Background

For section content background, refer to **Earthquake Magnitude** on pages 494C–D.

Preplanning

Refer to the Chapter Organizer on pages 494A–B.

1 Focus

Section Focus

Before presenting the lesson, display **Section Focus Transparency 58** on the overhead projector. L1 ELL

Tying to Previous Knowledge

Ask students whether they have ever sat in a small boat on a lake or river. If so, they should recall that boats pitch up and down, roll from side to side, and swivel horizontally (yaw) from side to side. Explain that the ground motion during an earthquake is similar, but some of the oscillations are slower.

505

Enrichment

Interpersonal Have interested students research the Good Friday earthquake that struck Alaska in 1964. Have students find out the location of the epicenter, the quake's magnitude on the Richter scale, its duration, its maximum intensity, the damage it caused, the number of casualties, the depth of the focus, the type of fault involved, and the tectonic setting that led to this earthquake. Have students include their findings in their science journals. Point out that the photo on page 505 shows some of the damage caused by this major quake. **L1**

Content Background

Earthquake magnitude is not the same as earthquake energy, but the two quantities are related. This relationship can be expressed as $\mathrm{Log}\, E = 5.24 + 1.44\, M$, or alternately as $\mathrm{Log}\, E = 4.8 + 1.5\, M$, where E is the energy in Joules, and M is the magnitude (M_s). Both formulas give comparable results for quakes with magnitudes higher than 3. According to these relationships, a magnitude-8 earthquake releases about $10^{16.8}$ J of energy, which is comparable to the energy released by a 16-megaton nuclear device. By comparison, the energy released by the atomic bomb that destroyed Hiroshima corresponded to the energy of a magnitude-5.3 earthquake.

Moment Magnitude Scale While the Richter scale can still be used to describe the magnitude of an earthquake, most seismologists today use a scale called the moment magnitude scale to measure earthquake magnitude. The **moment magnitude scale** takes into account the size of the fault rupture, the amount of movement along the fault, and the rocks' stiffness. Unlike Richter-scale values, which are based on the largest seismic waves generated by a quake, moment magnitude values are estimated from the size of several types of seismic waves produced by an earthquake.

Modified Mercalli Scale Another way to assess earthquakes is to measure the amount of damage done to the structures involved. This measure, called the intensity of an earthquake, is determined using the **modified Mercalli scale,** which rates the types of damage and other effects of an earthquake as noted by observers during and after its occurrence. This scale uses the Roman numerals I to XII to designate the degree of intensity. Specific effects or damage correspond to specific numerals; the higher the numeral, the worse the damage. A simplified version of the modified Mercalli intensity scale is shown in *Table 19-1.* Use the information given in this scale to try to rate the intensity of the earthquake that caused the damage shown in *Figure 19-13.*

Figure 19-13 *Use the modified Mercalli scale to determine the intensity of the earthquake that caused the damage to this grocery store in Washington State.*

Interpreting the Photo

Figure 19-13 Use the modified Mercalli scale to determine the intensity of the earthquake that caused the damage to this grocery store in Washington State. The quake had an intensity of between IV and VI on the modified Mercalli scale.

Resource Manager

Laboratory Manual, pp. 145–148 **L2**

Table 19-1 Modified Mercalli Intensity Scale

I.	Not felt except under unusual conditions.
II.	Felt only by a few persons. Suspended objects may swing.
III.	Quite noticeable indoors. Vibrations are like the passing of a truck.
IV.	Felt indoors by many, outdoors by few. Dishes and windows rattle. Standing cars rock noticeably.
V.	Felt by nearly everyone. Some dishes and windows break, and some plaster cracks.
VI.	Felt by all. Furniture moves. Some plaster falls and some chimneys are damaged.
VII.	Everybody runs outdoors. Some chimneys break. Damage is slight in well-built structures but considerable in weak structures.
VIII.	Chimneys, smokestacks, and walls fall. Heavy furniture is overturned. Partial collapse of ordinary buildings occurs.
IX.	Great general damage occurs. Buildings shift off foundations. Ground cracks. Underground pipes break.
X.	Most ordinary structures are destroyed. Rails are bent. Landslides are common.
XI.	Few structures remain standing. Bridges are destroyed. Railroad ties are greatly bent. Broad fissures form in the ground.
XII.	Damage is total. Objects are thrown upward into the air.

Earthquake intensity depends primarily on the amplitude of the surface waves generated. Because surface waves, like body waves, gradually decrease in size with increasing distance from the focus of an earthquake, the intensity also decreases as the distance from a quake's epicenter increases. Maximum intensity values are observed in the region near the epicenter; Mercalli values decrease to I at distances very far from the epicenter.

Modified Mercalli scale intensity values of places affected by an earthquake can be compiled to make a seismic-intensity map. Contour lines join points that experienced the same intensity. The maximum intensity is usually, but not always, found at the quake's epicenter. You will generate a seismic-intensity map when you do the *MiniLab* on the next page.

Depth of Focus Earthquake intensity is related to earthquake magnitude. Both measurements reflect the size of the seismic waves generated by the quake. Another factor that determines the intensity of an earthquake is the depth of the quake's focus. An earthquake can be classified as shallow, intermediate, or deep depending on the location of the quake's focus. Because a deep-focus earthquake produces smaller vibrations at the epicenter than a shallow-focus quake, a shallow-focus, moderate quake of magnitude-6, for example, may generate a greater maximum intensity than a deep-focus quake of

Topic: Bam, Iran
To learn more about damage caused by earthquakes, visit the Earth Science Web Site at earthgeu.com

Activity: Research the December 2003 earthquake in Bam, Iran. Describe what an eyewitness may have seen.

Discussion

Tell students that intensity values decrease with increasing distance from the epicenter because the amplitudes of surface waves decrease with travel distance. Have students speculate why this is so. Students should be able to deduce that some of this decrease in wave size is a result of friction. Refer students to **Figure 19-6** and help them conclude that most of the decrease in wave size is a result of geometric spreading because surface waves spread in a circular pattern centered on the epicenter.

✓ *Assessment*

Knowledge Present the following scenario to students. During an earthquake, all the windows of a well-constructed school building broke, and some of the desks and other heavy furniture inside were overturned. What is the modified Mercalli intensity value that corresponds to this type of damage?
a. IV
b. V
c. VIII
d. X
The correct answer is c.

Content Background

Almost all deep-focus earthquakes are associated with regions that lie landward of subduction zones. A seismologist named Hugo Benioff discovered that the depths of earthquake foci increase with distance from a suduction zone trench. These seismic regions are oriented about 45 degrees in relation to the surface and are called Benioff zones after the scientist who discovered them.

NY Core Curriculum Standards
Page 504: St 4 KI 2.1j
Page 505: St 4 KI 2.1j, St 6 KI 3
Page 506: St 6 KI 3
Page 507: St 6 KI 3

MiniLab

Purpose
Students will make and interpret a simple seismic-intensity map.

Process Skills
interpret data, draw a conclusion

Materials
pencil and paper

Teaching Strategies
- Review the concepts presented in Chapter 2 on contour maps before students begin this lab.
- Draw a fictitious seismic-intensity map on the chalkboard so that students can get an idea of what their maps will look like.
- Remind students that the numbers between contours should all be the same. Instruct them to omit the intensity-I contour.

Expected Results
Students should produce a contour map with the highest intensity (VIII) contour in SW Ohio. Contours should show a SSW-NNE trend in intensities.

Analyze and Conclude
1. The maximum intensity value is VIII.
2. It is located at stations L and N.
3. between stations L and N

✓Assessment

Knowledge Have students use the Earth Science Web Site at earthgeu.com to search for a seismic-intensity map of another earthquake. Have them answer the same questions presented in the MiniLab for the earthquake they choose in their science journals.

MiniLab

How is a seismic–intensity map made?

Make a Map using seismic–intensity data.

Procedure
1. Trace the map onto paper. Mark the locations indicated by the letters on the map.
2. Plot these Mercalli intensity values on the map next to the correct letter: A, I; B, III; C, II; D, III; E, IV; F, IV; G, IV; H, V; I, V; J, V; K, VI; L, VIII; M, VII; N, VIII; O, III.
3. Draw contours on the map to separate the intensity values.

Analyze and Conclude
1. What is the maximum intensity value?
2. Where is the maximum intensity value located?
3. Where is the earthquake's epicenter?

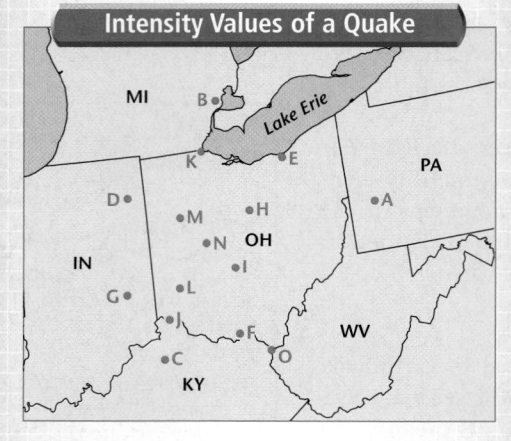

Intensity Values of a Quake

magnitude-8. Catastrophic quakes with high intensity values are almost always shallow-focus events.

LOCATING AN EARTHQUAKE

The exact location of an earthquake's epicenter and the time of the quake's occurrence are initially unknown. All epicenter locations, as well as times of occurrence, however, can be easily determined using seismograms and travel-time curves.

Distance to an Earthquake Look again at *Figure 19-9* on page 501. Suppose the separation time for the P-waves and S-waves is six minutes. Based on known travel times of seismic waves, the distance between the earthquake's epicenter and the seismic station that recorded the waves can only be 4500 km—no more, no less. This is because the known travel time over that distance is eight minutes for P-waves and 14 minutes for S-waves. At greater distances from the epicenter, the travel times for both types of waves increase. This results in a larger P-S separation because S-waves lag behind the faster P-waves. The distance to a quake's epicenter, then, is determined by the P-S separation. By measuring this separation on any seismogram as well as the distance on a travel-time graph at which the P-curve and S-curve have the same separation, the distance to a quake's epicenter can be determined. This distance is called the epicentral distance.

The distance between an earthquake's epicenter and a single seismic station does not provide sufficient information to determine the location of that epicenter—it could be located in any direction from the seismic station. The only thing that is certain is that the epicenter is located somewhere on a circle centered on the seismic station. The radius of this circle is equal to

Differentiated Instruction

Behaviorally Disordered Engage students by having them use the Earth Science Web Site at earthgeu.com to research an earthquake that occurred this year. Information gathered should include the date, location, magnitude, maximum intensity, depth of focus, casualties, and any other relevant information about the quake. **L1**

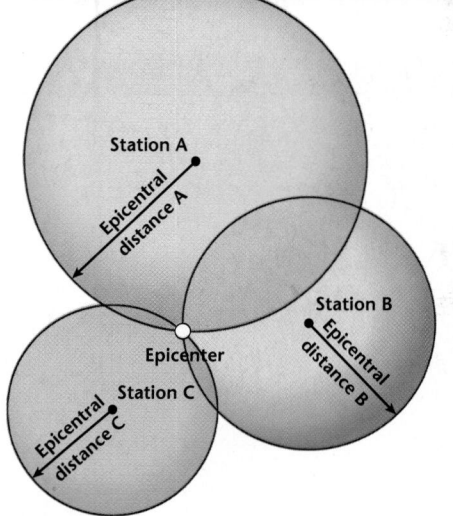

Figure 19-14 To determine the location of an earthquake's epicenter, the locations of three seismic stations are plotted on a map. A circle whose radius is equal to the corresponding epicentral distance is plotted around each station. The point of intersection of these circles is the earthquake's epicenter.

the epicentral distance. If the distances between three or more seismic stations and an earthquake's epicenter are known, the exact location of the epicenter can be determined, as shown in *Figure 19-14.* You will locate an actual epicenter in the *GeoLab* at the end of this chapter.

Time of an Earthquake The time of occurrence of an earthquake can be easily calculated, again by using the travel-time graph shown in *Figure 19-9.* The exact arrival times of the P-waves and S-waves at a seismic station can be read from the seismogram. The travel time of either wave at the epicentral distance of that station can be read from the travel-time graph. The time of occurrence of the earthquake is then determined by subtracting the appropriate travel time from the known arrival time of the wave.

SEISMIC BELTS

Over the years, seismologists have collected and plotted the locations of numerous earthquake epicenters. The global distribution of these epicenters, shown in *Figure 19-15* on the next page, reveals an interesting pattern. Earthquake locations are not randomly distributed. The majority of the world's earthquakes occur in relatively narrow seismic belts that separate large regions with little or no seismic activity. What causes this pattern of seismic activity?

Look back at *Figure 17-13* on page 455, which shows Earth's tectonic plates and the boundaries between them. How does this map compare with the map shown in *Figure 19-15?* By comparing the two maps, you can see that most earthquakes are associated with tectonic plate boundaries. Almost 80 percent of all earthquakes occur in the Circum-Pacific Belt. Another zone of significant seismic activity stretches across southern Europe and Asia. About 15 percent of the

Update For an online update of recent earthquakes, visit earthgeu.com and select the appropriate chapter.

Resource Manager

GeoLab and MiniLab Worksheets, p. 75 L2

Teaching Transparency 57 L2 ELL

Using Scientific Terms

Linguistic Have students use their dictionaries to each compile a list of at least ten scientific terms that contain the prefix *epi-.* Examples might include *epicenter, epiglottis, epiphyte, epidermis, epidural, epicycle,* and *epilepsy,* among others. Have students jot down a brief definition next to each term. L1

Interpreting the Illustration

Figure 19-14 Have students use the figure to explain why data from at least three seismic stations are necessary to locate the epicenter of an earthquake. Students should conclude that data from only two stations would result in two possible locations for the epicenter of the earthquake. Data from a third station pinpoint the quake's epicenter.

Interpreting the Illustration

Figure 19-15 Provide students with photocopies of **Figure 17-13.** Have students compare the figure with **Figure 19-15,** on the next page, as you explain that most Circum-Pacific earthquakes and those between the Indian and Eurasian Plates are related to plate convergence (compressional faulting) and subduction zones, and that most of the world's deep and intermediate-depth earthquakes occur there. Have students identify the major subduction zones in the Pacific and Indian Oceans. Explain, too, that the earthquakes in the Mediterranean area are the result of convergence between the African and Eurasian Plates. Finally, point out that ocean-ridge seismicity is the result of plate divergence (normal faulting).

Check for Understanding

Discussion

Have students compare and contrast two earthquakes: a shallow-focus, magnitude-6 quake and a deep-focus, magnitude-7 quake. Ask students the following questions. How do the earthquakes differ in released energy and in seismic wave size at the same distance from the focus? The waves of the magnitude-7 quake are ten times larger, and the energy released is 32 times greater than the energy released by the magnitude-6 quake. Which quake produces larger surface waves at the epicenter, and which quake has the greater maximum intensity? Why? The magnitude-6 quake produces larger surface waves and intensities at the epicenter because it originates closer to the surface.

Reteach

Have students each organize the information in the Check for Understanding item in a data table. Then have them add the same information for a deep-focus, magnitude-5 earthquake and a shallow-focus, magnitude-4 quake.

✓Assessment

Knowledge Ask students to compare and contrast the modified Mercalli and Richter scales. Both measure earthquake parameters. The modified Mercalli scale measures earthquake intensity, or the type of damage and other effects of a quake as noted by observers during and after the quake. The Richter scale measures earthquake magnitude, which is based on the size of the largest waves generated by the quake.

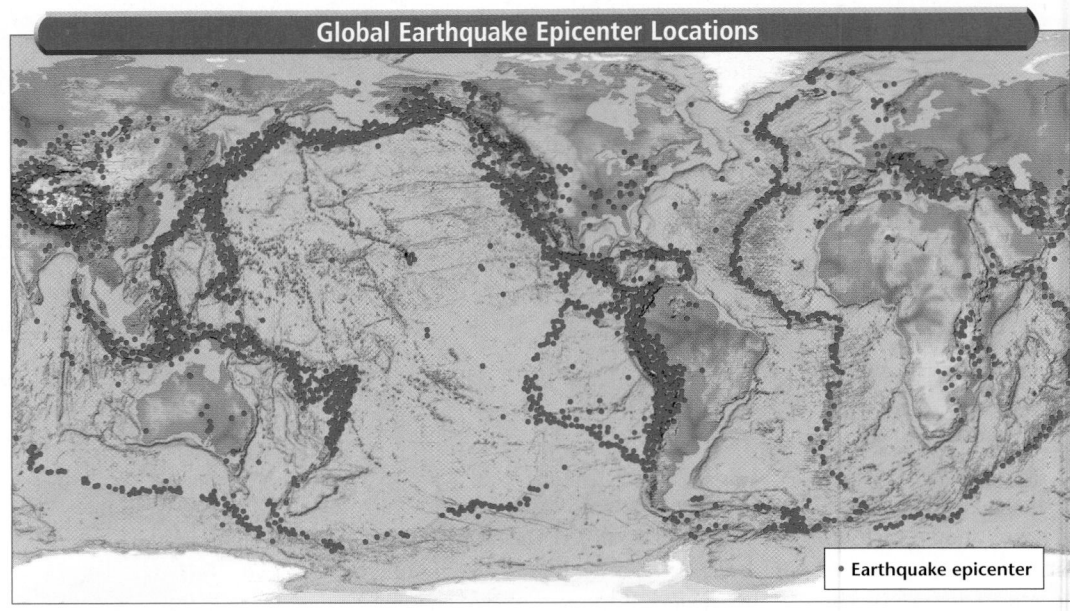

Global Earthquake Epicenter Locations

• Earthquake epicenter

Figure 19-15 This map shows the locations of earthquake epicenters.

world's earthquakes take place in this region, which is sometimes called the Mediterranean-Asian Belt. Most of the remaining earthquakes occur in narrow bands that run along the crests of ocean ridges. A very small percentage of earthquakes happen far from tectonic plate boundaries and are distributed more or less at random.

Look again at *Figure 19-15.* Do you live in an area prone to earthquakes? If so, how can you minimize the damage done by these seismic events?

SECTION ASSESSMENT

1. What is earthquake magnitude and how is it measured?
2. What is earthquake intensity and how is it measured?
3. Explain why earthquake data from at least three seismic stations are needed to locate an earthquake's epicenter.
4. **Thinking Critically** The separation of P-waves and S-waves on a seismogram recorded 4500 km from the epicenter of an earthquake is six minutes. On another seismogram that separation is seven minutes.

Is the second station closer to or more distant from the epicenter? Explain.

SKILL REVIEW

5. **Interpreting Scientific Diagrams** Use *Figure 19-15* above to determine which of the following countries has the most earthquakes: Ireland, Pakistan, South Africa, or Australia. Why does this country have more earthquakes than the other three countries? For more help, refer to the *Skill Handbook.*

 earthgeu.com/self_check_quiz

---

SECTION ASSESSMENT

1. The amount of energy released during a quake is related to the quake's magnitude. Magnitude can be measured on the Richter scale or the moment-magnitude scale.
2. Earthquake intensity is a measure of the damage caused by an earthquake and is measured on the modified Mercalli scale.
3. Data from only one station are insufficient because the epicenter could be in any direction from the station. Data from two stations result in two possible locations for the quake's epicenter.

Data from three stations intersect at only one point—the quake's epicenter.
4. P-waves always travel faster than S-waves. The greater the distance from the epicenter, the larger the time separation between P- and S-waves. A seismic station recording a P-S wave separation of seven minutes must be further from the epicenter than one recording a separation of six minutes.
5. Pakistan has more earthquakes than the other countries because it is located on a plate boundary in the Mediterranean-Asian Belt.

SECTION 19.4 *Earthquakes and Society*

Most earthquake damage results from the prolonged shaking of the ground by surface waves. During major quakes, this shaking can last longer than a minute. Many structures cannot withstand such violent motion. Collapsing buildings are responsible for many earthquake-related deaths. What other types of damage are caused by earthquakes? What kinds of factors affect the damage done during a quake? Is it possible to predict earthquakes?

SOME EARTHQUAKE HAZARDS

The damage produced by an earthquake is directly related to the strength or quality of the structures involved. The most severe damage occurs to unreinforced buildings made of stone, concrete, or other brittle building materials. Wooden structures, on the other hand, are remarkably resilient and generally sustain significantly less damage. Many high-rise, steel-frame buildings also sustain little damage during an earthquake because they are reinforced to make them earthquake resistant. Some buildings in earthquake-prone areas, such as California, even rest on large rubber structures that absorb most of the vibrations generated during a quake.

Structural Failure In many earthquake-prone areas, buildings are destroyed as the ground beneath them shakes. In some cases, the supporting walls of the ground floor fail and cause the upper floors, which initially remain intact, to fall and collapse as they hit the ground or lower floors. The resulting debris resembles a stack of pancakes, and thus, the process has been called "pancaking". This type of structural failure is shown in the photograph on page 494, and was a common result of the quake that rocked Turkey in 1999. You'll learn more about this quake and the damage it caused in the *Science in the News* feature at the end of this chapter.

Another type of structural failure is related to the height of a building. During the 1985 Mexico City earthquake, for example, most buildings between 5 and 15 stories tall collapsed or were otherwise completely destroyed as shown in *Figure 19-16.* Similar structures that were either shorter or taller, however, sustained only minor

OBJECTIVES

* **Discuss** *factors that affect the amount of damage done by an earthquake.*
* **Explain** *some of the factors considered in earthquake probability studies.*
* **Define** *seismic gaps.*

VOCABULARY

tsunami
seismic gap

Figure 19-16 The buildings damaged or destroyed during the 1985 Mexico City quake vibrated with the same period as the seismic waves.

Prepare

Section Background

For section content background, refer to **Vibrations and Resonance** on page 494D.

Preplanning

Refer to the Chapter Organizer on pages 494A–B.

1 Focus

Section Focus

Before presenting the lesson, display **Section Focus Transparency 59** on the overhead projector.
L1 ELL

Resource Manager

Study Guide for Content Mastery, p. 122 L2
Laboratory Manual, pp. 149–152 L2
Section Focus Transparency 59 L1 ELL

Demo

Build a small tower with soft-drink cans. Gently tap downward on the top of the tower with a hammer. Students will observe that the tower remains standing. Tap on the side of the bottom can with the same force. The tower will collapse. Explain that most buildings are constructed to withstand vertical forces, but not horizontal forces. Thus, buildings suffer little damage from vertical vibrations but may collapse as a result of horizontal vibrations.

NY Core Curriculum Standards

Page 510: St 4 KI 2.1n, St 6 KI 5
Page 511: St 1 Engin KI 1

Content Background

Refer to **Figure 19-5** on page 498. Because of their longitudinal motion, P-waves shake the ground nearly vertically. S-waves shake the ground mostly in the horizontal direction because of their transverse motion. Neither P- nor S-waves cause much damage because of their small amplitudes and high frequencies. Surface waves, on the other hand, have much larger amplitudes and much lower frequencies, and thus they are capable of causing catastrophic resonance in structures. Also, surface waves shake the ground much longer than body waves do. Love waves have horizontal transverse motion and shake the ground horizontally. Rayleigh waves have both horizontal and vertical motion. Both types of ground motion, especially when they act in concert, are capable of destroying buildings and other structures.

damage. Can you guess why? The shaking caused by the quake had the same period of vibration as the natural sway of the intermediate buildings, which caused them to sway violently during the quake. The ground vibrations, however, were too rapid to affect taller buildings, whose periods of vibration were longer than the earthquake waves, and too slow to affect shorter buildings, whose periods of vibration were shorter.

Land and Soil Failure In addition to their effects on structures made by humans, earthquakes can wreak havoc on Earth itself. In sloping areas, earthquakes may trigger massive landslides. Most of the estimated 30 000 deaths caused by the 7.8-magnitude earthquake that struck in Peru in 1970 resulted from a landslide that buried several towns. In areas with fluid-saturated sand, seismic vibrations may cause subsurface materials to liquefy and behave like quicksand, generating landslides even in areas of low relief. Soil liquefaction can also cause trees and houses to fall over or to sink into the ground and can cause underground pipes and tanks to rise to the surface.

In addition to causing soil liquefaction, earthquake waves can be amplified as they travel through a soil. Because soft materials have little resistance to deformation, seismic waves are amplified in such materials but are muted in more-resistant materials. Consequently, wave size and earthquake intensity are greatest in soft, unconsolidated sediments and relatively small in hard, resistant rocks such as

Figure 19-17 This fault scarp was produced by faulting associated with an earthquake that struck Mount Borah, Idaho, in 1983.

granite. The severe damage to structures in Mexico City during the 1985 earthquake is attributed to the fact that Mexico City is built on soft sediments. The thickness of the sediments caused them to resonate with the same frequency as that of the surface waves generated by the quake. This produced reverberations that greatly enhanced the ground motion and the resulting damage.

Fault Scarps Fault movements associated with earthquakes can produce areas of great vertical offset where the fault intersects the ground surface. These offsets are called fault scarps. As shown in **Figure 19-17,** a distinct fault scarp formed as the result of an earthquake that struck central Idaho in 1983. The magnitude-7.6 quake that rocked Taiwan in

Differentiated Instruction

Gifted Tall buildings have natural periods of oscillation and can be compared to upside-down pendulums. Have students contrast the periods and lengths of several pendulums by performing the following activity. **CAUTION:** *Wear safety goggles during this activity and insist that students do the same.* Instruct students to attach a weight (a heavy bolt or nut) to a long string, mark a fulcrum point on the string (1 m from the center of the weight), hold the string at the fulcrum, and, with everyone well out of the way, carefully swing

the weight with a relatively small amplitude. Have students count the number of swings (back and forth) per minute and calculate the period of oscillation by dividing 60 s by the number of swings. Have students change the length of the pendulum and repeat the activity several times with different lengths. Remind students to record the length and period for each new length of the pendulum. Have students plot the results to conclude that the period of a pendulum increases with the square root of its length.

NY Core Curriculum Standards

Page 512: St 1 Engin KI 1, St 5 KI 2.1n
Page 513: St 4 KI 2.1l, St 6 KI 5

Figure 19-18 Vertical offset along a fault caused this waterfall to form during the 1999 Taiwan earthquake.

1999 produced vertical offsets of up to 10 m, the greatest fault movement observed in recent history. An 8-m-high waterfall that formed where the fault crosses a river is shown in *Figure 19-18.*

Tsunami Another type of earthquake hazard is a **tsunami,** a large ocean wave generated by vertical motions of the seafloor during an earthquake. These motions displace the entire column of water overlying the fault, creating bulges and depressions in the water. The disturbance then spreads out from the epicenter in the form of extremely long waves. While these waves are in the open ocean, their height is generally less than 1 m. When the waves enter shallow water, however, they may form huge breakers with heights occasionally exceeding 30 m! These enormous wave heights, together with open-ocean speeds between 500 and 800 km/h, make tsunamis dangerous threats to coastal areas both near and far from the quake's epicenter. The magnitude-9.5 earthquake that struck Chile in 1960 generated a tsunami that destroyed many villages along an 800-km section of the South American coast. The wave then spread across the entire Pacific Ocean and struck Japan 23 hours later, killing 200 people. Even several days after the quake had struck, significant changes in water levels were observed in many coastal cities.

SEISMIC RISK

Recall that most earthquakes occur in areas called seismic belts. The probability of future quakes is much greater in these belts than elsewhere around the globe. The past seismic activity in any region is also a reliable indicator of future earthquakes and can be used to generate seismic-risk maps. A seismic-risk map of the United States is shown in *Figure 19-19* on the next page. Can you locate the areas of highest seismic risk on the map? In addition to Alaska, Hawaii, and some western states, there are several regions of relatively high

Using Math

Using Numbers The speed of tsunamis in the open ocean can reach 800 km/h. At this speed, how long, will it take a tsunami to travel from Japan to California, a distance of about 9000 km? If the waves are 160 km long, how far apart in time are the wave crests?

Collaborative Learning

Have students use metersticks to mark off a distance of 8 m on a sidewalk or in the hallway to get a sense of the vertical offset that produced the waterfall shown in **Figure 19-18.**

Using Math

speed = distance/time
travel time = distance/speed
= 9000 km/800 km/h
= 11.25 h or 11 h, 15 min

speed = wavelength/period
period = wavelength/speed
= 160 km/800 km/h
= 0.2 h or 12 min

Science Field Book

Earth Science
Journal

In their science journals, ask students to compare and contrast four earthquakes and their effects: a shallow, magnitude-8 quake at the Mid-Atlantic Ridge; a deep, magnitude-8 quake under Japan; a shallow, magnitude-6 quake in California; and a shallow, magnitude-6 quake in Turkey. Which of the quakes poses the greatest danger to populated areas? Why? Which is most likely to generate a tsunami? Explain. Which is probably the most harmless? Why? The Mid-Atlantic Ridge quake is too far from land to affect many people, but it might generate a tsunami. The Japan quake is too deep to generate dangerous intensities at the surface. The California and Turkey quakes are shallow and will generate high intensities in populated areas. California has more stringent building codes than Turkey. The Turkey quake is the most dangerous because of densely populated areas. Unless it generates a very large tsunami, the ocean-ridge earthquake is probably the least dangerous.

Project

Intrapersonal Have interested students research the building codes of your community and the compliance with the code of your school building. Ask students to find the answers to the following questions. Is your school earthquake proof? What earthquake hazards exist in and around the school? What would be the expected effects of an intensity VIII seismic event on your school and community? Have students report their findings to the class. Use the findings to conduct an earthquake drill.
L1

Time Line

Have students use references and the Earth Science Web Site to construct a time line that shows all earthquakes worldwide with magnitudes greater than 8 during the past 20 years. Have students indicate with "NA" which of these quakes occurred in North America. Recommend that students use a scale of 12 mm/y (1mm/mo).

Environmental Connection

Earthquakes can cause underground gas, water, and sewer lines to rupture. Therefore, in addition to earthquake damage and fires, the water supply in the epicentral area may become contaminated. Also, vertical ground displacement and the disruption of surface and subsurface drainage can have far-reaching consequences for the environment, such as uplifted coastal areas that can destroy marine habitats, drowned forests, and the loss of the water supply to large areas.

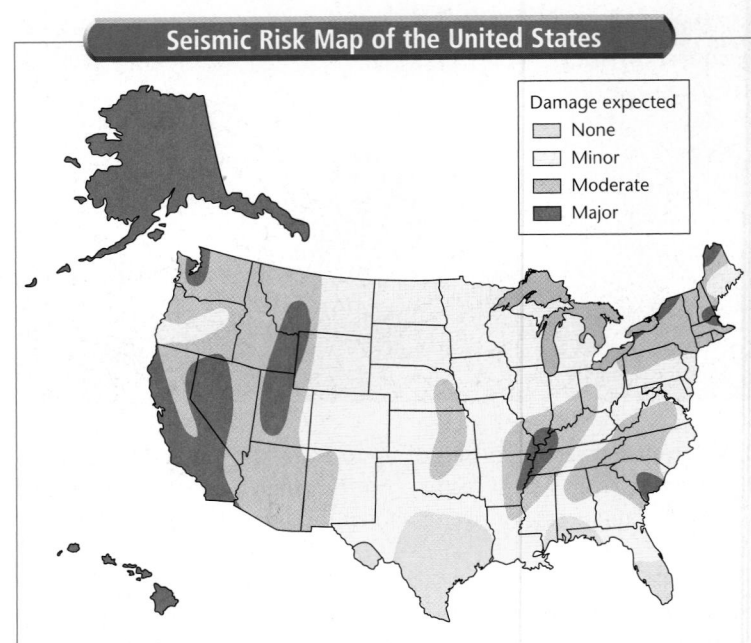

Figure 19-19 Areas of high seismic risk in the United States include Alaska, Hawaii, and some of the western states.

seismic risk in the central and eastern United States. These regions have suffered disastrous earthquakes in the past and probably will experience significant seismic activity in the future. Locate your state in *Figure 19-19.* What is the seismic risk of your area?

EARTHQUAKE PREDICTION

To minimize the damage and deaths caused by quakes, seismologists are searching for ways to predict these events. Earthquake prediction research is largely based on probability studies. The probability of an earthquake's occurring is based on two factors: the history of earthquakes in an area and the rate at which strain builds up in the rocks.

Earthquake History Earthquake recurrence rates can indicate that the fault involved ruptures repeatedly at regular intervals to generate similar quakes. The earthquake-recurrence rate at Parkfield, California, for example, shows that a sequence of quakes of approximately magnitude-6 shook the area about every 22 years from 1857 until 1966. This record indicates a 90-percent probability that a major quake will rock the area within the next few decades. Several kinds of instruments, including the lasers shown in *Figure 19-20,* are in place around Parkfield in an attempt to predict future quakes.

In-Text Question

Page 514 What is the seismic risk of your area? Answers will vary depending on your location. Help students locate your state on the map, if necessary.

Resource Manager

Teaching Transparency 58 **L2** **ELL**

Probability forecasts are also based on the location of seismic gaps. **Seismic gaps** are sections of active faults that haven't experienced significant earthquakes for a long period of time. One seismic gap in the San Andreas Fault cuts through San Francisco. This section of the fault hasn't ruptured since the devastating earthquake that struck the city in 1906. Because of this inactivity, seismologists currently predict that there is a 67-percent probability that the San Francisco area will experience a magnitude-7 or higher quake within the next 30 years.

Strain Accumulation The rate at which strain builds up in rocks is another factor used to determine the earthquake probability along a section of a fault. To predict when a quake might occur, scientists make several measurements. The strain accumulated in a particular part of the fault, together with how much strain was released during the last quake along that section of the fault, are two important factors in earthquake probability studies. Another factor is how much time has passed since an earthquake has struck that section of the fault.

Earthquake prediction is still a relatively new branch of geology. Being able to predict these destructive events can prevent damage to property, possibly reduce the number of injuries as a result of the quake, and, most importantly, save many lives.

Figure 19-20 Lasers are just one technique being used to study earthquake probability in the area around Parkfield, California. Lasers can record very small movements along a fault.

SECTION ASSESSMENT

1. Describe structural damage caused by earthquakes.
2. What are some of the effects caused by soil liquefaction?
3. How are tsunamis generated?
4. What are some of the factors considered in earthquake probability studies?
5. **Thinking Critically** Which structure is less likely to suffer severe damage during an earthquake: a high-rise, steel-frame hotel built on sediments, or a wood-frame house built on bedrock? Explain.

SKILL REVIEW

6. **Comparing and Contrasting** Compare and contrast the seismic risk of your state to at least three neighboring states. For more help, refer to the *Skill Handbook*.

earthgeu.com/self_check_quiz

19.4 *Earthquakes and Society* **515**

SECTION ASSESSMENT

1. Buildings are damaged or destroyed as the ground beneath them shakes. In some cases, ground floors fail and cause upper floors to collapse. Some structures are destroyed because they sway with the same period of vibration as the seismic waves.
2. Soil liquefaction can trigger landslides, cause buildings to sink or fall over, and cause underground pipes and tanks to rise to the surface.
3. Tsunamis are generated by the vertical displacement of the seafloor that results from a quake.
4. earthquake recurrence rates, seismic gaps, and strain-accumulation rates
5. A wood-frame house on bedrock is less likely to be damaged than a high-rise structure on sediments. Surface waves in sediments are much larger than in bedrock, and high-rise buildings are likely to sway with the same period of vibration as earthquake waves.
6. Answers will vary depending on your location. Have students explain any differences in seismic risk among geographically adjacent states.

515

GeoLab

GeoLab

Time Allotment

one class period

Process Skills

collect and interpret data, compare and contrast, draw a conclusion, use graphs, measure, use numbers, observe and infer, recognize cause and effect

Safety Precautions

Remind students to use their drafting compasses only as directed.

Preparation

You might want to provide photocopies of the map to students to cut back on the time needed to complete this lab. Make sure the copies are not reduced or enlarged, as smaller or larger copies will result in measurements different from those given in the data table.

Procedure

Teaching Strategies

- Have students work in groups of three or four. Make sure students follow the instructions step-by-step. Have them ask you about any steps that might be unclear.
- Due to the small map size, the data in the table are not accurate. Use a smaller-scale map for more accurate data.

Troubleshooting

- Some students may not be able to convert length measurements on the seismogram to time. Explain the procedure if necessary.
- Review how to use a map scale.
- Make sure students understand that each circle must be centered on the appropriate seismic station in order to accurately locate the quake's epicenter.

Locating an Epicenter

*T*he separation of P- and S-waves on a seismogram allows you to estimate the distance between the seismic station that recorded the data and the epicenter of that earthquake. If the epicentral distance from three or more seismic stations is known, then the exact location of the quake's epicenter can be determined.

Preparation

Problem

Determine the epicenter location and the time of occurrence of an actual earthquake, using the travel times of P- and S-waves recorded at three seismic stations.

Materials

Figures 17-13, 19-8, and *19-9*
map on facing page   calculator
drafting compass   metric ruler
tracing paper

Objectives

In this GeoLab, you will:

- **Determine** the arrival times of P- and S-waves from a seismogram.
- **Interpret** travel-time curves.
- **Plot** an epicenter location on a map.
- **Relate** seismic data to plate tectonics.

Safety Precaution

Procedure

1. The seismogram in *Figure 19-8* shows the arrival time of the first P-wave at 10 h, 50 min, 32 s GMT, Greenwich mean time. Estimate the arrival time of the first S-wave to the nearest tenth of a minute.

2. Subtract this S-wave time from the initial P-wave time. What is the P-S separation on the seismogram, in minutes and tenth of minutes? Enter this value in the data table for the Berkeley seismic station.

Sample Data

GEOLAB DATA TABLE			
Seismic Station	P-S Separation (min)	Epicenter Distance (km)	Map Distance (cm)
Berkeley, CA	4.3	2400	4.6
Boulder, CO	3.6	2000	3.8
Knoxville, TN	4.9	2700	5.2

3. The P-S separation observed on two other seismograms, which are not shown, are also listed in the table. Use the travel-time curves in *Figure 19-9* to determine the distances at which the P- and S-curves are separated by the time intervals listed in the table. Enter these distances in the table under the Epicenter Distance.

4. Carefully trace the map on this page. Accurately mark the three seismic station locations.

5. Determine the epicentral distances on your tracing, using a scale of about 0.9 cm = 500 km. Enter your values in the table under the Map Distance.

6. Use the compass to draw circles around each station on the map with the radius of each circle equal to the map distance, in cm, for that station.

7. Mark the point of intersection. This is the epicenter of the earthquake.

8. Determine the time of occurrence of this earthquake by reading the P-wave travel time from *Figure 19-9* for the epicentral distance for Berkeley.

United States and Mexico

Subtract this from the initial P-wave arrival time at Berkeley, which was 10 h, 50.5 min. Express this time in terms of hours, minutes, and seconds.

Analyze

1. Where is this epicenter located?
2. In which major seismic belt did this earthquake occur?
3. Use *Figure 17-13* to determine which plates form the boundary associated with this earthquake.

Conclude & Apply

1. What type of plate boundary is this?
2. Briefly describe the relative motion of the plates involved.
3. Describe the tectonic motions that caused the earthquake.

GeoLab **517**

Answers to Procedures

1. S-wave arrival: 10 h, 54.4 min GMT
2. P-S separation: 3.9 min
3. Berkeley: 2300 km
   Boulder: 1900 km
   Knoxville: 2600 km
5. Berkeley: 4.6 cm
   Boulder: 3.8 cm
   Knoxville: 5.2 cm
8. 10 h, 45 min, 18 s GMT

Analyze

1. north of Mazatlan, Mexico
2. Circum-Pacific Belt
3. the North American and Pacific Plates

Conclude & Apply

1. divergent
2. The Pacific Plate is moving toward the northwest in relation to the North American Plate.
3. The quake was caused by movements along the transform faults that offset the divergent boundary.

✔Assessment

Knowledge Pose the following questions to assess students' understanding of this lab. If the epicenter had been in Mexico City, how far would it have been from Berkeley? 3400 km What would have been the separation between the P- and S-waves on the seismogram? 5.0 min

---

Resource Manager

GeoLab and MiniLab Worksheets, pp. 76–78

NY Core Curriculum Standards

Page 516: St 1 Math KI 1 & 3, St 6 KI 2 & 5
Page 517: St 1 Math KI 1 & 3, St 6 KI 2 & 5

Purpose

Students will find out about the December 2003 earthquake that struck Bam, Iran, and the tectonic and human factors responsible for the vast devastation.

Content Background

The Bam quake occurred along the Bam Fault—Iran's version of the San Andreas Fault in California. The earthquakes in the region concentrate most of their energy at Earth's surface, thereby increasing the likelihood of damage and injuries.

Teaching Strategies

- Have students mark on a map of Iran the locations of quakes that have occurred along the Bam Fault in the twentieth century. Have students label each quake with the year it occurred using a different-colored pen for each decade. Students should observe any direction of earthquake epi-centers and infer if a threat to a densely populated city exists.
- Have students make a simple model of a strike-slip fault by placing two sheets of construction paper side by side on a tabletop. Have students erect a city over the fault line using plastic interlocking blocks. Instruct students to then pull the pieces of paper to simulate the horizontal movement that occurs along a strike-slip fault.

Science in the News

Earthquake in Iran

At 5:26 am local time on December 26, 2003, an earthquake rocked the city of Bam, located in southeastern Iran. Some residents were already sleeping outside due to a foreshock that occurred the previous evening. The earthquake had a magnitude of 6.6 and caused extensive damage in terms of human life and property, including leveling an ancient fortress that had been a World Heritage Site.

It is estimated that as many as 40,000 people were killed in the quake, up to 30,000 more were injured, and more than 75,000 people were left without homes. Eighty-five percent of the buildings in the city were damaged or destroyed, and the water supply system was damaged. A 2,000-year-old citadel, Arg-e Bam, thought to be the world's greatest mud fortress, was reduced to rubble as a result of the quake. The historic fortress was the city's most popular tourist attraction.

Tectonic Factors

The southeastern portion of Iran is a seismi-cally active area. Although no earthquakes have previously been reported in Bam, major earth-quakes have occurred in the region northwest of Bam. Between 1981 and 1998, four earthquakes with magnitudes greater than 5.6 occurred in this area. The origin of the December 26 quake is thought to be the Bam fault, a fault line that runs north-south through the region. According to the U.S. Geological Survey, the quake occurred as a result of stresses created by the motion of the Arabian plate northward against the Eurasian plate at a rate of approximately 3 cm/yr. The hori-zontal and vertical movement along a strike-slip fault resulted in the destruction of homes and buildings throughout Bam.

The Aftermath

Immediately following the quake, rescue efforts and humanitarian aid were launched by international organizations such as the United Nations and the Red Cross. Food, water, shelter, and medical services were provided to victims through relief efforts and donations. Search teams found one man alive beneath rubble 13 days after the quake struck. Initial estimates for recovery and rebuilding of the city of Bam were between $70 million and $1 billion dollars. The World Health Organization estimated that 30 mil-lion dollars would be needed to reestablish Bam's health services. Two hospitals were destroyed and half of Bam's health workers were killed in the earthquake. A minimum estimate of two years was given by the United Nations Office of Coordination of Human Affairs for rebuilding the fallen city.

Activity

Dealing with disasters of the magnitude of the Bam earthquake can seem overwhelm-ing. Contact emergency preparedness agen-cies in your area to find out what steps have been taken to locally prepare for nat-ural disasters. What kinds of disasters do these agencies primarily prepare for? Make a pamphlet to summarize your findings.

518 CHAPTER 19 *Earthquakes*

Activity

Display the pamphlets and discuss how the class might prepare for natural disasters that might strike your area.

Summary

SECTION 19.1
Forces Within Earth

Main Ideas
- Stress is a force per unit area that acts on a material. The deformation of materials in response to stress is called strain.
- Reverse faults form as a result of horizontal compression; normal faults, horizontal tension; strike-slip faults, horizontal shear.
- P-waves squeeze and pull rocks in the same direction along which the waves travel. S-waves cause rocks to move at right angles to the direction of the waves. Surface waves cause both an up-and-down and a side-to-side motion as they pass through rocks.

Vocabulary
epicenter (p. 499)
fault (p. 497)
focus (p. 499)
primary wave (p. 498)
secondary wave (p. 498)
strain (p. 496)
stress (p. 495)
surface wave (p. 498)

SECTION 19.2
Seismic Waves and Earth's Interior

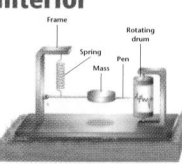

Main Ideas
- A seismometer has a frame that is anchored to the ground and a suspended mass. Because of inertia, the mass tends to stay at rest as the ground and, thus, the frame vibrate during a quake. The motion of the mass in relation to the frame is registered and recorded.
- Seismic waves are reflected and refracted as they strike different materials. Analysis of these waves has enabled scientists to determine the structure and composition of Earth's interior.

Vocabulary
seismogram (p. 500)
seismometer (p. 500)

SECTION 19.3
Measuring and Locating Earthquakes

Main Ideas
- Earthquake magnitude is a measure of the energy released during a quake and can be measured on the Richter scale. Intensity is a measure of the damage caused by a quake and is measured with the modified Mercalli scale.
- Data from at least three seismic stations are needed to locate an earthquake's epicenter.
- Most earthquakes occur in areas associated with plate boundaries called seismic belts.

Vocabulary
magnitude (p. 505)
modified Mercalli scale (p. 506)
moment magnitude scale (p. 506)
Richter scale (p. 505)

SECTION 19.4
Earthquakes and Society

Main Ideas
- Earthquakes cause structural collapse, landslides, soil liquefaction, fissures, fault scarps, uplift or subsidence, and tsunamis. Factors that affect the extent of damage done by a quake include the type of subsurface as well as the quality, height, and structure of buildings and other structures involved.
- The probability of an earthquake is based on the history of quakes in an area and the rate at which strain builds in the rocks.
- Seismic gaps are places along an active fault that haven't experienced significant earthquakes for a long period of time.

Vocabulary
seismic gap (p. 515)
tsunami (p. 513)

 earthgeu.com/vocabulary_puzzlemaker

---

Main Ideas

Summary statements can be used by students to review the major concepts of the chapter.

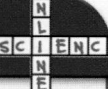

VOCABULARY PuzzleMaker

For additional help with vocabulary, have students access the Vocabulary Puzzlemaker online.

earthgeu.com/
vocabulary puzzlemaker

0:00 *Out of Time?*

If time does not permit teaching the entire chapter, use the GeoDigest at the end of the unit as an overview.

Earth Science online

Be sure to check the Earth Science Web Site for links to chapter material:
earthgeu.com

GLENCOE
Technology

Videotape/DVD
MindJogger Videoquizzes
Chapter 19: *Earthquakes*
Have students work in groups as they play the videoquiz game to review key chapter concepts.

Resource Manager

Chapter Assessment, pp. 109–114
MindJogger Videoquizzes DVD/VHS
ExamView® Pro CD-ROM
Performance Assessment in Earth Science

NY Core Curriculum Standards

Page 518: St 4 KI 2.1j & 2.1l
Page 519: St 4 KI 2.1j & 2.1n, St 6 KI 3 & 5
Page 520: St 1 Engin KI 1, St 4 KI 2.1j & 2.1n
Page 521: St 1 Math KI 3, St 4 KI 2.1j & 2.1n, St 6 KI 2, 3, & 5

Understanding Main Ideas

1. c
2. b
3. a
4. c
5. a
6. c
7. b
8. All are fractures along which movement takes place. Normal faults are caused by tension, reverse faults by compression, and strike-slip faults by shear. In normal and reverse faults, movement is vertical and horizontal. In strike-slip faults, movement is only horizontal.
9. Students' drawings should resemble **Figure 19-5**.
10. A recording drum moves in relation to a stationary mass. The relative motion of the mass is traced on the drum during a quake.
11. Seismic waves are reflected and refracted at interior boundaries. Seismic wave velocities depend on the composition of the material through which they travel.
12. When plotted on a map, the epicentral distances of three seismic stations intersect at only one point—the epicenter.
13. a reverse fault
14. horizontal compression
15. the surface between the arrows
16. Seismic belts are located at tectonic margins because most quakes are caused by motion between tectonic plates.
17. quake magnitude, depth of the focus, distance from the

Understanding Main Ideas

1. What is stress?
   a. movement of waves parallel to rock particles
   b. deformation of a material caused by applied forces
   c. forces per unit area acting on a material
   d. unit of measure on the Richter scale

2. What is strain?
   a. forces per unit area acting on a material
   b. deformation of a material caused by applied forces
   c. unit of measure on the Mercalli scale
   d. travel time of seismic waves

3. Which type of seismic wave causes rock particles to move in the same direction as the wave movement?
   a. P-wave
   c. tension wave
   b. S-wave
   d. shear wave

4. What part of Earth doesn't receive direct P-waves from a quake?
   a. epicenter
   c. shadow zone
   b. focus
   d. mantle

5. Which is used to measure magnitude?
   a. Richter scale
   c. shadow zone
   b. Mercalli scale
   d. seismic gap

6. What is earthquake intensity?
   a. a measure of the energy released
   b. a measure of seismic risk
   c. a measure of damage done
   d. a measure of the quake's focus

7. What is a seismic gap?
   a. a large fault scarp
   b. a part of an active fault that hasn't recently experienced seismic activity
   c. the time separation between P- and S-waves
   d. the liquefaction of soil during a quake

8. Compare and contrast the three types of faults.
9. Draw three diagrams to show how each type of seismic wave moves through rocks.
10. Explain how a seismometer works.
11. How have seismic waves been used to determine Earth's structure and composition?
12. Why are data from at least three seismic stations needed to locate an epicenter?

Use this figure to answer questions 13–15.

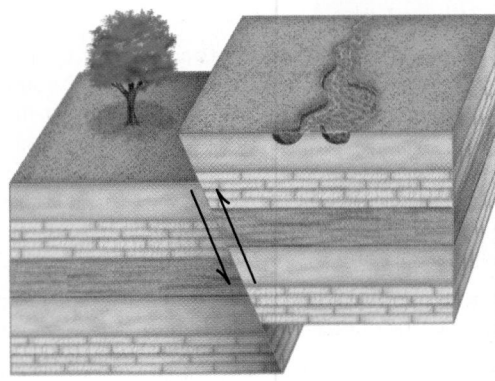

13. What type of fault is shown?
14. What type of force caused this fault to form?
15. Where is the fault plane?
16. Explain the relationship between worldwide earthquake distribution and tectonic boundaries.
17. What factors affect the damage done by an earthquake?

Test-Taking Tip

MORE THAN ONE GRAPHIC If a test question refers to more than one table, graph, diagram, or drawing, use them all. If you answer based on just one graphic, you'll probably miss an important piece of information.

---

epicenter, nature of the surface material, location of the epicenter relative to population centers, quality of structures
18. earthquake history, seismic gaps, and strain-accumulation rates

Applying Main Ideas

19. Materials deform elastically when exposed to low stresses (straight segment) and by ductile flow when exposed to high stresses (curved segment).

20. Surface waves are the largest seismic waves, and they move in two directions as they pass through rocks.
21. One records horizontal motion and the other vertical ground motion.
22. The fact that S-waves can't travel through liquids and didn't penetrate the outer core indicates that it is liquid. The fact that P-waves are reflected from the inner core indicates that it is solid.

18. What factors are studied in the field of earth-quake probability?

Applying Main Ideas

19. Explain why a stress-strain curve usually has two segments.

20. Why do surface waves cause so much destruction?

21. Why are two types of seismometers generally used to record the same earthquake?

22. How were P-waves and S-waves used to determine the physical state of Earth's core?

23. Compare and contrast the Richter scale and the moment magnitude scale.

24. Explain how shear stress is different from tension and compression.

25. Compare and contrast the composition of Earth's mantle and core with the composition of meteorites.

Thinking Critically

26. How do you think a thin, plastic, ruler would react to a small amount of stress? What would happen if the stress applied exceeded the elastic limit of the ruler?

27. Describe several reasons why an earthquake of magnitude-3 can cause more damage than a quake of magnitude-6.

28. Why are tsunamis so destructive?

29. If rocks below the lithosphere are too hot to undergo brittle fracture, how is it possible to have deep-focus earthquakes beneath island arcs?

30. Refer to *Figure 19-19* on page 514. Explain why some areas in the eastern part of the United States are prone to major earthquake damage even though these places are far from present tectonic plate boundaries.

earthgeu.com/standardized_test

Standardized Test Practice

1. What happens to a material when it undergoes stress that exceeds its strength?
   a. The material undergoes ductile formation.
   b. The material is deformed permanently.
   c. The material returns to its original state.
   d. The material breaks or fails.

2. What is the order in which seismic waves are recorded by a seismometer?
   a. S-wave, P-wave, surface wave
   b. surface wave, P-wave, S-wave
   c. P-wave, S-wave, surface wave
   d. S-wave, surface wave, P-wave

INTERPRETING DATA Use the table below to answer questions 3 and 4.

Some Earthquakes In Recent History		
Location	**Year**	**Richter Magnitude**
Chile	1960	8.5
California	1906	7.9
Alaska	1964	8.6
Columbia	1994	6.8
Taiwan	1999	7.6

3. Approximately how much more energy was released by the Chilean quake than the Taiwan earthquake?
   a. twice as much
   b. ten times as much
   c. thirty two times as much
   d. one thousand times as much

4. Approximately how much larger was the amplitude of the waves generated by the Alaskan quake than the Taiwan quake?
   a. about twice as large
   b. about ten times as large
   c. about one hundred times as large
   d. about one thousand times as large

23. The Richter scale is based on the size of seismic waves generated and underestimates the magnitude of large quakes. The moment-magnitude scale is based on actual fault dimensions, fault slip, and properties of the rocks, and gives a more accurate magnitude estimate.

24. Compression causes a material to shorten; tension causes a material to stretch. Shear stress distorts a material.

25. Meteorites consist mostly of iron, nickel, and chunks of rock similar to peridotite in roughly the same proportions as the rocks thought to make up Earth's core and mantle.

Thinking Critically

26. A plastic ruler would deform elastically under small stresses. It would deform permanently if the stresses exerted exceeded the elastic limit of the ruler.

27. A magnitude-3 quake can cause more damage than a magnitude-6 quake if the magnitude-3 quake strikes near a populated area, strikes an area underlain by sediments, or has a shallower focus than the magnitude-6 quake.

28. Tsunamis can be much higher and move much faster than large storm waves and can strike coastal regions far from a quake without warning.

29. Deep-focus quakes occur in subduction zones where cool, brittle slabs of lithosphere have penetrated the upper mantle.

30. These areas are sites of former plate boundaries that are still active deep beneath Earth's surface.

AMVIEW® PRO

Standardized Test Practice

1. d
2. c
3. c
4. b

se ExamView® Pro Testmaker D-ROM to:

Create **multiple versions** of tests.

Create **modified** tests with one mouse click for struggling students.

Edit existing questions and add your own questions.

Build tests based on national curriculum standards.

521

Chapter 20

Mountain Building

Refer to pages 8T–9T of the Teacher Guide for an explanation of the National Science Content Standards correlations.

Section	Objectives	National Science Content Standards	State/Local Standards
SECTION 20.1 **Crust-Mantle Relationships** 🕐 1 session 📦 ½ block	1. **Describe** the elevation distribution of Earth's surface. 2. **Explain** isostasy and how it pertains to Earth's mountains. 3. **Describe** how Earth's crust responds to the addition and removal of mass.	UCP.2, UCP.4; D.3	St 1 Math KI 2 & 3, St 4 KI 1.1i, St 4 KI 2.1j, 2.1l, 2.1n, 2.1o, 2.1p, 2.1q, & 2.1t St 6 KI 2, 3, & 4
SECTION 20.2 **Convergent-Boundary Mountains** 🕐 1 session 📦 ½ block	4. **Compare** and **contrast** the different types of mountains that form along convergent plate boundaries. 5. **Explain** how the Appalachian Mountains formed.	UCP.2; D.3	St 4 KI 2.1l, 2.1m, 2.1n, 2.1o, & 2.1p, St 6 KI 2, 3, 4, & 5
SECTION 20.3 **Other Types of Mountains** 🕐 4 sessions 📦 2 blocks	6. **Describe** the mountain ranges that form along ocean ridges. 7. **Compare** and **contrast** uplifted and fault-block mountains. 8. **Describe** the mountains that form as a result of hot spots in Earth's mantle.	UCP.2; UCP.4; A.2; D.3; E.1, E.2; G.1, G.3	St 1 Science KI 1 & Math KI 3, St 2 KI 1, St 4 KI 2.1l, 2.1m, 2.1n, 2.1o, 2.1p, & 2.1r, St 6 KI 2, 4, & 6

* *A complete Planning Guide is provided on pages 30T–32T.*

🕐 The number of recommended single-period sessions

📦 The number of recommended blocks

Activity Materials

Discovery Lab *page 523*
metric ruler, softwood blocks (8 cm × 8 cm × 2 cm and 8 cm × 8 cm × 4 cm), 1 hardwood block (8 cm × 8 cm × 2 cm), balance, plastic tub, water

GeoLab *pages 540–541*
metric ruler, graph paper, sharp pencil

MiniLab *page 536*
tracing paper; pencil; metric ruler; physiographic maps, at the same scale, of the Atlantic Ocean floor and the United States

Demo *page 538*
polystyrene foam

Need materials? Contact Science Kit at 1-800-828-7777 or at www.sciencekit.com on the Internet. For alternate materials, see the activity on the listed page.

Key to Teaching Strategies

L1 Level 1 activities should be appropriate for students with learning difficulties.

L2 Level 2 activities should be within the ability range of all students.

L3 Level 3 activities are designed for above-average students.

ELL ELL activities should be within the ability range of English-language learners.

COOP LEARN Cooperative learning activities are designed for small-group work.

P These strategies represent student products that can be placed in a best-work portfolio.

📦 These strategies are useful in a block-scheduling format.

Chapter Organizer

Glencoe Exclusive!
TeacherWorks™
All-In-One Planner and Resource Center

Activities/Features	Reproducible Masters	Transparencies
Discovery Lab: Model Crustal Differences, p. 523 **Using Math:** Using Numbers, p. 524 **Problem-Solving Lab:** Making and Interpreting Graphs, p. 526	**Study Guide for Content Mastery,** p. 123 **L2**	**Section Focus Transparency 60** **L1** **ELL** **Teaching Transparency 59** **L2** **ELL**
	Study Guide for Content Mastery, pp. 124–126 **L2** **Laboratory Manual,** pp. 153–156 **L2**	**Section Focus Transparency 61** **L1** **ELL** **Teaching Transparency 60** **L2** **ELL**
MiniLab: How large is an ocean ridge? p. 536 **GeoLab:** Making a Map Profile, pp. 540–541 **Science & Math:** The Roof of the World, p. 542	**Study Guide for Content Mastery,** pp. 127–128 **L2** **GeoLab and MiniLab Worksheets,** p. 79 **L2** **Laboratory Manual,** pp. 157–160 **L2** **GeoLab and MiniLab Worksheets,** pp. 80–81 **L2**	**Section Focus Transparency 62** **L1** **ELL** **Teaching Transparency 61** **L2** **ELL**

✔ Assessment

Chapter Assessment,
  pp. 115–120
Performance Assessment in the Science Classroom (PASC)
MindJogger Videoquiz DVD/VHS
Performance Assessment in Earth Science
ExamView® Pro CD-ROM
5 Days to the Regents Exam

GLENCOE'S
ASSESSMENT
ADVANTAGE

Additional Resources

Guided Reading Audio Program **ELL**
Cooperative Learning in the Science Classroom **COOP LEARN**
Lesson Plans
Block Scheduling
earthgeu.com
NY Lesson Plans
NY Block Scheduling
Review Handbook for Regents Earth Science Exam

◻ NATIONAL GEOGRAPHIC

Teacher's Corner

Products Available from National Geographic Society
To order the following products, call the National Geographic Society at 1-800-368-2728:

Curriculum Kits
GeoKit: *Dynamic Earth*
GeoKit: *Earth's History*

Content Background

Glacioisostatic Rebound
Section 20.1

If Earth scientists could push down on a section of Earth's crust and watch it rebound, they could learn a great deal about isostasy. At first thought, such an experiment seems impossible. However, the last several episodes of glaciation have provided the basis for such an experiment. The weight of continental ice sheets such as those that covered much of Earth during the last ice age depressed the crust significantly. At the close of a glacial episode, the excess weight on the crust is rapidly removed as ice sheets melt. This rebounding of

the crust is known as glacioisostatic rebound. Glacioisostatic rebound is currently occurring in parts of Scandinavia and Canada. The ice sheets that once covered these areas melted about 10 000 years ago, causing the crust in these regions to rebound. Measurements show that the crust in the northern Baltic Sea area is rising 1 cm/y. Such a rate can impact harbors, lakes, and river drainage patterns over several hundred years.

The Aleutian Arc
Section 20.2

The Aleutian Island Arc, which extends nearly 4000 km westward from Alaska, represents one of the largest oceanic subduction zones on Earth. This arc system contains 40 historically active volcanoes and is unique in that it involves an oceanic-oceanic convergent boundary to the west and an oceanic-continental convergent boundary to the east. Subduction in this region began during the Late Cretaceous Period when the former Kula Plate began to subduct beneath the North American Plate. The Kula Plate no longer exists; it has been subducted into the mantle. The trailing edge of the Kula Plate consisted of an ocean ridge called the Kula Ridge. During the Eocene Epoch of the Cenozoic Period, the Kula Ridge started to subduct. Because the ridge material was warm and therefore buoyant, however, it resisted subduction and jammed the subduction zone. By the Middle Miocene Epoch, subduction

Multiple Learning Styles

Kinesthetic Project, p. 530, Modeling, p. 537

Visual-Spatial Demo, pp. 526, 538, Reteach, p. 527

Interpersonal Collaborative Learning, p. 538

Linguistic Reinforcement, p. 531, Reteach, p. 539

GLENCOE
Technology

The following multimedia resources are available from Glencoe.

Vocabulary Puzzlemaker

TeacherWorks™ CD-ROM

MindJogger Videoquizzes DVD/VHS

ExamView® Pro CD-ROM

Interactive Chalkboard CD-ROM

Chapter Organizer

stopped. The Pacific Plate, however, continued to move northwest against the plugged subduction zone. Eventually, during the Pliocene Epoch, the cold, dense Pacific Plate broke free and began to subduct beneath the North American Plate. This subduction continues today.

The Colorado Plateau
Section 20.3

There are several hypotheses about what causes large regions of continental crust to move vertically with little or no horizontal deformation, as in the case of the Colorado Plateau of the southwestern United States. The thick, horizontal sedimentary rock layers exposed in the Grand Canyon represent a long period of regional stability. The last period of major structural deformation is marked by an angular unconformity beneath the Tapeats Sandstone. This unconformity represents a period of faulting, tilting, and erosion that occurred about 550 million years ago. Since then, this region of the North American Plate has remained intact and has undergone only vertical movements. This 500-million-year period of stability is unusual in that the surrounding Rocky Mountain and Basin and Range regions were being thrusted, stretched, and fractured at the same time. The final episode of vertical uplift of the Colorado Plateau region about 6 million years ago allowed the Colorado River to carve the awesome feature known as the Grand Canyon.

Identifying Misconceptions

Students might have the misconception that mountains are built during a single, continuous episode and are subsequently worn away by erosion. Most mountains and mountain ranges go through multiple stages of formation, or orogenesis. A rugged mountain range, for example, can form and be partially eroded. Many years later, renewed uplift can restore the mountain range's youthful, jagged stage. This process is called rejuvenation. The main orogenesis of the Rocky Mountains occurred during the Late Mesozoic Era and the Early Tertiary Period. The heights and shapes of the mountains we see today, however, are the result of rejuvenation caused by renewed uplift during the last 15 to 20 million years.

Assessment

Portfolio Assessment
Assessment, TWE, p. 539

Performance Assessment
Discovery Lab, SE, p. 523
Discovery Lab, TWE, p. 523
MiniLab, SE, p. 536
MiniLab, TWE, p. 536
GeoLab, SE, pp. 540–541
GeoLab, TWE, pp. 540–541

Knowledge Assessment
Problem-Solving Lab, TWE, p. 526
Section Assessment, SE, pp. 527, 534, 539
Chapter Assessment, SE, pp. 544–545
Assessment, TWE, p. 534

Skill Assessment
Assessment, TWE, p. 527

Be sure to check the Earth Science Web Site for links to chapter material: earthgeu.com

Mountain Building

Introducing the Chapter

Display a physiographic map of the world as you teach this chapter. Begin a discussion about mountains by asking students the following questions. What are the nearest mountains? Where are some other mountains located? Are all mountains the same? How might they be different? How do you think mountains form? You might want to have students record their answers to these questions in their science journals and correct any errors as you teach this chapter.

Interpreting the Photo

The Towers of Paine, some of which are shown here, are parts of a granite massif that rises over 2000 m above sea level in Chile's Paine Towers National Park, a UNESCO biospheric reserve.

Chapter Themes

The following themes from the National Science Content Standards are covered in this chapter. Refer to page 8T of the Teacher Guide for an explanation of the correlations.
Systems, order, and organization (UCP.1); Change, constancy, and measurement (UCP.3); Evolution and equilibrium (UCP.4)

⏱ (8:88) Out of Time?

If time does not permit teaching the entire chapter, use the Chapter Summary on page 543 and the GeoDigest found at the end of the unit as an overview.

What You'll Learn

• Why Earth's crust displaces the mantle on which it rests.

• How different processes create mountains that rise above Earth's surface.

Why It's Important

All mountains rise above the surrounding land, yet each of these awesome structures is unique. Understanding the various processes involved in mountain building is critical to our understanding of the dynamic planet on which we live.

Earth Science Online

To learn more about mountain building, visit the Earth Science Web Site at earthgeu.com

Mountain Building

Discovery Lab

Process Skills

measure, use numbers, collect and interpret data, draw a conclusion **L1** **ELL**

Preparation

Each group will need two softwood blocks, one 8 cm × 8 cm × 2 cm and one 8 cm × 8 cm × 4 cm, and a hardwood block 8 cm × 8cm × 2 cm. Provide a balance for the whole class to use.

Procedure

Troubleshooting

• Stress that depth measurements be made without pushing down on the blocks.

Analyze and Conclude

The softwood block floats higher than the hardwood block because it has a lower density. The thicker softwood block floats higher than the thinner softwood block. The hardwood block represents oceanic crust, and the softwood block represents continental crust.

Discovery Lab

Model Crustal Differences

Continental and oceanic crust have different densities. In this activity, you will model how both kinds of crust displace the mantle.

1. Obtain three wood blocks from your teacher. Determine the mass and volume of each. Calculate the density of each block. Record all of these values in a data table.

2. Half-fill a clear, plastic container with water. Place both of the 2-cm-thick blocks in the container.

3. Use a ruler to measure how much of each block is above the water surface. Record the measurements.

4. Replace the hardwood block with the 4-cm-thick softwood block.

5. Measure and record how much of each block is above the water surface.

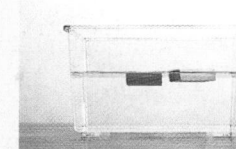

 **CAUTION:** *Always wear safety goggles and an apron in the lab.*

Analyze and Conclude Use your data to answer the following questions in your science journal. How does density affect the height of flotation? How does thickness affect the height of flotation? Which block represents oceanic crust? Continental crust?

SECTION 20.1 — *Crust-Mantle Relationships*

OBJECTIVES

- **Describe** *the elevation distribution of Earth's surface.*

- **Explain** *isostasy and how it pertains to Earth's mountains.*

- **Describe** *how Earth's crust responds to the addition and removal of mass.*

VOCABULARY

isostasy
isostatic rebound

Mountains are spectacular features of Earth's crust that rise high above their surroundings. Mountains can occur as individual peaks such as the Towers of Paine in southern South America, which are shown on the facing page, or as immense ranges that snake for many kilometers along the landscape. Why do these geologic wonders rise high above Earth's surface, and how are such vast masses of rock supported? The answers to these questions lie in the relationships between Earth's crust and the underlying mantle.

EARTH'S TOPOGRAPHY

When you look at a globe or a map of Earth's surface, you immediately notice the oceans and continents. From these models of Earth, you can estimate that about 70 percent of Earth's surface is below sea level, and that the remaining 30 percent lies above the ocean's surface. What isn't obvious from most maps and globes, however, is the change in elevation, or topography, of the crust. Look at *Figure 20-1* on the next page, which is a map of the general topography of Earth's crust. Where are

---

✓Assessment

Performance Have students predict how the blocks would float in liquids with densities greater than and less than that of water. Have students conduct simple experiments to test their predictions. Use the Performance Task Assessment for Designing an Experiment in **PASC,** p. 23.

Resource Manager

Study Guide for Content Mastery, p. 123 **L2**

Section Focus Transparency 60 **L1** **ELL**

Prepare

Section Background

For section content background, refer to **Glacioisostatic Rebound** on page 522C.

Preplanning

Refer to the Chapter Organizer on pages 522A–B.

1 Focus

Section Focus

Before presenting the lesson, display **Section Focus Transparency 60** on the overhead projector.
L1 **ELL**

Tying to Previous Knowledge

Active mountains can be thought of as battling between uplifting forces and the agents of erosion. Have students recall what they learned in Chapters 7 and 8 about erosion, weathering, and mass movement. Ask them to list some of the processes that wear down mountains.

Identifying Misconceptions

Some students may incorrectly think that Earth's crust is too thick to respond to added mass.

Uncover the Misconception
Before students read this section, ask them how they think Earth's crust would respond when mass is added to or removed from it.

Demonstrate the Concept
Push down on a thick block of polystyrene foam floating in an aquarium or a large, clear container of water. Have students describe the change in position of the block as you add and remove mass.

Assess New Knowledge
After you complete this section, have students describe a situation in which Earth's crust has isostatically adjusted to changes in load.

Using Math

The rate of erosion, 1 cm/y, equals 1 m/100 y, which is ten times faster than the rate of uplift, 1 m/1000 y.

Environmental Connection

The loss of mass resulting from the melting of continental glaciers during the last ice age is causing the crust in the Great Lakes region to rebound. The rebound has caused an increase in shoreline erosion along the southern margins of the lakes and is threatening coastal communities.

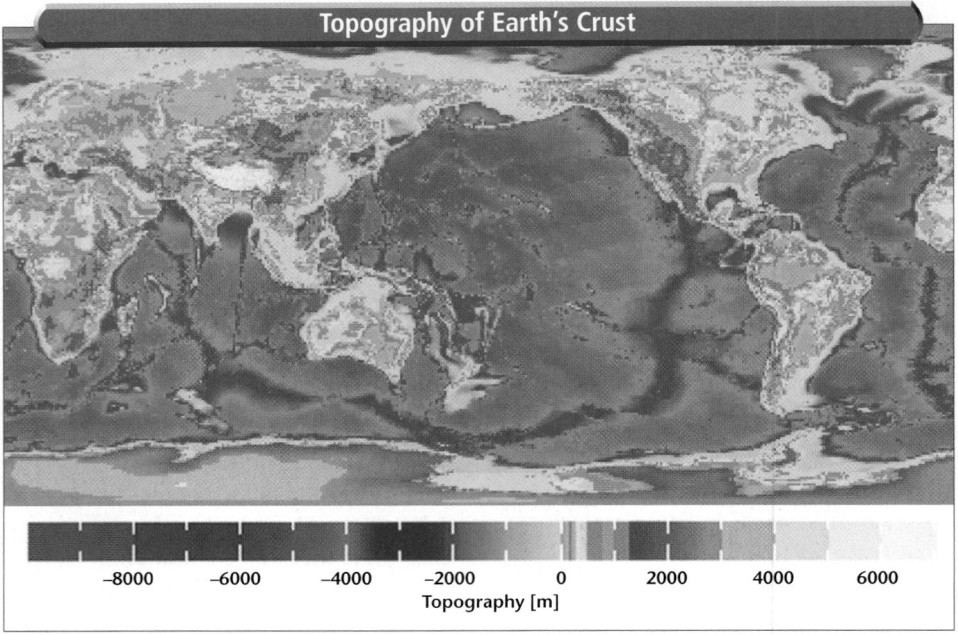

Topography of Earth's Crust

Topography [m]

Figure 20-1 The highest point on Earth is Mt.Everest in Asia. The lowest point on Earth is the Mariana Trench, which is in the Pacific Ocean.

Using Math

Using Numbers
Suppose a mountain is being uplifted at a rate of 1 m every 1000 years. It is also being eroded at a rate of 1 cm/y. Is this mountain rising faster than it is being eroded? Explain.

Earth's highest elevations? Where are Earth's lowest elevations?

When Earth's topography is plotted on a graph, a pattern in the distribution of elevations emerges, as shown in **Figure 20-2.** Note that there are two main elevation modes. Most of Earth's elevations cluster around these two modes: 0 to 1 km above sea level and 4 to 5 km below sea level. These two modes dominate Earth's topography and reflect the basic differences in density and thickness between continental and oceanic crust.

You observed in the *Discovery Lab* at the beginning of this chapter that blocks of wood with different densities displaced different amounts of water, and thus floated at various heights above the surface of the water. The block with the greatest density displaced the most water and floated lower in the water than the less-dense blocks. The results of this simple experiment are similar to the relationship that exists between Earth's crust and mantle. Recall from Chapter 1 that oceanic crust is composed mainly of basalt and that continental crust is composed primarily of granite. The average density of basalt is about 2.9 g/cm^3, while the average density of granite is about 2.8 g/cm^3. The slightly higher density of oceanic crust causes it to displace more of the mantle—which has a density of about 3.3 g/cm^3—than the same thickness of continental crust does.

Differences in elevation, however, are not caused by density differences alone. Recall from the *Discovery Lab* what happened when the

524 CHAPTER 20 *Mountain Building*

In-Text Questions

Pages 523–524 Where are Earth's highest elevations? Asia Where are Earth's lowest elevations? the Pacific Ocean

Differentiated Instruction

Gifted Have students research the elevation distribution of Mars and Venus and compare them to that of Earth. Have students hypothesize whether crustal isostasy plays any role on Mars and Venus. Scientists hypothesize that Venus may still be experiencing crustal rebound. Mars, however, being smaller, has cooled to the point at which its crust is too thick to rebound. **L3**

thicker wood block was placed in the water. It displaced more water than the other two blocks, but, because of its density, it floated higher in the water than the other two blocks. Continental crust, which is thicker and less dense than oceanic crust, behaves similarly. It extends deeper into the mantle because of its thickness, and it rises higher above Earth's surface than oceanic crust because of its lower density, as shown in *Figure 20-3.*

ISOSTASY

The displacement of the mantle by Earth's continental and oceanic crust is a condition of equilibrium called **isostasy.** The crust and mantle are in equilibrium when the force of gravity on the mass of crust involved is balanced by the upward force of buoyancy. This balance is familiar to you if you have ever watched people get in and out of a small boat. As the people boarded the boat, it sank deeper into the water. Conversely, as the people got out of the boat, it displaced less water and floated higher in the water.

A similar sinking and rising that result from the addition and removal of mass occurs with the crust that makes up Earth's mountains. Gravitational and seismic studies have detected thick roots of continental material that extend into the mantle below Earth's mountain ranges. According to the principle of isostasy, parts of the crust will rise or subside until these parts are buoyantly supported by their roots. In other words, a mountain range requires large roots to counter the enormous mass of the range above Earth's surface. Continents and mountains are said to float on the mantle because they are less dense than the underlying mantle and therefore project into the mantle to

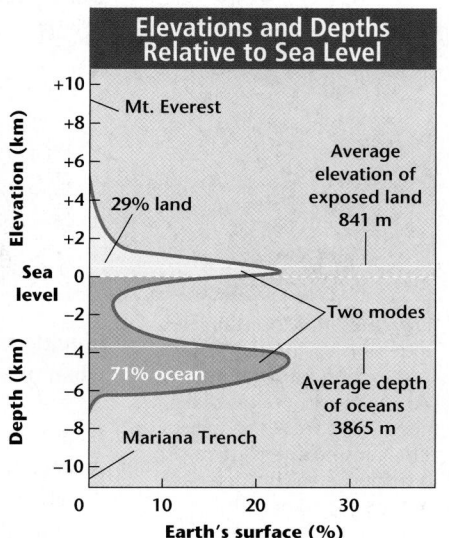

Figure 20-2 About 29% of Earth is land; 71% of Earth is water. Two elevations dominate Earth's surface: 0 to 1 km above sea level and 4 to 5 km below sea level. The average elevation above sea level is 841 m. The average depth of Earth's oceans is 3865 m.

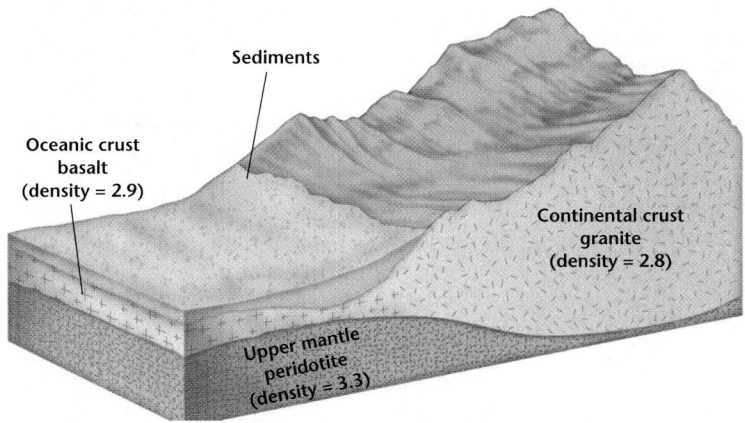

Figure 20-3 Continental crust is less dense and thicker than oceanic crust, and it thus extends higher above Earth's surface and deeper into the mantle than oceanic crust.

Content Background

Continental glaciers covered large regions of North America during the Pleistocene Epoch. The weight of the 3-kilometer thick mass of ice caused the underlying crust to subside. Scientists estimate that as much as 330 m of rebound has occurred in the Hudson Bay area since the ice sheets melted.

Interpreting the Illustration

Figure 20-2 Have students refer to this graph to answer the following questions. What percentage of Earth's surface is higher than 1 km in elevation? about 6 percent What percentage of Earth's surface is 5 km below sea level? about 14 percent

Resource Manager

Teaching Transparency 59
L2 ELL

Earth Science

Journal

Tell students that seamounts with flat, wave-eroded tops have been found thousands of meters below sea level. Additionally, patterns of circular fractures in the seafloor around these seamounts have been observed. Challenge students to write a paragraph or two explaining these features in their science journals.

Seamounts form as the result of hot spots in the mantle. The tops of the seamounts were eroded by waves as the oceanic crust isostatically sank as a result of the added mass. Eventually, the tops sank below the wave base. The downwarping of the crust caused the circular fractures.

NY Core Curriculum Standards

Page 522: St 4 KI 2.1m
Page 523: St 4 KI 1.1n, 2.1n, 2.1p, & 2.1q, St 6 KI 2
Page 524: St 1 Math KI 2, St 4 KI 2.1p & 2.1q
Page 525: St 4 KI 2.1j, 2.1l, & 2.1o, St 6 KI 2 & 4

In-Text Question

Page 526 What do you think happens when mass is removed from a mountain or mountain range? *Students should be able to deduce that the mountain or mountain range will rebound when mass is removed.*

Problem-Solving Lab

Purpose
Students will determine how the rate of isostatic rebound changes over time.

Process Skills
make and use graphs, analyze data, predict, think critically

Materials
graph paper, pencil

Teaching Strategies
- Tell students that the data represent rebound since the end of the last ice age. The ice melted 10 000 years ago, and rebound is measured in relation to sea level (0 m).
- Students should plot total rebound on the *y*-axis and time on the *x*-axis, which should have 10 000 years before present plotted at the far left end of the axis and 0 years plotted on the right end of the axis.
- Students' graphs should show exponential curves that rise steeply and level off between 2000 and 0 years before present.

Analysis
1. Rebound between 10 000 and 8000 years ago was 54 m. This is about half of the total rebound.

Thinking Critically
2. Extrapolating the curve will result in an estimated 6–8 m of additional rebound, which could take another 6000 to 8000 years.
3. The rate of rebound decreases by about one-half every 2000 years.

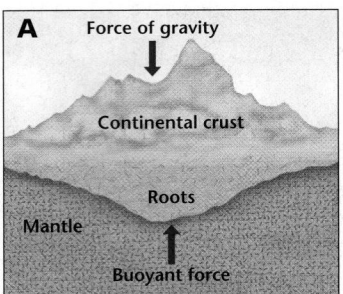 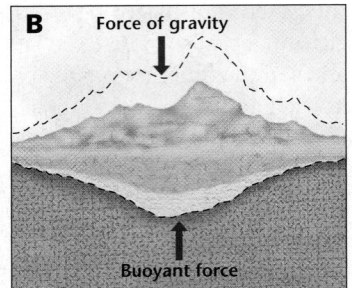 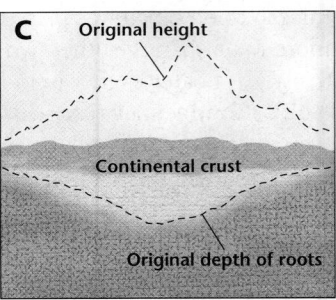

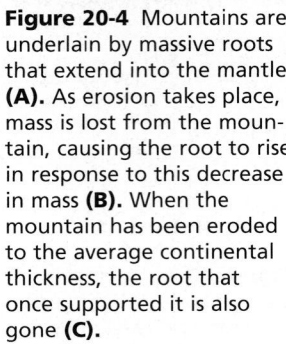

Figure 20-4 Mountains are underlain by massive roots that extend into the mantle **(A)**. As erosion takes place, mass is lost from the mountain, causing the root to rise in response to this decrease in mass **(B)**. When the mountain has been eroded to the average continental thickness, the root that once supported it is also gone **(C)**.

provide the necessary buoyant support. What do you think happens when mass is removed from a mountain or mountain range?

Isostasy and Erosion You might recall from Chapter 17 that the Appalachian Mountains formed millions of years ago when the North American continent collided with the European continent. Rates of erosion on land are such that these mountains should have been completely eroded long ago. Why, then, do these mountains still exist? As mountains rise above Earth's surface, deep roots form until isostatic equilibrium is achieved and the mountains are buoyantly supported. As peaks are eroded, mass decreases, and the roots become smaller, as shown in *Figure 20-4.* A balance between erosion and the decrease in the size of the root will continue for hundreds of millions of years until both the mountains and their roots disappear. This slow process of the

Problem-Solving Lab

Making and Interpreting Graphs

Graph isostatic rebound The rate of isostatic rebound changes over time. An initially rapid rate often declines to a very slow rate. Use the data in the table to generate a graph of isostatic rebound with time.

Isostatic Rebound Data	
Years Before Present	**Total Amount of Rebound (m)**
8000	54
6000	80
4000	93
2000	100
0	104

Analysis
1. How much of the total rebound occurred during the first 2000 years?

Thinking Critically
2. Predict how much rebound will still occur. Approximately how long will this take?
3. Study your graph. Describe how the rate of isostatic rebound decreases with time.

✓Assessment

Knowledge Ask students the following question. Would the rate of isostatic rebound be slower or faster if the viscosity of the upper mantle were less than it is now? *The rate would be faster.*

Demo

Visual-Spatial You can demonstrate the effect of isostatic rebound if the viscosity of Earth's mantle were greater than it is now with two small blocks of wood, a beaker 3/4 full of honey, and a beaker 3/4 full of water. Have students determine which setup represents the viscosity of Earth's mantle and which represents the hypothetical mantle. **CAUTION:** *Wipe up any spills immediately to prevent slipping or falling.*

crust's rising as the result of the removal of overlying material is called **isostatic rebound.** You can explore how the rate of isostatic rebound changes with time in the *Problem-Solving Lab* on page 526.

Crustal movements resulting from isostasy are not restricted to Earth's continents. Individual volcanic mountains called seamounts can form on the ocean floor as a result of a plate's moving over a hot spot in Earth's mantle. On the geologic time scale, these mountains form very quickly. What do you think happens to the seafloor after these seamounts form? The seamounts are added mass. As a result of isostasy, the oceanic crust around these peaks displaces the underlying mantle until equilibrium is achieved.

You've just learned that the elevation of Earth's crust depends upon the thickness of the crust as well as its density. You also learned that a mountain peak is countered by a root. Mountain roots can be many times as deep as a mountain is high. Mt. Everest, shown in *Figure 20-5,* towers nearly 9 km above sea level and is the tallest peak in the Himalayan Mountains. Some parts of the Himalayas are underlain by crustal roots nearly 80 km thick! You'll learn more about Mt. Everest in the *Science & Math* feature at the end of this chapter. Where do the immense forces required to produce such crustal thickening originate? You'll find out in the next section.

Figure 20-5 Mt. Everest, a peak in Asia, is currently the highest mountain on Earth. It is underlain by a very deep crustal root that supports its mass.

SECTION ASSESSMENT

1. If continental crust were thinner than its average thickness of 40 km, would it depress the mantle more or less than it does now? Explain.

2. What is isostasy?

3. Describe the distribution of Earth's elevations and explain what causes this distribution.

4. Why is the crust thicker beneath continental mountain ranges than it is under flat-lying stretches of landscape?

5. **Thinking Critically** The area around the Great Lakes was once covered by thick sheets of ice. Use the principle of isostasy to explain how the melting of these ice sheets has affected the land around the lakes.

SKILL REVIEW

6. **Recognizing Cause and Effect** Explain what happens in terms of isostasy to the land surrounding a mountain range as sediments are eroded from the mountains onto the nearby land. For more help, refer to the *Skill Handbook.*

earthgeu.com/self_check_quiz

Check for Understanding
Reinforcement
Inform students that the Mississippi River has deposited thousands of meters of sediment into the Gulf of Mexico. Ask students what effect this has had on Earth's offshore crust. The mass of the sediment has depressed the crust. Ask students whether this would cause sea level to rise or sink in relation to the shoreline. Sea level would rise in relation to the shoreline.

Reteach
 **Visual-Spatial** Have each student draw three diagrams that show blocks of wood with different thicknesses floating in water. Have them exchange drawings with a partner who should sequence the diagrams to show how a mountain and its roots change as the result of erosion. **ELL**

✓Assessment

Skill Have students describe at least two scenarios that would cause Earth's crust to isostatically subside deeper into the mantle. Possible answers include the formation of volcanoes, the accumulations of large volumes of sediment, and the formation of continental ice sheets.

SECTION ASSESSMENT

1. It would depress the mantle less than it does now, just as the thinner wood block in the Discovery Lab displaced less water than the thicker block of the same kind of wood.

2. a condition of equilibrium reached as the mantle is displaced by crust

3. There are two main elevation modes: 0–1 km above sea level and 4–5 km below sea level. These modes are caused by differences in thickness and density of continental and oceanic crust.

4. The mountain range is underlain by a deep root that provides the buoyant support necessary for this massive volume of crust.

5. The ice caused the crust to displace more of the mantle than the unglaciated crust. As the ice melted, the crust began to rebound.

6. As sediments are deposited, the additional mass causes the crust to displace more of the mantle until isostatic equilibrium is reached.

NY Core Curriculum Standards
Page 526: St 1 Math KI 3, St 4 KI 2.1o, 2.1p, & 2.1t, St 6 KI 2 & 3
Page 527: St 4 KI 2.1n, 2.1o, & 2.1p

527

Section Background

For section content background, refer to **The Aleutian Arc** on pages 522C–D.

Preplanning

Refer to the Chapter Organizer on pages 522A–B.

1 Focus

Section Focus

Before presenting the lesson, display **Section Focus Transparency 61** on the overhead projector. **L1** **ELL**

FOLDED ROCKS
Use with Chapter 20, Section 20.2

❶ Describe the rock layers pictured.

❷ These rocks were once sediments deposited in horizontal layers. What kinds of forces could have brought about the changes these rocks have undergone?

Section Focus Transparency   Earth Science: Geology, the Environment, and the Universe

Tying to Previous Knowledge

The rock andesite got its name from the Andes Mountains. Have students recall what they learned in Chapter 5 about igneous rocks. Ask them to classify andesite and state its composition. Andesite is an extrusive rock with an intermediate composition between those of basalt and granite.

SECTION 20.2

Convergent-Boundary Mountains

OBJECTIVES

• **Compare** *and* **contrast** *the different types of mountains that form along convergent plate boundaries.*

• **Explain** *how the Appalachian Mountains formed.*

VOCABULARY

orogeny

A quick glance at a world map will show that Earth's landscape is dotted with numerous mountain peaks and ranges. The Cascades and the Appalachians, for example, run north-south on either side of the United States. The Andes form the western border of South America, and the majestic Himalayas separate Nepal from Tibet. Mt. Kilimanjaro is a volcano that rises high above the African continent. Mauna Loa, another volcanic peak, is located in Hawaii. Most of these ranges and peaks, like most earthquakes and volcanoes, have formed as a result of tectonic interactions.

OROGENY

The processes that form all mountain ranges are called **orogeny.** Orogeny results in broad, linear regions of deformation known as orogenic belts. Most orogenic belts, as shown in *Figure 20-6,* are associated with plate boundaries. The greatest variety and the tallest of these belts are found at convergent boundaries. The compressive forces at these

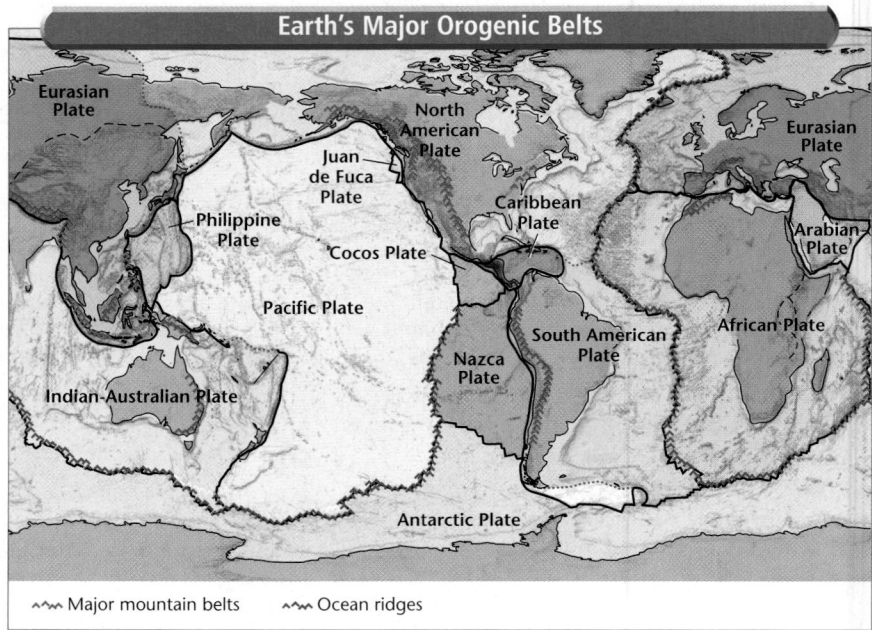

Earth's Major Orogenic Belts

⌃⌃⌃ Major mountain belts   ⌃⌃⌃ Ocean ridges

Figure 20-6 Most of Earth's mountain ranges have formed along plate boundaries.

528 CHAPTER 20 *Mountain Building*

Interpreting the Illustration

Figure 20-6 Have students use the figure to locate the mountains named in the introductory paragraph on this page. Ask students to name the type of boundary responsible for the formation of each of the mountains, except Mauna Loa, which did not form as the result of interactions along plate boundaries. The Cascades, the Appalachians, the Andes, and the Himalayas formed as the result of convergence. Kilimanjaro formed as the result of volcanism along a divergent boundary.

Differentiated Instruction

English-Language Learners Have students use their dictionaries to find the meanings of the word parts that make up the word *orogeny.* Students should find that *oro* means "mountain" and *geny* means "production." **ELL**

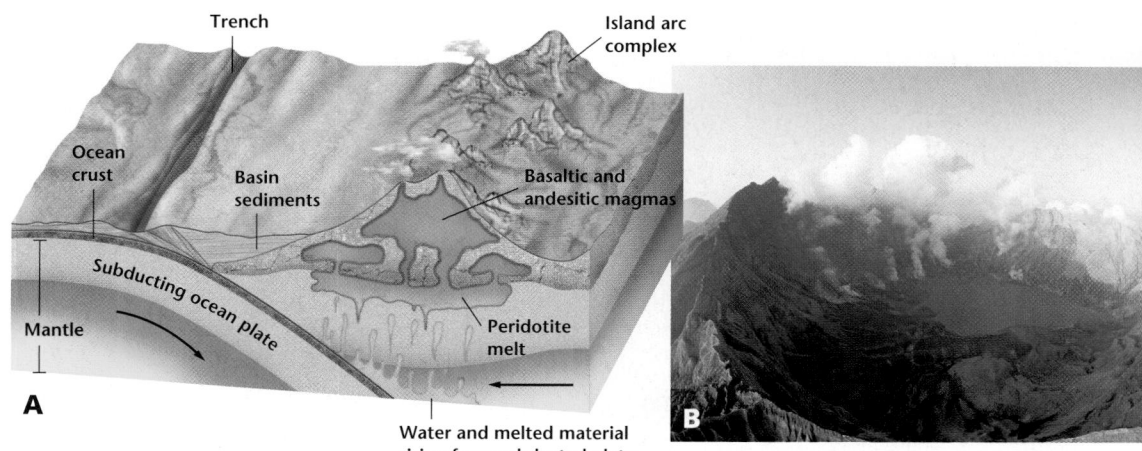

A

B

Figure 20-7 Convergence between two oceanic plates results in the formation of individual volcanic peaks that make up an island arc complex **(A)**. Mt. Pinatubo, shown here **(B)**, is one of several volcanic peaks that make up the island arc complex known as the Philippine Islands.

boundaries may cause the intense deformation—folding, faulting, metamorphism, and igneous intrusions—that is characteristic of orogenic belts. Interactions at each type of convergent boundary create different types of mountain ranges.

Oceanic-Oceanic Convergence When an oceanic plate converges with another oceanic plate, one plate descends into the mantle to create a subduction zone. As parts of the subducted plate melt, magma is forced upward to form a series of volcanic peaks called an island arc complex. The tectonic relationships and processes associated with oceanic-oceanic convergence are detailed in *Figure 20-7A.* Note that the crust along the island arc thickens to form a root. According to the principle of isostasy, it is the displacement of the mantle by this root that provides the necessary buoyancy for a mountain peak.

What kinds of rocks make up island arc complexes? Recall from Chapter 19 that seismic studies indicate that much of the mantle is made of an igneous rock called peridotite. The water released from a subducted plate and the sediments it carries causes the peridotite to melt. The melted rocks, along with bits of the subducted plate, are forced upward toward the surface, where more melting occurs. As the melted material comes into contact with the crust, magmas with different compositions form. Eventually, basaltic and andesitic magmas rise to the surface and erupt to form the island arc complex.

In addition to the volcanic rocks that make up an island arc complex, some large complexes contain sedimentary rocks. Between an island arc and a trench is a depression, or basin, which fills with sediments eroded from the island arc. If subduction continues for a long enough period of time, some of these sediments can be uplifted,

20.2 Convergent-Boundary Mountains **529**

Tying to Previous Knowledge

Have students recall what they learned about metamorphism in Chapter 6. Then ask what type of metamorphic temperature and pressure conditions they would expect to find at an oceanic-continental convergent boundary. low temperature because of the shallow depth in the crust and high pressure because of convergence

Content Background

The highly folded, faulted, and metamorphosed rocks found along the continental edge of a subduction zone are called subduction mélanges. These rock assemblages are very complex but are recognizable on the basis of their unique composition and structure. These intensely deformed mixtures of deep-sea sediments, continental sediments, and mafic-to-ultramafic-rocks derived from oceanic crust are found in no other tectonic setting. These mélanges are shown by the wavy pattern in **Figure 20-8B.**

Project

Kinesthetic Have pairs of students use different colors of modeling clay to make two-dimensional models of the mountains that form as the result of convergence between oceanic and continental plates. Have students use **Figures 20-7A** and **20-8B** as references. Be sure that students use the same color of clay to represent the same features in their models. **L2** **ELL** **COOP LEARN**

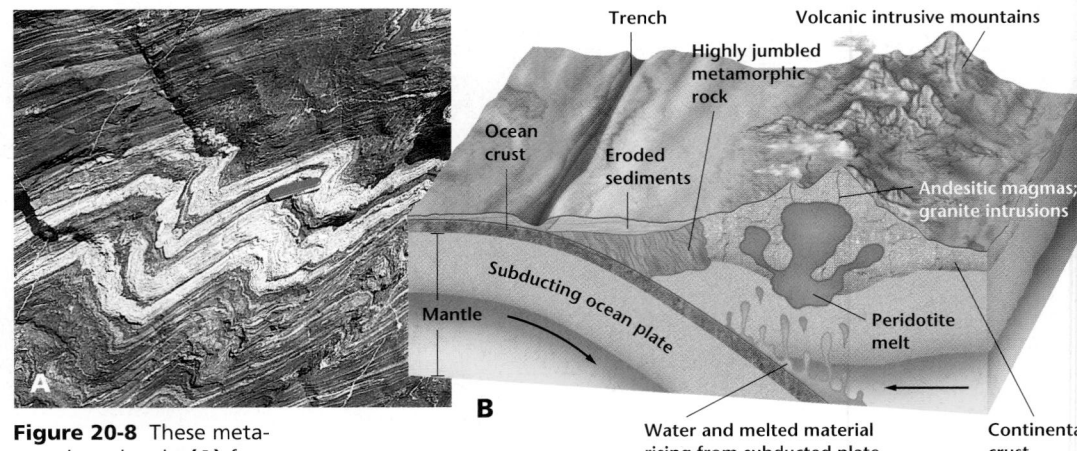

Figure 20-8 These metamorphosed rocks **(A)** from Catalina Island, California, formed as the result of convergence of an oceanic plate with a continental plate. At an oceanic-continental boundary **(B)** compression causes continental crust to fold and thicken. Igneous activity and metamorphism are also common along such boundaries.

Earth Science Online

Topic: Mt. Everest
To take a virtual tour of Mt. Everest, visit the Earth Science Web Site at earthgeu.com

Activity: High Altitudes
Research the effects of high altitudes on climbers. How does the density of air at 29 000 feet affect the human body? How do climbers cope with this effect?

folded, faulted, and thrust against the island arc to form a complex mass of sedimentary and island-arc volcanic rocks.

Oceanic-Continental Convergence Oceanic-continental boundaries are very similar to oceanic-oceanic boundaries in that convergence along both creates subduction zones and trenches. The similarity ends there, however, because convergence between oceanic and continental plates can produce major mountain belts. When an oceanic plate converges with a continental plate, the descending oceanic plate forces the edge of the continental plate upward. This uplift marks the beginning of orogeny, as detailed in **Figure 20-8B.** In addition to uplift, compressive forces may cause the continental crust to fold and thicken. As the crust thickens, higher and higher mountains form. Deep roots develop to support these enormous masses of rocks.

Another important orogenic process that occurs along an oceanic-continental boundary is the formation of magma, as illustrated in **Figure 20-8B.** As the subducting plate sinks into the mantle, parts of the plate begin to melt. As the magma moves upward through the continental crust, the magma becomes rich in silica and gives rise to granitic intrusions and volcanoes fueled by andesitic magma.

Sediments eroded from volcanic intrusive mountains may fill the low areas between the trench and the coast. These sediments, along with ocean sediments and material scraped off the descending plate, are shoved against the edge of the continent to form a jumble of highly folded, faulted, and metamorphosed rocks. The metamorphosed rocks shown in **Figure 20-8A** formed when the Pacific Plate subducted beneath the North American Plate millions of years ago.

Across the Curriculum

Math Have students use a physiographic atlas to compute and compare the total relief of the Andes Mountain Range with that of the Himalayan Mountains. Students may be surprised to find out that because of the depth of the Peru-Chile Trench, the total relief associated with the Andes Mountains is much greater than that of the Himalayas, which were formed and are still rising as the result of continental-continental convergence.

Interpreting the Illustration

Figure 20-8B Have students refer to the figure as you read the student page aloud. Pause after each sentence so that students can locate on the figure the major features (oceanic plate, continental plate, thickened continental crust, magma, volcanoes, granitic intrusions, eroded sediments, and trench) discussed in the text.

Continental-Continental Convergence Earth's tallest mountain ranges, including the Himalayas, are formed at continental-continental plate boundaries. Because of its relatively low density, continental crust cannot be subducted into the mantle when two plates converge. Instead, the energy associated with the collision is transferred to the crust involved, which becomes highly folded and faulted, as shown in *Figure 20-9A.* Compressional forces break the crust into thick slabs that are thrust onto each other along low-angle faults. This process can double the thickness of the deformed crust. Deformation can also extend laterally for hundreds of kilometers into the continents involved. The magma that forms as a result of continental-continental mountain building hardens beneath Earth's surface to form granite batholiths.

Another common characteristic of mountains that form when two continents collide is the presence of marine sedimentary rock near the mountains' summits. Where do you think this rock comes from? Such rock forms from the sediments deposited in the ocean basin that existed between the continents before their collision. Mount Godwin Austen, also known as K2 in the western Himalayas, for example, is composed of thousands of meters of marine limestone that sits upon a granite base. The limestone represents the northern portions of the old continental margin of India that were pushed up and over the rest of the continent when India began to collide with Asia about 50 million years ago.

NATIONAL GEOGRAPHIC

To learn more about Mt. Everest, the tallest peak in the Himalayas, go to the **National Geographic Expedition** on page 864.

Figure 20-9 Intense folding and faulting along continental-continental boundaries produce some of the highest mountain ranges on Earth **(A)**. K2, shown here **(B)**, is the second-highest peak in the Himalayas; only Mt. Everest is taller.

A

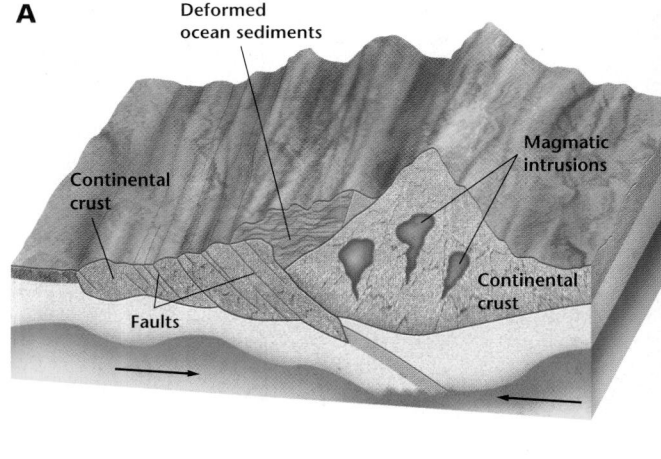

Deformed ocean sediments

Continental crust

Magmatic intrusions

Continental crust

Faults

B

531

Interpreting the Illustration

Figure 20-9A Again, have students refer to the diagram as you read the student page aloud. Have students identify on the diagram the following features discussed in the text: continental crust, faults, magmatic intrusions, and ocean sediments.

Reinforcement

Linguistic Have students write short paragraphs in their science journals to explain why it is more common to find marine fossils in the rocks of continental-continental convergent mountains than in the rocks of oceanic-continental convergent mountains. **L2**

Tying to Previous Knowledge

Have students refer to **Figure 17-13,** on page 455, which shows the rates and directions of movement of Earth's tectonic plates. Ask students to predict where another continental-continental convergent mountain range might form in the geologic future. The most likely regions are the area associated with the Arabian Plate and the area involved in the convergence between the African Plate and the Eurasian Plate.

Across the Curriculum

Biology Have interested students research how people living at high elevations in the Andes and the Himalayas have become acclimated to the oxygen-poor air present at these elevations.

NY Core Curriculum Standards

Page 530: St 4 KI 2.1l, 2.1m, & 2.1n

Page 531: St 4 KI 2.1l, 2.1m, & 2.1n

Concept Development

Have a geologic map that shows the major regions of the Appalachian Mountains available for students to use as you teach the material contained in the next three pages.

Enrichment

Use introductory historical or physical geology books to find a simple cross section that shows the major regions of the Appalachians. Reproduce and label the cross section on the chalkboard. Have students refer to the cross section as they interpret **Figure 20-11.**

In-Text Questions

Page 532 Why are these regions so different? The different types of rocks and structures characteristic of each region formed as the result of different tectonic processes. What kinds of processes led to their formation? Folding, faulting, metamorphism, and igneous activity produced the rocks and features found in the different regions of the Appalachians.

THE APPALACHIAN MOUNTAINS–A CASE STUDY

Recall from Chapter 17 that Alfred Wegener used the matching rocks and geologic structures in the Appalachians and mountains in Greenland and northern Europe to support his hypothesis of continental drift. In addition to Wegener, many other scientists have studied the Appalachians. In fact, the geology of this mountain range, which is located in the eastern United States, has been the subject of many studies for more than a hundred years. Based on these studies, geologists have divided the Appalachian Mountain Belt into several distinct regions, including the Valley and Ridge, the Blue Ridge, and the Piedmont Provinces. Each region is characterized by rocks that show different degrees of deformation. Rocks of the Valley and Ridge Province, for example, some of which are shown in *Figure 20-10,* are highly folded; most of the rocks that make up the Piedmont Province are not. Why are these regions so different? What kinds of processes led to their formation?

The Early Appalachians The tectonic history of the Appalachian Mountains began about 700 to 800 million years ago when ancestral North America separated from ancestral Africa along two divergent boundaries to form two oceans. The ancestral Atlantic Ocean was located off the western coast of ancestral Africa. A shallow, marginal sea formed along the eastern coast of ancestral North America. A continental fragment was located between the two divergent boundaries.

About 700 to 600 million years ago, the directions of plate motions reversed. The ancestral Atlantic Ocean began to close as the plates converged. This convergence resulted in the formation of a subduction zone and a volcanic island arc east of ancestral North America, as shown in *Figure 20-11A.*

Figure 20-10 These folded rocks in West Virginia are part of the Valley and Ridge Province of the Appalachian Mountains.

Across the Curriculum

History Early textile industries in the eastern United States required water power for factories and transport. Have students find out how the geology of the Appalachians was responsible for the locations of the first textile mills between the Piedmont Province and regions toward the west.

Students should find that rivers and streams flowing out of the folded regions to the west had steep gradients that provided the energy needed to turn waterwheels and operate other machinery. In the Piedmont Province, these same rivers had smaller gradients, which made them navigable to transport goods.

Figure 20-11 The Appalachians formed millions of years ago as a result of convergence.

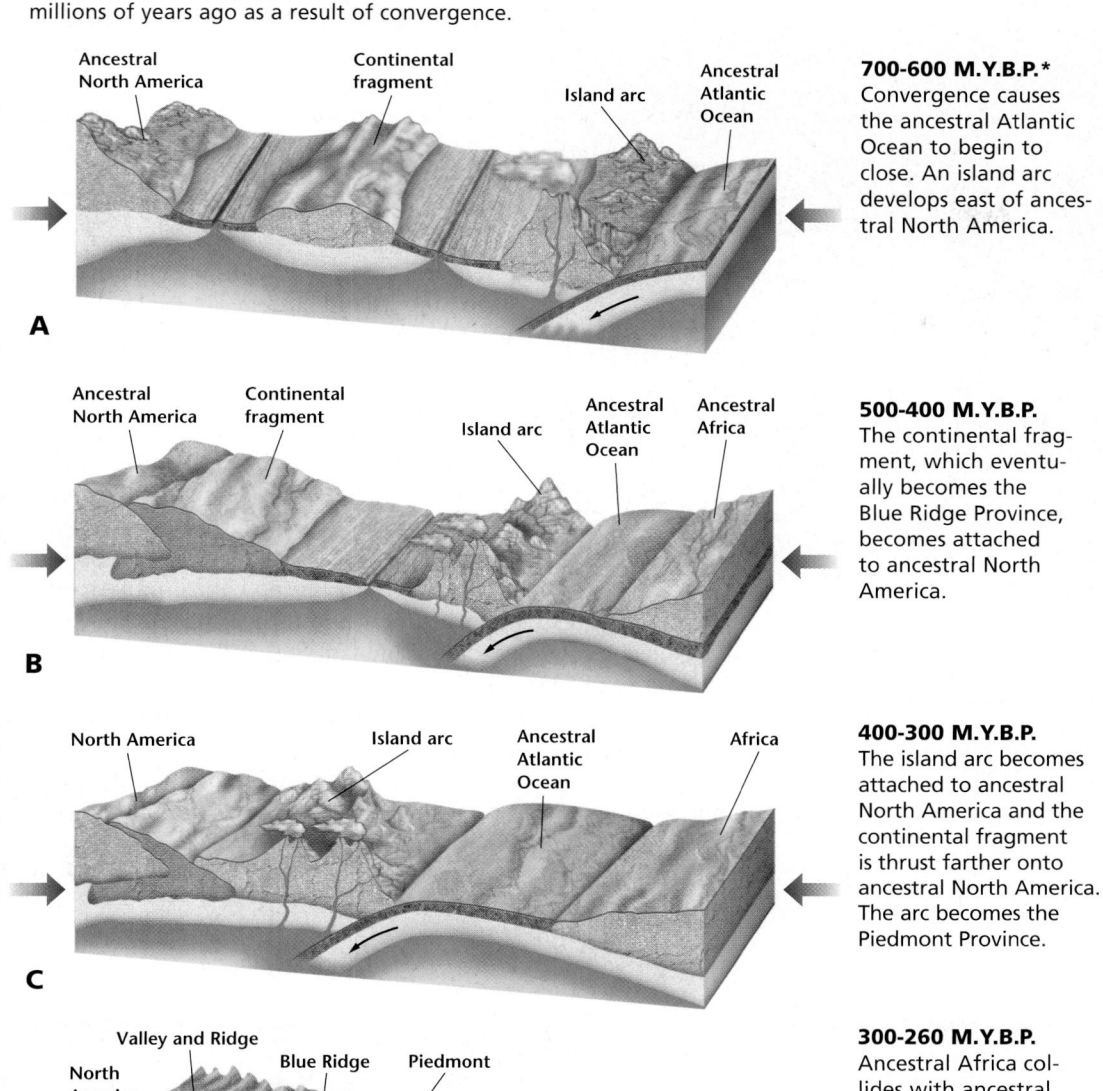

A

Ancestral North America — Continental fragment — Island arc — Ancestral Atlantic Ocean

700-600 M.Y.B.P.* Convergence causes the ancestral Atlantic Ocean to begin to close. An island arc develops east of ancestral North America.

B

Ancestral North America — Continental fragment — Island arc — Ancestral Atlantic Ocean — Ancestral Africa

500-400 M.Y.B.P. The continental fragment, which eventually becomes the Blue Ridge Province, becomes attached to ancestral North America.

C

North America — Island arc — Ancestral Atlantic Ocean — Africa

400-300 M.Y.B.P. The island arc becomes attached to ancestral North America and the continental fragment is thrust farther onto ancestral North America. The arc becomes the Piedmont Province.

D

Valley and Ridge — Blue Ridge — Piedmont — North America — Africa

300-260 M.Y.B.P. Ancestral Africa collides with ancestral North America to close the ancestral Atlantic Ocean. Compression forces the Blue Ridge and Piedmont rocks farther west and the folded Valley and Ridge Province forms.

* Million Years Before Present

20.2 Convergent-Boundary Mountains **533**

Interpreting the Illustration

Figure 20-11 Have students refer to the figure as you ask the following questions. Where is the convergent boundary in **Figure 20-11A?** The convergent boundary lies between the ancestral Atlantic and the island arc. Where are the divergent boundaries in **Figure 20-11A?** The divergent boundaries are located on either side of the continental fragment. What happened to the divergent boundaries between 500 and 300 M.Y.B.P.? They were destroyed as the result of convergence. Why are the rocks of the Valley and Ridge Province highly folded? The compressional forces associated with convergence caused the rocks to fold. Why are the rocks of the Blue Ridge and the Piedmont Provinces mostly deformed igneous and metamorphic rocks? These rocks formed as the result of volcanism (the island arc) and changes in pressure and temperature associated with igneous activity and convergence.

Tying to Previous Knowledge

Provide students with topographic maps of the Appalachians. Have students use what they learned in Chapter 9 to explain how the tectonic history of the Appalachian Region is reflected in the drainage patterns of the area. The major drainage patterns in the Appalachians are the result of the parallel folds that formed during the continental-continental convergence that closed the ancestral Atlantic Ocean.

NY Core Curriculum Standards

Page 532: St 4 KI 2.1l, 2.1n, & 2.1o

Page 533: St 4 KI 2.1l & 2.1n, St 6 KI 2, 3, 4, & 5

Applying Earth Science

Anthracite is a very hard, high-grade type of coal that has been mined in the Appalachian region. Appalachian coal beds began as swamps that existed during the Mississippian and Pennsylvanian Periods. When Pangaea formed several hundred million years ago, the forces involved in the formation of this supercontinent slowly turned the swamp material into anthracite.

Discussion

Ask the following questions to determine students' mastery of the information presented in this section. What type of plate boundary will result in the formation of an orogenic belt composed of volcanic, intrusive, and deformed continental rocks? an oceanic-continental convergent boundary What type of convergence results in towering mountains composed of continental crust and sedimentary rocks? a continental-continental convergence What type of convergent boundary leads to the formation of island arc complexes? an oceanic-oceanic convergent boundary

Reteach

Make giant flashcards of the types of convergent boundaries. On one side of each card, draw **Figures 20-7A, 20-8B,** and **20-9A** without their labels. On the reverse side of each card, include the same figure with its labels. Point to various features on each unlabeled diagram and have students identify them.

✓Assessment

Knowledge Ask students the following questions. What kinds of materials become attached to continental crust at subduction zones? sedimentary wedges What kinds of materials are subducted? Subducted materials include oceanic crust and deep-sea sediments.

Figure 20-12 The metamorphosed rocks in the foreground are parts of the Blue Ridge Province of North Carolina.

About 200 million years passed before the continental fragment became attached to ancestral North America, as shown in *Figure 20-11B* on page 533. These highly metamorphosed rocks, some of which are shown in *Figure 20-12,* were thrust over younger rocks to become the Blue Ridge Province.

The Final Stages of Formation

Between about 400 and 300 million years ago, the island arc became attached to North America, as shown in *Figure 20-11C* on page 533. Evidence of this event is preserved in the Piedmont Province as a group of metamorphic and igneous rocks. These rocks were also faulted over the continent, pushing the Blue Ridge rocks farther west.

Between about 300 and 260 million years ago, the ancestral Atlantic Ocean closed as ancestral Africa, Europe, and South America collided with ancestral North America to form Pangaea. This collision resulted in extensive folding and faulting, as illustrated in *Figure 20-11D* on page 533, to form the Valley and Ridge Province. When rifting caused Pangaea to break apart about 200 million years ago, the modern Atlantic Ocean formed.

The Appalachian Mountains are only one example of the many mountain ranges that have formed along convergent boundaries. In the next section, you'll find out about the orogeny that takes place along divergent plate boundaries, as well as some of the types of mountains that form far from plate margins.

SECTION ASSESSMENT

1. Describe how mountains form along a continental-continental plate boundary.

2. How do the mountains that form at oceanic-oceanic plate boundaries differ from the mountains that form at oceanic-continental plate boundaries?

3. **Thinking Critically** Locate the Aleutian Islands on the map shown in *Figure 20-6.*

How do you think these mountain peaks formed?

SKILL REVIEW

4. **Sequencing** Sequence the events that resulted in the formation of the Appalachian Mountains. For more help, refer to the *Skill Handbook.*

earthgeu.com/self_check_quiz

SECTION ASSESSMENT

1. Continental crust cannot be subducted. The energy associated with the collision causes extensive deformation that includes faulting and folding. These processes result in the formation of very tall mountain ranges.

2. The mountains that form at oceanic-oceanic boundaries are primarily volcanic because they are derived from the subducted plate. Mountains that form along oceanic-continental boundaries are much higher and consist of both volcanoes and nonvolcanic mountain peaks.

3. The Aleutian Islands are a volcanic island arc that has developed along an oceanic-oceanic subduction zone.

4. Convergence caused the ancestral Atlantic Ocean to begin to close. A continental fragment became attached to North America. An island arc became attached to North America. The ancestral Atlantic Ocean closed to cause the final deformation of the rocks that form the Appalachian Mountains.

SECTION 20.3 ♦ *Other Types of Mountains*

When ocean ridges were first discovered, they caused quite a stir in the scientific community simply because of their size. These mountains form a continuous chain that snakes along Earth's ocean floor for over 65 000 km! In addition to their being much longer and taller than most of their continental counterparts, these mountains formed as a result of different orogenic processes.

DIVERGENT-BOUNDARY MOUNTAINS

Ocean ridges are regions of very broad uplift that seems to be related to the rising convection cells that form deep in the mantle beneath these ridges. As matter is heated, it expands, which results in a decrease in density. Magma is less dense than surrounding mantle material, and thus it is forced upward, where it warms the overlying lithosphere. As a result of this increase in temperature, the lithosphere along a divergent boundary bulges upward and stands higher than the surrounding ocean crust to form a gently sloping mountain range, as shown in *Figure 20-13.* As newly formed lithosphere moves away from the central rift, it cools, contracts, and becomes more dense.

Ocean ridge mountain ranges can be thousands of kilometers wide. In the *MiniLab* on page 536, you will compare the size of one ocean ridge, the Mid-Atlantic Ridge, with the size of the continental United States.

OBJECTIVES

• **Describe** *the mountain ranges that form along ocean ridges.*

• **Compare** *and* **contrast** *uplifted and fault-block mountains.*

• **Describe** *the mountains that form as a result of hot spots in Earth's mantle.*

VOCABULARY

pillow basalt
uplifted mountain
fault-block mountain

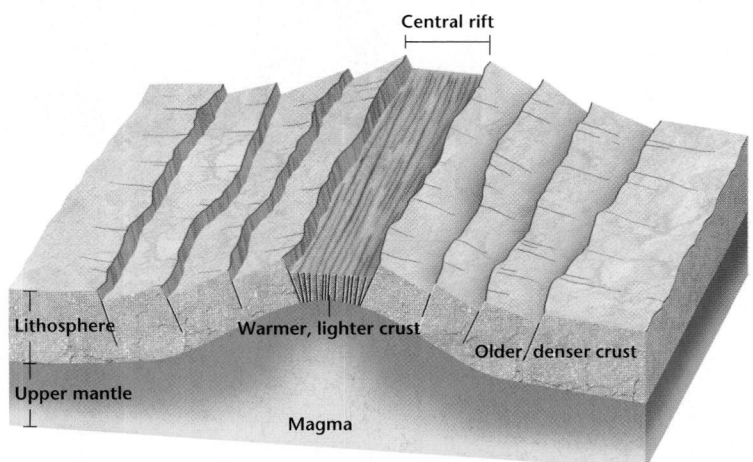

Central rift

Lithosphere
Warmer, lighter crust
Older/denser crust
Upper mantle
Magma

Figure 20-13 An ocean ridge is a broad, topographic high that forms as lithosphere bulges upward due to an increase in temperature along a divergent boundary.

Differentiated Instruction

Gifted Have students think about the forces and structures associated with ocean ridges and subduction zones. Ask students to predict what might happen if an ocean ridge is subducted. Then have them refer to **Figure 17-13,** on page 455, to identify a place where a ridge is being subducted. The Juan de Fuca Ridge, off the Pacific Northwest Coast of Washington State and Canada, is being subducted into the Cascadia Subduction Zone. **L3**

Resource Manager

Study Guide for Content Mastery, pp. 127–128 **L2**

Section Focus Transparency 62 **L1** **ELL**

Section 20.3

Prepare

Section Background

For section content background, refer to **The Colorado Plateau** on page 522D.

Preplanning

Refer to the Chapter Organizer on pages 522A–B.

1 Focus

Section Focus

Before presenting the lesson, display **Section Focus Transparency 62** on the overhead projector. **L1** **ELL**

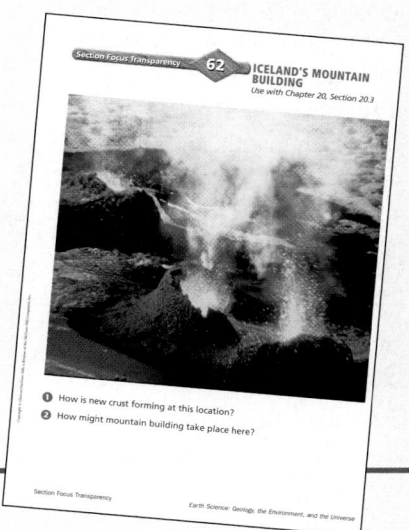

Section Focus Transparency **62** ICELAND'S MOUNTAIN BUILDING
Use with Chapter 20, Section 20.3

❶ How is new crust forming at this location?
❷ How might mountain building take place here?

Section Focus Transparency
Earth Science: Geology, the Environment, and the Universe

Tying to Previous Knowledge

Review the processes that occur along a divergent boundary as presented in Chapter 17.

NY Core Curriculum Standards

Page 534: St 4 KI 2.1l, 2.1n, & 2.1o

Page 535: St 4 KI 2.1l, 2.1m, & 2.1n, St 6 KI 2

535

Interpreting the Photo

Figure 20-14A Have students hypothesize how pillow basalts get their shape. As the hot lava comes into contact with the cold seawater, the lava rapidly cools to form the pillow-shaped rocks.

MiniLab

Purpose

Students will compare the width of part of the Mid-Atlantic Ridge to the size of the continental United States.

Process Skills

measure and use numbers, compare and contrast, think critically

Materials

physiographic maps of the Atlantic Ocean floor and the United States, tracing paper, pencil

Teaching Strategies

Be certain that the two maps are drawn at the same scale.

Expected Results

The width of the Mid-Atlantic Ridge is variable, but students will find that even a section of the ridge easily covers a tracing of the continental United States.

Analyze and Conclude

1. The width varies from less than 1000 km to more than 3000 km.
2. Depending upon where students place the ridge axis and which section of the ridge they traced, only Florida and the southern tip of Texas are not covered by the ridge.
3. The Mississippi River would be smaller because half of it would flow north. The Colorado River and the Rio Grande might actually be larger because they would receive more southerly drainage from the mountain. The climate in the Great Plains would be much different. The northern part would probably be much colder and drier, while

the southern part would be wetter and warmer.

Performance Have students choose another section of the ridge to trace and repeat this activity. Use the Performance Task Assessment for Scientific Drawing in **PASC,** p. 55.

MiniLab

How large is an ocean ridge?

Compare the width of part of an ocean ridge with the size of the United States.

Procedure

1. Obtain physiographic maps of the Atlantic Ocean floor and North America.
2. Use tracing paper to copy the general outline of a section of the Mid-Atlantic Ridge. The length of the section should be long enough to stretch from San Francisco to New York City. Mark the ridge axis on your tracing.
3. Place the same tracing paper on the map of North America with the ridge axis running east-west. Trace the general outline of the United States onto the paper.

Analyze and Conclude

1. How wide is the Mid-Atlantic Ridge?
2. Are there any parts of the United States that are not covered by your tracing?
3. If a mountain range the size of the Mid-Atlantic Ridge were located in the United States as you have drawn it, how would it affect the major river drainage patterns and climates in various parts of North America?

Ocean–Ridge Rocks Ocean ridges are composed mainly of igneous rocks. Recall from Chapter 17 that as tectonic plates separate along an ocean ridge, hot mantle material is forced upward. The partial melting of this material results in a mixture that accumulates in a magma chamber beneath the ridge. From the chamber, the mixture intrudes into the overlying rock to form a series of vertical dikes that resemble a stack of index cards standing on edge, as shown in *Figure 20-14B.* Some of the magma also pushes through the dikes and erupts onto the seafloor to form igneous rocks called **pillow basalts,** which, as you can see in *Figure 20-14A,* resemble a pile of sandbags.

A

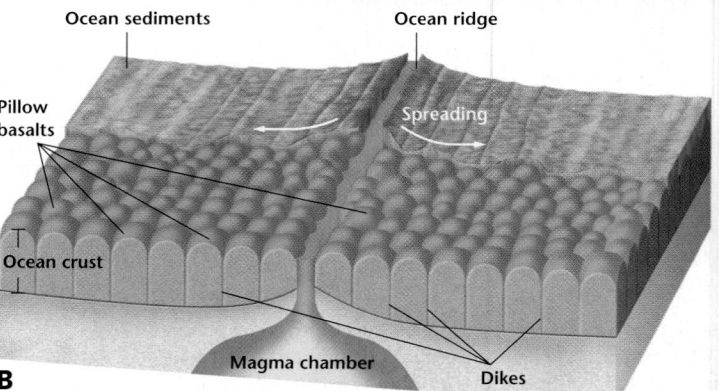

Figure 20-14 Vertical dikes overlain by pillow basalts, which are shown in the photo **(A),** are characteristic of ocean-ridge rocks **(B).**

B

Ocean sediments   Ocean ridge   Pillow basalts   Spreading   Ocean crust   Magma chamber   Dikes

Resource Manager

GeoLab and MiniLab Worksheets, p. 79 [L2]

Teaching Transparency 61 [L2] [ELL]

NONBOUNDARY MOUNTAINS

You've just learned that island arc complexes, intrusive volcanic mountain ranges, highly folded continental mountains, and ocean ridges are all associated with plate boundaries. While these types of mountains make up the majority of ranges and peaks on Earth, some mountains and peaks form in places far removed from tectonic boundaries. Three nonboundary types of mountains are uplifted mountains, fault-block mountains, and some volcanoes.

Uplifted Mountains As shown in *Figure 20-15B,* some mountains form when large regions of Earth have been slowly forced upward as a unit; these mountains are called **uplifted mountains.** The Adirondack Mountains in New York State, shown in *Figure 20-15A,* are uplifted mountains. Generally, the rocks that make up uplifted mountains undergo less deformation than rocks associated with plate boundary orogeny, which are highly folded, faulted, and metamorphosed.

The cause of large-scale regional uplift is not well understood. It is possible that warmer regions of the mantle heat these portions of the lithosphere. The heat causes the density of the crust to decrease, resulting in slow uplift as that section rebounds in response to isostasy. Another possible cause is upward movement in the mantle, which lifts regions of the crust without causing much deformation. Regional uplift can form broad plateaus, such as the Colorado Plateau, which extends through Colorado, Utah, Arizona, and New Mexico. Erosional forces eventually carve uplifted areas to form mountains, valleys, and canyons.

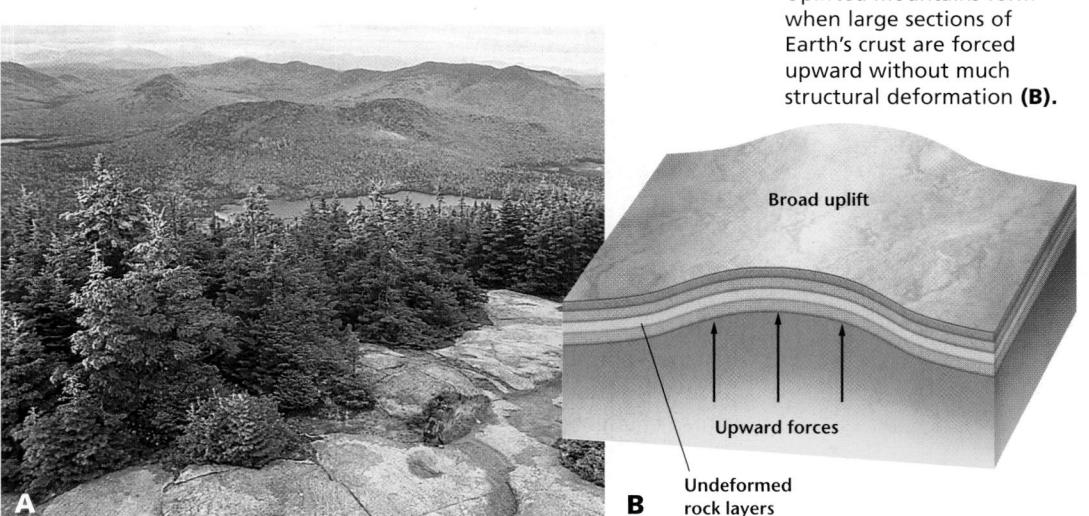

Figure 20-15 The Adirondack Mountains of New York State, shown in the photo **(A)**, are uplifted mountains. Uplifted mountains form when large sections of Earth's crust are forced upward without much structural deformation **(B)**.

Broad uplift

Upward forces

Undeformed rock layers

20.3 *Other Types of Mountains* **537**

Modeling

Kinesthetic Use eight rectangular pieces of felt of different colors, a small, round balloon, and a bicycle pump to demonstrate how uplifted mountains might form. Secure the neck of the balloon to the pump. Lie the felt pieces on top of one another over the balloon. Slowly fill the balloon with air from the pump. Have students describe what happens. The layers of felt bulge in the center to form a "mountain." Explain that the felt represents rock layers and that the inflating balloon represents uplifting forces. **ELL**

✔Assessment

Knowledge Ask: Which of the following statements is true?
a. The rocks in uplifted mountains are highly deformed.
b. Uplifted mountains are associated with plate boundaries.
c. Upward movement in the mantle causes uplifted mountains to form.
d. Uplifted mountains form as the result of erosion.
Statement c is true.

Discussion

Erosion in the Colorado Plateau region has resulted in many small plateaus that are isolated on all sides by vertical walls thousands of meters high. Ask students to hypothesize what happens to populations of organisms that are isolated on these plateaus. The populations can evolve to form new species.

NY Core Curriculum Standards

Page 536: St 4 KI 2.1m & 2.1n, St 6 KI 2 & 6
Page 537: St 4 KI 2.1l & 2.1n, St 6 KI 2

Demo

Visual-Spatial Use blocks of polystyrene foam to model parallel fault-block mountains. Cut rectangular pieces of foam to form polygons as shown below. Set the polygons side by side with every other block upside down and slightly raised to represent the mountains. Have students identify the fault planes in the model. Then demonstrate that fault-block mountains form as the result of relative uplift or subsidence of large blocks of fault-bounded rocks. **ELL**

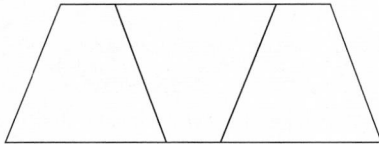

Collaborative Learning

Interpersonal Have groups of students work out a solution to the following scenario. Imagine that you are in the Basin and Range Province mining an underground silver deposit. You follow the veins of silver until they suddenly stop at a normal fault plane. Geologic mapping at the surface indicates that the fault has a vertical movement of 750 m. Where would you look for a continuation of the silver deposit? Students should simply tunnel up or down along the fault for 750 m until the silver veins are found on the opposite side of the fault. **COOP LEARN**

NY Core Curriculum Standards

Page 538: St 4 KI 2.1n, St 6 KI 2

Page 539: St 4 KI 2.1n

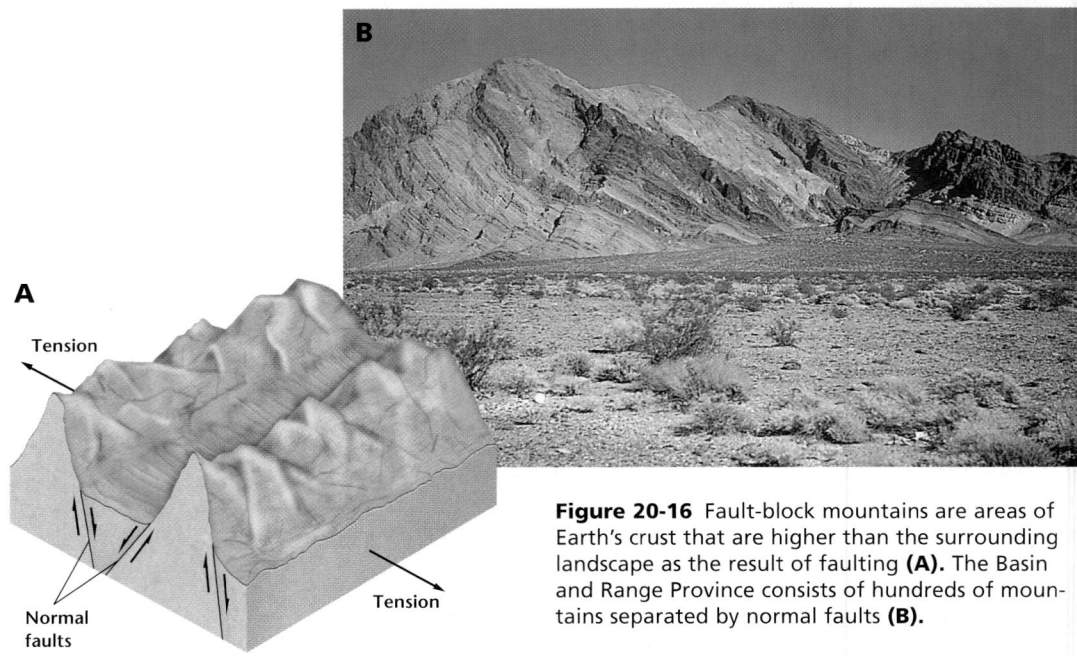

Figure 20-16 Fault-block mountains are areas of Earth's crust that are higher than the surrounding landscape as the result of faulting **(A)**. The Basin and Range Province consists of hundreds of mountains separated by normal faults **(B)**.

Fault-Block Mountains Another type of mountain that is not necessarily associated with plate boundaries is a fault-block mountain. **Fault-block mountains** form when large pieces of crust are tilted, uplifted, or dropped downward between large faults, as shown in *Figure 20-16A.* The Basin and Range Province of the southwestern United States and northern Mexico, a part of which is shown in *Figure 20-16B,* consists of hundreds of nearly parallel mountains separated by normal faults. The Grand Tetons in Wyoming are also fault-block mountains. You'll explore the topography of this range in the *Mapping Geolab* at the end of this chapter.

Volcanic Peaks Volcanoes that form along oceanic-continental convergent margins are usually parts of large mountain ranges. Volcanoes that form over hot spots, however, are generally solitary peaks that form far from tectonic plate boundaries. Recall from Chapter 18 that a hot spot is a region in Earth's mantle that is much hotter than the surrounding area. As a tectonic plate moves over a hot spot, plumes of mantle material are forced through the crust to form a volcanic peak. As the plate continues to move over the hot spot, a chain of volcanoes forms. The shield volcanoes that make up the state of Hawaii are volcanic peaks that formed as the Pacific Plate moved over a hot spot in the mantle. Mauna Kea, which is shown in *Figure 20-17,* is one of these volcanic peaks.

Across the Curriculum

Geography Closed drainage basins often form in the down-dropped valleys associated with fault-block mountains. The restricted circulation results in the formation of salt beds and dry lakes. Have students study maps of the western United States to locate some of these features. Some of these features include Sevier Lake and the Bonneville Salt Flats in Utah, Death Valley in California, Carson Sink in Nevada, and Alvord Desert in Oregon.

Resource Manager

Laboratory Manual, pp. 157–160 **L2**

Figure 20-17 Mauna Kea, and the small volcanoes that dot its flanks are some of the many volcanic peaks that make up the Hawaiian Islands, which formed as the Pacific Plate moved over a hot spot in Earth's mantle.

While all mountains are similar in that they tower high above the surrounding land, individual peaks and chains are unique, as you have discovered in this chapter. Some peaks and chains form along tectonic plate boundaries, while others form far from these boundaries. Some mountains are produced by faulting and folding; others form as the result of igneous activity and crustal uplift. No matter how they form, all mountains are evidence that Earth, unlike some of its neighbors, is truly a dynamic planet.

SECTION ASSESSMENT

1. What kinds of rocks are associated with ocean ridges?

2. Explain why an ocean ridge is higher than the surrounding crust.

3. How do volcanoes that form when a plate moves over a hot spot in the mantle differ from volcanoes that form along convergent plate boundaries?

4. Compare and contrast the formation of uplifted and fault-block mountains.

5. **Thinking Critically** Would you expect a volcano that forms on a continent to depress the crust as much as a volcano that forms on the ocean floor? Explain your reasoning.

SKILL REVIEW

6. **Concept Mapping** Use the following terms to construct a concept map that contrasts the mountain types discussed in this section. For more help, refer to the *Skill Handbook.*

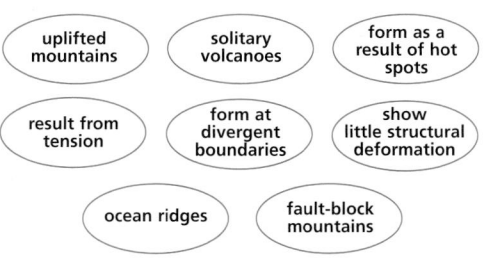

earthgeu.com/self_check_quiz

20.3 *Other Types of Mountains* **539**

SECTION ASSESSMENT

1. igneous rocks—primarily vertical dikes and pillow basalts

2. Rising magma warms the overlying lithosphere and causes it to bulge upward to form a gently sloping mountain range.

3. Hot-spot volcanoes are usually solitary mountains located far from plate boundaries. Convergent-boundary volcanoes are usually part of an orogenic belt.

4. Both form as the result of internal forces. Uplifted mountains form when large sections of relatively undeformed crust are uplifted as a unit. Fault-block mountains form when large pieces of Earth's crust are tilted, uplifted, or dropped downward between large faults.

5. No; oceanic crust is thinner and would therefore show a greater response to the added load of a volcanic mountain than continental crust would.

6. Terms should be linked as follows: ocean ridges—form at divergent boundaries; solitary volcanoes—form as a result of hot spots; uplifted mountains—show little structural deformation; fault-block mountains—result from tension.

---

3 Assess

Check for Understanding
Reinforcement

Ask students to name two types of mountains discussed in this section that form primarily as the result of tensional forces in Earth's crust. ocean ridges and fault-block mountains

Reteach

 **Linguistic** Have students use the bold headings to outline the major points of this section. L2

✔ Assessment

Portfolio Have each student write a creative but scientifically accurate poem about each of the mountain types discussed in this section. Each poem should be between six and eight lines in length. Have volunteers contrast poems about the same type of mountains. P

539

Time Allotment
60 minutes

Process Skills
interpret scientific illustrations, measure and use numbers, think critically

Preparation

- Review, if necessary, the information presented in Chapter 2 about topographic maps.

Procedure

Teaching Strategies
Discuss the concepts of relief and vertical exaggeration with students before they begin the activity.

Troubleshooting
Demonstrate how to transfer points from the map to the profile. Make a transparency of the map and the profile grid. Then cut a transparent strip to represent the paper strip. Use the overhead projector to show students how to transfer the points.

Mapping GeoLab

Making a Map Profile

A map profile, which is also called a cross section, is a side view of a geographic or geologic feature constructed from a topographic map. You will construct and analyze a profile of the Grand Tetons, a mountain range in Wyoming that formed when enormous blocks of rocks were faulted along their eastern flanks, causing the blocks to tilt to the west.

Preparation

Problem
How do you construct a map profile?

Materials
metric ruler   sharp pencil
graph paper

Procedure

1. On the graph paper, make a grid like the one shown on the facing page.
2. Place the edge of a paper strip along the profile line AA' and mark where each major contour line intersects the strip.
3. Label each intersection point with the correct elevation.
4. Transfer the points from the paper strip to the profile grid.
5. Connect the points with a smooth line to construct a profile of the mountain range along line AA'.
6. Label the major geographic features on your profile.

Analyze

1. Describe how the map profile changes with distance from point A.
2. What is the elevation of the highest point on the map profile? The lowest point?
3. What is the average elevation shown in the profile?
4. Calculate the total relief shown in the profile.

Conclude & Apply

1. Is your map profile a scale model of the topography along line AA'? Explain.
2. What determined the scale of this map profile?
3. Why are map profiles made from topographic maps often exaggerated vertically?

Differentiated Instruction

Visually Impaired Enlarge the map and grid on the facing page as much as possible to help students with visual impairments complete this lab.

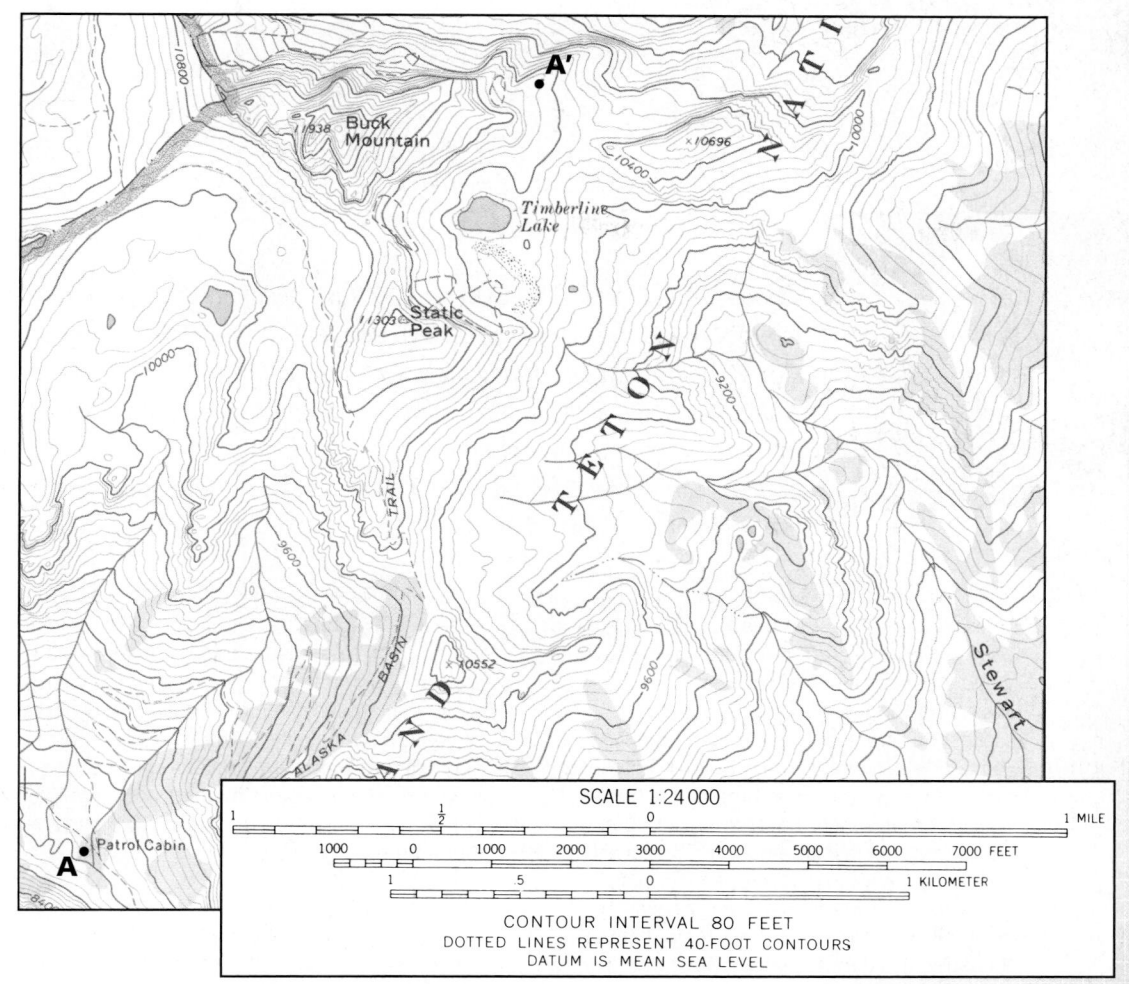

SCALE 1:24 000

1   ½   0   1 MILE

1000   0   1000   2000   3000   4000   5000   6000   7000 FEET

1   5   0   1 KILOMETER

CONTOUR INTERVAL 80 FEET
DOTTED LINES REPRESENT 40-FOOT CONTOURS
DATUM IS MEAN SEA LEVEL

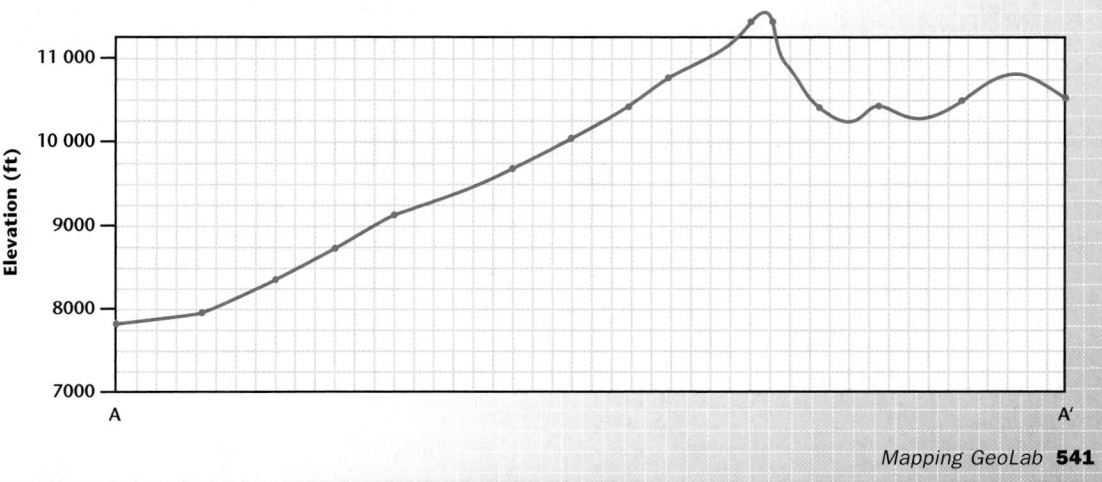

Analyze

1. Elevation steadily increases up to Static Peak. Elevation then decreases.
2. Static Peak is 11 303′ high. The Patrol Cabin is at 7840′.
3. The average elevation along the profile is about 9600′.
4. 11 303′ − 7840′ = 3463′

Conclude & Apply

1. No; the vertical and horizontal scales are different, and therefore the profile is not to scale.
2. The horizontal scale was determined by the scale of the map. The vertical scale was chosen to correspond to the total relief of the area in question.
3. In reality, the relief of Earth's surface is very small when compared to the horizontal distances. Vertical exaggeration is used to make details more obvious.

✓ Assessment

Performance Have students each draw a profile of this part of the Grand Tetons that is to scale without any vertical exaggeration. Use the Performance Task Assessment List for Scientific Drawing in **PASC,** p. 55.

Resource Manager

GeoLab and MiniLab Worksheets,
   pp. 80–81 L2

NY Core Curriculum Standards

Page 540: St 1 Science KI 1
Page 541: St 6 KI 2

Purpose

Students will find out how surveyors measured the elevation of Mt. Everest and will calculate how much Mt. Everest may have risen since 1954.

Content Background

- To determine an elevation with the Global Positioning System, exact measurements of both latitude and sea level are necessary. Finding sea level from atop the Himalayas is extremely difficult and uncertain.
- Some scientists argue that any measurement of Mt. Everest is actually the elevation of the mountain plus the snowpack at that time. Experts say that the snowpack can vary by at least 1 m over the course of a typical year.

Teaching Strategy

Point out to students that the surveyors in 1954 used chains, telescopes, and trigonometry to measure the mountain. Recent measurements are based on modern satellite technology but are only a little more than twice as accurate as the first surveys.

Science &
Math

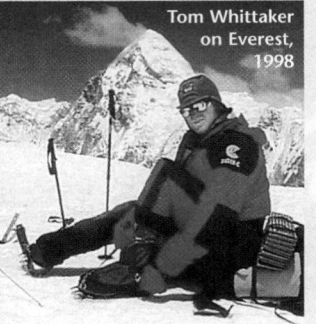

Tom Whittaker on Everest, 1998

The Roof of the World

Since 1953, more than 600 people have reached the summit of Mt. Everest to stand nearly 9 km above sea level on Earth's highest point. Brutal cold, oxygen deprivation, and treacherous conditions have claimed the lives of hundreds who attempted the climb. Preserved from decay by the dry, cold conditions and high altitude, most of their bodies remain on Everest, silent witnesses to the awesome forces that continue to build this mountain.

Since British surveyor Sir George Everest first measured the height of this Himalayan peak in 1852, many explorers have dreamed of reaching Mt. Everest's summit. One hundred years would pass from the initial measurement to the first successful attempt to reach the summit by Sir Edmund Hillary and Tenzing Norgay. An explorer named George Mallory led the first attempts to scale Everest during the 1920s. He did not return from his last attempt. The discovery of his body by climbers in 1999 reminded many of Mallory's reply when asked why he was trying to reach Mt. Everest's peak. His famous answer, "Because it's there," echoes the sentiments of many who have followed in his footsteps.

Measuring a Mountain

Some of those who have climbed Mt. Everest in the past 50 years have had another reason to scale this peak: to measure the elevation of Earth's tallest point. In 1954, an elevation of nearly 8848 m was determined by averaging altitude measurements taken from 12 different points around the mountain. Climbers with the Millennium Expedition, which took place from 1998 to 2000, utilized the highly accurate Global Positioning System to calculate an elevation of 8850 m for Earth's highest point.

Is Mt. Everest getting taller, or is the difference in elevation a result of the different instruments used to measure this mountain? The answer could be both. The collision between two tectonic plates is forcing the Indian subcontinent beneath Asia, causing Everest to rise at a rate of about 5 to 8 mm/y. Readings from GPS instruments on the mountain also suggest that Everest and other peaks in the range are moving toward China at about 6 cm/y.

Technology—Then and Now

The elevation determined in 1954 by the Survey of India was calculated by picking the unweighted mean of altitudes determined from the 12 survey stations around the mountain. These measurements varied by about 5 m. The data gathered by the GPS to calculate the elevation have a margin of error of just over 2 m.

Activity

Is Mt. Everest actually 2 m taller than it was in 1954? Use an average rate of uplift of 6.5 mm/y to determine how much Mt. Everest has risen since it was first measured. How does this compare with the newly calculated elevation?

Activity

Students should multiply the number of years since 1954 by 6.5 mm/y to calculate the answer. For the year 2001, 47 y × 6.5 mm/y = 305.5 mm total uplift since 1954. This is much less than the newly calculated increase in elevation of 2000 mm. Thus, students should conclude that the change in elevation of Mt. Everest is primarily a result of improved instrumentation and not necessarily uplift.

Summary

SECTION 20.1

Crust-Mantle Relationships

Main Ideas

- Earth's elevations cluster around two intervals: 0 to 1 km above sea level and 4 to 5 km below sea level. These modes reflect the differences in density and thickness of the crust.
- Isostasy is a condition of equilibrium. According to this principle, the mass of a mountain above Earth's surface is supported by a root that projects into the mantle. The root provides buoyancy for the massive mountain.
- The addition of mass to Earth's crust depresses the crust; the removal of mass from the crust causes the crust to rebound in a process called isostatic rebound.

Vocabulary

isostasy (p. 525)
isostatic rebound (p. 527)

SECTION 20.2

Convergent-Boundary Mountains

Main Ideas

- Orogeny is the cycle of processes that form mountain belts. Most mountain belts are associated with plate boundaries.
- Island arc complexes are volcanic mountains that form as a result of the convergence of two oceanic plates.
- Highly deformed mountains with deep roots may form as a result of the convergence of an oceanic plate and a continental plate.
- Earth's tallest mountains form along continental-continental plate boundaries, where the energy of the collision causes extensive deformation of the rocks involved.
- The Appalachian Mountains, which are located in the eastern United States, formed millions of years ago mainly as the result of convergence between two tectonic plates.

Vocabulary

orogeny (p. 528)

SECTION 20.3

Other Types of Mountains

Main Ideas

- At a divergent boundary, newly formed lithosphere moves away from the central rift, cools, contracts, and becomes more dense to create a broad, gently sloping mountain range called an ocean ridge. Rocks that make up ocean ridges include dikes and pillow basalts.
- Regional uplift can result in the formation of uplifted mountains that are made of nearly horizontal, undeformed layers of rock.
- Fault-block mountains form when large pieces of the crust are tilted, uplifted, or dropped downward between normal faults.
- Most solitary volcanic peaks form as a tectonic plate moves over a hot spot in Earth's mantle.

Vocabulary

fault-block mountain (p. 538)
pillow basalt (p. 536)
uplifted mountain (p. 537)

earthgeu.com/vocabulary_puzzlemaker

Main Ideas

Summary statements can be used by students to review the major concepts of the chapter.

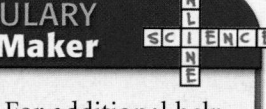
VOCABULARY PuzzleMaker

For additional help with vocabulary, have students access the Vocabulary Puzzlemaker online.

earthgeu.com/
vocabulary puzzlemaker

0:00 Out of Time?

If time does not permit teaching the entire chapter, use the GeoDigest at the end of the unit as an overview.

Earth Science Online

Be sure to check the Earth Science Web Site for links to chapter material:
earthgeu.com

GLENCOE
Technology

Videotape/DVD
MindJogger Videoquizzes
Chapter 20: *Mountain Building*
Have students work in groups as they play the videoquiz game to review key chapter concepts.

Resource Manager

Chapter Assessment, pp. 115–120
MindJogger Videoquizzes DVD/VHS
ExamView® Pro CD-ROM
Performance Assessment in Earth Science

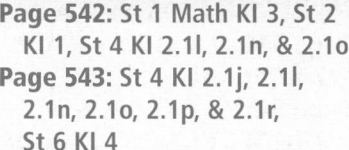
NY Core Curriculum Standards

Page 542: St 1 Math KI 3, St 2 KI 1, St 4 KI 2.1l, 2.1n, & 2.1o
Page 543: St 4 KI 2.1j, 2.1l, 2.1n, 2.1o, 2.1p, & 2.1r, St 6 KI 4

Understanding Main Ideas

1. a
2. c
3. b
4. b
5. b
6. c
7. Continental crust is thicker than oceanic crust and therefore requires a deeper root to achieve isostatic equilibrium.
8. The root decreases in size.
9. Convergent plate boundaries are most often associated with orogenic belts because the forces associated with convergence result in the formation of extensive mountain ranges.
10. Crust along an island arc thickens as a result of the convergence of two oceanic plates. During oceanic-continental convergence, crust thickens as the descending oceanic plate forces the edge of the continental plate upward. Compressional forces cause crust to thicken when two continental plates collide.
11. Rising magma warms the overlying lithosphere and causes it to bulge upward to form a mountain range.
12. There are two possible processes: the heating of the lithosphere by warm regions of the mantle or upward movement of the mantle, which lifts the overlying crust.

NY Core Curriculum Standards

Page 544: St 4 KI 2.1n, 2.1o, & 2.1p, St 6 KI 2
Page 545: St 4 KI 2.1l, 2.1n, & 2.1p, St 6 KI 2

Understanding Main Ideas

1. What causes differences in elevation on Earth?
   a. density and thickness of the crust
   b. vertical dikes and pillow basalts
   c. seamounts and hot spots
   d. uplifted and faulted mountains

2. Which of the following is *not* associated with orogeny at convergent boundaries?
   a. island arcs
   b. highly folded and faulted ranges
   c. ocean ridges
   d. deformed sedimentary rocks

3. What type of mountains are generally made up of undeformed rocks?
   a. fault-block mountains
   b. uplifted mountains
   c. convergent-boundary mountains
   d. continental mountains

4. What type of mountain would you expect to find at a convergent boundary involving two oceanic plates?
   a. fault-block mountain   c. uplifted mountain
   b. volcanic mountain   d. an ocean ridge

5. What is isostasy?
   a. a convergent-boundary mountain
   b. a condition of equilibrium
   c. a fault-block mountain
   d. a difference in crustal densities

6. Adding mass to the crust causes
   a. the crust to rebound.
   b. the mantle to rebound.
   c. the crust to become depressed.
   d. the mantle to displace the crust.

7. Explain why continental crust can displace more of the mantle than oceanic crust can.

8. What happens to a mountain's root as the mountain is eroded?

9. What type of plate boundary is most often associated with orogenic belts? Why?

10. Describe three mechanisms of crustal thickening that occur at convergent boundaries.

11. Explain why ocean ridges rise high above the surrounding ocean floor.

12. What processes might be responsible for regional uplift of continental crust?

13. Discuss the processes involved in the formation of the Appalachian Mountains.

Use the figure below to answer questions 14–16.

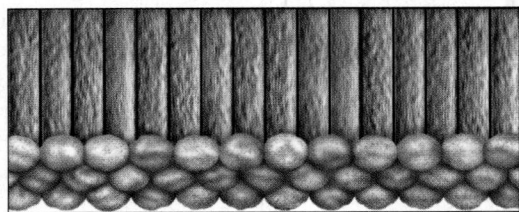

14. A geologist observed these two igneous rock beds in a coastal mountain range. Based on what you've learned in this chapter, where did these rocks form?

15. Explain how the two rock beds formed.

16. Are the rock beds in their original positions? Explain.

Test-Taking Tip

TEST YOURSELF Have a classmate make a practice test for you that covers the material discussed in this chapter. Take the test under test-like conditions. Show your practice test to one of your teachers for an objective assessment of your performance.

earthgeu.com/chapter_test

13. Convergence resulted in the formation of an island arc as well as the highly folded, faulted, and metamorphosed rocks that make up much of the mountain range.
14. They formed along an ocean ridge.
15. Intruding magma resulted in the formation of the vertical dikes, and underwater eruptions resulted in the formation of the pillow basalts.
16. No; the rocks have been overturned because pillow basalts form above the vertical dikes.

Standardized Test Practice

1. b
2. a
3. b
4. a
5. d

Applying Main Ideas

17. If Earth's mantle were denser than it is now, would continental crust displace more or less of it? Explain.

18. Explain what caused an island arc to develop east of the North American continent early in the tectonic history of the Appalachian Mountains.

19. Refer to *Figure 20-11*. Describe how the deformation due to orogeny changes among the provinces of the Appalachian Mountains.

20. What type of faulting occurs at a continental-continental convergent boundary? Explain your answer.

21. How are ocean ridges and fault-block mountains similar? How do they differ?

Thinking Critically

22. Thick ice sheets once covered the Great Lakes region. The area north of the Great Lakes has rebounded more than areas south of the lakes. What conclusion can you make about the thickness of the ice in these two areas? Explain your reasoning.

23. Suppose a mountain range is 4 km high. Explain why more than 4 km of material would have to be eroded before the mountain would be completely level.

24. When does the isostatic rebound of an area stop?

25. Why are dikes rather than sills common along ocean ridges?

26. The Appalachians mark the western side of the convergent boundary between North America and Africa. What kinds of structures do you think would be found on the eastern side of this boundary? Where would you look for these structures?

earthgeu.com/standardized_test

Standardized Test Practice

1. Why would a certain thickness of continental crust displace less of the mantle than the same thickness of oceanic crust?
   a. Continental crust is more dense.
   b. Continental crust is less dense.
   c. Continental crust is mainly basalt.
   d. Continental crust is closer to the mantle.

2. Which of the following can NOT form as the result of oceanic-oceanic convergence?
   a. rift zones   **c.** subduction zones
   b. trenches   **d.** island arc complexes

3. Which type of mountains form as the result of uplift far from plate boundaries?
   a. ocean ridges
   b. uplifted mountains
   c. faulted mountains
   d. volcanic ranges

INTERPRETING DIAGRAMS Use the diagram and *Figure 20-11* to answer questions 4 and

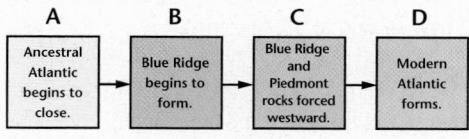

A	B	C	D
Ancestral Atlantic begins to close.	Blue Ridge begins to form.	Blue Ridge and Piedmont rocks forced westward.	Modern Atlantic forms.

4. Which of the following occurred between events B and C?
   a. The island arc attached to North America.
   b. Plate motions reversed.
   c. Africa collided with North America.
   d. The island arc developed.

5. Approximately when did event C occur?
   a. 800 to 700 M.Y.B.P.
   b. 700 to 600 M.Y.B.P.
   c. 500 to 400 M.Y.B.P.
   d. 300 to 200 M.Y.B.P.

Applying Main Ideas

17. The crust would displace less of the mantle and float higher in this denser medium.

18. Subduction of an oceanic plate into the mantle caused magma to form as the plate partially melted. The magma rose and fueled the volcanoes of the island arc complex.

19. Deformation increases from east to west; the rocks of the Valley and Ridge, and Blue Ridge Provinces are more deformed than the rocks of the Piedmont Province.

20. thrust faulting as the result of intense compressional forces

21. Both are mountains that form as the result of tension. Unlike ocean ridges, fault-block mountains are not associated with igneous activity.

Thinking Critically

22. Greater rebound in the north is indicative of a greater initial depression of the crust caused by thicker ice in the northern regions.

23. As the mountain is eroded, the root rises. To completely level the mountain, part of the root must also be eroded.

24. Rebound stops when the crust reaches its preload elevation.

25. Ocean ridges are areas of divergence. Divergence results in vertical fractures into which magma easily intrudes to form dikes.

26. Similarly folded rocks and thrust faults would be found on the eastern side of this boundary. These types of rocks and structures can be found along the western coast of Africa.

For a **preview** of Unit 5, study this GeoDigest before you read the chapters in the unit. After you have studied these chapters, you can use the GeoDigest to **review** the unit.

Prepare

Purpose

This GeoDigest can be used as an overview of plate tectonics and the processes and features associated with tectonism. If time is limited, you may wish to use this unit summary to teach the concepts presented in the chapters in Unit 5.

Key Concepts

Students are introduced to plate tectonics and some of the processes associated with tectonism, such as ridge push, slab pull, volcanism, seismicity, and orogeny.

1 Focus

Section Focus

Kinesthetic As you read the information about the three types of plate boundaries aloud, have students use their hands to model the movement associated with each boundary.
L1 **ELL**

0:00 *Out of Time?*

If time does not permit teaching the entire unit, use this GeoDigest as an overview.

NY Core Curriculum Standards

Page 546: St 4 KI 2.1k, 2.1l, 2.1m, 2.1n, & 2.1o

Page 547: St 4 KI 2.1j, 2.1k, 2.1m, 2.1n, & 2.1o

The Dynamic Earth

Plate Tectonics

Drifting Continents and Seafloor Spreading Continental drift, first hypothesized by Alfred Wegener, states that Earth's continents were once joined as a single landmass that broke up and drifted apart. Wegener used matching coastlines of Earth's continents, similar rocks and fossils, and ancient climatic data to support his hypothesis. Wegener, however, couldn't explain how or why the continents moved. The answer, seafloor spreading, was found by studying ocean-floor rocks and sediments. Magnetic patterns of ocean-floor rocks are symmetric in relation to ocean ridges, which indicates that oceanic crust on either side of the ridge is moving away from the ridge. Seafloor spreading occurs as magma rises toward the crust, cools and hardens to fill the gap that forms, and becomes a new section of oceanic crust.

The Theory of Plate Tectonics Earth's crust and the top of the upper mantle are broken into large slabs of rock called plates, which move at different rates over Earth's surface. Interactions occur at plate boundaries. At a divergent boundary, plates move apart; high heat flow, volcanism, and earthquakes are associated with divergent boundaries. At a convergent boundary, plates come together; deep-sea trenches, island arcs, and folded mountain ranges are associated with this type of boundary. At a transform boundary, plates slide past one another horizontally; faults and shallow earthquakes are associated with transform boundaries. Convection currents in Earth's mantle are related to

Soufrière, a composite cone in the West Indies

plate movements. Convection currents transfer energy through the movement of matter. Heat causes matter to expand and decrease in density. Warm matter is thus forced upward and cool matter is pulled downward. Ridge push is a tectonic process that occurs when the weight of an ocean ridge pushes a plate toward a subduction zone. Slab pull is a tectonic process that occurs when the weight of the subducting plate pulls a plate into a subduction zone.

Volcanic Activity

Magma The composition of magma is affected by temperature, pressure, and the presence of water. There are three main types of magma—basaltic, andesitic, and rhyolitic— that differ in the source rock from which they form, and also in composition, viscosity, silica content, amount of dissolved gases, and explosiveness.

Multiple Learning Styles

 *Kinesthetic* Section Focus, p. 546

 Visual-Spatial Project, p. 547

 Linguistic Reteach, p. 549

GeoDigest

Intrusive Activity

Magma can affect the crust in several ways. Magma can force overlying rock apart and enter the fissures formed, can cause blocks of rock to break off and sink into the magma chamber, and can melt the rock into which it intrudes. Plutons, which include batholiths, stocks, sills, dikes, and laccoliths, are classified according to their size, shape, and relationship to surrounding rocks.

Volcanoes

A volcano forms when lava repeatedly flows out through a vent and accumulates. A crater is a depression that forms around the vent at the summit of a volcano; a caldera is a large crater that forms when a volcano collapses during or after an eruption. There are three types of volcanoes—shield volcanoes, cinder-cone volcanoes, and composite volcanoes. Shield volcanoes are large, gently sloping volcanoes composed of basalt. Cinder-cone volcanoes have steep sides and are made of volcanic fragments. Composite volcanoes have relatively steep slopes and are made of layers of volcanic fragments that alternate with lava. Most volcanoes form along subduction zones and rifts, but they may also form over hot spots, which are especially hot areas in Earth's mantle.

Hot Spring, Africa

Earthquakes

Forces Within Earth

Stresses exist within Earth. Stress is the forces per unit area that act on a material. Strain is the deformation of a material in response to stress. Stress is released at breaks in Earth's crust called faults. Reverse faults form as a result of horizontal compression; normal faults as a result of horizontal tension; and strike-slip faults as a result of horizontal shear. Movements along many faults cause earthquakes. Earthquakes generate waves that pass through Earth in specific ways. P-waves squeeze and pull rocks in the same direction in which the waves travel. S-waves cause rocks to move at right angles to the direction of the waves. Surface waves cause both up-and-down and side-to-side motions. Seismic waves are reflected and refracted as they strike different materials. Analysis of these different waves have enabled scientists to infer the structure of Earth's interior.

Measuring and Locating Earthquakes

Most earthquakes occur along plate boundaries in areas called seismic belts. Earthquake epicenters are located with data from at least three seismic stations. Magnitude is a measurement of the energy released during an earthquake and is measured on the Richter scale or the moment-magnitude scale. Intensity is the measure of the damage caused by an earthquake as measured on the modified Mercalli scale.

Vital Statistics

Highest Peak per Continent

Africa	Kilimanjaro	5895 m
Antarctica	Vinson Massif	4897 m
Asia	Everest	8850 m
Australia	Kosciusko	2228 m
Europe	Elbrus	5642 m
North America	McKinley	6194 m
South America	Aconcagua	6960 m

GeoDigest **547**

Differentiated Instruction

Visually Impaired Have students use their sense of touch to contrast the textures of some extrusive rocks. **CAUTION:** *Remind students to be careful handling the rocks. Sharp edges can cut skin.* Provide students with samples of obsidian, scoria, pumice, and basalt. Students should describe the texture of obsidian as smooth and glassy. The other samples are rough, and scoria and pumice contain holes that formed as gases were released from the lava that cooled to form these rocks. **ELL**

Across the Curriculum

History In 1884, John Longmire opened a resort at the base of Mount Rainier, in Washington State. The resort, called Mineral Springs Resort, attracted many adventurous visitors, who sat in baths filled with water from bubbling-hot mineral springs. Historically, people have used these and other resources associated with volcanoes. Ask students to research and write reports that explain how people use and have used volcanic resources.

2 Teach

Interpreting the Photo

The volcano shown on page 546 is Soufrière, a composite volcano on the island of St. Vincent, in the West Indies. Have students identify the crater. Inform them that this is one of several craters that has formed as the result of repeated volcanic activity.

Project

Visual-Spatial Have pairs of students make a hollow volcanic cone out of modeling clay. Instruct them to fill the cone with baking soda and set the cone on its base on a tabletop. Tell students to slowly pour about 1/2 cup of white vinegar into the cone to simulate a volcanic eruption. **CAUTION:** *Make sure that students wear safety goggles and lab aprons during this entire activity.* **L1** **ELL**

Demo

Use a wooden stick to demonstrate how stress and strain are related. **CAUTION:** *Wear safety goggles when doing this activity.* Gently bend the stick and have students describe how it has changed. It bends. Release the stress and have students observe that the stick returns to its original shape. Exert enough stress to break the stick. Help students conclude that this breaking is similar to faulting.

Resource Manager

Study Guide for Content Mastery, pp. 129–130 **L2**

GeoDigest

GeoDigest

Enrichment

Use a coiled spring toy to demonstrate how the different types of earthquake waves move through rocks. To simulate the movement of P-waves, compress 20 or so coils and quickly release them. Students should observe that the movement of the coils is in the same direction as the compressional force that you applied to them. To demonstrate the movement of S-waves, have a volunteer hold one end of the spring. Set the spring in motion vertically by flicking your wrist while holding onto the free end of the spring. Students should observe that the motion of the spring is at right angles in relation to the direction of the applied force. With a volunteer, repeat both parts of this activity to simulate the movement in two directions of surface waves.

Using an Analogy

Ask students whether they have ever heard the expression "just the tip of the iceberg." Explain that this expression is often used when only a small part of a problem or situation is apparent. Also explain the basis for this expression—over 90 percent of an iceberg is below water. Relate this expression to Earth's mountains and their corresponding roots.

Earthquake damage, Guatemala

Earthquakes and Society Earthquakes can cause buildings and other structures to collapse, soil to behave like quicksand, fissures and fault scarps to form, uplift and subsidence of the crust, and tsunamis to form. The type of subsurface, the height and structure of buildings, the distance to the epicenter, and the depth of the earthquake's focus all affect the extent of damage done by an earthquake. The probability of an earthquake is determined by the history of earthquakes in an area and the rate at which strain builds up in the rocks.

Mountain Building

Isostasy According to the principle of isostasy, the mass of a mountain above Earth's surface is supported by a root that projects into the mantle. The root provides buoyancy for the mountain. Adding mass to Earth's crust results in a depression of the crust. Removing mass causes the crust to rebound. Earth's elevations cluster around two intervals: 0 to 1 km above sea level and 4 to 5 km below sea level. These modes reflect the differences in density and thickness of Earth's two kinds of crust.

548 UNIT 5

Types of Mountains The cycle of processes that forms mountain belts is called orogeny. Island-arc complexes are volcanic mountains that form as the result of convergence of two oceanic plates. When an oceanic plate converges with a continental plate, highly deformed mountains with deep roots form. When two continental plates converge and collide, very tall mountains result, along with extensive deformation of the rocks involved. Ocean ridges are mountains that form on ocean floors along divergent boundaries; they form topographic highs as the result of density differences—crust along the ridges is warmer and less dense than older, cooler crust farther from the ridges. Some mountains form far from plate boundaries. Uplifted mountains are made of nearly horizontal, undeformed layers of rock and form as the result of regional uplift. Fault-block mountains form when large pieces of the crust are tilted, uplifted, or dropped downward between large faults. Solitary volcanic peaks form as a result of a plate's moving over a hot spot in Earth's mantle.

FOCUS ON CAREERS

Volcanologist
A volcanologist is a scientist who studies volcanoes. A volcanologist must have at least a bachelor's degree, but often pursues a master's or doctoral degree in order to specialize in a specific aspect of volcanology. Some volcanologists work close to active volcanoes; others study data in labs, perhaps searching for relationships that will allow the prediction of eruptions.

Content Background

When two continental plates converge and collide, neither is dragged down, or subducted, into the mantle because of the relatively low density of continental crust. Instead, the energy involved in the collision is transferred to the rocks involved and results in extremely high, very deformed mountain ranges. The Himalayas are an example of such mountains.

✔Assessment

Portfolio Assessment
Assessment, TWE, p. 549

Knowledge Assessment
GeoDigest Assessment, SE, p. 549

The Dynamic Earth

ASSESSMENT

Understanding Main Ideas

1. The study of which of the following led to the proposal of seafloor spreading?
   a. ocean rocks and sediments
   b. soil liquefaction
   c. seismic wave travel times
   d. P-wave motions

2. Which of the following is the probable cause of plate movements?
   a. ocean currents
   b. topographic highs
   c. convection currents in the mantle
   d. strain

3. In addition to temperature and pressure, what other factor affects the composition of magma?
   a. seismic gap
   b. the presence of water
   c. explosiveness
   d. seismic waves

4. What are batholiths, stocks, sills, dikes, and laccoliths?
   a. types of plutons
   b. kinds of magma chambers
   c. seismic wave types
   d. topographic lows

5. Which of the following forms when a volcano collapses during an eruption?
   a. a vent   **c.** a lava pipe
   b. a crater   **d.** a caldera

6. Which type of fault forms as a result of horizontal tension?
   a. reverse   **c.** strike-slip
   b. normal   **d.** shear

7. Which of the following is not caused by earthquakes?
   a. collapse of buildings
   b. flood basalt
   c. soil liquefaction
   d. tsunamis

8. How is earthquake magnitude measured?
   a. on the modified Mercalli scale
   b. by seismic gaps
   c. on the Richter scale
   d. by the earthquake history of an area

9. Which type of mountain forms when large pieces of Earth's crust are tilted, uplifted, or dropped down between large faults?
   a. uplifted mountains
   b. island arcs
   c. fault-block mountains
   d. hot spot volcanoes

10. What is stress?
    a. the deformation of a material
    b. the force that acts on a material
    c. a series of P-waves
    d. a series of S-waves

Thinking Critically

1. Describe the process of seafloor spreading.
2. How do scientists determine the probability of an earthquake?

Sierra Nevada, California

549

ASSESSMENT

Understanding Main Ideas

1. a	**6.** b		
2. c	**7.** b		
3. b	**8.** c		
4. a	**9.** c		
5. d	**10.** b		

Thinking Critically

1. Magma is forced upward toward the crust, cools and hardens to fill the gap that forms, and becomes a new section of ocean crust, which moves slowly away from the ridge.
2. Scientists determine the probability of an earthquake by examining the earthquake history of an area and the rate at which strain builds up in rocks.

3 Assess

Check for Understanding
Discussion
Ask the following questions to assess students' understanding of tectonism and associated processes. What are tectonic plates? slabs of Earth's crust and the upper, rigid mantle How do plates interact? They move apart, they move toward one another, and they move horizontally past one another. Which type of boundaries are responsible for most earthquakes? divergent and transform boundaries Most volcanoes? divergent and convergent boundaries Most mountain ranges? convergent

Reteach
 Linguistic Have students write short essays that explain the relationship between plate tectonics and volcanoes, orogeny, and earthquakes.

✔Assessment

Portfolio Have students each research a volcanic eruption or earthquake that occurred within the past year and display their findings as posters. **P**

Geologic Time

Unit Overview

Changes over Time In Unit 6, students are introduced to the geologic time scale and to the concepts of geologic time, fossils, and how Earth's physical and biological features have developed over its 4.6-billion-year history. Students will learn how Earth's continents formed.

Chapter Breakdown Chapter 21 introduces the geologic time scale and its use in interpreting Earth's history. Methods by which rocks and fossils are dated, as well as the processes by which fossils form, are also explored. Chapter 22 begins with a discussion of the Precambrian Earth, including the development of Earth's atmosphere, oceans, and landmasses. The primitive life-forms that existed during the Precambrian are also described. Chapter 23 focuses on the Paleozoic Era and reveals the changes Earth underwent as its atmosphere and environment became hospitable to new forms of life. Mountain-building events and continental positioning also are covered. Chapter 24 covers the Mesozoic and Cenozoic Eras, during which mountain building continued and the continents moved to their present positions. Students will learn about the substantial changes in both animal and plant life that occurred during this time.

0:00 Out of Time?

If time does not permit teaching the entire unit, use the GeoDigest at the end of the unit as an overview.

Unit 6

Geologic Time

Volcanic eruptions, glaciations, tectonic collisions and mountain building have all occurred many times in various places on Earth. What information do we have today that tells us of these events? The rocks themselves! It has been said that a picture tells a thousand words. The photograph at right is worth many more than that. Recorded in the rock layers is evidence of geologic events that have helped to shape Earth's history. Along with these dramatic events, countless species of plants and animals have appeared and disappeared. Fossils of these organisms are evidence of these occurrences. By studying the characteristics of layered rocks and the changes in life through time, geologists have been able to unravel Earth's history.

Unit Contents

21 **Fossils and the Rock Record**

22 **The Precambrian Earth**

23 **The Paleozoic Era**

24 **The Mesozoic and Cenozoic Eras**

NATIONAL GEOGRAPHIC   Go to the National Geographic Expedition on page 892 to learn more about topics that are connected to this unit.

550

NATIONAL GEOGRAPHIC

e**X**peditions!

Dinosaurs Take Wing Some topics of Earth science deserve more attention than others because they're unusual, informative, or just plain interesting. The National Geographic Society has created visually exciting, multipage *Expeditions!* features that inform, excite, and motivate your students.

Expeditions! features are relevant to the Earth science content of the student edition. Assign them as a lead-in to special research projects and in-depth studies for extra credit. Use them as a basis for colorful visual displays and bulletin boards.

Capital Reef National Park, Utah

551

Introducing the Unit

Preconceptions The photograph shows the multicolored layers of rock in Capitol Reef National Park, Utah. Ask students what they think layers of rock have to do with studying geologic time and changes in Earth's flora and fauna. Explain that these rocks are all sedimentary, and that they are predominantly sandstones, limestones, and shales.

Ancient Environments Ask students what they recall about the deposition and formation of sedimentary rocks. Can they interpret the environments in which these rocks were deposited? Explain to students that a shallow sea once covered this area, and that these rock layers represent the onshore-to-offshore environments that existed during that time. Then, ask students what they might find in certain types of limestone and what information can be inferred from the limestone. Tell students that fossils are often components of limestone and that different types of fossils indicate whether the water that deposited these sediments was open-ocean, brackish, or lagoonal.

Changing Scenery Ask students whether they think anything has happened to these rock layers since they were deposited. The rocks have been tilted. They are dipping to the west. The layers are now a monocline. Have students again examine the photo of Capitol Reef National Park and ask them whether their perceptions of the rock layers have changed. Students should now perceive that the rock layers are full of information about the time of their formation.

Earth Science Online

Note Internet addresses that you find useful in the space below for quick reference.

_____

_____

_____

_____

_____

For Internet tips, see Glencoe's **Using the Internet in the Science Classroom.**

551

Chapter 21

Fossils and the Rock Record

Refer to pages 8T–9T of the Teacher Guide for an explanation of the National Science Content Standards correlations.

Section	Objectives	National Science Content Standards	State/Local Standards
SECTION 21.1 **The Geologic Time Scale** 🕐 2 sessions 📦 1 block	1. **Describe** the geologic time scale. 2. **Distinguish** among the following geologic time scale divisions: eon, era, period, and epoch.	UCP.5; A.1; C.3; D.3; F.3; G.1, G.2	St 1 Science KI 1, St 4 KI 1.2i & 1.2j, St 6 KI 2
SECTION 21.2 **Relative-Age Dating of Rocks** 🕐 ½ session 📦 ¼ block	3. **Apply** the principles for determining relative age to interpret rock sequences. 4. **Describe** an unconformity and how it is formed within the rock record.	UCP.2; A.1; D.3; G.3	St 1 Science KI 1, 2, & 3, St 4 KI 1.2j, 2.1n, & 2.1o, St 6 KI 2
SECTION 21.3 **Absolute-Age Dating of Rocks** 🕐 1½ sessions 📦 ¾ block	5. **Explain** the several different methods used by scientists to determine absolute age. 6. **Describe** how objects are dated by the use of selected radioactive elements. 7. **Explain** how annual tree rings and glacial varves are used to date geologic events.	B.2, B.3, B.6; D.2, D.3; E.1, E.2	St 4 KI 1.2d, 1.2i, & 1.2j
SECTION 21.4 **Remains of Organisms in the Rock Record** 🕐 2 sessions 📦 1 block	8. **Define** fossil. 9. **Explain** several methods by which fossils can be preserved. 10. **Describe** the characteristics of an index fossil. 11. **Discuss** how fossils can be used to interpret Earth's past physical and environmental history.	A.1, A.2; B.2, B.3; C.3, C.4; D.1, D.3; G.2	St 4 KI 1.2i, 1.2j, & 3.1b, St 6 KI 3

A complete Planning Guide is provided on pages 30T–32T.

🕐 The number of recommended single-period sessions

📦 The number of recommended blocks

Activity Materials

Discovery Lab *page 553*
Sand-microfossil mixture, petri dish, tweezers

GeoLab *pages 570–571*
poster board, meterstick, measuring tape, colored pencils, geologic time scale, encyclopedia, reference books, paper, pencil, calculator

MiniLab *page 558*
paper, colored pencils, scissors, ruler

Demo *page 553*
photos of the Grand Canyon

page 563
photos of things of obvious ages

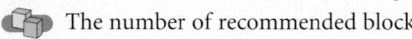

Need materials? Contact Science Kit at 1-800-828-7777 or at www.sciencekit.com on the Internet. For alternate materials, see the activity on the listed page.

Key to Teaching Strategies

L1 Level 1 activities should be appropriate for students with learning difficulties.

L2 Level 2 activities should be within the ability range of all students.

L3 Level 3 activities are designed for above-average students.

ELL ELL activities should be within the ability range of English-language learners.

COOP LEARN Cooperative learning activities are designed for small-group work.

P These strategies represent student products that can be placed in a best-work portfolio.

📦 These strategies are useful in a block-scheduling format.

Chapter Organizer

Glencoe Exclusive!
TeacherWorks™
All-In-One Planner and Resource Center

Activities/Features	Reproducible Masters	Transparencies
Discovery Lab: Fossil Hunt Activity, p. 553	**Study Guide for Content Mastery,** p. 131 L2 **Laboratory Manual,** pp. 161–164 L2	**Section Focus Transparency 63** L1 ELL **Teaching Transparency 62** L2 ELL
MiniLab: How is relative age determined? p. 558 **Problem-Solving Lab:** Interpreting Diagrams, p. 560	**Study Guide for Content Mastery,** pp. 132–133 L2 **GeoLab and MiniLab Worksheets,** p. 83 L2	**Section Focus Transparency 64** L1 ELL **Teaching Transparency 63** L2 ELL
Using Math: Using Numbers, p. 563	**Study Guide for Content Mastery,** pp. 134–135 L2 **Laboratory Manual,** pp. 165–168 L2	**Section Focus Transparency 65** L1 ELL **Teaching Transparency 64** L2 ELL
Design Your Own GeoLab: Interpreting History-Shaping Events, pp. 570–571 **Science in the News:** Frozen Mammoth, p. 572	**Study Guide for Content Mastery,** p. 136 L2 **GeoLab and MiniLab Worksheets,** pp. 84–86 L2 **Laboratory Manual,** pp. 161–164 L2	**Section Focus Transparency 66** L1 ELL **Teaching Transparency 65** L2 ELL

✔Assessment

Chapter Assessment, pp. 121–126
Performance Assessment in the Science Classroom (PASC)
MindJogger Videoquiz DVD/VHS
Performance Assessment in Earth Science
ExamView® Pro CD-ROM
5 Days to the Regents Exam

GLENCOE'S
ASSESSMENT
ADVANTAGE

Additional Resources

Guided Reading Audio Program ELL
Cooperative Learning in the Science Classroom COOP LEARN
Lesson Plans
Block Scheduling
earthgeu.com
NY Lesson Plans
NY Block Scheduling
Review Handbook for Regents Earth Science Exam

NATIONAL GEOGRAPHIC

Products Available from National Geographic Society
To order the following products, call the National Geographic Society at 1-800-368-2728:

Teacher's Corner

Curriculum Kits
GeoKit: *Earth's History*
GeoKit: *Rocks and Minerals*
Video
Fossils: Clues to the Past

Content Background

The Geologic Time Scale
Section 21.1

Earth scientists interpret Earth's fossil record and geologic events by the use of a chronologically sequenced chart known as the geologic time scale. The geologic time scale represents Earth's history from its formation 4.6 billion years ago to the present. The geologic time scale was designed so that the oldest divisions are at the bottom of the chart with each division above being successively younger. Eons, eras, periods, and epochs are divisions of time utilized on the chart and are used by geologists worldwide. However, the geologic history of a local region is as unique as the fossils and rocks found in the region. For example, the geologic events that resulted in the formation of the Grand Canyon are not the same as the events that formed the volcanic landscapes of the Hawaiian Islands. Thus, although the geologic histories of the Grand Canyon and the Hawaiian Islands are different, the geologic time scale is used for both areas as a tool for establishing a frame of reference for the timing of the geologic events that formed them. Often noted on the geologic time scale are significant events, such as the formation of the atmosphere and oceans, the advent of life, the "explosion of life" in the Cambrian Period, the uplifting of numerous mountain ranges, the rise of the dinosaurs, and mass extinction events.

Relative-Age Dating of Rocks
Section 21.2

The relative age of a geologic event, rock, or fossil can be determined by comparing it to other events, rocks, or fossils. Three primary principles are used by geologists to help determine the relative age of an object or event. These principles were originally put forth by Danish geologist Nicolaus Steno. They are the principle of superposition, the principle of original horizontality, and the principle of cross-cutting relationships. As a result of weathering and erosion, deposition, glaciation, earthquakes, and volcanism, Earth's surface features do not always conform to Steno's principles. Rock layers may be overturned, tilted, or eroded away. Gaps in the rock record are a result of erosion or nondeposition. These gaps are called unconformities. Depending on the cause of the unconformity, more than one unconformity may be present across the same rock layer. For example, a batholith intrusion will cause rock layers to fold upward. Subsequent erosion and burial will result in the formation of an angular unconformity on either side of the fold and a disconformity or nonconformity at the top of the fold.

With the use of Steno's principles and knowledge of the processes just discussed, an area's history can be interpreted without reference to absolute age.

Multiple Learning Styles

Visual-Spatial Modeling, p. 559, Reteach, p. 561

Interpersonal, Activity, pp. 557, 566, Collaborative Learning, p. 568

Intrapersonal Reteach, p. 556

GLENCOE
Technology

The following multimedia resources are available from Glencoe.

Vocabulary Puzzlemaker

TeacherWorks™ CD-ROM

MindJogger Videoquizzes DVD/VHS

ExamView® Pro CD-ROM

Interactive Chalkboard CD-ROM

Chapter Organizer

Absolute-Age Dating of Rocks
Section 21.3

The absolute ages of many rocks and fossils are determined using radioactive elements and their decay rates. The most commonly used radioactive elements are uranium-235, uranium-238, potassium-40, oxygen-18 and carbon-14. Annular tree rings, seasonally deposited glacial lake sediments called varves, and volcanic ash deposits can also be used to determine the absolute ages of objects or events. Millions of years from now, the ash from the eruption of Mt. Saint Helens will have become a key bed. Analysis of the radioactive elements within the ash will give geologists of the future the information needed to determine when the eruption occurred.

Fossils
Section 21.4

Fossils are the remains of or evidence of dead organisms. Fossils may be direct evidence, such as shells, bones, or plant fragments, or they may be indirect evidence, such as tracks, trails, or footprints. A fossil is considered to be originally preserved when the organism remains as it was when it died. A fossil is considered to be an altered hard part when all of the organic material has decomposed and minerals such as silica or calcite have replaced all of the original shell or bone in a process called permineralization. Petrified trees are the most famous type of permineralization, although shells of many marine organisms are also preserved in this way. Evidence in the form of footprints or trails are called trace fossils. Dinosaur footprints preserved in New Mexico have been used to calculate the speed at which dinosaurs walked or ran. Resting traces of trilobites are common and look surprisingly like deer hoofprints. Feeding traces of some burrowing worms indicate that they seldom left their burrows but sent their tentacles out instead. Coprolites are the fossilized feces of ancient animals. The diets of many animals have been determined through the analysis of coprolites.

Identifying Misconceptions

Students may read about, hear about, or see objects referred to as fossilized mud cracks, ripples, or raindrop impressions and may think that these objects are true fossils. While these objects are indeed old, as are fossils, they do not fit the definition of a fossil. A fossil is classically defined as the remains, imprint, or trace of a once-living organism. Therefore, ripples, mud cracks, and raindrop impressions are not true fossils because they are not remnants of once-living organisms.

✓ Assessment

Portfolio Assessment
GeoLab, TWE, pp. 570–571

Performance Assessment
MiniLab, TWE, p. 558
MiniLab, SE, p. 558
Discovery Lab, SE, p. 553
GeoLab, SE, pp. 570–571

Knowledge Assessment
Section Assessment, SE, pp. 556, 565, 569
Problem-Solving Lab, TWE, p. 560
Chapter Assessment, SE, pp. 574–575
Assessment, TWE, pp. 556, 560, 565, 569

Skill Assessment
Discovery Lab, TWE, p. 553
Assessment, TWE, p. 561

Be sure to check the Earth Science Web Site for links to chapter material: earthgeu.com

Introducing the Chapter

In this chapter, students will learn the basic principles that geologists use to interpret Earth's age and history as it is recorded within its rocks. Scientists developed the geologic time scale on the basis of fossils found within rocks.

Interpreting the Photo

Granite Rapids, on the Colorado River in Grand Canyon National Park, is almost at the very bottom of both the canyon and the geologic time scale. Here, Precambrian-aged rocks make up the walls and river bed. The rocks are either metamorphic or igneous. No sedimentary rock layers are present at the bottom.

Chapter Themes

The following themes from the National Science Content Standards are covered in this chapter. Refer to page 8T of the Teacher Guide for an explanation of the correlations.
Systems, order, and organization (UCP.1); Evidence, models, and explanation (UCP.2); Change, constancy, and measurement (UCP.3); Evolution and equilibrium (UCP.4)

⏱ Out of Time?

If time does not permit teaching the entire chapter, use the chapter summary on p. 573 and the GeoDigest found at the end of the unit as an overview.

Chapter 21

What You'll Learn

- How geologists divide Earth's long history.

- How certain geologic principles can be used to interpret age relations in layered rocks.

- How different techniques to determine the ages of rocks are used.

- What fossils are, how they form, and how they are used to interpret Earth's history.

Why It's Important

Fossils and rocks contain a record of Earth's history and can be used to make predictions about Earth's future. Some fossils can help identify potential sites of energy resources.

Earth Science Online

To learn more about fossils and the rock record, visit the Earth Science Web Site at earthgeu.com

552

Fossils and the Rock Record

Discovery Lab

Process Skills

hypothesize, classify, observe, infer, communicate
L1 ELL

Safety Precautions

- Students should wash their hands with soap when the lab is completed.

- Students should wear safety goggles and aprons during this lab.

Disposal
Return the microfossil sand to its container for future use.

Alternative Materials
If you live in an area that has fossil-enriched sands, weathered soils, or both, collect a full pail for classroom use.

Procedure

- Premeasure the sand-and-fossil mixture.

Discovery Lab
Fossil Hunt Activity

Have you ever found shells at a beach, along a river, or by a pond? If so, did you wonder where they came from or what type of animal might have lived in them? The shape, size, and composition of shells provide clues about the environment in which individual animals once lived. In this activity, you will make inferences about shells that you examine.

1. Obtain a mixture of sand and microfossils from your teacher.

2. Place the mixture on a petri dish or a small, shallow tray.

3. Use tweezers or a small, dry paintbrush to separate the fossils from the sandy sediment.

4. Categorize the fossils by shape, size, and composition.

 *CAUTION: Always wear safety goggles and an apron in the lab. Wash your hands when lab is completed.*

Observe In your science journal, explain how fossils can help determine the age of sediment or a rock. Does categorizing the fossils provide any further clues about the environment in which the fossiliferous sediment formed? Explain.

SECTION 21.1

The Geologic Time Scale

OBJECTIVES

• **Describe** *the geologic time scale.*

• **Distinguish** *among the following geologic time scale divisions: eon, era, period, and epoch.*

VOCABULARY

geologic time scale
eon
era
period
epoch

A hike down the Kaibab Trail in the Grand Canyon reveals the multicolored layers of rock that make up the canyon walls. These layers, or strata, are made of different types of sedimentary rock. Some of the rock layers have fossils in them. At the bottom of the Grand Canyon, is the Colorado River, which has been cutting downward through the rocks of the canyon for millions of years. Also at the bottom are rocks that date back 400 million years or more. These rocks record the many advances and retreats of oceans and the development of plants and animals. By studying the characteristics of rocks and the fossils within them, geologists can interpret the environments the rocks were deposited in, reconstruct Earth's history, and possibly predict events or conditions in the future.

THE ROCK RECORD

To help in the analysis of Earth's rocks, geologists have divided the history of Earth into time units based upon the fossils contained

21.1 The Geologic Time Scale **553**

Observe
Once the identity and age of a fossil is determined by comparison to reference books, the age of the rock or sediment the fossil was found in can be determined as well.

✔Assessment

Skill Hold a class discussion to compare each group's answers. Ask students to illustrate several characteristics that distinguish one microfossil from another.

Section Background

For section content background, refer to **The Geologic Time Scale** on page 552C.

Preplanning

Refer to the Chapter Organizer on pages 552A–B.

1 Focus

Section Focus

Before presenting the lesson, display **Section Focus Transparency 63** on the overhead projector.
L1 ELL

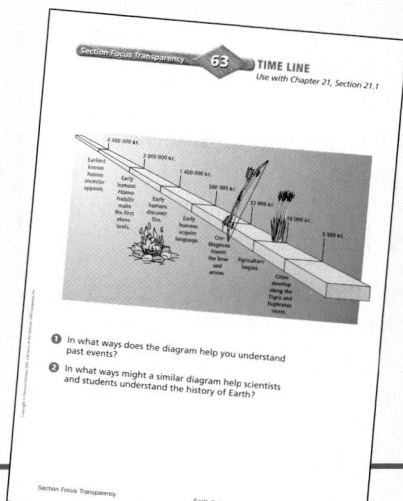

Demo

Pass out photos of the Grand Canyon at the Yavapai Point Overlook. Ask students to list and sketch, in their science journals, features that they see in the rock structures.

NY Core Curriculum Standards

Page 552: St 4 KI 1.2j
Page 553: St 1 Science KI 1, St 4 KI 1.2j

Identifying Misconceptions

Students may think that there is only one geologic history that applies to all of the continents and all areas of the world.

Uncover the Misconception
Ask students to compare and contrast the geologic history and time-scale units of their state with another state or country. This information can be acquired from the state Geological Survey unit.

Demonstrate the Concept
Explain that while the divisions of the geologic time scale are standard worldwide, the geologic histories of individual areas are not. Sequences of rocks and fossil assemblages, mountain-building events, tectonic activity, climatic conditions, and conditions of rock formation differ from one geologic province to another.

Assess New Knowledge
After you complete this section, have the students relate how the geologic time scale fits the geologic history of their local area. They may observe that parts are missing or find that the history of their region is somewhat distorted or unclear.

NY Core Curriculum Standards

Page 554: St 4 KI 1.2i & 1.2j
Page 555: St 4 KI 1.2i & 1.2j

Phanerozoic Eon

Cenozoic Era

Quaternary Period
1.6 M.Y.B.P.
Recent
Holocene Epoch 0.01 M.Y.B.P.
Pleistocene Epoch 1.6 M.Y.B.P.

Neogene Period
23 M.Y.B.P.
Pliocene Epoch 5 M.Y.B.P.
Miocene Epoch 23 M.Y.B.P.

Paleogene Period
66 M.Y.B.P.
Oligocene Epoch 35 M.Y.B.P.
Eocene Epoch 56 M.Y.B.P.
Paleocene Epoch 66 M.Y.B.P.

Mesozoic Era

Cretaceous Period
146 M.Y.B.P.

Jurassic Period
208 M.Y.B.P.

Triassic Period
245 M.Y.B.P.

Paleozoic Era

Permian Period
290 M.Y.B.P.

Pennsylvanian Period
323 M.Y.B.P.

Mississippian Period
362 M.Y.B.P.

Devonian Period
408 M.Y.B.P.

Silurian Period
439 M.Y.B.P.

Ordovician Period
510 M.Y.B.P.

Cambrian Period
540 M.Y.B.P.

Precambrian Time
Proterozoic Eon

2500 M.Y.B.P.

Archean Eon

4600 M.Y.B.P.

*Millions of years before present

Callout boxes (left):
- Homo sapiens evolves; most recent ice ages occur; Grand Canyon forms.
- Dinosaurs become extinct.
- Dinosaurs are dominant; first birds appear; mountain building continues in western North America.
- Many marine invertebrates become extinct; building of Appalachians ends; glaciers retreat.
- Amphibians are dominant; glacial advances occur.
- Corals and other invertebrates are dominant; warm, shallow seas cover much of North America.
- Trilobites, brachiopods, other marine invertebrates are abundant; thick sediments deposited in inland seas.

Callout boxes (right):
- Mammals are abundant; angiosperms are dominant; Alps and the Himalayas begin to rise.
- Angiosperms appear; Rocky Mountains begin to form.
- First mammals, and cycads appear; Atlantic Ocean begins to form, Pangaea breaks up.
- Reptiles evolve; coal swamps form; shallow seas begin to withdraw.
- Fish are dominant; first amphibians; Appalachians continue to form in North America and Europe.
- First land plants form, first insects.
- First fish appear; Appalachians begin to form.
- Ediacara organisms develop.
- Bacteria-like organisms form; several episodes of mountain building occur.

Figure 21-1 Earth's long history is divided into specific units of time in the geologic time scale.

within the rocks. These time units are part of the **geologic time scale,** a record of Earth's history from its origin 4.6 billion years ago to the present. Since the naming of the first geologic time period, the Jurassic, in 1797, development of the time scale has continued to the present. The names of the periods do not change, but the years marking the beginning and end of each unit of time are continually being refined. The geologic time scale is shown in *Figure 21-1.* This scale enables scientists from around the world to correlate the geologic events, environmental changes, and the development of life-forms that are preserved in the rock record.

GEOLOGIC TIME

The oldest division of time is at the bottom of the geologic time scale. Moving upward on the scale, each division is younger, just as the rock layers in the rock record grow generally younger as you move upward. The time scale is divided into units called eons, eras, periods, and epochs. An **eon** is the longest time unit and is measured in billions of years. The Archean, the Proterozoic, and the Phanerozoic are eons. An **era** is the next-longest span of time; it is measured in hundreds of millions to billions of years. Eras are defined by the differences in life-forms found in rocks; the names of eras are based on the relative ages of these life-forms. For example, in Greek, *paleo* means "old," *meso* means "middle," and *ceno* means "recent." *Zoic* means "of life" in Greek, and thus *Mesozoic* means "middle life." Precambrian Time, which makes up approximately 90 percent of geologic time, is divided into the Archean and Proterozoic Eons. The Proterozoic is the more recent of the two, and the end of it is marked by the first appearance of organisms with hard parts. All life-forms up until then had soft bodies and no shells or skeletons. Some of

---

Differentiated Instruction

Gifted The geologic time scale is depicted as a vertical continuum. Have students investigate other methods of illustrating geologic time, such as geologic time as it relates to a 24-hour day, geologic time represented by the calendar, or the geologic time scale mapped onto a football field. **L3**

Across the Curriculum

History Over a span of 225 years, the United States has experienced many events that have helped to mold it into a world leader. Have students create a time line illustrating the following historic events: the signing of the Declaration of Independence, the ratification of the Constitution, the Louisiana Purchase, the Industrial Revolution, the Civil War, the invention of the electric lightbulb, the introduction of automobile mass production, the Stock Market Crash, Neil Armstrong's walk on the Moon, and the American bicentennial.

these resembled organisms that exist today, such as sponges, snails, and worms, while others cannot be accurately assigned to any known animal or plant group.

Plants and Animals Evolve During the Paleozoic Era, the oceans became full of a wide diversity of plants and animals. Trilobites dominated the oceans in the Cambrian Period; land plants appeared and were followed by land animals; and swamps provided the plant material that became the coal deposits of the Pennsylvanian. The end of the Paleozoic Era is marked by the largest extinction event in Earth's history. As many as 90 percent of all marine invertebrate species became extinct. The era following the Paleozoic Era, the Mesozoic Era, is known for the emergence of dinosaurs, but other important developments occurred then as well. Reef-building corals and large predatory reptiles developed in the oceans. Amphibians began living on land as well as in water. Dinosaur populations began a slow decline in numbers throughout the Cretaceous Period as mammals evolved and grew in number. Flowering plants and trees evolved during the Cretaceous.

The end of the Mesozoic is also marked by a large extinction event. In addition to the remaining dinosaurs, many other groups of organisms, became extinct. Mammals increased both in number and diversity in the Cenozoic. Human ancestors developed at this time. Grasses and flowering plants expanded on land while ocean life remained relatively unchanged throughout this era.

Periods of Geologic Time **Periods** are defined by the life-forms that were abundant or became extinct during the time in which specific rocks were deposited. Periods are usually measured in terms of tens of millions of years to hundreds of millions of years. Some were named for the geographic region in which the rocks of that age were first observed, studied, and described. For example, the Mississippian Period was named for the distinctive limestone bluffs along the Mississippi River, as shown in *Figure 21-2.* The Jurassic Period was named for the rocks that were described in the Jura Mountains in Europe.

To learn more about dinosaurs and their evolution, go to the National Geographic Expedition on page 892.

Topic: Time Scales
To find out more about the geologic time scale, visit the Earth Science Web Site at earthgeu.com

Activity: Compare the span of time represented by the geologic time scale to the span of time represented by a 24-hour day. Apply the geologic time span to the 24-hour time span. How much time in a 24-hour day is represented by each era? Each period?

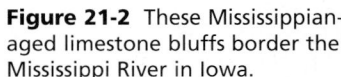

Figure 21-2 These Mississippian-aged limestone bluffs border the Mississippi River in Iowa.

21.1 The Geologic Time Scale **555**

Cultural Diversity

Dong Zhiming (1937–) Dong Zhiming was born in Weihai, China. He became fascinated by dinosaurs when he was very young. This fascination led to a distinguished career as a paleontologist. Newspapers and scientific journals have called him the world's most prolific dinosaur hunter. Zhiming has found, so far, 18 new genera, including the first Middle Jurassic Period dinosaur ever excavated in China. In 1975, he and his team of scientists discovered a vast dinosaur graveyard in Dashanpu, which yielded skeletons of more than 100 dinosaurs. Most were sauropods, *Datousaurus*, and *Ommeisaurus*. The Chinese government now protects this site. In 1985, Dong Zhiming helped to organize a $15 million dollar China-Canada Dinosaur Project, which identified 11 new species. This project has led to greater knowledge about dinosaur dispersal from Asia to North America.

Content Background

The geologic time scale was developed to help geologists understand Earth's history. It is arranged, and always depicted, with the names of the oldest units at the bottom and the youngest units at the top. The names of the periods are generally derived from the region where the rocks were first discovered and studied. The divisions of the geologic time scale are based upon the fossil record. The geologic history of an area varies from one region to another because the forces that constantly change the surface of Earth, such as weathering, erosion and deposition, earthquakes, volcanism, mountain building, and glaciation, vary from region to region.

Discussion

The Pennsylvanian Period was named for the distinct coal deposits that lie above Mississippian-aged rocks in Pennsylvania. Ask students how the geologic time scale might differ if the state had a different name. Have students look at a relief map of North America. Ask them to speculate about other locations where the names of rock formations might have been influenced by the geography of the locations.

Interpreting the Photo

Figure 21-2 Resistance to weathering has caused these Mississippian-aged limestones to stand out as bluffs along the Mississippi River in Illinois and Iowa. Weathering has caused many fossils to break free of the rock. Numerous crinoids and brachiopods, among others, can be collected from these rocks. Their presence is a testimony to the ocean that once covered this part of North America.

Reinforcement
Quiz students orally about the importance of geologists' knowing the geologic time scale when interpreting the past conditions during which rocks and fossils developed in a particular region.

Reteach

Intrapersonal Have each student make a list of at least ten of the most important events that have occurred in his or her life and to create a time line entitled Great Events of My Life.

✓ Assessment

Knowledge Have students list the major units of time that appear on the geologic time scale and the approximate number of years that each era represents. Ask students to briefly discuss how these time units help geologists to interpret Earth's history.

Figure 21-3 This fossil sycamore leaf is preserved in the Eocene-aged, Green River Formation in Wyoming.

Historically, the Cenozoic Era was divided into two periods, the Tertiary and the Quaternary. Currently, however, the Cenozoic is divided into three periods: the Paleogene, Neogene, and Quaternary. In contrast to the boundaries between the Paleozoic and the Mesozoic Eras, the boundaries between the periods of the Cenozoic are not marked by extinction events.

Epochs of Geologic Time Epochs are even smaller divisions of geologic time and are usually measured in millions of years to tens of millions of years. The fossil record of the Cenozoic Era is relatively complete because there has been less time for weathering and erosion to remove evidence of this part of Earth's history. Thus, rocks and fossils from this era are easily accessed and studied. Accordingly, the Cenozoic Periods have been further divided into epochs, such as the Paleocene and the Oligocene. Different groups of organisms have been used to distinguish the various epochs. For example, marine fossils were used to mark the Oligocene Epoch, and terrestrial plant fossils, such as those shown in *Figure 21-3,* were used to mark the Eocene Epoch.

Regardless of how a geologic period was defined, each unit contains specific characteristics that set it apart from the rest of geologic history. In the *Design Your Own GeoLab* at the end of this chapter, you will find out what makes each time unit unique.

SECTION ASSESSMENT

1. How did geologists determine the divisions of the geologic time scale?
2. What does the geologic time scale indicate about the change in life-forms over time?
3. What do the names of the three eras of the Phanerozoic mean?
4. What major change occurred in life-forms at the end of the Proterozoic?
5. How were the geologic time periods named? On what basis are they defined?
6. **Thinking Critically** Explain why the use of living faunas is acceptable for defining the periods and epochs of the Cenozoic Era.

SKILL REVIEW

7. **Graphing** Make a bar graph that shows the relative percentages of time that each period of the geologic time scale spans. For more help, refer to the *Skill Handbook.*

earthgeu.com/self_check_quiz

SECTION ASSESSMENT

1. Geologists have divided Earth's history into time units based upon the fossil record.
2. It indicates that a wide variety of life-forms existed in the past and that most of these have become extinct.
3. *Paleo* means "ancient" and *zoic* means "life" = "ancient life"; *meso* means "middle" and *zoic* means "life" = "middle life"; *cenos* means "recent" and *zoic* means "life" = "recent life."
4. Hard skeletons and shells developed.
5. They were named for the location where the rocks were first studied, for distinctive groups of people that lived nearby, or for a geographic feature. They are defined by the last fossil occurrence of a particular group of organisms.
6. Many plants and animals that exist today originated during the Cenozoic. Thus, their fossils can be used to define the epochs of the Cenozoic.

7. Era	Percentage of Time
Precambrian	90.0 %
Paleozoic	6.0 %
Mesozoic	4.0 %
Cenozoic	1.0 %

As late as the turn of the nineteenth century, the majority of the world believed that Earth was only about 6000 years old. This age had been determined by Archbishop James Ussher of Ireland, who used a chronology of human and Earth history to calculate Earth's age. As early as 1770, James Hutton, a Scottish physician and geologist, had begun to observe and to attempt to explain Earth's landscapes. Hutton's observations in Great Britain helped him to develop the principle of uniformitarianism, which attempts to explain the forces that continually change the surface features of Earth. Such processes include mountain building, erosion, earthquakes, and sea-level changes. The principle of **uniformitarianism** states that the processes occurring today have been occurring since Earth formed. Only the rate, intensity, and scale with which they occur have changed. For example, if you stand on the shore of an ocean watching the waves come in, you are observing a process that has not changed since the oceans were formed. The waves crashing on a Cambrian shore, a Jurassic shore, and a modern shore all share the same process. The resulting sediments and rocks all record a beach environment, where the sediments become finer with distance from shore and the fossils within the rocks preserve evidence of the life-forms that lived during the time of deposition.

PRINCIPLES FOR DETERMINING RELATIVE AGE

The concept of relative-age dating places the ages of rocks and the events that formed them in order, but without exact dates. This is done by comparing one event or rock layer to another.

OBJECTIVES

- **Apply** *the principles for determining relative age to interpret rock sequences.*
- **Describe** *an unconformity and how it is formed within the rock record.*

VOCABULARY

uniformitarianism
original horizontality
superposition
cross-cutting relationships
unconformity
correlation

Figure 21-4 The Colorado River, in Grand Canyon National Park, has cut through rock layers that span the Triassic through the Precambrian.

557

Prepare

Section Background

For section content background, refer to **Relative-Age Dating of Rocks** on page 552C.

Preplanning

Refer to the Chapter Organizer on pages 552A–B.

1 Focus

Section Focus

Before presenting the lesson, display **Section Focus Transparency 64** on the overhead projector. L1 ELL

Activity

Interpersonal Make a list of ten historical events that have occurred in the past 15 years, such as the election of a president, a home-run record, or your high school winning a state title. Cut the items in the list into strips. Give the strips to groups of four students and have them place the events in order from oldest to youngest. This will give students a good idea of how to determine relative age. L1 ELL

MiniLab

Purpose

Students will demonstrate how the principles of relative-age dating are used.

Process Skills

recognize cause and effect, interpret data, observe, infer, model

Materials

colored pencils, paper, scissors, metric ruler

Teaching Strategies

Have students work in pairs.

Expected Results

Students will observe that the determination of relative ages of rock layers is based upon the comparison of one layer or structure to another.

Analyze and Conclude

1. Use the principles of superposition, cross-cutting relationships, and original horizontality to determine the relative ages.
2. Because the intrusion cuts across layers 1, 2, and 3, but not layer 4, it is older than layer 4 and younger than layers 1, 2 and 3.
3. Line XY represents a fault. It is the youngest feature because it cuts across all other layers.

✓Assessment

Performance Divide students into groups of three. Have students examine a photograph of the Great Angular Unconformity in the Grand Canyon. Then, have students determine the relative ages of the rocks and events in the photograph and write their observations and analyses in their science journals. Use the Performance Task Assessment List for Science Journal in **PASC**, p. 103.

MiniLab

How is relative age determined?

Demonstrate how the principles of super-position, original horizontality, and cross-cutting relationships are used to determine the relative ages of rock layers.

Procedure

1. Draw a diagram of an outcrop with four horizontal layers. Label the layers 1 through 4.
2. Draw a vertical intrusion from layer 1 to layer 3.
3. Label the bottom-left corner of the diagram X and the top-right corner Y.
4. Cut the paper diagonally from X to Y. Move the left-hand piece 1.5 cm along the cut.

Analyze and Conclude

1. How can you determine the relative ages of the strata in your diagram?
2. How does the principle of cross-cutting relationships explain the age of the vertical intrusion?
3. What does line XY represent? Is line XY older or younger than the vertical intrusion and surrounding strata? Explain.

Figure 21-5 Using the principle of superposition, geologists have determined the relative ages of these rock layers.

Geologic Principles Many different horizontal or nearly horizontal layers of rocks make up the walls of the Grand Canyon, shown in *Figure 21-4.* Most of the rocks are sedimentary and were originally deposited millions of years ago by water or wind. The principle of **original horizontality** states that sedimentary rocks are deposited in horizontal or nearly horizontal layers. While we may not know the actual ages of the rock layers, we can assume that the oldest rocks are at the bottom and that each successive layer going toward the top is younger. Thus, we can infer that the Moenkopi Formation, which rims the top of the Grand Canyon, is much younger than the Vishnu Group found at the bottom of the gorge as shown in *Figure 21-5.* This is an application of the principle of **superposition,** which states that in an undisturbed rock sequence, the oldest rocks are at the bottom and each successive layer is younger than the layer beneath.

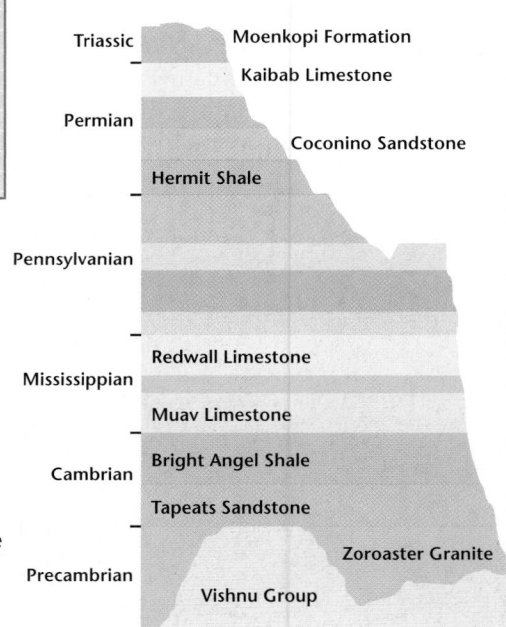

Triassic	Moenkopi Formation
	Kaibab Limestone
Permian	Coconino Sandstone
	Hermit Shale
Pennsylvanian	
Mississippian	Redwall Limestone
	Muav Limestone
Cambrian	Bright Angel Shale
	Tapeats Sandstone
	Zoroaster Granite
Precambrian	Vishnu Group

Rocks exposed in the deepest part of the Grand Canyon are some of the oldest in North America. These are mostly igneous and metamorphic rocks. Within the Vishnu Group at the bottom of the Grand Canyon sequence are dikes of granite. The principle of **cross-cutting relationships** states that an intrusion or a fault is younger than the rock it cuts across. Therefore, the granite is younger than the schist, because the granite cuts across the schist. In earthquake-prone areas, such as California, and in ancient, mountainous regions, such as the Adirondacks of New York, there are many faults. As you learned in Chapter 20, a fault is a fracture in Earth along which movement takes place. A fault is younger than the strata and surrounding geologic features because it cuts across them. You used geologic principles to determine relative ages of rocks in the *MiniLab* on the previous page.

Inclusions Relative age also can be determined where an overlying rock layer contains particles of rock material from the layer beneath it. The bottom layer was eroded, and the loose material on the surface became incorporated in the newly deposited top layer. These particles, called inclusions, indicate that the rocks in the lower layer are older than those on top. As you learned in Chapter 6, once a rock has been eroded, the resulting sediment may be transported and redeposited and recemented many kilometers away. In this case, although this newly formed rock may be Jurassic in age, the grains that make up the rock may be Cambrian in age. Another example of the use of eroded sediments to determine the relative ages of rocks is a cooled lava flow that has bedrock particles trapped within it. An inclusion layer that is formed during a lava flow is illustrated in *Figure 21-6*.

OTHER MEANS OF DETERMINING RELATIVE AGE

The fact that Earth is constantly changing as a result of processes such as weathering, erosion, earthquakes, and volcanism makes it difficult to find an undisturbed sequence of rock layers. For example, if rocks that record a volcanic eruption or the last occurrence of a particular fossil are eroded away, then the record of that particular

Figure 21-6 This pahoehoe lava flow in Hawaii most likely contains pieces, or inclusions, of the aa lava flow beneath it **(A)**. When lava or sediments are deposited on top of an eroded surface that contains loose fragments, the fragments become incorporated as inclusions in the top layer **(B)**.

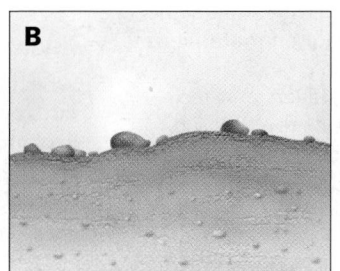

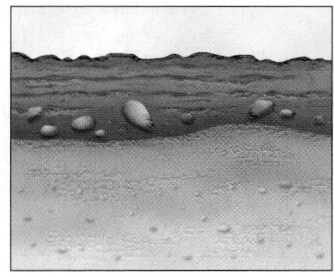

21.2 *Relative-Age Dating of Rocks* **559**

2 Teach

Identifying Misconceptions

Students may think that Earth's surface cannot change dramatically in a short period of time as a result of weathering, erosion, and deposition.

Uncover the Misconception
Have students predict what will happen to a pile of loose soil or sand during a rainstorm. Then, have them observe the material during an actual rainstorm.

Demonstrate the Concept
Explain that forces such as weathering and erosion can be accelerated by heavy rainfall and can destroy a landscape in a very short period of time.

Assess New Knowledge
After students have finished this section, have them compile a list of three geologic events that they think occur over a relatively long period of time and three geologic events that they think occur over a short period of time.

Modeling

 **Visual-Spatial** Supply groups of students with at least four different colors of modeling clay. Ask each group of students to construct a model that represents the principles of original horizontality, superposition, and cross-cutting relationships, and an angular unconformity. Have students draw and label the four models in their science journals.

L2 P 🎲

NY Core Curriculum Standards

Page 558: St 1 Science KI 1, 2, & 3, St 4 KI 1.2j, St 6 KI 2
Page 559: St 4 KI 1.2j
Page 560: St 4 KI 1.2j, St 6 KI 1
Page 561: St 4 KI 1.2j

Students will interpret the geologic history of the illustrated rock sequence.

Process Skills

interpret diagrams, observe, infer, apply, recognize cause and effect

Teaching Strategies

Assign student pairs. Have them record their observations and answers in their science journals. Ask selected groups to share their analysis of the block diagram with the class. Lead a class discussion.

Analysis

1. The sandstone (layer B) at the bottom of the outcrop is the oldest unit.
2. Erosional surfaces exist between layers D and F, and layers E and F. They are disconformities.
3. The rocks underwent a change in their mineral composition and structure as a result of contact metamorphism as the dike intruded.
4. A reverse fault occurred as the west side or hanging wall of the fault moved up relative to the footwall. This caused the layers to become offset.

Thinking Critically

5. According to the principle of cross-cutting relationships, the dike is the youngest feature because it cuts across the folded strata and is not folded itself.
6. deposition of layers B, C, D, and E; intrusion of unit A and folding of layers B, C, D, and E; erosion of unit A and layers B, C, D, and E; deposition of layers F, G, H, and I; faulting of layers B through H. The sequence was dated based on the principles of superposition, cross-cutting relationships, and on unconformities and contact metamorphism.

✓Assessment

Knowledge What are the differences among an unconformity, a disconformity, and a nonconfor-

event has been lost. Further changes may occur if the area is covered by a river during a flood or by the sea. Additionally, an erosional surface might become buried by the deposition of younger rocks. This buried erosional surface results in a gap in the rock record and is called an **unconformity.** When horizontal sedimentary rocks overlie horizontal sedimentary rocks, the unconformity is called a disconformity. A different type of unconformity exists when sedimentary rocks overlie nonsedimentary rocks such as granite or marble. Such an unconformity suggests a possible uplifting of the marble or granite and exposure at the surface by weathering and erosion. The contact point between the nonsedimentary and sedimentary rock is called a nonconformity. The formation of unconformities are illustrated in *Figure 21-7* on the following page.

When horizontal sedimentary rocks are uplifted and tilted, they are exposed to the processes of weathering and erosion. When deposition resumes, horizontal layers of sedimentary rocks are laid down on top of the erosional surface. The layers beneath the eroded surface of the folded layers remain intact, but they are at an angle to the eroded surface. This type of unconformity is called an angular unconformity. You will use several geologic principles to interpret the geologic history of an area in the *Problem-Solving Lab* on the this page.

Problem-Solving Lab

Interpreting Diagrams

Interpret the relative ages of rock layers Use the diagram to answer the following questions.

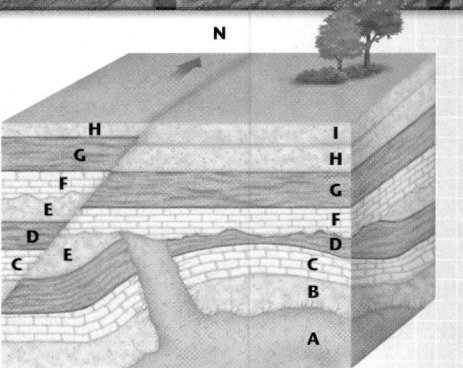

Analysis

1. Which is the oldest rock unit in the diagram?
2. An unconformity exists between which two layers of rock? Explain.
3. What happened to the rock that came in contact with the molten material of the intruded dike?
4. Explain why the rock layers and features on the left side of the diagram do not match the rock layers and features on the right side.

Thinking Critically

5. Which is the younger feature in the outcrop, the dike or the folded strata? Explain.
6. List the order of geologic events represented by this diagram. Which geologic principles did you use?

mity? An unconformity is a gap in geologic time. A disconformity is an unconformity with sedimentary rock layers overlying other sedimentary rock layers. A nonconformity occurs when nonsedimentary rock such as granite or gneiss is eroded and then covered by sedimentary rock.

✓Assessment

Knowledge Ask students the following question: How can you explain a sedimentary sequence consisting of Cambrian sandstone overlying Devonian limestone? The Cambrian sandstone was deposited first, followed by Ordovician and Silurian rocks. These were eroded and an unconformity formed when the Devonian limestone was deposited. The rock layers were then overturned.

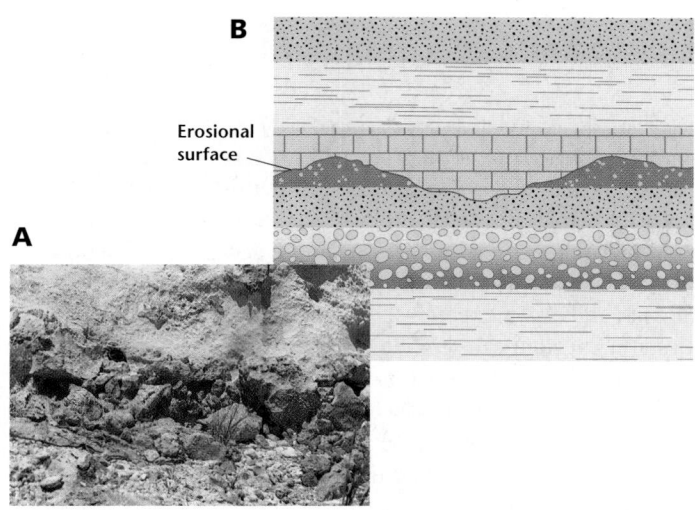

B

Erosional surface

A

C

Sedimentary rock

Erosional surface

Igneous rock

Figure 21-7 This disconformity on San Salvador Island, Bahamas, was formed by a soil that developed on top of a fossilized coral reef **(A)**. A disconformity forms when a sedimentary rock layer is deposited on top of an eroded sedimentary rock layer **(B)**. A nonconformity forms when a sedimentary rock layer is deposited on top of an eroded metamorphic or igneous rock layer **(C)**.

Correlation of Rock Strata The Permian Kaibab Formation rims the top of the Grand Canyon, but is also found about 300 km away at the bottom of a 200-m gorge in Capitol Reef National Park in Utah. How do geologists match rock layers such as these, which are far apart from each other? One method is by correlation. **Correlation** is the matching of outcrops of one geographic region to another. Geologists examine rocks for distinctive fossils and unique rock or mineral features to help correlate the rock layers. This information can be used to help in the exploration for oil or valuable minerals. For example, if a sandstone layer in one area contains oil, it is possible that the same layer in a different area also contains oil. Correlation allows geologists to accurately locate that same sandstone layer in another location.

SECTION ASSESSMENT

1. How would a geologist use the principle of superposition to determine the relative ages of the rocks in the Grand Canyon?

2. What is an unconformity?

3. Explain how inclusions at the base of a lava flow can help determine the relative age of the layers.

4. A fault or a dike cuts across a sequence of rocks. What does this suggest about the relative ages of the rocks?

5. **Thinking Critically** Explain how the principle of uniformitarianism is used to interpret Earth's past.

SKILL REVIEW

6. **Interpreting Data** Discuss how a sequence of strata can be correlated from one side of a canyon to another. For more help, refer to the *Skill Handbook*.

21.2 *Relative-Age Dating of Rocks* **561**

3 Assess

Check for Understanding
Reinforcement
Quiz students orally about the principles involved in determining the relative age of a sequence of strata as observed in natural settings, such as the Grand Canyon or Letchworth State Park in New York, which is also known as The Grand Canyon of the East.

Reteach

Visual-Spatial Review the principles used to determine the relative ages of rocks. Provide a visual illustration of each principle in a natural setting. If possible, provide illustrations from a local setting.

Assessment

Skill Have individual students come to the chalkboard and draw a variety of sequences that illustrate the principles of original horizontality, superposition, and cross-cutting relationships, as well as inclusions and unconformities. Students should be prepared to briefly explain their drawings to the class.

SECTION ASSESSMENT

1. Assuming that the horizontal rocks were not faulted or overturned, the oldest layer would be at the bottom of the sequence. Each layer overlying this layer would be successively younger.

2. An unconformity is a gap in the rock record where layers of rocks, and thus, a record of geologic time, are missing. Unconformities are the result of either weathering and erosion or periods of nondeposition.

3. Because inclusions are pieces of the rock layer below, according to the principle of superposition, the inclusions are older than the rock layer they are now in.

4. Both the fault and the dike cut across preexisting rock layers. Thus, according to the principle of cross-cutting relationships, the fault and dike are younger than the rock layers they cut across.

5. The principle of uniformitarianism attempts to explain the forces that continually change Earth's surface features. This principle assumes that these forces are the same today as they were in the past.

6. By observing and recording similarities, such as fossil content, color, and texture of rock layers on both sides of a canyon, strata can easily be correlated.

561

Section Background

For section content background, refer to **Absolute-Age Dating of Rocks** on page 552D.

Preplanning

Refer to the Chapter Organizer on pages 552A–B.

1 Focus

Section Focus

Before presenting the lesson, display **Section Focus Transparency 65** on the overhead projector. **L1** **ELL**

TREE RINGS AND DATING EVENTS
Use with Chapter 21, Section 21.3

❶ How old do you think this tree is? How can you tell?
❷ How might tree rings be used to help date past events?

Tying to Previous Knowledge

The relative-age dating of rocks and fossils is complemented by methods for determining absolute ages. Radiometric analyses of Precambrian rocks greatly help geologists determine a time frame for eras where fossils are rare.

SECTION 21.3 *Absolute-Age Dating of Rocks*

OBJECTIVES

- **Explain** *the several different methods used by scientists to determine absolute age.*
- **Describe** *how objects are dated by the use of certain radioactive elements.*
- **Explain** *how annual tree rings and glacial varves are used to date geologic events.*

VOCABULARY

radioactive decay
radiometric dating
half-life
dendrochronology
varve
key bed

As you have learned, relative-age dating is a method of comparing past geologic events based on the observed order of strata in the rock record. In contrast, absolute-age dating enables scientists to determine the actual age of a rock, fossil, or other object. Scientists have devised a method for dating very old objects using the decay rate of radioactive isotopes. These isotopes are found in igneous and metamorphic rocks, some fossils, and organic remains. Radioactive substances emit nuclear particles at a constant rate. As the numbers of protons and neutrons change with each nuclear emission, the element is converted to a different element. The original radioactive element is referred to as the "parent," and the new element is referred to as the "daughter." For example, a radioactive isotope of uranium, U-238, will decay into an isotope of lead, Pb-206, over a specific span of time, as illustrated in *Figure 21-8.* The emission of radioactive particles and the resulting change into other elements over time is called **radioactive decay.** Once the emission of these atomic particles begins, the rate remains constant regardless of environment, pressure, temperature, or any other physical changes. Thus, these atomic particles become accurate indicators of the absolute age of an object.

USE OF RADIOACTIVE ISOTOPES

In a process called **radiometric dating,** scientists attempt to determine the ratio of parent nuclei to daughter nuclei within a given sample of a rock or fossil. This ratio is then used to determine the absolute age of the rock or fossil. As the number of parent atoms decreases, the number of daughter atoms increases by the same amount and indicates the increasing age of an object. Because it often takes a long time for the entire amount of an isotope to decay, geologists use the length of time it takes for one-half of the original amount to decay. This

Figure 21-8 The decay of U-238 to Pb-206 follows a specific and never-changing path.

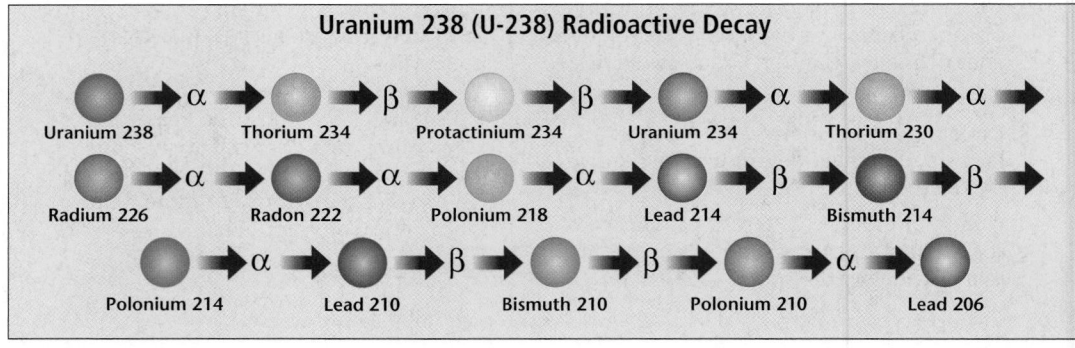

Uranium 238 (U-238) Radioactive Decay

Uranium 238 → α → Thorium 234 → β → Protactinium 234 → β → Uranium 234 → α → Thorium 230 → α →

Radium 226 → α → Radon 222 → α → Polonium 218 → α → Lead 214 → β → Bismuth 214 → β →

Polonium 214 → α → Lead 210 → β → Bismuth 210 → β → Polonium 210 → α → Lead 206

562 CHAPTER 21 *Fossils and the Rock Record*

Resource Manager

Study Guide for Content Mastery, pp. 134–135 **L2**

Section Focus Transparency 65 **L1** **ELL**

Table 21-1 Half-Lives of Selected Radioactive Isotopes		
Radioactive Isotope	**Approximate Half-Life**	**Decay Product**
Rubidium-87	48.6 billion years	Strontium-87
Thorium-232	14.0 billion years	Lead-208
Potassium-40	1.3 billion years	Argon-40
Uranium-238	4.5 billion years	Lead-206
Uranium-235	0.7 billion years	Lead-207
Carbon-14	5730 years	Nitrogen-14

period of time is called the **half-life.** *Table 21-1* lists some common radioactive isotopes and their half-lives.

Carbon-14 Another radioactive isotope that is commonly used to determine the absolute age of an object is carbon-14 (C-14). This isotope is especially useful for finding the age of materials that are of organic origin, such as amber, humanoid bones, papyrus, and charcoal fragments. This is because all organic materials contain carbon. C-14 decays into the stable, nonradioactive element nitrogen-14 (N-14). The half-life of C-14 is 5730 years, as shown in *Table 21-2.* When state-of-the-art technology is used, C-14 dating is accurate for objects up to 75 000 years old.

If U-238 is used for an object that is only a few hundred thousand years old, the ratio of parent to daughter atoms will be too large to be useful; therefore, a radioactive isotope with a shorter half-life than U-238, such as U-235, which has a half-life of 700 000 000 years, must be used. Conversely, for the dating of a particularly old rock sample, a radioactive isotope with a longer half-life must be used. Otherwise, there may come a point when the ratio of parent-to-daughter atoms is too small to measure but the age of the rock has not yet been determined. In essence, the isotope used for dating depends on the estimated general age of the rock or object being dated.

Using Math

Using Numbers A granite sample from Canada was dated using uranium-235, which has a half-life of 700 000 000 years. The rock was calculated to be 2.8 billion years old. How many half-lives have elapsed since the rock formed?

Table 21-2 Radioactive Decay of Carbon-14 to Nitrogen-14			
	Percent Parent Element	**Percent Daughter Element**	**Elapsed Years**	**Number of Half-Lives**
Time 1	100	0	0	0
Time 2	50	50	5730	1
Time 3	25	75	11 560	2
Time 4	12.5	87.5	17 090	3

21.3 *Absolute-Age Dating of Rocks* **563**

Using Math

$T\frac{1}{2}$ of U-235 = 700 000 000 y; $(2.8 \times 10^9)/(0.7 \times 10^9)$ = 4 half-lives

Content Background

Unlike relative-age dating techniques, which compare the relative ages of rocks and fossils, absolute-age dating methods incorporate the use of radioactive elements that decay to stable elements over a constant rate of time. If the ratio of parent material to daughter material can be determined, then the absolute age of the object can be determined. For example, cloth wrappings taken from a mummified Apis bull in a pyramid in Dashur, Egypt, were dated at 2050 years. This date agrees with the age of the pyramid as estimated from historical records. Samples collected from a pumice and ash deposit in Owens Valley, California have been dated at 700 000 years. This volcanic material overlies glacial drift and serves as a key bed in dating the glacial period before it. A quartz monzonite from Half Dome in Yosemite National Park has been dated at 80 000 000 years. The Pikes Peak Granite at the top of Pikes Peak, Colorado is dated at 1 030 000 000 years. Finally, samples from outcrops in southwestern Minnesota that have been dated at 3.6 billion years old are believed to be some of the oldest rocks in North America.

Differentiated Instruction

Behaviorally Disordered To engage students who are behaviorally disordered in this section's content, direct the students to the Earth Science Web Site at **earthgeu.com** and have them search for information about the development of the geologic time scale based on both relative- and absolute-age dating methods. Ask students to create a brochure describing absolute-age dating methods, such as radiometric dating and interpreting tree rings and varves. **L2**

Demo

Obtain several samples or photos of items whose absolute ages are known, such as a Precambrian rock, a Mesozoic dinosaur-bone fragment, a Miocene gastropod, and a Pleistocene tree fragment. Show students the selected items and ask them what they think the age of each specimen might be. Then, tell them the age and the radioactive isotope used to determine the absolute age of the specimen.

NY Core Curriculum Standards

Page 562: St 4 KI 1.2j
Page 563: St 4 KI 1.2j

Enrichment

Have students examine a cross section of a hardwood tree (e.g., maple, ash, or box elder) obtained from a local sawmill or someone who cuts wood. Assign students the task of drawing a diagram of the cross section and determining the age of the tree. Be sure to have students pay close attention to details, such as the width of the rings.

Interpreting the Photo

Figure 21-9 The Anasazi built their cliff dwellings in alcoves such as this for protection against the elements and their enemies. Additionally, freshwater springs were often present at the backs of the alcoves. Because the modern-day Pueblo Native Americans are believed to be the direct descendants of the Anasazi, the term *Anasazi* has been replaced by *Ancestral Puebloans.*

Earth Science Journal

Have students describe in their science journals the science of dendrochronology and how it is used not only to date the ages of trees, but also to interpret climatic changes. Have students draw diagrams showing a pair of tree rings that might indicate a drought, a rainy season, or a normal growth season. Also have them describe how dendrochronology has helped anthropologists to infer why the Anasazi disappeared. L2

Earth Science Online

Update For an online update on the oldest rocks found to date, visit the Earth Science Web Site at earthgeu.com

OTHER WAYS TO DETERMINE AGE

Determining the relative or absolute age of an object or event is not limited to the use of rocks or chemical elements. Naturally occurring materials, such as trees, lake-bottom sediment, and volcanic ash can also be used to help geologists determine the age of an object or event, such as a forest fire, a drought, a flood, or a volcanic eruption.

Tree Rings With the use of a technique from the science of forestry, the age of a tree can be determined by counting the number of annual tree rings in a cross section of the tree. During the spring months, a tree experiences its greatest growth, while in the winter, its growth is less. Thus, the widths of tree rings are directly related to the climatic conditions during growth periods. A pair of spring and winter growth rings represents an annual tree ring. **Dendrochronology** is the science of comparing annual growth rings in trees to date events and changes in past environments. For example, in Mesa Verde National Park in Colorado, the age of the wooden rafters used to build the pueblos of the Anasazi have been determined with the use of dendrochronology. *Figure 21-9* shows a pueblo from Mesa Verde National Park. The Anasazi were a group of Native Americans that lived in the southwestern United States. It has been calculated by other methods, that the pueblos were built between A.D. 1150 and A.D. 1200. It also has been determined that pueblos in the southwestern United States were abandoned by the Anasazi around A.D. 1300, most likely because of a severe drought that lasted from A.D. 1276 to A.D. 1299.

Seasonal Climatic Changes About 11 000 years ago, continental glaciers covered the northern part of the United States. During the summer months, the ice would partially melt. Large volumes of water containing fine glacial sediment were carried downstream and deposited in large lakes. Summer deposits are generally light-colored and relatively thick compared to the thinner, organically enriched,

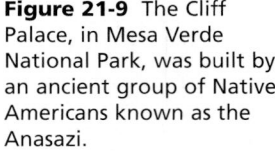

Figure 21-9 The Cliff Palace, in Mesa Verde National Park, was built by an ancient group of Native Americans known as the Anasazi.

Resource Manager

Laboratory Manual, pp. 165–168 L2
Teaching Transparency 64 L2 ELL

NY Core Curriculum Standards

Page 564: St 4 KI 1.2i
Page 565: St 4 KI 1.2d & 1.2j

and dark-colored sediments of winter. These bands of alternating light- and dark-colored sediments of sand, clay, and silt are called **varves.** Varves are similar to tree rings in that they show evidence of cyclic events—in this case, a cycle of summer to winter. Varves from different lakes can be compared to determine the ages of glacial lake sediments from about 15 000 to 12 000 years ago.

Distinctive Sediment Layers Scientists hypothesize that about 66 million years ago, an asteroid 10 km in diameter struck Earth in the region known today as the Yucatan Peninsula in Mexico. The blast threw out large amounts of crushed rock into Earth's atmosphere. Much later, when the asteroid's impact debris settled onto the surface of Earth, it formed a sediment layer that can be found in many parts of the world today. This layer lies between rocks deposited at the end of the Cretaceous Period of the Mesozoic Era and the beginning of the Paleogene Period of the Cenozoic Era. These geologic time units are shown in *Figure 21-1.* When such a layer is formed by an instantaneous or short-lived event, geologists may be able to determine the time of the event through radiometric dating. The layer then becomes a time marker called a **key bed,** which can be used to correlate rock layers across large areas. Key beds, such as the black coal bed shown in *Figure 21-10,* contain material that is distinctive and easy to recognize in the rock record.

Volcanic eruptions also create key beds. For example, when Mount St. Helens erupted in 1980, vast amounts of volcanic ash were distributed over many states. The ash will eventually become a thin, clay layer and will mark the date of the eruption. Clay layers such as this one occur throughout the rock record and attest to Earth's volcanic history. You will learn more about this history in Chapter 22.

Figure 21-10 This coal seam near Healy, Alaska can be used to correlate rock layers across a large area because it is exposed in many outcrops throughout the area.

SECTION ASSESSMENT

1. What is the difference between relative-age dating and absolute-age dating?

2. A scientist finds the charred remains of a tree in a layer of volcanic ash thought to be from the eruption of Mt. Mazama some 6600 years ago. Which radioactive isotope, U-238 or C-14, would you use to verify the actual age of the charred wood? Explain.

3. What is a key bed?

4. **Thinking Critically** Potassium-40 decays to the noble gas argon-40. What problems might arise when these radioactive isotopes are used for age dating?

SKILL REVIEW

5. **Comparing and Contrasting** Compare and contrast the uses of tree rings and varves in relative-age dating. For more help, refer to the *Skill Handbook.*

SECTION ASSESSMENT

1. Relative-age dating is based on the comparison of one event with another over time. Absolute-age dating is the determination of an object's actual age by means of radiometric dating, tree rings, or varves.

2. Because the tree was once living, it contains C-14. The half life of C-14 is 5700 years, long enough to be used to date an event that occurred 6600 years ago.

3. A key bed is generally formed as a result of a major geologic event such as a volcanic eruption. A key bed has material or characteristics that are easily recognized in the rock record.

4. The half-life of K-40 is 8.4 billion years; thus, with such a slow rate of decay, the ratios of K-40 to Ar-40 may be too small to accurately measure. Consequently, an accurate absolute age may be difficult to determine. Additionally, argon gas may escape and result in a ratio that indicates an age younger than it really is.

5. Tree rings and varves both record seasonal and yearly changes in climate. Varves accumulate in water and are made of sediment, whereas tree rings are part of a living tree.

Section Background

For section content background, refer to **Fossils** on page 552D.

Preplanning

Refer to the Chapter Organizer on pages 552A–B.

1 Focus

Section Focus

Before presenting the lesson, display **Section Focus Transparency 66** on the overhead projector.
`L1` `ELL`

Section Focus Transparency **66**
TRACE FOSSILS
Use with Chapter 21, Section 21.4

❶ How do you think these fossils were made?
❷ What can you infer about the organisms that made them?

Section Focus Transparency — Earth Science: Geology, the Environment, and the Universe

Activity

Interpersonal Have students make fossil collections, either from actual fossils or photographs of fossils. Descriptions should include whether the fossil was plant or animal, species name, rock type in which the fossil was found, inferred environmental conditions, location, geologic age, and any other pertinent information. Have students present their collections to their classmates at the end of this section. `L2` `ELL` `COOP LEARN`

SECTION 21.4

Remains of Organisms in the Rock Record

OBJECTIVES

- **Define** *fossil.*
- **Explain** *several methods by which fossils can be preserved.*
- **Describe** *the characteristics of an index fossil.*
- **Discuss** *how fossils can be used to interpret Earth's past physical and environmental history.*

VOCABULARY

fossil
evolution
original preservation
altered hard part
permineralization
index fossil
mold
cast

Fossils are the evidence or remains of once-living plants or animals. They provide evidence of the past existence of a wide variety of life-forms, most of which have become extinct. The fossil record also provides evidence that populations have undergone change through time in response to changes in their environments. This change in populations as a result of environmental change is **evolution.** Fossils preserved in the rock record also provide information about past environmental conditions. They can even be used to correlate rock layers from one area to another.

TYPES OF FOSSILS

Fossils with **original preservation** are the soft and hard parts of plant and animal remains that have not undergone any kind of change since the organisms' deaths. Such fossils are uncommon because their preservation requires extraordinary circumstances such as freezing, drying out, or oxygen-free environments. In Alaska, original woody parts of plants are imbedded in the permafrost from 10 000-year-old bogs. Soft parts of mammoths and saber-toothed cats are preserved in the sticky ooze of the La Brea Tar Pits in California. Tree sap from prehistoric trees that hardened into amber sometimes has fossil insects imbedded in it. You will read about the recent discovery of a mammoth carcass that is at least 20 000 years old in the *Science in the News* feature at the end of this chapter. Soft parts are also preserved when plants or animals have been dried out and their remains have been mummified. Most mummified remains are found in dry caves or are buried in desert sands. For example, in 1935, the mummified remains of a Native American were found in Mammoth Cave National Park in Kentucky. *Figure 21-11* shows another fossil with original preservation.

Figure 21-11 The Graubelle man was found in 1952 in a bog in Jutland, Denmark. It dates from between A.D. 80 to 170 B.C. Fossils like these are called bog bodies.

566

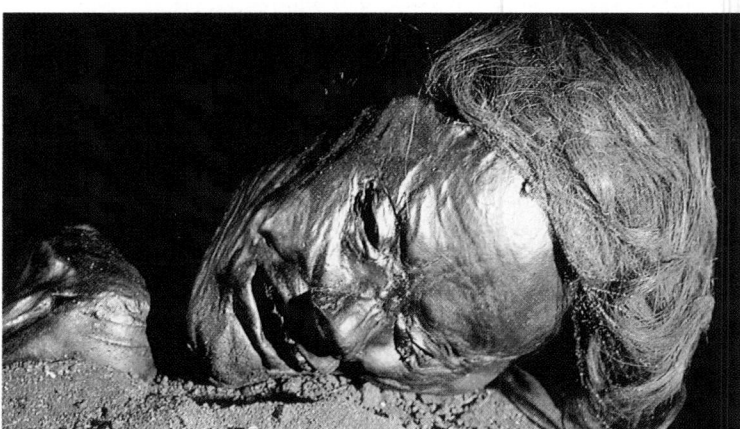

Differentiated Instruction

Visually Impaired Obtain very good samples of a trilobite, a brachiopod, a clam, and a crinoid for students with visual impairments to touch. Ask students to give a verbal description of each fossil and note the similarities and differences among the fossils. Have students tape-record their descriptions, play their recordings for the class, and then have classmates try to name the fossils from the descriptions.

Resource Manager

Laboratory Manual, pp. 161–164 `L2`
Teaching Transparency 65 `L2` `ELL`
Section Focus Transparency 66 `L1` `ELL`
Study Guide for Content Mastery, p. 136 `L2`
GeoLab and MiniLab Worksheets, pp. 84–86 `L2`

Figure 21-12 One year after the 1980 eruption of Mount St. Helens, in Washington State, these trees are slowly being converted to petrified wood **(A)**. This petrified tree stump in Theodore Roosevelt National Park, North Dakota, stands as testimony to an ancient volcanic eruption **(B)**.

2 Teach

Content Background

Geologists who study fossils are called paleontologists. Invertebrate paleontologists study fossils of organisms without backbones. These include marine organisms such as corals, brachiopods, and sponges, and terrestrial organisms such as insects. Vertebrate paleontologists study fossils of organisms with backbones. These include mammals, fishes, dinosaurs, and other reptiles. Paleobotanists study fossilized plants. Paleobiologists study fossils as individual organisms. In contrast, paleoecologists study and interpret the ecology of fossil organisms as a means of interpreting past environments and Earth's history. Finding spectacularly preserved fossils is rare; thus, most paleontologists learn to recognize individual fossil species by partial remains. It is newsworthy when an entire dinosaur is discovered.

Altered Hard Parts When all the organic material has been removed and the hard parts of a plant or animal have been changed either by mineral replacement or by recrystallization, their fossils are referred to as **altered hard parts.** The process by which pore spaces are filled in with mineral substances is called **permineralization.** For example, when volcanic ash spreads out and settles over a large geographic area, entire forests may become buried. Over a long period of time, quartz and other minerals in the ash combine with groundwater and slowly fill in the spaces between the cellular walls of the trees and silicify them. A common name for this type of fossilized tree is petrified wood. Modern and fossil examples are shown in *Figure 21-12.* Permineralization also occurs when groundwater combines with minerals in sediments. The mineral-rich water then reaches a buried organism and the replacement process begins, as illustrated in *Figure 21-13.*

Changes in temperature and pressure may also result in changes in shell or bone material. Shells, such as those of clams, or exoskeletons, such as those of corals, may be affected by a process called recrystallization. The exterior of the shell remains the same, but the shell microstructures are destroyed during this process.

Figure 21-13 The shells of spectacularly preserved Brachiopods, such as this *Echinauris,* from Permian-aged rocks in the Glass Mountains of Texas, were replaced by silica during permineralization **(A)**. This process is illustrated in **(B)**.

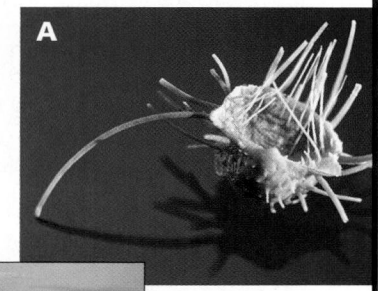

A

B

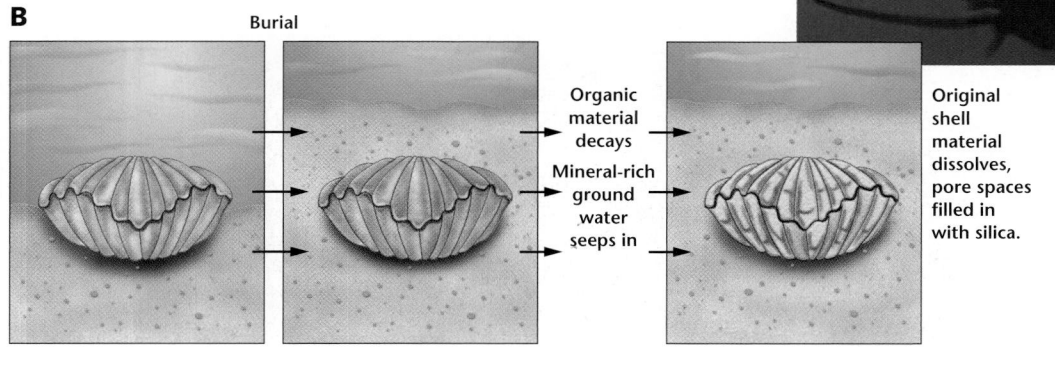

Burial

Organic material decays

Mineral-rich ground water seeps in

Original shell material dissolves, pore spaces filled in with silica.

21.4 Remains of Organisms in the Rock Record **567**

Activity

Petrified Forest National Park, Arizona, has one of the largest exhibits of petrified wood in the world. Have students research the formation of petrified wood to find answers to the following questions. Do the petrified remains of the trees show any characteristics of the original trees when they were alive? Why are the petrified logs and debris now exposed at Earth's surface? Why does the Park Service closely protect the petrified trees of Petrified Forest National Park?

Using Scientific Terms

How can coprolites help paleontologists to interpret the environmental conditions in which an animal may have lived? Coprolites may contain fossilized food particles such as plant material or bone fragments. They provide information about the diet of the animal that formed the coprolite.

Interpreting the Photo

Figure 21-13 Because the Glass Mountain fossils are composed of silica, extracting them from the limestone they're found in is very easy. Limestone contains calcite, and calcite dissolves in hydrochloric acid. Blocks of the limestone are put in tubs of acid and the fossils remain after the limestone dissolves.

NY Core Curriculum Standards

Page 566: St 4 KI 1.2i & 1.2j
Page 567: St 4 KI 1.2j & 3.1b

Environmental Connection

Pose the following question: Suppose a mammoth tusk was found stuck in the ocean floor 100 km off the coast of the northeastern United States. Assuming that the tusk had not been transported out of the mammoth's living area, what would a geologist conclude about the environment in this area 12 000–15 000 years ago?

Collaborative Learning

Interpersonal Have groups of students examine a photo of dinosaur trackways. Have students write in their science journals what they think they can learn about the dinosaur's size, height, and gaits from analyzing the trackways. Have a volunteer from each group walk across a muddy or sandy area near your school. Have another volunteer run across the area. Have students record the height of the volunteers. Ask each group to measure and sketch the volunteers' trackways, match each set of trackways with the student who made it, and explain how the group was able to match the trackways with the students who made them. Students should note the depth of a track versus the size of the student, the length of the strides relative to the trackmaker's height, and the distance between strides relative to whether the volunteer was walking or running. **L1** **ELL** **COOP LEARN**

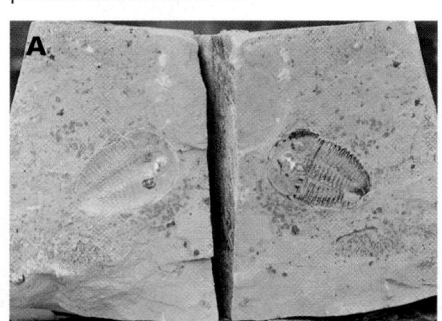

Figure 21-14 The characteristic shape of this mollusk, *Ecphora*, makes it easy to recognize and identify.

Figure 21-15 This mold and cast of the trilobite *Elrathia kingii*, from the Cambrian of Utah **(A)**, shows the results of the process illustrated in **B**.

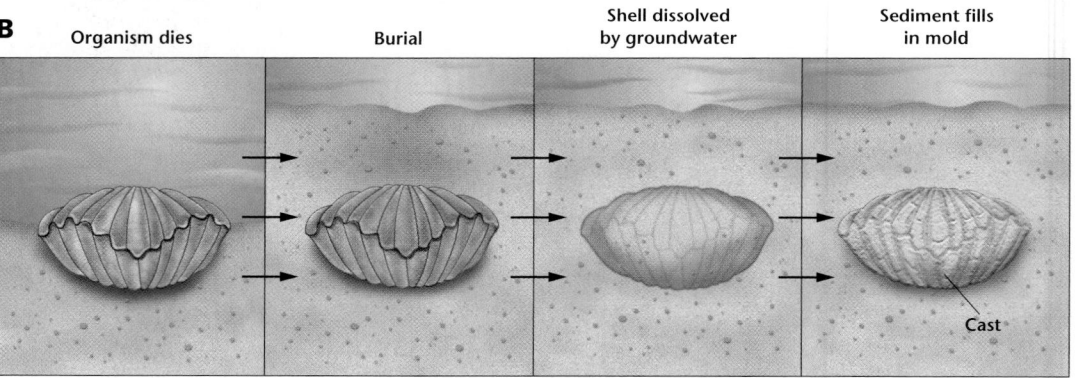

B

| Organism dies | Burial | Shell dissolved by groundwater | Sediment fills in mold |

Cast

Index Fossils Some fossils are more useful than others in relative age dating. **Index fossils** are remains of plants or animals that can be used by geologists to correlate rock layers over large geographic areas or to date a particular rock layer. An index fossil is easily recognized, abundant, and widely distributed geographically. It must also have lived during a short period of time. For example, the mollusk *Ecphora*, shown in *Figure 21-14,* is an excellent index fossil for the Mesozoic because of its distinctive shape and its abundance.

Molds and Casts Some fossils do not contain any shell or bone material. They may be molds and casts of shelled organisms, such as clams. A **mold** is formed when the original shell parts of an organism within a sedimentary rock are weathered and eroded. A hollowed-out impression, or mold, of the shells is left in their place. This cavity might later become filled with minerals or sediment to create a **cast** of the organism. A mold and cast are illustrated in *Figure 21-15.*

Indirect Evidence of Past Life Indirect evidence of plant and animal life are called trace fossils. Some examples are worm trails, burrows, and footprints. Trace fossils such as those shown in *Figure 21-16* can provide information about how an organism lived, how it moved, or how it obtained food. Dinosaur trackways in Texas and Connecticut provide scientists with clues about the size and walking characteristics of dinosaurs. Other trace fossils include gastroliths, smooth and rounded rocks that dinosaurs had in their stomachs to help them digest and grind their food, and coprolites, the remains of solid waste materials of animals. By analyzing the content of coprolites, scientists can learn about the eating habits of ancient animals.

Earth Science
Journal

Science Field Book

Have students find the Web address for your state's Geological Survey. Have them find the following items and write them in their science journals: state fossil (if applicable), state rock (if applicable), and common index fossils. Have students find the index fossil for the portion of the rock record that is represented in your local area. **L1**

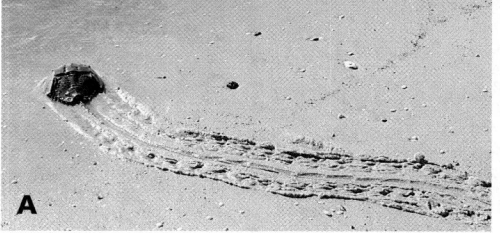

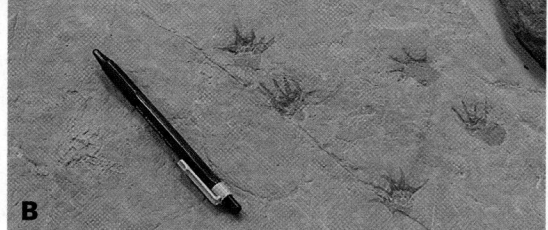

WHY STUDY FOSSILS?

The study of fossils allows scientists to interpret and describe Earth's history. Fossils from different geologic time periods describe how organisms have changed through time. Fossils also show evidence of ancient environmental conditions. They also may help scientists find patterns and cycles that can be used to predict future phenomena, such as climatic changes. The study of fossils further allows geologists to locate energy resources. For example, petroleum geologists use certain index microfossils to determine whether oil might be present at a particular site. These fossils provide information about the ages of rocks and, in some cases, information that indicates whether the temperature and pressure conditions needed to form oil or gas were present in those layers.

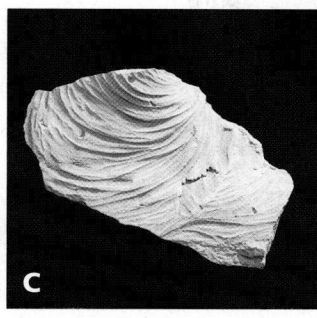

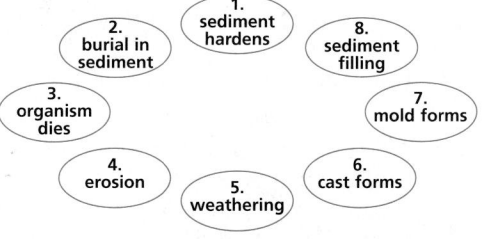

Figure 21-16 The tracks made by this horseshoe crab **(A)** may someday become preserved as did the tracks of this small Permian reptile **(B)**. Zoophycus **(C)** is interpreted to be the feeding trace of a wormlike, burrowing organism **(D)**. The sweeping lines are distinctive trace fossils.

SECTION ASSESSMENT

1. What is a fossil?

2. What is the difference between a fossil with original preservation and an altered hard part?

3. What are the characteristics of an index fossil?

4. Explain why the eruption of Mount St. Helens in 1980 resulted in the formation of a key bed.

5. **Thinking Critically** How might a mold or cast of a fossil help scientists to interpret the type of environment it lived in?

SKILL REVIEW

6. **Concept Mapping** Rearrange the following terms to construct a sequencing concept map to illustrate the formation of a mold and a cast. For more help, refer to the *Skill Handbook*.

1. sediment hardens
2. burial in sediment
3. organism dies
4. erosion
5. weathering
6. cast forms
7. mold forms
8. sediment filling

earthgeu.com/self_check_quiz

21.4 *Remains of Organisms in the Rock Record* **569**

DESIGN YOUR OWN GeoLab

Interpreting History-Shaping Events

What do volcanic eruptions, mountain building, flooding, and drought have in common? They are all events that in some way affect life and the surface of Earth. How strong an impact does each event have on the future of Earth? How different would things be if certain events in Earth's history had not happened?

Preparation

Problem

What are the most important events in Earth's history? Where do they fit in the long history of Earth's development? Why are these events important? Do some geologic time periods contain more history-shaping events than others?

Possible Materials

paper	colored pencils
pencil	geologic time scale
posterboard	calculator
meterstick	encyclopedia
tape measure	reference books

Hypothesis

Brainstorm about Earth's history and the changes that Earth has experienced over time. Hypothesize which events had the most impact on the direction that Earth's development has taken. Determine where additional data might be available and collect resources to use as your references. Describe the best way to list and illustrate your choices.

Objectives

In this GeoLab, you will:

- **Hypothesize** about important events in Earth's development.
- **Explain** why such events had a significant impact on Earth's history.
- **Communicate** your results and interpretations.

Plan the Experiment

1. Review the list of events in the table on the facing page.
2. As a group, decide on and make a list of events that you think can help support your hypothesis.
3. Choose two other resources and use them to find at least ten more events to add to your list.
4. Design and construct a way to exhibit and explain your results.
5. Check your plan. Make sure your teacher has approved your plan before you proceed.
6. Carry out your plan.

India), continental glaciation (in the northern and southern hemispheres), sea-level changes, the breaking apart of Pangaea, the mass extinction events at the end of the Permian and Cretaceous Periods, and significant evolutionary changes in plants and animals as recorded in the rock record.

- Encourage students to include the years in scientific notation (M.Y.B.P.) for each event.

Possible Procedures

Student methods and selection of Earth history-shaping events will vary. Ask students to write their procedures and descriptions of their presentation methods (poster, data table, and so on) in their science journals.

1. **Interpreting Observations** Did more history-shaping events seem to have occurred early in Earth's history or later on? Explain.
2. **Comparing and Contrasting** Plot your list of events on a copy of the geologic time scale. Compare and constrast the number of events in each era. Does any geologic time period contain more history-shaping events than others? Explain.
3. **Observing and Inferring** Choose one event in the Mesozoic and infer how Earth's history might have progressed had the event not happened.

Conclude & Apply

1. How do extinction events influence the development of life on Earth?
2. How do mountain-building events and glaciations affect the development of life on Earth?
3. If another planet experienced the same events that you chose, would that planet be identical to Earth? What would be similar or different?

EARTH HISTORY-SHAPING EVENTS

Origin of the solar system
Earth forms, 4.6 B.Y.B.P.
Oceans form, 4.0 B.Y.B.P
Primitive algae evolves, 3.3 B.Y.B.P
First fossil evidence of multicellular organisms, 1.2 B.Y.B.P.
Trilobites are abundant, algal reefs form, 600 M.Y.B.P.
First corals evolve, invertebrates dominate oceans, 500 M.Y.B.P.
First land plants evolve, insects appear, 440 M.Y.B.P.
Fishes are abundant, early amphibians evolve, 400 M.Y.B.P.
Forests that become coal swamps are present, 300 M.Y.B.P.
Earliest reptiles evolve, 300 M.Y.B.P.
Alleghenian Orogeny occurs, 270 M.Y.B.P.
Trilobites become extinct, 270 M.Y.B.P.
Earliest dinosaurs appear, 225 M.Y.B.P.
Pangaea breaks up, 225 M.Y.B.P.

Earliest mammals evolve, 200 M.Y.B.P.
Dinosaurs are abundant, 180 M.Y.B.P.
The first birds evolve, 180 M.Y.B.P.
Asteroid impact, 66 M.Y.B.P.
Modern groups of mammals appear, 60 M.Y.B.P.
Earliest horses evolve, 60 M.Y.B.P.
Large mammals evolve, 40 M.Y.B.P.
Carnivores abundant, 11 M.Y.B.P.
Adirondack mountains uplifted, 11 M.Y.B.P.
First humanoids evolve (*Australopithecus africanus*), 3 M.Y.B.P.
Ice Age of the Pleistocene begins, 1 M.Y.B.P.
Mammoths and mastodons are abundant, 1 M.Y.B.P.
Large ice sheets retreat ~ 10 000 years ago
Mount Vesuvius erupts and destroys Pompeii, A.D. 79
New Madrid Earthquake, 1811–1812
Chicago Fire, 1871
Krakatoa eruption in Java, 1883
Mt. St. Helens eruption in Washington, U.S., 1980

Conclude & Apply (continued)

process by extinction, isolation, or interactions of species.
3. Answers will vary depending on the planet selected. For example, if Mars was selected, weathering and erosion would be considerably different. Wind erosion and the alteration of surface features would be more prevalent on a planetwide basis as compared to Earth.

Assessment

Portfolio Have students each create a collage of at least four major Earth history-shaping events that they consider to be the most significant in the development of Earth. Collages may include text photos, student drawings, and diagrams found on the Internet.

Data and Observations

Have students record their Earth history-shaping event selections and other data in a table format. Create a transparency or computer-generated data table that accentuates the elements in students' data tables. Each event, its approximate date, and why the event was selected should be included. The events should be sequenced from oldest to youngest.

Analyze

1. Answers may vary depending on students' selections of Earth history-shaping events. The main idea is that there have been many such events throughout geologic time.
2. Answers will vary depending upon the events selected by students. Some students may think that the Mesozoic Era had the most Earth history-shaping events.
3. Answers will vary greatly. One example might represent a scenario in which dinosaurs did not become extinct. In this case, the significance of mammals might have been greatly reduced.

Conclude & Apply

1. The extinction of existing forms of life open environmental niches for surviving species to thrive and proliferate.
2. Large-scale mountain-building events, such as the one that formed the Alleghenies, create barriers, not only in terms of elevation, but also in terms of amount of precipitation and other climatic factors. Species are prevented from interacting, thus effectively impeding the evolutionary

Purpose

Students will learn about the recent discovery of an intact woolly mammoth in Central Siberia and the research efforts related to the discovery.

Content Background

- The expedition to remove and thaw the Jarkov mammoth was led by French polar explorer Bernard Buigues. The research team is led by Dick Mol, a Dutch paleontologist, and Larry Agenbroad, a paleontologist from Northern Arizona University in Flagstaff.
- Other members of the group Proboscidea include the American mastodon, the steppe mammoth, the straight-tusked elephant, the imperial mammoth, the Columbian mammoth, and the modern Indian and African elephants. Members of this group first appeared toward the end of the Miocene Epoch.
- Woolly mammoths were herbivores that were well-adapted to cold climates with their heavy coats of hair and humps of fat on their backs. Their bodies were protected by a 7–8 cm layer of fat.

Science in the News

Frozen Mammoth

The sound of jackhammers echoed across the tundra. As a helicopter hovered nearby, the last few cuts were made into the permanently frozen ground. Many hours later, a cube of frozen earth weighing more than 26 metric tons went soaring across the Siberian steppe as it dangled from the bottom of the helicopter.

A chunk of tundra may not seem to be important, but this chunk found in 1997, contained a valuable prize: a complete specimen of a woolly mammoth that had died about 20 000 years ago and became buried in the permafrost. Many fossils represent only the partial remains of once-living organisms. Thus, a complete mammoth with bones, skin, hair, and internal organs intact represents a unique opportunity for scientists to investigate the lifestyle of this animal and the environment in which it lived.

The mammoth was a member of one of the great herds of the species *Mammuthus primigenius*. These herds roamed the vast grasslands of Siberia during the Pleistocene Epoch. The mammoths, cousins of today's elephants, were the largest land mammals ever. They ranged from 2.5 to 4.2 m high at the shoulder, had trunks and tusks like today's elephants, and were covered with thick hair for protection from the cold. This mammoth was a tusked male, about 3.5 m tall, and was about 47 years old when it died.

Solving the Mystery

The mammoth was flown to an ice cave near the town of Khatanga in Central Siberia, where scientists used hair dryers to thaw it out one tiny piece at a time. Every square centimeter of the mammoth and the soil surrounding it will be examined. One thing scientists hope to find out is why mammoths became extinct. They may have been unable to adapt to climatic changes, they may have been over-hunted by early humans, or they may have died of disease. Tissue samples from the mammoth may help to solve this mystery.

"Pleistocene Park"

The amount of knowledge to be gained from the mammoth is tremendous. Some scientists even hope to find cells in the mammoth that could be cloned, and from them, to grow a living woolly mammoth. Other scientists hope to find sperm cells that they can use to cross-breed it with a living female elephant. The hybrid offspring would also be fertilized with mammoth sperm, and a nearly pure-bred mammoth would result after several generations. In a scene right out of "Pleistocene Park," the woolly mammoth might be returned to the steppe as an ecological tourist attraction.

Activity

The woolly mammoth is one of several species in the family Proboscidea. Visit the Earth Science Web Site at **earthgeu.com** to research the other members of this family. Make a poster telling when, where, and how they lived.

Teaching Strategies

- Show the Discovery Channel documentary about the Jarkov mammoth, called *Raising the Mammoth*, which first aired in March 2000.
- Divide the class into teams to debate whether or not cloning or cross-breeding an extinct species is a good idea.
- As a connection to biology, have students use reference sources to compare and contrast cloning and cross-breeding.

Activity

Encourage students to provide both the time in years and the geologic time periods during which the animals lived. Maps with plate movement can help explain migratory paths. Pictures of native grasses and shrubs can be related to the animals' teeth.

Summary

SECTION 21.1

The Geologic Time Scale

Main Ideas

- Geologists have separated Earth's history into divisions based upon the fossil record.
- The divisions of the geologic time scale, in descending order and decreasing length of time spans, are eons, eras, periods, and epochs.

Vocabulary

eon (p. 554)
epoch (p. 556)
era (p. 554)
geologic time scale (p. 554)
period (p. 555)

SECTION 21.2

Relative Age-Dating of Rocks

Main Ideas

- The principles of uniformitarianism, original horizontality, superposition, and cross-cutting relationships are used to interpret Earth's rock record and, thus, to describe the planet's history.
- Unconformities caused by weathering and erosion or by periods of nondeposition mark missing layers in the rock record.

Vocabulary

correlation (p. 561)
cross-cutting relationships (p. 559)
original horizontality (p. 558)
superposition (p. 558)
unconformity (p. 560)
uniformitarianism (p. 557)

SECTION 21.3

Absolute Age-Dating of Rocks

Main Ideas

- Absolute-age dating measures the actual age of an object such as a mineral, rock, or fossil.
- Radioactive decay is the emission of particles from a radioactive atom. The decay rate can be used to determine the age of a rock or fossil. The time it takes a radioactive element to decay to 50 percent of its original mass is known as its half-life.
- Tree rings and varves can also determine the dates of events and changes in the environment. Volcanic ash and meteorite-impact debris create key beds that mark the time of the event.

Vocabulary

dendrochronology (p. 564)
half-life (p. 563)
key bed (p. 565)
radioactive decay (p. 562)
radiometric dating (p. 562)
varve (p. 565)

SECTION 21.4

Remains of Organisms in the Rock Record

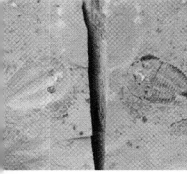

Main Ideas

- The remains and evidence of plants and animals that once lived on Earth are called fossils.
- Fossils preserved in the rock record provide information about past environmental conditions, evolutionary changes in life-forms, and help geologists to correlate rock layers from one area to another.

Vocabulary

altered hard part (p. 567)
cast (p. 568)
evolution (p. 566)
fossil (p. 566)
index fossil (p. 568)
mold (p. 568)
original preservation (p. 566)
permineralization (p. 567)

GLENCOE
Technology

Videotape/DVD
MindJogger Videoquizzes
Chapter 21: *Fossils and the Rock Record*
Have students work in groups as they play the videoquiz game to review key chapter concepts.

Resource Manager

Chapter Assessment, pp. 121–126
MindJogger Videoquizzes DVD/VHS
ExamView® Pro CD-ROM
Performance Assessment in Earth Science

Main Ideas

Summary statements can be used by students to review the major concepts of the chapter.

VOCABULARY PuzzleMaker

For additional help with vocabulary, have students access the Vocabulary Puzzlemaker online.

earthgeu.com/vocabulary_puzzlemaker

0:00 Out of Time?

If time does not permit teaching the entire chapter, use the GeoDigest at the end of the unit as an overview.

Earth Science Online

Be sure to check the Earth Science Web Site for links to chapter material:
earthgeu.com

NY Core Curriculum Standards

Page 572: St 4 KI 1.2i
Page 573: St 4 KI 1.2i & 1.2j

573

Understanding Main Ideas

1. c
2. d
3. d
4. b
5. b
6. b
7. b
8. a
9. c
10. b

Applying Main Ideas

11. Most of the rocks and fossils of the Precambrian have been destroyed as a result of weathering and erosion, mountain-building and deformation, and metamorphism.

12. A crater near the Yucatán Peninsula of Mexico, and a thin layer of sediment that consists of crushed rock and debris from impact. This layer forms a key bed, and has been dated to approximately 66 M.Y.B.P., at the end of the Cretaceous Period.

13. The Cambrian and Ordovician rock layers were overturned as a result of deformation or faulting.

14. No; an unconformity exists because the Permian and Triassic Periods are missing from the rock record.

15. C-14 is the best radioactive isotope to use because of the organic nature of the remains and because C-14 can help determine accurate ages up to about 75 000 years.

16. Both index fossils and key beds record specific times in Earth's history. Their presence helps geologists determine the age and history of a specific rock layer easily and quickly.

Understanding Main Ideas

1. Which geologic principle is used when a geologist observes an outcrop of rocks and determines that the bottom layer is the oldest?
   a. uniformitarianism
   b. original horizontality
   c. superposition
   d. inclusion

2. What is a magma intrusion that cuts across pre-existing rock layers called?
   a. sill   c. fault
   b. lava flow   d. dike

3. Which term does NOT describe a gap in geologic time?
   a. unconformity   c. disconformity
   b. nonconformity   d. key bed

4. Which of the following is NOT a characteristic of an index fossil?
   a. was commonplace while alive
   b. existed for a long period of time
   c. is geographically widespread
   d. is easily recognizable

5. How old is a mammoth's tusk if there is only 25 percent C-14 remaining in the sample?
   a. 5700 years   c. 17 100 years
   b. 11 400 years   d. 22 800 years

6. Trees that have been buried by volcanic ash are preserved in what manner?
   a. original preservation   c. mummification
   b. permineralization   d. recrystallization

7. What feature is formed when a sedimentary rock layer overlies a nonsedimentary rock layer?
   a. unconformity
   b. nonconformity
   c. disconformity
   d. contact metamorphism

8. Based on radioactive elements, what is the calculated age of Earth?
   a. 4.6 billion years   c. 15 billion years
   b. 5 million years   d. 1 million years

9. Which type of fossil forms when an organism's hard parts dissolve and leave a cavity that later fills with sediment?
   a. mold   c. cast
   b. coprolite d. gastrolith

10. What are glacial sediments that show cyclic deposition called?
    a. annual rings   c. tillites
    b. varves   d. unconformities

Applying Main Ideas

11. Why is it difficult to interpret the rock record of Precambrian Time?

12. What evidence is preserved to indicate that a large meteorite impact occurred at the end of the Mesozoic?

13. How would you explain a horizontal sedimentary rock layer containing Cambrian fossils lying on top of a rock layer containing Ordovician fossils?

14. Does an outcrop containing Jurassic dinosaur fossils overlying Pennsylvanian coal deposits represent uninterrupted deposition? Explain.

Test-Taking Tip

WRITE IT DOWN! Most tests ask you a large number of questions in a small amount of time. Write down your work wherever possible. Do math on paper, not in your head. Underline and reread important facts in passages and diagrams—don't try to memorize them.

earthgeu.com/chapter_test

Standardized Test Practice

1. d
2. b
3. c
4. b

15. What radioactive isotope would be best for determining the age of prehistoric human remains?

16. How is an index fossil like a key bed?

Thinking Critically

Use the diagram below to answer questions 17–23.

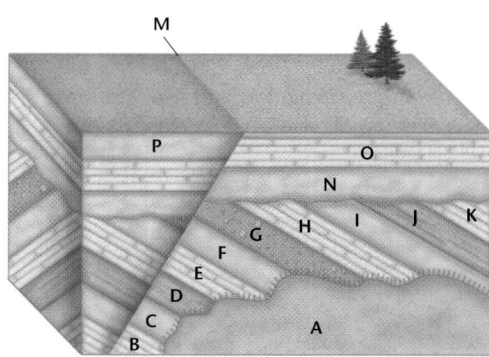

17. Which is the oldest rock unit in the diagram?

18. What has happened to the sedimentary rocks since they were first deposited?

19. Which is the youngest feature in the diagram, the fault or Layer P? Explain.

20. An unconformity exists between which two layers of rock? Explain your answer.

21. Why is rock unit P thicker on the left side of the diagram than on the right side?

22. Explain why the rock layers and features on the left side of the diagram do not match the rock layers and features on the right side.

23. List the order of geologic events represented in the diagram. List the principles you used to place the structures in order from oldest to youngest.

earthgeu.com/standardized_test

Standardized Test Practice

1. Which of the following constitutes the fewest number of years?
- **a.** eon
- **b.** era
- **c.** period
- **d.** epoch

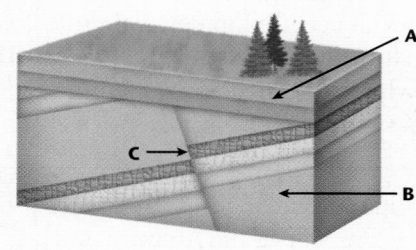

INTERPRETING SCIENTIFIC ILLUSTRATIONS
Use the diagram of the rock region above to answer questions 2 and 3.

2. Which principle for determining relative age is relevant to point A of this diagram of a rock region?
- **a.** The principle of original horizontality.
- **b.** The principle of superposition.
- **c.** The principle of cross-cutting relationships.
- **d.** The principle of uniformitarianism.

3. Which principle is relevant to point C of the diagram?
- **a.** The principle of original horizontality.
- **b.** The principle of superposition.
- **c.** The principle of cross-cutting relationships.
- **d.** The principle of uniformitarianism.

4. In which of the following do original structures of an organism remain?
- **a.** mold fossil
- **b.** permineralized fossil
- **c.** cast fossil
- **d.** all of the above

Assessment **575**

Thinking Critically

17. layer B

18. Layers B through L have been uplifted, tilted, and eroded.

19. The fault is the youngest feature because it cuts across layer P.

20. As a result of uplift, erosion, and deposition, angular unconformities exist between layers E through L and layer N; and nonconformities exist between intrusion A and layers B through I.

21. The rock unit P on the left side is thicker because of differences in deposition of sediment at different places in the prehistoric environment.

22. The left side of the outcrop has moved down relative to the right side of the outcrop as a result of faulting. This resulted in the offset of the layers.

23. From oldest to youngest:
1. layers B–L were deposited
2. igneous intrusion A was injected, resulting in uplift and erosion of layers B–L and contact metamorphism in layers B–I
3. deposition of layers N, O, and P
4. normal fault M, resulting in offset of all the layers; principles of superposition, cross-cutting relationships, and original horizontality

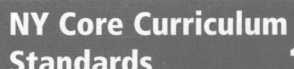

NY Core Curriculum Standards

Page 574: St 4 KI 1.2i & 1.2j
Page 575: St 4 KI 1.2i & 1.2j

The Precambrian Earth

Refer to pages 8T–9T of the Teacher Guide for an explanation of the National Science Content Standards correlations.

Section	Objectives	National Science Content Standards	State/Local Standards
SECTION 22.1 **The Early Earth** 🕐 ½ session 🧊 ¼ block	1. **Describe** the evidence used to determine the age of Earth. 2. **Understand** why scientists theorize that the early Earth was hot.	UCP.2; B.2, B.6; C.3; D.1, D.2, D.3	St 1 Science KI 1, 2, & 3, St 4 KI 1.2d, 1.2e, 1.2f, 1.2h, 1.2i, 1.2j, & 2.1a, St 6 KI 2 & 3
SECTION 22.2 **Formation of the Crust and Continents** 🕐 1 session 🧊 ½ block	3. **Explain** the origin of Earth's crust. 4. **Describe** the formation of the Archean and Proterozoic continents.	D.1, D.2, D.3	St 4 KI 1.2j, 2.1a, 2.1b, 2.1k, 2.1l, 2.1m, 2.1n, 2.1o, & 2.1p
SECTION 22.3 **Formation of the Atmosphere and Oceans** 🕐 ½ session 🧊 ¼ block	5. **Describe** the formation of Earth's atmosphere and oceans. 6. **Identify** the origin of oxygen in the atmosphere. 7. **Explain** the evidence that oxygen existed in the atmosphere during the Proterozoic.	UCP.2; B.3, B.6; C.3; D.1, D.2, D.3	St 1 Math KI 2 & 3, St 4 KI 1.2e, 1.2f, 1.2g, 1.2h, 1.2i, 1.2j, & 2.2c, St 6 KI 2 & 3
SECTION 22.4 **Early Life on Earth** 🕐 2 sessions 🧊 1 block	8. **Describe** the experimental evidence of how life developed on Earth. 9. **Distinguish** between prokaryotes and eukaryotes. 10. **Identify** when the first multicellular animals appeared in geologic time.	UCP.2, UCP.3; B.2, B.3; C.3; D.1, D.2, D.3; E.1, E.2; G.1, G.2, G.3	St 1 Science KI 3 & Math KI 3, St 4 KI 1.2c, d, e, f, h, i, j, 2.1a, 2.1b, 2.1k, 2.1l, 2.1m, 2.1n, & 2.1p, St 6 KI 2 & 3

A complete Planning Guide is provided on pages 30T–32T.

🕐 The number of recommended single-period sessions

🧊 The number of recommended blocks

Activity Materials

Discovery Lab *page 577*
250-mL beaker, dark food coloring, vegetable oil (175 mL), water, stirring rod, dropper

GeoLab *pages 594–595*
paper, pencil, colored pencils, metric ruler

MiniLab *page 587*
150-mL beaker, 50-mL graduated cylinder, water, household bleach, white sand, steel wool, watch glass, spoon or spatula, water

Demo *page 577*
blocks (25)

Key to Teaching Strategies

L1 Level 1 activities should be appropriate for students with learning difficulties.

L2 Level 2 activities should be within the ability range of all students.

L3 Level 3 activities are designed for above-average students.

ELL ELL activities should be within the ability range of English-language learners.

COOP LEARN Cooperative learning activities are designed for small-group work.

P These strategies represent student products that can be placed in a best-work portfolio.

🧊 These strategies are useful in a block-scheduling format.

Need materials? Contact Science Kit at 1-800-828-7777 or at www.sciencekit.com on the Internet. For alternate materials, see the activity on the listed page.

Chapter Organizer

Glencoe Exclusive!
Teacher Works™
All-In-One Planner and Resource Center

Activities/Features	Reproducible Masters	Transparencies
Discovery Lab: Density Separation, p. 577	**Study Guide for Content Mastery** p. 137 L2	**Section Focus Transparency 67** L1 ELL **Teaching Transparency 66** L2 ELL
	Study Guide for Content Mastery pp. 138–139 L2 **Laboratory Manual,** pp. 169–172 L2	**Section Focus Transparency 68** L1 ELL **Teaching Transparency 67** L2 ELL
Problem-Solving Lab: Calculate Mining Costs, p. 586 **MiniLab:** Why are red beds red?, p. 587	**Study Guide for Content Mastery** p. 140 L2 **Laboratory Manual,** pp. 173–176 L2 **GeoLab and MiniLab Worksheets,** p. 87 L2	**Section Focus Transparency 69** L1 ELL **Teaching Transparency 68** L2 ELL
Using Math: Using Numbers, p. 590 **GeoLab:** pp. 594–595 **Science in the News:** Martians or Meteorites? p. 596	**Study Guide for Content Mastery** pp. 141–142 L2 **GeoLab and MiniLab Worksheets,** pp. 88–90 L2	**Section Focus Transparency 70** L1 ELL

✔Assessment

Chapter Assessment, pp. 127–132
Performance Assessment in the Science Classroom (PASC)
MindJogger Videoquiz DVD/VHS
Performance Assessment in Earth Science
ExamView® Pro CD-ROM
5 Days to the Regents Exam

GLENCOE'S
ASSESSMENT
ADVANTAGE

Additional Resources

Guided Reading Audio Program ELL
Cooperative Learning in the Science Classroom COOP LEARN
Lesson Plans
Block Scheduling
earthgeu.com
NY Lesson Plans
NY Block Scheduling
Review Handbook for Regents Earth Science Exam

NATIONAL GEOGRAPHIC

Teacher's Corner

Products Available from National Geographic Society
To order the following products, call the National Geographic Society at 1-800-368-2728:
Curriculum Kits
GeoKit: *Earth's History*
GeoKit: *Oceans*

CD-ROM
111 Years of National Geographic Magazine
Video
Earth Alive
Fossils: Clues to the Past

Content Background

The Early Earth
Section 22.1

It is theorized that Earth formed at approximately the same time as the Sun and the planets in the solar system. As gas and solid particles collided, they combined to form larger masses called planetesimals. The further combination of planetesimals formed the planets. Some estimates suggest that a planet the size of Earth could form from planetesimals in as little as 1 million years.

A meteoroid and asteroid belt exists between Mars and Jupiter. Where did these asteroids and meteoroids come from? There are presently two well-supported hypotheses. The first is that they represent the remnants of a planet that was between Mars and Jupiter. The second hypothesis is that the huge gravitational field of Jupiter prevented the formation of a planet in the main belt of asteroids between Mars and Jupiter.

In this scenario, asteroids and meteoroids represent planetesimals, which because of the influence of the giant planet Jupiter, were never able to accrete together to form a planet. This second hypothesis is most widely accepted by planetary geologists today.

Greenstone Belts
Section 22.2

Shield areas often contain bodies of deformed rocks called greenstone belts. Nearly half of the rocks in the Superior and Slave Provinces of the Canadian Shield are comprised of greenstone belts. These rocks formed between 2.7 and 2.5 billion years ago. Greenstone belts typically consist of three layers. The two bottom layers are volcanic and the upper layer is sedimentary. Faulting, folding, and granitic intrusions have deformed these layers into discontinuous bands or belts. Low-grade metamorphism has produced the green mineral chlorite, which colors the volcanic rocks green. This is why geologists call them greenstone belts.

Our Changing Atmosphere
Section 22.3

Scientists use some of the oldest-known rocks on Earth to learn details about the evolution of oxygen and ozone in Earth's early atmosphere. These two key ingredients permitted and record the expansion of life. Precambrian sediments reveal a profound change in the chemical reactions involving sulfur and oxygen in the atmosphere. These reactions began before 2.5 B.Y.B.P. and continued to about 2.1 B.Y.B.P. They coincide with a time during which the oxygen levels in the atmosphere are known to have increased sharply.

Other gases have changed in their abundance in the atmosphere through geologic time as well. For example, Argon (Ar) gas represents 0.93% of the gas by volume in our atmosphere today, but we know that it was not always that way. The Ar that is present in today's

Multiple Learning Styles

 Visual-Spatial Demo, p. 581

 Interpersonal Collaborative Learning, p. 585, Activity, p. 589

 Linguistic Reteach, pp. 579, 583, 588, Enrichment, p. 584

GLENCOE Technology

The following multimedia resources are available from Glencoe.

Vocabulary Puzzlemaker

TeacherWorks™ CD-ROM

MindJogger Videoquizzes DVD/VHS

ExamView® Pro CD-ROM

Interactive Chalkboard Pro CD-ROM

atmosphere began to accumulate during the Early Precambrian. It forms when the radioactive isotope K-40 decays to Ar-40. Through this reaction, the amount of Ar has increased in the atmosphere at about the same rate that K-40 decays.

Origin of Eukaryotic Cells
Section 22.4

Fossils of prokaryotes are found in rocks older than rocks in which the fossils of eukaryotes are found. However, this order does not tell us how the evolution from a prokaryotic state to a eukaryotic state occurred. The most widely accepted theory held today is that this evolution resulted from the symbiosis of several different kinds of prokaryotic cells. Mutualism—a form of symbiosis—is a relationship between dissimilar organisms in which both partners benefit. Lichens, which were once thought to be plants, are a modern example of symbiosis between fungi and algae. Evolutionary paleobiologists hypothesize that two or more prokaryotes may have entered into a symbiotic relationship and, over time, the symbionts became so interdependent that they could no longer survive independently. The theory of endosymbiosis suggests that several prokaryotes developed symbiotic relationships, and that some eukaryote organelles, such as mitochondria and plastids, are actually the distant descendants of once free-living prokaryotic organisms.

Identifying Misconceptions

We have a tendency to think that the continents that exist today formed early in Earth's history. This is not exactly true. The crust that forms the cores of modern continents formed throughout the Archean. These ancient cores of the modern continents, called shields, are themselves mosaics of smaller pieces of ancient crust. Throughout Earth's history, these shields have accumulated younger rocks around their margins and have been in many different configurations. Sometimes, the continents have been all together in one great mass, and at other times, the continents have been separated into many more continental masses than exist today.

✔ Assessment

Portfolio Assessment
Assessment, TWE, pp. 583, 588, 593

Performance Assessment
MiniLab, TWE, p. 587
GeoLab, TWE, pp. 594–595
GeoLab, SE, pp. 594–595
Discovery Lab, SE, p. 577
MiniLab, SE, p. 587

Knowledge Assessment
Discovery Lab, TWE, p. 577
Assessment, TWE, p. 581

Section Assessment, SE, pp. 579, 583, 588, 593
Chapter Assessment, SE, p. 598–599

Skill Assessment
Assessment, TWE, p. 579
Problem-Solving Lab, TWE, p. 586

To find out more about the planet on which you live, visit the Earth Science Web Site at earthgeu.com

The Precambrian Earth

Introducing the Chapter

Ask students, "How old is Earth?" Have students write down their answers. This is their hypothesis of the age of Earth. Divide students into groups based on their answers about the age of Earth. From general observations that students have made throughout their lives, have them test their hypotheses about the age of Earth. Have some groups of students design ways to test their hypotheses as if it were 1750 and others with the resources available today.

Interpreting the Illustration

Based on the illustration, have students list features that are the same and those that are different from today's Earth. Same: active volcanoes, bodies of water, hot springs, and blue sky. Different: Widespread stromatolites, and no vegetation on land.

INTERACTIVE CHALKBOARD
with Image Bank

PowerPoint® Presentations

This CD is an editable Microsoft® PowerPoint® presentation that includes:
- Section presentations
- Section checks
- Image bank
- Links to Earth Science Online
- All transparencies
- Animations
- Audio

The Precambrian Earth

What You'll Learn
- How the age of Earth is determined.
- How the continents, atmosphere, and oceans formed.
- When life first appeared on Earth.
- What kinds of organisms populated the Precambrian Earth.

Why It's important

Most of Earth's history occurred during the Precambrian. During this time, the crust, atmosphere and oceans formed and life first appeared. Early life-forms produced oxygen through photosynthesis, and, thus, changed the atmosphere and the history of life on Earth.

Earth Science Online

To find out more about Precambrian Earth, visit the Earth Science Web Site at earthgeu.com

576

The Precambrian Earth

Discovery Lab

Process Skills

observe and infer, recognize cause and effect, communicate, model, predict L1 ELL

Safety Precautions

Caution students to handle the beaker with care. The contents of the beaker will stain clothing. Have students pour the contents of the beaker into a container that you provide.

Procedure
Troubleshooting

Any oil, including motor oil, can be used. The food coloring is optional, but it does help increase the contrast if a light colored oil is used. Pour the oil into the water slowly to avoid causing large bubbles to form. Bubbles can be popped with a toothpick if necessary.

Observe

The oil will float on the water because it is less dense. The average density of continental crust is 2.7 g/cm³ and 3.0 g/cm³ for oceanic crust. The average density of the mantle is about 3.3–5.7 g/cm³

Discovery Lab
Density Separation

Earth's core, mantle, and crust have different average densities. The core is the densest, and the crust is the least dense. Scientists hypothesize that when Earth formed, temperatures were hot enough for the materials that make up Earth to act, in part, like a liquid and flow. In this activity, you will model how liquids of different densities react when they are mixed together.

1. Fill a 250-mL beaker with 50 mL of tap water.

2. Add 2–3 drops of dark food coloring to the water.

3. Poor 175 mL of vegetable oil into the beaker and stir the contents.

CAUTION: *Always wear safety goggles and an apron in the lab.*

Observe In your science journal, describe what happened to the colored water and vegetable oil in the beaker. Explain how this is similar to what happened to the core and mantle when Earth formed.

SECTION 22.1 — *The Early Earth*

OBJECTIVES

- **Describe** *the evidence used to determine the age of Earth.*

- **Understand** *why scientists theorize that the early Earth was hot.*

VOCABULARY

zircon
asteroid
meteorite

For most of Earth's history, there was nothing like the plants and animals that exist today. In Chapter 21, you learned about the geologic time scale and how Earth's history is divided into time periods. In this chapter, you will learn about the earliest part of the geologic time scale, the Precambrian.

EARTH'S "BIRTH"

For about the first 4 billion years of Earth's 4.6-billion-year existence, most of the life-forms that inhabited Earth were unicellular organisms. What evidence did these organisms leave of their existence? What was Earth like when these organisms lived? How did Earth change during the Precambrian? How did these changes set the stage for the animal life that exists today? Answers to these questions not only help us to understand the history of Earth, but they also serve as a model for the search for life on other planets. In 1996, the announcement that a meteorite from Mars might contain microscopic fossils of bacteria rekindled scientific interest in the search for life elsewhere in the universe. You can read more about this meteorite in this chapter's *Science in the News* feature. It may be possible to

22.1 *The Early Earth* **577**

---

and 10–13 g/cm³ for the core. These density differences are a result of differences in composition (just as the compositions of water and oil are different) and differences in temperature and pressure.

✓Assessment

Knowledge Be sure students understand that the reason for the separation of the liquids is a result of compositional differences. Ask students to recall the compositions of the mantle and the core, and be sure they recognize that the mantle and core differ in composition.

Resource Manager

Section Focus Transparency 67 L1 ELL

Teaching Transparency 66 L2 ELL

Study Guide for Content Mastery, p. 137 L2

Section 22.1

1 Focus

Section Focus

Before presenting the lesson, display **Section Focus Transparency 67** on the overhead projector.
L1 ELL

Chapter Themes

The following themes from the National Science Content Standards are covered in this chapter. Refer to page 8T of the Teacher Guide for an explanation of the correlations.
Evidence, models, and explanation (UCP.2); Change, constancy, and measurement (UCP.3); Evolution and equilibrium (UCP.4)

0:00 Out of Time?

If time does not permit teaching the entire chapter, use the Chapter Summary on page 597 and the GeoDigest found at the end of the unit as an overview.

Tying to Previous Knowledge

There are numerous radioactive isotopes. Many of them, however, have relatively short half-lives. The radioactive isotopes that are useful for dating Precambrian rocks, and that contributed most to the internal heat of Earth, are those that are relatively abundant, have long decay series, and, long half-lives such as uranium and thorium.

Using an Analogy

Using the oldest rocks to date the age of Earth is like using the age of a person's oldest pair of shoes to determine how old the person is. You know that the person is at least as old as the shoes. You also know that shoes wear over time, and that the person is older than his or her shoes. The rocks that form Earth's crust also wear with time through the process of erosion. If there are minerals in a rock that are older than the oldest rocks on Earth, then Earth must be at least as old as the oldest mineral, not just the oldest rock.

Content Background

Lord Kelvin thought that the originally molten Earth had cooled over time to its current temperature. Using the size of Earth, and a geothermal gradient of 30 degrees per km, he reasoned that for Earth to have cooled to its present temperature, it must be 20 to 30 million years old. His reasoning was sound, but it had one major flaw that Kelvin did not know about. Radioactivity was discovered in 1896. Radioactivity was adding heat to Earth throughout Earth's history. Earth's cooling was not a simple closed system.

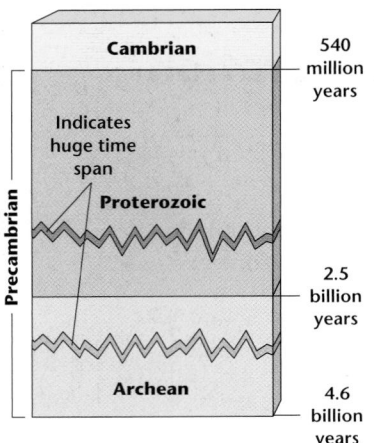

Figure 22-1 Most of Earth's history is contained within the 4 billion years that make up the Precambrian.

identify clues to the possible existence of life on other planets, even if rocks from those planets are the only evidence we have. After all, rocks are all that we have left of the Precambrian Earth, and as you will learn, there is evidence of life's humble beginnings on Earth in Precambrian rocks. The Precambrian portion of the geologic time scale is shown in *Figure 22-1.*

HOW OLD IS EARTH?

We know that Earth must be at least as old as the oldest rocks in the crust. Radiometric dating has determined that the age of the oldest rocks on Earth is between 3.96 to 3.8 billion years. But the rocks that form Earth's crust have been eroded over time. Evidence of 4.1- to 4.2-billion-year-old crust exists in the mineral zircon that is contained in metamorphosed sedimentary rocks in Australia. **Zircon** is a very stable mineral that commonly occurs in small amounts in granite. Radiometric dating has determined that the zircon grains in these sedimentary rocks are between 4.1 and 4.2 billion years old. The zircon existed before it became cemented into the sedimentary rocks, and scientists theorize that the zircon is the eroded residue left behind from 4.1- to 4.2-billion-year-old granitic crustal rocks. Based on this evidence, Earth must be at least 4.2 billion years old.

Meteorites, such as the one shown in *Figure 22-2,* have been radiometrically dated at between 4.5 and 4.7 billion years old. Most astronomers agree that the solar system, including Earth, formed at the same time, and therefore, Earth and meteorites should be about the same age. In addition, the oldest rock samples from the Moon, collected during the Apollo missions, are approximately 4.6 billion years old. Thus, taking all of the evidence into consideration, scientists commonly agree that the age of Earth is 4.6 billion years.

EARTH'S HEAT SOURCES

Earth was most likely extremely hot shortly after it formed, and there were three likely sources of this heat. The first source was radioactivity. Radioactive isotopes were more abundant during the past because, over time, radioactive decay has reduced the original amount of Earth's radioactive isotopes. One product of radioactive decay is energy, which generates heat. Much of Earth's current internal heat is attributed to the energy released by radioactivity. Because there were more radioactive isotopes in Earth's distant past, scientists infer that more heat was being generated then and that Earth was hotter.

The second source of Earth's heat was the impact of asteroids and meteorites. **Asteroids** are metallic or silica-rich objects that are

Interpreting the Illustration

Figure 22-1 represents the earliest part of the geologic time scale. Have students determine what percentage of Earth's history is represented by the Archean and what percentage is represented by the Proterozoic.

Differentiated Instruction

Behaviorally Disordered To engage students with behavioral disorders in section content, assign them the task of finding additional information about the age of meteorites and Moon rocks. Have students gather visual and written data from the library and from the Earth Science Web Site at <u>earthgeu.com</u>.

1 km to 950 km in diameter. Today, most asteroids orbit the Sun between the orbit of Mars and Jupiter. Meteoroids are small asteroids or fragments of asteroids. When meteoroids fall to Earth, we call them **meteorites.** Evidence from the surfaces of the Moon and other planets suggests that there were many more meteoroids and asteroids distributed throughout the early solar system than there are today, and therefore collisions were much more common. For this reason, scientists infer that for the first 500 to 700 million years of Earth's history, bombardment by meteorites and asteroids was common. These impacts generated a tremendous amount of thermal energy.

The third source of Earth's heat was gravitational contraction. As a result of meteor bombardment and the subsequent accumulation of meteorite material on Earth, the size of Earth increased. The weight of the material caused gravitational contraction of the underlying zones. The energy of the contraction was converted to thermal energy. The new material also caused a blanketing effect, which prevented the newly generated heat from escaping.

The combined effects of radioactive decay, meteorite and asteroid bombardment, and gravitational contraction made a hot and rather inhospitable beginning for Earth. However, cooling and subsequent crystallization laid the foundation for Earth's crust to form and prepared Earth for the next phase in its development.

Figure 22-2 This 10 000-year-old, 16-ton meteorite was found in Oregon on the tribal lands of the Willamette Native Americans.

SECTION ASSESSMENT

1. What is the age of Earth?
2. Describe the evidence used to determine the age of Earth.
3. How is zircon used to date igneous rocks?
4. Which of Earth's early sources of heat are not major contributors to Earth's present-day internal heat?
5. **Thinking Critically** If most astronomers hypothesize that the solar system formed all at once, why is it important that we use the age of the oldest rocks on Earth to determine the age of Earth rather than using only the age of meteorites?

SKILL REVIEW

6. **Comparing and Contrasting** Compare and contrast Earth's three early sources of heat. For more help, refer to the *Skill Handbook*.

earthgeu.com/self_check_quiz

22.1 *The Early Earth* **579**

SECTION ASSESSMENT

1. Earth is 4.6 billion years old.
2. The ages of the oldest rocks at Earth's surface, the oldest zircons in sedimentary rocks, moon rocks, and meteorites are used.
3. Zircon is radiometrically age-dated.
4. bombardment by meteorites
5. If any rocks on Earth or the Moon were older than meteorites, scientists would have to reject the hypothesis that meteorites represent material formed when the solar system formed or that the solar system formed all at once.

Because no rocks on Earth or the Moon are older than meteorites, the hypothesis is supported.
6. Decay of radioactive isotopes and the generation of heat; asteroid and meteorite impact and the generation of heat through thermal energy; gravitational contraction and generation of thermal energy and heat.

3 Assess

Check for Understanding
Discussion
Ask students why geologists theorize that Earth is 4.6 billion years old. This age predates the age of the oldest rocks on Earth's surface and corresponds to the ages of rocks from the Moon and meteorites, both of which are thought to have formed at nearly the same time as Earth.

Reteach
Linguistic Have students make data tables in their science journals of the sources of the early Earth's heat and identify whether the heat source was internal or external. L2

✔ Assessment

Skill Have students create concept maps to illustrate the age of Earth using the following dates and concepts: oldest rocks on Earth, 3.8–3.96 billion years; oldest minerals on Earth, 4.1–4.2 billion years; meteorites, 4.5–4.7 billion years; Moon rocks, 4.6 billion years; Earth and solar system formed at about the same time, age of Earth must be about 4.6 billion years.

NY Core Curriculum Standards

Page 576: St 4 KI 1.2k, 1.2m, 2.1h, & 2.1i
Page 577: St 1 Science KI 1, 2, & 3, St 4 KI 1.2i & 1.2j, St 6 KI 2 & 3
Page 578: St 4 KI 1.2j & 2.1a, St 6 KI 2
Page 579: St 4 KI 1.2d

579

Section Background

For section content background, refer to **Greenstone Belts** on page 576C.

Preplanning

Refer to the Chapter Organizer on pages 576A–B.

1 Focus

Section Focus

Before presenting the lesson, display **Section Focus Transparency 68** on the overhead projector.
L1 **ELL**

Tying to Previous Knowledge

Earth's crust and mantle are made of different minerals. List the minerals of Bowen's reaction series on the chalkboard. Have students determine which minerals from Bowen's reaction series are more common in the crust and in the mantle. The denser minerals such as olivine, pyroxene, and Ca-plagioclase are common in the mantle. All of the other minerals are intermediate or felsic, and are more common in the crust.

 SECTION 22.2

Formation of the Crust and Continents

OBJECTIVES

• **Explain** the origin of Earth's crust.

• **Describe** the formation of the Archean and Proterozoic continents.

VOCABULARY

differentiation
Precambrian shield
Canadian Shield
microcontinent
Laurentia

Were continents always present on Earth's surface? Early in the formation of Earth, the planet was molten, and numerous elements and minerals were mixed throughout the magma. Over time, the minerals became concentrated in specific zones and Earth became layered. As the magma reached the surface and cooled, landmasses began to form.

FORMATION OF THE CRUST

When Earth formed, iron and nickel, which are dense elements, concentrated in its core. Minerals with low densities tend to crystallize from magma at cooler temperatures than denser minerals do. Therefore, near the surface of Earth, where it is cooler, the rocks are generally composed of a high proportion of the less-dense minerals. For example, granite is common at Earth's surface. Granite is mainly composed of feldspar, quartz, and mica, which, as you learned in Chapter 4, are minerals with low densities. Lava flowing from the hot and partly molten interior of Earth concentrated the less-dense minerals near the surface of Earth over time. In contrast, the denser minerals, which crystallize at higher temperatures, concentrated deeper within Earth and formed the rocks that make up Earth's mantle. The process by which a planet becomes internally zoned when heavy materials sink toward its center and lighter materials accumulate near its surface is called **differentiation.** The differentiated zones of Earth are illustrated in *Figure 22-3.*

Geologists hypothesize that Earth's earliest crust formed as a result of the cooling of the uppermost mantle. Thus, the crust likely consisted of iron and magnesium-rich minerals similar to those found in basalt. As these minerals weathered, they formed sediments that covered the early crust. Geologists also hypothesize that as sediment-covered slabs of the crust were recycled into the mantle at subduction zones, the slabs partly melted and generated magmas with different mineral compositions. These magmas crystallized to form the first granitic continental crust, which was rich in feldspar, quartz, and mica. The formation of

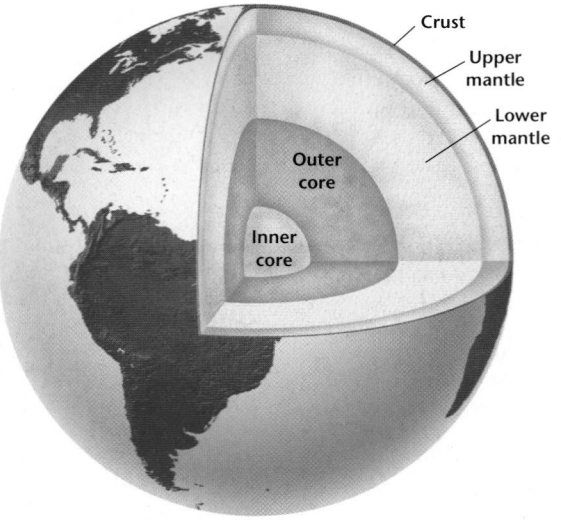

Figure 22-3 Earth's layers formed as a result of differentiation. The density of the minerals found within each layer decreases toward the crust.

Resource Manager

Section Focus Transparency 68 **L1** **ELL**

Teaching Transparency 67 **L2** **ELL**

Study Guide for Content Mastery, pp. 138–139 **L2**

Laboratory Manual, pp. 169–172 **L2**

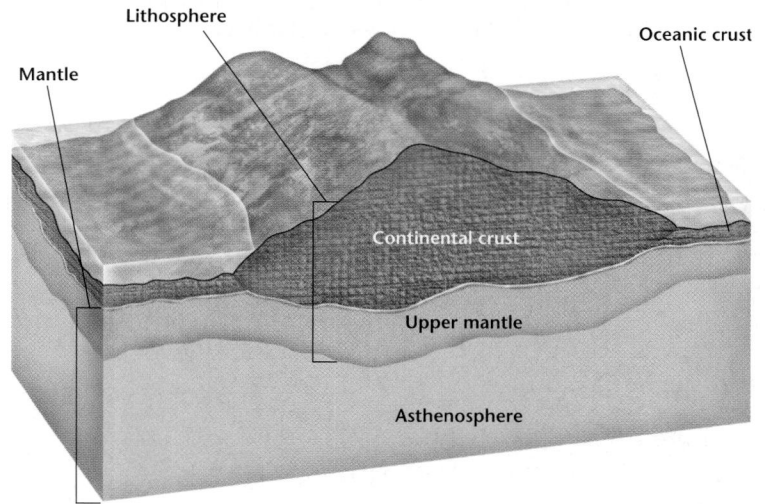

Lithosphere

Mantle

Oceanic crust

Continental crust

Upper mantle

Asthenosphere

Figure 22-4 The difference in density between the heavier ocean crust and the lighter continental crust allows the continental crust to float higher on the mantle, even when its thickness is greater.

granitic crust was a slow process. Most geologists hypothesize that the formation of the majority of crustal rocks that make up the low-density, granitic cores of continents was completed by about 2.5 billion years ago. The rocks of the earliest crust no longer exist because they were recycled in subduction zones long ago.

Less-dense material has a tendency to float on more-dense material. In the *Discovery Lab* at the beginning of this chapter, you observed that oil floats on top of water. This happens because oil is less dense than water. For this same reason, continental crust "floats" on top of the mantle below it. In addition, basaltic crust is more dense than granitic crust, and therefore, it does not float as high on the mantle as granitic, continental crust does. This difference in density is what causes the basaltic ocean floor to be lower in elevation than the less-dense granitic continental crust, as illustrated in *Figure 22-4.*

THE CORES OF THE CONTINENTS

Today's continents each contain a core of Archean and Proterozoic rock called a **Precambrian shield.** In some areas, the Precambrian shields are exposed at the surface, whereas in other areas, younger sedimentary rocks bury them. The buried and exposed parts of a shield together compose the craton, which is the stable part of a continent. In North America, the Precambrian shield is called the **Canadian Shield** because much of it is exposed in Canada. As shown in *Figure 22-5* on page 582, the Canadian Shield is also exposed in the northern parts of Minnesota, Wisconsin, and Michigan; in the Adirondack Mountains of New York; and over a large part of Greenland.

22.2 *Formation of the Crust and Continents* **581**

2 Teach

Content Background

Since Earth formed 4.6 billion years ago, it has undergone significant changes. Earth's interior differentiated into an inner and outer core, mantle, and crust. Earth has remained dynamic from the beginning. The continents have been moving across Earth's surface, coming together to form supercontinents, only to rift apart again. The crust formed as a result of the cooling of Earth's surface. Convection of the hot rock beneath this surface set plate tectonics in motion. Recycling of the crust concentrated the less dense, felsic minerals into the continental masses during the Precambrian.

✓ Assessment

Knowledge Ask students why the mantle is less dense than the core. The mantle is less dense because the denser material of the core concentrated at Earth's center through the process of differentiation.

Interpreting the Illustration

Figure 22-4 The oceanic crust is topographically lower than the continental crust. This is because the continental crust is less dense. Even in areas where the continental crust is substantially thicker than the oceanic crust, such as at a mountain chain, the continental crust will still float higher than the oceanic crust.

Demo

Visual-Spatial Heat a can of clam chowder (strain the clams and potatoes first if you like). Let the soup cool during the class period. Ask students to describe how and why the crust forms on the top of the soup. Have students relate this to the formation of an early crust on Earth. Have students think about the thickness of the soup crust relative to the soup and the thickness of Earth's crust relative to the mantle and core. In both cases, the crust is quite thin compared to the overall thickness.

NY Core Curriculum Standards

Page 580: St 4 KI 2.1a, 2.1b, 2.1k, & 2.1m

Page 581: St 4 KI 1.2j, 2.1b, 2.1k, 2.1l, & 2.1o

Interpreting the Illustration

Figure 22-5 Laurentia was positioned across the equator during the Late Precambrian and Early Cambrian. The rocks that were deposited on Laurentia would have been sedimentary, shallow sea deposits such as limestones, shales, and sandstones. Hurricanes were likely common then, as they are now, in equatorially positioned areas. The sediments would have shown the results of high-energy waves and wind. Evidence of strong storms can be seen in the large boulders and coarse gravel that make up sedimentary features of Cambrian age in parts of Wisconsin.

Figure 22-5 The oldest rocks in North America are found in the Precambrian shield rocks in Canada. They were the first-formed rocks of the North American continent.

The Precambrian Shield in North America

☐ Canadian shield-exposed and covered rocks

▨ Belts of folded strata

■ Stable platforms

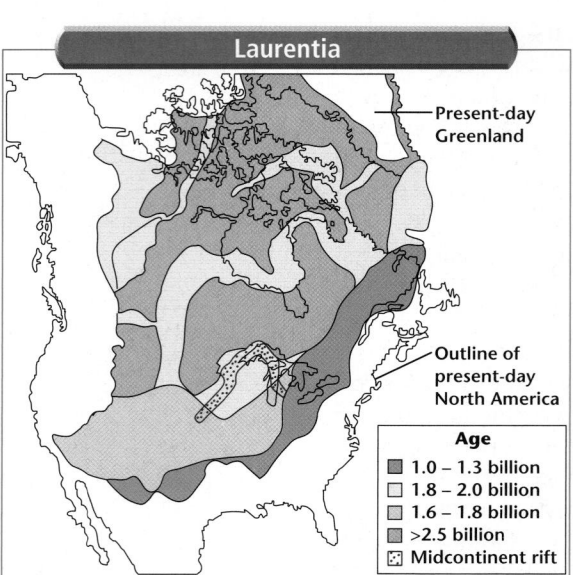

Laurentia

— Present-day Greenland

— Outline of present-day North America

Age
- ■ 1.0 – 1.3 billion
- ☐ 1.8 – 2.0 billion
- ☐ 1.6 – 1.8 billion
- ▨ >2.5 billion
- ▨ Midcontinent rift

Figure 22-6 From the beginning of its formation, the continent of Laurentia resembled the familiar shape of present-day North America.

GROWTH OF CONTINENTS

Early during the Proterozoic, small pieces of continental crust, called **microcontinents,** that formed during the Archean began to collide as a result of plate tectonics. The impact of the collisions jammed the microcontinents together, and they became larger continents. At each of these collision sites, the Archean microcontinents were sutured or fused together at orogens. These orogens are belts of rocks that were deformed by the immense energy of the colliding continents. The resulting mountain ranges have been deeply eroded since that time. By about 1.8 billion years ago, the core of modern-day North America had been assembled; it formed the ancient continent known as **Laurentia,** as shown in *Figure 22-6.* You will explore the technique of interpreting continental growth in the *Mapping GeoLab* at the end of this chapter.

Differentiated Instruction

English-Language Learners Have students whose second language is English use the library or the Earth Science Web Site to find the names of the igneous minerals (quartz, muscovite, potassium feldspar, plagioclase feldspar, biotite, amphibole, pyroxene, and olivine) in their native language. They will likely be surprised by the similarity to the English names.

Project

Have students determine where the closest Precambrian rocks are to your area. If you live in an area that is underlain by the Precambrian Shield, have students determine what province of the Precambrian Shield underlies your area.

Near the end of the Early Proterozoic, between 1.8 and 1.6 billion years ago, volcanic island arcs collided with the southern margin of Laurentia. This added more than 1000 km of continental crust to southern Laurentia. The final phase of Proterozoic growth of Laurentia is called the Grenville Orogeny. Recall that an orogeny is a mountain-building event. The Grenville Orogeny occurred between 1.2 billion and 900 million years ago and added a considerable amount of continental crust to the southern and eastern margins of Laurentia. Also by the end of the Proterozoic, nearly 75 percent of present-day North America had formed. The remaining 25 percent, as you will learn in Chapter 24, was added to the eastern and western margins of the North American craton during the Phanerozoic.

By the end of the Proterozoic, all of the major masses of continental lithosphere had formed on Earth. The lithospheric plates were moving around, periodically colliding with each other and suturing together. By the end of the Proterozoic, so many of these collisions had occurred that Rodinia, the first supercontinent, had formed. It was positioned so that the equator ran through Laurentia, as shown in *Figure 22-7*. Rodinia began to break apart at the end of the Proterozoic and continued to do so during the Early Phanerozoic. During this time, Earth also acquired an atmosphere and oceans. You will learn how they formed in the next section.

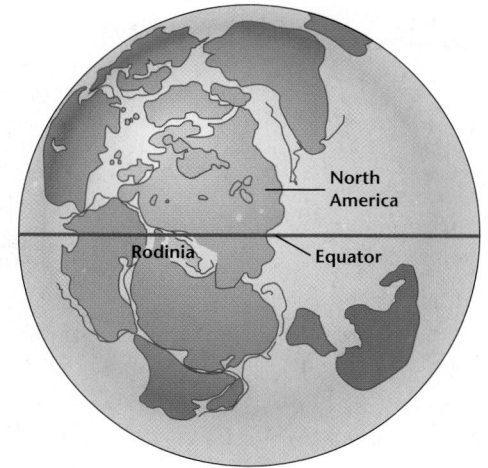

750 million years ago

Figure 22-7 Rodinia was the first supercontinent to form on Earth's surface. Similar rock types in eastern North America and western Africa are evidence of its existence.

SECTION ASSESSMENT

1. Describe the origin of Earth's crust.
2. How did the Archean and Proterozoic continents form?
3. How does a planet become internally zoned?
4. **Thinking Critically** The oceans are underlain by basaltic crust, and the continents are underlain by granitic crust. What would Earth be like if all of its crust were made of the same material?

SKILL REVIEW

5. **Sequencing** Suppose that you are a reporter about to witness the formation of a large continent. In your science journal, write your step-by-step eyewitness account of the event. For more help, refer to the *Skill Handbook*.

earthgeu.com/self_check_quiz

22.2 *Formation of the Crust and Continents* **583**

3 Assess

Check for Understanding
Discussion
Ask students to explain how and when the ancient continent of Laurentia formed. During the Proterozoic, the microcontinents that formed during the Archean collided as a result of plate tectonics and stuck together. These accreted microcontinents formed Laurentia.

Reteach

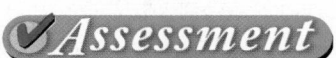 **Linguistic** Based on their observations in the Discovery Lab at the beginning of the chapter, have students explain, in their science journals, why the crust is composed of lighter minerals than the mantle or core. L2

✓Assessment

Portfolio Have students research the location of Precambrian shields on other continents. Have students plot the locations of the shields on a map of the world along with the ages of the rocks that make up these shields. Have students compare the ages of these shield rocks with the age of the Canadian Shield. P

SECTION ASSESSMENT

1. Earth's crust originated as a result of cooling of the uppermost mantle.
2. The Archean and Proterozoic continents formed through accretion of microcontinents. These microcontinents collided and stuck together. Today's continents have these Precambrian shields at their cores.
3. through the process of differentiation; The densest material concentrates at the core and is surrounded by progressively less-dense zones of material (e.g., core, mantle, and crust).
4. If all of Earth's crust were made of the same material, there would be no ocean basins as we know them. Because oceanic crust is denser than continental crust, the continental crust rides higher on the mantle. If there were not this marked difference in density, accumulations of seawater would be more random, the average depth of the ocean would be less, and possibly more of the surface of Earth would be covered by water. In addition, plate tectonics would be quite different because there would not be a denser slab of crust subducting beneath a less-dense slab of crust.
5. microcontinents move toward each other via plate tectonics; they join together making a larger continent; mountains form at the collision sites, continued microcontinent collisions increase the continent's size.

583

Section Background

For section content background, refer to **Our Changing Atmosphere** on pages 576C–D.

Preplanning

Refer to the Chapter Organizer on pages 576A–B.

1 Focus

Section Focus

Before presenting the lesson, display **Section Focus Transparency 69** on the overhead projector.
L1 ELL

Tying to Previous Knowledge

Have students research the composition of the present-day atmosphere. Have them hypothesize where argon in the atmosphere comes from. Argon is the only major atmospheric gas that students have not read about in this chapter, but it was mentioned in **Chapter 11.** Have students recall that through radioactive decay new elements may be formed.

Formation of the Atmosphere and Oceans

OBJECTIVES

• **Describe** the formation of Earth's atmosphere and oceans.

• **Identify** the origin of oxygen in the atmosphere.

• **Explain** the evidence that oxygen existed in the atmosphere during the Proterozoic.

VOCABULARY

cyanobacteria
stromatolite
banded iron formation
red bed

Figure 22-8 Steam and gas from Poas Volcano in Poas National Park, Costa Rica, rise high above the volcano's summit.

If you could travel back in time to the Early Precambrian, what would you take with you? Probably the most important thing that you could take for your survival would be a supply of oxygen! This is because Earth's early atmosphere was nothing like what it is today. The oxygen that early forms of algae produced through the process of photosynthesis affected the development of life on Earth in two very important ways. First, it changed the composition of the atmosphere and thus made life possible for oxygen-breathing animals. Second, it produced the ozone layer that filters ultraviolet (UV) radiation. Scientists refer to these types of processes, which modify a system, as feedback.

THE PRECAMBRIAN ATMOSPHERE

Hydrogen and helium probably dominated Earth's earliest atmosphere. However, because of their small masses, these gases could not remain near Earth for long. Earth's gravity is not strong enough to keep hydrogen and helium from escaping to space. However, gases that have greater masses, such as carbon dioxide and nitrogen, cannot escape Earth's gravity. This is why Earth's atmosphere is rich in carbon dioxide and nitrogen today.

There was considerable volcanic activity during the Early Precambrian. In Chapter 18, you learned that lava is not the only substance that erupts from volcanoes. Tremendous amounts of gases are also vented during volcanic eruptions in a process called outgassing, shown in *Figure 22-8.* The most abundant gases vented from volcanoes are water vapor (H_2O), carbon dioxide (CO_2), nitrogen (N_2), and carbon monoxide (CO). Many geologists hypothesize that outgassing formed Earth's early atmosphere. Thus, the early atmosphere must have contained large concentrations of water vapor, carbon dioxide, and nitrogen. In addition, the early atmosphere most likely contained methane (CH_4) and ammonia (NH_3), both of which may have formed as a result of chemical reactions among the volcanic gases. The argon (Ar) that is present in today's atmosphere began to accumulate during the Early Precambrian. It forms when the radioactive isotope potassium-40 (K-40) decays to argon-40 (Ar-40). Through this reaction, the amount of argon has increased in the atmosphere at about the same rate that K-40 decays.

Enrichment

Linguistic Have students research and report on the information currently available about water from outer space, via comets or otherwise. Have students visit the Earth Science Web Site at **earthgeu.com** for links to acquire more information.

OXYGEN IN THE ATMOSPHERE

No wonder life as we know it today did not exist during the Precambrian—there was no oxygen in the atmosphere to breathe! Volcanoes do not commonly give off oxygen; so, scientists do not think that the oxygen in Earth's atmosphere came from volcanoes. Where did the oxygen come from? The oldest known fossils which can help answer this question, are preserved in rocks that are about 3.5 billion years old. These fossils are the remains of tiny, threadlike chlorophyl bearing filaments of **cyanobacteria.** Such fossils are contained in 3.46-billion-year-old rocks called the Warrawoona Group, from western Australia. *Figure 22-9* compares fossilized cyanobacteria and modern cyanobacteria. Like their present-day counterparts, ancient cyanobacteria used photosynthesis to produce the nutrients they needed to survive. In the process of photosynthesis, solar energy is used to convert carbon dioxide and water into sugar. Oxygen is given off as a waste product.

Oxygen Producers Could microscopic cyanobacteria have produced enough oxygen to change the composition of Earth's early atmosphere? The abundance of cyanobacteria increased throughout the Archean until they became truly abundant during the Proterozoic. Large mats and mounds of billions of cyanobacteria, called **stromatolites,** dominated the shallow oceans of the Proterozoic. Modern stromatolites, such as those found in Australia today and shown in *Figure 22-10,* do not differ much from their ancient counterparts. The oldest stromatolites are preserved in 3.4-billion-year-old rocks from the Swaziland Supergroup of South Africa.

Evidence in the Rocks One way to test the hypothesis that there was oxygen in Earth's early atmosphere is to look for oxidized iron, or iron oxides, in Archean and Proterozoic rocks. The iron in rocks

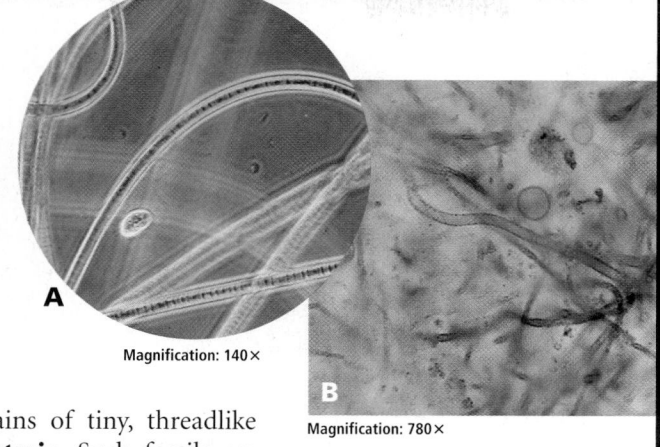

A

Magnification: 140×

B

Magnification: 780×

Figure 22-9 The cells of modern cyanobacteria are often identical in shape and size to some fossil cyanobacteria that are billions of years old. This micrograph is of the filamentous cyanobacterium, *Oscillatoria* **(A).** This fossil cyanobacterium is from the Gunflint Chert, Ontario, Canada **(B).**

ENVIRONMENTAL CONNECTION

Figure 22-10 Colonies of cyanobacteria form modern stromatolites in Hamelin Pool, Australia. Millions of individual cyanobacteria cells make up each colony **(A).** Fossil stromatolites are nearly identical to modern stromatolites. They provide evidence for the existence of a shallow sea in the areas where they are found **(B).**

A

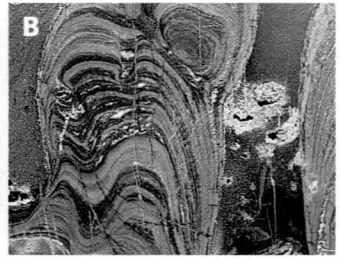

B

Interpreting the Photo

Figure 22-9 Have students compare and contrast the modern and fossil cyanobacteria. Ask students to list similarities and differences.

Collaborative Learning

Interpersonal Oxygen that is produced by plants benefits animals which breathe this oxygen. These animals respire CO_2, which benefits the plants. Have groups of students brainstorm other mutually beneficial relationships. **L2** **COOP LEARN**

Content Background

Earth's atmosphere developed from volcanic outgassing and possibly from water and gas from comets. Understanding the ancient atmosphere can improve our understanding of future atmospheric events such as global warming. To test the hypothesis that global warming is part of a natural cycle, a long-term record is needed. Understanding the details about the evolution of oxygen, ozone, and other gases in Earth's early atmosphere will help give us that record.

There has been an increase in global mean annual temperatures of approximately 0.7 degrees C over the past 100 years. The 1990's were the warmest decade since measurements began in the 1800's, with 1998 being the warmest year on record.

NY Core Curriculum Standards

Page 584: St 4 KI 1.2e
Page 585: St 4 KI 1.2h, 1.2i, & 1.2j
Page 586: St 1 Math KI 2 & 3, St 4 KI 1.2h, 1.2i, & 1.2j, St 7 KI 1
Page 587: St 4 KI 1.2e & 2.2b, St 6 KI 2 & 3

Across the Curriculum

Chemistry One of the most striking features of Earth's surface is that it is dominated by water. We know that liquid water on Earth's surface is necessary for life as we currently understand it. Have students write reports explaining why water exists on Earth in all three states: solid, liquid, and gas.

Differentiated Instruction

Visually Impaired To help students who are red-green color blind with the concept of a red bed, have students write detailed descriptions in their science journals about the color changes that they observed in the MiniLab. Next, have students research the chemical reactions responsible for the formation of red beds and write summaries of their research in their science journals as well.

Figure 22-11 The beautiful rocks of the Banded Iron Formation give testimony to the oxygenated atmosphere of the Precambrian. This sample is from the 2.1 billion year old Negaunee Formation, Michigan **(A)**. The Empire Iron Mine in Ishpeming, Michigan is well known for its iron production **(B)**.

reacts with free oxygen in the atmosphere to form iron oxides. Iron oxides are identified by their red color and provide undeniable evidence of free oxygen in the atmosphere. Some metamorphosed Archean sedimentary rocks contain mineral grains that would have been oxidized if there had been oxygen in the atmosphere. However, these minerals were not oxidized, which indicates that there was little or no free oxygen in the atmosphere throughout most of the Archean. However, there is evidence that near the end of the Archean and by the beginning of the Proterozoic, photosynthesizing stromatolites in shallow marine water increased oxygen levels in localized areas. These locally high concentrations of oxygen in otherwise oxygen-poor, shallow, ocean water allowed unique deposits to form. These deposits, which consist of alternating bands of chert and iron oxides are called **banded iron formations.** Today, these formations are mined as a source of iron, as shown in *Figure 22-11.* The *Problem-Solving Lab* should give you an example

Problem-Solving Lab

Profits from the Precambrian

Calculate mining costs Precambrian rocks contain many important mineral deposits, such as uranium, which is used in nuclear reactors. In a uranium oxide (U_3O_8) ore deposit in southern Ontario, the ore-containing rocks are an average of 3 m thick over an area that is 750 m long and 1500 m wide. Geochemical analysis of the deposit indicates that there are, on average, 0.9 kg of uranium oxide per metric ton of rock. Additionally, 0.3 cubic meters of the uranium-bearing rock weighs one ton (2000 lbs).

Analysis

1. How many pounds of ore does this new deposit contain?
2. It will cost $45 per cubic yard and 10 years to mine and extract the ore from the deposit. How much will this cost?

Thinking Critically

3. The current market price is $9.25 per pound of uranium oxide. Based on your answer to question 2, can the ore be mined for a profit?

Problem-Solving Lab

Purpose
Students will calculate the mass of uranium ore and the cost of mining the ore.

Process Skills
use numbers, predict

Materials
pencil, paper, calculator

Teaching Strategies
Determining the cost of the job compared to the income generated is essential in any business. Mining materials from Earth is a business, and a cost-benefit analysis is necessary before determining whether an area can be mined without the company going into debt. Ask students to describe similar cost-benefit analyses that they are familiar with (e.g., building a home, transporting goods).

Analysis

1. First, calculate the number of cubic feet of rock: $2500 \times 5000 \times 10 = 125\ 000\ 000$ ft³. Next, convert cubic feet of rock to short tons: $125\ 000\ 000$ ft³ ÷ 10 ft³ per short ton = $12\ 500\ 000$ short tons. Finally, determine the number of pounds of uranium: $12\ 500\ 000$ short tons $\times$ 2 lb of uranium per short ton = $25\ 000\ 000$ lb.

2. Students must figure out that there are 27 ft³ in one cubic yard. Then they can calculate the value of the uranium: $125\ 000\ 000$ ft³ ÷ 27 = $4\ 629\ 629.6296$ ft³ $\times$ $45 ft³ = $208 333 333

Thinking Critically

3. The current market value of the U_3O_8 in the deposit is $9.25/lb $\times$ $25\ 000\ 000$ lb = $231 250 000. Therefore, the deposit will turn a net profit of $22 916 667. This means that the mine will turn a profit of $2 291 666/y, because it will take 10 years to mine it.

✓Assessment

Skill Ask students how they could determine the price at which mining this uranium deposit neither makes money or loses money. $x \times 25\ 000\ 000 = \$208\ 333\ 333$ $x = \$8.33$. Therefore, if the market value of uranium dropped below $8.33/lb, the mine would lose money by mining the uranium.

Modeling
Ore can be extracted and concentrated from rocks by taking advantage of its magnetic properties. Have students model this process by concentrating a magnetic material from a sandy sediment. Give pairs of students about 200 mL of a sediment and iron filing mixture and a magnet. Have students devise methods of concentrating the sediment with the magnet and write down the steps they used.

of mining for a profit. Many sedimentary rocks that are younger than 1.8 billion years are rusty red in color and are called **red beds.** The presence of red beds in rocks that are Proterozoic and younger is strong evidence that the atmosphere by this time contained free oxygen. You will observe oxidation when you complete the *MiniLab* on this page.

IMPORTANCE OF OXYGEN

Oxygen is important not only because most animals require it for respiration, but also because it provides protection against UV radiation from the Sun. If you have ever read a label on sunscreen, you know that UV radiation can be harmful. Today, only a small fraction of the UV radiation that the Sun radiates toward Earth reaches its surface. This is because Earth is naturally protected from this radiation by ozone that is present in the lower part of Earth's upper atmosphere. An ozone molecule (O_3) consists of three oxygen atoms bonded together. Ozone forms when high-energy UV radiation splits oxygen gas molecules (O_2) and the single oxygen atoms combine with other oxygen molecules. This ozone layer filters out much of the Sun's UV radiation. Oxygen in Earth's atmosphere that was produced mainly through photosynthesis also contributes to the ozone layer. Early life, mainly the cyanobacteria that made up stromatolites, modified the atmosphere by generating large amounts of oxygen. Some of this oxygen also formed ozone, which, in turn, filtered out UV radiation so that other forms of life could survive on Earth's surface. It appears that nearly all the oxygen that we breathe today, and the oxygen that all animals have breathed in the geologic past, was released into the atmosphere by photosynthesis.

MiniLab

Why are red beds red?

Model the formation of red beds with iron, oxygen, and water.

Procedure 🖐 👓 🔥 🧪 CAUTION:
Steel wool can be sharp. Wear gloves in the lab.

1. Place 40 mL of white sand in a 150-mL beaker.
2. Add water so that the total volume is 120 mL.
3. Add 15 mL of bleach.
4. Place a piece of steel wool about the size of your thumbnail, in the beaker. Cover the beaker with a petri dish and allow it to stand in a quiet place for one day.
5. Remove the steel wool and stir the contents of the beaker. Allow the mixture to settle for five minutes after stirring.
6. Slowly pour off the water so that the iron-oxide sediment is left behind.
7. Stir the mixture again, then spoon some of the sand onto a watch glass and allow it to dry.

Analyze and Conclude

1. In your science journal, describe how the color of the sediment changed.
2. Where does the iron in the experiment come from?
3. Where in nature does the red in rocks come from?
4. What do you think is the function of the bleach?

MiniLab

Purpose 📦
Students will learn how iron oxidizes and stains sediment orange-red to form red beds.

Process Skills
model, recognize cause and effect, observe and infer

Materials 👓 🔥 🖐
140 mL beaker, graduated cylinder, water, bleach, white sand, steel wool (no soap on it), watch glass, spoon or spatula

Teaching Strategies
- Explain to students that even small amounts of impurities can cause color changes in transparent or light colored materials. For example, if you put just one drop of food coloring in a glass of water, it will color the water. However, if the fluid is dark to begin with, as motor oil is, one drop of food coloring will not change the color much. This is true of the staining of sediments. Quartz sand is generally light in color. Therefore, a small amount of iron can cause a color change.
- Handle bleach with care. It can discolor clothing.

Expected Results
The steel wool will oxidize. The iron oxide from this reaction will accumulate on the surface of the sand. When the sand and iron oxide are spooned onto the watch glass and allowed to dry, the iron oxide will stain the sand orange-red.

Analyze and Conclude
1. The sediment changed from white to orange-red.
2. It comes from the iron contained in the steel wool.
3. The red comes from the oxidized iron contained in iron-bearing minerals in the rocks.
4. The bleach speeds up the reaction, it is a catalyst.

Performance Have students design and conduct an experiment showing how a small amount of a coloring agent affects the color of light and dark colored materials. Have students write what these experiments tell us about red beds. Use the performance Task Assessment List for Designing an Experiment in **PASC**, p. 23.

Check for Understanding

Concept Development
Ask students to explain what the absence of red beds in rocks older than 1.8 billion years tells us about Earth's earliest atmosphere. It indicates that Earth's atmosphere did not contain free oxygen before about 1.8 billion years ago.

Reteach

Linguistic Have students write essays that compare and contrast the formation of the oceans and the formation of the atmosphere.

✓Assessment

Portfolio Have students use the Internet to research the hypothesis that much of Earth's water may be extraterrestrial. Have students access the Earth Science Web Site at <u>earthgeu.com</u> to find links to more information. Have students write about the discovery and the controversy surrounding it that every few seconds a snowball the size of a small house breaks apart as it approaches Earth and deposits a large cloud of water vapor into Earth's upper atmosphere.

Earth Science Online

Topic: Ozone Levels
To find out more about ozone in Earth's atmosphere, visit the Earth Science Web Site at <u>earthgeu.com</u>

Activity: Research the monthly concentrations of atmospheric ozone for a given year in the Antarctic or Arctic. Graph the ozone concentrations for each month in the year.

FORMATION OF THE OCEANS

Oceans are thought to have originated largely from the same process of outgassing that formed the atmosphere. A major component of the gas was water vapor. As the early atmosphere and the surface of Earth cooled, the water vapor condensed to form liquid water. You have probably observed the result of condensation on the sides of a cold glass of water. During the Archean, the entire atmosphere was rich with water vapor. When it began to cool, the result was a tremendous amount of rain, which slowly filled the low-lying, basalt-floored basins, thus forming the oceans. Rainwater dissolved the soluble minerals exposed at Earth's surface and just as they do today, rivers, runoff and groundwater transported these minerals to the oceans. These dissolved minerals made the oceans of the Precambrian salty just as they make the oceans salty today.

Another source of water may have played an important role in adding water vapor to Earth's atmosphere. A recent but controversial hypothesis suggests that some of Earth's water may have come from outer space! Earth is constantly bombarded with very small comets made of frozen gas and water. Based on the current rate of microcomet bombardment, some scientists calculate that a significant portion of Earth's surface waters might be extraterrestrial in origin.

Oxygen Causes Change The Precambrian began with an oxygen-free atmosphere and simple life-forms. Cyanobacteria then evolved, and their oxygen contribution caused the atmosphere to become filled with oxygen. This oxygen not only enabled new life-forms to evolve, but it also protected Earth's surface from the Sun's UV rays. Oceans formed from abundant water vapor in the atmosphere and possibly from outer space. Earth was then a hospitable place for new life-forms to inhabit.

SECTION ASSESSMENT

1. What are banded iron formations?
2. Describe the origin of the oxygen in the atmosphere.
3. Explain the relationship between red beds and oxygen in the atmosphere.
4. **Thinking Critically** If cyanobacteria had not produced as much oxygen as they did, how might life on Earth be different from how it is today?

SKILL REVIEW

5. **Comparing and Contrasting** Compare and contrast the formation of the atmosphere and the formation of the oceans. For more help, refer to the *Skill Handbook*.

SECTION ASSESSMENT

1. Precambrian rocks composed of alternating layers of chert and iron oxide
2. The oxygen that accumulated in Earth's early atmosphere came from photosynthetic cyanobacteria. Over geologic time, photosynthetic microorganisms produced the oxygen that we breathe today.
3. Red beds form through the oxidation of iron, which in turn stains sediment orange-red. When this sediment lithifies, it is called a red bed. Before there was an oxygenated atmosphere, there was no oxidation of iron. Red beds became common as atmospheric oxygen increased.
4. The atmosphere and oceans would never have become oxygen-rich and life would have had to develop the ability to survive in an anoxic environment. Also, there would be no ozone to protect life from UV radiation. Therefore, life would have had to adapt to environments with higher radiation.
5. Both formed through outgassing. As the atmosphere cooled, the water vapor condensed and rain fell to Earth. This water, plus possible water from microcomets filled low areas that became the ocean basins.

Of all the questions that humans have ever asked, none fascinates us more than those about the origin of life. "Where did life come from?" is a question that has been explored from many different perspectives. Today, we know that life comes from other life through reproduction. But where did the first life come from? What does science tell us about the origin of life?

ORIGIN OF LIFE ON EARTH

You have learned that Earth is about 4.6 billion years old and that fossil evidence indicates that life existed on Earth about 3.5 billion years ago. Thus, life must have begun during Earth's first 1.1 billion years. Earth probably could not have supported life until about 3.9 billion years ago because meteorites were constantly striking its surface. If life did begin during this time of meteorite bombardment, it is unlikely that it could have survived for long. This places the origin of life somewhere between 3.9 and 3.5 billion years ago.

Experimental Evidence During the first half of the twentieth century, scientists hypothesized that the early atmosphere contained carbon dioxide, nitrogen, water vapor, methane, and ammonia, but no free oxygen. They also theorized that numerous storms produced lightning and that the surface of Earth was relatively warm. Molecular biologists in the 1920s also suggested that an atmosphere containing abundant ammonia and methane but lacking free oxygen would be an ideal setting for the "primordial soup" in which life may have begun. A young graduate student named Stanley Miller, who was working with his graduate advisor, Nobel prize-winning chemist Harold Urey in 1953, was aware of these hypotheses.

Miller and Urey decided to create their own primordial soup. They set up an apparatus, like that shown in *Figure 22-12,* that contained a chamber filled with hydrogen, methane, and ammonia to simulate the early atmosphere. This atmospheric chamber was connected to a lower chamber that was designed to catch any particles that condensed in the atmospheric chamber.

OBJECTIVES

- **Describe** *the experimental evidence of how life developed on Earth.*
- **Distinguish** *between prokaryotes and eukaryotes.*
- **Identify** *when the first multicellular animals appeared in geologic time.*

VOCABULARY

amino acids
hydrothermal vent
prokaryote
eukaryote
Varangian Glaciation
Ediacara fauna

Figure 22-12 Dr. Stanley Miller is shown with a replica of the apparatus used to model Earth's early atmosphere in the Miller-Urey experiment.

22.4 *Early Life on Earth* **589**

2 Teach

Content Background

The essential elements (C, H, N, O, etc.) and the energy required to synthesize the "building blocks" of life existed shortly after Earth formed. It is nearly certain that amino acids existed, perhaps even in proteinlike chains, in an organic soup on the Archean Earth. The unanswered question is, How did these proteinlike substances develop into life which is capable of metabolism, growth, reaction to stimuli, and reproduction?

Using Math

Average Depth = 4 600 000 y × 1 in water ÷ 20 000 y = 230 000 in.

230 000 in × 2.54 cm/in =

584 200 cm = 5842 m

The average depth should be at least 5842 m. *Problem:* 97.2 percent of the water on Earth is in the oceans. *Possible Solutions:* Water has escaped Earth's atmosphere, the rate of bombardment is higher now than it was in the geologic past, or the water has dissociated and is a different form on Earth.

Using Math

Using Numbers
Some scientists argue that the influx of small comets into the atmosphere could add about one inch of water to Earth's surface every 20 000 years. The average depth of Earth's oceans is 3795 meters. If this influx has been constant for the past 4.6 billion years, what should be the minimum average depth of the oceans? How can you account for the difference in water volume?

Miller and Urey added sparks from tungsten electrodes to simulate lightning in the atmosphere. Only one week after the start of the experiment, the lower chamber contained a murky, brown liquid—the primordial soup! The "soup" that formed in this experiment contained organic molecules such as formaldehyde (H_2CO), and four different amino acids. **Amino acids** are the building blocks of proteins, and proteins are the basic substances from which life is built.

Continued experiments showed that 13 of the 20 amino acids known to occur in living things could be formed using experimental set-ups similar to the Miller-Urey method. Further experiments demonstrated that heat, cyanide, and certain clay minerals could cause amino acids to join together in chains like proteins. Proteins provide structure for tissues and organs, and are important agents in cell metabolism. Thus, the discovery that amino acids could be formed in this way was amazing. What Miller and Urey demonstrated, is that however life first formed, the basic building blocks of life were most likely present on Earth during the Archean.

The Role of RNA Not much is known about the next step required for the development of life. It is one thing for the proteins that are required for life to exist on the Archean Earth, but quite another for organic life to actually exist. One essential characteristic of life is the ability to reproduce. The nucleic acids RNA and DNA, shown in *Figure 22-13,* are the basic requirements for reproduction.

In modern organisms, DNA carries the instructions necessary for cells in all living things to function. Both RNA and DNA need enzymes to replicate and at least one of them is necessary for the synthesis of enzymes. Recent experiments have shown that types of RNA molecules, called ribozymes, can act as an enzyme. These RNA ribozymes can, therefore, replicate without

A

Magnification: 27 000×

B

Magnification: 10 800×

Figure 22-13 These are ribonucleic acid (RNA) polymerase molecules **(A)**. This is a single strand of deoxyribonucleic acid (DNA) **(B)**.

590 CHAPTER 22 *The Precambrian Earth*

Environmental Connection

Deep-sea hydrothermal vents teem with life today. It was not long ago that scientists thought the deep sea was a barren wasteland. With increasing knowledge of these ecosystems, there is an increased awareness of the diversity of life in all environments on Earth.

the aid of enzymes. This suggests that RNA molecules may have been the first replicating molecules on Earth. An RNA-based world may have been intermediate between an inorganic world and the DNA-based organic world that followed. The remaining mystery is figuring out how the first RNA molecule formed because RNA cannot be easily synthesized under the conditions that likely existed at the surface of the Archean Earth.

Hydrothermal Vents and the Beginnings of Life

The Urey-Miller model places the origin of life in shallow surface waters. But, life on Earth may have originated deep in the ocean, near active volcanic seafloor rifts. Ocean water seeps through the cracks in the ocean floor and is heated by the magma at the rifts. This heated water rises and is expelled from the ocean floor at hot-water vents called **hydrothermal vents,** as shown in *Figure 22-14.* All of the energy and nutrients necessary for the origin of life are present at these deep-sea hydrothermal vents. In fact, amino acids have been found there. This has led some scientists to hypothesize that during the Archaean, near hydrothermal vents, amino acids joined together on the surfaces of clay minerals to form proteins. Other scientists contend that this is not possible in such an environment. It is important to note that life is not being synthesized at these vents today, only because amino acids are quickly devoured by organisms that live near the vents. But in the Archaean, no organisms existed to eat the amino acids being produced.

PROTEROZOIC LIFE

At the beginning of the Proterozoic, life-forms were still quite simple. The only evidence of life-forms that existed before the Proterozoic is the fossilized remains of unicellular organisms called prokaryotes. A **prokaryote** is an organism that is composed of a single cell, which does not contain a nucleus and is the simplest kind of cell. All prokaryotes, including the cyanobacteria that make up stromatolites, belong to Kingdom Monera.

A **eukaryote** is an organism that is composed of cells that contain a nucleus. One way to determine whether an organism is a prokaryote or a eukaryote is by its size. As a general rule, eukaryotes are larger than prokaryotes. This general observation is useful in determining whether a fossil was a prokaryote or a eukaryote because it is rare for a fossil to be preserved in enough detail to determine whether its cells had nuclei. The oldest known fossil eukaryotes occur in a 2.1-billion-year-old banded iron formation in northern Michigan.

Figure 22-14 These sulfur encrusted, underwater geothermal vents bubble as volcanic gasses escape. They are located off Dobu Island, Papua, New Guinea.

Update For an on-line update on recent discoveries of life-forms at hydrothermal vents, visit the Earth Science Web Site at earthgeu.com

22.4 Early Life on Earth **591**

Cultural Diversity

Complex Precambrian Life Complex life-forms were thought to have developed in the Cambrian Period, around 550 million years ago. Recent findings in southern China, however, indicate much earlier beginnings. In the 570-million-year-old Doushantuo limestone formation in southern China, a team of scientists from Beijing and Harvard universities discovered ancient seaweed that is similar in many ways to modern species. Perhaps more importantly, they also found perfectly preserved embryos of bilateral organisms, whose right and left sides are symmetrical. Many complex organisms, including humans, share this feature. This amazing find provides evidence that eukaryotic organisms lived 30 million years earlier than was previously thought.

Interpreting the Illustration

Figure 22-15 This representation of Ediacaran life illustrates the current interpretation of these organisms' modes of life. Although no consensus has been reached regarding their placement in the animal or plant kingdom, some similarities to modern-day fauna have been recognized. For example, some paleontologists hypothesize that the sea pen-like organisms illustrated here are true ancestors of modern-day sea pens and related cnidarians.

There is growing evidence that a widespread glaciation, which occurred between 800 and 700 million years ago, played a critical role in the extinction of many members of a group of possible eukaryotes, the acritarchs. This glaciation event, called the **Varangian Glaciation,** was so widespread that some geologists liken Earth at that time to a giant snowball. Evidence from ancient glacial deposits suggests that glacial ice advanced nearly to the equator. Shortly after the ice retreated toward the poles, 700 million years ago, multicellular organisms first appeared in the fossil record.

EDIACARA FOSSILS

In 1947, the impressions of soft-bodied organisms were discovered in Late Proterozoic rocks in the Ediacara Hills of southern Australia. These fossils are collectively referred to as the **Ediacara fauna.** *Figure 22-15* shows an interpretation of the Ediacaran world. There has been much debate in the scientific community about the precise nature of these remarkable fossils. It is generally agreed that these fossils represent animals that were composed of different types of eukaryotic cells. Scientists are unsure, however, whether the Ediacara fauna are relatives of modern animal groups or whether they were completely different types of organisms.

The discovery of the Ediacara fauna at first seemed to solve one of the great mysteries in geology—why were there no fossils of the ancestors of the complex and diverse organisms that existed during the Cambrian Period. The Ediacara fauna seem to provide fossil

Figure 22-15 The Ediacara fauna contained a wide variety of organisms. It included floating organisms as well as those which were attached to the sea floor and possibly some organisms that were actively mobile.

evidence of an ancestral stock of complex Proterozoic animals. Indeed, many of the Ediacara fossils look quite similar in overall body shape to jellyfish, sea pens, segmented worms, arthropods, and echinoderms—just the kind of ancestral stock that geologists had been hoping to find.

Some scientists, however, hypothesize that the Ediacara fauna does not represent an ancestral stock of any modern group. These scientists consider the similarity in shape to animals in other phyla coincidental and that the Ediacara fauna represents a virtual dead end. None of the Ediacara fossils shows any evidence of a mouth, anus, or gut, and there is little evidence these animals could move. Arthropods, for example, leave tracks and trails when they move across the seafloor, but there is no evidence of such trace fossils associated with the Ediacara fossils. This has led some geologists to hypothesize that the Ediacara organisms were relatively immobile and that they fed by passively absorbing nutrients from seawater. These geologists point out that in the absence of any animal predators, there would have been no disadvantage to being a defenseless creature basking in the warm seawater and absorbing nutrients.

In recent years, geologists have found Ediacara fossils in all parts of the world. This suggests that these organisms were widely distributed throughout the shallow oceans of the Late Proterozoic. They seemed to have flourished between 670 and 570 million years ago. Then, in an apparent mass extinction, they disappeared before organisms that are likely related to modern phyla took over the oceans of the world.

> **Earth Science Online**
>
> **Topic: Ediacara Fossils**
> To find out more about the Ediacara fauna, visit the Earth Science Web Site at **earthgeu.com**
>
> **Activity:** Research the locations of Ediacara fossils. List some locations in your state where they may be found.

SECTION ASSESSMENT

1. Explain why the Miller-Urey experiment was important.

2. What kind of organisms do the earliest fossils represent?

3. What is the significance of the Varangian Glaciation?

4. Discuss the differences between prokaryotes and eukaryotes.

5. **Thinking Critically** Describe how early life might have changed if some of the Ediacaran fauna had been able to move and if predators had been present in their environment.

SKILL REVIEW

6. **Concept Mapping** Rearrange the following events into an events chain that describes the results of the Miller-Urey experiment. For more help, refer to the *Skill Handbook*.

chamber with cyanide, formaldehyde, and amino acids	heat and clay minerals added
chains of amino acids	simulated atmospheric lightning
chamber with hydrogen, methane, and ammonia	

earthgeu.com/self_check_quiz

22.4 *Early Life on Earth* **593**

3 Assess

Check for Understanding
Discussion
Have students discuss the "primordial soup" hypothesis and the hydrothermal vent hypothesis of the origin of life. In particular, ask students to think about the source of energy required for the synthesis of organic compounds in these different environments. Students should recognize that lightning was the source of energy in the "primordial soup" model, whereas Earth's internal heat was the source of energy in the hydrothermal vent model.

Reteach
Have students create timelines showing the origin of prokaryotic and eukaryotic life, the Varangian Glaciation, and the origin of eukaryotic animals (the Ediacara fauna).

Portfolio Have students research the Ediacara fauna using the Internet and literature and write a paper arguing that either the Ediacara fauna represents relatives of modern phyla, or it represents completely different kinds of organisms not related to modern fauna. Some students may think that some represent evolutionary dead ends and others represent an ancestral stock to modern phyla. **P**

SECTION ASSESSMENT

1. It demonstrated that the building blocks of proteins (amino acids) were likely quite abundant during the Archean.

2. prokaryotes; cyanobacteria

3. Earth was nearly turned into a giant snowball. It may have been responsible for an extinction event. In the aftermath of this glacial episode undisputed multicellular organisms first arose. It is not known if this glacial event triggered this evolution.

4. Prokaryotes are the simplest unicellular organisms and do not contain a nucleus. Eukaryotes are composed of one or more cells, which contain nuclei. They are larger and more complex than prokaryotes. Prokaryote fossils are known from early Archaen rocks. Eukaryotes did not appear until at least the Early Proterozoic.

5. The Ediacaran organisms would have had to develop some means of protecting themselves, possibly by burrowing into the sediment. Their world would not have been passive as is hypothesized by many paleontologists; it would have been quite similar to the predator-prey world of the Phanerozic.

6. chamber with hydrogen, methane and ammonia; simulated atmospheric lightning; chamber with cyanide, formaldehyde and amino acids; heat and clay minerals added; chains of amino acids

Mapping GeoLab

Time Allotment

45 minutes

Process Skills

interpret maps, communicate, analyze data, draw a conclusion, use numbers

Preparation

Special Instructions

- Place 12 samples of igneous or metamorphic rocks on desks relatively evenly spaced throughout the classroom.
- Put an index card with the sample indicating its radiometrically dated age.
- Use three 3.5 billion year old samples near the center of the room, three 3.0 billion year old samples on the north side of the room, three 2.5 billion year old samples on the west side of the room, three 2.0 billion year old samples on the east side of the room, and three 1.5 billion year old samples on the south side of the room.
- Alternatively, you could vary the dates somewhat; for example, instead of three cards labeled 3.5 billion years old, you might have one labeled 3.4 billion years old, another labeled 3.5 billion years old, and another labeled 3.6 billion years old.

Mapping Continental Growth

Plotting the distribution of the ages of rocks onto a map helps geologists to reconstruct the history of continental accretion. During the Precambrian, microcontinents and island arcs collided to form what would become the modern continents.

Preparation

Problem

How can the distribution of the ages of rocks plotted on a map be used to interpret the growth of a continent?

Materials

paper   colored pencils
pencil   metric ruler

Procedure

1. Your teacher will set up locations with a rock sample at each location.
2. Make an outline map of your classroom similar to the map on the next page, using the scale 1 cm = 100 km.
3. Visit each location where a rock sample has been set out. Plot each location and record the age of each rock on the map.
4. After you have recorded all the locations, use a pencil to draw lines on the map that separate rocks of different ages. Be careful not to simply connect the dots.
5. Use a different colored pencil to shade in the areas on the map that contain rocks of the same age. These are your geologic age provinces.
6. Make a key for your map by drawing a small rectangle for each different geologic age province. Name the oldest province "Province A," the next oldest "Province B," and so on for all provinces.

Analyze

1. Use the ruler to measure the east-to-west width of Province A. Convert the map scale to ground distance by using the scale 1 cm = 1 km.
2. Why do some of your classmates have different answers? Who is right?
3. Where is the oldest province located relative to all the other provinces?

Procedure

Teaching Strategies

- Have students work in pairs or in small groups.
- To increase students' proficiency in SI, have them give their answer to question 1 in Analyze in both English and SI units.

Troubleshooting

The scale is 1 cm on the map equals 1 km of the imaginary field area, not 1 cm in the room equals 1 km in the imaginary field area. Many students will simply draw circles around the similar numbers. Be sure they have only one line separating the provinces from each other.

Conclude & Apply

1. Based on the distribution of the geologic age provinces, describe the sequence of collisional events that formed the craton represented by your map.
2. According to your map, where would you find metamorphic rocks? What type of metamorphism would have occurred?
3. If your map represents an area composed of Precambrian-aged rocks, would the mountains that formed from collisions still be high and rugged? Explain.
4. Compare the distribution of age provinces on your map with *Figure 22-6.* What are the similarities?
5. Based on what you learned in this activity, describe the formation of the North American Craton.

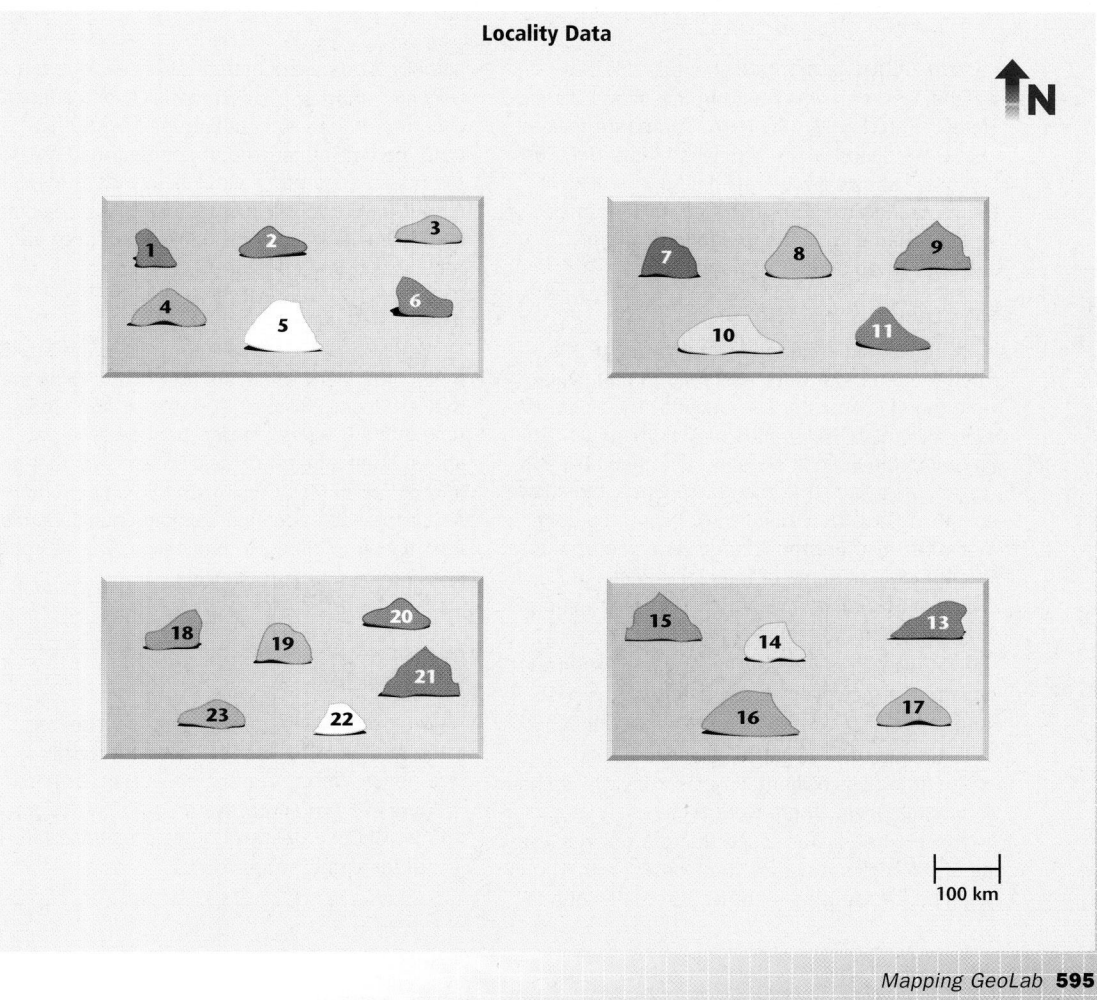

Locality Data

N

100 km

Mapping GeoLab **595**

Conclude & Apply *(continued)*

Craton, and the younger provinces are around the margin of the craton.

5. The younger provinces must have accreted around the margin of the craton over geologic time. That is, the craton grew by accreting younger provinces along its margins.

✓ Assessment

Performance Have students make timelines that suggest the order of accretion of the provinces of the North American Craton in **Figure 22-6.** This will not be as straightforward as that of the map that they drew. Have them develop multiple hypotheses about why the order is not as simple. Use the Performance Task Assessment List for Evaluating a Hypothesis in **PASC,** p. 31.

Data and Observations
Students will plot the data on the base map of the room and interpret the distribution of age provinces.

Analyze

1. For example: If the map is 8 cm wide, then the distance on the ground is 8 km.
2. The answers are all different. In order for the numbers to be all nearly the same, a very large number of data points would be needed. Thus there is no "right" answer, only answers that correctly model the data.
3. The oldest province is in the center of the map area.

Conclude & Apply

1. The younger provinces must have accreted around the oldest province.
2. Metamorphic rocks would be found at the province boundaries. Regional metamorphism would have resulted from the collisions. If any igneous activity was generated, contact metamorphism also could have occurred.
3. No; the mountains would have been exposed to the agents of weathering and erosion for so many years that the mountains would be worn down, rounded, and low in elevation as compared to newly formed mountains.
4. The distribution is similar. The oldest province is near the center of the North American

NY Core Curriculum Standards

Page 594: St 4 KI 1.2j, St 6 KI 2 & 3
Page 595: St 4 KI 1.2j, St 6 KI 2 & 3

Purpose

Students will learn that not everything that looks like a fossil is a fossil. Some objects that were first described by scientists as fossils have turned out to be inorganic.

Content Background

ALH 84001 is a meteorite that formed from molten lava about 4.5 billion years ago, possibly from an ancient Martian volcano. How do we know that ALH 84001 is from Mars? The strongest evidence for a Martian origin is that ALH 84001 contains traces of gases that are similar to those in the Martian atmosphere. We know the composition of the Martian atmosphere because the *Viking Lander* spacecraft analyzed it in 1976. The Martian atmosphere is different from Earth's atmosphere. In part, it contains less nitrogen and oxygen and more carbon dioxide.

In fact, there are 11 other meteorites that are also almost certainly from Mars. Long after ALH 84001 crystallized, about 4 billion years ago, it was heated again and deformed by a strong shock, probably from an asteroid or meteorite impact. Some time after this impact, possibly about 3.6 billion years ago, some kind of liquid flowed through ALH 84001 and deposited rounded globules of carbonate minerals. The so-called Martian fossils are in these carbonate globules. A more recent event that can be inferred from ALH 84001 is another shock event. This shock may have come from the meteorite impact that propelled ALH 84001 off Mars.

Science in the News

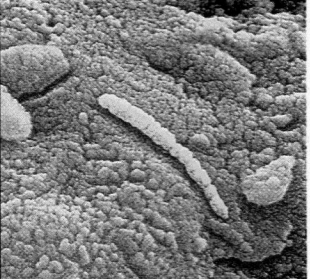

Martians or Meteorites?

Some of the rarest meteorites found on Earth come from Mars. One of these, ALH 84001, caused quite a stir in the scientific community when some scientists claimed to have found fossils in it. Many fossils, such as dinosaur bones and impressions of fern fronds, are obviously the remains of once-living things. Less-obvious evidence of life are the microscopic spheres and rods found in ALH 84001.

ALH 84001 is a potato-shaped rock that weighs 1.9 kg. It was found in the Allan Hills Ice Field, Antarctica, in 1984. The meteorite formed about 4.5 billion years ago, when Mars did. The "fossils," shown above, are found in cracks in the rock and are more than one million times smaller than a typical bacterial cell and are 1/100th the diameter of human hair.

Mystery on Earth

A similar situation took place in the 1860s, when features that were assumed to be fossils were found in limestone in Canada. The features were millimeter-thick bands of dark minerals separated into blobs and layers by light minerals. This "fossil" was named *Eozoon canadense,* the "dawn animal of Canada." This discovery created quite a stir, because *Eozoon canadense* came from the Precambrian, in some of the oldest rocks in North America. Scientists hailed it as "the greatest discovery in geology for half a century."

Not everyone was so taken with *Eozoon canadense,* however. Within months, the first doubts that it was truly a fossil were published.

Gradually, the weight of evidence turned against the possibility that *Eozoon canadense* had an organic origin. There were three main lines of evidence. First, it was found that the original layering of the rock cut across the "fossil," rather than being parallel to it as it should if the animal had actually lived on the bottom of an ancient sea. Second, mapping showed that *Eozoon canadense* occurred around igneous intrusions. The heat from the cooling magma, it seemed, had created the appearance of fossils. Finally, nearly identical features were found in limestone blocks ejected by a volcano, again showing that heat, not life, had formed these features.

What are they?

What about the so-called fossils in the Martian meteorite? Many scientists now do not think that they are fossils. One reason is their size. Their volume is 2000 times smaller than the smallest known living things—parasitic organisms that live in other cells. Many scientists think that something so tiny probably could not contain enough genetic information to direct life processes. The search goes on for extraterrestrial life.

Activity

What other kinds of geologic features can be mistaken for fossils? Visit the Earth Science Web Site at **earthgeu.com** or a library to find more examples of pseudofossils. Choose one and, in your science journal, describe how it forms.

Teaching Strategies

Have students search at **earthgeu.com** for information about fossils in Martian meteorites and ALH 84001. Have students compare and contrast the story of the so-called fossils from ALH 84001 with that of *Eozoon canadensis.*

Activity

Students will find that there are many pseudofossils. In fact, a pseudofossil is by definition a natural object, structure, or mineral of inorganic origin that may resemble or be mistaken for a fossil. Therefore, any object that someone mistakenly thinks is a fossil is, in essence, a pseudofossil.

Summary

SECTION 22.1
The Early Earth

Main Ideas
- Geologists have used radiometric dating to show that Earth must be at least 4.2 billion years old.
- Because the solar system formed all at the same time, Moon rocks and meteorites that are approximately 4.6 billion years old suggest that Earth is 4.6 billion years old too.
- The early Earth was a very hot place because of abundant radioactive isotopes, bombardment by meteorites, and gravitational contraction.

Vocabulary
asteroid (p. 578)
meteorite (p. 579)
zircon (p. 578)

SECTION 22.2
Formation of the Crust and Continents

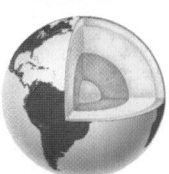

Main Ideas
- Earth's early crust formed by the cooling of the uppermost mantle. This early crust weathered and formed sediments.
- Sediment-covered slabs of this early crust were subducted and generated magmas that contained granitic minerals.
- During the Archean, microcontinents collided with one another throughout the Proterozoic and formed the cores of the continents. By the end of the Proterozoic, the first supercontinent, Rodinia, had formed.

Vocabulary
Canadian Shield (p. 581)
differentiation (p. 580)
Laurentia (p. 582)
microcontinents (p. 582)
Precambrian shield (p. 581)

SECTION 22.3
Formation of the Atmosphere and Oceans

Main Ideas
- Earth's early atmosphere and the oceans formed mainly by the process of outgassing.
- Nearly all of the oxygen in the atmosphere is a result of photosynthesis.
- Certain minerals oxidize, or rust, in the presence of free oxygen. Proterozoic red beds are sedimentary rock deposits that contain oxidized iron. They are the evidence that there was free oxygen in the atmosphere during the Proterozoic.

Vocabulary
banded iron formation (p. 586)
cyanobacteria (p. 585)
red bed (p. 587)
stromatolite (p. 585)

SECTION 22.4
Early Life on Earth

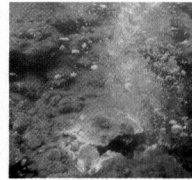

Main Ideas
- All the ingredients were present on the early Earth to form proteins, the building blocks of life. Amino acids, the molecules that make up proteins, were present on the surface of the early Earth.
- Prokaryotic cells are generallly small and contain no nuclei. Eukaryotic cells contain nuclei and are generally larger and more complex than prokaryotic cells.
- The first evidence of multicellular animals are fossils of 2.1 billion year old eukaryotic algae.

Vocabulary
amino acids (p. 590)
Ediacara fauna (p. 592)
eukaryote (p. 591)
hydrothermal vent (p. 591)
prokaryote (p. 591)
Varangian Glaciation (p. 592)

Main Ideas

Summary statements can be used by students to review the major concepts of the chapter.

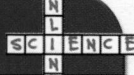

VOCABULARY PuzzleMaker

For additional help with vocabulary, have students access the Vocabulary Puzzlemaker online.

earthgeu.com/ vocabulary puzzlemaker

0:00 *Out of Time?*

If time does not permit teaching the entire chapter, use the GeoDigest at the end of the unit as an overview.

Earth Science online

Be sure to check the Earth Science Web Site for links to chapter material: earthgeu.com

---

GLENCOE
Technology

Videotape/DVD
MindJogger Videoquizzes
Chapter 22: *The Precambian Earth*
Have students work in groups as they play the videoquiz game to review key chapter concepts.

Resource Manager

Chapter Assessment, pp. 127–132
MindJogger Videoquizzes DVD/VHS
ExamView® Pro CD-ROM
Performance Assessment in Earth Science

NY Core Curriculum Standards

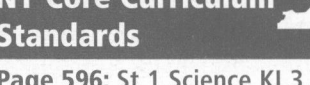

Page 596: St 1 Science KI 3, St 4 1.2d, 1.2i, & 2.1j
Page 597: St 4 KI 1.2c, 1.2f, 1.2h, 1.2i, 2.1a, 2.1k, & 2.1m
Page 598: St 4 KI 1.2c, 1.2e, 1.2f, 1.2h, 2.1a, 2.1b, 2.1l, 2.1n, & 2.1p
Page 599: St 4 KI 1.2e, 1.2i, 2.1l, & 2.1n

Understanding Main Ideas

1. c
2. d
3. b
4. d
5. a
6. a
7. d
8. c
9. b
10. It protects organisms from harmful UV radiation.
11. These gases are heavier than other gases and are unable to escape Earth's gravity.

Applying Main Ideas

12. upper mantle cooled and crystallized, crust weathered, sediments formed, sediments drawn down into subduction zones, partial melting of sediments and subducted slab, magma with new chemical composition formed, granitic crust formed as magma crystallized, subduction continued forming more magma

13. Radiometric dating was used to determine the ages of the oldest rocks and minerals from the surface of Earth and the rocks collected from the Moon. These ages were compared to those from radiometrically dated meteorites. None of the samples was older than the oldest meteorites, which are 4.66 billion years old. Based on these tests, geologists theorize that Earth formed about 4.6 billion years ago, at or shortly after the formation of the oldest meteorites.

14. The continents formed as Earth cooled and a crust

Understanding Main Ideas

1. What is the commonly accepted age of Earth?
   a. 4.6 million years
   c. 4.6 billion years
   b. 46 million years
   d. 46 billion years

2. Which of the following was not a source of heat for the early Earth?
   a. meteor bombardment
   b. gravitational contraction
   c. radioactivity
   d. hydrothermal energy

3. What are small asteroids called?
   a. comets
   c. cratons
   b. meteoroids
   d. microcontinents

4. What is the process by which a planet becomes internally zoned when heavy materials sink toward its center and lighter materials accumulate near its surface?
   a. photosynthesis
   c. accretion
   b. dewatering
   d. differentiation

5. Where is most of the North American Precambrian shield exposed at the surface?
   a. Canada
   c. Wisconsin
   b. Minnesota
   d. Michigan

6. What mineral can be used to radiometrically date Earth's age?
   a. zircon
   c. hematite
   b. quartz
   d. feldspar

7. Refer to *Figure 22-6*. What name is given to the core of the modern-day North American continent that formed in the Proterozoic?
   a. Baltica
   c. Grenville
   b. Yavapai
   d. Laurentia

8. What is the name of the first supercontinent, which formed near the end of the Proterozoic?
   a. Laurentia
   c. Rodinia
   b. Grenville
   d. Pangaea

---

9. What volcanic process most likely formed Earth's atmosphere?
   a. differentiation
   c. crystallization
   b. outgassing
   d. photosynthesis

10. Why is ozone a necessary component of Earth's atmosphere?

11. Why is Earth's atmosphere rich in nitrogen (N) and carbon dioxide (CO_2) today?

Applying Main Ideas

12. Rearrange the following phrases to create a cycle map that describes the formation of Earth's early crust.

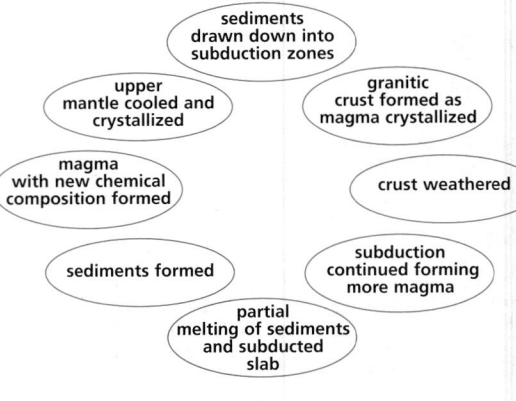

Test-Taking Tip

KEEP A CLEAR MIND When you take a test, each new question should be a clean slate. Once you have read a question, considered the answers, and chosen one, put that question behind you. Don't let one or two troublesome questions distract you while you're working on other questions.

earthgeu.com/chapter_test

---

developed. Convection in the mantle caused pieces of lithosphere to move and collide with one another. Some lithosphere was subducted, melted, and became magma. This magma erupted through volcanoes. Outgassing from these volcanoes formed the early atmosphere. Condensation of water vapor resulted in rain. The water that accumulated on Earth's surface filled in the low areas to form oceans. Water may also have been added to Earth from space via comets.

15. Banded iron formations indicate that some oxygen was accumulating, at least locally, during the Late Archean and Early Proterozoic.

16. red beds; the red color of these beds is a result of iron oxide minerals that form only in an oxidizing environment

17. Prokaryotes are small, simple unicellular organisms, do not have nuclei, and appeared first. Eukaryotes are more complex, are larger, and contain a nucleus.

13. Explain how geologists have determined the age of Earth.

14. Discuss the relationships among the formation of the continents, the atmosphere, and the oceans.

15. What is the geologic significance of banded iron formations?

16. What geologic evidence suggests that free oxygen was accumulating in Earth's atmosphere during the Proterozoic?

17. What is the difference between prokaryotes and eukaryotes? Which appeared first in the fossil record?

18. What characteristics of continental crust allow it to "float" higher on the mantle than oceanic crust?

19. Why are orogens deformed?

20. What is the significance of the Ediacara fauna?

21. Discuss the evidence that suggests that most members of the Ediacara fauna were immobile.

Thinking Critically

22. Explain how the production of oxygen through photosynthesis by cyanobacteria affected the composition of the atmosphere and the development of other organisms.

23. A rock sample from Mars is reported to contain fossil evidence of life. What kind of fossil would you expect it to be? Explain your answer.

24. Where in North America would you look if you wanted to find evidence of Archean life? Explain your answer.

25. When making a map of geologic age provinces, as you did in the *Mapping GeoLab* in this chapter, why did you draw the lines between the data points instead of connecting them?

26. How might Earth's surface be different if water vapor had not been a product of outgassing?

earthgeu.com/standardized_test

Standardized Test Practice

1. Which of the following is NOT a likely source of the Precambrian Earth's heat?
   a. radioactivity
   b. asteroid impact
   c. increased solar activity
   d. gravitational contraction

2. What does orogeny refer to?
   a. the drifting of microcontinents
   b. the building of mountain ranges
   c. the formation of volcanic islands
   d. the breaking apart of the supercontinents

3. Which of the following was NOT a source of information about the early presence of oxygen on Earth?
   a. red beds   c. stromatolites
   b. banded iron   d. meteorites
      formations

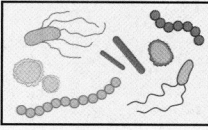
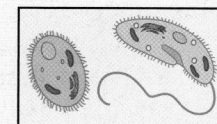

Group A   Group B

INTERPRETING SCIENTIFIC ILLUSTRATIONS
Use the diagrams to answer questions 4 and 5.

4. How do members of Group A differ from members of Group B?
   a. They belong to the Kingdom Plantae.
   b. They can be found in Proterozoic fossils.
   c. They contain no nuclei.
   d. They are all unicellular.

5. Where did members of Group B probably originate?
   a. glaciers   c. Australian fauna
   b. hydrothermal vents   d. oil deposits

Assessment **599**

18. The minerals that make up continental crust have lower densities than those of the oceanic crust.

19. The great compressive pressure that occurs when lithospheric masses collide causes deformation.

20. It provides evidence that complex, multicellular life-forms had evolved before the Paleozoic.

21. There are no trace fossils of Ediacaran organisms. Additionally, they do not seem to have any appendages adapted for swimming or walking.

Thinking Critically

22. Oxygen created through photosynthesis allowed ozone to form which, in turn, allowed more advanced organisms to survive on Earths' surface.

23. simple, unicellular organisms; the presence of microbial life in extreme environments on Earth suggests that perhaps microbial life could also exist on Mars

24. in the Precambrian rocks of the Canadian Shield

25. The lines are drawn between the dots because no data are available to determine exactly where one province begins and the other ends.

26. Earth probably would not have large bodies of water.

The Paleozoic Era

Refer to pages 8T–9T of the Teacher Guide for an explanation of the National Science Content Standards correlations.

Section	Objectives	National Science Content Standards	State/Local Standards
SECTION 23.1 **The Early Paleozoic** 🕐 1 session 📦 ½ block	1. **Describe** the Cambrian paleogeography of Laurentia. 2. **Discuss** the concept of a passive margin. 3. **Describe** the Cambrian fauna.	UCP.2; D.3	St 1 Science, KI 2, St 4 KI 2.1i, 2.1j, 2.1o, 2.1t, 2.1v, & 2.1w, St 6 KI 2 & 3
SECTION 23.2 **The Middle Paleozoic** 🕐 1 session 📦 ½ block	4. **Describe** the Middle Paleozoic paleo-geography. 5. **Explain** the concept of an active margin and the formation of a clastic wedge. 6. **Describe** the Middle Paleozoic fauna. 7. **Define** the concept of mass extinction.	UCP.2, UCP.4; B.3; C.3; D.3; E.1	St 1 Math KI 1, St 4 KI 1.2i, 1.2j, 2.1m, 2.1n, 2.1o, 2.1w, & 3.1a, St 6 KI 2 & 3
SECTION 23.3 **The Late Paleozoic** 🕐 3 sessions 📦 1 block	8. **Describe** the formation of Pangaea. 9. **Explain** how cyclothems formed. 10. **Identify** the importance of amniote eggs. 11. **Discuss** the causes of the Late Permian mass extinction.	UCP.2, UCP.4; A.1; B.3; C.3; D.3; G.1	St 1 Science KI 1, St 4 KI 1.2i, 1.2j, 2.1n, 2.1o, 2.1w, & 3.1a, St 6 KI 2 & 3

A complete Planning Guide is provided on pages 30T–32T.

🕐 The number of recommended single-period sessions

📦 The number of recommended blocks

Activity Materials

Discovery Lab *page 601*
unglazed brick or sandstone, dropper, water

GeoLab *pages 618–619*
fossil brachiopods (4 different), fossil bivalves (4 different), paper, pencil

MiniLab *page 616*
white modeling clay (500 g), yellow modeling clay (250 g), metric ruler, calculator

Demo *page 602*
plastic butter tub with lid, sand, large deep pan, water, black grease pencil

Need materials? Contact Science Kit at 1-800-828-7777 or at www.sciencekit.com on the Internet. For alternate materials, see the activity on the listed page.

Key to Teaching Strategies

L1 Level 1 activities should be appropriate for students with learning difficulties.

L2 Level 2 activities should be within the ability range of all students.

L3 Level 3 activities are designed for above-average students.

ELL ELL activities should be within the ability range of English-language learners.

COOP LEARN Cooperative learning activities are designed for small-group work.

P These strategies represent student products that can be placed in a best-work portfolio.

📦 These strategies are useful in a block-scheduling format.

Chapter Organizer

Glencoe Exclusive!
TeacherWorks™
All-In-One Planner and Resource Center

Activities/Features	Reproducible Masters	Transparencies
Discovery Lab: Where is oil found? p. 601	**Study Guide for Content Mastery** pp. 143–144 L2	**Section Focus Transparency 71** L1 ELL **Teaching Transparency 69** L2 ELL
Problem-Solving Lab: Interpreting Graphs, p. 610	**Study Guide for Content Mastery** pp. 145–146 L2 **Laboratory Manual** pp. 177–180 L2	**Section Focus Transparency 72** L1 ELL **Teaching Transparency 70** L2 ELL
MiniLab: Collisions and Shelves, p. 616 **Using Math:** Calculating Percentages, p. 616 **GeoLab:** Symmetry, Shape and Shells, pp. 618–619 **Science & the Environment:** Mass Extinctions, p. 620	**Study Guide for Content Mastery** pp. 147–148 L2 **GeoLab and MiniLab Worksheets** p. 91 L2 **GeoLab and MiniLab Worksheets** pp. 92–94 L2 **Laboratory Manual** pp. 181–184 L2	**Section Focus Transparency 73** L1 ELL **Teaching Transparency 71** L2 ELL

✔Assessment

Chapter Assessment, pp. 133–138
Performance Assessment in the Science Classroom (PASC)
MindJogger Videoquiz DVD/VHS
Performance Assessment in Earth Science
ExamView® Pro CD-ROM
5 Days to the Regents Exam

GLENCOE'S
ASSESSMENT
ADVANTAGE

Additional Resources

Guided Reading Audio Program ELL
Cooperative Learning in the Science Classroom COOP LEARN
Lesson Plans
Block Scheduling
earthgeu.com
NY Lesson Plans
NY Block Scheduling
Review Handbook for Regents Earth Science Exam

◼NATIONAL GEOGRAPHIC

Products Available from National Geographic Society
To order the following products, call the National Geographic Society at 1-800-368-2728:
Curriculum Kits
GeoKit: *Earth's History*
GeoKit: *Rocks and Minerals*

Teacher's Corner

CD-ROM
111 Years of National Geographic Magazine
Videos
Fossils: Clues to the Past

Content Background

The "Cambrian Explosion"
Section 23.1

Major events of the Late Precambrian, including the breakup of Rodinia, the expansion of Earth's oceans over many continental areas, and dramatic changes in ocean chemistry (most notably, an increase in oxygen levels), resulted in a rise and later diversification of multicellular organisms, including complex animals. Between the time of the Late Proterozoic Ediacaran fauna (600 M.Y.B.P. to 544 M.Y.B.P.), which included the oldest definitive animals, and about 518 M.Y.B.P., representatives of most multicellular marine animals and plants had evolved. Experimentation with body types for various habitats also had occurred. Most soft-bodied organisms of the Ediacaran fauna had become extinct by the end of the Precambrian. The Cambrian Period was a time of fundamental change in life-forms. By the beginning of the Cambrian Period, predation had become a significant factor in biological evolution and probably had a causal link (along with various geochemical factors) to the development of mineralized skeletons.

Also by the Early Cambrian, the transition from a microbial mat-dominated, sediment-water interface (i.e., stromatolites) to a blurry interface that was burrowed by organisms in shallow marine settings was well underway. This time of rapid change among marine animals, experimentation with new body types, and shifting ecological settings is referred to as the "Cambrian explosion." The Cambrian explosion represents an important biological phenomenon: the rapid appearance and development of many animal groups within a short amount of geological time. With the appearance of complete skeletons, the rich fossil record of the Phanerozoic began.

The Paleozoic Fauna
Section 23.2

Fauna consisting of trilobites, inarticulate brachiopods, early mollusks, and primitive echinoderms dominated the Cambrian seas. These Cambrian fauna were replaced in the Early Ordovician. Articulate brachiopods, corals, cephalopod mollusks, and crinoids became dominant in the shallow seas that covered the continents. In addition, a new phylum of colonial animals called bryozoans debuted in the Ordovician. Bryozoans commonly form branching colonies that house microscopic animals. These microscopic animals are thought to be distantly related to the brachiopods because they, like brachiopods, feed with a featherlike structure called a lophophore. Two major groups of corals were common during the Middle Paleozoic. The dominant reef-building corals were tabulate corals. These colonial corals, along with stromotoporoids, were the main reef builders responsible for the spectacular reefs in the Great Lakes region. The corals of the second group

Multiple Learning Styles

 Visual-Spatial Modeling, p. 607

 Interpersonal Reteach, p. 611, Collaborative Learning, p. 615

 Linguistic Project, p. 605, Earth Science Journal, p. 613, Project, p. 615

 **Logical-Mathematical** Reinforcement, p. 615

GLENCOE Technology

The following multimedia resources are available from Glencoe.

Science and Technology Videodisc Series (STVS)
Biodiversity
Solar System

Vocabulary Puzzlemaker

TeacherWorks™ CD-ROM

MindJogger Videoquizzes DVD/VHS

ExamView® Pro CD-ROM

Interactive Chalkboard CD-ROM

Chapter Organizer

were usually solitary. They commonly grew unattached to other corals. These corals, called rugose corals, were horn shaped; thus, they are commonly referred to as horn corals. Graptolites, a group of colonial hemichordates, also appeared in the Ordovician. There were two major groups of graptolites. The members of one group, called the dendroid graptolites, were rooted to the seafloor in shallow marine environments. The graptoloid graptolites were planktonic, meaning that they floated freely in the oceans. Graptolites are most commonly found as fossils in black shale that was deposited in deep water. Graptoloid graptolites are excellent index fossils for the relative-age dating of Middle Paleozoic deep-marine shale deposits because they are widespread, common, and evolved rapidly.

Sinking Coal Swamps
Section 23.3

During the Late Paleozoic, the paleogeography of North America, combined with the many river systems that drained the enormous mountains that resulted from the Allegheny Orogeny, made a perfect setting for the formation of large swamps. These swamps covered vast lowlands between the mountains and the ocean on the east side of North America. The climate was warm and humid—just right for the growth of dense forests. Under the weight of the sediment that was being deposited from the eroding mountains, the coastal plains were subsiding. This subsidence was important because it meant that space for deposition was continuously being created. The continuously increasing space allowed for the deposition of the thick sandstone and coal deposits that characterize the Late Paleozoic rocks of eastern North America.

Identifying Misconceptions

Many people think that life in the distant past was not very diverse or complicated. This is a vast oversimplification of the truth. During the Early Paleozoic Era, life became quite diverse. All of the major modern phyla had evolved by the end of the Ordovician Period. With this amazing diversity, complex ecological relationships between organisms developed. The Paleozoic was indeed a time of major changes that set the evolutionary stage for the ecological play of life during the Phanerozoic Eon.

Assessment

Portfolio Assessment
Assessment, TWE, p. 617

Performance Assessment
Assessment, TWE, p. 608
MiniLab, SE, p. 616
Discovery Lab, SE, p. 601
GeoLab, SE, pp. 618–619

Knowledge Assessment
Section Assessment, SE, pp. 604, 611, 617
Discovery Lab, TWE, p. 601
Assessment, TWE, p. 611
Chapter Assessment, SE, pp. 622–623

Skill Assessment
Assessment, TWE, p. 604
Problem-Solving Lab, TWE, p. 610
MiniLab, TWE, p. 616
GeoLab, TWE, pp. 618–619

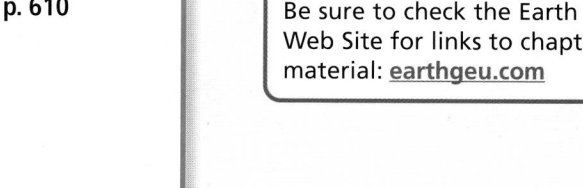

Earth Science Online

Be sure to check the Earth Science Web Site for links to chapter material: earthgeu.com

GLENCOE'S ASSESSMENT ADVANTAGE

The Paleozoic Era

Introducing the Chapter

The Paleozoic Era was a time of great change for life on Earth. To help students appreciate this, have small groups research Paleozoic organisms such as trilobites, brachiopods, crinoids, bryozoans, placoderms, cephalopods, lobe-finned fishes, corals, sphenopsids, lycopods, or conodonts. Have each group give an oral presentation about its organism.

Interpreting the Photo

Tectonic collisions of microcontinents with the eastern margin of North America resulted in the formation of the Valley and Ridge Province. A portion of this province can be seen in the mountains and valleys of the Otter Creek Wilderness in Monongahela National Forest, West Virginia. Intense thrust faulting and folding formed these mountains during several Paleozoic orogenies.

INTERACTIVE CHALKBOARD
with Image Bank

PowerPoint® Presentations

This CD is an editable Microsoft® PowerPoint® presentation that includes:
• Section presentations
• Section checks
• Image bank
• Links to Earth Science Online
• All transparencies
• Animations
• Audio

Chapter 23

The Paleozoic Era

Otter Creek Wilderness, Monongahela National Forest, WV

What You'll Learn
• How the Appalachian and Ouachita Mountains formed.
• When and on what scale three mass extinctions occurred.
• Why coal is common in Pennsylvanian-aged rocks.
• How the development of seeds and eggs affected the evolution of life.

Why It's Important
The tectonic setting of eastern North America provided a hospitable environment not only for a wide variety of animals and plants, but also for the vast swamps that ultimately formed the rich coal deposits of eastern North America.

Earth Science Online

To find out more about the Paleozoic Era, visit the Earth Science Web Site at earthgeu.com

600

Discovery Lab

Process Skills
observe and infer, recognize cause and effect, communicate, model, predict **L1** **ELL**

Procedure
Troubleshooting
• This activity works best with a very porous sandstone. The fractured side of a broken brick will also work well.

• Students should drop the water slowly, a little at a time. It may take 15–20 minutes for them to get 10 to 50 mL of water into the brick or rock.

Observe
The water enters the rock or brick under the influence of gravity. The water is filling the void spaces between the grains in the rock or brick.

Assessment

Knowledge Ask students what happened to the water. Be sure they understand that it is now in the pore spaces in the rock or brick. Have students apply this information by asking them to answer the

Discovery Lab

Where is oil found?

Many sedimentary rocks contain oil and water in the pore spaces between their grains. For example, as you will learn later in this chapter, there is abundant oil in the Paleozoic-aged, sedimentary rocks of West Texas. In this activity, you will observe how oil or water can be stored in solid rock.

1. Place an unglazed brick or sandstone sample on your table.

2. Using a dropper, slowly squeeze three to five drops per minute, of water or oil, for ten minutes.

Infer In your science journal, sketch a cross-section of the rock or brick. Include both before and after you added the water to it. Include in your sketches what the inside of the brick might look like. Infer what happened to the water.

SECTION 23.1 — *The Early Paleozoic*

OBJECTIVES

• **Describe** *the Cambrian paleogeography of Laurentia.*

• **Discuss** *the concept of a passive margin.*

• **Describe** *the Cambrian fauna.*

VOCABULARY

paleogeography
passive margin
transgression
regression
Burgess Shale

Clues from the Paleozoic Era help us to understand how the diversity of life developed. Today, the Appalachian Mountains of the eastern United States border a tectonically calm coastline. But this area was much different in the past. The Paleozoic story explains how early life-forms moved from water to land, why the Appalachians exist, and why they contain the vast coal deposits that fueled the industrial revolution. The Paleozoic portion of the geologic time scale is shown in *Figure 23-1* on page 602.

CONTINENTAL SETTING

Geologists refer to the ancient geographic setting of an area as its **paleogeography.** The supercontinent Rodinia, was present at the end of the Proterozoic. By the Cambrian, the ancient North American continent of Laurentia had split off from Rodinia, was located near the equator, and was surrounded by ocean. In addition, it was almost completely covered by a shallow, tropical sea.

Throughout the Cambrian Period, there was no plate tectonic activity on Laurentia. There were no collisional tectonic events, so there were no mountain ranges actively forming at that time. The edge of a continent is called a margin; when there is no tectonic activity

23.1 *The Early Paleozoic* **601**

following question in their science journals: If more than 10 to 50 mL of water can be stored in the rock or brick, how much oil can be stored in rocks that underlie West Texas? A great deal of oil can be stored. Students should come away from this Discovery Lab understanding that most water and oil in Earth are stored within rocks and sediment, not as underground lakes or rivers.

Section Focus

Before presenting the lesson, display **Section Focus Transparency 71** on the overhead projector. **L1 ELL**

Chapter Themes

The following themes from the National Science Content Standards are covered in this chapter. Refer to page 8T of the Teacher Guide for an explanation of the correlations.
Evidence, models, and explanation (UCP.2); Change, constancy, and measurement (UCP.3); Evolution and equilibrium (UCP.4)

 **·Out of Time?**

If time does not permit teaching the entire chapter, use the Chapter Summary on page 621 and the GeoDigest found at the end of the unit as an overview.

Resource Manager

Study Guide for Content Mastery, pp. 143–144 **L2**

Section Focus Transparency 71 L1 ELL

Teaching Transparency 69 L2 ELL

NY Core Curriculum Standards

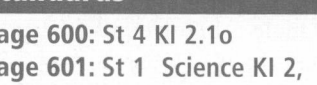

Page 600: St 4 KI 2.1o
Page 601: St 1 Science KI 2, St 4 KI 2.1o, St 6 KI 2

Content Background

Laurentia was surrounded by passive margins throughout the Cambrian Period, so there were no major tectonic events. Sea-level changes in this passive margin setting are recognizable by the fining upward sequences of sandstone-shale-limestone such as those preserved in the Grand Canyon. These sequences are a result of calm conditions farther and farther from the shoreline. Sandy beach areas had higher energy, so the fine sediment washed out to deeper water, where it was deposited as mud that ultimately lithified to shale. Beyond this area of sediment influx was calm, warm water, where carbonate sediment accumulated. The stacking order of sedimentary rocks indicates whether sea level was rising or lowering. The observation that sediments that are deposited adjacent to each other become vertically stacked as a result of a change in sea level is called Walther's principle.

Demo

Fill a plastic butter tub with sand and put the lid on it. Place the tub in a large, deep pan filled with enough water to cover half of the tub. Use a black grease pencil to mark the tub where the waterline is. Explain to students that this mark represents a sandy beach and that shale would be deposited in the water just below the mark. Add water to the pan so that the mark indicating where the beach was is now covered. Make a new mark to indicate that the beach is now at the higher water level. Explain to students that, now, the deeper water where the shale is being deposited is where the beach was before sea level rose.

Figure 23-1 The Paleozoic Era spans 290 million years and is divided into seven periods. The rocks of the Paleozoic Era, tell of the great changes in both the tectonic setting and the life-forms that developed during that era.

Paleozoic Era	
	— 245 M.Y.B.P.
Permian Period	
	— 290 M.Y.B.P.
Pennsylvanian Period	
	— 323 M.Y.B.P.
Mississippian Period	
	— 362 M.Y.B.P.
Devonian Period	
	— 408 M.Y.B.P.
Silurian Period	
	— 439 M.Y.B.P.
Ordovician Period	
	— 510 M.Y.B.P.
Cambrian Period	
	— 540 M.Y.B.P.

along a margin, it is called a **passive margin.** Laurentia was completely surrounded by passive margins throughout the Cambrian Period.

Characteristic Sediments The paleogeographic setting of Laurentia, as shown in *Figure 23-2,* set the stage for a characteristic pattern of sandstone-shale-limestone deposits that represent increasing water depth from shore. The exposed land surface was flat, and the floor of the shallow sea that covered Laurentia dipped gently away from the shoreline. On land, the exposed Precambrian rocks were deeply eroded. Large, sandy beaches formed as fragments of quartz were weathered from the rocks of the Precambrian Shield and transported to Laurentia's shoreline. Clay-sized sediments were carried by strong tides and deposited in slightly deeper water. Carbonate sediment accumulated in even deeper water as organisms whose skeletons were composed of calcium carbonate died and fell to the seafloor. Over time, the sand that had been deposited on the beaches became sandstone, the clay-sized sediments compacted to form shale, and the carbonate sediment became limestone. The most famous location where the sandstone-shale-limestone deposits of the Cambrian are exposed is the Grand Canyon. This sequence is shown in *Figure 23-3.*

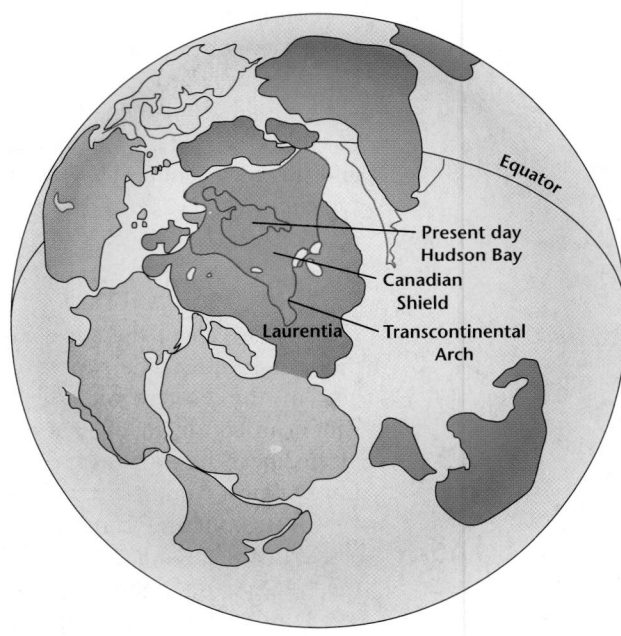

Figure 23-2 Laurentia was positioned at the equator during the Early Paleozoic. Strong, tropical storms, much like today's hurricanes, contributed to erosion and formation of sandy beaches. Corals thrived in the warm ocean waters and ultimately contributed to the formation of limestone.

Across the Curriculum

Biology Much of the calcium carbonate that makes up limestone comes from organisms that once lived in the ocean. Have students use the library or visit the Earth Science Web Site at earthgeu.com to discover what modern-day organisms contribute to the calcium-carbonate sediment of oceans.

Differentiated Instruction

Behaviorally Disordered To encourage students who are behaviorally disordered to learn the section content, ask them to find additional information about the Paleozoic sedimentary rocks of the Grand Canyon. Encourage students to use the library and the Earth Science Web Site at earthgeu.com to collect both descriptive and visual materials. Students can also contact the National Park System for more information.

CHANGES IN SEA LEVEL

The sandstone-shale-limestone sequence deposited during the Cambrian was a side-by-side, or lateral, sequence from shallow to deeper water. Why, then, are the layers of sandstone, shale, and limestone stacked one on top of the other in the Grand Canyon? The sediments themselves reflect the energy of the water and often, the water depth. Thus, any changes in sediments may indicate changes in sea level.

A **transgression** occurs when sea level rises and the shoreline moves further inland. Think of a sandy beach. In water slightly deeper than that at the beach, there is clay-rich sediment, and beyond this, in even deeper water, is carbonate-rich sediment. As sea level rises, the water floods inland and the shoreline moves inland. The beach is now located where dry land had been. The area of slightly deeper water where clay-sized sediments are deposited also moves shoreward on top of the old beach. The result of the transgression is deeper-water deposits overlying shallower-water deposits, as shown in *Figure 23-4.*

A **regression** occurs when sea level falls and causes the shoreline to move seaward. This results in shallow-water deposits overlying deeper-water deposits. A stacked sequence of limestone-shale-sandstone is evidence of a regression. As sea level rises or falls, sediments that are lateral to each other become stacked one on top of another.

Figure 23-3 This sequence of rocks is evidence of a rise in sea level during the Cambrian. The beach environment that existed during the Cambrian is preserved in the Tapeats Sandstone **(A).** Slightly deeper water is represented by the Bright Angel Shale **(B).** The fossiliferous Muav Limestone represents the deepest, offshore environment **(C).**

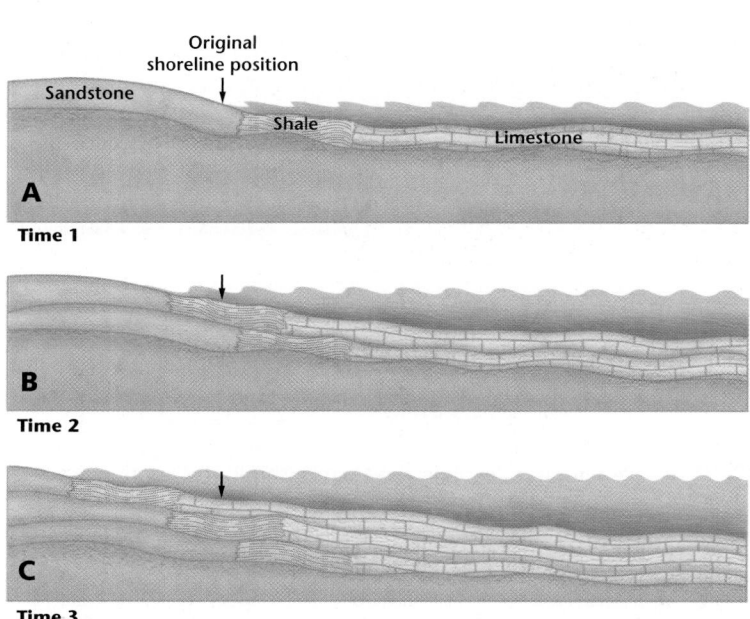

Figure 23-4 Time 1—sand is deposited at the shoreline and shale and limestone are deposited farther out **(A).** Time 2—sea level has risen, the shoreline has moved inland and shale is deposited at the original shoreline position **(B).** Time 3—sea level has risen again and limestone is deposited at the original shoreline position. The result is a sedimentary sequence of sandstone–shale–limestone **(C).**

23.1 *The Early Paleozoic* **603**

Environmental Connection

The Burgess Shale provides insight into the Cambrian ecosystem because it contains both soft-bodied and shelled organisms. Have the class make a list of organisms that are in an aquatic environment near your school, including invertebrates that do not have mineralized shells (such as worms). Discuss how our interpretation of this environment would be different if we did not know about the soft-bodied organisms.

Interpreting the Illustration

Figure 23-5A Represented in this illustration, clockwise from the top left are: sponges (conical, ribbed organism), trilobites, brachiopods, *Hyolithes* (a cone-shaped organism of uncertain phylum), and a polychaete worm.

603

3 Assess

Check for Understanding

Reinforcement

Ask students what sequence of sedimentary rocks they would expect to find overlying limestone in a marine regression. The limestone should be overlain by shale, and the shale should be overlain by sandstone. **L2**

Reteach

Have students predict what kind of sedimentary rock would be deposited stratigraphically above a layer of shale during a transgression and during a regression. During a transgression, limestone would be deposited above the shale, and during a regression, sandstone would be deposited above the shale. **L2**

✓Assessment

Skill Mix up the phrases below, then have students organize the phrases into a cycle map that describes the deposition of sedimentary rocks as sea level changes through time: sea level rises, transgression of the ocean, limestone is deposited over shale, sea level falls, regression of the ocean, sandstone is deposited over shale

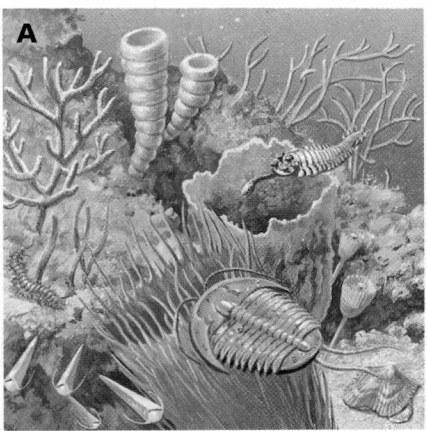

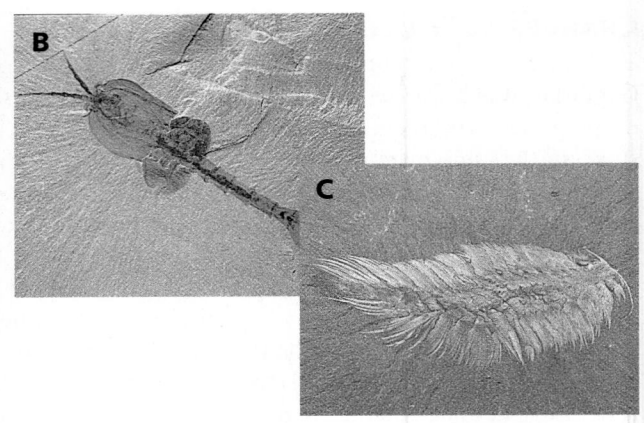

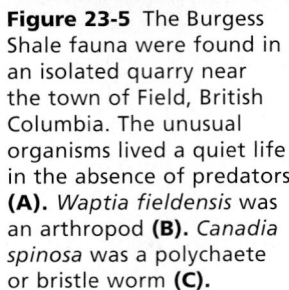

Figure 23-5 The Burgess Shale fauna were found in an isolated quarry near the town of Field, British Columbia. The unusual organisms lived a quiet life in the absence of predators **(A)**. *Waptia fieldensis* was an arthropod **(B)**. *Canadia spinosa* was a polychaete or bristle worm **(C)**.

You have learned that these distinct sequences of rock are the result of changes in sea level. While sea level was changing throughout the Paleozoic, so were the types of plants and animals that lived in the seas.

EARLY PALEOZOIC LIFE

There was such an increase in diversity and abundance of life-forms near the beginning of the Cambrian Period that some call this the Cambrian "explosion." Organisms representing all but one of the major marine groups appeared at this time. The development of mineralized skeletons or hard parts also mark the Cambrian explosion.

Some of the best fossilized Cambrian organisms come from the **Burgess Shale,** in the Canadian Rocky Mountains. A spectacular array of soft-bodied organisms, as well as organisms with hard parts, are preserved. This deposit includes wormlike animals of unknown affinity and many other animals that do not fit into any living phylum, as shown in *Figure 23-5.*

SECTION ASSESSMENT

1. What was the paleogeography of Laurentia during the Cambrian?

2. What is a passive margin?

3. Briefly describe the significance of the Cambrian fauna.

4. Describe how sedimentary sequences change when sea level lowers.

5. **Thinking Critically** If there were a major ice age today, explain the effect it would have on the sediments that are currently being deposited in the oceans and at sea level.

SKILL REVIEW

6. **Communicating** In your science journal, explain the relationship between the meanings of the words Cambrian *explosion* and the *explosion* of an object. For more help, refer to the Skill Handbook.

earthgeu.com/self_check_quiz

SECTION ASSESSMENT

1. Laurentia was geographically located over the equator during the Cambrian Period.

2. A passive margin is an edge of a continent along which there is no tectonic activity.

3. The Cambrian fauna marks a change in Earth's life-forms from soft-bodied, passive organisms to mobile, sometimes predatory organisms with hard parts.

4. When sea level lowers, the result is shallow-water deposits, such as sandstone, overlying deeper-water deposits, such as shale and limestone.

5. If a major ice age occurred today, sea level would fall. Water that evaporates from the ocean falls in the form of snow and forms the glaciers of an ice age. Global sea level would fall by the approximate volume of water in the ice and cause a regression. This regression would cause deeper-water deposits to be overlain by shallow-water deposits, as described in the answer to question 4.

6. In the first case, explosion is a noun *describing* an event, as in the sudden appearance of Cambrian organisms. In the second case, the explosion is an actual event. It is a noun, as in an explosion of a bomb.

The Middle Paleozoic

The passive margin that existed around Laurentia continued into the Early Ordovician Period. The paleogeography of Laurentia, as shown in *Figure 23-6A,* was still equatorial, with the paleo-equator running from approximately modern-day New Mexico through Minnesota.

SEA LEVEL CHANGES AGAIN

Sea level rose during the Early Ordovician and, once again, a beach environment covered much of Laurentia's margins. The base of the rock layers that were deposited is marked throughout much of central North America by the pure quartz sand of the St. Peter Sandstone, shown in *Figure 23-7* on page 606. The sandstone is overlain by minor amounts of shale and by extensive limestone deposits. These limestone deposits contain a tremendously diverse array of organisms, including the first corals that built organic reefs.

Organic reefs are structures composed of carbonate skeletons made by living organisms. Corals require warm, clear, shallow water of normal marine salinity in order to thrive. For this reason, they are confined to latitudes between 30° north and south of the equator. During the Middle Ordovician, corals and a group of sponges called stromatoporoids became common and began to build reefs in the shallow sea that covered Laurentia.

Reefs affect the environments in which they grow. They commonly form in long, linear mounds parallel to islands or continents, where they absorb the energy of waves that crash against them on their oceanward side. This protects the environments behind reefs from the waves' energy. The calm areas behind reefs, are called lagoons.

OBJECTIVES

- **Describe** the Middle Paleozoic paleogeography.
- **Explain** the concept of an active margin and the formation of a clastic wedge.
- **Describe** the Middle Paleozoic fauna.
- **Define** the concept of mass extinction.

VOCABULARY

Taconic Orogeny
Caledonian Orogeny
Acadian Orogeny
Antler Orogeny
Paleozoic fauna
vascular plant
mass extinction

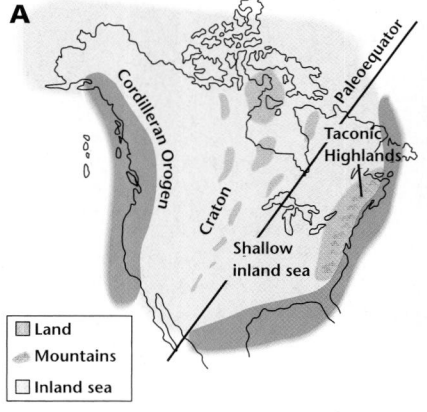
Ordovician Paleogeographic setting of Laurentia

A
Cordilleran Orogen
Paleoequator
Taconic Highlands
Craton
Shallow inland sea

☐ Land
⬡ Mountains
☐ Inland sea

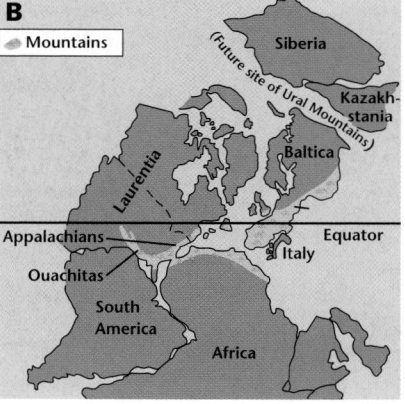
Pennsylvanian World Paleogeography

B
⬡ Mountains
Siberia
(Future site of Ural Mountains)
Kazakhstania
Baltica
Laurentia
Appalachians
Ouachitas
Equator
Italy
South America
Africa

Figure 23-6
Laurentia was positioned across the equator during the Early Ordovician. The Taconic Orogeny formed the Taconic Highlands along Laurentia's eastern margin **(A)**. Orogenic activity continued during the Pennsylvanian. Mountains formed along the line of collision. All of the continents were assembled as one supercontinent, Pangaea **(B)**.

23.2 *The Middle Paleozoic* **605**

Project

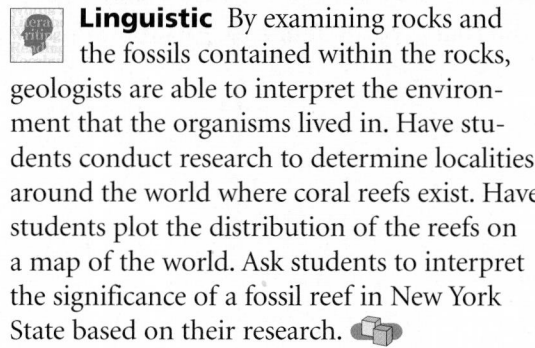
Linguistic By examining rocks and the fossils contained within the rocks, geologists are able to interpret the environment that the organisms lived in. Have students conduct research to determine localities around the world where coral reefs exist. Have students plot the distribution of the reefs on a map of the world. Ask students to interpret the significance of a fossil reef in New York State based on their research.

Content Background

The first major orogeny of the Phanerozoic occurred during the Middle Paleozoic. Two major deformational events, the Taconic and Acadian Orogenies, occurred along what is now the eastern margin of North America. Huge, wedge-shaped deposits of clastic material formed next to the mountains formed by these orogenies. Also during the Middle Paleozoic, life suffered two mass extinction events, both apparently caused by climatic cooling. Life, however, also made great evolutionary strides during this time. Perhaps most notably, plants and animals began to colonize the land.

Interpreting the Illustration

Figure 23–8 The reef shown in the illustration is a barrier reef. This kind of reef exists today along the eastern coast of Australia and is called the Great Barrier Reef. Lead students to notice that the lagoon is protected from the waves that pound against the oceanward side of the reef. The back-reef lagoon setting is quite calm, and because there is little connection with the open ocean, the salinity of the water may rise as a result of evaporation. If restriction from the ocean continues for extended periods of time, the water in the lagoon may become saline enough for the precipitation of evaporite minerals.

Figure 23-7 Glass is made from silica sand such as the very pure and clear St. Peter sandstone.

Here fragile organisms can thrive as shown in *Figure 23-8.* Reefs also can restrict water flow from the lagoon to the ocean. The shallow, quiet water in lagoons warms in the tropical sunlight and water evaporates at a high rate. When this happens, lagoon waters may become oversaturated with calcium and sodium. These elements combine with other elements or compounds in the water and precipitate out of solution as evaporite minerals such as gypsum and halite.

The Great Lakes area of North America contains huge deposits of Silurian-aged evaporite minerals that are mined commercially. Surrounding many of these evaporite deposits are reefs that almost certainly played a role in restricting the flow of water, thus making conditions right for the deposition of evaporite minerals. In the Michigan Basin, periodic restriction and deposition of evaporites resulted in deposits of halite and anhydrite more than 700 m thick! The Ohio Basin and the Appalachian Basin also were sites of evaporite deposition during the Late Silurian. *Figure 23-9* shows the locations of these basins. Today, these evaporite deposits are important sources of gypsum, which is used to make plaster and drywall, and halite, which is mainly used as road salt.

MIDDLE PALEOZOIC TECTONICS

During the Middle Ordovician, an ocean-continent collisional boundary, an active margin, developed in what is now eastern North America. As shown in *Figure 23-6A,* this resulted in a mountain building event called the **Taconic Orogeny,** named for the Taconic

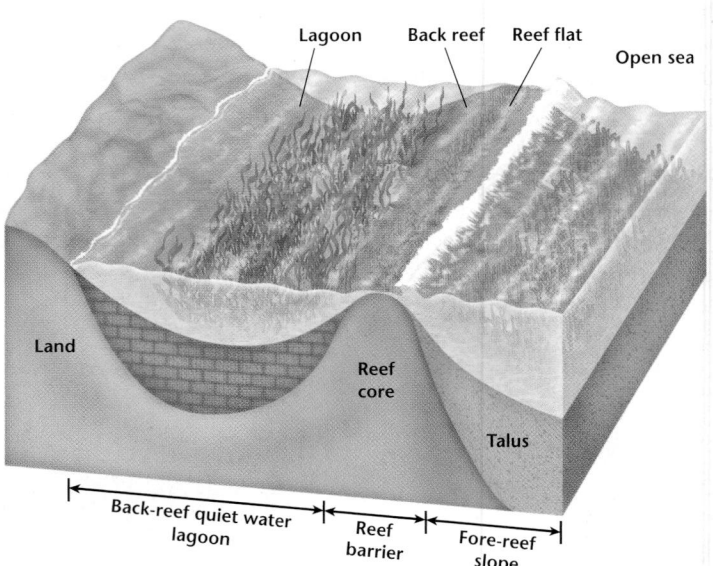

Figure 23-8 The sheltered, quiet water behind a coral reef is an ideal place for fragile organisms to thrive.

Differentiated Instruction

Gifted Salt is mined from regions of the world other than those discussed in this section. Have students conduct research to discover where else salt is mined. Have them compare the different geological and environmental settings where these salt deposits occur. L3

Resource Manager

Teaching Transparency 70 L2 ELL

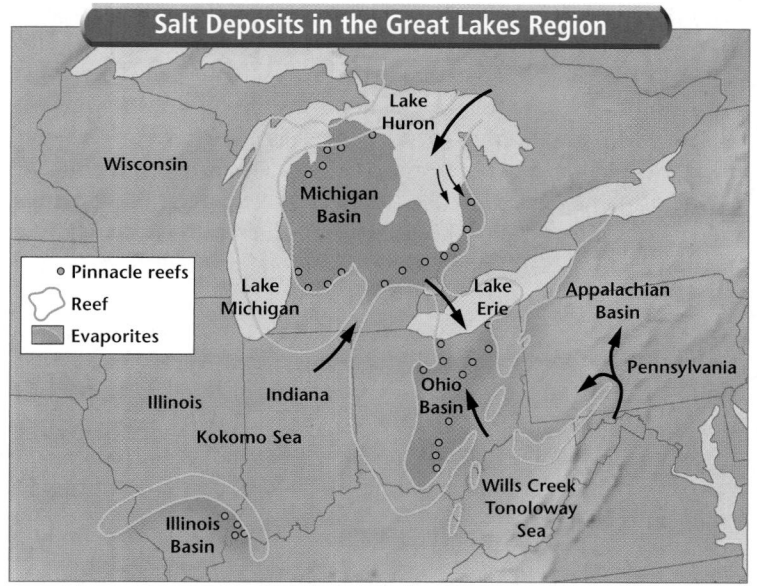

Salt Deposits in the Great Lakes Region

Lake Huron

Wisconsin

Michigan Basin

Lake Michigan

○ Pinnacle reefs
◇ Reef
▨ Evaporites

Lake Erie

Appalachian Basin

Pennsylvania

Illinois

Indiana

Ohio Basin

Kokomo Sea

Wills Creek Tonoloway Sea

Illinois Basin

Figure 23-9 The barrier reefs that grew within these basins most likely restricted the flow of water from time to time. This, coupled with increased evaporation, resulted in the formation of halite and other evaporite minerals.

Mountains of eastern New York State. A series of volcanic islands also formed as a result of this mountain building event.

How do we know that this Taconic Orogeny occurred? Geologists look for clues and evidence in the rocks like detectives at a crime scene. One form of evidence is angular unconformities. Rocks that are older than the Middle Ordovician of eastern New York are tilted at a different angle than those of the younger Silurian rocks. This means that something, such as a tectonic collision, tilted the rocks after the Middle Ordovician but before the Silurian. Volcanic activity also provides evidence of the Taconic Orogeny. Lava flows and volcanic ash deposits that are Middle-to-Late Ordovician in age exist in present-day eastern North America. There are also igneous intrusions and regional metamorphic features that have been radiometrically dated as being between 480 and 440 million years old. The final piece of evidence of the Taconic Orogeny is the wedge of sediment, some of which is shown in *Figure 23-10,* that formed as the mountains from the Taconic Orogeny eroded. In a cross section, such a deposit has a triangular wedge shape, and is called a clastic wedge.

Orogenies and Deformation Tectonism continued during the Late Silurian and into the Devonian when Laurentia collided with Baltica, an ancient continent that consisted of what are now northern Europe and Russia west of the Ural Mountains. This collision joined Laurentia and Baltica into a larger continent known as Laurasia, pictured in *Figure 23-6B* on page 605.

Figure 23-10 Erosion and transport of material from rising mountains to the east resulted in the formation of these coarse-grained, layered deposits. They are part of a large clastic wedge called the Queenston Delta and are exposed in Genesee Gorge in Letchworth State Park, NY.

Modeling

Visual-Spatial All salt deposits are precipitated by water. Normal ocean water contains about 3.5 percent salt. Prepare water with normal marine salinity by adding 35 g of salt to 965 mL of water. Tell students that the solution has a salinity of 35 parts per thousand (ppt). Pour the solution into a shallow baking pan, then allow the water to evaporate and the salt to precipitate. Ask students to imagine how many liters of seawater must have evaporated to produce salt deposits that are hundreds of meters thick, given that 1 L of normal marine water must evaporate to precipitate just 35 g of salt.

Applying Earth Science

Evaporites continued to form throughout the Paleozoic and Mesozoic. Because salt is less dense than other sedimentary rocks, it rises upward toward the surface and forms pillar-shaped structures called salt domes. This upward pressure deforms the surrounding rock layers. Oil and gas may get trapped in these layers. Evaporation and formation of salt deposits during the Mesozoic produced more than 1000 m of salt in what is now the Gulf of Mexico. Today, the Gulf of Mexico is the site of active oil and gas exploration and production in such domes. In addition to oil and gas, salt domes are mined for the salt itself.

Tying to Previous Knowledge

One of the lines of evidence used to demonstrate that the Taconic Orogeny occurred is the presence of volcanic ash. Ask students why Ordovician volcanic ash deposits support the idea that there was Ordovician orogenic activity.

Enrichment

Ask students to discuss how they would determine the age of volcanic ash. The best ways would be the radiometric age-dating of mineral crystals that are part of the ash ejected from the volcano and the use of fossils in strata above and below the ash bed to determine its relative age.

NY Core Curriculum Standards

Page 606: St 4 KI 2.1n, 2.1w, & 3.1a

Page 607: St 4 KI 2.1m & 2.1n

Figure 23-11 These rocks were deformed and faulted during the collisional events of the Taconic and Acadian Orogenies.

This collisional tectonic event, known as the **Caledonian Orogeny,** closed the ocean that had separated these two continents. Shortly after Baltica collided with Laurentia, a microcontinent called Avalonia, which is now Newfoundland, collided with the southeastern margin of Laurasia. This tectonic event, known as the **Acadian Orogeny,** affected the same general area as the Ordovician Taconic Orogeny. The deformation caused by the Acadian Orogeny added folds, faults, and igneous intrusions to the already deformed rocks of the Taconic Orogeny. *Figure 23-11* shows some of the complex folds that resulted. During the Late Devonian and into the early Mississippian, the passive western margin of Laurentia was affected by a collisional tectonic event called the **Antler Orogeny.** It was most likely caused by a microcontinent or island arc that collided with what is now western North America, as shown in *Figure 23-12.* As you will learn in the next chapter, one of the problems with interpreting the Paleozoic geology of western North America is that it has been complicated by numerous younger orogenic events.

Figure 23-12 The mountains of the Antler Orogeny bordered an inland sea to the east. The collision of a microcontinent with Laurentia is thought to be the cause of the orogeny.

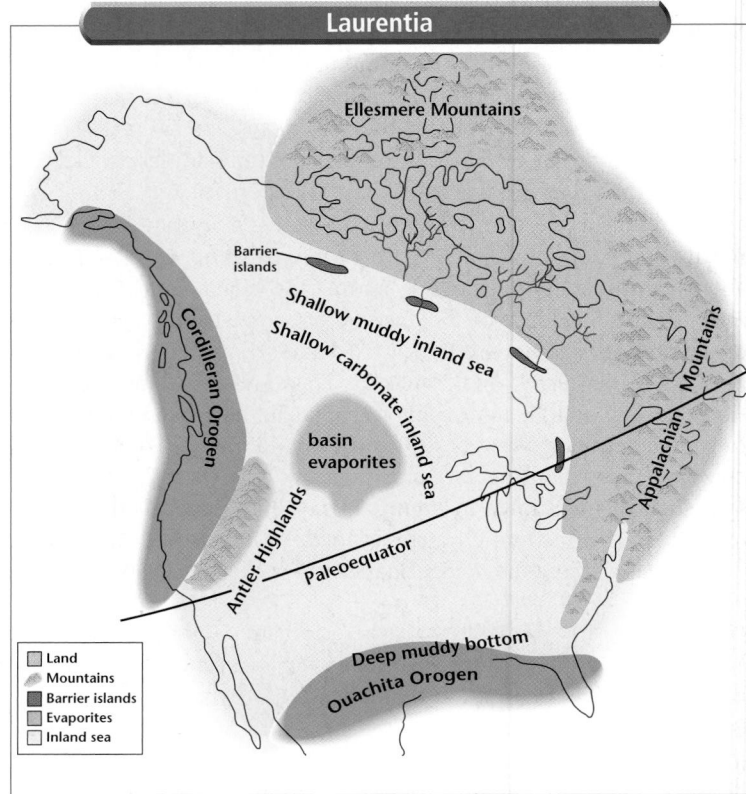

Laurentia

Ellesmere Mountains

Barrier islands

Cordilleran Orogen

Shallow muddy inland sea

Shallow carbonate inland sea

basin evaporites

Antler Highlands

Paleoequator

Appalachian Mountains

Deep muddy bottom

Ouachita Orogen

- ☐ Land
- ⫽ Mountains
- ■ Barrier islands
- ☐ Evaporites
- ☐ Inland sea

608 CHAPTER 23 *The Paleozoic Era*

Resource Manager

Laboratory Manual, pp. 177–180 L2

MIDDLE PALEOZOIC LIFE

The Middle Paleozoic seas were dominated by animals that are collectively called the **Paleozoic fauna.** The animals that dominated the Cambrian seas were replaced during the Early Ordovician by a variety of new organisms. Representatives of the Paleozoic fauna are shown in *Figure 23-13.*

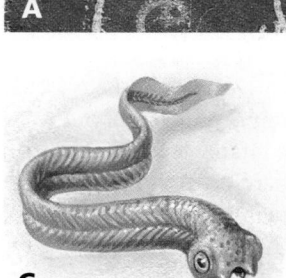

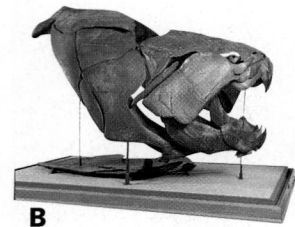

Biologists have observed that modern corals deposit thin layers of carbonate, called growth lines, to their skeletons each day. Seasonal variations in length of day cause yearly changes in the spacing of these growth lines. The Devonian horn coral, *Heliophyllum,* pictured in *Figure 23-13D,* displays these types of growth lines. Based upon the spacing and number of growth lines in a cycle, paleontologists have deduced that, during the Devonian, the days were about 22 hours long and there were about 400 days in a year. The corals thus indicate that Earth was rotating more rapidly during the Paleozoic and, like a top, has been slowing ever since. You will calculate the lengths of days of other periods in the *Problem-Solving Lab* on page 610.

LIFE MOVES TO LAND

The seas were not the only places where life was developing during the Middle Paleozoic. For the first time in the history of life on Earth, land was colonized. Fossilized plant parts and spores suggest that some form of land plant existed during the Late Ordovician. **Vascular plants** have tissue for circulating water and nutrients through their stems and leaves. It was the development of this tissue that allowed plants to spread out on land. Fossils that undisputedly represent vascular plants are found in Early Silurian rocks. These plants were small, leafless, grew along the ground, and reproduced by spores.

New Plants Emerge By the Late Devonian, three important groups of vascular spore-bearing plants were living on land. One group, the ferns, still thrive today. The second group, the sphenopsids, were joint-stemmed plants. A modern species of sphenopsid is the horsetail or scouring rush, shown in *Figure 23-14,* whose common name is derived from its use by early plains settlers to scour their dishes. The last group is the lycopods. The leaves of the lycopods grew directly from their stems, leaving diamond-shaped scars on the fossilized stems.

Figure 23-13 Graptolites lived in shallow, marine waters **(A)**. The Early Paleozoic fishes had internal skeletons of cartilage. This *Dunkleosteus,* from Ohio was a top predator in the Devonian Seas **(B)**. Conodonts were eel-like swimmers whose only hard-parts were tooth-like structures. They are excellent index fossils because they are widespread, existed during a short period of time, and have distinct characteristics **(C)**. The growth lines on this Devonian horn coral, *Heliophyllum,* help determine the length of a Devonian year **(D)**.

Content Background

An important component of the Paleozoic marine fauna was a group of organisms that are represented in the rocks by their toothlike hard parts, called conodont elements. Conodont animals appeared in the Cambrian and became extinct at the end of the Triassic. In 1983, preserved soft parts of conodonts were discovered. Conodont elements were concentrated in the head region of an eel-like animal. Conodont elements are composed of calcium phosphate, much like teeth, and recent work has shown that conodont elements contain enamel and bonelike microstructures. Many paleontologists now think that conodonts are a group of extinct marine vertebrates. Because conodont elements are widespread and common, and the conodont animal evolved rapidly, they are excellent index fossils for Paleozoic and Triassic (Early Mesozoic) marine rocks.

Cultural Diversity

Estella Leopold (1927–   ) Paleoecology is the study of prehistoric organisms and their environments. Estella Leopold attempts to re-create ancient landscapes by comparing modern assemblages of pollen, spores, and leaves to fossilized vegetation. In this way, she creates images of past landscapes.

After graduating from Yale in 1955, Leopold worked for the U. S. Geological Survey and studied rocks in the Rocky Mountains to reconstruct the evolution of ancient forests. Leopold found that patterns of evolution and extinction are linked to climatic changes. She found that the older species of trees lived in moderate climates. Thus, the moderate climates were more capable of sustaining older species.

Leopold has won many awards from the National Science Foundation for her work. She has also served on such conservationist boards as the National Audubon Society, the Nature Conservancy, and the Colorado Wildlife Foundation.

Students will infer the number of hours in a day in the geologic past and use this knowledge to predict what will happen to the length of days in the future.

Process Skills

use graphs, predict

Teaching Strategies

Ask students whether they think it is more likely that Earth's rotation is slowing down or speeding up over time. Earth's rotation is slowing down. Use the analogy of Earth as a top that is spinning on its axis as it revolves around the Sun. Ask students whether a top that is spinning speeds up or slows down over time. It slows down. Ask them why a top doesn't speed up over time. Air friction causes the top to slow down.

Analysis

1. 400 million years ago, there were about 21.2 hours in a day.
2. 200 million years ago, there were about 22.6 hours in a day.

Thinking Critically

3. There will be 24.5 hours in a day about 50 million years from now. This is determined by extending the line on the graph into the future and assuming that the rate of slowing will roughly follow the trend that it has for the past 500 million years.

Assessment

Skill Ask students to determine how many minutes per million years Earth has slowed during the past 200 million years. If a day was 22.6 hours long 200 million years ago and it is 24 hours long now, then it has slowed by 1.4 hours, or 84 minutes, over the past 200 million years. 84 minutes/200 million years = 0.42 minutes/million years = 25.2 seconds/million years.

Figure 23-14 This modern horsetail **(A)** and this fossil horsetail from Italy **(B)** exhibit strikingly similar features such as the individual joints and clusters of leaves along the stem. This fossil fern is from Piesberg, Germany **(C)**.

During the Late Devonian, the seed ferns developed. The most important aspect of these plants was the development of seeds. Seeds contain their own moisture and food source. They are covered by a hard coating that prevents drying and protects them. Seeds allowed plants to spread out and colonize dry land. Until the development of the seed, plants required water to complete their reproductive cycles. Thus, with the development of seeds, the surface of the continents was changed forever.

MASS EXTINCTIONS

Two of the greatest extinction events in Earth's history occurred during the Middle Paleozoic. When an unusually large number of organisms become extinct over a relatively short period of geologic time, it

Problem-Solving Lab

Interpreting Graphs

Determine the length of a Paleozoic day Geologists study the shapes and compositions of fossil organisms to interpret how and in what types of environments they lived. Fossils can even be used to interpret climatic changes. For example, rugose corals exhibit lines on their shells that represent yearly growth cycles. Ultimately, paleontological data such as this can be used to interpret the past and to predict future events. Use the figure at the right to answer the following questions.

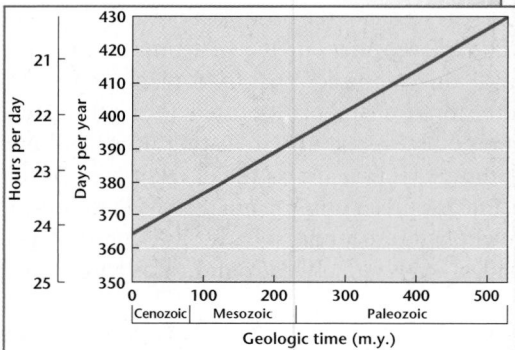

Geologic time (m.y.)

Analysis

1. How many hours were in a day 400 million years ago?

2. How many hours were in a day 200 million years ago?

Thinking Critically

3. When will there be 24.5 hours in a day?

is called a **mass extinction.** The first mass extinction occurred at the end of the Ordovician Period. Approximately 57 percent of all marine genera became extinct. Those that survived suffered large but not complete losses in their numbers of species and genera.

What caused the Late Ordovician mass extinction? One clue is that there are Late Ordovician glacial deposits preserved in what is now northern Africa. Another clue is that species that were adapted to warm environments were the hardest hit. Geologists hypothesize that an episode of global cooling, plus the rapid lowering of sea level that accompanied the glaciations, caused the extinction of many species that were adapted to warm environments.

Global Cooling and Overturning A second mass extinction occurred during the late Devonian when approximately 50 percent of the marine genera were wiped out, including many species of corals and stromatoporoids. Again, the polar communities were not severely affected. Was global cooling again the cause? There is evidence that glaciation occurred on some continents at this time. The cooling of Earth's atmosphere may have caused a tremendous disturbance in the ocean system. This created overturning, a process in which oxygen-poor, deep ocean water rises up, creating surface waters that contain little or no oxygen.

Evidence of overturning exists in the form of black shale. Black sediment indicates a lack of oxygen. Black shale deposits from the Late Devonian are common worldwide, and therefore, suggests that the seawater at that time contained reduced amounts of oxygen. The lack of oxygen in the water stressed the organisms to the point at which many species became extinct.

Update To find out more about present-day extinctions, visit the Earth Science Web Site at earthgeu.com

3 Assess

Check for Understanding
Discussion
Ask students why the development of the seed was important. Seeds are protective capsules that allowed plants to colonize the land.

Reteach

Interpersonal As a class, have students make a list of reasons for geologists' theory that eastern North America was the site of collisional plate tectonics during the Middle Paleozoic. Mountain ranges border the eastern and southeastern margins of the continents. **L2** **COOP LEARN**

✓Assessment

Knowledge In their science journals, have students explain how climatic cooling can lead to mass extinction. As climate changes, the types of vegetation change or simply die out. Animals that rely on that food will die, and so on up the food chain. Alternatively, animals and plants that are unable to adapt to the changing climate may simply die.

SECTION ASSESSMENT

1. Where was Laurentia positioned on Earth during the Middle Paleozoic?

2. Explain how evaporite deposits formed during the Middle Paleozoic.

3. What kinds of evidence do geologists use to determine whether an area was subjected to an orogeny?

4. What were the common causes of the Late Ordovician and Late Devonian mass extinctions?

5. **Thinking Critically** In Chapter 19, you learned about different kinds of faults. What kinds of faults would you expect to have been associated with the Acadian Orogeny? Why?

SKILL REVIEW

6. **Recognizing Cause and Effect** Explain how the appearance of land plants led to the appearance of land animals.

earthgeu.com/self_check_quiz

23.2 *The Middle Paleozoic* **611**

SECTION ASSESSMENT

1. Laurentia was positioned equatorially through the Middle Paleozoic.
2. Barrier reefs often caused the restriction of seawater in basins. In such cases, restriction meant that seawater could not flow from the ocean to replace the water that was evaporating. This caused the restricted seawater to become oversaturated with salts, and the salts precipitated to form evaporites.
3. angular unconformities, volcanic rocks and

ash, igneous intrusions, regional metamorphism, and clastic wedges
4. Global cooling was common to both extinction events.
5. Reverse faults and thrust faults would be associated with the Acadian Orogeny. This is because the Acadian Orogeny was a compressional event that occurred as the microcontinent of Avalonia collided with Laurasia. Reverse and thrust faults form as

a result of compressional forces, and therefore, these types of faults are associated with collisional orogenic events.
6. Many land animals are herbivores or plant eaters. With plants well established on land, food sources for land animals were well established too.

The Late Paleozoic

Prepare

Section Background

For section content background, refer to **Sinking Coal Swamps** on page 600D.

Preplanning

Refer to the Chapter Organizer on pages 600A–B.

1 Focus

Section Focus

Before presenting the lesson, display **Section Focus Transparency 73** on the overhead projector. **L1** **ELL**

Tying to Previous Knowledge

One line of evidence used to support the theory that Pangaea existed as a supercontinent is the distribution of fossils. **Figure 17-2** shows the paleobiogeography of some important fossils that support the theory of Pangaea's existence.

OBJECTIVES

- **Describe** *the formation of Pangaea.*
- **Explain** *how cyclothems formed.*
- **Identify** *the importance of amniote eggs.*
- **Discuss** *the causes of the Late Permian mass extinction.*

VOCABULARY

Gondwana
cyclothem
Ouachita Orogeny
Ancestral Rockies
Alleghenian Orogeny
amniote egg

During the Late Paleozoic, the supercontinent Pangaea formed. In the previous section, you learned that Laurentia, Baltica, and the microcontinent Avalonia were joined together by the end of the Devonian. *Figure 23-15* shows how, as a result of similar collisional events, South America, Africa, India, and Antarctica joined to form the large continent in the southern hemisphere called **Gondwana.**

SEA LEVEL AND DEPOSITION

The Late Paleozoic began with Laurasia still covered by a shallow tropical sea. This setting provided the perfect environment for the deposition of carbonate sediment. Thus, Mississippian rocks throughout North America are predominantly limestone. The end of the Mississippian was marked by a major regression of the sea.

The Pennsylvanian Period began with a slow transgression. The sediments that were deposited have quite different characteristics from those of the underlying Mississippian carbonates. The Pennsylvanian and Permian rocks in central and eastern North America are predominantly river and delta deposits.

The Pennsylvanian Period is known for the coal deposits that accumulated in heavily vegetated lowland swamps. As you have learned, coal forms through the compaction of plant material. Why

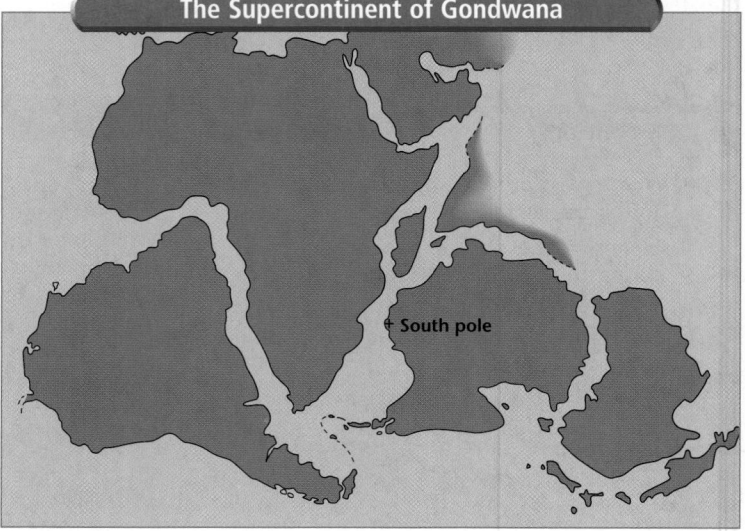

Figure 23-15 The mountain building and subsequent erosion that occurred as Gondwana formed resulted in the formation of clastic wedges in front of the mountains. The mountain building events are sometimes referred to as the Gondwanan Orogeny.

Resource Manager

Study Guide for Content Mastery, pp. 147–148 **L2**

Section Focus Transparency 73 **L1** **ELL**

Teaching Transparency 71 **L2** **ELL**

Differentiated Instruction

Visually Impaired Make cutouts of the continents from cardboard and place them on a flat map of the world. Use a string to designate the equator. Then, move the continents to form Pangaea relative to the equator. Point out Gondwana and the north and south poles.

are coal deposits not common in older rocks? The answer lies in the development of plant life on land. Not enough plant material had accumulated on land to form significant coal deposits until the Mississippian. Because a shallow sea covered Laurasia during the Mississippian, and because coal deposits generally form on land, there are few Mississippian-aged coal deposits in North America.

Cyclothems Pennsylvanian rocks in North America display a repeating cyclic pattern of sediments stacked one on top of another. Such a sequence as pictured in *Figure 23-16* is called a **cyclothem.** Cyclothems record two changes in sea level. A regression is represented by layers of marine limestone, and sandstone. A transgression is represented by sandstone, clay, coal, shale and marine limestone. In some parts of Laurentia, as many as 40 to 50 of these sequences were stacked one on top of the other. What could have caused the seas to transgress and regress 50 times? Most geologists hypothesize that glaciation was responsible. Glaciers grow by the accumulation of snow. Most of the water that freezes into snow comes from the evaporation of seawater. Thus, when glaciers are growing, sea level is falling. Gondwana was located in part over the south pole during the Pennsylvanian and large, glacial ice sheets developed on land. It is likely that glaciers grew during cooler periods during the Pennsylvanian and caused sea level to drop, which, in turn, caused a regression. The glaciers partially melted during warmer periods and caused sea level to rise, which resulted in a transgression. In this way, numerous cyclothems were deposited one on top of the other.

REEFS AND EVAPORITES

During the Permian, much of what is now eastern North America was dry land and a shallow sea covered most of what is now western North America. A spectacular fossilized barrier reef complex was formed during the Permian in what is now western Texas, southeastern New Mexico, and northern Mexico. Sponges and algae built this reef complex, known as the Great Permian Reef Complex, the remains of which are shown in *Figure 23-17* on page 614. Because these barrier reefs restricted the flow of water, large evaporite deposits formed behind the reefs during the Middle and Late Permian.

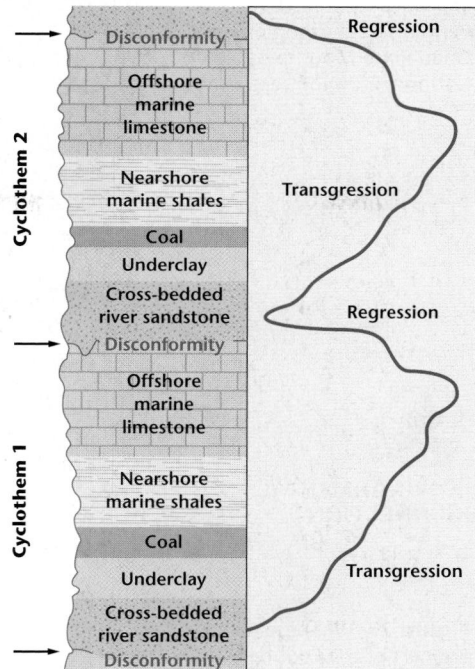

Figure 23-16 The general rock sequence of a cyclothem from base to top, is sandstone-clay-coal-shale-limestone.

Content Background

The supercontinent Pangaea formed during the Late Paleozoic. Reptiles evolved from amphibians and invaded the dry land during the Late Paleozoic. A particularly successful group of reptiles that appeared during the Pennsylvanian were the fin-backed pelycosaurs. The sail on a pelycosaur was made of skin stretched over long spines that extended from the vertebrae. Most paleontologists agree that the main function of the sail was to regulate the animal's temperature. Pelycosaurs were most likely cold-blooded and could not regulate their body temperatures. The sail probably was used to catch the Sun's rays and warm the blood that was pumped through the skin. When it was too hot, the pelycosaurs could face the wind to cool their blood, much the same way that a radiator circulates fluid to cool a car's engine.

Interpreting the Illustration

Figure 23-16 Each rock layer in the cyclothem represents a specific environment. The coal layers are nonmarine and might contain plant and land animal fossils and possibly an ancient soil called a paleosol. The limestone and shales are marine and might contain fossils of crinoids, brachiopods, bivalves, and trilobites. The sandstone represents a river environment and may contain cross beds and ripple marks.

Earth Science
Journal

Science Field Book

Linguistic The cyclothems discussed in this section have different characteristics in Kansas, in Illinois, and in the Appalachian Mountains. Ask students to research cyclothems in these different areas. Have students describe in their science journals how and why the cyclothems in these regions are both different from and similar to each other.

Figure 23-17 The best
exposure of the Great
Permian Reef Complex is at
Guadalupe Mountains
National Park in West Texas.

Tying to Previous Knowledge

Ask students why the rocks exposed at Garden of the Gods, Colorado, shown in **Figure 23-18,** are red in color. These rocks are red because they contain oxidized iron. Refer students to the MiniLab in Chapter 22.

Concept Development

Ask students the following question: Why would the coarse-grained rocks of the Great Permian Reef Complex be better oil reservoirs than the salt deposits associated with them? There is very little porosity in the salt deposits, and thus there are no spaces in the salt to store oil. The coarse-grained reef deposits have a high degree of porosity and therefore many spaces in which to store oil.

ENVIRONMENTAL CONNECTION

Figure 23-18 These rocks are part of the Fountain Formation, a unit whose sediments were derived from erosion of Pennsylvanian-aged arkoses. As a result of continued faulting, the layers are standing literally on end.

These evaporites and the Great Permian Reef Complex are very important deposits. As you learned in the *Discovery Lab* at the beginning of this chapter, pore spaces in rocks and sediment can be filled with oil or water. The pore spaces in Permian reefs and in the surrounding coarse-grained rocks are filled with oil making these reefs important oil reservoirs. The evaporites associated with these reefs are important for a different reason. The thick salt deposits have very low permeability and, thus, virtually no liquids move through them. This makes them an excellent environment for long-term storage of nuclear waste. In the thick salt deposits in southeastern New Mexico, a large facility has been built for the disposal of various kinds of nuclear waste.

CONTINENTAL COLLISIONS AND MOUNTAIN BUILDING

The Late Paleozoic was a time of active mountain building. Gondwana collided with the southeastern margin of Laurasia during the **Ouachita Orogeny.** The Ouachita Orogeny formed the Ouachita Mountains of Arkansas and Oklahoma and the mountains in the Marathon area of West Texas.

The collision between Gondwana and Laurasia was so intense that it caused the crust to uplift inland as far as present-day Colorado. Geologists call the mountain range that formed the **Ancestral Rockies.** Large vertical faults lifted the Paleozoic rocks more than 2 km. The uplifted rocks eventually eroded and were deposited as red sandstone beds. The most famous of these deposits are the beautiful exposures at Garden of the Gods in Colorado Springs, shown in *Figure 23-18.*

As the collision between the two supercontinents continued, it closed the ocean that separated Gondwana from Laurasia. The part of Gondwana that is now Africa began to collide with Laurasia during the Late Pennsylvanian, causing the **Alleghenian Orogeny.**

Resource Manager

Laboratory Manual, pp. 181–184 L2
GeoLab and MiniLab Worksheets, p. 91 L2

Interpreting the Photo

Figure 23-18 The mountain-building event that created the landscape surrounding the Garden of the Gods included large-scale thrust faulting. The result of this can be seen in the photo. The rocks that appear to be sticking straight up out of the ground are doing just that. The original layers have been tilted up on their sides and are now oriented vertically.

NY Core Curriculum Standards

Page 614: St 4 KI 1.2j & 2.1n
Page 615: St 4 KI 1.2i, 1.2j, & 2.1n
Page 616: St 4 KI 1.2i, St 6 KI 2
Page 617: St 4 KI 1.2i & 1.2j

Figure 23-19 This fossil crinoid is from the Silurian **(A).** Living crinoids feed by spreading out their arms to catch and filter food particles from the water and pass them down to their mouths through grooves in their arms **(B).**

It continued through the Permian along the southeastern margin of Laurasia. The Alleghenian Orogeny was the last of the three major mountain-building events to affect what is now eastern North America and resulted in the formation of the Appalachian Mountains. Pangaea had formed. This is summarized in *Figure 23-6B* on page 605.

LATE PALEOZOIC LIFE

The invertebrate marine organisms that flourished during the Middle Paleozoic continued to dominate the marine environment. One group, the crinoids, shown in *Figures 23-19A* and *B,* became dominant during the Mississippian. Crinoids were so abundant that some Mississippian limestones are made almost entirely of fossilized crinoid stem fragments.

Changes in the Ocean Following the extinction of many fishes during the Late Devonian, sharks and other ray-finned fishes, some of which still exist today, became more abundant. Lobe-finned fishes appeared during the Late Devonian, but became more abundant during the Late Paleozoic. Their club-shaped fins were supported by thick bones that made it possible for some of these fishes to walk on land. Of the three groups of lobe-finned fishes, two of them, the lungfishes and the coelacanths, are still living today. The third group of lobe-finned fishes gave rise to the amphibians.

On land, the true ferns, sphenopsids, lycopods, and seed ferns that appeared during the Late Devonian had thoroughly

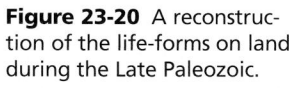

Figure 23-20 A reconstruction of the life-forms on land during the Late Paleozoic.

Project

Linguistic Have students work individually or in small groups to find out about current extinction rates and global diversity. Have students use the numbers that they find to estimate the longest time and the shortest time before 96 percent of all current species become extinct. Have each student group report its results to the class. On the chalkboard, keep a list of estimated extinction rates, estimated global biodiversity, and calculations of time before a 96 percent mass extinction occurs. Have students incorporate these data in their science journals. **L2**

Collaborative Learning

Interpersonal The Devonian has been called the Age of Fishes because of the great diversification of fishes that occurred at this time. Many of these groups continued to flourish through the Late Paleozoic. Important groups of jawed fishes that lived at this time include the ostracoderms, acanthodians, placoderms, lobe-finned fishes, cartilaginous fishes (chondrichthyes), and ray-finned fishes. Divide the class into groups. Have each group conduct research on one of these groups of fishes. Have the groups present their research to the class. You may wish to have students restrict their research to only Middle to Late Paleozoic representatives of these groups; otherwise, students studying groups that are extant, such as chondrichthyes, may end up talking about modern sharks. **L2**
COOP LEARN

Reinforcement

Logical-Mathematical Have students each construct a data table that includes the three orogenies that deformed eastern North America during the Middle and Late Paleozoic in one column, and the time when each occurred in the other column. **L2**

Interpreting the Illustration

Figure 23-20 Cycads are shown in the foreground of this swampy area. In the background at the right are trees of the genus *Lepidodendron*, which are characterized by a distinct spiral pattern of leaf scars on their trunks. Dragonflies with wingspans of approximately .5 m fly just to the left of center. Most Carboniferous insects were of normal size, by today's standards. Only one giant insect species is known.

96 percent of 10 million species = 9.6 million species

5.5 species/day × 364 days/year = 2002 species/year

9.6 million species/2002 species/year = 4795 years

Even if these estimates are off by a factor of 100, this would still mean that 96 percent of all species on Earth would become extinct within only half a million years.

MiniLab

Purpose
Students will use clay models to calculate how the continental shelf areas of one supercontinent and two individual continents differ.

Process Skills
construct models, measure, calculate, infer

Materials
modeling clay: 500 g of white, 250 g of yellow; metric ruler; calculator

Teaching Strategies
Ask students to imagine two small pizzas with the same area of toppings and sauce as one large pizza and to determine which has the most crust, the two small pizzas or the single large pizza. The small pizzas have more crust, just as two small continents have more continental shelf than a single continent.

Expected Results
The combined area of the continental shelf for the two small models should be greater than the area of the large model.

Analyze and Conclude
1. two small continents; because their shelf area is a greater proportion of the total area.
2. If there is only one supercontinent and part of it is situated over the equator, then the area of a warm, shallow-water habitat is restricted to only that part of one

MiniLab

Collisions and Shelves

Model the difference in continental shelf area between individual continents and one supercontinent.

Procedure
1. Using 250 g of modeling clay, make a sphere and flatten it into a disk that is 1/2 cm thick. This represents a craton.
2. Divide another 250 g of clay into 2 equal spheres and flatten them as above.
3. Roll 250 g of modeling clay into 3 long cylinders with 1/2 cm diameters. Wrap the cylinders around the edges of the clay disks. These represent continental shelves.
4. Using the formula area = πr^2, calculate the area of the large craton and the area of the large craton plus the continental shelf. Subtract the craton area from the total area. This equals the area of the continental shelf.
5. Repeat step 4 for each of the small models.

Analyze and Conclude
1. Which has more shelf area, two small continents or one large continent? Why?
2. Tropical oceans contain the greatest diversity of animals. If there is only one supercontinent how does this further limit the amount of habitat space?
3. Explain how reduced habitat space, Pangaea, and the mass extinction at the end of the Permian are related.

continent. However, if there are many continents in tropical latitudes, then the area of habitat space is much greater.
3. Pangaea formed over the equator; tropical marine habitat space was reduced; and diverse organisms were forced into a smaller space, which stressed the communities and caused Earth's greatest extinction event.

invaded the low, swampy land of the Pennsylvanian as illustrated in *Figure 23-20.* The warm, wet lowlands that developed at the base of the newly formed Appalachian Mountains was a perfect environment for plants to grow in and ultimately gave rise to the great coal swamps of the Pennsylvanian. They were a breeding ground for insects as well as plants. In fact, the largest insects that ever lived were preserved in coal swamps, including cockroaches that reached more than 10 cm in length and centipedes that were longer than 30 cm. The largest of all was a dragonfly with a 74-cm wingspan.

The coal swamps also housed amphibians. Although they were most likely sluggish and ate only fish, insects, vegetation, and smaller amphibians, they were the top carnivores on the land. Amphibians have one major limitation: they must lay their eggs in water because their eggs have no protective coating to prevent them from drying out on land. Thus, although early amphibians could colonize the land, they had to remain close to a source of water. Sometime during the Late Mississippian, this dependence on water was overcome. Reptiles that evolved from the early amphibians developed a new type of egg, the **amniote egg.** It has a shell that protects the embryo, which is surrounded by a liquid-filled sac that contains a food sac and a waste sac. Early reptiles were small, agile, and had more advanced teeth and jaws than amphibians. During the Permian, the more rapidly moving and stronger reptiles became abundant on land and displaced the amphibians as the top land carnivores.

THE PERMIAN MASS EXTINCTION
The largest mass extinction in the history of life on Earth defines the end of the Paleozoic Era. It is called the Permo-Triassic Extinction Event and it marks the end of

✓ Assessment

Skill Have students sketch a profile from the continental shelf to the abyssal plain and explain what would happen to habitat space if there were a marine regression. Have students also explain how the formation of Pangaea plus a marine regression, would have shrunk the habitat area for tropical marine life.

nearly 95 percent of all species including trilobites. You will learn more about this event in the *Science & the Environment* feature at the end of this chapter.

In contrast to the mass extinctions of the Middle Paleozoic, this extinction did not affect only the marine animals. Many of the terrestrial organisms that thrived in the swamps of the Late Paleozoic became extinct as well. More than 65 percent of the amphibians and reptiles did not survive, nor did almost one third of all insects. What could have caused such a widespread catastrophe?

A Major Marine Regression One possible cause of the Permo-Triassic Extinction Event was a major marine regression. Now, as then, most marine animals live in the relatively shallow water called the continental shelf. When sea level is high, the entire continental shelf is flooded, and there is quite a large area where marine animals can live. During regression, however, the continental shelf can become very narrow, leaving little space on the continental shelf for marine animals to live. This situation would have been particularly critical when there was only one continent. You learned about the consequences of reduced continental shelf space in the *MiniLab* on the previous page.

The end of the Paleozoic was a stressful time for life on Earth. Marine habitats shrank as a result of the major regression that occurred around Pangaea. Whether additional stresses were acting on life at that time is not known. What is known, however, is that regardless of the ultimate cause, life on Earth was irrevocably changed at the end of the Paleozoic.

Using Math

Calculating Percentages Is Earth currently in the middle of a mass extinction? If ten million species exist today, and 5.5 species extinctions occur every day, calculate how many years it would take for 96 percent of the species living today to become extinct.

SECTION ASSESSMENT

1. Explain the geologic events that resulted in the formation of Pangaea.

2. What is the relationship between cyclothems and glaciation?

3. What do scientists hypothesize were the main causes of the Late Permian mass extinction?

4. **Thinking Critically** In the previous section, you learned about the development of the seed. In this section, you learned about the development of the amniote egg. Explain the similarities between

these two important developments in the history of life on Earth.

SKILL REVIEW

5. **Concept Mapping** Reorganize the events below into an events chain that describes the formation of Pangaea. Ouachita Orogeny occurs; Ancestral Rockies uplifted; North America joined to Gondwana; Pangaea formed; Part of Gondwana collides with eastern Laurasia; Alleghenian Orogeny occurs; Part of Gondwana collides with SE Laurasia.

earthgeu.com/self_check_quiz

Check for Understanding

Discussion

Ask students: What conditions existed during the Permian extinctions that did not exist during the mass extinctions at the ends of the Ordovician and Devonian? A supercontinent existed and therefore there was less shelf area. Also, there is evidence that there was climatic warming at the end of the Permian, whereas at the ends of the Ordovician and Devonian, there was climatic cooling.

Reteach

The evolution of the amniote egg is similar to the invention of the submarine. The submarine allows humans to survive in an undersea environment, where we would otherwise drown. The amniote egg allows reptile embryos to survive in an environment in which they would dry out and die without the protection of the shell.

✓ Assessment

Portfolio Many of the largest coal deposits on Earth accumulated during the Late Paleozoic. Have students each create a poster that illustrates how this coal formed from plant material. **P**

SECTION ASSESSMENT

1. Pangaea formed as a result of the collision of Laurasia and Gondwana. This collision resulted in the Ouachita Orogeny, the uplift of the Ancestral Rockies, and the Alleghenian Orogeny. The Ouachita Mountains and the Appalachian Mountains formed as a result of these collisional events.

2. Cyclothems are sedimentary rock sequences that record the multiple changes in sea level that occurred during the Pennsylvanian Period. The changes in sea level

were likely caused by periods of glaciation.

3. the formation of a supercontinent that reduced the habitat space available for tropical marine organisms and a major marine regression that further reduced habitat space

4. The development of the seed and amniote egg were similar in that both of these evolutionary changes allowed organisms to colonize dry land. Both a seed and an amniote egg are capsules that protect the embryo

and carry materials vital for survival in the absence of constantly available liquid water.

5. Initiating Event: part of Gondwana collides with southeastern Laurasia, then: Ouachita Orogeny occurs, Ancestral Rockies uplifted, part of Gondwana collides with eastern Laurasia, Alleghenian Orogeny occurs, North America joined to Gondwana, Pangaea formed

GeoLab

Time Allotment

40 minutes

Process Skills

observe and infer, analyze data, classify, recognize relationships

Preparation

- Select large specimens to facilitate ease in handling.
- Select spiriferid brachiopods to best show brachiopod symmetry.
- Specimens may have sharp edges. Caution students to handle specimens with care.

Procedure

Teaching Strategies

- Discuss the concept of symmetry with students using common examples such as the bilateral symmetry of chordates.
- Have students identify the plane of symmetry in drawings of animals such as humans, dogs, fishes, and birds.
- Some brachiopods have smooth shells, while others have coarse ribs on their shells. There is a correlation between the textures of modern brachiopod shells and the environments in which they live. Modern brachiopods that live in low-energy, deep-water environments have smooth

GeoLab · Symmetry, Shape and Shells

Brachiopods and bivalves have been present in Earth's oceans since the Cambrian. Both have two shells and live in marine environments. But the similarity ends there. How can you tell the two apart? Oysters are bivalves that are known for the pearls they secrete inside their shells. Can you distinguish an oyster from a brachiopod? If you were searching for pearls, you would want to know how!

Preparation

Problem

Distinguish between brachiopods and bivalves and interpret the environment where a brachiopod lived based on its shell.

Materials

fossil brachiopods (4), each belonging to a different species
fossil bivalves (4), each belonging to a different species
paper
pencil

Objectives

In this GeoLab you will:

- **Determine** if a fossil is a brachiopod or a bivalve.
- **Describe** the symmetry of fossil brachiopods and bivalves.
- **Infer** the environment in which different fossil brachiopods lived.

Safety Precautions

Always wear safety goggles and an apron in the lab.

shells, whereas those that live in shallow, high-energy environments have coarse-ribbed shells. Have students divide the brachiopods into two groups based on whether they lived in a deep-water, low-energy environment or a shallow-water, high-energy environment. Students should record these groupings in their data tables.

Resource Manager

GeoLab and MiniLab Worksheets, p. 92–94 L2

| FOSSIL DATA | | |
Specimen	Brachiopod or Bivalve	Deeper water, low energy environment or shallow water, high-energy environment
1		
2		
3		

Procedure

1. Design a data table like the one above. You may choose to add more columns to record additional data.
2. Examine the fossils provided by your teacher.
3. Determine where the plane of symmetry is for each specimen. An organism that can be divided into two nearly identical halves has bilateral symmetry.
4. Identify the specimens as brachiopods or bivalves based on their symmetry and record this in your data table. Brachiopod symmetry runs across both shells. Bivalve symmetry runs between the shells.
5. Divide the brachiopods into two groups based on whether you think they lived in a deeper water, low energy environment, or in a shallow water, high-energy environment. Record this in your data table.

Analyze

1. **Interpreting Observations** Explain how symmetry is useful in determining whether a fossil is a brachiopod or a bivalve.
2. **Applying and Interpreting** If you only had one shell, how could you determine if it was the shell of a brachiopod or the shell of a bivalve?
3. **Comparing and Contrasting** Explain the similarities and differences between a streamlined auto and a smooth brachiopod, in terms of their place in wind or water.

Conclude & Apply

1. What principle did you use to determine the environment in which the fossil brachiopods lived? Explain.
2. Hypothesize about the reasons for the different shell types for brachiopods that live in different environments.
3. All living brachiopods pump water through their shells and filter organic particles out of that water to feed. Some brachiopod shells close along a straight line, whereas others close along a zig-zag line. What is the benefit of having a zig-zag opening for a filter feeding brachiopod?

GeoLab **619**

✔ Assessment

Skill Have students each construct a flow-chart key to classify bivalved animals according to whether they are brachiopods or bivalves and according to the environments in which they lived.

Data and Observations

Students will recognize that brachiopods are bilaterally symmetrical about a vertical plane that divides the shell, whereas in bivalves, the two shells are bilaterally symmetrical about a horizontal plane between the shells.

Analyze

1. Each shell of a brachiopod is bilaterally symmetrical, while bivalve shells are asymmetrical. This is useful because, many times, only a single shell of a fossil is found.
2. If the shell was bilaterally symmetrical, it would be a brachiopod; if it was not bilaterally symmetrical, it would be a bivalve.
3. Streamlined autos are not highly affected by air friction. Similarly, currents flow over and around smooth brachiopods with little obstruction.

Conclude & Apply

1. The principle of uniformitarianism; the lifestyles of modern organisms are used to infer the lifestyles of ancient organisms.
2. Winged and ribbed shells are found in higher energy water. These shapes help keep the shell oriented in the current. Smooth shells are not protected in this way. Thus, they are commonly found in quieter waters.
3. A zig-zag opening between the shells is larger than a straight opening. Greater volumes of water and food can be passed through this opening with roughly the same amount of energy in the same amount of time.

Science & the Environment

Science & the Environment

Purpose

Students will learn about the scale of major mass extinctions, and about how mass extinctions clear the way for new organisms to fill the niches left behind. Students will also learn that we are likely in the midst of a very large extinction event, which is threatening some biological resources that humans may need.

Content Background

The Permo-Triassic extinction event is the most devastating mass extinction known from the fossil record. This extinction event separates the Paleozoic from the Mesozoic on the geologic time scale. The Mesozoic organisms represent descendents of those that survived the Permo-Triassic extinction event. The extinction left many open niches, and these were filled by opportunistic organisms.

Teaching Strategies

Remind students of the calculations that they made in the Using Math feature on page 617. Have students access earthgeu.com to research other ideas about modern extinction rates and the areas that are most at risk.

Trilobite

Mass Extinctions

Most organisms that have ever lived on Earth are now extinct. For shallow-water, ocean-dwelling species, the average lifetime of a species is about 4 million years. That works out to an average of two or three species becoming extinct every year. The fossil record also indicates that, at certain times, many species became extinct over a short time.

The extinction of the dinosaurs and many other forms of life at the end of the Cretaceous Period has received much attention. For sheer numbers, though, these extinctions can't compare with the extinctions that ended the Paleozoic Era.

The Big Extinction Event

At the end of the Mesozoic, 65 to 75 percent of all species on Earth became extinct. When the Paleozoic ended, as many as 95 percent of all species became extinct. This event is called the Permo-Triassic Extinction Event.

Some marine organisms that became extinct during this Extinction Event were fusilinid foraminifera, rugose corals, and trilobites. On land, therapsids or mammal-like reptiles, became extinct, and insects suffered their only major extinction in their 390 million year history.

Paleontologists once thought that the Permo-Triassic extinctions took place over millions of years. However, recent research indicates that the extinctions were much more rapid. The causes are not well understood, but the extinctions appear to be the result of a fatal combination of changes in sea level, reduced oxygen levels, massive volcanic eruptions and global warming.

Opportunities Lost and Gained

Although the biosphere took millions of years to recover from each mass extinction, such extinctions are not entirely negative. The Permo-

Triassic Extinction Event cleared the way for new kinds of life, including the dinosaurs. The extinction at the end of the Mesozoic cleared the way for mammals to dominate. Without those extinctions, humans might not be here.

Many scientists believe that we are currently in the midst of another mass extinction. Over a thousand species of animals, and probably even more species of plants, are in danger of becoming extinct within our lifetime. This extinction is not caused by a regression or climatic changes, but by the impact of human activities.

Drugs to fight everything from AIDS to cancer have been found in organisms ranging from sponges to trees. Plants might be discovered that can be used to feed the world's hungry people. If a species becomes extinct, we lose the possibility of discovering any potential uses it might have had.

Activity

Go to earthgeu.com to find links to more information about the use of drugs derived from plants or animals to fight disease. Summarize where the drug is found, whether the plant or animal is in danger of becoming extinct, and how it is used to fight disease in humans.

Activity

Students should find that many medicines are derived from plants and animals. They should also find that a large proportion of these plants and animals are from areas that are threatened by humans such as tropical rain forests.

Summary

SECTION 23.1

The Early Paleozoic

Main Ideas

- The ancient North American continent of Laurentia was located near the equator and surrounded by ocean during the Cambrian Period. A shallow sea covered most of Laurentia.
- Laurentia was completely surrounded by passive margins throughout the entire Cambrian Period.
- Many new organisms developed during the Cambrian explosion. Fossils of trilobites and articulate brachiopods are particularly common in Cambrian rocks.
- When environments change position laterally due to changes in sea level, adjacent depositional facies overlie each other in vertical succession.

Vocabulary

Burgess Shale (p. 604)
paleogeography (p. 601)
passive margin (p. 602)
regression (p. 603)
transgression (p. 603)

SECTION 23.2

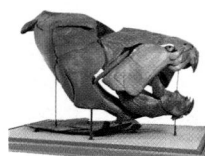

The Middle Paleozoic

Main Ideas

- High evaporation rates in lagoon settings cause the water to become oversaturated with calcium and sodium. These elements combine with other elements or compounds in the water and precipitate out of solution as the evaporite minerals.
- Clastic wedges provide evidence for orogenic events.
- The seas were dominated by articulate brachiopods, corals, mollusks, bryozoans, crinoids, graptolites and conodonts. Fishes were the top predators of the seas during the Devonian. Ferns, sphenopsids, and lycopods covered the landscape by the Late Devonian.
- Two mass extinctions occurred. A mass extinction occurs when an unusually large number of organisms become extinct over a relatively short period of geologic time.

Vocabulary

Acadian Orogeny (p. 608)
Antler Orogeny (p. 608)
Caledonian Orogeny (p. 608)
mass extinction (p. 611)
Paleozoic fauna (p. 609)
Taconic Orogeny (p. 606)
vascular plant (p. 609)

SECTION 23.3

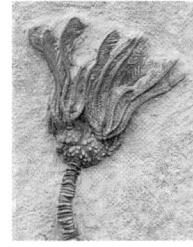

The Late Paleozoic

Main Ideas

- Pangaea formed as Laurasia (North America + Europe) collided with Gondwana (South America, Africa, India, Australia and Antarctica).
- Cyclothems consist of transgressive and regressive rock sequences stacked one on top of another. They represent cycles of glacial-interglacial periods.
- Seeds evolved and allowed plants to colonize dry land. The amniote egg evolved and allowed reptiles to colonize dry land.
- One possible cause of the Permo-Triassic Extinction Event was regression. Marine habitats around Pangaea shrank. Feedback from this event caused global warming, which affected organisms on land as well as in the sea.

Vocabulary

Alleghenian Orogeny (p. 614)
amniote egg (p. 616)
Ancestral Rockies (p. 614)
cyclothem (p. 613)
Gondwana (p. 612)
Ouachita Orogeny (p. 614)

 earthgeu.com/vocabulary_puzzlemaker

Main Ideas

Summary statements can be used by students to review the major concepts of the chapter.

VOCABULARY PuzzleMaker

For additional help with vocabulary, have students access the Vocabulary Puzzlemaker online.

earthgeu.com/ vocabulary puzzlemaker

0:00 Out of Time?

If time does not permit teaching the entire chapter, use the GeoDigest at the end of the unit as an overview.

Earth Science Online

Be sure to check the Earth Science Web Site for links to chapter material:
earthgeu.com

GLENCOE Technology

Videotape/DVD MindJogger Videoquizzes
Chapter 23: *The Paleozoic Era*
Have students work in groups as they play the videoquiz game to review key chapter concepts.

Resource Manager

Chapter Assessment, pp. 133–138
MindJogger Videoquizzes DVD/VHS
ExamView® Pro CD-ROM
Performance Assessment in Earth Science

NY Core Curriculum Standards

Page 620: St 4 KI 1.2i & 1.2j
Page 621: St 4 KI 1.2i, 1.2j, 2.1n, 2.1w, & 3.1a

Understanding Main Ideas

1. c
2. a
3. a
4. b
5. c
6. b
7. a
8. c
9. b
10. c
11. c

Applying Main Ideas

12. Burgess Shale fossils are unique because many of the preserved animals did not have mineralized shells.
13. The shale overlain by limestone indicates that a transgression occurred. The sandstone overlying the limestone indicates that a regression occurred.
14. The Paleozoic fauna consisted of new organisms such as graptolites, armored fishes, and conodonts. The Cambrian fauna were less diverse and dominated by trilobites.
15. Geologists look for angular unconformities, extrusive and intrusive igneous rocks, volcanic ash deposits, regional metamorphic rocks, folded rocks, and clastic wedges.

Understanding Main Ideas

1. Where was Laurentia located during the Paleozoic?
   a. over the south pole
   b. over the north pole
   c. over the equator
   d. where it is today

2. During what period was Laurentia completely surrounded by passive margins?
   a. the Cambrian
   b. the Ordovician
   c. the Devonian
   d. the Permian

3. What term describes a drop in sea level and the resulting seaward movement of the shoreline?
   a. regression
   b. excursion
   c. explosion
   d. transgression

4. What are the most common fossils of the Cambrian fauna?
   a. sharks
   b. trilobites
   c. crinoids
   d. rugose corals

5. What is the calm area behind a reef called?
   a. a clastic wedge
   b. a passive margin
   c. a lagoon
   d. a continental shelf

6. Which of the following is not an evaporite mineral?
   a. anhydrite
   b. quartz
   c. halite
   d. gypsum

7. What evaporite mineral is used to make plaster and drywall?
   a. gypsum
   b. aragonite
   c. halite
   d. quartz

8. What is a triangular-shaped sedimentary rock deposit that was deposited adjacent to an uplifted area called?
   a. a passive margin
   b. an active margin
   c. a clastic wedge
   d. an orogeny

9. What landmass collided with Laurentia and caused the Acadian Orogeny?
   a. Gondwana
   b. Avalonia
   c. Baltica
   d. Siberia

10. What group of fishes were able to walk on land?
    a. ray-finned fishes
    b. sharks
    c. lobe-finned fishes
    d. Dunkleosteus

11. What group of fishes gave rise to the amphibians?
    a. acanthodians
    b. sharks
    c. lobe-finned fishes
    d. Dunkleosteus

Applying Main Ideas

12. What is special about the fossils of the Burgess Shale?

Use the figure below to answer question 13.

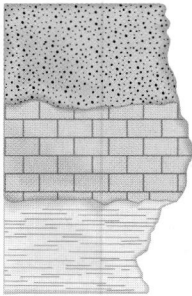

13. What change(s) in sea level is/are represented by the sequence of rocks?

Test-Taking Tip

DRAWINGS AND DIAGRAMS WITH TEXT
If a written description is included with a drawing or diagram, read it carefully. Sometimes the written description can clarify or change the meaning of the graphic.

earthgeu.com/chapter_test

Standardized Test Practice

1. c
2. d
3. c
4. b

14. Describe the differences between the Cambrian and Paleozoic fauna.

15. What kind of clues do geologists use to determine whether an area was the site of an orogeny in the geologic past?

16. How did paleontologists use rugose corals to determine that Earth rotated more rapidly in the geologic past than it does now?

17. How did the Pennsylvanian cyclothems form?

Thinking Critically

18. Explain why many paleontologists consider the development of the seed and the amniote egg to be two of the most important events in Earth's history.

19. How do the many coral reef deposits in the Great Lakes area of North America support the hypothesis that Laurentia was positioned across the equator in the Late Paleozoic?

20. Explain how identical clastic wedges formed on either side of the mountains that were formed by the Acadian Orogeny.

21. Distribution of plants occurs with the help of animals that eat them. Explain how the evolution of the seed ensured the success of this type of plant distribution.

Standardized Test Practice

1. What is it called when the sea level rises and shorelines move inland?
a. regression   **c.** transgression
b. passive Margin   **d.** laurentia

2. Which tectonic event was probably caused by a small microcontinent or island arc that collided with present-day western North America?
a. Taconic Orogeny   **c.** Acadian Orogeny
b. Caledonian Orogeny   **d.** Antler Orogeny

INTREPRETING SCIENTIFIC ILLUSTRATIONS
Use the figure to answer question 3.

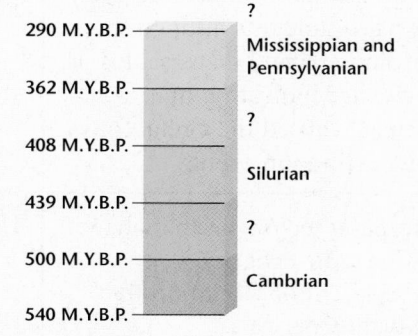

3. During the last period of the Paleozoic Era, much of what is now western North America was covered with dry land. What was this period called?
a. Pennsylvanian   **c.** Permian
b. Devonian   **d.** Ordovician

4. What was formed in North America when Gondwana and Laurasia collided?
a. Ancestral Rocky Mountains
b. Appalachian Mountains
c. Ouachita Mountains
d. Great Permian Reef

earthgeu.com/standardized_test

Assessment **623**

16. They used the daily and seasonal growth lines on the shells of rugose corals to determine the number of days in the year.

17. Pennsylvanian cyclothems formed as a result of sea-level changes associated with glacial and interglacial periods.

Thinking Critically

18. The development of the seed and the amniote egg allowed plants and vertebrate animals to colonize the dry land, away from a continuous source of water.

19. Today, coral reefs grow only in tropical regions near the equator. Based on the principle of uniformitarianism, this suggests that reefs in the distant past must have been located in tropical latitudes. Therefore, the Great Lakes area must have been located in tropical latitudes during the Middle Paleozoic.

20. Clastic wedges formed on both sides of the mountains that were formed by the Acadian Orogeny because as the mountains weathered, sediment was carried by mountain streams that flowed down each side of the mountain. The streams deposited the sediment along the margins of the mountains to form aprons of clastic debris that are called clastic wedges.

21. Seeds have protective coatings that can pass through the digestive systems of some animals. As animals that eat the seeds move from one area to another, they deposit the seeds along with with fecal material in a new location.

EXAMVIEW® PRO

Use ExamView® Pro Testmaker CD-ROM to:
• Create **multiple versions** of tests.
• Create **modified** tests with one mouse click for struggling students.
• **Edit** existing questions and add your own questions.
• **Build** tests based on national curriculum standards.

The Mesozoic and Cenozoic Eras

Refer to pages 8T–9T of the Teacher Guide for an explanation of the National Science Content Standards correlations.

Section	Objectives	National Science Content Standards	State/Local Standards
SECTION 24.1 **Mesozoic Paleogeography** 🕐 1 session 📦 ½ block	1. **Explain** the breakup of Pangaea. 2. **Distinguish** between the different characteristics of the Mesozoic Orogenies.	UCP.2, UCP.5; D.3	St 1 Science KI 1, 2, & 3, St 4 KI 1.2j, 2.1n, St 6 2.1o, 2.1p, & 2.1w, KI 2 & 3
SECTION 24.2 **Mesozoic Life** 🕐 1 session 📦 ½ block	3. **Discuss** why many paleontologists theorize that birds are descended from dinosaurs. 4. **Describe** how paleontologists distinguish among reptile, dinosaur, and mammal fossils. 5. **Explain** the evidence indicating that a meteorite impact caused the Cretaceous-Paleogene mass extinction event.	UCP.4; C.3	St 4 KI 1.2i & 1.2j, St 6 KI 5
SECTION 24.3 **Cenozoic Paleogeography** 🕐 1 session 📦 ½ block	6. **Describe** the type of tectonism that characterized the Cenozoic orogeny. 7. **Understand** the extent of glaciation that occurred in North America.	UCP.2, UCP.3; C.3; D.3	St 1 Math KI 2 & 3, St 4 KI 1.2i, 1.2j, 2.1n, 2.1o, 2.1p, 2.1r, 2.1u, 2.1v, & 2.1w, St 6 KI 2 & 3
SECTION 24.4 **Cenozoic Life** 🕐 2 sessions 📦 1 block	8. **Describe** the landscape of the Oligocene. 9. **Discuss** the changes in animals in North America during the Cenozoic. 10. **Identify** the characteristics of primates. 11. **Explain** what separates hominids from the other hominoids.	UCP.2, UCP.5; A.1; C.3; D.3	St 1 Math KI 2, Science KI 1 & 2, St 4 KI 1.2i, 1.2j, 2.1m, 2.1n, 2.1o, 2.1p, 2.1t, & 2.1u

A complete Planning Guide is provided on pages 30T-32T.

🕐 The number of recommended single-period sessions

📦 The number of recommended blocks

Activity Materials

Discovery Lab *page 625*
1-L beaker, water, plasticene

Problem-Solving Lab *page 637*
map, calculator

GeoLab *pages 642–643*
Internet access, pencil, paper

MiniLab *page 636*
1-L glass jars (3), crushed ice, gravel, sand, silt, clay, water

Need materials? Contact Science Kit at 1-800-828-7777 or at www.sciencekit.com on the Internet. For alternate materials, see the activity on the listed page.

Key to Teaching Strategies

L1 Level 1 activities should be appropriate for students with learning difficulties.

L2 Level 2 activities should be within the ability range of all students.

L3 Level 3 activities are designed for above-average students.

ELL ELL activities should be within the ability range of English-language learners.

COOP LEARN Cooperative learning activities are designed for small-group work.

P These strategies represent student products that can be placed in a best-work portfolio.

📦 These strategies are useful in a block-scheduling format.

Chapter Organizer

Glencoe Exclusive!
TeacherWorks™
All-In-One Planner and Resource Center

Activities/Features	Reproducible Masters	Transparencies
Discovery Lab: Determining the Effect of Shape on Buoyancy, p. 625	**Study Guide for Content Mastery,** p. 149 ▣	**Section Focus Transparency 74** ▣ ▣ **Teaching Transparency 72** ▣ ▣
Using Math: Using Numbers, p. 633	**Study Guide for Content Mastery,** pp. 150–152 ▣ **Laboratory Manual,** pp. 185–188 ▣	**Section Focus Transparency 75** ▣ ▣ **Teaching Transparency 73** ▣ ▣
MiniLab: Glaciers and Deposition, p. 636 **Problem-Solving Lab:** Using Math, p. 637	**Study Guide for Content Mastery,** p. 153 ▣ **GeoLab and MiniLab Worksheets,** p. 95 ▣	**Section Focus Transparency 76** ▣ ▣ **Teaching Transparency 74** ▣ ▣
Internet GeoLab: Huge Appetites, pp. 642–643 **Science & Math:** Weighing a Dinosaur, p. 644	**Study Guide for Content Mastery,** p. 154 ▣ **GeoLab and MiniLab Worksheets,** pp. 96–98 ▣ **Laboratory Manual,** pp. 189–192 ▣	**Section Focus Transparency 77** ▣ ▣ **Teaching Transparency 75** ▣ ▣

✔Assessment

Chapter Assessment,
   pp. 139–144
Performance Assessment in the Science Classroom (PASC)
MindJogger Videoquiz DVD/VHS
Performance Assessment in Earth Science
ExamView® Pro CD-ROM
5 Days to the Regents Exam

Additional Resources

Guided Reading Audio Program ▣
Cooperative Learning in the Science Classroom COOP LEARN
Lesson Plans
Block Scheduling
earthgeu.com
NY Lesson Plans
NY Block Scheduling
Review Handbook for Regents Earth Science Exam

NATIONAL GEOGRAPHIC

Products Available from National Geographic Society
To order the following products, call the National Geographic Society at 1-800-368-2728:
Curriculum Kit
GeoKit: *Earth's History*
GeoKit: *Dynamic Earth*

Teacher's Corner

CD-ROM
111 Years of National Geographic Magazine
Videos
What's the Earth made of?
Our Dynamic Earth

Content Background

Pangaea Breaks Apart
Section 24.1

The breakup of Pangaea can best be described as a five-stage process. The first stage involved the separation of North America from Africa and South America during the Late Triassic. The second and third stages occurred during the Jurassic. The second stage involved the separation of South America and Africa from Antarctica, Australia, and India. During the third stage, India separated from Antarctica and Australia. The fourth stage occurred during the Late Jurassic with the separation of Africa and South America. As Africa separated from South America, it began to collide with Europe. The fifth stage involved the separation of North America and Europe during the Cenozoic.

The Palisades of the Hudson River, in New York, are a thick basalt sill that formed as a result of extensional tectonism that began in the Mesozoic. Some of the large valleys formed by the rifting filled with sediment. Rift basins that are filled with Late Triassic and Jurassic sediments are common along the eastern margin of North America from New York to North Carolina.

Ornithischian Dinosaurs
Section 24.2

Ornithischian dinosaurs included the ornithopods, pachycephalosaurs, ceratopsians, stegosaurs, and ankylosaurs. The ornithopods and pachycephalosaurs walked primarily on their hind limbs, but ornithopods had well-developed forelimbs that allowed them to also walk on all four limbs. The ornithopods included the crested, duck-billed hadrosaurids that thrived during the Cretaceous. The pachycephalosaurs had thick, domed heads. Although some paleontologists suggest that these dinosaurs engaged in head-butting competitions for mates, fossils of pachycephalosaur skulls show no evidence of such collisions.

There is a very good fossil record of the ceratopsians, or horned dinosaurs. The most well-known ceratopsian was *Triceratops,* which lived during the Late Cretaceous. Although the large, bony frill on a *Triceratops's* head probably made it appear quite menacing, it would have been of little use for protection because it was basically a bony frame with skin stretched over it.

The familiar genus *Stegosaurus* was typical of the stegosaurs. These dinosaurs were quadrupedal. They had bony, spiked tails and plates along their backs that had intricate chambers for blood to flow through, much like the chambers on the radiator of a car. Paleontologists theorize that these bony plates acted like radiators to cool the giant herbivores. As blood was pumped into the bony plates and a stegosaur faced the wind, its blood was cooled. The cooled blood then returned to the stegosaur's body and cooled it.

Multiple Learning Styles

- **Visual-Spatial** Demo, p. 631, Reteach, p. 634
- **Interpersonal** Project, p. 630
- **Intrapersonal** Activity, p. 635, Modeling, p. 640
- **Linguistic** Project, p. 631, Reteach, p. 638
- **Logical-Mathematical** Reteach, p. 627

GLENCOE Technology

The following multimedia resources are available from Glencoe.

The Infinite Voyage Series
The Great Dinosaur Hunt
Life in the Balance

Vocabulary Puzzlemaker

TeacherWorks™ CD-ROM

MindJogger Videoquizzes DVD/VHS

ExamView® Pro CD-ROM

Interactive Chalkboard CD-ROM

The last group of Ornithischians were the armored ankylosaurs. They had bony armor that covered them from head to tail. The end of the tail was a large, club-shaped hunk of bone that was used for protection.

Drying of the Mediterranean Sea
Section 24.3

The Mediterranean Sea is the remnant of the Tethys Sea, which once separated Africa and India from Eurasia. The narrow connection between the Mediterranean Sea and the Atlantic Ocean at the Strait of Gibraltar is the only thing preventing the Mediterranean Sea from drying and becoming a large desert. A 2-km-thick sequence of evaporites beneath the Mediterranean Sea led geologists to theorize that, during the Late Miocene, the sea did dry up and became a vast desert. The simple drying of the Mediterranean Sea would have created only about 25 m of evaporites. Many geologists theorize that there were multiple events of filling with water followed by evaporation and deposition of evaporites. Some other geologists theorize that because of the region's arid climate, the water in the Mediterranean Sea reached saturation and precipitated the evaporites without ever drying.

Hominids
Section 24.4

There currently is controversy about the relationship between *Homo erectus* and modern humans, *Homo sapiens.* Some scientists theorize that *H. sapiens* evolved from a group of *H. erectus* that lived in Africa. These scientists theorize that *H. sapiens* then migrated from Africa to populate other parts of Earth and drove *H. erectus* to extinction. Other scientists theorize that modern humans did not have an isolated origin from Africa, but that they arose from separate populations throughout Europe and Asia. These scientists theorize that occasional contact and interbreeding between populations were responsible for the overall similarity of humans, while regional differences were maintained.

Identifying Misconceptions

Some people think that all large reptiles were dinosaurs. This is not true. There were many large flying and swimming reptiles, but these were not dinosaurs. Dinosaurs were all terrestrial and none of them could fly. Dinosaurs had upright postures that reflected a different hip structure than that of any other reptile group.

✔ Assessment

Portfolio Assessment
Assessment, TWE, p. 638

Performance Assessment
Assessment, TWE, p. 627
GeoLab, SE, pp. 642–643
GeoLab, TWE, pp. 642–643
Discovery Lab, SE, p. 625
MiniLab, SE, p. 636

Knowledge Assessment
Discovery Lab, TWE, p. 625
Assessment, TWE, p. 626
MiniLab, TWE, p. 636

Chapter Assessment, SE, pp. 646–647
Section Assessment, SE, pp. 627, 634, 638, 641

Skill Assessment
Problem-Solving Lab, TWE, p. 637

Be sure to check the Earth Science Web Site for links to chapter material: earthgeu.com

Chapter 24

The Mesozoic and Cenozoic Eras

Introducing the Chapter

The giant reptiles of the Mesozoic have fascinated people for generations. While dinosaurs were the rulers of the land during the Mesozoic, in the air and in the sea, there were other amazing giant reptiles. Divide the class into three groups and have them access the Earth Science Web Site at **earthgeu.com** to find links for research about pterosaurs, ichthyosaurs, and plesiosaurs. Each group can then present its research to the class.

Interpreting the Photo

Albertosaurus was one of the gigantic tyrannosaurids from the Upper Cretaceous. Its lower jaw was modified so that it could increase its gape to bite very large prey such as this *Centrosaurus,* a ceratopsian, or horned dinosaur.

INTERACTIVE CHALKBOARD with Image Bank

PowerPoint® Presentations

This CD is an editable Microsoft® PowerPoint® presentation that includes:
- Section presentations
- Section checks
- Image bank
- Links to Earth Science Online
- All transparencies
- Animations
- Audio

Chapter 24

What You'll Learn

- How plate tectonics shaped the landscape of western North America.

- What the characteristics of a dinosaur are.

- How dinosaurs and many other organisms became extinct at the end of the Mesozoic Era.

Why It's Important

As the physical geology of Earth changed, so did the biosphere. Reptiles ruled the land during the Mesozoic, but their reign ended abruptly with the dawn of the Cenozoic.

Earth Science Online

To find out more about the Mesozoic and Cenozoic Eras, visit the Earth Science Web Site at **earthgeu.com**

The Mesozoic and Cenozoic Eras

Albertosaurus and *Centrosaurus* from the Cretaceous of Alberta, Canada

Discovery Lab

Process Skills

observe and infer, recognize cause and effect, model

Procedure

Troubleshooting

Making the plasticine spines may require multiple attempts. It is important that the spines be long enough to significantly increase the surface area. However, because plasticine is very ductile, if the spines are too thin they will deform and the effect on buoyancy will be severely diminished.

Observe

The spines will increase the surface area of the object, and therefore it will sink more slowly. Some planktonic organisms take advantage of this phenomenon to help them float high in the water column. Tell students that, for this same reason, it is easier for them to float in water when they spread their arms apart.

Discovery Lab

Determining the Effect of Shape on Buoyancy

How can the shape of a micro-fossil help paleontologists determine whether it floated or whether it lived on the seafloor? In this lab, you will learn how the shape of a fossil shell affected the animal's buoyancy, and how this information helps paleontologists determine how the animal lived.

1. Fill a 1000-mL beaker with water.

2. Using plasticene, make two solid spheres that are each 1.5 cm diameter.

3. Deform one of the spheres by pinching the plasticene into 5 "spines" that extend around the sphere.

4. Drop both spheres into the beaker at the same time and observe what happens.

Observe In your science journal, record your observations. What effect does the shape of the spheres have on their buoyancy? The photos on this page show marine microfossils. Based on your observations in this lab, which one do you think floated in the water? Which one lived on the seafloor? Explain your reasoning.

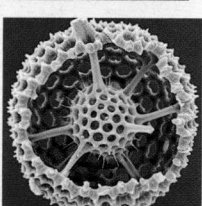

Section Focus

Before presenting the lesson, display **Section Focus Transparency 74** on the overhead projector.
L1 ELL

Chapter Themes

The following themes from the National Science Content Standards are covered in this chapter. Refer to page 8T of the Teacher Guide for an explanation of the correlations.
Evidence, models, and explanation (UCP.2); Change, constancy, and measurement (UCP.3); Evolution and equilibrium (UCP.4)

SECTION 24.1 *Mesozoic Paleogeography*

OBJECTIVES

• **Explain** *the breakup of Pangaea.*

• **Distinguish** *between the different tectonic characteristics of the Mesozoic Orogenies.*

VOCABULARY

Cordillera

The Mesozoic Era consisted of the Triassic, Jurassic, and Cretaceous periods, as shown in ***Figure 24-1*** on page 626. Movies such as *Jurassic Park* and *The Lost World* have popularized the Mesozoic as the age of the dinosaurs. What was the world like in which dinosaurs such as those pictured on page 624 lived? Why did this chapter in Earth's history end? These and other questions make the Mesozoic one of the most fascinating times of study in Earth's history.

THE BREAKUP OF PANGAEA

An important event that occurred during the Mesozoic Era was the breakup of Pangaea. Because heat causes solid objects to expand, the heat coming from within Earth beneath Pangaea caused the continent to expand. By the Late Triassic, the brittle lithosphere of Pangaea had cracked and broken apart. As some of the large cracks, or rifts, widened and as the landmasses spread apart, the ocean flooded the rift valleys. This resulted in the formation of new oceans that divided the newly separated continents.

24.1 Mesozoic Paleogeography **625**

✓Assessment

Knowledge Have students give examples of other organisms or objects that use the same principle of increasing their surface area to stay afloat in water or suspended in the air. Answers may include water fowl that have webbed feet, seeds with extensions, such as maple seeds, or snowshoes used to walk in deep snow.

Resource Manager

Study Guide for Content Mastery,
p. 149 L2

Section Focus Transparency 74 L1 ELL

Teaching Transparency 72 L2 ELL

0:00 *Out of Time?*

If time does not permit teaching the entire chapter, use the Chapter Summary on page 645 and the GeoDigest found at the end of the unit as an overview.

Using an Analogy

Heat causes solid objects to expand. For this reason, running hot water on the metal lid of a glass jar loosens the lid. Because metal is a better conductor of heat than glass is, the heat causes the lid to expand faster than the glass jar expands. The expanded lid becomes looser, and the jar can be opened. Similarly, the heat beneath Pangaea caused the continent to expand. By the Late Triassic, continued expansion caused the brittle lithosphere of Pangaea to begin to break apart. This form of tectonism is called extensional tectonism.

Project

Evidence of the extensional tectonism that occurred during the breakup of Pangaea is found near New York City. Have students use the library or the Glencoe Science Web Site to research the Palisades of the Hudson River. Ask them how the Palisades and other features along the eastern margin of North America support the theory that extensional tectonism occurred in that part of North America during the Late Triassic and Jurassic. Students should discover the presence of rift basins filled with sediments and the basalt intrusions of the Palisades.

✓Assessment

Knowledge Have students make a list of evidence that geologists use to support the theory that two seas covered Central North America during the Mesozoic.

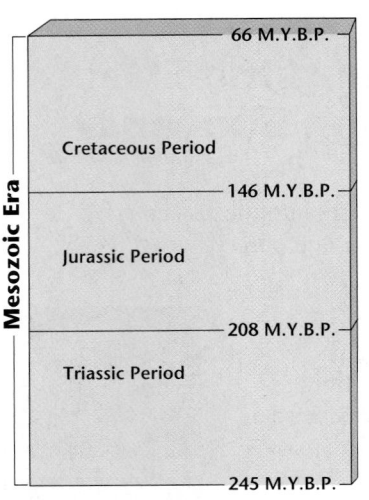

Figure 24-1 Each Mesozoic period is distinct. Pangaea broke apart and new seaways formed during the Triassic. Dinosaurs dominated the land during the Mesozoic. Flowering plants evolved during the Cretaceous. You'll learn more about these events as you study this chapter.

Figure 24-2 These Paleozoic limestones in the Sawtooth Mountains, MT were faulted and thrust eastward during the second Mesozoic orogeny.

The breakup of Pangaea resulted in the formation of the Atlantic Ocean. As North America rifted away from Europe and Africa, some of the spreading areas joined together to form a long, continuous rift system called the Mid-Atlantic Ridge. The Mid-Atlantic Ridge is still active today.

ACTIVE TECTONISM IN WESTERN NORTH AMERICA

In contrast to the passive margin that existed along eastern North America during the Mesozoic, active subduction along the western coast continued through the Middle Triassic. Geologists refer to the mountain ranges that formed in western North America during this time as the **Cordillera,** which means "mountain range" in Spanish.

Deformation along the western margin of North America increased substantially when Pangaea broke apart. Three major episodes of orogenies—mountain building—occurred along the western margin of North America during the Mesozoic. Different types of deformation occurred during each of these orogenies.

The oldest orogeny was characterized by a tremendous number of igneous intrusions. Large bodies of granite called batholiths exist throughout the cordillera. The spectacular exposure of Half-Dome at Yosemite National Park was intruded during this orogeny.

The next orogeny was characterized by low-angle thrust faulting and folding. This was caused by collisional tectonism along the western margin of North America. This type of deformation began in the Late Jurassic and continued through the Late Cretaceous. The thrust faults run north-south and place older rocks on top of younger rocks in Utah, Idaho, Wyoming, western Canada, and Montana, shown in *Figure 24-2.*

Content Background

Not all rifts remain active. When rifting stops and a continent is no longer being split apart, the rift is called a failed rift or an aulacogen. An aulacogen in North America runs beneath present-day Arkansas, Louisiana, western Tennessee, and Mississippi. It is called the Mississippi Embayment and has periodically been flooded with ocean water since the Jurassic. Today, it is filled with thick sediments and is the southern drainage basin of the Mississippi River.

Differentiated Instruction

Gifted The Nevada, Sevier, and Laramide Orogenies all occurred along the western margin of North America as a result of collisional tectonism. Have students access the Earth Science Web Site at earthgeu.com and find links to sites that contain information about how collisional tectonism caused these three different styles of deformation. Students' research should include the rate and angle of subduction of the Pacific Plate. **L3**

The third Mesozoic orogenic event was characterized by vertical uplifts. This orogeny mainly affected the area east of the folds and faults caused by the second orogeny. Deformation caused by the third orogeny began during the Late Cretaceous and continued into the Cenozoic.

SEAWAYS AND SAND DUNES

Throughout the Early and Middle Triassic, the supercontinent Pangaea and a single global ocean defined Earth's paleogeography. As Pangaea began to split apart, numerous rift basins formed in eastern North America, and large blocks of crust collapsed to form deep valleys. The Triassic ended with a rapid drop in sea level that caused sedimentation in the western United States to change dramatically during the Late Triassic and Early Jurassic. Western North America became much more arid, and it was covered by a thick blanket of sand. Strong winds shaped the sand into dunes. Evidence of this ancient desert is preserved in large-scale, cross-bedded sandstone deposits some of which are shown in *Figure 24-3.*

Sea level rose again in the Jurassic, and a shallow sea covered central North America. The Appalachian Mountains still rose high in the east, and the newly formed mountains of the Cordillera rose high in the west. As the mountains continued to uplift in the west, large river systems transported sediments from the mountains into the sea. The deposits of the Late Jurassic river systems are preserved today as multicolored sandstones, siltstones, and mudstones. They are well known for large numbers of dinosaur fossils.

The ocean continued to rise onto North America during the Cretaceous Period, and the Gulf of Mexico flooded the entire southeastern margin of North America. As a result, a sea covered the interior of North America from Texas to Alaska.

Figure 24-3 The effects of the wind is preserved in these sand dunes in the Vermillion Cliffs Wilderness, AZ.

SECTION ASSESSMENT

1. Explain why Pangaea rifted apart.
2. Describe the difference between the three major episodes of mountain building that occurred during the Mesozoic.
3. **Thinking Critically** What might happen if a continent stops rifting apart?

SKILL REVIEW

4. **Recognizing Cause and Effect** Explain how heat that is generated in Earth's interior can cause continents to rift apart, as in the case of Pangaea. For more help, refer to the *Skill Handbook.*

earthgeu.com/self_check_quiz

24.1 *Mesozoic Paleogeography* **627**

SECTION ASSESSMENT

1. Heat built up beneath Pangaea because of the blanketing effect that continental masses have on the hotter asthenosphere below. This heating caused expansion, which in turn caused the brittle lithosphere of Pangaea to begin to rift apart.
2. All three orogenies were the result of compressional tectonism. The first orogeny was characterized by large igneous intrusions, the second orogeny was characterized by low-angle thrust faults, and the third was characterized by vertical uplifts.
3. If a continent begins to rift apart and then stops, the area of the failed rift will become a depression, or basin. This basin will fill with sediment and become a natural site for rivers to flow toward.
4. Just as heat causes objects to expand, Earth's internal heat causes the lithosphere to expand. Expansion reaches a critical point, at which time the land breaks or rifts apart.

Collaborative Learning

Have students discuss where vast deserts that have large sand dunes occur on Earth. Have students locate these areas on a map and discuss what these locations suggest about the climate and paleogeography of western North America during the Late Triassic and Early Jurassic. **L2** **COOP LEARN**

3 Assess

Check for Understanding

Reinforcement
Ask students whether the three Mesozoic orogenies resulted from compressional or extensional tectonism. They resulted from compressional tectonism.

Reteach

Logical-Mathematical
Have students explain the evidence of orogenic activity in the Cordillera during the Mesozoic.

✓ Assessment

Performance Have students construct a data table illustrating the timing and characteristics of orogenies that deformed western North America during the Mesozoic. The table should list each orogeny, the area of deformation, and the type of deformation. Use the Performance Task Assessment List for Data Table in **PASC,** p. 37.

NY Core Curriculum Standards

Page 624: St 4 KI 2.1o
Page 625: St 1 Science KI 1, 2, & 3, St 4 KI 2.1l & 2.1o
Page 626: St 4 KI 2.1m & 2.1n, St 6 KI 3
Page 627: St 4 KI 2.1n, 2.1o, 2.1p, & 2.1w

627

Section Background

For section content background, refer to **Ornithischian Dinosaurs** on pages 624C–D.

Preplanning

Refer to the Chapter Organizer on pages 624A–B.

1 Focus

Section Focus

Before presenting the lesson, display **Section Focus Transparency 75** on the overhead projector. **L1** **ELL**

75 A LIVING FOSSIL
Use with Chapter 24, Section 24.2

❶ How do the present-day ginkgo leaf and the fossil leaf compare?

❷ What can you infer about the history of the ginkgo plant throughout geologic time?

Tying to Previous Knowledge

In Chapter 22, students learned how oxygen accumulated in the atmosphere through the process of photosynthesis. In this section, students learn that phytoplankton make their own food through photosynthesis, and that these organisms are at the base of the food chain. Ask students to explain why phytoplankton are considered to be at the base of the food chain.

SECTION **24.2** *Mesozoic Life*

OBJECTIVES

- **Discuss** *why many paleontologists theorize that birds are descended from dinosaurs.*
- **Describe** *how paleontologists distinguish among reptile, dinosaur, and mammal fossils.*
- **Explain** *the evidence indicating that a meteorite impact caused the Cretaceous-Paleogene mass extinction event.*

VOCABULARY

modern fauna
angiosperm
dinosaur
Ornithischia
Saurischia
ectotherm
endotherm
iridium

ENVIRONMENTAL CONNECTION

Figure 24-4 These phytoplankton are diatoms; tiny freshwater or marine plants. Upon death, their silica shells contribute to the ocean floor sediment.

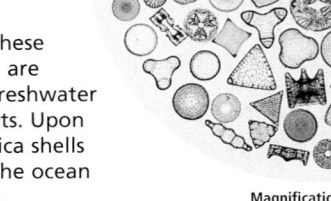

Magnification 48×

The Mesozoic is commonly referred to as the Age of Reptiles. However, the Mesozoic also was a time of some other very important biological firsts, such as the first mammals, the first birds, and the first flowering plants. The mass extinction at the end of the Paleozoic Era had left Earth's biosphere quite barren, and therefore ripe for the appearance of new organisms.

As Pangaea began to split apart during the Triassic, much of the habitat on the continental shelves that was lost during the formation of Pangaea became available again. New marine organisms, which are collectively called the **modern fauna,** evolved which filled this habitat. The modern fauna includes crabs, lobsters, shrimps, sponges, sea urchins, modern corals, snails, and clams. The major marine vertebrate groups include bony fishes, sharks, aquatic reptiles, and aquatic mammals.

LIFE IN THE OCEANS

Much attention is given to the large animals of the Mesozoic. It is important, however, to remember that then, as now, the base of the food chain that supported all the large animals consisted of tiny, ocean-dwelling organisms called phytoplankton, shown in *Figure 24-4.* Phytoplankton float near the surface of oceans and lakes and make their own food through the process of photosynthesis. You examined the relationship between shape and floating ability in the *Discovery Lab* on page 625.

 Reef Builders Arise Again As you learned in Chapter 23, the Permo-Triassic Extinction Event wiped out the reef-building corals of the Paleozoic. By the end of the Triassic, the modern corals had evolved to fill this same niche. In addition to corals, a new group of clams called rudists developed the ability to build reefs during the Cretaceous. Rudists are important because the reefs that they built were very porous and today contain some of the largest Cretaceous oil deposits in areas such as West Texas.

628 CHAPTER 24 *The Mesozoic and Cenozoic Eras*

Resource Manager

Study Guide for Content Mastery, pp. 150–152 **L2**

Teaching Transparency 73 **L2** **ELL**

Section Focus Transparency 75 **L1** **ELL**

Laboratory Manual, pp. 185–188 **L2**

Important Index Fossils Ammonites are related to modern nautiluses, octopuses, and squids. Ammonites were abundant and diverse throughout the Late Paleozoic and Mesozoic, and their abundance indicates that they were very successful predators. Several ammonites are shown in *Figure 24-5*. Ammonite fossils are widespread and abundant. Because ammonite species were also short-lived, they are excellent index fossils.

Figure 24-5 These ammonites are from the Lower Jurassic of Europe. Their distinct shell shape and ornamentation adds to their usefulness as index fossils. The use of ammonites to determine the age of Mesozoic rocks is usually much more accurate than radiometric dating.

While the ammonites were successful Mesozoic marine predators, they were by no means the top predators of the Mesozoic. In fact, swimming reptiles ruled the Mesozoic oceans. Ichthyosaurs resembled modern dolphins while plesiosaurs were more like walruses and seals. Predatory mosasaurs lived only during the Cretaceous, but for that time in the history of life, the sea was theirs to rule. These Mesozoic reptiles are shown in *Figure 24-6*.

LIFE ON THE LAND

Life on land changed dramatically as the cool climate that characterized the end of the Paleozoic over many parts of Earth came to an end during the Mesozoic. The large, temperate coal swamps dried up, and the climate gradually warmed. Fossils of insects that dominated the Paleozoic coal swamps, such as flies, mosquitoes, wasps, and bees, were also present but were not as common in Mesozoic rocks.

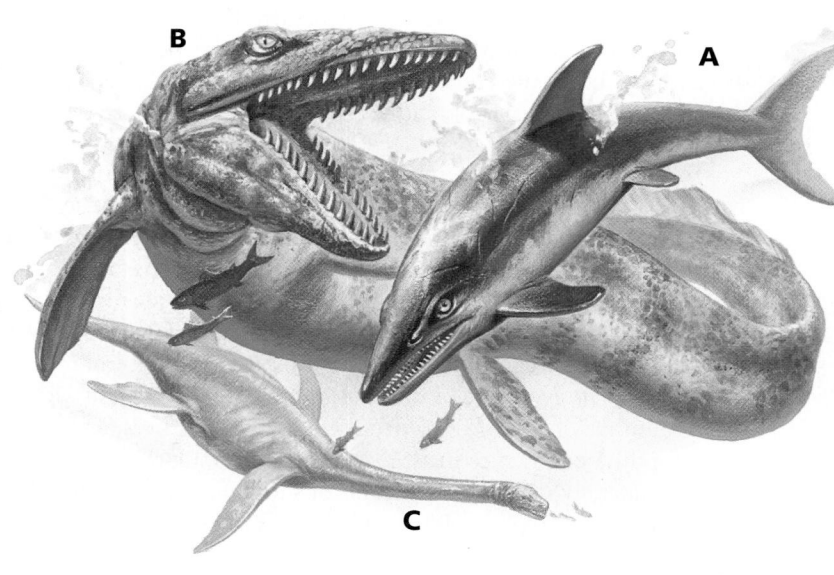

Figure 24-6 The presence in the oceans of aggressive marine predators, such as ichthyosaurs (A), mosasaurs (B), and plesiosaurs (C), no doubt kept their intended prey on alert.

24.2 *Mesozoic Life* **629**

Interpreting the Photo

Figure 24-5 Ammonites belong to a larger group of cephalopods called ammonoids. In addition to the coiled forms shown in this photo, ammonoids also grew straight shells and shells that were combinations of both. Such forms are called heteromorphs. The largest straight ammonoids were Ordovician endoceratoids with shell lengths of 9 to 10 m. Cretaceous ammonoids reached diameters of 3 m and would have been 18 m if unrolled.

Interpersonal Mosasaurs were amazing Mesozoic aquatic reptiles. Mosasaurs propelled themselves through the water with their long tails, using flipperlike arms and legs to steer. Some grew to over 10 m in length. A mosasaur's lower jaw had an extra hinge so that it could increase the gape of its mouth to engulf prey that was larger than its mouth. Have students access the Earth Science Web Site to find links to information about mosasaurs. Divide the class into four groups and have them find information about one of the four major groups of mosasaurs: *Clidastes, Platecarpus, Tylosaurus,* and *Mosasaurus.* Ask the groups to find out whether there are any modern animals that have adapted a means of eating prey larger than their mouths.

Concept Development

Mammals have two sets of teeth during their lives, and the teeth are differentiated as incisors, canines, and molars. In contrast, reptiles generally have only one type of tooth, and their teeth continually grow and replace older teeth throughout their lives. Show students sets (or photos of sets) of mammal and reptile teeth. Discuss the different uses of each type of mammal tooth (i.e., molars—chewing; canines—holding, grabbing; incisors—slicing) and compare these to reptile teeth.

Using Scientific Terms

Deciduous, in the sense of deciduous trees, means to "shed or lose leaves seasonally." Ask students to list other applications of the word *deciduous.* deer have deciduous antlers, dogs have deciduous fur, snakes have deciduous skin

Figure 24-7 Cycads have a limited distribution today. They grow only in the southern hemisphere, in Central America and in Florida. Only one species of ginkgo survives today, *Ginkgo biloba,* and it is quite common.

Figure 24-8 Fossils clearly show the progressive enlargement of one of the lower jawbones in mammal-like reptiles and its evolution into a single jawbone, which is characteristic of mammals. At the same time, the other jawbones decreased in size and became ear bones.

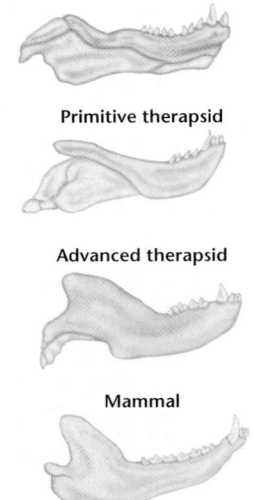

Primitive mammal-like reptile

Primitive therapsid

Advanced therapsid

Mammal

The land flora also changed substantially during the Mesozoic. Paleobotanists rightly call the Mesozoic the Age of Cycads. Cycads are seed plants that do not have true flowers. During the Jurassic, tall cycad trees along with ginkgoes and conifers dominated the landscape, as shown in *Figure 24-7.*

Angiosperms Evolve A new kind of plant evolved during the Cretaceous that would come to dominate the terrestrial landscape. This important group of plants was the **angiosperms,** which are seed-bearing plants that have flowers. Before the Cretaceous, there were no flowers. By the Middle Cretaceous, however, flowering plants were common. By the end of the Cretaceous, the land was covered with flowering trees, shrubs, and vines.

Early Mammals Small, primitive mammals evolved during the Late Triassic. Mammals are easily recognizable today because they are warm-blooded, have hair or fur, and mammary glands. How do scientists identify fossils of mammals? One method is to examine the structure of the lower jaw, middle ear, and teeth. A reptile has one ear bone and multiple lower jawbones, whereas a mammal has one lower jawbone and three ear bones. Early mammals arose from mammal-like reptiles. The evolution of the mammal jaw is illustrated in *Figure 24-8.* Mammals have two sets of teeth during their lives, and their teeth are differentiated as incisors, canines, and molars. In contrast, reptiles generally have only one kind of tooth, and their teeth continually grow and replace older teeth throughout their lives.

Across the Curriculum

Biology The last surviving species of ginkgo, *Ginkgo biloba,* would most likely be extinct if it weren't for some rather unusual circumstances. In the 1690s, a German traveler was intrigued by the distinctive, "duck-foot shaped" leaves of some ginkgo trees that were preserved in a Chinese monastery. After this discovery of the ginkgo by the western world, it was reintroduced and is now quite common.

Interpreting the Illustration

Figure 24-7 There is a cycad in the right foreground, seed ferns in the left foreground, ginkgo trees in the right background, and a red oak-like ancestor (*Brachyphyllum*) in the left background.

Flying Reptiles Pterosaurs, as shown in *Figure 24-9,* were flying reptiles that dominated the air during the Mesozoic. The earliest pterosaurs were small and had long tails and wingspans of less than 60 cm. Their descendents had no tails and were generally much larger. One species had a wingspan of more than 12 m. Pterosaurs had light, hollow bones, like modern birds. The modification that allowed them to fly was the growth of a membrane from a greatly lengthened fourth finger.

Two groups of reptiles that arose during the Mesozoic and still exist are the crocodiles and turtles. Why crocodiles and turtles survived the great extinction at the end of the Mesozoic, while the mosasaurs, plesiosaurs, icthyosaurs, and dinosaurs did not, puzzles paleontologists to this day.

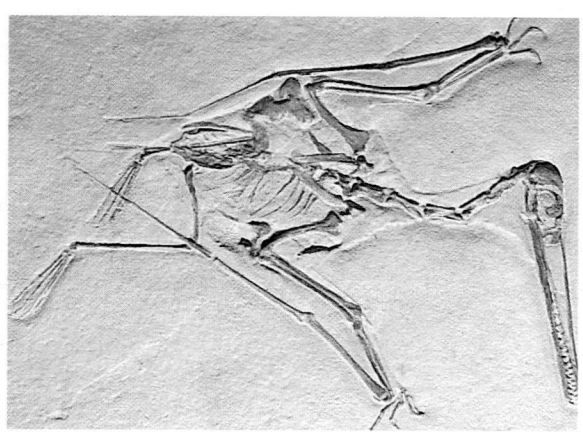

Figure 24-9 This pterosaur fossil was found in Jurassic-aged rocks in Germany. The membrane that was attached to the fourth finger was actually a flap of tough skin that stretched from the finger to the sides of the pterosaur's body.

DINOSAURS RULE THE LAND

No other group of animals has captured the human imagination as much as the dinosaurs have. **Dinosaurs** were a group of reptiles that developed an upright posture about 228 million years ago. Even though our understanding of these rulers of the Mesozoic land has changed, our fascination with dinosaurs has remained. Dinosaurs came in all sizes, from the very small to the extraordinarily large, and all were terrestrial. You can learn how to estimate a dinosaur's weight in the *Science and Math* feature on page 644. Although the largest dinosaurs were most likely slow and plodding animals, many of them were quick and agile. All reptiles other than dinosaurs have a sprawling posture, that is, their legs are not set directly underneath their bodies. In contrast, as shown in *Figure 24-10,* dinosaurs' legs were set directly underneath their bodies because their hips and ankles were different from those of other reptiles.

Figure 24-10 The characteristic sprawling posture of reptiles is shown here. Dinosaurs, with their straight shoulders, ankles, and hips, stood apart from the reptiles.

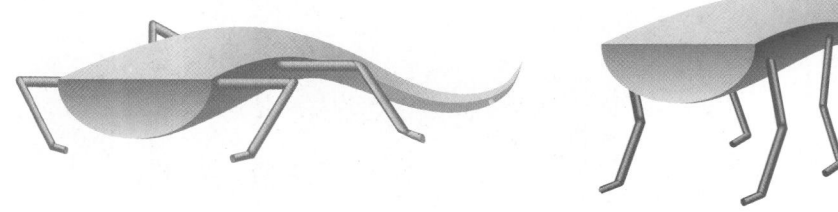

Included among the sauropods are *Apatosaurus* (commonly called *Brontosaurus*), *Diplodocus*, and the more than 55-metric-ton *Brachiosaurus*. There is evidence from partial skeletal remains that some sauropods were even larger than *Brachiosaurus*. The names *Amphicoelias, Giganotosaurus, Supersaurus, Seismosaurus,* and *Ultrasaurus* have been given to these partial remains. One estimate suggests that *Amphicoelias* was up to 60 m long and weighed over 150 metric tons! Compare this to an adult African elephant which weighs between 5 to 7.5 metric tons and is 5 to 7.5 m long. Fossil trackways have provided evidence that sauropods moved in large herds. Their large size and herding behavior were likely the best protection that sauropods had from meat-eating predators, such as the theropods.

Discussion

Ask students whether they think birds evolved from dinosaurs. Have students access the Earth Science Web Site at **earthgeu.com** for links to information on this topic. Based on their opinions after the research is completed, divide the class into two groups, those in favor and those not in favor of the theory that birds evolved from dinosaurs. Hold a debate in class with each side presenting and defending its ideas. **L2** 🗃️

NY Core Curriculum Standards

Page 632: St 4 KI 1.2i, St 6 KI 5
Page 633: St 4 KI 1.2i & 1.2j
Page 634: St 4 KI 1.2i
Page 635: St 4 KI 2.1n, 2.1o, 2.1p, & 2.1r, St 6 KI 3

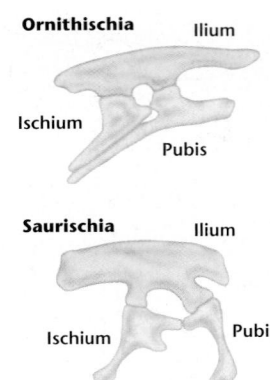

Ornithischia — Ilium, Ischium, Pubis
Saurischia — Ilium, Ischium, Pubis

Figure 24-11 The arrangement of hip bones in dinosaurs serves as a basis for their classification.

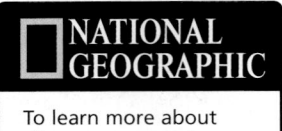

NATIONAL GEOGRAPHIC

To learn more about dinosaurs, go to the **National Geographic Expedition** on page 892.

Dinosaur Hips Two major groups of dinosaurs are recognized based on their hip structure: Ornithischia and Saurischia. Three bones comprised the hip, as shown in *Figure 24-11.* The ischium and pubis were parallel to one another in ornithischian dinosaurs. This is similar to the orientation of these bones in modern birds, which is why scientists named this group of dinosaurs **Ornithischia,** meaning "bird-hipped". This name is unfortunate, however, because birds likely did not evolve from Ornithischia. The ischium and pubis were at an angle to one another in Saurischia, similar to the orientation observed in modern lizards. **Saurischia** means "lizard hipped." Scientists hypothesize that birds are actually descended from the Saurischia.

There were five different groups of ornithischian dinosaurs: stegosaurs, ankylosaurs, pachycephalosaurs, ceratopsians, and ornithopods. All ornithischian dinosaurs were plant eaters, also called herbivores. There were two different groups of saurischian dinosaurs: sauropods and theropods. Although they shared a similar hip structure, these two groups of dinosaurs were quite different. The sauropods were all quadrupedal—walked on four legs—plant eaters, and some grew to enormous sizes. They were the largest land animals to have ever lived. In contrast to the sauropods, all theropods were bipedal—walked on two legs—carnivores. Your research results from the *GeoLab* on page 642 will help you interpret what dinosaurs ate. *Figure 24-12* shows some representative Mesozoic dinosaurs.

Figure 24-12 Herbivores such as *Parasaurolophus* (right) and *Triceratops* (center) had to constantly be on the lookout for carnivores such as *Tyrannosaurus.*

632 CHAPTER 24 *The Mesozoic and Cenozoic Eras*

Differentiated Instruction

Visually Impaired Construct simple models of the ornithischian and saurischian hip structures using modeling clay. Have students with visual impairments use these models to enhance their understanding of the different hip structures of these two dinosaur groups.

Dinosaurs to Birds? The idea that birds are related to dinosaurs stems from the amazing similarities between theropods and the oldest known bird, *Archaeopteryx*. Fossils of feather impressions and a wishbone provide clear evidence that *Archaeopteryx* was definitely a bird, even though it did have teeth and a theropod-like skeleton.

Ectotherm or Endotherm? All living reptiles are **ectotherms,** meaning that their body temperatures vary in response to outside temperatures. All living mammals and birds are **endotherms,** meaning that they maintain relatively constant body temperatures, regardless of temperatures outside. Some paleontologists hypothesize that at least some groups of dinosaurs were endotherms. One reason is that bones of endotherms typically have more passageways for blood than bones of ectotherms do, and dinosaur bones have numerous passageways. Critics of the hypothesis that some dinosaurs were endotherms correctly point out that the bones of crocodiles and turtles also have numerous passageways, and yet they are ectotherms.

A recent discovery of a possible fossilized heart in a dinosaur supports the hypothesis that some dinosaurs were endothermic. The heart has four chambers and one aortal arch, which is a condition that exists only in endothermic animals. Whether dinosaurs were ectotherms or endotherms is still controversial, but for now, there seems to be evidence that perhaps some dinosaurs were endotherms.

MASS EXTINCTIONS

A major mass extinction event ended the Mesozoic. Most major groups of organisms were devastated and all known species of dinosaurs, pterosaurs, ammonites, mosasaurs, and plesiosaurs

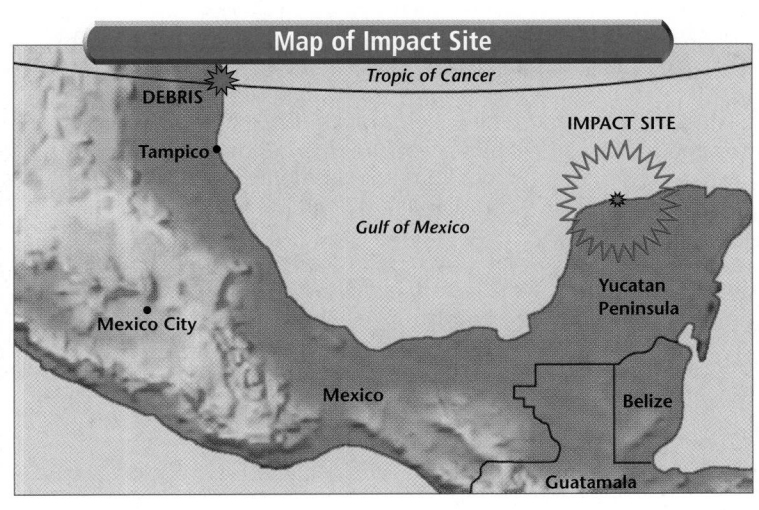

Map of Impact Site

Figure 24-13 The circular shape and underlying layer of melted iridium-rich rock provides evidence of a meteorite impact. It was named the Chicxulub crater after a nearby village.

Using Math

Using Numbers The end of the Permian is marked by an extinction event in which 80 percent of all marine genera became extinct, and the end of the Cretaceous is marked by an extinction event in which 50 percent of all marine genera became extinct. How many times greater was the Permian extinction event than the Cretaceous extinction event?

Enrichment

The recent discovery of a possible fossilized heart in a dinosaur supports the hypothesis that some dinosaurs were endothermic. Have students compare the appearance of this heart to the hearts of various ectotherms and endotherms. Have students access the Earth Science Web Site for links to information on this topic.

Content Background

There is some evidence that separate iridium spikes and layers with glass spheres occur both above and below the Cretaceous-Paleogene boundary. This suggests that there may have been multiple meteorite impacts, but such physical evidence is more consistent with the volcanic activity theory. The theory that a period of extended darkness caused plant communities to collapse, which killed off the large herbivores, which, in turn, killed off the large carnivores, has also been challenged. Studies of plant extinctions at the Cretaceous-Paleogene boundary reveal that most of the plants that became extinct were adapted to temperate climates; they had mechanisms for surviving the winter. Tropical plants, which lack mechanisms for seed dormancy, were barely affected. Critics of the impact hypothesis suggest that this does not fit with the impact scenario.

Across the Curriculum

Biology Have students research predator–prey relationships among modern endotherms and ectotherms. Have them use this information to either support or challenge the hypothesis that dinosaurs were endotherms. Students should find that it takes more energy to be an endotherm than it does to be an ectotherm; thus, endotherms must eat more and eat often. Studies show that predator–prey ratios of modern mammals are relatively low. This means that for every one endothermic predator, there are many smaller endothermic prey. This is because it takes quite a few prey to support one endothermic predator. Predator–prey ratios for dinosaurs were also low. This supports the hypothesis that dinosaurs were endotherms. However, it also assumes that the fossil record accurately reflects the predator–prey ratio for a given community. Many paleontologists suggest that this level of detailed demographics is not obtainable from the fossil record.

Using Math

$80\% \div 50\% = 0.80/0.50 = 1.6$. Therefore, the Permian mass extinction was 1.6 times greater than the Cretaceous mass extinction.

Check for Understanding

Discussion

Ask students to discuss the most important organisms of the Mesozoic flora and fauna.

Reteach

 **Visual-Spatial** Ask students to make a sketch of a dinosaur and a nondinosaurian reptile. Have students identify the characteristics in each sketch that do or do not make it a dinosaur. **L1** **ELL**

✓Assessment

Skill Divide the class into two groups and conduct a debate about whether the extinction at the end of the Cretaceous was caused by a meteorite impact or some other cause. One group should defend and the other group should refute the meteorite-impact theory.

Earth Science Online

Topic: Meteor Impacts and Extinctions
To find out more about mass extinction, visit the Earth Science Web Site at earthgeu.com

Activity: Prepare a map of the world showing three large meteor impacts besides the Chicxulub impact. Indicate the approximate dates on your map. Do any of these dates correspond to other mass extinctions?

---

became extinct. Geologists theorize that a large meteorite, at least 10 km in diameter, slammed into the Yucatan Peninsula shown in *Figure 24-13* on page 633, at a speed of up to 240 000 kph. Such an impact would have blown 25 trillion metric tons of rock and sediment high into the atmosphere. Organisms lucky enough to have survived the impact would have faced a millennium of greenhouse warming and increased levels of UV radiation from the Sun.

The chemistry of a clay layer that separates Cretaceous from Paleogene rocks in Italy provides evidence of such a meteorite impact. An unusually high amount of **iridium,** a metal that is rare in rocks at Earth's surface but is relatively common in meteorites and asteroids, is found not only in Italy but in Cretaceous-Paleogene boundary sites worldwide. Soot and charcoal, which are evidence of widespread fires, are also common in the sediments.

A buried crater in the Gulf of Mexico contains iridium, which has a radiometrically dated age of approximately 65 million years. This age is close to the time of the Late Cretaceous mass extinctions. It is important to note, however, that elevated amounts of iridium are also present in Earth's interior, and thus, volcanic deposits can be enriched with iridium. During the Late Cretaceous, massive volcanic eruptions occurred in India.

Today, most scientists agree that both a large meteorite impact and massive volcanism occurred at the end of the Cretaceous. In the midst of a stressful time of climatic cooling, changing plant populations and a gradual decline in dinosaur diversity and abundance, a large meteorite struck Earth. The extraordinary stress that the impact added to an already stressed ecosystem likely caused the climax of the Cretaceous-Paleogene mass extinction.

SECTION ASSESSMENT

1. How do paleontologists distinguish between fossils of mammals and fossils of reptiles?

2. Discuss how *Archaeopteryx* supports the hypothesis that birds are descended from dinosaurs.

3. Explain why a cycad is not an angiosperm.

4. What is the main characteristic that separated dinosaurs from all other reptiles?

5. Describe the differences between Saurischia and Ornithischia.

6. **Thinking Critically** What conclusions can be stated, based on tooth characteristics, regarding the differences in diet between reptiles and mammals?

SKILL REVIEW

7. **Comparing and Contrasting** Compare and contrast the evidence for meteorite impact and volcanism at the end of the Cretaceous. For more help, refer to the *Skill Handbook.*

 earthgeu.com/self_check_quiz

---

SECTION ASSESSMENT

1. They use the structure of the lower jaw and middle ear. Reptiles have one ear bone and multiple lower jawbones; mammals have one lower jawbone and three ear bones.

2. *Archaeopteryx* and the skeletons of advanced theropod dinosaurs have many characteristics that are indistinguishable from birds. *Archaeopteryx* had feathers and a wishbone, which only birds possess. The skeleton of *Archaeopteryx* is a good candidate for a form that is transitional between dinosaur and bird.

3. Cycads do not have true flowers.

4. posture; all reptiles other than dinosaurs have sprawling postures; dinosaurs had upright postures

5. the orientation of their hip bones; the illium and ischium were parallel to each other in ornithischian dinosaurs, whereas in saurischian dinosaurs, these bones were at an angle to one another

6. Mammals may eat a more varied diet requiring teeth for chewing, biting, and cutting.

7. The evidence for a meteorite includes iridium anomaly, soot and charcoal, and the Chicxulub crater. All but the crater could also have been caused by tremendous volcanic activity, for which there is evidence in India.

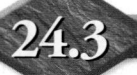

You are living during the Cenozoic, which means "recent life." The Cenozoic Era encompasses approximately the last 66 million years of Earth's history. The Cenozoic portion of the geologic time scale is shown in *Figure 24-14*. The final breakup of Pangaea occurred during the Cenozoic. Earth's life-forms and surface features continued to change, evolving into their present form. The Cenozoic has been a time of major climate changes, which have been in part, caused by the positions of the continents.

The Ice Ages As Australia split apart from Antarctica during the Middle-to-Late Eocene, the warm climate began to deteriorate. A change in ocean circulation is thought to be the cause. When Antarctica and Australia were connected as shown in *Figure 23-15* on page 612, a current of warm water from the north moderated the temperature of Antarctica. When Antarctica split apart from Australia during the Oligocene, it was isolated over the south pole. A cold current began to flow around Antarctica, and glaciers began to form.

The climate began to warm again during the Early Miocene. The glaciers on Antarctica began to melt, and the sea rose onto the margin of North America. In the *Problem-Solving Lab* on page 637, you will consider glacial melting and the length of time involved. Glaciers returned to Antarctica during the Middle and Late Miocene. During the Pliocene, the water of the Arctic Ocean began to freeze to form an arctic ice cap, which set the stage for the ice ages of the Late Pliocene and the Pleistocene.

During the Late Pliocene through the Pleistocene, the northern hemisphere experienced extensive glaciation, or an ice age. Glaciers from the arctic advanced and retreated in at least four stages over North America. The paths of the Ohio River and the Missouri River roughly mark the southernmost point to which glaciers advanced in North America. During the peak of Pleistocene glaciation, glaciers up to 3 km-thick covered some areas north of these rivers. You will model the effect glaciers have on sediment deposition when you complete the *MiniLab* on page 636.

TECTONIC EVENTS

Western North America had been tectonically active throughout the Cenozoic. The orogenic events that occurred at the end of the Mesozoic uplifted massive

OBJECTIVES

- **Describe** *the type of tectonism that characterized the Cenozoic orogeny.*
- **Understand** *the extent of glaciation that occurred in North America.*

VOCABULARY

Basin and Range Province
Tethys Sea

Figure 24-14 Although the last Ice Age began about 2 million years ago during the Pleistocene, ice age conditions really began about 40 million years ago during the Oligocene Epoch.

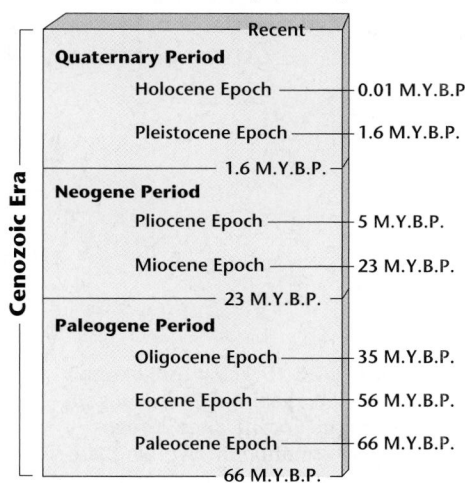

Cenozoic Era		
	Recent	
Quaternary Period		
	Holocene Epoch	0.01 M.Y.B.P.
	Pleistocene Epoch	1.6 M.Y.B.P.
	1.6 M.Y.B.P.	
Neogene Period		
	Pliocene Epoch	5 M.Y.B.P.
	Miocene Epoch	23 M.Y.B.P.
	23 M.Y.B.P.	
Paleogene Period		
	Oligocene Epoch	35 M.Y.B.P.
	Eocene Epoch	56 M.Y.B.P.
	Paleocene Epoch	66 M.Y.B.P.
	66 M.Y.B.P.	

24.3 *Cenozoic Paleogeography* **635**

Section 24.3

Prepare

Section Background

For section content background, refer to **Drying of the Mediterranean Sea** on page 624D.

Preplanning

Refer to the Chapter Organizer on pages 624A–B.

1 Focus

Section Focus

Before presenting the lesson, display **Section Focus Transparency 76** on the overhead projector.
L1 ELL

Activity

Intrapersonal Sediment deposited by melting glaciers is called till. Have students access the Earth Science Web Site to find information about locating the till deposits nearest to your school and the age of those deposits. L2

Differentiated Instruction

Behaviorally Disordered To engage students who are behaviorally disordered in section content, assign them the task of finding additional information about the spectacularly preserved fossils of the Green River Formation. Encourage students to find books in the library that have pictures of the fossils, and to use the Internet.

Resource Manager

Study Guide for Content Mastery, pp. 153 L2
Teaching Transparency 74 L2 ELL
Section Focus Transparency 76 L1
GeoLab and MiniLab Worksheets, p. 95 L2

Demo

Sketch two diagrams of Antarctica over the south pole. One diagram should have Antarctica and Australia connected. The other should have them separated. Show with arrows how a circumpolar current around an isolated Antarctica never enters into warm latitudes, and how warm currents would have deflected along the coast to moderate the temperature when Australia was connected to Antarctica.

MiniLab

Purpose

Students will observe the differences in sediment deposition and sediment characteristics that result from glacial ice and moving water.

Process Skills

model, observe, infer

Materials

two large, glass jars; finely crushed ice; sediment mixture of gravel, sand, silt, and clay particles

Teaching Strategies

Remind students that ice is an agent of erosion. Sediment contained in glacial ice is a product of the erosive power of ice.

Troubleshooting

• Put ice cubes in a cloth bag and use a hammer to crush the ice.
• Stir the sediment and ice mixture thoroughly.

Expected Results

The water-deposited sediment will show grading from coarse to fine; the ice-deposited sediment will not.

Analyze and Conclude

1. The water-only jar will have the coarse grains at the bottom and the finer grains at the top. The sediment sizes in the ice-and-sediment jar will be randomly distributed.
2. The sediment in the jar that contained water is sorted, and

MiniLab

Glaciers and Deposition

Model the deposition of sediment by melting glaciers.

Procedure

1. Pour water into a large, wide-mouthed jar until it is approximately 3/4 full.
2. Add a mixture of clay, silt, sand, and pebbles to the jar. Put the lid tightly on the jar.
3. Shake the jar for 30 seconds and allow the contents to settle.
4. Finely crush enough ice to fill approximately three-fourths of a second large, wide-mouthed jar. Stir a mixture of clay, silt, sand, and pebbles into the ice and pour the mixture into the jar.
5. Allow the ice to melt and the particles to settle overnight.

Analyze and Conclude

1. Describe the differences in the way the sediments settled in the two jars.
2. Compare and contrast the sorting of the grain sizes in the two jars.
3. How could geologists use this information to determine whether sediment had been deposited by a glacier or by running water?

the sediment in the jar that contained the ice is poorly sorted.
3. Sediment that is very poorly sorted suggests that the sediment was not deposited by moving water, but by melting ice.

Assessment

Knowledge Have students explain how the distribution of rocks composed of poorly

blocks of crust to form the Rocky Mountains. Large basins that formed adjacent to the Rocky Mountains were filled with as much as 3000 m of sediment from the uplifted and eroded mountains. The sediment that filled these basins contains beautifully preserved fish, insect, frog, plant, and bird fossils. A fossil fish from the most famous of these deposits, the Green River Formation in Wyoming, is shown in **Figure 24-15.** The basins in Wyoming that filled with huge, swampy, river deposits provided an ideal environment for the accumulation of vast amounts of coal. These coal seams are close to Earth's surface, and some are more than 50 m thick. Wyoming is one of the largest coal mining regions in the world. The coal there is especially valuable because it has a very low sulfur content, and thus, it burns cleanly.

Subduction in the West Volcanism returned to the western coast of North America at the end of the Eocene. The Cascade Mountains in the Pacific Northwest are the result of the subduction of an oceanic plate beneath the western coast of North America. During the Miocene, the North American Plate was forced over the East Pacific Rise resulting in the creation of the San Andreas Fault. Because there is currently

Figure 24-15 Fossil fish, like this 50 million year old *Phareodus sp.* from the Eocene-aged, Green River formation in Wyoming, are preserved in spectacular detail.

sorted sediment that have been interpreted by geologists to have been deposited by glaciers can help determine the former position of continental lithospheric plates. Continental glaciers usually form in high-latitude regions (usually at least 40°). Therefore, if there is rock composed of glacial deposits on a continent that is presently located over the equator, the continent was located at higher latitudes in the geologic past.

no subduction beneath southern and central California, the volcanoes in most of California are geologically inactive.

The subduction of the East Pacific Rise beneath the North American plate coincides with pull-apart, or extensional, tectonism in the southwestern United States and north-central Mexico. A series of mountains that trend north-to-slightly-northeast are separated by long, linear valleys and extend from Nevada and western Utah to north-central Mexico. This area, shown in *Figure 24-16,* is called the **Basin and Range Province.** As extensional tectonism has pulled the crust apart, large blocks of the crust have dropped down along normal faults to form the basins, leaving other blocks at higher elevations to form the mountain ranges. This extension is still occurring today.

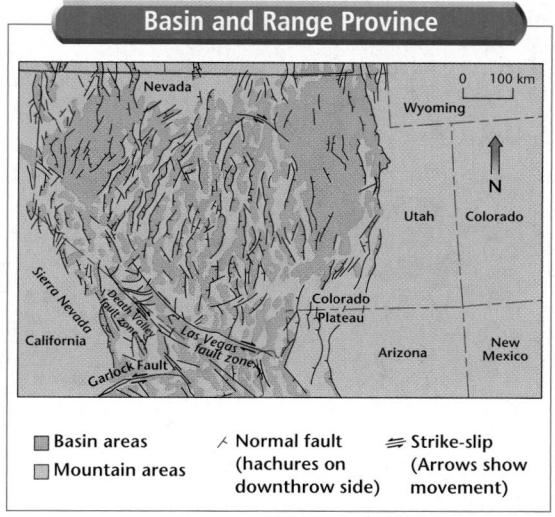

Basin and Range Province

- Basin areas
- Mountain areas
- Normal fault (hachures on downthrow side)
- Strike-slip (Arrows show movement)

Figure 24-16 The extensive development of basins and mountain ranges in this area is a clear example of the results of extensional tectonism.

Hot Spots in the West In Chapter 18, you learned that hot spots are mantle plumes that rise to Earth's surface. Some of the hot spots that occur in the western United States are related to the continuing subduction along the western coast of North America. Yellowstone National Park is famous for its beautiful geysers and hot springs. The land that makes up Yellowstone National Park is situated on a hot spot that has been active since the Early Cenozoic. The rocks at Yellowstone

Problem-Solving Lab

Using Math

New Continental Shorelines? If all the ice on Earth were to melt, sea level would rise to approximately 50 m above its current level. Sea level is rising today at an average rate of 2 mm per year. Assuming that sea level will continue to rise at this rate, how long will it take for all the ice on Earth to melt and sea level to rise to its maximum? Use the relationship distance = rate × time. Remember that 1000 mm = 1 m.

Analysis

1. What assumption is this calculation based on?
2. How realistic are the average rates?
3. What are some possible shortcomings of this calculation?
4. What major cities would this rise in sea level endanger?

Thinking Critically

5. Where, if at all, would new coral reefs grow? Why?

Content Background

The cause of Basin and Range extension is debatable. It may be that the subduction of the East Pacific Rise's spreading center is still active beneath North America; or that the shearing movement of the San Andreas Fault is somehow responsible; or that rising magma from a piece of subducted oceanic lithosphere caused partly molten magma to rise beneath the crust of the Basin and Range Province. Pressure from beneath the crust is causing it to thin and split apart.

✓Assessment

Skill Ask students to estimate local average high temperatures for January–June and to use this information to predict the average temperatures for August–November. Remind students that sea level has both risen and fallen in the past. Ask them to relate average temperature change to average sea-level change.

Problem-Solving Lab

Purpose

Students will use a real estimate of modern sea-level change to model sea-level change in the future. They will also learn the dangers associated with assumptions in this kind of extrapolation.

Process Skills

use math, interpret data, infer, form hypotheses

Materials

calculator, relief map of the world or of North America that shows the locations of major cities

Teaching Strategies

- This is a d (distance) = r (rate) × t (time) problem.
- First, make sure that all units are the same, such as 50 m = 50 000 mm.
- Distance = 50 000 mm and rate = 2 mm/y.
  50 000 mm = 2 mm/y × time.
  (50 000 mm)/(2 mm/y) = time.
  25 000 y = time.
  It would take 25 000 years.

Analysis

1. that there is a constant rate of sea-level rise, and that this constant rate will continue
2. It is unrealistic because very few, if any, natural processes behave in linear, predictable ways. Sea level has risen and fallen throughout geologic time, and using the average of a variable system to predict behavior in the distant future is not appropriate.
3. Shortcomings are that the problem suggests that all the ice will melt, that sea level will continue to rise at a rate of 1.2 mm/y, and that all rises in sea level are a result of melting ice.
4. Most major coastal cities would be in danger of severe flooding.

Thinking Critically

5. New coral reefs would grow in the clear, shallow, warm, tropical waters that would cover the low-lying lands that are currently exposed, such as Florida.

Check for Understanding

Reinforcement

Ask students to describe where extensional tectonism and compressional tectonism are currently active in western North America.

Reteach

Linguistic Have students outline in their science journals the main points about climate and tectonics in this section. Ask students to include specific examples in support of each point.

✓Assessment

Portfolio Have students select one of the North American glacial periods (Nebraskan, Kansan, Illinoian, or Wisconsinin). Have them visit the Earth Science Web Site at earthgeu.com to find links leading to information about the maximum southern extent of glaciation for the glacial period. Students should use this information to create informative posters.

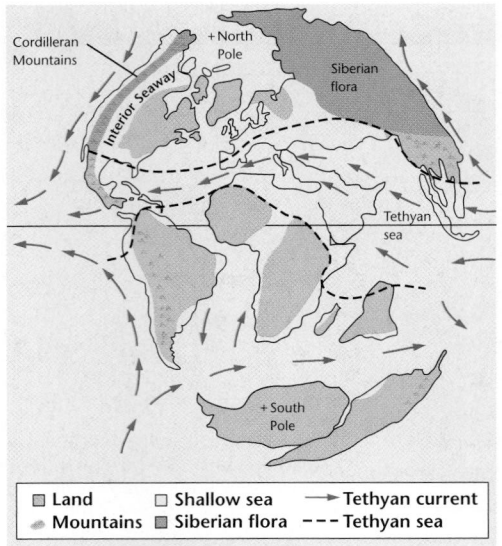

Figure 24-17 The Tethys Sea had a strong, westward-flowing current that transported organisms across large distances. Cretaceous-aged fossils that resemble fossils from the Tethys Sea area are found as far west as the Hawaiian Islands.

indicate that, in the past, this hot spot generated tremendous volcanic activity. Volcanic rocks that are Pleistocene in age record episodes of explosive volcanism. In fact, the yellow color of the extrusive volcanic rock rhyolite is responsible for the name of the river and the national park.

Continental Collisions While the final breakup of Pangaea occurred during the Cenozoic, plate tectonics also brought continents together during this time. The spectacular result of one such collision is the Himalayan Mountains. India traveled north and collided with the southern margin of Asia. The force of this tremendous continent-to-continent collision resulted in the formation of the Himalayan Mountains, which contain the point of highest elevation on Earth, Mt. Everest. The rocks at the top of Mt. Everest are Ordovician marine limestones. Tectonic forces have pushed what was the seafloor during the Ordovician to the top of the world!

Africa also drifted north after the breakup of Pangaea and collided with the connected landmass of Europe and Asia, or Eurasia. This continent-to-continent collision formed the Alps. Before Africa collided with Eurasia, a narrow sea called the **Tethys Sea** separated the two continents, as shown in *Figure 24-17*. The collision between Africa and Eurasia continues today, and it is almost certain that in the geologic future, the last remnant of the Tethys Sea will dry up.

SECTION ASSESSMENT

1. What kind of tectonic deformation characterized the Cenozoic?
2. What was the southern boundary of Pleistocene glaciation in the Central United States?
3. What is the relationship between the East Pacific Rise, the North American Plate and the San Andreas Fault?
4. **Thinking Critically** The positioning of Antarctica over the south pole helped trigger the Cenozoic ice ages. There would be a major rise of sea level if all the ice on Antarctica melted. If Antarctica were to move north of the south pole, as India did, it is likely that all the ice on the continent would melt. Explain why the movement of Antarctica should or should not be considered in predicting how a sea level change would affect the climate today.

SKILL REVIEW

5. **Recognizing Cause and Effect** Discuss the tectonic activity on the western coast of North America and the effect it had on the Basin and Range Province. For more help, refer to the *Skill Handbook*.

earthgeu.com/self_check_quiz

SECTION ASSESSMENT

1. A variety of tectonic deformations including extension, large-scale uplifts, and transform faulting (San Andreas) characterize the Cenozoic.
2. The southern boundary in the Central U.S. is approximately the trace of the Ohio and Missouri Rivers.
3. The East Pacific Rise was, in part, subducted beneath the North American Plate. A transform plate boundary formed between these two plates. This transform boundary is the San Andreas Fault.
4. The movement of continental lithosphere occurs very slowly. Even if Antarctica were moving off the south pole, such a journey would take millions of years. Therefore, such plate movements are not significant in terms of climatic change on a human time scale. As far as modern climate models are concerned, the positions of lithospheric plates are essentially fixed.
5. The western coast of North America was an ocean-continent collisional boundary. When part of the spreading center, the East Pacific Rise, subducted beneath North America, part of this plate boundary became a transform boundary. It is thought that the extensional tectonism of the Basin and Range Province is a result of the subducted spreading center underneath the North American Plate.

The modern marine fauna, including clams, snails, sea urchins, crustaceans, bony fishes, and sharks, survived the Cretaceous mass extinction to populate the modern oceans. Whales and dolphins evolved during the Cenozoic as completely aquatic mammals. Walruses and sea lions returned to the oceans. These mammals are still partly terrestrial today, but, like plesiosaurs were, they are much more at home in the water than on land.

LIFE ON LAND

Most of the currently living groups of mammals had evolved by the Eocene. Forests dominated North America during the Paleocene and Eocene. As the climate cooled during the Late Eocene, however, the forests gave way to open land. Grasses, which were important to many large mammals, appeared during the Eocene. Grasses spread out over the plains, and by the Late Oligocene, grassy savannas, like those in East Africa today, were common from Texas to South Dakota. The grasslands supported a large diversity of mammals, most of which are members of groups living today. These included dogs, cats, rodents, rabbits, camels, horses, pronghorn antelope, and mastodons. The rocks in Badlands National Park in South Dakota, shown in *Figure 24-18,* contain a treasure trove of fossils from the Oligocene. The rocks are made of clay, silt, and sand that were deposited in marshes and lakes and by slowly moving streams.

Pleistocene Mammals As the Pliocene ice age began, the great savannas were replaced by more arid land. The change in climate caused many of the savanna mammals to become extinct. A new group of animals evolved to populate the land as the Late Pliocene-Pleistocene ice age sent a chill across North America. Several of these animals are shown in *Figure 24-19* on page 640.

Figure 24-18 The Badlands of South Dakota may resemble a moon-scape but they were far from a lifeless plain. In fact, the abundant and diverse mammal fossils found here have inspired some paleontologists to call the Oligocene the Golden Age of Mammals.

OBJECTIVES

- **Describe** the landscape of the Oligocene in Central North America.
- **Discuss** the changes in animals in North America during the Cenozoic.
- **Identify** the characteristics of primates.
- **Explain** what separates hominids from the other hominoids.

VOCABULARY

primate
hominoid
hominid
Homo sapiens

24.4 *Cenozoic Life* **639**

Section 24.4

Prepare

Section Background

For section content background refer to **Hominids** on page 624D.

Preplanning

Refer to the Chapter Organizer on pages 624A–B.

1 Focus

Section Focus

Before presenting the lesson, display **Section Focus Transparency 77** on the overhead projector.
L1 ELL

Resource Manager

Study Guide for Content Mastery, p. 154 L2

Teaching Transparency 75 L2 ELL

Section Focus Transparency 77 L1 ELL

GeoLab and MiniLab Worksheets, pp. 96–98 L2

Laboratory Manual, pp. 189–192 L2

Tying to Previous Knowledge

Grasses evolved during the Tertiary. Have students identify the group of plants that grasses belong to. angiosperms, because grasses are flowering plants

NY Core Curriculum Standards

Page 636: St 4 KI 2.1l, 2.1n, 2.1o, 2.1p, 2.1u, 2.1v, & 2.1w, St 6 KI 2

Page 637: St 1 Math KI 2 & 3, St 4 KI 2.1n, 2.1o, & 2.1p

Page 638: St 4 KI 2.1n & 2.1o

Page 639: St 4 KI 1.2i & 1.2j

Content Background

Large mammals dominated the grassy plains through the Pliocene. Some of the more spectacular animals included the hornless rhinoceros *Paracerantherium,* which stood more than 4 m tall at the shoulder and weighed more than 4 metric tons; the giant three-clawed plant-eater *Moropus;* and the shovel-tusked mastodon *Ambelodon.* As one might expect, if there were many large herbivores, there must have been carnivores. Hyenalike mammals and large cats were the dominant predators of the land.

Modeling

Intrapersonal
Stereoscopic vision is very important in primates, especially for depth perception. To illustrate this, have students choose a partner (student A and student B). Have student A shut her eyes, and cover them with her hands. Have student B move to a different place in front of student A. Have student B extend an arm about 0.5–1 m in front of student A. Have student A remove one hand from one eye so that she can see only with one eye. Have student A try to grasp the arm of Student B. It will be difficult to do; Student A has lost depth perception because she has no stereoscopic vision. Ask students to imagine how hard they think it would be to jump from tree branch to tree branch without stereoscopic vision. **L1** **ELL** **COOP LEARN**

NY Core Curriculum Standards

Page 640: St 4 KI 1.2i & 1.2j
Page 641: St 4 KI 1.2i

Figure 24-19 The woolly mammoth, dire wolf, and the sabre-toothed cat are a few of the Pleistocene animals that evolved abilities to withstand the cold.

PRIMATES AND HUMANS

One of the most difficult problems to overcome in studies of the origin of humans and our relationship to other primates is the scarcity of fossils. This makes this area of study dynamic, partly because the discovery of a single new fossil can dramatically change our understanding.

Primates Primates are distinguished from other mammals by a grasping hand with an opposable thumb and two eyes directed forward that result in stereoscopic vision. Such vision allows primates to judge distance quite accurately. Other primate characteristics include smaller, fewer, and less-specialized teeth than other mammals and a relatively large brain.

Our species, *Homo sapiens,* belongs to a group of primates called hominids. In turn, hominids are part of a larger group called **hominoids** that includes the great apes. The fossil record of hominids extends back approximately 4.4 million years. What is it that separates a hominid from the other hominoids? The most recognizable feature is that all **hominids** are bipedal. That is, they have an upright posture resulting from a modification of the hipbone and they walk on two legs. Hominids also have larger brains, smaller canine teeth, and smaller faces than other hominoids, and they use sophisticated tools and have greater manual dexterity.

The Rise of *Homo Sapiens* Tracing the ancestry of **Homo sapiens,** the species to which humans belong, to earlier hominids began in the 1850s, when a fossilized skull was discovered in Neander Tal near Dusseldorf, Germany. *Tal* is the German word for "valley". Since that time, paleoanthropologists have scoured Earth looking for fossils of hominids in an attempt to piece together the ancestry of *Homo sapiens.*

Earth Science Online

Update To find out more about hominid fossil finds, visit the Earth Science Web Site at earthgeu.com

Gifted A tremendous variety of animals are preserved in the Rancho La Brea tar pits. Have students research the environment that existed at Rancho La Brea, how the tar pits formed, and why they contain such spectacularly preserved flora and fauna. **L3**

Mary Leakey (1913–1996), an archaeologist, worked at the famous sites of Olduvai Gorge and Laetoli in Kenya. In 1959, she found a hominid skull determined to be 1.8 million years old and proved the antiquity of human species in East Africa. She classified it *Australopithecus boisei.* In 1976, Leakey found fossilized, humanlike footprints formed 3.5 M.Y.B.P. These provided evidence that early humans were bipedal much earlier than had been thought. Leakey's finds have contributed significantly to the field of paleoanthropology.

What about the fossils from Neander Tal? These hominids are commonly called Neanderthals. Most fossil evidence indicates that Neanderthals were most likely a side branch of *H. sapiens* and not direct ancestors of modern humans. The Neanderthals were hunters that inhabited Europe and the Near East approximately 200 000 to 30 000 years ago. Neanderthals differed from modern humans in a number of ways; differences in their skulls are shown in *Figure 24-20.* Neanderthals had heavy brows, mouths that projected forward, and receding chins. They had short, thick limbs and more massive, muscular bodies. Perhaps most surprising is that they had slightly larger brains than modern humans do. Neanderthals did live in caves and used a variety of tools. There is evidence that they buried their dead and placed items such as tools in their graves.

It may seem strange that scientists do not have a more complete understanding of the relationships among the hominids. After all, the fossil skeleton of one of the earliest known hominid species, *Australopithecus afarensis,* provides evidence that bipedal, upright-walking hominids existed at least 3.5 million years ago. However, compared to the rest of the fossil record, there are relatively few hominid fossils. As a result, our understanding of the evolution of many other groups of animals is much better than our understanding of the evolution of hominids. Subsequently, each new find yields information that could dramatically change previous ideas.

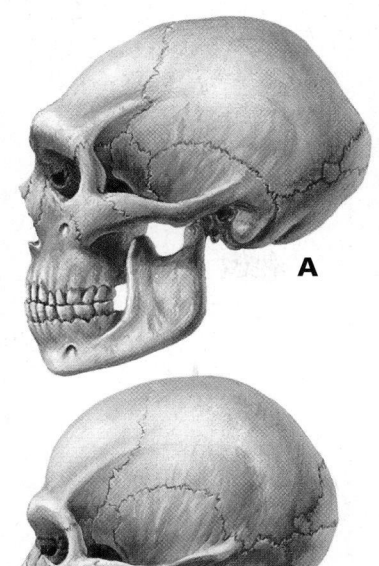
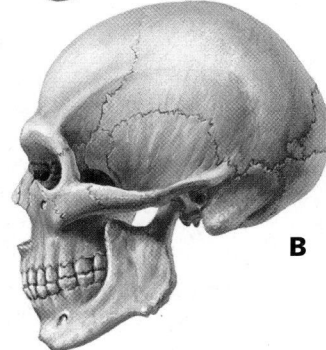

Figure 24-20 A characteristic of Neanderthals is a gap that occurs between the rear teeth and the jaw bone **(A).** Modern humans do not possess this **(B).**

SECTION ASSESSMENT

1. What kind of plants dominated the landscape of Central North America during the Oligocene?

2. How did the flora and fauna change in response to climatic changes during the Cenozoic?

3. What characteristics distinguish primates from other mammals?

4. What separates hominids from the other hominoids?

5. Discuss why it is difficult to reconstruct the evolutionary history of hominids.

6. **Thinking Critically** Explain why the evolution of grasses was a significant event for the mammals of central North America.

SKILL REVIEW

7. **Communicating** Suppose you are a journalist. In your science journal, write a press-release describing the recent discovery of a group of Neanderthal hominids. For more help, refer to the *Skill Handbook.*

earthgeu.com/self_check_quiz

Internet GeoLab

Time Allotment

one week to visit Web sites and answer questions

Process Skills

form hypotheses, communicate, collect data, interpret data, observe and infer, form conclusions

Preparation

Special Instructions

If you do not have access to the Internet, use reference books about dinosaurs from the library. Also use reference books that describe the feeding behavior of modern carnivorous and herbivorous animals.

Possible Hypotheses

Hypotheses will vary. Many students will use the size of the animal as a starting point. This is related to the amount of food that the animal consumed, but it will not help much in distinguishing plant eaters from meat eaters. Encourage students to think about aspects of the skeleton, especially tooth structure.

Plannning

Teaching Strategies

Encourage students to think about animals that they are familiar with (e.g., dogs cats, cows, and horses) and the diets of these animals.

Huge Appetites

The study of how an organism interacts with its environment is called ecology. Ecology includes how an organism obtains energy from its environment. Animals do this by eating. Determining the diet of modern animals is relatively easy to do. We can observe them in their habitat and watch what they eat, or we can examine their feces. Paleoecology is the ecology of ancient organisms. Part of dinosaur paleoecology includes determining what and how dinosaurs ate. Imagine how much food some dinosaurs must have eaten!

Preparation

Problem

How do paleontologists tell what types of food different dinosaurs ate?

Hypothesis

What kind of evidence might you use to determine what type of diets dinosaurs ate? What are the diets of different animals today? Think about the characteristics of these different animals. Do most meat eaters share certain characteristics? What about plant eaters? **Form a hypothesis** about the skeletal characteristics of plant eaters and meat eaters.

Objectives

- **Gather** data and **communicate** interpretations about the characteristics of meat eaters and plant eaters.
- **Form conclusions** about the characteristics of plant eating and meat eating dinosaurs.
- **Discover** how sauropods might have shared food resources.

Data Sources

Go to the Earth Science Web Site at **earthgeu.com** to find links to fossil data on the Internet. You can also visit your library or local natural history museum to gather information about dinosaur diets.

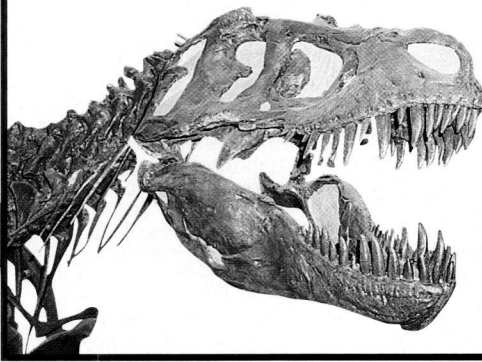

This Late Cretaceous *Tyrannosaurus* is from Alberta, Canada.

Possible Procedures

Students will gather data from Internet sites that can be accessed through the Earth Science Web Site at **earthgeu.com**. Students will post their hypotheses and indicate whether or not the data they collected support their hypotheses.

Procedure

Data and Observations

- Students should pay close attention to tooth structure and skeletal structure, which related to the browsing height of sauropods.
- Herbivores were more abundant than carnivores.

Plan the Experiment

1. Find a resource that describes skeletal characteristics of meat-eating and plant-eating dinosaurs. The Earth Science Web Site lists sites with information about dinosaurs.
2. Gather information from the links on the Earth Science Web Site or the library about the environments that these two types of dinosaurs lived in and which dinosaurs lived in the same environments.
3. Design a data table to record your research results. Include categories such as Dinosaur Name, Meat or

Plant Eater, Food Preference, Skeletal Characteristics, Jaw and Teeth Characteristics, and so on.

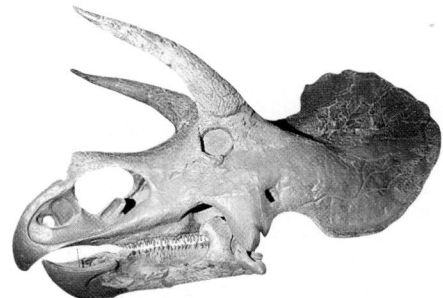

Triceratops was an herbivore.

Procedure

1. Complete your data table, including all information that you think is important.
2. Go to the Earth Science Web Site at <u>earthgeu.com</u> to post your data.
3. Visit sites listed on the Earth Science Web Site for more information on the diets of dinosaurs.

Conclude & Apply

Sharing Your Data Find this Internet GeoLab on the Earth Science Web Site at <u>earthgeu.com</u>. Post your data in the table provided for this activity. Use the additional data from other students to complete your chart and answer the Conclude and Apply questions.

1. What part of a dinosaur skeleton is most important in determining its diet? Why? What is the likelihood that this part of a skeleton will be preserved?
2. What are some other characteristics associated with dinosaur skeletons

that help paleontologists determine what their diets were like?
3. Which were more abundant, meat-eating dinosaurs or plant-eating dinosaurs? Why?
4. How did sauropods share food resources? Describe the evidence used by paleontologists to determine how sauropods shared food resources.
5. How could the same evidence that is used to determine the diets of dinosaurs be used for other animals?

Internet GeoLab **643**

Conclude & Apply

1. Dentition (tooth structure) is one of the most abundant lines of evidence useful for determining dinosaur diets. Tooth shape and form evolved in response to food sources. Teeth are more likely to be fossilized.
2. Body size and shape also can be used to infer diet. Large sauropods were cowlike, with large guts. Leaner body types equipped with claws were adapted for attacking and eating prey.
3. Plant eaters were more abundant. If there had been too many meat eaters, they soon would have exhausted their supply of food, the plant eaters, and starved.
4. Sauropods shared food resources by selectively eating vegetation of a specific kind or at a different height from the vegetation that other sauropods ate. Different wear patterns on teeth and the skeletal structures of the skulls of different sauropods are used by paleontologists to support the hypothesis that sauropods shared food resources in this way.
5. Teeth and skeletal structure can be used to infer whether any animal was or is an herbivore or carnivore. The same relationships are usually true.

✓ Assessment

Performance Using a poster that shows many different dinosaurs, have students identify which dinosaurs were carnivores and which were herbivores. If you do not have a poster, make a collage poster by printing dinosaur images and posting them on a large poster board. Use the Performance Task Assessment List for Poster in **PASC,** p. 73.

Sharing Your Data

Post your data on the Glencoe Science Web Site. Compare your ideas with other classrooms around the country.

NY Core Curriculum Standards
Page 642: St 1 Science KI 1 & 2
Page 643: St 1 Science KI 1 & 2

Science & Math

Purpose

Students will learn how a scale model can be used to determine the approximate weight of an extinct organism.

Content Background

The largest living land animals are African elephants, which can be more than 4 m tall and weigh more than 6.5 metric tons. Although not all dinosaurs were large, over half of the known species weighed more than 2 metric tons. Today, only about 2 percent of all mammals weigh that much. These include elephants, rhinoceroses, hippopotamuses, and the largest animals that ever lived on Earth: whales.

Teaching Strategies

Explain to students how water is displaced by an object. Use the example of getting into a bathtub. If the water is at the brim of the tub, when a person gets in the tub, the water will spill over. This is because the person's body displaced the water. Explain that the volume of water that spills out of a completely full tub when a person gets into it is equal to the volume of the person's body.

Data and Observations

The volume of a scale model that is 1-to-40 is 40 × 40 × 40 (that length × height × width for all the dinosaur parts), which is 64 000. To find the weight in this example use the following equation: volume of dinosaur × water displaced by model × weight of living tissue. If the 1-to-40 scale dinosaur displaced 50 mL of water, then it would have weighed

3 200 000 gm (64 000 × 50 mL × 0.9 g/mL), or 3200 kg.

Sources of Error

- A potential source of error is the reading of the water level. Be sure that students read the value from an eye-level position. If they read from either above or below the water level, they will not get an accurate reading.

Science & Math

Weighing a Dinosaur

How do you weigh a dinosaur? Since the last one died 66 million years ago, you can't exactly ask one to step on a scale.

Model of *Parasaurolophus*, actual dinosaur was 10 m tall.

Weight is a much better indicator of overall size than length or height. A python may be longer than an elephant, and a giraffe may be taller, but most people would agree that the heavier elephant was the bigger animal.

How to Weigh a Dinosaur

Two methods have been employed to estimate the weights of dinosaurs. The first uses a formula derived from the cross-sectional area of the leg bones. Since the legs supported the animal, their strength is an approximation of that animal's weight. Heavier animals have thicker bones.

The second method estimates the volume of a dinosaur, then multiplies the volume by the specific gravity. Most living animals have a specific gravity of around 0.9 kilograms per liter, but this can vary from 0.8 to just over 1. But how do you obtain the volume of a dinosaur? Calculating the volumes of simple shapes like cubes and spheres is easy, but dinosaur shapes were not simple.

One way is to measure the volume of an accurate scale model, then multiply that volume by the scale cubed (since the real dinosaur increased in length, width, and height by the scaled amount). The easiest way to obtain the volume is to immerse the model in water and measure how much water is displaced.

Procedure

1. Obtain several waterproof models of dinosaurs. You will also need a ruler, a calculator, and a graduated cylinder large enough to hold your biggest model.
2. Calculate the scale of each model. Measure the length of the model. The length of the actual dinosaur divided by the length of the model is the scale. Example: a model *Tyrannosaurus* is 30 cm long. A real *Tyrannosaurus* skeleton is 12 meters (1200 cm) long, so the scale is 1/40.
3. Fill the empty graduated cylinder with enough water to cover the model. Record that amount. Completely submerge the model and record the new level of the water. The difference between the first reading and second is the volume of the model.
4. Multiply the volume of the model by the cube of the scale. The result is the volume of the living dinosaur.
5. Multiply the volume of the living dinosaur by the density of living tissue (about 0.9 g/cc). The result is the weight of the living dinosaur, in grams. Convert that number into kilograms.

To find out more about dinosaur sizes and weights, visit the Earth Science Web Site at earthgeu.com

- If the model floats, gently push it in the water until it is submerged.
- Be sure that no water splashes out of the graduated cylinder.
- Be sure that there are no large bubbles of air trapped by the dinosaur model.

Summary

SECTION 24.1
Mesozoic Paleogeography

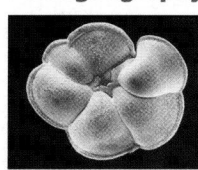

Main Ideas
- Geologists hypothesize that Pangaea broke apart as heat built up beneath it. Expansion occurred and ultimately resulted in the rifting apart of Pangaea.
- The first orogeny is characterized by igneous intrusions, whereas the second orogeny is characterized by thrust faulting and folding.

Vocabulary
Cordillera (p. 626)

SECTION 24.2
Mesozoic Life

Main Ideas
- The modern marine fauna include crabs, lobsters, shrimps, sponges, sea urchins, modern corals, snails, and clams. The major vertebrate groups of the modern fauna include bony fishes, sharks, aquatic reptiles, and aquatic mammals.
- The oceans contained vast numbers of ammonites that are now index fossils. The most common land plants were cycads, and the dominant land animals were dinosaurs.
- An upright posture distinguishes dinosaurs from other reptiles.

Vocabulary
angiosperm (p. 630)
dinosaur (p. 631)
ectotherm (p.633)
endotherm (p. 633)
iridium (p. 634)
modern fauna (p. 628)
Ornithischia (p. 632)
Saurischia (p. 632)

SECTION 24.3
Cenozoic Paleogeography

Main Ideas
- The Cenozoic tectonism is characterized by vertical normal faulting.
- During the Pleistocene, glaciers extended as far south as the courses of the Ohio and Missouri Rivers.

Vocabulary
Basin and Range Province (p. 637)
Tethys Sea (p. 638)

SECTION 24.4
Cenozoic Life

Main Ideas
- Large mammals evolved to feed on the abundant grasslands that developed during the Cenozoic. As the ice ages approached, many of the mammals that lived on these grasslands became extinct and were replaced by large mammals that were adapted to the cold and arid land south of the glaciers.
- Primates are mammals that developed specialized traits, including a grasping hand with an opposable thumb; stereoscopic vision; smaller, fewer, and less-specialized teeth, and a relatively large brain.

Vocabulary
hominid (p. 640)
hominoid (p. 640)
Homo sapiens (p. 640)
primate (p. 640)

earthgeu.com/vocabulary_puzzlemaker

Main Ideas

Summary statements can be used by students to review the major concepts of the chapter.

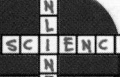

VOCABULARY PuzzleMaker

For additional help with vocabulary, have students access the Vocabulary Puzzlemaker online.

earthgeu.com/ vocabulary puzzlemaker

0:00 *Out of Time?*

If time does not permit teaching the entire chapter, use the GeoDigest at the end of the unit as an overview.

Earth Science Online

Be sure to check the Earth Science Web Site for links to chapter material:
earthgeu.com

GLENCOE *Technology*

Resource Manager

Chapter Assessment, pp. 139–144
MindJogger Videoquizzes DVD/VHS
ExamView® Pro CD-ROM
Performance Assessment in Earth Science

Videotape/DVD
MindJogger Videoquizzes
Chapter 24: *The Mesozoic and Cenozoic Eras*
Have students work in groups as they play the videoquiz game to review key chapter concepts.

NY Core Curriculum Standards

Page 644: St 1 Math KI 2
Page 645: St 4 KI 2.1l & 2.1n

Understanding Main Ideas

1. b
2. c
3. d
4. a
5. b
6. a
7. a
8. d
9. a
10. see student page
11. c
12. d

Applying Main Ideas

13. During the Mesozoic, Pangaea broke apart. The rift system that formed between what are now North America and Africa and Europe became the Mid-Atlantic Ridge.

14. the presence of large-scale cross-bedded sandstones that were deposited as sand dunes

15. dinosaur bone structure; The number of passageways for blood is similar to the bones of endotherms. Also, a possible fossilized heart has four chambers and one aortal arch. This too, is characteristic of endotherms.

NY Core Curriculum Standards

Page 646: St 4 KI 1.2i, 1.2j, & 2.1n, St 6 KI 2
Page 647: St 4 KI 1.2i, 1.2j, 2.1m, 2.1n, 2.1o, 2.1p, 2.1t, & 2.1u

Understanding Main Ideas

1. Which term describes down-dropped blocks of crust bounded by steeply dipping normal faults?
   a. volcanic arcs
   b. basins
   c. red beds
   d. batholiths

2. What are tiny organisms that float in the oceans and make their own food through the process of photosynthesis called?
   a. echinoids
   b. gastropods
   c. phytoplankton
   d. teleosts

3. What makes a dinosaur different from other reptiles?
   a. Dinosaurs were large.
   b. Dinosaurs laid eggs.
   c. Dinosaurs were carnivores.
   d. Dinosaurs had upright postures.

4. The Saurischia were one main group of dinosaurs. What was the other one?
   a. Ornithischia
   b. Sugoschia
   c. *Australopithecus*
   d. *Smilodon*

5. Which of the following best describes all theropod dinosaurs?
   a. herbivores
   b. carnivores
   c. omnivores
   d. quadrupedal

6. Which of the following best describes all sauropod dinosaurs?
   a. herbivores
   b. carnivores
   c. omnivores
   d. bipedal

7. What seed-bearing, flowering plants first appeared during the Cretaceous?
   a. angiosperms
   b. phytoplankton
   c. prosimians
   d. cycads

8. What flying reptiles became extinct at the end of the Cretaceous?
   a. plesiosaurs
   b. mosasaurs
   c. icthyosaurs
   d. pterosaurs

9. What region in the southwestern United States and North-Central Mexico is characterized by northeast-trending mountains and long, linear valleys?
   a. Basin and Range
   b. Colorado Plateau
   c. Sierra Nevada
   d. Mississippi Embayment

10. Use the following terms to complete the concept map below: pterosaurs, ichthyosaurs, primitive mammals, reptiles, rudists & corals, cycads, ammonites, angiosperms, dinosaurs, phytoplankton, turtles, mosasaurs, predatory reptiles.

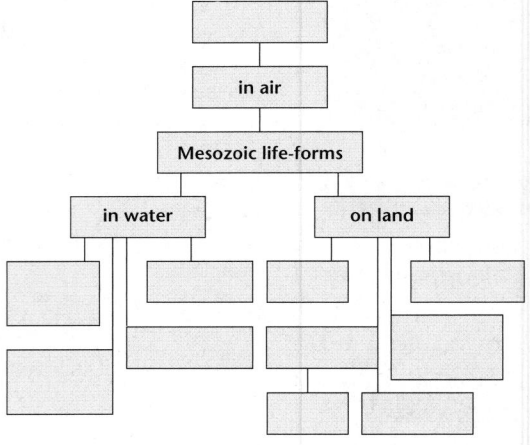

Test-Taking Tip

IF IT LOOKS TOO GOOD TO BE TRUE... Beware of answer choices in multiple-choice questions that seem ready-made and obvious. Remember that only one answer choice for each question is correct. The rest are made up by the test-makers to distract you. This means that sometimes they look very appealing. Check each answer choice carefully before finally selecting it.

earthgeu.com/chapter_test

16. When Australia was connected to Antarctica, a warm current from the north moderated the temperature of Antarctica. A cold, circumpolar current began to flow around Antarctica after the two continents split apart. Without the moderating warm current, the climate of Antarctica became much cooler and glaciers began to form.

17. an opposable thumb, stereoscopic vision, relatively larger brains, and smaller, fewer, less-specialized teeth

11. What mountain range formed as a result of the collision of India with Asia?
a. Rocky Mountains
b. Andes Mountains
c. Himalayan Mountains
d. Alps

12. What genus do Neanderthals belong to?
a. *Australopithecus* c. *Smilodon*
b. *Ardipithicus* d. *Homo*

Applying Main Ideas

13. Discuss how and when the Mid-Atlantic Ridge formed.

14. What evidence indicates that during the Late Triassic and Early Jurassic, western North America was arid?

15. What evidence suggests that dinosaurs were endothermic?

16. How did the paleogeography of Antarctica and Australia affect the climate during the Oligocene?

17. What characteristics separate primates from other mammals?

Thinking Critically

18. Compare the body shapes of ichthyosaurs and plesiosaurs to those of dolphins and whales. What can you conclude about these body shapes?

19. If a meteorite struck Earth at the end of the Cretaceous, does this mean that the impact caused the extinction of the dinosaurs? Explain why or why not.

20. Cite several reasons why the evolutionary history of ammonites is better supported than theories about hominid evolution.

21. Do the characteristics of today's coral reefs suggest that they might become oil reservoirs as the rudist reefs did? Explain.

earthgeu.com/standardized_test

Standardized Test Practice

1. What characterizes the second orogeny that affected western North America in the Mesozoic Era?
a. low-angle faults c. igneous intrusions
b. block faults d. clastic wedges

INTERPRETING DATA Use the table below to answer questions 2 and 3.

Mass Extinction Theories	
Evidence for meteor impact	Unusually high levels of iridium in Cretaceous-Paleogene boundary sediments; Discovery of Chicxulub crater
Evidence for massive volcanic activity	Volcanic eruptions during the Late Cretaceous in India; Unusually high levels or iridium, soot, and charcoal in Cretaceous-Paleogene boundary sediments

2. How does the presence of iridium at the Cretaceous-Paleogene boundary support the theory of massive volcanic activity?
a. Iridium is deposited after a large fire is extinguished.
b. Iridium is a common byproduct of combustion reactions.
c. Iridium is found in abundance in Earth's core.
d. All of the above.

3. Underneath the Chicxulub crater is a large layer of melted rock and a layer of jumbled rocks. Why are these rocks jumbled?
a. They have been broken up by water erosion.
b. They contain a higher level of iridium.
c. They are pieces of the meteorite that broke off upon impact.
d. They fell into the crater after the impact.

Assessment **647**

Thinking Critically

18. The body shape of ichthyosaurs was very similar to the body shape of dolphins, and the shape of plesiosaurs was similar to the shape of walruses. These body shapes are well-adapted for their environments and suggest that, through natural selection, aquatic tetrapod vertebrates will evolve these types of body plans.

19. No; the impact of a meteorite at the end of the Cretaceous was one event, and the terminal Cretaceous extinction event was another. There is strong evidence that both events happened at, or near, the same time. There also is evidence that these two events had a cause-and-effect relationship. However, it is also possible that both events occurred but had nothing to do with each other. Temporal correlation of events does not mean that the events are connected.

20. There are many more fossils of ammonites than there are of hominids. Because there is much more data, the evidence is much stronger. In addition, there is a much longer record of ammonite fossils than there is of hominids.

21. Yes, there are many open areas in-between the branching and irregularly shaped coral structures. After death and burial, if these open spaces remain, oil could get stored within them.

Standardized Test Practice

1. a
2. c
3. d

For a **preview** of geologic time, study this GeoDigest before you read the chapters.
After you have studied geologic time, use the GeoDigest to **review** the unit.

Prepare

Purpose

This GeoDigest can be used as an overview of the concepts of geologic time and the changes on Earth throughout geologic time. If time is limited, you may wish to use this unit summary to teach these concepts in place of the chapters in Unit 6.

Key Concepts

Students are introduced to geologic dating methods and the geologic time scale. They learn about relative-age dating, absolute-age dating, and the geologic eras.

1 Focus

Section Focus

Linguistic Before beginning the lesson, make a copy of the geologic time scale found at the back of the book and delete the names. Provide copies to students, and ask students to fill it in with the names of eons, eras, and periods. They can use this time scale to record major events throughout geologic time, which are discussed throughout Unit 6. This activity will familiarize students with the hierarchy of eons, eras, and periods, as well as the spellings and pronunciations of these words.
L2

0:00 **Out of Time?**

If time does not permit teaching the entire unit, use this GeoDigest as an overview.

Geologic Time

Fossils and the Rock Record

Geologists have separated Earth's history into divisions based upon the fossil record and organized these divisions into the geologic time scale. The divisions found on the geologic time scale—in descending order of length—are eons, eras, periods, and epochs. The principles of uniformitarianism, original horizontality, superposition, and cross-cutting relationships are used to interpret Earth's rock record—and thus describe our planet's history. Unconformities caused by weathering and erosion or by periods of nondeposition indicate missing layers in the rock record. Fossils are the remains and evidence of plants and animals that once lived on Earth. Fossils preserved in the rock record provide information about past environmental conditions and evolutionary changes in life-forms. They thus help to correlate rock layers from one area to another.

Absolute Age of Rocks Absolute age dating measures the actual age of an object such as a mineral, rock, or fossil. Radioactive dating uses the decay rates of various types of radioactive minerals to determine the actual age of a rock or fossil. Radioactive decay is the random emission of particles from the nucleus of a radioactive atom at a constant rate. The time it takes a radioactive isotope to decay fifty percent of its original mass to a nonradioactive element is known as the mineral's half-life. Tree rings and varves are other methods of determining the dates of events and changes in the environment. Key beds in the rock record that mark the time of their occurrence include volcanic ash and meteorite-impact debris that spread out over large areas of Earth in a small amount of time.

The Precambrian

Geologists have used radiometric dating to show that Earth must be at least 4.2 billion years old. Because all of the objects in the solar system formed at the same time, and Moon rocks and meteorites are dated at 4.6 billion years old, Earth is assumed to be 4.6 billion years old also. Early Earth was hot because of abundant radioactive isotopes, bombardment by meteorites, and gravitational contraction. Earth's crust formed when the uppermost portion of the mantle cooled. The early crust weathered and formed sediments. Sediment-covered slabs of early crust were subducted and generated magmas with granitic compositions. During the Archaean Eon, granitic crust formed microcontinents. The microcontinents collided with one another throughout the Proterozoic Eon to form the cores of today's continents. Earth's early

Fossil snake

Multiple Learning Styles

 Linguistic Section Focus, p. 648; Earth Science Journal, p. 650

 Interpersonal Project, p. 650

 Visual-Spatial Activity, p. 649

atmosphere and the oceans formed through the process of outgassing. Nearly all of the oxygen in the atmosphere is a result of photosynthesis. Certain minerals oxidize, or rust, in the presence of free oxygen. Proterozoic red beds are sedimentary rock deposits that contain oxidized iron. They are evidence that there was free oxygen in the atmosphere during the Proterozoic Eon.

Early Life on Earth
All the ingredients were present on the early Earth to form proteins, which are the building blocks of life. Experiments have demonstrated that amino acids, the molecules that make up proteins, were likely abundant on the surface of early Earth. The first life was likely prokaryotic cells, which are small and contain no nuclei. Eukaryotic cells, which contain nuclei and are generally larger and more complex than prokaryotic cells, emerged later. The first evidence of multicellular organisms are fossils of eukaryotic algae from a 2.1 billion year old banded iron formation in northern Michigan. By about 670 million years ago, the multicellular Ediacaran organisms began to flourish throughout the world.

The Paleozoic Era
Early in the Paleozoic, a shallow sea covered the ancient North American continent of Laurentia, which was located near the equator. Laurentia's continental margin was passive—no tectonic activity was occurring. The fauna included many new

Vital Statistics	
Half-Lives of Radioactive Isotopes	
Carbon 14	5730 (+/- 30) years
Uranium 235	700 million years
Rubidium 87	4.9 billion years
Uranium 238	4.5 billion years

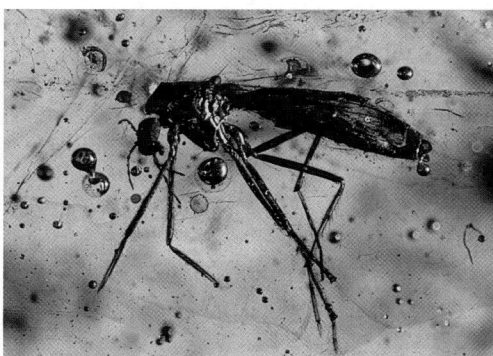
Insect in amber

organisms that evolved during the Cambrian explosion. Fossils of trilobites and articulate brachiopods are common. Sea level changes cause depositional environments to change position laterally. This results in adjacent depositional sequences overlying each other in vertical succession.

Middle Paleozoic
Deposits of evaporite minerals such as gypsum, and halite formed in the mid-Paleozoic as areas of ocean water were isolated and evaporated. Collisional tectonism occurred, causing mountain building along active continental margins. Clastic wedges formed as a result of mountain building as deposits of sedimentary rocks formed adjacent to uplifted areas in wedge-shaped formations. Articulate brachiopods, corals, and many other organisms dominated the seas. Fishes evolved as top ocean predators and plants moved onto land. At the end of the Ordovician and in the Late Devonian, large numbers of organisms became extinct in relatively short periods of time. This phenomenon is called a mass extinction.

Late Paleozoic
In the Late Paleozoic, continents collided to form Pangaea. Cycles of glacial/interglacial periods during the Pennsylvanian are represented by cyclothems—stacked deposits of

GeoDigest **649**

2 Teach

Activity

Visual-Spatial To demonstrate the concept of correlation (determining age relationships between geographically separated rocks), superposition, original horizontality, and unconformities, have students correlate hypothetical outcrop sections that are placed on tables at the front of the room. Make "outcrops" by setting rocks out in a specific vertical order. Students will duplicate this arrangement on paper and then draw lines to correlate the "outcrop" sections. Any type of rocks can be used. A sample setup might be:

Outcrop 1 (west)	Outcrop 2 (central)	Outcrop 3 (east)
limestone	limestone	granite
shale	granite	sandstone
granite	sandstone	fossilifeous limestone

Using an Analogy
Earth is 4.6 billion years old. Of this, the Phanerozoic Eon is only the most recent 542 million years. If we could compress the Phanerozoic Eon into one year, dinosaurs would appear in mid-April and die out in late October. Humans would not appear until the very end of the year, approximately two hours before midnight on New Years' Eve!

Content Background
During the Archean Eon, 4.6–2.5 billion years ago, Earth was much hotter than it is today. Earth gave off gases that became Earth's atmosphere. Water vapor was also released by degassing. As Earth cooled, the water vapor condensed into rain and remained on Earth's surface as the oceans.

NY Core Curriculum Standards

Page 648: St 4 KI 1.2i, 1.2j, & 2.1l

Page 649: St 4 KI 1.2h, 1.2i, & 1.2j

GeoDigest

Earth Science
Journal

Linguistic Have students each write an essay in their science journals in which they describe a dinosaur of their choice. They should include characteristics such as whether the dinosaur was a saurischian or an ornithischian, its size, and any specialized characteristics. [L2]

Time Line

Have students each create a time line that includes the following events: the breakup of Pangaea, the formation of Rodinia, a Mesozoic orogeny, the formation of Pangaea, and a Cenozoic orogeny. In addition, have students research the timing of the Taconic, Acadian, and Alleghenian Orogenies and add them to their time lines.

Project

Interpersonal Have students work in small groups to research an invertebrate fossil type of their choice, such as trilobites, cephalopods, mollusks, crinoids, ammonoids, or foraminifera. Ask student groups to write a summary for presentation to the class. The summary should include a labeled diagram of the group's fossil and information about the animal's range, habitat, and other distinguishing characteristics. Ask students to answer the following question: If a geologist were to find this fossil in a rock, what could the geologist infer about the depositional environment of that rock?
COOP LEARN

alternating transgressive and regressive rock sequences. The ocean shrank during glacial periods and expanded during interglacial periods. Seeds and the amniote egg developed during the Late Paleozoic, developments that allowed plants and reptiles to move onto dry land. Regression of the ocean and climate change led to a mass extinction at the end of the Permian Period.

The Mesozoic and Cenozoic Eras

Mesozoic Era In the Mesozoic, Pangaea broke up. Geologists hypothesize that the size of the supercontinent led to a heat buildup and expansion of the landmass, resulting in rifting that broke it up. Two orogenies occurred. The first orogeny is characterized by igneous intrusions whereas the second orogeny is characterized by thrust faulting and folding. Ammonites were prevalent in the Mesozoic ocean; the most common land plants were cycads; and the dominant land animals were dinosaurs. High levels of iridium, and the Chicxulub structure in the rocks at the Cretaceous-Paleogene boundary indicate that a meteorite hit Earth at the end of the Cretaceous Period. This meteorite may have led to the extinction of the dinosaurs. Dinosaurs are distinguished from reptiles by their upright posture. Birds may be descended from dinosaurs. The fossil *Archaeopteryx*, which contains features of both dinosaurs and birds, is cited as evidence for the relationship. The fossils of reptiles are distinguished from the fossils of mammals by tooth shape, and the number of lower jawbones.

Cenozoic Era The major orogeny of the Cenozoic is characterized by vertical normal faulting. During the Pleistocene ice ages, glaciers extended as far south as the courses of the Ohio and Missouri rivers. By the Oligocene, grassy savannas covered much of Central North America. Large

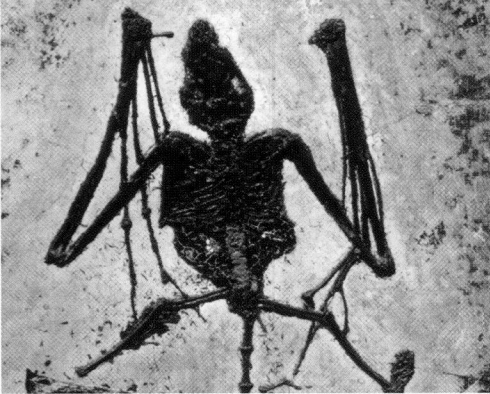

Fossil bat

mammals evolved to feed in these abundant grasslands. As the ice ages approached, many grazers became extinct and were replaced by large mammals that were adapted to cold and arid climates. Primates emerged during the Cenozoic. Primates are mammals that developed specialized traits such as a grasping hand with an opposable thumb; smaller, fewer, and less specialized teeth; stereoscopic vision; and a relatively large brain.

FOCUS ON CAREERS

Paleoecologist
Paleoecologists study the ecology of ancient animals and plants. Where did a fossil specimen live? What did it eat? What ate it? What were the limiting factors in its environment? Paleontology, biology, and ecology are put together to complete pictures of ancient environments. Curiosity and patience are essential to a paleoecologist, but advanced degrees are also required.

Differentiated Instruction

Learning Disabled Make two copies of the complete geologic time scale. Use one copy to cut each eon, era, and period into separate strips of paper. Give students with learning disabilities the pieces of the time scale and the whole time scale. Ask them to reconstruct the time scale from the pieces using the whole geologic time scale as a guide.

Resource Manager

Study Guide for Content Mastery, pp. 155–156 [L2]

ASSESSMENT

Understanding Main Ideas

1. What feature, caused by weathering and erosion or by periods of nondeposition, indicates missing layers in the rock record?
   a. uniformitarianism
   b. unconformity
   c. horizontality
   d. cross-cutting

2. What is the random emission of particles from the nucleus of a radioactive atom at a constant rate called?
   a. radioactive minerals
   b. half-life
   c. radioactive decay
   d. uranium

3. What formed when the uppermost portion of Earth's mantle cooled?
   a. meteorites
   b. radioactive isotopes
   c. sediment
   d. Earth's crust

4. Earth's early atmosphere and the oceans formed through what process?
   a. photosynthesis
   b. free oxygen
   c. outgassing
   d. Proterozoic red beds

5. The first life on Earth was a small cell with no nucleus called what?
   a. a prokaryotic cell
   b. a eukaryotic cell
   c. algae
   d. Ediacaran organisms

6. What forms when areas of ocean water are isolated and evaporate?
   a. collisional tectonism
   b. clastic wedges
   c. evaporite minerals
   d. brachiopods

Fossil conifer cone

7. What sequence represents alternating glacial/interglacial periods during the Pennsylvanian?
   a. cyclothems   **c.** clastic wedges
   b. amniote egg   **d.** microcontinent

8. What were the most common land plants of the Mesozoic?
   a. ammonites   **c.** cycads
   b. conifers   **d.** embayments

9. Which of these land features was prominent in Central North America during the Oligocene?
   a. grasslands   **c.** primates
   b. forests   **d.** glaciation

10. Which of the following is a trait of primates?
   a. more-specialized teeth
   b. smaller brain
   c. hooves
   d. stereoscopic vision

Thinking Critically

1. Put the following geologic time divisions in order from shortest to longest: period, eon, epoch, era.

2. Describe why early Earth was hot.

3. Discuss how paleontologists distinguish reptiles from mammals in the fossil record.

---

3 Assess

Check for Understanding
Using Scientific Terms
Have students compare and contrast the terms *relative age* and *absolute age*. Ask students to describe the significance of each dating method.

Reteach

Use soft, wrapped candies to demonstrate the concept of radioactive mineral decay and half-lives. Start off with a given number of candies for different isotopes. You might use potassium-40, whose half-life is 1.3 billion years, and rubidium-87, whose half-life is 4.7 billion years. Use a clock with a second hand to estimate time, where 1 minute is equal to 1 billion years. After 1 minute, tell students to remove one-half of their candies, and so on. Soft, chewable candies are good to use because they can be easily cut into halves and fourths.

✔Assessment

Skill Have students each make a graph of the percent of original radioactive isotopes versus the number of half-lives up to four half-lives. The x,y coordinates should be 0, 100; 1, 50; 2, 25; 3, 12.5; 4, 6.25.

ASSESSMENT

Understanding Main Ideas

1. b	**3.** d	**5.** a	**7.** a	**9.** a
2. c	**4.** c	**6.** c	**8.** c	**10.** d

Thinking Critically

1. The geologic time divisions, in order from shortest to longest, are epochs, periods, eras, and eons.

2. The early Earth was hot because of abundant radioactive isotopes, bombardment by meteorites, and gravitational contraction.

3. The fossils of reptiles are distinguished from the fossils of mammals by the number of ear bones and the number of lower jawbones.

NY Core Curriculum Standards

Page 650: St 4 KI 1.2h, 1.2i, & 1.2j
Page 651: St 4 KI 1.2e, 1.2h, & 2.1p

Resources and the Environment

Unit Overview

Populations and Resources
In Unit 7, students are introduced to the relationships among populations and natural resources. Students will learn how the availability of natural resources affects population growth. They will also learn about the types of natural resources provided by Earth, and how the use of these resources has impacts on Earth. Students will identify resources as renewable or nonrenewable, and also will examine each type of resource. They will learn about traditional energy resources such as fossil fuels, as well as discover alternative energy resources.

Chapter Breakdown Chapter 25 introduces natural resources and develops the idea that the availability of such resources determines the size of any population in a given area. The types of natural resources used to provide energy for human populations are explored in Chapter 26. In this chapter, students will study traditional energy sources as well as many alternative energy sources. Chapter 27 continues the discussion about resources by describing the impacts that human use of resources has upon the land, air, and water resources on Earth.

(0:00) Out of Time?

If time does not permit teaching the entire unit, use the GeoDigest at the end of the unit as an overview.

Resources and the Environment

Herds of scimitar-horned oryx meander across the rolling hills and meadows of The Wilds, a unique, 4000 ha wildlife preserve and environmental education center in rural Ohio. The Wilds was developed on land donated by a local power company after the area was strip-mined for coal. When resources such as coal are removed by surface mining, reclamation not only can restore the area to its former contours, but also can provide new educational and recreational activities for local residents.

Unit Contents

25 **Earth Resources**

26 **Energy Resources**

27 **Human Impact on Earth Resources**

NATIONAL GEOGRAPHIC

Go to the National Geographic Expedition on page 898 to learn more about topics that are connected to this unit.

652

NATIONAL GEOGRAPHIC

eXpeditions!

Streams of Hope Some topics of Earth science deserve more attention than others because they're unusual, informative, or just plain interesting. The National Geographic Society has created visually exciting, multipage *Expeditions!* features that inform, excite, and motivate your students.

Expeditions! features are relevant to the Earth science content of the student edition. Assign them as a lead-in to special research projects and in-depth studies for extra credit. Use them as a basis for colorful visual displays and bulletin boards.

Scimitar-horned Oryx,
The Wilds, Cumberland, Ohio

653

Introducing the Unit

Preconceptions The photograph shows a herd of scimitar-horned oryx grazing and resting on a hill overlooking a small lake in a nature preserve called The Wilds, located in eastern Ohio. Ask students what they think a nature preserve has to do with the chapters in this unit. Then explain that The Wilds is built on land that was donated by the local power company after reclamation of a former coal strip-mine. Ask whether any students have visited a strip-mine or underground mine. If so, ask them to describe what the land area around an operating mine looks like. If students have visited an operating mine, they may be aware that mining companies leave behind piles of waste rock that have been crushed or pulverized to extract the resource.

Resource Distribution

Display a world map that includes resources in its legend. Have students look at the map and locate the areas on Earth in which most of the coal, petroleum, natural gas, and peat reserves are found. Ask students to identify the countries in which most of these fossil fuels are consumed. Ask students whether the countries that consume fossil fuels also produce them. Students should recognize that there is a disparity between those countries with particular natural resources and those that need those resources to support their standards of living. In the last chapter of this unit, students will learn how humans impact their environments.

Earth Science Online

Note Internet addresses that you find useful in the space below for quick reference.

For Internet tips, see Glencoe's **Using the Internet in the Science Classroom.**

653

Earth Resources

Refer to pages 8T–9T of the Teacher Guide for an explanation of the National Science Content Standards correlations.

Section	Objectives	National Science Content Standards	State/Local Standards
SECTION 25.1 **What are resources?** 🕐 1 session 📦 ½ block	1. **Distinguish** between renewable and non-renewable resources. 2. **Identify** renewable and nonrenewable resources.	UCP.4; D.2, D.3; F.3, F.6	St 1 Math KI 1 & St 1 Science KI 2, St 6 KI 2, 4, & 5
SECTION 25.2 **Land Resources** 🕐 1½ sessions 📦 1 block	3. **Describe** why land is considered to be a natural resource. 4. **Recognize** the need to protect Earth's land as a resource. 5. **Explain** how humans adjust to the uneven distribution of land resources.	UCP.4; B.2; F.3, F.5, F.6	St 4 KI 2.1t, 3.1a, & 3.1b, St 6 KI 4 & 6, St 7 KI 1
SECTION 25.3 **Air Resources** 🕐 1½ sessions 📦 1 block	6. **Recognize** that the atmosphere is an Earth resource. 7. **Describe** the importance of clean air.	UCP.2, UCP.4; F.3, F.4, F.5, F.6	St 1 Math KI 1, 2, & 3, St 4 Ki 1.2e, & 2.2d, St 6 KI 2, 4, & 5, St 7 KI 2
SECTION 25.4 **Water Resources** 🕐 2 sessions 📦 1 block	8. **Explain** the importance of clean freshwater. 9. **Analyze** how water is distributed and used on Earth. 10. **Identify** ways in which humans can reduce the need for increasing production of freshwater resources.	UCP.2, UCP. 4; B.1, B.2; D.1, D.3; E.1, E.2; F.3, F.4, F.5, F.6	St 1 Science KI 1, 2, Engin KI 1, St 4 KI 1.1i, 1.2g, 2.1a, 3.1b, St 6 KI 1, 2, 4, & 6, St 7 KI 1

A complete Planning Guide is provided on pages 30T–32T.

🕐 The number of recommended single-period sessions

📦 The number of recommended blocks

Activity Materials

Discovery Lab *page 655*
variety of items found in the classroom, such as pieces of natural chalk, glass slide, microscope, paper, pencil

GeoLab *pages 676–677*
clear plastic, large pans, salt water, collecting containers, lamp, glass pan or beaker, hot plate

MiniLab *page 674*
baby-food jars and lids (6), water samples (5), distilled water, liquid soap, pencil, paper, labels, dropper, 100-mL graduated cylinder

Demo *page 655*
bicycle wheel

page 661
400-mL beakers (2), dropper, food coloring, Epson salts, laundry detergent, water

Need materials? Contact Science Kit at 1-800-828-7777 or at www.sciencekit.com on the Internet. For alternate materials, see the activity on the listed page.

Key to Teaching Strategies

L1 Level 1 activities should be appropriate for students with learning difficulties.

L2 Level 2 activities should be within the ability range of all students.

L3 Level 3 activities are designed for above-average students.

ELL ELL activities should be within the ability range of English-language learners.

COOP LEARN Cooperative learning activities are designed for small-group work.

P These strategies represent student products that can be placed in a best-work portfolio.

📦 These strategies are useful in a block-scheduling format.

Chapter Organizer

Glencoe Exclusive!
Teacher Works™
All-In-One Planner and Resource Center

Activities/Features	Reproducible Masters	Transparencies
Discovery Lab: Origins of Resources, p. 655	**Study Guide for Content Mastery,** p. 157 L2	**Section Focus Transparency 78** L1 ELL
	Study Guide for Content Mastery, p. 158 L2	**Section Focus Transparency 79** L1 ELL **Teaching Transparency 76** L2 ELL
Problem-Solving Lab: Interpreting Graphs, p. 665	**Study Guide for Content Mastery,** pp. 159–160 L2 **Laboratory Manual,** pp. 193–196 **Exploring Environmental Problems,** pp. 29–32	**Section Focus Transparency 80** L1 ELL **Teaching Transparency 77** L2 ELL
MiniLab: Hard Water, p. 674 **GeoLab:** Designing a Solar Desalinator, pp. 676–677 **Science in the News:** Glass from the Past, p. 678	**Study Guide for Content Mastery,** pp. 161–162 L2 **Geolab and MiniLab Worksheets,** p. 99 L2 **Geolab and MiniLab Worksheets,** pp. 100–102 L2 **Laboratory Manual,** pp. 197–200	**Section Focus Transparency 81** L1 ELL **Teaching Transparency 78** L2 ELL

Assessment

Chapter Assessment,
  pp. 145–150
**Performance Assessment in
  the Science Classroom
  (PASC)**
**MindJogger Videoquiz
  DVD/VHS**
**Performance Assessment in
  Earth Science**
ExamView® Pro CD-ROM
5 Days to the Regents Exam

GLENCOE'S
ASSESSMENT
ADVANTAGE

Additional Resources

**Guided Reading Audio
  Program** ELL
**Cooperative Learning in the
  Science Classroom**
  COOP LEARN
Lesson Plans
Block Scheduling
earthgeu.com
NY Lesson Plans
NY Block Scheduling
Review Handbook for
  Regents Earth Science
  Exam

**NATIONAL
GEOGRAPHIC**

**Teacher's
Corner**

**Products Available from
National Geographic Society**
*To order the following products,
call the National Geographic
Society at 1-800-368-2728:*
Videos
What's the Earth Made Of?
Recycling: The Endless Circle

Every Stone Has a Story
Water: A Precious Resource
Curriculum Kits
GeoKit: *Dynamic Earth*
GeoKit: *Rocks and Minerals*

Content Background

What are resources?
Section 25.1

Earth supplies a wide variety of natural resources. All organisms on Earth, including humans, use resources provided by the environment. Living things use, change, and reuse many Earth resources. The word *resource* itself comes from the French word *resourdre*, meaning "to rise anew." The natural resource needs of human societies have changed over time. For example, obsidian and chert once were important resources because they were necessary for making tools and weapons. The resources used in technology today are different from those of the past. Bauxite is an example of a natural resource that had little significance to humans in the past. Today, however, it is the principle source of aluminum and is widely used in industrialized countries.

Land Resources
Section 25.2

Land can be thought of as a natural resource, both because it contains natural resources and because the land surface itself can support many uses. Landmasses hold many valuable rocks and minerals that humans use for a variety of purposes. The following are obtained from rocks and minerals found in Earth's crust. Iron is used in the production of steel, a material used widely in bridges, automobile frames, buildings, and machinery. Copper is used in the production of electrical wiring and brass. Lead is important in the manufacture of storage batteries, solder, and protective radiation shielding. Zinc, combined with copper, is used to produce brass and to coat iron and steel to prevent rusting. Aluminum has many uses, including the production of cans.

Titanium is a valuable resource commonly used for surgical implants. Chromium and nickel are used to make surgical instruments, kitchenware, and automobile parts. Gold, nickel, and silver are commonly used for jewelry and coins.

Air Resources
Section 25.3

All living things depend on gases in the atmosphere. All organisms depend on atmospheric oxygen for cellular respiration, the process in which a cell uses oxygen to break down carbohydrates to release energy needed for cell maintenance, growth, and reproduction. The waste products of cellular respiration are water and carbon dioxide. All photosynthetic organisms, including green plants, cyanobacteria, and some protists, also require carbon dioxide for the process of photosynthesis. The products of photosynthesis are oxygen and water. On Earth, living things are connected to one another through

Multiple Learning Styles

- **Visual-Spatial** Modeling, p. 660, Demo, p. 661, Project, p. 664, Reteach, p. 675
- **Interpersonal** Project, p. 657, Collaborative Learning, pp. 667, 672
- **Intrapersonal** Earth Science Journal, p. 660
- **Linguistic** Reteach, pp. 658, 668
- **Naturalist** Project, p. 672

GLENCOE Technology

The following multimedia resources are available from Glencoe.

The Infinite Voyage Series
Crisis in the Atmosphere
Secrets From a Frozen World

Vocabulary Puzzlemaker

TeacherWorks™ CD-ROM

MindJogger Videoquizzes DVD/VHS

ExamView® Pro CD-ROM

Interactive Chalkboard CD-ROM

these two processes and many other geochemical cycles. As a result, changes in the atmosphere can affect all life on Earth. There is evidence that human activities have significantly affected the quality of the atmosphere. Understanding the interrelationships among living things, all of which depend on atmospheric resources, will lead students to an appreciation and acceptance of the need for the protection of air resources.

Water Resources
Section 25.4

The National Institute for Water Resources (NIWR) is a network of research institutes located in each of the states and territories in the United States. Each state and territory has a research institute, located at a designated college or university, whose role is to promote research, training, and information dissemination. The primary impact of water resource issues is at the local or state level. Thus, water

resources generally are managed at these levels. Federal agencies get involved when water issues cross state boundaries. The Secretary of Interior oversees and periodically evaluates each state institute with assistance from the U.S. Geological Survey. Concern and care for water resources is a global issue that begins locally. Because most of Earth's freshwater supply is frozen, the care and use of available freshwater resources is crucial to the maintenance of the quality of life on Earth.

Identifying Misconceptions

Students have a tendency to think that recycling is a new idea and that it is a relatively recent phenomenon. However, Earth processes have always involved cycles, which are natural forms of recycling. Earth has a set amount of matter and energy. Over the 4.6 billion years of Earth's existence, this matter and energy have been reused over and over. When humans recycle, they are applying basic principles: the laws of conservation of matter and energy. These laws state that matter and energy cannot be created nor destroyed, but both can be transformed and transferred.

✔*Assessment*

Portfolio Assessment
Assessment, TWE, p. 663

Performance Assessment
Discovery Lab, TWE, p. 655
Discovery Lab, SE, p. 655
MiniLab, TWE, p. 674
MiniLab, SE, p. 674
GeoLab, SE, pp. 676–677

Knowledge Assessment
Assessment, TWE, pp. 656, 658, 661, 668, 672
GeoLab, TWE, pp. 676–677

Section Assessment, SE,
pp. 658, 663, 668, 675
Chapter Assessment, SE, pp. 680–681

Skill Assessment
Assessment, TWE, p. 675
Problem-Solving Lab, TWE, p. 665

Be sure to check the Earth Science Web Site for links to chapter material: earthgeu.com

Earth Resources

Introducing the Chapter

Ask students to list what they did before they came to school today. Students may include activities such as bathing, getting dressed, eating breakfast, and taking the bus. Then ask students to list every item they used to get ready for school. They may list clothing, foods, vehicles, gasoline, and so on. Point out to students that all of the materials they listed are resources.

Interpreting the Photo

Earth resources include rocks and soil. The first tools used by humans probably were sharp rocks found on the land surface. As time went on, humans were able to shape rocks so that they could be used to build structures, such as this archway. Point out to students that the archway shown here is made up of many flat stones lying upon one another.

INTERACTIVE CHALKBOARD
with Image Bank

PowerPoint® Presentations

This CD is an editable Microsoft® PowerPoint® presentation that includes:
- Section presentations
- Section checks
- Image bank
- Links to Earth Science Online
- All transparencies
- Animations
- Audio

Earth Resources

What You'll Learn
- What materials are considered to be Earth resources.
- Which Earth resources are renewable and which are nonrenewable.
- How Earth resources are used.

Why It's Important
Earth resources can be derived from either living or nonliving things. Many Earth resources are essential for life. Once used, some resources cannot be replaced, whereas others can be replaced in relatively short periods of time. The use of Earth resources must be balanced for life on Earth to continue.

Earth Science Online

To learn more about earth resources, visit the Earth Science Web Site at earthgeu.com

---

Earth Resources

Ancient ruins in Cork, Ireland

Discovery Lab

Process Skills

observe and infer, classify, make and use tables, compare and contrast, think critically **L1** **ELL**

Preparation

Set out on display in front of the classroom a group of common objects. The objects may include paper, an apple, popcorn, an empty jar, a balloon filled with air, a shirt, a toy car, and so on.

Procedure

- It makes little difference what objects are displayed as long as some came from living things and some did not.

Observe

Objects such as paper, an apple, and popcorn came from living things; the others did not. A shirt may be either. If it is made of cotton or silk, it would be classified as having come from living things. Determining which objects are easily replaceable may involve an extended discussion and will depend on students'

Discovery Lab — Origins of Resources

All the material goods that you use every day are matter. One way in which matter can be classified is whether it comes from living things or from nonliving things. In this activity, you will identify the origins of some common materials.

1. In your science journal, make a data table with the headings "Item," "Living," "Nonliving," "Easily Replaced," and "Not Replaceable."

2. Look around your classroom and list common items that you see in the first column of your table.

3. Classify the matter in each item as coming from either living or non-living things, and as being either easily replaced or not replaceable, by placing check marks in the appropriate columns.

Classify Compare your data table with those of several other students. Which of the items were identified as coming from living things? Which came from nonliving things? Which are easily replaced? Which are not replaceable? What criteria did you use to classify each item? Were you unable to classify any item using just these categories? Explain.

SECTION 25.1 — *What are resources?*

OBJECTIVES

- **Distinguish** *between renewable and non-renewable resources.*

- **Identify** *renewable and nonrenewable resources.*

VOCABULARY

natural resource
renewable resource
sustainable yield
nonrenewable resource

 Did you eat an apple or a banana for breakfast this morning? Every day, you eat food and drink water because these resources are necessary for you to live. You and every other living thing on Earth must have certain resources to grow, develop, maintain life processes, and reproduce. In addition to food and water, most animals also need shelter. Think about the resources used to provide shelter for you and your family. Maybe your home is made of brick or stone, or perhaps it has wood shingles or aluminum siding. All of these materials come from Earth.

NATURAL RESOURCES

The resources that Earth provides are known as **natural resources.** Natural resources include Earth's air, water, and land; all living things; and nutrients, rocks, and minerals in the soil and deep in Earth's crust. Recall from Chapter 3 that neither matter nor energy can be

25.1 *What are resources?* **655**

Section 25.1

1 Focus

Section Focus

Before presenting the lesson, display **Section Focus Transparency 78** on the overhead projector.
L1 ELL

Chapter Themes

The following themes from the National Science Content Standards are covered in this chapter. Refer to page 8T of the Teacher Guide for an explanation of the correlations.
Evidence, models, and explanation (UCP.2); Change, constancy, and measurement (UCP.3); Form and function (UCP.5)

---

backgrounds. Lists derived from home may vary widely but should follow the same procedure used in class.

✓ Assessment

Performance Have students assemble a new group of items and classify each as either having come from living things or not. Place the separated items in a display case with a sign inviting students in other classes to add items. Use the Performance Task Assessment List for Making Observations and Inferences in **PASC**, p. 17.

Resource Manager

Study Guide for Content Mastery, p. 157 L2

Section Focus Transparency 78 L1 ELL

0:00 Out of Time?

If time does not permit teaching the entire chapter, use the Chapter Summary on page 679 and the GeoDigest found at the end of the unit as an overview.

Using Scientific Terms

Deciduous trees are trees that lose their leaves during the winter season and grow new leaves in the spring. The biosphere is the part of Earth that supports living things. The biosphere is related to other Earth systems: the atmosphere, the hydrosphere, and the lithosphere. The atmosphere includes the gases of Earth, the lithosphere includes rocks and minerals on Earth, the hydrosphere includes water on Earth, and the biosphere includes all living things found on Earth.

Environmental Connection

Write the following quotation on the chalkboard at the beginning of class. "Sustainability is an economic state where the demands placed upon the environment by people and commerce can be met without reducing the capacity of the environment to provide for future generations. It can also be expressed in the simple terms of an economic golden rule for the restorative economy: Leave the world better than you found it, take no more than you need, try not to harm life or the environment, make amends if you do." (Paul Hawken, *The Ecology of Commerce*) Ask students to explain what this statement means in terms of their daily lives.

Enrichment

Aluminum cans are the most recycled product in North America, with a recycling rate of 62.8 percent. Ninety-five percent of the energy needed to produce an aluminum can is saved by recycling. A recycled aluminum can typically is back in use in just 60 days.

Figure 25-1 Trees are renewable resources because they are living things that reproduce within a relatively short period of time.

created or destroyed, but both can be changed from one form to another. You will find out how some natural resources are transformed in the *Science in the News* feature at the end of this chapter. One way in which natural resources are changed is through cycling, as in the carbon, nitrogen, and water cycles that you learned about in previous chapters.

Have you ever recycled an aluminum can? If you recycle, you probably are already aware that some resources cannot be replaced in a reasonable amount of time. If you have ever mowed a lawn or planted a garden, you know that some other natural resources can be used and replaced through natural processes in a short period of time. Both types of natural resources are necessary for life on Earth.

RENEWABLE RESOURCES

Do you live in an area that has an autumn season? During the autumn, as the amount of sunlight declines, deciduous trees stop producing chlorophyll and become dormant so that they can survive the cold winter season. When the leaves of trees do not contain the green pigment chlorophyll, many other colors can be seen, as shown in *Figure 25-1*. Eventually, all of these colorful leaves fall to the ground. However, in the spring, new leaves appear and the trees continue their life cycles. If you cut down a tree, you can replace that tree by planting a seedling in its place. Trees are examples of **renewable resources**, which are natural resources that it is possible to use indefinitely without causing a reduction in the available supply. Renewable resources include fresh air; fresh surface water in lakes, rivers, and streams; most groundwater; fertile soil; elements that cycle through Earth's systems, such as nitrogen, carbon, and phosphorus; and all living things. Resources that exist in an inexhaustible supply, such as solar energy, also are renewable resources. Renewable resources are replaced through natural processes at a rate that is equal to, or greater than, the rate at which they are being used.

Living Things Organisms in the biosphere are important renewable resources. Plants and animals reproduce, and therefore, as long as some mature individuals of a species survive, they can be replaced. Crops can be planted every spring and harvested every fall from the same land as long as the Sun shines, the rain falls, and the required nutrients are provided by organic matter or fertilizers. Animals that are raised for food, such as chickens and cattle, also can be replaced in short periods of time. Forests that are cut down for the production of

656 CHAPTER 25 *Earth Resources*

Assessment

Knowledge Ask students which of the following resources are renewable: freshwater, sunlight, trees, gold, copper, diamonds, and oil. renewable: water, sunlight, trees; nonrenewable: gold, copper, diamonds, and oil

Differentiated Instruction

Gifted Students with strong science backgrounds may be interested in researching the processes involved in recycling a particular resource. Allow advanced students to research a topic of their choice and evaluate the effectiveness of the process in relation to costs and effects on other resources. In their reports, have students include suggestions for improvements in the recycling processes. Have students report their findings to the rest of the class. **L3**

paper products can be replanted and ready for harvest again in 10 to 20 years. Trees that are cut down for timber also can be replaced after a period of up to 60 years. Humans who use natural resources responsibly are practicing management techniques to replace resources as they are used, as shown in *Figure 25-2.* The replacement of renewable resources at the same rate at which they are consumed results in a **sustainable yield.**

Sunlight Some of Earth's renewable resources are not provided by Earth. The Sun provides an inexhaustible source of energy for all processes on Earth. Sunlight is considered to be a renewable resource because it will continue to be available for at least the next 5 billion years.

NONRENEWABLE RESOURCES

Suppose you visit a fine jewelry store. You notice that diamonds, such as those shown in *Figure 25-3,* are very expensive. Why are diamonds so expensive? After all, they form through geologic processes, just like quartz and feldspar do. Diamonds are expensive because the supply of diamonds is limited. When all the diamond mines that currently exist have been exhausted, no more natural diamonds will become available. Diamonds are an example of a **nonrenewable resource,** a resource that exists in a fixed amount in various places in Earth's crust and can be replaced only by geological, physical, and chemical processes that take hundreds of millions of years. Resources such as fossil fuels, diamonds and other gemstones, and elements such as gold, copper, and silver are therefore considered to be nonrenewable. Nonrenewable resources are exhaustible because they are being extracted and used at a much faster rate than the rate at which they were formed.

DISTRIBUTION OF RESOURCES

Do you live in an area that has coal mines, oil wells, or deposits of bauxite, the ore that contains aluminum? Perhaps you live near a scenic river or a hot spring. Wherever you live, you probably have noticed that natural resources are not distributed evenly on Earth. The availability of natural resources helps determine the wealth and the power of countries around the world. Countries with many natural resources, such as the United States, are able to support higher living standards for their citizens than countries with fewer resources. However, smaller countries may have an abundance of

Figure 25-2 Paper companies may cut down entire forests to provide wood for pulp and paper, but they also manage the forests and replant on a regular schedule so that the forest resources are always available.

Figure 25-3 Diamonds form through geologic processes. *Why is a diamond ring so expensive?*

Interpreting the Photo

Figure 25-2 When timber companies manage forests for sustainable yields, they clear-cut some sections of the forest while replanting other sections. In this photo, students can see sections of the forest that are mature, sections that have tiny seedling trees, and sections that have young trees.

Project

Interpersonal Have a brainstorming session with students to determine what natural resources are available in their community. Have students work in small groups to identify where they may find out what resources are available. Students may interview community members and town officials or conduct research at the local library or town or county offices. Looking in the yellow pages of local telephone books may also offer some clues. Warn students that many local resources are often taken for granted and that they should be careful not to overlook some of the more obvious resources in their community and its surroundings. Once each group has accumulated a list of local resources, compile a master list to be displayed in the classroom. Students may add to the list as they become aware of additional resources. **L2 COOP LEARN**

Figure Caption Question

Figure 25-3 Why is a diamond ring so expensive? Diamonds are rare, and like other gemstones, are nonrenewable resources, which, once used, cannot be replaced.

NY Core Curriculum Standards

Page 654: St 1 Science KI 2
Page 655: St 1 Science KI 2
Page 656: St 6 KI 4
Page 657: St 6 KI 4 & 5

Reinforcement

Ask students how the words *replaceable* and *renewable* relate to one another. If something is renewable, it means that it can be replaced. The word *replaceable* can also refer to using something in place of the original material that would fulfill the same need.

Reteach

Linguistic Have students each make a list of the new vocabulary words that they find in the text of this section. Ask them to list the words and their definitions in their science journals. Have students each write one new word on an index card. On the back of each card, have students scramble the letters in the word. Then have students use the scrambled side of each card to quiz a fellow student. The student being quizzed should first identify the scrambled word and then define it. **COOP LEARN**

Assessment

Knowledge Ask students to observe a picture cut out of a magazine and identify which objects in the picture are renewable and which are nonrenewable.

NY Core Curriculum Standards

Page 658: St 1 Math KI 1, St 6 KI 2
Page 659: St 6 KI 4, & 6

Figure 25-4 This graph shows the percentage of crude oil that is consumed by the United States and worldwide. Note that the United States consumes 27 percent of the total crude oil used each day.

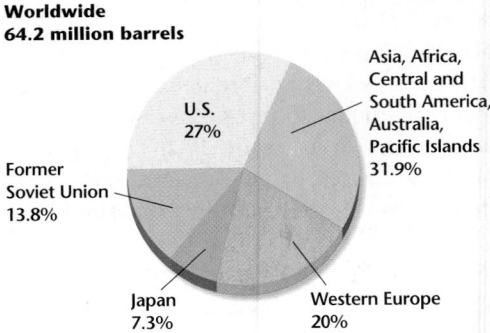

Oil Use Per Day

Worldwide
64.2 million barrels

- U.S. 27%
- Asia, Africa, Central and South America, Australia, Pacific Islands 31.9%
- Former Soviet Union 13.8%
- Japan 7.3%
- Western Europe 20%

one natural resource that is needed by many other countries. Surinam and Guyana, in South America, for example, have some of the richest reserves of bauxite in the world. Saudi Arabia and Kuwait have some of the richest petroleum reserves.

The United States has a high standard of living and it consumes approximately 30 percent of Earth's mineral and energy resources each year, even though it has only 6 percent of the world's population. Some countries with larger populations have lower standards of living than the United States, and thus, these countries do not consume as many resources. One nonrenewable resource that developed countries consume in ever-increasing amounts is crude oil. *Figure 25-4* shows the percentage of total worldwide consumption of crude oil versus the amount used in the United States daily.

SECTION ASSESSMENT

1. What is a natural resource?
2. Explain the difference between a renewable resource and a nonrenewable resource.
3. Name three renewable resources and three nonrenewable resources.
4. Explain why it is important to know whether a resource that you are using is renewable or nonrenewable.

5. **Thinking Critically** Fossil fuels are derived from the remains of once-living organisms, and living things are renewable resources. Why, then, are fossil fuels considered to be nonrenewable resources?

SKILL REVIEW

6. **Concept Mapping** Make a concept map of the major ideas in this section using the section headings and the vocabulary terms. For more help, refer to the *Skill Handbook*.

earthgeu.com/self_check_quiz

SECTION ASSESSMENT

1. a resource available on Earth
2. Renewable resources can be replenished in a reasonable amount of time, whereas nonrenewable resources are limited in quantity and not replenishable.
3. Renewable resources include wood, wheat, and milk. Nonrenewable resources include oil, coal, and diamonds. Accept all reasonable answers.
4. It is important to recognize whether a resource is renewable so that it can be conserved if necessary. If a resource is nonrenewable, incentives can be provided to develop alternative resources.
5. These fuels are considered to be nonrenewable because of the extremely long period of time necessary to produce more fossil fuels—that is, millions of years.
6. Make sure that student concept maps include the following concepts: natural resources, renewable resources, living things, sustainable yield, nonrenewable resources, and distribution of resources.

Land Resources

In the springtime, many people visit garden centers and buy sand, mulch, peat moss, topsoil, and different kinds of rocks for landscaping purposes. These materials all are derived from land, a valuable natural resource. Land provides places for humans and other organisms to live and interact. Land also provides spaces for the growth of crops, forests, grasslands, and for wilderness areas.

PROTECTED LAND

Of all the land in the United States, 42 percent is certified as public land, which consists of forests, parks, and wildlife refuges. Of this public land, 73 percent is located in Alaska, and 22 percent is located in the western states. These land areas are federally administered to protect timber, grazing areas, minerals, and energy resources. Some public land, such as national forests, is managed for sustainable yield and includes multiple-use areas where resources are used for many purposes, including recreation. Public land includes grasslands, prairies, deserts, scrub forests, and other open spaces. Some of these more remote areas eventually may become wilderness areas, places that are maintained in their natural state and protected from development.

The national park system preserves scenic and unique natural landscapes, preserves and interprets the country's historic and cultural heritage, protects wildlife habitats and wilderness areas, and provides areas for various types of recreation. About 49 percent of the land in the national park system is designated as wilderness.

National wildlife refuges provide protection of habitats and breeding areas for wildlife, and some provide protection for endangered species, as shown in *Figure 25-5.* Other uses of the land in wildlife refuges, such as fishing, trapping, farming, and logging, are permitted as long as they are compatible with the purpose of each individual refuge.

SOIL

Do you know what is in the soil under your feet? It can take up to 1000 years to form just a few centimeters of topsoil, yet it can be lost in a matter of minutes as a result of erosion by wind or water. Plowing and leaving bare ground without plant cover can increase topsoil loss. The loss of topsoil makes soil less fertile and less able to hold water. The result is poorer crops. Today, topsoil is eroding faster than it forms on about

OBJECTIVES

• **Describe** *why land is considered to be a natural resource.*

• **Recognize** *the need to protect Earth's land as a resource.*

• **Explain** *how humans adjust to the uneven distribution of land resources.*

VOCABULARY

desertification
bedrock
aggregate
ore
gangue

Figure 25-5 The Aransas National Wildlife Refuge was established in 1937 to protect the vanishing wildlife of coastal Texas. The whooping crane, an endangered migratory bird species in the United States, makes its winter home in this refuge.

25.2 *Land Resources* **659**

Resource Manager

Study Guide for Content Mastery, p. 158 L2
Teaching Transparency 76 L2 ELL
Section Focus Transparency 79 L1 ELL

Section 25.2

Prepare

Section Background

For section content background, refer to **Land Resources** on page 654C.

Preplanning

Refer to the Chapter Organizer on pages 654A–B.

1 Focus

Section Focus

Before presenting the lesson, display **Section Focus Transparency 79** on the overhead projector.
L1 ELL

Demo

Display posterboards with pictures from magazines pasted on them. The pictures should show some type of land use. Pictures could portray factories, mines, parks, or houses. Ask students to list the land use shown in each of the pictures.

Content Background

Land itself is a valuable resource. It provides space for humans and other organisms to live. Land areas also are important as resources for cropland, forests, rangelands, parks, and wilderness areas. The economic value of land varies from one location to another, and the economic value of any one parcel of land may change over time. However, the intrinsic value of land may be considered priceless because there is only a given amount of land on Earth.

Modeling

Visual-Spatial Have students work in small groups to develop scenes of conditions that lead to desertification using shadow-box models. On top of each shadow box, the following question should be posed: How does this scene show a condition that has led to desertification? Scenes may portray overgrazing or heavy machinery use. Give students the option to divide the shadow box in half, with one side showing overgrazing and the other side showing what the area would look like after corrective measures have been implemented.

Interpreting the Photo

Figure 25-7 The marble in this quarry is cut by machines and loaded onto trucks for transport to construction sites and to studios for use by sculptors. Carrara marble is famous for its fine grain and for its white color.

Figure 25-6 When animals are allowed to graze on marginal land in arid or semi-arid climates, the topsoil can be eroded easily, and desertification can result.

Figure 25-7 The finest-grained marble in the world is obtained from the bedrock at Carrara, Italy.

660

one-third of Earth's croplands. Each decade, Earth loses about seven percent of its topsoil, yet the eroded croplands must feed an ever-increasing human population. In arid and semi-arid areas of the world, the loss of topsoil leads to **desertification,** which is the process whereby productive land becomes desert. Desertification can occur when too many grazing animals are kept on arid lands, as shown in *Figure 25-6,* or when soil is compacted by large herds of heavy animals or heavy farm equipment.

Desertification is a growing problem in cattle-producing areas in North Africa south of the Sahara, in the Middle East, in the western half of the United States, and in Australia. Desertification also occurs when trees and shrubs are cut down for use as fuel in areas with few energy resources. When these plants are not replaced, erosion can lead to the loss of topsoil. Desertification can be prevented by reducing overgrazing and by planting trees and shrubs to anchor soils and retain water.

BEDROCK

Underneath the topsoil is a layer of soil consisting of inorganic matter, including broken-down rock, sand, silt, clay, and gravel. This deeper soil layer lies on a base of unweathered parent rock called **bedrock.** Bedrock is solid rock, and it may consist of limestone, granite, marble, or other rocks that can be mined in quarries, as shown in *Figure 25-7.* Slabs of bedrock are often cut from quarry faces. Such large pieces of bedrock are used in the construction of buildings, monuments, flooring, and fireplaces.

AGGREGATES

Have you ever watched a highway being built? You may have seen construction workers place layers of crushed or broken stone, pebbles, or sand on the ground before they began to build the highway surface. The materials used for this first layer come from an **aggregate,** which is a mixture of gravel, sand, and crushed stone that naturally accumulates on or close to Earth's surface. Some aggregates are found on floodplains in river valleys and in alluvial fans in mountainous areas. Other aggregates were deposited by glacial activity in moraines, eskers, kames, and outwash plains. Some aggregates contain erratics, shown in *Figure 25-8,* which are rocks or rock fragments deposited by glaciers far from their origins.

Science Field Book

Earth Science

Journal

Intrapersonal Have students write letters in their science journals from the perspective of a developer who wishes to convince local town officials that it is in their best interests to allow the building of a major-league ice-hockey rink in an area that is currently a gravel pit. **L2**

Aggregates used in construction are mixed with cement, lime, gypsum, or other materials to form concrete or mortar. An aggregate provides volume and stability to the resulting mixture, and it also makes the finished surface more resistant to erosion and weathering. The most commonly used natural aggregates are sand, crushed or broken rocks, and gravel.

ORES

An **ore** is a natural resource that can be mined at a profit; that is, it can be mined as long as its value on the market is greater than the cost of its extraction. For example, the mineral hematite (Fe_2O_3) is an iron ore because it contains 70 percent iron by weight. Other minerals, such as limonite, also contain iron, but they are not considered to be ores because the percentage of iron contained in them is too low to make extraction profitable. Ores can be classified by the manner in which they formed. Some ores are associated with igneous rocks, whereas others are formed by processes at Earth's surface.

Settling of Crystals Ores associated with igneous rocks may contain iron, chromium, and platinum. Chromium and platinum ores can form when minerals crystallize and settle to the bottom of a cooling body of magma. Chromite ore deposits are often found near the bases of sills and other igneous intrusions. One of the largest deposits of chromium and platinum in the world is the Bushveldt Complex in South Africa.

Hydrothermal Fluids The most important sources of metallic ore deposits are hydrothermal fluids. Hot water and other fluids may be part of the magma that is injected into surrounding rock during the last stages of magma crystallization. Because atoms of metals such as copper and gold do not fit into the crystals of feldspar and other minerals during the cooling process, they become concentrated in the remaining magma. Eventually, a solution rich in metals and silica moves into the surrounding rocks to create ore deposits, known as hydrothermal veins. Hydrothermal veins, such as the one shown in *Figure 25-9,* commonly form along faults and joints.

Chemical Precipitation Ores of manganese and iron most commonly originate from chemical precipitation in layers. Iron ores in sedimentary rocks are often found in bands made up of alternating layers of iron–bearing minerals and chert. The origin of these ores,

Figure 25-8 Glaciers often deposit erratics in areas with rocks that are vastly different. Some erratics are deposited on softer rocks, which erode more quickly, and thus, the erratics are left perched on top.

Figure 25-9 This gold nugget contains a hydrothermal vein that is composed of quartz.

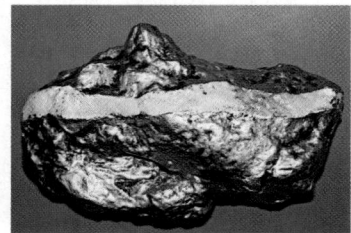

✓Assessment

Knowledge Ask students whether a mineral found in two different types of deposits can be identical in composition but still not be considered an ore. Yes, if the mineral does not exist in amounts that would be profitable if it were mined.

Demo

Visual-Spatial Wear splash goggles, an apron, and gloves for this demonstration. To demonstrate a chemical precipitate, place 30 g of a laundry detergent in 250 mL of warm water in a glass beaker and stir. In another beaker, place 50 mL of warm water and 30 g of Epsom salts and stir. Add one or two drops of food coloring to the Epsom solution. Fill a dropper with the Epsom solution. Slowly squeeze the dropper into the detergent solution. Have students watch the precipitate form. **ELL**

Tying to Previous Knowledge

In Chapter 8, the formation of glacial features was described. In this chapter, it is important for students to recall that glacial deposits in moraines, eskers, and kames may be associated with sediment being carried as a glacier moves and melts. The longer that sediments are carried by the melting water, the greater the opportunity for the material to be sorted by size before it settles. This is how gravel and sand pits form. Sediments that were deposited directly by the glacial ice and were not carried by water are usually unsorted and a mix of all sizes.

Enrichment

An ore may be described based on its concentration factor. An ore's concentration factor is equal to the concentration of the ore deposit divided by the average concentration of the ore in Earth's crust. The higher the concentration factor, the richer the deposit. In general, the minimum concentration factor needed to be considered for profitable mining is inversely proportional to the average concentration found in Earth's crust. Exceptions to this general rule exist; for example, gold is so valuable that even small amounts may be worth mining.

Applying Earth Science

When houses are built, gravel is often placed around their bases. This is done to aid in the drainage of water away from the house. Gravel is also used in the leach fields of individual home septic systems to help drain away and filter the water.

Identifying Misconceptions

Many students think that humans have existed on Earth for a much longer time than they actually have.

Uncover the Misconception

Ask students the following question: Compared to the length of time since Earth was formed, how long have humans had an impact on Earth resources? Ask students to compare the history of Earth to a 24-hour day. Ask them to identify when, over the 24-hour period, humans began to have an impact on Earth resources. Many students will say the last six hours.

Demonstrate the Concept

Draw a picture of a clock on the chalkboard. Explain to students that Earth is theorized to have formed between 5 and 4.6 billion years ago. This period of time represents one 24-hour day, or twice around a 12-hour clock, for the purposes of this analogy. Tell students that the fossil record shows that the earliest humans can be traced back to one million years ago, which is just one second before midnight of the 24-hour day. All of the concern about resource use has occurred during this time period.

Assess New Knowledge

Ask students which of the following statements are true. Many of the resources of concern being depleted have been used only during the past century. true Some Earth resources are required for the existence of life on Earth. true Human ingenuity can replace all resources required by life on Earth. false The resources used by humans have changed over time. true

---

called banded iron formations, is not fully understood. Banded iron formations may have resulted from volcanic activity or weathering and then may have been deposited in layers in shallow, water-filled basins during the Precambrian to form sedimentary rocks. Banded iron deposits are discussed in more detail in Chapter 22.

Placer Deposits Some sediments, such as grains of gold and silver, are heavy. When stream velocity decreases, as, for example, when a stream flows around a bend, heavy sediments may be dropped by the water and deposited in bars of sand and gravel. Sand and gravel bars that contain heavier sediments such as gold nuggets, gold dust, diamonds, platinum, and gemstones, as well as rounded pebbles of tin and titanium oxides, are known as placer deposits. Some of the gold found during the Gold Rush in California during the late 1840s was located in placer deposits.

Concentration by Weathering Some ores form when the minerals in rocks are concentrated by weathering. For example, aluminum forms in bauxite through weathering in tropical climates. Other metals that become more concentrated as rocks weather include nickel, copper, silver, lead, tin, mercury, uranium, and manganese.

OTHER LAND RESOURCES

Are there many brick buildings where you live? Bricks are made from clay, another resource found on land. Clay is a sediment, and a group of minerals, made up of tiny particles with diameters of less than 0.004 mm. In addition to bricks, clay is used to make china, ceramics, tiles, and pottery. It is also used in the paper-making process.

Salt, or sodium chloride, also occurs in deposits both on Earth's surface and underground. One of the most famous salt mines in the world, the Wieliczka Salt Mine in Poland, is shown in **Figure 25-10**. Other mineral resources found on land include gypsum, which is used to make plaster; talc, which is used in cosmetics; and graphite, which is used as a lubricant. Both salt and gypsum deposits can form when seawater evaporates.

Figure 25-10 The Wieliczka Salt Mine in Poland has been mined continuously since the thirteenth century. Today, it is well known for its many rock-salt structures, including the underground Queen Kinga's Chapel. The statues, chandeliers, railings, altars, and candlesticks are carved from rock salt.

Content Background

Scientists using submersible research vessels have discovered hydrothermal fluids gushing from mid-ocean ridges on the seafloor. Many of the precious-metal deposits in the western United States are the result of hydrothermal deposits associated with plate boundary activities.

USING LAND RESOURCES

Although many of the resources that you have learned about in this section can be extracted with little impact on the surrounding environment, the extraction of others can have negative impacts. Mines that are used to remove materials from the ground surface destroy the original ground contours. Open-pit mines leave behind waste rock that can weather and release pollutants into the air and water. The extraction of mineral ores often involves grinding parent rock to separate the ore. The material left after the ore is extracted, called **gangue,** may release harmful chemicals into groundwater or surface water. Sometimes, chemicals that harm the environment are used to separate ores. Mercury is used to extract gold from alluvial deposits of sand along rivers in the Amazon River Basin. Liquid mercury dissolves the gold particles in these deposits, forming a solution. When the solution is heated, as shown in *Figure 25-11,* the mercury evaporates, leaving the gold behind. Miners who have inhaled mercury vapors and people who live downstream from the mining operations have been poisoned by mercury. Mining sometimes exposes other materials, such as pyrite, that form acids as they weather and pollute groundwater. In addition to causing environmental problems, mining itself is a dangerous activity. In fact, the National Safety Council has identified mining as the most dangerous occupation in the United States: of all occupations, it has the highest yearly death rate.

Figure 25-11 Small-scale miners in the Amazon River Basin use mercury to extract gold.

SECTION ASSESSMENT

1. Describe two resources found on land.
2. Why is the loss of topsoil through erosion considered to be a worldwide problem?
3. Name five ways in which ores can form, and give an example of a mineral that forms in each way.
4. What is the difference between an aggregate and an ore?
5. **Thinking Critically** What options would humans have if a land resource became depleted?

SKILL REVIEW

6. **Predicting** Many developing countries would like to have the same standard of living as that enjoyed by citizens of the United States. As these countries become industrialized, what may happen to the demand for land resources? How can this demand be met? For more help, refer to the *Skill Handbook.*

earthgeu.com/self_check_quiz

Check for Understanding
Discussion
Ask students to explain how chemistry, biology, and math are related to the study of land resources. Many land resources were formed through chemical processes, such as chemical precipitation. Some of the processes affecting land resources involve interactions with living things, such as the involvement of animals in desertification. Math is applied when designing structures best suited for a particular environment.

Reteach
Have students outline this section of the chapter. Then have students exhange outlines with one another and fill in portions that may have been overlooked.

Portfolio Have students collect information on one particular land resource and place all the information that they find in a folder to be kept in the classroom as a class resource. Encourage students to include photographs, drawings, and even samples if possible. Videotapes and audiotapes may be collected to add to the classroom resources. P

SECTION ASSESSMENT

1. topsoil, bedrock, minerals
2. The loss of topsoil makes soil less fertile and less able to hold water, which leads to poorer crops. As the human population grows worldwide, more crops will be needed.
3. Ores can form by settling of crystals (chromium); through hydrothermal fluids (gold); through chemical precipitation (manganese); in placer deposits (gold); and through concentration by weathering (aluminum).
4. An aggregate is a mixture of gravel, sand, and crushed stone that accumulates naturally on Earth's surface. An ore is a mineral resource that can be mined at a profit.
5. Humans would have to find alternative materials or develop alternative measures to meet the needs formerly provided by the depleted resource.
6. There will be more of a demand upon the same resources. Measures to conserve current supplies will be necessary, as will be the development of alternative materials and land-use methods.

NY Core Curriculum Standards
Page 662: St 4 KI 2.t
Page 663: St 7 KI 1

Prepare

Section Background

For section content background, refer to **Air Resources** on pages 654C–D.

Preplanning

Refer to the Chapter Organizer on pages 654A–B.

1 Focus

Section Focus

Before presenting the lesson, display **Section Focus Transparency 80** on the overhead projector.
L1 ELL

Project

Visual-Spatial Have students make posters about one aspect of air pollution. Hang the posters around the school to make others aware of the problems and solutions. L1 ELL P

NY Core Curriculum Standards

Page 664: St 4 KI 1.2e, & 2.2d, St 6 KI 4
Page 665: St 1 KI 1, 2, & 3, St 6 KI 2, 4, & 5, St 7 KI 2

OBJECTIVES

- **Recognize** *that the atmosphere is an Earth resource.*
- **Describe** *the importance of clean air.*

VOCABULARY

pollutant
air pollution

Figure 25-12 The forests of the Amazon River Basin are sometimes called the lungs of Earth. They help to balance gas exchange for the entire planet.

Resource Manager

Study Guide for Content Mastery, pp. 159–160 L2
Laboratory Manual, pp. 193–196 L2
Teaching Transparency 77 L2 ELL
Section Focus Transparency 80 L1 ELL
Exploring Environmental Problems, pp. 29–32 L3

Have you ever gone outside after a rainstorm and noticed how clean and fresh the air smelled? Most of the time, people don't think about air. However, air contains substances that all organisms need to survive, including nitrogen, oxygen, carbon dioxide, hydrogen, methane, and ozone. Water vapor can make up as much as five percent of air by volume. For humans and all other animals, the most important component of air is oxygen. Oxygen makes up 21 percent of air.

ORIGIN OF OXYGEN

Most organisms on Earth require oxygen or carbon dioxide to maintain their life processes. Oxygen has not always been a part of Earth's atmosphere. Scientists hypothesize that 4.6 to 4.5 billion years ago, Earth's atmosphere was similar to the mixture of gases released by erupting volcanoes. These gases include carbon dioxide, nitrogen, and water vapor. As Earth cooled and became more solid, rains washed most of the carbon dioxide out of the atmosphere and into the oceans. Early life-forms in the seas used carbon dioxide during photosynthesis and released oxygen and water vapor. Over time, oxygen in the atmosphere built up to levels that allowed the evolution of organisms that required oxygen for life processes.

DISRUPTING EARTH'S CYCLES

The geochemical cycles of Earth's atmosphere are in a delicate balance. Volcanic eruptions release various gases and dust particles into the atmosphere. Photosynthetic organisms in the oceans and on land take in and use carbon dioxide and release oxygen. Other organisms take in this oxygen and release carbon dioxide. Life on Earth continues to survive as a result of this balanced gas exchange.

However, human activities are disrupting these cycles. For example, humans burn fossil fuels to produce electricity and burn forests to clear land. These two activities release carbon dioxide into the atmosphere. Increased amounts of carbon dioxide are thought to play a role in global warming, which is the gradual rising of Earth's average surface temperature. The human alteration of the carbon cycle has the potential to change global climate and therefore the environments of food-producing regions. Rainfall patterns in the tropical rain forests of the Amazon River Basin have already changed as a result of the loss of forest cover. One of these rain forests is shown in **Figure 25-12.** You will find out how deforestation is affecting tropical rain forests worldwide in the *Problem-Solving Lab* on the next page.

Humans also disrupt other geochemical cycles. By burning fossil fuels and using fertilizers that contain nitrogen, humans release about three times as much nitrogen oxide and ammonia gas into the atmosphere as do the natural processes of the nitrogen cycle. In the atmosphere, nitrogen oxides are converted to nitric acid, which returns to Earth in acid precipitation and damages surface water, plants, and soil. Human activities also release sulfur into the atmosphere when coal and oil are burned to produce electricity. Sulfur in the atmosphere is converted to sulfuric acid, which also returns to Earth in the form of acid precipitation. Both the excess nitrogen oxides and sulfur are **pollutants,** which are substances that can adversely affect the survival, health, or activities of organisms. These are only a few of the chemicals that human activities release into the atmosphere. Small amounts of toxic metals, such as lead, cadmium, and arsenic, also are released. When pollutants in air occur in quantities that become harmful to human health and the health of the environment, **air pollution** results.

Problem-Solving Lab

Interpreting Graphs

Calculate the rate of deforestation
Many experts are concerned about the loss of the forest cover in tropical rain forests worldwide. In the Amazon River Basin, for example, scientists estimate that 1 hectare (ha, about 2.47 acres) of forest is cut down each hour. Nearly 20 million ha of rain forest is destroyed each year worldwide. If this rate continues, there will be no tropical rain forests left in just 40 years. The graph indicates the fate of the world's tropical rain forests if the current rate of deforestation continues.

Analysis

1. How much tropical rain forest has been depleted since the year you were born?
2. According to the graph, when will all the rain forests be depleted?

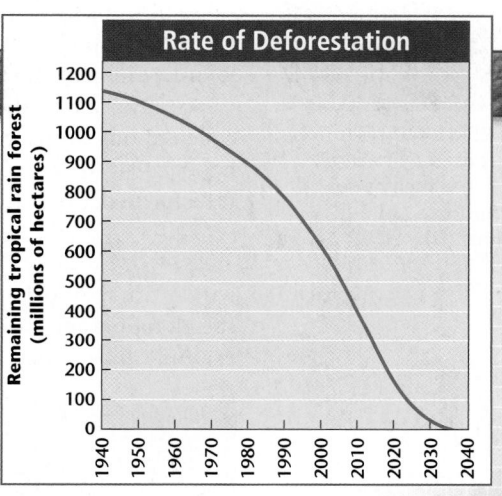

Thinking Critically

3. What are the rates of deforestation for the 1950–1985 and 1985–2000 time periods?
4. How do the rates of deforestation between 1950–1985 and 1985–2000 compare?
5. What might be the reason for the change in the rate of deforestation between these two time periods?

Cultural Diversity

Wangari Maathai (1940–) Wangari Maathai, a Kenyan environmentalist, began the greenbelt movement in Kenya in the 1970s in response to the deforestation of her country. Almost 90 percent of the population in Kenya depended on wood for fuel, and forests were being depleted at an alarming rate. The women had to travel long distances in search of firewood, and the lack of firewood often meant a lack of food for poorer families. The greenbelt movement established community nurseries and provided free tree seedlings. A small payment was made for every tree that was planted and maintained by villagers. By 1977, the greenbelt movement had spread throughout Africa. It provided compensation for 80 000 people and resulted in the reintroduction of more than 10 million native trees. Today the greenbelt movement has spread throughout the world, and is sponsored by many countries and international environmental organizations.

Problem-Solving Lab

Purpose
Students will gain an understanding of the rapid rate of deforestation of Earth's tropical rain forests.

Process Skills
hypothesize, make and use graphs, predict, recognize cause and effect

Materials
paper, pencil

Teaching Strategies
Ask students to locate several tropical rain forests on a world map. Then ask them why these forests are important resources. Share with students that the loss of the rain forests is of concern because 25 percent of the medicines used in the United States to treat cancer, mental illness, and coronary heart disease come from rain forests. In addition, the tropical rain forests contain 50 percent of the species of the world, many of which have not yet been named or described.

Troubleshooting
Review basic graph-reading skills with students who appear to have difficulty in this area.

Analysis
1. depends on students' ages
2. about 2035

Thinking Critically
3. approximately 7.1 million ha/y; approximately 16.0 million ha/y
4. The rate of deforestation has nearly doubled between the 1950–1985 and the 1985–2000 periods.
5. increasing populations in tropical countries, resulting in cutting rain forests to provide space for farming, settlements, and logging

Assessment

Skill Ask students the following questions: What is expected to happen to the amount of tropical rain forest during the time you spend in high school? It will continue to be reduced in size. How old will you be when the tropical rain forest is expected to disappear? Answers will vary depending on students' current ages.

Concept Development

In the mid 1970s, an index directly relating air pollution to human health was developed. Known as the Pollutant Standards Index (PSI), it rates air pollution levels on a scale from 0-500 for each of the following pollutants: carbon monoxide, ozone, sulfur dioxide, nitrogen dioxide, and suspended particulates. Pollutant levels above 100 are considered to be unhealthful, whereas those above 300 are considered to be hazardous. This index allows ordinary people to have a basic understanding of levels that indicate potential health hazards.

Figure 25-13 Air pollution can be caused by natural phenomena, such as volcanic eruptions **(A)** and forest fires **(B)**.

SOURCES OF AIR POLLUTION

Air pollution has both natural and human origins. Two natural sources of air pollution are shown in *Figure 25-13.* Human sources of air pollution include gases, smoke, and dust. One of the biggest sources of air pollution is the burning of fossil fuels. Power plants that generate electricity burn coal and oil, which produce many types of air pollution. However, the single largest source of air pollution in the United States is the exhaust from motor vehicles that burn fossil fuels in the form of gasoline. In the United States, motor vehicles cause 90 percent of the carbon monoxide pollution in cities. In cities such as Los Angeles, Rome, and Mexico City, shown in *Figure 25-14,* motor vehicles are responsible for 80 to 88 percent of the air pollution.

Air pollution can make humans ill. When humans inhale harmful gases, the gases can be absorbed by the bloodstream and interfere with various body systems. Carbon monoxide, a colorless and odorless gas, interferes with the body's ability to absorb oxygen and causes headaches, chest pains, dry throat, and nausea. Pollution can also cause burning eyes, irritated throats, and breathing difficulties. Some chemical air pollutants can cause cancer, birth defects, brain damage, long-term injury to lungs, and even death.

As clean air in the troposphere moves across Earth's surface, it collects both naturally occurring and human-made pollutants. What happens to these pollutants? They may be transported, diluted, transformed, or removed from the atmosphere.

Transport and Dilution Some pollutants may be carried downwind from their origin. Transport depends upon wind direction and speed, topographical features, and the altitude of the pollutants. For example, hills, valleys, and buildings interrupt the flow of winds and

Figure 25-14 Air pollution from vehicles in Mexico City is so concentrated that people who have breathing difficulties often listen to the radio to find out whether it is safe for them to go outdoors.

Differentiated Instruction

Visually Impaired One way to assist students with visual impairments is to enlarge all handouts that are duplicated. Make sure that diagrams are clear and labels are not located over background material and colors. Sometimes, black-and-white handouts and diagrams are more distinguishable than colored diagrams. It is also best to talk with students to determine which options best suit students' individual needs.

Demo

Cut a piece of masking tape approximately 20 cm long and tack it high on a wall for one week. At the beginning of this section, take the tape down and have students observe what may be stuck to it. Have them compare the strip of tape to a freshly cut piece of tape. Have students list what they observed on the tape in their science journals and predict how each item made its way to the tape. Students likely will indicate that the materials on the tape were carried by air.

NY Core Curriculum Standards

Page 666: St 4 KI 2.2d
Page 667: St 4 KI 2.2d

thus influence the transport of pollutants. Many of the pollutants in the acid precipitation that falls in the Adirondack Mountains of New York State were transported from coal-burning power plants in the midwestern states. If air movement in the troposphere is turbulent, some pollutants are diluted and spread out, which reduces their concentration.

Transformation and Removal Other pollutants undergo chemical changes, called photochemical changes, that are triggered by reactions with ultraviolet (UV) radiation. Photochemical smog, for example, forms when a mixture of nitrogen oxides and volatile organic compounds interact under the influence of sunlight.

Some other air pollutants undergo physical changes. For example, dry particles may clump together and become heavy enough to fall back to Earth's surface. These and other air pollutants are removed from the atmosphere in precipitation, which includes snow, mist, and fog as well as rain.

INDOOR AIR POLLUTION

Have you ever shopped at a fabric store? Some people cannot even enter such a store because they are sensitive to the chemical formaldehyde, which is used in fabrics to prevent damage from insects. About 90 percent of the furniture sold in the United States also contains formaldehyde. Formaldehyde is just one of the many air pollutants that occurs indoors, as shown in *Figure 25-15.*

Earth Science Online

Topic: Indoor Air Pollution
To find out more about air pollution, visit the Earth Science Web Site at earthgeu.com

Activity: Research some ways to reduce indoor air pollution. Design a brochure that informs readers about reducing indoor air pollution.

Figure 25-15 Major indoor air pollutants are shown in this diagram of a new house.

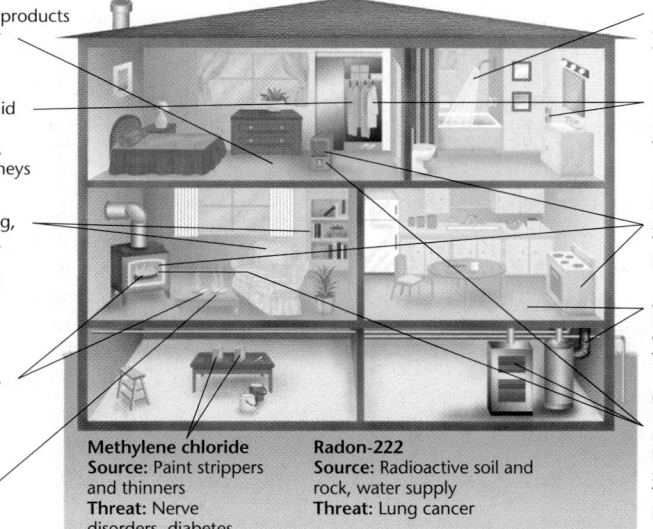

Styrene
Source: Carpets, plastic products
Threat: Kidney and liver damage

Tetrachloroethylene
Source: Dry-cleaning fluid fumes on clothes
Threat: Nerve disorders, damage to liver and kidneys

Formaldehyde
Source: Furniture stuffing, paneling, particle board, foam insulation
Threat: Irritation of eyes and lungs; nausea; dizziness

Benzo-a-pyrene
Source: Tobacco smoke, wood stoves
Threat: Lung cancer

Tobacco smoke
Source: Cigarettes
Threat: Lung cancer, respiratory ailments

Methylene chloride
Source: Paint strippers and thinners
Threat: Nerve disorders, diabetes

Radon-222
Source: Radioactive soil and rock, water supply
Threat: Lung cancer

Chloroform
Source: Chlorine-treated water in hot showers
Threat: Cancer

Para-dichlorobenzene
Source: Air fresheners, mothball crystals
Threat: Cancer

Nitrogen oxides
Source: Unvented gas stoves, wood stoves
Threat: Irritated lungs, headaches

Asbestos
Source: Pipe insulation, vinyl tiles
Threat: Lung cancer

Carbon monoxide
Source: Faulty furnaces, unvented gas stoves and kerosene heaters, wood stoves
Threat: Headaches, irregular heartbeat

Science Field Book

Earth Science
Journal

Have students locate an article on air pollution in a newspaper, magazine, journal, or on the Internet. Ask them to read the article and summarize its contents in outline form in their science journals. Ask students to share one or two major points of their articles with the class.

Across the Curriculum

Chemistry When elements are written, such as uranium-238 or radon–222, the number refers to mass number. The mass number is equal to the total number of neutrons and protons in the atom's nucleus. Radioactive materials are chemically unstable and give off neutrons, which results in a change in mass number.

Collaborative Learning

Interpersonal Hang a map of the local community at the front of the classroom. Place a piece of clear acetate over the map. Have each student use a marking pen to make a dot on the acetate to indicate where he or she lives. Tell students that they will study air pollution in their community and will be responsible for collecting data at home. If no students live in certain areas, ask for student volunteers to take on an extra site or two so that all sections of the community will be represented. Decide as a class what data to collect, when to collect them, and how the data will be collated. Student ideas may include hanging strips of masking tape for a predetermined amount of time for the same time period. Visual observations will be necessary at each site. Once the data are collected, different acetate overlays can be developed for the different types of data collected. In some cases, students may be able to draw isolines from the collected data. Ask students to draw conclusions from the data at the end of the activity. **L2**
COOP LEARN

Interpreting the Illustration

Figure 25-15 Students may not realize that so many potential pollutants exist in any house. Ask students to identify those pollutants that they think might be found in their school buildings. One possible pollutant in school buildings is asbestos, a material that once was used as insulation for heating ducts and hot water pipes. Have interested students find out if asbestos remains in their school buildings and, if so, what the school administration plans to do about it.

3 Assess

Check for Understanding
Activity
Ask students to draw a landscape or the inside of a building in their science journals. Have students label all the forms of air pollution that might be associated with their drawings. Have students share their drawings and what forms of air pollution they noted with a lab partner. Ask partners to check to see whether any forms of air pollution were missed. If so, have students add these onto their drawings.

Reteach
 **Linguistic** Have students write newspaper articles about pollution in their community. Ask students to define the type of pollution in their articles. Post articles on the classroom bulletin board. **L1**

✔Assessment

Knowledge Ask students what the following abbreviations stand for: EPA and UV. Environmental Protection Agency; ultraviolet radiation

Figure 25-16 A radon test kit is a simple device that measures the amount of radon gas infiltrating a building over a week's time.

"Sick" Buildings Studies conducted by the United States Environmental Protection Agency (EPA) and by scientists in European countries have linked indoor air pollutants to headaches, coughing, sneezing, burning eyes, nausea, chronic fatigue, and flu-like symptoms. When these symptoms are experienced by 20 percent of the occupants of a building, the building is said to be "sick." Often, these symptoms disappear when the affected people go outside. New buildings are more likely to be "sick" than older buildings. This is because newer buildings tend to be airtight so that heating and cooling costs can be kept to a minimum, and because new furniture and carpeting release many indoor air pollutants, including styrene and formaldehyde.

Radon Gas The gas known as radon-222 is colorless, odorless, tasteless, and naturally occurring. Radon-222 is produced by the radioactive decay of uranium-238. Small amounts of uranium-238 are found in most soils and rocks, and in underground deposits. Usually, radon gas from such deposits seeps upward through the soil and is released into the atmosphere, where it is diluted to harmless levels. However, when buildings are constructed with hollow concrete blocks, or when they have cracks in their foundations, radon gas can enter and build up to high levels indoors. Once indoors, radon gas decays into radioactive elements that can be inhaled. Scientists have traced approximately 13 000 lung-cancer deaths in the United States each year to high levels of radon gas in homes.

Because it is impossible to see or smell a buildup of radon gas in a building, the EPA suggests that people test the radon levels in their homes and offices. Radon test kits, such as the one shown in *Figure 25-16,* measure the levels of radon in buildings. 🍃

SECTION ASSESSMENT

1. Why is air considered to be an Earth resource?
2. How did oxygen originate on Earth?
3. Explain how the oxygen and carbon-dioxide cycles on Earth are related.
4. Describe how air can be polluted by both natural processes and human activities.
5. **Thinking Critically** Explain why photochemical smog is a major problem in large cities that have little public transportation.

SKILL REVIEW

6. **Comparing and Contrasting** Compare and contrast the components of indoor air pollution and the components of atmospheric air pollution. Is one type of air pollution more damaging than the other? Explain. For more help, refer to the *Skill Handbook.*

earthgeu.com/self_check_quiz

SECTION ASSESSMENT

1. It contains gases essential to life and the maintenance of balanced ecosystems on Earth.
2. The origin of oxygen is believed to be a byproduct of photosynthesis.
3. The carbon dioxide and oxygen cycles are related in that plants take in carbon dioxide and give off oxygen during the photosynthetic process. All living things take in oxygen and release carbon dioxide during the process of respiration.
4. A natural source of air pollution is gases given off by erupting volcanoes. A human-generated source of air pollution is the gases produced from the burning of fossil fuels.
5. Automobile exhausts produce conditions that contribute to photochemical smog. If there is little public transportation, more vehicles are on the road, contributing to air pollution.
6. Both indoor and outdoor pollution degrade the quality of air and can be equally harmful. Indoor pollution, however, can be much worse because the levels of pollutants are concentrated indoors. Chemicals such as formaldehyde are released from new furniture, and with little air circulation, these chemicals remain in a building. The newer the building, the more airtight it may be, resulting in less mixing with outdoor air and a higher level of air pollution.

When astronauts first took photographs of Earth from space, many people were surprised to see how much of Earth's surface is covered by water. One such photograph is shown in *Figure 25-17.* The oceans contain 97 percent of the planet's water, which means that only 3 percent of Earth's water is freshwater. Of this freshwater, about 2.997 percent is either locked up in ice caps and glaciers or stored as groundwater that is too deep to extract. This leaves only 0.003 percent of Earth's total volume of water available to humans for domestic, agricultural, and industrial purposes. This fraction of freshwater is in the form of surface water, water vapor, and obtainable groundwater.

THE IMPORTANCE OF WATER

About 71 percent of Earth's surface is covered by water. However, this is not the only reason that Earth is sometimes called the "water planet." The world's oceans help regulate climate, provide habitats for marine organisms, dilute and degrade many pollutants, and even have a role in shaping Earth's surface. Freshwater is an important resource for agriculture, transportation, recreation, and numerous other human activities. In addition, the organisms that live on Earth are made up mostly of water. Most animals are about 50 to 65 percent water by weight, and even trees may be composed of up to 60 percent water. Without water, life as we know it could not exist on Earth.

Liquid Water Why is water such an important resource? Water is a unique substance with many desirable qualities. Water can exist as a liquid over a wide range of temperatures because of the hydrogen bonds between water molecules. Recall from Chapter 3 that water molecules are polar molecules with positive and negative ends. Hydrogen bonds form when the positive ends of some water molecules are attracted to the negative ends of other water molecules.

OBJECTIVES

• **Explain** *the importance of clean freshwater.*

• **Analyze** *how water is distributed and used on Earth.*

• **Identify** *ways in which humans can reduce the need for increasing production of freshwater resources.*

VOCABULARY

desalination

Figure 25-17 This composite photograph was created by a satellite as it orbited Earth. It depicts the entire surface of Earth, showing the relative sizes of land masses and oceans and their true colors. From this photograph, it is easy to see why Earth is sometimes called the "water planet."

25.4 *Water Resources* **669**

Section 25.4

Prepare

Section Background

For section content background, refer to **Water Resources** on page 654D.

Preplanning

Refer to the Chapter Organizer on pages 654A–B.

1 Focus

Section Focus

Before presenting the lesson, display **Section Focus Transparency 81** on the overhead projector. L1 ELL

Tying to Previous Knowledge

In Chapter 17, students learned about plate tectonics. Some scientists hypothesize that plate movement can be linked to the distribution of resources on Earth's surface.

669

Content Background

The water budget is a concise representation of the amount of water received, used, and stored in a particular location. Studying an area's water budget can show whether the area has surplus water, whether the area experiences deficits or water shortages, and when during the year the area's water supply typically is recharged, including the water stored in the ground. The local water budget is dependent upon the availability of solar energy and the amount of precipitation.

Demo

Demonstrate a unique property of water by filling a glass to the top with water. Ask students to look at the glass of water, and ask them how full it is. Some students will simply say the glass is filled. More astute students will notice that the water actually is higher than the top edge of the glass. Ask these students how a glass can be more than filled with a liquid. The water molecule's atoms are arranged with the hydrogen atoms on one side of the molecule and the oxygen atom on the other side of the molecule. This causes the water molecule to be polar; although it is electrically balanced as a molecule, it does have a positive side and a negative side. This enables water molecules to attract each other and form links with other molecules. Thus, water molecules can stick together and overfill a glass.

Figure 25-18 Perspiration is the body's way of helping you cool off. As the water in perspiration evaporates, it removes heat from your skin.

Figure 25-19 Ice is less dense than liquid water, and therefore it floats on top of water.

The hydrogen bonds cause water's surface to contract and allow water to adhere to and coat a solid. These properties enable water to rise from the roots of a plant through its stem to its leaves. Water also has a high boiling point, 100°C, and a low freezing point, 0°C. As a result, water remains a liquid in most of the environments on Earth.

Heat-Storage Capacity Liquid water can store a large amount of heat without a correspondingly high increase in temperature. This property protects organisms that live in water from abrupt temperature changes, and it is also responsible for water's ability to regulate Earth's climate. Because of this same property, water is used as a coolant for automobile engines, power plants, and other heat-generating processes. Have you ever perspired heavily while participating in an outdoor activity on a hot day? Evaporation of perspiration from your skin, shown in *Figure 25-18,* helps you cool off because water absorbs large quantities of heat as it changes into water vapor.

Water as a Solvent Liquid water also can dissolve a wide variety of compounds. This ability enables water to carry nutrients into, and waste products out of, the tissues of living things. The diffusion of water across cell membranes enables all cells to regulate their internal pressure. Water also dilutes water-soluble waste products of humans and thus serves as an all-purpose cleanser.

Solid Water Expands Unlike most liquids, water expands when it freezes. Because ice has a lower density than liquid water, it floats on top of water, as shown in *Figure 25-19.* As a result, bodies of water freeze from the top down. If water did not have this property, ponds and streams would freeze solid, and aquatic organisms would die each winter. The expansion of water as it freezes also can fracture rocks when ice crystals form in preexisting cracks and force the cracks to widen. Thus, ice forming in cracks becomes part of the weathering process.

LOCATION OF FRESHWATER RESOURCES

Freshwater resources are not distributed evenly across Earth's landmasses. Although the United States has plenty of freshwater, much of it is concentrated in certain areas or has been contaminated by agricultural or industrial processes. The eastern states receive ample precipitation, and most freshwater in these states is used for cooling, energy production, and manufacturing. By contrast, western states often have too little precipitation. Thus, in the West, the largest use of freshwater is for irrigation. Water tables in the West are dropping as farmers and cities continue to sink wells into aquifers and use the groundwater faster than it can be recharged.

Differentiated Instruction

Visually Impaired Have students with visual impairments work with models of oxygen and hydrogen to make a water molecule. Give students tennis-ball-sized foam spheres to use for oxygen atoms and smaller golf-ball-sized foam spheres to use for hydrogen. Have students attach two hydrogen spheres at an angle of about 100° from one another on one oxygen sphere to represent a water molecule.

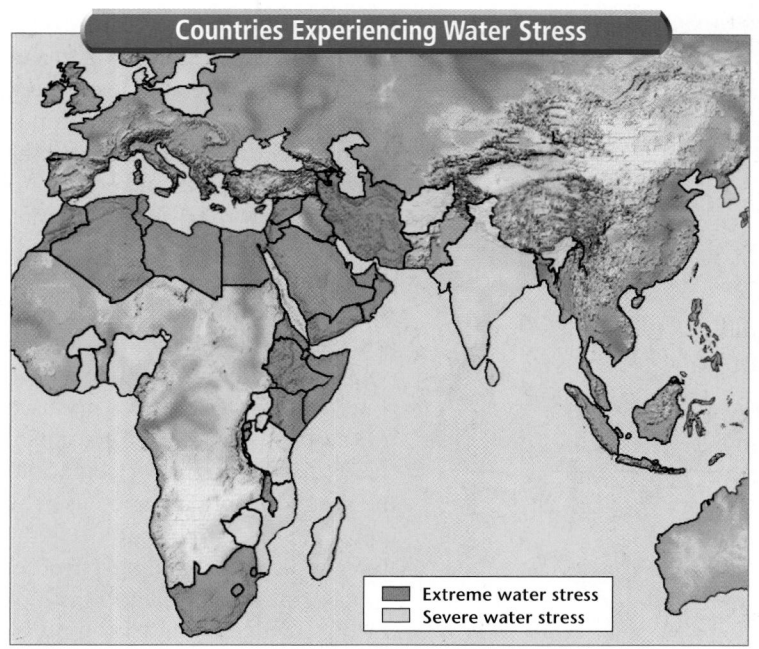

Countries Experiencing Water Stress

■ Extreme water stress
□ Severe water stress

Figure 25-20 Countries experience severe water stress when there is less than 1000 m³ of freshwater per person. Extreme water stress occurs when there is less than 500 m³ of freshwater per person. Increased populations will impose even greater demands on the freshwater available in these countries.

Worldwide, water distribution is a continuing problem, even though most continents have plenty of water. Since the 1970s, scarcity of water has caused the deaths of more than 24 000 people worldwide each year and created huge numbers of environmental refugees. In areas where water is scarce, women and children often walk long distances each day to collect a meager supply of water for domestic uses. Millions of people also try to survive on land that is prone to drought. About 25 countries, primarily in Africa, experience chronic water shortages, as shown in *Figure 25-20.* That number is expected to rise to 90 countries by the year 2025.

USE OF FRESHWATER RESOURCES

As you learned in Chapters 9 and 10, freshwater on Earth is held either in surface waters, such as lakes, rivers, and streams, or in the ground as groundwater. Recall that the upper surface of groundwater is called the water table, and that the water-saturated layers of sand, gravel, or bedrock through which groundwater flows are called aquifers. Aquifers are refilled naturally as rain percolates downward through soil and rock in the process known as natural recharge. Many humans worldwide rely on wells drilled into the ground that tap aquifers for freshwater supplies.

The current rate of withdrawal of freshwater from both surface and groundwater sources worldwide is five times greater than it

NATIONAL GEOGRAPHIC

To learn more about water, go to the **National Geographic Expedition** on page 898.

Using Scientific Terms

The word *riparian* refers to the banks of a body of water, including rivers, streams, lakes, and even seashores. A riparian doctrine outlines the water rights of people who own land alongside streams and rivers. Riparian rights differ among states and countries. In some places, the first person to own land along a stream and use a certain amount of water in the stream is entitled to continue to use that same amount forever. This means that landowners who come later must not interfere with the amount of water that an earlier landowner downstream is supposed to receive. Other riparian laws contain guarantees about the quality of the water that each landowner is entitled to.

Across the Curriculum

History The availability and use of water has political ramifications. Access to bodies of water often is of concern to more than one country, state, or province. To avoid conflicts, more than 2000 treaties dealing with the issue of water rights are in existence. The use of water downstream is as important as the use of water upstream. Assuring access to water has contributed to disagreements and military conflicts, such as the war between several Arab nations and Israel in 1967.

Resource Manager

Laboratory Manual, pp. 197–200

NY Core Curriculum Standards

Page 670: St 4 KI 2.1a, St 6 KI 4
Page 671: St 1 Engin KI 1, St 6 KI 4, St 7 KI 1

Collaborative Learning

Interpersonal Ask for student volunteers to join a panel to either support or oppose the building of dams and reservoirs. Have each panel research its respective point of view and prepare for a classroom debate. Have other students take notes on the facts presented in the debate and share their notes in a post-debate class discussion. **COOP LEARN**

Project

Naturalist Have student groups research a particular dam or reservoir. Each group can research the history of the dam, including the reason it was built and facts about its construction. Students may be able to find photographs of dam construction. Ask each group to make a presentation about its dam. Students should identify the advantages as well as the disadvantages of the dam. **L2 COOP LEARN**

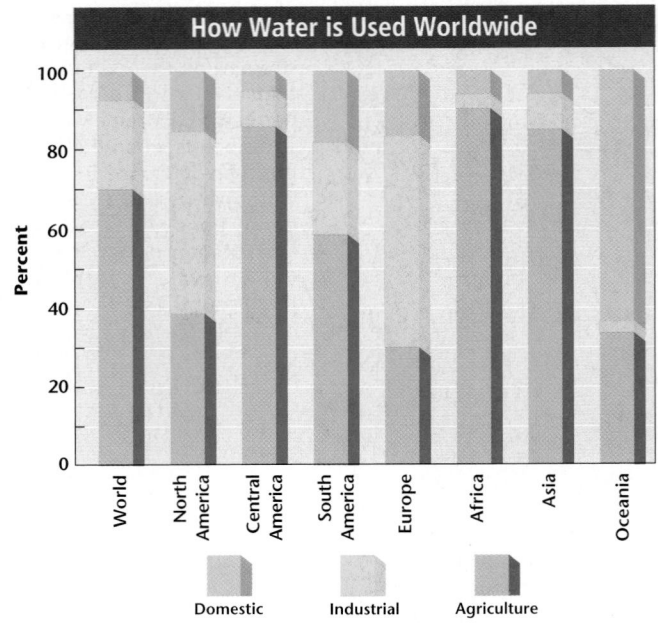

Figure 25-21 This bar graph identifies the uses of freshwater worldwide. *Where in the world is the most water used for industrial purposes?*

Figure 25-22 The purpose of the Three Gorges Dam is to reduce China's reliance on coal for energy production and to regulate the annual flooding of areas along the Yangtze River.

was just 50 years ago. This increase has occurred primarily to meet the drinking-water and agricultural needs of an increasing human population. Withdrawal rates for freshwater resources are expected to double again within the next 20 years.

Uses of freshwater vary worldwide, but about 70 percent of the water withdrawn each year is used to irrigate 18 percent of the world's croplands. However, much of the water used for irrigation is not used by the plants; nearly 80 percent of this water evaporates or seeps into the ground before it can be used by crops. About 23 percent of freshwater is used for cooling purposes in power plants, for oil and gas production, and in industrial processing. Domestic and municipal uses account for only seven percent of the freshwater withdrawn from surface and groundwater resources. The uses of freshwater worldwide are shown in *Figure 25-21*.

MANAGING FRESHWATER RESOURCES

The dam shown in *Figure 25-22* is being built to hold back the floodwaters of the Yangtze River in China. Called the Three Gorges Project, the construction of this dam will provide freshwater and supply power to 150 million people. However, the dam will also flood large areas of farmland and displace about 1 million people who live nearby. Some critics think that the Three Gorges Project will ruin the water quality of the Yangtze River and create more severe flooding as the dam fills up with sediment and eventually overflows. However, most countries manage their supplies of freshwater by building dams, by transporting surface water, or by tapping groundwater. Some countries also have had success removing the salts from seawater to provide needed freshwater supplies.

Dams and Reservoirs Building dams is one of the primary ways that countries try to manage their freshwater resources. Large dams are built across river valleys, usually to control flooding downstream, and the reservoirs behind dams capture the rivers' flow as well as rain and melting snow. The water captured in these reservoirs can be released as necessary to provide water for irrigation and municipal

✓ Assessment

Knowledge Ask students to distinguish between a dam and a reservoir. Ask students to give two reasons for, and two reasons against, the building of dams.

NY Core Curriculum Standards

Page 672: St 1 Engin KI 1, St 6 KI 2 & 4, St 7 KI 1
Page 673: St 6 KI 4 & 6, St 7 KI 1

uses, such as in homes and businesses, or to produce hydroelectric power. Reservoirs also provide opportunities for recreational activities, such as fishing and boating. Dams and reservoirs currently control between 25 and 50 percent of the total runoff on every continent.

Transporting Surface Water If you were to visit Europe, you would likely see many ancient aqueducts like the one shown in *Figure 25-23A*. The Romans built aqueducts to bring water from other locations into their cities 2000 years ago. Today, many countries use aqueducts, tunnels, and underground pipes to bring water from areas where it is plentiful to areas in need of freshwater supplies.

The California Water Project is one example of the benefits, as well as the costs, of transporting surface water. In California, about 75 percent of the precipitation occurs north of the city of Sacramento, yet 75 percent of the state's population lives south of that city. The California Water Project uses a system of dams, pumps, and aqueducts to transport water from northern California to southern California. Most of this water, 82 percent, is used for agriculture. The residents of Los Angeles and San Diego are withdrawing groundwater faster than it is being replenished. As a result, there is a demand for even more water to be diverted to the south. However, the residents of northern California object, because the diversion of more water would harm the Sacramento River and threaten fisheries. As this example illustrates, conflicts over the transport of surface water will probably increase as human populations increase and create higher demands for water.

Tapping Groundwater Most people in the United States obtain drinking water by turning on a faucet in their kitchens or bathrooms. But do you know where this water comes from? In this country, about 23 percent of all freshwater used is groundwater pumped

Figure 25-23 Roman aqueducts, such as this one still standing in France, were considered to be architectural wonders when they were first built **(A)**. This present-day aqueduct transports water from water-rich northern California to semi-arid and arid areas in southern California **(B)**.

Update For an online update of the progress of the Three Gorges Project in China, visit earthgeu.com and select the appropriate chapter.

Environmental Connection

There are more than 100 000 dams on rivers and streams in the United States. Most dams and reservoirs are built to regulate water, especially as a means for controlling flooding. However, opponents of dam construction argue that dams only shift flooding to another site. They also contend that the availability of cheap water encourages wasteful consumption while adding federal costs to localities and states. In addition, opponents claim that dams cause significant changes to downstream ecosystems and pose a potential threat to life and property that could far outweigh any damage from flooding the dam was intended to prevent.

Enrichment

Scientists and government officials use Geographic Information Systems (GIS) to gather, store, retrieve, integrate, analyze, and display information relating to water distribution patterns on Earth's surface. GIS technology makes possible the integration of many database systems to help officials make sound decisions. GIS can show scenarios relating to storm probabilities and create three-dimensional models. Using these tools, officials can determine the impacts of possible dam failures and visualize the extent of possible flooding and thus determine the extent of risk and plan for evacuation. Satellite data can be obtained using the Global Positioning System (GPS) to determine the exact positions of storms on Earth's surface. Using these systems, along with computers, scanners, digitizers, and plotters, scientists can create very sophisticated maps and conduct detailed studies.

MiniLab

Purpose
Students will compare the hardness of water samples.

Process Skills
collect and interpret data, draw a conclusion, make and use tables

Materials
water samples (5), distilled water, graduated cylinder, baby food jars with lids (6), labels for jars, dropper, liquid soap, paper, pencil

Alternate Materials
Use pure soap for best results. If they are available, use plastic rather than glass jars.

Teaching Strategies
Remind students to measure carefully to ensure the best results. Also tell students to securely tighten the lids on the jars before shaking. Water samples should include water from wells and lakes, rainwater, softened water, and so on.

Safety Precautions
Tell students that if a glass bottle is broken, they must inform you immediately.

Expected Results
Students should recognize that suds are produced in some water samples more easily than in others.

Analyze and Conclude
1. Student answers will vary.
2. Softer water will make suds more easily and will feel silkier to the touch than hard water.
3. More soap is needed to get things clean; scum often forms in sinks, tubs, or around clothes in the washing process.

✔Assessment

Performance Give each group three unmarked bottles of water and ask the group to determine which one is the distilled water. The distilled water will produce the greatest amount of suds when it is mixed with liquid soap. Use the Performance Task Assessment List for Making Observations and Inferences in **PASC,** p. 17.

MiniLab

Hard Water

Determine the hardness of water samples by observing how easily soap suds can be produced.

Procedure
1. Obtain six clean baby-food jars. Label them A through F.
2. Measure 20 mL of one water sample. Pour the water into the jar marked A.
3. Repeat step 2 four more times, using a different water sample for jars B through E.
4. Measure 20 mL of distilled water. Pour this water into jar F.
5. Make a data table in your science journal. In the first column, write the letters A–F.
6. Place one drop of liquid soap in sample jars A through E. Do not place any soap in jar F. Tighten the lids. Then shake each jar vigorously for five seconds.
7. Using the following rating scale, record in your data table the amount of suds in each jar: 1—no suds, 2—few suds, 3—moderate amount of suds, 4—lots of suds.

Analyze and Conclude
1. List the water samples in order from hardest to softest.
2. What is the difference between hard and soft water?
3. What are some disadvantages of hard water?

---

from aquifers. In some states, such as Florida, Hawaii, and Nebraska, more than 90 percent of the population depends upon groundwater from aquifers for drinking water. Sometimes, groundwater contains substances that make it difficult to use for domestic purposes. For example, water that contains calcium and magnesium ions, known as hard water, does not form suds when soap is added. You will determine the hardness of water samples in the *MiniLab* on this page.

Groundwater normally moves from points of high elevation and pressure to points of lower elevation and pressure. This movement of water is relatively slow; water moves through the ground at a rate of only about 1 m/year. If the withdrawal rate of an aquifer exceeds its natural recharge rate, the water table around the withdrawal point is lowered. This lowering of the water table is known as drawdown. If too many wells are drilled into the same aquifer in a limited area, the drawdown can lower the water table below the bottoms of the wells, and as a result, the wells will run dry. Because groundwater is the source of many streams in the United States, groundwater depletion also affects stream flow. In coastal areas, drawdown of groundwater can also result in the intrusion of salt water into shallow aquifers.

Desalination With all the water available in the oceans, some countries have explored the possibility of removing salt from ocean water to provide freshwater in a process called **desalination.** Desalination occurs when salt water is distilled. The water is first heated until it evaporates, then it is condensed and collected. This evaporation process leaves the salts behind. Most countries that use desalination to produce freshwater use solar energy to evaporate sea water. Although the evaporation of seawater

---

Resource Manager

GeoLab and MiniLab Worksheets, p. 99 L2

Earth Science
Journal

Ask students to do some research on hard and soft water and to write position papers on why they would rather have hard or soft water in their homes. Ask students to include their position papers in their science journals. Students' position papers should include facts that support their positions. References should be cited at the end of the position papers.

by solar energy is a slow process, it is an inexpensive way to provide needed freshwater. Some desalination plants use fuel to distill seawater, but because this process is expensive, it is used primarily to provide drinking water. You will find out how a simple desalinator works in the *Design Your Own GeoLab* at the end of this chapter.

Reducing Freshwater Use The increasing need for freshwater supplies has led to some extremely creative solutions. You may have heard about a plan to tow an Antarctic iceberg to the Middle East to provide needed freshwater to arid countries in that region. However, most experts agree that the best way to meet the need for freshwater is to use available supplies more efficiently. For example, irrigation of field crops loses vast amounts of freshwater to evaporation. Farmers can prevent evaporation of irrigation water by changing their irrigation methods. Trickle irrigation, shown in *Figure 25-24,* provides water directly to plant roots, and thus considerably reduces evaporation rates. Some farmers also monitor the soil and provide irrigation only when necessary. Water can be used more efficiently by industries when they use recycled water instead of clean, freshwater for manufacturing processes.

Domestic uses of water, such as flushing toilets, bathing, and washing dishes and clothing, account for about 78 percent of the water used in a typical home in the United States. In the summer, watering lawns and gardens may account for 80 percent of a home's daily water usage. Many of these domestic uses can be reduced by installing low-flow toilets, using plants that are drought-resistant for landscaping, and fixing leaky pipes and faucets.

Figure 25-24 Trickle irrigation uses a system of perforated pipes to release trickles of water next to plant roots. This minimizes evaporation and seepage and brings 80 to 90 percent of the irrigation water directly to the crops.

SECTION ASSESSMENT

1. Why is clean water important to life on Earth?

2. How does the distribution of freshwater resources affect humans?

3. Describe three ways in which humans provide for their freshwater needs.

4. How can the amount of water used for irrigation be reduced?

5. **Thinking Critically** Many people from the northeastern part of the United States have moved to the sunny southwestern states of Arizona and New Mexico. These new residents increase local populations. How does this relocation of people affect the demand for freshwater resources?

SKILL REVIEW

6. **Predicting** Some aquifers are found deep underground and receive very little recharge. These aquifers are sometimes referred to as fossil aquifers. Once water is taken from a fossil aquifer, it rarely fills up again. Is water from fossil aquifers a renewable resource? Explain. For more help, refer to the *Skill Handbook.*

earthgeu.com/self_check_quiz

SECTION ASSESSMENT

1. Water is a major component of the bodies of living organisms.

2. Historically, people have settled in areas near water supplies. Industries also have located near ample water resources to meet their needs.

3. by drilling deep wells to access water supplies, holding water behind dams in reservoirs for use as needed, and building aqueduct systems to carry water from one location to another

4. by using a trickle or drip method, which releases water at plants' roots instead of generally flowing water over the entire field

5. The same amount of water will have to be shared as the population increases. Demand will increase as supplies generally remain the same.

6. If the water will be depleted and is not replenishable, water from a fossil aquifer would be considered a nonrenewable resource.

---

3 Assess

Check for Understanding

Project
Have students work in small groups to research a large, metropolitan area's water sources and water-management plans. Students should include in their reports the numbers of people affected, maps, descriptions of systems that transport the water, and conflicts that exist between the city and the source regions. Each group should summarize its material on a bulletin board.

Reteach

Visual-Spatial Have students draw maps of their own community's water systems in their science journals. The maps should include the water sources used, as well as treatment plants for both drinking water and wastewater. Major land-use features should be noted on each map, along with some indication of topography and vegetation.
L2 **P**

✓Assessment

Skill Ask each student to develop a water system that could be used on an oceanographic research vessel that remains at sea for six months at a time. Have students list issues that need to be addressed.

NY Core Curriculum Standards

Page 674: St 1 Science KI 1, St 6 KI 4, St 7 KI 1
Page 675: St 6 KI 6

DESIGN YOUR OWN GeoLab
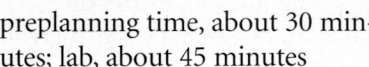

Time Allotment

preplanning time, about 30 minutes; lab, about 45 minutes

Process Skills

design an experiment, draw a conclusion, formulate models, observe and infer, recognize cause and effect, think critically

Preparation

The materials used will depend on student designs, accessibility, and cost.

Possible Hypothesis

The Sun's energy can be collected to desalinate salt water by using mirrors to focus the energy and evaporate the water, then condensing it again.

Plan the Experiment

Teaching Strategies

- A few days before the lab, brainstorm with students how a desalinator could be made. This will give students some ideas to begin with.
- Have a variety of materials available for students to use.

Safety Precautions

If any cutting tools are required to build the model, make sure students follow appropriate safety guidelines.

Tying to Previous Knowledge

Remind students that incoming solar radiation can be trapped and heat accumulated with a structure similar to a greenhouse.

DESIGN YOUR OWN GeoLab

Designing a Solar Desalinator

Most of Earth's surface is covered with salty ocean water. Ocean water can be used for drinking water and other purposes if the salts are first removed. Solar energy can be used to evaporate water from seawater, leaving the salts behind. The evaporated water can then be condensed into freshwater.

Preparation

Problem

How can you build a small-scale, working solar desalinator?

Possible Materials

clear plastic or Plexiglas
large pans to hold water
salt water
collecting containers
lamp
glass pan or beaker
hot plate

Hypothesis

The Sun's energy can be collected to desalinate salt water.

Objectives

In this GeoLab, you will:

- **Design** a model of a working solar desalinator.
- **Assemble** the model from design plans.
- **Test** the effectiveness of the design model.
- **Analyze** the model to suggest possible improvements.

Safety Precautions 🥽 ☝️ ✋ ⚡

Always wear safety goggles and an apron in the lab. Be careful when handling hot materials.

Troubleshooting

Some designs may not hold in enough heat to allow for a rapid rate of evaporation and condensation. Setups may have to remain in place for several hours to collect water. Additional light sources may be used to speed up the process.

Possible Procedures

Students need to develop some type of basic box structure with a clear side that will allow the light to enter. The structure should also include material on the inside that will absorb the heat and allow it to build up to a high enough temperature to evaporate water within the structure. Dark colors are usually helpful, and angled surfaces for the accumulation of condensing evaporated water are necessary components. Exact designs will vary widely.

Plan the Experiment

1. Use the library and go to earthgeu.com to identify designs of solar desalinators.
2. Draw a design for your model desalinator. (Hint: Solar energy must be collected in some way that allows sunlight to enter and causes an increase in temperature inside the container so that water in saturated air can condense and be collected.)
3. Make a list of the materials you will need, and then collect them.
4. Construct the desalinator you designed.
5. Test the desalinator by recording how long it takes to collect the purified water and how much water was collected.
6. Test the water to see if it has been purified by boiling the water away. If any salt remains in the container after the water has evaporated, your desalinator did not remove all of the salts from the salt water.

Analyze

1. **Interpreting Scientific Illustrations** Draw the desalinator that you constructed.
2. **Interpreting Observations** How well did your desalinator work? On what criteria did you base the effectiveness of your desalinator?
3. **Observing and Inferring** What problems did you encounter in this investigation?
4. **Comparing and Contrasting** Compare and contrast your desalinator with one of your classmates'. What were the advantages or disadvantages of your design?

Conclude & Apply

1. What factors affected the efficiency of the desalinator?
2. How did your solar desalinator's efficiency compare with the efficiencies of other students' models?
3. How could you improve your desalinator?
4. What conclusions could be drawn from your investigation regarding the viability and use of solar-powered desalinators?

Design Your Own GeoLab **677**

Data and Observations

Have students draw scaled model diagrams as part of their report on the experiment. Data should include the length of time required to obtain the amount of water collected.

Analyze

1. Models should be drawn to scale and be accompanied by a list of materials used.
2. The length of time needed to collect a suitable sample may be the criterion used to determine effectiveness. Water quality may also be a criterion.
3. Problems will vary. Students may run into difficulty sustaining a warm enough environment to keep the evaporation and condensation cycle going.
4. Answers will vary.

Conclude & Apply

1. Factors that can affect a desalinator's efficiency may include its ability to hold in solar heat and the water-collection design.
2. Answers will vary.
3. Possible suggestions for future models may include making it larger or insulating it better.
4. Solar-powered desalinators may be viable in consistently sunny locations.

✓Assessment

Knowledge Have students indicate on a world map regions of the world where desalination would be feasible. Students are likely to select desert areas with high levels of solar intensity.

NY Core Curriculum Standards

Page 676: St 1 Science KI 2 & Engin KI 1
Page 677: St 1 Science KI 2 & Engin KI 1

Purpose

Students will learn how Earth resources have been used by humans to develop new materials. The art of glassmaking makes use of land and water resources.

Content Background

Glass has been known to exist for thousands of years. Natural glass from volcanic eruptions was used by prehistoric humans for arrowheads and simple tools. Evidence of the first human-made glass dates to around 4000 B.C. Evidence indicates that glassblowing first occurred in 1 B.C.

Many glassblowers in the 1700s and 1800s came to the Americas from Germany. Often, these glassblowers were brought over by glassmakers on contracts that forbade them to work for any other glassmakers. The glaze on pottery is actually a thin layer of glass that melts during firing and fuses to the surface of the pot. Colored glass can be made by adding different minerals.

Teaching Strategies

- As a connection to art, have students compare and contrast the making of pottery and the making of glass. Have each student make a table showing the similarities and differences.
- Invite a glassblower to speak to your class. Ask him or her to emphasize how different substances are used to create different kinds and colors of glass.

Science in the News

Glass from the Past

In the autumn of 1739, Caspar Wistar opened a glass factory in southern New Jersey—the first successful glassworks in North America. He chose a location that had the chief resources he needed to make and ship glass: sand, wood, and water.

From glass fragments, old documents, and even old advertisements, historians have pieced together the history of Wistar's glassworks. It was likely a wooden building constructed around a large, beehive-shaped furnace. The furnace was built of clay bricks and was divided into three levels. The bottom level held the fire; it had an opening at one end where wood could be added and the condition of the coals could be checked. The middle level of the furnace held specially-made pots into which the ingredients for the glass itself were placed. The pots had to withstand the extreme heat of molten glass—a broken pot meant that the furnace shut down, and production ceased. Completed pieces were placed in the top level of the furnace, the annealing chamber, where they cooled slowly so that they would retain their strength.

Ingredients for Success

The ingredients for making glass have remained the same since the earliest days of glassmaking, about 4000 years ago. The primary ingredient in all glass is sand. In the eighteenth century, glass was made from sand dug from the ground. The dry ingredients, sand, potash—which is potassium carbonate found in wood ashes—lime, and other minerals used for coloring, were mixed in large troughs. The dry mixture was then placed in the hot pots in the

middle level of the furnace. The ingredients melted together to form molten glass.

In addition to sand, glass makers needed a continuous supply of wood because the fire in the furnace could never be allowed to go out. Wistar built his factory near both wood and sand; thus, he never ran out of either resource.

Importance of Water

Being close to water was important in the location of Wistar's factory for two reasons. First, having water nearby meant that fires could be put out quickly. Many early glassworks were destroyed by fire. Second, being close to water made the shipping of finished pieces much easier. The fewer times that glass had to be handled on its way to the marketplace, the less breakage there was. Given the heaviness of glass, shipping it by water was the transportation method of choice.

Activity

A variety of minerals and compounds from Earth's crust are used to make different colors of glass. Use the library or go to **earthgeu.com** to research the different materials used to produce different colors of glass. Record your findings in a data table. Are any of the materials you found surprising? Why?

Activity

Students will find that the following compounds make the following colors.

Red	copper, gold, selenium
Yellow	iron, selenium
Green	iron, chromium, copper
Blue	copper, cobalt
Purple	manganese, nickel
White	zinc, tin

Summary

SECTION 25.1

What are resources?

Main Ideas
- Natural resources are the resources that Earth provides, including air, water, land, organisms, rocks, minerals, and nutrients.
- Renewable resources are replaced by natural processes at a rate that is equal to or greater than the rate at which they are being used.
- Nonrenewable resources exist in a fixed amount and can be replaced only by geological, physical, and chemical processes that take hundreds of millions of years.

Vocabulary
natural resource (p. 655)
nonrenewable resource (p. 657)
renewable resource (p. 656)
sustainable yield (p. 657)

SECTION 25.2

Land Resources

Main Ideas
- Land resources include topsoil, rocks, and minerals. Land also provides space for agriculture, housing, roadways, and protected areas such as national forests, wildlife refuges, and national parks.
- Topsoil is a complex mixture of decaying organic matter, eroded rock, minerals, nutrients, oxygen, and water. In arid areas, loss of topsoil can lead to desertification.
- Bedrock is unweathered parent rock.
- Aggregates, including sand, gravel, and crushed stone, are found in glacial deposits.
- An ore is a natural resource that can be mined at a profit. Ores may be associated with igneous rocks or formed by processes at Earth's surface.

Vocabulary
aggregate (p. 660)
bedrock (p. 660)
desertification (p. 660)
gangue (p. 663)
ore (p. 661)

SECTION 25.3

Air Resources

Main Ideas
- The atmosphere contains mostly nitrogen and oxygen, as well as various other gases in smaller amounts. Early Earth had no oxygen; this was supplied by photosynthetic organisms.
- The geochemical cycles of Earth's atmosphere are delicately balanced. Human activities disrupt this balance, and air pollution results.
- Clean air is necessary to most organisms. Both outdoor and indoor air pollution are harmful to living things.

Vocabulary
air pollution (p. 665)
pollutant (p. 665)

SECTION 25.4

Water Resources

Main Ideas
- Freshwater is necessary to all life and to many Earth processes. Water is recycled continually through the water cycle.
- Water has unique properties that allow life to exist on Earth.
- Water is not evenly distributed on Earth's surface.
- Water-management methods distribute freshwater resources more evenly through the use of dams, aqueducts, and wells.

Vocabulary
desalination (p. 674)

 earthgeu.com/vocabulary_puzzlemaker

Main Ideas

Summary statements can be used by students to review the major concepts of the chapter.

VOCABULARY PuzzleMaker

For additional help with vocabulary, have students access the Vocabulary Puzzlemaker online.

earthgeu.com/ vocabulary puzzlemaker

0:00 *Out of Time?*

If time does not permit teaching the entire chapter, use the GeoDigest at the end of the unit as an overview.

Earth Science Online

Be sure to check the Earth Science Web Site for links to chapter material:
earthgeu.com

GLENCOE *Technology*

Videotape/DVD
MindJogger Videoquizzes
Chapter 25: *Earth Resources*
Have students work in groups as they play the videoquiz game to review key chapter concepts.

Resource Manager

Chapter Assessment, pp. 145–150
MindJogger Videoquizzes DVD/VHS
ExamView® Pro CD-ROM
Performance Assessment in Earth Science

NY Core Curriculum Standards

Page 678: St 1 Engin KI 1
Page 679: St 1 Engin KI 1, St 4 KI 2.1t, St 6 KI 4

679

Understanding Main Ideas

1. c
2. a
3. a
4. d
5. a
6. c
7. c
8. b
9. b
10. c
11. b
12. d
13. b

Applying Main Ideas

14. The atmosphere contains oxygen and carbon dioxide, which are used by living things in the processes of photosynthesis and respiration. It also is part of the natural geochemical cycles on Earth, such as the carbon cycle, water cycle, and so on.

Understanding Main Ideas

1. Which of the following is a renewable resource?
   a. oil
   b. natural gas
   c. trees
   d. coal

2. What portion of Earth's atmosphere consists of oxygen?
   a. 21 percent
   b. 78 percent
   c. 3 percent
   d. trace amounts

3. What is the origin of oxygen in Earth's atmosphere?
   a. photosynthetic organisms
   b. volcanic eruptions
   c. meteorites
   d. burning fossil fuels

4. Marble is what type of land resource?
   a. an aggregate
   b. an ore
   c. soil
   d. bedrock

5. Which of the following is a nonrenewable resource?
   a. bauxite
   b. carbon
   c. water
   d. nitrogen

6. Of Earth's surface waters, what percent is freshwater available for human use?
   a. 97 percent
   b. 3 percent
   c. less than 1 percent
   d. 21 percent

7. Which of these is NOT a way to manage water resources?
   a. building dams
   b. using aqueducts
   c. settling crystals
   d. desalination

8. What is the process by which productive land becomes desert?
   a. deforestation
   b. desertification
   c. desalination
   d. respiration

Use the following table to answer questions 9 and 10.

Efficiencies of Irrigation Methods in Texas		
Irrigation Method	Percent Efficiency	Water Needed to Add 100 mm to Root Zone
Conventional furrow	60%	167 mm
Furrow with surge valve	80%	125 mm
Low-pressure sprinkler	80%	125 mm
Trickle irrigation	95%	105 mm

9. Which of the irrigation methods requires the most water to add 100 mm to the root zone of plants?
   a. low-pressure sprinkler
   b. conventional furrow
   c. trickle irrigation
   d. furrow with surge valve

10. Which of the irrigation methods appears to be the most efficient use of water?
    a. low-pressure sprinkler
    b. conventional furrow
    c. trickle irrigation
    d. furrow with surge valve

11. Which air pollutant is more harmful to human health inside a building than outside?
    a. smog
    b. radon gas
    c. carbon dioxide
    d. nitrogen oxide

Test-Taking Tip

TABLES If a test question involves a table, skim the table before reading the question. Read the title, column heads, and row heads. Then read the question and interpret the information in the table.

earthgeu.com/chapter_test

Standardized Test Practice

1. a
2. a
3. c
4. d
5. c

NY Core Curriculum Standards

Page 680: St 1 Engin KI 1, St 4 KI 1.2g, St 6 KI 2, St 7 KI 1
Page 681: St 1 Engin KI 1, St 4 KI 3.1b, St 6 KI 1

12. Which of these is NOT a manner in which ores form?
  a. crystal settling
  b. weathering
  c. chemical precipitation
  d. photochemical changes

13. Which of the following is NOT a property of water?
  a. It has a high heat-storage capacity.
  b. It exists mostly as a gas.
  c. It expands when it freezes.
  d. It dissolves many compounds.

Applying Main Ideas

14. What is the atmosphere's role in the exchange of gases on Earth?

15. Why is the loss of the forest cover in the Amazon River Basin a worldwide concern?

16. What is the best way to prevent loss of topsoil?

17. How would planting forests help control desertification in arid areas?

Thinking Critically

18. If Earth processes recycle water resources, why is water pollution a problem?

19. Most of the water resources on Earth are salt water. Why can't all of the human population's freshwater needs be supplied by the desalination of salt water?

20. Suppose that you recently moved into a new house. Shortly thereafter, you began to feel ill. How can you determine whether the house is "sick"?

21. Volcanic eruptions and other natural events result in air pollution. Why is the air pollution produced by human activities a concern?

earthgeu.com/standardized_test

Standardized Test Practice

INTERPRETING SCIENTIFIC ILLUSTRATIONS
Use the illustrations below to answer questions 1 and 2.

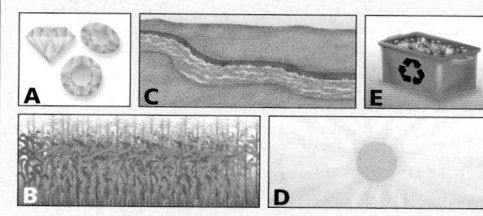

1. Which shows a nonrenewable resource?
  a. A   **c.** C
  b. B   **d.** D

2. Which resource is replaced through natural processes more quickly than it is used?
  a. B   **c.** D
  b. C   **d.** E

3. Which of the following is NOT an example of a material that is mined at a profit?
  a. hematite   **c.** limonite
  b. diamonds   **d.** chromium

4. Which is the greatest source of air pollution in the U.S.?
  a. power plants
  b. industrial smokestacks
  c. agricultural processes
  d. motor vehicles

5. Which is the most expensive and least commonly used method of providing water to areas that need it?
  a. tapping groundwater
  b. aqueducts
  c. desalination
  d. dams

Assessment **681**

15. Forests on Earth remove carbon dioxide and add oxygen to the atmosphere. The loss of forest cover may increase the amount of carbon dioxide in the atmosphere, resulting in an increase in average atmospheric temperatures. Also, with fewer trees, there would be less oxygen available for respiration.

16. to keep vegetation growing on it

17. Planting forests would retain topsoil in the area and would prevent the area from being overgrazed.

Thinking Critically

18. Although water is recycled on Earth, there is little freshwater available at any one time. Pollutants can be removed from water, but purification through the water cycle alone takes a long time.

19. Desalination is expensive, and it would be difficult to produce the quantity of water needed through this process alone.

20. Have the air inside the house tested. Also, see whether you feel better when you leave the house.

21. With an increasing human population, humans are producing more and more pollutants. In addition, human activities are producing unnatural forms of pollution that are not part of Earth's natural processes of recycling.

EXAMVIEW® PRO

Use ExamView® Pro Testmaker CD-ROM to:
- Create **multiple versions** of tests.
- Create **modified** tests with one mouse click for struggling students.
- **Edit** existing questions and add your own questions.
- **Build** tests based on national curriculum standards.

Energy Resources

Refer to pages 8T–9T of the Teacher Guide for an explanation of the National Science Content Standards correlations.

Section	Objectives	National Science Content Standards	State/Local Standards
SECTION 26.1 **Conventional Energy Resources** 🕐 2 sessions 📦 1 block	1. **Recognize** the Sun as the ultimate source of most energy on Earth. 2. **Describe** how energy changes from one form to another. 3. **Identify** materials that are used as fuels. 4. **Explain** how fossil fuels form.	UCP.1, UCP.2, UCP.3; A.1; B.2, B.3, B.5, B.6; C.5; D.1, D.2; F.3, F.4, F.5, F.6; G.3	St 1 Science KI 1, 2, & 3, St 4 KI 1.1f, 1.2g, 1.2j, 2.1a, 2.1i, 2.1m, 2.1o, 2.1w, 2.2a, 2.2b, 2.2c, & 3.1c, St 6 KI 1, 2, 4, 5, & 6, St 7 KI 1
SECTION 26.2 **Alternative Energy Resources** 🕐 1 session 📦 ½ block	5. **Identify** alternative energy resources. 6. **Compare** the advantages and disadvantages of the various alternative energy resources.	B.1, B.2, B.3, B.4, B.6; C.5; D.1, D.2; E.1; F.3, F.4, F.5, F.6	St 1 Math KI 1, 3, & Engin KI 1, St 4 KI 1.1f, 1.2g, 2.1a, 2.1b, 2.1c, 2.1i, 2.1l, 2.1w, 2.2a, 2.2b, 2.2c, & 3.1c, St 6 KI 1, 5, & 6, St 7 KI 1 & 2
SECTION 26.3 **Conservation of Energy Resources** 🕐 2 sessions 📦 1 block	7. **Recognize** the need for the conservation of energy resources. 8. **Identify** ways to conserve energy resources.	UCP.1, UCP.3, UCP.5; A.1; B.2, B.3, B.6; C.4, C.5; D.1; E.2; F.3, F.4, F.5, F.6; G.3	St 1 Math KI 1, 2, 3, Science KI 1, 2, 3, & Engin K1 1, St 2 KI 1, 2, & 3, St 4 KI 1.2g, 2.1a, 2.1b, 2.1i, 2.1k, 2.1w, 2.2a, 2.2b, 2.2c, & 3.1c, St 6 KI 1, 2, 4, 5, & 6, St 7 KI 1 & 2

A complete Planning Guide is provided on pages 30T–32T.

🕐 The number of recommended single-period sessions

📦 The number of recommended blocks

Activity Materials

Discovery Lab *page 683*
250-mL glass beaker, tap water, hot plate

GeoLab *pages 704–705*
glass or clear plastic, cardboard boxes, scissors, tape, glue, thermometers, paints, paper, aluminum foil, foam board, stones, mirrors, fabric, light source

MiniLab *page 688*
cooking oil, sand, colored aquarium gravel, 100-mL graduated cylinder, tap water

Demo *page 690*
250-mL beakers (2), light source, thermometers (2), soil, water

page 693
250-mL Erlenmeyer flask, 1-hole rubber stopper, water, hot plate, glass tubing

page 694
electric fan, paper, scissors, plastic straw, straight pin

Key to Teaching Strategies

L1 Level 1 activities should be appropriate for students with learning difficulties.

L2 Level 2 activities should be within the ability range of all students.

L3 Level 3 activities are designed for above-average students.

ELL ELL activities should be within the ability range of English-language learners.

COOP LEARN Cooperative learning activities are designed for small-group work.

P These strategies represent student products that can be placed in a best-work portfolio.

📦 These strategies are useful in a block-scheduling format.

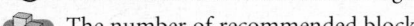

Need materials? Contact Science Kit at 1-800-828-7777 or at www.sciencekit.com on the Internet. For alternate materials, see the activity on the listed page.

Chapter Organizer

Glencoe Exclusive!
TeacherWorks™
All-In-One Planner and Resource Center

Activities/Features	Reproducible Masters	Transparencies
Discovery Lab: Sources of Energy, p. 683 **MiniLab:** Oil Migration, p. 688	**GeoLab and MiniLab Worksheets,** p. 103 L2 **Study Guide for Content Mastery,** pp. 163–164 L2	**Section Focus Transparency 82** L1 ELL **Teaching Transparency 79** L2 ELL
Using Math: Calculating Wind Speed, p. 695	**Study Guide for Content Mastery,** pp. 165–167 L2 **Laboratory Manual,** pp. 201–204 L2 **Laboratory Manual,** pp. 205–208 L2	**Section Focus Transparency 83** L1 ELL **Teaching Transparency 80** L2 ELL
Problem-Solving Lab: Changes in Energy Resource Use, p. 699 **GeoLab:** Designing an Energy-Efficient Building, pp. 704–705 **Science & the Environment:** Preserving the Rain Forest, p. 706	**GeoLab and MiniLab Worksheets,** pp. 104–106 L2 **Study Guide for Content Mastery,** p. 168 L2 **Exploring Environmental Problems,** pp. 37–40 L2 **Exploring Environmental Problems,** pp. 41–44 L2	**Section Focus Transparency 84** L1 ELL **Teaching Transparency 81** L2 ELL

 **Assessment**

Chapter Assessment,
pp. 151–156
Performance Assessment in the Science Classroom (PASC)
MindJogger Videoquiz DVD/VHS
Performance Assessment in Earth Science
ExamView® Pro CD-ROM
5 Days to the Regents Exam

GLENCOE'S
ASSESSMENT
ADVANTAGE

Additional Resources

Guided Reading Audio Program ELL
Cooperative Learning in the Science Classroom
COOP LEARN
Lesson Plans
Block Scheduling
earthgeu.com
NY Lesson Plans
NY Block Scheduling
Review Handbook for Regents Earth Science Exam

 **NATIONAL GEOGRAPHIC**

Products Available from National Geographic Society
To order the following products, call the National Geographic Society at 1-800-368-2728:
Videos
Pollution: World at Risk
Recycling: The Endless Circle

Teacher's Corner

Every Stone Has a Story
Fossils: Clues to the Past
Curriculum Kits
GeoKit: *Rocks and Minerals*
GeoKit: *Earth's History*
GeoKit: *Oceans*

Content Background

Conventional Energy Resources
Section 26.1

Energy use in the United States is heavily dependent on Earth's oil supply. Although it has been estimated that the United States once had ten percent of Earth's oil supply, over half of this oil has already been consumed, and the country's net oil reserves have been steadily declining each year. The United States' energy appetite consumes more than 40 percent of all energy resources used in any one year. Some analysts predict that at this rate of use, Earth's oil supply will be depleted in just a few decades. A careful review of energy use will help students understand the magnitude of the course that has been charted by the lifestyles of Americans.

Some people think that conventional energy resources will continue to be found on Earth and thus they are not overly concerned about the limited resources. Most experts in the field disagree, however, and stress that while other, poorer sources of petroleum are available, these resources are not very promising. Petroleum-industry experts have indicated that recent explorations have not been very successful and are not encouraging. Experts believe that all the oil resources that are easily accessible through offshore drilling have already been discovered. The remaining resources are buried deep in Earth's crust, and exploiting them will be expensive. Conservation practices will help extend current supplies and help provide time for additional exploration and for the development of changes in energy-usage patterns and technology.

Alternative Energy Resources
Section 26.2

Because conventional sources of energy are clearly in limited supply, efforts must be made to find and use alternative energy sources. This is especially true if people in developed countries such as the United States are to maintain a high standard of living. These people likely will continue to demand the energy needed to maintain their lifestyles. The premise of using alternative energy sources suggests that limited conventional resources can be replaced with other energy sources; however, this task will not be easily accomplished. It will require a concerted effort and possibly some concessions or adjustments in expectations.

Solar energy is an abundant source of energy that is expected to last throughout human existence. Solar energy is the result of nuclear fusion. On the Sun, hydrogen is converted into helium in the process of fusion. The amount of energy produced is enormous: it is produced at

Multiple Learning Styles

 **Kinesthetic** Modeling, pp. 692, 702

Interpersonal Collaborative Learning, pp. 684, 695

Intrapersonal Tying to Previous Knowledge, p. 683, Project, pp. 685, 700

GLENCOE Technology

The following multimedia resources are available from Glencoe.

The Infinite Voyage Series
Crisis in the Atmosphere

Vocabulary Puzzlemaker

TeacherWorks™ CD-ROM

MindJogger Videoquizzes DVD/VHS

ExamView® Pro CD-ROM

Interactive Chalkboard CD-ROM

Chapter Organizer

a continuous rate of 10^{26} J/s. This is possible because the Sun is composed mostly of hydrogen. According to Einstein's theory of relativity, $E = mc^2$, mass is converted into energy. Earth receives only a very small fraction of all the energy that is continuously radiated from the Sun. Because this amount is enormous, the amount of energy that Earth receives from the Sun would be sufficient to meet the world's energy needs if additional methods can be developed to capture and store solar energy.

Conservation of Energy Resources
Section 26.3

As more countries worldwide become developed, the demand for energy will increase. If more energy is not available, the energy that is available will have to be shared among more people. To meet this inevitable increase in demand, we need to learn how to make our energy resources go further. Throughout history, humans have used their ingenuity

to develop ways to extend their energy resources. From the use of draft horses to the invention of machinery, humans have been able to meet their increasing needs for energy. The development of energy resources has historically been accompanied by social and economic changes. The process of change was slow for most industrialized countries, but for some, the changes were made relatively quickly. The move from rural to urban environments hastened the changes and greatly increased the demand for energy. Electricity, which is now considered to be indispensable, has been available only since the late 1800s. The U.S. Government has responded to the need to conserve energy resources through the development of regulatory agencies and legislation. Conserving energy affects many aspects of daily life.

Identifying Misconceptions

Students may think that humans could exist on Earth without the Sun. Ask students to think about how we would be able to survive on Earth if the Sun suddenly stopped shining. They may think that humans could find alternative sources of energy. For each alternative energy source that students suggest, ask what would happen when that source of energy is used up. Explain to students that we don't have the knowledge of, or the technology to travel to, another viable solar system. In essence, life on Earth would quickly end without the Sun's radiation. Earth would continue to radiate heat until it had a much colder surface temperature. Geothermal energy would be the last energy source once other fuels had been used up. Share with students that the Sun is expected to be around for billions of years to come.

✓ Assessment

Portfolio Assessment
Assessment, TWE, pp. 689, 697

Performance Assessment
MiniLab, TWE, p. 688
MiniLab, SE, p. 688
Discovery Lab, SE, p. 683
GeoLab, SE, pp. 704–705

Knowledge Assessment
Section Assessment, SE, pp. 689, 697, 703
Chapter Assessment, SE, pp. 708–709
Assessment, TWE, pp. 686, 692, 694
GeoLab, TWE, pp. 704–705
Discovery Lab, TWE, p. 683

Skill Assessment
Problem-Solving Lab, TWE, p. 699
Assessment, TWE, p. 703

Be sure to check the Earth Science Web Site for links to chapter material: earthgeu.com

Energy Resources

Introducing the Chapter

Ask students what they and a desk, water, and a pen all have in common. In a class discussion, lead students to the chapter title as a hint. The common link among all matter on Earth is energy.

Interpreting the Photo

Windmills have been used to pump water and grind grain in Europe since the twelfth century, but the earliest references to the use of windmills dates back to Persia in A.D. 644. Windmills have been used as a source of electrical power since 1890.

INTERACTIVE CHALKBOARD with Image Bank

PowerPoint® Presentations

This CD is an editable Microsoft® PowerPoint® presentation that includes:

- Section presentations
- Section checks
- Image bank
- Links to Earth Science Online
- All transparencies
- Animations
- Audio

NY Core Curriculum Standards

Page 682: St 4 KI 2.1a, St 6 KI 1, 5, & 6
Page 683: St 1 Science KI 3, St 4 KI 1.2g & 2.2a

What You'll Learn

- What energy resources are found on Earth.
- What alternatives to traditional energy resources exist.
- How conservation can extend both traditional and alternative energy resources.

Why It's Important

Life on Earth could not exist without energy resources. Many commonly used energy resources are nonrenewable; thus, energy conservation and the development of alternative energy resources are necessary to ensure a continuous energy supply.

Earth Science Online

To find out more about energy resources, visit the Earth Science Web Site at earthgeu.com

---

Energy Resources

Windmills in the Netherlands

Discovery Lab

Process Skills

observe and infer, recognize cause and effect, communicate, model, measure in SI L1 ELL

Safety Precautions

Caution students to handle the hot water with care. Remind students to wear splash goggles and aprons and to allow the water in the beaker to cool before attempting to move it at the end of the lab.

Procedure

- Ask students the following questions. What is happening to the water? Is it remaining in the beaker? If not, where is it going?

Observe

As the water heats up in the beaker, small bubbles form and rise to the top. The bubbles become larger and eventually, the water boils. Some water evaporates, leaving less liquid water in the beaker. The ultimate source of most of the energy on Earth is the Sun. A power plant provided the electricity used by the hot plate. Whatever type of power plant

Discovery Lab

Sources of Energy

Energy cannot be created or destroyed, but it can change form and be transferred. Thus, the same energy can be used over and over again. In this activity, you will observe a type of energy transfer that occurs every day.

1. Add 200 mL of water to a 250-mL glass beaker.

2. Place the beaker on a hot plate.

3. Turn on the hot plate. Observe what happens to the water as it heats up and begins to boil.

CAUTION: *Always wear safety goggles and an apron in the lab. Allow the beaker*

to cool before moving it at the end of the activity.

Observe In your science journal, trace the energy source used to bring the water to a boil back to its origin. Describe what happened to the energy as it was used to heat and boil the water. In your description, include an explanation of the source of most energy on Earth. Infer where the energy went when the water began to boil.

SECTION 26.1

Conventional Energy Resources

OBJECTIVES

• **Recognize** *the Sun as the ultimate source of most energy on Earth.*

• **Describe** *how energy changes from one form to another.*

• **Identify** *materials that are used as fuels.*

• **Explain** *how fossil fuels form.*

VOCABULARY

fuel fossil fuel
peat

 What kinds of activities do you engage in each morning? Do you turn on lights or run water for a shower? In the kitchen, you might toast bread or use a microwave oven to heat up your breakfast. You may ride a bus to school or drive a car. All of these activities depend upon energy. Where does most of the energy that you use each morning come from? The energy that humans and all other organisms use comes mostly from the Sun.

TRANSFER OF SOLAR ENERGY

How is solar energy used by organisms? Green plants, protists such as algae, and cyanobacteria are producers that capture the Sun's energy in the process of photosynthesis. In these photosynthetic organisms, solar energy is used for maintenance, growth, and reproduction. Whatever energy is not used right away is stored by the organisms. When consumers eat producers, they use that stored

26.1 *Conventional Energy Resources* **683**

---

produced the electricity, ultimately, its energy source was derived from the Sun.

✓Assessment

Knowledge Ask students the following questions. What is the ultimate source of most of the energy on Earth? the Sun What happens to energy on Earth? It changes from one form to another as it is transferred from one object or phase to another. In the overall Earth system, is energy lost or gained? Neither, it is transferred and may change form.

Resource Manager

Study Guide for Content Mastery, pp. 163–164 L2

Section Focus Transparency 82 L1 ELL

Section 26.1

1 Focus

Section Focus

Before presenting the lesson, display **Section Focus Transparency 82** on the overhead projector.
L1 ELL

Section Focus Transparency

82 NOW YOU'RE COOKING
Use with Chapter 26, Section 26.1

❶ What material is used to heat food here?

❷ Do you think this material is better or worse for cooking than what you use at home?

Section Focus Transparency   Earth Science: Geology, the Environment, and the Universe

Chapter Themes

The following themes from the National Science Content Standards are covered in this chapter. Refer to page 8T of the Teacher Guide for an explanation of the correlations.
Evidence, models, and explanation (UCP.2); Change, constancy, and measurement (UCP.3); Evolution and equilibrium (UCP.4)

0:00 Out of Time?

If time does not permit teaching the entire chapter, use the Chapter Summary on page 707 and the GeoDigest found at the end of the unit as an overview.

2 Teach

Content Background

The first fuels used by humans were wood and coal. The use of wood for fuel took time and effort, from cutting down trees and dragging them home, to cutting branches into the proper length for a firepit or oven, to watching to make sure the fire didn't go out. Although coal is heavy, dirty, and somewhat cumbersome to use, the use of coal was considered to be an improvement over wood because coal burns steadily for hours without needing much attention. It is estimated that, currently, coal is used by only 20 percent of the homes in the United States. However, coal is used by over half of the electrical power-generation plants in the United States.

Collaborative Learning

Interpersonal Have students work in groups to compile a list of the energy sources that each group member uses in one week. Tell student groups that they must devise a system of collecting data from individuals that includes measurements of the amount of energy used. Each group must compile data and make a presentation to the class. Have one group prepare a summary chart or data table that includes the data collected from all the other groups. Ask the group that prepares the class summary data to answer the following questions as part of the group report. What were the most common energy sources listed? What were the most common uses of energy? A general conclusion for the class as a whole might be that students' lives are dependent on many sources of energy. **L2**

COOP LEARN

Figure 26-1 Wheat plants in a field trap the Sun's energy during photosynthesis **(A)**. When you eat a breakfast cereal made from wheat **(B)**, you are consuming solar energy in another form.

Figure 26-2 People who live in cold climates require energy to stay warm.

energy for their own life processes. For example, when you eat a breakfast cereal made from grain such as oats or wheat, as illustrated in *Figure 26-1,* you are consuming the energy stored by those green plants. In this way, trapped solar energy is transferred through the food chains found in most ecosystems. A food chain is a model that shows how solar energy flows from the Sun to producers and then to consumers in an ecosystem.

Humans also need energy to keep them warm in cold climates, to cook food, to pump water, to grind grain, and to provide light. The energy for all of these purposes also comes primarily from the Sun. Traditional sources of energy, such as wood and peat, are derived from producers such as plants. Even gasoline and kerosene are derived from decayed organisms that first obtained energy from the Sun. When organic materials such as these are burned, the energy stored in them is released.

TRADITIONAL SOURCES OF ENERGY

Do you live in an area that has four seasons each year? As you can see in *Figure 26-2,* some people live in climates that are very cold for part of the year. Humans have been able to survive in such cold climates primarily because of their ability to alter the environment to meet their needs. Living in cold areas requires humans to use energy to provide heat. Most humans also use energy to provide light and to cook food. The energy for all of these activities is provided by **fuels,** which are materials that are burned to produce heat or power. Probably the earliest use of fuels occurred when humans found pieces of wood that had been struck by lightning and were still burning, and then used them to start fires back at their homesteads. Archaeologists have discovered fire pits in caves that provide evidence that humans burned wood to cook their food many thousands of years ago. Traditional fuels include renewable resources such as wood, dried field crops, and dried fecal material from animals such

Differentiated Instruction

Learning Disabled Have students use the letters in the word *energy* to develop a simple crossword puzzle composed of energy-related words. Have students include their completed puzzles in their science journals. **L1**

as cows and bison. In fact, any material that is in good supply and also burns can be used as fuel.

The total amount of living things in an ecosystem is its biomass. Thus, fuels derived from living things are called biomass fuels. In many developing countries, biomass fuels are used to provide energy for cooking and heating. By far, the most commonly used traditional biomass fuel is wood. Today, wood is the primary source of energy for more than half of the world's population.

Wood Humans have been using wood as an energy source for thousands of years. While wood is currently the primary source of energy for only about four percent of households in the United States, roughly 1.5 billion people throughout the world use wood as their primary source of fuel for heating and cooking. Many of these people live in developing countries, which use half of the world's wood supply. Unfortunately, the need to use wood as a fuel has led to deforestation in many areas of the world. As the forests near villages are cut down for fuel, people travel farther and farther away to gather the wood they need. In some parts of the world, this demand for wood has led to the complete removal of forests, which, in turn, has resulted in erosion and the loss of topsoil. In industrialized countries such as the United States and Canada, trees are cut down for lumber and paper production rather than fuel. However, these uses of forest resources can have the same negative impact on the environment.

Field Crops When wood is scarce, humans use other materials, including field crops, as fuel. The simplest way to use field crops, such as corn, hay, and straw, is to burn them directly. Crop residues left after harvest, including the stalks, hulls, pits, and shells from corn, oats, rice, wheat, and nuts, are other sources of energy. All of these can be burned to provide heat. Crops and their residues are most commonly burned for fuel on farms and in homes.

Fecal Material Feces are the solid wastes of animals. In many cases, dried feces contain undigested pieces of grass that help the material to burn. Fecal material from cows often meets the energy needs of people in developing countries that have limited forest resources. People who live in villages in India, Pakistan, and Afghanistan collect animal dung for fuel and dry it on the outside walls of their stables or compounds, as illustrated in *Figure 26-3.*

Figure 26-3 Traditional energy sources usually are those available locally. Where wood is scarce, people rely on other resources for fuel, such as dried fecal material from cows.

Environmental Connection

On average, one American uses more than 272 kg of paper annually compared to the 6 kg used by one Chinese person. Share these facts with students to serve as a basis for developing awareness of the interrelationships between humans and trees.

Enrichment

Oil seed crops, such as sunflowers, okra, soybeans, and sesame, can be used to make vegetable oil and can be substituted for diesel fuel. High-cellulose crops and crop residues including hay, straw, cornstalks, and wood chips can be burned directly.

Project

Intrapersonal Divide the class into research groups. Have each group work on designing an experiment to determine the possibility of using a crop for fuel. It is important for each group to consider equipment needs, criteria for types of plants, rating criteria, and potential uses. Each design should be presented with an overview of the research, a hypothesis, necessary materials, a procedure to follow, safety precautions, questions to answer, and references. **L3**
COOP LEARN

Cultural Diversity

A Quote from Chief Seattle

"Every shining pine needle, every sandy shore, every mist in the dark woods, every clearing and humming insect is holy in the memory and experience of my people. Teach your children what we have taught our children, that the Earth is our mother. And what is man without the beasts? If all the beasts were gone, man would die from a great loneliness of spirit. This we know. The Earth does not belong to man, man belongs to the Earth. Man did not weave the web of life; he is merely a strand in it. All things are connected like the blood, which unites one family. All things are connected." These words were first spoken by Chief Seattle of the Suquamish tribe, Washington Territory, when he addressed the assembly to sign the Native American treaties in 1854. This quotation is known in many cultures and embodies the ideals of the modern ecology movement.

NY Core Curriculum Standards

Page 684: St 4 KI 1.1f, 2.1a, 2.1i, 2.2a, 2.2b, & 2.2c
Page 685: St 4 KI 2.1a, St 6 KI 4, 5, & 6, St 7 KI 1

Content Background

Large beds of peat can be found in Europe, North America, and northern Asia. Millions of metric tons of peat are burned annually in Ireland, and considerable quantities are burned in Russia, Sweden, Germany, and Denmark. Peat is used for domestic purposes in England and Scotland. However, peat is used for fuel only where other energy resources are lacking. Dried peat can be burned directly in furnaces, made into briquettes, or burned to produce gas.

Discussion

Ask students to propose materials that may become tomorrow's fossil fuels. Ask students what characteristics the materials should have to be used as fossil fuels. Students may note that materials would have to be readily preserved and changed to a usable form. In addition, materials would have to be located where they are accessible.

Using an Analogy

It is sometimes difficult for students to develop a feel for how much longer 1 million years is than 100 or 1000 years. Sometimes, comparing numbers, such as 1 million, 1 billion, and 1 trillion, with the use of examples can help. For example, a pinch of salt might contain a thousand grains, a cup of salt might contain a million grains, a bathtub of salt might contain a billion grains, and a classroom of salt might contain a trillion grains.

NY Core Curriculum Standards

Page 686: St 4 KI 2.1a, 2.1w, & 3.1c
Page 687: St 4 KI 1.2j, 2.1a, 2.1m, 2.1w, 2.1o, & 3.1c, St 6 KI 5 & 6, St 7 KI 1

Figure 26-4 Peat is cut into blocks, dried in the Sun, and then burned in stoves and furnaces to provide heat for homes. When it burns, peat has an earthy smell that many people enjoy.

Peat Bogs are poorly drained areas with spongy, wet ground that is composed mainly of dead and decaying plant matter. Plants in bogs include *Sphagnum* moss, which forms large mats on top of the water. When plants in a bog die, they fall into the water. Bog water is acidic and has low levels of oxygen; these conditions slow down or stop the growth of the bacteria that decompose dead organic matter, including plants. As a result, dead and partially decayed plant material builds up on the bottom of the bog. Over time, as the plant material is compressed by the weight of water and by other sediments that accumulate above, it becomes a light, spongy material called **peat,** shown in *Figure 26-4.* Most of the peat used as fuel today is several thousands of years old.

Peat has been used as a low-cost fuel for centuries because it can easily be cut out of a bog, dried in the sun, and then burned directly in a stove or furnace to produce heat. Highly decomposed peat burns with greater fuel efficiency than wood. Today, peat is still used to heat homes in Ireland, England, parts of northern Europe, and the United States.

FOSSIL FUELS

Peat is one of the **fossil fuels,** which are energy sources that formed over geologic time as a result of the compression and partial decomposition of plants and other organic matter. Although peat and all fossil fuels originally formed from once-living things, these energy sources are considered to be nonrenewable because their formation occurred over thousands or even millions of years. The formation of peat is the first step in the development of coal.

Fossil fuels also include coal, natural gas, and petroleum. The high concentration of carbon and hydrogen in fossil fuels makes them very efficient energy sources. Most industrialized countries of the world today, including the United States, depend primarily on coal, natural gas, and petroleum to fuel power plants that provide electricity and to fuel vehicles. You can find out how one oil company preserves the environment while prospecting for fossil fuels in the *Science & the Environment* feature at the end of this chapter. Although fossil fuels are diverse, all of them originated from organic matter trapped in sedimentary rock.

Across the Curriculum

History Ask students to write reports on the history of coal mining in the United States. Ask students to include the following information in their reports: the location of mines, the effect of mines on the country's economy, the health issues of workers, environmental concerns, the quality of coal, transportation issues, the introduction and use of technology, and the future of coal mining in the United States. **L2**

✓Assessment

Knowledge Have students answer the following questions to check their understanding. Which of the following are fuels: wood, coal, peat, natural gas, petroleum, fecal materials, rice, straw, and corn? all of them Which of these fuels are fossil fuels? coal, peat, natural gas, and petroleum

A   B   C   D

Figure 26-5 Peat **(A)** is light and spongy. Lignite **(B)** is a soft, brown coal. Bituminous coal **(C)** and anthracite **(D)** differ mainly in hardness, color, and carbon content.

Coal During periods of coal formation, tectonic plate movements caused some landmasses to move near Earth's equator. As a result, these areas experienced humid, tropical conditions that supported abundant plant growth. Generations of swamp plants, such as ferns and sedges, grew in the warm, tropical swamps. As each generation died, the organic material settled to the bottom of the swamp and became covered with subsequent generations of dead plants. The limited supply of oxygen was used up quickly, which resulted in a slow rate of decay. Over time, oxygen and hydrogen were lost from the organic matter, and the concentration of remaining carbon increased. Eventually, this compressed organic matter became coal.

Coal can be classified according to the amount of pressure under which it formed and the amount of time involved. *Figure 26-5* shows types of coal. When peat continues to be compressed, it becomes a type of coal called lignite, a soft, brown, low-grade coal. Over time, and under increasing pressure, lignite develops into higher grades of coal as it changes from soft bituminous coal to hard anthracite, the highest grade of coal. Carbon concentrations in lignite are generally around 40 percent. In bituminous coal, carbon concentrations can be as high as 85 percent, and in anthracite, these concentrations reach 90 to 95 percent. The higher the carbon concentration, the hotter and cleaner the coal burns.

Anthracite is the most efficient and most cleanly burning coal. However, less than one percent of the coal reserves in the United States are anthracite. Most coal reserves in the United States are bituminous coal; thus, many of the electric power plants in the United States burn this type of coal. When bituminous coal burns, it releases carbon and sulfur and nitrogen oxides into the air, causing air pollution. Although lignite has a low sulfur content—less than 1 percent—and is less expensive than bituminous coal, lignite is a less-efficient fuel; more of it must be burned than other types of coal to provide the same amount of energy.

Earth Science Online

Topic: Fossil Fuels
To find out more about fossil fuels, visit the Earth Science Web Site at earthgeu.com

Activity: World Reserves
Research the amount of petroleum that geologists think is left in the world (reserves). How many barrels are left? How many years will it last?

26.1 *Conventional Energy Resources* **687**

Resource Manager

GeoLab and MiniLab Worksheets, p. 103 [L2]
Teaching Transparency 79 [L2] [ELL]

Content Background
The location and quantity of the coal reserves on Earth are known. Currently, most coal exploration involves the evaluation of coal reserves. Core samples of the coal are taken to determine its quality and to identify the geologic structures in which it is found. Satellites and advanced sensors help in the creation of safe and economical mining plans. Today, with the assistance of computers, planning can be completed in seconds. This process saves time and money, and it also eliminates the dangerous physical exploration that once was done by humans.

Tying to Previous Knowledge
Remind students of the geologic time scale to help them keep in perspective the length of time it takes coal to form. Most of the coal deposits in Europe and in the eastern United States began to form in the Paleozoic Era. This was the time of the trilobites, crinoids, and early fishes. Coal deposits in the western United States formed later, during the Mesozoic Era, the time when dinosaurs ruled the land.

Enrichment
Geologists have determined that the formation of a layer of coal 1 m thick required a layer of plants approximately 20 m thick. Coal is found in deposits ranging in thickness from a few centimeters to over 30 m.

NY Core Curriculum Standards

Page 688: St 1 Science KI 2 & 3, St 4 KI 2.1a & 3.1c, St 6 KI 2 & 5
Page 689: St 1 Science KI 1, St 4 KI 2.1w & 3.1c, St 6 KI 2 & 5

Purpose

Students will demonstrate how oil migrates upward through the pores in permeable rocks.

Process Skills

model, recognize cause and effect, observe and infer, predict

Materials

cooking oil, sand, colored aquarium gravel, tap water, 100-mL graduated cylinder, carbonated soft drink (optional)

Teaching Strategies

- Have students work in small groups.
- Students may already understand that oil is less dense than water and that it will float on the surface of water.

Safety Precautions

Have students wear safety goggles and an apron while performing this activity.

Expected Results

Students will observe that adding water causes the oil to move upward through the sand and gravel. When a carbonated drink is added, the gas bubbles also rise to the liquids' surface.

Analyze and Conclude

1. crude oil; layers of rocks and their pores
2. The oil moves until it is floating on top of the water. It is less dense than water.
3. Students may predict that the bubbles of the soft drink will rise to the top as the drink sinks to the bottom of the cylinder. The bubbles in the soft drink represent natural gas.

✓Assessment

Performance Have students design and conduct an experiment to determine how an increase in temperature affects the cooking oil, sand, gravel, and water mixture. Use the Performance Task Assessment List for Designing an Experiment in **PASC,** p. 23.

MiniLab

Oil Migration

Model the migration of oil and natural gas upward through layers of porous rocks.

Procedure 🧤🥽🧪

1. Pour 20-mL of cooking oil into a 100-mL graduated cylinder.
2. Carefully pour sand into the graduated cylinder until the sand-oil mixture reaches the 40-mL mark.
3. Now add a layer of colored aquarium gravel above the sand until the gravel reaches the 70-mL mark.
4. Pour tap water into the graduated cylinder until the water reaches the 100-mL mark.
5. Let stand and observe for 5 minutes.

Analyze and Conclude

1. What does the cooking oil represent? What do the sand and aquarium gravel represent?
2. What happens when water is added to the mixture in the graduated cylinder? Why does adding water cause this change?
3. Predict what might occur in the graduated cylinder if a carbonated soft drink was added to the mixture instead of water. What would the bubbles represent?

Figure 26-6 La Brea Tar Pits in Hancock Park, Los Angeles, California, are fossil-bearing seeps that ooze crude oil.

Petroleum and Natural Gas The word *petroleum* comes from the Greek word *petra,* meaning "rock," and the Latin word *oleum,* meaning "oil"; thus, petroleum was originally known as rock oil. Today, the term *petroleum* is used to refer to the natural crude oil found underground and on Earth's surface in natural seeps, which are areas on Earth's surface where shallow deposits of crude oil ooze upward into pits or creeks, or along beaches. One such seep is illustrated in *Figure 26-6.* Crude oil is a mixture of compounds of hydrogen and carbon called hydrocarbons, which can be burned to release energy. Crude oil that is collected on Earth's surface or pumped out of the ground is refined into a wide variety of petroleum products, such as gasoline and kerosene.

Most geologists hypothesize that oil originated organically, in a manner similar to the formation of coal. Millions of years ago, much of Earth's land surface was covered by shallow seas. Rivers carrying mud and silt, along with other sediments, emptied into these seas. Organisms that died in or near the water became part of the sediment load and fell to the bottom of the seas. As layers of sediment accumulated, they were pressed down by the weight of overlaying layers and eventually became sedimentary rocks.

Concept Development

Many high-tech instruments are used to locate oil supplies. Satellites are used to make maps of Earth. Magnetic resonance imaging helps to provide three-dimensional views of the ground and its underlying structure. These technologies help to pinpoint oil and gas reserves, and thus fewer holes need to be drilled into Earth's surface. Also, drilling horizontally rather than vertically helps to reveal more natural gas and oil. Some horizontal wells are only 10 cm wide.

Across the Curriculum

Math Crude oil is often measured in barrels. A barrel of oil is equal to 159 L (42 gal). When reporters discuss the price of a barrel of oil, they are referring to the price of the crude oil before it has been refined and distributed for sale. To help students understand how oil prices vary over time, ask them to research the price of a barrel of crude oil for each year that they have been alive.

Most scientists hypothesize that crude oil and natural gas originated with once-living organisms partly because sedimentary rocks associated with oil deposits, such as sandstone and shale, contain fossils of ancient organisms. Also, because little oxygen could reach the layers of organic matter at the bottom of the seas, bacteria that do not require oxygen partially decomposed the accumulated organisms, and released a waste product called methane, which is one of the components of natural gas.

Migration Crude oil and natural gas migrate sideways and upward from their place of formation. As they migrate, they move through the pores of permeable sedimentary rocks such as limestone and sandstone. These pores in permeable rocks are the reservoirs in which crude oil and gas accumulate. As the oil and gas rise upward, they displace some, but not all, of the water that originally filled the pores. You can find out how oil migrates in the *MiniLab* on the previous page. Oil and gas continue to rise until they reach a barrier of impermeable rock, such as slate or shale, that prevents their continued upward movement. This barrier effectively seals the reservoir and creates a trap for the petroleum. In some petroleum traps, the natural gas forms a gas cap above the oil, but at high pressures, the gas may form a layer below the crude oil. Geologic formations such as faults and anticlines can trap petroleum deposits, as shown in *Figure 26-7*. Because most geologists accept the hypothesis that oil and natural gas originated with the sedimentation of once-living organisms, the search for crude oil and natural gas often begins in areas with thick beds of sedimentary rocks. Today, geologists search for oil deposits using remote sensors, magnetometers, and seismographic equipment that create subsurface maps.

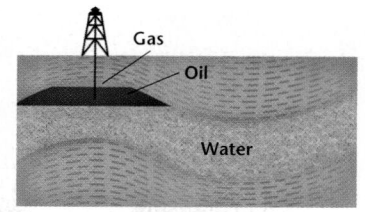

A   Anticline

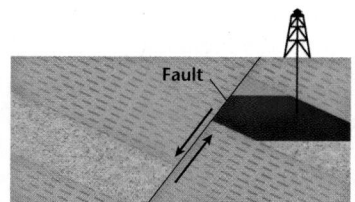

B   Normal fault

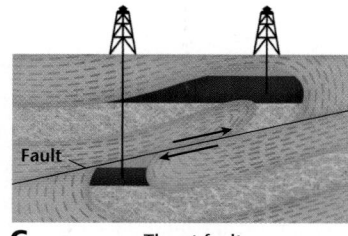

C   Thrust fault

Figure 26-7 These diagrams show typical structural traps for oil and gas deposits.

SECTION ASSESSMENT

1. What is the primary source of energy on Earth?

2. How does coal form?

3. How does petroleum form?

4. **Thinking Critically** Explain how the energy released by a burning candle originated from the Sun.

SKILL REVIEW

5. **Comparing and Contrasting** Compare and contrast the formation of peat and the formation of crude oil. How are these two energy sources alike? How are they different? For more help, refer to the *Skill Handbook*.

earthgeu.com/self_check_quiz

SECTION ASSESSMENT

1. the Sun

2. Plants that lived in warm, swampy areas died, and their remains accumulated under the water. Over time, organic matter decayed slowly, eventually developing into peat, lignite, bituminous coal, and finally anthracite.

3. Petroleum formed underneath ancient seas where organic matter from decaying organisms was subjected to increasing pressure, increasing temperatures, and other chemical and bacterial changes over millions of years.

4. The Sun's energy in the form of sunlight reached plants on Earth's surface. The plants transformed the Sun's energy into food. Some of this food was released by the plants as nectar in flowers and incorporated in the energy in pollen. Bees collected nectar and pollen and used this food to produce wax to build their hives as well as honey to fill the hives. After the honey was collected, the wax was used to make candles. When candles burn, they release light and heat, energy that originally came from the Sun.

5. Peat and crude oil both originate from living things. Peat originates from organisms that died and accumulated in swampy areas. Oil originates from organisms that died and accumulated in shallow seas.

3 Assess

Check for Understanding

Demo
Show students samples of peat, lignite, bituminous coal, and anthracite. Ask students what types of comparisons they can and cannot make just by looking at and handling the samples. Students should recognize that they are not able to assess the samples' ability to burn, amount of heat generated by burning, and cleanliness of combustion.

Reteach

Have students make data tables of conventional energy resources. Students should include in their tables how each energy resource is formed, where it is found, its uses, and its availability.

✓*Assessment*

Portfolio Have students draw maps of Earth. Ask students to include symbols representing locations that use conventional energy resources. Have students include their maps in their portfolios.

Section Background

For section content background, refer to **Alternative Energy Resources** on pages 682C–D.

Preplanning

Refer to the Chapter Organizer on pages 682A–B.

1 Focus

Section Focus

Before presenting the lesson, display **Section Focus Transparency 83** on the overhead projector.
L1 **ELL**

Section Focus Transparency **83** SOLAR OVEN
Use with Chapter 26, Section 26.2

❶ What are some advantages of using a solar-heated oven like this one?
❷ How practical would it be to use this type of oven in your home?

Section Focus Transparency   Earth Science: Geology, the Environment, and the Universe

Tying to Previous Knowledge

Ask students to think back to a hot, sunny day. Ask students why it feels cool underneath a tree on a hot day. Students are likely to make the connection that it feels cool under a tree because they are not in direct sunlight. Direct sunlight transfers radiant energy to objects that it falls upon. This is the basis for harnessing the power of solar energy.

OBJECTIVES

- **Identify** *alternative energy resources.*
- **Compare** *the advantages and disadvantages of the various alternative energy resources.*

VOCABULARY

photovoltaic cell
geothermal energy
biogas
gasohol

As you have learned, many of the fuels used today are renewable resources, including wood. Most people, however, rely on nonrenewable fossil fuels for their energy needs. Recently, it has become clear that humans are using up nonrenewable fuels at an alarming rate. Even though there are known reserves of fossil fuels around the world, development of such reserves may be too dangerous, too expensive, or too damaging to the environment to be practical. Some experts estimate that petroleum resources may be used up within the next 60 years. Scientists, private companies, and government agencies are all studying renewable alternatives to traditional energy resources. These alternative energy resources include solar energy, wind, water, geothermal energy, nuclear energy, and biomass.

SOLAR ENERGY

Have you ever used a calculator like the one shown in *Figure 26-8?* This calculator has batteries, but it also has a solar collector that uses the Sun's energy to provide power. As you have learned, the Sun is the ultimate source of most energy on Earth. The main advantages of solar energy are that it is free and it doesn't cause any kind of pollution.

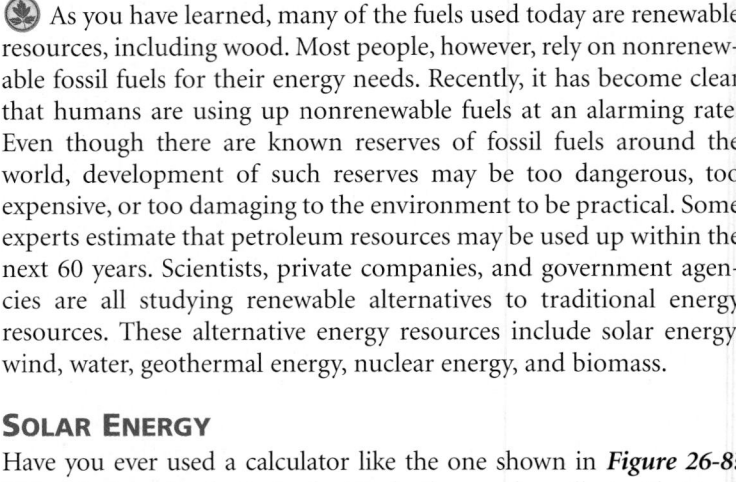

Figure 26-8 This hand-held calculator uses solar energy for power.

Passive Solar Heating Have you ever sat on the vinyl seat of a car that had been in direct sunlight for a few hours? If so, you know that the Sun can heat up the inside of a car or a building just by shining through the windows. The sunporch of the house shown in *Figure 26-9* uses this principle to capture sunlight directly and convert it into heat. The Sun's energy also can be captured in floors and walls made of concrete, adobe, brick, stone, or tile, which have heat-storing capacities. These materials collect solar energy during the daytime and slowly release it during the evening. In some warm climates, these materials alone provide enough energy to keep a house warm. Passive solar designs can provide up to 70 percent of the energy needed to heat a house, as well as up to 60 percent of the energy needed to cool it. Although a passive solar house can be slightly more expensive to build than a traditional home, the cost of operating such a house is 30 to 40 percent lower.

Active Solar Heating Even in areas that do not receive consistent sunlight, the Sun's energy can still be used for heating. Active solar-heating systems include collectors such as solar panels that absorb solar energy

690 CHAPTER 26 *Energy Resources*

Demo

Wear goggles and have students wear goggles if you are not using a safety shield for this demonstration. Obtain two beakers, then fill one with soil and the other with water. Place a thermometer 1 cm below the surface of the soil in the first beaker, and another thermometer 1 cm below the surface of the water in the second beaker. Place a light source equidistant from both beakers and leave the light on for 15 minutes. Have students note any changes in temperature on either thermometer at the end of the 15 minutes. Students should observe that the light energy was more readily absorbed by the soil and therefore the thermometer in the soil registered a higher temperature.

and fans or pumps that distribute that energy throughout the house. Solar panels mounted on the roof, as shown in the house in *Figure 26-9,* have unobstructed exposure to the Sun. Heat collected by these solar panels can be used to heat a house directly, or it can be stored for later use in insulated tanks that contain rocks, water, or a heat-absorbing chemical. Solar panels mounted on a roof can heat water up to 65°C (149°F), which is hot enough to wash dishes and clothing.

Solar Cookers Have you ever heard a weather forecaster say that temperatures will be hot enough to cook eggs on a sidewalk? The Sun's energy can cook food when it is focused correctly. Solar cookers can be used effectively where fuels are scarce or expensive, as in countries that have cut down most of their forests. A solar cooker can be as simple as an enclosed box with reflectors to direct the Sun's rays inside the box. More-sophisticated types of solar cookers, such as the parabolic cooker shown in *Figure 26-10,* can provide enough heat to boil water by focusing sunlight on one point. When the Sun's rays are focused in this way, however, they can damage eyesight, and therefore dark glasses must be worn when solar cookers are used.

Photovoltaic Cells All of the uses of solar energy described so far rely on direct sunlight. Using direct sunlight is relatively easy, but energy is also needed during hours of darkness and on cloudy days. On overcast days and in areas that don't get much direct sunlight, solar energy cannot be used directly. In addition, solar energy is difficult to store. An economical and practical method of storing large amounts of solar energy for long periods of time has not yet been developed. If such a method were to be developed, there might be no need for any other energy resources.

Until such a method is developed, solar energy is converted into electrical energy by **photovoltaic cells,** which are thin, transparent wafers made up of layers of boron- and phosphorus-enriched silicon. When sunlight falls on a photovoltaic cell, it releases a flow of electrons that creates an electrical current. Although a photovoltaic cell produces only a small amount of electricity, many such cells can be wired together in a panel that provides 30 to 100 W of power. In the same way, several panels wired together increase the amount of power produced. The electricity produced by photovoltaic cells can be stored in batteries.

Figure 26-9 This house incorporates both passive and active solar heating in its design. Deciduous trees help block the Sun in the summer to keep the house cool. In the winter trees lose their leaves, allowing the Sun to warm the house directly.

Figure 26-10 This parabolic solar cooker focuses sunlight on the spot where the cooking pot is placed.

26.2 *Alternative Energy Resources* **691**

Differentiated Instruction

English-Language Learners Students from other areas of the world may have rich experiences to share with the class. Cultural differences in the use of energy may provide a student from another cultural background the opportunity to share another perspective and personal experiences. Encourage students from other cultures to share their own experiences with energy resources with the class.

Identifying Misconceptions

Some students might think that Earth's distance from the Sun is the reason that the tropics are warmer than northern or southern locales.

Uncover the Misconception
Ask students why it is warmer in the summer than in the winter. Typically, students will say that it is warmer on Earth during the summer because the Sun is closer or providing more energy to Earth at that time.

Demonstrate the Concept
Turn on a flashlight and point it directly at the chalkboard. Have students note the bright ring of light. Then shine the flashlight at an angle to the chalkboard. The light will form more of an oval shape and be less bright. Ask students whether the flashlight is still producing the same amount of light energy and whether the flashlight is still the same distance away. Students should answer yes to both questions. Students will see that it is the angle of the Sun's rays that determines the intensity of the energy being received.

Assess New Knowledge
Ask students the following true-false questions. The amount of solar energy reaching Earth is comparable each day of the year. true The angle of the Sun's rays is the major factor in determining the amount of energy absorbed by Earth. true

Modeling

 **Kinesthetic** Ask students to work in small groups to design models of working hydroelectric power plants. Students should first draw designs for their models. Computer-generated designs might be an option for student groups with computer access. Once you have approved their designs, have students build their models. The models should be small enough so that they can use a water source, such as a sink in the classroom or an outside water tap. Each group should demonstrate its model and explain the principles behind its operation to the class.

L2 **COOP LEARN** **P**

Figure 26-11 A power tower is surrounded by banks of solar panels that reflect and concentrate sunlight onto the tower, where the sunlight is collected and stored in batteries.

Photovoltaic cells are reliable, quiet, and typically should last more than 30 years. They can be installed quickly and can be moved easily. Large-scale groups of cell panels can be set up in deserts and in other land areas that are not useful for other purposes. Today, more than 20 public utility companies in the United States use photovoltaic cells in their operations. Power towers are being used to collect solar energy and produce electricity, as shown in *Figure 26-11.* Some scientists estimate that power towers may someday supply 30 percent of the electric power used worldwide.

ENERGY FROM WATER

Are you familiar with the waterfall pictured in *Figure 26-12?* This is Niagara Falls, a waterfall in the Niagara River that straddles the border between the United States and Canada. This waterfall produces electricity for both countries. Water from the falls is diverted into massive turbines. As water falls over the turbines, they turn, producing mechanical energy that drives a generator and produces electrical energy. Energy produced in this way is called hydroelectric power.

The power of falling water also can be harnessed to produce electricity when a dam is built across a large river to create a reservoir. The water stored in the reservoir flows through huge pipes at controlled rates and causes turbines to spin to produce electricity. Today, hydroelectric power provides about 20 percent of the world's electricity and 6 percent of its total energy. Approximately 10 percent of the electricity used in the United States is generated by water, while Canada obtains more than 70 percent of its electricity from this source. Many of the hydroelectric power resources of North America and Europe have already been developed, but in Africa, Latin America, and Asia, many potential sites for hydroelectric power plants have not yet been explored.

One advantage of hydroelectric power is that it is nonpolluting. Dams built to harness hydroelectric energy provide additional

Figure 26-12 The water diverted from Niagara Falls powers huge turbines. Hydroelectric power presently provides 26 percent of the electricity needs of Upstate New York.

✓ Assessment

Knowledge Ask students to explain how energy is transferred and changed in a hydroelectric power plant. The energy of moving water, kinetic energy, is used to move a portion of a wheel. When the water hits the wheel, the wheel moves forward, thus changing kinetic energy into mechanical energy. With the use of turbines, this mechanical energy is transformed into electrical energy.

benefits in the form of recreational opportunities, drinking water, flood control, and water for irrigation. Dams also have negative impacts, however. When the reservoirs behind dams fill, they flood large areas and force people to move, destroy wildlife habitats, interrupt migration routes for fish, and change the natural pattern of water flow. This causes sediments to accumulate in the reservoir, streambeds downstream to erode, and water quality to degrade.

Energy from the Oceans Ocean water is another potential source of energy. The kinetic energy in waves, which is created primarily by wind, can be used to generate electricity. Barriers built across estuaries or inlets can capture the energy associated with the ebb and flow of tides for use in tidal power plants. One such plant exists at the mouth of La Rance River in France. While power from moving ocean water is renewable and nonpolluting, barriers in the ocean can change the water level and may disrupt coastal and marine ecosystems.

To learn more about water, go to the **National Geographic Expedition** on page 898.

GEOTHERMAL ENERGY

Most of the energy sources you have studied in this chapter so far came from the Sun. However, one energy source used today originates from Earth's own internal heat. Some of the hot springs at Yellowstone National Park, in the western United States, regularly shoot out geysers, tall fountains of steam mixed with hot water. Old Faithful is one of the best-known geysers in the world. What causes geysers? Water trapped underground in fractures or in porous rock is heated by Earth's internal heat. Some of the water becomes steam. When the heated water and steam escape through cracks in Earth's crust, they explode upwards in spectacular displays. Energy produced by naturally occurring steam and hot water is called **geothermal energy.** While some geothermal energy escapes from Earth in such small amounts that it is barely noticeable, large amounts of geothermal energy are released at other surface locations. In these areas, which usually coincide with plate boundaries, geothermal energy can be harnessed to heat homes and businesses, used in power plants to produce electricity, and even used to provide recreational opportunities, as illustrated in *Figure 26-13.*

The U.S. Department of Energy estimates that if the geothermal reservoirs in the United States were developed, they could provide up to 30 times as much energy as the country currently uses.

Figure 26-13 Geothermal reservoirs are most common in areas of high volcanic and seismic activity. In Reykjavik, Iceland, almost 80 percent of the buildings are heated by power plants that draw hot water directly from geothermal wells underneath the city.

Science Field Book
Earth Science
Journal

Have students each write a poem or short story about harnessing some form of Earth's energy in their science journals. Encourage students to augment their writing with drawings or photographs. You may wish to collect copies of students' work to be made into a booklet for conferences and open houses. **P**

Enrichment

An eponym is the name of some particular thing that is given to all other similar things. For example, the word *geyser* is an eponym because it originated from a fountain of hot water and steam, called "Geysir," that erupted in Iceland. Another eponym in geology is the word *volcano*. All volcanoes are named after a mountain, called "Volcano," that erupted in the sea off the coast of Italy.

Project

Have students who are comfortable with computer research use the Internet and go to **earthgeu.com** to find out the timing of eruptions of a particular geyser and the duration of each eruption. The data collected can then be placed on a spreadsheet and used to generate computer graphs. Students can study the eruption patterns of several geysers and make some comparisons and conclusions. Ask students to offer explanations for differences or similarities that they find. The results of students' research can be presented to the class and displayed in the classroom. **L2**
COOP LEARN

Demo

Use a safety shield for this demonstration and wear splash goggles. Have all students put on splash goggles and aprons before beginning this demonstration. Place a stopper in a Pyrex Erlenmeyer flask half-filled with water. Secure a glass tube with a fine, eyedropper-shaped opening in the stopper. Make sure that the tip of the glass tube is pointing upward toward the ceiling. Heat the water in the flask until it boils and water begins to spurt out the top. This is similar to what happens when a geyser erupts. As the water changes to steam, pressure builds up inside the flask. Underground, this pressure eventually forces the hot water and steam out of any openings in Earth's surface.

Discussion

Conduct a class discussion based on the reasons that geothermal energy exists. Students often think that Earth contains hot material within it because it was once molten and is cooling off. Share with students that scientists have calculated the rate of cooling since Earth formed and that, given the time that has passed since Earth's formation, it should now be completely solid. Therefore, there must be another source of heat within Earth. Scientists hypothesize that this source is radioactivity.

Demo

Make a paper pinwheel by cutting and folding a piece of paper. Attach the pinwheel to a plastic straw by placing a straight pin through the center of the pinwheel and through the straw. Place an electric fan with different speed settings on a table. Remind students to keep their hands away from the fan's blades. Turn on the fan at the lowest speed and have students count the number of times the pinwheel turns in one minute. Increase the fan's speed and have students count the number of pinwheel turns in one minute. Continue with each of the fan's speeds. Then have students calculate the speed of the fan in terms of turns of the pinwheel.

Earth Science Online

Topic: Alternative Energy
To find out more about alternative energy sources, visit the Earth Science Web Site at earthgeu.com

Activity: Fuel Cells
Research fuel cells as alternatives to petroleum to power automobiles. What issues must be resolved to make fuel cells practical?

Figure 26-14 Wind farms such as this one in California produce one percent of the state's electricity.

Advantages and Disadvantages of Geothermal Energy

One advantage of geothermal energy is that it is abundant and reliable at the sites where it occurs. However, as the water heated by geothermal energy is tapped, cooler water replaces it. To provide continuous power, geothermal energy reservoirs must be managed carefully. For example, in Rotorua, New Zealand, homes are heated with geothermal energy, but the availability of water is decreasing and restrictions are now being placed on its use. Geothermal steam is generally pollution-free, but water heated by geothermal energy frequently contains large amounts of minerals that can clog pipes and pollute surface water. These problems can be eliminated with systems that hold hot water and steam from geothermal reservoirs in closed containers. A greater disadvantage of geothermal energy is that its development can disrupt ecosystems and can cause local air and water pollution. Also, geothermal energy is useful only near sites where it exists, because transporting it is not practical.

WIND ENERGY

Have you ever seen a windmill? Windmills in the Netherlands have been capturing wind power for human use for more than 2000 years. Today, wind farms, such as the one shown in *Figure 26-14,* are replacing the more traditional windmills that farmers once used to pump water from underground wells. The windmills on a wind farm are more properly called wind turbines, because they convert the energy of the wind to mechanical energy, which is then used to produce electrical energy. Wind energy increases with the cube of the wind speed. For example, when wind velocity doubles, the wind's capacity to generate power increases 8 times.

Most of the wind farms in the United States are in California, yet nearly all of the energy needs of the country could be met if wind farms were built in just three states that experience consistent, steady winds: North Dakota, South Dakota, and Texas. Wind turbines currently provide three percent of the electricity used in Denmark. Experts suggest that wind power could supply more than 10 percent of the world's electricity by the year 2050.

Advantages and Disadvantages of Wind Energy

Wind is a virtually unlimited energy resource at favorable sites worldwide. Locations at high altitudes generally produce the strongest, most consistent winds. Another advantage of using wind energy is that wind farms can be built quickly and expanded as needed. They are nonpolluting and do not require water for cooling purposes, and the land

NY Core Curriculum Standards

Page 694: St 4 KI 2.1b, 2.1c, 2.1i, 2.2a, 2.2b, & 2.2c, St 6 KI 6, St 7 KI 1 & 2
Page 695: St 1 Math KI 1 & 3, St 4 KI 3.1c, St 6 KI 6, St 7 KI 1 & 2

Assessment

Knowledge Ask students which of the following are true statements about geothermal energy. Geothermal energy is always associated with geysers. false Geothermal energy is not abundant enough to make a significant difference in meeting energy needs. false Geothermal energy is energy left within Earth from the time of Earth's origin. false Geothermal energy is not available in arctic regions. false

Resource Manager

Laboratory Manual, pp. 205–208 [L2]

underneath wind turbines can be used for cattle grazing or other farming activities. As a result, wind energy is one of the least expensive ways to produce electricity.

Why isn't wind power used to provide more of the world's electricity? Wind power is economical only in areas with steady winds. When the wind dies down, people have to rely on backup systems for power, including traditional fossil fuel-burning power plants. Other disadvantages of wind farms are that they are not very attractive and they have been shown to interfere with and even kill migrating birds, as well as birds of prey. Windmills also can be noisy and interfere with radio and television reception.

NUCLEAR ENERGY

As you learned in Chapter 3, atoms lose particles in the process of radioactive decay. One process by which atomic particles are given off is called nuclear fission. Nuclear fission is the process in which a heavy nucleus (mass number greater than 200) divides to form smaller nuclei and one or two neutrons. This process releases a large amount of energy. Radioactive elements consist of atoms that have a natural tendency to undergo nuclear fission. Uranium is one such radioactive element that is commonly used in the production of nuclear energy. Nuclear energy is one other energy source that does not come directly from the Sun.

In the late 1950s, power companies in the United States began developing nuclear power plants because scientists suggested that nuclear power could produce electricity at a much lower cost than coal and other types of fossil fuels. Another advantage was that nuclear power plants do not produce carbon dioxide or any other greenhouse gases. After 50 years of development, however, 424 nuclear reactors in 25 countries currently are producing only 17 percent of the world's electricity. Construction of new nuclear power plants in Europe has come to a halt, and no new nuclear plants have been built in the United States since 1978.

What happened to the promise of nuclear power? Poor management, high operating costs, poor reactor designs, and public concerns about safety and disposal of radioactive wastes contributed to the decline of nuclear power. In addition, nuclear accidents such as those at Three Mile Island, shown in *Figure 26-15,* and at

Using Math

Calculating Wind Speed Wind energy increases with the cube of the wind speed. What increase in wind energy would occur if the wind speed quadrupled?

Figure 26-15 The nuclear power plant at Three Mile Island near Harrisburg, Pennsylvania, lost its coolant water as a result of mechanical failure and human error in 1979. About 70 percent of the core was damaged, and unknown amounts of radioactive materials escaped into the atmosphere.

Collaborative Learning

Interpersonal Much information is available on both positions regarding the use of nuclear energy. It is important for students to be given the opportunity to hear all the issues so that they can develop their own reasons for supporting or not supporting further development of nuclear energy. Ask for volunteers to select either the supporting or opposing side of this issue and participate in a debate. Take a vote at the end of the debate to see how the class now views the issue.

Earth Science
Journal

Intrapersonal Ask students to each write a paragraph or two in their science journals that express their personal opinions about the future use of nuclear energy. Tell students to make sure they include the reasons for their viewpoints.

Using Math

Because wind energy increases with the cube of wind speed, if the wind speed quadrupled, the wind energy would be 64 times greater than it was initially.

Modeling

Have students work in groups to design a structure to collect wind energy—a type of windmill. Encourage students to disregard what they know about the designs of conventional windmills so that they do not limit themselves in the designing process. After designs have been approved and models built, have students test their models outside in the presence of wind. Have students determine a method to evaluate the effectiveness of their models. Students may suggest that the effectiveness of a model can be determined by how easily the wind can move the parts of the model to generate electricity. Ask each group to determine the size that the model should be if it were built in the real world to produce energy from the wind.

L2 **COOP LEARN** **P**

Enrichment

Energy cannot be created or destroyed; it can only be changed from one form to another. Albert Einstein discovered the mathematical formula for this law, $E = mc^2$. E represents energy, m represents mass, and c represents the speed of light. Einstein helped to prove that matter can be changed into energy. Under special circumstances, the energy that holds together the basic units of matter can be released and used.

Content Background

Many electrical power plants in the United States are fueled with waste biomass. These power plants are generally located near waste-disposal sites, and the electricity generated is often considered to be a by-product. Using waste biomass in this manner relieves the problems of the accumulation and disposal of waste biomass.

Enrichment

Although biomass releases carbon dioxide into the atmosphere when it is burned, scientists call this part of a "closed loop." This means that the amount of carbon dioxide released is equal to that previously taken in by the same plants during photosynthesis. As a result, there is no net increase in carbon dioxide in the atmosphere when biomass is burned for energy.

Content Background

Biomass such as corn can be changed to liquid fuels, including methane or methanol (methyl alcohol) and ethane or ethanol (ethyl alcohol). Both of these liquids can fuel internal-combustion engines such as those in automobiles. Today, many mass-transportation vehicles such as city buses use methanol as a fuel. Ethanol is important in the production of solvents, chemicals, detergents, and cosmetics. In the 1880s, ethanol was the fuel of the first automobiles and was mixed with gasoline to operate farm machinery in the 1920s under the name of agrifuel. Gasoline shortages in the 1970s led to the resurgence of this mixture under the new name of gasohol. Gasohol is a mixture of gasoline diluted with approximately ten percent ethanol.

Figure 26-16 Bales of bagasse are burned to produce the energy that powers this steam locomotive in Java, Indonesia.

Chernobyl, Ukraine, in 1986, alerted people worldwide about the hazards of nuclear power plants. Because of its hazards, nuclear power is no longer considered to be the solution to providing for the world's energy needs, although nuclear power plants continue to provide energy in many countries.

BIOMASS

Biomass is a renewable energy resource as long as the organisms that provide the biomass are replaced. Biomass fuels include wood, dried field crops, and dried fecal materials from animals. One way to produce biomass fuel is to plant large numbers of rapidly growing plants, such as cottonwood trees, in biomass plantations. After harvest, these plants can be burned directly, converted into gas, or fermented into alcohol fuel.

Bagasse, which is the residue of sugar cane after the juice has been extracted, is another source of biomass that is burned to produce power as illustrated in *Figure 26-16*. The burning of bagasse produces approximately 10 percent of Hawaii's electricity supply, and thus, it eliminates the need for approximately 2.7 million barrels of oil each year. Other types of biomass fuels are produced when bacteria and chemical processes are used to convert solid biomass into gaseous and liquid biofuels, such as biogas, liquid ethanol, and liquid methanol. A disadvantage of biomass fuels is that when they are burned, they release carbon dioxide and particulate matter into the atmosphere. Biomass is the main source of energy for more than half of the world's population.

Biogas **Biogas** is a mixture of gases that includes 50 to 70 percent methane gas and 30 to 48 percent carbon-dioxide gas. Plant and animal wastes can be converted into methane gas in simple containers, called digesters, by the action of bacteria. In China, more than 8 million biogas digesters are in use in individual households. In a biogas digester the gas is separated from the solid wastes and piped into homes for use as a cooking fuel. The leftover solid wastes then can be used as fertilizer on food crops, because the high temperatures inside the digester destroy harmful bacteria.

Ethanol and Methanol Liquid ethanol is another name for grain alcohol. Ethanol can be made from sugar and grain crops, including sugar cane, sugar beets, sorghum, and corn. Currently, ethanol produced from corn is used in gasoline mixtures around the world. Gasoline mixed with ethanol makes **gasohol,** which can be

Across the Curriculum

Chemistry Methane, also called marsh gas, is a gas at room temperature. In fact, it is a gas at temperatures higher than −161°C. The chemical formula of methane is CH_4. Methane is colorless, odorless, lighter than air, and flammable. Methane is also called a greenhouse gas because it traps atmospheric heat; it has been estimated to be 21 times more effective in trapping atmospheric heat than carbon dioxide. In the past 200 years, the amount of methane in the atmosphere is believed to have doubled.

Biology The basis of biomass energy is the process of photosynthesis, in which solar energy is converted into food by green plants and other photosynthesizing organisms. One product of photosynthesis is sugar, a basic carbohydrate. Energy stored in sugar can later be released. While the efficiency of solar energy captured in this way is relatively low (8–15 percent), the amount of harvestable biomass is 100 times the total annual energy consumption.

burned in conventional gasoline engines. The use of gasohol can extend gasoline supplies and reduce dependency on foreign petroleum reserves. Ethanol fuels burn more cleanly than pure gasoline. Liquid methanol, which is wood alcohol, is made mostly from natural gas, but it can also be made from wood, wood wastes, agricultural wastes, sewage sludge, garbage, or coal.

ENERGY FROM OIL SHALE AND TAR SAND

You have learned that crude oil and natural gas can be found in porous sedimentary rocks. Sometimes, other hydrocarbon mixtures become trapped in different types of rocks. For example, oil shale, shown in *Figure 26-17,* is a fine-grained rock that contains a solid, waxy mixture of hydrocarbon compounds called kerogen. Oil shale can be mined, then crushed and heated until the kerogen vaporizes. The kerogen vapor can then be condensed to form a heavy, slow-flowing, dark-brown oil known as shale oil. Shale oil is processed to remove nitrogen, sulfur, and other impurities before it can be sent through pipelines to a refinery. At present, the cost of processing oil shale is higher than the cost of crude oil sold by countries that have abundant oil supplies.

Tar sand is a mixture of clay, sand, water, and bitumen, which is a heavy, black, high-sulfur oil. Tar sand also can be mined, then heated until the bitumen fluid softens and floats to the top. Bitumen can be purified and upgraded into a type of crude oil. However, the processing of oil shale and tar sand requires large amounts of energy and produces air and water pollution. 🍁

Figure 26-17 Shale oil is extracted from oil shale, a fine-grained rock. Some oil shale can actually ignite and burn on its own, as this photo shows.

SECTION ASSESSMENT

1. Identify one alternative energy resource that is associated with each of Earth's systems: the atmosphere, hydrosphere, biosphere, and lithosphere.

2. Compare passive and active solar energy.

3. What is gasohol?

4. What alternative energy source would be the least damaging to the environment if the required technology could be developed to harness and use it? Explain.

5. **Thinking Critically** Although solar energy could supply all of the world's energy needs, why isn't it used to do so?

SKILL REVIEW

6. **Making Tables** Prepare a table that compares the advantages and disadvantages of alternative energy resources, including solar energy, hydroelectric energy, geothermal energy, wind, nuclear energy, and biomass. In your table, include the following headings: Location, Limits to Use, Health Hazards, Affordability, Major Advantage, and Major Disadvantage. For more help, refer to the *Skill Handbook.*

697

SECTION 26.3

Conservation of Energy Resources

Section Background

For section content background, refer to **Conservation of Energy Resources** on page 682D.

Preplanning

Refer to the Chapter Organizer on pages 682A–B.

1 Focus

Section Focus

Before presenting the lesson, display **Section Focus Transparency 84** on the overhead projector. **L1** **ELL**

84 HYBRID CAR
Use with Chapter 26, Section 26.3

❶ What would be some advantages of buying this car?
❷ Would you buy this car? Why or why not?

Project

Have students ask their parents or guardians how energy use has changed over their lifetimes. Have students report on the differences or similarities in their parents' or guardians' opinions and their own. Ask students how the information they obtained compares to the information presented in the table in the Problem-Solving Lab on the next page.

OBJECTIVES

- **Recognize** *the need for the conservation of energy resources.*
- **Identify** *ways to conserve energy resources.*

VOCABULARY

energy efficiency
cogeneration
sustainable energy

🍁 As you have learned, traditional energy resources such as fossil fuels are nonrenewable and in limited supply. Yet industrialized countries continue to consume these resources at ever increasing rates. *Figure 26-18* compares the energy resources used in industrialized countries to those used in developing countries. The graphs in *Figure 26-18* show that renewable resources account for 41 percent of the energy used in developing countries, in comparison to industrialized countries where renewable resources account for only 10 percent of the energy used. Experts have concluded that the best way to meet energy needs is a combination of improved energy efficiency and increased use of locally available, renewable energy resources. This means that it is better to use a variety of energy resources at all times than to depend upon a single, nonrenewable energy resource such as oil, coal, or natural gas. For example, a community that has hydroelectric energy resources may also use solar energy to generate electricity in months when water levels are low.

ENERGY EFFICIENCY

Energy efficiency is the use of energy resources in the ways that are most productive. This means using the same amount of a resource but getting more from it. To find ways to use resources more efficiently, scientists study exactly how energy resources are used and where improvements are needed. Using resources more efficiently is a type of conservation.

Figure 26-18 This graph shows the relative amounts of energy used by industrialized and developing countries worldwide.

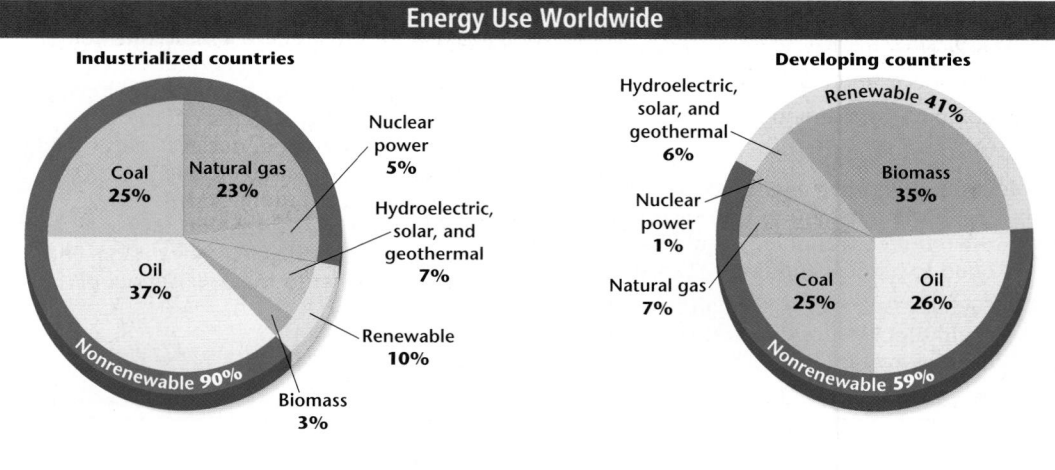

Energy Use Worldwide

Industrialized countries
- Coal 25%
- Natural gas 23%
- Nuclear power 5%
- Hydroelectric, solar, and geothermal 7%
- Renewable 10%
- Biomass 3%
- Oil 37%
- Nonrenewable 90%

Developing countries
- Hydroelectric, solar, and geothermal 6%
- Renewable 41%
- Biomass 35%
- Nuclear power 1%
- Natural gas 7%
- Coal 25%
- Oil 26%
- Nonrenewable 59%

Demo

Pass out a sheet of paper to each student. Ask students to write their names, addresses, and telephone numbers on the paper. Have students return the sheets of paper to you. Count out loud the number of sheets of paper used. Announce that you have only 50 sheets of paper, including those you have already used, and that you will conduct this activity in all your classes. Count the remaining unused pieces of paper. Tell students the number of remaining students you have in your other classes. Ask them for suggestions on how to deal with the paper shortage. Students will likely suggest cutting the paper into smaller sheets or using the other side of the used paper. Relate the limitation of paper to the limitation of energy resources.

How can energy efficiency be improved? Energy analysts have suggested several ways of doing so. People can recycle old appliances and vehicles, and purchase newer, more energy-efficient models. They also can improve the energy efficiency of older homes by adding insulation, installing solar panels, or by installing new windows, or they may purchase newer, energy-efficient homes. Local power companies can use energy from alternative resources in areas where they are available to decrease their dependence on petroleum. Governments also can help by offering tax savings to people who buy more-efficient vehicles and appliances, and by funding research and development projects related to energy efficiency.

Conservation of Energy Resources Do you wet your toothbrush, then turn off the water while you brush your teeth? When you leave an empty room, do you turn off the lights? You can probably think of many other ways that you could conserve energy at home, at school, and in the workplace. Conserving energy is, in the long run, less expensive than finding new energy sources. You can find out how energy use has changed in the *Problem-Solving Lab* on this page.

Problem-Solving Lab

Changes in Energy Resource Use

Analyze how the use of energy resources has changed Many types of energy resources are used throughout the world. Over time, fluctuations occur in the amount of each resource used. The data in the table show the changes that have occurred in world energy use between 1900 and 1997. Are these changes good or bad?

Analysis

1. Plot the data in the table on a graph. Use a different color for each year.

Thinking Critically

2. Of all the energy used between 1900 and 1997, what percentage was nonrenewable?

3. What trend in the use of renewable energy sources is evident?
4. What concerns are reflected by the data? How can these concerns be addressed?

World Energy Use		
Energy Source	**Percent of Total Energy Provided**	
	1900	**1997**
Coal	55	22
Oil	2	30
Natural gas	1	23
Nuclear power	0	6
Alternatives (biomass, hydroelectric energy, wind, solar energy, geothermal energy)	42	19

Resource Manager

Teaching Transparency 81 L2 ELL

Study Guide for Content Mastery, p. 168 L2

Section Focus Transparency 84 L1 ELL

Assessment

Skill Ask students to each make a bar graph of the data presented in the Problem-Solving Lab. Ask students which type of graph they think best represents the data, which one they prefer, and why.

Problem-Solving Lab

Purpose
Students will analyze how the use of energy resources has changed over time.

Process Skills
use numbers, make and use graphs, draw conclusions, think critically

Materials
paper, pencil, graph paper, colored pencils

Teaching Strategies
- Ask students how they think energy use has changed since they were born. Have students share their opinions before proceeding with this activity.
- Review graphing procedures with students. Remind students that a graph needs a title, legend, and appropriate scales on the x and y axes.

Analysis
1. Students should have little difficulty plotting the graph. Assist students who are experiencing difficulty.

Thinking Critically
2. 58 percent (1900); 81 percent (1997)
3. The use of renewable energy sources decreased from 42 percent to 19 percent.
4. The use of nonrenewable energy resources has increased by 23 percent over 97 years. Emphasis should be shifting toward the use of renewable resources, but the trend shows otherwise. Emphasis needs to be placed on developing affordable and available renewable energy resources. The government should provide incentives to encourage renewable energy use to ensure that future energy needs are met.

Project

Intrapersonal Have students each keep a log of how much electricity they use for one week. Possible headings for the log include: Date, Activity, Appliance Wattage, Length of Time in Use, and Electricity Consumed. At the end of the week, have students each find the total amount of electricity that they used during the week. Have students repeat the procedure for another week. This time, ask students to make a concerted effort to reduce their electrical use, noting in a separate column on the log what they did or did not do to reduce their total electrical use for each log entry. On a summary sheet, list each student's name and the total kilowatts of electricity saved by that student. Total the list to determine the cumulative amount of electrical energy saved by the class in one week. Have students calculate how much energy they could save if they continued to save energy at that rate for one year. L1

Figure 26-19 Fluorescent lightbulbs like this one can be used in most lamps to save energy.

GETTING MORE FOR LESS

The usual approach to energy use in industrialized countries has been to spend more to get more. Higher demand requires a greater supply and results in higher costs. The price that people in these countries pay for energy is high. This is especially true of electrical energy. Electricity is costly to produce and it is not efficiently used in homes or industry. In the United States, approximately 43 percent of the energy used by motor vehicles and to heat homes and businesses is wasted. One solution is to shift to the more efficient use of energy rather than the search for more energy. If this became the norm, less energy would be needed, thus helping the total cost of energy to go down.

One example of this concept involves merely changing the type of lightbulb in a lamp. Replacing an incandescent lightbulb with a compact fluorescent lightbulb, shown in *Figure 26-19*, would save the consumer $35 to $50 over the 10-year life of the lightbulb. Replacing just 25 incandescent lightbulbs in a house with fluorescent ones could save between $87 to $125 each year in electricity costs. Use of fluorescent lightbulbs or other energy-efficient lighting could save businesses in the United States alone billions of dollars per year in the cost of electricity. In addition, less energy would be used. This would help to reduce the amount of coal or other fossil fuels needed for generation of electricity, which could in turn decrease the amount of carbon dioxide and sulfur dioxide emitted into the atmosphere. The net effect would be a reduction in air pollution.

Cogeneration When power plants generate electricity, waste heat is given off during the process. However, it is possible to recover this waste heat and use it to produce another form of energy. The production of two usable forms of energy, such as steam and electricity, at the same time from the same process is called **cogeneration.** Cogeneration can produce income and reduce the need for additional energy resources. One secondary use of the heat given off by the generation of electricity is the warming of buildings or water. Another is the operation of electrical devices in the power plant, such as scrubbers, which remove sulfur from the air emitted from smokestacks. Cogeneration has enabled Central Florida to operate the nation's cleanest coal-powered electric facility. Sweden has achieved an 85-percent energy efficiency rating while releasing only a fraction of the nitrogen-oxide and sulfur-oxide emissions that are permitted for coal-powered facilities in the United States.

700 CHAPTER 26 *Energy Resources*

Earth Science
Journal

Have students each make a list of the appliances used in their homes and the wattage used by each appliance. Ask students to place a star next to the appliance with the highest wattage requirements.

Across the Curriculum

History Ask students to each write a report about a person who was important to the history of electricity. Possibilities include the following: Otto von Guericke, the inventor of the static electric generator in 1675; Alosio Galvani, who invented the first current generator in 1780; Samuel Morse, who invented the telegraph in 1840; and Thomas Edison, who invented the incandescent lightbulb in 1880 and the first central power station to produce electricity.

Figure 26-20 Electric cars generally are smaller than gasoline-powered vehicles, and they have a limited range. However, for trips close to home at moderate speeds, these vehicles are extremely efficient and non-polluting.

Improving Efficiency in Transportation Transportation is necessary to move food and other goods from one place to another, and to move people from their homes to workplaces, schools, stores, and other places. Although transportation requires the use of fuel, conservation practices can help reduce dependency on the fuel resources used for transportation.

The use of fuel-efficient vehicles is one way to reduce the amount of petroleum resources consumed. Automobile manufacturers now have the ability to build vehicles that achieve high rates of fuel efficiency without sacrificing performance. Laws that lower speed limits help improve fuel efficiency, because engines burn fuel more completely at lower speeds. The future of this industry looks especially promising as hybrid and electric cars, such as the one shown in *Figure 26-20,* begin to reach the consumer market.

People who live in metropolitan areas can improve energy efficiency by using public transportation. When it is necessary to drive private automobiles, carpooling can reduce the number of vehicles on the highways and reduce gasoline consumption. Carpooling also eases congestion on major highways in and around large cities. Some metropolitan areas, such as Washington, DC, encourage carpooling by providing express lanes for cars with multiple passengers, as illustrated in *Figure 26-21.* In Europe, mass transportation includes long-distance rail systems, as well as electric trams and trolleys in the major cities.

People who live in rural areas are often dependent on automobiles. In many rural areas, modes of transportation other than the automobile are limited or nonexistent. However, with the increasing importance

Figure 26-21 Special lanes for car pools encourage people to leave their cars at home and travel with a friend or two to work each day, thus reducing total vehicle emissions.

26.3 *Conservation of Energy Resources* **701**

Discussion

Bring to students' attention the fact that certain landscaping techniques can reduce energy needs. For example, the strategic location of trees around buildings can reduce energy needs. Trees can block the wind and thus may be able to reduce heating costs. Trees can also reduce cooling costs by providing shade and thereby reducing absorption of solar energy. In these ways, the external environment of a building can be as important as the internal features of the building when it comes to conserving energy. In addition, the leaves of trees use carbon dioxide and thus reduce the amount of carbon dioxide in the atmosphere.

Modeling

Kinesthetic Have students work in groups to design and build a landscape model of some type of new construction, such as a school or mall. Designs should include the placement of appropriate landscaping to help reduce energy use by the new facility. Cardinal directions and scale must be noted on the designs. Each design also should be accompanied by a written description explaining how the design will save energy. Each group's finished model can be displayed in the classroom and critiqued by other groups.

L3 **COOP LEARN** **P**

NY Core Curriculum Standards

Page 702: St 1 Math KI 1, 2, & Engin KI 1, St 6 KI 1 & 6, St 7 KI 1 & 2

Page 703: St 1 Engin KI 1, St 6 KI 1, 4, & 6, St 7 KI 1 & 2

Figure 26-22 Insulation is rated by its R-value, which is the resistance to heat flow. An R-value of 18 indicates that this insulation is more efficient at retaining energy than insulation with an R-value of 3.

of computers and access to the Internet, more jobs can be performed from home. The use of bicycles for short distances is another option in some places. In China, a country of 1.3 billion people, approximately 300 million bicycles are in use.

Improving Efficiency in Industry While industries use one-third of all energy produced in the United States, cogeneration has allowed some industries to increase production while leveling off their energy use. This has been accomplished in part by the use of more efficient machinery. Industries can further improve their energy efficiency by making greater efforts to reduce their use of both materials and the energy used to produce those materials. For example, packaging can be reduced overall, and unnecessary packaging can be eliminated. These efforts would cut down on resource use, lower costs, and also reduce the amount of solid waste.

Increasing Efficiency at Home People can do many things in their own homes to conserve energy. For example, fluorescent lights last longer than incandescent bulbs and need to be replaced less frequently. The use of energy-efficient appliances can also make a significant difference in energy consumption. This is especially true of appliances that consume large amounts of energy, such as refrigerators, water heaters, and ovens.

The use of more-efficient insulation on existing homes can result in dramatic savings on heating costs, especially in climates with cold winters. As warm air rises, heat escapes through windows, chimneys, and roofs. Weather-stripping around doorways and caulking around older windows can help keep cold air outside and warm air inside. Insulating pipes and water heaters also reduces energy consumption.

Building materials and windows are rated according to their insulation abilities. Construction materials are labeled with these ratings, known as R-values, as shown in *Figure 26-22.* The use of materials with high insulation values can significantly reduce energy consumption. Replacing older windows can save so much money in reduced energy costs that the windows pay for themselves in just a few years.

When new structures are built, the use of energy-efficient materials and windows can have a major impact on future energy needs. Designs for new buildings that incorporate

---

Differentiated Instruction

Visually Impaired Pair a visually impaired student with another student. Collect several types of insulation. Have the visually impaired student handle each material and describe it as the other student writes down the description. Then ask the visually impaired student to rank the materials in order from the one with the best insulating ability to the least. Have the other student write down the rankings, then examine the materials to identify their R-values. Have the student share this information with the visually impaired student to see how accurate the student's rankings were. Be careful with fiberglass; some students may have skin reactions to it.

passive and active solar heating also can reduce the need for the consumption of traditional energy resources. Find out more about solar heating in the *Design Your Own GeoLab* at the end of this chapter. Some window manufacturers now triple-glaze their windows, as shown in *Figure 26-23,* or place an inert gas between the panes to reduce energy loss. Superinsulation and air barriers in new homes built in Minnesota recently resulted in heating savings of 68 percent. Newly constructed buildings that are designed to save energy cost more initially, but they can save money and resources in the long run.

Figure 26-23 A triple-glazed window is one that has either three panes of glass or two panes of glass with a middle layer of plastic film. Some triple-glazed windows also have an inert gas, such as argon or krypton, between the layers to improve the insulating ability of the windows.

SUSTAINABLE ENERGY

All humans have needs for energy, but these needs vary. Energy resources on Earth are interrelated, and they affect one another. **Sustainable energy** involves the global management of Earth's natural resources to meet current and future energy needs without causing environmental damage. A good management plan incorporates both conservation and energy efficiency. The development of new technology to extend current resources and provide additional energy resources is a vital part of such a plan. Global cooperation can help ensure the necessary balance between protection of the environment and economic growth. The achievement of these goals will depend on the commitment made by all to ensure that future generations have access to the energy resources required to maintain a high quality of life on Earth. 🍁

SECTION ASSESSMENT

1. Why should you be concerned about energy efficiency?

2. Describe three ways in which you could conserve electrical energy in your home.

3. How does cogeneration save energy resources?

4. Why is it important to conserve resources instead of seeking new sources of energy?

5. **Thinking Critically** Why is there such a difference in energy consumption among different countries, such as the United States and India?

SKILL REVIEW

6. **Concept Mapping** Use the following terms to construct a concept map of the major concepts in this section. For more help, refer to the *Skill Handbook*.

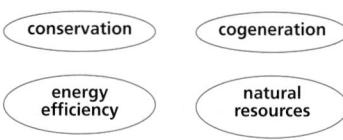

conservation
cogeneration
energy efficiency
natural resources

earthgeu.com/self_check_quiz

26.3 *Conservation of Energy Resources* **703**

SECTION ASSESSMENT

1. Without the use of methods to conserve energy, many of our resources will soon become exhausted.

2. use more-efficient appliances, turn off lights when no one is in a room, do things manually instead of using electrical appliances

3. Using the same energy source to complete two tasks saves the energy needed to do the second task.

4. By conserving the energy resources currently being used, the resources will last longer and allow more time for the discovery and development of additional energy sources.

5. The United States is a highly industrialized nation. Industrialized countries require more energy resources to operate factories and to maintain technological developments.

6. Conservation of natural resources can be accomplished by achieving energy efficiency both at home and in industry, for example, by cogeneration.

SECTION ASSESSMENT

---

3 Assess

Check for Understanding
Project
Have students work together as a class to develop an evaluation of how energy is conserved in your school. Have them develop categories such as heating, lighting, transportation, use of natural resources, degree of recycling, and so on. After students have gathered information to support their evaluation, have them present it to the school principal.

Reteach

Have students work in pairs to review section material. After 15 minutes, have each student make up five questions for the other student to answer. Add up the total number of questions that the pair correctly answered. Ask each pair to ask the questions that they missed to others in the class.
COOP LEARN

✓Assessment

Skill Have each student develop five questions based on the information in this section. Have students write each question on a piece of paper. Shuffle the pieces of paper and have all students stand up and take turns to answer the questions. When a question is missed, the student should be seated. Students who are seated can join the standing students if they can answer any of the questions missed. Make sure the correct answers to all questions are eventually discussed.

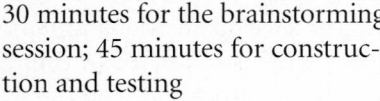

DESIGN YOUR OWN GeoLab

Time Allotment

30 minutes for the brainstorming session; 45 minutes for construction and testing

Process Skills

design an experiment, formulate models, hypothesize, observe and infer

Preparation

- Hold the brainstorming session a few days before students make and test their buildings.
- Review the reason for and use of a control.
- Have references on hand in the classroom on the topic of energy-efficient building designs.

Possible Hypotheses

Student hypotheses may suggest that insulating their buildings with materials such as foam board will hold in the heat and keep out the cold. Students may plan for few windows or windows facing the south. Colors may be chosen to absorb or reflect sunlight. Many options are possible.

Plan the Experiment

Teaching Strategies

Allow students to be creative. Offer suggestions only if a student is headed in a direction that won't allow the student to learn the lesson. Allow students to make small errors in their designs so that they can analyze their results easily. Make sure students have used a control during the testing phase.

DESIGN YOUR OWN GeoLab

Designing an Energy-Efficient Building

Buildings can be designed to conserve heat energy. Some considerations involved in the design of a building that conserves heat include the materials that will be used in construction, the materials that will store heat, and the overall layout of the building.

Preparation

Problem

How can a building be designed to conserve energy? What building materials will work best, and what other factors need to be considered?

Possible Materials

glass or clear plastic
sturdy cardboard boxes
scissors
tape
glue
thermometers
paints of various colors
materials to cover the building (paper, aluminum foil, foamboard, and so on)
interior materials (stones, mirrors, fabric, and so on)
light source

Hypothesis

Brainstorm a list of design features that might contribute to the energy efficiency of a building. Hypothesize how you could incorporate some of these features into an energy-efficient building. Find out what materials are used in heat-efficient homes and research local sources of materials for your design.

Decide how you will determine the heat efficiency of the building you construct. Be sure to plan for a control building for comparison.

Objectives

In this Geolab, you will:
- **Research** what materials are used in the construction of energy-efficient buildings.
- **Design** a building that is energy efficient.
- **Construct** the building that you design.
- **Determine** the heat efficiency of the building by comparing it to a control building.
- **Interpret** the data that you collect to determine your success in developing an energy-efficient building.

Safety Precautions

Be careful when you are using scissors. Make sure to handle the light source carefully when it is hot. Always wear safety goggles and an apron in the lab.

Troubleshooting

Keep a watchful eye over students as they build and test their setups to help them avoid any serious mistakes.

Resource Manager

GeoLab and MiniLab Worksheets,
p. 104–106 **L2**

Plan the Experiment

1. Review the data that you collected about building energy-efficient buildings. Also review your list of possible design features.
2. Design your building. Make a list of the heat-conserving issues that you addressed.
3. Decide on the materials that you will use to build your house. Collect those materials.
4. Construct the building and a control building for comparison.
5. Devise a way to test the heat-holding ability of each building.
6. Proceed with the test on each building. To test the buildings' heat energy efficiency, it may be necessary to heat the buildings and determine how long heat is conserved within each one. **CAUTION:** *Make sure the heat*

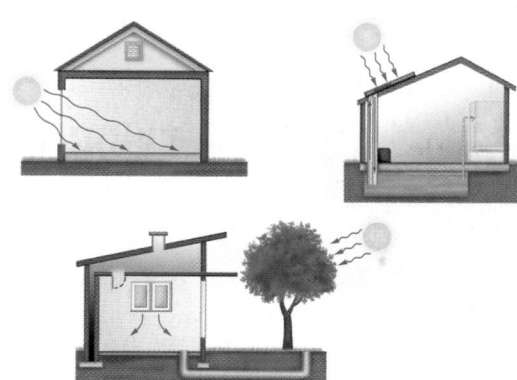

source is far enough away from the building materials so that they do not burn or melt.

7. Record your data in a table. Then, make a graph of your data.
8. Make modifications to the design to improve the building's efficiency.

Analyze

1. **Checking Your Hypothesis** Was the building that you designed more energy-efficient than the control building? Why did you construct a control building?
2. **Interpreting Observations** What problems did you encounter, and how did you solve them?
3. **Observing and Inferring** How did your observations affect decisions that you might make if you were to

repeat this lab? Why do you think your design worked or did not work?
4. **Comparing and Contrasting** Compare and contrast the building you designed and the control building. Compare and contrast your design and the designs of your classmates.
5. **Thinking Critically** Suppose you could use only naturally occurring materials. Would that limit your design? Explain your answer.

Conclude & Apply

1. How could you incorporate some of your design elements in your own home?
2. How could your design be improved?
3. How could using different energy sources affect your results?

Design Your Own GeoLab **705**

Possible Procedures

Students may design buildings that are small and compact as well as well insulated. Strategic landscaping may be incorporated into design plans. The direction of the Sun in the sky and the influence of topography and weather patterns may also have been taken into consideration.

Data and Observations

Students should use thermometers in their buildings and in the control building to identify their energy efficiencies. The data should be collected in a data table and a comparison graph should be made.

Analyze

1. Students should be able to use the data that they collected from their models and the control to determine the effectiveness of their designs.
2. Students must be assured that listing problems is important in any experiment.
3. Evaluating by observing and inferring helps students to make concrete applications of the concept of heat storage and of the scientific process.
4. Lead students to understand that if the control and design models showed no difference, then the methods employed likely did not affect what was being measured—either heat absorbed or heat retained.
5. Asking students to consider specific materials will help them realize that decisions sometimes have to be made after balancing the options. To make a decision of this type, priorities may need to be established and compromises made.

Conclude & Apply

Student answers will vary depending on their designs and their success. In all cases, improvements will be possible either in the type or amount of material used and in the orientation of the buildings. Possible sources of error in the testing phases are also important to look for and consider when analyzing the results obtained.

✓ Assessment

Knowledge Ask students which of the following statements apply to their designs. A smaller building will heat up faster than a larger one. Buildings with more insulation heat up and cool off more slowly than buildings with less insulation. Some materials hold in heat better than others. All of these statements apply.

Purpose

Students will learn that cooperative ventures between those who want to protect the rain forest and those who want to use the products from the rain forest can be achieved to the benefit of both.

Content Background

The third-largest rain forest on Earth, and the largest rain forest in the Asia-Pacific region, is in Papua New Guinea. This tropical rain forest has a great diversity of animals and plants, including lowland and mangrove forests, grasslands, alpine vegetation, and savanna woodland. Over half of the species found in this rain forest are endemic to Papua New Guinea. This means that they are found nowhere else in the world. Some species are under the threat of extinction. The culture of the area is a mix of Melanesians, Torres Strait Islanders, and Australian Aboriginals. For the most part, New Guineans still live in tribal societies.

Teaching Strategies

- Have students research the rain forests of the world, including the reasons that humans are so interested in the rain forests from both economic and environmental perspectives.
- Display a large world map and have students place rain forest symbols in locations where rain forests currently exist on Earth. If a particular rain forest is in danger, students should place a red symbol at that location. If the rain forest has not yet been affected by human activities, have students place

Science & the Environment

Preserving the Rain Forest

Papua New Guinea's rain forest is home to a diverse population of living things. Huge butterflies glide through the air along with more than 700 species of tropical birds. This paradise also contains extinct volcanoes and beautiful waterfalls.

Imagine the distress the people of Papua New Guinea must have felt when a multinational petroleum company announced that it had plans to search for oil in their rain forest home. Plans to begin drilling for oil in the Kikori area of Papua New Guinea met with local opposition immediately. The oil company responded by teaming up with the government of Papua New Guinea to develop a comprehensive environmental plan. This plan called for the study of archaeological, cultural, and socioeconomic impacts that the extraction of oil would have on the rain forest. In addition, the company enlisted the help of an international wildlife organization to study the environmental impacts of oil extraction. The Kikori Integrated Conservation and Development Plan is the result of that study. It includes a major biodiversity survey of the area, experimental projects in ecotourism and ecoforestry, and training of personnel in conservation management. The project has now become a model for development in Papua New Guinea.

Protecting the Ecosystem

Since the beginning of oil drilling in the Kikori area, most of the rain forest has been left intact. The clearings for oil drilling equipment are small; only as much room as is needed has been cleared of vegetation. When crews are finished working in an area, it is reseeded with native plants. Only essential roads have been built; most roads are narrow and hard to see from above. Supplies are brought in by boats or seaplanes.

Birds Tell the Tale

Once oil drilling operations in tropical rain forests begin, wildlife often leave. However, in the Kikori area, tropical birds such as the bird of paradise remain. Bird watchers are amazed to see that many endangered species of birds still call the rain forest home. These include the double-wattled cassowary, shown in the photograph above, a flightless bird that is related to emus.

Other Benefits

The oil company has built schools and trained local residents in health and sanitation methods. In addition, the company has donated money to a fund that protects tropical birds. In these ways, oil companies can continue to search for and extract oil while preserving the environment.

Activity

Research the endangered bird species found in Papua New Guinea. Choose one bird species and report on how it nests, what it eats, what part of the rain forest it lives in, and so on. Find a photograph of the bird in a book or go to <u>earthgeu.com</u> and make a drawing of the bird to include in your report.

a green symbol at that location. Ask the class to draw conclusions from the information on the completed map. The threat to rain forests should be apparent. Follow up with a discussion about how this problem can be addressed. Students should then see the importance of the Kikori Integrated Conservation and Development Plan currently being implemented in Papua New Guinea's rain forest.

Activity

There are approximately 700 bird species in Papua New Guinea. Students can find links to sites that have information about bird species in Papua New Guinea by visiting the Earth Science Web Site at <u>earthgeu.com</u>

Summary

CHAPTER 26
Study Guide

SECTION 26.1
Conventional Energy Resources

Main Ideas
- The Sun is the ultimate source of most energy on Earth. The Sun's energy is transferred from photosynthetic organisms to all other living things.
- Materials derived from living things, known as biomass, have been used as renewable fuels by humans for thousands of years.
- Wood continues to serve as a fuel for over half of the world's population.
- Fossil fuels, such as natural gas, coal, and petroleum, formed from organisms that lived millions of years ago. The burning of these fossil fuels releases sulfur into the atmosphere, and thus contributes to air pollution.

Vocabulary
fossil fuel (p. 686)
fuel (p. 684)
peat (p. 686)

SECTION 26.2
Alternative Energy Resources

Main Ideas
- Alternative energy resources, such as solar energy, water, geothermal energy, wind, nuclear energy, and biomass, can supplement dwindling conventional energy resources.
- Solar energy is unlimited, but technological advances are needed to find practical solutions to collect and store it.
- Hydroelectric power is derived from the energy of moving water and is commonly used in the production of electricity. Geothermal energy is a product of Earth's internal heat. Its usefulness is limited to areas where it is found near Earth's surface. Wind is a source of energy in areas that have consistently strong winds.
- Nuclear energy results when atoms of radioactive elements emit particles in the process known as fission.
- Oil shale and tar sand contain secondary oil resources that are expensive to extract.

Vocabulary
biogas (p. 696)
gasohol (p. 696)
geothermal energy (p. 693)
photovoltaic cell (p. 691)

SECTION 26.3
Conservation of Energy Resources

Main Ideas
- Energy resources will last longer if conservation and energy efficiency measures are developed and used. Energy efficiency results in the use of fewer resources to provide more usable energy.
- Cogeneration, in which two usable forms of energy are produced at the same time from the same process, saves resources in the long run.
- The achievement of sustainable energy use will ensure that current and future energy needs are met while maintaining standards of living and at the same time protecting the environment.

Vocabulary
cogeneration (p. 700)
energy efficiency (p. 698)
sustainable energy (p. 703)

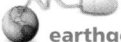
 earthgeu.com/vocabulary_puzzlemaker

Main Ideas

VOCABULARY PuzzleMaker

 For additional help with vocabulary, have students access the Vocabulary Puzzlemaker online.

earthgeu.com/vocabulary puzzlemaker

0:00 *Out of Time?*

If time does not permit teaching the entire chapter, use the GeoDigest at the end of the unit as an overview.

Earth Science Online

Be sure to check the Earth Science Web Site for links to chapter material:
earthgeu.com

Resource Manager

Chapter Assessment, pp. 151–156
MindJogger Videoquizzes DVD/VHS
ExamView® Pro CD-ROM
Performance Assessment in Earth Science

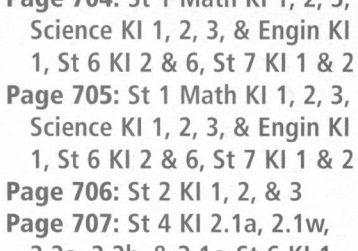
GLENCOE
Technology

Videotape/DVD
MindJogger Videoquizzes
Chapter 26: *Energy Resources*
Have students work in groups as they play the videoquiz game to review key chapter concepts.

NY Core Curriculum Standards

Page 704: St 1 Math KI 1, 2, 3, Science KI 1, 2, 3, & Engin KI 1, St 6 KI 2 & 6, St 7 KI 1 & 2
Page 705: St 1 Math KI 1, 2, 3, Science KI 1, 2, 3, & Engin KI 1, St 6 KI 2 & 6, St 7 KI 1 & 2
Page 706: St 2 KI 1, 2, & 3
Page 707: St 4 KI 2.1a, 2.1w, 2.2a, 2.2b, & 3.1c, St 6 KI 1, 4, 5, & 6, St 7 KI 1 & 2

Understanding Main Ideas

1. c
2. a
3. d
4. d
5. a
6. b
7. d
8. b
9. d
10. c
11. b
12. b
13. a

Applying Main Ideas

14. To be useful as an energy source, wind must be consistent and steady. Winds in the northeastern part of the United States don't meet these criteria.

15. It is hard to store solar energy, and on overcast days, other energy sources must be used.

16. Oil shale must be mined and processed to retrieve the oil. Both oil shale and coal have to be located and mined out of the ground as a solid.

Understanding Main Ideas

1. What is the ultimate source of most energy on Earth?
   a. tides   c. the Sun
   b. radioactivity d. the mantle

2. Which product can be made from crude oil?
   a. kerosene   c. cornmeal
   b. peat   d. biogas

3. Which is NOT derived from living things?
   a. petroleum   c. peat
   b. coal   d. photovoltaic cells

4. Which is NOT a biomass energy resource?
   a. wood   c. fecal material
   b. sugar cane   d. wind

5. In which process is the Sun's energy captured and used for food production in living things?
   a. photosynthesis c. radioactivity
   b. respiration   d. combustion

6. What organic fuel is derived from moss and other bog plants?
   a. bagasse   c. biogas
   b. peat   d. oil shale

7. Which is NOT a fossil fuel?
   a. crude oil   c. lignite
   b. bituminous coal d. biogas

8. What percentage of the world's electricity is provided by falling water?
   a. 50 percent   c. 30 percent
   b. 20 percent   d. 60 percent

9. How many nuclear reactors are producing electricity in the world today?
   a. 25   c. 17
   b. 50   d. 424

---

10. Which is NOT a type of fuel?
    a. wood   c. the Sun
    b. kerosene   d. coal

Use the diagram to answer questions 11, 12, and 13.

11. The diagram represents a house in New York with a glass-enclosed porch. Which direction should the porch be facing to take advantage of passive solar heating?
    a. north   c. east
    b. south   d. west

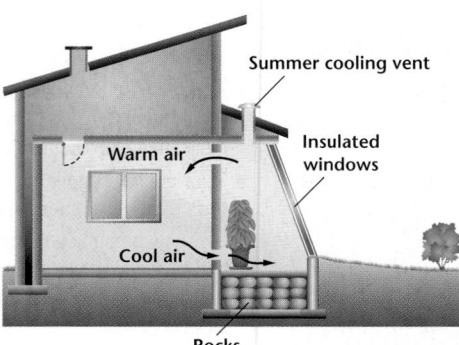

Summer cooling vent

Insulated windows

Warm air

Cool air

Rocks

12. What material should be used as flooring in the porch to reduce the need for a furnace to heat the room?
    a. wall-to-wall carpeting c. oak
    b. slate   d. vinyl tile

THE PRINCETON REVIEW — **Test-Taking Tip**

DIAGRAMS If a test question requires you to understand a diagram, check the labels carefully. Then test yourself by mentally explaining the diagram.

---

17. • Use more energy-efficient appliances.
    • Use appliances for less time.
    • Do things manually instead of using electrical appliances.
    • Insulate the home better to hold in heat.
    • Replace old windows.

18. Accidents at nuclear power plants that have harmed and killed people, as well as problems with the storage of radioactive wastes, have led to a general belief that nuclear energy is no longer the panacea it once was thought to be.

13. To make full use of the energy-conservation abilities of this house, what landscape plants should be planted in front of the porch?
  a. tall deciduous trees
  b. short evergreen bushes
  c. short evergreen trees
  d. ornamental grasses

Applying Main Ideas

14. Why isn't wind energy used to provide electricity in most parts of the northeastern United States?

15. What are two problems associated with the use of solar energy?

16. How is the production of oil from oil shale similar to coal mining?

17. Describe five ways in which you could improve energy efficiency in your home.

18. Explain why nuclear energy is no longer considered to be a solution to providing for the world's energy needs.

Thinking Critically

19. How can a household that uses only electricity be responsible for depleting fossil fuel reserves?

20. Why is the deforestation of tropical rain forests a global concern?

21. What might be some negative consequences of a nation being dependent on foreign energy resources?

22. Explain how using closed containers in geothermal reservoirs is similar to saving energy in cogeneration.

THE PRINCETON REVIEW **Test Practice**

INTERPRETING SCIENTIFIC ILLUSTRATIONS
Use the illustration below to answer questions 1 and 2.

1. How could this kitchen be made more energy efficient?
  a. by maintaining older appliances instead of replacing them with newer ones
  b. by replacing the fluorescent light bulb with an incandescent one
  c. by washing the dishes in the dishwasher instead of the sink
  d. by replacing the old windows with newer ones

2. If this kitchen was located in a house in China, which alternative energy source would most likely be used in it?
  a. bagasse   **c.** gasohol
  b. biogas   **d.** oil shale

3. Which type of coal is the most efficient and burns most cleanly?
  a. peat   **c.** bituminous coal
  b. lignite   **d.** anthracite

4. Which is NOT a good way to conserve transportation energy?
  a. drive at a lower speed
  b. make frequent stops
  c. work from home
  d. use a hybrid or electric car

Assessment **709**

Thinking Critically

19. Many electrical generating plants use coal as a fuel.

20. Deforestation reduces the number of trees on Earth available to use the carbon dioxide present in the atmosphere. Increasing levels of carbon dioxide are thought to contribute to global warming. In addition, the loss of forests reduces the habitats for many forms of wildlife and thus reduces biodiversity. Specialized products derived from rain forests will no longer be available and soil erosion will increase. Changing one portion or aspect of Earth can affect Earth as a whole.

21. Dependency on foreign energy supplies may result in inconsistent supplies of the resource and no control over costs.

22. Using closed containers to hold geothermal water and steam allows for the transfer of heat to another source that can be used for another purpose. As in cogeneration, the same energy can be used for more than one purpose.

EXAMVIEW® PRO

Use Exam*View*® Pro Testmaker CD-ROM to:

- Create **multiple versions** of tests.
- Create **modified** tests with one mouse click for struggling students.
- **Edit** existing questions and add your own questions.
- **Build** tests based on national curriculum standards.

Standardized Test Practice

1. d
2. b
3. d
4. b

Human Impact on Earth Resources

Refer to pages 8T–9T of the Teacher Guide for an explanation of the National Science Content Standards correlations.

Section	Objectives	National Science Content Standards	State/Local Standards
SECTION 27.1 **Populations and the Use of Natural Resources** ⏱ 1 session 📦 1 block	1. **Summarize** the typical pattern of the population growth of organisms. 2. **Describe** what happens to populations when they reach carrying capacity. 3. **Identify** environmental factors that affect population growth.	F.2, F.3, F.4, F.5, F.6	St 1 Science KI 1 & 2, St 6 KI 1, 2, 5, & 6, St 7 KI 1 & 2
SECTION 27.2 **Human Impact on Land Resources** ⏱ 1 session 📦 ½ block	4. **Describe** the environmental impact of mineral extraction. 5. **Discuss** the environmental problems created by agriculture and forestry, and their solutions. 6. **Explain** the environmental impact of urban development.	UCP.2; C.4; F.3, F.4, F.5, F.6	St 1 Engin KI 1, St 6 KI 1, 2, 4, 5, & 6, St 7 KI 1 & 2
SECTION 27.3 **Human Impact on Air Resources** ⏱ 1 session 📦 ½ block	7. **Describe** the types and sources of air pollution. 8. **Differentiate** between the greenhouse effect and global warming. 9. **Sequence** the reactions that occur as CFCs cause ozone depletion. 10. **Identify** the causes and effects of acid precipitation.	UCP.2, UCP.3; B.3; F.4, F.5, F.6	St 1 Engin KI 1, St 4 KI 2.2d, St 6 KI 2 & 5, St 7 KI 1
SECTION 27.4 **Human Impact on Water Resources** ⏱ 2 sessions 📦 1½ blocks	11. **Summarize** the types and sources of water pollution. 12. **Describe** some methods of controlling water pollution. 13. **Identify** ways to conserve water.	UCP.2, UCP.3; A.2; C.4; F.2, F.3, F.4, F.5, F.6	St 1 Science KI 1 St 1 Engin KI 1, St 4 KI 2.2d, St 6 KI 2, 5, & 6, St 7 KI 1 & 2

A complete Planning Guide is provided on pages 30T–32T.

⏱ The number of recommended single-period sessions

📦 The number of recommended blocks

Activity Materials

Discovery Lab *page 711*
paper, pencil, various items found in pockets and backpacks of students

GeoLab *pages 734–735*
metric ruler, pencil

MiniLab *page 718*
paper plate, paper napkin, plastic knife, two iced, cream-filled cupcakes

Demo *page 725*
thermometer, glass jar or aquarium with tight lid

page 727
limestone, 10 percent hydrochloric acid solution

page 731
250 mL beakers (3), food coloring, water, soil

Need materials? Contact Science Kit at 1-800-828-7777 or at www.sciencekit.com on the Internet. For alternate materials, see the activity on the listed page.

Key to Teaching Strategies

- **L1** Level 1 activities should be appropriate for students with learning difficulties.
- **L2** Level 2 activities should be within the ability range of all students.
- **L3** Level 3 activities are designed for above-average students.
- **ELL** ELL activities should be within the ability range of English-language learners.
- **COOP LEARN** Cooperative learning activities are designed for small-group work.
- **P** These strategies represent student products that can be placed in a best-work portfolio.
- 📦 These strategies are useful in a block-scheduling format.

Chapter Organizer

Glencoe Exclusive!
TeacherWorks™
All-In-One Planner and Resource Center

Activities/Features	Reproducible Masters	Transparencies
Discovery Lab: A Pocketful of Resources, p. 711	**Study Guide for Content Mastery** pp. 169–170 **L2** **Exploring Environmental Problems,** pp. 37–40 **L2**	**Section Focus Transparency 85** **L1** **ELL** **Teaching Transparency 82** **L2** **ELL**
MiniLab: Reclamation, p. 718 **Using Math:** Finding Percentages, p. 721	**Study Guide for Content Mastery,** pp. 171–172 **L2** **GeoLab and MiniLab Worksheets,** p. 107 **L2** **Laboratory Manual,** pp. 209–212 **L2** **Exploring Environmental Problems,** pp. 29–32, 33–36 **L2**	**Section Focus Transparency 86** **L1** **ELL** **Teaching Transparency 83** **L2** **ELL**
Problem-Solving Lab: Using Graphs, p. 728	**Study Guide for Content Mastery,** p. 173 **L2** **Exploring Environmental Problems,** pp. 17–20, 21–24 **L2**	**Section Focus Transparency 87** **L1** **ELL** **Teaching Transparency 84** **L2** **ELL**
GeoLab: Pinpointing a Source of Pollution, pp. 734–735 **Science & the Environment:** Methane Hydrates: Hope or Hype?, p. 736	**Study Guide for Content Mastery,** p. 174 **L2** **Laboratory Manual,** pp. 213–216 **L2** **GeoLab and MiniLab Worksheets,** pp. 108–110 **L2**	**Section Focus Transparency 88** **L1** **ELL** **Teaching Transparency 85** **L2** **ELL**

Assessment

Chapter Assessment, pp. 157–162
Performance Assessment in the Science Classroom (PASC)
MindJogger Videoquiz DVD/VHS
Performance Assessment in Earth Science
ExamView® Pro CD-ROM
5 Days to the Regents Exam

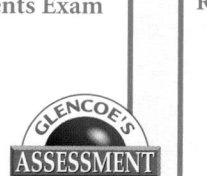

Additional Resources

Guided Reading Audio Program **ELL**
Cooperative Learning in the Science Classroom **COOP LEARN**
Lesson Plans
Block Scheduling
earthgeu.com
NY Lesson Plans
NY Block Scheduling
Review Handbook for Regents Earth Science Exam

NATIONAL GEOGRAPHIC

Teacher's Corner

Products Available from National Geographic Society
To order the following products, call the National Geographic Society at 1-800-368-2728:
Videos
Pollution: World at Risk
Recycling: The Endless Circle

Fresh Water: Resource at Risk
Toxic S.W.A.T.
Technology's Price
Healing the Earth
Curriculum Kits
GeoKit: *Pollution*

Chapter 27 Human Impact on Earth Resources

Content Background

Managing Population Growth
Section 27.1

Fifty years ago, the populations of many developing countries entered a period of exponential growth. This was a result of a combination of advances in agriculture and improvements in the availability of medical care. Mortality rates began to fall, while fertility rates did not. Developing countries took one of two approaches to population growth. Countries such as South Korea, Taiwan, and Thailand mounted efforts to reduce family size. This led to a cycle of higher savings, higher living standards, and falling fertility rates. Other developing countries, particularly India and those located in Africa, maintained high birth rates. Rising populations are currently overwhelming these countries. Governments are unable to either provide schooling and jobs or deal with the environmental effects of overpopulation.

Bioremediation
Section 27.2

Bioremediation is rapidly becoming one of the most effective ways to clean up pollution from toxic metals and organic compounds. Bioremediation typically takes one of two forms: augmentation or stimulation. During augmentation, organisms are added to the contaminated site. During stimulation, nutrients are provided that stimulate the growth of organisms that are already present. Both naturally occurring and genetically modified bacteria have successfully been used in bioremediation. Some of these microbes have enzymes that chemically reduce toxic cations of metals to much less toxic and less soluble forms. One branch of bioremediation called phytoremediation uses plants instead of bacteria. Plants have been used to remove toxic selenium from soils in Central California. More recently, crabgrass, normally considered a weed, is showing great potential in cleaning up heavily oil-polluted soils around wellheads in Texas and Arkansas.

Indoor Air Pollution
Section 27.3

Recent studies have indicated that air within buildings can be more polluted than outside air. Many people spend approximately 90 percent of their time indoors, so the risk to health from indoor air pollution may be greater than from

Multiple Learning Styles

- **Kinesthetic** Modeling, p. 714
- **Visual-Spatial** Activity, pp. 719, 722, Project, p. 727
- **Interpersonal** Collaborative Learning, p. 720, Project, p. 725
- **Intrapersonal** Enrichment, pp. 712, 731, Activity, p. 724
- **Linguistic** Enrichment, p. 714, Reteach, p. 723
- **Logical-Mathematical** Reteach, p. 715

GLENCOE
Technology

The following multimedia resources are available from Glencoe.

The Infinite Voyage Series
Life in the Balance
Crisis in the Atmosphere

Vocabulary Puzzlemaker

TeacherWorks™ CD-ROM

MindJogger Videoquizzes DVD/VHS

ExamView® Pro CD-ROM

Interactive Chalkboard CD-ROM

outside air pollution. In addition, people who are exposed to indoor air pollution for the longest periods—infants, the elderly, and the chronically ill—are often those most susceptible. Indoor air pollution is caused by sources that release gases or particulate matter combined with inadequate ventilation. Sources of indoor air pollution include combustion sources such as oil, gas, kerosene, wood, and tobacco; pressed-wood building materials; damp carpets; cleaning products, air fresheners, and outdoor air pollution that is trapped indoors.

Mining Aquifers
Section 27.4

One of the most serious environmental challenges that humans will face in the coming years is the depletion of underground water supplies. Some farmers use deep wells and powerful pumps to pull groundwater to the surface for the irrigation of crops in regions where rainfall is inadequate. In many cases, the water is used faster than it is recharged, and water tables are steadily dropping. These farmers are essentially mining the aquifers. In some parts of India and China, the water tables are dropping by 1m/year. In the United States, the most serious groundwater depletion is from the Ogallala Aquifer, located beneath central and southwestern states. When water tables drop too low, farmers must abandon their fields. This puts a large portion of the world's food production in jeopardy. The Ogallala Aquifer provides water for 20 percent of the land that is irrigated in the United States. In India, 25 percent of the grain production is in danger. In light of rising populations, the loss of these irrigated lands could create serious food shortages in some countries.

Identifying Misconceptions

Most students underestimate the amount of solid waste that they generate. One way to correct this misconception is to have students carry a bag in which they put all their trash for one day. Make sure students consider solid wastes they generate that they cannot carry in a plastic bag, such as bulk food containers used in the school cafeteria and cleaning compounds. Another way is to have students realize how much trash is generated by the school each week by observing the dumpsters before trash-pickup day.

✔ Assessment

Portfolio Assessment
Problem-Solving Lab, TWE, p. 728
GeoLab, TWE, pp. 734–735

Performance Assessment
Discovery Lab, TWE, p. 711
Discovery Lab, SE, p. 711
Assessment TWE, p. 729
MiniLab, SE, p. 718
GeoLab, SE, pp. 734–735

Knowledge Assessment
Section Assessment, SE, pp. 715, 723, 729, 733
Chapter Assessment, SE, pp. 738–739
MiniLab, TWE, p. 718
Assessment, TWE, pp. 723, 726

Skill Assessment
Assessment, TWE, pp. 715, 733

Be sure to check the Earth Science Web Site for links to chapter material: earthgeu.com

Introducing the Chapter

Have students make a list of ten ways that humans impact Earth and evaluate each in terms of its positive or negative impact. Ask students what determines the level of impact, and whether the impacts discussed are permanent or temporary.

Interpreting the Photo

The photo illustrates Central Park in New York City. Although students cannot observe human activities in the photo, they should be able to infer the types of activities that take place in the park.

Chapter Themes

The following themes from the National Science Content Standards are covered in this chapter. Refer to page 8T of the Teacher Guide for an explanation of the correlations.
Systems, order, and organization (UCP.1); Evidence, models, and explanations (UCP.2); Change, constancy, and measurement (UPC.3); Evolution and equilibrium (UCP.4)

⏱ Out of Time?

If time does not permit teaching the entire chapter, use the Chapter Summary on page 737 and the GeoDigest found at the end of the unit as an overview.

What You'll Learn
- Why all populations require natural resources to exist.
- How the use of natural resources affects Earth's land, air, and water.

Why It's Important
As a result of increasing human population growth, natural resources are being used at increasing rates. The development and use of natural resources may have impacts upon the environment. Humans need to find ways to extract and use natural resources that minimize these impacts.

Earth Science Online

To learn more about human impact on natural resources, visit the Earth Science Web Site at earthgeu.com

710

Human Impact on Earth Resources

Discovery Lab

Process Skills
observe and infer, collect and interpret data, make and use tables **L1** **ELL** 🔲

Alternative Materials
Small objects from the classroom may be used.

Preparation
Organize several boxes of small, everyday objects if you are going to supply items to the students.

Procedure
- Ask a student to define *renewable resources* and *nonrenewable resources*.
- Discuss with the class materials that can easily be recycled, such as paper, metals, and glass.

Troubleshooting
- It may be difficult for students to determine where items were made. In this case, students can consult with other groups.

Observe
Answers will vary depending upon the collection of objects. Typically, students will observe metals,

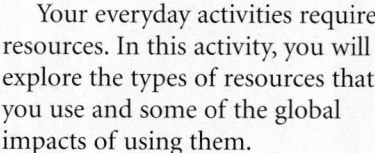

Discovery Lab

A Pocketful of Resources

Your everyday activities require resources. In this activity, you will explore the types of resources that you use and some of the global impacts of using them.

1. Make a pile of 10 to 15 items that you brought into the classroom.

2. Combine your pile with those of two or three other students so that you have about 30 different items.

3. In your science journal, make a data table for your items.

4. For each item, record as much of the following information as you can.

- What resources were used to make the item?
- Are the resources renewable or nonrenewable?
- Where was the item made?

CAUTION: Always wear an apron and safety goggles in the lab.

Observe How many different resources are represented by the items in your collection? What are the percentages of renewable and nonrenewable resources? Where were each of the objects made?

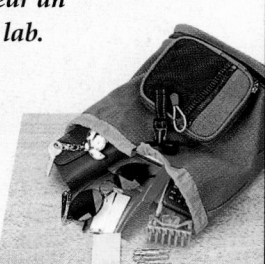

SECTION 27.1

Populations and the Use of Natural Resources

OBJECTIVES

- **Summarize** the typical pattern of the population growth of organisms.
- **Describe** what happens to populations when they reach carrying capacity.
- **Identify** environmental factors that affect population growth.

VOCABULARY

exponential growth
carrying capacity
density-independent factor
density-dependent factor

Suppose you and some of your friends plan to spend a day at the park. Some of your friends start a volleyball game, while others unpack the cooler and light the barbecue. Later on, maybe all of you will go for a bicycle ride. Did you know that in each of these activities you and your friends would be using natural resources?

RESOURCES AND ORGANISMS

Take a deep breath right now, then let it out again. When you inhale, you take oxygen gas out of the air and into the cells of the blood vessels in your lungs. When you exhale, you release oxygen and carbon dioxide gas and water vapor back into the air. Oxygen, carbon dioxide, and water are examples of natural resources that you, as well as many other living things, use every day.

Like all organisms, you need particular natural resources to maintain life, grow, and reproduce. Among the resources that organisms require are air, food, water, and, in some cases, shelter. To meet their

27.1 Populations and the Use of Natural Resources **711**

---

paper, plastics, cloth such as cotton and wool, leather, rubber, and synthetic fabrics. The collection of objects should reflect a global impact.

✓ Assessment

Performance Have each pair of students select some aspect of their data and make a bar graph. Examples include the number of items made in different parts of the world and the number of items made of different materials. Use the Performance Task Assessment List for Graph from Data in **PASC,** p. 39.

Resource Manager

Study Guide for Content Mastery,
  pp. 169–170 L2

Section Focus Transparency 85 L1 ELL

Exploring Environmental Problems,
  pp. 37–40 L2

Section 27.1

Prepare

Section Background

For section content background, refer to **Managing Population Growth** on page 710C.

Preplanning

Refer to the Chapter Organizer on pages 710A–B.

1 Focus

Section Focus

Before presenting the lesson, display **Section Focus Transparency 85** on the overhead projector. L1 ELL

Tying to Previous Knowledge

Students should be able to recall that the primary components of the air we breathe are oxygen, carbon dioxide, nitrogen, and water vapor.

NY Core Curriculum Standards

Page 710: St 6 KI 5 & 6, St 7 KI 1 & 2

Page 711: St 1 Science KI 1 & 2, St 6 KI 2

Enrichment

Intrapersonal Some people believe that genetically engineered plants are needed to increase crop yields to meet the growing demand for food. Other people insist that these plants pose a significant environmental hazard. Ask students to research the pros and cons of this issue and form opinions about which side they agree with. **L2** **P**

Enrichment

Have students research termite mounds to find out why termites alter their environment in this way and what advantages it offers.

Figure 27-1 Some organisms alter their environment to better provide for their needs. In the middle of their newly created ponds, beavers build domed lodges where they live, nest, and raise their young **(A)**. Tropical termites are highly social organisms that live in colonies where each termite has an assigned role that helps the society survive **(B)**.

basic needs, most organisms are adapted to their immediate environment; they live in a balance with the natural resources their environment provides. For example, songbirds live in grassy meadows, forage for grass seeds to eat, weave nests out of dried grasses and twigs, and drink water from ponds or streams nearby. Painted turtles live in ponds, swamps, and slow-moving streams, where they eat aquatic plants, insects, and other small animals.

Other organisms, however, alter their environment to better meet their needs. For example, beavers build dams across streams to create ponds where none previously existed. Such alteration of the environment has both positive and negative impacts: it kills some trees and displaces both aquatic and terrestrial organisms, but at the same time, it creates a new wetland environment for other organisms. Termites in tropical areas also create environments that are favorable to themselves by building tall mounds. Both a beaver dam and a termite mound, shown in *Figure 27-1,* alter the environment to provide for the basic needs of the organisms that build them. Many other organisms alter their environments to improve their chances of survival. For example, corals build huge, underwater reefs that provide homes for all kinds of marine organisms. Of all organisms, however, humans have an unequaled capacity to modify their environments. This capacity allows us to live in every terrestrial environment on Earth. As a result, humans also have the greatest impact on Earth's natural resources.

RESOURCES AND POPULATION GROWTH

Any type of organism can have an impact on its environment if its population becomes large enough. For example, your consumption of oxygen and release of carbon dioxide usually has little effect on your

Differentiated Instruction

Learning Disabled Have students breathe onto a mirror to observe the resulting condensation. This will provide visual proof that water vapor is being released into the surrounding air and impacting the local environment.

Resource Manager

Teaching Transparency 82 **L2** **ELL**

NY Core Curriculum Standards

Page 712: St 6 KI 1
Page 713: St 6 KI 1, 2, & 6

Figure 27-2 A large elephant population can damage natural resources, such as forests and riverbeds, which other populations depend upon for survival.

immediate environment. However, if you were in a closed room crowded with people, there would soon be less oxygen and more carbon dioxide than the amount people are used to. If no additional fresh air entered the room, everyone eventually would become uncomfortable and would leave the room. As any population increases, its demand for natural resources increases as well. *Figure 27-2* illustrates what happens when an elephant population exceeds the ability of the environment to provide the necessary natural resources.

Population growth is defined as an increase in the size of a population over time. A graph of a growing population resembles a J-shaped curve at first. Whether the population is one of dandelions in a lawn, squirrels in a city park, or herring gulls on an isolated island, the initial increase in population is small because the number of adults capable of reproducing is low. As the number of reproducing adults increases, however, the rate of population growth increases rapidly. The population then experiences **exponential growth,** a pattern of growth in which a population grows faster as it increases in size. As shown in *Figure 27-3,* exponential growth results in a population explosion.

LIMITS TO POPULATION GROWTH

If the graph in *Figure 27-3* was extended for a longer period of time, what do you think would happen to the size of the population? Would it continue to grow exponentially? Many of Earth's natural resources are in limited supply, and therefore, most populations cannot continue to grow forever. Eventually, one or more *limiting factors,* such as the

Figure 27-3 This graph shows a rapid increase over time in the population of bacteria after just a few individuals were added to a petri dish full of necessary nutrients.

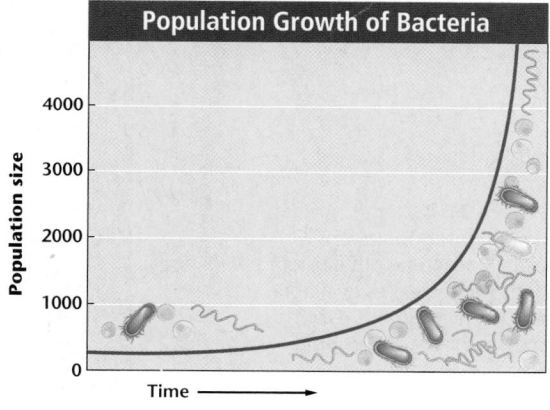

Population Growth of Bacteria

Interpreting the Photo

Figure 27-2 Have students study the photo, which shows environmental damage caused by elephants. Ask students to identify the types of damage shown in the photo. Ask students the following questions. How have the elephants caused this damage? How is the damage related to population density?

Discussion

Ask students whether they can think of any other examples of exponential growth. Some examples are radioactive decay and half-lives of radioactive elements, nuclear reactions, the change in the intensity of light with distance, the velocity of a falling object, and earthquake-magnitude scales.

Across the Curriculum

Biology In addition to exhaling gases, humans also release heat into the environment. Have students research metabolic processes to find answers to the following questions. Where does this heat come from? The heat comes from chemical reactions as humans break down their food. How is the heat generated? Most of the heat is generated by muscular activity. Can the amount of heat vary from person to person? Yes; a person at rest will generate less heat than a person exercising. Also, a large person will generate more heat than a smaller person.

Differentiated Instruction

Gifted Fire ants are an imported species that is causing serious problems in the United States. Have students research fire ants and give short presentations to the class in which they answer the following questions. Where did the ants come from? How quickly are they spreading? What impacts are they having on ecosystems? Why haven't the populations of fire ants reached carrying capacity?

Modeling

Kinesthetic Have students place about 30 paper clips in a shoebox lid and shake the lid. Then have them place the lid flat on a desk and remove any paper clips that are touching one another. Have students repeat the shaking and removal, and keep track of how many paper clips they remove each time. Then, ask students the following questions. Does the number of paper clips removed increase or decrease? decrease Is this shaking and removal an example of a density-dependent or density-independent factor? density-dependent How could you model a density-independent factor? drop the lid and turn it upside down

Enrichment

Linguistic Ask students to find out whether the population growth curves for individual countries match the overall curve shown in the text. Have students research and report on population graphs for several countries. L3

Figure Caption Question

Figure 27-5 What does this graph tell you about the growth of the human population on Earth? The human population on Earth is still experiencing exponential growth.

NY Core Curriculum Standards

Page 714: St 6 KI 2 & 5
Page 715: St 6 KI 5

availability of food, water, or clean air, will cause a population to stop increasing. This leveling-off of population size results in an S-shaped curve, similar to the one in *Figure 27-4.*

The number of organisms that any given environment can support is its **carrying capacity.** When population size has not yet reached the carrying capacity of a particular environment, there will continue to be more births than deaths. If the population size exceeds the carrying capacity temporarily, the number of deaths will increase, or the number of births will decrease, until the population size returns to the carrying capacity. A population that is at the carrying capacity for its environment is in equilibrium. It continues to fluctuate around the carrying capacity as long as natural resources remain available.

Environmental Limits Have you ever seen television or newspaper coverage of the aftermath of a tornado or other violent storm? Storms are environmental factors that limit population growth. Environmental factors that affect population growth, such as storms, extreme changes in temperatures, droughts, floods, and pollution, are **density-independent factors.** These factors affect all populations that they come in contact with, regardless of population size. A flood affects not only the humans whose homes are destroyed, but also trees, birds, and many other populations of organisms.

Other environmental factors that affect population growth, such as disease, parasites, and lack of food, are called **density-dependent factors.** Density-dependent factors increasingly affect a population as the population's size increases. For example, in a large population members may live close together. This enables disease organisms to spread quickly from one member of the population to another. If a population is very dense, disease may wipe out the entire population.

Figure 27-4 Under normal conditions, populations usually reach an equilibrium with the resources available in the environment. From that point on, the population size will fluctuate around the carrying capacity.

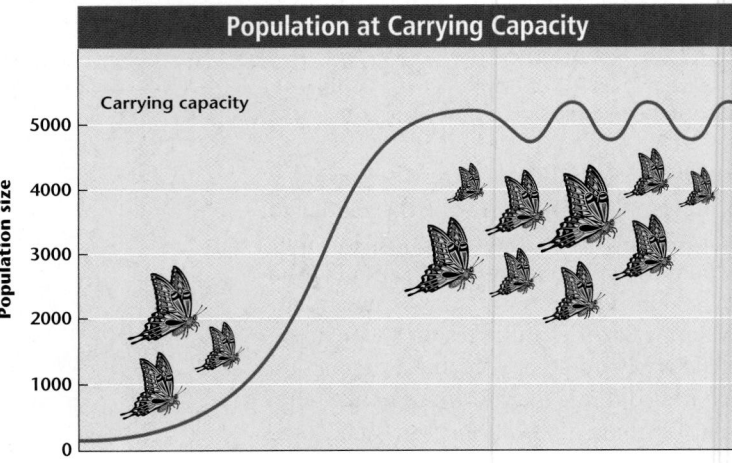

Population at Carrying Capacity

714 CHAPTER 27 *Human Impact on Earth Resources*

Across the Curriculum

Math Ask students to solve the following problems. A species of bacteria divides every ten minutes. If there is one bacterium to begin with, how many will there be after one hour? $2^6 = 64$ bacteria After six hours? $2^{36} = 68.7$ million bacteria

Earth Science

Journal

Ask students to write a paragraph about what life would be like in the United States if the population doubled just ten years from now. Have them include their paragraphs in their science journals.

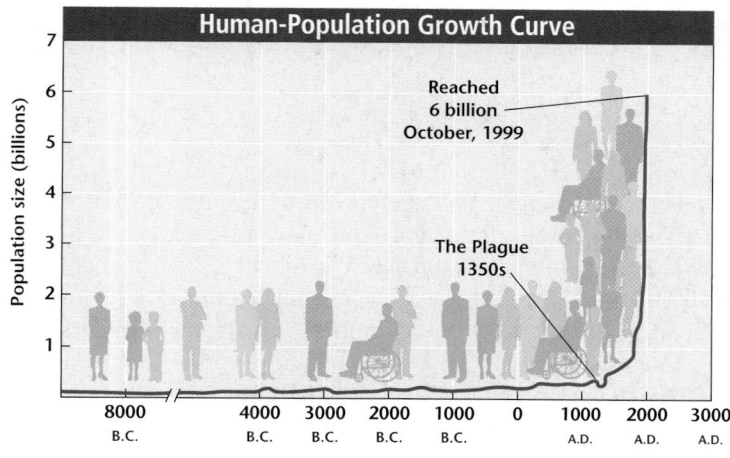

Human-Population Growth Curve

Population size (billions): 1–7

8000 B.C., 4000 B.C., 3000 B.C., 2000 B.C., 1000 B.C., 0, 1000 A.D., 2000 A.D., 3000 A.D.

Reached 6 billion October, 1999

The Plague 1350s

Figure 27-5 A graph of human-population growth still shows a J-shaped curve. *What does this graph tell you about the growth of the human population on Earth?*

HUMAN POPULATION GROWTH

No matter where you live, you probably have seen an increase during your lifetime in the number of cars, houses, and roads. The human population on Earth is still growing. As shown in *Figure 27-5,* the growth curve of the human population is still in the J-shaped stage. The human population is expected to continue to grow for at least another 50 years.

Although the human population has not yet reached the carrying capacity of Earth, the current rate of growth clearly cannot continue forever. As the population continues to increase, human demand for natural resources also will continue to increase steadily. Although humans are not the most abundant species on Earth, our use of natural resources has impacted the environment on a global scale. ❧

SECTION ASSESSMENT

1. Why do populations stop increasing when they reach carrying capacity?

2. Explain why a hurricane is a density-independent factor that limits population growth.

3. Suppose that a small population of bacteria is placed in a petri dish with limited nutrients. Predict how the population will change over time.

4. **Thinking Critically** What might happen if a human population temporarily exceeded the carrying capacity of an area?

SKILL REVIEW

5. **Making Graphs** Make a graph that extends the human-population growth curve shown in *Figure 27-5.* Base your graph on the assumption that the carrying capacity of Earth for humans will be reached in the year 2150. For more help, refer to the *Skill Handbook.*

earthgeu.com/self_check_quiz

27.1 *Populations and the Use of Natural Resources* **715**

SECTION ASSESSMENT

1. Once carrying capacity is reached, available resources will not support larger populations, and births are balanced by deaths.

2. A hurricane is a density-independent factor because the amount of destruction does not depend on population density. A hurricane affects all populations in an area regardless of size or type.

3. The bacteria population will grow slowly at first, then exponentially. As the nutrients begin to run out, the population will reach a maximum and then quickly decrease when all the nutrients have been consumed.

4. Unless resources can be imported, or humans migrate to another area, the human population will decrease as people die from starvation, exposure, disease, and so on.

5. Student graphs should extend the current J-shaped population curve into an S-shaped curve that levels off around the year 2150.

3 Assess

Check for Understanding
Activity
Have students each sketch a copy of **Figure 27-5** and superimpose a line on the graph that represents the rate of resource demand. Ask students whether it is possible for resource demand to increase faster than the population increases. Ask them whether the reverse is also possible and to explain why or why not. A line representing resource demand would most likely mirror the population growth curve. However, the amount of resources consumed per person can increase. In this case, the resource curve will increase faster than the population curve. If attempts are made to conserve resources, the per capita consumption can decrease and the resource curve will decrease more slowly than the population curve.

Reteach
Logical-Mathematical Ask students how many breaths they take per minute. Have them calculate how many breaths the class takes per minute. Then, ask them to identify the resource being consumed when this population breathes. Finally, ask how this is related to populations and resource demand. L2

✓Assessment
Skill Have students make a list of the factors that can affect human populations and identify each as density-dependent or density-independent.

715

Section 27.2

Prepare

Section Background

For section content background, refer to **Bioremediation** on page 710C.

Preplanning

Refer to the Chapter Organizer on pages 710A–B.

1 Focus

Section Focus

Before presenting the lesson, display **Section Focus Transparency 86** on the overhead projector.
L1 **ELL**

Tying to Previous Knowledge

Have students refer back to Chapter 6. Ask students what type of sediments sand and gravel are. clastic sediments Ask them where they would expect to find large deposits of these materials for mining. along high-energy rivers near mountains, glacial outwash plains, and coastlines

SECTION 27.2

Human Impact on Land Resources

OBJECTIVES

- **Describe** *the environmental impact of mineral extraction.*
- **Discuss** *the environmental problems created by agriculture and forestry, and their solutions.*
- **Explain** *the environmental impact of urban development.*

VOCABULARY

reclamation
biodiversity
monoculture
deforestation
bioremediation

How much land do you think is necessary to grow the food and provide the other materials that you consume and use? Each year, a typical person in North America consumes resources equal to the renewable yield from approximately 5 ha (about 12.35 acres) of forest and farmland. Through our use of mineral resources, food, lumber, and living space, humans have a significant impact on Earth's surface.

EXTRACTION OF MINERAL RESOURCES

Do you spend much time talking on the telephone? Perhaps you use a microwave oven to heat up after-school snacks. Many of the materials in telephones and microwave ovens are derived from land. Modern societies require huge amounts of land resources, including iron, aluminum, copper, sand, gravel, and limestone. Unfortunately, the extraction of these resources often disturbs large areas of Earth's surface. Finding a balance between the need for mineral resources and controlling the environmental change caused by extraction can be difficult.

Surface Mining Mineral and ore deposits found just beneath Earth's surface, such as iron, bauxite (aluminum ore), copper, coal, and gold, can be extracted through mining techniques that involve removing huge amounts of overlying soil and rock, as shown in *Figure 27-6.* Unfortunately, extracting land resources in this way completely changes the landscape.

Figure 27-6 Surface-mining techniques include strip-mining and open-pit mining. In a coal strip-mine, surface material up to 60-m deep may be removed to expose the coal seam below **(A).** In an open-pit mine, the mineral resources are extracted from the surface downward, and a gaping hole is gouged into Earth's surface **(B).**

Resource Manager

GeoLab and MiniLab Worksheets, p. 107 **L2**

Study Guide for Content Mastery, pp. 171–172 **L2**

Section Focus Transparency 86 **L1** **ELL**

Underground Mining Underground mining, also called subsurface mining, is used where mineral resources lie deep under the ground. Underground mining is less disruptive to Earth's surface than surface mining, but it still has impacts on the environment. For example, although the underground mine in *Figure 27-7* cannot be seen, the mountains of waste rock dug from under the ground are clearly visible. Rainwater seeping through these piles of mining waste can dissolve toxic metals as well as other chemicals and move them into nearby streams and rivers, where they will cause water pollution. Although many mining companies build large holding ponds to contain polluted water until it can be treated, these ponds sometimes leak.

Responsible mining companies make efforts to protect the land during mining operations. In the United States, the Surface Mining Control and Reclamation Act of 1977 requires mining companies to restore the land to its original contours and to replant vegetation in the process of **reclamation.** *Figure 27-8* shows a strip-mined area both before and after reclamation. Although reclamation repairs much of the damage that surface mining causes, it can be extremely difficult to restore land to its original contours, as you will discover in the *MiniLab* on the following page.

Figure 27-7 Much of the material brought to the surface of underground mines is waste material that must be removed before miners can extract the mineral resource.

Figure 27-8 Layers of soil and rock have been stripped away to expose the coal in this strip mine **(A).** During reclamation, soil and rock are replaced and the area is replanted **(B).**

2 Teach

Content Background

Abandoned mines may be more of an environmental danger than operating mines are. It is estimated that there are about 16 000 abandoned mines in the western United States, each of which poses serious water contamination problems. In most cases, the original mine operators are no longer in business, so cleanup costs will have to be borne by the public. To restore these sites will require a tremendous amount of tax dollars.

Discussion

Ask students whether reclamation could work for underground mining as well as surface mining. It would not work very well; it would be expensive to put all the rocks back underground, and they would not all fit because there would be additional air spaces between the rocks and between broken particles.

NY Core Curriculum Standards

Page 716: St 6 KI 4
Page 717: St 1 Engin KI 1, St 6 KI 6, St 7 KI 1 & 2

Purpose

Students will model the process of reclamation after strip-mining.

Process Skills

acquire and analyze information, apply concepts, draw a conclusion

Materials

paper plate, paper napkin, plastic knife, two iced, cream-filled cupcakes

Teaching Strategies

- If supplies are short, this lab may be done as a demo for the class.
- You may prefer to have several cupcakes wrapped in clear plastic to use for comparisons to cut cupcakes.
- Have students work in groups of two to four.

Safety Precautions

Caution students to use care when handling plastic knives.

Expected Results

The restored cupcake will be shorter and flatter than the original cupcake.

Analyze and Conclude

1. The icing represents the topsoil; the cream represents the extracted resource.
2. The reclaimed cupcake resembles the untouched cupcake but it is shorter and has a broken surface.
3. Reclamation cannot restore the original contours because some material has been removed.

✓Assessment

Knowledge Ask students to discuss what would be necessary for a mining company to restore a strip-mined area to its original contours. Ask them to consider how reclamation might affect the environment in nearby areas. Material would need to be brought in from somewhere else. This would create a new excavation to be restored in another location.

MiniLab

Reclamation

Model the procedure used by mining companies to reclaim an area after strip-mining.

Procedure

1. Using a plastic knife, make four or five cuts across the icing of one cream-filled, iced cupcake. Remove the pieces of icing.
2. Make four or five cuts down into the cake until you reach the cream filling. Cut horizontally just above the cream filling and remove the cake pieces.
3. Remove the cream filling. To restore the area, use the pieces of cake that you cut out to fill in the hole left when you removed the cream filling. Make the surface of the cupcake as level as possible.
4. Replace the icing so that it covers the surface of the restored cupcake.

Analyze and Conclude

1. On the restored cupcake, what does the icing represent? What does the cream filling represent?
2. Does the reclaimed cupcake resemble the original, untouched cupcake?
3. Can reclamation of an area that has been strip-mined restore the land to its original contours? Explain your answer.

Figure 27-9 Many farmers in the United States grow just one plant species in their fields.

Discussion

Ask students the following question. How have consumers played a role in excessive pesticide use? American consumers expect their fruits and vegetables to be 100 percent free of insect damage and other blemishes. Farmers therefore use excess pesticides so that they can sell their products.

AGRICULTURE

In natural ecosystems, such as a forest, many species of organisms interact with one another and with their environment to create a stable ecosystem. For example, scientists have identified as many as 300 species of trees on just 1 ha of land in a tropical rain forest. Even city parks can have a wide variety of different species, called **biodiversity.** In a recent study of a park in Hartford, Connecticut, scientists found and identified a total of 1369 species of organisms in just one 24-hour period. Ecosystems that have high biodiversity are more stable than those with fewer species because they are able to recover more quickly from harmful events such as disease and drought.

Monoculture When land is cleared for food production, a biologically diverse ecosystem is often replaced with a single plant species, such as corn or wheat. The planting of just one species in a field is called **monoculture.** Growing a monoculture crop makes it easier for a farmer to sow, fertilize, and harvest a crop, but this efficiency also brings risks. For example, in a monoculture of corn, illustrated in *Figure 27-9,* a fungus or a parasite that destroys corn can spread rapidly and destroy the entire crop. In contrast, in a field that contains several species of crops, disease organisms cannot spread as quickly because they have a more difficult time finding the target species. Even if the entire corn crop in such a field is eventually lost, the farmer can still harvest the other crops growing in the field.

Differentiated Instruction

Learning Disabled Have students count the number of species in an aquarium to illustrate biodiversity. Help students compare this number to the number of species in the classroom outside of the aquarium.

Pesticides A variety of pesticides, including fungicides and insecticides, have played an important role in boosting food production worldwide by eliminating organisms that destroy crops. However, the use of pesticides has drawbacks. Some pesticides remain in the environment for long periods of time. As they slowly accumulate in the food chain, they may harm beneficial organisms, such as fishes and birds. Some pesticides also kill beneficial insect predators along with destructive insects. When pesticides kill decomposers, such as worms, the overall fertility of topsoil deteriorates. In addition, insect populations can quickly develop resistance to an insecticide, causing some farmers to use ever-increasing amounts in an attempt to control pests. Further problems are created when wind and rain carry pesticides away from a farm and cause pollution in nearby waterways.

Topsoil It can take thousands of years for topsoil to form, and thus, once it is lost, it is hard to replace. Erosion of topsoil occurs when forests or grasslands are cleared for the first time, but even established farms can suffer from the loss of topsoil. As shown in *Figure 27-10,* whenever fields are plowed and the plants whose roots hold the soil in place are removed, topsoil becomes vulnerable to erosion by wind and water. The addition of fertilizers helps replace some of the nutrients that are depleted by topsoil erosion, but there are other substances in topsoil that fertilizers cannot provide. Topsoil contains trace minerals as well as organisms such as earthworms, which aerate the soil and provide space for plant roots to grow, and nitrogen-fixing bacteria, which take nitrogen out of the air and make it available to plants. Topsoil also has an abundance of organic matter, including fecal material from organisms that live in the soil and dead and dying organisms such as grasses and insects. As organic matter decomposes, it releases nutrients back into the soil.

Figure 27-10 Plowing a field in preparation for planting can result in the loss of topsoil.

Cultural Diversity

Ronald Brooks (1935–1989) An African-American chemist, Dr. Ronald Brooks led research units at General Electric to develop oil-eating microorganisms that cleaned up environmentally damaging oil spills in ocean environments. The oil-digesting microbes helped to metabolize, or break down, the hydrocarbons in petroleum into carbon dioxide and water, thus decreasing the toxic effects of petroleum. Brooks received many awards, and in addition to his scientific career, he was known for his work with inner-city youth. He was killed in an auto accident before he was able to patent his invention for combating oil spills.

Have students research the problem of plant pests, such as insects, bacteria, and fungi, developing resistance to pesticides. Ask students to find out what causes the development of resistance and what is being done to combat the problem.

Collaborative Learning

Interpersonal Have groups of students discuss the following question. Is topsoil a renewable or nonrenewable resource? If it is renewable, why is topsoil loss such a problem?

L2 **COOP LEARN**

Reinforcement

Have students make a data table showing how topsoil can be lost and ways to prevent the loss.

Content Background

Legumes, such as alfalfa, clover, lupines, peas, and beans, are often used as cover crops because they actually add nitrogen to soil. Before planting, the seeds are inoculated with *Rhizobium* bacteria, which fix atmospheric nitrogen and convert it into a form usable by plants. There is a natural symbiotic relationship between legumes and *Rhizobium*. The bacteria live in small nodules that form on the plants' roots.

Enrichment

Have students investigate the following question: How can growing a cover crop replenish nutrients in a field? Cover crops usually add nutrients to the soil that other crops have depleted.

Figure 27-11 Good farming practices can help conserve topsoil. In no-till farming, the crop residue is left on the field after harvest to hold soil in place. In the spring, seeds are planted right through the crop residue **(A)**. To stabilize the soil and replenish nutrients in a field used for monoculture, farmers plant cover crops such as clover every few years **(B)**.

Figure 27-12 In selective logging, foresters mark trees that will be cut down as well as those that will be left standing.

To maintain the fertility of their land, many farmers use methods that help preserve topsoil, such as those shown in *Figure 27-11.* When fertilizers are necessary, responsible farmers carefully monitor their use to prevent runoff into streams. Because fertilizers are expensive, farmers also save money by using only as much as the plants require. Methods used by farmers to selectively apply fertilizers where they will provide the greatest benefit include soil analysis, careful mapping of fields, and monitoring of plant growth.

FORESTRY

The clearing of forested land is another way in which topsoil is lost. Worldwide, thousands of hectares of forests are cut down annually to meet the demand for firewood, charcoal, paper, and lumber. In many parts of the world, the clearing of forested land results in **deforestation,** which is the removal of trees from a forested area without adequate replanting. Deforestation often involves clear-cutting, the complete removal of all the trees in an area. Clear-cutting may result in the loss of topsoil through erosion and in the clogging of nearby streams with excess sediment. Fortunately, the negative environmental impacts of deforestation can be minimized through the practices of selective logging, as shown in *Figure 27-12,* and the retention of buffer zones of trees along streambeds. In selective logging, workers remove only designated trees rather than clear-cutting an entire forest. This practice reduces the amount of ground left bare and thus helps prevent erosion. In the United States, new logging laws require that buffer zones of trees be left along the banks of streams. Buffer zones of trees slow runoff by catching the sediment that has been eroded from bare ground before it reaches streams.

Across the Curriculum

Biology Have students identify how decomposers fit into the nutrient-energy cycle. Ask them why soil fertility decreases when decomposers are killed by pesticides. Decomposers break down organic matter into simpler molecules that can be used by other organisms as nutrients. Thus, decomposers complete the cycle of energy through the environment. If decomposers are killed off by pesticides, some nutrients remain locked up and soil fertility decreases.

Across the Curriculum

Chemistry Ask students what three elements are found in most fertilizers. nitrogen, potassium, and phosphorus Have students find out what role each of these nutrients plays in plant growth. Nitrogen is involved in protein production and gives plants their deep green color. Phosphorus is involved in root growth and flower production. Potassium's role is less well understood but may be involved in protein and cell-wall construction.

URBAN DEVELOPMENT

Do you live in the country, or in a town or city? As the human population continues to increase, more and more people live in cities and towns. For example, 70 percent of the population in North America now lives in urban and suburban areas, and an estimated 5 billion people worldwide will be living in cities and towns by the year 2025.

The development of land for the growth of urban areas has many impacts on the environment. When towns and cities expand into rural areas, natural habitats are lost as forests are cleared and wetlands are filled to provide land for roads, houses, and other buildings. When land is prepared for construction, erosion of topsoil often increases until new landscaping can be established.

Development also takes land away from agricultural use, which puts pressure on the remaining farmland for increased production. Other problems are created when concrete and asphalt cover large land areas; because there are fewer opportunities for rainwater to soak into the ground, groundwater supplies are not recharged and flooding increases during heavy rains. Increasing urbanization also produces large volumes of solid waste, as illustrated in *Figure 27-13.* Each person in the United States generates an average of 1.5 kg of solid waste per day. Where does it all go? Much of it is buried in landfills. People once thought that because buried waste was out of sight, it was no longer a problem. Many old landfills, however, are creating pollution problems as dangerous chemicals leak out and contaminate water supplies.

Additional contamination occurs as a result of industrial processes. Heavy metals, such as lead and mercury, and poisonous chemicals, such as arsenic, are by-products of many industrial processes and can

Using Math

Finding Percentages
If 61 million metric tons of the solid waste generated in the United States each year are reclaimed, and if this represents 28 percent of the total solid waste generated, how much total solid waste is generated in the United States each year?

Using Math

$(28\%)X = 61$ million metric tons

$X = 61 \div 0.28$

$X = 217.86$ million metric tons of solid waste

Solid Waste Generated Each Year

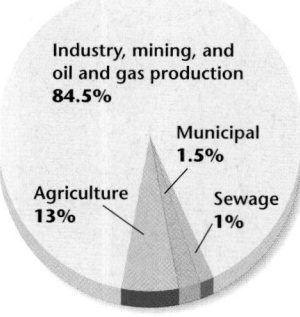

Industry, mining, and oil and gas production **84.5%**

Municipal **1.5%**

Agriculture **13%**

Sewage **1%**

Figure 27-13 This graph shows the percentage of solid waste generated by various users of natural resources in the United States annually. Municipal wastes are those wastes contributed by homes and businesses.

Resource Manager

Exploring Environmental Problems,
pp. 29–32, 33–36 L2

NY Core Curriculum Standards

Page 720: St 1 Engin KI 1, St 6 KI 6, St 7 KI 1 & 2
Page 721: St 6 KI 1

Demo

To demonstrate the effects of vegetation on erosion, take the class outside and pour a bucket of water (or use a hose) on a patch of bare soil. Then, pour a bucket of water on a patch of grass or other ground cover. More soil will be eroded from the bare patch of soil than from the patch covered with vegetation.

Activity

Visual-Spatial Have students draw cross-sectional diagrams comparing old landfills with modern landfills. Ask students to identify the pollution problems that were created by the old types of landfills and the solutions that are incorporated in the new designs. **L2**

Enrichment

Lead (Pb) is a heavy metal that can be a problem if it contaminates the environment. Have students research the effects of lead contamination, where the lead comes from, and what is being done to remove lead from the environment. Ask them to find out what other heavy metals cause environmental problems.

Figure 27-14 During construction, barriers such as these slow water flow and prevent erosion from the site.

Figure 27-15 Modern landfills are designed to have the least possible impact on the environment.

pollute the soil and groundwater in urban areas. Some of this type of contamination was caused by industries that operated before the dangers of improper waste disposal were known. However, accidental spills and illegal dumping continue to be sources of contamination. Even though it is possible to clean up contaminated sites, the processes involved in doing so are difficult and extremely expensive.

Solutions Although urban development can create many environmental problems, most of these problems can be solved. People are becoming aware of the need to protect the environment, and communities are making increased efforts to do so. For example, developers are often required to place barriers, such as those shown in *Figure 27-14,* around construction sites to catch sediment from increased erosion. In the United States, wetlands are now recognized as valuable ecosystems and are protected from development. In some cases, if developers destroy a wetland area, they are required to build wetlands somewhere else in return.

Problems associated with waste disposal are more difficult, primarily because the volume of trash is so large. Modern landfills, however, are very different from the dumps of the past; they are carefully designed to minimize leakage of toxic liquids. Impermeable clay or plastic layers are placed beneath a landfill, and each day's trash is compacted by huge machines and buried under a layer of dirt to reduce volume and eliminate wind-blown trash. Ventilation pipes in landfills release methane and other gases that are generated as the garbage decomposes. A diagram of a modern landfill is shown in *Figure 27-15.*

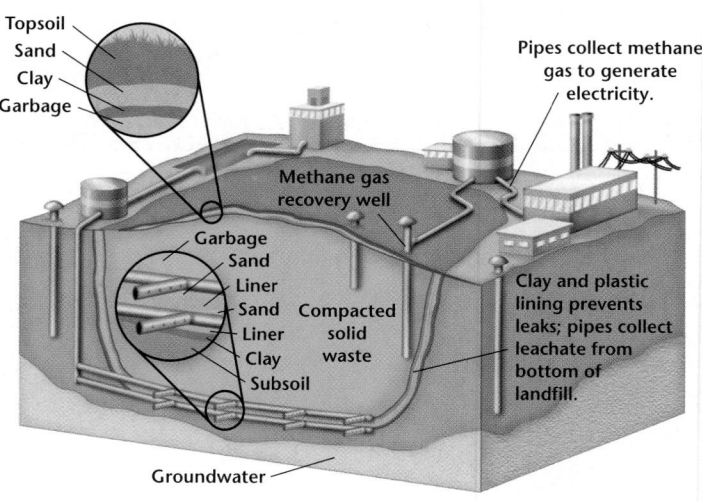

Resource Manager

Teaching Transparency 83 **L2** **ELL**
Laboratory Manual, pp. 209–212 **L2**

NY Core Curriculum Standards

Page 722: St 1 Engin KI 1, St 7 KI 1 & 2
Page 723: St 1 Engin KI 1, St 6 KI 6, St 7 KI 1

Figure 27-16 In one type of bioremediation, plants that contain bacterial genes are grown in soils contaminated with toxic compounds. The bacterial genes enable the plants to convert these compounds into nontoxic substances, which the plants then release.

Several methods are available for cleaning up industrial toxic-waste sites. In one method, all the contaminated soil is removed and incinerated at temperatures high enough to destroy the toxic chemicals. The drawbacks to this method are that it can be very expensive when large volumes of soil are involved and it also produces toxic ash. Another method that shows great promise is **bioremediation,** the use of organisms to clean up toxic wastes, illustrated in *Figure 27-16.* In some cases, naturally occurring bacteria can be found that eat toxic materials and convert them to less-harmful substances. This technique has been especially useful for contamination caused by spilled gasoline and oil. 🍂

SECTION ASSESSMENT

1. What are some of the ways in which mining activities affect the land surface?

2. Compare the positive and negative aspects of pesticide use.

3. What are some of the ways in which urbanization affects the local land environment?

4. **Thinking Critically** If fertilizers cause environmental damage and are expensive, why do farmers use them?

SKILL REVIEW

5. **Concept Mapping** Use the following terms to fill in the concept map below to organize the major ideas in this section: erosion, topsoil loss, water pollution, waste rock, and mineral extraction. For more help, refer to the *Skill Handbook.*

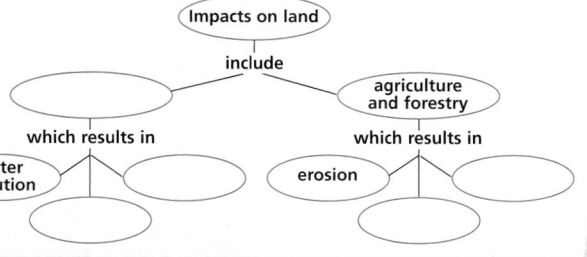

3 Assess

Check for Understanding

Project
Have small groups of students each make a data table summarizing the advantages and disadvantages of urban development as well as possible solutions to the disadvantages. **L2** **COOP LEARN**

Reteach

Linguistic Have students summarize human impacts on land resources by making an outline of this section. Students can use the headings for each subsection in their outlines.

✓*Assessment*

Knowledge Ask students to identify two environmental problems that can be caused by all four of the following human activities: mining, logging, farming, and urban development. erosion and subsequent loss of topsoil; habitat loss

---

SECTION ASSESSMENT

1. Mining activities can disturb the land surface by burial (tailing piles) or removal (strip-mining), and they can pollute waterways with mine runoff that carries toxic chemicals and heavy metals.

2. Positive aspects of pesticides are the control of disease-carrying and damaging insects, such as mosquitoes and termites, and increased crop production. Negative aspects are the destruction of beneficial insects, increased costs, accumulation in the food chain, and the development by insects of resistance to pesticides.

3. Some effects of urbanization are loss of habitat, loss of farmland, increased runoff, and increased pollution from pesticides, fertilizers, and sewage.

4. When they are used properly, fertilizers can help restore soil fertility, improve plant health, and increase crop yields without harming the environment. However, in some cases, economic factors force farmers to squeeze as much crop production as possible from the land, leading to damaging overuse of fertilizers.

5. See the annotations on the student page.

723

Section Background

For section content background, refer to **Indoor Air Pollution** on pages 710C–D.

Preplanning

Refer to the Chapter Organizer on pages 710A–B.

1 Focus

Section Focus

Before presenting the lesson, display **Section Focus Transparency 87** on the overhead projector. **L1** **ELL**

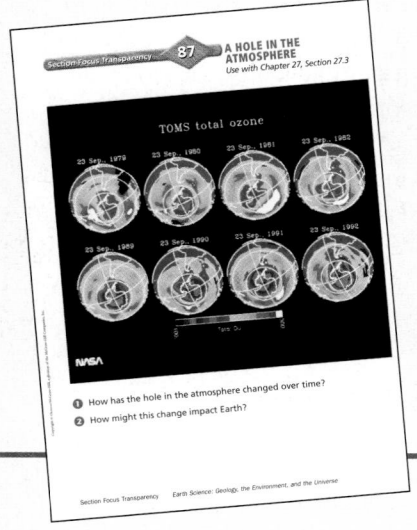

Activity

Intrapersonal Ask each student to label an index card with his or her name and date, and then stick a 5-cm piece of double-sided tape on the card. Have students place their cards around the school and leave them for two days. They should then use hand lenses to study the pieces of tape. Ask students to make a list of the types of particulate air pollution that they find on the pieces of tape. **L1** **ELL**

SECTION 27.3

Human Impact on Air Resources

OBJECTIVES

- **Describe** *the types and sources of air pollution.*
- **Differentiate** *between the greenhouse effect and global warming.*
- **Sequence** *the reactions that occur as CFCs cause ozone depletion.*
- **Identify** *the causes and effects of acid precipitation.*

VOCABULARY

smog
ozone
global warming
acid precipitation

Can you see the haze that seems to hover above the buildings in *Figure 27-17*? This yellow-brown haze is a type of air pollution called **smog,** which is a photochemical haze caused by the action of solar radiation on an atmosphere polluted with hydrocarbons and nitrogen oxides mostly from automobile exhaust systems. When smog occurs in a city, the air becomes harmful to breathe, especially for those who already have some difficulty breathing. The major chemical in smog is **ozone** (O_3), a gas molecule made up of three oxygen atoms. Recall that in the upper atmosphere, solar radiation converts oxygen gas into ozone. Ozone in the upper atmosphere is beneficial because it absorbs and filters out harmful ultraviolet (UV) radiation. However, ground-level ozone is produced when combinations of air pollutants, including nitrogen oxides, carbon monoxide, and hydrocarbons, are exposed to sunlight. Ozone irritates the eyes, noses, throats, and lungs of humans, and it also has harmful effects on plants.

Air pollution also occurs in the form of particulate matter. The solid particles of such materials as ash, dust, pollen, and asbestos fibers range in size from microscopic bits to large grains. When humans breathe in particulates, they can lodge in lung tissues, disrupt normal functions, and cause breathing difficulties and lung disease.

Figure 27-17 The air in many cities is polluted by smog, a word created by the combination of the words *smoke* and *fog.*

Resource Manager

Study Guide for Content Mastery, p. 173 **L2**

Section Focus Transparency 87 **L1** **ELL**

GLOBAL IMPACTS OF AIR POLLUTION

Recently, it has become clear that human activities can affect Earth on a global scale. The global atmospheric effects of air pollution include global warming, ozone depletion, and acid precipitation.

Global Warming Recall from Chapter 14 that the greenhouse effect is a natural phenomenon in which Earth's atmosphere traps heat in the troposphere to warm Earth. A phenomenon related to the greenhouse effect is **global warming,** which is the increase in Earth's average surface temperature. Whereas the greenhouse effect is a natural phenomenon, global warming is partly caused by humans. Human activities, especially the burning of fossil fuels by automobiles, are largely responsible for increased levels of carbon dioxide, which is the main greenhouse gas that causes global warming. Fossil fuels contain carbon, and when they are burned, the carbon combines with oxygen to form carbon dioxide. Since the beginning of the industrial revolution, around 1850, humans have been burning fossil fuels at an ever-increasing rate. *Figure 27-18* shows how atmospheric carbon dioxide has increased over the past 250 years.

Studies indicate that Earth's mean surface temperature has risen about 0.5°C in the last century. Some scientists hypothesize that this warming trend is the result of global warming and predict that global warming could raise average temperatures by 1 to 3.5°C in the next 100 years. Although this may not seem like much of a temperature change, the consequences could be extreme. Wind and rainfall patterns might

Update To find out more about global warming, visit the Earth Science Web Site at <u>earthgeu.com</u>

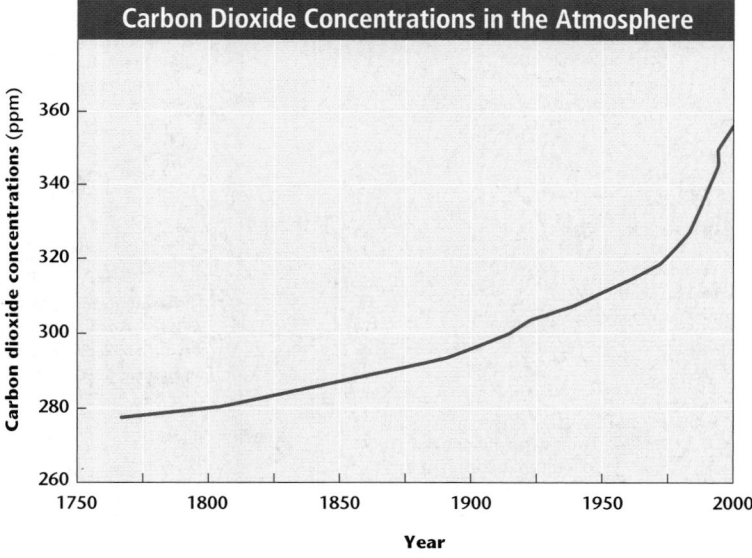

Figure 27-18 The amount of atmospheric carbon dioxide has increased greatly since the 1850s.

27.3 *Human Impact on Air Resources* **725**

Content Background

One of the more serious long-term effects of ozone depletion is melanoma, or skin cancer. Studies have shown a link between exposure to ultraviolet radiation and the development of melanoma later in life, especially in people with light-colored skin. Currently, the worst ozone depletion is found at high latitudes in the southern hemisphere. Health officials are particularly concerned about increased melanoma risks in Australia.

Earth Science Journal

Have students write their responses to the following scenario in their science journals. Imagine that one of the long-term climatic effects of global warming is that your region receives half as much rainfall as normal. How would this change your environment? What if rainfall were to double?

✔ Assessment

Knowledge Ask students to identify the products of burning fossil fuels and which of these products is a greenhouse gas.

---

change and affect the major agricultural belts. If climate patterns change too rapidly, plant and animal species may be unable to adapt and may become extinct. Glaciers and ice caps could melt, raising the sea level and flooding low-lying areas. Other scientists, however, assert that humans have not kept weather records long enough to tell whether the present rate of global warming is an artificial or a natural phenomenon. They argue that the increase in Earth's temperature could be part of a natural pattern of climatic change.

Ozone Depletion Another global change that is a result of human activity involves the ozone layer in the stratosphere. The ozone layer serves as a protective shield as it absorbs and filters out harmful UV radiation, which has been linked to human eye damage and skin cancer, as well as reduced crop yields. In the early 1970s, scientists first suggested that chlorofluorocarbons (CFCs) could destroy ozone in the upper atmosphere. Although CFCs are stable and harmless near Earth's surface, scientists now know that they destroy ozone molecules when they migrate into the upper atmosphere, as shown in **Figure 27-19.** Since the mid-1980s, atmospheric studies have detected a thinning of the ozone layer, including an extremely thin area over Antarctica that was publicized in the news media as an "ozone hole." Because all of the CFCs in the atmosphere were released from old refrigerators, cleaning agents, and propellants in aerosol cans, this ozone depletion is entirely a result of human activity.

Figure 27-19 Just a few chlorine atoms from CFCs can destroy many ozone molecules.

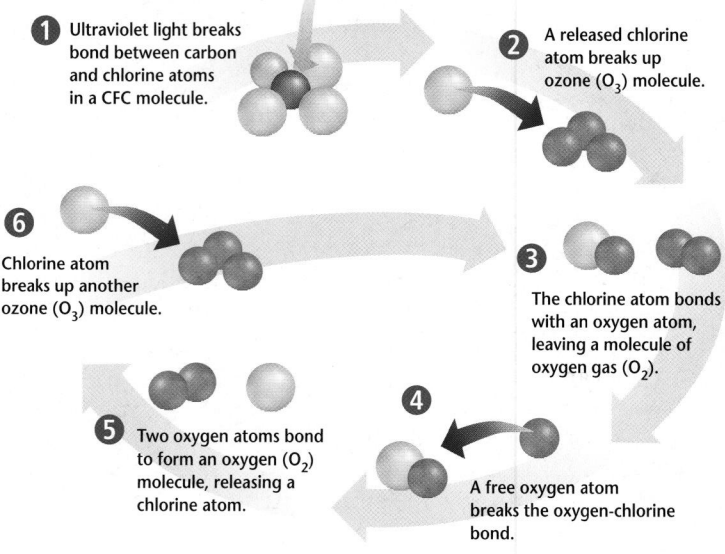

1 Ultraviolet light breaks bond between carbon and chlorine atoms in a CFC molecule.

2 A released chlorine atom breaks up ozone (O_3) molecule.

3 The chlorine atom bonds with an oxygen atom, leaving a molecule of oxygen gas (O_2).

4 A free oxygen atom breaks the oxygen-chlorine bond.

5 Two oxygen atoms bond to form an oxygen (O_2) molecule, releasing a chlorine atom.

6 Chlorine atom breaks up another ozone (O_3) molecule.

Across the Curriculum

Chemistry Ask students whether they know what an acid is. Acids are substances that release H+ ions into solution. Write the chemical formulas for sulfuric acid, H_2SO_4, and nitric acid, HNO_3, on the chalkboard. Ask students how sulfur dioxide and nitrogen oxides react with water to form sulfuric acid and nitric acid. The chemical reactions are as follows: $SO_2 + 2H_2O = H_2SO_4$; $2NO + H_2O = 2HNO_3$. Ask a volunteer to write the chemical reactions on the chalkboard and to balance the equations.

Resource Manager

Teaching Transparency 84 L2 ELL

Exploring Environmental Problems, pp. 17–20, 21–24 L2

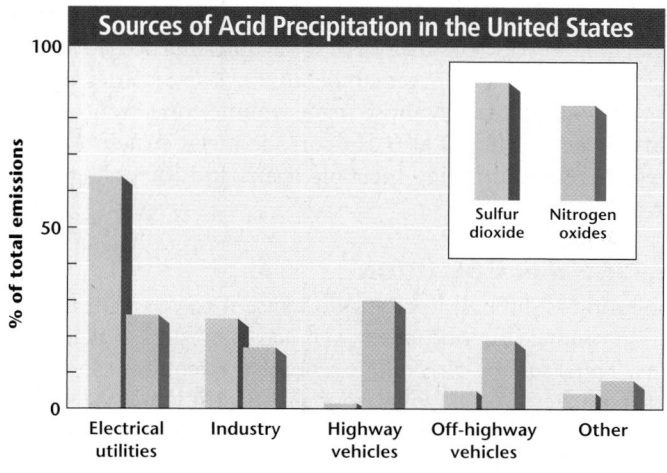

Sources of Acid Precipitation in the United States

Figure 27-20 Most of the nitrogen oxides that cause acid precipitation come from automobiles. *What is the greatest source of the sulfur dioxide that causes acid precipitation?*

Acid Precipitation Another major air pollution problem is **acid precipitation,** which is defined as precipitation with a pH of less than 5.0. Recall from Chapter 3 that pH is a measure of the acidity of a substance on a scale of 0 to 14, with 7 being neutral. Natural precipitation has a pH of about 5.0 to 5.6, which is slightly acidic. Acid precipitation forms when sulfur dioxide and nitrogen oxides combine with atmospheric moisture to create sulfuric acid and nitric acid. Acid precipitation includes acidic rain, snow, fog, mist, gas, and dust. Although volcanoes and marshes add sulfur gases to the atmosphere, 90 percent of the sulfur emissions in eastern North America are of human origin. *Figure 27-20* shows a comparison of the different sources of acid precipitation.

The type of acid precipitation that has received the most attention is caused by coal-burning power plants in the midwestern United States. These plants burn coal that contains significant amounts of the mineral pyrite (FeS_2) and other sulfur-bearing compounds. When sulfur-rich coal is burned, large amounts of sulfur dioxide are released. The sulfur dioxide generated by midwestern power plants rises high into the air and is carried by winds towards the eastern coast of the United States and Canada. When acids are carried into wet weather, they become part of the rain, snow, or fog that falls to the ground in areas far from their source.

When acid precipitation makes its way into surface waters, such as lakes, streams, ponds, and rivers, it causes damage to aquatic ecosystems and vegetation. Acid precipitation also affects plants and soil. Although trees in areas affected by acid precipitation usually aren't killed outright, acid precipitation weakens them so that they become

Figure 27-21 Buildings and outdoor artwork are damaged by acid precipitation.

Activity

Obtain pH test kits to test the pH of rainwater in your area. Have students collect rainwater as well as surface water after a rainstorm and test the water for its pH level. Have students determine whether their region suffers from acid precipitation. **L2**

Figure Caption Question

Figure 27-20 What is the greatest source of the sulfur dioxide that causes acid precipitation? electric utilities

Project

Visual-Spatial Have student groups research the effects of acid on aquatic organisms and create poster displays to share with the class. At least one group should focus on the steps being taken to raise the pH levels of lakes and streams that have already been affected by acid precipitation. **L2** **ELL**

Discussion

Ask students to discuss this question: How does acid precipitation affect the availability of nutrients in soil? When the pH of soil changes, some nutrients form compounds that are insoluble and cannot be absorbed by plants. Other nutrients are converted to more soluble forms and are quickly leached from the soil.

Demo

Simulate the effects of acid precipitation on stone by placing a few drops of a 10 percent solution of hydrochloric acid on limestone. **CAUTION:** *Wear an apron, safety goggles, and gloves when you perform this demonstration. Have students wear safety goggles to observe. Take care to avoid splashing acid on clothing or skin.*

NY Core Curriculum Standards

Page 724: St 4 KI 2.2d
Page 725: St 4 KI 2.2d, St 6 KI 5
Page 726: St 4 KI 2.2d
Page 727: St 4 KI 2.2d, St 6 KI 2

Problem-Solving Lab

Purpose
Students will identify changes in the levels of air pollutants over the last 30 years.

Process Skills
interpret graphs, recognize cause and effect, think critically

Materials
paper, pencil

Teaching Strategies
Review line graphs with students. Remind them of the axes and what each axis represents. Point out that each air pollutant has a different line on the graph. Students with poor graphing skills should be paired with more capable students.

Analysis
1. The amount of lead has dropped significantly. This is mostly a result of the phasing out of leaded gasoline.
2. CO_2 has dropped from 129 million metric tons to 88 million metric tons per year. NO_2 has actually increased slightly from 21 million metric tons to 24 million metric tons per year.

Thinking Critically
3. There are more cars being driven more often each year. Even though they burn fuel more efficiently, there is more total nitrous oxide being released.

✓Assessment

Portfolio Have students each make a data table that compares 1970 and 1995 emission rates for the pollutants shown on the graph. Students can include their tables in their portfolios. **L2** **P**

NY Core Curriculum Standards

Page 728: St 4 KI 2.2d, St 6 KI 2, St 7 KI 1
Page 729: St 1 Engin KI 1

---

more susceptible to damage from insect pests and disease. In addition, acid precipitation depletes the soil of some nutrients needed by plants.

Acid precipitation damages stone buildings and statues, as shown in *Figure 27-21,* especially those made of limestone, by accelerating the rate of weathering. It also can corrode metal structures such as bridges, thereby shortening their life spans and increasing maintenance costs.

REDUCING AIR POLLUTION

Air pollution is difficult to control because it travels with the wind; pollution produced in one area travels across borders to neighboring regions. Thus, solving air pollution problems requires the cooperation of both state and national governments. In the last decade, the governments of many nations have met several times in an attempt to reduce global air pollution, especially that caused by carbon dioxide

Problem-Solving Lab

Using Graphs

Identify changes in air pollutants The Clean Air Act of 1972 was an attempt to reduce the amount of air pollution in the United States. The emission rates of six major air pollutants are graphed to the right. Use this graph to answer the following questions.

Analysis
1. In 1970, the main source of lead (Pb) air pollution was leaded gasoline. What has happened to the amount of lead emitted into the atmosphere since 1970? What do you think may have caused this change?
2. Modern cars emit significantly fewer air pollutants, such as carbon monoxide and nitrogen dioxides, than cars from the 1970s and earlier. How have the emission rates of these two air pollutants changed since 1970?

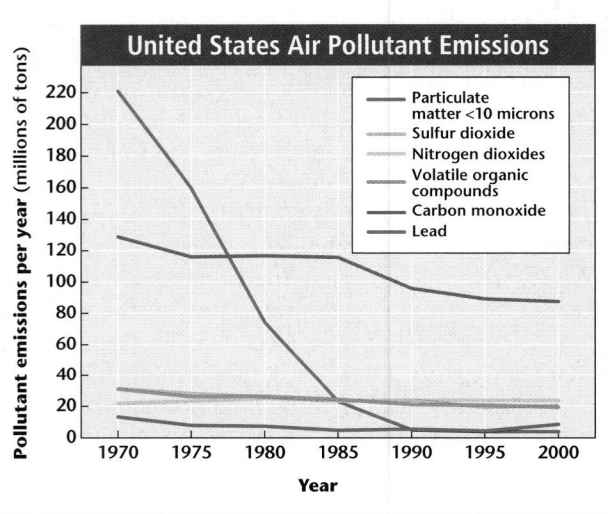

Thinking Critically
3. If modern cars are more efficient and less polluting, how would you explain the small amount of change in the levels of nitrogen dioxides over the years?

Differentiated Instruction

English-Language Learners Have students use a dictionary to define the following terms: *precipitation, rain, snow,* and *fog.* Ask students to explain why *acid precipitation* is a more accurate term to use than acid *rain.* **L1** **ELL**

Across the Curriculum

Chemistry Review acids, bases, and neutralization reactions. Then, ask students the following questions. What chemical equation represents the effects of acid precipitation on limestone? $H_2SO_4 + CaCO_3 \rightarrow CO_2 + H_2O + CaSO_4$. How might this reaction be used to change the pH levels of lakes that have been affected by acid precipitation? Powdered limestone can be added to acidified lakes to raise their pH levels.

and CFCs. In the United States, Congress has passed laws to reduce air pollution. For example, the 1990 Clean Air Act set specific reduction goals and enforcement policies for many types of air pollution. This act called for the United States to reduce its sulfur dioxide emissions to 50 percent of their 1980 levels by the year 2000, and to reduce emissions of nitrogen oxides as well. You will find out how the amount of air pollutants in the United States has changed since the 1970s in the *Problem-Solving Lab* on the previous page.

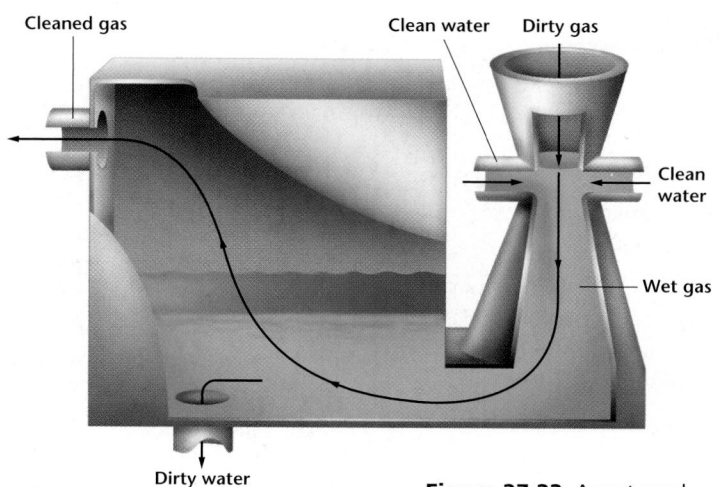

Figure 27-22 A wet scrubber installed on a smokestack of a coal-burning power plant reduces sulfur-dioxide emissions.

Many coal-burning power plants have installed a device such as the wet scrubber illustrated in **Figure 27-22** to reduce emissions of particulate matter and sulfur dioxide. In North America and Western Europe, the use of low-sulfur coal and natural gas have helped to reduce such emissions. However, scientists agree that the most effective way to reduce air pollution is to remove older, highly polluting vehicles from roadways. It is estimated that just 10 percent of the motor vehicles in operation produce 50 to 60 percent of the air pollution generated by gasoline-powered engines. Switching to newer cars with more efficient engines could significantly reduce air pollution throughout the world.

3 Assess

Check for Understanding
Discussion
Have a discussion about the major air pollution problems in your region. What are the sources of the problems, and what is being done to alleviate the problems?

Reteach
Have students each make a list of five human activities that cause air pollution and describe the type of air pollution that is generated. L2

✔Assessment

Performance Have students each make a data table comparing the three global air-pollution problems: ozone depletion, acid precipitation, and global warming. Ask students to list the chemicals that cause each problem and to explain where these chemicals originate. Use the Performance Task Assessment List for Data Table in **PASC,** p. 37.

SECTION ASSESSMENT

1. Name two forms of pollutants found in air. What are some of the natural and human sources of these pollutants?

2. How is global warming related to the greenhouse effect?

3. How do CFCs cause ozone depletion?

4. What are the effects of acid precipitation on ecosystems?

5. **Thinking Critically** At some point, humans will run out of inexpensive coal resources to burn for fuel. What impact might this have on global warming?

SKILL REVIEW

6. **Predicting** The atmosphere of Venus is 90 percent carbon dioxide. Based on this information, what could you infer about the average surface temperature of Venus? Explain your answer. For more help, refer to the *Skill Handbook*.

SECTION ASSESSMENT

1. gases and particulate matter; Particulates come from forest fires, volcanic eruptions, mining activities, farming, and construction. Gases come from cars, industry, and power plants.

2. The greenhouse effect is the ability of Earth's atmosphere to heat and maintain surface temperatures on Earth. Global warming is the increase in Earth's average surface temperature. Global warming may be caused by an increase in the amount of atmospheric greenhouse gases.

3. UV radiation frees chlorine atoms from CFCs in the upper atmosphere. These chlorine atoms break up ozone molecules.

4. Acid precipitation lowers the pH levels of lakes and streams, thereby harming aquatic organisms, and changes soil chemistry so that nutrients are unavailable to plants.

5. Burning less coal means that less CO_2 is released into the atmosphere. This could decrease global warming.

6. The average surface temperature of Venus would be much higher than the average surface temperature of Earth. This higher temperature is a result of an extreme greenhouse effect caused by the high carbon-dioxide concentration. The average surface temperature on Venus is about 480°C (900°F).

Section Background

For section content background, refer to **Mining Aquifers** on page 710D.

Preplanning

Refer to the Chapter Organizer on pages 710A–B.

1 Focus

Section Focus

Before presenting the lesson, display **Section Focus Transparency 88** on the overhead projector. **L1** **ELL**

Tying to Previous Knowledge

Ask students to review the amount of freshwater available on Earth. Remind them that most of the freshwater on Earth is frozen in glaciers, leaving only 0.003 percent of total water resources immediately available for use in surface and ground-water resources.

SECTION **27.4**

Human Impact on Water Resources

OBJECTIVES

- **Summarize** *the types and sources of water pollution.*
- **Describe** *some methods of controlling water pollution.*
- **Identify** *ways to conserve water.*

VOCABULARY

point source
nonpoint source

Humans depend on water in many ways. In 1995, the United States consumed 378 billion L of water per day. Since 1960, freshwater use has nearly doubled, and the demand is expected to continue to increase. Most people use freshwater in their homes for bathing, drinking, cooking, and washing. The irrigation of crops also requires water, but much of it is wasted because it often evaporates or seeps into the ground before it can be used by crops. Still, the greatest demand on water supplies comes from industry, including power plants that use water for cooling purposes. *Figure 27-23* shows how water supplies in the United States are distributed among users.

Because water supplies are not distributed evenly on Earth, some areas have less water than is needed. When water supplies are limited, conflicts occur between the needs of people and the needs of other users, including wildlife.

WATER POLLUTION

Pollution is another area in which humans have an impact on water supplies. Some supplies of water have been polluted by human activities and are no longer usable. Water-pollution sources are grouped into two main types. **Point sources** generate pollution from a single point of origin, such as a sewage-treatment plant or an industrial site, while **nonpoint sources** generate pollution from widely spread areas.

Use of Water in the United States

Figure 27-23 This graph illustrates the percentage of total water supplies used for various purposes in the United States.

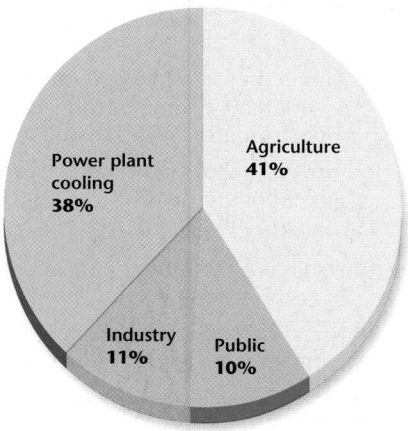

Power plant cooling 38%

Agriculture 41%

Industry 11%

Public 10%

Differentiated Instruction

Learning Disabled Have students cut out magazine photos showing different types of water use. Students should attach the photos to posterboard and write a sentence next to each photo describing how water is being used.

Resource Manager

Study Guide for Content Mastery, p. 174 **L2**

Section Focus Transparency 88 **L1** **ELL**

Teaching Transparency 85 **L2** **ELL**

Laboratory Manual, pp. 213–216 **L2**

Point Sources Common point sources of water pollution include bacteria and viruses that enter water systems through improper disposal of sewage, and toxic wastes that enter streams from both illegal dumping and accidental spills. In addition, industries that divert water from streams to use in manufacturing processes may return polluted water to the streams, as shown in *Figure 27-24.*

Nonpoint Sources Rainwater, a nonpoint source of water pollution, absorbs air pollutants and may become acidic itself. Rainwater also dissolves pesticides and fertilizers and carries them into streams as it drains from farms and lawns. Runoff from roads and parking lots that includes oil, gasoline, and other chemicals is another nonpoint source of water pollution.

Pollution of Groundwater Leaking chemical-storage barrels, underground gasoline-storage tanks, landfills, road salts, nitrates from fertilizers, sewage from septic systems, and other pollutants can seep into the ground and foul underground water supplies. Polluted groundwater may find its way into the drinking-water supplies of people who rely on wells. Once groundwater is contaminated, the pollutants can be very difficult to remove.

Pollution in the Oceans Although human activities have the greatest impact on freshwater supplies, pollution of ocean waters is also a concern. For years, it was thought that the oceans were so big that human activities could not affect them. This may be true for the oceans as a whole, but it is not true for near-shore regions. Nearly 50 percent of the U.S. population lives near coastlines in areas such as San Francisco, shown in *Figure 27-25.* Pollutants from such cities often end up in estuaries and other near-shore regions.

Sewage water is a major source of near-shore pollution around coastal areas. Even after treatment, human waste-water contains high levels of nitrogen and phosphorus. These nutrients can create blooms of cyanobacteria that later die and use up the oxygen in the water as they decompose. Some coastal cities dispose of their untreated sewage by pumping it through pipelines that run along the ocean floor and extend far out into the ocean. This practice can create large dead zones on the ocean floor where there are no living organisms. You will identify possible types and sources of pollution along a hypothetical coastline in the *Mapping GeoLab* at the end of this chapter.

Figure 27-24 Point-source pollution such as this can be identified and cleaned up more easily than nonpoint source pollution.

Figure 27-25 The area around San Francisco Bay has a high population density, which can lead to pollution of the ocean nearby.

27.4 *Human Impact on Water Resources* **731**

2 Teach

Modeling

Have groups of students create maps of hypothetical streams, rivers, or lake systems. Students should then add several possible pollution sources and label them as point or nonpoint sources.

Tying to Previous Knowledge

Ask students to recall what type of rock holds groundwater. sedimentary rock, usually sandstone or porous limestone

Enrichment

Intrapersonal Have students research the local water supply to find out where their water comes from and how is it treated to ensure that it is safe to drink. **L2**

Demo

Fill three clear containers with water. Add some food coloring to one of the containers, add nothing to the second container, and add a little soil to the third to make it muddy. Ask students which water sample is unsafe to drink. Students may say that the muddy water is not safe to drink but that the colored water is. Most students will also say that the clear water is safe to drink, but point out that it could be contaminated with any number of colorless chemicals.

Earth Science
Journal

Science Field Book

Have students write in their science journals about how they use water every day. They should also try to estimate how much water each activity requires.

NY Core Curriculum Standards

Page 730: St 6 KI 2 & 5
Page 731: St 6 KI 5

Figure 27-26 In the late 1970s, Ohio's Cuyahoga River was one of the most severely polluted rivers in the world. Today, the river again provides recreational activities for the residents of Akron and Cleveland.

To learn more about controlling water pollution, go to the **National Geographic Expedition** on page 870.

REDUCING WATER POLLUTION

In recent decades, many steps have been taken to prevent and reduce water pollution as people have found that it is much cheaper and more efficient to prevent pollution than it is to clean it up later. Two major laws have been passed in the United States to combat water pollution: the Safe Drinking Water Act and the Clean Water Act. The Safe Drinking Water Act of 1974 was designed to ensure that everyone in the United States has access to safe drinking water. Progress is being made, but many water supplies still do not meet the standards consistently. In 1998, 20 percent of public water supplies were in violation of the act at least once in a one-year period. The goal of the Safe Drinking Water Act is to reduce this number to less than 5 percent by the year 2005.

The Clean Water Act of 1972 is the primary federal law that protects our nation's waters. The act was amended in 1977, 1981, and again in 1987. The two main goals of the Clean Water Act are to eliminate discharge of pollutants into rivers, streams, lakes, and wetlands, and to restore water quality to levels that allow for recreational uses of waters, including fishing and swimming. One positive result of this act is shown in *Figure 27-26.*

Is the Clean Water Act working? Since 1972, the number of people served by sewage-treatment plants has increased from 85 million to 190 million. During that same time period, the annual rate of wetland losses has *decreased* from 146 000 ha to about 32 000 ha. Two-thirds of the nation's waters are now safe for swimming and fishing, compared to only one-third in 1972. However, more improvements must be made; in 1998, 35 percent of U.S. rivers and streams were still in violation of established water-quality levels at some point during that year.

WATER CONSERVATION

When there is not enough water to go around, populations have two choices: decrease demand or develop new supplies. In many cases, new supplies are not readily available or may be too expensive to develop. Therefore, water conservation is the most common solution to excessive demand. Because irrigation can waste so much water, efficient irrigation practices can greatly reduce the demand for water. Landscaping with plants that require less water, as illustrated in *Figure 27-27,* monitoring soil moisture, improving delivery systems, and raising water prices have all been effective in minimizing the amount of water used for irrigation. Industries can also conserve

732 CHAPTER 27 *Human Impact on Earth Resources*

Figure 27-27 In arid and semiarid areas, landscaping may include plants adapted to a dry climate. This form of landscaping is called xeriscaping, for the Greek word *xeros*, meaning "dry."

water; many are developing ways to recycle cooling water and wastewater, especially when they are charged high rates for water usage. Manufacturing processes often can use recycled water, or they can be redesigned to conserve water.

Is there a leaky faucet in your home? In the United States alone, 20 to 35 percent of the water taken from public water supplies is lost through leaky pipes, toilets, bathtubs, and faucets. Some cities don't even have water meters to measure, and thus charge for, the public water that households use. Not surprisingly, when water meters were introduced in Boulder, Colorado, the use of water was reduced by more than 30 percent. People tend to fix leaks and conserve water when they have to pay for it. If every person used a little less water, the water conserved would add up to a large volume. Installing more efficient showerheads, as shown in *Figure 27-28,* and toilets is just one way to decrease personal water consumption. Consider how you use water. What are some of the ways you might conserve water in your everyday life?

Figure 27-28 Many communities offer low-flow showerheads like these to their residents at low cost to help conserve water.

SECTION ASSESSMENT

1. What are some of the ways in which surface water can be polluted?

2. What are some ways to minimize the need for irrigation?

3. How might residents of a city reduce water consumption?

4. What are some of the positive impacts of the Clean Water Act?

5. **Thinking Critically** Which type of pollution is easier to eliminate, point source or nonpoint source? Give an example of each type and explain how it might be controlled.

SKILL REVIEW

6. **Interpreting Graphs** Based on the graph in *Figure 27-23,* what percentage of water supplies in the United States is used to provide you with food and the electricity needed to cook it? For more help, refer to the *Skill Handbook.*

earthgeu.com/self_check_quiz

3 Assess

Check for Understanding
Reinforcement
Ask students to identify what two laws have been passed in the United States to reduce water pollution and what the primary focus of each law is. Ask them whether these laws have been effective. The Safe Drinking Water Act was designed to ensure clean drinking water for all Americans. It has resulted in improvements, but some people still lack clean drinking water. The Clean Water Act was designed to prevent pollution of U.S. waters and protect aquatic environments. However, 35 percent of waters are still not in compliance with the laws.

Reteach
Have students make flashcards about different mechanisms of water pollution. The back of each card should identify whether it is a point or nonpoint source of pollution.

Skill Have students compare and contrast different methods of water conservation. Ask them which provide the greatest water savings with the least amount of effort.

SECTION ASSESSMENT

1. sewage, chemicals from industry, runoff from streets and farms, acid precipitation, and oil spills
2. planting crops that need less water, raising prices, using drip-irrigation systems, and careful monitoring of soil moisture
3. fixing leaks, installing low-flow showerheads and toilets, and watering yards during the morning and evening when evaporation rates are lower
4. a decrease in the rate of wetland loss,

an increase in the number of sewage-treatment plants, and the fact that two-thirds of waterways are now safe for swimming and fishing

5. A point source is easier to eliminate because the location can be identified and the problem can be corrected. For example, an industry that releases effluent into a local stream can be identified and required to stop releasing materials into surface water. Educating homeowners and creating

barriers to slow runoff before it reaches streams and lakes might control nonpoint source pollution, such as fertilizer runoff from yards.

6. If agriculture is responsible for 41 percent of water use and power plant cooling is responsible for 38 percent of water use, then food and the electricity needed to cook it is responsible for approximately 79 percent of water use.

Mapping GeoLab

Time Allotment

60 minutes

Process Skills

interpret maps, apply concepts, predict, analyze information

Preparation

No special preparation is required.

Procedure

Teaching Strategies

- Read through the information presented in the Procedure section with the class. This section contains clues that will help students to answer the lab questions.
- Explain to students that this scenario is based upon a real region.

Troubleshooting

- Make sure that students understand the different symbols and colors on the map.
- Some students may need an enlarged copy of the map.

Data and Observations

Many of the questions are open-ended and thus have multiple answers. Accept any student responses that are well supported. In the real world, environmental problems seldom have clear, simple answers. This lab can generate class discussions that successfully illustrate this point.

Mapping GeoLab

Pinpointing a Source of Pollution

*I*ris City and the surrounding region are shown in the map on the facing page. Iris City is a medium-sized city of 100 000. It is experiencing many types of environmental impacts. Study the map and the information given to identify these problems and possible solutions.

Preparation

Problem

How can the residents of Iris City identify the source of local water pollution?

Materials

metric ruler
pencil

Procedure

1. Iris City obtains its drinking water from Opal Lake. Studies of the lake have detected increased levels of nitrogen, phosphorus, hydrocarbons, sewage, and silt. The northwest end of Opal Lake is experiencing increased development, while the remainder of the watershed is a mix of forest and logging clear-cuts.

2. Last spring, blooms of cyanobacteria choked parts of the Vista Estuary Nature Preserve. Commercial shellfish beds in Iris Bay have been closed because of sewage contamination.

3. A natural-gas power plant has been proposed for location A, near the Vista Cutoff, an abandoned channel of the Vista River. The plant would provide jobs as well as generate electricity. The company plans to divert 25 percent of the Vista River down the Vista Cutoff.

4. The Lucky Mine was abandoned 60 years ago. A mining company has applied for permits to reopen the mine. An estimated 1 million ounces of gold can be recovered using modern techniques.

Analyze

1. What are some possible sources of water pollution in Opal Lake? What steps might the residents of Iris City take to protect their drinking water?

2. How are the blooms of cyanobacteria and the closing of the shellfish beds in Iris Bay related?

3. What are the positive and negative aspects of diverting water from the Vista River through the Vista Cutoff?

4. If the Lucky Mine is reopened, what effects might it have on the populations of Carlton, Vista, and Iris City?

Analyze

1. Possible pollution sources are increased development around the lake, logging operations, and power boating. Solutions include controlling runoff from development, buffer zones and selective cutting during logging, and banning powerboats from Opal Lake.

2. One cause of cyanobacterial blooms is sewage waste containing excess nutrients. If the cities and dairy farms along the Vista River were releasing improperly treated sewage into the river, this would cause both cyanobacterial blooms and the contamination of shellfish beds.

3. Positive aspects are new jobs, more electricity production, and possibly new wetlands at the mouth of Vista Cutoff. Negative aspects are increased pollution and reduction in freshwater flow to the Vista estuary region, which will cause saltwater intrusion and loss of habitat.

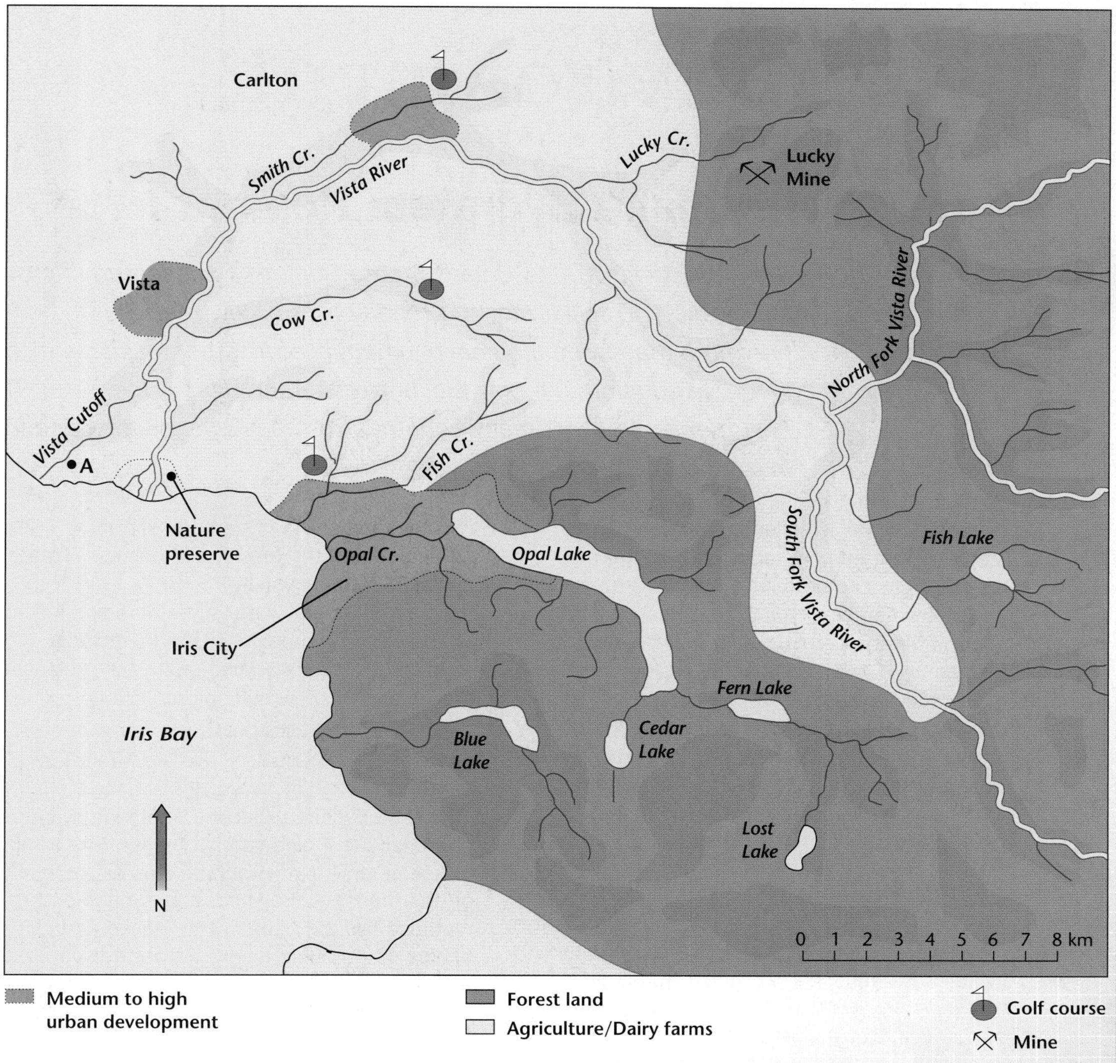

Map

Carlton

Smith Cr.

Vista River

Lucky Cr.

Lucky Mine

Vista

Cow Cr.

North Fork Vista River

Vista Cutoff

• A

Fish Cr.

Nature preserve

Opal Cr.

Opal Lake

South Fork Vista River

Fish Lake

Iris City

Fern Lake

Iris Bay

Blue Lake

Cedar Lake

Lost Lake

N

0 1 2 3 4 5 6 7 8 km

Medium to high urban development

Forest land

Agriculture/Dairy farms

Golf course

Mine

Conclude & Apply

1. Identify the sources of water pollution in Iris Bay. Are these point or nonpoint sources of pollution?
2. How could you identify the source of pollution causing cyanobacteria blooms in the Vista Estuary?
3. If the Vista Cutoff is used to divert water from the Vista River, how will the aquatic habitats of the river be affected?
4. If the Lucky Mine is reopened, what could the mining company do to minimize negative environmental impacts?

Mapping Geolab **735**

4. There will be economic benefits for all three cities. Pollution problems from mining activities will primarily affect Vista and Carlton because they are located along the river.

Conclude & Apply

1. Fertilizer and pesticides can come from farming operations, golf courses, and general urban development. Oil and gasoline pollution comes from street runoff, powerboats, and harbor operations. Excess silt comes from urban development and logging. Unfortunately, most of these are nonpoint sources and difficult to control. Each golf course and farm could be considered a point source.
2. The source of pollution could be located by analyzing water samples while traveling up the Vista River until the source was identified.
3. The Vista River will have lower flow downstream of the diversion. This could result in shallower water and increased temperature. Also, the freshwater-saltwater balance in the estuary would be changed, resulting in loss of habitat and organisms.
4. The mining company could build containment ponds and filtration barriers to prevent liquid wastes from entering the streams. The tailing piles could be landscaped to help replace the habitat that was buried.

✓ Assessment

Portfolio Have groups of students discuss the following question. Should development, logging, and power boating be allowed on and around a lake used as a source of public drinking water? Why or why not? Have students write responses in their science journals, then share their opinions in a class discussion.

Resource Manager

GeoLab and MiniLab Worksheets, pp. 108–110 L2

NY Core Curriculum Standards

Page 734: St 1 Science KI 1 & Engin KI 1, St 7 KI 1 & 2
Page 735: St 1 Science KI 1 & Engin KI 1, St 7 KI 1 & 2

Science & the Environment

Purpose

Students will become familiar with an energy source that is newly under development: frozen methane hydrates in Earth's crust.

Content Background

At moderately high pressure and low temperatures, the methane molecules in methane hydrates are caught in a cage of water molecules and frozen into a solid hydrate. To exploit methane hydrates, scientists must first develop technology to recover them. In addition, this recovery process must be studied to determine its economic feasibility.

Teaching Strategies

- Remind students that a resource must be recoverable at a reasonable cost before companies are willing to invest in it. Lead a discussion about factors that affect the cost of recovering a resource, such as the price of other fuels, the development of new technology, and environmental costs.
- Have students make data tables of various energy resources that include methane hydrates.

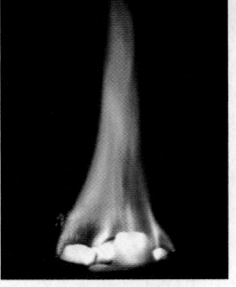

Methane Hydrates: Hope or Hype?

On April 4, 2000, the United States Congress passed a bill providing nearly $50 million for the research of a new fuel. This new fuel has more than twice the energy potential of all other fossil fuels combined. In addition, the new fuel is plentiful throughout the world. This new fuel could allow many countries to reach energy independence in the new century.

This new fuel is called methane hydrate. Methane hydrates are molecules of frozen methane gas captured inside crystals of regular ice. Many methane hydrate deposits are found deep within the permafrost in arctic regions. Methane gas released when dead plants and animals decay becomes frozen within the ice. Larger deposits of methane hydrates are found under the oceans, particularly along the continental slopes. Heat generated by tectonic processes is thought to release methane gas. The gas first rises, then freezes deep beneath the oceanic crust.

Something Old

Geologists have known about methane hydrates for a long time. The crystal structure of methane hydrates is strong, but not stable. When a hydrate bed is disturbed, the crystals break down and the methane is released as a gas. The rapid breakdown of the hydrate bed causes areas above the bed to slump. This phenomenon has been a major problem for offshore oil drilling platforms, which need a stable ocean floor to rest upon.

Something New

What's new is the idea of mining the hydrates from permafrost or from beneath the ocean floor. Fluctuations in fuel prices have led to an interest in harvesting the energy from this source. Research is underway in Japan, India, Canada, and the United States to develop ways to tap into the methane hydrate beds and remove useful amounts of the fuel. The instability of the hydrates is the biggest stumbling block. The hydrates must either be kept stable and frozen all the way to the processing area to avoid unwanted releases of methane, or the released gas must somehow be captured on-site.

What are the drawbacks to methane hydrates? First, removing hydrates from the seafloor may cause massive slumping along the continental shelves. Second, methane hydrates are fossil fuels, and burning them would cause the same environmental problems as the burning of other fossil fuels. Third, a disruption of the methane hydrate beds might release a large bubble of methane. Scientists have discovered that just such a "big burp" of methane, released 55 million years ago, led to climatic changes and a major extinction of deep-sea species.

Activity

Research and report on the potential advantages and disadvantages of the use of methane hydrates as fuel. Why are scientists interested in using methane hydrates? How might slumping impact the coastal environment?

Activity

Scientists expect methane hydrates to be a rich source of energy in the near future because they are plentiful and easy to convert into gas. However, slumping has been a problem for companies with offshore oil platforms. Slumping on the continental shelf happens suddenly and spontaneously, undermining the platforms. Undersea cables are also affected. In addition, slumping has been associated with tsunamis.

Summary

SECTION 27.1
Populations and the Use of Natural Resources

Main Ideas
- All organisms use resources to maintain their existence. The use of these resources has an impact on the environment.
- As populations increase, the demand for resources also increases. Because resources are limited, populations eventually will reach the carrying capacity of the environment and stop growing.
- At early stages, populations grow exponentially. Earth is currently experiencing a human population explosion.

Vocabulary
carrying capacity (p. 714)
density-dependent factor (p. 714)
density-independent factor (p. 714)
exponential growth (p. 713)

SECTION 27.2
Human Impact on Land Resources

Main Ideas
- Modern societies require large amounts of land resources. The extraction of land resources can disrupt Earth's surface.
- Growing populations increase the demand for food. Food production can cause habitat loss, erosion, and water pollution.
- Urban development causes habitat loss, increased erosion, and pollution of nearby areas.
- The impact of using land resources can be minimized through the use of modern techniques.

Vocabulary
biodiversity (p. 718)
bioremediation (p. 723)
deforestation (p. 720)
monoculture (p. 718)
reclamation (p. 717)

SECTION 27.3
Human Impact on Air Resources

Main Ideas
- Many human activities create air pollution. Air pollution can cause human health problems.
- Humans have affected Earth's atmosphere on a global scale. Acid precipitation, ozone depletion, and global warming are all caused by human activities.

Vocabulary
acid precipitation (p. 727)
global warming (p. 725)
ozone (p. 724)
smog (p. 724)

SECTION 27.4
Human Impact on Water Resources

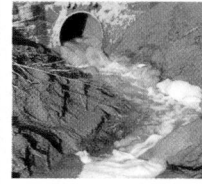

Main Ideas
- Humans require freshwater to live. In some regions, there is not enough freshwater to meet the demand. Conservation of existing supplies is the best way to stretch supplies of freshwater.
- Human activities can pollute freshwater supplies and render them unusable.
- The Safe Drinking Water Act and the Clean Water Act are two sets of laws designed to decrease water pollution in the United States.

Vocabulary
nonpoint source (p. 730)
point source (p. 730)

earthgeu.com/vocabulary_puzzlemaker

Study Guide **737**

GLENCOE
Technology

Videotape/DVD
MindJogger Videoquizzes
Chapter 27: *Human Impact on Earth Resources*
Have students work in groups as they play the videoquiz game to review key chapter concepts.

Resource Manager

Chapter Assessment, pp. 157–162
MindJogger Videoquizzes DVD/VHS
ExamView® Pro CD-ROM
Performance Assessment in Earth Science

CHAPTER 27
Study Guide

Main Ideas

Summary statements can be used by students to review the major concepts of the chapter.

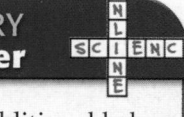

VOCABULARY PuzzleMaker

For additional help with vocabulary, have students access the Vocabulary Puzzlemaker online.

earthgeu.com/ vocabulary_puzzlemaker

(0:00) *Out of Time?*

If time does not permit teaching the entire chapter, use the GeoDigest at the end of the unit as an overview.

Earth Science Online

Be sure to check the Earth Science Web Site for links to chapter material:
earthgeu.com

NY Core Curriculum Standards

Page 736: St 6 KI 5
Page 737: St 4 KI 2.2d, St 6 KI 5 & 6

Understanding Main Ideas

1. a
2. d
3. d
4. b
5. b
6. b
7. a
8. a
9. a
10. mining and oil and gas production
11. sewage
12. 84.9 percent
13. Answers will vary. Municipalities and industry would have the greatest impact on landfills, but mining and oil and gas drilling would have the greatest impact on the total amount.

Applying Main Ideas

14. As the population grows, the number of reproducing individuals increases, and the rate of population growth accelerates.
15. The rate of population increase will slow down and the total population will fluctuate around an equilibrium number.
16. Mining companies build containment ponds to hold wastewater, reclaim the land surface, control dust, and place waste rock piles carefully to reduce pollution.

Understanding Main Ideas

1. What is the rapid growth rate of a population after a period of slow growth called?
   a. exponential growth
   b. overconsumption
   c. a point source
   d. the carrying capacity

2. Which of the following consumes the largest amount of freshwater in the United States?
   a. sewage-waste disposal
   b. irrigation
   c. drinking water
   d. industrial uses

3. What is the use of organisms to help clean up pollution called?
   a. the greenhouse effect
   b. reclamation
   c. recycling
   d. bioremediation

4. What type of pollution comes from multiple places?
   a. point source
   b. nonpoint source
   c. irrigation
   d. reclamation

5. What is the process in which a mining company restores the land after mineral extraction?
   a. bioremediation
   b. reclamation
   c. pollution
   d. open-pit mining

6. Which of the following is a gas molecule composed of three oxygen atoms?
   a. nitrogen oxide
   b. ozone
   c. sulfur dioxide
   d. smog

7. Which of the following is the primary source of carbon-monoxide air pollution?
   a. motor vehicles
   b. volcanoes
   c. urban development
   d. power plants

8. Which of the following gases is (are) responsible for ozone depletion in the upper atmosphere?
   a. chlorofluorocarbons
   b. carbon dioxide
   c. sulfur dioxide
   d. carbon monoxide

9. What is the variety of species in a habitat called?
   a. biodiversity
   b. monoculture
   c. bioremediation
   d. biology

Use the following graph to answer questions 10 through 13.

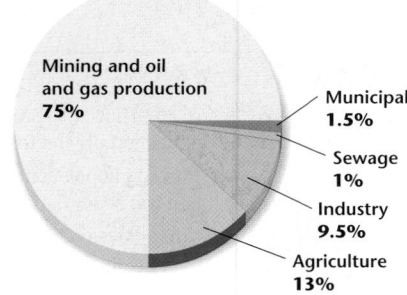

Solid Wastes Generated Annually in the U.S.

Mining and oil and gas production 75%
Municipal 1.5%
Sewage 1%
Industry 9.5%
Agriculture 13%

10. What activity is the largest producer of solid wastes in the United States each year?

11. What source produces the smallest amount of solid wastes in the United States each year?

12. What is the total percentage of solid waste produced by industry and resource extraction activities in the United States each year?

13. If you wanted to reduce the total amount of solid wastes produced each year, in what area would you concentrate your efforts? Why?

Test-Taking Tip

ROOT WORDS Use roots to learn. Roots can help you group words together as you learn them. If you learn that *bene-* means "good" as in beneficial, you can then group new words such as benefit, benefactor, and benevolent with beneficial, a word you already know.

earthgeu.com/chapter_test

17. Monocultures can deplete soil nutrients and cause a greater risk of insect, disease, and fungal damage.
18. Modern landfills are lined to prevent leakage, have drainage systems to collect liquids and gases, and undergo daily compaction and soil covering to reduce wind-blown trash.
19. A hurricane affects all populations equally without regard to population size; thus, it is density independent. A new disease may affect one population more than another, especially in dense populations, where the disease can spread more easily. Thus, disease is usually density dependent.
20. They have to increase the amount because they killed off the susceptible organisms earlier, and the organisms left are more resistant to the pesticide.

Applying Main Ideas

14. What causes populations to experience periods of explosive growth?

15. What will happen to human population numbers as carrying capacity is approached?

16. How do mining companies protect the environment when they extract mineral resources?

17. What are some of the risks of planting a monoculture?

18. What steps are taken in modern landfills to reduce environmental pollution?

19. Explain why a hurricane is a density-independent factor in limiting population size, whereas a new disease such as the Ebola virus is density-dependent.

20. Why do farmers who use chemical pesticides to control pests have to increase the amount applied to their fields each year?

Thinking Critically

21. What are some of the environmental costs involved in developing a new gold mine, and how might this affect the decision to open the mine?

22. Why is ground-level ozone worse on a sunny weekday than on a sunny weekend?

23. If midwestern power plants generate most of the air pollution, why does most acid precipitation fall in the northeastern United States?

24. How does urban development impact coastal waters?

25. What would be some of the positive environmental effects of reducing consumption of electricity?

earthgeu.com/standardized_test

Standardized Test Practice

INTERPRETING DATA Use the graphic below to answer the following questions.

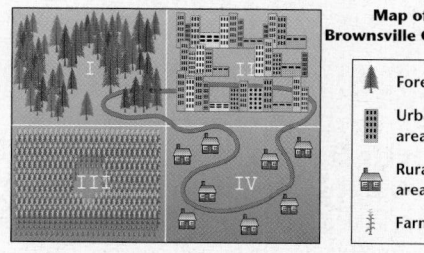

Map of Brownsville County

- Forest
- Urban area
- Rural area
- Farm

1. Which area of Brownsville is most likely to have problems with flooding during heavy rains?
   a. I   **b.** II   **c.** III   **d.** IV

2. Which area of Brownsville is most likely to have problems with nonpoint source pollution from fertilizer runoff?
   a. I   **b.** II   **c.** III   **d.** IV

3. If Brownsville County decided to clear area I in order to expand area III, Brownsville might develop problems with topsoil erosion and pesticide pollution. What might be one way to minimize harmful effects?
   a. deforestation   **c.** monoculture
   b. clear-cutting   **d.** selective logging

4. What will happen if the size of Brownsville's human population reaches the carrying capacity for its environment?
   a. There will be more births than deaths.
   b. The death rate will increase and the birth rate will increase.
   c. The population will reach equilibrium.
   d. There will be no more births until the death rate increases.

Thinking Critically

21. Environmental costs would include treating wastewater, monitoring and containing dangerous chemicals, storing waste-rock piles, and reclaiming the land surface. If the environmental costs are greater than the value of the extractable gold, the mine will probably not be opened.

22. Much of the air pollution that reacts to form ozone comes from cars. More cars are on the road during weekdays than weekends because people are commuting to and from work.

23. The prevailing wind patterns carry the air pollution from the Midwest to the Northeast. The air pollution doesn't hit moist, rainy weather until it reaches the Northeast, where it reacts to form acid precipitation.

24. Urban development impacts coastal water in the form of fertilizer runoff, sewage disposal, oil and other toxic runoff from streets, increased flooding, increased sediment, and erosion.

25. Some of the positive environmental effects of reducing electricity consumption are derived from decreased production. Less production means less acid precipitation, less strip-mining of coal, less CO_2 in the atmosphere, less water used for cooling and therefore less thermal pollution, and fewer dams needed for hydroelectric power.

EXAMVIEW® PRO

Use ExamView® Pro Testmaker CD-ROM to:

- Create **multiple versions** of tests.
- Create **modified** tests with one mouse click for struggling students.
- **Edit** existing questions and add your own questions.
- **Build** tests based on national curriculum standards.

Standardized Test Practice

1. b
2. c
3. d
4. c

For a **preview** of resources and the environment, study this GeoDigest before you read the chapters. After you have studied the topic, you can use the GeoDigest to **review** the unit.

Prepare

Purpose

This GeoDigest can be used as an overview of the concepts of Earth resources and the impacts of their use. If time is limited, you may wish to use this unit summary to teach these concepts in place of the chapters in Unit 7.

Key Concepts

Students are introduced to natural resources on Earth. They will learn about renewable and nonrenewable resources, traditional as well as alternative energy resources, and the impact of using Earth resources.

1 Focus

Section Focus

 Visual-Spatial Use a block of foam board and a block of clay of the same size to make models of a meteorite crater. Cut the foam board and mold the clay into the shape of a crater. Then tell students that you wish to make a volcano from these same materials. Ask students which of the two materials can be reused to make the new model. Students will recognize that the clay can be reused more readily than the foam board. Inform students that the same is true of Earth resources; some are reused easily, whereas others cannot be reused.

0:00 Out of Time?

If time does not permit teaching the entire unit, use this GeoDigest as an overview.

Resources and the Environment

Earth Resources

Resources Natural resources, which include air, water, land, organisms, rocks, minerals, and nutrients, are resources that Earth provides. Geochemical cycles that move substances through Earth's hydrosphere, lithosphere, biosphere, and atmosphere are also natural resources. Renewable resources, which include living things, surface water, groundwater, fertile soil, air, solar energy, and elements that cycle such as carbon and nitrogen, are replaced by natural processes at a rate that is at least equal to the rate at which they are used. Nonrenewable resources exist in fixed amounts in Earth's crust and can be replaced only by geological, physical, or chemical processes that take hundreds of millions of years. Nonrenewable resources include fossil fuels, such as coal and petroleum, and elements such as gold, copper, and silver. Natural resources are not distributed evenly on Earth.

in buildings and monuments. Aggregates such as sand, gravel, and crushed stone, are used in construction. An ore is a natural resource that can be mined at a profit. Ores may be associated with igneous rocks or formed by processes at Earth's surface. Some uses of land resources may have negative effects on the environment.

Land Resources Land resources include topsoil, rocks, minerals, and space for agriculture, housing, roadways, and protected areas such as wildlife refuges and national parks. In the United States, 42 percent of the land is protected from some uses. Topsoil is a mixture of decaying organic matter, eroded rock, minerals, nutrients, oxygen, and water. It takes thousands of years for topsoil to form, yet poor farming practices and erosion can lead to its rapid loss and even to the formation of deserts. Bedrock is unweathered parent rock, which is used

Air Resources Earth's atmosphere is mostly composed of nitrogen and oxygen, with small amounts of other gases. Early in Earth's history, its atmosphere had no oxygen; over time, oxygen was provided by photosynthetic organisms. When human activities disrupt the balance of the geochemical cycles in Earth's atmosphere, pollution results. Both indoor and outdoor pollution are harmful. Outdoors, pollutants can be transported, diluted, transformed, or removed. Indoor air pollutants remain trapped, resulting in "sick" buildings.

Multiple Learning Styles

 Visual-Spatial Section Focus, p. 740

 Interpersonal Collaborative Learning, p. 741

 Intrapersonal Applying Earth Science, p. 742, Reteach, p. 743

GeoDigest

Water Resources Only three percent of the water on Earth is freshwater and it is continually recycled through the water cycle. Water has unique properties that allow life to exist on Earth. It is a liquid over a wide range of temperatures, has high heat-storage capacity, dissolves many substances, and expands when it freezes. Because water is not evenly distributed on Earth, water management techniques and plans are developed to ensure a continuing supply. Management methods include building dams and reservoirs, transporting surface water, tapping groundwater, and desalinating seawater.

Energy Resources

The Sun is Earth's primary energy source. The Sun's energy is transferred from photosynthetic organisms to all other living things. Materials from living things have been used as fuels throughout history. Renewable biomass fuels release energy when they are burned, decomposed, or digested, and thus produce heat and electricity. Wood still serves as a fuel for over half of the world's population. Field crops such as hay, corn, straw, and sugar cane are also used as fuels. Fossil fuels, such as coal and petroleum, formed from organisms that lived millions of years ago. The burning of fossil fuels releases sulfur into the atmosphere and causes air pollution. As ancient organisms died and settled to the bottom of swamps, their remains partially decayed and formed peat. When the peat was subjected to high temperatures and pressure, coal formed. Types of coal include lignite, bituminous coal, and anthracite.

Natural gas and petroleum formed from accumulations of ancient organic material, primarily plankton, in shallow seas. Refined crude oil yields gasoline, kerosene, fertilizer, plastics, lubricants, and medicines.

Alternative Energy Resources

Alternative energy resources are those other than fossil fuels. Solar energy is unlimited, but advances in technology are needed to find better ways to collect and store it. Both passive and active solar techniques are used. Hydroelectric power is derived from the energy of falling or moving water and is commonly used in the production of electricity. In coastal areas, tidal power can be used to produce electricity. Geothermal energy is available in certain areas and is a product of Earth's internal heat. In areas with consistently strong winds, wind is a source of energy. Nuclear energy results when atoms of radioactive elements emit particles in the process known as fission. Technological advances are needed to dispose of or render harmless the dangerous waste products of nuclear energy. Biomass energy comes from the burning, decomposition, or digestion of organic materials such as wood, crops, and animal-waste material. Alcohols that form from biomass can be mixed with fuels such as gasoline to produce gasohol. Biogas, a mixture of methane and carbon dioxide, forms from the decomposition of animal wastes.

Conservation of Energy Resources

Energy resources will last longer if conservation and energy efficiency are further developed, so that fewer resources are used to provide more energy. Making vehicles more fuel efficient and improving efficiency in industry and homes will reduce the rate at which natural resources are used. Achieving sustainable energy use will ensure that current and future energy needs are met while guarding against the degradation of our environment.

GeoDigest **741**

✔**Assessment**

Portfolio Assessment
Assessment, TWE, p. 743

Knowledge Assessment
GeoDigest Assessment, SE, p. 743

Resource Manager

Study Guide for Content Mastery,
pp. 175–176

---

2 Teach

Modeling

Fill a set of beakers or clear containers with the following: marbles, jelly beans, table-tennis balls, clay, and colored water. Ask students which of the containers are models of aggregates. those filled with marbles, jellybeans, and table-tennis balls

Discussion

Place a glass of ice water on a desk in the front of the classroom. Ask students what substances found in the room currently exist in all three states of matter at the same time. water, as liquid water, ice, and water vapor in the atmosphere

Collaborative Learning

Interpersonal Have students work in small groups to research "sick" buildings. Encourage students to use magazines, newspapers, and the Internet in their research. Have student groups present their findings to the class. Then have each group cut out magazine illustrations or photos to develop a class bulletin board on the topic. Ask students to consider possible issues of concern within the school building. Have students develop a plan to check the air quality in the school and identify what steps they can take if they think a problem exists.

Interpreting the Photo

Ask students to identify each of the uses of water shown in the photograph. Then ask students to suggest ways in which water could be conserved in each of the uses shown.

Using an Analogy

Ask students to compare the following scenario to the use and conservation of Earth's resources. A group of students went on a white-water rafting trip. They carried enough food with them to last for four days. On the second day of the trip, their raft overturned in the rapids, and most of their food supply fell overboard and disappeared downstream. To survive the next two days of their trip, the students had to conserve the remaining food supply and look for alternative food resources in the environment. Students should recognize that the rafters' food supply is comparable to Earth's resources.

Humans and Resources

Populations All organisms use resources to exist and the uses of these resources have an impact on the environment. As populations increase, the demand for resources also increases. At first, populations grow exponentially. But because resources are limited, populations eventually reach the carrying capacity of the environment and stop growing. Earth's current human population explosion has a huge impact on resources and environments.

Impact on Land, Air, and Water The extraction of the mineral resources that modern societies need can disrupt land surfaces and create toxic chemical wastes. Growing populations may increase the demand for food production, which causes habitat loss, erosion, and water pollution. Urban development also causes habitat loss, erosion, and pollution of nearby areas. Many cities are taking steps to preserve habitats, control erosion at construction sites, and clean up pollution. Air pollution causes human health problems. Ground-level ozone is the major component of smog, a type of air pollution common in cities. Humans affect Earth's atmosphere on a global scale, as demonstrated by acid precipitation, ozone depletion, and

global warming. Controlling air pollution requires government help because wind blows air pollution across state and national boundaries. Conservation of existing supplies is the best way to ensure that freshwater is available in areas where there is not enough to meet human needs. Pollution of freshwater supplies comes from sewage, pesticide and fertilizer runoff, and chemical and oil spills. The Clean Air, Safe Drinking Water, and Clean Water Acts are laws designed to decrease pollution in the United States.

A Sustainable Society When the total environmental cost of developing and using a resource is considered, some resources may be uneconomical to develop. Resources will run out if the current rate of consumption is not decreased. For a society to be sustainable, it must manage its resources to minimize demand and environmental impact. Reducing, reusing, and recycling materials decreases the demand for resources.

Vital Statistics

Most Populous Cities: 2003	Population
1. Mumbai (Bombay), India	12 383 100
2. Buenos Aires, Argentina	12 116 400
3. Karachi, Pakistan	10 537 200
4. Manila, Philippines	10 232 900
5. Delhi, India	10 203 700
6. São Paulo, Brazil	10 195 000
7. Seoul, South Korea	9 630 600
8. Istanbul, Turkey	9 419 000

FOCUS ON CAREERS

Urban Planner
An urban planner develops ideas for how a city will develop and use its land—now and in the future. He or she works with city leaders to make a plan that meets the needs of all citizens. The urban planner examines the need for greenbelts and parks, and determines how traffic will move through an area. Urban planners usually have bachelor's degrees, and an advanced degree is sometimes necessary.

Earth Science *Journal*

Have students each make a data table in their science journals that compares the supply, source, advantages, and disadvantages of energy resources, such as wood, oil, and coal.

Applying Earth Science

Intrapersonal Pop some popcorn before class. Ask students to suggest ways to rid the classroom of the popcorn smell. Students will suggest opening windows, using fans, or removing the source of the smell. Ask students how this smell models a source of air pollution and how the method they used to solve the problem compares to an actual method used to clean up air pollution. **ELL**

Resources and the Environment

ASSESSMENT

Understanding Main Ideas

1. What are resources called that are replaced by natural processes at a rate that is at least equal to the rate at which they are used?
  a. nonrenewable resources
  b. fossil fuels
  c. renewable resources
  d. minerals

2. What type of resources are topsoil, rocks, minerals, and space for agriculture, housing, and roadways?
  a. land   **c.** water
  b. air   **d.** solar

3. What causes a building to become "sick"?
  a. outdoor air pollution
  b. thinning of the ozone
  c. indoor air pollution
  d. acid precipitation

4. What types of methods are building dams and reservoirs, tapping groundwater, and desalinating seawater?
  a. soil conservation
  b. water management
  c. transportation
  d. cleaning up pollution

5. Which of the following is not a type of coal?
  a. lignite
  b. bituminous coal
  c. anthracite
  d. peat

6. What is the ultimate source of most forms of energy on Earth?
  a. fossil fuels   **c.** biomass
  b. the Sun   **d.** tidal power

7. Which of these is not a property of water?
  a. liquid over wide temperature range
  b. high heat storage capacity
  c. contracts when it freezes
  d. dissolves many substances

8. What happens when populations reach the carrying capacity of the environment?
  a. They stop growing.
  b. They explode.
  c. They grow exponentially.
  d. They outgrow cities.

9. Acid precipitation, ozone depletion, and global warming demonstrate what type of effects by humans on the atmosphere?
  a. local   **c.** national
  b. regional   **d.** global

10. Which of these is a land resource that can be mined at a profit?
  a. bedrock   **c.** ore
  b. aggregate   **d.** topsoil

Thinking Critically

1. Compare and contrast renewable and non-renewable resources.
2. Describe how gasoline is derived from living things.
3. Explain why governments get involved in controlling pollution.

Bauxite

GeoDigest **743**

3 Assess

Check for Understanding
Project
Take students on a walking field trip around the school grounds. As they walk, have students record natural, energy, and human resources that they notice along the way. In a discussion following the field trip, ask students to identify resources that they did not find on the trip.

Reteach

Intrapersonal Have students develop study cards that each have a picture or photograph of a resource on one side and the definition and facts about the resource on the opposite side of the card.

✓Assessment

Portfolio Ask students to each write a short story about an imaginary planet and how its life and resources need to be managed. Tell students that their stories should reflect the same problems that exist on Earth. Grade the content of students' work based on their development of the concepts of this unit.

ASSESSMENT

Understanding Main Ideas

1. c **3.** c **5.** d **7.** c **9.** d
2. a **4.** b **6.** b **8.** a **10.** c

Thinking Critically

1. Renewable resources are those that can be replaced at a rate that is at least equal to the rate at which they are used. Nonrenewable resources exist in fixed amounts and can be replaced only by Earth processes that take millions of years.

2. Gasoline is a petroleum product derived from crude oil. Crude oil is a fossil fuel that formed from the remains of organisms that lived millions of years ago.

3. Pollution often crosses borders, as in air pollution and water pollution. Governments become involved because the activities in one country can have impacts on a neighboring country.

NY Core Curriculum Standards

Page 740: St 4 KI 1.2e
Page 741: St 4 KI 2.1a
Page 742: St 6 KI 5
Page 743: St 4 KI 2.1a, St 6 KI 5

743

Beyond Earth

Unit Overview

Astronomy In Unit 8, students are introduced to the universe beyond Earth and the relationships between planets and moons, and stars and galaxies. The formation of the universe led to the formation of galaxies and stars, and during the formation of some stars, planetary systems developed. The planets in our solar system contain clues to the solar system's formation. The two astronomical bodies that have the most dramatic impact on Earth are the Sun and the Moon, which influence Earth's climates and tides, and provide the dramatic displays of eclipses and lunar phases.

Chapter Breakdown Chapter 28 emphasizes astronomical observations and the effects of the Sun-Earth-Moon system on our daily lives, while Chapter 29 explores our solar system and its origin and helps to put Earth in context by a comparison with other planets. Chapters 30 and 31 bring students into the realm of deep space and cosmology through discussions of the Sun and other stars, in Chapter 30, and of galaxies and the universe as a whole, in Chapter 31.

0:00 Out of Time?

If time does not permit teaching the entire unit, use the GeoDigest at the end of the unit as an overview.

Unit 8

Beyond Earth

The nighttime sky appears to contain only stars, which belong to the Milky Way (right). However, a variety of objects, such as planets, stars, nebulae, and galaxies can be found. Despite their distance, each of these objects impacts our existence here on Earth. Galaxies provide a place for stars to develop. Nebulae provide the materials to form stars. Stars, like the Sun, provide energy and create elements. Star formation often results in the formation of planets.

Unit Contents

NATIONAL GEOGRAPHIC

Go to the National Geographic Expedition on page 902 to learn more about topics that are connected to this unit.

744

NATIONAL GEOGRAPHIC

NASA's Eye in the Sky Some topics of Earth science deserve more attention than others because they're unusual, informative, or just plain interesting. The National Geographic Society has created visually exciting multipage *Expeditions!* features that inform, excite, and motivate your students.

Expeditions! features are relevant to the Earth science content of the student edition. Assign them as a lead-in to special research projects and in-depth studies for extra credit. Use them as a basis for colorful visual displays and bulletin boards.

Unit 8

Introducing the Unit

Preconceptions This composite photograph shows a desert landscape superimposed over an image of the Milky Way Galaxy. What do students think that the Milky Way contains? Students may say that it contains only stars, but ask them to hypothesize what stars are made of and whether all stars are the same. Ask students whether they've ever observed the Milky Way. If so, ask them how it was different from the photograph. Can they give possible reasons for any differences?

Formation History Galaxies contain gas and dust, as well as stars. Interstellar gas and dust can be observed either as dark clouds blocking light or glowing clouds. These clouds are the birthplaces of stars and planets. Stars are mostly gas, while planets are collections of dust and gas. Rocky planets, such as Earth, are mostly large collections of dust, while planets such as Jupiter are mostly gas. Stars evolve as they fuse elements within their cores.

Milky Way Galaxy

745

Earth Science Online Note Internet addresses that you find useful in the space below for quick reference.

_____

_____

_____

_____

_____

For Internet tips, see Glencoe's **Using the Internet in the Science Classroom.**

Chapter 28

The Sun-Earth-Moon System

Refer to pages 8T–9T of the Teacher Guide for an explanation of the National Science Content Standards correlations.

Section	Objectives	National Science Content Standards	State/Local Standards
SECTION 28.1 **Tools of Astronomy** 🕐 1 session 📦 ½ block	1. **Describe** electromagnetic radiation. 2. **Explain** how telescopes work. 3. **Describe** space exploration.	UCP.1, UCP.2, UCP.3, UCP.5; D.1; E.1, E.2; F.6; G.1, G.3	St 1 Math KI 1 & Engin KI 1, St 6 KI 3, St 7 KI 1, St 4 KI 1.lf
SECTION 28.2 **The Moon** 🕐 1 session 📦 ½ block	4. **Describe** the development of exploration of the Moon. 5. **Identify** features on the Moon. 6. **Explain** the theories about how the Moon formed.	UCP.2, UCP.3, UCP.4; A.2; D.3; E.2; F.6; G.1	St 1 Science KI 1, St 4 KI 1.1b, 1.2c, & 1.2d, St 6 KI 2
SECTION 28.3 **The Sun-Earth-Moon System** 🕐 3 sessions 📦 2 blocks	7. **Identify** the relative positions and motions of Earth, the Sun, and the Moon. 8. **Describe** the phases of the Moon. 9. **Explain** eclipses of the Sun and Moon.	UCP.1, UCP.2, UCP.3, UCP.4, UCP.5; A.1, A.2; B.4; D.1, D.3; E.1; G.2, G.3	St 1 Math KI 1, 2, 3, & Science KI 2, St 4 KI 1.1a, 1.1c, 1.1d, 1.1e, 1.1f, 1.1g, 1.1h, & 1.1i, St 6 KI 2, 3, 4, & 5

A complete Planning Guide is provided on pages 30T–32T.

🕐 The number of recommended single-period sessions

📦 The number of recommended blocks

Activity Materials

Discovery Lab *page 747*
meterstick, drawing compass, scissors, paper, pencil

GeoLab *pages 768–769*
pencil, paper, ruler

MiniLab *page 761*
drawing compass, protractor, ruler, paper, pencil

Demo *page 747*
prism, light source, white paper

page 749
magnifying glass, paper

page 755
cake pan, colored sand, flour, rocks of assorted sizes

page 758
globe, flashlight

page 764
globe, foam ball, pointer or arrow

Key to Teaching Strategies

L1 Level 1 activities should be appropriate for students with learning difficulties.

L2 Level 2 activities should be within the ability range of all students.

L3 Level 3 activities are designed for above-average students.

ELL ELL activities should be within the ability range of English-language learners.

COOP LEARN Cooperative learning activities are designed for small-group work.

P These strategies represent student products that can be placed in a best-work portfolio.

 These strategies are useful in a block-scheduling format.

Need materials? Contact Science Kit at 1-800-828-7777 or at www.sciencekit.com on the Internet. For alternate materials, see the activity on the listed page.

Chapter Organizer

Glencoe Exclusive!
TeacherWorks™
All-In-One Planner and Resource Center

Activities/Features	Reproducible Masters	Transparencies
Discovery Lab: Make a Scale Model, p. 747 **Using Math:** Using Numbers, p. 748	**Study Guide for Content Mastery,** p. 177 **L2** **Laboratory Manual,** pp. 221–224 **L2**	**Section Focus Transparency 89** **L1** **ELL** **Teaching Transparency 86** **L2** **ELL**
	Study Guide for Content Mastery, pp. 178–179 **L2**	**Section Focus Transparency 90** **L1** **ELL** **Teaching Transparency 87** **L2** **ELL**
MiniLab: The Sun's Position, p. 761 **Problem-Solving Lab:** Interpreting Scientific Illustrations, p. 766 **Mapping GeoLab:** Relative Ages of Lunar Features, pp. 768–769 **Science & Math:** The Size of Earth, p. 770	**Study Guide for Content Mastery,** pp. 180–182 **L2** **GeoLab and MiniLab Worksheets,** p. 111 **L2** **GeoLab and MiniLab Worksheets,** pp. 112–114 **L2** **Laboratory Manual,** pp. 217–220 **L2**	**Section Focus Transparency 91** **L1** **ELL** **Teaching Transparency 88** **L2** **ELL** **Teaching Transparency 89** **L2** **ELL**

✓Assessment

Chapter Assessment, pp. 163–168
Performance Assessment in the Science Classroom (PASC)
MindJogger Videoquiz DVD/VHS
Performance Assessment in Earth Science
ExamView® Pro CD-ROM
5 Days to the Regents Exam

GLENCOE'S
ASSESSMENT
ADVANTAGE

Additional Resources

Guided Reading Audio Program **ELL**
Cooperative Learning in the Science Classroom
Lesson Plans
Block Scheduling
earthgeu.com
NY Lesson Plans
NY Block Scheduling
Review Handbook for Regents Earth Science Exam

NATIONAL GEOGRAPHIC

Teacher's Corner

Products Available from National Geographic Society
To order the following products, call the National Geographic Society at 1-800-368-2728:
Curriculum Kits
GeoKit: *Astronomy*

Videos
Sun, Earth, Moon
The Sun: Earth's Star
Maps
The Earth's Moon

Content Background

Tools of Astronomy
Section 28.1

The speed of light (and of all electromagnetic radiation) is constant in a vacuum. The speed of light is a little slower in any medium such as air, glass, or water. In most transparent media, the speed of light is very close to its speed in a vacuum, and often, the difference can be ignored. However, the media through which light travels have important effects on light. For example, refraction, the bending of light as it passes through a boundary between media, is caused by the shift in light speed at the boundary. A refracting telescope focuses light by bending it. A reflecting telescope relies on a curved mirror, usually parabolic in shape, to bring light to a focus. A radio telescope uses a curved dish to bring radio waves to a focus, much like a reflecting telescope. Many radio telescopes have wire mesh dishes because the wavelengths of radio waves are longer than the spaces between the mesh, so radio waves are still reflected. Gamma rays and X rays cannot be reflected in a conventional method. Because they have such high frequencies and short wavelengths, these rays must be reflected by a series of grazing, or low-angle, reflections. Otherwise, they travel right through a material.

The Moon
Section 28.2

Lunar surface features, particularly the major craters that are readily observed from Earth, are generally named after important people in astronomy.

However, other conventions are used as well. The maria are so named because Galileo thought they were seas, and they were given names corresponding to human feelings or moods, for example, the Sea of Tranquility. Mountainous regions on the Moon are named after mountain ranges on Earth. Small features that were not identified until humans explored the Moon were named by astronauts, and some are quite colloquial.

The Moon has a very tenuous atmosphere. It is composed primarily of hydrogen, helium, neon, and argon. The atmosphere was extremely difficult for Apollo astronauts to measure. It is so tenuous that the exhaust gases from the Apollo lander seriously contaminated it. In fact, if the Moon's atmosphere were compressed down to the density of water, the entire atmosphere would fit into a cube measuring 1 m on each side. Earth's atmosphere, in contrast, would fit into a cube measuring 170 km on each side.

Multiple Learning Styles

- **Kinesthetic** Modeling, p. 760
- **Visual-Spatial** Demo, pp. 747, 749, 755, 758
- **Interpersonal** Collaborative Learning, p. 756
- **Intrapersonal** Enrichment, p. 762
- **Linguistic** Reteach, p. 757
- **Logical-Mathematical** Reteach, p. 752

GLENCOE
Technology

The following multimedia resources are available from Glencoe.

The Infinite Voyage Series
Sail On, Voyager
Unseen Worlds

The Planets
Moon

Vocabulary Puzzlemaker

TeacherWorks™ CD-ROM

MindJogger Videoquizzes DVD/VHS

ExamView® Pro CD-ROM

Interactive Chalkboard CD-ROM

Chapter Organizer

The Sun-Earth-Moon System
Section 28.3

Earth's rotation is the basis for human timekeeping. Even today, the world's clocks are set according to the solar day through precise astronomical observations made by such institutions as the U.S. Naval Observatory, whose timekeeping service sets the official U.S. clocks, which are coordinated with others throughout the world. Atomic clocks, known for their precision, measure only relative time, not absolute time (i.e., not the time of day as read on a clock). Earth's rotation is slowing very gradually, requiring that a leap second be added to official clocks from time to time.

The Moon is far more massive relative to Earth than most other satellites are in relation to their planets. Thus, the Moon has a substantial gravitational effect on Earth. Calculations have shown that Earth's rotational axis would tend to shift as a result of small outside forces if not for the stabilizing effect of the Moon's gravity. If Earth's axis were not stable, climates would undergo extreme fluctuations over short or long periods of time. It has been suggested that life might not have been able to form on Earth without the stabilizing effect of the Moon. If life's presence on Earth requires the Moon, then life in the universe may be rare, because our Moon is unusual, as described in Section 28.2.

Identifying Misconceptions

Many students might think that the main purpose of a telescope is to magnify objects or to enable the observer to see farther. Neither is correct; the main purpose of a telescope is to enable the observer to see objects fainter than the human eye can detect. This often does involve far-away objects, depending on the luminosity of the objects being viewed. A secondary purpose of telescopes is to enable the observer to see details in images, which is called resolution, but this is not the same as magnification. Magnification makes an image larger but not necessarily clearer, as increased resolution does.

✔ Assessment

Portfolio Assessment
Assessment, TWE, p. 759

Performance Assessment
Discovery Lab, SE, p. 747
MiniLab, SE, p. 761
Assessment, TWE, p. 767
GeoLab, SE, pp. 768–769

Knowledge Assessment
Assessment, TWE, pp. 748, 756, 757, 763
GeoLab, TWE, pp. 768–769
Section Assessment, SE, pp. 752, 757, 767
Chapter Assessment, SE, pp. 772–773

Skill Assessment
Discovery Lab, TWE, p. 747
Assessment, TWE, p. 752
MiniLab, TWE, p. 761
Problem-Solving Lab, TWE, p. 766

GLENCOE'S ASSESSMENT ADVANTAGE

Earth Science Online

Be sure to check the Earth Science Web Site for links to chapter material: earthgeu.com

The Sun-Earth-Moon System

Introducing the Chapter

Spark student interest by discussing what astronomers do and how their branch of science relates to the other branches already discussed in the text. Ask students how astronomy relates to their daily lives, despite its seemingly remote nature. You may need to prompt students by asking them what they observe in the skies.

Interpreting the Photo

This total solar eclipse sequence was photographed over the Keck Observatory on the island of Mauna Kea, Hawaii, on July 11, 1991. A multiple-exposure photograph produced the multi-image progression of the eclipse. Depending on an observer's location, totality lasted from about three minutes to over six minutes.

PowerPoint® Presentations

This CD is an editable Microsoft® PowerPoint® presentation that includes:
• Section presentations
• Section checks
• Image bank
• Links to Earth Science Online
• All transparencies
• Animations
• Audio

The Sun-Earth-Moon System

What You'll Learn
• How light and telescopes are used to explore the sky.
• How to identify features on the Moon.
• What theories are used to describe the Moon's origin.
• How to analyze the motions of the Sun, Earth, and the Moon.

Why It's Important
The motions of the Sun-Earth-Moon system affect Earth physically, as well as play an important role in our timekeeping system.

Earth Science Online

To find out more about the Sun-Earth-Moon system, visit the Earth Science Web Site at earthgeu.com

746

The Sun-Earth-Moon System

Discovery Lab

Process Skills

compare and contrast, formulate models, measure in SI, interpret data, use numbers, recognize spatial relationships **L1** **ELL**

Safety Precautions

Caution students to handle scissors and drawing compasses with care.

Procedure

Observe

Scaled diameters: the Moon—1 cm; Earth— 3.7 cm; the Sun—403.3 cm. Scaled distances: Earth-Moon— 111 cm; Earth-Sun—44 400 cm. The size of the cutouts is small in comparison to the scaled distance between them. The cutouts are not very different in size, but a cutout of the Sun would be dramatically larger. A cutout of the Sun would be larger than a normal piece of paper, and if it were placed at the proper distance, the model would not fit in a classroom. Students would have to apply a new scale to

Make a Scale Model

The Sun is about 109 times larger in diameter than Earth, and Earth is about 3.7 times larger in diameter than the Moon. The Moon is 30 times farther from Earth than Earth's diameter, and the Sun is 400 times farther away from Earth than is the Moon. In this activity, you will compare relative sizes and distances within the Sun-Earth-Moon system.

1. Calculate the diameters of Earth and the Sun using a scale in which the Moon's diameter is equal to 1 cm.

2. Using your calculations in step 1, calculate the distance between Earth and the Moon and the distance between Earth and the Sun.

3. Cut out circles to represent your scaled Earth and Moon, and place them at the scaled distance apart.

CAUTION: *Always handle sharp objects with care.*

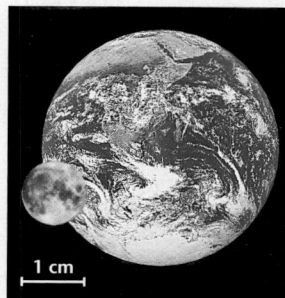
1 cm

Observe In your science journal, describe the sizes of your cutout Earth and Moon compared to the distance between them. Infer why you were not instructed to cut out a scaled Sun and place it at the scaled distance. How would you change this model so that it would fit in your classroom?

Tools of Astronomy

OBJECTIVES

- **Describe** *electromagnetic radiation.*
- **Explain** *how telescopes work.*
- **Describe** *space exploration.*

VOCABULARY

refracting telescope
reflecting telescope
interferometry
spinoff

The best tool, and in most cases the only tool, that astronomers can use to learn about the universe is the light that comes to Earth from distant objects. Apart from a few solar-system objects that have been sampled by direct probes and particles and fragments that have made their way into Earth's atmosphere, there is no other way to study the cosmos except to analyze the light that we receive from it. Therefore, it is necessary to understand the nature of light.

RADIATION

Light is a common term for electromagnetic radiation, which consists of electric and magnetic disturbances, traveling through space as waves. The human eye can sense only a limited range of all the various wavelengths of electromagnetic radiation. This range is called visible light. Electromagnetic radiation includes not just visible light, but also infrared and ultraviolet radiation, radio waves, microwaves, X rays, and gamma rays.

28.1 *Tools of Astronomy* **747**

---

the system by setting the distance between Earth and the Sun equal to the length of the classroom.

✔Assessment

Skill Ask students to measure the classroom and apply their scale to that measurement. Students should then compare and contrast the scaled measurement of the classroom to the distances among Earth, the Moon, and the Sun.

Resource Manager

Section Focus Transparency 89 L1 ELL

Study Guide for Content Mastery, p. 177 L2

Section Focus

Before presenting the lesson, display **Section Focus Transparency 89** on the overhead projector. L1 ELL

Chapter Themes

The following themes from the National Science Content Standards are covered in this chapter. Refer to page 8T of the Teacher Guide for an explanation of the correlations.
Systems, order, and organization (UCP.1); Evidence, models, and explanation (UCP.2); Change, constancy, and measurement (UCP.3); Form and function (UCP.4)

0:00 Out of Time?

If time does not permit teaching the entire chapter, use the Chapter Summary on page 771 and the GeoDigest found at the end of the unit as an overview.

Activity

Have students find out the frequency at which their favorite radio stations broadcast, and then calculate the wavelength of the broadcast using $\lambda = c/f$.

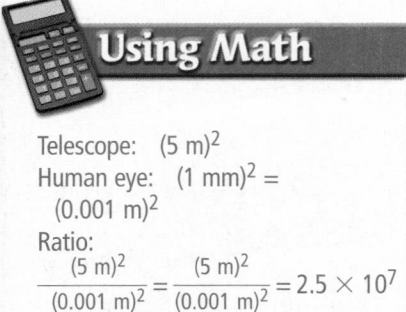

Using Math

Telescope: $(5 \text{ m})^2$
Human eye: $(1 \text{ mm})^2 =$
$(0.001 \text{ m})^2$
Ratio:
$$\frac{(5 \text{ m})^2}{(0.001 \text{ m})^2} = \frac{(5 \text{ m})^2}{(0.001 \text{ m})^2} = 2.5 \times 10^7$$

✓Assessment

Knowledge Ask students to each list the various forms of electromagnetic radiation in order from shortest to longest wavelengths. Also have students list the forms of electromagnetic radiation in order from lowest to highest frequency. From shortest to longest wavelengths are gamma rays, X rays, ultraviolet radiation, visible light, infrared radiation, microwaves, and radio waves. From lowest to highest frequency are radio waves, microwaves, infrared radiation, visible light, ultraviolet radiation, X rays, and gamma rays.

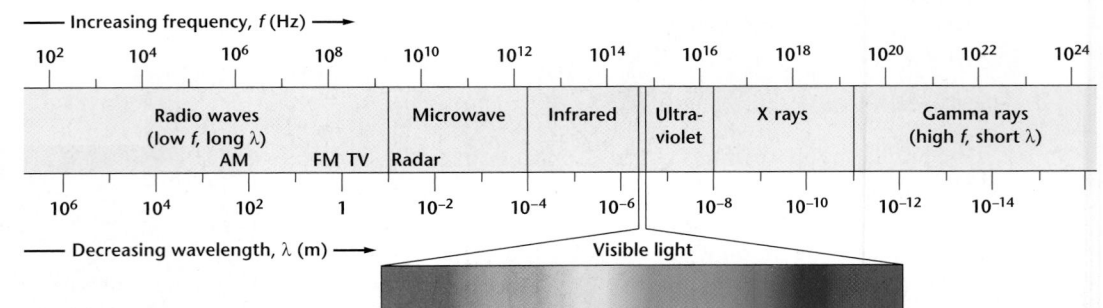

Increasing frequency, f (Hz) →

| 10^2 | 10^4 | 10^6 | 10^8 | 10^{10} | 10^{12} | 10^{14} | 10^{16} | 10^{18} | 10^{20} | 10^{22} | 10^{24} |

Radio waves (low f, long λ) AM | FM TV Radar | Microwave | Infrared | Ultra-violet | X rays | Gamma rays (high f, short λ)

| 10^6 | 10^4 | 10^2 | 1 | 10^{-2} | 10^{-4} | 10^{-6} | 10^{-8} | 10^{-10} | 10^{-12} | 10^{-14} |

← Decreasing wavelength, λ (m)

Visible light

Figure 28-1 The electromagnetic spectrum ranges from radio waves to gamma rays. Wavelength and frequency are related by $c = \lambda f$. Notice how small the range of visible light is compared to the rest of the spectrum.

Using Math

Using Numbers For a circular telescope, the collecting area is πr^2, where r is the telescope's radius. If one telescope is twice as large as another, it will collect four times as much light. How much more visible light will a visible-light telescope with a radius of 5 m collect than a human eye that has a pupil with a 1 mm radius?

You may be familiar with some forms of electromagnetic radiation. For example, ultraviolet radiation causes sunburn, and X rays help doctors diagnose diseases and observe internal injuries. All the types of electromagnetic radiation, arranged according to wavelength and frequency, form the electromagnetic spectrum, illustrated in *Figure 28-1.*

Electromagnetic radiation is classified by its wavelengths. Wavelength is the distance between peaks on a wave. You can see in *Figure 28-1* that red light has longer wavelengths than blue light, and radio waves have longer wavelengths than gamma rays. Electromagnetic radiation also can be classified according to frequency, which is the number of waves or oscillations occurring per second. Visible light has frequencies ranging from 4.3×10^{14} to 7.5×10^{14} Hz. There is a mathematical relationship between frequency and wavelength. Frequency is related to wavelength by $c = \lambda f$, where c is the speed of light (3.0×10^8 m/s), λ is the wavelength, and f is the frequency. Note that all types of electromagnetic radiation travel at the same speed, because c is constant.

TELESCOPES

Objects in space emit radiation in all portions of the electromagnetic spectrum. The ability to attach different detectors to telescopes to observe all wavelengths, especially those the human eye cannot detect, is just one of the benefits of using a telescope. Another benefit is that a telescope brings much more light to a focus than the human eye can. A telescope collects light from a distant object and focuses it at a point where the image of the object can be studied or recorded. The human eye does the same thing with visible light, but the eye is much more limited. A typical human-eye pupil has a diameter of up to 7 mm when it is adapted to darkness, whereas a telescope might be as large as 10 m in diameter. The area of the opening through which

748 CHAPTER 28 *The Sun-Earth-Moon System*

Interpreting the Illustration

Figure 28-1 Have students examine the electromagnetic spectrum and demonstrate the relationship between frequency and wavelength. As wavelength increases, frequency decreases, and vice versa.

Resource Manager

Laboratory Manual, pp. 221–224

light enters determines the light-collecting power of a telescope. The larger the opening, the more light that can be gathered. A telescope's ability to collect a large amount of light allows astronomers to observe faint objects.

A third benefit of telescopes is that they allow astronomers to use specialized equipment. A photometer, for example, is used to measure the intensity of visible light. A fourth benefit is that telescopes can be used to make time exposures with the aid of cameras or other imaging devices. In time exposures, light is collected over a long period of time. This is something the human eye cannot do. The human eye "photographs" what it sees about 10 times per second, so an object too dim to be perceived in one-tenth of a second cannot be seen. This is why telescopes are able to detect objects that are too faint for the human eye to see.

Refracting and Reflecting Telescopes Two different types of telescopes are used to focus visible light. The first telescopes, invented around the year 1600, used lenses to bring visible light to a focus and are called **refracting telescopes,** or refractors. The largest lens on such a telescope is called the objective lens. *Figure 28-2A* illustrates how a simple refracting telescope works. In 1668, a new telescope was designed that used mirrors. Telescopes that bring visible light to a focus with mirrors are called **reflecting telescopes,** or reflectors. *Figure 28-2B* illustrates how a simple reflecting telescope works.

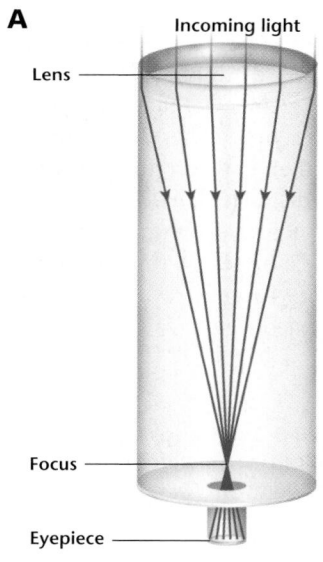
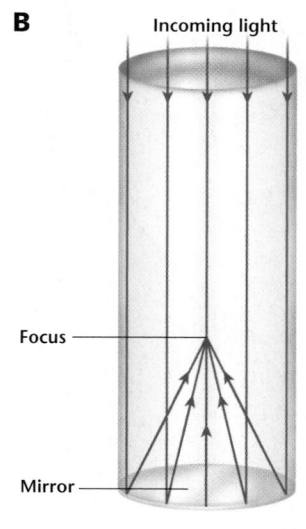

Figure 28-2 A refracting telescope **(A)** uses a lens to bring light to a focus. The largest lens is called the objective lens. A reflecting telescope **(B)** uses a mirror to bring light to a focus. The largest mirror is called the primary mirror.

Differentiated Instruction

Gifted The resolution of a telescope, meaning the smallest angular detail it can detect, is given by $\theta = 2.5 \times 10^5(\lambda/D)$, where θ is expressed in arcseconds (1 arcsecond = 1/60 of one minute of arc, which is 1/60 of a degree), λ represents the wavelength being observed, and D is the aperture diameter in meters. Explain to students that 1 arcsecond is roughly the angular diameter of a dime seen from a distance of 3 km. Have students calculate θ for a human eye with a pupil diameter of 2 mm, a 10-cm telescope, and a 5-m telescope, assuming that the observed wavelength is 6×10^{-7} m.

	Diameter	θ
Human eye	0.002 m	75 arcseconds
Telescope 1	0.1 m	1.5 arcseconds
Telescope 2	5 m	0.03 arcseconds

NY Core Curriculum Standards

Page 746: St 4 KI 1.1f
Page 747: St 6 KI 3
Page 748: St 1 Math KI 1, St 7 KI 1
Page 749: St 7 KI 1, St 1 Engin KI 1

Content Background

Reflectors have several advantages over refractors. The mirror of a reflector needs only one perfectly shaped surface, while a lens needs two. The glass in a lens must be clear and flawless, but because light does not travel through a mirror, the glass in a mirror does not have to be perfect. Mirrors can also be very large because they can be supported from behind. Lenses cannot be very large because they can be supported only around the edge and will sag if they are too large. Reflectors can also use a variety of mirror arrangements to bring light to a focus.

Environmental Connection

As a result of the numerous rocket launches and space exploration missions, space around Earth is filled with debris. These fragments of rockets and other debris will eventually fall into Earth's atmosphere and burn up, but until that time, this debris must be tracked. A small piece of debris can cause severe damage to a spacecraft or satellite because it is moving very quickly. The U.S. Space Command tracks over 7000 objects that are bigger than a few centimeters across. Occasionally, a large piece of debris doesn't burn up completely in Earth's atmosphere, and it crashes to the ground.

NY Core Curriculum Standards

Page 750: St 1 Engin KI 1, St 7 KI 1

Page 751: St 1 Engin KI 1, St 7 KI 1

Although both refracting and reflecting telescopes are still in use today, the majority are reflectors. Most telescopes used for scientific study are located at observatories far from city lights, usually at high elevations where there is less atmosphere overhead to blur images. Some of the best observatory sites in the world are located high atop mountains in the southwestern United States, along the peaks of the Andes Mountains in Chile, and on the summit of Mauna Kea, the gigantic volcano on the island of Hawaii.

Telescopes at Other Wavelengths In addition to using visible-light telescopes, astronomers observe the universe at wavelengths that the human eye cannot detect. For all telescopes, the goal is to bring as much radiation as possible to a focus. Infrared and ultraviolet radiation can be focused by mirrors in much the same way as visible light. X rays cannot be focused by normal mirrors, and thus, special designs must be used. Because gamma rays cannot be focused, telescopes designed to detect the extremely short wavelengths of this type of radiation can determine little more than the general direction from which the rays come.

Figure 28-3 shows a radio telescope consisting of a large dish, or antenna, which resembles a satellite TV dish. The dish plays the same role as the primary mirror in a reflecting telescope, by reflecting radio waves to a focus above the dish. There, a receiver converts the radio waves into electrical signals that can be stored in a computer for analysis. A process called interferometry, which has been used with radio telescopes for a number of years, is now being applied to other telescopes as well. **Interferometry** is the process of linking separate telescopes together so that they act as one telescope. The detail in the images that they produce improves as the distance between the telescopes increases. One of the best-known examples of this technology is the Very Large Array near Socorro, New Mexico.

NATIONAL GEOGRAPHIC

To learn more about the *Hubble Space Telescope,* go to the **National Geographic Expedition** on page 902.

Figure 28-3 The Owens Valley Radio Telescope in California is a typical radio telescope.

Earth Science Journal

Have each student choose a major observatory and research its location, the size and nature of its telescope, and the characteristics of the site that make it ideal for astronomical observations. Students should organize their information into reports that explain the features and advantages of the observatories.

Resource Manager

Teaching Transparency 86 [L2] [ELL]

SATELLITES, PROBES, AND SPACE-BASED ASTRONOMY

Astronomers often have to send their instruments into space to collect the information they seek. One reason for this is that Earth's atmosphere blocks infrared radiation, ultraviolet radiation, X rays, and gamma rays. In addition, when Earth's atmosphere does allow certain wavelengths to pass through, the images are blurred. Another reason for sending instruments into space is to make close-up observations and even obtain samples from nearby objects in the solar system. Since the late 1960s, American, European, Soviet (later, Russian), and Japanese space programs have launched many space-based observatories to collect data in different wavelengths.

One of the best-known space-based observatories, shown in *Figure 28-4,* is the *Hubble Space Telescope (HST),* which was launched in 1990 and is scheduled to operate until 2010. *HST* was designed to obtain sharp visible-light images without atmospheric interference, and also to make observations in infrared and ultraviolet wavelengths. Other space-based telescopes, such as the *Far Ultraviolet Spectroscopic Explorer,* the *Chandra X-Ray Observatory,* and the *Spitzer Space Telescope,* are used to observe other wavelengths that are blocked by Earth's atmosphere.

Spacecraft In addition to making observations from above Earth's atmosphere, space-based exploration can be achieved by sending spacecraft directly to the bodies being observed. Robotic probes make close-up observations and sometimes land to collect information directly. Probes are practical only for objects within our solar system, because the stars are much too far away. The robot *Sojourner,* part of the *Pathfinder* probe, explored Mars for almost 3 months in 1997. More recently, the twin robots *Spirit* and *Opportunity* conducted scientific experiments on Mars in 2004 (*Figure 28-5*).

Figure 28-4 On April 25, 1990, the *Hubble Space Telescope* was released from the shuttle *Discovery* during mission STS-31.

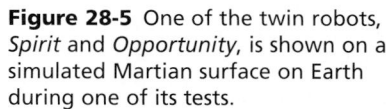

Figure 28-5 One of the twin robots, *Spirit* and *Opportunity,* is shown on a simulated Martian surface on Earth during one of its tests.

28.1 *Tools of Astronomy* **751**

Content Background

The launch of the American space station *Skylab* in 1973 enabled humans to live in space for up to 84 days. A Soviet (later Russian) space station, *Mir,* began operation in 1986 and ended in 2001. The maximum stay there was 366 days.

Tying to Previous Knowledge

HST and other Earth-orbiting spacecraft are powered by the same kinds of solar panels that are sometimes used as alternative energy sources for buildings on Earth. The solar arrays on *HST* and other spacecraft convert sunlight into electricity, which is stored in batteries onboard. The operations of spacecraft require that the solar panels be exposed to the Sun at all times.

Check for Understanding

Discussion

Tell students that astronomers are considering the idea of placing an observatory on the Moon. Ask students to discuss the advantages and disadvantages of doing so. The Moon has no atmosphere, so the telescope would obtain sharp images and could observe all wavelengths. The possibility of building a far larger telescope than is feasible for an orbiting spacecraft would be another advantage. The chief disadvantages would be cost and the difficulty of servicing the telescope.

Reteach

Logical-Mathematical Have students each make a summary table listing the advantages of telescopes and the criteria for deciding where to locate them, that is, whether they should be in space or on Earth, and if they are on Earth, where the best location is. For each criterion listed, ask students to give an example of a telescope that meets it. **L2**

✓Assessment

Skill Have students explain how refracting and reflecting telescopes work, and why each type is beneficial. Ask students to use their knowledge of how visible-light telescopes work and to draw sketches, similar to the illustrations in **Figure 28-2,** of a radio telescope.

NY Core Curriculum Standards

Page 752: St 1 Engin KI 1, St 7 KI 1
Page 753: St 4 KI 1.1b

Figure 28-6 This photo shows the partially completed *International Space Station* as it orbits Earth.

Human Spaceflight Exploring objects in space has been a top priority for scientists, but they have also been very interested in exploring the effects of space, such as weightlessness. The most recent human explorations and studies have been accomplished with the space shuttle program, which began in 1981. The space shuttle provides an environment for scientists to study the effects of weightlessness on humans, plants, the growth of crystals, and other phenomena. However, because shuttle missions last a maximum of just 17 days, long-term effects must be studied in space stations.

A multi-country space station called the *International Space Station,* shown in *Figure 28-6,* is the ideal environment to study the long-term effects of space. Human habitation and research aboard the *International Space Station* began in 2000.

Spinoffs Space-exploration programs have benefited our society far beyond our increased understanding of space. Many technologies that were originally developed for use in space programs are now used by people all over the world. Did you know that the technology for the space shuttle's fuel pumps led to the development of pumps used in artificial hearts? Or that the Apollo program led to the development of cordless tools? In fact, more than 1400 different NASA technologies have been passed on to commercial industries for common use, and are called **spinoffs.** Each year, new technologies are developed that not only benefit astronomers and space exploration, but society also.

SECTION ASSESSMENT

1. How do the various types of electromagnetic radiation differ from each other?

2. What are the advantages of using a telescope compared to making observations with the unaided eye?

3. What is interferometry, and how does it affect the images that are produced?

4. Why do astronomers send telescopes and probes into space?

5. How are space stations beneficial?

6. **Thinking Critically** How would humans' lives and our perceptions of the universe be different without space-based technology and exploration?

SKILL REVIEW

7. **Comparing and Contrasting** Compare and contrast refracting telescopes and reflecting telescopes. For more help, refer to the *Skill Handbook.*

SECTION ASSESSMENT

1. in wavelength or frequency
2. a larger light-collecting area, sharper images, the ability to make time exposures, and the use of instruments to analyze light
3. Interferometry is the linking of separate telescopes so they act as one large telescope. The images have much more detail.
4. Telescopes are sent into space to avoid the effects of Earth's atmosphere, which blurs images and blocks some wavelengths. Probes obtain close-up measurements and images and, in some cases, obtain samples for analysis.
5. They provide long-term, weightless environments for various experiments and tests.
6. Students may answer that we would have a very limited understanding of other celestial objects, and we'd lack spinoffs.
7. To focus visible light, refractors use lenses, while reflectors use mirrors. Both increase the amount of light collected and can have instruments attached to them.

The Moon is a familiar object in the night sky. Despite its proximity to Earth, however, the origins and nature of the Moon have been elusive. Only with advances in telescope and spacecraft technology over the past 100 years have people begun to understand the Moon.

REACHING FOR THE MOON

Astronomers have learned much about the Moon from telescopic observations. However, most of our knowledge of the Moon comes from explorations by space probes, such as *Lunar Prospector* and *Clementine,* and astronauts. Plans for a crewed lunar expedition began in the late 1950s. The first step was taken in 1957 with the launch of the first satellite, *Sputnik I,* by the Soviet Union. Shortly thereafter, in 1961, Soviet cosmonaut Yuri A. Gagarin became the first human in space.

The United States' Project Mercury launched the first American, Alan B. Shepard Jr., shown in *Figure 28-7,* into space on May 5, 1961. Project Gemini launched two-person crews into space, and on July 20, 1969, the Apollo program landed Neil Armstrong and Buzz Aldrin on the Moon, during *Apollo 11.*

Lunar Properties Earth's moon is unique among all the moons in the solar system. It is one of the largest moons, especially compared to the size of the planet it orbits. The Moon's radius is about 27 percent of Earth's radius, and its mass is more than 1 percent of Earth's mass, as shown in *Table 28-1.* Most moons are much smaller than this in relation to the size of the planets they orbit.

The orbit of the Moon is also unusual in that the Moon is relatively farther from Earth than most moons are from the planets they orbit. Earth's moon is a solid, rocky body, in contrast to the icy composition of the moons of the outer planets Jupiter, Saturn, Uranus, Neptune, and Pluto. Also, Earth's moon is the only large moon among the inner planets. Mercury and Venus have no moons at all, and the moons of Mars are just two tiny chunks of rock.

OBJECTIVES

- **Describe** *the development of exploration of the Moon.*
- **Identify** *features on the Moon.*
- **Explain** *the theories about how the Moon formed.*

VOCABULARY

albedo
highland
mare
impact crater
ejecta
ray
rille
regolith

Figure 28-7 American astronaut Alan B. Shepard Jr., in the *Mercury 7* capsule, prepares for launch.

Table 28-1 The Moon and Earth		
	The Moon	**Earth**
Mass (kg)	7.349×10^{22}	5.9736×10^{24}
Radius (km)	1737.4	6378.1
Volume (km³)	2.1968×10^{10}	1.08321×10^{12}
Density (kg/m³)	3340	5515

753

2 Teach

Content Background

The first successful reconnaissance of the far side of the Moon was accomplished by the Soviet Union, whose *Luna 3* spacecraft photographed the far side of the Moon in 1959. For this reason, many of the features on the Moon's far side have Russian names.

Interpreting the Photo

Figure 28-8B This image shows that ejecta from impacts on the Moon are brighter than the surrounding surface. The reason for this is that ejecta consist of materials from below the Moon's surface that may have a different composition and have not been exposed to the darkening effects of radiation and particles from space for as long as the surrounding surface has. Craters with visible rays of ejecta are all relatively young.

Time Line

Have students each create a time line of unpiloted probes that were sent to the Moon. Be sure that students include the probes of other countries besides the United States. L2

GLENCOE
Technology

**Videotape/DVD
The Planets: Moon**

The Lunar Surface Although the Moon is the brightest object in our nighttime sky, the lunar surface is actually quite dark. The **albedo** of the Moon, the amount of sunlight that its surface reflects, is very small—only about 0.07 (7 percent). In contrast, Earth has an average albedo of nearly 0.31 (31 percent). The sunlight that is absorbed by the surface of the Moon is responsible for the extreme differences in temperatures on its surface. Because the Moon has no atmosphere, sunlight can heat the Moon's surface to temperatures as high as 400 K (127°C). During the absence of sunlight, the Moon's surface temperature can drop to a chilly 100 K (−173°C).

The physical surface of the Moon is very different from that of Earth. There is no erosion on the Moon—except for surface creep and wear caused by recent impacts—because it has no atmosphere or flowing water. The surface of the Moon consists of several features. Regions called **highlands,** shown in *Figure 28-8A,* are light in color, mountainous, and heavily covered with craters. Regions called **maria** (*singular,* mare), shown in *Figure 28-8A,* are dark, smooth plains, which on average are 3 km lower in elevation than the highlands. All of the craters on the Moon are **impact craters,** formed when objects from space crashed into the lunar surface. The material blasted out during these impacts fell back to the surface as **ejecta.** Some craters have long trails of ejecta, called **rays,** that radiate outward. Rays are visible on the Moon as light-colored streaks, as shown in *Figure 28-8B.*

In contrast to the crater-covered highlands, the surfaces within maria are quite smooth. However, the maria do have a few scattered craters and **rilles,** which are meandering, valleylike structures, as illustrated in *Figure 28-8D.* In addition, around some of the maria are mountain ranges, shown in *Figure 28-8C.*

Why does the Moon have many craters, while Earth has few? Early in the formation of the solar system, Earth was bombarded just as heavily as the Moon, but erosion on Earth has eliminated traces of all but the youngest craters. On the Moon, craters are preserved until one impact covers another.

A

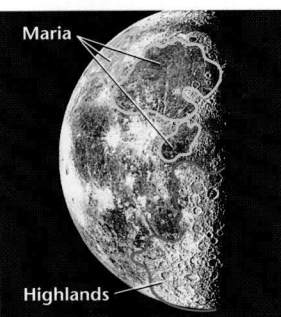

Maria

Highlands

B

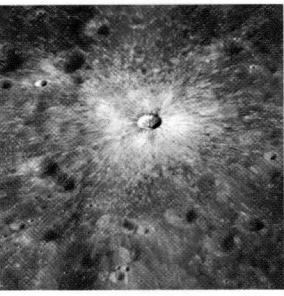

C

D

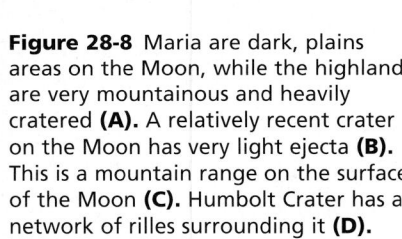

Figure 28-8 Maria are dark, plains areas on the Moon, while the highlands are very mountainous and heavily cratered **(A).** A relatively recent crater on the Moon has very light ejecta **(B).** This is a mountain range on the surface of the Moon **(C).** Humbolt Crater has a network of rilles surrounding it **(D).**

754 CHAPTER 28 *The Sun-Earth-Moon System*

Composition The Moon is made up of minerals similar to those of Earth—mostly silicates. The highlands, which cover most of the lunar surface, are predominately lunar breccias, which are rocks formed by the fusing together of smaller pieces of rock during impacts. Unlike sedimentary breccias on Earth, most of the lunar breccias are composed of plagioclase feldspar, a silicate containing high quantities of calcium and aluminum but low quantities of iron. The maria are predominately basalts that differ from those on Earth in that they contain no water.

HISTORY OF THE MOON

The entire lunar surface is very old. Radiometric dating of lunar rocks from the highlands indicates an age between 3.8 and 4.6 billion years. Based on the ages of the highlands and the frequency of the impact craters that cover them, scientists theorize that the Moon was heavily bombarded during its first 800 million years, which resulted in the breaking and heating of rocks on the surface of the Moon. This formed a layer of loose, ground-up rock, called **regolith,** on the surface of the Moon. The regolith averages several meters in thickness, but it varies considerably depending on location.

The maria, only slightly younger than the highlands, are between 3.1 and 3.8 billion years old. After the period of intense bombardment in which the highlands formed, lava welled up from the Moon's interior and filled in the large impact basins to form the maria. The maria have remained relatively free of craters because fewer impacts have occurred on the Moon since the time when they formed. However, flowing lava in the maria scarred their surfaces with rilles, which are much like lava tubes found on Earth. During the formation of the maria, the lava often did not fill the basins completely. Instead, the rims of the basins remained above the lava and formed the mountain ranges that now exist around many of the maria. As shown in *Figure 28-9,* there are virtually no maria on the far side of the Moon, which is covered almost completely with highlands. Scientists hypothesize that this is because the crust is twice as thick on the far side, which would have made it increasingly difficult for lava to reach the lunar surface. You will determine the relative ages of the Moon's surface features in the *Mapping GeoLab* at the end of this chapter.

Figure 28-9 This photo of the far side of the Moon, shows the heavily cratered surface of the highlands.

Concept Development

Build a crater out of clay in a rimmed pan. Fill the clay crater with water, but don't allow it to overflow, to model the formation of a mare in a crater. Add more water so that the crater overflows and water fills the pan. Point out to students that the rim sticking out of the water is similar to the mountain ranges on the Moon.

Enrichment

Have students compare the geological history of the Moon with that of Earth. Points that students should include in the comparison are the formation processes, the importance of differentiation, internal heat sources, internal structures, tectonic activity, formation of surface features, relative impact rates, and atmospheres. **L2**

Tying to Previous Knowledge

The many precise dates given in the text for the formation of lunar regions are based on radiometric dating, which involves exactly the same techniques that are used to date rock samples on Earth. Radiometric dating was possible for lunar rocks only with the success of the Apollo program, which returned samples of lunar rocks to Earth, where their isotopic ratios could be measured.

Demo

Visual-Spatial Fill a large cake pan with different layers of colored sand. Place a layer of flour on top to model regolith. Throw different-sized rocks into the pan to model crater formation and how it disturbs the layers of the surface. Vary the size of the rocks as well as the speed with which they are thrown. Ask students how size and speed affect the size and shape of a crater.

NY Core Curriculum Standards

Page 754: St 4 KI 1.2d
Page 755: St 4 KI 1.2d

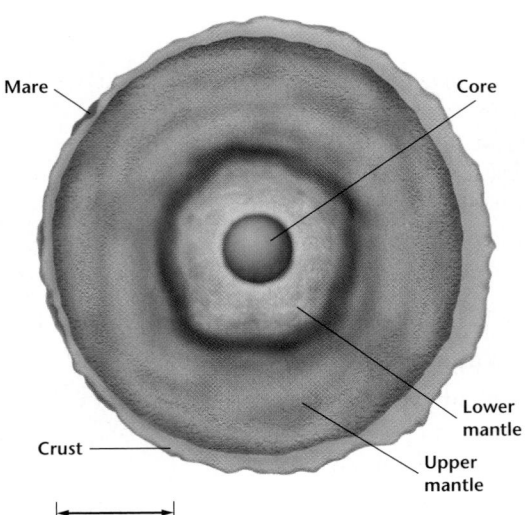

Mare

Core

Lower mantle

Upper mantle

Crust

|← 1000 km →|

Figure 28-10 The Moon has a layered structure similar to Earth's.

Tectonics on the Moon? Mountain ranges around maria were not formed tectonically, as mountain ranges on Earth are. But is that enough evidence to conclude that the Moon is not tectonically active? Scientists infer from seismometer data that the Moon, like Earth, has a layered structure, which consists of the crust, the upper mantle, the lower mantle, and the core, as illustrated in *Figure 28-10*. The crust varies in thickness and is thickest on the far side. The Moon's upper mantle is solid, its lower mantle is partially molten, and its core is made of solid iron. Seismometers also measure moonquake strength and their frequency. Although the Moon experiences a moonquake that would be strong enough to cause dishes to fall out of a cupboard approximately once a year, scientists theorize that the Moon is not tectonically active. The fact that the Moon has no active volcanoes and no significant magnetic field supports scientists' theory that tectonics are not occurring on the Moon.

Formation Theories Several theories have been proposed to explain the Moon's unique properties. One of these is the capture theory, which proposes that as the solar system was forming, a large object ventured too near to the forming Earth, became trapped in its gravitational pull, and formed into what is now the Moon. One problem with this theory is that something would have had to slow down the passing object for it to become trapped instead of continuing on its original path. Another problem with the capture theory is that Earth and the Moon are composed of very similar elements. If the Moon had been captured, we would expect the crusts of the Moon and Earth to have different compositions, rather than similar ones.

Another theory, called the simultaneous formation theory, accounts for the problems with the capture theory. According to this theory, the Moon and Earth formed at the same time and in the same general area, and thus the materials from which they formed were essentially the same. Also, because they formed in the same general area, the Moon did not have to be slowed down to become gravitationally trapped. This theory does not account for the different amounts of iron on Earth and on the Moon, however. The Moon is iron poor, while on Earth, iron is relatively abundant.

756 CHAPTER 28 *The Sun-Earth-Moon System*

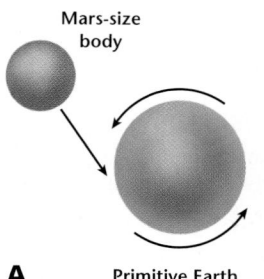
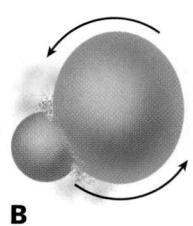
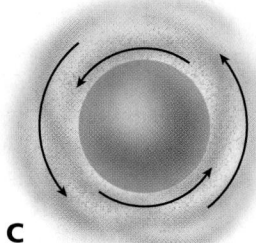
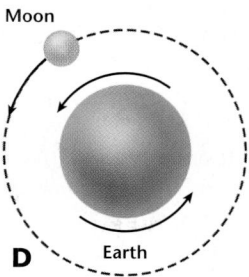

A Mars-size body

A Primitive Earth **B** **C** **D** Moon Earth

The most commonly accepted theory of how the Moon formed, the impact theory, can explain astronomers' observations as a whole. Computer models indicate that the Moon formed as the result of a gigantic collision between Earth and a Mars-sized object about 4.5 billion years ago, when the solar system was forming. As a result of the collision, materials from the incoming body and from Earth's outer layers were ejected into space, where they then merged together to form the Moon, as illustrated by *Figure 28-11.* This model accounts for why the Moon is so similar to Earth in chemical composition. If this model is correct, then the Moon is made up of material that was originally part of Earth's iron-deficient crust as well as material that was once part of Earth's mantle. Heat produced by the impact would have evaporated any water that was present and resulted in lunar minerals lacking water. Despite scientists' uncertainty about how the Moon formed, we do know that it plays a vital role in the Sun-Earth-Moon system, as you will learn in the following section.

Figure 28-11 The impact theory suggests that a Mars-sized body **(A)** collided with Earth. The impact **(B)** threw material from the body and Earth into space **(C)**. This material eventually merged together to form the Moon **(D)**. (Not to scale)

SECTION ASSESSMENT

1. How is Earth's moon different from the moons of other planets?

2. Why are there many visible craters on the Moon, but few on Earth?

3. Why do scientists believe that tectonic activity is not occurring on the Moon?

4. What is the most accepted theory of how the Moon formed, and what are the problems with the other theories?

5. **Thinking Critically** How would the surface of the Moon look different if the crust on the far side were the same thickness as the crust on the near side?

SKILL REVIEW

6. **Concept Mapping** Use the following terms to construct a concept map to organize the major ideas in this section. For more help, refer to the *Skill Handbook.*

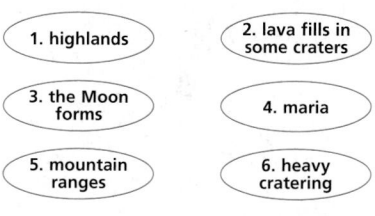

1. highlands | 2. lava fills in some craters | 3. the Moon forms | 4. maria | 5. mountain ranges | 6. heavy cratering

28.2 *The Moon* **757**

SECTION ASSESSMENT

1. The Moon is much more massive relative to Earth, and it is farther from its parent planet than is typical of other satellites.

2. The Moon has essentially no erosion, and Earth does.

3. There is no evidence of current volcanic activity, significant quakes, or a magnetic field.

4. the impact theory; the capture theory does not explain the chemical similarities between Earth

and the Moon, or how a passing object was slowed. The simultaneous formation theory cannot explain the differences in the amount of iron on Earth and the Moon.

5. The Moon would probably be covered with more maria. The far side would be smoother and darker.

6. 3–6–1–2– both 4 and 5

SECTION ASSESSMENT

3 Assess

Check for Understanding
Project
To help students realize how unique the Moon is in comparison with other planetary satellites, have students each make a data table containing information about the Moon and at least ten other satellites in the solar system. Have students include the following properties in their tables: mass, ratio of mass to parent planet's mass, orbital radius, and ratio of orbital radius to the radius of the parent planet. Students will see how much larger these ratios are for the Moon than for other satellites.

Reteach

 **Linguistic** Have students each choose a lunar surface feature and write a paragraph describing how it formed. **L2**

✓*Assessment*

Knowledge Ask students to explain why the Moon's surface is a more accurate record of the solar system's history than Earth's surface is. Because the Moon has no atmosphere, its surface has not been altered by erosion, weathering, chemical processes, or biological effects, all of which have affected Earth's surface. Thus, the Moon's surface reflects conditions and processes that prevailed early in the solar system's history, while Earth's surface displays only the effects of processes that have occurred more recently.

Section Background

For section content background, refer to **The Sun-Earth-Moon System** on page 746D.

Preplanning

Refer to the Chapter Organizer on pages 746A–B.

1 Focus

Section Focus

Before presenting the lesson, display **Section Focus Transparency 91** on the overhead projector.
L1 **ELL**

Resource Manager

Section Focus Transparency 91
L1 **ELL**

Study Guide for Content Mastery, pp. 180–182 **L2**

SECTION 28.3

The Sun-Earth-Moon System

OBJECTIVES

- **Identify** *the relative positions and motions of Earth, the Sun, and the Moon.*
- **Describe** *the phases of the Moon.*
- **Explain** *eclipses of the Sun and Moon.*

VOCABULARY

ecliptic
summer solstice
winter solstice
autumnal equinox
vernal equinox
synchronous rotation
solar eclipse
perigee
apogee
lunar eclipse

The relationships between the Sun, Moon, and Earth are important to us in many ways. The Sun provides light and warmth, and it is the source of most of the energy that fuels our society. Additionally, the Moon raises tides in our oceans and illuminates our sky with its monthly cycle of phases. Every society from ancient times to the present has based its calendar and its timekeeping system on the apparent motions of the Sun and Moon.

DAILY MOTIONS

The most obvious pattern of motion in the sky is the daily rising and setting of the Sun, the Moon, the stars, and everything else that is visible in the sky. The Sun rises in the east and sets in the west, as do the Moon, planets, and stars. Today, we understand that these daily motions result from Earth's rotation. The Sun, Moon, planets, and stars do not orbit around Earth every day. It only appears that way to us because we observe the sky from a planet that rotates once every day, or 15° per hour. But how do we know that Earth is rotating?

Earth's Rotation There are two relatively simple ways to demonstrate that Earth is rotating. One is to use a pendulum, which is a weight on a string or wire that is suspended from a support and can swing freely. A Foucault pendulum, which has a long wire and a heavy weight, will swing in a constant direction. But as Earth turns, it appears from our point of view that the pendulum gradually shifts its orientation. With a Foucault pendulum, pegs are often placed on the floor in a circle so that as Earth turns, the pendulum, shown in *Figure 28-12,* eventually knocks over each of the pegs. The second method of demonstrating that Earth rotates makes use of the fact that flowing air and water on Earth are diverted from a north-south direction to an east-west direction as a result of Earth's rotation. This diversion of direction is called the Coriolis effect, which you learned about in Chapter 12.

Figure 28-12 A Foucault pendulum, such as this one at the Griffith Observatory in Los Angeles, California, demonstrates that Earth is rotating.

Demo

Visual-Spatial Use a globe and a bright flashlight to illustrate why the length of day and the Sun's intensity both vary during the year. Set the globe on a table on one side of a darkened room with the southern hemisphere of Earth tilted toward the far side of the room. Stand in the center of the room and shine the flashlight on the globe from the level of the globe's center. Have a student spin the globe at a steady rate, and point out that the length of day is longer than the length of night in the northern hemisphere. Then, have a student move the globe to a table on the other side of the room keeping the tilt oriented in the same direction, so that the northern hemisphere is tipped away from you. Shine the flashlight on the globe while a student spins it, and have students observe the length of day compared to the length of night in the northern hemisphere.

The length of a day as we observe it is a little longer than the time it takes Earth to rotate once on its axis. This is because as Earth rotates, it also moves along in its orbit and has to turn a little farther. The time period from one sunrise or sunset to the next is called a solar day. Our timekeeping system is based on the solar day.

ANNUAL MOTIONS

As you know, the weather changes throughout the year. The length of days varies, and temperatures may range from cold to hot, depending on the latitude where you live. These annual changes are the result of Earth's orbital motion about the Sun. The plane in which Earth orbits about the Sun is called the **ecliptic,** as illustrated in *Figure 28-13.*

The Effects of Earth's Tilt Earth's axis is tilted relative to the ecliptic at approximately 23.5°. As Earth orbits the Sun, the orientation of Earth's axis remains fixed in space, so that, at one point, the northern hemisphere of Earth is tilted toward the Sun, while at another point, six months later, the northern hemisphere is tipped away from the Sun. Our seasons, as discussed in Chapter 14, are created by this tilt and by Earth's orbital motion around the Sun.

The way in which altitude is measured is illustrated in *Figure 28-14.* As a result of the tilt of Earth's axis and Earth's motion around the Sun, the Sun changes its altitude in the sky. You've probably

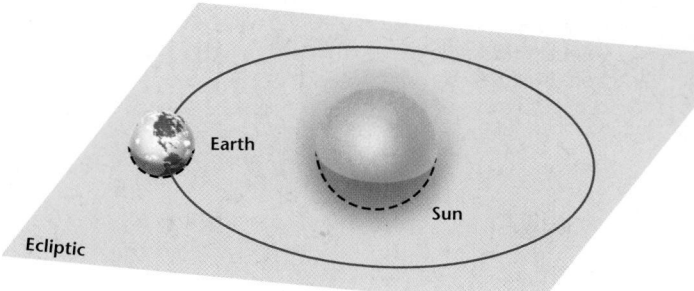

Figure 28-13 The ecliptic is the plane that contains Earth's orbit around the Sun. (Not to scale)

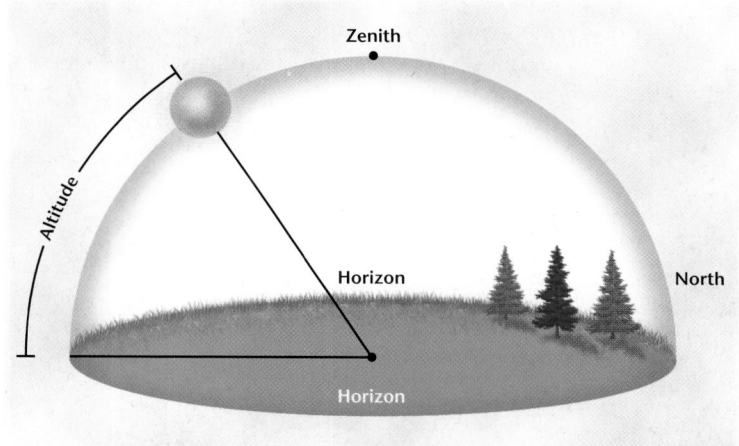

Figure 28-14 Altitude is measured in degrees from the observer's horizon to the object. There are 90 degrees from the horizon to the point directly overhead, called the zenith of the observer.

Content Background

People sometimes exaggerate the importance of the Coriolis effect on small scales. For example, the circulation of water in a toilet bowl or a sink is often attributed to Earth's rotation. In fact, the Coriolis effect is far too weak over a scale of a few centimeters or meters to have any noticeable effect. The direction of water flow in a toilet or a sink is determined by the direction in which water enters or by the shape or slope of the bowl or sink, not by Earth's rotation.

✔Assessment

Portfolio Ask students to each write a short essay on what would happen if timekeeping were based on the time it takes Earth to rotate once on its axis rather than on the solar day. Have students include in their essays how this would impact life on Earth. This would cause a steady shifting of the time of sunrise and sunset during a year, so that clocks would be out of synchronization with day and night.

Differentiated Instruction

Learning Disabled Use a globe and a flashlight in a darkened room to illustrate how Earth's rotation, not the motion of the Sun, is responsible for day and night. Put a marker on the globe at your position on Earth, so that students can more easily see how their location enters daylight and darkness as Earth rotates. This demonstration will help students who have difficulties with visualization based on drawings. **L1** **ELL**

☐ NATIONAL GEOGRAPHIC

CD-ROM
Solar System Picture Show
Sun, Earth, and Moon

NY Core Curriculum Standards

Page 758: St 4 KI 1.1a, 1.1d, 1.1e, 1.1h, & 1.1i
Page 759: St 4 KI 1.1a, 1.1d, & 1.1f

Ask students to think of ways to demonstrate that Earth actually is moving in an orbit around the Sun. As in the case of Earth's rotation, there is no obvious way to demonstrate this. A good point that some students might make is the difference between the length of the solar day and the time it takes Earth to rotate once on its axis, which we explain as being a result of Earth's motion about the Sun. Another good point is that we explain the seasons by assuming that Earth orbits the Sun (and has a tilted axis). However, the seasons could also be explained if the Sun orbited Earth in a complex path.

Modeling

Kinesthetic Have students mark the Tropic of Cancer, the Tropic of Capricorn, and the equator on a ball with tape. Then, have students use a flashlight to represent the Sun and model Earth's changing position around the Sun and the solstices and equinoxes. **L1** **ELL**

NY Core Curriculum Standards

Page 760: St 4 KI 1.1a, 1.1c,1.1f, & 1.1g
Page 761: St 6 KI 2, St 4 KI 1.1a, 1.1c, 1.1f, & 1.1g

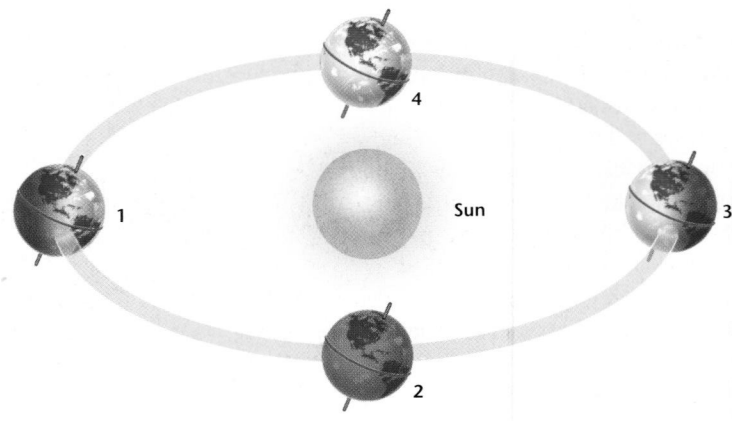

Figure 28-15 As Earth orbits the Sun, Earth's tilted axis points in the same direction. (Not to scale)

noticed the change in altitude of the Sun during the northern hemisphere's summer, when the Sun appears higher in the sky than it does during the northern hemisphere's winter. This change occurs gradually throughout Earth's orbit in a cyclic pattern.

Solstices Earth's varying position in its orbit around the Sun and the tilt of Earth's axis are illustrated in *Figure 28-15.* As Earth moves from position 1, through position 2, to position 3, the altitude of the Sun decreases in the northern hemisphere. Once Earth is at position 3, the Sun's altitude starts to increase as Earth moves through position 4 and back to position 1. Position 1 corresponds to the Sun's maximum altitude in the sky in the northern hemisphere. At this position, called the **summer solstice,** the Sun is directly overhead at the Tropic of Cancer, which is at 23.5° north latitude, as illustrated in *Figure 28-16A.* On the summer solstice, which occurs around June 21 each year, the number of daylight hours for the northern hemisphere is at its maximum, while it is at its minimum for the southern hemisphere. During the summer solstice, the Sun does not set in the region within the arctic circle, and it does not rise in the region within the antarctic circle.

Figure 28-16 The Sun's rays are vertical at the Tropic of Cancer during the summer solstice **(A),** at the Tropic of Capricorn during the winter solstice **(B),** and at the equator during the autumnal equinox **(C)** and the vernal equinox **(D).**

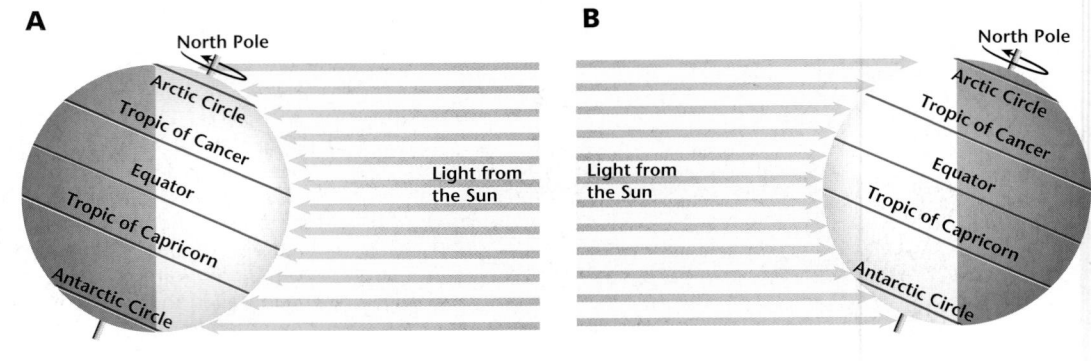

Applying Earth Science

Earth's distance from the Sun varies by about 5 million km during the year, because Earth's orbit is not perfectly circular. Have students compare this variation with the average Sun-Earth distance of 150 million km and comment on whether the change in distance is likely to affect Earth's seasons. The variation is 3 percent of the average Sun-Earth separation, which is not enough to have a noticeable effect on Earth's climate.

Interpreting the Illustration

Figure 28-16 Students should note that the Sun's rays are perpendicular to Earth's surface at the Tropic of Cancer in **Figure 28-16A,** and perpendicular to Earth's surface at the Tropic of Capricorn in **Figure 28-16B.** In **Figures 28-16C** and **D,** the Sun's rays are perpendicular to Earth's surface at the equator, and hence the Sun is directly overhead, corresponding to the equinoxes.

Conversely, when Earth is in position 3 and the northern hemisphere is tilted away from the Sun, the Sun has reached its lowest altitude in the sky. At this position, called the **winter solstice,** the Sun is directly overhead at the Tropic of Capricorn at 23.5° south latitude, as illustrated in *Figure 28-16B.* On the winter solstice, which occurs around December 21 each year, the number of daylight hours in the northern hemisphere is at its minimum, while it is at its maximum for the southern hemisphere. During the winter solstice, the Sun never rises in the region within the arctic circle, and it never sets in the region within the antarctic circle. You will model the Sun's position as seen from your location during the summer solstice in the *MiniLab* on this page.

Equinoxes At positions 2 and 4 in *Figure 28-15,* Earth's axis is not pointed at the Sun. As a result, both hemispheres receive equal amounts of sunlight, and the Sun is directly overhead at the equator. Thus, the lengths of day and night are equal for both the northern and southern hemispheres when Earth is at position 2, called the **autumnal equinox,** illustrated in *Figure 28-16C,* and position 4, called the **vernal equinox,** illustrated in *Figure 28-16D.* The term *equinox* means "equal nights." For an observer at the Tropic of Cancer or Tropic of Capricorn, the Sun is

MiniLab

The Sun's Position

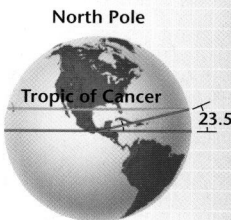
North Pole

Model the overhead position of the Sun at various latitudes during the summer solstice.

Procedure
1. Draw a circle to represent Earth. Also draw the equator.
2. Use a protractor to find the location of the Tropic of Cancer. Draw a line from Earth's center to the Tropic of Cancer.
3. Using a map, locate that latitude at which you live. With the protractor, mark that latitude on your diagram. Draw a line from Earth's center to this location.
4. Measure the angle between the line to the Tropic of Cancer and the line to your location.
5. Choose two different latitudes, then repeat steps 3 and 4 for these latitudes.

Analyze and Conclude
1. How does the angle vary with latitude?
2. At what southern latitude would you not see the Sun above the horizon?
3. How would the angle change if you used the Tropic of Capricorn?

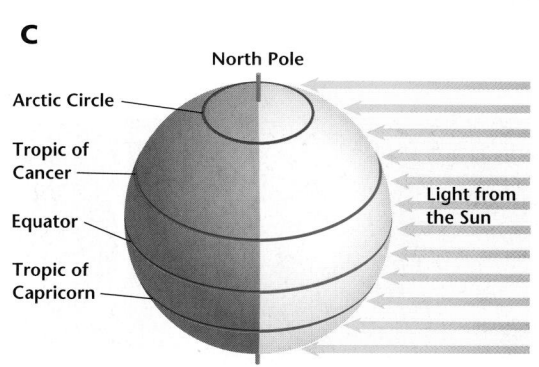
C

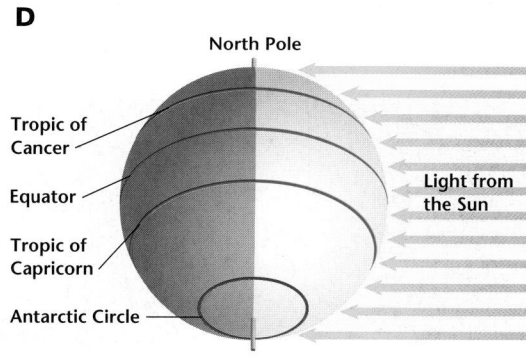
D

28.3 *The Sun-Earth-Moon System* **761**

MiniLab

Purpose
Students will use simple geometry to determine the Sun's midday altitude above the southern horizon as seen from different latitudes at the time of the summer solstice.

Process Skills
use scientific illustrations, interpret data, use numbers, recognize spatial relationships

Materials
paper, drawing compass, protractor, metric ruler

Teaching Strategies
This can be either an individual activity or one performed by small groups of students.

Safety Precautions
Have students handle drawing compasses with care.

Troubleshooting
Making the drawing of Earth the same diameter as the protractor may help. If the circle is too small, it will be difficult for students to make the measurements.

Expected Results
Students will see that the Sun's altitude above the southern horizon increases with proximity to the equator.

Analyze and Conclude
1. The farther north your location, the more the angle between the line to the Tropic of Cancer and the line to your location increases. Hence, the Sun is lower in the sky on the solstices for more northerly latitudes.
2. 66.5° south latitude
3. The angle would be larger. For any latitudes above 66.5° north, the angle would be more than 90°.

Assessment

Skill Ask students to illustrate how their results would be different if Earth's axis were not tilted. If Earth's axis were not tilted, there would still be variations in the Sun's altitude as seen from different latitudes, but there would be no variations during the year.

761

Reinforcement

People who live north of the Tropic of Cancer often think that the Sun is always to the south of their position. However, this is not so. Between the spring and fall equinoxes, the Sun rises and sets to the north of due east or due west. This is easily observed, but many people don't seem to notice. Ask students to note where the Sun rises and sets relative to the east-west direction after late March.

Enrichment

Intrapersonal Have students visualize being at the north pole, and ask them to describe the daily motion of the Sun as seen from there on the solstices and the equinoxes. At the summer solstice, the Sun stays overhead all day, circling the horizon at an altitude of 23.5°. At each equinox, the Sun circles right on the horizon, and at the winter solstice, it stays 23.5° below the horizon all day.

Figure Caption Question

Figure 28-18 What are the phases in between called? starting with second from the left: first quarter, waxing gibbous, full moon, waning gibbous, third quarter

NY Core Curriculum Standards

Page 762: St 4 KI 1.1a & 1.1f
Page 763: St 4 KI 1.1a & 1.1f

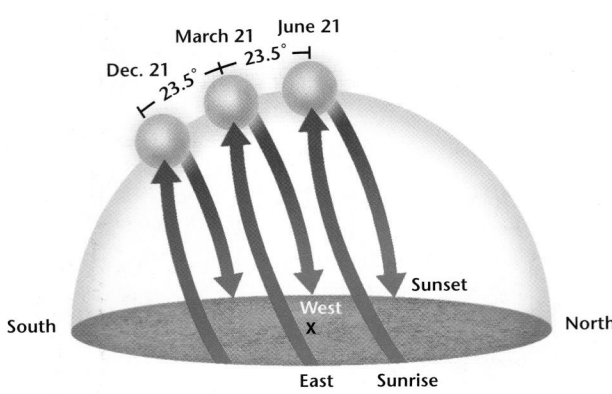

Figure 28-17 For a person standing at the *x* at 23.5° north latitude, the Sun would appear in these positions on the winter solstice, the vernal equinox, and the summer solstice. On the autumnal equinox, the Sun would be at the same altitude as on the vernal equinox.

Figure 28-18 These photos show the phases of the Moon, except the new moon phase, in which no portion of the Moon's illuminated surface is visible from Earth. The photo starts on the left with a waxing crescent, and ends on the right with a waning crescent. *What are the phases in between called?*

23.5° from the point directly overhead during the equinoxes. In the *Science & Math* feature at the end of this chapter, you will learn how Eratosthenes, an ancient Greek mathematician, used the Sun's position and shadows to calculate the circumference and radius of Earth.

Figure 28-17 illustrates how the Sun would appear in the sky to a person at 23.5° north latitude during the solstices and the equinoxes. As you can see, the position of the Sun affects how directly sunlight strikes Earth. When the Sun is at a lower altitude, the sunlight that strikes Earth is spread out over a larger area.

PHASES OF THE MOON

Just as the Sun appears to change its position in the sky, so, too, does the Moon. This is a result of the movement of the Moon around Earth and of our changing viewpoint on Earth relative to the Sun. The sequential changes in the appearance of the Moon are called lunar phases, shown in *Figure 28-18.* To understand lunar phases, look at the Sun-Earth-Moon system as a whole.

You have learned that the Moon does not emit visible light. Instead, we see the Moon's reflection of the Sun's light. When the Moon is between Earth and the Sun, however, we cannot see the Moon because of the Sun's glare and because the sunlit side is facing away from us. This dark Moon positioned between Earth and the Sun is called a new moon.

As the Moon moves along in its orbit, the amount of reflected sunlight that we can see increases. The increase in the portion of the sunlit side of the Moon that we see is called waxing. When we can see less than half of the sunlit portion of the Moon during this increase, it is called a waxing crescent. When we can see more than half of the sunlit portion of the Moon during this increase, it is called a waxing

---

Resource Manager

Laboratory Manual, pp. 217–220 L2

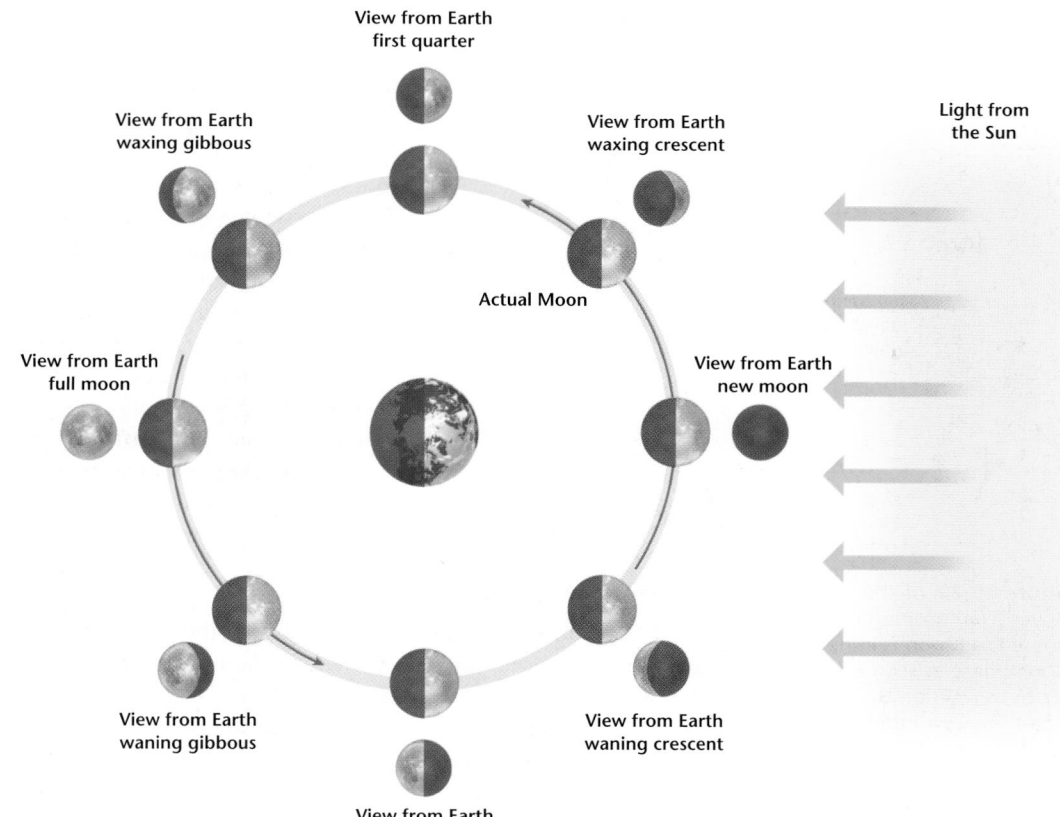

View from Earth
first quarter

View from Earth
waxing gibbous

View from Earth
waxing crescent

Light from
the Sun

Actual Moon

View from Earth
full moon

View from Earth
new moon

View from Earth
waning gibbous

View from Earth
waning crescent

View from Earth
third quarter

Figure 28-19 As the Moon orbits Earth, the portion of the illuminated side of the Moon that we see from Earth changes, thus creating phases. (Not to scale)

gibbous. Between these phases, the Moon reaches a point in its orbit when we see half of the sunlit side. This is called the first quarter.

As the Moon continues farther in its orbit, as illustrated in *Figure 28-19*, it moves to a position where it is once again aligned with the Sun. This time, Earth is between the Moon and Sun, and we are able to see the entire sunlit side of the Moon. This is known as a full moon. Once a full moon is reached, the portion of the sunlit side that we see begins to decrease as the Moon moves back toward the new-moon position. The decrease in the amount of the sunlit side of the Moon that we see is called waning. As in the waxing phases, there is a period during the waning phases when we can see more than half of the sunlit portion of the Moon, as well as a period when we can see less than half of the sunlit portion. These phases are called waning gibbous and waning crescent, respectively. In the middle of the waning phases, the Moon is in a position in its orbit where we can see half of the sunlit portion. This is called the third quarter.

Content Background

The phases of the Moon can be correlated to the times of the rising and setting of the Moon and the Sun. If the Moon rises at the same time as the Sun, it is in the new moon phase. The Moon rises approximately 6 hours after the Sun during the first quarter. The Moon rises 12 hours after the Sun during the full moon, or in other words, it rises as the Sun sets. During the third quarter, the Moon rises approximately 6 hours after the Sun sets, or 18 hours after the Sun rises. These times of rising and setting correspond to the positions of the Sun, Earth, and the Moon.

✓Assessment

Knowledge Ask students what phase the Moon is in when the Sun and Moon rise at the same time. new moon Ask what phase the Moon is in when it rises 12 hours after the Sun rises, or while the Sun sets. full moon

Using Scientific Terms

Students may question why a quarter moon is so named when half of the disk is visible. *Quarter* refers to the fact that the Moon rises a quarter of a day later (first quarter) than or three-quarters of a day later (third quarter) than the Sun does.

Differentiated Instruction

Learning Disabled To help illustrate the phases of the Moon, use a ball representing the Moon and a strong flashlight in a darkened room. Place the ball on a table in front of students and shine the light on the ball from different angles. Be careful not to shine the light into students' eyes. When you stand behind the students and illuminate the ball, this simulates a full moon. When you stand at right angles to the students' line of sight, this simulates the quarter moon phases, and when you illuminate the ball from behind, this simulates a new moon. You can simulate the crescent and gibbous phases by illuminating the Moon from intermediate positions. This demonstration is useful for students who have difficulty with spatial visualization. **L1** **ELL**

Demo

Students might be confused about the Moon's rotation and think that the Moon does not rotate at all because the same side is always facing Earth. Place a globe on a table to represent Earth and use a smaller foam ball to represent the Moon. Attach a small arrow or pointer to the Moon at one point, so that students can easily keep track of its orientation. Walk around the globe that represents Earth while holding the Moon and keeping the pointer always fixed in the same direction. Students should see that different sides of the Moon face Earth at different points in the Moon's orbit. Then repeat the demonstration, rotating the Moon so that the pointer always points toward Earth. In this case, students should see that the Moon is rotating once during each orbit.

Discussion

Ask students to discuss how the phases of the Moon would be affected if the Moon's rotation were not synchronous. There would be no change.

Enrichment

The time between consecutive high or low tides is always a bit longer than 12 hours, and the daily cycle of two high and two low tides is longer than 24 hours. Ask students to try to work out why this is so. The Moon moves along in its orbit, so Earth has to rotate a little more than one full spin to return to the same alignment with the Moon. This is analogous to the difference between the solar day and the time it takes Earth to rotate once on its axis, or the difference between the lunar month and one revolution of the Moon about Earth.

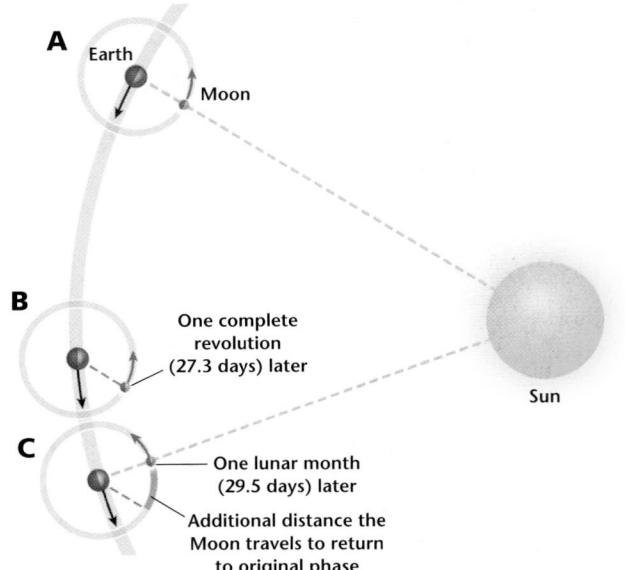

Figure 28-20 As the Moon moves from position **A**, where the Moon is in new moon phase as seen from Earth, to position **B**, it completes one revolution and is in the waning crescent phase as seen from Earth. At position **C**, the Moon has traveled for another 2.2 days and is back to the new moon phase, completing a lunar month. (Not to scale)

Synchronous Rotation You might have noticed that the illuminated surface of the Moon always looks the same. As the Moon orbits Earth, the same side faces Earth at all times. This is because the Moon is rotating with a period equal to its orbital period, so it spins exactly once each time it goes around Earth. This is not a coincidence. Scientists theorize that Earth's gravity slowed the Moon's original spin until the Moon reached **synchronous rotation,** the state at which its orbital and rotational periods are equal.

MOTIONS OF THE MOON

The length of time it takes for the Moon to go through a complete cycle of phases, for example, from one full moon to the next, is called a lunar month. The length of a lunar month is about 29.5 days, which is longer than the 27.3 days it takes for one revolution, or orbit, around Earth, as illustrated in *Figure 28-20.* The Moon also rises and sets 50 minutes later each day because the Moon has moved 13° in its orbit over a 24-hour period, and Earth has to turn an additional 13° for the Moon to rise.

Tides One of the Moon's effects on Earth is the formation of tides. The Moon's gravity pulls on Earth along an imaginary line connecting Earth and the Moon, and this creates bulges of ocean water on both the near and far sides of Earth. Earth's rotation also contributes to the formation of tides, as you learned in Chapter 15. As Earth rotates, these bulges remain aligned with the Moon, so that a person at a shoreline on Earth's surface would observe that the ocean level rises and falls every 12 hours.

The Sun's gravitational effect on the formation of tides is about half that of the Moon's, because the Sun is farther away. However, when the Sun and Moon are aligned along the same direction, the effects of the Sun and Moon combine, and tides are higher than normal. These tides, called spring tides, are especially high when the Moon is nearest Earth and Earth is nearest the Sun in their slightly noncircular orbits. When the Moon is at a right angle to the Sun-Earth line, the result is lower-than-normal tides, called neap tides.

Content Background

Earth's gravity slowed the Moon's spin until it reached synchronous rotation. The slowing was not a direct result of the force of attraction between Earth and the Moon, but of the difference between the forces acting on the near side and the far side of the Moon. This difference is called a differential gravitational force, or a tidal force. Such a force tends to stretch a body, so the Moon is slightly elongated along the line toward Earth, and Earth, especially its oceans, is elongated along this line as well.

SOLAR ECLIPSES

A **solar eclipse** occurs when the Moon passes directly between the Sun and Earth and blocks our view of the Sun. Although the Sun is much larger than the Moon, it is much farther away, which causes the Sun and Moon to appear to be the same size when viewed from Earth. When the Moon perfectly blocks the Sun's disk, we see only the dim, outer gaseous layers of the Sun. This spectacular sight, shown in *Figure 28-21,* is called a total solar eclipse. A partial solar eclipse is seen when the Moon blocks only a portion of the Sun's disk.

The difference between a partial and a total solar eclipse can be explained by the fact that the Moon casts a shadow on Earth. This shadow consists of two regions, as illustrated in *Figure 28-22.* The inner portion, which does not receive direct sunlight, is called the umbra. People who witness an eclipse from the umbra see a total solar eclipse. People in the outer portion of this shadow, where some of the Sun's light reaches, are in the penumbra. They see a partial solar eclipse where part of the Sun's disk is still visible. Typically, the umbral shadow is never wider than 270 km, so a total solar eclipse is visible from a very small portion of Earth, whereas a partial solar eclipse is visible from a much larger portion.

Topic: Next Solar Eclipse
To find out more about solar eclipses, visit the Earth Science Web Site at earthgeu.com

Activity: Research future solar eclipses. When will the next solar eclipse be visible in your area?

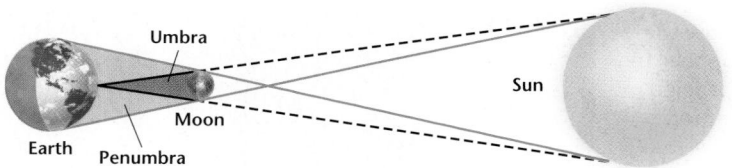

Figure 28-22 During a solar eclipse, the Moon passes between the Sun and Earth. People within the umbral shadow witness a total solar eclipse, while people within the penumbral shadow witness a partial solar eclipse. (Not to scale)

Content Background

Besides being spectacular sights, total solar eclipses have significant scientific value. While the Sun's disk is blocked by the Moon, it is possible to observe the dim layers of the Sun's outer atmosphere, known as the chromosphere and corona. A famous scientific observation of a total solar eclipse occurred in 1919, when astronomers were able to successfully test Albert Einstein's then-new theory of general relativity. The test involved precisely measuring the position of a star very close to the edge of the Sun's disk and verifying that the star's position had shifted as a result of the Sun's gravity, as predicted. Biologists have also conducted eclipse-based research, observing the reactions of plants and animals to the sudden fall of night in the middle of the day.

Activity

Have students find out the number of solar and lunar eclipses that occurred over some definite period of time in the past ten years. Ask students to compare the numbers of solar and lunar eclipses and to explain any difference they find. Lunar eclipses occur more frequently because the alignment required is not as precise as it is for a solar eclipse.

Cultural Diversity

Eclipse Legends Almost every culture throughout history has legends about eclipses, which often were thought to be omens or harbingers of disaster. One Chinese legend was that an invisible dragon devoured the Sun and caused a solar eclipse. According to the legend, making loud noises by banging on pots or even shooting guns would frighten the dragon and return the world to daylight. Have students research legends about eclipses and share their findings with the class.

NY Core Curriculum Standards

Page 764: St 4 KI 1.1a, 1.1f, & 1.1i, St 6 KI 4
Page 765: St 4 KI 1.1a & 1.1f

Purpose

Students will use model drawings to predict the appearance of solar eclipses.

Process Skills

predict, recognize spatial relationships

Materials

paper, pencil

Alternate Materials

colored pencils

Teaching Strategies

This is a good project for students to do in pairs.

Troubleshooting

Refer students to the diagram on page 765 if they have difficulty getting started.

Analysis

1. See art for Thinking Critically.

Thinking Critically

2. & 3.

Location of observer	What the observer sees there	
Point A (umbra)		Total eclipse
Point B (penumbra)		Partial eclipse
Point C (umbra)		Total eclipse
Point D (penumbra)		Partial eclipse
Point E (penumbra)		Annular eclipse

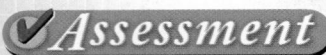

✔Assessment

Skill Ask students how the appearance of eclipses would be affected if Earth's distance from the Sun were increased. Total solar eclipses would be more frequent because the Sun would appear to be smaller than the Moon, and the alignment required for the Moon to totally block the Sun would not have to be as precise. Lunar eclipses would also be more frequent because Earth's shadow would be larger at the Moon's distance from Earth.

Figure 28-23 This annular eclipse, partly obscured by clouds, was photographed in San Diego, California, in January, 1992.

The Effects of Orbits You might wonder why a solar eclipse does not occur every month, as the Moon passes between the Sun and Earth during the new moon phase. This does not happen because the Moon's orbit is tilted 5° relative to the ecliptic. Usually, the Moon passes north or south of the Sun as seen from Earth, so no solar eclipse takes place. Only when the Moon crosses the ecliptic is it possible for the proper alignment for a solar eclipse to occur, but even that is not enough to guarantee a solar eclipse. The plane of the Moon's orbit also rotates slowly around Earth, and a solar eclipse occurs only when the intersection of the Moon and the ecliptic is in a line with the Sun and Earth. Hence, the proper alignment for solar eclipses does not occur every month with each new moon.

Not only does the Moon move above and below the plane of Earth and the Sun, but also, the Moon's distance from Earth increases and decreases as the Moon moves in its elliptical orbit around Earth. The closet point in the Moon's orbit to Earth is called **perigee,** and the farthest point is called **apogee.** When the Moon is near apogee, it appears smaller as seen from Earth, and thus it does not completely block the disk of the Sun during an eclipse. This is called an annular eclipse because from Earth, a ring of the Sun called an annulus is visible around the dark Moon, as shown in *Figure 28-23.* You'll experiment with the different types of solar eclipses in the *Problem-Solving Lab* on this page.

Interpreting Scientific Illustrations

Predict how a solar eclipse will look Depending on an observer's location, a solar eclipse can look different.

Analysis

1. Make a drawing of how the solar eclipse would appear to an observer at each labeled location in the illustration.

Thinking Critically

2. Design a data table showing your drawings of how the eclipse would appear at each location.

3. What type of eclipse does each of your drawings represent? Include this information in your data table.

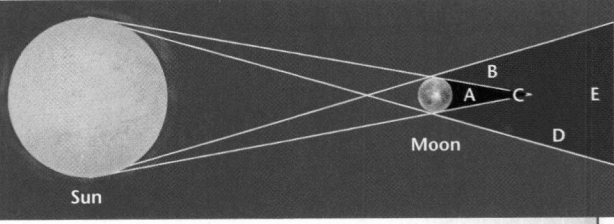

Content Background

The Moon's orbital plane precesses with a period of 18 years, causing the line of intersection between the orbital planes of the Moon and Earth to rotate with a period of 18 years. The result is an 18-year repeating pattern of solar and lunar eclipses.

Teaching Transparency 89 L2 ELL

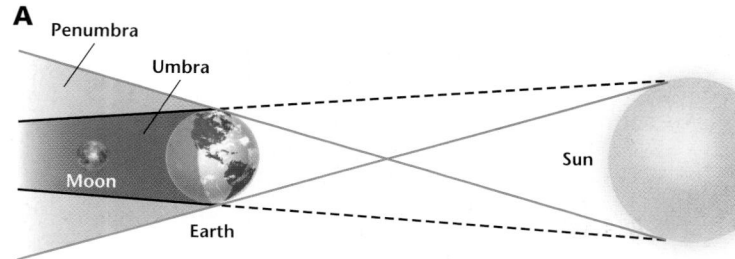

A
Penumbra
Umbra
Moon
Earth
Sun

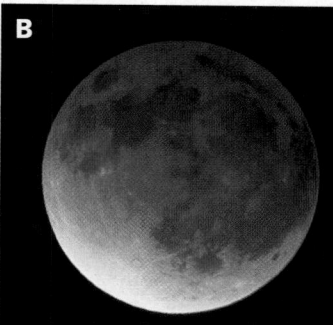

B

Figure 28-24 When the Moon is completely within the umbra of Earth's shadow **(A)**, we observe a total lunar eclipse **(B)**. (Illustration not to scale)

LUNAR ECLIPSES

A **lunar eclipse** occurs when the Moon passes through Earth's shadow. As illustrated in **Figure 28-24A,** this can happen only at the time of a full moon, when the Moon is in the opposite direction from the Sun. The shadow of Earth has umbral and penumbral portions, just as the Moon's shadow does. A total lunar eclipse occurs when the entire Moon is within Earth's umbra, and totality lasts for approximately two hours. During a total lunar eclipse, the Moon is faintly visible, as shown in **Figure 28-24B,** because sunlight that has passed near Earth has been refracted by Earth's atmosphere. This light can give the eclipsed Moon a reddish color as Earth's atmosphere bends the red light into the umbra, much like a lens. Like solar eclipses, lunar eclipses do not occur every full moon because the Moon in its orbit usually passes above or below the Sun as seen from Earth.

Solar and lunar eclipses occur in almost equal numbers, with slightly more lunar eclipses. The maximum number of eclipses, solar and lunar combined, that can be seen in a year is seven. The last time this occurred was in 1982, and it won't happen again until 2038.

SECTION ASSESSMENT

1. What are the causes of the seasons on Earth?

2. What would our seasons be like if Earth's axis were not tilted?

3. Explain why the Moon goes through phases as seen from Earth.

4. Describe solar and lunar eclipses.

5. **Thinking Critically** If Earth's axis were tilted 45°, at what latitudes would the Sun be directly overhead on the summer and winter solstices, and on the vernal and autumnal equinoxes?

SKILL REVIEW

6. **Formulating Models** If you were to observe Earth from the Moon, you would see that it goes through phases. Draw a diagram illustrating these phases and the positions of the Sun, Earth, and the Moon. For more help, refer to the *Skill Handbook.*

28.3 The Sun-Earth-Moon System **767**

SECTION ASSESSMENT

1. Earth orbits the Sun, and Earth's axis is tilted.
2. There would be no seasonal variations.
3. We see varying portions of the Moon's sunlit side as it orbits Earth.
4. A solar eclipse occurs when the Moon partially or completely blocks the Sun's disk as seen from Earth. A lunar eclipse occurs when the Moon passes through Earth's shadow.

5. summer solstice—45°N; winter solstice—45°S; equinoxes—equator
6. When the Moon is directly between Earth and the Sun, Earth is in full Earth phase. When Earth is directly between the Moon and the Sun, Earth is in new Earth phase. When the Moon is in first quarter, Earth is in third quarter. When the Moon is in third quarter, Earth is in first quarter.

---

3 Assess

Check for Understanding

Discussion
Have students summarize the role of the Moon in forming both tides and eclipses.

Reteach

To verify student understanding of tides, ask students what the tides would be like if Earth were in synchronous rotation with the Moon, that is, if the same side of Earth always faced the Moon. The Moon would hover over a fixed spot on Earth, and there would be two permanent, non-moving bulges in the oceans on the sides of Earth facing toward and away from the Moon. The tides would not rise and fall at any location on Earth; sea level would simply be higher or lower, depending on the location relative to the Moon's direction.

✓ Assessment

Performance Have students model the positions of the Sun, Earth, and the Moon during solar and lunar eclipses, spring and neap tides, and the phases of the Moon with balls and a flashlight. Use the Performance Task Assessment List for Model in **PASC,** p. 51.

NY Core Curriculum Standards

Page 766: St 4 KI 1.1a &1.1f, St 6 KI 2
Page 767: St 4 KI 1.1a &1.1f, St 6 KI 2

767

Time Allotment

30 minutes

Process Skills

sequence, observe and infer, recognize cause and effect, recognize spatial relationships

Preparation

Special Instructions

Briefly review with students the principle of cross-cutting relationships.

Procedure

Teaching Strategies

- Team students who are visually impaired with students who can easily discern fine details.
- Have students work on the first photo, check their work, and then continue.

Troubleshooting

Have students review the formation of the Moon's surface features, especially the maria.

Mapping GeoLab — Relative Ages of Lunar Features

*I*t is possible to use the principle of cross-cutting relationships, discussed in Chapter 21, to determine the relative ages of surface features on the Moon. By observing which features cross-cut others, you can infer which is older.

Preparation

Problem
How can you use images of the Moon to interpret relative ages of lunar features?

Materials
metric ruler
pencil

Procedure

1. Observe photos I and II. Use the letters to identify the oldest feature in each photo using the principle of cross-cutting relationships. List the other features in order of their relative ages.
2. Observe photo III. List the mare, rille, and craters in order of their relative ages.
3. Observe photo IV. Use the principle of cross-cutting relationships, along with your knowledge of lunar history, to identify the features and list them in order of their relative ages.

Analyze

1. What problems did you encounter?
2. Based on information from all the photos, what features are usually the oldest? The youngest?
3. Could scientists use the process you did to determine the exact age difference between two overlapping craters? Why or why not?
4. If the small crater in photo II, labeled A, is 44 km across, what is the scale for that photo? What is the size of the large crater, labeled D?

Conclude & Apply

1. Which would be older, a crater that had rays crossing it, or the crater that caused the rays? Explain.
2. Is there some type of relative-age dating that scientists can use to analyze craters on Earth? Explain.
3. What do you think caused the chain of craters in photo I? If the crater labeled A is approximately 17 km across, how long is the chain of craters?

Data and Observations

Photo I: A is older than D; B is older than C.
Photo II: D is the oldest; A is younger than D; E is younger than D; B and C are younger than E.
Photo III: B is the oldest; D is the next oldest; then E and A; C is the youngest.
Photo IV: D is the oldest; A is the next oldest; C or B is the youngest.

I

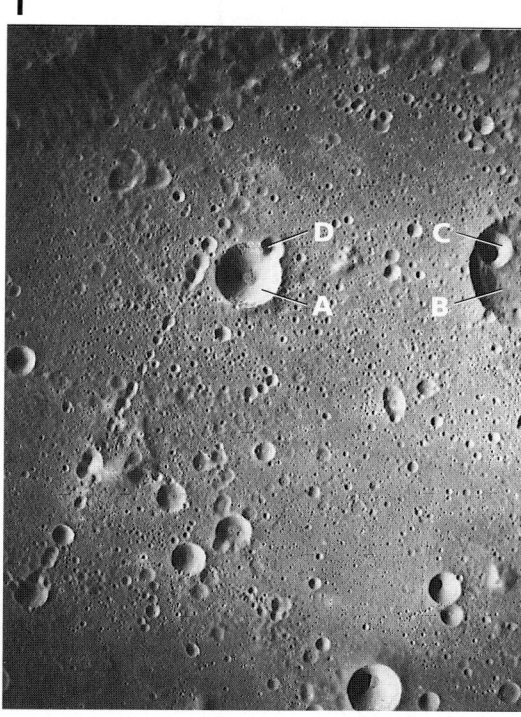

II

III

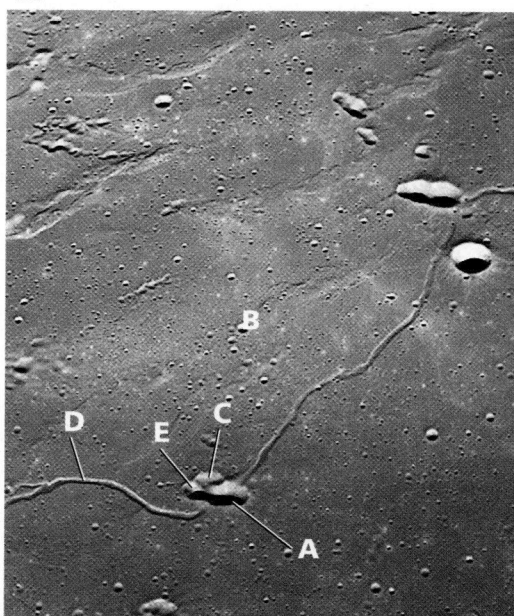

IV

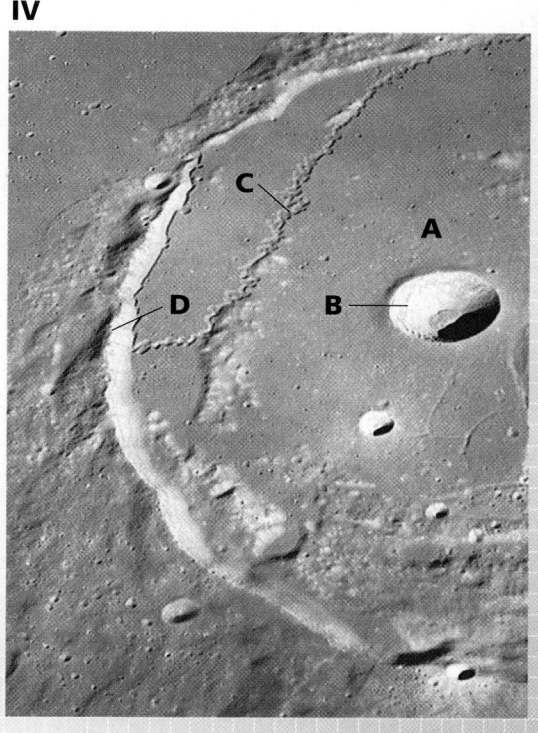

Mapping GeoLab **769**

Science & Math

Purpose 🎲

Students will learn how a scientist in ancient times estimated the size of Earth, and they will also learn how simple geometric techniques based on local observations can provide significant information about larger systems.

Content Background

Eratosthenes was not only a mathematician, but also an astronomer, a poet, a geographer, and a librarian. His method for measuring Earth's circumference was based on a simple principle of geometry: that the ratio of an arc to the circumference of a circle is equal to the angle that the arc subtends to 360°. This calculation works only when the assumption is made that the Sun is sufficiently far away that its rays of light are parallel.

Teaching Strategies

- Show students that half of the circumference corresponds to 180°, a quarter of the circumference corresponds to 90°, and so on. This will help students to understand why a 7° angle corresponds to 7/360 of the full circumference of Earth.
- Be sure that students have the basic algebra skills necessary to solve the equations.

Procedure

Students need to use basic algebra to solve the ratio expression given in item 3.

Science & Math

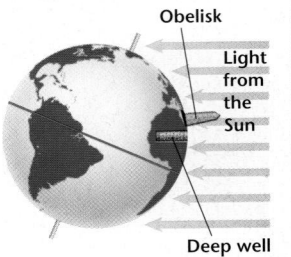

Obelisk
Light from the Sun
Deep well

The Size of Earth

We know that Earth is round, but how do we know how large it really is? Have you ever wondered how we measure such a large object? Long ago, before the development of high-tech computers and space shuttles, one man used his knowledge of geometry to determine the circumference of Earth.

Using Geometry

An ancient Greek mathematician, Eratosthenes (276–194 B.C.), was the first to develop a method for determining the circumference of Earth. It was known during his time that at noon on the summer solstice, when the Sun was directly overhead in Syene, Egypt, sunlight reached the bottom of a local well. However, to the north, in Alexandria, the Sun cast a shadow off an obelisk on the same day and at the same time.

Eratosthenes knew that the distance between the two cities was approximately 4900 stadia, an ancient form of measurement equivalent to 770 km by today's estimate. He measured the height of the obelisk and the length of the shadow. Then, by using the relationship

$$\arctan\left(\frac{\text{length of shadow}}{\text{height of obelisk}}\right)$$

he calculated that the Sun was 7° lower than directly overhead. Knowing that Earth was round, and that round objects have a total of 360°, Eratosthenes determined that the difference in latitude of the two cities was 7°. Because sunlight could be seen at the bottom of the well in Syene on the summer solstice, Eratosthenes determined that Syene was at latitude 23.5°N and that Alexandria was at latitude 30.5°N.

Procedure

1. Using a compass and a sheet of paper, draw a diagram of Earth. Mark the equator.

2. Using a protractor, locate Syene at latitude 23.5°N and Alexandria at latitude 30.5°N.
3. Knowing that the difference in latitudes of the two cities is 7° and that a circle has 360°, you can determine what portion of a circle is 7°. This ratio of 7° to 360° can be represented by

$$\frac{d}{C} = \frac{7°}{360°}$$

where d is the distance between Alexandria and Syene, and C is Earth's circumference. Given that $d = 770$ km (4900 stadia), solve the equation for C. Then find Earth's radius using $C = 2\pi r$.

4. Use your answers in step 3 to determine Earth's diameter.

Challenge

1. Earth's radius is actually 6378.1 km. How do your measurements compare to this?
2. What is the percent deviation of your measurement?

$$\text{Percent deviation} = \frac{\text{difference from accepted value}}{\text{accepted value}} \times 100$$

Earth Science Online

To learn more about Eratosthenes' contributions to science and math, visit the Earth Science Web Site at <u>earthgeu.com</u>

Data and Observations

1. & 2.

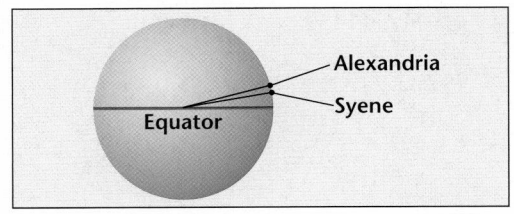

Alexandria
Syene
Equator

3. $C = 39\ 600$ km
$r = 6302.5$ km

4. diameter = 12 605.0 km

Challenge

1. Students' values should be too small by 75.6 km.
2. 1.2 percent (Note: There is some uncertainty among modern scholars about the conversion factor between the ancient stadia and modern units such as kilometers, so it is not clear that the value of Eratosthenes was as accurate as is portrayed here.)

Summary

SECTION 28.1

Tools of Astronomy

Main Ideas

- Visible light, radio waves, infared and ultraviolet radiation, X rays, and gamma rays are types of electromagnetic radiation.
- A telescope collects light over a large area, makes time exposures, and can use other instruments to analyze light.
- Visible-light telescopes can be made using lenses, as in refracting telescopes, or mirrors, as in reflecting telescopes.
- Space is explored by telescopes, satellites, probes, and humans.

Vocabulary
interferometry (p. 750)
reflecting telescope (p. 749)
refracting telescope (p. 749)
spinoff (p. 752)

SECTION 28.2

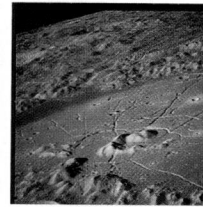

The Moon

Main Ideas

- The first step toward exploration of the Moon was the launch of the Soviet satellite *Sputnik 1*. The American spacecraft *Apollo 11* was the first crewed exploration of the Moon.
- The Moon's surface has many features that are not present on Earth because the Moon lacks an atmosphere and therefore its surface does not undergo erosion.
- Scientists theorize that the Moon formed simultaneously with Earth, was captured by Earth's gravity, or formed as a result of an object colliding with Earth.

Vocabulary
albedo (p. 754)
ejecta (p. 754)
highland (p. 754)
impact crater (p. 754)
mare (p. 754)
ray (p. 754)
regolith (p. 755)
rille (p. 754)

SECTION 28.3

The Sun-Earth-Moon System

Main Ideas

- The entire sky appears to rotate daily because we observe it from a rotating Earth. Our timekeeping system is based on the solar day, the length of day as observed from Earth.
- Our view of the Sun's position changes throughout the year as Earth moves in its orbit about the Sun. Seasons occur on Earth because Earth's axis is tilted.
- The Moon goes through a cycle of phases each lunar month that correspond to our changing view from Earth of the sunlit side of the Moon.
- Tides are caused by the gravitational attraction of the Moon, and to a lesser extent, the gravitational attraction of the Sun.
- A solar eclipse occurs when the Moon lies directly between Earth and the Sun. A lunar eclipse occurs when the Moon passes through Earth's shadow.

Vocabulary
apogee (p. 766)
autumnal equinox (p. 761)
ecliptic (p. 759)
lunar eclipse (p. 767)
perigee (p. 766)
solar eclipse (p. 765)
summer solstice (p. 760)
synchronous rotation (p. 764)
vernal equinox (p. 761)
winter solstice (p. 761)

Study Guide **771**

CHAPTER 28
Study Guide

Main Ideas

Summary statements can be used by students to review the major concepts of the chapter.

VOCABULARY PuzzleMaker

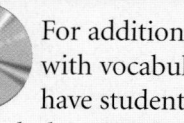

For additional help with vocabulary, have students access the Vocabulary Puzzlemaker online.

earthgeu.com/ vocabulary puzzlemaker

0:00 Out of Time?

If time does not permit teaching the entire chapter, use the GeoDigest at the end of the unit as an overview.

Earth Science Online

Be sure to check the Earth Science Web Site for links to chapter material:
earthgeu.com

GLENCOE
Technology

Videotape/DVD
MindJogger Videoquizzes
Chapter 28: *The Sun-Earth-Moon System*
Have students work in groups as they play the videoquiz game to review key chapter concepts.

Resource Manager

Chapter Assessment, pp. 163–168
MindJogger Videoquizzes DVD/VHS
ExamView® Pro CD-ROM
Performance Assessment in Earth Science

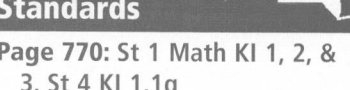

NY Core Curriculum Standards

Page 770: St 1 Math KI 1, 2, & 3, St 4 KI 1.1g
Page 771: St 4 KI 1.1a, 1.1c, 1.1f, 1.1h, & 1.1i

Understanding Main Ideas

1. b
2. d
3. a
4. a
5. b
6. b
7. gamma rays, X rays, ultraviolet radiation, visible light, infrared radiation, microwaves, radio waves
8. to avoid blurring by the atmosphere and to observe wavelengths that don't penetrate Earth's atmosphere
9. Top: dark shadow—umbra; light shadow—penumbra; total lunar eclipse
   Bottom: dark shadow—umbra; light shadow—penumbra; partial lunar eclipse
10. oscillating electric and magnetic waves that travel through space
11. through continual overturning of the uppermost layer of the lunar crust by impacts
12. the length of time it takes for the Moon to go through a complete cycle of phases; 29.5 days
13. visible light
14. Mountain ranges around maria are remnants of crater walls of large impact basins that rose above the level of the lava flows that filled the basins after the impacts.
15. There is no atmosphere or oceans to transport heat around the Moon and smooth out the extreme temperature differences.

Understanding Main Ideas

1. On what does the light-collecting power of a telescope depend?
   a. the type of telescope
   b. the area of the opening through which light enters
   c. the location of the telescope
   d. the distance from the telescope to the object being observed

2. What is the same for all types of electromagnetic radiation?
   a. frequency   c. color
   b. wavelength   d. speed

3. What type of radiation does not have to be observed above Earth's atmosphere?
   a. visible light   c. gamma rays
   b. X rays   d. ultraviolet radiation

4. During which of the following is the Sun directly overhead at 23.5° north latitude?
   a. summer solstice   c. winter solstice
   b. vernal equinox   d. autumnal equinox

5. Which of the following provides evidence that Earth is rotating?
   a. The Sun rises and sets.
   b. The plane of a Foucault pendulum appears to shift its orientation.
   c. The Moon goes through phases.
   d. The same side of the Moon always faces Earth.

6. Which of the following is in the correct order?
   a. waning crescent, third quarter, waning gibbous, new moon
   b. waxing gibbous, full moon, waning gibbous, third quarter
   c. new moon, waning gibbous, first quarter, waning crescent
   d. waxing crescent, new moon, waning crescent, first quarter

---

7. List the various forms of electromagnetic radiation according to wavelength, from shortest to longest.

8. Why must some telescopes be launched into space?

Use the diagrams below to answer question 9.

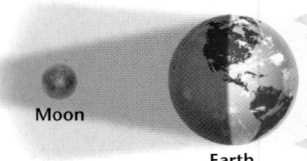

Moon   Earth   Light from the Sun

Moon   Earth   Light from the Sun

9. List the types of shadows as well as the types of eclipses that will be seen by an observer on the unlit side of Earth.

10. What is electromagnetic radiation?

11. How was the lunar regolith formed?

12. Describe how a lunar month is defined. How long is it?

13. Of all types of electromagnetic radiation, which can the human eye detect?

Test-Taking Tip

CROSSING OUT Cross out choices you've eliminated. If you can't write in the test booklet, list the answer choice letters on the scratch paper and cross them out there. You'll save time and stop yourself from choosing an answer you've mentally eliminated.

earthgeu.com/chapter_test

Applying Main Ideas

16. During a full moon, the Sun, Moon, and Earth are in a line, with Earth between the Sun and Moon; during a new moon, the Sun, Moon, and Earth are in a line, with the Moon between the Sun and Earth.

17. because of the tilt of Earth's axis

18. No; to be in synchronous rotation, the Moon must rotate once on its axis for every revolution. Otherwise, the same side would not always face Earth.

19. During each lunar month, there would be both a total solar eclipse and a total lunar eclipse.

20. Scattered light from a city makes it difficult or impossible to see dim objects in the sky.

14. How did the mountain ranges around the maria on the Moon form?

15. Why are the temperature fluctuations on the surface of the Moon so extreme compared to those on Earth?

Applying Main Ideas

16. What are the Moon's positions relative to the Sun and Earth when we observe a full moon and a new moon?

17. Why does the Sun's altitude in the sky change throughout the year?

18. If the Moon rotated twice on its axis for every one time it orbited Earth, would it be in synchronous rotation? Explain.

19. Suppose the Moon's orbital plane were exactly aligned with Earth's orbital plane. How often would eclipses occur?

20. Why is it best to get away from city lights to view the nighttime sky?

Thinking Critically

21. How would Earth's surface look if Earth did not have an atmosphere?

22. Why did one-half of the Moon's surface remain hidden from human sight until the era of space probes, which started in 1959?

23. When observers on Earth can see a total lunar eclipse, what kind of eclipse would be seen by an observer on the Moon?

24. In some maria, there are craters. Which are younger, the maria or the craters?

25. How would the topography of the Moon be different if the Moon had an atmosphere?

earthgeu.com/standardized_test

Standardized Test Practice

1. What is debris from an impact that falls back to the surface of the Moon called?
a. rilles   **c.** ejecta
b. maria   **d.** albedo

2. In December, the South Pole is tilted farther toward the Sun than at any other time of the year, and the North Pole is tilted its farthest away from the Sun. What is the northern hemisphere experiencing at that time?
a. the winter solstice
b. the summer solstice
c. the vernal equinox
d. the autumnal equinox

INTERPRETING SCIENTIFIC ILLUSTRATIONS
Use the diagram below to answer questions 3 and 4.

Earth   The Moon   The Sun

3. What results on Earth when the Sun and the Moon are aligned along the same direction, as in the diagram?
a. spring tides   **c.** the autumnal equinox
b. neap tides   **d.** the summer solstice

4. If the Moon in this diagram were passing directly between the Sun and Earth, thereby blocking our view of the Sun, what would we be experiencing on Earth?
a. a lunar eclipse   **c.** umbra
b. a solar eclipse   **d.** penumbra

Thinking Critically

21. Its surface would look similar to the surface of the Moon. It would be covered by craters and lava flows, and there would be no features resulting from erosion.

22. That side of the Moon is never visible from Earth as a result of the Moon's synchronous rotation.

23. When a total lunar eclipse is observed on Earth, the Moon is in Earth's shadow. At that time, an observer on the Moon would experience a total solar eclipse.

24. When craters are within maria, the craters are younger than the maria.

25. If the Moon had an atmosphere, there would be sources of erosion, which would gradually erase old features such as early craters. The erosional process would be much more effective if the atmosphere were thick enough so that liquid water could exist and if there were a hydrological cycle, as there is on Earth.

EXAMVIEW® PRO

Use ExamView® Pro Testmaker CD-ROM to:
- Create **multiple versions** of tests.
- Create **modified** tests with one mouse click for struggling students.
- **Edit** existing questions and add your own questions.
- **Build** tests based on national curriculum standards.

Standardized Test Practice

1. c
2. a
3. a
4. b

NY Core Curriculum Standards
Page 772: St 4 KI 1.1a, 1.1d, & 1.1f, St 6 KI 2
Page 773: St 4 KI 1.1a, 1.1f, & 1.1h, St 6 KI 5

Our Solar System

Refer to pages 8T–9T of the Teacher Guide for an explanation of the National Science Content Standards correlations.

Section	Objectives	National Science Content Standards	State/Local Standards
SECTION 29.1 **Overview of Our Solar System** 🕐 1½ sessions 📦 1 block	1. **Describe** early models of our solar system. 2. **Examine** the modern heliocentric model of our solar system. 3. **Relate** gravity to the motions of celestial bodies.	UCP.1, UCP.2, UCP.3, UCP.4; A.1; B.4; E.2; G.2, G.3	St 1 Math KI 1, 2, 3, Science KI 1, & 3, St 2 KI 1, St 4 KI 1.1a, 1.1b, 1.1f, & 1.2c, St 6 KI 1 & 2
SECTION 29.2 **The Terrestrial Planets** 🕐 1 session 📦 ½ block	4. **Describe** the properties of the terrestrial planets. 5. **Compare** Earth with the other terrestrial planets.	UCP.1, UCP.2, UCP.3, UCP.4; B.2, B.4; D.3; G.2, G.3	St 1 Math KI 2, Science KI 1, 2, & 3, St 4 KI 1.1a, 1.1b, 1.2c, & 1.2d, St 6 KI 2 & 4
SECTION 29.3 **The Gas Giant Planets** 🕐 1 session 📦 ½ block	6. **Describe** the properties of the gas giant planets. 7. **Identify** the unique nature of the planet Pluto.	UCP.1, UCP.2, UCP.3, UCP.4; A.1, A.2; B.2, B.4; G.3	St 1 Math KI 1, 2, 3, Science KI 1 & 2, St 4 KI 1.1a, 1.1b, 1.2c, & 1.2d, St 6 KI 2, 3, & 4
SECTION 29.4 **Formation of Our Solar System** 🕐 2½ sessions 📦 1½ blocks	8. **Summarize** the properties of the solar system that support the theory of the solar system's formation. 9. **Describe** how the planets formed from a disk surrounding the young Sun. 10. **Explore** remnants of solar system formation.	UCP.1, UCP.2, UCP.3, UCP.4, UCP.5; A.1, A.2; B.2, B.4; D.3; E.2; G.3	St 1 Math KI 1, 2, 3, Science KI 1, 2, 3, & Engin KI 1, St 2 KI 1 & 2, St 4 KI 1.1a, 1.1.b, 1.2c, & 1.2d, St 6 KI 1, 2, 3, 4, & 5

A complete Planning Guide is provided on pages 30T–32T.

🕐 The number of recommended single-period sessions

📦 The number of recommended blocks

Activity Materials

Discovery Lab *page 775*
Internet access, paper, pencil

GeoLab *pages 798–799*
meterstick, masking tape, stopwatch, measuring tape, calculator, marker, round objects of assorted sizes

MiniLab *page 777*
string, cardboard, thumbtacks, meterstick, paper, ruler

Demo *page 783*
toy top or gyroscope

page 790
flashlight, meterstick

Need materials? Contact Science Kit at 1-800-828-7777 or at www.sciencekit.com on the Internet. For alternate materials, see the activity on the listed page.

Key to Teaching Strategies

L1 Level 1 activities should be appropriate for students with learning difficulties.

L2 Level 2 activities should be within the ability range of all students.

L3 Level 3 activities are designed for above-average students.

ELL ELL activities should be within the ability range of English-language learners.

COOP LEARN Cooperative learning activities are designed for small-group work.

P These strategies represent student products that can be placed in a best-work portfolio.

📦 These strategies are useful in a block-scheduling format.

Chapter Organizer

Glencoe Exclusive!
Teacher Works™
All-In-One Planner and Resource Center

Activities/Features	Reproducible Masters	Transparencies
Discovery Lab: Exploring Our Solar System, p. 775 **MiniLab:** Eccentricity, p. 777 **Using Math:** Using Numbers, p. 778	**Study Guide for Content Mastery,** p. 183 **L2** **Laboratory Manual,** pp. 229–232 **L2** **GeoLab and MiniLab Worksheets,** p. 115 **L2**	**Section Focus Transparency 92** **L1** **ELL** **Teaching Transparency 90** **L2** **ELL**
	Study Guide for Content Mastery, p. 184 **L2**	**Section Focus Transparency 93** **L1** **ELL**
Problem-Solving Lab: Using Numbers, p. 791	**Study Guide for Content Mastery,** pp. 185–186 **L2** **Laboratory Manual,** pp. 225–228 **L2**	**Section Focus Transparency 94** **L1** **ELL** **Teaching Transparency 91** **L2** **ELL**
Design Your Own GeoLab: Scaling the Solar System, pp. 798–799 **Science in the News:** Discovering New Planets, p. 800	**Study Guide for Content Mastery,** pp. 187–188 **L2** **GeoLab and MiniLab Worksheets,** pp. 116–119 **L2**	**Section Focus Transparency 95** **L1** **ELL** **Teaching Transparency 92** **L2** **ELL**

✓ Assessment

Chapter Assessment, pp. 169–174
Performance Assessment in the Science Classroom (PASC)
MindJogger Videoquiz DVD/VHS
Performance Assessment in Earth Science
ExamView® Pro CD-ROM
5 Days to the Regents Exam

Additional Resources

Guided Reading Audio Program **ELL**
Cooperative Learning in the Science Classroom **COOP LEARN**
Lesson Plans
Block Scheduling
earthgeu.com
NY Lesson Plans
NY Block Scheduling
Review Handbook for Regents Earth Science Exam

☐ NATIONAL GEOGRAPHIC

Teacher's Corner

Products Available from National Geographic Society
To order the following products, call the National Geographic Society at 1-800-368-2728:
Curriculum Kit
GeoKit: *Astronomy*

Videos
The Sun: Earth's Star
Maps
Solar System/Celestial Family

Content Background

Overview of Our Solar System
Section 29.1

The struggle to learn the true nature of the solar system and of planetary motion took centuries. The many false starts and incorrect hypotheses along the way help to illustrate some important principles of science. One of these principles is the notion of simplicity: a scientific theory that is simple, and that depends on the fewest unsupported assumptions, is most likely to be correct. Some of the early models of the solar system were far from simple; they involved multiple nested spheres or complex circles upon circles, whose sizes and motions were arbitrarily chosen to reproduce the observed positions of the planets. Then, during the Renaissance, Kepler found that a very simple figure called the ellipse describes planetary motions much more accurately than the older models, and

Newton showed that a few mathematical relationships could explain and predict the motions of the planets. Thus, our understanding of the structure and motions of the solar system provides an excellent example of simplicity in nature.

The Terrestrial Planets
Section 29.2

People have long been fascinated with the possibility that life may exist on Mars. In the late 1800s, telescopic observations seemed to reveal a network of lines on Mars. These were soon interpreted to be canals, suggesting that a technological civilization on the red planet had built these structures. Interest in this idea culminated with the famous 1938 radio broadcast, "The War of the Worlds," which led many people to believe that Earth was actually being invaded by Martians. By the 1960s, speculation about life on Mars waned, largely because the first probes showed Mars to be barren and cratered. However, there was evidence of ancient rivers and lakes, so the idea persisted that conditions conducive to life might once have existed on Mars. Then, in 1996, new excitement arose when a meteorite of Martian origin was interpreted as possibly containing fossil microorganisms. Later studies showed this is not likely, but interest in possible Martian fossils remains high, and the current NASA program to explore Mars is focused on a search for such fossils, or possibly, living microorganisms. Another flurry of excitement occurred in 2000, when NASA released images suggesting that liquid water may exist on Mars today. In the next few years, a series of new NASA probes to Mars may help end the speculation and firmly establish whether Mars once was home to life.

Multiple Learning Styles

- **Kinesthetic** Modeling, p. 796
- **Visual-Spatial** Activity, p. 775, Demo, pp. 778, 783
- **Interpersonal** Collaborative Learning, p. 781
- **Linguistic** Earth Science Journal, pp. 776, 795
- **Logical-Mathematical** Earth Science Journal, p. 782, Reteach, p. 792

GLENCOE Technology

The following multimedia resources are available from Glencoe.

The Infinite Voyage Series
Sail On, Voyager

Vocabulary Puzzlemaker

TeacherWorks™ CD-ROM

MindJogger Videoquizzes DVD/VHS

ExamView® Pro CD-ROM

Interactive Chalkboard CD-ROM

The Gas Giant Planets
Section 29.3

The *Voyager 2* mission came very close to completing a path through the outer solar system that had long been referred to as the Grand Tour. All of the outer planets were to be aligned on the same side of the Sun in the 1980s, and astronomers recognized long before then that this could be an opportunity to visit all of these planets very economically. A single spacecraft could go from one planet to the next, using the gravitational field of each planet along the way to boost the spacecraft to the next planet. However, Congressional funding constraints quashed the idea. Oddly enough, once *Voyager 2* was well on its way and was operating successfully, NASA found that with a few course adjustments, most of the Grand Tour could be completed after all. Funding extensions were granted to allow it to do so. Ultimately, *Voyager 2* made close flyby approaches to all four of the gas giants and returned vast amounts of images and data, which have been invaluable in studies of these planets.

Formation of Our Solar System
Section 29.4

Meteorites preserve information about the early history of the solar system. Therefore, scientists seek them out for laboratory analysis aimed at gaining mineralogical and chemical clues to the origin of the solar system. One difficulty in conducting such research is identifying meteorites once they are on the ground, because rocks from space can closely resemble Earth rocks. Perhaps surprisingly, the best place to search for meteorites is Antarctica. Earth rocks in Antarctica are buried under thousands of meters of ice, so rocks sitting on top of ice caps stand out, and they are usually identified as meteorites. Hence, part of the job of a scientist studying meteorites is to make occasional forays onto the ice sheet of Antarctica looking for rocks that are out-of-place.

Identifying Misconceptions

The planets influence each other to some extent because of their mutual gravitational attraction, but not as much as some scientists once hypothesized. On two recent occasions, an alignment of most or all of the planets occurred, leading some to expect catastrophic consequences. In 1982, all nine of the planets were lined up in the same direction from the Sun (within 90°), and there were dire predictions that their combined gravitational force would cause tidal disruption of the Sun, which would in turn have catastrophic effects on Earth. Others expected some sort of celestial epiphany on the occasion, and dubbed the event the "harmonic convergence." Somehow, the precise date of the alignment was determined to be March 10, 1982. Nothing unusual happened.

Assessment

Portfolio Assessment
Assessment, TWE, pp. 785, 792

Performance Assessment
Discovery Lab, SE, p. 775
Discovery Lab, TWE, p. 775
MiniLab, SE, p. 777
GeoLab, SE, pp. 798–799

Knowledge Assessment
Assessment, TWE, pp. 779, 782, 784, 789, 797
Problem-Solving Lab, TWE, p. 791
GeoLab, TWE, pp. 798–799
Section Assessment, TWE, pp. 779, 785, 792, 797
Chapter Assessment, TWE, pp. 802–803

Skill Assessment
MiniLab, TWE, p. 777
Assessment, TWE, p. 790

Be sure to check the Earth Science Web Site for links to chapter material: earthgeu.com

Chapter 29

Our Solar System

Introducing the Chapter

Have students use a current sky map from the Internet, or from a popular magazine such as *Sky & Telescope* or *Astronomy,* to identify which planets should be visible at this time of the year. The planets that are visible, along with the Moon if it is up, delineate the plane of our solar system's disk. This activity will illustrate the system of planets that students will study in this chapter.

Interpreting the Photo

The visitation of the comet Hale-Bopp into our solar system in the spring of 1997 created quite a stir. This photo of Hale-Bopp over Mono Lake, in the Sierra Nevada of California, shows the comet's stunning tails. The star trails in this and other images are a result of time-lapse photography, telescope motion, and Earth's rotation.

INTERACTIVE CHALKBOARD with Image Bank

PowerPoint® Presentations

This CD is an editable Microsoft® PowerPoint® presentation that includes:
- Section presentations
- Section checks
- Image bank
- Links to Earth Science Online
- All transparencies
- Animations
- Audio

Chapter 29

Our Solar System

What You'll Learn
- How gravity and orbits are related.
- The characteristics of planets and interplanetary bodies.
- What theory is used to describe the formation of the solar system.

Why It's Important
The laws of motion and universal gravitation explain how gravity governs the motions of the planets and other planetary bodies. Scientists base the model of our solar system on observations of the organization and nature of the planets and interplanetary bodies.

Earth Science Online

To find out more about our solar system, visit the Earth Science Web Site at earthgeu.com

Comet Hale-Bopp over Mono Lake

Discovery Lab

Process Skills
compare and contrast, outline

Procedure
This lab may be done in small groups.

Troubleshooting
You can find information about older probes in books at a library if you don't have access to the Internet.

Observe
Student answers will vary. An example would be *Mars Pathfinder* (lander), launched December 4, 1996. It arrived July 4, 1997, and was operated by NASA and JPL. It took photographs, analyzed rock composition, measured winds, and monitored weather.

Discovery Lab

Exploring Our Solar System

All nine planets in our solar system have been explored by uncrewed space probes, or soon will be. You can learn about these missions and their discoveries by finding information on the Web. The agency that sponsors a mission, the scientists involved, or both, usually create extensive Web sites full of information about the design, operation, and scientific goals of the mission.

1. Find at least one Web site for missions to four different planets. Or go to science.glencoe.com and follow the links.

2. Make a list of some of the key aspects of each mission.

Summarize Make an outline for each mission. Include the type of mission (flyby, lander, or orbiter), the scientific goals, the launch date and the date of arrival at the planet, and a summary of what was learned, or what scientists hope will be learned.

SECTION 29.1 — Overview of Our Solar System

OBJECTIVES

- **Describe** *early models of our solar system.*
- **Examine** *the modern heliocentric model of our solar system.*
- **Relate** *gravity to the motions of celestial bodies.*

VOCABULARY

retrograde motion
astronomical unit
perihelion
aphelion
eccentricity

Earth is one of nine planets revolving around, or orbiting, the Sun. All the planets, as well as most of their moons, also called satellites, orbit the Sun in the same direction, and all their orbits, except Pluto's, lie near the same plane. The planets of our solar system have various sizes, surface conditions, and internal structures. Scientists have gathered much information about our solar system through the use of technologies developed in the twentieth century, but human beings have been watching the sky for thousands of years, and early ideas about the solar system were developed solely on the basis of Earth-based observations of the sky.

EARLY IDEAS

When viewed from Earth, the planets slowly change position each night relative to the position of the stars. Therefore, ancient astronomers could recognize the difference between stars and planets. These astronomers assumed that the Sun, planets, and stars orbited a stationary Earth in what is now known as a geocentric model, meaning "Earth centered."

29.1 Overview of Our Solar System **775**

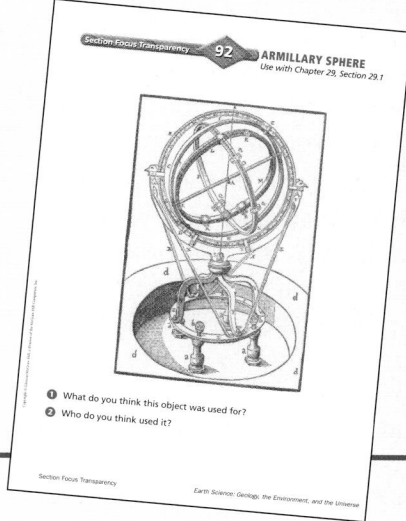

Using an Analogy

Explain to students that retrograde motion is very similar to cars passing one another. To a person riding in a car that passes another car on the freeway, it appears that the slower car is moving backwards in relation to the background. The same is true when the faster-moving Earth passes a slower planet, such as Mars.

Discussion

Have students discuss whether or not it is possible for Venus and Mercury to undergo retrograde motion as seen from Earth. Venus and Mercury do undergo retrograde motion because retrograde motion occurs whenever Earth passes or is passed by another planet. The retrograde motions of Venus and Mercury occur when they are near the Sun, so the motions are difficult to see.

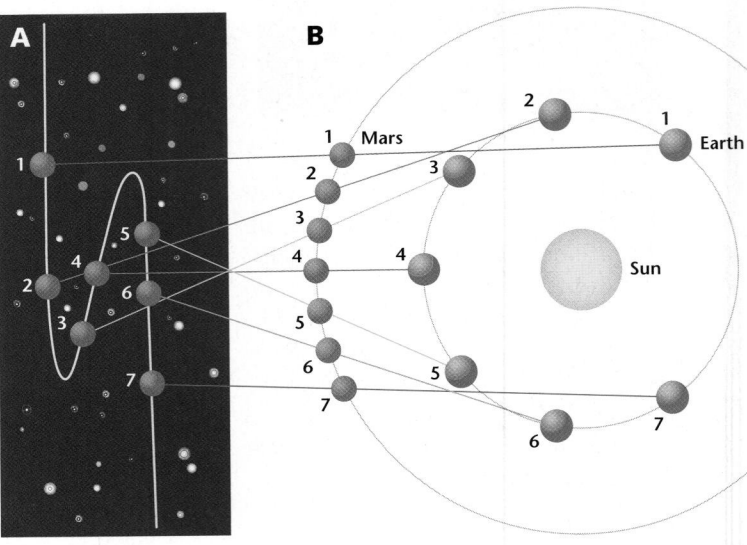

Figure 29-1 Mars appears to move from east to west (positions 3 and 4) for a short time **(A)** during its retrograde motion. The heliocentric model **(B)** explains retrograde motion. Follow the lines from Earth's orbital positions to Mars's orbital positions, and then to Mars's position in the sky. Retrograde motion is similar to passing a slower car on the freeway. It appears that the slower car is moving backwards relative to the background. (not to scale)

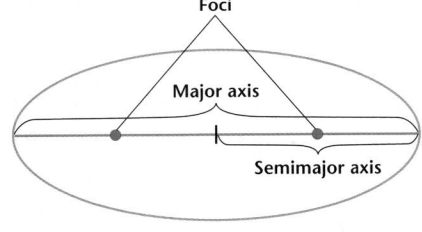

Figure 29-2 The major axis passes through the foci of an ellipse, while the semimajor axis is half of the major axis.

However, some aspects of planetary motion were difficult to explain with a geocentric model. For example, the normal direction of motion for all planets, as observed from Earth, is toward the east. Occasionally, however, a planet will move in the opposite direction across the sky in what is called **retrograde motion.** The retrograde motion of Mars is shown in *Figure 29-1A.* The search for a simple scientific explanation for retrograde motion motivated early astronomers to keep searching for a better model of our solar system.

In 1543, Polish scientist Nicolaus Copernicus suggested that the Sun was the center of the solar system. In this sun-centered, or heliocentric, model, Earth and the other planets orbit the Sun. This model provided a simple explanation of retrograde motion. In a Sun-centered model, the inner planets move faster in their orbits than the outer planets do. As Earth bypasses a slower-moving outer planet, as illustrated in *Figure 29-1B,* it appears that the outer planet temporarily moves backward in the sky.

Kepler's First Law The ideas of Copernicus were not initially accepted by the scientific community, but within a century, other astronomers were finding evidence that supported the heliocentric model. For example, from 1576–1601, a Danish astronomer, Tycho Brahe, made many accurate observations of planetary positions. Using Brahe's data, Johannes Kepler demonstrated that each planet orbits the Sun in a shape called an ellipse, rather than in a circle. This is known as Kepler's first law.

Content Background

Each planet has its own sidereal period, which is the time it takes a planet to return to the starting place in its orbit. However, from a point of view on Earth, the orbital period of any planet is the length of time it takes for that planet to return to the same alignment relative to the Sun-Earth line, called the synodic period. In this chapter and in Appendix J, only sidereal orbital periods are used for the planets.

Earth Science Journal

Linguistic Have each student choose a planet and gather detailed information about its orbit. Students can then put this information together using Kepler's third law and the parameters of an ellipse to develop comprehensive pictures of the motions of their chosen planets. L2 P

An ellipse is an oval shape that is centered on two points instead of a single point, as in a circle. The two points are called the foci (*sing.* focus). The major axis is the line that runs through both foci; it is the maximum diameter of the ellipse, as illustrated in *Figure 29-2.* You will experiment with the foci and shapes of ellipses in the *MiniLab* on this page.

Each planet's elliptical orbit is a different shape and size, and the Sun is always at one focus. For each Sun-planet pair, half of the length of the major axis is called the semimajor axis. It is the average distance between the Sun and the planet. For the Sun and Earth, it is 1.496×10^8 km, or 1 **astronomical unit** (AU). The average distances between the Sun and each planet are measured in astronomical units, and therefore these distances are relative to Earth's average distance from the Sun.

Eccentricity A planet in an elliptical orbit is not at a constant distance from the Sun. When a planet is closest to the Sun in its orbit, it is at **perihelion,** and when it is farthest away, it is at **aphelion,** as shown in *Figure 29-3.* The shape of a planet's elliptical orbit is defined by **eccentricity,** which is the ratio of the distance between the foci to the length of the major axis. Eccentricity values range from 0 to 1. An eccentricity of 0 is a perfect circle, and an eccentricity of nearly 1 is a very elongated oval. An eccentricity equal to 1 is a parabola. Most of the planets have orbits that are not very eccentric, as shown in *Appendix J,* and are thus close to being circles. The length of time it takes for a planet or other body to travel a complete elliptical orbit around the Sun is called the orbital period.

Figure 29-3 A planet is at perihelion when it is closest to the Sun in its orbit and at aphelion when it is farthest. (not to scale)

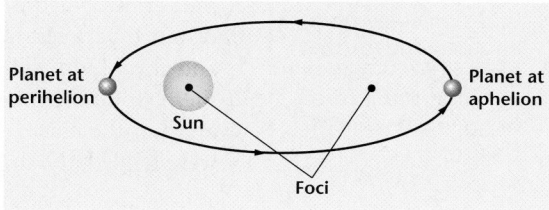

Planet at perihelion — Sun — Foci — Planet at aphelion

MiniLab

Eccentricity

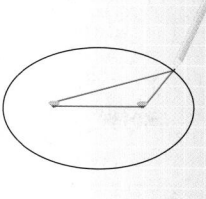

Measure the eccentricity of different ellipses. Eccentricity is the ratio of the distance between the foci to the length of the major axis.

Procedure

1. Tie a piece of string into a loop that fits on a piece of cardboard when it is laid out in a circle.
2. Place a sheet of paper on the cardboard.
3. Stick two pins through the paper close to the center but separated from each other by a few centimeters. Use caution when using sharp objects.
4. Loop the string over the pins and use the pencil to trace around them. Keep the string taut.
5. Measure the major axis and the distance between the pins. Calculate the eccentricity.
6. Repeat steps 3–5 for different separations of the pins.

Analyze and Conclude

1. What do the two pins represent?
2. How does the eccentricity change as the distance between the pins changes?
3. What kind of figure would you form if the two pins were at the same location? What would its eccentricity be?

Differentiated Instruction

Gifted If the semimajor axis and the eccentricity of an elliptical orbit are both known, it is possible to calculate the perihelion and aphelion distances. If a is the semimajor axis of the orbit, e is the eccentricity, and P is the perihelion distance, then $P = a(1 - e)$. For example, Earth's semimajor axis is 1.000 AU and its eccentricity is 0.0167, so its perihelion distance is $P = 1.000(1 - 0.167) = 0.983$ AU. The formula for aphelion, A, is $A = a(1 + e)$.

For Earth, $A = 1.000(1 + 0.0167) = 1.0167$ AU. Hence, Earth's distance from the Sun varies between 0.983 and 1.0167 AU. The same formula is used to calculate perigee and apogee for an Earth-orbiting satellite. Ask students to calculate the perihelion and aphelion distances for other planets. Semimajor axes and eccentricities can be found in Appendix J. **L3**

MiniLab

Purpose

Students will learn how to model planetary orbits and will also learn some basic properties of ellipses.

Process Skills

measure in SI, use numbers, collect and organize data, interpret data

Materials

string, cardboard, thumbtacks or push pins, paper, metric ruler or meterstick

Teaching Strategies

Students can work in pairs or small groups.

Safety Precaution

Caution students to take care when using push pins, which are sharp.

Troubleshooting

Thumbtacks should not be pushed in all the way so that the string can move freely.

Expected Results

Students should observe that the closer together the two foci are, the more circular the orbit.

Analyze and Conclude

1. The two pins represent the foci of the elliptical orbit.
2. The eccentricity becomes smaller as the two pins are moved closer together, and larger as the pins become more widely separated.
3. If the two pins were at the same location, the figure would be a circle. Its eccentricity would be zero because the numerator in the eccentricity formula, the distance between foci, would be zero.

Assessment

Skill Have students each create ellipses with the following eccentricities: 0.2, 0.6, and as close to 1.0 as they can get. This is probably most easily done by trial and error, by adjusting the pin separation until the correct eccentricity is found.

Interpreting the Illustration

Figure 29-4 Have students examine the illustration and identify why a planet sweeps out equal areas in equal amounts of time. Farther from the Sun, a planet moves more slowly, so the area is long, but narrow. Close to the Sun, a planet moves more rapidly, so the area is wider, but short. Speed and distance balance each other.

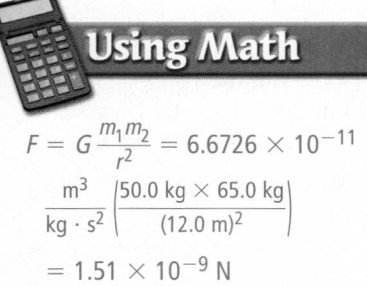

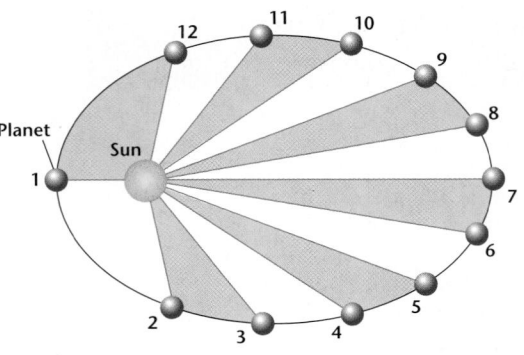

Figure 29-4 Because a planet moves fastest when close to the Sun and slowest when far from the Sun, equal areas are swept out in equal amounts of time, which is Kepler's second law. (not to scale)

Using Math

Using Numbers
Newton's law of universal gravitation, found on the next page, can be applied to any two objects that have mass. If one student has a mass of 50.0 kg and is 12.0 m away from another student that has a mass of 65.0 kg, what is the force of gravity between them?

Kepler's Second and Third Laws In addition to discovering the true shapes of planetary orbits, Kepler found that an imaginary line between the Sun and a planet sweeps out equal amounts of area in equal amounts of time, as illustrated in *Figure 29-4.* This is known as Kepler's second law. Kepler also derived a mathematical relationship between the size of a planet's ellipse and its orbital period. He found that the square of the orbital period (P) equals the cube of the semimajor axis of the orbital ellipse (a). This relationship, called Kepler's third law, is $P^2 = a^3$, where P is a unit of time measured in Earth years, and a is a unit of length measured in astronomical units. You will apply Kepler's third law to each planet in our solar system in the *Problem-Solving Lab* later in this chapter.

While Kepler was developing his ideas, Italian scientist Galileo Galilei became the first person to use a telescope to observe the sky. Galileo made many important discoveries that supported Copernicus's idea that the planets, including Earth, orbit the Sun. The most famous of Galileo's discoveries was that four moons orbit the planet Jupiter. This observation proved that not all celestial bodies orbit Earth, and therefore, Earth is not necessarily the center of the solar system. The underlying explanation for the heliocentric model still remained unknown, however, until 1684, when English scientist Isaac Newton published a mathematical and physical explanation of the motions of celestial bodies. Newton's concepts included the law of universal gravitation, which provided an explanation of how the Sun governs the motions of the planets.

GRAVITY AND ORBITS

Newton developed an understanding of gravity by observing the Moon's motion, the orbits of the planets, and the acceleration of falling objects on Earth. He realized that any two bodies attract each other with a force that depends on their masses and the distance between the two bodies. The force grows stronger in proportion to the product of the two masses, but diminishes as the square of the distance between them. For example, if the distance between Earth and the Moon were twice as great, the gravitational force between them would be only one-fourth as strong. At their normal distance apart, if the mass of the Moon were doubled and the mass of Earth were tripled, the force would be greater by a factor of 6.

Demo

Visual-Spatial Demonstrate the concept of center of mass by attaching two balls of equal weight to the ends of a rod and showing that the balance point is at the center of the rod. Then, use a pair of balls of very different weights and show that the balance point is much closer to the heavier ball. If you rotate the rod on a pivot such as a pencil point, you can demonstrate that the center of mass remains fixed as the balls rotate around it, just as the Sun and a planet remain fixed while they orbit the center of mass between them. Explain to the class that for a Sun-planet pair, the center of mass is so close to the Sun that it is actually inside the Sun, except in the case of the Sun and Jupiter, where the balance point is just above the Sun's surface.

Gravity Newton's statement of the relationship among the masses of two bodies and the force and distance between them is known as the law of universal gravitation. This law can be stated as follows: Every pair of bodies in the universe attract each other with a force that is proportional to the product of their masses and inversely proportional to the square of the distance between them, or

$$F = G\frac{m_1 m_2}{r^2}.$$

F is the force measured in newtons, and G is the universal gravitation constant, or 6.6726×10^{-11} meters cubed per kilogram per second squared. m_1 and m_2 are the masses of the bodies measured in kilograms, and r is the distance between the two bodies measured in meters.

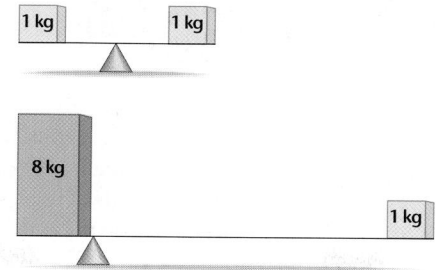

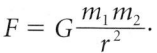

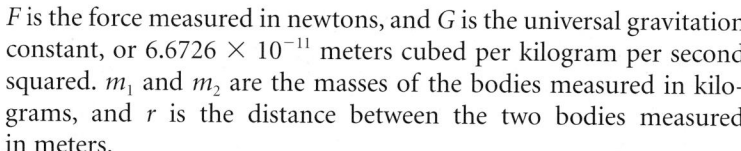

Figure 29-5 The center of mass is halfway between two equal mass objects, but closer to the heavier object when the objects are of unequal mass, similar to the pivot of a see-saw.

Center of Mass Newton also determined that each planet orbits a point between it and the Sun called the center of mass. The center of mass is the balance point between two orbiting bodies, similar to the pivot point on a see-saw. If one person on a see-saw is much heavier than the other, the balance point is closer to the heavier person, as shown in *Figure 29-5*. In space, the same is true. If one of two bodies orbiting each other is more massive than the other, the center of mass is closer to the more massive body. If the two bodies have similar masses, the center of mass is near the middle position between them. For any planet and the Sun, the center of mass is just above the surface of the Sun, or within the Sun, because the Sun is much more massive than any planet, as you will learn in the following sections.

SECTION ASSESSMENT

1. Why is retrograde motion an apparent motion?

2. What were the contributions of Copernicus, Kepler, and Galileo in developing the Sun-centered model of the solar system?

3. Describe how the force between two bodies depends on their masses and the distance between them.

4. **Thinking Critically** Your weight is the gravitational force between you and

Earth, and the separation between you and Earth is equal to Earth's radius. How would your weight be different if Earth's radius were larger or smaller than it is but Earth's mass remained the same?

SKILL REVIEW

5. **Comparing and Contrasting** Compare and contrast the geocentric and the heliocentric models of the solar system. For more help, refer to the *Skill Handbook*.

earthgeu.com/self_check_quiz

SECTION ASSESSMENT

1. The planet does not go backward and then forward again; it only looks that way because of the difference in orbital speed between Earth and the planet.

2. Copernicus suggested the Sun-centered model. Kepler found that the orbits of the planets are ellipses, and he found mathematical relationships between the sizes and periods of the orbits. Galileo developed observational arguments favoring the Sun-centered model.

3. The force between two bodies is proportional to the product of their masses and inversely proportional to the square of the distance between them.

4. less if Earth's radius were larger, and greater if Earth's radius were smaller

5. In the geocentric model, which could not explain retrograde motion, Earth is at the center. In the heliocentric model, all bodies orbit the Sun. Retrograde motion and seasons can be explained by the heliocentric model.

3 Assess

Check for Understanding

Discussion

Ask students to think about what would happen if the force of gravity between the Sun and planets was suddenly "turned off." The planets would continue to travel in straight lines in the direction they were going when gravity stopped.

Reteach

Have students summarize the arguments favoring the Sun-centered theory of the solar system over the Earth-centered model. The Sun-centered model is much simpler, requiring just an ellipse to describe each orbit. This model also has the advantage of explaining retrograde motion very simply, and it explains the seasons if Earth's tilt is recognized.

✓ Assessment

Knowledge Ask students what would happen if the masses of Earth and the Sun were comparable, instead of the Sun's mass being much greater. The center of mass would be close to the center point between the Sun and Earth. Because both the Sun and Earth orbit the center of mass, both would have comparably large orbital motions.

779

Section 29.2

Prepare

Section Background

For section content background, refer to **The Terrestrial Planets** on page 774C.

Preplanning

Refer to the Chapter Organizer on pages 774A–B.

1 Focus

Section Focus

Before presenting the lesson, display **Section Focus Transparency 93** on the overhead projector.
L1 **ELL**

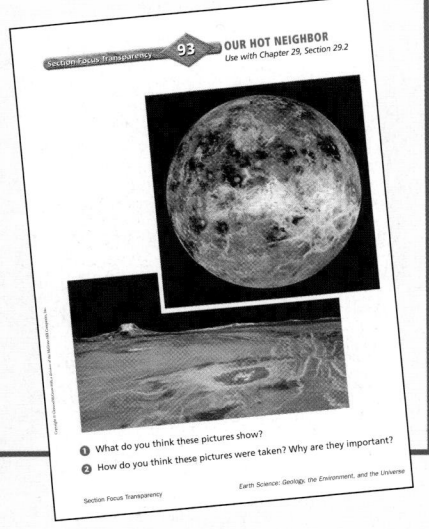

Activity

Have students look up basic data on the terrestrial planets, such as their masses, radii, and average densities. Have students each create a data table comparing these values with those for Earth. This will help students keep in mind how each planet compares to Earth as they learn about the planets in more detail. **L2**

OBJECTIVES

- **Describe** *the properties of the terrestrial planets.*
- **Compare** *Earth with the other terrestrial planets.*

VOCABULARY

terrestrial planet
gas giant planet
precession

The nine planets of our solar system can be grouped into two main categories according to their basic properties. The inner four planets, called **terrestrial planets,** are close to the size of Earth and have solid, rocky surfaces. The terrestrial planets are Mercury, Venus, Earth, and Mars, in order from closest to farthest from the Sun. The next four planets from the Sun, called **gas giant planets,** are much larger, more gaseous, and lack solid surfaces. The gas giants include Jupiter, Saturn, Uranus, and Neptune. Pluto, the ninth planet from the Sun, has a solid surface, but it does not fit into either category. On the next several pages, we'll discuss each planet.

MERCURY

Mercury is the closest planet to the Sun and has no moons. Mercury is about one-third the size of Earth and has a smaller mass and radius, as shown in *Appendix J.* Radio observations in the 1960s revealed that Mercury has a slow spin of 1407.6 hours. After Mercury completes one orbit around the Sun, it has rotated one and a half times, and the opposite side of the planet faces the Sun. In two orbits, Mercury spins three times and the side originally facing the Sun faces the Sun again. Thus, in two of Mercury's years, three of Mercury's days have passed.

Atmosphere Unlike Earth, Mercury has essentially no atmosphere, and what little does exist is composed primarily of oxygen and sodium, as illustrated in *Figure 29-6.* The daytime surface temperature on Mercury is 700 K (427°C), while temperatures at night fall to 100 K (-173°C). This is the largest day-night temperature difference of all the planets in our solar system.

Surface Most of what we know about Mercury is based on radio observations and images from a United States space probe mission, called *Mariner 10,* which passed close to Mercury three times in 1974 and 1975. Images from *Mariner 10* show that Mercury's surface, similar to the Moon's surface, is covered with craters and plains, as shown in *Figure 29-7A.* The plains of Mercury's surface are smooth and relatively crater free. It is thought that the plains were formed from lava flows that covered cratered terrain, much like the maria on the Moon. The surface gravity of Mercury is much greater than that of the Moon, and thus crater walls and peaks are lower and ejecta are shorter in length than those on the Moon. Mercury has a planetwide system of cliffs, called scarps, as shown in

Figure 29-6 The major components in Mercury's atmosphere are oxygen, sodium, hydrogen, helium, and potassium.

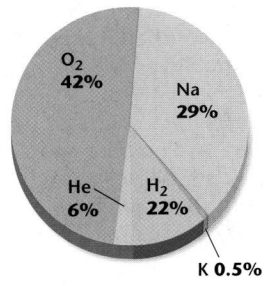

O₂ 42%
Na 29%
He 6%
H₂ 22%
K 0.5%

Resource Manager

Section Focus Transparency 93
L1 **ELL**

Study Guide for Content Mastery, p. 184
L2

GLENCOE
Technology

Videotape/DVD
The Planets: Terra Firma
The Planets: Atmosphere

Figure 29-7B. Scientists hypothesize that the scarps developed as Mercury's crust shrank and fractured early in the planet's geological history.

Interior Although scientists have no seismic data with which to analyze the interior of Mercury, the high density of the planet suggests that Mercury has an extensive nickel-iron core, filling about 42 percent of Mercury's volume. The detectable magnetic field, only 1 percent of Earth's magnetic field strength, suggests that Mercury has a molten zone in its interior. Mercury's small size, high density, and probable molten interior zone resemble what Earth might be like if its crust and mantle were removed. These observations suggest that Mercury was originally much larger, with a mantle and crust similar to Earth's, and that the outer layers may have been lost in a collision with another celestial body early in its history.

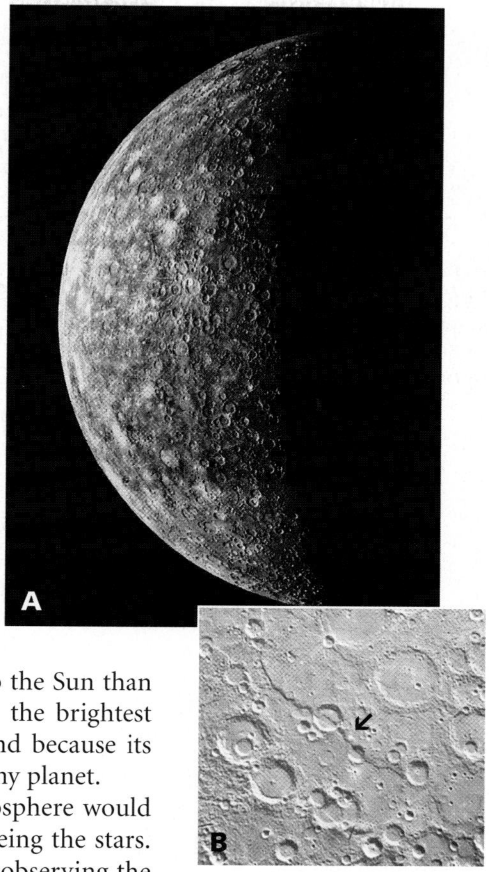

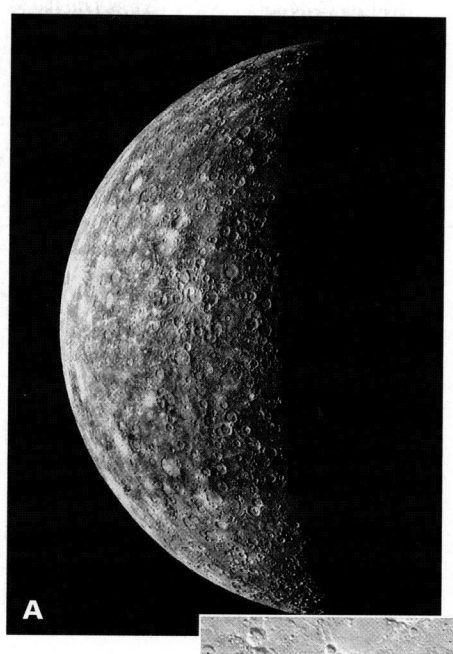

Figure 29-7 This composite image of Mercury **(A)** was photographed by *Mariner 10.* Discovery Scarp **(B)** is 500 km long and 2 km high.

VENUS

Venus and Mercury are the only two planets closer to the Sun than Earth. Like Mercury, Venus has no moons. Venus is the brightest planet in Earth's nighttime sky because it is close and because its albedo is 0.75. The albedo of Venus is the highest of any planet.

The thick clouds that are present in Venus's atmosphere would prevent an observer on the surface of Venus from seeing the stars. These clouds also prevent astronomers from directly observing the surface, except at radio wavelengths. In the 1960s, radar measurements showed that the surface of Venus is very hot, and that Venus is rotating slowly. One day on Venus is 243 Earth days in length. Radar measurements also revealed Venus's clockwise spin, which is opposite the spin of most planets. The backward spin exhibited by Venus, called retrograde rotation, means that for an observer on Venus, the Sun would rise in the west and set in the east. Astronomers hypothesize that the retrograde rotation of Venus may have been caused by a collision between Venus and another body early in our solar system's history.

Today, astronomers know a lot about Venus as a result of close-up observations made by several United States and Soviet (later Russian) spacecraft. Some probes landed on the surface of the planet and made observations there, while others flew by. The 1978 *Pioneer-Venus* and the 1989 *Magellan* missions of the United States used radar to map up to 98 percent of the surface of Venus.

2 Teach

Activity

Have students research why it is often difficult to observe Mercury. Have them create diagrams to accompany their explanations. Mercury is difficult to observe because it is always very near the Sun.

Collaborative Learning

Interpersonal Have students compare images of the Moon and Mercury. Ask students to identify features on the Moon and then find comparable features on Mercury. Remind students how rilles and scarps are different despite their similar appearances in many distant images.

Content Background

Conventions for naming surface features on planets and satellites are governed by the International Astronomical Union (IAU), the major, worldwide organization of professional astronomers. In most cases, a consistent theme is adopted for naming features. For example, prominent craters on the Moon are named after historically important scientists such as Copernicus. For Venus, the convention is to name features after prominent women in science, history, and mythology, such as Aphrodite. Mercury's craters are named for famous artists and musicians of the past, such as Beethoven.

Differentiated Instruction

Visually Impaired A graphic and tactile method of teaching students with visual impairments is to illustrate the relative sizes of the terrestrial planets by having students handle balls with corresponding relative sizes. It is useful to include the Moon as well.

Cultural Diversity

Mae C. Jemison (1956-) The first African-American woman in space was Mae C. Jemison. She served as a mission specialist on the shuttle *Endeavor* in 1992 and studied the effects of weightlessness on organisms. Dr. Jemison earned a medical degree from Cornell University and now is president of the Jemison Group, Inc., which works to improve health care in western Africa. Dr Jemison considers recruiting women and minorities into the various scientific fields to be some of her most important work.

NY Core Curriculum Standards

Page 780: St 1 Math KI 2 & Science KI 1, St 4 KI 1.1a, 1.1b, & 1.2c, St 6 KI 2
Page 781: St 1 Science KI 1, St 4 KI 1.1a

Enrichment

Venus has far fewer impact craters than either the Moon or Mercury, and on Venus, there are no small craters. Ask students for an explanation. The thick atmosphere of Venus prevents small objects from reaching the surface with enough speed to form craters. The smallest impact craters on Venus have diameters of about 3 km, which suggests that meteoroids smaller than 29 m are slowed by the atmosphere and cannot form craters.

✓Assessment

Knowledge Ask students to compare the degrees of tectonic activity on Earth, the Moon, and Venus. Earth is tectonically active, with seafloor spreading, subduction, and volcanism. The Moon is tectonically inactive. Venus has had extensive lava flows in the past, but it does not appear to be active at present.

In-Text Question

Page 782 How does this compare to Earth's atmospheric composition? Earth's atmosphere is primarily nitrogen and oxygen. There is very little carbon dioxide in Earth's atmosphere compared to Venus's.

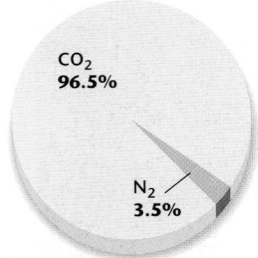

Figure 29-8 The major components of Venus's atmosphere are carbon dioxide and nitrogen.

CO₂ 96.5%
N₂ 3.5%

Figure 29-9 The clouds in the atmosphere of Venus **(A)** obscure the surface. By using the radar of *Magellan*, astronomers have been able to map the surface and discover features like the volcano Maat Mons and the surrounding surface smoothed by volcanic lava flows **(B)**.

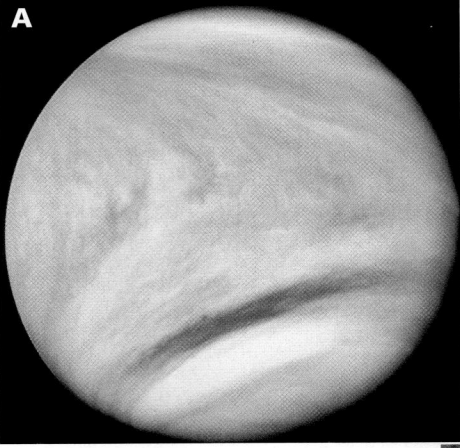

Atmosphere Venus is the planet most similar to Earth in physical properties, such as diameter, mass, and density, as shown in *Appendix J*, but its surface conditions are vastly different from those on Earth. The average surface temperature of Venus is extremely hot, about 737 K (464°C), as compared to Earth's average surface temperature of 288 K (15°C). On the surface of Venus, it is hot enough to melt lead! The atmospheric pressure on Venus is 92 atmospheres—much higher than the 1 atmosphere at sea level on Earth. The pressure from the atmosphere on Venus would make you feel like you were under 915 m of water.

The atmosphere of Venus is primarily carbon dioxide and nitrogen, as illustrated in *Figure 29-8*. How does this compare to Earth's atmospheric composition? Similar to Earth, Venus has clouds. But instead of being composed of water vapor and ice, clouds on Venus, shown in *Figure 29-9A*, are made of sulfuric acid and are 35 km thick. If it were to rain on Venus, the rain would be sulfuric acid.

Venus has a greenhouse effect, like Earth, but Venus's is more efficient. As you learned in Chapter 14, greenhouse gases in Earth's atmosphere trap infrared radiation and keep Earth at higher temperatures than those that would exist if there were no atmosphere. Carbon dioxide, one of Earth's greenhouse gases, has a high concentration in Venus's atmosphere, which prevents infrared radiation from escaping and keeps the surface extremely hot. In fact, it is so hot that liquid water can't exist. Venus is the hottest planet, even though it is not the closest to the Sun.

Surface The *Magellan* orbiter used radar reflection measurements to map the surface of Venus in fine detail. The surface has been smoothed by volcanic lava flows, as shown in *Figure 29-9B*, and it has only a few impact craters. The most recent global episode of volcanic activity took place about 500 million years ago, and therefore the surface of Venus is relatively young. Unlike Earth, there is little evidence of current tectonic activity on Venus, and there is no well-defined system of crustal plates.

Content Background

The circulation of Venus's atmosphere is far simpler than that of Earth's because of the slow rotational rate of Venus and also because of the lack of significant surface temperature variations on Venus compared to the contrasts between the temperatures of oceans and continents on Earth. There are no strong pressure differentials and no rotary winds on Venus, as there are on Earth. The lower atmosphere of Venus appears to be quite static.

Earth Science
Journal

Logical-Mathematical Have students each create a comprehensive data table that summarizes various aspects of the atmospheres of the terrestrial planets, such as pressure, temperature, and the major compounds present. Once they complete their data tables, students should think about how to explain the differences and similarities. **L2**

Interior The size and density of Venus are similar to Earth, so the internal structure is most likely similar. However, astronomers have no seismic data with which to prove this. It is theorized that Venus has a liquid metal core that extends halfway to the surface. There is no measurable magnetic field despite this liquid core, which is probably due to Venus's slow rotation rate.

EARTH

Earth, shown in *Figure 29-10,* is the third planet from the Sun. Earth has many unique properties when compared with the other planets. Its distance from the Sun and its nearly circular orbit allow liquid water to exist on its surface in all three states: solid, liquid, and gas. Liquid water is required for life, and Earth's vast abundance of liquid water has been important for the development and existence of life on our planet. In addition, our planet's moderately dense atmosphere, which is composed primarily of 78 percent nitrogen and 21 percent oxygen, and a mild greenhouse effect also support conditions suitable for life.

Precession Earth's axis is tilted, as you have learned, and this tilt creates our seasons. As you learned in Chapter 14, Earth's axis is wobbling, like a toy top that wobbles if you give it a small sideways push while it is spinning. This wobble in Earth's rotational axis, shown in *Figure 29-11,* is called **precession.** It takes Earth's rotational axis about 26 000 years to go through one cycle of precession. The sideways pull that causes precession comes from the Moon's gravitational force on Earth, as well as the Sun's gravitational force. However, the Sun's gravitational force plays a lesser part in Earth's precession.

Figure 29-10 This shows Earth as seen by the Apollo astronauts orbiting the Moon.

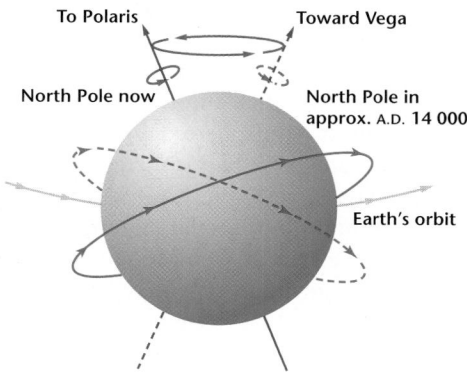

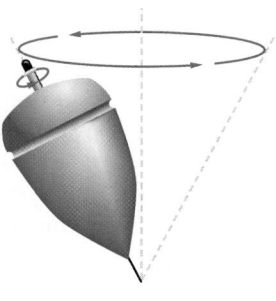

Figure 29-11 Earth precesses, or wobbles, on its axis, much like a toy top. In 12 000 years, our new north star will be Vega.

29.2 *The Terrestrial Planets* **783**

Tying to Previous Knowledge

Tying to Previous Knowledge

Earth is highly differentiated, and the majority of its iron is in the core. Mars is not so highly differentiated, and a greater fraction of its iron remains in the crust. Iron at the surface of Mars combines with oxygen to form iron oxide. This is why Mars has a reddish color.

Enrichment

Have interested students find current images of Mars. Ask students to summarize recent findings and present them to the class.

Assessment

Knowledge Ask students to summarize the role of water on Mars. Dry river channels show that Mars once had flowing water, and possible ancient shorelines in Valles Marineris suggest that there also may have been lakes. Most of this water is absent today, although some is present in the form of water ice in the northern polar cap, traces of water vapor in the atmosphere, and possibly subsurface ice deposits.

NY Core Curriculum Standards

Page 784: St 1 Science KI 1, St 4 KI 1.1a, 1.2c, & 1.2d, St 6 KI 2

Page 785: St 1 Science KI 1 & 2, St 4 KI 1.1a & 1.2c, St 6 KI 2

Figure 29-12 This view of Mars, taken by the *Hubble Space Telescope (HST),* shows its surface, its atmosphere, and one of its polar caps.

Figure 29-13 The major components of Mars's atmosphere are carbon dioxide, nitrogen, argon, and oxygen.

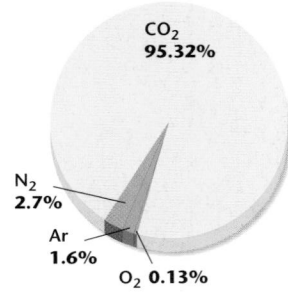

CO$_2$ 95.32%

N$_2$ 2.7%

Ar 1.6%

O$_2$ 0.13%

MARS

Mars is the fourth planet from the Sun and the outermost of the terrestrial planets. It is often referred to as the red planet because of its reddish surface color, shown in **Figure 29-12,** which is caused by a high iron content in the soil. Mars is smaller and less dense than Earth, as shown in *Appendix J,* and has two irregularly-shaped moons, Phobos and Deimos, which are most likely captured asteroids.

Mars has been explored by telescopes on Earth and with probes that have flown by, orbited, or landed. In the 1960s, the United States sent a spacecraft, *Mariner 4,* to explore Mars. Later missions included *Mariner 9,* in 1971, and two *Viking* landers in 1976. More recent missions have been the *Mars Climate Orbiter* in 1998 and the *Mars Exploration Rover Mission* in 2003, which are all part of a long-term NASA plan to explore Mars for evidence of preexisting life.

Atmosphere The composition of Mars's atmosphere, shown in **Figure 29-13,** is similar to Venus's atmosphere, but the density and pressure in Mars's atmosphere are much lower, and therefore Mars does not have a strong greenhouse effect, as Venus does. Although the atmosphere is thin, it is turbulent, so there is a constant wind on Mars. Dust storms in the atmosphere may last for weeks at a time.

Surface The southern and northern hemispheres of Mars have different types of surfaces. The southern hemisphere is a heavily cratered, highland region, resembling the highlands of the Moon. The northern hemisphere is dominated by plains that are sparsely cratered. Scientists theorize that great lava flows covered the once-cratered terrain of the northern hemisphere. Four gigantic shield volcanoes are located in the northern hemisphere, near a region called the Tharsis Plateau. The largest volcano is Olympus Mons, which is also the largest mountain in the solar system. The base of Olympus Mons would cover the state of Colorado; it is three times higher than Mt. Everest. An enormous canyon, Valles Marineris, shown in **Figure 29-14,** lies on the Martian equator and splits the Tharsis Plateau. This canyon seems to have formed as a fracture when the Tharsis Plateau was uplifted more than 3 billion years ago.

Content Background

Mars has a much more eccentric orbit than Earth does, and seasons on Mars are affected by the varying distances of the planet from the Sun. The overall result is that seasonal variations in the northern part of Mars are moderate, while the variations in the south are extreme. During southern spring, when the weather is making a dramatic shift from cold to hot, the temperature contrast drives major global wind storms that sometimes raise so much dust that the surface of Mars is obscured.

Other Martian surface features include dried river and lake beds, outflow channels, and runoff channels. These are all erosional features that suggest that liquid water once existed on the surface of Mars. Astronomers hypothesize that the atmosphere must have once been much warmer, thicker, and richer in carbon dioxide, which would have allowed water to exist on Mars. Although there is a relatively small amount of ice at the poles, astronomers are still searching for water at other locations on the Martian surface today.

Mars has polar ice caps covering both poles. The caps grow and shrink with the seasons on Mars. Martian seasons are caused by a combination of a tilted axis and a highly elongated orbit. Both caps are made of carbon dioxide ice, which you may know as "dry ice." Water ice lies beneath the carbon dioxide ice in the northern cap, shown in *Figure 29-12,* and is exposed during the northern hemisphere's summer when the carbon dioxide ice evaporates. There may also be water ice beneath the southern cap, but the carbon dioxide ice never completely evaporates to expose the water ice.

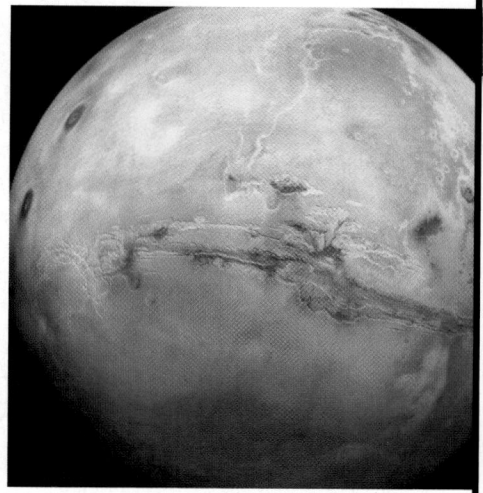

Figure 29-14 Valles Marineris stretches for more than 4000 km. A few large volcanoes can be seen in the upper left.

Interior Astronomers are unsure about the internal structure of Mars. They hypothesize that there is a core of iron and nickel, and possibly sulfur, that extends somewhere between 1200 km and 2400 km from the center of the planet. Because Mars has no magnetic field, astronomers hypothesize that the core is probably solid. Above the solid core is a mantle. There is no evidence of current tectonic activity or tectonic plates on the surface of the crust.

SECTION ASSESSMENT

1. List the similarities and differences between Mercury and the Moon, and between Mercury and Earth.

2. Explain why surface conditions on Venus and Earth are so different.

3. Why do astronomers hypothesize that the southern polar cap of Mars has water ice under the carbon dioxide ice?

4. What evidence do astronomers use to support the hypothesis that there was once tectonic activity on Mercury, Venus, and Mars?

5. **Thinking Critically** What do you think the terrestrial planets would be like today if major impacts had not played a role in their formation and evolution?

SKILL REVIEW

6. **Making Graphs** Using *Appendix J,* create a graph showing the distance from the Sun for each terrestrial planet on the *x*-axis and the orbital period in Earth days on the *y*-axis. For more help, refer to the *Skill Handbook.*

Check for Understanding

Project

Ask students to rank the terrestrial planets according to the following properties: mass, diameter, density, degree of present-day tectonic activity, and atmospheric pressure. Mass: Earth, Venus, Mars, Mercury. Diameter: Earth, Venus, Mars, Mercury. Density: Earth, Mercury, Venus, Mars. Tectonic activity: Earth, Venus, Mars, Mercury (students should note that only Earth is definitely active today). Atmospheric pressure: Venus, Earth, Mars, Mercury.

Reteach

Have students summarize the surface features of the terrestrial planets. **L2**

✓Assessment

Portfolio Have students each make a booklet that summarizes the characteristics of the terrestrial planets and the compositions of their atmospheres. **P**

SECTION ASSESSMENT

1. The surfaces of Mercury and the Moon look very similar, although Mercury has scarps that the Moon lacks. Both lack current tectonic activity. Mercury is much smaller than Earth but is comparable in density. Mercury does not have as extensive a mantle as Earth does. Earth has erosion as a result of its atmosphere, and Earth has tectonic activity, while Mercury does not.

2. Venus has a thick CO_2 atmosphere and a very strong greenhouse effect.

3. The presence of water ice in the northern cap increases the possibility that there could be water ice under the southern cap as well.

4. Venus and Mars both show volcanic surface structures, while Mercury has the scarp system.

5. Mercury might be larger and less dense, Venus might have a more rapid rotation in the normal direction, and Earth might not have a moon.

6.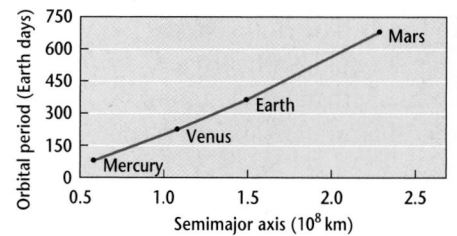

785

Section Background

For section content background, refer to **The Gas Giant Planets** on page 774D.

Preplanning

Refer to the Chapter Organizer on pages 774A–B.

1 Focus

Section Focus

Before presenting the lesson, display **Section Focus Transparency 94** on the overhead projector.
L1 ELL

Section Focus Transparency **94** GAS GIANT PLANETS
Use with Chapter 29, Section 29.3

❶ What two planets do you think these are?
❷ How do the two planets differ in appearance?

Section Focus Transparency   Earth Science: Geology, the Environment, and the Universe

Tying to Previous Knowledge

Most gas giant planets have clouds similar to those on Earth. However, as a result of the rapid rotation of these gas giant planets, the clouds get stretched out into bands. The clouds of gas giants are made of hydrogen, helium, methane, and ammonia, rather than water vapor.

OBJECTIVES

- **Describe** the properties of the gas giant planets.
- **Identify** the unique nature of the planet Pluto.

VOCABULARY

liquid metallic hydrogen
belt
zone

The interiors of the gas giant planets are composed of fluids, either gaseous or liquid, and possibly small, solid cores. They are composed primarily of lightweight elements such as hydrogen, helium, carbon, nitrogen, and oxygen, and they are very cold at their surfaces. The gas giants have many satellites as well as ring systems, and, as their name implies, they are all very large, ranging from 15 to more than 300 times the mass of Earth, and from about 4 to more than 10 times Earth's diameter. You will compare the relative sizes and distances from the Sun of the nine planets in the *Design Your Own GeoLab* at the end of the chapter.

JUPITER

Jupiter is the largest planet and the fifth planet from the Sun. The diameter of Jupiter is 11 times larger than Earth's, and only 10 times smaller than the Sun's. Jupiter's mass, shown in *Appendix J*, makes up 70 percent of all planetary matter in our solar system. From Earth, Jupiter appears quite bright because of its albedo of 0.343. Telescopic observations reveal that Jupiter has a banded appearance, as shown in *Figure 29-15A*, as a result of flow patterns in its atmosphere. Jupiter has four major satellites, which were discovered by Galileo, in addition to many smaller ones, which were discovered by flyby space probes and recent observations.

Jupiter has been explored by several United States space probes. The first were the *Pioneer 10* and *Pioneer 11* missions, which arrived at Jupiter in 1973 and 1974, respectively. In 1979, the *Voyager 1* and *Voyager 2* missions discovered several new satellites and a thin, dim ring around Jupiter. They also detected volcanic activity on Jupiter's closest major moon, Io. In 1995, the United States spacecraft *Galileo* arrived at Jupiter and dropped a probe into the clouds while the main spacecraft orbited the planet for five years and made observations.

Figure 29-15 Jupiter **(A)**, as photographed by *Voyager 1*, has a banded appearance. *Voyager 1* also photographed Jupiter's Great Red Spot **(B)**.

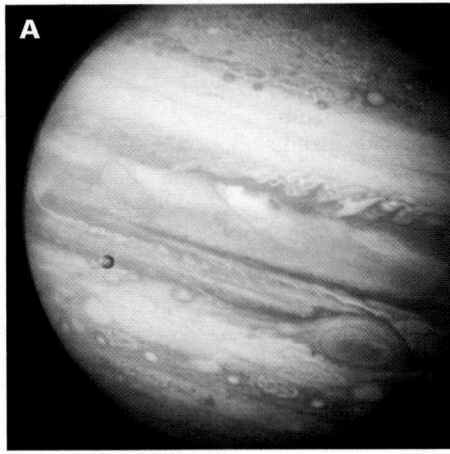

A

B

Resource Manager

Section Focus Transparency 94 L1 ELL
Study Guide for Content Mastery, pp. 185–186 L2

GLENCOE
Technology

Videotape/DVD
The Planets: Giants

Atmosphere Jupiter has a low density, 1326 kg/m³, for its huge size because it is composed of lightweight elements. Hydrogen and helium make up the majority of Jupiter's atmospheric gas, as illustrated in *Figure 29-16.* In Jupiter's atmosphere, these elements remain in a gas or liquid form. Below the liquid hydrogen, there is a layer of **liquid metallic hydrogen,** a form of hydrogen that has properties of both a liquid and a metal, which can exist only under conditions of very high pressure. Electric currents exist within the layer of liquid metallic hydrogen and generate Jupiter's magnetic field. Theoretical models of Jupiter suggest that Jupiter might have an Earth-sized solid core made of heavier elements that have sunk to the center of the planet.

The rotation of Jupiter is extremely rapid for its huge size. Jupiter spins on its axis in a little less than 10 hours, making it the shortest day in the solar system. This rapid rotation distorts the shape of the planet so that the diameter through its equatorial plane is 7 percent larger than the diameter through its poles. Jupiter's rapid rotation causes its clouds to flow rapidly as well, in alternating cloud types called belts and zones. **Belts** are low, warm, dark-colored clouds that sink, and **zones** are high, cool, light-colored clouds that rise. These are similar to the rotation-driven flows in Earth's atmosphere. *Figure 29-15B* shows Jupiter's Great Red Spot, which is an atmospheric storm that has been rotating around Jupiter for more than 300 years.

Moons and Rings Jupiter's four largest moons, Io, Europa, Ganymede, and Callisto, are called Galilean satellites, after their discoverer. All but one of them are bigger than Earth's moon, and all are larger than Pluto. These four moons are composed of ice and rock mixtures. The ice content is lower in Io and Europa, shown in *Figure 29-17,* because they have been squeezed and heated to a greater extent by Jupiter's gravitational force than the outer moons. In fact, Io has been heated to the point of becoming almost completely molten inside and undergoes constant volcanic eruptions. Gravitational heating has melted the ice in Europa, at least in the past, and astronomers hypothesize that this moon still has a subsurface ocean of liquid water.

The ring of Jupiter was discovered in images from the *Voyager 1* mission. Jupiter's ring is 6400 km wide. Its discovery proved that Saturn is not the only gas giant that has rings. In fact, it is now known that all four of the gas giant planets have rings.

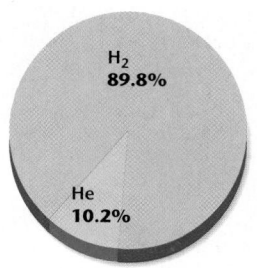

Figure 29-16 The major components of Jupiter's atmosphere are hydrogen and helium.

H₂ 89.8%
He 10.2%

Figure 29-17 Io is the closest major moon to Jupiter **(A)**. The next closest is Europa **(B)**.

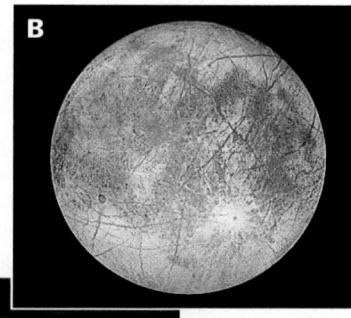
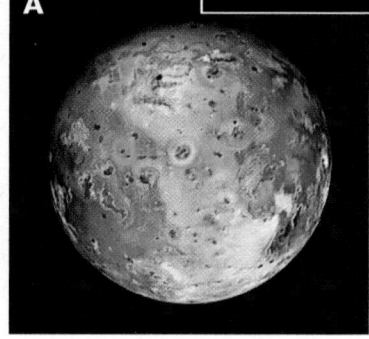

29.3 *The Gas Giant Planets* **787**

Tying to Previous Knowledge

The Coriolis force drives horizontal wind flows into rotary patterns called cyclonic and anticyclonic flows. On Jupiter, the Coriolis force is enhanced as a result of the planet's rapid rotation. Cyclones and anticyclones on Earth usually lose their energy and dissipate within a few days as a result of friction with landmasses and loss of solar thermal energy to drive them. However, on Jupiter, there are no landmasses, and internal thermal energy, rather than sunlight, drives the convection that triggers atmospheric flows. Thus, storms last longer on Jupiter than on Earth. The Great Red Spot is an anticyclonic storm (circulation around a high-pressure region) in the southern hemisphere, so its flow direction is counterclockwise.

Content Background

The possibility that Europa may have vast oceans of liquid water beneath its surface ice has led to speculation that life may have developed on this moon of Jupiter. All of the conditions known to have been present when life formed on Earth would be satisfied: the presence of liquid water, the availability of the basic chemicals required by life (Europa is known to have a variety of complex carbon compounds), and a source of energy (tidal heating from Jupiter).

Across the Curriculum

Chemistry After hydrogen and helium, the next most-abundant elements in the solar system are carbon, nitrogen, and oxygen. The dominant compounds in Jupiter's atmosphere are combinations of hydrogen and each of these three elements. Hydrogen and carbon combine to form methane (CH_4), which is known on Earth as natural gas and is used widely as a source of heat for houses and stoves. The combination of hydrogen and nitrogen yields ammonia (NH_3), which is commonly used in cleaning fluids. And, of course, the combination of hydrogen and oxygen is oxygen dihydride (H_2O), better known as water. Helium does not appear in compounds because it is inert and has no valence electrons available for chemical bonding.

NY Core Curriculum Standards

Page 786: St 1 Math KI 2 & Science KI 1, St 4 KI 1.2c, St 6 KI 3
Page 787: St 1 Science KI 1, St 4 KI 1.1a & 1.2c, St 6 KI 2 & 4

Reinforcement

Ask students to compare and contrast Jupiter and Saturn. Both are gas giants of similar size, composition, and atmospheric flow patterns, and both have extensive systems of rings and moons. Contrasts are that Jupiter is larger but less dense; Saturn has a much more prominent ring system; and Jupiter's magnetic axis is tilted relative to the rotational axis while Saturn's magnetic field is aligned with its rotational axis.

Content Background

Galileo was the first to observe the rings of Saturn, but he had no idea what he was observing. In 1610, Galileo noted that the image of Saturn was elongated and therefore referred to Saturn as the planet with "ears." However, it was not until 1655 that Dutch astronomer Christiaan Huygens was able to deduce the explanation for the strange appearance of Saturn.

Environmental Connection

Probes to the outer planets travel too far from the Sun for solar panels to be useful power sources. Instead, NASA uses small nuclear power sources called radioisotope thermoelectric generators (RTGs), which are based on the decay of plutonium, a highly toxic radioactive element. RTGs have been in use in space probes for more than 29 years without incident. However, environmental activists have been concerned that an accident during the launch of a spacecraft could release plutonium into the atmosphere and cause a widespread health hazard. The 1997 launch of the *Cassini* mission to Saturn led to a heated debate over the potential dangers.

Figure 29-18 This image of Saturn was captured by *HST*, on December 1, 1994.

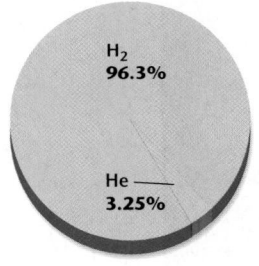

Figure 29-19 The major components of Saturn's atmosphere are hydrogen and helium.

H₂ 96.3%

He 3.25%

SATURN

Saturn is the sixth planet from the Sun and the second-largest planet in the solar system. Saturn is shown in *Figure 29-18.* Four space probes have visited Saturn, including *Pioneer 10, Pioneer 11,* and *Voyager 1* and *2.* In 2004, the United States *Cassini* mission, launched in 1997, will arrive at Saturn and go into orbit around the planet. It will also release a probe into the atmosphere of Titan, Saturn's largest moon, to explore surface conditions there.

Atmosphere Saturn is not quite as large as Jupiter and has an average density, shown in *Appendix J,* that is actually lower than that of water. Similar to Jupiter, Saturn rotates rapidly for its size and has flowing belts and zones. Saturn's atmosphere is dominated by hydrogen and helium, as illustrated in *Figure 29-19,* but it also includes ammonia ice near the top of the clouds. The internal structure of Saturn is also probably similar to Jupiter. It is most likely fluid throughout with a small, solid core and a magnetic field that is 1000 times stronger than Earth's. Saturn's magnetic field is aligned with its rotational axis, which is unusual among the planets.

Moons and Rings The most striking feature of Saturn is its ring system, shown in *Figure 29-20,* which has much broader and brighter rings than those of the other gas giant planets. Saturn's rings are composed of pieces of rock and ice that range from microscopic to the size of houses. There are seven major rings, but each ring is actually made up of narrower rings, called ringlets, and many open gaps. These ringlets and gaps are caused by the gravitational effects of the many moons of Saturn. The rings are very thin, less than 200 m thick, because rotational forces keep all the particle orbits confined to Saturn's equatorial plane. The ring particles have not combined to form a large satellite because Saturn's gravity prevents particles very close to the planet from sticking together. This is why the major moons of the gas giant planets are always found farther out than the rings.

Until recently, astronomers hypothesized that the ring particles were simply left over from the time when Saturn and its moons formed. Now, however, many astronomers hypothesize it more likely that the ring particles are debris left over when a moon was destroyed by a collision with an asteroid or other object, or was ripped apart by Saturn's gravity. Some astronomers hypothesize that Saturn and the other gas giant planets may form new ring systems from time to time as collisions or gravitational effects occasionally destroy their moons.

788 CHAPTER 29 *Our Solar System*

Saturn's many satellites include the giant Titan, seven intermediate-sized moons, and a number of small moons. Titan is larger than Earth's moon, and its atmosphere is made of nitrogen and methane. Methane may exist as a gas, a liquid, and ice on Titan's surface, similar to the three phases of water on Earth's surface.

URANUS

The seventh planet from the Sun, Uranus, was discovered accidentally in 1781. A bluish object was spotted through a telescope, and after tracking it for a couple of days, it was found that the object moved relative to the stars. It was a planet. In 1787, two of Uranus's larger moons, Titania and Oberon, were discovered. Today, we know that Uranus has many moons and 10 rings. In 1986, the United States *Voyager 2* mission visited Uranus and provided detailed information about the planet, including the existence of new moons and rings.

Atmosphere Uranus is 4 times as large and 15 times as massive as Earth, as shown in *Appendix J.* It has a blue, velvety appearance, as shown in *Figure 29-21A,* which is caused by its atmospheric composition. The methane gas in Uranus's atmosphere reflects blue light back into space, although most of the atmosphere is composed of helium and hydrogen, as illustrated in *Figure 29-21B.* There are very few clouds present, and they differ little in brightness and color from the surrounding atmosphere, making them difficult to detect. In addition, there are no distinct belts or zones like those observed on Jupiter and Saturn, which contributes to Uranus's featureless appearance. The internal structure of Uranus is similar to Jupiter and Saturn; it is completely fluid except for a small, solid core. Uranus also has a strong magnetic field.

The rotational axis of Uranus is tipped over so far that the north pole almost lies in its orbital plane. Astronomers hypothesize that Uranus was knocked sideways by a massive collision with a passing object, such as a very large asteroid, early in the solar system's history. Each pole on Uranus spends 42 Earth years in darkness and 42 Earth years in sunlight due to this tilt and Uranus's long trip around the Sun. Uranus's atmosphere keeps the planet at a temperature of 58 K (–215°C).

Figure 29-20 This image taken by *Voyager 1* shows the many ringlets that comprise the rings of Saturn.

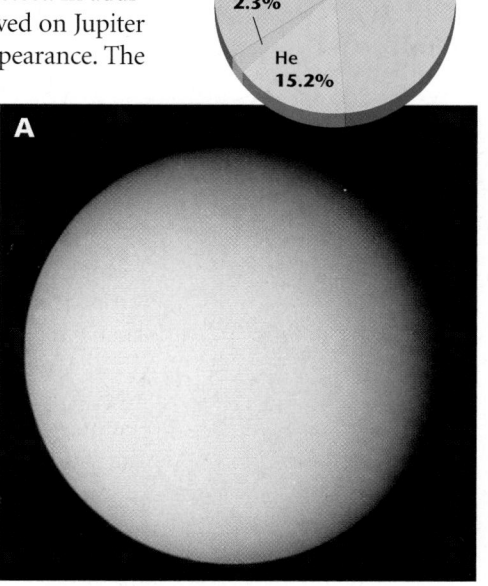

Figure 29-21 Uranus **(A)**, photographed by *Voyager 2,* appears to be blue and featureless because of the methane (CH$_4$) in its atmosphere **(B).**

Interpreting the Photo

Figure 29-20 The brightest of Saturn's rings are the A and B rings. The outer band of rings in this photo is the A ring, and the thicker band is the B ring. The dark band between them is the Cassini division, first noticed by Giovanni Cassini in 1675. The division is dark because it has fewer ring particles to reflect light. Although the Cassini division appears to be devoid of material, it does have some small ringlets within it. The dark ring on the surface of Saturn is the shadow of the rings.

✔Assessment

Knowledge Ask students to summarize the key features of Saturn. banded atmosphere, many moons, complex ring structure, fluid interior, solid icy core

Discussion

Have students discuss solstices and equinoxes on Uranus, keeping in mind that its axis is tipped by just over 90°. During the solstices, one of the hemispheres is pointed directly toward the Sun, so that the entire hemisphere experiences daylight all the time. The opposite hemisphere is in complete darkness at the same time. During the equinoxes, all latitudes experience equal periods of day and night. These periods are equal to one-half of the rotational period of 17.24 hours.

Content Background

The blue colors of Uranus and Neptune are caused by methane gas in their outer atmospheres. Methane, or natural gas, absorbs red light while allowing blue light to pass through it. Thus, when sunlight passes through the outer layers of Uranus's and Neptune's outer atmospheres in the process of being reflected from the clouds below, the red wavelengths are absorbed, and blue light is visible.

NY Core Curriculum Standards

Page 788: St 1 Science KI 1, St 4 KI 1.1a & 1.2c, St 6 KI 2 & 4

Page 789: St 1 Science KI 1, St 4 KI 1.1a, 1.2c, & 1.2d, St 6 KI 2

Interpreting the Photo

Figure 29-22 This photo is a black-and-white image of the rings of Uranus taken by *Voyager 2*. Many color images taken by *Voyager 2* are false-color, or colorized, images.

Content Background

The seventh planet from the Sun, Uranus, was discovered accidentally in 1781. An English astronomer, William Herschel, noticed a bluish object through his telescope and thought it was a star. Herschel tracked the position of the object for a period of time and found that the object moved relative to the stars. He then knew he had found a planet. In 1787, Herschel discovered two of Uranus's larger moons, Ariel and Umbriel. In 1846, a German astronomer, Johannes Galle, discovered Neptune in the location that had been predicted by other astronomers based on discrepancies in the motion of Uranus.

✅ *Assessment*

Skill Have students compare the properties of Pluto and Earth's moon. The two are comparable in size, but the Moon is much denser.

Figure 29-22 The rings of Uranus, photographed by *Voyager 2,* are very dark. Astronomers hypothesize that they are made of carbon compounds.

Figure 29-23 Like Uranus, the major components of Neptune's atmosphere are hydrogen, helium, and methane.

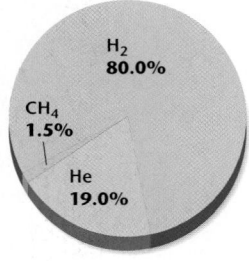

H₂ 80.0%
CH₄ 1.5%
He 19.0%

Moons and Rings The known moons and rings of Uranus orbit in the planet's equatorial plane. New moons are frequently being discovered, so Uranus's moon counts, like Jupiter's and Saturn's, are always changing. Uranus's rings, shown in *Figure 29-22,* are very dark—almost black. This is why they weren't discovered until the brightness of a star behind the rings dipped as Uranus moved in its orbit and the rings blocked the light.

NEPTUNE

The existence of Neptune was predicted before it was discovered. The prediction was based on small deviations in the motion of Uranus and the application of Newton's universal law of gravitation. In 1846, Neptune was discovered where astronomers had predicted it. Few details can be observed on Neptune with an Earth-based telescope, but the *Voyager 2* probe flew past this planet in 1989 and sent back new data and images of the planet.

Atmosphere Neptune is slightly smaller and denser than Uranus, but it is still about four times as large as Earth, as shown in *Appendix J*. Other similarities between Neptune and Uranus include their bluish color caused by methane in the atmosphere, atmospheric compositions, as illustrated in *Figure 29-23,* temperatures, magnetic fields, interiors, and particle belts. Unlike Uranus, however, Neptune, shown in *Figure 29-24A,* has distinctive clouds and atmospheric belts and zones similar to those of Jupiter and Saturn. In fact, Neptune had a persistent storm, the Great Dark Spot, with characteristics similar to Jupiter's Great Red Spot. The storm disappeared from Neptune in 1994.

Moons and Rings Neptune has many moons, the largest being Triton. Triton, shown in *Figure 29-24B* has a retrograde orbit, which means that it orbits backward, unlike virtually every other large satellite in the solar system. Triton also has a thin atmosphere and nitrogen geysers. The geysers are caused by nitrogen gas below the surface in Triton's south polar ice cap expanding and erupting when heated by the Sun.

The *Voyager 2* flyby increased our knowledge of Neptune's rings, which previously had been only indirectly observed. The six rings are composed of microscopic-sized dust particles. Some parts of the outermost ring appear much brighter than other parts because of the clumping of material. Scientists theorize that these clumps do not spread out evenly in the ring because of the gravitational effects of Neptune's moons.

790 CHAPTER 29 *Our Solar System*

NY Core Curriculum Standards

Page 790: St 1 Science KI 1 & 2, St 4 KI 1.1a & 1.2c, St 6 KI 2, 3, & 4
Page 791: St 1 Math KI 1, 2, 3, & Science KI 1, St 4 KI 1.1a, 1.1b, & 1.2c, St 6 KI 2, 3, & 4

Demo

Visual-Spatial The rings of Uranus were detected by a method called stellar occultation. A telescope on Earth was aimed at a star in the distance beyond Uranus, and as the planet passed in front of the star, the rings caused the star to blink off and on. A similar effect can be created in the classroom by using a flashlight and passing a rod or bar in front of it. Turn all the lights off and cover the windows, if possible, so that students see only the point of light created by the flashlight. Then move the rod or a series of rods across the face of the flashlight. Students will observe the light alternately dim and brighten in the same manner that astronomers saw the background star dim and brighten as the rings of Uranus passed in front of it.

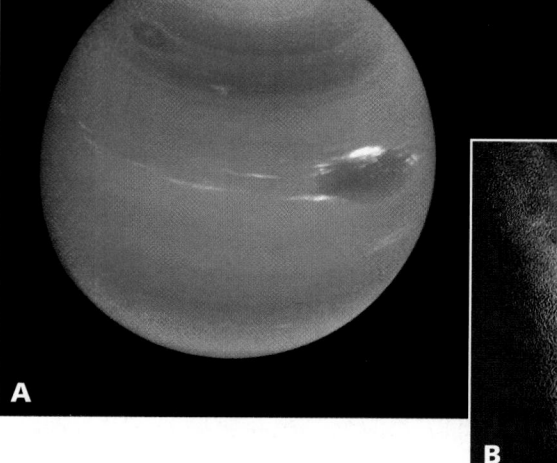

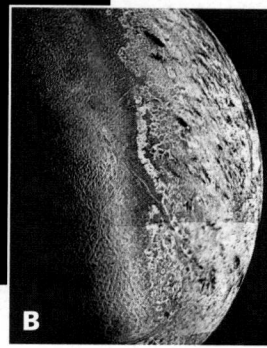

Figure 29-24 Neptune **(A)** has bands in its atmosphere. This image, taken before 1994, shows the Great Dark Spot right of center. This image of Triton **(B)**, taken by *Voyager 2*, shows the sooty material of the nitrogen geysers that have been blown downwind by Triton's thin atmosphere.

PLUTO

The ninth planet in our solar system, Pluto, was discovered in 1930. Pluto is very different from the other eight planets of our solar system. Even though it has a solid surface, Pluto is not classified as a terrestrial planet because of its low density and small size. With its solid surface, Pluto does not have properties characteristic of the gas giant planets either. The density of Pluto indicates that it is made of half ice and half rock, and it is smaller than Earth's moon. The atmosphere is composed of methane and nitrogen, but in unknown quantities.

Problem-Solving Lab

Using Numbers

Test Kepler's third law For the six planets closest to the Sun, Kepler observed that $P^2 = a^3$, where P is the orbital period in years and a is the semimajor axis in AU.

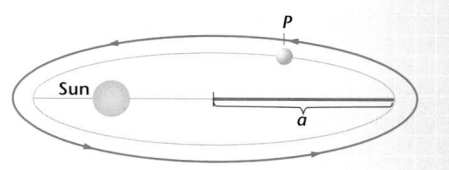

Analysis

1. Use data from *Appendix J* to calculate P^2 and a^3 for each of the nine planets.
2. Compare P^2 to a^3 for each planet.

Thinking Critically

3. Does Kepler's third law fit each of the planets?

4. If Uranus, Neptune, and Pluto had been discovered in Kepler's time, do you think he would have still believed in his law? Explain.
5. What would be the orbital period of an asteroid orbiting the Sun at 2.5 AU?
6. What is the semimajor axis for comet Halley, which has an orbital period of 76 years?

29.3 The Gas Giant Planets **791**

Problem-Solving Lab

Purpose
Students will perform simple calculations to demonstrate the validity of Kepler's third law for each of the planets.

Process Skills
use numbers, interpret data

Materials
calculator, paper, pencil

Teaching Strategies
Students may find it easier to compare data by constructing a data table.

Troubleshooting
When they get to the outermost planets, students will find small discrepancies between P^2 and a^3. This is normal. Students will also have to convert days into years and kilometers into astronomical units.

Analysis

1.

	P^2	a^3
Mercury	0.0580	0.0580
Venus	0.3785	0.3784
Earth	1.0000	1.0000
Mars	3.5375	3.5363
Jupiter	140.7020	140.9608
Saturn	867.6945	879.8843
Uranus	7057.7321	7078.9230
Neptune	27 154.3579	27 127.6203
Pluto	61 343.2043	60 400.9898

2. For the inner planets, the law agrees nicely. For planets farther away from the Sun, there are some discrepancies.

Thinking Critically

3. Kepler's third law reasonably fits each of the planets.
4. If Kepler had been aware of the outermost three planets, he would have found that his law applied to them as well as to the inner six planets. Students could argue that the discrepancies may have been enough to lead him to conclude that his law did not hold true.
5. $P = 3.95$ y
6. $a = 17.9$ AU (Remind students that this represents Halley's average distance from the Sun. The actual distance varies between 0.6 and 35.3 AU.)

✓Assessment

Knowledge Ask students whether they think Kepler's third law is wrong or whether the discrepancies might be a result of measurement error. The discrepancies are a result of measurement error; the periods and orbital sizes of the outer planets are not known to the required accuracy.

Check for Understanding

Discussion

Have students discuss the reasons that some astronomers don't consider Pluto to be a planet. Pluto's properties are very different from those of both the terrestrial and gas giant planets. Pluto resembles one of the giant moons of the outer planets more closely than anything else. Furthermore, Pluto has a highly eccentric orbit that is highly tilted as well.

Reteach

Logical-Mathematical
Have students rank all nine planets in order from the highest to the lowest density. This is a very useful way of demonstrating the contrast between the terrestrial and gas giant planets, and it also helps to show how Pluto does not fit into either group. **L2**

✔Assessment

Portfolio Have students each research the moons and rings of the gas giant planets and make a booklet that shows the contrasts and similarities among the moons and rings.

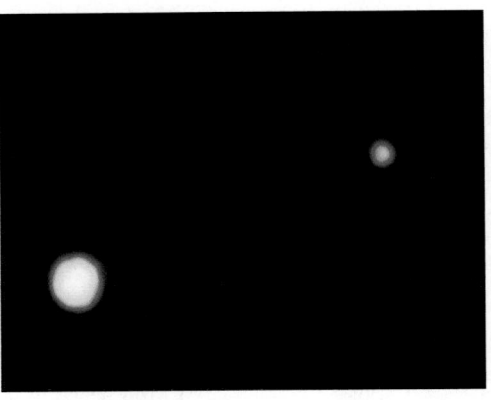

Figure 29-25 This image of Pluto and Charon, taken by *HST* on February 21, 1994, is the best image to date of the pair. Pluto and Charon are separated by a distance of 19 640 km.

The orbit of Pluto is so eccentric that at aphelion, it is 50 AU from the Sun, and at perihelion, it is almost 30 AU from the Sun. While at perihelion, Pluto is closer to the Sun than Neptune is. This happened last between 1978 and 1998. No space probes have traveled out to Pluto, although NASA is planning a flyby mission of Pluto.

Pluto's rotational axis is tipped so far over that its north pole actually points south of its orbital plane. Pluto has a satellite, called Charon, which orbits in Pluto's equatorial plane. Pluto and Charon, shown in *Figure 29-25,* have masses that are the most similar of any planet-satellite pair in the solar system. They are in synchronous rotation with each other, which means that each one keeps the same side facing the other. If you visited Pluto at a location on the side facing Charon, you would always see Charon in the sky overhead, throughout day and night.

Many of Pluto's properties, shown in *Appendix J*, are more similar to those of the gas giants' large moons than they are to those of any other planet. One theory suggests that Pluto was once a satellite of Neptune that escaped as a result of a near-collision with Triton. This would help explain Pluto's highly eccentric, tilted orbit and the unusual tilt of its rotational axis, as well as Triton's backward orbital motion. According to another theory, Pluto's composition and eccentric orbit suggest that it is related to a comet.

SECTION ASSESSMENT

1. In what two ways does Jupiter's rapid rotation affect the planet?
2. Describe the rings of Saturn and how they are thought to have formed.
3. What are the similarities between Uranus and Neptune?
4. Describe properties of Pluto that exclude it from being classified as either a terrestrial planet or a gas giant planet.
5. **Thinking Critically** Pluto and Neptune's orbits are arranged in such a way that Pluto is sometimes within Neptune's orbit. Despite this, collisions between the two are not possible. What are some possible reasons for this?

SKILL REVIEW

6. **Using Tables** Using values from *Appendix J,* compare the mass of Jupiter with the total mass of the other eight planets. Also, compare the total mass of all the planets, including Jupiter, with the mass of the Sun. For more help, refer to the *Skill Handbook.*

earthgeu.com/self_check_quiz

SECTION ASSESSMENT

1. Jupiter's rapid rotation forces atmospheric flows into belts and zones and flattens the planet a bit.
2. They are made of ice particles and include gaps and narrow ringlets. Astronomers theorize that the rings formed as a result of the destruction of a satellite.
3. Uranus and Neptune have similar masses and densities, color (as a result of methane absorption), and atmospheric flow patterns, and both have multiple moons and ring systems.
4. Pluto has a small diameter and mass, an intermediate density, a highly eccentric and highly inclined orbit, and a satellite that is about half its size. Pluto has a hard surface but a low density.
5. Their orbital planes are highly tilted in rela-

tion to each other, and the ratio of their orbital periods prevents them from aligning close to the same direction from the Sun.
6. Jupiter's mass is 1.8986×10^{27} kg, or 2.5 times the sum of the masses of the other planets (7.6955×10^{26} kg). The Sun's mass is 1.99×10^{30} kg, or about 746 times the mass of all the planets (2.6681×10^{27} kg).

Now that you know some of the characteristics of the solar system and the nature of the celestial bodies that occupy the Sun's vicinity, you are prepared to think about how the solar system formed. Astronomers use Earth-based observations and data from probes to derive theories about how our solar system formed. The significant observations related to our solar system's formation include the shape of our solar system, the differences among the planets, and the oldest planetary surfaces, asteroids, meteorites, and comets.

A COLLAPSING INTERSTELLAR CLOUD

Stars and planets form from clouds of gas and dust, called interstellar clouds, which exist in space between the stars. The interstellar clouds consist mostly of gas, especially hydrogen and helium. Dust makes interstellar clouds look dark because the dust blocks the light from stars within or behind the clouds. The dust can be thought of as a kind of interstellar smog. Conversely, light from stars reflects off the dust and partially illuminates the clouds. The clouds can also be heated by stars, which can cause them to glow on their own. This is why the interstellar clouds often appear as blotches of light and dark, as shown in *Figure 29-26.*

Many interstellar clouds can be observed along the Milky Way in regions that have relatively high concentrations of interstellar gas and dust. The density of interstellar gas is very low, much lower than even the best laboratory vacuums created by scientists. However, an interstellar cloud can start to condense as a result of gravity and become concentrated enough to form a star and possibly planets. Astronomers hypothesize that our solar system began in this way.

OBJECTIVES

- **Summarize** *the properties of the solar system that support the theory of the solar system's formation.*
- **Describe** *how the planets formed from a disk surrounding the young Sun.*
- **Explore** *remnants of solar system formation.*

VOCABULARY

planetesimal
asteroid
meteoroid
meteor
meteorite
comet
coma
nucleus
meteor shower

Figure 29-26 This mosaic of images of the Orion Nebula was taken by *HST.* The Orion Nebula is home to newly forming stars.

793

Section 29.4

Prepare

Section Background

For section content background, refer to **Formation of Our Solar System** on page 774D.

Preplanning

Refer to the Chapter Organizer on pages 774A–B.

1 Focus

Section Focus

Before presenting the lesson, display **Section Focus Transparency 95** on the overhead projector. **L1 ELL**

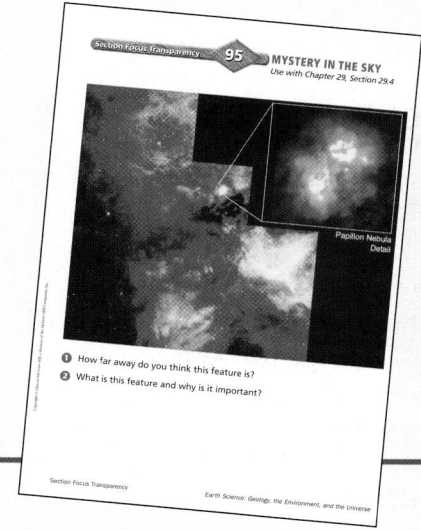

Resource Manager

Section Focus Transparency 95 L1 ELL
Study Guide for Content Mastery, pp. 187–188 L2

Tying to Previous Knowledge

Astronomers use radiometric dating to establish the ages of meteorites and interplanetary dust particles. The ages of these bodies are thought to be the best indicators of the age of the solar system itself, because meteorites and interplanetary dust particles are theorized to be left over from the time before the planets formed.

NY Core Curriculum Standards

Page 792: St 1 Math KI 1, 2, 3, & Science KI 1, St 4 KI 1.1a, 1.2c, & 1.2d, St 6 KI 2, 3, & 4
Page 793: St 1 Science KI 2, St 4 KI 1.2b, 1.2c, & 1.2d, St 6 KI 1, 2, & 4

Tying to Previous Knowledge

The density of Earth's atmosphere at sea level is roughly 2×10^{19} molecules per cubic centimeter, usually expressed as $2 \times 10^{19}/cm^3$. Point out to students that the maximum densities ever observed in interstellar clouds, the ones that look totally black on astronomical photographs, are never higher than about $10^6/cm^3$, a trillion times less dense than Earth's atmosphere. In other words, the densest interstellar clouds, the ones that form stars and planets, have lower densities than the best human-made vacuums on Earth. The reason an interstellar cloud looks so dark is that there are tiny solid particles, called interstellar dust grains, mixed in with the interstellar gas. The dust grains absorb and scatter starlight very efficiently, and prevent the light of background stars from shining through the cloud.

Using an Analogy

In biological reproduction, the first animal that is born in a litter or a spawning often becomes dominant and eats more than its share. Jupiter may be viewed in a similar light. Before its neighboring planets formed, Jupiter was already accreting material from its surroundings. This helped Jupiter to become the dominant planet in the solar system and deprived its neighbors of matter that they might have accreted.

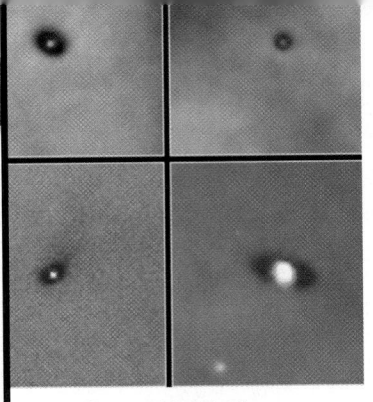

Figure 29-27 These images, taken by *HST* on November 20, 1995, show four young stars with disks of gas and dust around them. Astronomers often use radio and infrared telescopes which can penetrate the interstellar clouds to find these young stars.

NATIONAL GEOGRAPHIC

To learn more about The *Hubble Space Telescope,* go to the **National Geographic Expedition** on page 902.

At first, the collapse is slow, but it accelerates and the cloud soon becomes much denser at its center. If a cloud was rotating at all to begin with, it will spin faster and faster as it contracts, for the same reason that ice-skaters spin faster as they pull their arms close to their bodies. As the collapsing cloud spins, the rotation slows the collapse in the equatorial plane, and the cloud becomes flattened. The cloud eventually becomes a rotating disk with a dense concentration at the center, as shown in *Figure 29-27.*

SUN AND PLANET FORMATION

The disk of dust and gas that formed the Sun and planets is known as the solar nebula. The dense concentration of gas at the center of this rotating disk eventually became the Sun. You will learn more about the Sun's formation as well as the formation of other stars in Chapter 30.

In the disk surrounding the young Sun, the temperature varied greatly with location. It was hottest close to the Sun, possibly as hot as 2000 K (1726°C), and coolest near the edge of the disk, far from the Sun. As the disk began to cool, different substances were able to condense into a liquid or solid form. One of the first elements to form would have been tungsten, because of its high condensing temperature. As the disk cooled further, more elements and compounds, such as aluminum oxide, iron, and silicates, were able to condense.

Eventually, the condensation of materials into liquid and solid forms slowed. The area closest to the Sun was still warm because of the Sun's proximity and energy, while at the outer edge of the disk, it was cold because the Sun was so distant. Thus, different elements and compounds were able to condense depending on their distance from the Sun, as illustrated in *Figure 29-28,* which impacted the compositions of the forming planets.

The Growth of Objects Once the condensing slowed, the tiny grains of condensed material started to accumulate and merge together to form larger bodies. These solid particles gradually built up in size as grains collided and stuck together, and as gas particles collected on the surfaces of the grains. As the solid bodies continued to grow, they eventually reached hundreds of kilometers in diameter. These objects are called **planetesimals.** Further growth continued through collisions and mergers of planetesimals. These events were violent and sometimes destroyed the planetesimals. However, the overall result was a smaller number of larger bodies: the planets.

Merging into Planets In the outer solar system, the first large planet to develop was Jupiter. As Jupiter increased in size through mergers of icy planetesimals, its gravity began to attract additional

Across the Curriculum

Physics There is a principle in physics called conservation of angular momentum. Angular momentum is a measure of mass, rotational speed, and radius. For an object in a circular orbit, the angular momentum is the product of mass times speed times orbital radius. Because angular momentum is conserved, if one of these three parameters changes, one or both of the others must change as well to compensate. An example is the increase in the rotational speed of a figure skater when his or her arms are pulled in close to the body; the decrease in body diameter is compensated by an increase in rotational speed (while the mass remains constant). In the solar nebula, the decrease in diameter as the cloud contracted was similarly compensated by an increase in rotational speed. Because of conservation of angular momentum, the young Sun that formed at the center of the nebula was born with a very high rotational speed, much higher than the Sun's rotational speed today.

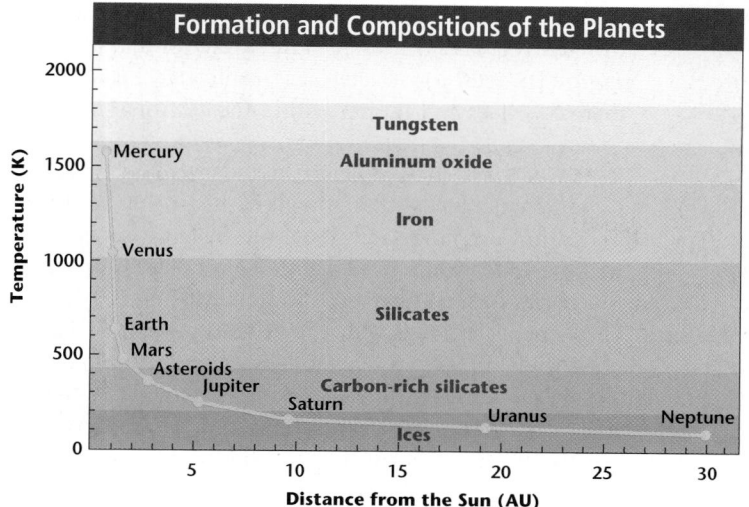

Formation and Compositions of the Planets

Tungsten
Mercury
Aluminum oxide
Venus
Iron
Earth
Mars
Silicates
Asteroids
Jupiter
Carbon-rich silicates
Saturn
Uranus
Neptune
Ices

Temperature (K): 2000, 1500, 1000, 500

Distance from the Sun (AU): 5, 10, 15, 20, 25, 30

Figure 29-28 Elements and compounds that were able to condense close to the Sun, where it was warm, are called refractory elements, and far from the Sun, where it was cool, volatile elements could condense. Refractory elements, such as iron, comprise the terrestrial planets, which are close to the Sun. Volatile elements, such as ices and gases like hydrogen, comprise the planets farther from the Sun, where it is cool.

gas, dust, and planetesimals, so Jupiter grew even larger. Saturn and the other gas giants formed similarly, but they could not become as large because Jupiter had collected so much of the material in the vicinity. As each gas giant acquired material from its surroundings, a disk formed in its equatorial plane, much like the disk of the early solar system. In the disk, matter coalesced to form satellites.

In the inner part of the main disk, near the young Sun, planets also formed by the merging of planetesimals. These planetesimals, however, were composed primarily of refractory elements, so the inner planets are rocky and dense, in contrast to the gaseous outer planets. Also, the Sun's gravitational force is theorized to have swept up much of the gas in the area of the inner planets and prevented them from acquiring much additional material from their surroundings. Thus, the inner planets initially ended up with no satellites.

Debris Eventually, the amount of interplanetary debris thinned out as it crashed into planets or was diverted out of the solar system. However, not all debris was ejected out of the solar system. The planetesimals in the area between Jupiter and Mars, known as the asteroid belt, remained there because Jupiter's gravitational force prevented them from merging to form a planet.

ASTEROIDS

There are thousands and thousands of bodies that orbit the Sun within the planetary orbits. They are leftovers from the formation of the solar system and are called **asteroids.** Asteroids range from a

Update For an online update on our solar system, visit the Earth Science Web Site at <u>earthgeu.com</u>

Interpreting the Illustration

Figure 29-28 Have students examine the graph and create data tables showing the temperature ranges in which different materials could condense. Then, by noting where each planet is located, students should include in their tables the possible materials that each planet could contain. Student tables should show temperature bands that correspond to the top and bottom of each color band; the possible materials would be anything located in and above the band in which the planet formed.

Content Background

Asteroids are not confined to the asteroid belt. Some asteroids are in Jupiter's orbit, and others, called Earth-crossing asteroids, have orbital paths that cross the orbit of Earth.

Enrichment

Have interested students plot the orbits of the ten largest asteroids on a scale drawing of the solar system. For this purpose, all the orbits can be assumed to be circular, so there is no need to take eccentricity into account. It will be awkward to make a scale drawing for the entire solar system, so suggest to students that they go only as far as Saturn's orbit, at just under 10 AU. A scale of 1 cm = 1 AU might be convenient.

Earth Science

Journal

Linguistic Have students find information and record in their science journals the estimated sizes and masses of the asteroids, as well as their orbital periods and semimajor axes. Ask students to compare these asteroids to planets such as Earth and to satellites such as the Moon. Finally, students should add up the masses of the ten largest asteroids and compare the result with the mass of Earth. Students should find that even the largest asteroids are smaller than the Moon, and that the total mass of the top ten asteroids is tiny compared with the mass of Earth. **L2**

NY Core Curriculum Standards

Page 794: St 1 Science KI 1, St 4 KI 1.2b & 1.2c, St 6 KI 1, 2, & 4

Page 795: St 1 Science KI 1, St 4 KI 1.2b, 1.2c, & 1.2d, St 6 KI 1, 2, 3, & 4

Identifying Misconceptions

Many students may think that only a large meteoroid can form a large crater.

Uncover the Misconception
Show students a photo of the Barringer Meteor Crater in Arizona. Ask them how large they think the meteoroid that formed the crater was.

Demonstrate the Concept
Tell students that the walls of the Barringer Meteor Crater rise about 46 m above the desert floor, and that the crater is about 174 m deep and 1.6 km wide. The meteoroid that formed the crater was only about 46 m wide, weighed 270 000 metric tons, and was traveling at about 64 400 km/h. The width of the meteoroid was only about 3 percent of the width of the crater it formed.

Assess New Knowledge
Have students extrapolate and explain why a tiny piece of material in space could seriously damage the space shuttle.

Modeling

Kinesthetic Create a model of a comet orbiting the Sun. Explain to students that the tails of a comet always point away from the Sun. **L1** **ELL** **P**

Figure 29-29 Gosses Bluff in central Australia **(A)** is 6 km in diameter and has a rim that is 200 m high. The asteroid Ida **(B),** photographed by *Galileo,* is 56 km in length and has its own moon, Dactyl.

Figure 29-30 Comet Hale-Bopp was visible in 1997, and it will not be visible again until the year 4397.

few kilometers to about 1000 km in diameter and have pitted, irregular surfaces, like the surface of Ida, shown in **Figure 29-29B.** Most asteroids are located between the orbits of Mars and Jupiter within the asteroid belt.

Pieces of Asteroids The asteroids were once thought to represent planets that somehow had been destroyed. Today, however, they are thought to be leftover planetesimal pieces from the time of the solar system's formation that never formed planets. Astronomers estimate that the total mass of all the asteroids is only about 0.08 percent of Earth's mass. As the asteroids orbit, they occasionally collide and break into fragments. When this, or any, interplanetary material falls toward Earth and enters Earth's atmosphere, it is called a **meteoroid.** When a meteoroid falls toward Earth, it burns up in Earth's atmosphere and produces a streak of light called a **meteor.** If the meteoroid does not completely burn up, part of it will collide with the ground, and it is then called a **meteorite.** If the meteorite is large, it will cause an impact crater when it collides with the ground. There is evidence of impact craters on Earth, such as Meteor Crater in Arizona and Gosses Bluff in Central Australia, shown in **Figure 29-29A.** Any craters visible on Earth must be relatively young because otherwise they would have been erased by erosion.

COMETS

Other remnants from solar system formation are comets. **Comets** are small, icy bodies that have highly eccentric orbits around the Sun. Comets are made of ice and rock, and they range from 1 to 10 km in diameter. There are two clusters, or clouds, of comets: the Kuiper belt and the Oort cloud. The Kuiper belt is close to Pluto and is between 30 and 50 AU from the Sun. The Oort cloud lies more than 100 000 AU from the Sun. Occasionally, a comet is disturbed by the gravity of another object and is thrown into the inner solar system from one of these clusters.

The Orbits of Comets Cometary orbits are highly eccentric. Some stretch far beyond the orbit of Pluto at aphelion, while others come very close to the Sun at perihelion. When a comet is within 3 AU of the Sun, it begins to evaporate, becomes much brighter, and forms a head and one or more tails. You may have seen the head and tails of comet Hale-Bopp, shown in **Figure 29-30,** when it lit up our night skies in the spring of 1997.

The head of a comet consists of the **coma** (KOH muh), an extended volume of glowing gas, and the **nucleus,** the small solid core, as shown in *Figure 29-31.* When the nucleus is heated, it releases gases and dust particles that form the coma and tails. The tails are pushed away from the coma by particles and ions coming from the Sun, as well as by the pressure of radiation from the Sun. This is why the tails of comets point away from the Sun, no matter what direction the comet is moving.

Periodic Comets Comets that repeatedly orbit into the inner solar system are known as periodic comets. For example, Comet Halley is a well-known short-period comet with a 76-year period. Halley last appeared in 1985–1986, and it is expected again in 2061. Each time a periodic comet comes near the Sun, the Sun vaporizes some of the comet's ice, and the comet loses some of its matter. Eventually, it may break apart completely as the remaining ice evaporates.

When Earth intersects a cometary orbit, we experience a **meteor shower** as particles from the comet burn up upon entering Earth's upper atmosphere. Most meteors are caused by dust particles from comets, while most meteorites, the solid chunks of rock or metal that reach Earth's surface, are fragments of asteroids.

Astronomers theorize that solar system formation occurs commonly among stars. Thus, this has driven the search for planets and systems of planets orbiting other stars. You will learn more about these planets and their detection in the *Science in the News* feature at the end of this chapter.

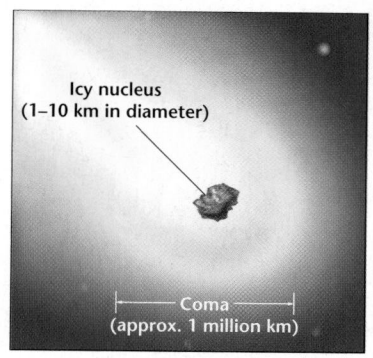

Figure 29-31 A comet consists of a nucleus, a coma, and tails pointing away from the Sun (not to scale).

SECTION ASSESSMENT

1. Explain why the material surrounding a young star forms a disk.

2. Describe why the inner planets are dense and rocky, while the outer planets have low densities and no solid surfaces.

3. Why is it theorized that the asteroids did not merge to form a planet?

4. For what reason did the inner planets not collect gas like the gas giants did?

5. **Thinking Critically** Why are there no comets in an orbit that is always close to the Sun?

SKILL REVIEW

6. **Concept Mapping** Use the following terms to construct a concept map to organize the correct sequence of events. For more help, refer to the *Skill Handbook.*

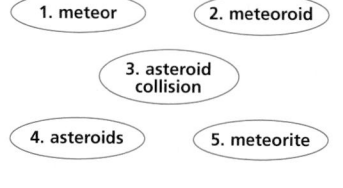

1. meteor   2. meteoroid
3. asteroid collision
4. asteroids   5. meteorite

earthgeu.com/self_check_quiz

SECTION ASSESSMENT

1. Rotation forces the material surrounding a young star to form a disk.

2. The high temperature in the central region of the young solar system prevented lightweight elements from condensing, leaving only the rocky and metallic elements to form the inner planets.

3. Jupiter's gravitational force disturbed the motions of asteroids and prevented them from merging.

4. The higher temperatures in the inner solar system and the Sun's gravitational force acted to drag gases away from the inner planets.

5. A comet whose orbit always kept it close to the Sun would quickly evaporate and dissipate.

6. 4–3–2–1 or 5, or 4–3–2–1–5; depending on the situation, either could occur.

---

3 Assess

Check for Understanding
Discussion

Have students discuss the reasons that meteorites and interplanetary dust particles are considered to be good indicators of the age and early conditions of the solar system. They are known to be of extraterrestrial origin and also to be very old—older than any rocks on Earth. Therefore, these objects represent conditions during the time when the planets were forming.

Reteach

To help students put events in the correct chronological context, have them each draw a time line starting 4.6 billion years ago and indicate the times of the following events: the formation of comets, Earth, and the Moon; the appearance of oceans on Earth; the beginnings of life on Earth; and the beginnings of the major geological eras. The astronomical events on the time lines should be clustered at the beginning, about 4.6 billion years ago.

✓Assessment

Knowledge Ask students to describe the differences and similarities between asteroids and comets. Asteroids: solid, rocky, metallic, high densities, roughly circular orbits. Comets: ice, loosely agglomerated, low densities, release gases when heated, highly eccentric orbits. Both are very old and are remnants of the formation of the solar system.

Time Allotment

one class period

Process Skills

compare and contrast, formulate models, organize data, recognize spatial relationships, make and use tables

Preparation

Data required to do this GeoLab can be found in Appendix J.

Possible Hypotheses

- For a model to fit in a 12.2 m classroom with the planets in a line, 1 AU = 0.30 m. For a football field, 1 AU = 2.29 m. Students will predict the size of their model based on the scale they choose.
- Using the football field, the diameter of Pluto would be approximately 0.035 cm, which is really too small to be modeled. Students should hypothesize that to include other measurements such as diameter, rotational rates, and so on, the model needs to be fairly large.

Plan the Experiment

Teaching Strategies

- Have students make a list on the chalkboard of different measurements they want to include, such as distance from the Sun and rotational rates.
- Use the illustration provided, and review with students how to create and use a scale.

Scaling the Solar System

Astronomers are familiar with both the small, such as interstellar dust particles, and the large, such as the solar system. In order to understand the variety of sizes in the solar system, astronomers use models. These models can be as simple as putting people or objects in marked places or as complex as elaborate computer simulations. The most difficult task with many models is choosing a scale that will display all the information needed, such as distance, rotation rates, and size.

Preparation

Problem

How can the size of the solar system be converted to a scale that will easily demonstrate relative distances between objects in the solar system? Is distance the only measurement that can be demonstrated in a scale model?

Possible Materials

calculator	tape measure
meterstick	stopwatches
marker	masking tape
variety of sizes	
of common	
round objects	

Hypothesis

Brainstorm about possible models and data needed to create them. Determine where these data are available, and collect them to use as a reference for your model. To have your model fit in your chosen area, make a hypothesis about the appropriate scale to use for distance from the Sun to each planet. Hypothesize how additional solar system measurements can be included in your model. For example, think about including planet diameters, rotation rates, etc.

Objectives

In this GeoLab, you will:
- **Calculate** the distance from the Sun for each planet based on your scale.
- **Determine** how to incorporate additional solar system measurements into your model, or design another model to show that information.
- **Interpret** your results based on your scale, and decide if your scale was an appropriate one based on the problems that may have resulted.

Troubleshooting

Students may find that the scale they used initially is too small to include all the information they intended to. They may have to go through a series of scales before they find one that is appropriate. If students want to show the entire orbit in their scale, then the amount of space they need will double.

Possible Procedures

Student procedures will vary. However, the general organization of students' tables of measurements and converted measurements should be similar. Organizing the information according to planets and writing the converted measurements next to the actual measurements will help.

Plan the Experiment

1. As a group, make a list of possible ways you might test your hypotheses. Keep the available materials in mind as you plan your procedure.
2. Be sure your scale is appropriate for the information you are representing. Remember that a model should have the same scale throughout. You may have to try more than one scale before you are successful.
3. Record your procedure and list every step. Determine what materials are needed and the amounts of each.
4. Design and construct a data table for recording your original data and your scaled data.
5. Check the plan. Make sure your teacher has approved your plan before you proceed with your experiment.
6. Carry out your plan.

Mars   Venus   Mercury

1 cm = 4000 km

Analyze

1. **Checking Your Hypothesis** Which scale worked the best for your model? Explain.
2. **Interpreting Observations** What problems did you have in finding a scale? Explain how you corrected the problems.
3. **Calculating Results** List and explain the conversions that you used to create your scale model. If multiple steps were necessary to convert to your scale units, how could they be combined to make the process simpler?
4. **Observing and Inferring** What possible problems could result from using a very large scale? A small scale? Explain why depicting a scale model of the solar system on a sheet of notebook paper is extremely difficult.
5. **Compare and Contrast** Compare and contrast your model with one of your classmates'. What were the advantages of the scale you used? What were the disadvantages? How would you improve your model?
6. **Thinking Critically** Suppose that the outer planets are three times farther away than they are now. How would this affect your model? What scale would you choose now? Explain.

Conclude & Apply

1. Proxima Centauri, the closest star to our Sun, is about 4.01×10^{13} km from the Sun. Based on your scale, how far would Proxima Centauri be from the Sun in your model? If you were to fit the distance between the Sun and Proxima Centauri into your classroom, how small would the scaled distance between Pluto and the Sun be?
2. An interstellar dust particle is 1.0×10^{-6} m in length. Convert this measurement to your scale. How many dust particles could fit in the distance between the Sun and Jupiter? Between Mars and Uranus?

Design Your Own GeoLab **799**

Data and Observations

Have students record their data tables and turn them in at the end of class. Have students indicate whether their scales worked to incorporate all the information they wanted to include. Make transparencies of sample tables and use them in class the following day to illustrate different scales and data.

Analyze

1. Students' answers will vary. Generally, larger scales will include more information.
2. Answers will vary. Initially, students will typically choose a scale that is too small.
3. Conversions will vary. If students converted from AUs to kilometers to meters, they can multiply their conversion factors to convert directly from AUs to meters.
4. Answers will vary. Large scales can be unmanageable, while small scales make it difficult to fit all the details in. Using a sheet of notebook paper makes it difficult because all the inner planets are crunched together.
5. Answers will vary.
6. Answers will vary.

Conclude & Apply

1. Answers will vary depending on students' scales.
2. Answers will vary depending on students' scales.

Resource Manager

GeoLab and MiniLab Worksheets, pp. 116–119 L2

✓Assessment

Knowledge Ask students to discuss how their models would be different if Pluto were not a planet, or if another planet beyond Pluto was discovered. Without Pluto, the scale of the model could be a bit larger, because Pluto's distance from the Sun is nearly 29 percent greater than Neptune's distance. Conversely, if there were a planet beyond Pluto, the model scale would have to be smaller to accommodate this larger orbit.

NY Core Curriculum Standards

Page 798: St 1 Math KI 1, 2, 3, & Engin KI 1, St 4 KI 1.1a, 1.1b, 1.2c, & 1.2d, St 6 KI 1, 2, & 3

Page 799: St 1 Math KI 1, 2, 3, & Engin KI 1, St 4 KI 1.1a, 1.1b, 1.2c, & 1.2d, St 6 KI 1, 2, & 3

Purpose

Students will learn about the techniques used to discover planets orbiting other stars.

Content Background

All of the extrasolar planets detected so far have been gas giants rather than terrestrial planets. It is important for students to recognize that this does not mean that all extrasolar planets are gas giants; instead, it reflects the fact that the gas giants are easiest to detect. Furthermore, gas giants orbiting close to their parent stars are easier to detect than similar planets orbiting farther away, so we can't necessarily assume that the closer gas giants are more common than those farther out. In time, when more systems have been observed, it will be possible to reach statistical conclusions that will tell us more about whether or not our solar system actually is unusual.

Teaching Strategies

- Review with students the concept of center of mass.
- The method by which a star's small motion is detected is the Doppler shift, a shifting in wavelength of light resulting from the motion between the source and the observer. Small wavelength shifts in a star's light must be detected to determine that the star is undergoing orbital motion about the center of mass. The Doppler shift is discussed in more depth in Chapter 30.
- The presence of Jupiter-like planets very close to their parent stars is a puzzle for astronomers, because these

---

Science in the News

Discovering New Planets

Have you ever looked up at the night sky and wondered whether there are other Earth-like planets? We know that there are other stars similar to the Sun in the galaxy. In 1995 the first evidence of a planet was discovered.

In 1995, after a year of careful measurements, Swiss astronomers announced the discovery of a planet orbiting around the star 51 Pegasi. A planet found outside of our solar system is called an extrasolar planet. Shortly after the discovery of the first extrasolar planet, several more were discovered. More than 100 extrasolar planets have been detected, with the number of discoveries increasing with every passing month.

Detecting Planets

The presence of these extrasolar planets was inferred, not directly detected. The gravitational attraction of a star and a planet causes both bodies to orbit around a center of mass. Because the star is much larger and brighter than the planet, astronomers actually detect the small movement of the star around the center of mass, rather than directly observing the planet. Then, by using Newton's law of universal gravitation, astronomers can determine information such as the planet's minimum mass and orbital period.

In addition to single planets orbiting around stars, astronomers have found more than one planet orbiting around a single star. On April 15, 1999, astronomers announced the discovery of three planets orbiting around the star Upsilon Andromedae. This discovery was significant because scientists then had evidence of a multiple-planet system, similar to our solar system with its nine planets. On March 29, 2000, two planets smaller than Saturn were discovered.

Until this time, only larger planets close to the size of Jupiter had been discovered.

Direct Evidence?

In the fall of 1999, astronomers using Earth-based telescopes recorded the distinct dimming of light from a star in the constellation Pegasus. Previously, a planet had been inferred from gravitational effects, but astronomers did not have direct evidence. However, the dimming occurred where the gravitational effects predicted the planet to be. This dimming was caused by the light from the star being blocked out by an extrasolar planet passing in front of the star. This provided direct evidence of an extrasolar planet.

No Earth-sized planets have yet been discovered, but scientists theorize that they exist. Two NASA missions, the *Space Interferometry Mission (SIM)* and the *Terrestrial Planet Finder Mission (TPF)*, will be used to study the extrasolar planets. *SIM* will have special telescopes that will be able to detect Earth-sized extrasolar planets. Later, the *TPF* will be used to study the compositions of the atmospheres and surfaces of the planets.

Activity

Visit your library or the Earth Science Web Site at **earthgeu.com** to research the most recent extrasolar planet discoveries. Present your findings to the class on a poster or in an oral report.

---

planets could not possibly have formed there, where heat from the stars would have prevented lightweight elements from condensing to form planets. Therefore, astronomers are considering mechanisms by which gas giant planets could form far from their parent stars and then drift inward to the close orbits that are observed.

Activity

Have students go to the Earth Science Web Site at **earthgeu.com**, as well as other news sources, to find the results of recent observations of extrasolar planets.

Summary

SECTION 29.1	Main Ideas	Vocabulary
Overview of Our Solar System 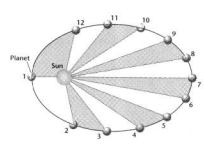	• Early astronomers explained the motions of the planets with geocentric models, including epicycles. • Copernicus, Brahe, Kepler, and Galileo developed evidence supporting a heliocentric solar system model. • Newton developed a law of gravitation that was used to demonstrate the validity of the heliocentric model.	aphelion (p. 777) astronomical unit (p. 777) eccentricity (p. 777) perihelion (p. 777) retrograde motion (p. 776)

SECTION 29.2	Main Ideas	Vocabulary
The Terrestrial Planets 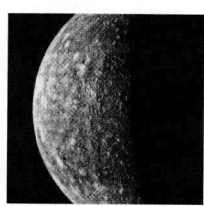	• The terrestrial planets include the four planets closest to the Sun. They are relatively small and dense, and they have rocky surfaces. • Mercury has a surface similar to the Moon's, but a very different interior. • Venus has an extremely hot surface as a result of greenhouse heating, but is similar to Earth in other properties. • Earth is suitable for life because of its unique orbital position that allows water to exist in all three phases on the surface. • Mars shows signs of having once had tectonic activity.	gas giant planet (p. 780) precession (p. 783) terrestrial planet (p. 780)

SECTION 29.3	Main Ideas	Vocabulary
The Gas Giant Planets 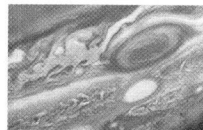	• The gas giant planets are very large and have low densities, no solid surfaces, ring systems, and many moons. • Jupiter is the largest of the planets. It has a fluid interior, except for a small rocky core, and several moons. Saturn is slightly smaller than Jupiter and has a more extensive ring system. • Uranus and Neptune are very similar in size and composition. • Pluto is not classified as a gas giant or a terrestrial planet.	belt (p. 787) liquid metallic hydrogen (p. 787) zone (p. 787)

SECTION 29.4	Main Ideas	Vocabulary
Formation of Our Solar System 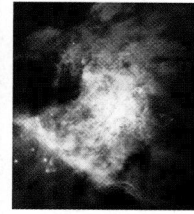	• The solar system formed from a collapsing interstellar cloud that flattened into a disk from which the planets formed. • Terrestrial planets formed from refractory materials in the hot inner disk, and gas giants formed from volatile elements in the cold outer disk. • Asteroids are rocky remnants of the early solar system. Most of them orbit the Sun between Mars and Jupiter. • Comets have highly eccentric orbits and are made of rock and ice. When they are close to the Sun, they glow brightly and have a head and tails of gas and dust.	asteroid (p. 795) coma (p. 797) comet (p. 796) meteor (p. 796) meteor shower (p. 797) meteorite (p. 796) meteoroid (p. 796) nucleus (p. 797) planetesimal (p. 794)

 earthgeu.com/vocabulary_puzzlemaker

Study Guide **801**

Main Ideas

Summary statements can be used by students to review the major concepts of the chapter.

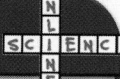

VOCABULARY
PuzzleMaker

 For additional help with vocabulary, have students access the Vocabulary Puzzlemaker online.

earthgeu.com/ vocabulary_puzzlemaker

(0:00) Out of Time?

If time does not permit teaching the entire chapter, use the GeoDigest at the end of the unit as an overview.

Be sure to check the Earth Science Web Site for links to chapter material:
earthgeu.com

GLENCOE
Technology

Videotape/DVD
MindJogger Videoquizzes
Chapter 29: *Our Solar System*
Have students work in groups as they play the videoquiz game to review key chapter concepts.

The Planets: Different Worlds

Resource Manager

Chapter Assessment, pp. 169–174
Performance Assessment in Earth Science
MindJogger Videoquizzes DVD/VHS
ExamView® Pro CD-ROM

NY Core Curriculum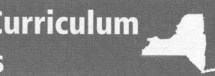
Standards

Page 800: St 1 Science KI 1, 2, & 3, St 2 KI 1 & 2, St 6 KI 1, 4, & 5
Page 801: St 1 Science KI 1, St 4 KI 1.1a, 1.1b, 1.2c, & 1.2d, St 6 KI 2 & 4

Understanding Main Ideas

1. b
2. d
3. a
4. c
5. b
6. b
7. a
8. a
9. Kepler's third law states that the square of the orbital period of a planet equals the cube of the planet's semimajor axis, if the period is expressed in years and the semimajor axis is expressed in astronomical units, $P^2 = a^3$.
10. Pluto, because its properties do not fit into either classification
11. The surface temperature on Venus is so hot because the greenhouse effect is very strong on Venus as a result of its thick atmosphere of carbon dioxide.
12. See the student page.
13. Its atmospheric density is much lower than that of Venus.
14. planetesimals left over from the time of the solar system's formation that were prevented by Jupiter's gravity from merging to form a planet

NY Core Curriculum Standards

Page 802: St 1 Math KI 1, 2, & Science KI 1, St 4 KI 1.1a, 1.1b, & 1.2c, St 6 KI 2 & 4
Page 803: St 1 Math KI 1, 2, & Science KI 1, St 4 KI 1.1a, 1.1b, 1.2c, & 1.2d, St 6 KI 2 & 4

Understanding Main Ideas

1. What is a planet's backward motion in the sky called?
   a. revolving
   b. retrograde motion
   c. planetary spin
   d. geocentric motion

2. What point in a planet's orbit is closest to the Sun?
   a. focus
   b. semimajor axis
   c. aphelion
   d. perihelion

3. What model of our solar system did Copernicus propose?
   a. a heliocentric model
   b. a retrograde model
   c. a geocentric model
   d. a nested-sphere model

4. A planet's average distance from the Sun is also what part of the orbital ellipse?
   a. the distance between the foci
   b. the eccentricity
   c. the semimajor axis
   d. the circumference

5. How were the plains on Mercury hypothesized to have formed?
   a. from large oceans smoothing out the surface
   b. from lava flows
   c. from wind eroding high points
   d. from landslides on the scarps

6. Why does the Sun rise in the west and set in east when viewed from Venus?
   a. Venus is the closest planet to Earth.
   b. Venus has a retrograde rotation.
   c. Venus's orbital period is 224 Earth days.
   d. The semimajor axis of Venus is only 0.723 AU from the Sun.

7. What two planets have similar appearances, atmospheric compositions, interiors, and particle belts?
   a. Neptune and Uranus
   b. Mars and Venus
   c. Saturn and Neptune
   d. Saturn and Uranus

8. Which condensed into solid form closest to the Sun?
   a. refractory elements
   b. volatile elements
   c. gas giants
   d. the Oort cloud

9. What does Kepler's third law state?

10. Which planet is not classified as a gas giant or a terrestrial planet? Why?

11. Why is the surface temperature of Venus 750 K (476°C)?

Use the diagram below to answer question 12.

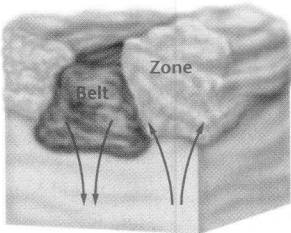

12. Identify a belt and a zone. What is the direction of movement of each?

Test-Taking Tip

MNEMONICS Use memory devices to help you remember terms and orders. For example, My Very Elegant Monkey Just Sat Upon Nancy's Petunias can help you remember the order of the planets in our solar system.

earthgeu.com/chapter_test

---

15. the discovery of Jupiter's ring
16. about half rock and half ice

Applying Main Ideas

17. It was simple, it explained retrograde motion, and Kepler and Newton were able to discover laws that fit the model.
18. Venus and Earth are similar in diameter, mass, density, and, presumably, internal structure. Venus has a far denser and hotter atmosphere than Earth made of carbon dioxide, and Venus has no liquid water on its surface.
19. Jupiter's gravity, specifically its tidal force, acts to stretch and squeeze each of the moons. The moons closest to Jupiter contain almost no ice, while those farther out do contain ice.
20. Asteroids are rocky and/or metallic in composition, they have roughly circular orbits, and most of them orbit between Mars and Jupiter. Comets have icy compositions and highly eccentric orbits that range far beyond all of the planets.

13. If the Martian atmosphere is 95 percent carbon dioxide, why doesn't Mars have a strong greenhouse effect?

14. Where are asteroids hypothesized to have originated?

15. What new discovery was made from the *Voyager 1* and *Voyager 2* visits to Jupiter?

16. What does the density of Pluto indicate that it is made of?

Applying Main Ideas

17. What were some of the advantages of the Sun-centered model proposed by Copernicus?

18. How are Venus and Earth similar, and how are they different?

19. How has Jupiter's gravitational force affected the geology of its four major moons?

20. What are the differences between asteroids and comets?

21. How did collisions during the formation of the planets affect Earth, Mercury, Venus, and Uranus?

22. Would it be possible for a gas giant to form close to the Sun? Explain.

23. How are the rings of the gas giants theorized to have formed?

Thinking Critically

24. Why are the volcanoes on Mars so much larger than those on Earth?

25. Why are the rings of each gas giant planet closer to the planet than its large moons are?

26. Should Pluto be considered a planet or a planetesimal? Explain.

27. How would a circular orbit affect Kepler's second and third laws? Restate these laws using the radius of a circle.

earthgeu.com/standardized_test

Standardized Test Practice

INTERPRETING SCIENTIFIC ILLUSTRATIONS
Use the diagram below to answer questions 1 and 2.

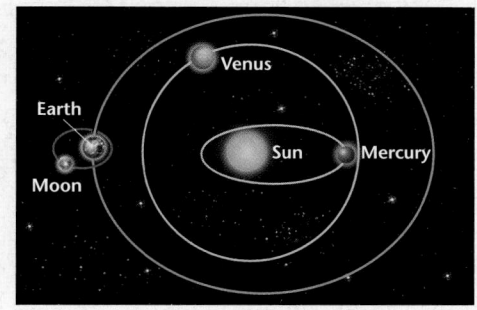

1. Which planet is located at aphelion in its orbit?
  a. Mercury   **c.** Earth
  b. Venus   **d.** none of the above

2. Which orbit shown has an eccentricity that is closest to 0?
  a. Mercury   **c.** Earth
  b. Venus   **d.** the Moon

3. How are Mercury and the Moon similar?
  a. Both are covered with craters and plains.
  b. Both have the same night-day temperature difference.
  c. They have the same strength of surface gravity.
  d. Both have an extensive nickel-iron core.

4. What is a piece of interplanetary material that burns up in Earth's atmosphere called?
  a. a meteorite   **c.** a meteor
  b. an asteroid   **d.** a meteoroid

Assessment **803**

---

21. Earth's moon apparently formed as a result of a massive collision of a large planetesimal with Earth; Mercury appears to be the remnant of an originally larger planet whose mantle was blown off in a giant collision; Venus has a slow retrograde rotation that is theorized to have resulted from a collision; and Uranus is tipped over by about 90° as a result of a massive collision early in its history.

22. No, because the Sun swept up much material in that vicinity and the gases couldn't condense that close, where it was hot.

23. by the fragmentation of moons in collisions

Thinking Critically

24. Mars does not have plate tectonics or continental drift, so the volcanic vent remains in one place and can build up.

25. Tidal forces prevent moons from forming closer to the planet than a certain distance.

26. There is no definitive answer to the question of whether Pluto is a planet or not. Physically, it is more like a large member of the Kuiper belt than a proper planet, but historically, it has always been considered a planet.

27. The laws would still be valid. Kepler's second law wouldn't change, and his third law would be $P^2 = r^3$.

Standardized Test Practice

1. a
2. b
3. a
4. c

Chapter

30

Stars

Refer to pages 8T–9T of the Teacher Guide for an explanation of the National Science Content Standards correlations.

Section	Objectives	National Science Content Standards	State/Local Standards
SECTION 30.1 **The Sun** 🕐 1 session 📦 ½ block	1. **Explore** the structure of the Sun. 2. **Describe** the solar activity cycle and how the Sun affects Earth. 3. **Compare** the different types of spectra.	UCP.2, UCP.3, UCP.4, UCP.5; A.1, A.2; B.1, B.2, B.3, B.4, B.6; D.1, D.4; E.2; F.4	St 1 Math KI 1, 2, 3, Science KI 1, 3, & Engin KI 1, St 2 KI 1, St 4 KI 1.1f, 1.2b, 1.2c, & 2.2a, St 6 KI 2, 3, 4, & 5
SECTION 30.2 **Measuring the Stars** 🕐 2 sessions 📦 1½ blocks	4. **Describe** star distribution and distance. 5. **Classify** the types of stars. 6. **Summarize** the interrelated properties of stars.	UCP.1, UCP.2, UCP.3, UCP.5; A.1, A.2; B.2, B.4, B.6; G.1, G.2, G.3	St 1 Math KI 1, 2, 3, Science KI 1, 2, 3, & Engin KI 1, St 4 KI 1.1a, 1.1b, 1.1f, 1.1g, & 1.2b, St 6 KI 1, 2, 3, & 5
SECTION 30.3 **Stellar Evolution** 🕐 3 sessions 📦 1½ blocks	7. **Explain** how astronomers learn about the internal structure of stars. 8. **Describe** how the Sun will change during its lifetime and how it will end up. 9. **Compare** the evolutions of stars of different masses.	UCP.1, UCP.2, UCP.3, UCP.4, UCP.5; A.1, A.2; B.2, B.3, B.4, B.6; E.1, E.2; G.2, G.3	St 1 Math KI 1, 2, 3, Science KI 1, 2, & 3, St 2 KI 1, 2, & 3, St 4 KI 1.2b, St 6 KI 1, 2, 3, 4, & 5

A complete Planning Guide is provided on pages 30T–32T.

🕐 The number of recommended single-period sessions

📦 The number of recommended blocks

Activity Materials

Discovery Lab *page 805*
Internet access, pencil, paper

Demo *page 808*
2 bar magnets

GeoLab *pages 826–827*
ruler, calculator, pencil, paper

MiniLab *page 817*
meterstick, string, protractor, graph paper

Need materials? Contact Science Kit at 1-800-828-7777 or at www.sciencekit.com on the Internet. For alternate materials, see the activity on the listed page.

Key to Teaching Strategies

L1 Level 1 activities should be appropriate for students with learning difficulties.

L2 Level 2 activities should be within the ability range of all students.

L3 Level 3 activities are designed for above-average students.

ELL ELL activities should be within the ability range of English-language learners.

COOP LEARN Cooperative learning activities are designed for small-group work.

P These strategies represent student products that can be placed in a best-work portfolio.

📦 These strategies are useful in a block-scheduling format.

Chapter Organizer

Glencoe Exclusive!
TeacherWorks™
All-In-One Planner and Resource Center

Activities/Features	Reproducible Masters	Transparencies
Discovery Lab: Monitoring the Sun, p. 805 **Problem-Solving Lab:** Using Numbers, p. 810	**Study Guide for Content Mastery,** pp. 189–190 L2 **Laboratory Manual,** pp. 233–236 L2	**Section Focus Transparency 96** L1 ELL
Using Math: Using Numbers, p. 816 **MiniLab:** Parallax in the Classroom, p. 817	**Study Guide for Content Mastery,** pp. 191–192 L2 **Laboratory Manual,** pp. 237–240 L2 **GeoLab and MiniLab Worksheets,** p. 121 L2	**Section Focus Transparency 97** L1 ELL
GeoLab: Identifying Stellar Spectral Lines, pp. 826–827 **Science in the News:** Chandra—An Eye on the Universe, p. 828	**Study Guide for Content Mastery,** pp. 193–194 L2 **GeoLab and MiniLab Worksheets,** pp. 122–125 L2	**Section Focus Transparency 98** L1 ELL **Teaching Transparency 93** L2 ELL

✔Assessment

Chapter Assessment,
   pp. 175–180
**Performance Assessment in
   the Science Classroom
   (PASC)**
**MindJogger Videoquiz
   DVD/VHS**
**Performance Assessment in
   Earth Science**
ExamView® Pro CD-ROM
5 Days to the Regents Exam

GLENCOE'S
ASSESSMENT
ADVANTAGE

Additional Resources

**Guided Reading Audio
   Program** ELL
**Cooperative Learning in the
   Science Classroom**
   COOP LEARN
Lesson Plans
Block Scheduling
earthgeu.com
NY Lesson Plans
NY Block Scheduling
Review Handbook for
   Regents Earth Science
   Exam

NATIONAL GEOGRAPHIC

Teacher's Corner

**Products Available from
National Geographic Society**
*To order the following products,
call the National Geographic
Society at 1-800-368-2728:*
Curriculum Kit
GeoKit: *Astronomy*

Videos
Stars and Constellations
Maps
Solar System/Celestial Family

Content Background

The Sun
Section 30.1

Studies of the Sun have proven to be very helpful for astronomers studying other stars. Research on other stars has also helped to provide a better understanding of the Sun. Astronomers can measure details on the solar surface, and they have obtained a centuries-long record of the Sun's activity cycle. These data are helpful in interpreting surface phenomena and activity cycles of other stars. In the same way, data on how other stars change with time help astronomers to deduce where the Sun is in its life cycle, how it looked in the distant past, and what will happen to it far in the future. The so-called solar-stellar connection has been a very fruitful area of research for astronomers.

Measuring the Stars
Section 30.2

The only definite proofs that Earth is revolving around the Sun come from precise measurements of stars. The first observation that definitively proved Earth's motion about the Sun involved the aberration of starlight. Earth's motion perpendicular to the line of sight toward a star causes an apparent displacement of the star's position. This is analogous to the apparent slant of rainfall as you run through a storm; your motion makes the raindrops appear to fall toward you. The aberration of starlight was first observed in 1727.

A second method of proving that Earth is revolving around the Sun is to observe stellar parallax, the apparent shifting in position of a nearby star as seen from different points in Earth's orbit about the Sun. Parallax is described in this section. The first successful detection of parallax occurred in 1838. A third proof that Earth orbits the Sun was established in 1888 with the first accurate measurements of Doppler shifts in stellar spectra. Wavelengths of light from a star shift back and forth as Earth orbits the Sun, and alternately approaches the Sun and recedes from it. Doppler shifts are also described in this section.

Some names of stars have long histories. Many of the brightest stars were named by Arabic astronomers, and in many cases these reflect the roles of the stars in the earlier Greek constellation mythology. Examples of Arabic names include Vega, Fomalhout, Deneb, and Sirius. Centuries later, astronomers adopted a more systematic nomenclature, using Greek letters to indicate rank within a constellation. In this system, Betelgeuse, the brightest star in Orion, is α Orionis. In this system, the rank is designated by a Greek letter but the constellation name is given in Latin. Numbers

Multiple Learning Styles

Visual-Spatial Activity, p. 806, Demo, p. 808, Reteach, p. 812, Demo, p. 815

Interpersonal Collaborative Learning, p. 807, Discussion, p. 811

Intrapersonal Reteach, p. 820

Logical-Mathematical Project, p. 808

GLENCOE
Technology

The following multimedia resources are available from Glencoe.

The Planets
Star

Vocabulary Puzzlemaker

TeacherWorks™ CD-ROM

MindJogger Videoquizzes DVD/VHS

ExamView® Pro CD-ROM

Interactive Chalkboard CD-ROM

are used when there are more bright stars in a constellation than there are letters in the Greek alphabet. Once telescopes came into use, many more stars were cataloged, and the fainter ones are generally listed only by numbers rather than names.

Stellar Evolution
Section 30.3

In 1987, stellar evolution suddenly attracted the attention of the general public, as well as astronomers, when the first supernova visible to the unaided eye occurred in nearly 400 years. A star in the Large Magellanic Cloud, a neighboring galaxy of the Milky Way, exploded. Photos of the event made the covers of *Time, Newsweek,* and other popular magazines, and science articles were dominated by the news of the supernova. Not only did this event help to make people aware that stars really do change, but also, it was a goldmine for astronomers studying stellar evolution.

A great deal of new information about how stars become unstable and explode, how they form and disperse new elements in the process, how they differ from one galaxy to another, and even new insights into the nature of elementary particles (neutrinos) and the "dark matter" problem in cosmology, all came from studies of the supernova of 1987.

Identifying Misconceptions

Many people think that stars are eternal, and that they don't change. This is because most changes in stars take place only over very long periods of time —much longer than a human lifetime. There are exceptions, such as nova and supernova outbursts, but for the most part, humans are not able to see stars move or change. Astronomers deduce how stars evolve by observing them in different phases of their life cycles and by using models. Stellar motions are actually quite rapid by human standards, but stars are so far away that we can't see the shifts in their positions without precise instruments. To our eyes, the constellations still look the same as they did 5000 years ago, when the first myths about the sky arose.

✔Assessment

Portfolio Assessment
Discovery Lab, TWE, p. 805
Assessment, TWE, p. 825

Performance Assessment
Discovery Lab, SE, p. 805
MiniLab, SE, p. 817
GeoLab, SE, pp. 826–827

Knowledge Assessment
Assessment, TWE, pp. 807, 820
Problem-Solving Lab, TWE, p. 810
Section Assessment, SE, pp. 812, 820, 825
Chapter Assessment, SE, pp. 830–831

Skill Assessment
Assessment, TWE, p. 812
MiniLab, TWE, p. 817
GeoLab, TWE, pp. 826–827

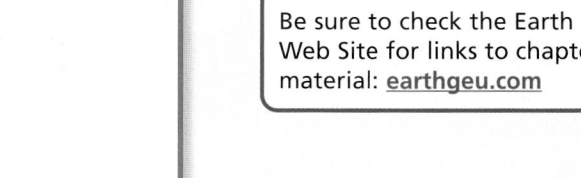

Be sure to check the Earth Science Web Site for links to chapter material: earthgeu.com

Introducing the Chapter

Stars are the building blocks of elements in the universe. Throughout their life cycles, stars produce iron and lighter elements by fusion. Heavier elements are produced when massive stars explode at the ends of their lives. All stars can be described by a few key properties including mass, temperature, composition, luminosity, and diameter.

Interpreting the Photo

The nebula NGC 3603 shows different stages in the evolution of stars. In the pillars of gas, stars are forming. To the lower left of the star cluster in the center is an elliptical blob, which may be the result of a protoplanetary disk. The star cluster in the center is a group of hot, young stars, and to the upper left is an evolved blue supergiant that has ejected a ring of gas.

INTERACTIVE CHALKBOARD with Image Bank

PowerPoint® Presentations

This CD is an editable Microsoft® PowerPoint® presentation that includes:
- Section presentations
- Section checks
- Image bank
- Links to Earth Science Online
- All transparencies
- Animations
- Audio

Chapter 30

Stars

What You'll Learn
- What the structure and processes of the Sun are.
- What properties are used to observe and measure stars.
- How stars change during their lives and what is left when they die.

Why It's Important

The Sun is vital to life on Earth. To understand the Sun, which is a star, it is necessary to understand how all stars function and evolve. Stars are also the building blocks of our galaxy and the source of most elements in the universe.

Earth Science Online

To find out more about the Sun and other stars, visit the Earth Science Web Site at earthgeu.com

NGC 3603

804

Discovery Lab

Process Skills

observe, infer, compare and contrast L1 ELL

Procedure
- This lab may be done by small groups of students.
- If time and Internet access permit, allow students to view the same set of images over a period of several days.

Observe

Students should observe that the Sun is more dynamic and active during the peak of the activity cycle. Comparisons of images will vary depending on images used. X-ray images look much more violent than visible-light images.

Discovery Lab

Monitoring the Sun

Although the Sun is an average star, it has many complex processes. We get a glimpse of these processes through the solar activity cycle. The activity cycle of the Sun refers to how active its surface is. During the peak of the activity cycle, the surface is violent and eruptive and has numerous dark spots. The activity cycle varies with a period of approximately 11 years and last peaked in late 2000.

1. Find sites on the Web that provide current images of the Sun and observe how the Sun looks today when viewed at different wavelengths. Or, go to **earthgeu.com** and follow the links.

2. Make notes of features that you observe and the wavelengths from which you observe them.

3. Find out where the Sun currently is in its activity cycle, and compare what you actually observe with what you would expect for this time in the cycle.

Observe Is the Sun near the peak of its activity cycle? Do the solar images that you observed fit with your expectation of where the Sun is in its activity cycle? Compare and contrast the images obtained at different wavelengths.

Section Focus

Before presenting the lesson, display **Section Focus Transparency 96** on the overhead projector.
L1 ELL

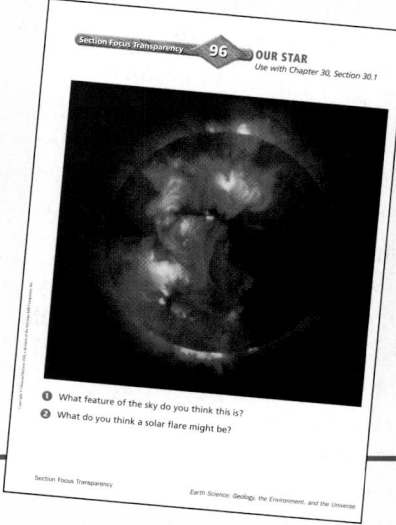

Chapter Themes

The following themes from the National Science Content Standards are covered in this chapter. Refer to page 8T of the Teacher Guide for an explanation of the correlations.
Systems, order, and organization (UCP.1); Evidence, models, and explanation (UCP.2); Change, constancy, and measurement (UCP.3); Evolution and equilibrium (UCP.4)

SECTION 30.1 — *The Sun*

OBJECTIVES

- **Explore** the structure of the Sun.
- **Describe** the solar activity cycle and how the Sun affects Earth.
- **Compare** the different types of spectra.

VOCABULARY

photosphere	solar flare
chromosphere	prominence
corona	fusion
solar wind	fission
sunspot	spectrum

Humans have probably always been aware of the Sun. However, it has been only recently that astronomers have begun to understand its nature. Through observations and probes such as the *Solar Heliospheric Observatory* (SOHO) and the *Ulysses* mission, astronomers have begun to unravel the mysteries of the Sun. Astronomers still rely on computer models for an explanation of the interior of the Sun because the interior cannot be directly observed.

PROPERTIES OF THE SUN

The Sun is the largest object in the solar system, in both size and mass. It would take 109 Earths lined up edge to edge to fit across the Sun, or almost 10 Jupiters. The Sun is about 330 000 times as massive as Earth and 1048 times the mass of Jupiter. In fact, the Sun contains more than 99 percent of all the mass in the solar system. It should therefore come as no surprise that the Sun's mass controls the motions of the planets and other objects.

30.1 The Sun **805**

✓ Assessment

Portfolio Have each student make a poster of the Sun in different wavelengths. Have students include the wavelengths of the images, descriptions of the features, and the dates that the images were taken. Also have them include plots of the solar activity cycle and indicate at which point in the cycle each image was taken. P

Resource Manager

Section Focus Transparency 96 L1 ELL
Study Guide for Content Mastery, pp. 189–190 L2

0:00 Out of Time?

If time does not permit teaching the entire chapter, use the chapter summary on page 829 and the GeoDigest found at the end of the unit as an overview.

Activity

Visual-Spatial While it is extremely dangerous to look directly at the Sun, it is easy to create small solar images that can be viewed safely. A small pinhole in a piece of cardboard can act as a lens that projects a solar image onto a sheet of paper a meter or so away. Have students work in groups to perform this activity. **CAUTION:** *Make sure that students do not directly view the Sun.* One student can hold the cardboard perpendicular to the Sun's direction, while another student can hold the sheet of paper directly behind the pinhole. A small solar image will appear on the sheet of paper. Students will observe that the size of the image increases with the separation between the pinhole and the paper. This activity works best when the sheet of paper is shaded from above, so that direct sunlight does not drown out the solar image. **ELL** **COOP LEARN**

Using Scientific Terms

The history of astronomy is apparent in the names given to astronomical phenomena. Many of these names are derived from Latin or Greek, and words from these two languages are often intermixed. For example, *chromosphere* comes from the Greek *chromos,* meaning "red," and *sphere. Corona* is a Latin word for "crown."

Table 30-1 Properties of the Sun			
	Sun	**Earth**	**Jupiter**
diameter (km)	1.392×10^6	1.2756×10^4	1.4298×10^5
mass (kg)	1.99×10^{30}	5.9736×10^{24}	1.8986×10^{27}
density (kg/m³)	1.408×10^3	5.515×10^3	1.326×10^3

The Sun's average density is similar to the densities of the gas giant planets, represented by Jupiter in *Table 30-1.* Astronomers can deduce densities at specific points inside the Sun, as well as other information, only by using computer models that explain the observations that they make. These models show that the density in the center of the Sun is about 1.50×10^5 kg/m³, which is about thirteen times the density of lead! A pair of dice having this density would weigh about two pounds. However, unlike lead, which is a solid, the solar interior is gaseous throughout because of its high temperature—about 1×10^7 K in the center. At this high temperature many of the gases are completely ionized, meaning that they are composed only of atomic nuclei and electrons. This state of matter is known as plasma. The outer layers of the Sun are not quite hot enough to be plasma.

THE SUN'S ATMOSPHERE

The lowest layer of the Sun's atmosphere, approximately 400 km in thickness, is called the **photosphere.** This is the visible surface of the Sun, as shown in *Figure 30-1A.* You may wonder why the photosphere is the visible surface when it is also the lowest layer of the Sun's atmosphere. This is because most of the light emitted by the Sun comes from this layer. The two layers above are transparent at most wavelengths of visible light. Additionally, the top two layers are very dim in the wavelengths that they do emit. The average temperature of the photosphere is about 5800 K.

Above the photosphere is the **chromosphere,** which is approximately 2500 km in thickness and has a temperature of nearly 30 000 K at the top. Normally, the chromosphere is visible only during a solar eclipse, when the photosphere is blocked.

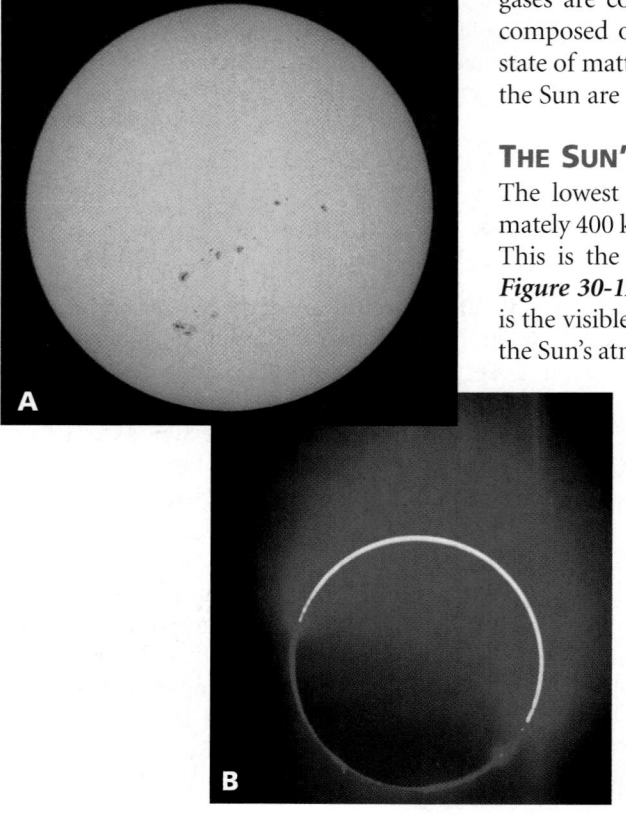

Figure 30-1 The photosphere **(A)** is the visible surface of the Sun. This annular eclipse **(B)** on May 30, 1994 shows the red chromosphere of the Sun in the lower half of the image.

Interpreting the Photo

Figure 30-1A Knowing that the Sun's diameter is approximately 109 times Earth's diameter, students can estimate the sizes of the sunspots that are visible in this photo and compare them with the size of Earth. Many of these sunspots have diameters that are approximately 1.73 times Earth's diameter.

CD-ROM
Solar System PictureShow
Sun, Earth, and Moon

Figure 30-2 The faint corona was a fabulous sight during the eclipse on July 11, 1991 in Baja, California.

However, astronomers can use special filters to observe the chromosphere when the Sun is not eclipsed. The chromosphere appears red, as shown in *Figure 30-1B,* because it emits most strongly in a narrow band of red wavelengths.

The top layer of the Sun's atmosphere, called the **corona,** extends several million kilometers from the top of the chromosphere and has a temperature range of 1 million to 2 million K. The density of the gas in the corona is very low, which explains why the corona is so dim that it can be seen only when the photosphere is blocked by either special instruments, as in a coronagraph, or by the Moon during an eclipse, as in *Figure 30-2.*

Solar Wind The corona of the Sun does not end abruptly. Instead, gas flows outward from the corona at high speeds and forms the **solar wind.** As this wind of charged particles, or ions, flows outward through the entire solar system, it bathes each planet in a flood of particles. At 1 AU, Earth's distance from the Sun, the solar wind flows at a speed of about 400 km/s. The charged particles are deflected by Earth's magnetic field and are trapped in two huge rings in Earth's magnetic field called the Van Allen belts. The high-energy particles in these belts collide with gases in Earth's atmosphere and cause the gases to give off light that we see as the aurora, shown in *Figure 30-3.*

Figure 30-3 The aurora is the result of the particles from the Sun colliding with gases in Earth's atmosphere. It is most easily viewed from regions around the poles of Earth.

Concept Development

One of the basic properties of radiation from heated bodies or objects is that the wavelength at which an object glows most brightly is inversely proportional to the temperature of the emitting object. This explains why the Sun's photosphere emits in visible wavelengths, while the much hotter corona glows most brightly in the X-ray portion of the electromagnetic spectrum. This principle also explains the different colors of stars of different temperatures. Red stars are cool, while blue stars are hot.

✔ Assessment

Knowledge Have each student rank the photosphere, chromosphere, and corona in order of thickness and again in order of temperature. From thickest to thinnest: corona, chromosphere, photosphere. From highest to lowest temperature: corona, chromosphere, photosphere.

Collaborative Learning

Interpersonal Have students brainstorm ideas explaining why the aurora has so many different colors. The colors correspond to different gases in Earth's atmosphere. Colors also depend on the height at which the particles from the Sun collide with the different elements in the gases.

Content Background

Students may wonder why the chromosphere and especially the corona are hotter than the solar surface. The source of this increased heating in the chromosphere and corona lies in the turbulent zone just below the photosphere, where convection causes the gases to churn and overturn. The kinetic energy associated with the motions of these gases is transported by magnetic field lines to higher levels, above the photosphere, where it is deposited as thermal energy.

GLENCOE
Technology

Videotape/DVD
The Planets: Star

NY Core Curriculum Standards

Page 804: St 4 KI 1.2b
Page 805: St 1 Science KI 1 & 3, St 2 KI 1, St 4 KI 1.2b, St 6 KI 2 & 3
Page 806: St 1 Math KI 2, Science KI 1, & 3, St 6 KI 3
Page 807: St 1 Science KI 1 & 3, St 4 KI 2.2a, St 6 KI 4

Project

Logical-Mathematical
Historical numbers of sunspots can be found at earthgeu.com. Have students each make a graph of the annual numbers of sunspots over a period of some decades so they can examine the 11-year cycle of maxima. Students can use their skills in using calculators or computers to graph their data. **L2**

Content Background

Astronomers can measure the Sun's rate of rotation by observing how long it takes a particular sunspot or group of sunspots to go completely around the Sun. The Sun rotates most rapidly at the equator, which completes an entire rotation in 25 days, and most slowly at the poles, which take 35 days to rotate completely. Not only does the rate of solar rotation vary with latitude on the Sun, but also, it varies with depth inside the Sun. This is known from the analysis of subtle pulsations that the solar surface undergoes, which reflect internal density and rates of rotation. The solar core rotates much more rapidly than the surface. The science of analyzing solar pulsations to infer interior conditions is called helioseismology.

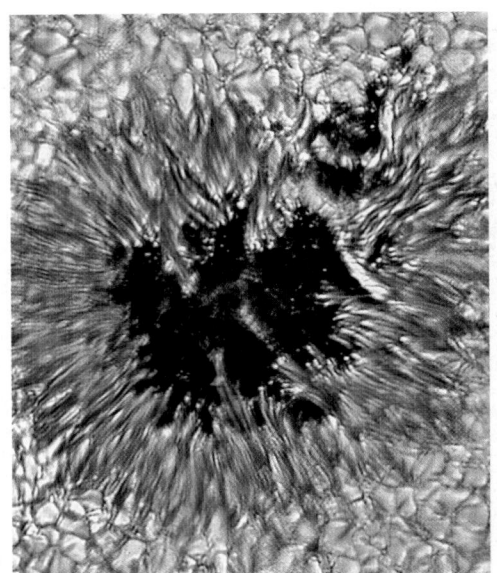

Figure 30-4 Sunspots consist of two regions: the lighter outer ring called the penumbra, and the dark inner ring called the umbra.

Figure 30-5 The dark regions in this X-ray image are coronal holes.

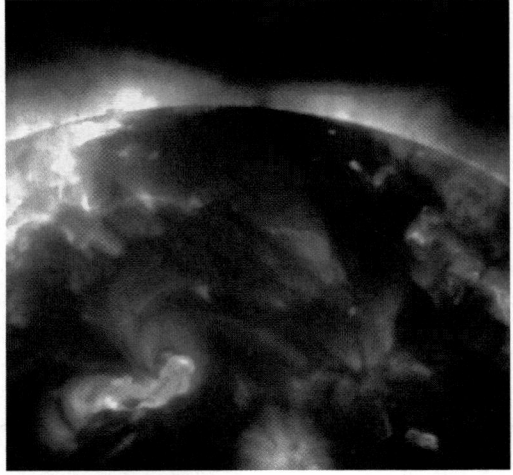

Solar Activity

While the solar wind and layers of the Sun's atmosphere are permanent features, other features on the Sun change over time in a process called solar activity. The Sun's magnetic field disturbs the solar atmosphere periodically and causes new features to appear. The most obvious features are **sunspots,** shown in *Figure 30-4,* which are dark spots on the surface of the photosphere. Sunspots are actually very bright, but they appear darker than the surrounding areas on the Sun because they are cooler. They are located in regions where the Sun's intense magnetic fields poke through the photosphere. These magnetic fields prevent hot gases inside the Sun from rising to the surface and heating the spots. Sunspots typically last two months. They occur in pairs with opposite magnetic polarities—with a north and a south pole like a bar magnet.

Solar Activity Cycle Astronomers have observed that the number of sunspots changes regularly and on average, reaches a maximum number every 11.2 years on average. Scientists therefore hypothesized that the solar activity cycle is 11.2 years in length. However, when the polarity of the Sun's magnetic field is taken into account, the length of the cycle doubles to 22.4 years. The Sun's magnetic field reverses, so that the north magnetic pole becomes the south magnetic pole and vice versa. When the polarities of the Sun's magnetic poles reverse, the polarities of pairs of sunspots also reverse, because sunspots are caused by magnetic fields. Thus, the solar activity cycle starts with minimum spots and progresses to maximum spots. Then the magnetic field reverses in polarity, and the spots start at a minimum number and progress to a maximum number again. The magnetic field then switches back to the original polarity and completes the solar activity cycle.

Other Solar Features Coronal holes, shown in *Figure 30-5,* are often located over sunspot groups. Coronal holes are areas of low density in the gas of the corona. They are the main regions from which the particles that comprise the solar wind escape. These holes are visible in the X ray region of the electromagnetic spectrum.

Demo

Visual-Spatial Label the poles of two bar magnets. Put the north and south poles together to demonstrate that they are opposite. Then, flip one magnet so that the like poles are together, and demonstrate to students that like poles repel. Hold one bar magnet with the north pole pointed up. Explain that the magnetic field of the Sun is aligned like this for 11 years. Then, flip the bar magnet so that the south pole is pointing up, and explain that the Sun's magnetic field is aligned this way for another 11 years. Flip the magnet again so that the north pole is pointing up, and explain that this represents the completion of the 22-year solar activity cycle.

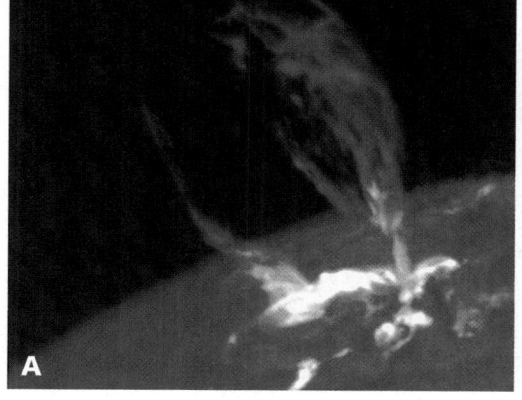
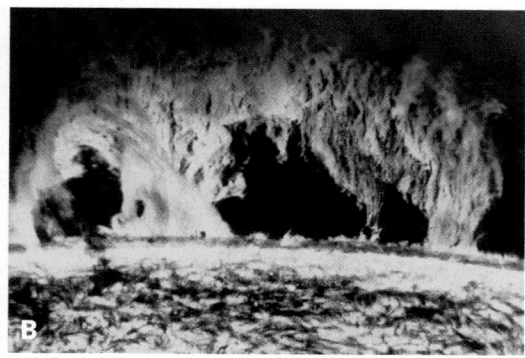

Figure 30-6 This solar flare **(A)** was observed by the National Solar Observatory, and this solar prominence **(B)** was observed by the Big Bear Solar Observatory of the New Jersey Institute of Technology.

Highly active solar flares also are associated with sunspots. **Solar flares** are violent eruptions of particles and radiation from the surface of the Sun, as shown in *Figure 30-6A*. Often, the released particles escape the surface of the Sun in the solar wind and Earth gets bombarded with the particles a few days later. The largest solar flare on record, which occurred in April 2001, hurled particles from the Sun's surface at 7.2 million km/hr.

Another active feature, sometimes associated with flares, is a **prominence**, shown in *Figure 30-6B*, which is an arc of gas that is ejected from the chromosphere, or gas that condenses in the inner corona and rains back to the surface. Prominences can reach temperatures greater than 50 000 K and can last from a few hours to a few months. Like flares, prominences also are associated with sunspots, and hence, occurrences of both vary with the solar activity cycle.

Impact on Earth There is evidence that the solar activity cycle affects climates on Earth. For example, some scientists have found evidence of subtle climate variations within 11-year periods. Also, there were severe weather changes on Earth during the latter half of the 1600s when the solar activity cycle stopped and there were no sunspots for nearly 60 years. No one knows why the Sun's cycle stopped. Those 60 years were known as the "Little Ice Age" because the weather was very cold in Europe and North America during those years.

The Solar Interior

You may be wondering where all the energy that causes solar activity and light comes from. Within the core of the Sun, where the pressure and temperature are extremely high, fusion occurs. **Fusion** is the combining of lightweight nuclei, such as hydrogen, into heavier nuclei. This is the opposite of the process of **fission**, which is the splitting of heavy atomic nuclei into smaller, lighter atomic nuclei.

ENVIRONMENTAL CONNECTION

Environmental Connection

Solar flares can have dramatic effects on Earth, especially in this technological age. When a major flare occurs in a position on the Sun such that the released radiation and particles strike Earth, there are widespread effects. The X-ray radiation reaches Earth in eight minutes and affects the ionization in Earth's upper atmosphere, but it has little effect on the ground. The charged particle burst takes from two to four days to reach Earth's atmosphere, and when it does, it can disrupt the upper atmosphere and the radiation belts. Some particles can even reach the ground, where they can disrupt electrical circuits. A massive solar flare in 1989 triggered the loss of electrical power throughout a large region in Canada and also interrupted radio and telecommunications worldwide.

Using an Analogy

Because of the Sun's rotation, the solar wind does not radiate outward from the Sun directly, but instead describes a spiraling path. The motion of water from a rotary lawn sprinkler is analogous to this motion of the solar wind. As the sprinkler turns, water drops follow curved paths as they move outward. This analogy helps to explain why a solar flare that is observed on the side of the Sun facing Earth will not necessarily affect Earth. For the burst of particles from a flare to reach Earth, the flare must occur at a location on the Sun from which the solar wind's curving path will intersect Earth.

Content Background

Around the time of maximum solar activity, the increased flux of radiation and charged particles from the Sun heats Earth's upper atmosphere, causing it to expand. This, in turn, creates extra drag on Earth-orbiting satellites that can cause them to spiral into the atmosphere. This is what happened to the U.S. *Skylab* space station in 1979, when its orbit decayed and it fell to Earth several years sooner than expected.

Earth Science

Science Field Book

Journal

Have students monitor solar activity on a daily basis for at least a week or two and make entries in their science journals. Students can go to <u>earthgeu.com</u> to obtain this information. Ask students to report on what they found. This project will be most interesting to students around the time of maximum rather than minimum solar activity.

In the core of the Sun, helium is a product of the process in which hydrogen nuclei fuse. The mass of the helium nucleus is less than the combined mass of the hydrogen nuclei, which means that mass is being lost during the process somehow. Albert Einstein's theory of special relativity showed that mass and energy are equivalent, and that matter can be converted into energy and vice versa. This relationship can be expressed as $E = mc^2$, where E is energy measured in joules, m is the quantity of mass that is converted to energy measured in kilograms, and c is the speed of light measured in m/s. This theory explains that the mass lost in the fusion of hydrogen to helium is converted to energy, which powers the Sun. At the Sun's rate of hydrogen fusing, it is about halfway through its lifetime, with another 5 billion years or so left.

Energy from the Sun The quantity of energy that arrives on Earth every day from the Sun is enormous. Above Earth's atmosphere, 1354 J of energy is received in 1 m² per second (1354 W/m²). In other words, thirteen 100-W lightbulbs could be operated with the solar energy that strikes a 1-m² area. However, not all of this energy reaches the ground because some is absorbed and scattered by the atmosphere. You will learn how energy from the Sun can be converted to electricity with solar panels in the *Problem-Solving Lab* on this page.

Problem-Solving Lab

Using Numbers

Calculate energy output from solar panels The energy from the Sun striking the top of Earth's atmosphere is 1354 W/m², about half of which reaches the ground. The energy output is measured in watts, because it is energy received per second. Assume that solar panels can convert about 15 percent of the Sun's energy into electricity.

Analysis
1. How much energy from the Sun reaches the ground per square meter per second?
2. How much of the Sun's energy would a 1-m² solar panel receive per second?

3. After the 1-m² solar panel converts the energy to electricity, how much electricity is available per second?

Thinking Critically
4. How many 1-m² solar panels would be needed to produce 1000 W of electricity for a house?
5. How would a cloudy region affect the energy production of solar panels? Is there anything that could be done to counteract this? Explain.

Applying Earth Science

Many people think that nuclear fusion could be a safe and plentiful source of energy. However, fusion requires very high densities and temperatures, conditions that are very difficult to reproduce on Earth. Fusion has been achieved in hydrogen bombs, where hydrogen nuclei fuse and instantaneously release tremendous amounts of energy. So far, however, sustained and controlled fusion has not been achieved.

Solar Zones If the energy of the Sun is produced in the core, how does it get to the surface before it travels to Earth? The answer lies in the two zones in the solar interior. Above the core is a region called the radiative zone, which extends approximately 86 percent of the way to the photosphere. In this zone, energy is transferred from particle to particle by radiation, as atoms continually absorb energy and then re-emit it. Above the radiative zone is the convective zone. In this zone, moving volumes of gas carry the energy the rest of the way to the Sun's surface through convection, which you learned about in Chapter 11. The radiative and convective zones are illustrated in *Figure 30-7.*

SPECTRA

You are probably familiar with the rainbow that appears when white light is shined through a prism. This rainbow is a **spectrum,** which is visible light arranged according to wavelengths. There are three types of spectra: continuous, emission, and absorption, as shown in *Figure 30-8.* All three types will be discussed on the next few pages. A spectrum that has no breaks in it, such as the one produced when light from an ordinary bulb is shined though a prism, is called a continuous spectrum. A continuous spectrum also can be produced by a glowing solid or liquid, or by a highly compressed, glowing gas. However, if you were to observe a spectrum coming from a non-compressed gas, you would see bright lines at certain wavelengths. This is called an emission spectrum, and the lines are called emission lines. The wavelengths of the lines you see depend on the element being observed, because each element has its own characteristic emission spectrum.

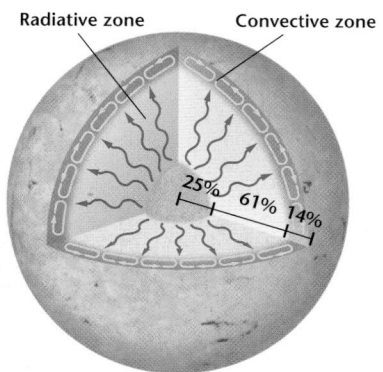

Figure 30-7 It takes about 170 000 years to transfer energy to the surface of the Sun through these zones.

Figure 30-8 A continuous spectrum is produced by a hot solid, liquid, or dense gas. When a cloud of gas is in front of this hot source, an absorption spectrum is produced. A cloud of gas without a hot source behind it will produce an emission spectrum **(A).** The Sun's spectrum **(B)** is an absorption spectrum.

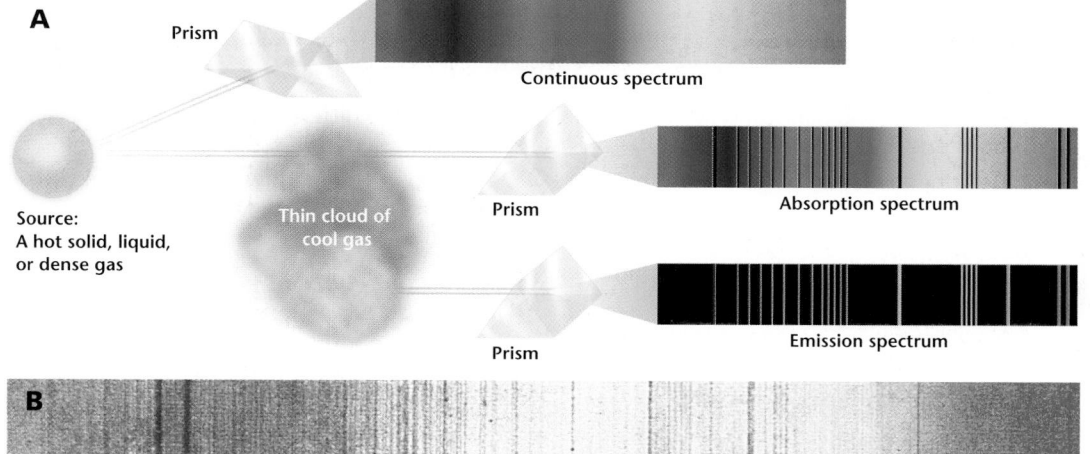

A

Prism

Continuous spectrum

Source:
A hot solid, liquid,
or dense gas

Thin cloud of
cool gas

Prism

Absorption spectrum

Prism

Emission spectrum

B

30.1 *The Sun* **811**

Content Background

Even though electromagnetic radiation travels at the speed of light, it can take a very long time for radiation produced in the Sun's core to emerge at the solar surface. The reason for the slow-down is that in a medium as dense as the deep solar interior, light is readily absorbed by atoms and ions. A particle of radiation, known as a photon, can travel only a very short distance before being absorbed. The atom or ion that absorbs the photon quickly emits it again, but in a random direction. The photon may be re-emitted in the same direction it came from or in some other direction. The path followed by a photon in a dense medium is called a random walk.

Discussion

Interpersonal Have students work in groups to find data tables summarizing the bulk chemical composition of the Sun and of Earth. Have students report on the differences and similarities and discuss them as a class. The Sun is dominated by hydrogen and helium, whereas these two elements are relatively rare on Earth. Students should recall that the Sun and Earth formed from the same material, but that the light-weight elements hydrogen and helium were unable to condense during the formation of the solar system and therefore were not retained by Earth. **COOP LEARN**

Enrichment

The process by which the Sun fuses hydrogen into helium is three step, as follows:

$$^1H + {}^1H \rightarrow {}^2H + e^+ + \upsilon$$
$$^2H + {}^1H \rightarrow {}^3He + \gamma$$
$$^3He + {}^3He \rightarrow {}^4He + {}^1H + {}^1H$$

Check for Understanding

Activity

Have each student create an illustration that summarizes the types of electromagnetic radiation coming from the Sun. Have students identify the layer or zone from which each type of radiation is emitted. ELL P

Reteach

Visual-Spatial Have students each make a graph of the temperature range from the Sun's center to the surface and out to the corona. Graphs should plot temperature against radius. Data can be found at earthgeu.com. L2

✔Assessment

Skill Ask students to discuss the role of convection in the Sun and in Earth. Convection is the mechanism of thermal energy transport in the outer zones of the solar interior. Similarly, convection is responsible for thermal energy transport in Earth's interior.

Interpreting the Illustration

Figure 30-9 The percentages in this illustration total 100.067% due to rounding errors in the data.

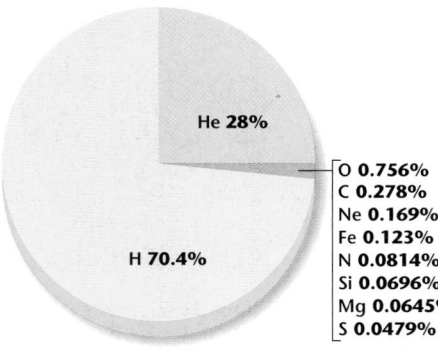

Composition of the Sun by Mass

He 28%

O 0.756%
C 0.278%
Ne 0.169%
Fe 0.123%
N 0.0814%
Si 0.0696%
Mg 0.0645%
S 0.0479%

H 70.4%

Figure 30-9 The Sun is primarily composed of hydrogen and helium. Trace elements in the Sun that are not listed are Li, Be, B, F, Al, P, Cl, Ar, K, Ca, Sc, Tr, V, Cr, Mn, Co, Ni, Cu, and Zn.

Conversely, if you observe the light from the Sun in a spectrum, you will see a series of dark bands. These dark spectral lines are caused by different chemical elements that absorb light at specific wavelengths. This is called an absorption spectrum, and the lines are called absorption lines. Absorption is caused by a cooler gas in front of a source that emits a continuous spectrum. The absorption lines caused by the element in the gas are in the exact same location as the emission lines made by the same element. Thus, by comparing laboratory spectra of different gases with the dark lines in the solar spectrum, it is possible to identify the elements that make up the Sun's outer layers. You will experiment with identifying spectral lines in the *GeoLab* at the end of this chapter.

SOLAR COMPOSITION

The Sun consists of hydrogen, about 70.4 percent by mass, and helium, 28 percent, as well as a small amount of other elements, as illustrated in *Figure 30-9.* This composition is very similar to that of the gas giant planets, which suggests that the Sun and the gas giants represent the composition of the interstellar cloud from which the solar system formed, while the terrestrial planets have lost most of the lightweight gases, as you learned in Chapter 29. The Sun's composition represents that of the galaxy as a whole. Most stars have proportions of the elements similar to the Sun. Hydrogen and helium are the predominant gases in stars, as well as in the entire universe. All other elements are in very small proportions compared to hydrogen and helium.

SECTION ASSESSMENT

1. How do astronomers know what conditions exist inside the Sun?

2. Describe the layers of gas above the Sun's visible surface.

3. How does energy produced in the core of the Sun reach the surface? How long does it take?

4. How are the Sun's magnetic field and its activity cycle related?

5. How are the different types of spectra created?

6. **Thinking Critically** How would the Sun affect Earth if Earth did not have a magnetic field?

SKILL REVIEW

7. **Comparing and Contrasting** Compare and contrast solar flares, prominences, and sunspots. For more help, refer to the *Skill Handbook.*

earthgeu.com/self_check_quiz

SECTION ASSESSMENT

1. from a combination of observations of external conditions and mathematical models of interior conditions

2. The Sun's visible surface, the photosphere, has a temperature of about 5800 K. Above this is the chromosphere, which is about 2500 km thick and reaches a temperature of about 30 000 K. Above this is the corona, which has a temperature ranging

from 1 million to 2 million K.

3. by the radiative and convective regions; about 170 000 years

4. The activity cycle is caused by the solar magnetic field and is on the same time scale as the polarity reversals.

5. Continuous spectra are created by a hot solid, liquid, or dense gas; emission lines are created by low-density, hot gas; and absorption lines are created by a cool gas in front of a hot continuous source.

6. Nothing would protect Earth's surface from the solar wind or solar flare particles. This would effect life and communications.

7. Solar flares are instantaneous releases of large quantities of radiation and particles from active solar regions; prominences also originate from active solar regions and are outflows or arcs of gas; and sunspots are small regions of locally intense magnetic fields that appear dark relative to their surroundings.

SECTION 30.2 *Measuring the Stars*

When you look up at the sky at night, you can often see the brightest stars, even in the city. These stars appear to be fairly isolated from each other. However, away from city lights, you would notice many more stars grouped together.

GROUPS OF STARS

Long ago, many civilizations looked at the brightest stars and named groups of them after animals, mythological characters, or everyday objects. These groups of stars are called **constellations.** Today, we group stars by the 88 constellations named by ancient peoples. Some constellations can be seen all year long, depending on the observer's location. In the northern hemisphere, you can see constellations that appear to move around the north pole of Earth. These constellations are called circumpolar constellations. Ursa Major, also known as the Big Dipper, is a circumpolar constellation for the northern hemisphere.

Unlike circumpolar constellations, the other constellations can be seen only at certain times of the year because of Earth's changing position in its orbit around the Sun, as illustrated in **Figure 30-10.** For example, the constellation Orion can be seen only in the northern hemisphere's winter, and the constellation Hercules can be seen only in the northern hemisphere's summer. This is why constellations are classified as summer, fall, winter, and spring constellations. For maps of the constellations, see *Appendix K.*

Star Clusters Although the stars in constellations appear to be close to each other, very few are gravitationally bound to one other. The reason that they appear to be close together is that human eyes can't distinguish how far or near stars actually are. Two stars could

OBJECTIVES

- **Describe** *star distribution and distance.*
- **Classify** *the types of stars.*
- **Summarize** *the interrelated properties of stars.*

VOCABULARY

constellation
binary star
parallax
apparent magnitude
absolute magnitude
luminosity
Hertzsprung-Russell diagram
main sequence

Figure 30-10 Depending on the time of year, only certain constellations are visible. (not to scale)

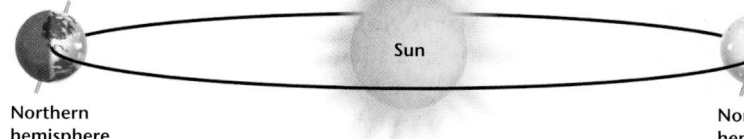

Hercules

Sun

Northern hemisphere summer

Orion

Northern hemisphere winter

30.2 *Measuring the Stars* **813**

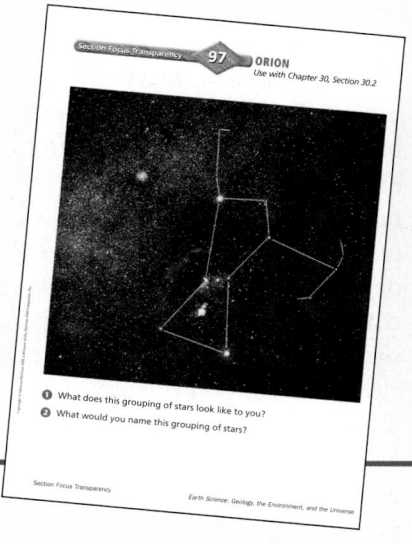

Content Background

Binary stars provide the best opportunity for astronomers to measure the masses of stars. Stellar masses are measured using another form of Kepler's third law. The masses of the two stars can be found if both the orbital period and semimajor axis can be observed. Typical stellar masses range from just below 0.1 times the Sun's mass up to about 50 solar masses.

Interpreting the Photos

Figures 30-11A and **30-11B**
The more dense a star cluster is, the more frequently stars come close to each other. Stars affect each other through their gravitational forces, and close encounters between stars can alter their orbits. The result of many encounters is a rounded, smooth cluster shape, as in the globular cluster shown in **Figure 30-11B.** Clusters that are not so dense take a lot longer to reach this state. **Figure 30-11A,** depicts a relatively young cluster with fewer members and an irregular overall shape. Globular clusters are not only dense, but also are the oldest objects in the galaxy, and thus, many close encounters between stars have occurred in such clusters.

Figure 30-11 The Pleiades **(A)** is an open cluster, and M13 **(B)** is a densely packed globular cluster.

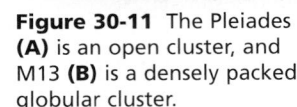

Figure 30-12 The bright star Sirius and its companion white dwarf, on the left, are a binary system.

appear to be right next to each other, almost touching, but one might be 1 trillion km away from Earth, and the other might be 2 trillion km away from Earth. However, by measuring distances to stars and observing how they interact with each other, scientists can determine which stars are gravitationally bound to each other. A group of stars that are gravitationally bound to each other is called a cluster. The Pleiades, in the constellation Taurus, shown in *Figure 30-11A,* is an open cluster because the stars are not densely packed. In contrast, a globular cluster is a group of stars that are densely packed into a spherical shape, such as M13, in the constellation Hercules, shown in *Figure 30-11B.*

Binaries When only two stars are gravitationally bound together and orbit a common center of mass, they are called a **binary star.** More than half of the stars in the sky are either binary stars or members of multiple-star systems. The bright star Sirius is actually a binary system, as shown in *Figure 30-12.* Most binary stars appear to be single stars to the human eye, even with a telescope. The two stars are usually too close together to appear separately and one of the two is often much brighter than the other. Astronomers are able to identify binary stars through several methods. For example, even if only one star is visible, accurate measurements can show that its position shifts back and forth as it orbits the center of mass between it and the unseen companion star. Also, the orbital plane of a binary system can sometimes be seen edge-on from Earth. In such cases, the two stars alternately block each other out and cause the total brightness of the two-star system to dip each time one star eclipses the other. This type of binary star is called an eclipsing binary.

814 CHAPTER 30 *Stars*

NY Core Curriculum Standards

Page 814: St 1 Science KI 1, St 4 KI 1.1a & 1.2b, St 6 KI 1 & 3

Page 815: St 1 Math KI 1, 2, & Science KI 1, St 4 KI 1.1a, 1.1f, & 1.2b, St 6 KI 1, 2, & 3

STELLAR POSITIONS AND DISTANCES

Astronomers use two units of measure for long distances. One, which you are probably familiar with, is a light-year (ly). A light-year is the distance that light travels in one year, equal to 9.461×10^{12} km. Astronomers often use a larger unit than a light-year, a parsec. A parsec (pc) is equal to 3.26 ly, or 3.086×10^{13} km.

Precise position measurements are an important tool for finding distances to stars. To estimate the distance of stars from Earth, astronomers make use of the fact that nearby stars shift in position as observed from Earth. This apparent shift in position caused by the motion of the observer is called **parallax.** In this case, the motion of the observer is the change in position of Earth as it orbits the Sun. As Earth moves from one side of its orbit to the opposite side, a nearby star appears to be shifting back and forth, as illustrated in *Figure 30-13.* The closer the star, the larger the shift. The distance to a star can be estimated from its parallax shift. In fact, a parsec is defined as the distance at which an object has a parallax of 1 arcsecond. Using the parallax technique, astronomers only could find accurate distances to stars up to about 100 pc, or approximately 300 ly, away until recently. Now with advancements in technology, such as the *Hipparcos* satellite, astronomers can find accurate distances up to 500 pc by using parallax. In the *MiniLab* later in this section, you will experiment with distance and how it affects parallax shifts.

Basic Properties of Stars

The basic properties of stars include diameter, mass, brightness, energy output (power), surface temperature, and composition. The diameters of stars range from as little as 0.1 times the Sun's diameter to hundreds of times larger, while their masses vary from a little less than 0.01 to 20 or more times the Sun's mass. The most massive stars can be as massive as 50 to 100 Suns but are extremely rare.

Figure 30-13 The shift in position of a star as viewed from opposite sides of Earth's orbit around the Sun is called parallax.

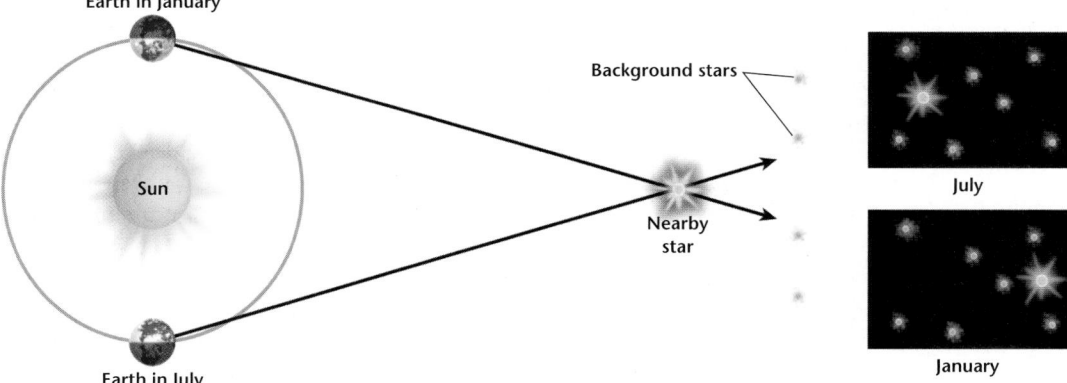

Discussion

Ask students how they think astronomers can tell whether a close pair of stars are a true binary system (two stars in mutual orbit) or an optical double, which refers to a pair of stars at different distances that happen to appear to be close together in the sky. Stars in a true binary system must be orbiting a common center of mass. If there is orbital motion, it may be seen directly, or it may be discovered through Doppler shifts in the spectra of the stars.

Content Background

The unit of distance called the parsec is derived from stellar parallax measurements. Ask students to envision a very long, skinny right triangle whose base is 1 AU and whose apex angle is 1 arcsecond. One arcsecond is equal to 1/60 of an arcminute, which in turn is equal to 1/60 of a degree. Thus, an arcsecond is 1/3600 of a degree. The length of the other leg of this triangle is 206 265 times the length of the base. This is the parsec, which stands for "parallax second." More specifically, one parsec is the distance to a star whose parallax angle (the apex angle as just described) is one arcsecond. Thus, one parsec = 206 265 AU, which is 3.26 ly.

Enrichment

Have interested students calculate the length of a light-year for themselves, multiplying the speed of light ($c = 2.998 \times 10^8$ m/s) by the number of seconds in a year. The number of seconds in a year is $365.24 \times 24 \times 60 \times 60 = 3.156 \times 10^7$ s; multiplying this times the speed of light yields 1 ly = 9.46×10^{15} m.

Using Scientific Terms

The words *luminosity* and *power* mean exactly the same thing: energy per second. A physicist uses power to describe what an astronomer calls luminosity. In the SI system of units, power is expressed in watts, where 1 watt = 1 joule/second.

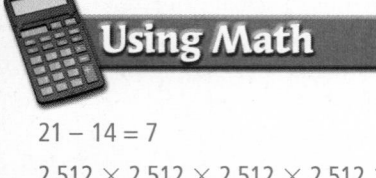

Using Math

$21 - 14 = 7$

$2.512 \times 2.512 \times 2.512 \times 2.512 \times 2.512 \times 2.512 \times 2.512 = 2.512^7 = 631.2$

Discussion

Lead students in a discussion of the relationship between absolute magnitude and luminosity. This will help students understand why astronomers go to the trouble of defining and measuring absolute magnitudes. Luminosity is an intrinsic property of a star, and it therefore does not depend on distance. Thus, to determine luminosity, a star's distance must be taken into account. Because astronomers normally measure stellar brightnesses using the magnitude system, the use of absolute magnitudes is a convenient way to allow for distance. Once the absolute magnitude is determined, finding a star's luminosity is a simple matter of using a conversion factor.

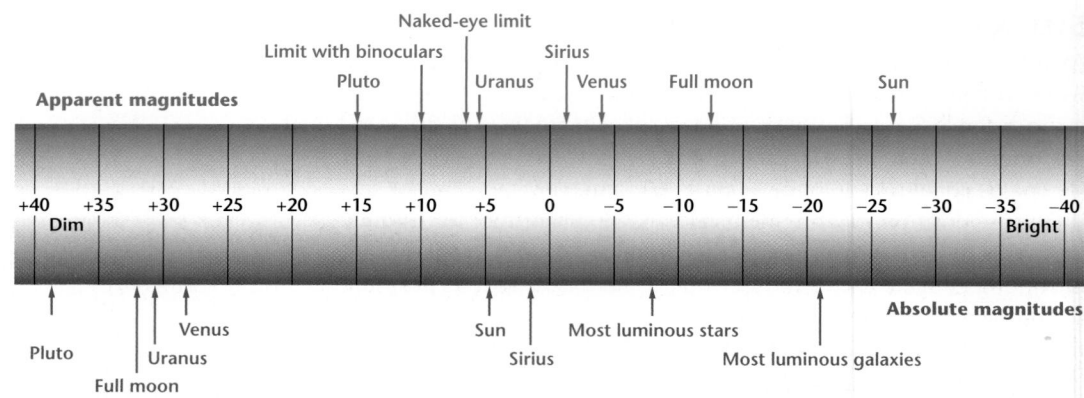

Figure 30-14 This shows the apparent and absolute magnitudes of some familiar celestial objects.

Using Math

Using Numbers The difference in brightness between a magnitude +12 star and a magnitude +9 star is $2.512 \times 2.512 \times 2.512 = 2.512^3 = 15.85$. What is the difference in brightness between a magnitude +21 star and a magnitude +14 star?

Magnitude One of the most basic observable properties of a star is how bright it appears. The ancient Greeks established a classification system based on the brightnesses of stars. The brightest stars were given a ranking of +1, the next brightest +2, and so on. Today's astronomers still use this system, but they have refined it.

Apparent Magnitude Astronomers have defined the ancient Greek system of classification as **apparent magnitude,** or how bright a star appears to be. In this system, a difference of 5 magnitudes corresponds to a factor of 100 in brightness. Thus, a magnitude +1 star is 100 times brighter than a magnitude +6 star. A difference of 1 magnitude corresponds to a factor of 2.512 in brightness. The modern magnitude system extends to objects that are both brighter and fainter than those that were included in the ancient Greek system. For objects brighter than magnitude +1, such as the Sun, the Moon, Venus, and some of the very brightest stars, negative numbers are assigned. The apparent magnitudes of several objects are shown in **Figure 30-14.**

Absolute Magnitude Apparent magnitude does not actually indicate how bright a star is, because it does not take distance into account. A faint star can appear to be very bright because it is relatively close to Earth, while a bright star can appear to be faint because it is far away. To account for this phenomenon, astronomers have developed another classification system for brightness. **Absolute magnitude** is the brightness an object would have if it were placed at a distance of 10 pc. The classification of stars by absolute magnitude allows comparisons that are based on how bright the stars would appear at equal distances from an observer. The absolute magnitudes for several objects are shown in **Figure 30-14.** The disadvantage of absolute magnitude is that it can be calculated only when the actual distance to a star is known.

Across the Curriculum

Math Real stars don't fall neatly into the whole-number magnitude classes assigned by the ancient Greeks, so fractional magnitudes must be used. Furthermore, telescopes enable astronomers to observe stars that are much too faint for the human eye to detect, so magnitudes greater than 6 must be used. The faintest objects visible with the *Hubble Space Telescope* have magnitudes greater than 30. Also, the original category of first magnitude includes stars that have a wide range of brightnesses, so magnitudes of zero or smaller must be used. For example, Sirius, the brightest star in the sky, has a magnitude of −1.47. A comprehensive expression using logarithms to relate a magnitude difference to a brightness ratio is used by astronomers; this expression allows for both negative and fractional values. The expression is $m_1 - m_2 = 2.5\log(b_2/b_1)$, where m_1 and m_2 are two magnitudes, and b_2/b_1 is the corresponding ratio of the brightnesses. The term *log* refers to the common logarithm, base 10.

Luminosity Apparent magnitudes do not give an actual measure of energy output. To measure the energy output from the surface of a star per second, called its **luminosity,** an astronomer must know both the star's apparent magnitude and how far away it is. The brightness we observe for a star depends on both its luminosity and its distance, and because brightness diminishes with the square of the distance, a correction must be made for distance. Luminosity is measured in units of energy emitted per second, or watts. The Sun's luminosity is about 3.85×10^{26} W. This is equivalent to 3.85×10^{24} 100-W lightbulbs! The values for other stars vary widely, from about 0.0001 to more than a million times the Sun's luminosity. No other stellar property varies by so much.

Spectra of Stars

You have learned that the Sun has dark absorption lines at specific wavelengths in its spectrum. Other stars also have dark absorption lines in their spectra and are classified according to their patterns of absorption lines.

Classification Stars are assigned spectral types in the following order: O, B, A, F, G, K, and M. Each class is subdivided into more specific divisions with numbers from 0 to 9. For example, a star may be classified as being a type A4 or A5. The classes were originally based only on the pattern of spectral lines, but astronomers later discovered that the classes correspond to stellar temperatures, with the O stars being the hottest and the M stars being the coolest. Thus, by examination of a star's spectrum, it is possible to estimate its temperature. The Sun is a type G2 star, which corresponds to a surface temperature of about 5800 K. Surface temperatures range from about 50 000 K for the hottest O stars to as low as 2000 K for the coolest M stars.

MiniLab

Parallax in the Classroom

Model stellar parallax and the change in parallax angle with distance.

Procedure

1. Place a meterstick at a fixed position and attach a 4-m piece of string to each end.
2. Stand away from the meterstick and hold the two strings together to form a triangle. Be sure to hold the strings taut. Measure your distance from the meterstick. Record your measurement.
3. Measure the angle between the two pieces of string with a protractor. Record your measurement of the angle.
4. Repeat steps 2 and 3 for different distances from the meterstick by shortening or lengthening the string.
5. Make a graph of the angles versus their distance from the meterstick.

Analyze and Conclude

1. What does the length of the meterstick represent? The angle?
2. What does the graph show? How does parallax angle depend on distance?
3. Are the angles that you measured similar to actual stellar parallax angles? Explain.

Resource Manager

GeoLab and MiniLab Worksheets, p. 121
L2

Skill Ask students to use their results to define a new unit of distance that corresponds to the distance to a meterstick whose parallax angle is 1°. This unit of distance would be 57.3 m.

MiniLab

Purpose
Students will learn about stellar parallax by measuring parallax angles in the classroom.

Process Skills
use numbers, recognize spatial relationships, measure in SI, formulate models

Materials
meterstick, string, protractor, graph paper

Teaching Strategies
This lab is best performed in groups of three. One student can hold the meterstick, one can hold the strings, and the other can make the measurements.

Safety Precautions
Make sure that students wear goggles and aprons during the lab.

Troubleshooting
• Make sure that students hold the strings taut.
• Make sure that the students use very different distances from the meterstick for their multiple measurements. The non-linear relationship is best illustrated when students use very different distances.
• Refer students to **Figure 30-13** to answer question 1.

Expected Results
Students will find that the angle between the strings diminishes as the distance from the meterstick becomes longer. This is analogous to the decrease of a stellar parallax angle with increasing stellar distance.

Analyze and Conclude
1. The meterstick represents 2 AU. The angle represents the parallax angle.
2. The graph shows the relationship between parallax angle and distance. This is an inverse proportionality.
3. The angles measured in this experiment are far larger than any actual stellar parallax angles.

Interpreting the Photo

Figure 30-15 Astronomers often use black and white spectra. The spectra pictured here are actually computer generated, based on real stellar data.

Tying to Previous Knowledge

Students' knowledge of atomic structure (discussed in Chapter 3) can help them understand why spectral classes of stars depend on temperature. The electrons orbiting the nucleus of an atom are responsible for forming spectral lines. Each element has its own unique pattern of electron orbits, and this pattern determines the wavelengths of spectral lines that the element can create.

Content Background

The spectral-line wavelengths of an element change if one or more electrons are missing—that is, if the gas is ionized. In a hot gas, electrons are freed by collisions between atoms. The degree of ionization, or loss of electrons, depends on temperature. Thus, a hot star will have a different spectrum from that of a cool star, because in the hot star, more of the atoms are ionized, and ions have different spectra from those of atoms. Two stars with identical compositions but different temperatures can have very different spectral lines.

Figure 30-15 These are the typical black and white absorption spectra of a class B5 star **(A)**, a class F5 star **(B)**, a class K5 star **(C)**, and a class M5 star **(D)**.

All stars, including the Sun, have nearly identical compositions, despite the differences in their spectra, shown in *Figure 30-15*. The differences in the appearance of their spectra are almost entirely a result of temperature effects. Hotter stars have fairly simple spectra while cooler stars have spectra with more lines. The coolest stars have bands in their spectra due to molecules, such as titanium oxide, in their atmospheres. Typically, about 73 percent of a star's mass is hydrogen, about 25 percent is helium, and the remaining 2 percent is composed of all the other elements. While there are some variations in the composition of stars, particularly in that final 2 percent, all stars have this general composition.

Wavelength Shifts Spectral lines provide other information about stars in addition to composition and temperature. Spectral lines are shifted in wavelength by motion between the source of light and the observer. The shifts in spectral lines are an example of the Doppler effect.

Figure 30-16 As a star moves towards or away from an observer, light is blueshifted or redshifted, respectively.

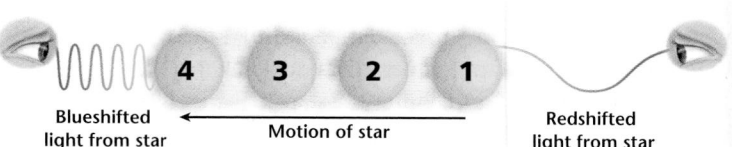

Cultural Diversity

Antonia Maury (1866–1952) Antonia Maury was born in Cold Spring, New York in 1866. From early childhood she was immersed in science. Her younger sister was a paleontologist, her father an editor of a geographic magazine. She worked for 25 years at the Harvard College Observatory. Her focus was the study of stellar spectra, wavelengths of the light from stars. She improved upon existing method of the classification of spectral lines that correspond to different stars. Students will learn more about spectral lines in the GeoLab in this chapter. Maury's system was later improved upon by Annie Cannon, but Maury's classification system is still an integral aspect of theoretical astrophysics.

If a star is moving toward the observer, the spectral lines are shifted toward shorter wavelengths, or blueshifted. However, if the star is moving away, the wavelengths become longer, or redshifted, as illustrated in *Figure 30-16*. The higher the speed, the larger the shift, and thus careful measurements of spectral line wavelengths can be used to determine the speed of a star's motion.

Because there is no Doppler shift for motion that is sideways to the line of sight, astronomers can learn only about the portion of a star's motion that is directed toward or away from Earth. The Doppler shift in spectral lines can be used to detect binary stars as they move about their center of mass towards and away from Earth with each orbit.

H-R Diagrams The properties of mass, luminosity, temperature, and diameter are closely related. Each class of star has a specific mass, luminosity, magnitude, temperature, and diameter. These relationships can be demonstrated on a graph called the **Hertzsprung-Russell diagram** (H-R diagram) with absolute magnitude plotted on the vertical axis and temperature or spectral type plotted on the horizontal axis, as shown in *Figure 30-17*. This graph was first plotted in the early twentieth century. An H-R diagram with luminosity plotted on the vertical axis looks very similar to the one in *Figure 30-17*.

About 90 percent of stars, including the Sun, fall along a broad strip of the H-R diagram called the **main sequence,** which runs diagonally from the upper-left corner, where hot, luminous stars are represented, to the lower-right corner, where cool, dim stars are represented. The interrelatedness of the properties of these stars indicates that all these stars have similar internal structures and functions.

Figure 30-17 This H-R diagram shows the relationship between absolute magnitude, surface temperature, and spectral type. Mass decreases from left to right, while luminosity increases from bottom to top.

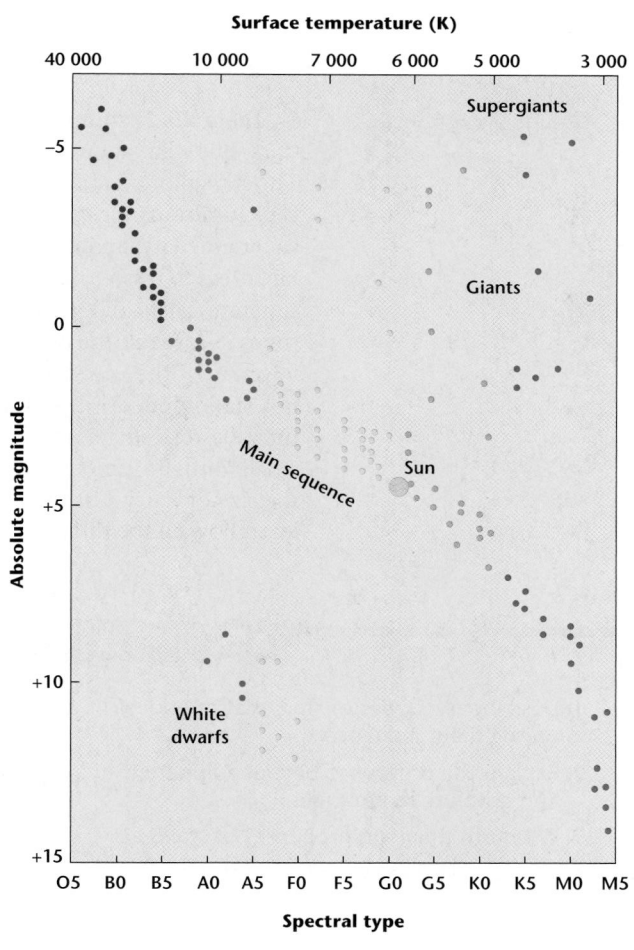

Sound waves undergo shifts similar to Doppler shifts. The shifts in sound waves are much easier to observe in everyday situations. Ask students whether they have ever noticed the change in pitch of a police or ambulance siren as the emergency vehicle passed by. Ask them whether the pitch of the sound became higher or lower. Higher as it approached, and lower as it receded. How do the changes in pitch compare with redshifts and blueshifts? It is analogous.

Content Background

The terms *red giant* and *white dwarf* suggest that stars have colors. This is indeed what the human eye sees. For example, Betelgeuse, the bright red giant in Orion's shoulder, looks reddish in color, while Rigel, one of Orion's feet, has a bluish white color. Stellar color differences are actually rather subtle, because all stars emit light over the full visible range and are therefore basically white. The reason for the slight differences in color is that the peak emission, the wavelength at which a star emits most strongly, depends on the surface temperature of the star. A hot star emits most strongly in the blue or even the ultraviolet portion of the spectrum, whereas a cool star emits most strongly in the red or the infrared portion. The Sun, which is intermediate in temperature, is brightest in the yellow portion of the spectrum.

Applying Earth Science

Students may be interested to know that police make use of the Doppler effect in timing the speeds of cars. Radar or an infrared laser emission from a radar gun is reflected from an oncoming car and is shifted in wavelength by the motion of the car. The device has circuitry to measure the wavelength shift and determine the car's speed. Ask students whether this is a redshift or a blueshift. a blueshift

Differentiated Instruction

English-Language Learners The Hertzsprung-Russell diagram is a useful way to summarize the properties of stars in a visual way so that English-language learners can focus on content. Use the diagram to summarize the brightnesses, temperatures, spectral types (stellar classes), and masses of stars. **ELL**

NY Core Curriculum Standards

Page 818: St 1 Science KI 1, St 4 KI 1.1a & 1.2b, St 6 KI 2 & 5
Page 819: St 1 Science KI 1 & 3, St 4 KI 1.2b, St 6 KI 1, 2, & 3

Reinforcement

Ask students to summarize what kinds of information can be obtained from observations of stellar positions, brightnesses, and spectra. positions: motions, distances, and distribution; brightnesses: luminosities; spectra: compositions, temperatures, and motions through the Doppler shift.

Reteach

Intrapersonal A different approach to teaching students about stellar properties is to have each student pick a particular star and learn as much as possible about that one star. Students can each find out a star's name, its designation in different catalogs, its magnitude, its position, its spectral type, its mass, its luminosity, and so on, and then write reports summarizing what they found. A comparison of stars chosen by different students can then be used to emphasize the range of properties that stars can have. L2

✓Assessment

Knowledge Ask students what they could conclude about the properties of a star that lies in the upper center of the H-R diagram, above the A stars on the main sequence. This star would have a midrange temperature of around 10 000 K, and it would be a giant or supergiant.

Table 30-2 Properties of Main-Sequence Stars

Spectral Type	Mass*	Surface Temperature (K)	Luminosity*	Radius*
O5	40.0	40 000	5×10^5	18.0
B5	6.5	15 500	800	3.8
A5	2.1	8500	20	1.7
F5	1.3	6580	2.5	1.2
G5	0.9	5520	0.8	0.9
K5	0.7	4130	0.2	0.7
M5	0.2	2800	0.008	0.3

*These properties are given relative to the Sun. For example, an O5 star has a mass 40 times that of the Sun, or $40 \times 1.99 \times 10^{30}$ kg = 7.96×10^{31} kg. The mass, luminosity, and radius of the Sun are 1.99×10^{30} kg, 3.846×10^{26} W, and 6.96×10^5 km, respectively.

Table 30-2 summarizes the basic properties of main sequence stars. But what about the stars that do not lie on the main sequence? The stars plotted at the upper right of the H-R diagram are cool, yet very luminous. Because cool surfaces emit much less radiation per square meter than hot ones do, these cool stars must have large surface areas to be so bright. For this reason, these larger, cool, luminous stars are called red giants. Red giants are so large—more than 100 times as large as the Sun in some cases—that Earth would be swallowed up if the Sun were to become a red giant! Conversely, the dim, hot stars plotted in the lower-lefthand corner of the H-R diagram must be very small, or else they would be far more luminous. These small, dim, hot stars are called white dwarfs. A white dwarf is about the size of Earth but has a mass about as large as the Sun's. You will learn how all the different stars are formed in the following section.

SECTION ASSESSMENT

1. Describe two types of stars that are not on the main sequence.
2. Explain the difference between apparent and absolute magnitudes.
3. What are the main properties of stars?
4. How do astronomers know that some stars are binary stars?
5. **Thinking Critically** How do the Sun's properties compare with those of other stars?

SKILL REVIEW

6. **Interpreting Diagrams** Use the H-R diagram in **Figure 30-17** to describe the properties of an A and an M star on the main sequence. For more help, refer to the *Skill Handbook*.

earthgeu.com/self_check_quiz

SECTION ASSESSMENT

1. Giants have larger diameters and greater luminosities than main sequence stars; white dwarfs are hot but dim, and small.
2. Apparent magnitude refers to the observed magnitude of a star; absolute magnitude is the magnitude a star would have if it were located 10 pc from Earth.
3. mass, luminosity, surface temperature, diameter, and composition
4. by measuring position for orbital motion, and by looking for dips in brightness resulting from eclipses by the companion star
5. The Sun is average or close to average in all the basic properties.
6. An A star is hotter and much more luminous than an M star, as well as more massive.

Using observations as their guide, astronomers have developed models of stars that successfully explain the properties that you have just learned about. These models, like the solar model, are based on equations describing physical processes that occur inside stars. However, these models are accepted only when they reproduce the external properties that have been observed.

BASIC STRUCTURE OF STARS

Mass governs a star's temperature, luminosity, and diameter. In fact, astronomers have discovered that the mass and the composition of a star determine nearly all its other properties. The more massive a star is, the greater the gravity pressing inward, and the hotter and denser the star must be inside to balance gravity. The temperature inside a star governs the rate of nuclear reactions, which in turn determines the star's energy output, or luminosity. The balance between gravity squeezing inward and pressure from nuclear fusion and radiation pushing outward, called hydrostatic equilibrium, must hold for any stable star; otherwise, the star would expand or contract, as illustrated in *Figure 30-18*. This balance is governed by the mass of a star.

Fusion Inside a star, conditions vary in much the same way that they do inside the Sun. The density and temperature increase toward the center, where energy is generated by nuclear fusion. Stars on the main sequence all produce energy by fusing hydrogen into helium, as the Sun does. Stars that are not on the main sequence either fuse different elements in their cores or do not undergo fusion at all.

Fusion reactions involving elements other than hydrogen can occur. Once a star's core has been converted into helium, the helium may fuse to form carbon if the temperature is high enough. At even higher temperatures, carbon can react with helium to form oxygen, then neon, then magnesium, and then silicon. Other types of reactions can produce even heavier elements, but few heavier than iron. Each of these reactions produces energy according to the equation $E = mc^2$ as a small fraction of mass is converted into energy. This energy stabilizes a star by producing the pressure needed to counteract gravity.

OBJECTIVES

- **Explain** *how astronomers learn about the internal structure of stars.*
- **Describe** *how the Sun will change during its lifetime and how it will end up.*
- **Compare** *the evolutions of stars of different masses.*

VOCABULARY

nebula
protostar
neutron star
supernova
black hole

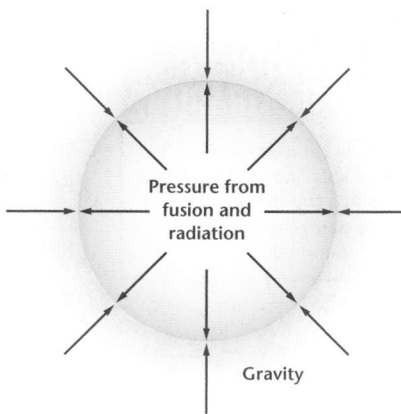

Figure 30-18 This star is stable and will not expand or contract.

Pressure from fusion and radiation

Gravity

30.3 Stellar Evolution **821**

Section 30.3

Prepare

Section Background

For section content background, refer to **Stellar Evolution** on page 804D.

Preplanning

Refer to the Chapter Organizer on pages 804A–B.

1 Focus

Section Focus

Before presenting the lesson, display **Section Focus Transparency 98** on the overhead projector. **L1** **ELL**

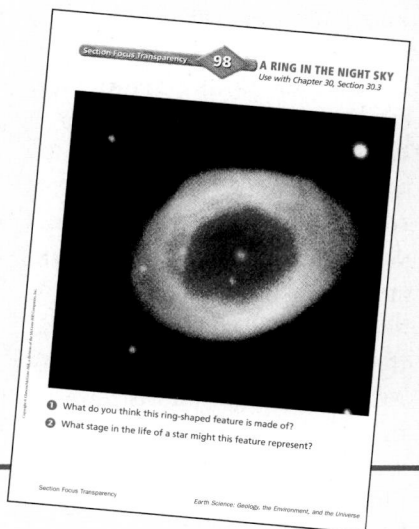

Section Focus Transparency **98** **A RING IN THE NIGHT SKY**
Use with Chapter 30, Section 30.3

❶ What do you think this ring-shaped feature is made of?
❷ What stage in the life of a star might this feature represent?

Section Focus Transparency   *Earth Science: Geology, the Environment, and the Universe*

Resource Manager

Section Focus Transparency 98 **L1** **ELL**
Study Guide for Content Mastery, pp. 193–194 **L2**

Tying to Previous Knowledge

Many people expect that, because the Sun is average in its physical properties, there must be comparable numbers of stars both more and less massive. Stars smaller in mass are far more numerous. Stars more massive are extremely rare. The Sun is average only in the sense that its properties fall in the middle of the range for all stars.

NY Core Curriculum Standards

Page 820: St 1 Science KI 1, St 4 KI 1.2b, St 6 KI 1, 2, & 3
Page 821: St 1 Science KI 1, St 4 KI 1.2b, St 6 KI 1, 2, 3, & 4

Discussion

Every stable object, including a star, a planet, a moon, and a basketball, is in hydrostatic equilibrium. Ask students what forces are in balance for each object, keeping it in equilibrium. A star is stabilized by a balance between inward gravity and outward gas pressure; a planet and a moon balance inward gravity with rigid body forces and fluid pressure (if they are partially fluid); and the inward force on a basketball is the tension in the outer shell, which is balanced by air pressure.

Tying to Previous Knowledge

Infrared radiation is sometimes known as heat radiation, because we sense it as heat even though we can't see it with our eyes. Ask students to imagine a stovetop with several electric burners, all turned off except one, which is set at a low temperature. If they were to wave their hands over the stovetop, students could tell right away which burner is on because their skin would sense the infrared radiation from it. Astronomers detect protostars in the same manner by the infrared radiation coming from these hotspots within cold interstellar gas clouds.

Using an Analogy

When a star uses up its nuclear fuel, its source of internal pressure diminishes and the star will contract unless it experiences a new source of pressure. This is similar to a balloon with a leak: when the air escapes, the balloon contracts because the inward force of the tension in the rubber remains while the outward pressure decreases.

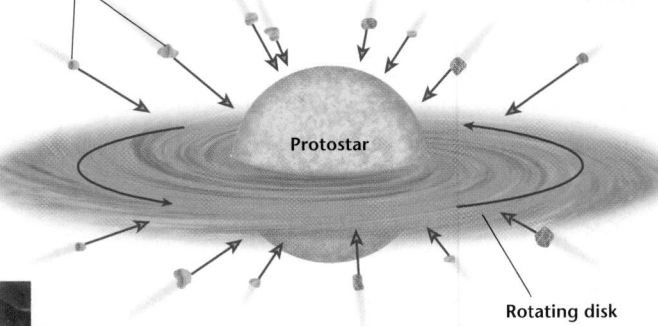

Figure 30-19 A protostar, formed from a disk of gas and dust **(A),** will become a star when fusion begins. The Triffid Nebula **(B)** is illuminated by new stars, as shown by the *Hubble Space Telescope.*

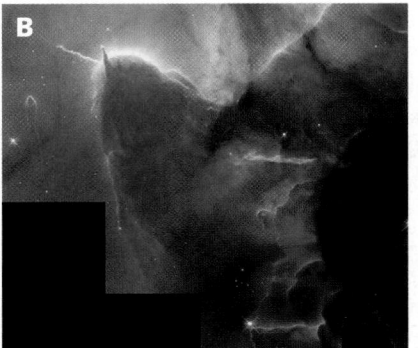

NATIONAL GEOGRAPHIC

To learn more about the *Hubble Space Telescope,* go to the National Geographic Expedition on page 902.

STELLAR EVOLUTION AND LIFE CYCLES

A star changes as it ages because its internal composition changes as nuclear fusion reactions in the star's core convert one element into another. As a star's core composition changes, its density increases, its temperature rises, and its luminosity increases. Eventually, the nuclear fuel runs out. Then the star's internal structure and mechanism for producing pressure must change to counteract gravity.

Star Formation All stars form in much the same manner as the Sun did. The formation of a star begins with a cloud of interstellar gas and dust, called a **nebula** (*pl.* nebulae), which collapses on itself as a result of its own gravity. As the cloud contracts, its rotation forces it into a disk shape with a hot condensed object at the center, called a **protostar,** as illustrated in *Figure 30-19A.* The condensed object will become a new star. A protostar is brightest at infrared wavelengths.

Fusion Begins Eventually, the temperature inside a protostar becomes hot enough for nuclear fusion reactions to begin. The first reaction to ignite is always the conversion of hydrogen to helium. Once this reaction begins, the star becomes stable because it then has sufficient internal heat to produce the pressure needed to balance gravity. The object is then truly a star and takes its place on the main sequence according to its mass. A new star often illuminates the gas and dust surrounding it, as shown in *Figure 30-19B.*

THE SUN'S LIFE CYCLE

What happens during a star's life cycle depends on its mass. For example, as a star like the Sun converts hydrogen into helium in its core, it gradually becomes more luminous because the core density and temperature rise slowly and increase the reaction rate. It takes

Differentiated Instruction

Gifted The reason that a star becomes a red giant after using up its core hydrogen is not obvious, even to experienced astronomers. Interested students may ask about this. The main reason for the expansion of a star into a red giant is that after hydrogen fusion stops in the inner core of the star, the same reaction continues in a shell outside the core. This shell source emits huge quantities of energy, which cannot escape quickly because the outer layers of the star are opaque—that is, the gas absorbs light very readily. Therefore, the energy from the shell source becomes trapped in the outer layers of the star, forcing these layers to expand. As these outer layers expand, they cool because the pressure decreases, and thus the temperature at the surface decreases. As the star expands and its luminosity increases as a result of its increased surface area, it also becomes redder (cooler). Thus, a former main sequence star becomes a red giant. **L3**

about 10 billion years for a star with the mass of the Sun to convert all of the hydrogen in its core into helium. Thus, such a star has a main sequence lifetime of 10 billion years.

Only the innermost 10 percent or so of a star's mass can undergo reactions because temperatures outside of this core never get hot enough for reactions to occur. Thus, when the hydrogen in its core is gone, a star has a helium center and outer layers made of hydrogen-dominated gas. Some hydrogen continues to react in a thin layer at the outer edge of the helium core, as illustrated in *Figure 30-20.* The energy produced in this layer forces the outer layers of the star to expand and cool. The star then becomes a red giant, because its luminosity increases while its surface temperature decreases due to the expansion.

While the star is a red giant, it loses gas from its outer layers. The star is so large that its surface gravity is very low and thus the outer layers can be driven away by small expansions and contractions or pulsations, of the star due to instability. Meanwhile, the core of the star becomes hot enough, at 100 million K, for helium to react and form carbon. The star contracts back to a more normal size, where it again becomes stable for awhile. The helium-reaction phase lasts only about one-tenth as long as the earlier hydrogen-burning phase. Afterwards, when the helium in the core is all used up, the star is left with a core made of carbon.

A Nebula Once Again A star of the Sun's mass never becomes hot enough for carbon to react, so the star's energy production ends at this point. The outer layers expand once again and are driven off entirely by pulsations that develop in the outer layers. This shell of gas is called a planetary nebula. It has nothing to do with planets, despite its name. In the center of a planetary nebula, shown in *Figure 30-21,* the core of the star becomes exposed as a small, hot object about the size of Earth. The star is then a white dwarf made of carbon.

Pressure in White Dwarfs A white dwarf is stable despite the lack of nuclear reactions because it is supported by the resistance of electrons being squeezed close together, and does not require a source of heat to be maintained. This pressure counteracts gravity and can support the core as long as the mass of the remaining core is less than about 1.4 times the mass of the Sun.

A star that has less mass than that of the Sun has a similar life cycle, except that helium may never form carbon in the core, and the star ends as a white dwarf made of helium. The main sequence lifetime of such a star is much longer, however, because low-mass stars are dim and do not use up their nuclear fuel very rapidly.

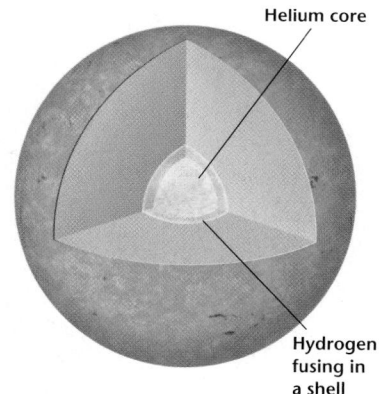

Helium core

Hydrogen fusing in a shell

Figure 30-20 After hydrogen fusing is done in the core, it continues in a shell. (not to scale)

Figure 30-21 NGC 6751 is a planetary nebula. This image was taken by the *Hubble Space Telescope.* The white dwarf is the white object at the center of the nebula.

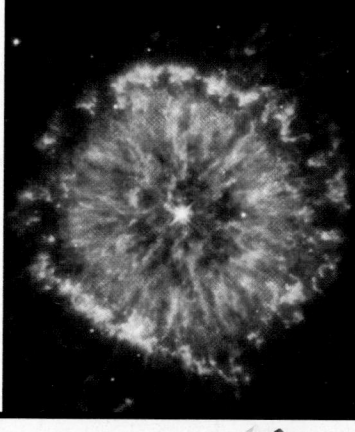

Interpreting the Photo

Figure 30-21 This image was produced by combining images taken with three different filters that isolate gases of different temperatures. Blue represents the hottest gas and red represents the coolest gas. The central star has a temperature of approximately 1.4×10^5 K on the surface, and its winds and radiation are responsible for the features of the nebula. The nebula is approximately 0.8 ly in diameter, but it is expanding at approximately 40 km/s. The nebula is 6500 ly away, in the constellation Aquila.

Using Scientific Terms

The ejected gas from a star that has lost its outer layers is called a planetary nebula because the ejected shell often appears round like a planet, and because many of these nebulae appear blue-green in color, resembling the planets Uranus and Neptune. The blue-green color comes from emission lines resulting from twice-ionized oxygen atoms.

Enrichment

The elements beyond iron in the periodic table are formed by neutron capture reactions, in which a neutron is added to a nucleus. Often, the neutron then decays to a proton, which changes the atomic number of the nucleus and creates a new element. Successive neutron captures can build up heavier nuclei.

Content Background

A comparison of H-R diagrams for different clusters shows that some have complete main sequences, while others are missing the upper portion, where the most massive stars would be. Instead, these clusters have a number of red giants. These observations led astronomers to realize that massive stars evolve faster than lower-mass stars do, and that when they leave the main sequence, stars become red giants.

Resource Manager

Teaching Transparency 93 L2 ELL

NY Core Curriculum Standards

Page 822: St 1 Science KI 1, St 4 KI 1.2b, St 6 KI 1, 2, 4, & 5
Page 823: St 1 Science KI 1, St 4 KI 1.2b, St 6 KI 1, 2, 4, & 5

Identifying Misconceptions

People generally think that a black hole has extra gravity that enables it to reach out and suck material into itself.

Uncover the Misconception
Ask students what would happen to Earth's orbit if the Sun were to collapse and turn into a black hole.

Demonstrate the Concept
Explain that the Sun's mass would not change if it were to become a black hole, and its gravitational force on Earth would be no different. The only region where the Sun's gravity is exceptionally strong is within the Sun's original radius, and even there, a body such as a planet could orbit without falling in. Only very close to the center is the gravitational field so strong that space is distorted and light is unable to escape. However, from a distance, a black hole behaves like an ordinary object.

Assess New Knowledge
Ask students what would happen in a binary star system if one of the stars collapsed and became a black hole. How would the other star be affected? There would be no effect on the companion star. It would continue to orbit the center of mass just as before.

NY Core Curriculum Standards

Page 824: St 1 Science KI 1, St 4 KI 1.2b, St 6 KI 1, 2, 3, 4, & 5
Page 825: St 1 Science KI 1, St 4 KI 1.2b, St 6 KI 1, 2, 3, 4, & 5

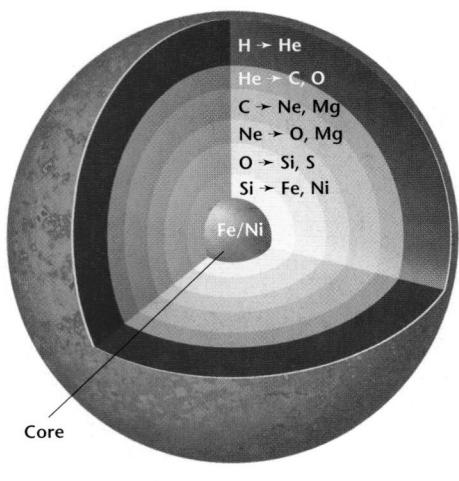

Figure 30-22 A massive star can have many shells fusing different elements. Massive stars are responsible for producing heavier elements. (not to scale)

Figure 30-23 The core of the star collapses **(A)** forming a neutron star **(B)**, on which infalling material bounces off and causes a supernova **(C)**. (not to scale)

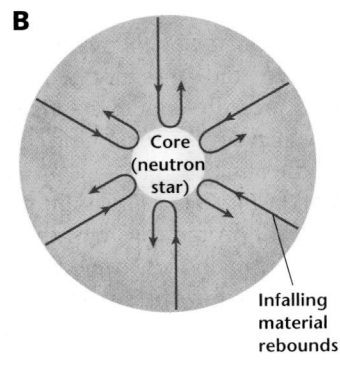

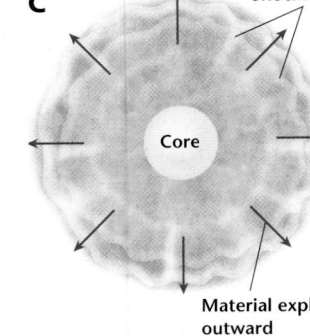

LIFE CYCLES OF MASSIVE STARS

For stars more massive than the Sun, evolution is very different. A more-massive star begins its life in the same way, but much higher on the main sequence, with hydrogen being converted to helium. However, the star's lifetime in this phase is short, because the star is very luminous and uses up its fuel quickly.

A massive star undergoes many more reaction phases and thus produces a rich stew of many elements in its interior. The star becomes a red giant several times as it expands following the end of each reaction stage. As more shells are formed by the fusion of different elements, illustrated in *Figure 30-22,* the star expands to a larger size and becomes a supergiant, such as Betelgeuse in the Orion constellation.

A massive star loses much of its mass during its lifetime as gas drifts from its outer layers, or is driven away by a stellar wind. A star that begins with as many as 8 times the Sun's mass may end up as a white dwarf with a final mass less than 1.4 times the Sun's mass. The composition of a white dwarf is determined by how many reaction phases the star went through before it stopped reacting altogether. Thus, there can be white dwarfs made of oxygen, white dwarfs made of neon, and so on.

Supernovae Some stars do not lose enough mass to become white dwarfs. A star that begins with a mass between about 8 and 20 times the Sun's mass will end up with a core that is too massive to be supported by electron pressure. Such a star comes to a very violent end. Once reactions in the core of the star have created iron, no further energy-producing reactions can occur, and the core of the star violently collapses in on itself, as illustrated in *Figure 30-23A.* As it does so, protons and electrons in the core merge to form

Across the Curriculum

Physics Students will have learned in previous science classes that like electrical charges repel each other. This makes fusion difficult, because nuclei are positively charged. The repulsion between nuclei can be overcome only if they collide at very high speeds. Only then can the nuclei come close enough together to merge. Collision speed depends on temperature, and a star is hottest in its center, which explains why fusion occurs only in stellar cores. The larger the nuclei, the greater the electrical charges, and the higher the speed needed to make nuclei fuse. Massive stars reach higher internal temperatures than lower-mass stars, so heavy elements can be formed only in massive stars. Thus, these very rare stars play the dominant role in forming heavy elements in the universe.

neutrons. Like electrons, neutrons can't be squeezed too closely together. Their resistance to being squeezed creates a pressure that halts the collapse of the core, and the core becomes a **neutron star,** as illustrated in *Figure 30-23B.* A neutron star has a mass of 1.5 to 3 times the Sun's mass but a radius of only about 10 km! The density is incredibly high—about 100 trillion times more dense than water—and is comparable to that of an atomic nucleus.

A neutron star forms quickly while the outer layers of the star are still falling inward. This infalling gas rebounds when it strikes the hard surface of the neutron star as illustrated in *Figure 30-23B,* and explodes outward, as illustrated in *Figure 30-23C.* The entire outer portion of the star is blown off in a massive explosion called a **supernova** (*pl.* supernovae), shown in *Figure 30-24.* This explosion creates elements that are heavier than iron and enriches the universe.

Black Holes Some stars are too massive even to form neutron stars. The pressure from the resistance of neutrons being squeezed together cannot support the core of a star if the star's mass is greater than about 3 times the mass of the Sun. A star that begins with more than about 20 times the Sun's mass will end up above this mass limit, and it cannot form a neutron star. The resistance of neutrons to being squeezed is not great enough to stop the collapse and the core of the star simply continues to collapse forever, compacting matter into a smaller and smaller volume. The small, but extremely dense, object that remains is called a **black hole** because its gravity is so immense that nothing, not even light, can escape it. You will learn about the search for black holes in the *Science in the News* feature at the end of this chapter.

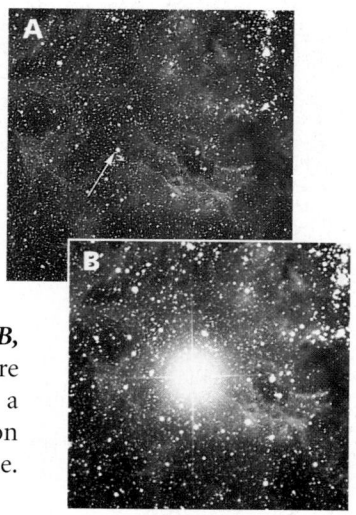

Figure 30-24 The top image **(A),** shows the region before Supernova 1987A in the Large Magellanic Cloud, while the bottom image **(B)** shows the supernova in full bloom.

SECTION ASSESSMENT

1. How do astronomers learn about the internal structure and evolution of stars?

2. How does a new star form?

3. What causes a supernova to occur? Explain.

4. Is the lifetime of a massive star shorter or longer than a star like the Sun? Why?

5. In what ways is the evolution of a massive star similar to the evolution of the Sun, and in what ways is it different?

6. **Thinking Critically** How would the universe be different if massive stars did not explode at the ends of their lives?

SKILL REVIEW

7. **Comparing and Contrasting** Compare and contrast how pressure and gravity are balanced or not balanced in main-sequence stars, white dwarfs, neutron stars, and black holes. For more help, refer to the *Skill Handbook.*

Check For Understanding

Reinforcement

Ask students to summarize the reasons that stars evolve. The composition of a star's core changes as a result of nuclear fusion reactions, and the star must adjust so it can maintain equilibrium.

Reteach

Ask students to summarize which stellar mass ranges lead to which kinds of stellar remnants. initial masses less than about 8 solar masses: white dwarfs; between about 8 and 20 solar masses: supernovae and neutron stars; more massive than 20 solar masses: black holes

✓ Assessment

Portfolio Have each student create a poster illustrating the evolution of the Sun. Ask students to include descriptions of what is occurring within the Sun at each stage.

SECTION ASSESSMENT

1. through observations of stars in different stages of evolution and model calculations

2. A nebula collapses, density and temperature increase in the center, and fusion begins.

3. Fusion stops and electron pressure can't support the iron core. As the core collapses, protons and electrons combine. The outer layers continue to collapse, bounce off the neutron star, and explode outward.

4. shorter; it fuses its fuel more quickly

5. A massive star and the Sun both fuse another nuclear fuel when one runs out. However, a massive star becomes much hotter, undergoes many more reaction stages, and evolves much more rapidly. A massive star may become a supernova, and neutron star, whereas the Sun will become a white dwarf.

6. Heavy elements would not be dispersed and they would not be available for incorporation into later generations of stars or for the formation of planets in a solar system.

7. In main sequence stars, gravity is balanced by ordinary gas pressure. In a white dwarf, the pressure from the repulsion of electrons balances gravity, and in a neutron star, gravity is balanced by the pressure from the repulsion of neutrons. In a black hole, nothing counteracts gravity.

GeoLab

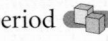

Time Allotment

one class period

Process Skills

use numbers, collect and organize data

Preparation

Review the information from this chapter about how spectral lines are related to the structure of the atom.

Procedure

Teaching Strategies

- Emphasize to students the importance of making measurements as precisely as possible, because precise wavelengths are often needed to identify spectral lines.
- Star 1 is an A5 star. Star 2 is an O5 star.

Troubleshooting

- Not all wavelengths in the table are used, and not all spectral lines in Star 2 (left end) are measured and included in the table.
- You may need to go through some example wavelength calculations with students to ensure that they know what to do.
- It may help for students to make a template (using a small card or piece of paper) on which the known spectral lines are marked on the same scale as the unknown spectrum. The template can be slid back and forth along the unknown spectrum until a match in spacing

GeoLab

Identifying Stellar Spectral Lines

An astronomer studying a star or other type of celestial object often starts by identifying the lines in the object's spectrum. The identity of the spectral lines gives astronomers information about the chemical composition of the distant object, along with data on its temperature and other properties.

Preparation

Problem

Identify stellar spectral lines based on two previously identified lines.

Materials

ruler

Objectives

In this Geolab, you will:
- **Develop** a scale based on the separation between two previously identified spectral lines.
- **Measure** wavelengths of spectral lines.
- **Compare** measured wavelengths to known wavelengths of elements to determine composition.

Procedure

1. Measure the distance between the two identified spectral lines on star 1. Be sure to use units that are small enough to get accurate measurements.
2. Calculate the difference in wavelengths between the two identified spectral lines.
3. Set up your scale by dividing the difference in wavelengths by the measured distance between the two identified spectral lines. This will allow you to measure wavelengths based on your distance measurement unit. For example, 1 mm = 12 nm.
4. Measure the distance to spectral lines from one of the two previously identified spectral lines.
5. Convert your distances to wavelengths using your scale. You have measured the difference in wavelength. This difference must be added or subtracted to the wavelength of the line you measured from. If the line you measured from is to the right of the line you are identifying, then you must subtract. Otherwise, you add.
6. Compare your wavelength measurements to the table of wavelengths emitted by elements, and identify the elements in the spectrum.
7. Repeat this procedure for star 2.

is found, which will lead to the identification of the unknown spectral lines.

Data and Observations

The scale for Star 1 is approximately 1 mm = 1.86 nm. The scale for Star 2 is approximately 1 mm = 2.36 nm.

Analyze

1. Star 1

   H (383.5 nm, 388.9 nm, 397.0 nm, 410.2 nm, 434.1 nm, 486.1 nm, 656.3 nm)

   Ca^+ (393.4 nm)

   Na (589.6 or 589.0—too close to tell)

   Star 2

   H (383.5 nm, 388.9 nm, 397.0 nm, 410.2 nm, 656.3 nm)

   He (402.6 nm, 447.1 nm, 587.6 nm,

Star 1

397.0 nm | 656.3 nm

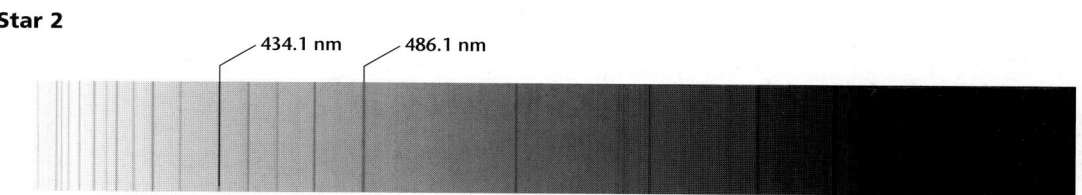

Star 2

434.1 nm | 486.1 nm

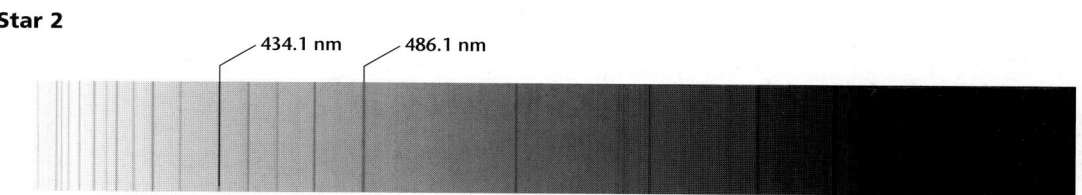

Analyze

1. What elements are present in the stars?
2. How does your list of elements compare with the list of elements seen in the periodic table in *Appendix G?*

3. Can you see any clues in the star's spectrum about which elements are most common in the stars? Explain.

Conclude & Apply

1. Do both stars contain the same lines for all the elements in the table?
2. You should notice that some absorption lines are wider than others. What are some possible explanations for this?
3. How do the thicker absorption lines of some elements in a star's spectrum effect the accuracy of your measurements? Is there a way to improve your measurements? Explain.

4. Using the following formula, calculate the percent deviation for 5 of your measured lines.

$$\text{Percent deviation} = \frac{\text{difference from accepted value}}{\text{accepted value}} \times 100$$

Is there a value that has a high percent deviation? If so, what are some possible explanations for this?

POSSIBLE ELEMENTS AND WAVELENGTHS

Element/Ion	Wavelengths (nm)
H	383.5, 388.9, 397.0, 410.2, 434.1, 486.1, 656.3
He	402.6, 447.1, 492.2, 587.6, 686.7
He$^+$	420.0, 454.1, 468.6, 541.2, 656.0
Na	475.2, 498.3, 589.0, 589.6
Ca$^+$	393.4, 480.0, 530.7

GeoLab **827**

4. Student answers will vary. Possibly, students could have identified a different, adjacent line. Also, measurements are very sensitive.

Skill Have students each create a data table summarizing the measured wavelengths, and the wavelengths and elements that they correspond to. Have students identify the star in which they measured that line.

Resource Manager

GeoLab and MiniLab Worksheets, pp. 122–125 L2

686.7 nm)
He$^+$ (420.0 nm, 454.1 nm, 468.6 nm, 686.7 nm)
Ca$^+$ (393.4 nm)

2. Based on the elements students identify in this lab, they are likely to indicate that there is a very small number of elements in stars compared to the periodic table. In actuality, most elements in the periodic table are also in the stars. Higher resolution spectra are needed to identify them.
3. Most of the lines are hydrogen and helium lines. Thickness of spectral lines is an indication, but it also depends on the temperature.

Conclude & Apply

1. No. Star 1 does not have identifiable helium (neutral or ionized) in this spectrum. Star 2 does not have identifiable sodium lines in this spectrum. In reality, both stars have all the same elements. The difference in their spectra is as a result of temperature effects.
2. Students might suggest such reasons as different temperatures, different abundances, and so on.
3. To correct for this, students should measure from the middle (width), where the line is darkest. As the band increases in width, it will increase the same amount on both sides. Thus, always measuring from the center will eliminate any error from increased width.

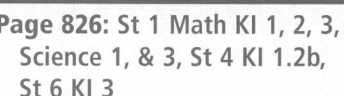

NY Core Curriculum Standards

Page 826: St 1 Math KI 1, 2, 3, Science 1, & 3, St 4 KI 1.2b, St 6 KI 3
Page 827: St 1 Math KI 1, 2, 3, Science 1, & 3, St 4 KI 1.2b, St 6 KI 3

Science in the News

Purpose

Students will become acquainted with current events in astronomy.

Content Background

Stellar black holes are best observed in binary star systems, where the analysis of the visible star may lead to the conclusion that the unseen star has too much mass to be anything other than a black hole. The *Chandra X-Ray Observatory* is especially well-equipped to detect emissions from hot gases surrounding black holes.

Teaching Strategies

Point out to students that some black holes are not formed from the collapse of individual, massive stars, but instead form from the mergers of many stars at the cores of galaxies. Many of the black holes detected by *Chandra* are of this second type, rather than being stellar black holes as discussed in this chapter. Galactic black holes are described in the next chapter.

Science in the News

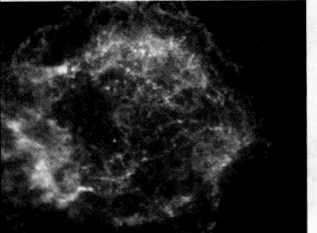

Supernova remnant Cassiopeia A

Chandra—An Eye on the Universe

*S*ome of the hottest action in the universe—action that takes place in black holes, exploding stars, and colliding galaxies—can't be observed with the naked eye. With the 1999 launch of the Chandra X-ray Observatory, however, scientists now have an unprecedented view.

Chandra is the third of NASA's Great Observatories—space telescopes designed to capture images beyond the reach of Earth-based telescopes. Unlike the Hubble Space Telescope and the Compton Gamma-Ray Observatory, which take pictures created by visible light and gamma rays, Chandra studies X rays. These rays are absorbed by Earth's atmosphere. Thus, they are best studied from a position high above our planet.

The Keen Eye

X-ray telescopes are not new. However, Chandra represents a vast improvement in technology. According to NASA, Chandra is a billion times more powerful than the first X-ray telescope, built just decades ago. "Chandra's resolving power," a NASA document explains, "is equivalent to the ability to read a 1- cm newspaper headline at the distance of a half-mile."

The $2.8 billion observatory is composed of three separate elements. The spacecraft system contains computers, data recorders, and communication equipment to transmit information back to Earth. The telescope system includes an assembly of high-resolution mirrors, the largest and most polished of their kind. The science instrument system is equipped with a high-resolution camera to record X-ray images of turbulent, high-temperature events, such as supernovae. Armed with this space-age technology,

Chandra is in a unique position to help scientists solve some of astronomy's most baffling puzzles.

Black Holes

Chandra has turned its eye toward black holes—high-gravity objects that can suck in entire stars. Black holes are thought to exist at the center of galaxies. They may be the source of the astounding amounts of energy and radiation emitted by galactic centers. Because nothing, not even light, can escape from black holes, they cannot be observed directly. However, when matter is pulled into a black hole, it is heated to incredibly high temperatures. The matter becomes so hot that it emits X rays. Chandra is studying these X-ray emissions, documenting particles of matter up until the very millisecond before they disappear into the black hole. Using this information, scientists hope to learn more about the nature of black holes and the energy they produce. The information Chandra gathers promises to change our views of the universe.

Activity

Chandra was originally called the Advanced X-ray Astrophysics Facility. Go to **earthgeu.com** to find links to more information on how the observatory received its new name. Who was it named for? Why?

Activity

Chandra was named in honor of the late Subrahmanyan Chandrasekhar, who died on August 21, 1995. He was one of the first scientists to combine the fields of physics and astronomy. Early in his career, he demonstrated that a white dwarf could be no more massive than 1.4 solar masses, now called the Chandrasekhar limit. He was a Nobel laureate in physics in 1983.

Summary

SECTION 30.1		
The Sun 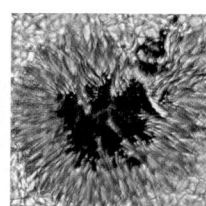	**Main Ideas** • The Sun contains most of the mass in the solar system and is made up primarily of hydrogen and helium. • Astronomers learn about conditions inside the Sun by a combination of observation and theoretical models. • The Sun's atmosphere consists of the photosphere, the chromosphere, and the corona. • The Sun has a 22-year activity cycle caused by reversals in its magnetic field polarities. • Sunspots, solar flares, and prominences are active features of the Sun. • The solar interior consists of the core, where fusion of hydrogen into helium occurs, and the radiative and convective zones.	**Vocabulary** chromosphere (p. 806) corona (p. 807) fission (p. 809) fusion (p. 809) photosphere (p. 806) prominence (p. 809) solar flare (p. 809) solar wind (p. 807) spectrum (p. 811) sunspot (p. 808)

Main Ideas

Summary statements can be used by students to review the major concepts of the chapter.

VOCABULARY PuzzleMaker

For additional help with vocabulary, have students access the Vocabulary Puzzlemaker online.

earthgeu.com/ vocabulary puzzlemaker

SECTION 30.2		
Measuring the Stars 	**Main Ideas** • Positional measurements of the stars are important for measuring distances through stellar parallax shifts. • Stellar brightnesses are expressed in the systems of apparent and absolute magnitude. • Stars are classified according to the appearance of their spectra, which indicate the surface temperatures of stars. • The H-R diagram relates the basic properties of stars: class, mass, temperature, and luminosity.	**Vocabulary** absolute magnitude (p. 816) apparent magnitude (p. 816) binary star (p. 814) constellation (p. 813) Hertzsprung-Russell diagram (p. 819) luminosity (p. 817) main sequence (p. 819) parallax (p. 815)

⏱ Out of Time?

If time does not permit teaching the entire chapter, use the GeoDigest at the end of the unit as an overview.

SECTION 30.3		
Stellar Evolution 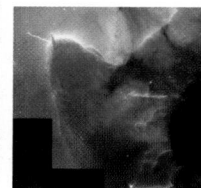	**Main Ideas** • The mass of a star determines its internal structure and its other properties. • Gravity and pressure balance each other in a star. • If the temperature in the core of a star becomes high enough, elements heavier than hydrogen but lighter than iron can fuse together. • Stars such as the Sun end up as white dwarfs. Stars up to about 8 times the Sun's mass also form white dwarfs after losing mass. Stars with masses between 8 and 20 times the Sun's mass end as neutron stars, and more massive stars end as black holes. • A supernova occurs when the outer layers of the star bounce off the neutron star core, and explode outward.	**Vocabulary** black hole (p. 825) nebula (p. 822) neutron star (p. 825) protostar (p. 822) supernova (p. 825)

Earth Science Online

Be sure to check the Earth Science Web Site for links to chapter material: earthgeu.com

 earthgeu.com/vocabulary_puzzlemaker

GLENCOE *Technology*

Videotape/DVD
MindJogger Videoquizzes
Chapter 30: *Stars*
Have students work in groups as they play the videoquiz game to review key chapter concepts.

Resource Manager

Chapter Assessment, pp. 175–180 L2
MindJogger Videoquizzes DVD/VHS
ExamView® Pro CD-ROM
Performance Assessment in Earth Science

NY Core Curriculum Standards

Page 828: St 1 Science KI 1 & 3, St 2 KI 1, 2, & 3, St 6 KI 4
Page 829: St 1 Science KI 1, St 4 KI 1.2b, St 6 KI 1, 2, 3, 4, & 5

Understanding Main Ideas

1. c
2. a
3. a
4. d
5. c
6. b
7. a
8. Fusion reactions are the merging of lightweight nuclei into heavier nuclei, whereas fission is the splitting of large nuclei into smaller nuclei.
9. The solar activity cycle is about 22 years long because the Sun's magnetic field reverses about every 11 years. Thus, it takes 22 years for the field to complete a full cycle.
10. They are cooler than their surroundings.
11. the conversion of hydrogen to helium in the stellar core
12. The Doppler shift provides information only along the line of sight. Motion perpendicular to the line of sight cannot be determined by the Doppler shift.
13. See the student page.
14. Light from the photosphere drowns out the faint light from the chromosphere and corona.

Understanding Main Ideas

1. Which of the following is not a part of the Sun's atmosphere?
   a. the corona
   b. the chromosphere
   c. the solar wind
   d. the photosphere

2. Which of the following is not created by the Sun's magnetic field?
   a. the radiative zone
   b. prominences
   c. solar flares
   d. sunspots

3. Which type of spectrum, if any, does the Sun emit?
   a. an absorption spectrum
   b. an emission spectrum
   c. a continuous spectrum
   d. no spectrum

4. Where does nuclear fusion in the Sun occur?
   a. in the convective zone
   b. in the radiative zone
   c. in the photosphere
   d. in the core

5. If a star begins its evolution with 10 times the mass of the Sun, but ends with 2 times the mass of the Sun, what type of object does it form?
   a. a white dwarf
   b. a nebula
   c. a neutron star
   d. a black hole

6. How would you calculate how much brighter a magnitude +4 star is than a magnitude +7 star?
   a. 2.512×2.512
   b. $2.512 \times 2.512 \times 2.512$
   c. $2.512 \times 2.512 \times 2.512 \times 2.512$
   d. $2.512 \times 2.512 \times 2.512 \times 2.512 \times 2.512$

7. Which of the following is the correct order of units from largest to smallest?
   a. pc, ly, AU, km
   b. ly, pc, km, AU
   c. km, pc, ly, AU
   d. km, AU, pc, ly

8. What is the difference between nuclear fusion reactions and nuclear fission reactions?

9. Why do we say that the Sun's activity cycle is 22 years long, when the number of sunspots follows an 11-year pattern?

10. Why do sunspots appear to be darker than their surroundings?

11. What is the energy source for all main-sequence stars?

12. Does the Doppler shift provide complete information about the motion of a star? Explain.

Use the diagram below to answer question 13.

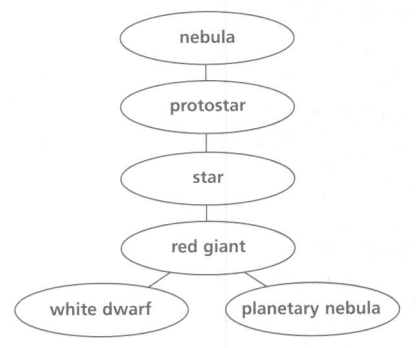

13. Use the following terms to fill in the concept map of the evolution of a star like the Sun.

   star   nebula   red giant
   protostar   white dwarf   planetary nebula

Test-Taking Tip

SLOW DOWN Read the questions and answer choices carefully. Remember that doing most of the problems and getting them right is always preferable to doing all the problems and getting many of them wrong.

Applying Main Ideas

15. A star whose initial mass is between 8 and 20 solar masses explodes as a supernova when its core collapses following iron formation. The core forms a neutron star, and the outer layers of the star rebound explosively when they fall onto the neutron star.

16. The core shrinks and becomes hotter. If the star is massive enough, in time, helium will react to form carbon; if the star is not massive enough to ignite helium, the core becomes a helium white dwarf.

17. It must lose enough mass during its lifetime to end up below the 1.4 solar mass limit.

18. A magnitude −3 star is three magnitudes, or a factor of $2.512 \times 2.512 \times 2.512 = 15.9$ times brighter than a magnitude 0 star.

19. composition, temperature, and motion with Doppler shifts

20. There would be no activity cycle, prominences, flares, or sunspots.

14. Why can the Sun's chromosphere and corona be observed without special instruments only during times of total solar eclipses?

Applying Main Ideas

15. Why do some stars explode as supernovae?

16. What happens to a star when the hydrogen in its core has all been converted into helium?

17. If a white dwarf can exist only if its mass is less than 1.4 times the Sun's mass, how can a star having 5 times the Sun's mass end as a white dwarf?

18. Is a magnitude −3 star brighter or dimmer than a magnitude 0 star? By how much?

19. What can astronomers learn about a star from its spectral lines?

20. How would the appearance of the Sun be different if it did not have a magnetic field?

Thinking Critically

21. Why does a star change over time?

22. Why do the most massive stars end up as black holes instead of neutron stars?

23. Why do the Sun and the gas giant planets have similar compositions? Why are the terrestrial planets different?

24. How would astronomers know if the theory of hydrostatic equilibrium inside the Sun were not correct?

25. How would an increase in mass affect the basic properties of a star? You may want to use an H-R diagram to help you.

26. Is a star's eventual fate determined by its initial mass or by the mass it has at the end of its life? Explain.

earthgeu.com/standardized_test

Standardized Test Practice

1. What causes sunspots on the Sun?
 a. intense magnetic fields poking through the photosphere
 b. charged particles flowing outward into the solar system
 c. spots on the surface of the photosphere which are hotter than the surrounding areas
 d. areas of low density in the gas of the Sun's corona

INTERPRETING DATA Use the table below to answer questions 2–4.

Stellar Magnitudes		
Star	**Apparent Magnitude**	**Absolute Magnitude**
Procyon	+0.38	+2.66
Altair	+0.77	+2.22
Becrux	+1.25	−3.92
Bellatrix	+1.64	−1.29
Denebola	+2.14	+1.54

2. Which is the brightest star as seen from Earth?
 a. Procyon   **c.** Bellatrix
 b. Becrux   **d.** Denebola

3. Which is the brightest star as seen from 10 parsecs?
 a. Procyon   **c.** Bellatrix
 b. Becrux   **d.** Denebola

4. Which is the dimmest star as seen from 10 parsecs?
 a. Bellatrix   **c.** Procyon
 b. Altair   **d.** Becrux

Thinking Critically

21. Its core composition changes, which causes the core density and temperature, and hence the star's luminosity, to change. More significant changes occur when the core nuclear fuel runs out and the star must readjust its equilibrium.

22. They are too massive to be supported by degenerate neutron gas pressure, and they collapse.

23. The Sun and gas giants have similar compositions because they retained essentially all of the elements that made up the solar nebula. The terrestrial planets are different because they were not able to retain the lightweight elements, and they are therefore composed primarily of rocky and metallic materials.

24. If the Sun were not in hydrostatic equilibrium, it would either be expanding or contracting.

25. Luminosity, temperature, and magnitude would increase, but the lifetime would decrease.

26. A star's eventual fate is determined by its final mass, not its initial mass. The final mass determines whether the star can be supported by degenerate electron gas pressure (as in a white dwarf), degenerate neutron gas pressure (as in a neutron star), or by nothing at all (as in a black hole).

EXAM*VIEW*® PRO

Use Exam*View*® Pro Testmaker CD-ROM to:

- Create **multiple versions** of tests.
- Create **modified** tests with one mouse click for struggling students.
- **Edit** existing questions and add your own questions.
- **Build** tests based on national curriculum standards.

Standardized Test Practice

1. a
2. a
3. b
4. c

Chapter 31

Galaxies and the Universe

Refer to pages 8T–9T of the Teacher Guide for an explanation of the National Science Content Standards correlations.

Section	Objectives	National Science Content Standards	State/Local Standards
SECTION 31.1 **The Milky Way Galaxy** 🕐 1 session 📦 ½ block	1. **Determine** the size and shape of the Milky Way, as well as Earth's location within it. 2. **Describe** how the Milky Way formed.	UCP.1, UCP.2, UCP.3, UCP.4; A.1, A.2; B.2, B.4, B.6; D.3, D.4; G.2, G.3	St 1 Math KI 1, 2, 3, Science KI 1, 2, 3, & Engin KI 1, St 4 KI 1.2b, St 6 KI 1, 2, 3, & 4
SECTION 31.2 **Other Galaxies in the Universe** 🕐 1½ sessions 📦 1 block	3. **Describe** how astronomers classify galaxies. 4. **Identify** how galaxies are organized into clusters and superclusters. 5. **Describe** the expansion of the universe.	UCP.1, UCP.2, UCP.3, UCP.4, UCP.5; A.1, A.2; B.2, B.4, B.6; D.4; E.2; G.2, G.3	St 1 Math KI 1, 2, 3, Science KI 1, 2, 3, & Engin KI 1, St 4 KI 1.2a & 1.2b, St 6 KI 1, 2, 3, 4, & 5
SECTION 31.3 **Cosmology** 🕐 2½ sessions 📦 1½ blocks	6. **Explain** the different theories about the formation of the universe. 7. **Describe** the possible outcomes of universal expansion.	UCP.1, UCP.2, UCP.3, UCP.4; A.1, A.2; B.2, B.4, B.6; D.4; E.1, E.2; G.2, G.3	St 1 Math KI 1, 2, 3, Science KI 1, 2, 3, & Engin KI 1, St 2 KI 1, 2, & 3, St 4 KI 1.2a & 1.2b St 6 KI 1, 2, 3, 4, & 5

A complete Planning Guide is provided on pages 30T–32T.

🕐 The number of recommended single-period sessions

📦 The number of recommended blocks

Activity Materials

Discovery Lab *page 833*
paper, pencil, ruler, calculator

GeoLab *pages 852–853*
Internet access, pencil, paper

MiniLab *page 845*
felt-tip marker, balloon, string, meterstick

Demo *page 837*
large tub, paddle, water, food coloring

Need materials? Contact Science Kit at 1-800-828-7777 or at www.sciencekit.com on the Internet. For alternate materials, see the activity on the listed page.

Key to Teaching Strategies

L1 Level 1 activities should be appropriate for students with learning difficulties.

L2 Level 2 activities should be within the ability range of all students.

L3 Level 3 activities are designed for above-average students.

ELL ELL activities should be within the ability range of English-language learners.

COOP LEARN Cooperative learning activities are designed for small-group work.

P These strategies represent student products that can be placed in a best-work portfolio.

📦 These strategies are useful in a block-scheduling format.

Chapter Organizer

Activities/Features	Reproducible Masters	Transparencies
Discovery Lab: Model the Milky Way, p. 833	**Study Guide for Content Mastery,** pp. 195–197 L2 **Laboratory Manual,** pp. 241–244 L2	Section Focus Transparency 99 L1 ELL Teaching Transparency 94 L2 ELL
Problem-Solving Lab: Making and Using Graphs, p. 843 **MiniLab:** Measuring Redshifts, p. 845	**Study Guide for Content Mastery,** p. 198 L2 **Laboratory Manual,** pp. 245–248 L2 **GeoLab and MiniLab Worksheets,** p. 127 L2	Section Focus Transparency 100 L1 ELL Teaching Transparency 95 L2 ELL
Using Math: Using Numbers, p. 850 **Internet GeoLab:** Classifying Galaxies, pp. 852–853 **Science & Technology:** The Early Universe, p. 854	**Study Guide for Content Mastery,** pp. 199–200 L2 **GeoLab and MiniLab Worksheets,** pp. 128–130 L2	Section Focus Transparency 101 L1 ELL

✔Assessment

Chapter Assessment, pp. 181–186
Performance Assessment in the Science Classroom (PASC)
MindJogger Videoquiz DVD/VHS
Performance Assessment in Earth Science
ExamView® Pro CD-ROM
5 Days to the Regents Exam

GLENCOE'S ASSESSMENT ADVANTAGE

Additional Resources

Guided Reading Audio Progam ELL
Cooperative Learning in the Science Classroom COOP LEARN
Lesson Plans
Block Scheduling
earthgeu.com
NY Lesson Plans
NY Block Scheduling
Review Handbook for Regents Earth Science Exam

⬛NATIONAL GEOGRAPHIC

Teacher's Corner

Products Available from National Geographic Society
To order the following products, call the National Geographic Society at 1-800-368-2728:
Curriculum Kit
GeoKit: *Astronomy*

Videos
Stars and Constellations
Maps
Solar System/Celestial Family

Content Background

The Milky Way
Section 31.1

One of the earliest methods used by astronomers to discover the shape of the Milky Way and the location of the solar system within it was to count stars in all directions. The idea was to map out a three-dimensional view of the distribution of stars, a seemingly simple idea. But when this was first done in detail in 1906, the result was stunning: the density of stars in space dropped off in all directions. This suggested that the solar system is at the center of the galaxy, an idea that immediately aroused skepticism. History had shown that Earth does not occupy any special place in the universe,

so it seemed implausible that it should be located at the very center of a galaxy of billions of stars. The skeptics were correct; the solar system is not located near the center of the galaxy. This was demonstrated in the 1920s by methods discussed in this chapter. It was not until 1930 when astronomers finally understood why the star-count method had yielded the wrong result: the galaxy is permeated with a haze of fine particles called interstellar dust, and this makes stars appear to be farther away than they really are. The dimming of stars as a result of interstellar dust made it appear that the density of stars in space drops off in all directions from Earth.

Other Galaxies in the Universe
Section 31.2

Perhaps the most important image ever taken by the *Hubble Space Telescope (HST)* was a picture of nothing. In 1993, the *HST* was pointed at a blank spot on the sky for several days in a row, and it took image after image of apparent darkness. The spot was chosen deliberately to be as blank as any spot on the sky that could be found. The goal was to see whether the sky might be covered with distant galaxies too faint to be seen by the largest telescopes on Earth. It is. The individual images were added together to create the Hubble Deep Field, a glorious window into the universe, full of color and light. No less than 1500 faint galaxies were found in a patch of sky only 30 arcminutes square. Most of these galaxies

Multiple Learning Styles

- **Kinesthetic** Modeling, p. 841
- **Visual-Spatial** Activity, p. 836, Demo, p. 837, Activity, p. 848
- **Interpersonal** Collaborative Learning, p. 841, Discussion, p. 848
- **Linguistic** Earth Science Journal, p. 835, Enrichment, p. 836
- **Logical-Mathematical** Using an Analogy, p. 840

GLENCOE
Technology

The following multimedia resources are available from Glencoe.

The Infinite Voyage Series
Unseen Worlds

Vocabulary Puzzlemaker

TeacherWorks™ CD-ROM

MindJogger Videoquizzes DVD/VHS

ExamView® Pro CD-ROM

Interactive Chalkboard CD-ROM

are so far away that they appear as they were about 10 billion years ago, when the universe was only a fraction of its present age. Astronomers have gained an enormous amount of new information about the evolution of galaxies and the early universe from a picture of "nothing."

Cosmology
Section 31.3

The discovery of the cosmic background radiation in 1965 is recognized as one of the most important ever for our understanding of the nature of the universe. Interestingly, the radiation could have been discovered at least 15 years earlier, following the prediction of its existence in the late 1940s and the development of appropriate technology in the 1940s and 1950s. Studies of element formation in a hot, expanding universe (now known as the Big Bang model) showed that the early universe would have been filled with high-energy radiation, which, by the present time, would have cooled and shifted into the microwave portion of the spectrum. Radar technology is appropriate for detecting this radiation, and radar was developed during and after World War II. However, the scientists who made the prediction considered it an insignificant sideline to their main interest in element formation, and they did not attempt to look for the radiation. In 1965, a new prediction was made, independent of the earlier one, and then the radiation was discovered accidentally, without knowledge of either prediction.

Indentifying Misconceptions

Astronomers find that distant galaxies move away from us, and that the farther away a galaxy is, the faster it recedes. Thus, it is tempting to conclude that Earth must be at the center of the universe. However, this is not the case. Later in this chapter, the analogy is made that on the surface of a balloon that is being inflated, any point on the surface recedes from every other point. This analogy can also be used to demonstrate that there is no center of expansion. Ask students to consider the balloon's surface, ignoring the volume inside the balloon. There is no one point on the surface that represents the center of expansion. They can consider any particular point, and they will find that all other points move away from that point. There is no center, just as there is no center of the universe.

✔*Assessment*

Portfolio Assessment
Assessment, TWE, p. 838

Performance Assessment
Discovery Lab, SE, p. 833
Assessment, TWE, p. 844
MiniLab, SE, p. 845
GeoLab, SE, pp. 852–853

Knowledge Assessment
Assessment, TWE, pp. 837, 846, 850, 851
Problem-Solving Lab, TWE, p. 843
MiniLab, TWE, p. 845
GeoLab, TWE, pp. 852–853
Section Assessment, SE, pp. 838, 846, 851
Chapter Assessment, SE, pp. 856–857

Skill Assessment
Discovery Lab, TWE, p. 833
Assessment, TWE, pp. 841, 843

Be sure to check the Earth Science Web Site for links to chapter material: earthgeu.com

GLENCOE'S ADVANTAGE
ASSESSMENT

Galaxies and the Universe

Introducing the Chapter

The best way for students to get a feeling for the scope of our galaxy is to observe the Milky Way. This can be done at any time of the year. However, it is essential to do this on a moonless night, and to get to a place far removed from city lights. The Milky Way will be visible as a hazy band of light stretching across the sky.

Interpreting the Photo

These two galaxies, NGC 2207 (bottom) and IC 2163 (top), are slowly destroying each other. Astronomers predict that NGC 2207 will eventually consume IC 2163 because NGC 2207 is larger. As these two galaxies collide, new starbirth is triggered, and dust is thrown about.

INTERACTIVE CHALKBOARD with Image Bank

PowerPoint® Presentations

This CD is an editable Microsoft® PowerPoint® presentation that includes:
- Section presentations
- Section checks
- Image bank
- Links to Earth Science Online
- All transparencies
- Animations
- Audio

Galaxies and the Universe

What You'll Learn
- What the Milky Way Galaxy is like.
- How galaxies are distributed and what their characteristics are.
- What astronomers know about the origin and history of the universe.

Why It's Important
The study of galaxies and the structure of the universe helps scientists to better understand the origin of our solar system as well as Earth's origin.

Earth Science Online

To find out more about galaxies and the universe, visit the Earth Science Web Site at earthgeu.com

Collision between NGC 2207 and IC 2163

Discovery Lab

Process Skills

use numbers, recognize spatial relationships, interpret data, formulate models, compare and contrast
L1 ELL

Preparation

Make sure that students have their calculators.

Procedure

This lab may be done in small groups.

Troubleshooting

Point out to students that this activity is similar to using scales on maps.

1. 1.30×10^5 ly
2. 1.26×10^{-3} ly
3. 130 000 mm or 130 m
4. 28 000 mm or 28 m
5. 1.26×10^{-3} mm

Observe

The model on this 1 mm = 1 ly scale would be too large to fit in a room, except possibly the school gym or cafeteria. Showing the size of the solar system on the same model would be difficult because everything would have to be very small. To include the

Discovery Lab

Model The Milky Way

Our solar system seems large when we compare it to the size of Earth. However, the Milky Way dwarfs the size of our solar system.

1. The Milky Way has a diameter of approximately 8.25×10^9 AU. Given that 206 265 AU = 3.26 ly, what is the diameter of the Milky Way in light-years?

2. Given that the orbit of Pluto has a diameter of 80 AU, what is the diameter of Pluto's orbit in ly?

3. If you were to apply the scale 1 mm = 1 ly, how large would the Milky Way be?

4. The Sun is located 28 000 ly from the center of the Milky Way. Based on the scale that you used in question 3, how many millimeters away from the center of the Milky Way would the Sun be?

5. If you included Pluto's orbit in your model, how many millimeters across would its orbit be?

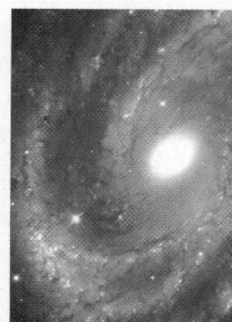

Observe In your science journal, describe what your model of the Milky Way would look like if you actually built it. Explain why it would be a problem to show the size of our solar system in comparison to the Milky Way. Explain how you would change your model to include the size of Earth.

SECTION 31.1

The Milky Way Galaxy

OBJECTIVES

- **Determine** *the size and shape of the Milky Way, as well as Earth's location within it.*

- **Describe** *how the Milky Way formed.*

VOCABULARY

variable star
RR Lyrae variable
Cepheid variable
halo
spiral density wave

When you see the hazy band of light across the sky known as the Milky Way, you are looking at our galaxy from the inside. It is an awesome sight, but one that you can see only if you get away from city lights on a moonless night. The Milky Way is a great disk made of stars orbiting a central point in the disk. Our Sun is just one of perhaps 100 billion stars that make up the Milky Way.

DISCOVERING THE MILKY WAY

When we look at the Milky Way, it is difficult to see its size and shape because not only are we too close, but we are also inside the galaxy. We see the band of stars stretching across the sky, and it's not hard to imagine that this is an edge-on view of a disk. However, we can't tell how big it is, where its center is, or what Earth's location is within it. These were some of the mysteries that astronomers were interested in solving. In fact, astronomers are still refining their measurements.

31.1 The Milky Way Galaxy **833**

size of Earth in the model would require an enormous expansion of the scale.

Skill Have students compare and contrast scales that would be useful for modeling Earth, the Sun-Earth-Moon system, the solar system, the Milky Way, and a group of galaxies about 2 million ly in diameter.

Resource Manager

Section Focus Transparency 99 L1 ELL
Study Guide for Content Mastery, pp. 195–197 L2

Section 31.1

1 Focus

Section Focus

Before presenting the lesson, display **Section Focus Transparency 99** on the overhead projector.
L1 ELL

Chapter Themes

The following themes from the National Science Content Standards are covered in this chapter. Refer to page 8T of the Teacher Guide for an explanation of the correlations.
Systems, order, and organization (UCP.1); Evidence, models, and explanation (UCP.2); Change, constancy, and measurement (UCP.3); Evolution and equilibrium (UCP.4)

 **Out of Time?**

If time does not permit teaching the entire chapter, use the Chapter Summary on page 855 and the GeoDigest found at the end of the unit as an overview.

Tying to Previous Knowledge

In the previous chapter, students were introduced to the use of parallax to measure stellar distances. That method depends on measuring the tiny angular shift in a star's position that is caused by Earth's motion about the Sun. Stellar parallax is accurate to distances of about 1500 light years due to technology advancements and the *Hipparcos* satellite. The variable star method is capable of determining distances up to thousands or even millions of light years, expanding the distance scale for astronomers by a huge factor. However, the relationship between period and luminosity for variable stars had to be established by finding some variables whose distances were known by other techniques. None are close enough for parallax measurements, so other, less accurate, methods had to be used. As a result, the period-luminosity relation was not well determined at first, leading to confusion over the size scale of our galaxy.

Enrichment

Have interested students find images of the Milky Way at wavelengths other than visible light. Have them present their findings to the rest of the class.

Figure 31-1 Globular clusters are located above and below the plane of the disk of the Milky Way. The Milky Way is the white band across the middle of this photo.

Variable Stars In the 1920s, astronomers mapped out the locations of globular clusters. These huge, spherical star clusters are located above or below the plane of the galactic disk, shown in *Figure 31-1.* Astronomers estimated the distances to the clusters by identifying variable stars in them. **Variable stars** are stars in the giant branch of the Hertzsprung-Russell diagram, discussed in Chapter 30, that pulsate in brightness because of the expansion and contraction of their outer layers. For certain types of variable stars, there is a relationship between a star's luminosity and its pulsation period, which is the time between brightenings. For example, **RR Lyrae variables** have periods of pulsation between 1.5 hours and 1 day, and on average, they have the same luminosity. **Cepheid variables,** however, have pulsation periods between 1 and 100 days. The longer the period of pulsation, the greater the luminosity of the star. By measuring a star's period of pulsation, astronomers can determine the star's luminosity. This, in turn, allows them to compare the star's luminosity, or absolute magnitude, to its apparent magnitude and calculate how far away the star must be to appear as dim or bright as it does.

The Galactic Center Astronomers used RR Lyrae variables to determine the distances to the globular clusters. They discovered that these clusters are located very far from our solar system, and that their distribution in space is centered on a distant point, 28 000 ly away. Astronomers reasoned that the globular clusters were orbiting the center of the Milky Way. The center is a region of very high star density, as shown in *Figure 31-2,* much of which is obscured by interstellar gas and dust. The direction of the galactic center is toward the constellation Sagittarius.

Content Background

In 1906, at the Harvard Observatory, Henrietta Leavitt was investigating variable stars in the Magellanic Clouds, two small galaxies orbiting the Milky Way. She found that the apparent magnitudes of these stars were related to their pulsation periods. Because the stars were all at approximately the same distance from Earth, this meant that their absolute magnitudes, or luminosities, must be related to the pulsation periods.

THE SHAPE OF THE MILKY WAY

Only by mapping the galaxy with radio waves have astronomers been able to determine its shape. This is because radio waves can penetrate the interstellar gas and dust without being scattered or absorbed. Astronomers have discovered, by measuring radio waves as well as infrared radiation, that the galactic center, also called the nucleus, is surrounded by a nuclear bulge, which sticks out of the galactic disk much like the yolk in a fried egg. Around the nuclear bulge and disk is the **halo,** a spherical region where globular clusters are located, as illustrated in *Figure 31-3.*

Spiral Arms Knowing that our galaxy has a disklike shape with a central bulge, astronomers speculated that it might also have spiral arms, as many other galaxies do. This was very difficult to prove, however, because astronomers have no way to get outside of the galaxy and look down on the disk. Astronomers have used hydrogen atoms to discover the spiral arms.

Hydrogen atoms in a very low-density gas can emit radiation at a wavelength of 21 cm. The use of this hydrogen emission for mapping the spiral arms of our galaxy has several advantages: first, hydrogen is the most abundant element in space; second, the interstellar gas, composed mostly of hydrogen, is concentrated in the spiral arms; and third, the 21-cm wavelength of hydrogen emission can penetrate the interstellar gas and dust and be detected all the way across the galactic disk. Using the 21-cm hydrogen emission as a guide, astronomers have identified four major spiral arms and numerous minor arms in the Milky Way. The Sun is located in the minor arm Orion at a distance of about 28 000 ly from the galactic center. The Sun's orbital speed is about 220 km/s, and thus its orbital period is about 240 million years. It is hypothesized that in its 5 billion-year life, the Sun has orbited the galaxy approximately 20 times.

Figure 31-2 The center of the Milky Way is densely populated by stars, many of which are obscured by dust.

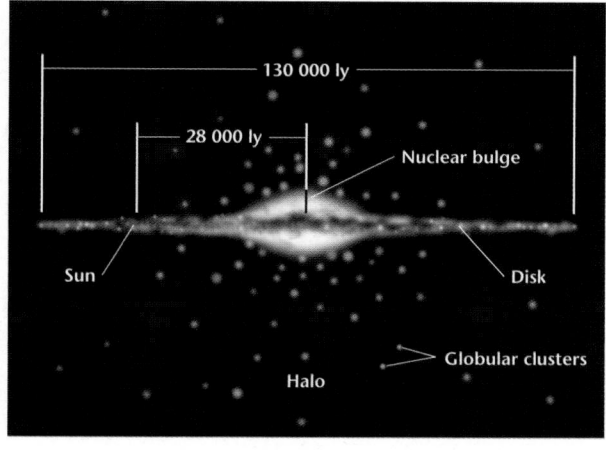

130 000 ly

28 000 ly

Nuclear bulge

Sun

Disk

Globular clusters

Halo

Figure 31-3 The Milky Way consists of a nuclear bulge in the center of a disk. The disk and bulge are surrounded by a spherical region called the halo. (not to scale)

Interpreting the Illustration

Figure 31-3 Ask students to study the diagram of the Milky Way. Have them describe the shape of the galaxy and our solar system's location relative to the center of the galaxy and the outer edge of the galaxy.

Using an Analogy

Anyone who has taken off in an airplane from a hazy or smoggy city will have experienced an effect similar to the dimming caused by interstellar dust. When you are on the ground, you can't see very far into the distance because of the haze or smog. However, as the plane climbs, you rise above the haze layer and begin to see much farther. Living in the plane of the Milky Way's disk is like being in the aircraft on the ground. Unfortunately, we have no way of lifting off and getting above the disk of the galaxy. Hence, we can see only a fraction of the way toward the galactic center, because we can't get clear of the "smog."

Earth Science

Journal

Linguistic The Milky Way is a naturally spiral-shaped object. There are others in nature. Have each student make an illustrated list of spirals in nature. Have students explain whether each spiral is governed by rotation. Possible examples: cyclonic storms, snail shells, certain oceanic flows, and the solar wind. All except snail shells are influenced by rotation. **L2**

Resource Manager

Teaching Transparency 94 L2 ELL

NY Core Curriculum Standards

Page 832: St 1 Science KI 1, St 6 KI 2

Page 833: St 1 Math KI 1, 2, 3, Science KI 1, 2, & Engin KI 1, St 4 KI 1.2b, St 6 KI 2 & 3

Page 834: St 1 Science KI 1 & 2, St 4 KI 1.2b, St 6 KI 3 & 4

Page 835: St 1 Science KI 1 & 3, St 4 KI 1.2b

Content Background

The ages of globular clusters are estimated from H-R diagrams. The age of a cluster of stars can be estimated by noting that the upper main sequence stars are missing from the H-R diagram because these massive stars have evolved into red giants. A young cluster will have a complete main sequence, while an older cluster will be missing the upper part of its main sequence. A typical globular cluster has only a very short main sequence, with only the lower portion present, and many red giants. Thus, these clusters are very old, with ages estimated to be as great as 14 billion years.

Activity

Visual-Spatial The galactic center object Sagittarius A* has been observed with telescopes at many different wavelengths, particularly radio, infrared, and X-ray wavelengths. Have students find as many images of this object as they can. Students can work in groups and prepare posters showing their collections of images. Have students compare and contrast their images. **L1** **ELL** **P**

Enrichment

Linguistic Have interested students research and write brief summaries about other possible forms of dark matter beyond stellar remnants.

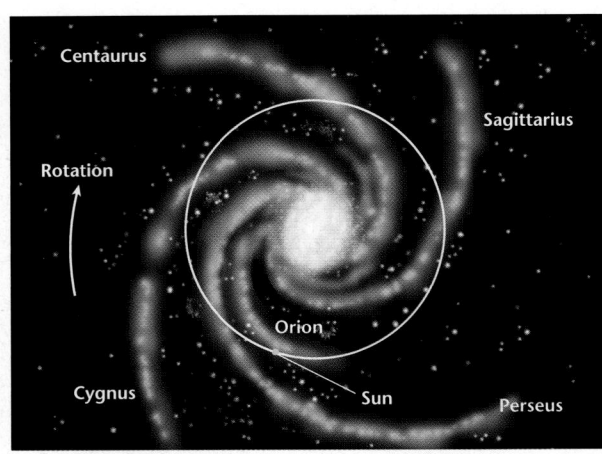

Figure 31-4 The Sun is located on the minor arm Orion and follows an orbital path around the nuclear bulge as shown. (not to scale)

MASS OF THE MILKY WAY

The mass located within the circle of the Sun's orbit through the galaxy, outlined in *Figure 31-4,* is about 100 billion times the mass of the Sun. Because the Sun is about average in mass, astronomers have concluded that the galaxy contains about 100 billion stars within its disk.

However, astronomers have found evidence that much more mass exists outside the disk of the galaxy. The stars and gas clouds that orbit in the outer disk are moving faster than they would if the galaxy's mass were concentrated near the center of the disk. Evidence indicates that as much as 90 percent of the galaxy's mass is contained in the halo. This mass is not observed in the form of normal stars, however. Some of this unseen matter is probably in the form of dim stellar remnants such as white dwarfs, neutron stars, or black holes, but the nature of the remainder of this mass is a mystery. As you'll discover, the problem of unseen matter, usually called dark matter, extends to other galaxies and to the universe as a whole.

A Galactic Black Hole Careful studies of the motions of the stars that orbit close to Sagittarius A*, the center of the galaxy, indicate that this area has about 2.6 million times the mass of the Sun but is smaller than our solar system. Data gathered by the *Chandra X-Ray Observatory* reveal intense X-ray emissions as well. Astronomers believe that Sagittarius A* is a supermassive black hole that glows brightly because of the hot gas surrounding it and spiraling into it. This black hole probably formed early in the history of the galaxy, at the time when the galaxy's disk was forming. Gas clouds and stars within the disk probably collided and merged to form a single, massive object that collapsed to form a black hole.

STARS IN THE MILKY WAY

The halo of the Milky Way contains the oldest-known objects in the galaxy: globular clusters. These clusters are estimated to be as old as 12 to 14 billion years. Stars in the globular clusters have extremely small amounts of elements that are heavier than hydrogen and helium. All stars contain small amounts of these heavy elements, but in globular clusters, the amounts are mere traces. Stars like the Sun are composed of about 98 percent hydrogen and helium, whereas in

Differentiated Instruction

Gifted The mass of the Milky Way and other disklike galaxies can be calculated using Kepler's third law. Newton showed that the relationship between P^2 and a^3 is affected by the sum of the masses of the two orbiting objects, the Sun and planet in our previous usage in Chapter 29. The law becomes $(m_1 + m_2)P^2 = a^3$, where P is the period in years, a is the semimajor axis in AU, and $m_1 + m_2$ is the sum of the masses in solar mass units. Taking the Sun and the galaxy as the two masses, the sum reduces to simply M, the mass of the galaxy, because the Sun's mass is insignificant by comparison. Thus, Kepler's third law becomes $MP^2 = a^3$, where P is the Sun's orbital period and a is its orbital radius. Have students convert the Sun's orbital radius, $a = 28\ 000$ ly, to astronomical units, then use this value with $P = 240$ million years to find M in solar mass units. The value of a converts to 1.77×10^9 AU, and $M = a^3/P^2 = 9.6 \times 10^{10}$ solar masses. Note that this method measures only the mass in the central region of the galaxy, inside the Sun's orbit. **L3**

globular cluster stars, this proportion can be as high as 99.9 percent. This indicates their extreme age. The nuclear bulge of the galaxy also contains stars with compositions like those of globular cluster stars.

Stellar Populations Most of the young stars in the galaxy are located in the spiral arms of the disk, where the interstellar gas and dust are concentrated. Most star formation takes place in the arms. There is little interstellar material and very few stars currently forming in the halo or the nuclear bulge of the galaxy. In fact, the galaxy could be divided into two components: the round part made up of the halo and bulge, where the stars are old and contain only traces of heavy elements; and the disk, especially the spiral arms, where stars are still forming, as illustrated in *Figure 31-5.* Astronomers divide stars in these two regions into two classes. Population I stars are those in the disk and arms and have small amounts of heavy elements. Population II stars are those in the halo and bulge and contain only traces of heavy elements. The Sun is a Population I star.

FORMATION AND EVOLUTION OF THE MILKY WAY

The fact that the halo and bulge are made exclusively of old stars suggests that these parts of the galaxy formed first, before the disk that contains only younger stars. Astronomers therefore hypothesize that the galaxy began as a spherical cloud in space. The first stars formed while this cloud was round. This explains why the halo, which contains the oldest stars, is spherical. The nuclear bulge, which is also round, represents the inner portion of the original cloud. The cloud eventually collapsed under the force of its own gravity, and rotation forced it into a disklike shape. Stars that formed after this time have orbits lying in the plane of the disk.

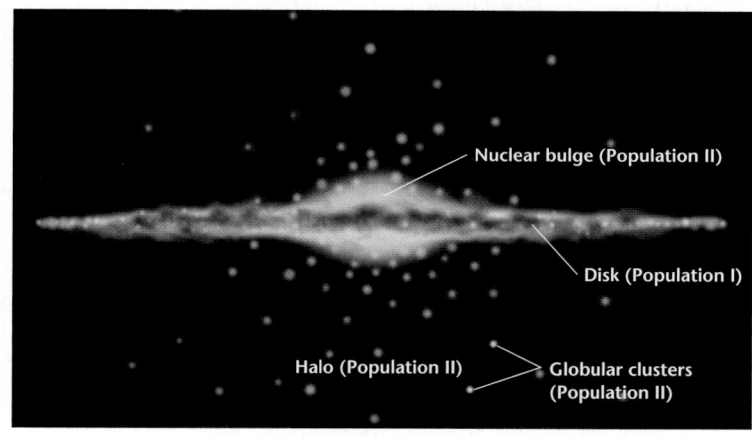

Figure 31-5 Globular clusters and the nuclear bulge contain old stars poor in heavy elements. The disk contains young stars that have a higher heavy element content. (not to scale)

Nuclear bulge (Population II)

Disk (Population I)

Halo (Population II)

Globular clusters (Population II)

31.1 *The Milky Way Galaxy* **837**

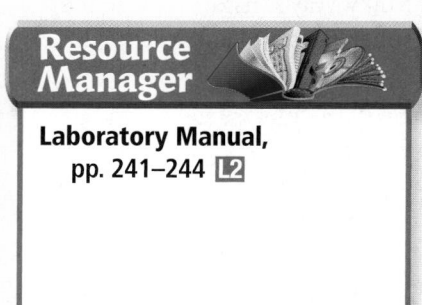

Check for Understanding

Activity

Locate a good-quality color photograph of a portion of the Milky Way, preferably one that includes the central region of the galaxy. Have students examine the photo and identify all of the objects they can. Students should be able to identify parts of the galaxy, star clusters, gas and dust clouds, and individual stars. **L2** **ELL**

Reteach

As a means of reinforcing student knowledge about star formation and the formation of the Milky Way, have students compare the formation of the Sun and planets with the formation of the galaxy. Students should point out that each formation process started with a rotating cloud of gas, which collapsed gravitationally and was flattened into a disk by rotation. Also, in each case, a central object formed that contained a great deal of mass, and objects orbit the center of mass.

✔Assessment

Portfolio Have students create posters that diagram the Milky Way and identify its parts. For each identifier, have students write brief descriptions. For example, for globular clusters, students could include Population II, old stars, located in the halo, and formed early in the Milky Way's history, before the spherical cloud collapsed. **P**

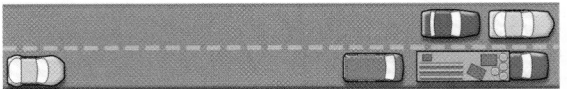

Figure 31-6 A slow truck on a highway causing a buildup of cars around it is similar to how spiral density waves create spiral arms in a galaxy.

They also contain greater quantities of heavy elements because they formed from gas that had been enriched by previous generations of massive stars.

MAINTAINING SPIRAL ARMS

Most of the main features of the galaxy are clearly understood by astronomers, except for the way in which the spiral arms are maintained. The Milky Way is subject to gravitational tugs by neighboring galaxies and is periodically disturbed by supernovae explosions, both of which can create spiral arms. There are two different theories about how these arms are maintained. One is that a kind of wave called a spiral density wave is responsible. You can think of a **spiral density wave** as alternating dense and less-dense regions that are frozen in place and rotate as a rigid pattern. As the wave moves through gas and dust, it causes a temporary buildup of material, like a slow truck on the highway that causes a buildup of cars, illustrated in *Figure 31-6*. The other theory is that the spiral arms are not permanent structures but instead are continually forming as a result of disturbances such as supernovae explosions. The Milky Way has a broken spiral-arm pattern, which most astronomers think fits this second model best. However, some galaxies have a prominent 2-armed pattern, almost certainly created by density waves.

SECTION ASSESSMENT

1. How did astronomers determine where Earth is located within the Milky Way?

2. What do measurements of the mass of the Milky Way indicate?

3. How are Population I stars and Population II stars different?

4. How can variable stars be used to determine the distance to globular clusters?

5. **Thinking Critically** If our solar system were slightly above the disk of the Milky Way, why would astronomers still have difficulty determining the shape of the galaxy?

SKILL REVIEW

6. **Concept Mapping** Use the following terms to construct a concept map to organize the major ideas in this section. For more help, refer to the *Skill Handbook*.

- 1. cloud collapses
- 2. globular clusters form
- 3. spherical cloud
- 4. disk forms
- 5. stars and spiral arms form
- 6. galaxy nucleus forms

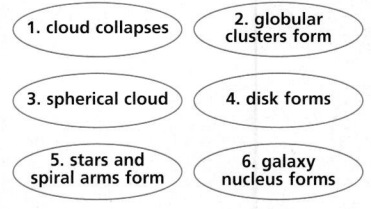

earthgeu.com/self_check_quiz

SECTION ASSESSMENT

1. by finding the center of the galaxy through the study of the distribution of globular clusters

2. contains about 100 billion stars, and a great deal more mass resides in the outer galaxy, in the halo

3. Population I stars orbit in the plane of the galactic disk and the spiral arms, and they have higher abundances of heavy elements than Population II stars, which reside in the central bulge and the halo of the galaxy. Population II stars are old, while Population I stars can be very young.

4. The period-luminosity relationship in variable stars can be used to find the luminosity, and hence the distance, of a star once its period has been measured.

5. The Milky Way is so large that our solar system would have to be quite some distance above the galactic plane to make the shape of the galaxy clearly visible.

6. 3–2–1–4–6–5 Some of these events, such as the formation of the nucleus and of stars and spiral arms, probably happened at the same time.

Our galaxy is just one of billions of galaxies in the universe. We live in a cosmos of galaxies that have a wide variety of sizes and shapes. By observing those galaxies that are farthest away, astronomers get an idea of how the universe looks as a whole. Because it takes so long for light to reach us from remote galaxies, these far away galaxies also provide an idea of what the universe was like long ago.

DISCOVERING OTHER GALAXIES

Astronomers were aware of galaxies outside the Milky Way long before they knew what these objects were. Many objects had been observed scattered throughout the sky, some with spiral shapes, but astronomers disagreed about their nature. Some astronomers hypothesized that these objects were nebulae or star clusters within the Milky Way. Others hypothesized that they were distant galaxies, as large as the Milky Way.

The question of what these objects were was answered by Edwin Hubble in 1924, when he discovered Cepheid variable stars in the Great Nebula in the Andromeda constellation. Using these stars to measure the distance to the nebula, Hubble showed that they were much too far away to be located in our own galaxy. The Andromeda Nebula then became known as the Andromeda Galaxy, shown in *Figure 31-7.*

Classification of Galaxies Hubble went on to study galaxies and sort them into categories according to their shapes. The disklike galaxies with spiral arms were called spiral galaxies. These were divided into two subclasses: normal spirals and barred spirals. Barred spirals have

OBJECTIVES

- **Describe** *how astronomers classify galaxies.*
- **Identify** *how galaxies are organized into clusters and superclusters.*
- **Describe** *the expansion of the universe.*

VOCABULARY

supercluster
Hubble constant
radio galaxy
active galactic nucleus
quasar

Figure 31-7 The Andromeda Galaxy is a spiral galaxy like the Milky Way. The two bright elliptical objects are small galaxies orbiting the Andromeda Galaxy.

839

Tying to Previous Knowledge

The masses of galaxies, and of clusters of galaxies, are determined by the application of Kepler's and Newton's laws of orbits and gravitation to such remote objects.

Section 31.2

Prepare

Section Background

For section content background, refer to **Other Galaxies in the Universe** on pages 832C–D.

Preplanning

Refer to the Chapter Organizer on pages 832A–B.

1 Focus

Section Focus

Before presenting the lesson, display **Section Focus Transparency 100** on the overhead projector.
L1 ELL

NY Core Curriculum Standards

Page 838: St 1 Science KI 1 & 3, St 4 KI 1.2b, St 6 KI 1 & 4
Page 839: St. 1 Science KI 1 & 3, St 6 KI 1, 2, & 3

Content Background

At one point in time, Hubble's tuning-fork diagram was viewed as an evolutionary diagram for galaxies. It was theorized that all galaxies started out as ellipticals and eventually evolved into spirals. As astronomers were able to look farther into the universe, and hence farther back in time, spirals as well as ellipticals were observed. If astronomers were looking so far back in time, then the young galaxies should be ellipticals, but this was not the case. The tuning-fork diagram is simply a convenient way to organize the different classes.

Using an Analogy

Logical-Mathematical

According to the classification method developed by Edwin Hubble, an elliptical galaxy is classified as E0 to E7, depending on the ratio of the long axis to the short axis of the galaxy. If a is the long axis and b the short axis, then the degree of ellipticity is given by $10(1 - b/a)$. A round galaxy, with $a = b$, has an ellipticity of 0 and is classified as an E0 galaxy. A galaxy whose long axis is twice its short axis (i.e., $a = 2b$) is an E5 galaxy. Have students measure the ellipticities of familiar objects such as soccer balls and footballs, bananas, toothpicks, and lemons. How are these objects analogous to galaxies? Elliptical galaxies have measured ellipticities up to 7; thus, E7 galaxies are the most elongated elliptical galaxies known. Some of the objects suggested above, such as the banana and the toothpick, may exceed this ellipticity. **L2**

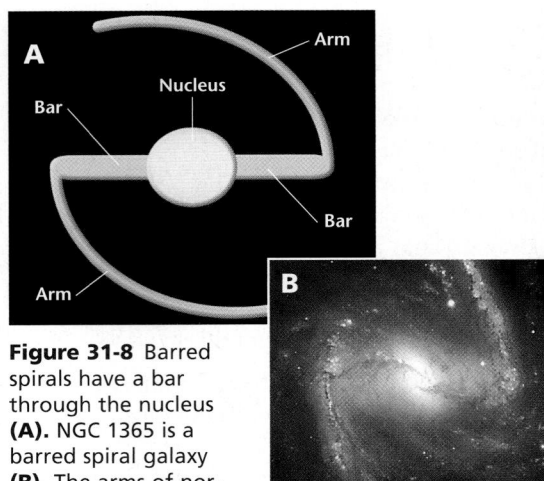
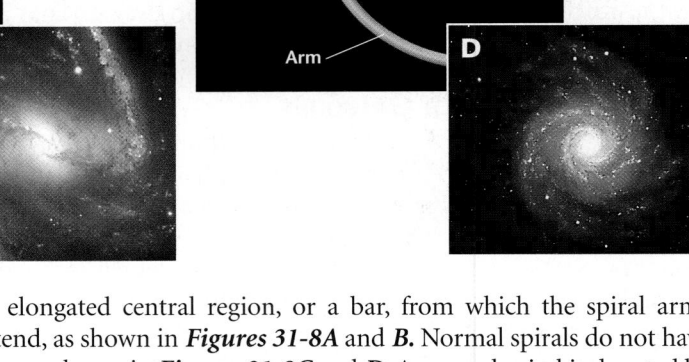

Figure 31-8 Barred spirals have a bar through the nucleus **(A)**. NGC 1365 is a barred spiral galaxy **(B)**. The arms of normal spirals extend directly from the nucleus **(C)**. NGC 628 is a normal spiral galaxy **(D)**.

Figure 31-9 This galaxy, M32, is an elliptical galaxy. Notice the uniform distribution of stars throughout the galaxy. Despite their flat appearance, ellipticals are three-dimensional, and are similar in shape to a football.

an elongated central region, or a bar, from which the spiral arms extend, as shown in *Figures 31-8A* and **B.** Normal spirals do not have bars, as shown in *Figures 31-8C* and **D.** A normal spiral is denoted by the letter *S*, and a barred spiral is denoted by *SB*. Normal and barred spirals are further subdivided based on how tightly the spiral arms are wound, as well as the size and brightness of the nucleus. The letter *a* represents tightly wound arms and a large, bright nucleus. The letter *c* represents loosely wound arms and a small, dim nucleus. The letter *b* represents characteristics between those of *a* and *c*. Thus, a normal spiral with class *a* arms and nucleus is denoted *Sa*, while a barred spiral with class *a* arms and nucleus is denoted *SBa*. Galaxies with flat disks, that do not have spiral arms are denoted *S0*. When an *S0* galaxy is observed edge-on, it often has a band of dark dust crossing the nuclear bulge.

In addition to spiral galaxies, there are galaxies that are not flattened into disks and do not have spiral arms, as shown in *Figure 31-9.* These are called elliptical galaxies. Ellipticals are divided into subclasses based on the apparent ratio of their major and minor axes. Round ellipticals are classified as *E0*, while very elongated ellipticals are classified as *E7*. Others are denoted by the letter *E* followed by a numeral *1* through *6*. The classification of both spiral and elliptical galaxies can be summarized by Hubble's tuning-fork diagram, illustrated in *Figure 31-10.* You will learn more about galaxy classification in the *Internet GeoLab* at the end of this chapter.

Some galaxies do not have distinct shapes, and thus do not fit into either the spiral or elliptical classification. These are called irregular galaxies and are denoted by *Irr*. The Large and Small Magellanic Clouds are irregular galaxies that are close to the Milky Way.

840 CHAPTER 31 *Galaxies and the Universe*

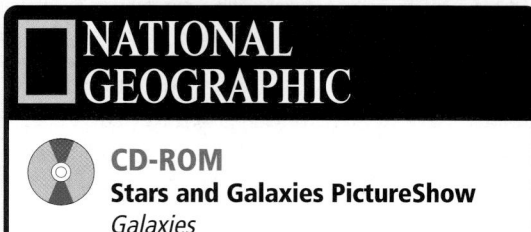

NATIONAL GEOGRAPHIC

CD-ROM
Stars and Galaxies PictureShow
Galaxies

Resource Manager

Teaching Transparency 95 L2 ELL
Laboratory Manual, pp. 245–248 L2

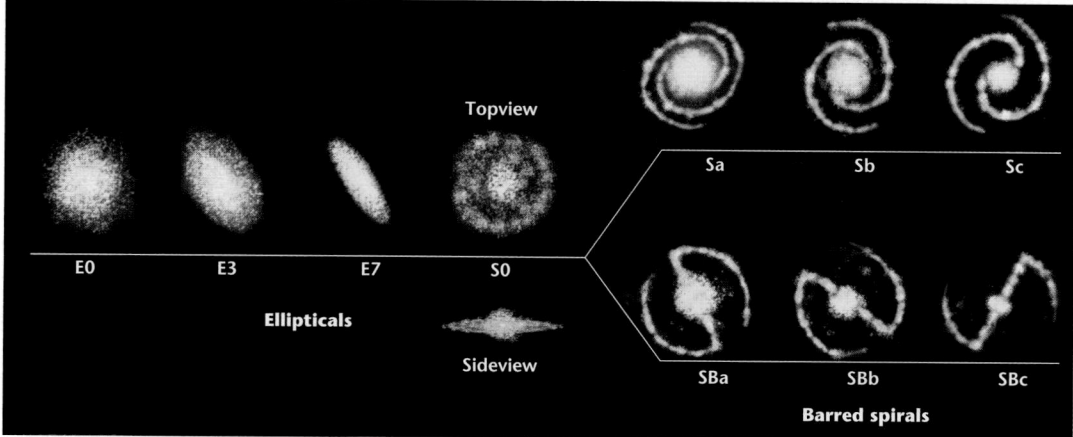

E0   E3   E7   S0

Ellipticals

Topview

Sideview

Sa   Sb   Sc

SBa   SBb   SBc

Barred spirals

Masses of Galaxies Masses of galaxies range from the dwarf ellipticals, which have masses of perhaps one million Suns; to large spirals, such as the Milky Way, with masses of around 100 billion Suns; to the largest galaxies, called giant ellipticals, which have masses as high as 100 trillion times the Sun's mass. Measurements of the masses of many galaxies indicate that they have extensive halos containing more mass than is visible, just as the Milky Way does.

Figure 31-10 The Hubble tuning fork diagram summarizes the Hubble classification scheme for non-unusual galaxies. An S0 galaxy is related to both spirals and ellipticals.

GROUPS AND CLUSTERS OF GALAXIES

Most galaxies are located in groups, rather than being spread uniformly throughout the universe. The Milky Way belongs to a small cluster of galaxies called the Local Group. The diameter of the Local Group is roughly 2 million ly. There are about 35 known members, most of which are dwarf ellipticals. The Milky Way and Andromeda Galaxies are the largest galaxies in the group.

Clusters larger than the Local Group may have hundreds of members and diameters in the range of about 5 to 30 million ly. The Virgo cluster is shown in *Figure 31-11.* Most of the galaxies in the inner region of a large cluster are ellipticals, while there is a more even mix of ellipticals and spirals in the outer portions.

In regions where galaxies are as close together as they are in large clusters, gravitational interactions among galaxies have many important effects. Galaxies often collide and form strangely shaped galaxies,

Figure 31-11 Galaxies are located in groups, or clusters, like the Virgo cluster.

31.2 Other Galaxies in the Universe **841**

Interpreting the Photo

Figure 31-12B This photo is a close-up of the nuclear region of the Andromeda Galaxy, taken by the *Hubble Space Telescope.* The small, fainter bright spot is considered to be the real nucleus of the Andromeda Galaxy because rotation occurs around this point. The other bright spot is possibly the nucleus of another galaxy that collided with Andromeda and will eventually merge with the real nucleus.

Using an Analogy

Explain to students that the way in which galaxies separate from each other as the universe expands is similar to the way raisins in dough separate from each other as a loaf of bread rises. Each raisin moves away from the others, and the greater the separation between raisins, the faster they move apart.

Using Scientific Terms

Astronomers use the term *visible mass* to refer to all the mass that is producing light that we can see, such as stars in a galaxy. Mass is often dark, such as dark matter, so it is not easy to detect, and is thus, not visible.

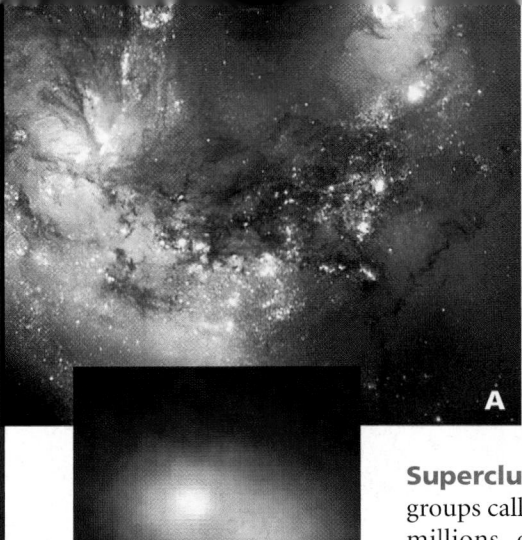

Figure 31-12 Strangely shaped galaxies, such as the Antennae Galaxies (NGC 4038 and NGC 4039) **(A),** are often the result of a collision. At the center of the Andromeda Galaxy, the *Hubble Space Telescope* uncovered two nuclei **(B),** which are probably a result of one galaxy being consumed by another.

such as those shown in *Figure 31-12A,* or galaxies with more than one nucleus, such as the Andromeda Galaxy, shown in *Figure 31-12B.*

Masses of Clusters For clusters of galaxies, the mass determined by analyzing the motion of member galaxies is always much larger than the sum of the visible masses of the galaxies. This suggests that most of the mass in a cluster of galaxies is invisible, which provides astronomers with the strongest evidence that the universe contains a great amount of dark matter. The nature of dark matter is still unknown.

Superclusters Clusters of galaxies are organized into even larger groups called **superclusters.** These gigantic formations, hundreds of millions of light-years in size, can be observed only when astronomers map out the locations of many galaxies ranging over huge distances. These superclusters appear in sheetlike and threadlike shapes, giving the appearance of a gigantic bubble bath with galaxies located on the surfaces of the bubbles, and the inner air pockets void of galaxies.

THE EXPANDING UNIVERSE

Edwin Hubble made yet another dramatic discovery, this time in 1929. It was known at the time that most galaxies have redshifts in their spectra, indicating that all galaxies are moving away from Earth. Hubble measured the redshifts and distances of many galaxies and found that the redshift of a galaxy depends on its distance from Earth. The farther away a galaxy is, the faster it is moving away. The universe is expanding.

You might infer from this that Earth is at the center of the universe. Actually, this is not the case. An observer located in any galaxy, at any place in the universe, will observe the same thing we do: all other galaxies move away with speeds that depend on their distances. In a medium that is uniformly expanding, all points are moving away from all other points, and no point has to be at the center. You will experiment with uniform expansion in the *MiniLab* later in this section.

Hubble's Law Hubble determined that the universe is expanding by making a graph of the speed at which a galaxy is moving versus its distance. The result is a straight line, which can be expressed as a simple equation, $v = Hd$, where v is the speed at which a galaxy is moving away measured in kilometers per second; d is the distance to the galaxy measured in megaparsecs (Mpc), where 1 Mpc = 1×10^6 pc; and H is

NY Core Curriculum Standards

Page 842: St 1 Math KI 1, Science 1, 2, 3, & Engin KI 1, St 4 KI 1.2a, St 6 KI 2, 3, & 4
Page 843: St 1 Math KI 1, 2, 3, Science KI 1, 2, & 3, St 4 KI 1.2a, St 6 KI 1, 2, 3, 4, & 5

Cultural Diversity

Margaret J. Geller (1947–) Margaret Geller earned a Ph.D. in physics from Princeton in 1975, and at that time, she was only the second woman to do so. She is now a professor at Harvard University and also is associated with the Smithsonian Astrophysical Observatory. Geller and her partner, John Huchra, map the positions of galaxies in three-dimensional space. Geller is one of the pioneers in mapping the universe. She has served on several advisory committees to NASA and the NSF, and has received numerous awards.

Across the Curriculum

History The human view of Earth's place in the cosmos has changed drastically on several occasions in history. Each time, the new perception placed Earth in a less central position, so that now, we realize that Earth orbits an ordinary star far from the center of a galaxy that is one of billions, occupying no special place in the universe. Have each student choose one of these major changes in perception and write a brief essay about its historical context. How was the new concept received by scientists and the public?

a number called the **Hubble constant,** that is measured in kilometers per second per megaparsec. H represents the slope of the line. You will plot Hubble's law in the *Problem-Solving Lab* on this page.

To measure H requires finding distances and speeds for many galaxies, out to the largest possible distance, and constructing a graph to find the slope. This is a difficult task, because it is hard to measure accurate distances to the most remote galaxies. Hubble himself could obtain only a crude value for H. Measuring an accurate value for H was one of the key goals of astronomers who designed the *Hubble Space Telescope.* It took nearly ten years after the *Hubble Space Telescope*'s launch to gather enough data to pinpoint the value of H to the satisfaction of most astronomers. Currently, the best measurements indicate a value of approximately 70 kilometers per second per megaparsec.

Once the value of H is known, it can be used to find distances to far away galaxies. By measuring the speed at which a galaxy is moving, astronomers can locate that speed on the graph and can then determine the corresponding distance of the galaxy on the graph. This method works for the most remote galaxies that can be observed, and it allows astronomers to measure distances to the edge of the observable universe.

To learn more about the *Hubble Space Telescope,* go to the National Geographic Expedition on page 902.

Problem-Solving Lab

Making and Using Graphs

The Hubble constant The table lists distances and speeds for a number of galaxies.

Analysis

1. Use the data to construct a graph. Plot the distance on the *x*-axis and the speed on the *y*-axis.
2. Use a ruler to draw a straight line through the center of the band of points on the graph, so that about as many points lie above the line as below it. Make sure your line starts at the origin.
3. Measure the slope by choosing a point on the line and dividing the speed at that point by the distance.

Thinking Critically

4. What does the slope represent?
5. How accurate do you think your value of H is? Explain.
6. How would an astronomer improve this measurement of H?

Galaxy Data			
Distance (Mpc)	Speed (km/s)	Distance (Mpc)	Speed (km/s)
3.0	210	26.5	2087
8.3	450	33.7	2813
10.9	972	36.8	2697
16.2	1383	38.7	3177
17.0	1202	43.9	3835
20.4	1685	45.1	3470
21.9	1594	47.6	3784

31.2 Other Galaxies in the Universe **843**

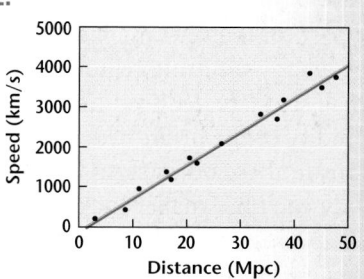

Interpreting the Photo

Figure 31-13 shows two images of the giant elliptical galaxy M87. One image shows a normal-looking elliptical galaxy, while the other reveals the vast jet of super-heated gas extending outward from the galaxy's core. The jet does not appear in the upper photo because this photo was exposed for a longer period of time than the lower photo.

Using Scientific Terms

The word *quasar* is a contraction of the original designation of these objects, which was *quasi-stellar objects*. Some astronomers refer to them as *QSOs*.

Content Background

The conclusion that the energetic objects in the cores of AGNs and quasars are black holes was based in part on the very small sizes of the energy-emitting regions. The small sizes are deduced from the rapidity of the brightness variations in these objects. An emitting body can't be smaller than the distance light travels in the time it takes for the object to change its brightness. Hence, a galactic nucleus or quasar that varies in a day's time can't be any larger in diameter than a light-day, or about the size of the solar system. The only object astronomers know of that can contain such vast amounts of mass in such a small space is a black hole.

Figure 31-13 M87 is a large radio galaxy **(A)**. In addition to radio lobes, M87 has a jet of gas that emits visible light **(B)**.

Figure 31-14 From a ground-based telescope, a quasar (right of center) looks much like a star **(A)**. From the *Hubble Space Telescope*, a quasar can be seen in the nucleus of a dim galaxy **(B)**.

ACTIVE GALAXIES

Radio-telescope surveys of the sky have revealed a number of galaxies that are extremely bright. These galaxies, called **radio galaxies,** are often giant elliptical galaxies that emit as much as or more energy in radio wavelengths than they do in wavelengths of visible light. Radio galaxies have many unusual properties. The radio emission usually comes from two huge lobes of very hot gas located on opposite sides of the visible galaxy. These lobes are linked to the galaxy by jets of very hot gas. The type of emission that comes from these regions indicates that the gas is ionized, and that electrons in the gas jets are traveling nearly at the speed of light. Many radio galaxies have jets that can be observed only at radio wavelengths. One of the brightest of the radio galaxies, a giant elliptical called M87, shown in *Figure 31-13,* also has a jet of gas that emits visible light extending from the galactic center out toward one of the radio-emitting lobes.

In some unusual galaxies, some sort of highly energetic object or activity exists in the core. This object or activity emits as much or more energy than the rest of the galaxy. The output of this energy often varies over time, sometimes as little as a few days. The cores of galaxies where these highly energetic objects or activities are located are called **active galactic nuclei,** or AGNs.

QUASARS

In the 1960s, astronomers discovered another new type of object. These objects looked like ordinary stars, but some were strong radio emitters. Most stars are not. The spectra of these new objects were completely different from the spectra of normal stars. Whereas most stars have spectra with absorption lines, these new objects had mostly

✓ Assessment

Performance Ask students to summarize the similarities among radio galaxies, active galactic nuclei, and quasars. Have students create a data table on the chalkboard outlining the results of their summaries. All three are sources of huge amounts of energy coming from small volumes of space, all involve jets of ionized gas, and all can vary in energy over a period of days. Use the Performance Task Assessment List for Data table in **PASC**, p. 37.

Differentiated Instruction

Learning Disabled The notion of vast energies and explosions often holds the attention of students. Have students work out how many 100-megaton nuclear bombs would have to explode every second to match the luminosity of a quasar. A 100-megaton bomb releases 4.2×10^{17} J, and the luminosity of a quasar is approximately 10^{40} W. Have students recall that 1 W = 1 J/s and provide students with scientific calculators if they do not have one of their own. 2.4×10^{22} bombs per second.

emission lines in their spectra. These starlike objects with emission lines in their spectra are called **quasars.** A quasar is shown in *Figure 31-14A.* At first, astronomers could not identify the emission lines in the spectra of quasars. Finally, they realized that the emission lines were spectral lines of common elements, such as hydrogen, shifted very far toward longer wavelengths. Soon, astronomers also discovered that many quasars vary in brightness over a period of a few days. Once astronomers had identified the large spectral-line shifts of quasars, they wondered whether these could be redshifts caused by the expansion of the universe.

The redshifts of quasars were much larger than any that had been observed in galaxies up to that time, which would mean that the quasars were much farther away than any known galaxy. Some astronomers at first doubted that quasars were far away, but in the decades since quasars were discovered, more evidence supports the hypothesis that quasars are indeed far away. One bit of supporting evidence is that some quasars are associated with clusters of galaxies with the same redshift, verifying that they are the same distance away. Another, more important discovery is that most quasars are nuclei of very dim galaxies, as shown in *Figure 31-14B.* The quasars appear to be extra-bright active galactic nuclei—so much brighter than their surrounding galaxies that astronomers could not even see the galaxies at first.

Looking Back in Time Because many quasars are far away, it takes their light a long time to reach Earth. For this reason, astronomers observing a quasar are seeing it as it was a long time ago. For example, it takes light from the Sun approximately eight minutes to reach Earth. When we observe that light, we are seeing the Sun as it

MiniLab

Measuring Redshifts

Model uniform expansion of the universe and the redshifts of galaxies that result from expansion.

Procedure 👓 🧤

1. Use a felt tip marking pen to make four dots in a row, each separated by 1 cm, on the surface of an uninflated balloon. Label the dots 1, 2, 3, and 4.
2. Partially inflate the balloon. Using a piece of string and a meterstick, measure the distance from dot 1 to each of the other dots. Record your measurements.
3. Inflate the balloon further, and again measure the distance from dot 1 to each of the other dots. Record your measurements.
4. Repeat step 3 with the balloon fully inflated.

Analyze and Conclude

1. Are the dots still separated from each other by equal distances? Explain.
2. How far did each dot move away from dot 1 after each inflation?
3. What would be the result if you had measured the distances from dot 4 instead of dot 1? From dot 2?
4. How does this activity illustrate uniform expansion of the universe and redshifts of galaxies?

31.2 Other Galaxies in the Universe **845**

Resource Manager

GeoLab and MiniLab Worksheets, p. 127
L2

✔Assessment

Knowledge Ask students how this exercise would be different if the separations between the dots were not equal to begin with. There would be no significant change. The separations would still increase in proportion to the original distances between dots.

MiniLab

Purpose
Students will use a model to help them understand the uniform expansion of the universe.

Process Skills
measure in SI, analyze, formulate models, recognize spatial relationships

Materials
felt-tip marker, large uninflated balloon, meterstick, string

Teaching Strategies
This should be done in groups of three or four, with each group having its own balloon.

Expected Results
Students should find that the dots become more widely separated as the balloon expands. They should also find that the rate of separation of dots is proportional to their initial separation, for example, dot 4 will increase its separation from dot 1 at twice the rate that dot 2 increases its separation from dot 1.

Analyze and Conclude

1. The dots are still separated from each other by equal distances, because the separations have grown uniformly as the balloon was inflated.
2. The distance of each dot from dot 1 should increase in proportion to its original separation from dot 1. Thus at an intermediate point dot 2 would be 2 cm from dot 1 instead of 1 cm, dot 3 would be 4 cm from dot 1 instead of 2 cm, and so on. At a later point, the separations would all be tripled, and so on.
3. The result would have been the same no matter which dot was chosen as the reference point.
4. It shows how galaxies (the dots) move away from each other at rates that are proportional to their original separations, and it shows that the observed expansion looks the same from any galaxy.

Check for Understanding

Discussion

Ask students to discuss the reasons why quasars are valuable probes of the large-scale properties of the universe.

Reteach

Ask students to summarize the basic properties of normal and active galaxies.

✓Assessment

Knowledge Ask students the following question. If the universe were not expanding uniformly, how would this effect the balloon model? The dots would move away from each other, but not uniformly. This would be analogous to having very strong portions of rubber in the balloon so that some galaxies wouldn't move far and weak spots that would stretch more so that galaxies would move farther.

was eight minutes earlier. When we observe the Andromeda Galaxy, we see the way it looked two million years earlier. The most remote quasars are several billion light-years away, which indicates that they existed billions of years ago. If quasars are extra-bright galactic nuclei, then the many distant ones are nuclei of galaxies as they existed when the universe was young. This suggests that many galaxies went through a quasar stage when they were young. In that case, today's active galactic nuclei might be former quasars that are not quite as energetic as they were long ago.

Source of Power The AGNs and quasars emit far more energy than ordinary galaxies, but they are as small as solar systems. This suggests that all of these objects are supermassive black holes. Recall that our own galaxy is hypothesized to contain such an object within its core, and that this object has a mass of about one million Suns. The black holes in the cores of AGNs and quasars are much more massive, up to hundreds of millions of times the mass of the Sun. The beams of charged particles that stream out of the cores of radio galaxies and form jets are probably created by magnetic forces. As material falls into a black hole, the magnetic forces push the charged particles out into jets. There is evidence that similar beams or jets occur in other types of AGNs and in quasars. In fact, radio-lobed quasars have jets that are essentially related to radio galaxies.

The role of AGNs and especially quasars as early stages in the evolution of galaxies provide important clues for astronomers as they study the origin and evolution of the universe itself. With the discovery of new and more distant objects, astronomers are getting closer to unraveling the story of the universe.

Earth Science Online

Update For an online update on quasars, visit the Earth Science Web Site at earthgeu.com

SECTION ASSESSMENT

1. How did astronomers discover that there are other galaxies beyond the Milky Way?

2. Why do astronomers theorize that most of the matter in galaxies and clusters of galaxies is dark matter?

3. Why is it difficult for astronomers to accurately measure a value for the Hubble constant, *H*? Once a value is determined, what can it be used for?

4. Explain the differences among normal spiral, barred spiral, elliptical, and irregular galaxies.

5. **Thinking Critically** How would the nighttime sky look from Earth if we lived in an elliptical galaxy?

SKILL REVIEW

6. **Using Numbers** Suppose that a distant galaxy is moving away from Earth at a velocity of 20 000 km/s. Assuming that the value of the Hubble constant is 70 kilometers per second per megaparsec, how far away is this galaxy? For more help, refer to the *Skill Handbook*.

earthgeu.com/self_check_quiz

SECTION ASSESSMENT

1. Edwin Hubble determined the distance to the Andromeda Nebula and found it to lie well outside of our own galaxy.

2. Mass estimates for our own galaxy show that most of the mass is in the outer regions, in some invisible form. Mass measurements for clusters of galaxies show, similarly, that the masses far exceed the masses of the visible galaxies.

3. it requires measuring both the speeds and distances to very far-away galaxies using other methods; distance

4. Normal spiral and barred spiral galaxies are differentiated on the basis of the shape of the central bulge. In a normal spiral, the central bulge is circular, whereas in a barred spiral, the central bulge is elongated. Elliptical galaxies are not flattened into a plane. Irregular galaxies are those that do not fit into either the spiral or elliptical category.

5. The nighttime sky would show a uniform distribution of stars, with no preferred plane of location.

6. $d = v/H = 20\,000/70 = 286$ Mpc

You've learned about Earth, the planets, the Sun, stars, and galaxies. Now you are ready to consider the universe as a whole. The study of the universe, its current nature, and its origin and evolution, is called **cosmology.**

As in other areas of science, astronomers use a combination of observations and theoretical models in cosmology. One difference between cosmology and other areas of study is that in cosmology, objects that have a range of properties cannot be compared, as they can be in the study of stars, for example. Astronomers have only one universe to consider and nothing to compare it with. However astronomers can use particle accelerators to learn about the universe, as you'll learn in the *Science & Technology* feature at the end of this chapter.

MODELS OF THE UNIVERSE

The fact that the universe is expanding implies that it had a beginning. The theory that the universe began as a point and has been expanding ever since is called the **Big Bang theory.** The Big Bang theory is not an explosion into space, but instead is an expansion of space with matter going along for the ride. Not all astronomers agree that the universe had a beginning, which led to an alternative theory. The **steady-state theory** proposes that the universe looks the same on large scales to all observers, and that it has always looked that way. The steady-state universe doesn't change with time. However, if the universe is expanding, how can this be true? Supporters of the steady-state theory propose that new matter is created and added to the universe as it expands, and thus, the overall density of the universe does not change, as illustrated in *Figure 31-15.*

OBJECTIVES

- **Explain** the different theories about the formation of the universe.
- **Describe** the possible outcomes of universal expansion.

VOCABULARY

cosmology
Big Bang theory
steady-state theory
cosmic background radiation
inflationary universe

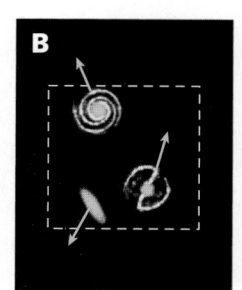
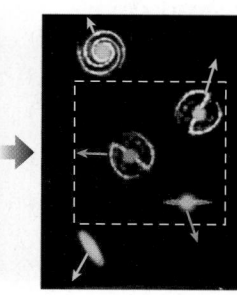
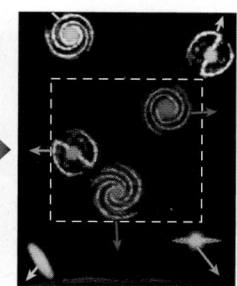

Figure 31-15 Without the creation of new matter, the area within the dotted box would not contain 3 galaxies after a time **(A).** The steady-state theory requires new matter to be added so that the area within the dotted box always contains 3 galaxies **(B).**

Section 31.3

Prepare

Section Background

For section content background, refer to **Cosmology** on page 832D.

Preplanning

Refer to the Chapter Organizer on pages 832A–B.

1 Focus

Section Focus

Before presenting the lesson, display **Section Focus Transparency 101** on the overhead projector.
L1 **ELL**

Resource Manager

Section Focus Transparency 101 **L1** **ELL**
Study Guide for Content Mastery, pp. 199–200 **L2**

Tying to Previous Knowledge

It is essential for students to realize that distance measurements to the most faraway galaxies and quasars depend on measurements to closer objects. Every distance-measurement method depends on the one before it, and the first method is stellar parallax, which is based on the Sun-Earth distance (see Chapter 30).

NY Core Curriculum Standards

Page 846: St 1 Math KI 1, 2, 3, Science KI 1, & 2, St 4 KI 1.2a & 1.2b, St 6 KI 1, 4, & 5
Page 847: St 1 Science KI 1, 3, & Engin KI 1, St 4 KI 1.2a, St 6 KI 1, 2, 4, & 5

Using Scientific Terms

The word *cosmology,* from the Greek *kosmos,* refers to the science of the universe as it is today. Technically, the word for studies of the origin of the universe is *cosmogony,* which dates back to times when philosophers thought that the solar system was the entire universe. Today, most scientists use *cosmology* to describe any study of the universe, including its origin.

Discussion

Interpersonal Divide students into groups to debate the merits of the steady-state model versus the Big Bang model. The debate can be held when this section is completed, but the assignment should be made at the beginning, so that students can begin gathering data for their arguments. Some outside reading will be needed to be sure that all the important points are covered. Caution students that the debate will include only scientific arguments based on logic and observation.

COOP LEARN

Activity

Visual-Spatial The *WMAP* made several important observational discoveries about background radiation. Have students work in groups to prepare posters that summarize results from *WMAP.* **L2**

COOP LEARN **P**

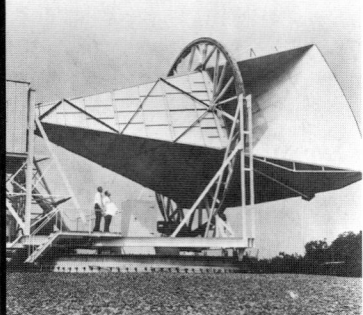

Figure 31-16 The cosmic background radiation was discovered accidentally with this radio antenna at Bell Labs, in Holmdel, New Jersey.

Figure 31-17 The map of the cosmic background radiation made by *COBE* shows areas that are slightly warmer than 2.735 K (pink) and slightly cooler than 2.735 K (blue).

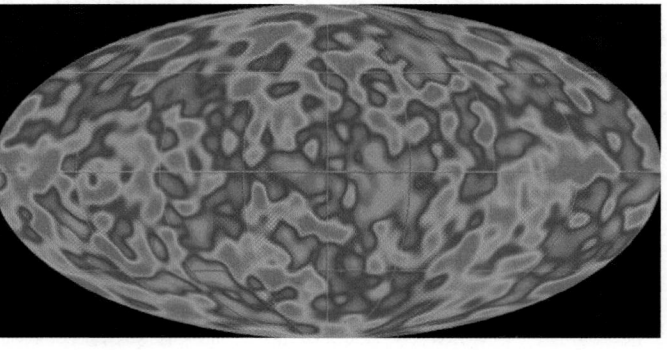

Many observational tests can be conducted to provide support for either the Big Bang or the steady-state theory. Each theory predicts what the universe should look like. By observing the universe, astronomers can determine which predictions are actually met. This in turn provides support for one theory or the other. Today, the evidence weighs in favor of the Big Bang.

Cosmic Background Radiation If the universe began in a highly compressed state, as the Big Bang theory suggests, it would have been very hot, and the high temperatures would have filled it with radiation. If radiation filled the universe back then, that same radiation should still fill the universe. Originally, when the radiation was able to escape, it would have been in the form of visible light and infrared radiation, which have high energy and short wavelengths. However, as the universe expanded and cooled, the radiation would have been Doppler shifted to lower energies and longer wavelengths.

The existence of such radiation in the universe today would not support the steady-state theory of the universe, which does not predict such radiation. In 1965, some scientists discovered a persistent background noise in their radio antenna, shown in *Figure 31-16.* This noise was caused by weak radiation, called the **cosmic background radiation,** that appeared to come from all directions in space and corresponded to an emitting object having a temperature of about 2.735 K (−270°C). This was very close to the temperature predicted by the Big Bang theory, and the radiation was interpreted to be from the beginning of the Big Bang.

Mapping the Radiation Since the discovery of the cosmic background radiation, extensive observations have confirmed that it matches the properties of the predicted leftover radiation from the early, hot phase in the expansion of the universe. Earth's atmosphere blocks much of the radiation, so it is best observed from high-altitude balloons or satellites. An orbiting observatory called the *Cosmic Background Explorer (COBE),* launched by NASA in 1989, mapped the radiation in detail, as shown in *Figure 31-17. COBE* operated for more than ten years. The peak of the radiation it measured has a wavelength of approximately 1 mm; thus, it is microwave radiation in the radio portion of the electromagnetic spectrum.

848 CHAPTER 31 *Galaxies and the Universe*

Environmental Connection

Life-forms on Earth's surface are subjected to many forms of radiation. The cosmic background radiation is one of these, but it is so low in intensity that it has no effect on organisms. Other kinds of natural radiation include both electromagnetic waves and subatomic particles. Particle radiation comes from naturally occurring radioactive elements in Earth's crust and from cosmic rays from space. Fortunately, Earth's atmosphere stops most of these from reaching the ground.

Differentiated Instruction

Gifted The notion that the universe is expanding from a single point dates back to the early 1920s, even before the expansion of the universe was discovered. A universal origin in a hot, dense state was predicted by Belgian scientist and clergyman Georges LeMaître, based on a solution to equations from Einsten's theory of general relativity. Have students read about LeMaître's prediction and write brief reports about it.

Proponents of the steady-state universe theory have not succeeded in explaining the cosmic background radiation. This is one of the major reasons that most astronomers do not accept this model. Other tests that can be used to validate either the steady-state theory or the Big Bang theory are whether or not each theory can explain redshifts of galaxies, the evolution of galaxies, and quasars.

THE BIG BANG MODEL

In the Big Bang model, there is a competition between the outward momentum of the expansion of the universe and the inward force of gravity as the matter in the universe acts to slow the expansion, as illustrated in *Figure 31-18A.* What ultimately will happen depends on which of these two forces is stronger. There are three possible outcomes for the universe: an open universe, in which the expansion will never stop; a closed universe, in which the expansion will stop and turn into a contraction; and a flat universe, in which the expansion will slow to a halt in an infinite amount of time—but it will never contract. All three cases, illustrated in *Figure 31-18B,* are based on the premise that the rate of expansion has slowed down since the beginning of the universe. The question would then appear to be, How much further will it slow down?

The Critical Density The total amount of matter in the universe is one of the factors that will determine whether or not the expansion will stop. The total amount of matter in the universe is expressed in terms of the average density of matter, something that astronomers can observe. The *critical density,* about 10^{-26} kg/m^3, is the dividing point between a closed or open universe. If the average density is higher than the critical density, the universe is closed, but if the average density is lower than the critical density, the universe is open. If the density equals the critical density, the universe is flat. By observing the average density of matter, astronomers can predict how the universe will change on a large scale. Observations of visible galaxies reveal an average density much less than the critical density. However, as you've learned, there is evidence that a great amount of dark matter exists in the universe, which impacts the average density.

Figure 31-18 Gravity competes with the momentum of the expansion **(A).** The universe could be open, flat, or closed **(B).** The flat universe line will gradually become a horizontal line, while the open universe line will keep increasing.

A

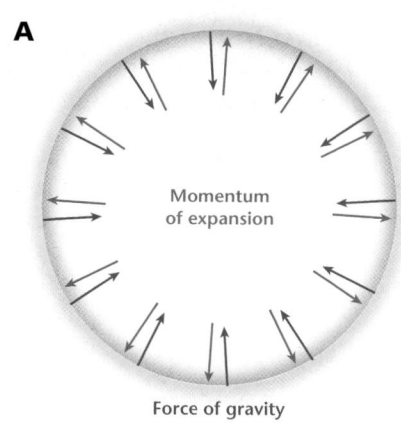

Momentum of expansion

Force of gravity

B

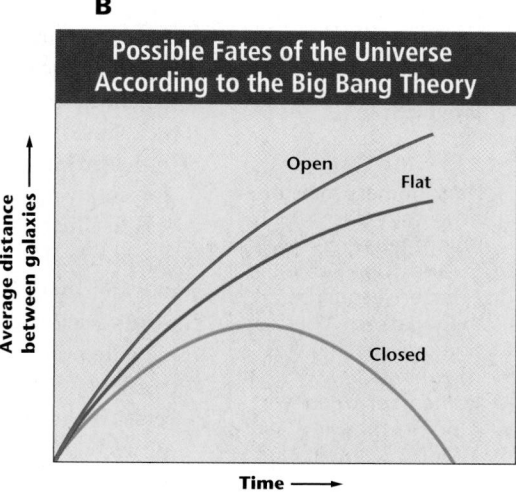

Possible Fates of the Universe According to the Big Bang Theory

Average distance between galaxies →

Open

Flat

Closed

Time →

31.3 Cosmology **849**

Content Background

Students might wonder where the first matter in the universe came from. Einstein's theory of special relativity provides the answer, and experiments done in particle accelerators confirm it: matter can be created from energy. A photon of electromagnetic radiation can spontaneously form a pair of particles of matter with equal but opposite properties. Visible light does not contain enough energy to produce particles, but higher-energy photons, especially gamma rays, can.

Interpreting the Photo

Figure 31-17 The different-colored regions in this *WMAP* map correspond to different temperatures above and below the average temperature. As students will observe, it is a rather clumpy pattern. Astronomers hypothesize that this clumpiness may have been enough to trigger galaxy formation.

The Using Math feature on this page illustrates how the value of H is related to the age of the universe, the time when it began to expand. The relationship $t = 1/H$ is very simply obtained, from a formula most students learn in elementary school: distance equals speed times time; or time equals distance divided by speed. Substituting d for distance, Hd for speed, and t for time, $t = d/Hd = 1/H$ is obtained. In cosmology, things are not quite this simple, because the speed of expansion has slowed since the beginning of the universe. Thus, a correction factor is needed. Its value ranges between 2/3 and about 9/10 in modern forms of the Big Bang model. Simply using $t = 1/H$ provides a good first estimate for students, however.

Using Math

$$50 \frac{km}{Mpc \cdot s} \times \frac{1 \; Mpc}{3.1 \times 10^{19} \; km}$$

$$= 1.61 \times 10^{-18} \; s^{-1}$$

$$t = \frac{1}{H} = \frac{1}{1.61 \times 10^{-18} \; s^{-1}}$$

$$= 6.21 \times 10^{17} \; s = 1.97 \times 10^{10} \; years$$

$$100 \frac{km}{Mpc \cdot s} \times \frac{1 Mpc}{3.1 \times 10^{19} \; km}$$

$$= 3.23 \times 10^{-18} \; s^{-1}$$

$$t = \frac{1}{H} = \frac{1}{3.23 \times 10^{-18} \; s^{-1}}$$

$$= 3.10 \times 10^{17} \; s = 9.8 \times 10^9 \; years$$

NY Core Curriculum Standards

Page 850: St 1 Math KI 1, 2, 3, Science KI 1, 2, & Engin KI 1, St 4 KI 1.2a, St 6 KI 2, 4, & 5

Page 851: St 1 Math KI 2, Science KI 1, 2, 3, & Engin KI 1, St 4 KI 1.2a, St 6 KI 1, 2, 3, 4, & 5

Figure 31-19 This distant cluster of galaxies, Abell 2218, allows astronomers to look back into time.

Using Math

Using Numbers The time since the expansion of the universe began can be calculated by

$$t = \frac{1}{H}.$$

Astronomers hypothesize that H is somewhere between 50 and 100 kilometers per second per megaparsec. What age does each value of H predict? Remember to convert Mpc to km, using 1 Mpc $= 3.1 \times 10^{19}$ km.

Expansion Rate Another approach to determining the fate of the universe is to measure how much slowing has occurred so far in its expansion. This will indicate how much further it will slow down. The slowing of the expansion of the universe can be measured by comparing the expansion rate today with the rate long ago. Recall that when astronomers observe the most distant galaxies, such as the ones shown in *Figure 31-19,* they are observing the galaxies as they existed far back in time. By measuring the redshifts of the most remote galaxies, it is possible for astronomers to determine the expansion rate long ago. This also requires finding the distances to those very far away galaxies.

The most recent observations of the change in the expansion rate of the universe have been startling. Astronomers have found that the rate of expansion is speeding up! It appears that the rate of expansion slowed for a while but is now gathering speed. The only explanation offered so far is that a previously unknown force is acting to push the galaxies apart. According to this explanation, when the universe was smaller and denser, gravity was strong enough to slow the expansion, but some time ago this unknown force began to dominate over gravity.

The Inflationary Model The combination of the observed density of the universe, including an allowance for dark matter, and the apparent acceleration of the expansion, fit together into a model in which the universe is flat. A flat universe was predicted in the 1980s by a version of the Big Bang model called the inflationary universe. In the **inflationary universe** model, the universe began as a fluctuation in a vacuum and expanded very rapidly for a fraction of a second, as illustrated in *Figure 31-20,* before settling into a more orderly expansion. The initial inflationary step is similar to what can happen in water that is supersaturated with soap: if the water is disturbed, it forms a sea of bubbles almost instantaneously.

When the rate of expansion of the universe is known, it is possible to calculate the time since the expansion started, or the age of the universe. When the distance to a galaxy and the rate at which it is moving away from Earth are known, it is simple to calculate how long ago that galaxy and the Milky Way were together. In astronomical terms,

850 CHAPTER 31 *Galaxies and the Universe*

✓ Assessment

Knowledge Ask students to summarize how the value of H, the Hubble constant, is measured. *H is measured by determining distances and speeds for a number of galaxies, using the greatest distance possible.*

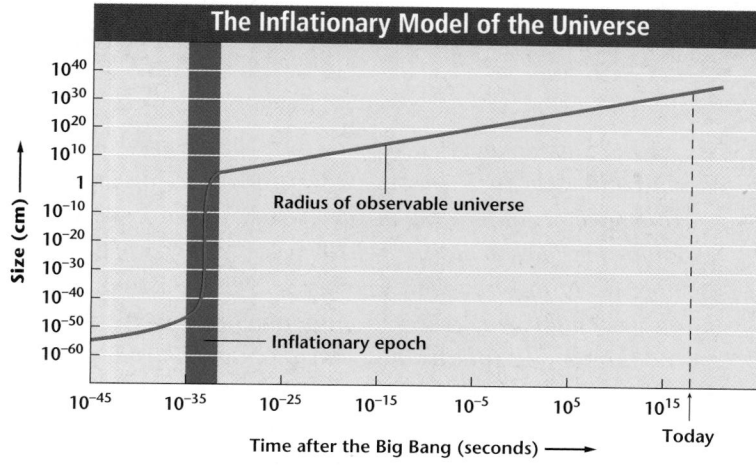

The Inflationary Model of the Universe

Size (cm) — y-axis: 10^{40}, 10^{30}, 10^{20}, 10^{10}, 1, 10^{-10}, 10^{-20}, 10^{-30}, 10^{-40}, 10^{-50}, 10^{-60}

Radius of observable universe

Inflationary epoch

Time after the Big Bang (seconds) — x-axis: 10^{-45}, 10^{-35}, 10^{-25}, 10^{-15}, 10^{-5}, 10^5, 10^{15}, Today

Figure 31-20 According to the inflationary model, the universe expanded very quickly in the early portion of the Big Bang. The time in which inflation occurred is the shaded portion of the graph, where the size of the universe increases drastically.

if the value of *H*, the expansion constant, is known, then the age of the universe can be determined. A correction is needed to allow for the fact that the expansion was more rapid at the beginning, and now it seems that this correction must also take into account the acceleration of the expansion that is occurring now. Based on the best value for *H* that has been calculated from *Hubble Space Telescope* data, as well as the appropriate corrections, the age of the universe is hypothesized to be about 13.5 billion years. This fits with what astronomers know about the age of our own galaxy, which is estimated to be between 12 and 14 billion years, based on the ages of the oldest star clusters. However, refinements to these measurements are still being made.

SECTION ASSESSMENT

1. What are the differences between the steady-state model of the universe and the Big Bang model of the universe?

2. Describe the inflationary model and its predicted impact on the structure of the universe.

3. Why is dark matter important in determining the density of matter in the universe?

4. Why was the cosmic background radiation an important discovery?

5. **Thinking Critically** How would a large value of *H*, the Hubble constant, affect the age of the universe? What about a small value of *H*?

SKILL REVIEW

6. **Comparing and Contrasting** Compare and contrast an open universe, a closed universe, and a flat universe. For more help, refer to the *Skill Handbook*.

 earthgeu.com/self_check_quiz

31.3 *Cosmology* **851**

SECTION ASSESSMENT

1. The steady-state model assumes that the universe had no beginning, will have no end, and is the same at all times. The Big Bang model assumes that the universe had a beginning in a highly condensed state and has been expanding and changing ever since.

2. For a very brief period at the beginning of the Big Bang, the universe expanded very quickly. This model predicts a flat universe.

3. Dark matter has the same gravitational effect as visible matter. Hence, the density of dark matter

must be included in the comparison with the critical density to determine whether the universe is open, closed, or flat.

4. The radiation was predicted by the Big Bang model and is considered to be very strong support for that model.

5. It would be small; it would be large.

6. open universe: will expand forever; flat universe: will slow to a halt in an infinite amount of time; closed universe: will slow, stop, and contract.

Time Allotment

1 hour

Process Skills

classify, observe and infer, compare and contrast

Preparation

Possible Hypotheses

Students should hypothesize that the galaxy images they find on the Internet will match classifications from Hubble's system, but they may find that some galaxies don't fit, and this might alter their hypotheses to suggest that not all galaxies fit the scheme.

Planning

Teaching Strategies

- Students can work in groups.
- Provide students with a set of galaxy images and classifications, which students can use for comparison as they look for galaxies of each type.
- Explain to students that galaxy images are not uniform in size, color, or resolution, and that they need to try to look at the overall properties of each image.

Possible Procedures

Students will gather data from Internet sites that can be accessed through the Earth Science Web Site. Students can post their data on the site and obtain data from other schools around the country.

Internet GeoLab

Classifying Galaxies

Edwin Hubble developed rules for classifying galaxies according to their shapes as seen in telescopic images. Astronomers are interested in the classification of galaxies. This information can indicate whether a certain type of galaxy is more likely to form than another and helps astronomers unravel the mystery of galaxy formation in the universe. Using the resources of the Internet and sharing data with your peers, you can learn how galaxies are classified.

Preparation

Problem

How can different galaxies be classified?

Hypothesis

How might galaxies be classified using Hubble's classification system? Are there absolute classifications based solely on shape? **Form a hypothesis** about how you can apply Hubble's galaxy classification system to galaxy images on the Internet.

Objectives

- **Gather** and **communicate** details about galaxy images on the Internet.
- **Form conclusions** about the classification of different galaxies.
- **Reconstruct** the tuning-fork diagram with images that you find.

Data Sources

Go to the Earth Science Web Site at earthgeu.com to find links to galaxy images on the Internet. You can also visit a local library or observatory to gather images of galaxies and information about them.

Plan the Experiment

1. Find a resource with multiple images of galaxies and, if possible, names or catalog numbers for the galaxies. The Earth Science Web Site lists sites that have galaxy images.
2. Choose one of the following types of galaxies to start your classification: spirals, ellipticals, or irregular galaxies.
3. Gather images and information, such as catalog numbers and names of galaxies, from the links on the Earth Science Web Site or the library.
4. Sort the images by basic types: spirals, ellipticals, or irregular galaxies.

852 CHAPTER 31 *Galaxies and the Universe*

Procedure

Sources of Error

The quality of the image, or the duration of the time exposure used to make the photograph, can affect one's perception of a galaxy's shape and form.

Data and Observations

Students will compare the galaxy images they find on the Internet with each other and possibly with images of galaxies whose classifications are known. Students will search for galaxies that match each type of galaxy in the Hubble classification system.

5. For each basic type, compare the galaxies to each other and decide which galaxy best represents each class and subclass of Hubble's galaxy classification system: Sa, Sb, Sc, SBa, SBb, SBc, S0, E0–E7, and Irr. Try to find at least one galaxy for each sub-class.

6. Arrange the galaxy images to construct a tuning-fork diagram like Hubble's.

GALAXY DATA

Galaxy Name	Sketch of Galaxy	Classification	Notes
NGC 3486		Sc	

Procedure

1. Complete the data table. Add any additional information that you think is important.

2. Go to the Earth Science Web Site at **earthgeu.com** to post your data.

3. Visit sites listed on the Earth Science Web Site for information about other galaxies.

Conclude & Apply

Sharing Your Data Find this Internet GeoLab on the Earth Science Web Site at **earthgeu.com**. Post your data in the table provided for this activity. Use the additional data from other students to complete your chart and answer the Conclude & Apply questions.

1. Were there any galaxy classes or sub-classes that were difficult to find images for? If so, which ones?

2. How many of each type of galaxy—normal spiral, barred spiral, elliptical, and irregular—did you find?

3. Calculate the percentages of the total number of galaxies that each type represents. Do you think this reflects the actual percentage of each type of galaxy in the universe? Explain.

4. Were there any galaxy images that you found that didn't fit your classification scheme? If so, why?

5. Was it difficult to distinguish between a normal spiral and a barred spiral in some cases? Explain your method.

6. What problems did you have with galaxies that are edge-on as seen from Earth?

7. Ellipticals are usually a difficult type of galaxy to classify. Why?

Internet GeoLab **853**

Purpose 📦

Students will learn more about how studies of the early expansion of the universe are aided by laboratory experiments on subatomic particles.

Content Background

The *Hubble Deep Field* image has had a huge impact on modern astronomy, because it provides unprecedented information about the nature of galaxies as they were many billions of years ago. It is theorized that the first 3–4 minutes of the Big Bang was the time when all the matter in the universe formed, first as subatomic particles, then as atoms. Experiments in particle accelerators can simulate the conditions of the early universe, and help teach physicists and astronomers many of the details about the origin of the universe.

Teaching Strategies

- Before students read this feature, explain to them that matter can form spontaneously from energy in the form of photons of electromagnetic radiation. Cite Einstein's equation $E = mc^2$, which gives the quantitative conversion of energy to density, and remind students that the energy of a photon is proportional to its frequency (and inversely proportional to its wavelength). The early universe was filled with high-frequency electromagnetic radiation, which contains enough energy to form particles.

Science & Technology

The Early Universe

Imagine looking back 10 billion years to a time when the universe was young and galaxies were just beginning to form. The Hubble Deep Field (HDF), pictured at left, is a snapshot of the early universe by the Hubble Space Telescope. *The HDF shows at least 1500 galaxies in various stages of evolution. Some are so far away that we see them now as they looked less than 1 billion years after the Big Bang.*

Back in Time

Images such as the HDF offer tantalizing clues to questions about conditions in the early universe. Did it resemble the universe we know today? How did the universe begin? Most astronomers hypothesize that the universe was formed by the Big Bang. This violent event left particles rushing away from each other at tremendous speeds. The energy created billions of years ago still propels galaxies away from each other as the universe continues to expand.

Accelerated Particles

Scientists learn about the world by making observations about events in progress, or by creating specific conditions that will cause an event to occur. Because the Big Bang can neither be observed nor recreated, other methods must be used to study it. One tool that scientists use to replicate conditions in the early universe is the particle accelerator, a machine that smashes charged particles into various targets at speeds close to the speed of light. The particle accelerator allows scientists to test models of how matter and energy behaved as soon as 1×10^{-11} s after the Big Bang.

All particle accelerators are based on the principle that electrically charged objects exert a force on each other. Intense magnetic fields are applied to charged particles moving through tubes. Particles gain speed until they crash into some target. High-speed collisions between particles often result in strange particles that scientists have never before observed.

Limitations

In 1989, workers began digging miles of tunnels in a geologically stable area in Texas where the Supercolliding Superconductor (SCC) was to be built. A 54-mile (86.9-km) oval, the SCC would have been the world's largest, most powerful particle accelerator, allowing astronomers to probe deeper into the early conditions of the universe. Despite the efforts of physicists and astronomers worldwide, however, Congress cut off funding for the project in 1993. Until larger, more powerful particle accelerators are built, scientists are limited in what they can learn about the early universe.

Activity

The Fermilab Tevatron is the world's most powerful accelerator. Go to the Earth Science Web Site at **earthgeu.com** to research Fermilab. Do you think particle accelerators should be built despite their large cost? Why?

- Remind students that only during the early expansion of the universe did the cosmic radiation field contain photons with enough energy to form subatomic particles such as neutrons, protons, and electrons; therefore, it is theorized that virtually no new matter has been formed since that time, according to the Big Bang model.

Activity

Students will have differing opinions. There are benefits to using particle accelerators beyond astronomy, such as in both chemistry and physics. And, like spinoffs of the space program, there have been spinoffs from the development of particle accelerators such as the development of the World Wide Web.

Summary

SECTION 31.1

The Milky Way Galaxy

Main Ideas

- Because our solar system is inside the Milky Way galaxy, it was difficult at first for astronomers to determine the size and shape of our galaxy, and where Earth is located within it.
- The Milky Way consists of a nuclear bulge, a disk, and a halo. Much of the mass of the galaxy is not visible.
- It is hypothesized that the Milky Way began as a spherical cloud of gas that eventually collapsed into a disk.
- Population I stars contain small amounts of heavy elements and are located in the arms and disk. Population II stars are located in the bulge and halo, and contain only trace amounts of heavy elements.

Vocabulary

Cepheid variable (p. 834)
halo (p. 835)
RR Lyrae variable (p. 834)
spiral density wave (p. 838)
variable star (p. 834)

SECTION 31.2

Other Galaxies in the Universe

Main Ideas

- Galaxies are classified according to their shapes as normal spirals, barred spirals, ellipticals, irregulars, or dwarf ellipticals.
- Most galaxies occur in clusters, which are further organized into superclusters.
- The universe is expanding, and the Hubble constant, *H,* measures the rate of expansion.
- Because it takes the light from very distant galaxies so long to reach Earth, when astronomers observe these galaxies, they are looking back in time.
- Many galaxies have energetic objects or activities at their cores called active galactic nuclei.

Vocabulary

active galactic nucleus (p. 844)
Hubble constant (p. 843)
quasar (p. 845)
radio galaxy (p. 844)
supercluster (p. 842)

SECTION 31.3

Cosmology

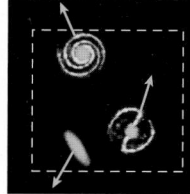

Main Ideas

- The Big Bang theory proposes that the universe began as a single point and has been expanding ever since.
- The steady-state theory proposes that the universe is the same as it always has been.
- The universe is filled with cosmic background radiation that is left over from the early, hot stages in the Big Bang expansion of the universe.
- In the Big Bang model, the universe could be open, closed, or flat.
- The inflationary model can explain the walls and voids of the distribution of galaxies. It also predicts that the universe is flat, which is supported by observations.
- Current observations indicate that an unknown force is accelerating the expansion of the universe.

Vocabulary

Big Bang theory (p. 847)
cosmic background radiation (p. 848)
cosmology (p. 847)
inflationary universe (p. 850)
steady-state theory (p. 847)

earthgeu.com/vocabulary_puzzlemaker

Main Ideas

Summary statements can be used by students to review the major concepts of the chapter.

VOCABULARY PuzzleMaker

For additional help with vocabulary, have students access the Vocabulary Puzzlemaker online.

earthgeu.com/ vocabulary puzzlemaker

0:00 *Out of Time?*

If time does not permit teaching the entire chapter, use the GeoDigest at the end of the unit as an overview.

Earth Science Online

Be sure to check the Earth Science Web Site for links to chapter material:
earthgeu.com

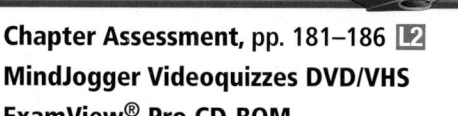
Resource Manager

Chapter Assessment, pp. 181–186 L2
MindJogger Videoquizzes DVD/VHS
ExamView® Pro CD-ROM
Performance Assessment in Earth Science

GLENCOE
Technology

Videotape/DVD
MindJogger Videoquizzes
Chapter 31: *Galaxies and the Universe*
Have students work in groups as they play the videoquiz game to review key chapter concepts.

NY Core Curriculum Standards

Page 854: St 1 Science KI 1, 3, & Engin KI 1, St 2 KI 1, 2, & 3, St 4 KI 1.2a, St 6 KI 2
Page 855: St 1 Science KI 1, 2, 3, & Engin KI 1, St 4 KI 1.2a & 1.2b, St 6 KI 1, 2, 4, & 5

Understanding Main Ideas

1. a
2. c
3. a
4. d
5. b
6. c
7. They have a period-luminosity relationship. The pulsation period determines the luminosity, which can then be used to calculate distance.
8. by mapping the 21-cm emissions of atomic hydrogen
9. Stars in the outer galaxy move faster than they would if most of the mass were at the center of the galaxy.
10. dim stellar remnants such as white dwarfs, neutron stars, and black holes, or other unknown objects
11. The motions of stars indicate that there is a lot of mass concentrated in a small area at the center.
12. measurement error, and the fact that the expansion of the universe is accelerating
13. They are old and they have very low abundances of heavy elements.
14. No. All galaxies move away from all others in a uniformly expanding universe.
15. It is the rate at which the universe is expanding.
16. Many quasars are seen at high redshifts and thus at very great distances. The light we receive today from quasars was emitted billions of years ago.

Understanding Main Ideas

1. What are the oldest objects in the Milky Way?
   a. globular clusters
   b. Cepheid variables
   c. spiral arms
   d. Population I stars

2. Where in the Milky Way are new stars being formed?
   a. in the nuclear bulge
   b. in globular clusters
   c. in the spiral arms
   d. in the halo

3. Where does the energy emitted by AGNs and quasars most probably come from?
   a. material falling into a supermassive black hole
   b. a neutron star
   c. a supernova explosion
   d. a pulsar

4. What theory proposes that the universe does not change with time?
   a. the Big Bang
   b. the cosmological constant
   c. the heliocentric universe theory
   d. the steady-state universe theory

5. What is the origin of the cosmic background radiation?
   a. It is emitted by stars.
   b. It is a remnant of the Big Bang.
   c. It is emitted by radio galaxies.
   d. It comes from the steady-state universe.

6. In the Big Bang model, which of the following describes a universe that will stop expanding and begin to contract?
   a. open
   b. flat
   c. closed
   d. inflationary

7. Why are pulsating variable stars useful for finding distances to globular clusters?

8. How do astronomers observe the spiral structure of our galaxy?

9. Why do astronomers think that there is a great amount of mass in the halo of the Milky Way?

10. What possible forms might the dark matter in the halo of the Milky Way be in?

11. Why do astronomers hypothesize that there is a supermassive black hole at the center of the Milky Way?

Use the diagram below to answer question 12.

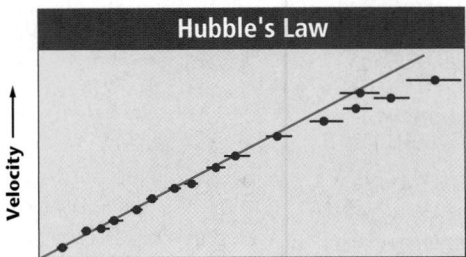

Hubble's Law

Velocity ——

12. The straight line represents Hubble's law, $v = Hd$, and the points are actual data for galaxies. Why don't the points agree with the straight line of Hubble's law?

13. Why are the stars in globular clusters classified as Population II stars?

14. Does the fact that all galaxies are receding from Earth suggest that it is located at the center of the universe? Explain.

15. What is the significance of the Hubble constant?

16. What evidence indicates that many quasars existed long ago?

Test-Taking Tip

MISTAKES Your mistakes can teach you. The mistakes you make before the test are helpful because they show you the areas in which you need more work.

earthgeu.com/chapter_test

17. The steady-state model assumes that the universe had no beginning and does not change with time, while the Big Bang model assumes that the universe had a beginning and has changed with time.
18. open: the universe will expand forever; flat: it will slow to a stop in an infinite amount of time; closed: it will stop and turn into a contraction

Applying Main Ideas

19. because it takes light from distant objects a long time to reach Earth
20. Masses measured in clusters and our own galaxy always reveal greater masses than are seen in the form of visible matter.
21. It can be compared with the critical density to determine the universe's fate.

17. What are the main differences between the steady-state model and the Big Bang model of the universe?

18. What would be the different outcomes of the open, flat, and closed universe models?

Applying Main Ideas

19. Why are astronomers actually looking into the past when they observe objects that are very far away?

20. What evidence indicates that much of the mass in the universe is in an invisible form called dark matter?

21. Why is it important for astronomers to determine the average density of the universe?

22. How did Edwin Hubble reach the conclusion that the universe is expanding?

23. Why do astronomers theorize that many quasars are active nuclei of young galaxies?

Thinking Critically

24. How would a star that forms in our galaxy a few billion years in the future compare with the Sun?

25. How is the formation of our galaxy like the formation of a star?

26. A quasar and three galaxies are observed, and the ranking of their redshifts is as follows: galaxy 1, largest redshift; galaxy 2, second-largest redshift; the quasar, third-largest redshift; and galaxy 3, fourth-largest redshift. List these objects in order from the nearest to the farthest from Earth.

27. How do the properties of quasars suggest that the steady-state model of the universe is not accurate?

earthgeu.com/standardized_test

Standardized Test Practice

USING GRAPHS Use the graph below to answer question 1.

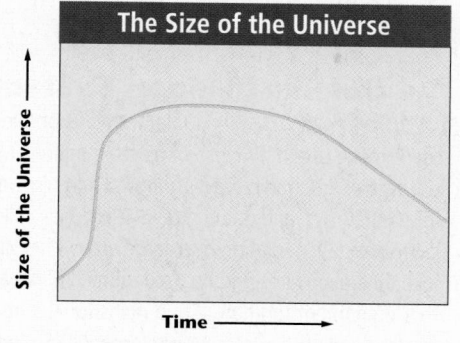

The Size of the Universe

Size of the Universe (y-axis)

Time (x-axis)

1. What possible fate of the universe does this represent?
a. flat
b. open
c. closed
d. steady

2. Without doing any calculations, what can astronomers determine from a variable star's period of pulsation?
a. distance
b. apparent magnitude
c. luminosity
d. age

3. What two measurements are required to determine the Hubble constant?
a. distance and speed
b. distance and absolute magnitude
c. apparent magnitude and speed
d. apparent and absolute magnitudes

4. Which of the following does the existence of the cosmic background radiation support?
a. critical density
b. the steady-state theory
c. the inflationary model
d. the Big Bang theory

Assessment **857**

22. He found that all galaxies are receding from Earth with recession speeds proportional to distance.

23. The emission and energy output of quasars are similar to active galactic nuclei; because quasars are seen predominantly at large redshifts, meaning that many existed long ago, when galaxies were young; and because quasars are found to be the cores of faint galaxies.

Thinking Critically

24. It will have a higher abundance of heavy elements than the Sun does, because it will form later in galactic history, after stellar nuclear reactions will have formed a higher abundance of heavy elements than exists today.

25. Both start with a rotating, spherical gas cloud, and both flattened into a disklike structure as a result of rotation.

26. galaxy 3, the quasar, galaxy 2, and galaxy 1

27. Many quasars are seen at very great distances, which means that they existed long ago. Quasars are not as common now as they were in the past, which shows that the universe is changing with time.

Standardized Test Practice

1. c
2. c
3. a
4. d

NY Core Curriculum Standards

Page 856: St 1 Math KI 1, Science KI 1, 2, & 3, St 4 KI 1.2a & 1.2b, St 6 KI 1, 2, 4, & 5

Page 857: St 1 Math KI 1, Science KI 1, 2, & 3, St 4 KI 1.2a & 1.2b, St 6 KI 1, 2, 4, & 5

UNIT 8
GeoDigest

For a **preview** of the universe beyond Earth, study this GeoDigest before you read the chapters. After you have studied these chapters, you can use the GeoDigest to **review** the unit.

Prepare

Purpose

This GeoDigest can be used as an overview of the concepts of astronomy and Earth's place in the universe. If time is limited, you may wish to use this unit summary to teach these concepts in place of the chapters in Unit 8.

Key Concepts

Students are introduced to the science of astronomy, the nature of the nighttime sky, and what astronomers know about the solar system, stars, galaxies, and the universe as a whole. Students will also learn how astronomers have developed their knowledge of the universe.

1 Focus

Section Focus

Visual-Spatial Have students look at images of different astronomical objects, such as stars, planets, galaxies, nebulae, lunar phases, and eclipses. Have students describe what they see and, if possible, the causes. **L1** **ELL**

⏰ Out of Time?

If time does not permit teaching the entire unit, use this GeoDigest as an overview.

Beyond Earth

The Sun-Earth-Moon System

Tools of Astronomy Different types of telescopes make use of all types of electromagnetic radiation: visible light, radio waves, infrared and ultraviolet radiation, X rays, and gamma rays. Telescopes collect electromagnetic radiation over large areas. They can make time exposures and be used with cameras and other equipment to analyze and measure electromagnetic radiation. Refracting telescopes use lenses to bring light to a focus, whereas reflecting telescopes use mirrors. Some forms of radiation are blocked by Earth's atmosphere, and thus telescopes that collect these forms of radiation must be placed in space. Space probes make observations from space or land and take samples for analysis.

John Glenn with suit technicians, 1998

858 UNIT 8

The Moon The Moon has surface features that survive due to its lack of an atmosphere and erosion. Earth's moon is larger and more distant, relative to the size of its planet, than any other satellite in the solar system. These characteristics may be a result of the Moon's being formed in a collision between Earth and a Mars-sized body. The Moon is covered with highlands and maria.

The Sun-Earth-Moon System From a rotating Earth, the sky appears to rotate daily. Our timekeeping system is based on the solar day as observed from Earth. On Earth, we see the Moon go through phases that complete a lunar month. The phases correspond to our changing view of the sunlit side of the Moon. A lunar eclipse occurs when the Moon passes through Earth's shadow; a solar eclipse occurs when the Moon passes between Earth and the Sun, and the Moon's shadow intersects the surface of Earth. Earth's tilt on its axis and its changing position in orbit causes seasons. Tides are caused by the gravitational pull of the Moon and the Sun on the water on Earth's surface.

The Solar System

Motion and Formation Early astronomers explained the motions of the planets with geocentric models. Copernicus, Brahe, Kepler, and Galileo collected data that supported a heliocentric model of the solar system. Newton's law of gravitation demonstrated the validity of the heliocentric model. The solar system formed from a collapsing

---

Multiple Learning Styles

 Linguistic Project, p. 860, Reteach, p. 861

 Visual-Spatial Section Focus, p. 858

 Logical-Mathematical Reinforcement, p. 860

GeoDigest

Olympus Mons, Mars

interstellar cloud that flattened into a disk. The terrestrial planets formed from refractory materials in the hot, inner disk; the gas giants formed from volatile elements in the cold, outer disk. Planets orbiting other stars have recently been discovered.

The Planets The terrestrial planets are the four planets closest to the Sun. Mercury has a surface similar to the Moon's. Venus's surface is heated to extreme temperatures through the greenhouse effect. Liquid water exists on Earth, making it suitable for life. Mars may have once had active tectonics. Between Mars and Jupiter is a belt of asteroids, which are rocky remnants of the early solar system. The huge gas giant planets have low densities, no solid surfaces, ring systems, and many moons. Jupiter, the largest and most massive planet, has a fluid (gas or liquid) interior, a small, rocky core, and many moons. Saturn is slightly smaller than Jupiter and has an extensive ring system. Uranus and Neptune are similar in size, composition, and the presence of moons and rings. Pluto is neither a gas giant nor a terrestrial planet. Its moon is close to its own size. Comets are made of rock and ice, and they have highly eccentric orbits. When comets are close to the Sun, they glow brightly and have tails of gas and dust that point away from the Sun.

Stars

The Sun Astronomers learn about the Sun through observations and models. They have found that the Sun contains most of the mass in the solar system and is made primarily of hydrogen and helium. The layers of its atmosphere are the photosphere, chromosphere, and corona. The interior of the Sun consists of radiative and convective zones that transfer energy. The nuclear fusion of hydrogen into helium within the core powers the Sun. Surface features of the Sun include sunspots, solar flares, and prominences. The Sun has an 11-year sunspot cycle and a 22-year activity cycle.

Measurement of Stars Positional measurements of the stars are important for measuring distances through apparent shifts in position, called parallax. Stellar brightness is expressed by apparent and absolute magnitude. The appearance of stars' spectra classifies them by their surface temperatures. Stellar characteristics—class, mass, temperature, magnitude, diameter, and luminosity—are related on a diagram called the Hertzsprung-Russell diagram. The mass of a star determines its internal structure and other properties; gravity and pressure are balanced in a star.

Evolution of Stars If the temperature in the core of a star becomes high enough, elements heavier than hydrogen but lighter than iron can fuse together. When the hydrogen in a star is used up, the star may go through several red-giant phases as reaction stages begin and end. Stars like the Sun end as white dwarfs. Stars up to about 8 times the Sun's mass also become white dwarfs after losing mass. Stars between 8 and 20 times the Sun's mass become supernovae and end as neutron stars. Stars more than 20 times as massive as the Sun end as black holes.

GeoDigest **859**

2 Teach

Interpreting the Photo

Olympus Mons is the largest-known volcano and mountain in the solar system. Located on Mars, Olympus Mons is over 600 km in diameter at its base, which is wider than the entire Hawaiian Island chain. Olympus Mons rises 24 km above the surrounding plain.

Content Background

The fact that we on Earth experience total solar eclipses, in which the Moon's disk just blocks the Sun, is a coincidence, one that would not be expected to happen elsewhere. The angular diameters of the Sun and Moon match almost perfectly, because while the Sun is about 400 times farther away than the Moon, it also just happens to be about 400 times larger, so the apparent sizes (angular diameters) of the Sun and Moon are nearly equal.

Applying Earth Science

The geologies of all planets are driven by the same basic forces that govern Earth. Heat flow from the warm or hot interior toward the coldness of space is a primary factor, creating convection in the form of rising currents, both in the interior and in the atmosphere (if the planet has one). Rotation of the planet also plays a role, particularly in atmospheric circulation. Among the planets, we see forces at work that are in many ways similar to the forces that shape Earth, but that also have many contrasts. The study of the planets has helped scientists to understand Earth, just as Earth science has helped in the understanding of other planets.

GeoDigest

Enrichment

The stellar-magnitude scale used by astronomers to measure the brightnesses and luminosities of stars is a logarithmic scale, in which a numerical scale based on the sensitivity of the human eye corresponds to multiplying factors in stellar light intensity. For every magnitude difference of one unit, the ratio of the brightnesses of two stars is increased by a factor of 2.512.

Reinforcement

Logical-Mathematical To reinforce student understanding of sizes and distance scales in the universe, have them rank the following from smallest to largest: 8 superclusters of galaxies, 6 the distance to the nearest galaxy, 3 the Sun-Earth distance, 5 the diameter of the Milky Way, 4 the distances between stars in our galaxy, 1 the diameter of Earth, 9 the distances of the most remote galaxies, 2 the diameter of the Sun, 7 and the size of a typical cluster of galaxies.

🗘 Project

Linguistic Arrange a field trip to a local planetarium, an observatory, or a dark area away from city lights. Have students record everything they see in their science journals and describe how the objects are related to each other. It might be handy to take along a field guide or star chart if you take the class to a dark area outside, rather than a planetarium or observatory.

COOP LEARN

GeoDigest

Galaxies

The Milky Way The Milky Way consists of a nuclear bulge, a disk, and a halo; much of its mass is not visible. In the galaxy, Population I stars contain small amounts of heavy elements and are located in the arms and disk. Population II stars are located in the bulge and halo, and contain only trace amounts of heavy elements. Because Earth is inside the Milky Way, it has been difficult to determine the size and shape of the galaxy, and also where Earth is located within it.

Other Galaxies Most galaxies occur in clusters that are further organized into superclusters. Galaxies are classified according to their shapes as normal spirals, barred spirals, ellipticals, or irregulars. Some galaxies have energetic objects or activities at their cores called active galactic nuclei. The universe is expanding, as measured by the Hubble constant. When astronomers observe distant galaxies, they are looking back in time because the light takes so long to reach Earth.

Cosmology Cosmology is the study of the universe as a whole. The Big Bang model proposes that

Star trails around Polaris

the universe began as a single point and has been expanding ever since. The universe is filled with cosmic background radiation that is left over from the early, hot stages in the Big Bang's expansion. According to the Big Bang model, the universe could be open, closed, or flat. The steady state theory of cosmology, which proposes that the universe is and always will be the same, is not accepted by most astronomers. The inflationary theory explains the walls and voids in the distribution of galaxies. Current observations indicate that the expansion of the universe is accelerating.

Vital Statistics	
The Sun's Nearest Neighbors	
Star	**Distance from the Sun**
1. Proxima Centauri	4.24 ly
2. Alpha Centauri	4.34 ly
3. Barnard's Star	5.97 ly
4. Wolf 359	7.80 ly
5. Lalande 21185	8.19 ly
6. Luyten 726-8	8.55 ly
7. Sirius	8.68 ly
8. Ross 154	9.52 ly
9. Ross 248	10.37 ly

FOCUS ON CAREERS

Cosmologist
Cosmologists study the universe as a whole in an attempt to discover how it formed and how it will end. They usually obtain doctoral degrees in physics, astronomy, or both and have a strong background in math and computer analysis. Cosmologists usually work and teach at universities, or other research institutions.

Differentiated Instruction

Gifted Have students each create a poster showing the different sizes of objects in the universe and how they are related. Students could start with the universe itself, then superclusters, clusters of galaxies, a galaxy, a star cluster, a star, a solar system, a planet, a moon, asteroids, meteors, and then humans. **L3**

▢ NATIONAL GEOGRAPHIC

 CD-ROM

Solar System PictureShow
Sun, Earth, and Moon
The Planets
Stars and Galaxies PictureShow
Stars
Galaxies

ASSESSMENT

Understanding Main Ideas

1. A telescope that uses mirrors rather than lenses to bring light to a focus is what kind of telescope?
   a. refracting
   b. reflecting
   c. electromagnetic
   d. probing

2. What is one theory about how the Moon formed?
   a. Numerous asteroids were pulled together.
   b. Earth and Mars collided.
   c. Earth and a Mars-sized body collided.
   d. Earth captured an existing moon from Mars.

3. The planets formed from a collapsing interstellar cloud that flattened into a disk. From which part of the disk did terrestrial planets form?
   a. the inner section of the disk
   b. the outer section of the disk
   c. the exact center of the disk
   d. sections throughout the entire disk

4. Which planets have low densities, no solid surfaces, ring systems, and many moons?
   a. the terrestrial planets
   b. the gas giants
   c. Pluto and Mercury
   d. Mars and Earth

5. The atmosphere of which object in the solar system is made up of the photosphere, the chromosphere, and the corona?
   a. Earth
   b. Jupiter
   c. Venus
   d. the Sun

6. What tool of astronomy relates the class, mass, temperature, magnitude, diameter, and luminosity of stars?
   a. parallax
   b. absolute magnitude
   c. absolute brightness
   d. the Hertzsrpung-Russell diagram

7. Stars that are 8 to 20 times more massive than the Sun end up as what kind of stars?
   a. red giants
   b. white dwarfs
   c. neutron stars
   d. black holes

8. Where are Population II stars located in the Milky Way?
   a. in the bulge and halo
   b. in the arms
   c. in the disk
   d. in the heavy elements

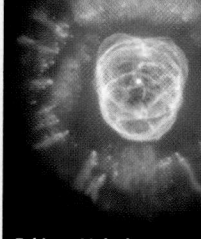

Eskimo Nebula, NGC 2392

9. How are galaxies classified?
   a. by size
   b. by closeness to Earth
   c. by shape
   d. by the Hubble constant

10. What is the study of the universe as a whole?
   a. astronomy
   b. cosmology
   c. physics
   d. astrometry

Thinking Critically

1. Compare lunar and solar eclipses.
2. Sequence the following star outcomes in order of the mass of the original star, with the smallest mass first: neutron star, white dwarf, and black hole.
3. Explain the Big Bang model of the formation of the universe.

GeoDigest **861**

3 Assess

Check for Understanding
Discussion
Have students discuss the different planets in our solar system. Have them compare and contrast the planets' characteristics and create a data table summarizing those characteristics for each planet.

Reteach
Linguistic Have students write essays summarizing the life cycles and evolution of stars of different masses. Remind them to be sure to include what happens to the stars when fusion stops. **L2**

✔Assessment

Portfolio Have students find and summarize information about a telescope used for each portion of the electromagnetic spectrum, including visible light, infrared radiation, radio waves, ultraviolet radiation, X rays, and gamma rays.

ASSESSMENT

Understanding Main Ideas

1. b	3. a	5. d	7. c	9. c
2. c	4. b	6. d	8. a	10. b

Thinking Critically

1. A lunar eclipse occurs when the Moon passes through Earth's shadow; a solar eclipse occurs when the Moon passes between Earth and the Sun, and the Moon's shadow intersects the surface of Earth.

2. white dwarf; neutron star; black hole

3. It proposes that the universe began as a single point and has been expanding ever since. Evidence for the Big Bang is that the universe is filled with cosmic background radiation left over from the early, hot stages in the Big Bang's expansion. According to this model, the universe could be open, closed, or flat.

NY Core Curriculum Standards

Page 860: St 4 KI 1.2a & 1.2b
Page 861: St 4 KI 1.2a, 1.2b, & 1.2c

NATIONAL GEOGRAPHIC eXpeditions!

Explore the *Titanic*...
Tame the mighty Colorado River...
Dig for dinosaurs...

What is it like to map the highest mountain on Earth? Or to explore the ghostly wreck of the "unsinkable" *Titanic?* The **National Geographic Expeditions** allow you to share in the excitement and adventures of explorers, scientists, and lovers of the environment as they delve into the unknown. You can explore the sparkling beauty of a cave in a river of ice. Or watch the explosion of a dying star. Each Expedition will take you on a journey that reaches from the distant galaxies to the depths of the oceans.

As you learn about our dynamic planet, you can use the **National Geographic Expeditions** to extend your knowledge and challenge yourself. To learn more about the Expeditions, go to the **Earth Science Web Site** (earthgeu.com) and click on the **National Geographic Expeditions** link. Or read the original **National Geographic Society** magazine articles to find out how geologists work to discover how a volcano erupts and try to predict future eruptions. The goal is to save lives! It's explorers and scientists like these that discovered the fascinating topics you are studying in your Glencoe **Earth Science: Geology, the Environment, and the Universe** textbook.

862

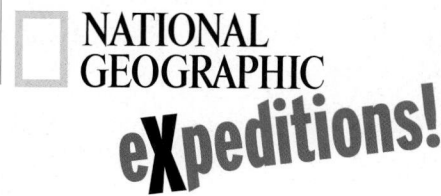

NATIONAL
GEOGRAPHIC
e**X**peditions!

National Geographic Expeditions!
are referenced within the chapters
at point of use, to support or
extend chapter content.

Table of Contents

e**X**peditions!

Purpose

Students will learn about the problems faced in an expedition to photograph and map Mount Everest. They will also be introduced to various strategies used to map mountainous areas such as the Himalayas.

Background

Until recently, the process of mapping high-elevation areas such as the Himalayas was extremely difficult. Before the advent of aerial photography, the only way to map an area was to physically survey it. This was a monumental task in a mountain range characterized by steep slopes, highly inclement weather, and low levels of oxygen. Aerial reconnaissance has simplified the task so that much of the mapping can now be done from the air. Today, high-resolution satellite photography allows for even more detailed and accurate maps.

864

✔ PORTFOLIO

Everest Explorers

Have students research and write reports about the history of efforts to scale Mount Everest. Student reports should mention who the mountain is named after and why, brief biographies of the early explorers who attempted to scale the summit, and information about the first team to actually reach this goal. Pique students' interest by telling them about English explorer George Mallory, who led several expeditions to Mount Everest in the early 1900s. Historians still debate whether Mallory actually reached the peak before a raging blizzard killed him and his climbing companion. Mallory's body was found by climbers in 1999. It was Mallory who, when asked why he wanted to scale Mount Everest, responded, "Because it's there."

NATIONAL GEOGRAPHIC eXpeditions!

Taking Cartography to New Heights

Mapping Mount Everest

● **ABOVE:** The earliest maps of Mount Everest, compiled in 1921, relied on the work of British surveyors Henry Morshead (right) and Oliver Wheeler. "They were the giants on whose shoulders we stood," said Bradford Washburn, who remapped Everest more recently.

● **LEFT:** The highest point on Earth, Everest proved to be a tough subject for remapping. In 1984 a jet plane with sophisticated photographic equipment provided the basis for more accurate depictions than the cartographers of the 1920s were able to achieve.

No one could accuse
Bradford Washburn of rushing into his plan to map Mount Everest. Before embarking on such an enormous undertaking, the climber-cartographer thought things over for a while. For 48 years, in fact.

What got Washburn thinking was a conversation at National Geographic Society headquarters in Washington, D.C. It was January 1936, and Washburn was working on a report about an expedition he'd led to the Yukon. At the National Geographic Society he ran into an old friend and hero, Captain Albert W. Stevens, who was an aviator and photographer.

NOT-SO-CASUAL CONVERSATION

Stevens was writing about his trip aboard the *Explorer II*, a hot-air balloon that had reached the record height of 22 080 meters (72 395 feet). The flight had given Stevens an idea: Why not fly over Everest? Aerial photographs would be an invaluable tool for mapping Earth's tallest peak. "It's a terrific project," he exulted.

Washburn never forgot those words. They took on new force in 1980, when he retired after decades as director of Boston's Museum of Science. "As I looked around to see what a 70-year-old cartographer with a keen interest in mountains could do," wrote Washburn, "I remembered that long-ago conversation with Steve." The project still sounded terrific.

865

Display

▨ **Visual-Spatial** Have groups of students use photographs from magazines, the Earth Science Web Site, and other sources to make displays illustrating the tallest mountain peaks on each continent. Assign a different continent to each group. Each display should include the name and height of the tallest peak, the year it was mapped, and a description or illustration of the peak and its mountain range. Afterwards, students should compare their results and rank their mountain ranges according to size and elevation. L2 ELL COOP LEARN P

Earth Science Journal

Have the class brainstorm the various items that must be obtained and the tasks that must be completed before undertaking a major expedition. Then have students each develop a plan for an expedition of their choice. Students should write their plans in their science journals.

Earth Science Online Note Internet addresses that you find useful in the space below for quick reference.

_____

_____

_____

_____

_____

_____

For Internet tips, see Glencoe's **Using the Internet in the Science Classroom.**

NATIONAL GEOGRAPHIC
eXpeditions!

Enrichment

Have interested students compile a list of the dangers involved in exploring the Himalayas on foot. Students will likely mention the danger of climbing steep slopes, the problems imposed by the lack of oxygen at high altitudes, the threat of hazardous weather conditions, the problems associated with transporting food and equipment, and the lack of emergency medical care. Accept all reasonable answers.

Going Further

Extreme weather conditions pose many problems to high-altitude explorers. Have students use their knowledge of the atmosphere to infer why the weather conditions at high altitudes are so much more extreme than those at lower elevations. Students may note that high elevations are generally colder and winds are stronger because there is less friction with Earth's surface. Also, heavy snowfalls are common because air is forced upward, which causes the water vapor in the air to condense and fall as snow.

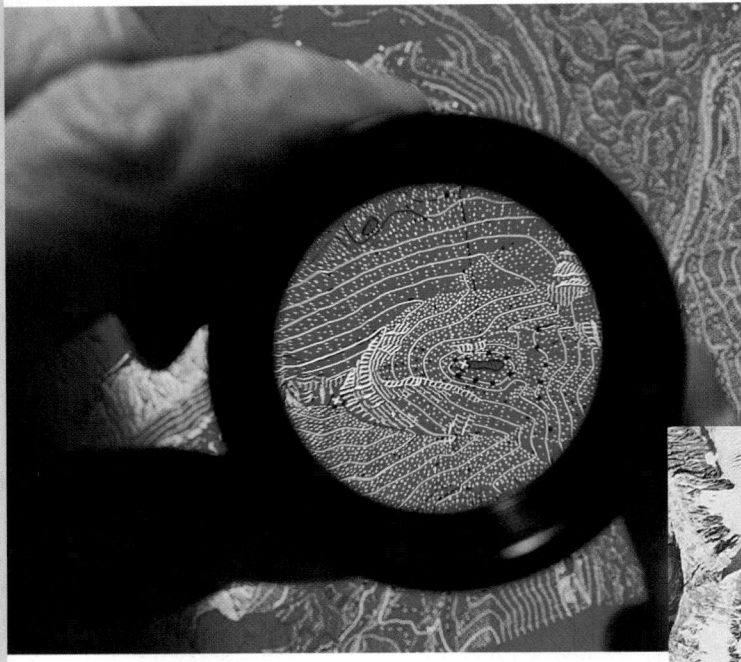

● **LEFT:** In a process that took two years, stereophotographs of Mount Everest and its environs were converted into a conventional contour map, which showed the dramatic lay of the land in remarkable detail.

● **ABOVE:** A portrait of Mount Everest from directly above is one of 160 images obtained in the jet's overflight. The mountain is discernable as a huge pyramid (center left) flanked by glaciers.

POLITICS AND PLANNING

Washburn began with a goal: To map 777 square kilometers (300 square miles) of the world's most rugged mountain wilderness. The vision was simple; bringing it to life would not be. In fact, it took several years.

First, Washburn had to chart a political landscape because Mount Everest straddles the China-Nepal border. Nepal approved the project after China's consent. "We visited China," wrote Washburn, "and when we returned we carried with us a treasure that no one had ever brought out of China before—permission to map Everest from the air."

Next, Washburn needed money. Half of the flight costs came from his former employer, Boston's Museum of Science. National Geographic provided the rest.

Finally the team had to schedule the flight carefully. "To make an accurate map," explained Washburn, "we needed not only cloudless weather but also a mountainscape that was free of loose snow." December looked like the best time for the expedition. The gales that hit Everest late each fall would sweep the peak clean, and the skies should be clear all winter.

In 1984, after almost half a century, Bradford Washburn was ready to map Mount Everest.

866

Differentiated Instruction

Gifted Students learned about the Global Positioning System (GPS) in Chapter 2. This system uses a network of satellites to pinpoint exact locations on Earth. Have students research how the GPS was used in 1999 to update the estimated height of Mount Everest.

TO THE BRINK AND BACK

He wasn't ready for what happened next. The Washburns had barely arrived in Nepal for the long-awaited aerial expedition when Barbara Washburn's temperature began soaring. Her doctors could find no cause, and the fever raged on.

Washburn took his wife to Bangkok, Thailand, for specialized medical labs. Thai doctors delivered grim news. Barbara Washburn was dying of cancer and needed to return home immediately.

Frantic, Bradford Washburn recruited Barry Bishop to lead the team. Bishop, an Everest veteran, was vice chairman of National Geographic's Committee for Research and Exploration. Expert pilot Werner Altherr, who worked for Swissair Photo + Surveys of Zurich, agreed to oversee the aerial photography. The expedition would go on—without the Washburns.

They were back in Boston, where doctors gladly lifted Barbara Washburn's death sentence. She did not have cancer; she had a rare blood disease. They had caught it just in time.

SANTA WITH A SWISS ACCENT

Barbara Washburn was home from the hospital in time for Christmas. The Washburn's holiday began with a phone call. Werner Altherr was calling from Switzerland.

"I've just arrived at Zurich," he said, "In my briefcase are 160 gorgeous negatives of Everest. This news and my love are a Christmas present to you both from the team in Kathmandu!"

● **ABOVE:** Leader of the project to create a new map of Mount Everest, Bradford Washburn, at left, examines the map (see detail at left) with surveying experts in Berne, Switzerland.

● **LEFT:** An artist uses an airbrush to create the stark relief on the most accurate and detailed aerial survey of Mount Everest ever accomplished.

NATIONAL GEOGRAPHIC eXpeditions!

Activity

Linguistic Surveying is the process of determining the elevations of known objects from the ground. Have students research the instruments and techniques used in surveying. If possible, have a representative of a local engineering firm speak to the class and demonstrate surveying equipment. Students can survey the elevation of their school using the known elevation of a nearby location as a reference point. **L2**

Teaching Strategies

The most recently estimated height of Mount Everest is 8850 m, or 29 035 ft. The measured height in 1954 was 8848 m, or 29 028 ft. Have students calculate the rate at which Mount Everest is growing and predict the height of the mountain in the year 2050.

Interpreting the Photo

The photograph of the artist at work on the Mount Everest map shows only one step in the creation of a map. After students have finished reading this feature, have them list the steps involved in mapping an area such as Mount Everest.

867

Project

Visual-Spatial Students have learned how contour maps can be used to determine the elevations of locations on Earth's surface. To help students visualize the enormous height of mountain ranges such as the Himalayas, have students locate the highest elevation on a contour map of the United States. Then have them compare this elevation with that of Mount Everest (more than 8850 m, or 29 035 ft). Students can use the U.S. map and its contour interval to determine how many more contour lines would be necessary to accurately map Mount Everest. **L2**

Identifying Misconceptions

Have students study the illustration of the overview of the Himalayan chain. Ask students whether the art represents the mountains in winter or in summer. Students may see the snow-covered peaks and assume that the art depicts the mountains in winter. Tell students that these mountain peaks are so high that average temperatures remain cold, and therefore the peaks are covered by snow year-round.

Tying to Previous Knowledge

Students have been introduced to the concept of plate tectonics, wherein Earth's plates move in response to internal forces. Ask students to identify other mountain ranges caused by the collision of Earth's plates. The Rocky Mountains of North America and the Andes in South America are good examples.

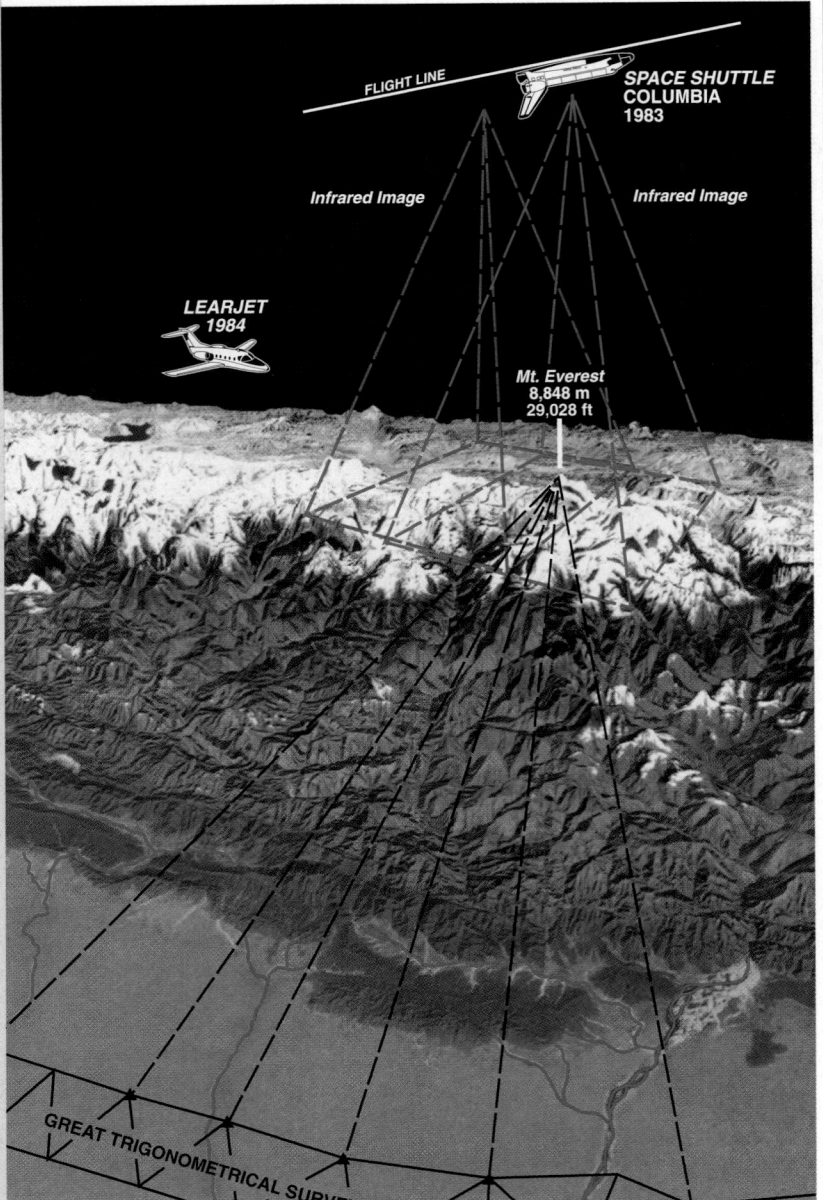

The flight had gone perfectly, he reported. Aboard a Learjet, the team spent three and a half hours photographing Everest and its Himalayan neighbors. Three hours later, the images were already developed. "It all seemed so very fast," mused Washburn, "so very easy at the end of so many years of dreaming, hoping, planning."

868

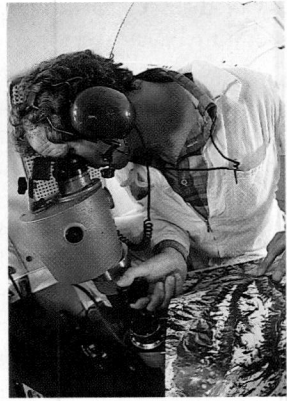

BELOW: The view of Everest from 12 300 kilometers (40 000 feet) aboard a Learjet was "utterly hazeless, like the surface of the moon," said aerial photographer Kurt Keller.

LEFT: Mapping of Mount Everest in the 1980s was preceded by surveys almost 150 years older. British surveyors in the 1840s took sightings of Himalayan peaks from six stations in northern India (bottom of diagram). In 1852, the position and elevation of the peak were determined. It took until 1954, however, to establish the height of Everest at 8848 meters (29 028 feet). The new map in the 1980s made use of this information, plus photos from the Learjet and stereophotographs taken from space by equipment on the space shuttle *Columbia* in 1983. Subsequent investigations, in the late 1990s, established Everest's peak two meters (7 feet) higher, at 8850 meters (29 035 feet).

This text is based on "Mount Everest, Surveying the Third Pole," in the November 1988 issue of NATIONAL GEOGRAPHIC. Use resources to read about a 1999 expedition that sought to measure Mount Everest.

Teaching Strategies

The jet that was used in the Washburn expedition would most likely not have encountered rain or snow on its flight over Mount Everest. Ask students to infer why. The plane would have been flying at an elevation of at least 9144 m, or 30 000 ft—well above the height of most precipitation-producing clouds.

FAST FLIGHT, PAINSTAKING PROCESSING

The next stage of the project was not fast. Valuable though they were, the aerial images were just a starting point for cartographers. The photographs had to be studied carefully and compared with a variety of other resources, including a computer database of old British, Chinese, and Austrian maps of the region.

NASA provided infrared images taken when the space shuttle *Columbia* orbited 250 kilometers (156 miles) above Everest in December 1983. The crystal-clear shots helped Washburn and his team confirm the location of key points. "These are as important to the map," stressed Washburn, "as a high-quality steel framework is to a big building."

Once the team was satisfied with the data, mapmakers in Switzerland went to work. Portraying the convoluted terrain took thousands of patient hours. Some days a cartographer might complete only a single square inch. Meanwhile, National Geographic researchers worked with experts in Nepal and China to ensure the accuracy of each place-name.

The final product—blue, gray, and beautiful—accompanied the November 1988 issue of NATIONAL GEOGRAPHIC. It was, indeed, a triumph.

NATIONAL GEOGRAPHIC eXpeditions!

● **LEFT:** Space shuttle photographs were useful in evaluating the accuracy of earlier maps of the Himalaya. Because clouds obscured part of the range in this 1984 image made from *Challenger* as it passed over Everest, the mapping team relied on photographs from the 1983 *Columbia* flight.

Expeditions Activity

Despite the accuracy of high-tech equipment for surveying mountain systems and measuring the height of peaks, the figures that scientists have obtained are subject to change even today. Discuss factors that might lead to new measurements and more accurate images of Everest. What are the possibilities for geological changes that would actually alter Everest's vital statistics?

869

Going Further

Logical-Mathematical
Have students research and explain why the Himalayan Mountains are still growing. The Indian subcontinent, which drifts northward at a rate of about 10 cm/y, is colliding with the Eurasian Plate. This collision, whereby the Indian subcontinent is being shoved under Eurasia, has formed the Himalayan Mountains. As India moves northward, the continuing collision between these continental plates causes the Himalayas to grow. **L3**

Expeditions Activity

Answers will vary. Students may say that improved technology may lead to new measurements and more accurate images of Mount Everest. Plate tectonics could continue to alter Mount Everest's shape and height. Accept all reasonable answers.

Be sure to check the Earth Science Web Site for links to chapter material:
earthgeu.com

Purpose

Students will learn how humans changed a sporadically raging Colorado River with a huge dam known as the Glen Canyon Dam.

Background

Water was an essential factor in the development of the American West. Because the water in the Colorado River is needed to feed into the far western states, many disputes developed over control and access to the river's water. The River Compact of 1922 was instituted to insure that the upper basin states, which include Colorado, Utah, Wyoming, and New Mexico, allow a specific amount of water to flow each year into the lower basin states, which include Nevada, Arizona, and California. Without access to this water, the lower basin states would be in dire need of water. The need to store water became apparent and in the late 1920s the United States government approved building dams along the Colorado River. As a result the Hoover Dam was built to store water for the lower basin states. The upper basin states needed additional water so a number of years later the Glen Canyon Dam was built.

870

Science Field Book

Earth Science
Journal

Intrapersonal Have students write a letter an early western settler may have written to family back home in the east regarding the water situation. Their letters should reflect the difference in water availability in the east vs. the west and the constant concern the water issue was for them as they traveled to settle in the west.

Cultural Diversity

Saving Zeugma As water rose three feet a day, an international team of archaeologists worked against the clock to save artifacts and mosaics from the ancient Turkish city of Zeugma. The site was threatened by waters from the newly-erected Biric Dam, which is part of a Turkish energy and irrigation project. Zeugma dates back to 300 B.C., and was an ancient trading center on the Euphrates with Greek and Roman settlements.

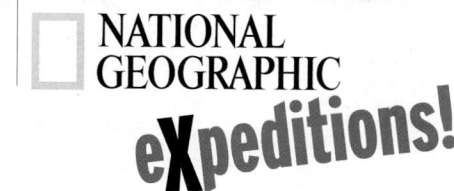
Grand Managed Canyon

The Remaking of a River

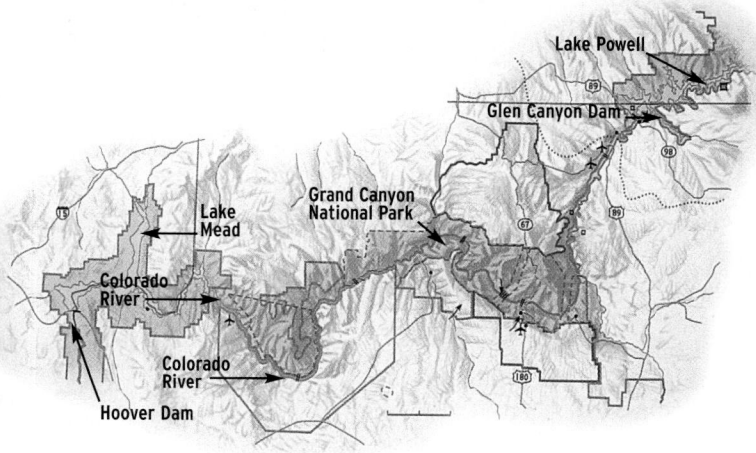

ABOVE: The Colorado River, which used to rage with spring floods, is restricted now by Glen Canyon Dam. Today the river rises and falls according to the demand for electric power.

LEFT: Water rocketed from outlet tubes at the base of Glen Canyon Dam for seven days in the spring of 1996. The artificial flood was designed to gather sediment from the riverbed to rebuild downstream beaches long eroded by the dam's fluctuating outflows.

"You're not going to write about this, are you?" boatman Martin Litton joked to writer Mike Long. The two men, along with several other passengers from a dory called the *Sequoia*, were drying off after capsizing in the Colorado River, the mighty stream that carved the Grand Canyon.

Long had come to the Colorado to study the effects of Glen Canyon Dam, built in 1963 to provide a reservoir for the thirsty Southwest and to generate hydroelectric power. As part of his fieldwork for NATIONAL GEOGRAPHIC, he embarked on a 451-kilometer (280-mile) ride downstream. The trip started well. Long saw incredible scenery and gathered tales about river life.

Then came Crystal Rapids—"the centerpiece," wrote Long, "of one of the most intimidating half miles of white water in North America." To make matters worse, an oar escaped from Litton's left hand, and the passengers aboard *Sequoia* found themselves heading straight into a two-story-high wave. "I see wavelets frothing on the curling crest," Long wrote, "and instantly we are flipped like frying eggs, sunny-side down, into the green, wet womb of the Colorado." No one suffered more than scrapes or bruised pride, but Long's baptism made one thing clear— rivers may be dammed, but not necessarily tamed.

871

Interpreting the Photo

The purpose of a dam is to hold back water and control the flow of water from the reservoir area. The outlets shown in the photograph on page 870 show water being allowed to flow downstream and leaving the reservoir under great pressure. This force can erode the stream's base level and change rates of flow, amounts of sediment deposition, and stream level. When humans interfere or change the natural flow of a stream, both the negative and positive aspects of the change must be considered.

Tying to Previous Knowledge

Students may have used a hose to water a garden or lawn or to wash a car. The nozzle on a hose may be changed to produce a fine stream of water with much force or a larger stream of water with less force. The size of the opening on a nozzle can usually be changed mechanically by turning the nozzle in a particular direction or squeezing the triggering mechanism. In each case what is being changed is the size of the opening the water is being forced through. On a dam, the size of the tube, which allows water to flow through, will determine the force of the moving water and therefore its ability to erode.

Differentiated Instruction

Learning Disabled Students learn best when able to experience first hand the concept that is being explained. Connect a typical garden hose to an outdoor tap and have students change the force of the water moving through the hose to reflect the fact that water moving through a large opening will have less pressure than the same amount of water being forced through a small opening. Use only cold or tepid water and have students wear safety goggles. By doing this themselves and having fun at the same time, these students will internalize and remember the concept relating force to size of outlet. Ask students where they may have seen this concept applied in their everyday lives. They may respond with answers such as a car wash and other forms of power washers.

Identifying Misconceptions

Students often do not realize the difficulties involved in building a dam. Show students pictures of a famous dam such as Hoover Dam. Ask them if they think it was a very difficult task to build such a dam. Tell students that the construction occurred in the hottest and driest area of the United States and in very dangerous conditions. The dam took years to complete and 112 people lost their lives during construction, while many others were injured or got sick in the process. Thousands worked on the project nonstop for four years. The dam is over 60 stories high (more than 200 meters) and as wide as two football fields. It has two protective spillways that are large enough to hold a battleship with a channel height equivalent to a ten-story building. The Hoover Dam is considered an engineering marvel and has been called the eighth wonder of the world.

WATER WARS

Not that people haven't tried to tame rivers. Americans at the start of the twentieth century largely saw nature as an obstacle to overcome. Minor details such as a desert climate were no reason not to settle in Arizona, Nevada, or southern California. American ingenuity would get water there somehow.

"Somehow" turned out to be more complicated than anyone expected, especially for states along the Colorado River. The very question of who owned the water sparked controversy, and the Colorado, according to a *Denver Post* columnist, "earned the reputation as the most legislated, litigated, and debated river in the world."

In 1922, seven western states signed the Colorado River Compact, which determined each state's share of the water. Two decades later, the U.S. guaranteed a portion of the flow to Mexico. Enforcing all these agreements meant wresting control of the river from Mother Nature.

DAMS, DAMS, EVERYWHERE!

With scores of reservoirs and diversion dams, hundreds of miles of aqueducts and tunnels, dozens of pumping stations, thousands of miles of canals, and more than 30 hydroelectric plants, the Colorado River basin contains one of the world's most controlled river systems. Among the jewels in this technological crown is Glen Canyon Dam, authorized by the U.S. Congress in 1956. Located near Page, Arizona,

● **ABOVE:** On the Colorado River, boaters travel an ecosystem transformed upriver by Glen Canyon Dam. Now available to the masses, Rainbow Bridge is only a half-mile stroll after a comfortable two-hour boat ride from Wahweap Marina on Lake Powell. In predam days, before Lake Powell existed, a mere handful of visitors trudged here. Today more than 300 000 people make the trip each year.

This text is based on "Grand Managed Canyon" in the July 1997 issue of NATIONAL GEOGRAPHIC.

872

Project

Kinesthetic Have students work in small groups with stream tables to try to build a dam in a river system. This can be done by allowing water to flow through a large flat container that contains soil. As the water flows through the container, a stream develops. It would be best to have a drain to allow for the continuous flow of water. Make sure any water spilled on the floor is quickly cleaned up. Once the system is established, students can carry out their attempt to build a dam. Allow students to look at the attempts of other lab groups to see how different problems are being addressed. Have students keep a log of the problems they encounter and methods of resolution. Students should come away with the understanding that building a dam is not an easy task. **L2 COOP LEARN**

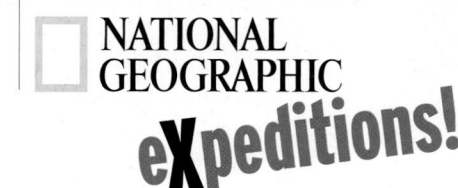
the dam is 92 meters (300 feet) thick at its base. It stands 217 meters (710 feet) high, creating an upstream reservoir known as Lake Powell.

The dam's influence also extends downstream, for nearly 483 kilometers (300 miles). Decades ago, the Colorado raged fierce and wild seasonally through the Grand Canyon. Now it runs year-round like water in a pipe, controlled not by nature but by human need.

NEW, IMPROVED NATURE?

"The predam Colorado, muddy and fierce," wrote Long, "rose and fell with the seasons. Carrying millions of tons of sediment, its floods scoured streamside vegetation while depositing enormous sandbars at the river's edge. A mud-caked cadre of river runners mucked it up in the world-class rapids during the few months of the strong flow, which ebbed to a chilled trickle in winter."

That all changed once the dam was built. Seasonal shifts gave way to a steady flow of clear, cool water. Depending on the amount pumped through Glen Canyon's hydroelectric plants, the river level rises and falls daily, sometimes by about 4 meters (13 feet). The Colorado now carries much more debris, which alters the dynamics of the river and creates new rapids—including the white water that soaked Mike Long.

WHOSE ECOSYSTEM IS IT, ANYWAY?

"One ecosystem was destroyed and replaced by another," said Ron Arnberger, superintendent of Grand Canyon National Park. Willow and tamarisk plants now crowd the Colorado's banks. The foliage sustains insects and migratory birds. Yet other birds—cliff swallows and endangered Bell's vireos, for instance—have declined. Three fish species have vanished. A fourth, the humpback chub, is endangered.

Experts disagree on what's best for the Colorado River ecosystem, and the human thirst for water and electricity further complicates the issue. According to former Secretary of the Interior Bruce Babbitt, "The more we look into our relation to the land, the more likely we will reaffirm natural visions. But final decisions will be made by the American people."

● **ABOVE:** A Bewick's wren brings its brood a meal of insect larva in a tamarisk tree.

● **LOWER LEFT:** Tamarisks stand on the shoreline at Eminence Break. Brought to the United States from the Middle East nearly 200 years ago, they now crowd many western waterways. Here they offer food and shelter to birds.

Expeditions Activity

Draining Lake Powell and abandoning the Glen Canyon Dam is a subject of much debate. Develop arguments both for and against this possibility. A good place to start might be the Web sites of the Glen Canyon Institute and of the Friends of Lake Powell. You can also search the Environmental News Network for recent developments: Click on their link at earthgeu.com

873

Teaching Strategies

When a dam is built, a reservoir of water is formed behind the dam. In the case of the Glen Canyon Dam, Lake Powell was formed. The lake covers an area formerly not covered by water, so ecosystems changed. The ecosystems below the dam also changed because the amount of water flowing changed. Environmentalists point out that frequently the backwater areas used by spawning fish are not restored. This also affects the habitats of water fowl and birds dependent upon the water. To insure that all aspects of the ecosystem are taken into consideration close collaboration must exist between different types of scientists—biologists as well as Earth scientists. Some argue that if the Glen Canyon Dam had been built during a time when the Environmental Protection Agency (EPA) existed, it would not have been approved.

Expeditions Activity

Some environmentalists are promoting draining Lake Powell. Their arguments contend that draining the lake will result in a reduction of pollution caused by boating activities on the lake. Others argue that to do so would cost millions of dollars, there would be a great loss from a reduction in electric generation, and the economy would suffer as a result of a reduction of tourism.

Activity

Interpersonal Divide the class into two groups. Have each group take opposing sides and conduct a debate on the issue of whether or not dams should be built. **COOP LEARN**

✔ PORTFOLIO

A Study of Dams

Interpersonal Have students work in groups and research different dams. Their research should include pictures, location of the dam, specific data relating to size and amount of water affected, a timeline of construction, costs, and effects on the economy and environment. The work of each group can be presented on a poster. Following the presentations to the class the locations of each dam researched can be plotted on a large map posted in the classroom. Have students determine if there is a pattern to where the dams were built. Students may also rate each dam based on number of people affected and on the effects on the area's economy and environment. Students should develop an understanding of the conflicting opinions regarding the need for human intervention in natural processes.

Purpose

Students will learn about caves formed of ice that may be found in glaciers and of the perils and different conditions that an ice caver may experience.

Background

Typically, the word *cave* brings to mind an opening in the ground surrounded by rock, that might be interesting to explore. Caves, however, also can be found in glaciers; these caves, called glacier caves, are formed in the ice by the erosive power of water as it flows to the lowest levels possible within the glacier. In contrast, the term *ice caves* refers to caves composed of bedrock that contain ice, such as the great ice caves found in the Austrian Alps. In ice caves, the ice seldom covers the walls but instead takes the form of year-round icicles and ice flows. The term *ice cave* thus may be interpreted and used loosely. Caves of ice can be found all over the world. Some of the most famous caves are found on Mer de Glace glacier in Chamonix, France, on the Gornergletscher and Spitzbergen glaciers in Switzerland, as well as in glaciers in Greenland and Iceland.

874

Earth Science
Journal

Science Field Book

Intrapersonal Have students draw a series of pictures of an imaginary trip into a cave. Have students write a caption for each picture. Along with the picture sequence, have students write a log that includes some of the experiences of the caver during the journey. Have students share their journals with their lab partners for feedback and to answer questions the other students may have. **L1**
COOP LEARN **P**

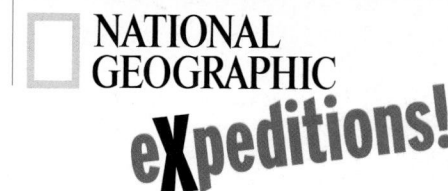
Ice Cavers

Really Cool Caves

Some of the toughest spelunkers—people who explore caves—don't see a single rock on their slow, dangerous, exhilarating journeys. That's because these cavers, a relatively new breed, navigate caves of ice.

Icy labyrinths twist and turn within the glaciers that cover 10 percent of the planet's land surface. The determined adventurers who brave those frigid mazes find them at least as challenging and diverse as the more familiar caves of rock that lie underground.

● **ABOVE:** Specially designed screws for securing one's steps in ice enable Stefan Geissler to reach this point, some 15 meters (50 feet) above the floor of an ice cave in southern Germany.

● **LEFT:** An ice shaft more than 91 meters (300 feet) deep surrounds rappelling adventurers in the Greenland ice sheet. A new breed of explorer is discovering that cave systems in glaciers can be just as challenging as caves underground.

BIRTH OF A GLACIER

Glaciers, huge masses of ice that inch over Earth's surface, form when snow piles up faster than it can melt. Each new snowfall compresses the layers beneath until what were once snowflakes fuse into solid ice.

As the ice forms, growing thicker and thicker and heavier and heavier, it begins to creep downward, driven by the force of gravity. As soon as a mass of ice starts moving, it becomes a glacier.

Glaciers come in two varieties. Alpine glaciers, which form on mountainsides, resemble frozen rivers. Continental glaciers, also called ice sheets, have a wide mound in the center and spread out in all directions, like pancake batter on a griddle. Ice sheets blanket most of Greenland and Antarctica.

875

Enrichment

When discussing caves and caving explorations, it is helpful to use the correct terminology as specified by the American Geological Institute (AGI). According to the AGI, speleology is the exploration and scientific study of caves, including the physical, biological, and geologic studies of their origin, morphology, and composition. A spelunker is a person who explores caves, or a caver. The act of caving is spelunking, while a scientist who studies caves is referred to as a speleologist, and the process of cave formation is speleogenesis. The root of these terms is derived from the Latin word *spelunca*, which means "cave."

Tying to Previous Knowledge

If your area experiences snow in the winter season, students likely will be familiar with snow sculptures. To make a snow sculpture, the snow is shaped and patted until it is a solid mass; such a mass is similar to a glacier, in which snow is compacted under its own weight. Snow sculptures, because of their density, last longer than snow on the ground and often contain the last snow to melt.

Differentiated Instruction

Visually Impaired Students who are visually impaired are likely to have a keenly developed sense of touch. This activity will not only provide a sensory approach to learning about ice, but will also give students who are visually impaired the opportunity to excel in describing what they feel as opposed to what they see. Give each student an ice cube. Caution students not to put the ice cubes in their mouths. Ask them to describe the surface of the ice cube, especially the irregularities. Explain to students that similar irregularities may be found on ice forming in glaciers.

NATIONAL GEOGRAPHIC
eXpeditions!

Teaching Strategies

- Ask students what is meant by the term *glacial pace* and whether they can relate it to any similar phrase that they have heard. One similar phrase is "a snail's pace." Both mean a very slow rate of movement.
- Ask students why glacial caves are called "chameleon caves." A chameleon changes its color according to its environment. Glacial caves are very changeable; hence the reference to chameleon caves.

Interpreting the Photo

Glacial crevasses are deep, usually vertical, cracks or fissures in a glacier or snowfield. They are the result of stresses related to the movement of the ice mass. Crevasses can be extremely dangerous for those who trek across glaciers. People who trek over glacial areas wear special gear to protect them from the cold as well as to help them navigate on the ice. Teamwork is essential, and the use of ropes is common. Sometimes, ladders are carried to help bridge the larger crevasses. Each step must be carefully taken, and the trekker must be constantly alert.

GLACIERS ON THE GO

There's a reason people complain when something moves at a "glacial pace." Driven by gravity, glaciers generally creep ever so slowly over the landscape, some advancing by only a few centimeters a day. Alpine glaciers drift downhill, slicing their way through valleys. Continental glaciers spread outward slowly from the center.

The layers of a glacier move at different rates. The bottom trudges, slowed by friction with soil and rocks. Icy layers in the middle move more swiftly, and the brittle crust at the top moves fastest of all—fast, that is, for a glacier.

Those varying speeds of movement create enormous pressures within glaciers. As the ice flows toward the margin of the glacier, it may encounter obstacles that cause the ice to slow down. The ice may also speed up if the slope of the glacier becomes steeper. The resulting stresses within the glaciers may cause the surface to fracture into deep cracks known as crevasses or produce shifting spaces that form glacial caves deep within.

CHAMELEON CAVES

"They are the chameleons of caves," says German photographer-spelunker Carsten Peter of the glacial caves he has explored in Europe

876

ABOVE: In search of the perfect ice cave, a team of Italian cavers carefully crosses Moreno Glacier, on Lake Argentino, in the Andes mountains of Argentina. They have to watch for hidden, deep crevasses and for ice that may thinly cover a cave.

RIGHT: Rising heat from geothermal springs melts an Iceland glacier from the inside out, creating a huge hollow in the ice. Layers of ice, marked by bands of volcanic ash, form a monstrous "eye" that casts its frozen stare on caver Arne Kaiser.

✔ PORTFOLIO

Cave Reports

Linguistic Ask students to each develop a report on a cave of their choice. The cave may or may not be local and may be a glacial, ice, or bedrock cave. Ask students to include in their reports a history of how the cave was found and interesting stories that spelunkers have shared about their experiences in the cave. Each report should also include a map showing the location of the cave and a three-dimensional model of the cave as it currently is known to exist. Have students briefly tell the class about the caves they reported on. Post maps of the caves on the classroom bulletin board and place models around the room for students to study.

and Greenland. "They change all the time."

Summer warmth often melts some of the ice and snow atop a glacier, creating torrents that both form and erase caves. Slithering through tiny fractures, meltwater can drip down into caves, where frigid temperatures turn the water back into ice. The result: enormous icicles that dangle like bizarre crystal chandeliers. They are an ice cave's version of stalactites.

In addition, geothermal springs within Earth give off heat that melts glaciers from the inside out. The melting makes and endlessly remakes large bowl-like chambers within the ice. Iceland is particularly noted for its geothermal and volcanic activity.

Each fall, as the deluge of meltwater recedes, cavers return to Greenland and other glacier sites to explore the latest batch of creations. It's an opportunity traditional spelunkers can only dream about. "As often as I return," says Carsten Peter, "I have never entered the same glacial cave twice."

BLEAK BEAUTY

During their short lives, glacial caves can be hauntingly gorgeous. Depending on how thick the ice is, refracted sunlight may reach deep into a cave, causing walls to glow deep blue, or slick cave walls may gleam like mirrors.

Caves near a glacier's surface may even have "skylights"—thin, clear sheets of ice that offer glimpses of Sun and clouds.

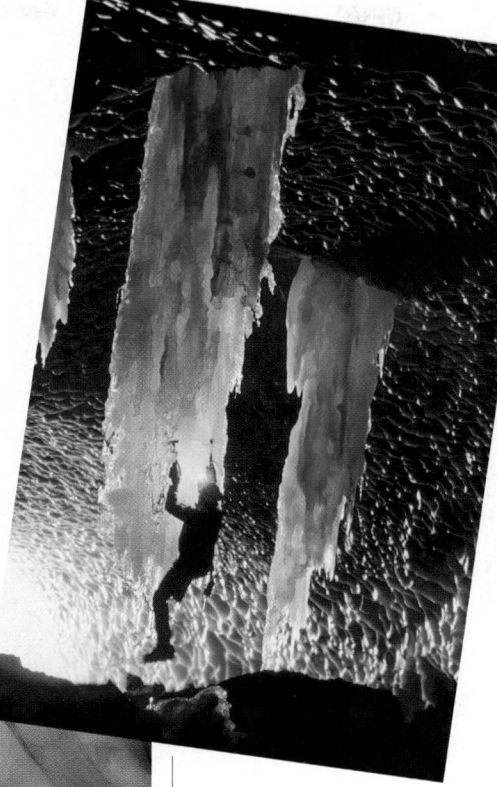

● **ABOVE:** With his helmet light casting a warm glow, Daniel Jehle uses ice axes to climb huge ice stalactites in a cave in Germany. The stalactites formed when meltwater from the surface dripped through tiny fractures and into the cave, where cold air froze it into huge icicles.

877

Going Further

Students may be surprised to find out that glaciers and volcanic activity can be occurring in the same locations. The Vatnajokull ice cap on the southeastern portion of Iceland overlies several volcanoes, one of which is Kverkfjoll. The area is geothermally active; there are numerous hot springs and gas vents. The heat melts portions of the glaciers, causing streams to flow within the glaciers and caves to form. Because of this continuous activity, the glaciers and their caves are constantly changing, and thus the hazards associated with caving within these glaciers are compounded. In addition, the difficulty of deciphering just what is being seen makes the danger greater in this tenuous environment. The best time to explore these glacial caves is between the summer melt and the beginning of the winter snows, which is a relatively short period of time.

Teaching Strategy

Intrapersonal Ask students when icicles form and how they change. Icicles form when the Sun melts the snow and ice from roofs and causes the water to flow down the sides of the roofs. In the evening, in the absence of radiant heat from the Sun, the water freezes again and forms the long icicle shapes. In the same way, ice stalactites form in ice caves and glacial caves.

Project

Kinesthetic Tell students that they will be using ice that is both in block form and in sheets for this project. Have students decide on the containers in which to form the ice blocks and sheets. They may select any solid container for the ice blocks and may choose a cookie sheet for the ice sheets. Have students place the containers filled with water in the freezer. Once the water is frozen, have students shine a light on a piece of ice.

Ask them to record their observations. Students should readily notice that the light reflects off of the ice as it would off of a mirror. Have students look through the sheet of ice, towards the sky. The ice will look blue. Ask students to write in their science journals how what they have experienced in this activity has helped them to understand what someone caving in a glacial cave would see and what difficulties it would present to the caver.

Identifying Misconceptions

Students may misjudge the dangers associated with caving. Ask students whether they have ever seen a cave or gone into a cave. Share with students that there are many different kinds of caves, and that even though an area may have the same types of caves, each one is different and may have unexpected conditions within. There likewise is an array of specialty caving equipment and a number of survival strategies and precautions that serious spelunkers learn and practice before they enter caves. People who do not know about the perils associated with caving are placing themselves in great danger if they attempt to explore an unknown cave.

Earth Science nline

Be sure to check the Earth Science Web Site for links to chapter material:
earthgeu.com

INTO AN ICY WORLD

Glacial caves lure spelunkers willing to face discomfort and danger in order to enjoy the fragile beauty. To do so, ice cavers use some of the same tools that traditional cavers employ: ropes, lamps, helmets, and more. Ice cavers also bring tools specially designed for their frozen world. These include screws that dig deep into icy walls, boots with long spikes that keep spelunkers from slipping, and ice axes.

In 1995, an Italian expedition took a new approach to exploring glacial caves in Argentina. They suited up like scuba divers and plunged into a flooded maze. With the water barely a degree above freezing, the spelunkers could not stay under for more than a few minutes. Twice, divers found that the air valves on their breathing devices had frozen. Despite these obstacles, the expedition located one of the longest glacial caves yet recorded—1037 meters (3400 feet).

The team also faced a challenge that might surprise traditional

● **ABOVE:** Tracing the path of a stream over ice was a difficult chore, so the Italian cavers in Argentina used fluorescent dye to mark the water, making following its path much easier.

● **RIGHT:** Some ice caves form extremely close to the surface of a glacier, as this one did in southern Argentina. Only a fragile skin of ice covered the tubular cave—until it broke.

This text is based on "Into the Heart of Glaciers" in the February 1996 issue of NATIONAL GEOGRAPHIC.

878

Science Field Book

Earth Science

Journal

Intrapersonal Have students write in their science journals reasons why they would or would not explore glacial caves. Ask for volunteers to share their decisions and reasons. This is a good time to point out to students the range of people and interests that exist just within their own classroom and to emphasize the importance of diversity of interests and the willingness to explore.

Differentiated Instruction

Gifted Have students research and write a report on the use of ice caves in the Badlands, El Malpais, in western New Mexico by the Acoma, Zuni, and Navajo. These Native Americans of the Southwest have a rich history of using the ice caves for shelter, storage, and as a source of water. The caves are held in high esteem, and are only approached by some Native Americans after performing rites that may include offerings, gifts, and prayers.

spelunkers—distinguishing the water from the walls. "The ice is blue, the water is blue," explained diver Antonio De Vivo. "It is very difficult to tell the difference between the ice and the water." Their creative solution? Add fluorescent yellow dye to the water.

A season later, of course, that notable cave might have melted away, but the turmoil beneath the surface of Earth's glaciers always promises replacements—brief, blue, and beautiful.

● **ABOVE:** Swimming in a flooded ice cave presents its own peculiar difficulty—distinguishing the blue water from the blue ice. Diver Matteo Diana gets help in finding the icy wall with a flashlight.

Expeditions Activity

The article describes perils that glacial spelunkers face due to the nature of the ice and water. What advantages might there be to caving in glaciers? Research typical spelunking and compare the dangers that explorers of rock caves face with the dangers faced by those who probe into glaciers.

879

Display

Visual-Spatial Have students bring in magazine photographs and downloaded photographs from the Earth Science Web Site, **earthgeu.com**, of glaciers and various types of ice caves. Use the photographs to make a class collage. Encourage students who are especially interested in language arts to write a poem based on the collage. **COOP LEARN** **P**

Activity

Ask students to think about what it would be like to be in a house of mirrors. Some students may have experienced this at a carnival. Also have students float a piece of ice in a glass or clear container. Have them notice how, unless they look carefully, they may not notice the ice. Put an ice cube in colored water and ask students to note the difference in their ability to distinguish the ice from the water. Students may also be able to relate this phenomenon to invisible "black ice." Black ice occurs on roadways when the temperature drops just to freezing. Many serious automobile accidents have occurred because black ice conditions have distorted the vision of drivers. Similar optical illusions would be experienced by a person in a glacial cave.

Cultural Diversity

International Ice Cores A group of Japanese scientists working at Dome Fugi in eastern Antarctica as part of the International Geosphere and Biosphere Program study paleoclimates by extracting and analyzing ice cores from glaciers. In addition to providing information about past climates, these studies can help scientists to determine the possible effects of global warming and rising sea levels.

Expeditions Activity

Have students use the Earth Science Web Site to find information on how cave spelunkers prepare to explore land caves and the safety equipment used. Document any historical caving tragedies and explain which safety techniques and equipment were developed as a result.

e**X**peditions!

Purpose

Students will learn about the scientific discovery of the wreckage of the *Titanic* deep within the Atlantic Ocean.

Background

When the *Titanic* was launched by the White Star Line in 1912, it was touted as being "unsinkable" by the media—a great engineering feat. It was thought to exemplify all of the modern conveniences and technology of the time. Ironically, it was partly this over-confidence that doomed the ship to disaster. Contrary to all of the propaganda about the *Titanic,* it was a product of the safety short-cuts that often were taken to cut costs in the building of steamships at that time. Divers who have examined the wreck have found evidence that the ship was constructed of brittle steel. Also, the designers decided to build a single hull instead of a double hull to make more room for cargo and passengers. The designers also added doors in watertight bulk-heads, and chose to install a grand staircase instead of a watertight deck. The new wireless was not fully operational, which inhibited communication with other ships in dangerous seas. The ship also lacked a speaker system that would have allowed better com-munication as the ship was sink-ing. There was also the infamous shortage of lifeboats, as well as questionable loading procedures. The disaster led to painful lessons about safety and travel on the high seas, the vulnerability of humans, and the effects of greed and ego on human lives.

880

Finding the *Titanic*

Plunging Into History

● **ABOVE:** A proud and allegedly unsinkable R.M.S. *Titanic* departs her berth in Southampton, England, in April 1912, on her fateful maiden voyage to the North Atlantic.

● **LEFT:** The ghostly hulk of the *Titanic* lies in her grave more than two miles deep, her bow festooned by decades of rust and sediment.

"God himself could not sink this ship," boasted a crewman aboard the R.M.S. *Titanic.* Famous last words. Many aboard the sumptuous liner—the largest and most expensive ship of her era—shared the sailor's optimism. As the ship left England on her maiden voyage, she seemed the very emblem of technological triumph.

Probably most people in America know the unhappy ending. The *Titanic* hit an iceberg at 11:40 P.M. on April 14, 1912. She sank about two hours later, killing 1522 people. (The ship's lifeboats saved 705 others.) The "unsinkable" ship didn't survive a single Atlantic crossing.

Yet by sinking, the *Titanic* achieved gruesome immortality. When scientists found the shipwreck in 1985, they earned attention seldom given to marine exploration.

DEADLY DECISION

Fred Fleet was on lookout duty the night the *Titanic* sank. From his perch in the crow's nest, he spotted an iceberg directly in the ship's path, only a quarter of a mile away. He phoned the bridge with a terse, terrifying warning: "Iceberg right ahead!"

The officer-in-charge tried to reverse engines while turning hard to starboard (to the right)—a combination that proved fatal. Because the ship was in reverse, the change in steering actually moved her to port

Interpreting the Photo

Ask students to observe the stern in the photograph on page 880. Discuss with them the color caused by the bacteria present on the stern. The bacteria are brown, yellow, and red. These bacteria helped to oxidize the iron in the wreck, creating rusticles. Scientists are collecting samples of these bacteria so that they can estimate the rate of the ship's decomposition. It is predicted that the ship will be naturally weathered by 2020 into a pile of debris. **L1** **ELL**

Be sure to check the Earth Science Web Site for links to chapter material: earthgeu.com

881

Identifying Misconceptions

Many students falsely believe that it was possible for people who were left in the water to survive long enough to be rescued by lifeboats. Discuss with students how long a person could survive in such conditions before succumbing to the freezing water. The water of the Atlantic was approximately -2°C (28°F). It is theorized that those who made it into the water lived only 10 to 15 minutes before freezing to death. Because the people who managed to get onto lifeboats were afraid that panic-stricken survivors in the water would overturn the boats, only one lifeboat returned to search for survivors. Days later, 330 bodies buoyed by life vests were recovered. Other bodies were thought to have been swept into the Gulf Stream. Those that sank to the ocean floor were probably quickly decomposed by the many bacteria present there.

Teaching Strategies

Ask students to select and research a legend of the *Titanic:* the band continuing to play as the ship sank; the behavior of famous people during the sinking, such as John Jacob Astor, Molly Brown, and Ben Guggenheim; the appearance of a mystery ship nearby; and so on. Students can then use their research to write newspaper editorials to support or refute the legends. **L2** **P**

(to the left), and the *Titanic*'s starboard side hit the iceberg. Six out of 16 watertight compartments flooded, pulling the bow (front) into frigid water.

Ironically, the *Titanic* might have survived a crash head-on. Two or three watertight compartments might have flooded, but that wouldn't have been enough to sink the ship.

OUT OF SIGHT, MUCH IN MIND

Shivering in icy terror, survivors watched the *Titanic* disappear shortly after 2 A.M. on April 15. "I saw that ship sink," recalled Eva Hart. "I saw all the horror of its sinking. And I heard, even more dreadful, the cries of drowning people." Eventually, the screams gave way to utter silence: No one remaining in the -2°C (28°F) North Atlantic waters was left alive.

Hart and 704 others were the last people to see the *Titanic* for 73 years. Various expeditions searched for the wreck, but they were defeated by the unpredictable North Atlantic weather, the enormous depth to which the ship sank, and conflicting accounts of her final hours.

Meanwhile, books and movies—notably, *A Night to Remember,* by Walter Lord—helped keep the story alive. The Titanic Historical Society gathered memorabilia, documents, and survivors' stories. In addition, a *Titanic* memorial by the Potomac River was included with the many monuments of Washington, D.C.

HIGH TECH ON THE HIGH SEAS

On June 28, 1985, a French-American expedition set out to search for the *Titanic* with the most advanced tools available: side-scan sonar, sonic beacons, submersible video cameras, computers, and much more. Led by Robert D. Ballard and Jean-Louis Michel, the team examined a 386-square-kilometer (150-square-mile) target zone about 644 kilometers (400 miles) south of Newfoundland. Like gardeners mowing a lawn, the expedition's ships patiently went back and forth, surveying strips of the seafloor.

● **ABOVE:** A storage area for *Titanic* lifeboats (top) serves as a landing platform for the manned submersible *Alvin,* resting on the deck at the far right. This scene was photographed by the remotely operated robot *Jason Jr.,* which is taking a closer look at the same spot (below), peering into a first-class cabin.

Cultural Diversity

Richard Glenn (1963–) Richard Glenn is an expert on sea ice. The son of an Inupiat mother and a white father, Glenn studied geology at the University of San Jose and at the University of Alaska to help his people in the fishing and shipping industries. He moved to Barrow, Alaska as an adult. Barrow lies 350 miles inside the arctic circle, and most of its residents are Inupiat. Inupiat culture centers on whale hunting; thus, the Inupiat have intimate knowledge of the changeable character of sea ice. Richard Glenn combines his Inupiat heritage with his knowledge of geology to study sea-ice strength. His work is used in oil exploration, in the shipping industry, and in submarine navigation. He is committed to improving the economic conditions of Inupiat communities.

Their perseverance paid off at 1:05 A.M. on September 1, 1985. Video cameras aboard the *Argo,* a submersible research vessel, focused on one of the *Titanic*'s enormous boilers. It lay some 4000 meters (13 000 feet) beneath the surface.

Over the next four days, the expedition shot more than 20 000 pictures of the well-preserved wreck. Marine organisms had devoured much of the wood-work—and any human remains—but the bulk of the ship looked achingly familiar.

FACE-TO-FACE WITH THE SHIP

On a second expedition, in 1986, Ballard and two colleagues became the first people to actually visit the wreck. Scrunched up in the research submersible *Alvin,* they had a mishap-filled descent to the bottom. Sonar died, salt water seeped into the sub's batteries, alarms wailed. The navigator, back at the surface in a support ship, was having difficulty directing them.

Hollywood could have scripted the next scene. Just as the pilot was ready to abort the mission, Ballard spotted "an endless slab of black steel rising out of the bottom." *Titanic!* Ballard truly was the first

● **ABOVE:** The research vessel *Knorr,* from the Woods Hole Oceanographic Institution in Woods Hole, Massachusetts, floats more than two miles above *Titanic.* Serving as a support ship for the submersible search vessel *Argo, Knorr* is specially equipped to allow it to maneuver sideways as well as forward and backward.

● **LEFT:** Robert Ballard and other members of the joint French-American search team monitor video screens during a descent by *Argo.*

883

Tying to Previous Knowledge

Many students are aware of legends about the *Titanic.* However, they may not know that the location of the shipwreck was not discovered until 1985 by Ballard. Ask students to discuss why scientists and treasure hunters seek out shipwrecks, what they intend to do once they have found the wrecks, and what methods they use to find the wrecks.

Activity

Have students work in small groups with maps of the northern Atlantic Ocean. Have students trace the intended path of the *Titanic*'s maiden voyage. Then ask students to locate the site of the shipwreck. stern: 41'43'35" N, 49'56'54" W; boilers: 41'43'32" N, 49'56'49"W; bow: 41'43'57" N, 49'56'49" W Ask students to compare these coordinates to the coordinates given by crew members in the distress signal: 41'46' N, 50'14' W. **L2 COOP LEARN**

Earth Science Online

Note Internet addresses that you find useful in the space below for quick reference.

_____

_____

_____

_____

_____

_____

For Internet tips, see Glencoe's **Using the Internet in the Science Classroom.**

Going Further

Have students investigate the class system for cabin assignments that prevailed on the ship. Ask students to research how many passengers were in each class and how classes were kept apart onboard. Have students examine how the class system and the policy of boarding women and children first affected who ended up on the lifeboats. Ask students to also research how many of the survivors were assigned to the second, third, and steerage classes on the ship. **L2**

Earth Science Journal

Have students select a piece of equipment or a type of technology used to locate the *Titanic*. Ask them to write about the role the instrument or technology played in searching for the *Titanic* and to describe how it is used for other types of research. Equipment and technology might include satellites, submersibles, and sonar.

High-tech Explorer Plumbs New Depths

ALVIN

1 Still camera with strobe
2 Manipulator arm with lights and still and video cameras **3** Cable winch and reel **4** Scanning sonar
5 Hatch **6** Titanium sphere
7 Viewing port **8** Jettisonable iron ballast **9** Acoustic telephone
10 Hoisting bitt **11** Tanks for air and variable seawater ballast
12 Batteries **13** Pressure housings for electric controls
14 Thrusters **15** Emergency tether cutter **16** Down-looking, low-light-level, black-and-white TV camera **17** Forward-looking, low-light-level, black-and-white TV camera

PAINTING BY WILLIAM H. BOND,
NATIONAL GEOGRAPHIC ARTIST

person to see the wreck—a moment he'd spent a lifetime dreaming about and working for.

Ballard and his team made 11 more dives. They also dispatched a "swimming eyeball"—a robotic submersible called *Jason Jr.*—to explore parts of the wreck too small or too dangerous for humans. Such robots, Ballard has argued, represent an essential advance for marine exploration.

SURPRISES ON THE SEAFLOOR

Many *Titanic* experts had believed the doomed ship went down in one piece. But the wreckage suggests a different story. The bow (front) and stern (rear) lie some 400 meters (1200 feet) apart. Ballard theorized that the ship tore apart at the surface. The bow descended first. The stern plunged afterwards and may have rotated en route. "In short," said Ballard, "the bow landed, the stern crashed."

884

● **ABOVE:** The three-person submersible *Alvin* carries a tethered robot named *Jason Jr.* in a so-called garage at the front of the vehicle. *Alvin* can park and let *Jason Jr.* explore areas that are too isolated or dangerous for the manned vehicle to enter.

● **LEFT:** Above the wreck site, divers stand atop the submersible *Alvin* to secure safety lines that hold *Jason Jr.*'s garage as the vehicles are lifted out of the water to the deck of the support ship. Both vehicles are operated by the Woods Hole Oceanographic Institution in Woods Hole, Mass.

This text is based on four NATIONAL GEOGRAPHIC articles: "How We Found Titanic*" (December 1985), "A Long Last look at* Titanic*" (December 1986)," "Epilogue for* Titanic*" (October 1987), and "Titanic: Tragedy in Three Dimensions" (August 1998).*

✔ PORTFOLIO

The *Alvin*

Ask students to imagine that they could ride in the *Alvin* down to explore the wreck of the *Titanic*. Have them write a story describing what they think the experience would be like, what they would see, and what part of the ship they would choose to investigate. **L1** **P**

Even more surprising was the starboard bow. *Titanic* accounts had always assumed that the iceberg slashed open the hull, but the expedition found no such wound. Either the fatal gash was lower on the bow, an area that lay buried in mud, or it never existed. Ballard noted, "*Titanic*'s massive steel plates probably would have been been bent or forced apart rather than ripped open by ice."

TRAGEDY FOR SALE

Ballard hoped that only "gentle exploration" would befall the wreck he found: "It would be wrong to attempt recovery of any of the remains." Not all agreed, and an American entrepreneur secured salvage rights to the ship. *Titanic* buffs can now see artifacts on exhibit or even buy pieces of coal meant to power the ship.

Late in the 1990s, the *Titanic* inspired a Broadway musical and a Hollywood movie—the first film to gross a billion dollars. The unsinkable ship that sank still sails on in millions of imaginations.

NATIONAL GEOGRAPHIC
eXpeditions!

- **ABOVE:** A grenadier fish eyes *Alvin*'s mechanical arm as it pauses above a china cup on the seafloor. The cup still bears the emblem of the White Star Line, a white star on a red flag.

- **LEFT:** A brass-and-crystal light fixture dangles, decorated by a feathery sea pen. Handsome features abounded in areas such as the skylighted grand staircase (lower) connecting first-class decks.

Expeditions Activity

Robert Ballard has discovered the hulks of other famous ships from the 20th century, as well as ancient vessels lost at sea. Which other ships has he discovered? Were the techniques used to find these more recently found vessels similar to the techniques used to find *Titanic*? Research Robert Ballard—like him, you'll start to discover some amazing information.

Enrichment

Interpersonal When Ballard located the *Titanic*, he kept the coordinates a secret to preserve the *Titanic*'s watery grave. He believed that the site should remain untouched as a memorial to those who died. In 1987 a company acquired salvaging rights to the shipwreck. Since then, many artifacts have been recovered, with some being archived in museums, and others, such as coal from the ship, being made available for sale. Ask students to investigate the current locations of various *Titanic* artifacts and the marine laws governing their recovery, and to develop informed opinions about what should happen to the site. Have students role-play a hearing to determine what should happen to the *Titanic*'s remains. Have students represent scientists, entrepreneurs, victims' relatives, and historians to present their views to the jury (the rest of the class). After all of the evidence has been heard, ask the jury to make a recommendation about what should happen to the remains. **L2 COOP LEARN**

Expeditions Activity

Have students go to **earthgeu.com** to find links to sites about Robert Ballard and his shipwreck-hunting activities.

Project

Students may choose to investigate the various theories about why the *Titanic* sank. Many theories over the years have been presented as the one and only reason that the *Titanic* sank. Some people believe that the brittle steel used in construction significantly contributed to the damage done to the ship. Others believe that the increasing speed (22–23 knots) and disregard of other ships' warnings about the ice field caused the disaster. The stoppage of the engines and the sharp turn made by the ship also are thought to have increased the severity of the situation. Some people believe that, had the watertight bulkheads been left open, the ship would have remained afloat longer. Still others blame the faulty wireless and poor safety features. Students should work in teams and select a theory about what led to the sinking of the *Titanic* to investigate. Each team should prepare a report on its theory and present it to the class. **L2 COOP LEARN**

886

NATIONAL GEOGRAPHIC
eXpeditions!

Purpose

Students will learn about the effects of a volcanic eruption on a populated area and about scientists' ability to predict the eruption.

Background

The Volcano Disaster Assistance Team (VDAT), which is based at the Cascade Mountain Observatory, is a division of the United States Geological Survey. The VDAT was formed to provide scientific monitoring and analysis in areas of active volcanism. The team, which consists of a group of scientists, is mobilized when the United States Office of Foreign Disaster Assistance receives a request. The VDAT arrived in the Philippines in 1991 at the request of the Philippine government and worked with a group of international scientists to monitor the activity of Mount Pinatubo. A volcano-hazards assessment map generated by the scientists helped to predict the size and severity of the impending eruption—crucial information that was used to safely evacuate thousands of people.

✔ PORTFOLIO

A Narrow Escape

Have students imagine that they are passengers in the vehicle shown in the photograph. Have students each write a paragraph or two describing how they feel and what they see as they look out of the back window of the vehicle. Ask for volunteers to read their descriptions. Some students might want to include their paragraphs in a best-work portfolio. Inform students that the people in the vehicle escaped unharmed.

Cultural Diversity

Volcanoes and Tourism There are 22 active volcanoes in the Philippines—enough to provide volcano enthusiasts with many possibilities to view volcanic eruptions. In the interest of safety, the Philippine Government and the Institute of Volcanology and Seismology are working to establish a program for tourists interested in observing these spectacular, but often-dangerous, phenomena. One stipulation of the program mandates that tourists not be allowed within a 7-km danger zone of an active volcano.

Mount Pinatubo's Eruption

One Hot Topic

● **ABOVE:** Much of the damage inflicted by Mount Pinatubo's eruption in the Philippines in June 1991 was not immediate. The weight of accumulated ash on roofs, particularly after it mixed with torrential rains, eventually brought down thousands of sheds and homes.

● **LEFT:** At full blast, Mount Pinatubo lies completely hidden by turbulent clouds of super-heated ash that surge from the volcano.

Someone was screaming. Yowls of terror woke NATIONAL GEOGRAPHIC's Noel Grove, who was on the Philippine island of Luzon researching an article about volcanoes. He'd borrowed a bed in a small, crowded boardinghouse about 19 kilometers (12 miles) from Mount Pinatubo. The creaking structure didn't inspire confidence. "I worry about the house," said the owner. "It isn't solid."

Seismic waves, rolling through the Earth, struck that night, jolting the house and its edgy inhabitants. Then came those screams, and the veteran writer noticed he was shaking. So was his bed. So was his room. Only then did Grove realize who was yelling—he was.

A DAY OF GEOLOGIC DRAMA

Noel Grove, and anyone else near Pinatubo in June 1991, had good reason to be nervous. In the first hours of June 15, the 1760-meter (5770-foot) volcano roared awake after a six-century sleep. Pinatubo belched clouds of gas and ash known as pyroclastic flows. Their temperature: 816°C (1500°F). Streams of ash and sulfur dioxide rocketed 40 kilometers (25 miles) into the stratosphere.

Another blast at dawn blew away the side of the mountain. So much ash and pumice choked the air that the sky grew black by

887

Interpreting the Photo

Refer students to the photograph on the facing page. Explain that the force of the eruption of Mount Pinatubo was comparable to the force of the nuclear bombs dropped on Hiroshima and Nagasaki during World War II.

Teaching Strategies

- Review, if necessary, the information on pyroclastic flows presented in Chapter 18.
- Refer students to **Figure 18-2** on page 473. Have them locate Mount Pinatubo. Then refer students to **Figure 17-13** on page 455. Have students compare the two maps to determine what kind of tectonic boundary is responsible for the formation and eruption of Mount Pinatubo. Mount Pinatubo and other volcanoes in the Philippines formed and are active as the result of convergence between an oceanic plate and a continental plate. Have a volunteer briefly explain what happens at a convergent boundary involving an oceanic plate and a continental plate.

Be sure to check the Earth Science Web Site for links to chapter material: earthgeu.com

Differentiated Instruction

Learning Disabled Ask a few students to bring in unopened 1-L bottles of unsweetened seltzer. Have students describe what they see and hear when the bottles are opened. Fill a cup with seltzer and have students hold their hands above the cup and describe what they feel. Explain that the release of carbon dioxide gas from the bottle and the cup is similar to the release of gases from volcanoes such as Mount Pinatubo. **CAUTION:** *Wipe up any spills immediately.* **L1** **ELL**

Tying to Previous Knowledge

Have students recall from Chapter 18 that a caldera is a volcanic crater that can form when a part of a volcano collapses into the magma chamber that fuels the volcano.

Enrichment

Have students research the geologic events that preceded the 1980 eruption of Mount St. Helens. Ask students to compare the events with the information on Mount Pinatubo presented in the caption on this page.

Demo

Visual-Spatial To help students visualize the speed of lahars, create a model of these volcanic hazards. Obtain a meter-long piece of PVC pipe, about 10 cm in diameter. Saw the pipe in half before bringing it to the classroom. Make a mixture of sand and gravel in a 1000-mL beaker; this mixture will be used to simulate a volcanic avalanche. Combine sand, gravel, and water in another 1000-mL beaker; this mixture will be used to simulate a lahar. Place a bucket on the floor, and prop a section of the PVC pipe between a desk and the bucket to form a sloped chute. Have students use a stopwatch to determine the time it takes each mixture to travel completely down the chute. **CAUTION:** *Wear safety goggles and aprons during this demo and insist that the students do the same. Wipe up any spills immediately.*

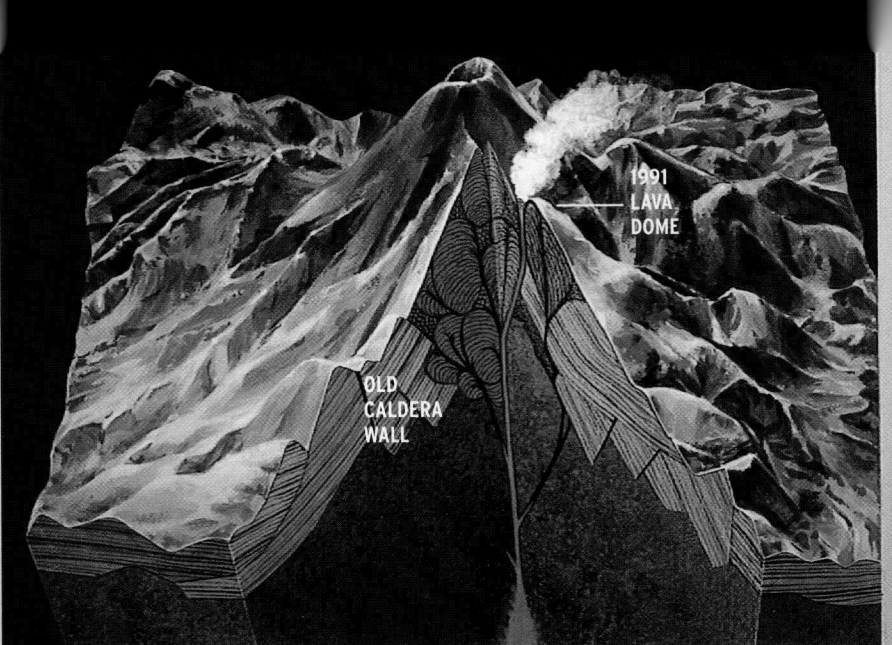

1991 LAVA DOME

OLD CALDERA WALL

Eve of eruption

Pinatubo sits in the center of a five-kilometer-wide (three-mile) caldera, a depression from an earlier eruption that had made the volcano collapse in upon itself (tilted blocks at left). A new cone formed—a dome of thick clumps of dacite rock overlain by layers of ash-flow deposits. Geothermal vents on the north side of the mountain gave the only clue that the volcano was still active. On April 2, 1991, steam and ash erupted from the site. Monitoring instruments were quickly installed.

afternoon, and chunks of volcanic rock fell like dirty hail. Meanwhile, new pyroclastic flows swept down Pinatubo's remaining slopes, filling canyons and ravaging farmland. Some flows reached as far as 18 kilometers (11 miles) from the volcano.

Evening brought new trauma—earthquakes. Pinatubo's eruption had created an underground cavern that finally caved in on itself, creating tremors. The remorseless assaults of June 15 now came from below as well as above. It was, said a woman in Manila, "like the end of the world."

JUST ADD WATER

July 1991 brought new suffering, as typhoons struck Luzon, where huge amounts of ash covered the landscape. Pinatubo had ejected enough ash to cover Washington, D.C., 15 stories high.

Water and ash blended into a cement-like slurry that soon charged over the terrain in streams called lahars. They snapped power-line poles like twigs and moved cars like cardboard stage props. Lahars also wrecked bridges and waterworks, and obliterated fields and villages. In fact, the deadly torrents destroyed twice as many homes as did the original eruption.

ABOVE: Quiet for 600 years, Mount Pinatubo was an innocent-looking peak in central Luzon. Then, in April 1991, vigorous steam eruptions, swarms of shallow earthquakes, increased sulfur dioxide emissions, and rapid growth of a lava dome heralded a powerful eruption. Scientists from the Philippine Institute of Volcanology and Seismology, later joined by a team from the U.S. Geological Survey, monitored the vents and called for evacuation of nearby villages. A series of minor explosions began on June 12.

This text is based on the article "Crucibles of Creation: Volcanoes," in the December 1992 NATIONAL GEOGRAPHIC.

888

Making matters even worse, lahars reappeared each year during the rainy season. The recurring floods of sludge defeated efforts to rebuild around Pinatubo and left more than a million people homeless. "In terms of magnitude, Mount Pinatubo is unprecedented," said volcanologist Kelvin Rodolfo. "No lahar flows of this magnitude and duration have ever been recorded [before]," he said.

PINATUBO'S PRICE TAG

Nine hundred people perished during the eruption. Five hundred others died of disease or exposure in the rudimentary camps that sheltered some 200 000 evacuees. Volcanic fallout destroyed 42 000 homes, and lahars washed away 110 000 more.

Ash laid waste to 40 500 hectares (100 000 acres) of farmland, and that was just one aspect of the devastation that left 650 000 Filipinos with no way to make a living. Damages were estimated conservatively at $440 million. Rebuilding would cost billions.

THE SCIENCE OF SURVIVAL

Stunned, homeless, and jobless, the 200 000 people evacuated from the area around Pinatubo before the eruption probably did not feel all that lucky. Yet only a generation earlier, the volcano might have killed

● **BELOW:** A small dam built to restrain lahars, which are floods of rain-soaked volcanic ash, was undercut by the lahars that followed Pinatubo's eruption. They scoured out a channel under the dam 18 meters (60 feet) deep.

● **LEFT:** Masked against the choking gloom of volcanic ash, jobless young men seek assistance—a few of the 650 000 Filipinos who were left without a source of income.

NATIONAL GEOGRAPHIC
eXpeditions!

889

Earth Science Online

Note Internet addresses that you find useful in the space below for quick reference.

_____

_____

_____

_____

_____

For Internet tips, see Glencoe's **Using the Internet in the Science Classroom.**

Teaching Strategies

After students have read this page, ask the following questions. What were the earliest indications that Mount Pinatubo was about to erupt? plumes of steam rising from vents in the volcano How were tiltmeters and seismometers used to study the volcano? Tiltmeters were used to detect swelling in the mountainsides. Seismometers were used to measure movements of the ground beneath the volcano. What did increases in sulfur dioxide in the air indicate to scientists? New and active magma was rising toward the surface. Why did scientists study old photos of the area? They were looking for evidence of prior eruptions.

Tying to Previous Knowledge

Have students recall how the eruption of Tambora affected the environment as presented in the Science & the Environment feature on page 490. Ask interested students to research the environmental effects of Mount Pinatubo on climate.

Expeditions Activity

Visual-Spatial Students should consider various aspects of emergency planning, such as early detection, evacuation routes, emergency communication systems, panic control, and relocation planning. Students can summarize their findings as volcano-preparedness brochures.

P

them. The difference resulted from scientists' increasing ability to detect volcanic activity early and predict its severity.

The first signs that Pinatubo's long nap was ending came on April 2, 1991, when villagers spotted plumes of steam rising from vents in the mountainside. Filipino scientists raced to the scene, and colleagues came from the United States to pitch in.

The volcanologists deployed seismometers to measure movements beneath Pinatubo and tiltmeters to detect any swelling in the mountainsides. "There are no magic new machines," seismologist Paul Okubo told Grove, "only steady improvement in using what we have."

Airborne instruments monitored gases escaping from the volcano. By May, sulfur dioxide levels had increased tenfold—a warning that new and active magma was rising toward the surface.

The scientists also conducted field studies and examined aerial photographs for geological evidence of the extent of previous eruptions. The team found volcanic debris 16 kilometers (10 miles) from the mountain, a sign that Pinatubo had a seriously violent past. The next blast was likely to be dramatic and deadly.

By June 11, Pinatubo was beginning to emit ash, and the mountain's lava dome

had doubled in size. Explosion was imminent. Based on the scientists' findings, Filipino authorities evacuated everyone within 24 kilometers (15 miles) of the volcano. When villagers balked at leaving home, the savvy officials didn't waste time on lengthy arguments. Instead they showed a video of pyroclastic flows and lahars. Viewers packed quickly.

EARTH NEVER SLEEPS

Mount Pinatubo's 1991 eruption was extraordinary—perhaps the mightiest of the entire twentieth century. Yet it was also oddly ordinary, part of Earth's long history of violent change. The planet, after all, is home to some 550 known active volcanoes, and a dozen or two are erupting at any given moment.

For humans in harm's way, such eruptions amount to unspeakable tragedy. Yet for Earth itself, represent an essential, vibrant cycle.

890

● **BELOW:** Steaming vents called fumaroles were still active eight months after Pinatubo's violent eruption. Rainwater had collected into a lake in the base of the massive crater.

Expeditions Activity

A great many people live close to volcanoes that could erupt in their lifetime. What kinds of precautions should they take? Break up into groups. Each group should act as if it is responsible for emergency planning for a community near a volcano. Consider specific plans for detecting an eruption and for organizing a mass evacuation. Compare plans among the groups.

Earth Science

Journal

Science Field Book

Have students find out about the following instruments commonly used to monitor volcanic activity: seismometers, tiltmeters, and spectrometers. Have students describe in their science journals how each instrument works and how it is used by volcanologists to monitor volcanic activity.

Pinatubo's insides

What caused the eruption? Scientists believe that an earthquake in July 1990 allowed floating rock from the upper mantle to squeeze into the magma chamber, which was filled with red-hot, melted stone material. That injection energized the shimmering reservoir and created a fluid, gas-charged magma called andesite. This magma soon rose toward the surface, building a new dome on the northeast slope that corked the system. Pressure in the magma chamber built up rapidly. Probing its way to the surface, the magma finally found a clear conduit, or path. Gas exploded from the lava, and the volcano blasted skyward, destroying the newest dome.

PYROCLASTIC FLOW

PYROCLASTIC FLOW

MAGMA CHAMBER

How volcanoes become killers

Majestic cones can turn into lethal monsters. Towering columns of ash collapse (**1**), raining hot rock and burying whatever lies below, as at Mount Vesuvius, in Italy. Unexpected landslides, like the one at Mount St. Helens in 1980 (**2**), unleash devastating lateral blasts. Lava domes cave in (**3**), releasing burning pyroclastic flows, as at Uzen, in Kazakhstan. Lahars, rivers of water-soaked ash (**4**), smother towns and fields, as they did at Mount Pinatubo and Nevado del Ruiz, in Colombia. A cone can build so steeply that it can't support itself and collapses in huge landslides (**5**) that send debris miles downslope—a process discovered in Hawaii. Flowing lava rarely kills, but it can cause widespread property loss.

Interpreting the Illustration

Have students study the small numbered figures on the right as you read aloud the caption associated with each figure. Stop between each caption to answer any questions that students might have.

Going Further

Have students view *Dante's Peak*, a popular Hollywood account of a volcanic eruption. Have students describe the actions of the scientists and identify scientific inaccuracies within the film. Then ask students to research what volcanologists would really do in such a situation and to compare their actions to those of scientists depicted in the film.

Project

Interpersonal Reiterate to students that hundreds of volcanoes are classified as active. Scientists believe that about 100 of these need constant monitoring and that another 300 or so need constant watching. In the case of Mount Pinatubo, $50 million was spent in monitoring and evacuation, and an estimated 200 000 lives and $250 million in property damage were saved.

Have students debate the establishment of volcano-monitoring observatories near Earth's 100 most dangerous volcanoes. Among the points to debate are who should pay for these observatories, who should staff them, and what benefits might arise from international cooperation in these efforts. **COOP LEARN**

NATIONAL GEOGRAPHIC

eXpeditions!

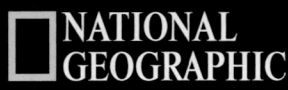

Purpose

Students will learn about the recent discovery of a *Sinosauropteryx prima,* which has contributed to the hypothesis that birds are descended from dinosaurs. Other species of feathered dinosaurs, such as *Caudipteryx zoui,* and the earliest bird, *Archaeopteryx,* also are discussed.

Background

The shapes of feathers on birds and theropod dinosaurs indicate whether the feathers were used for flight or something else, such as insulation for warmth. Asymmetric feathers were used for flight, whereas symmetric feathers were not. Birds are hypothesized to have descended from theropods—a group of saurischian dinosaurs.

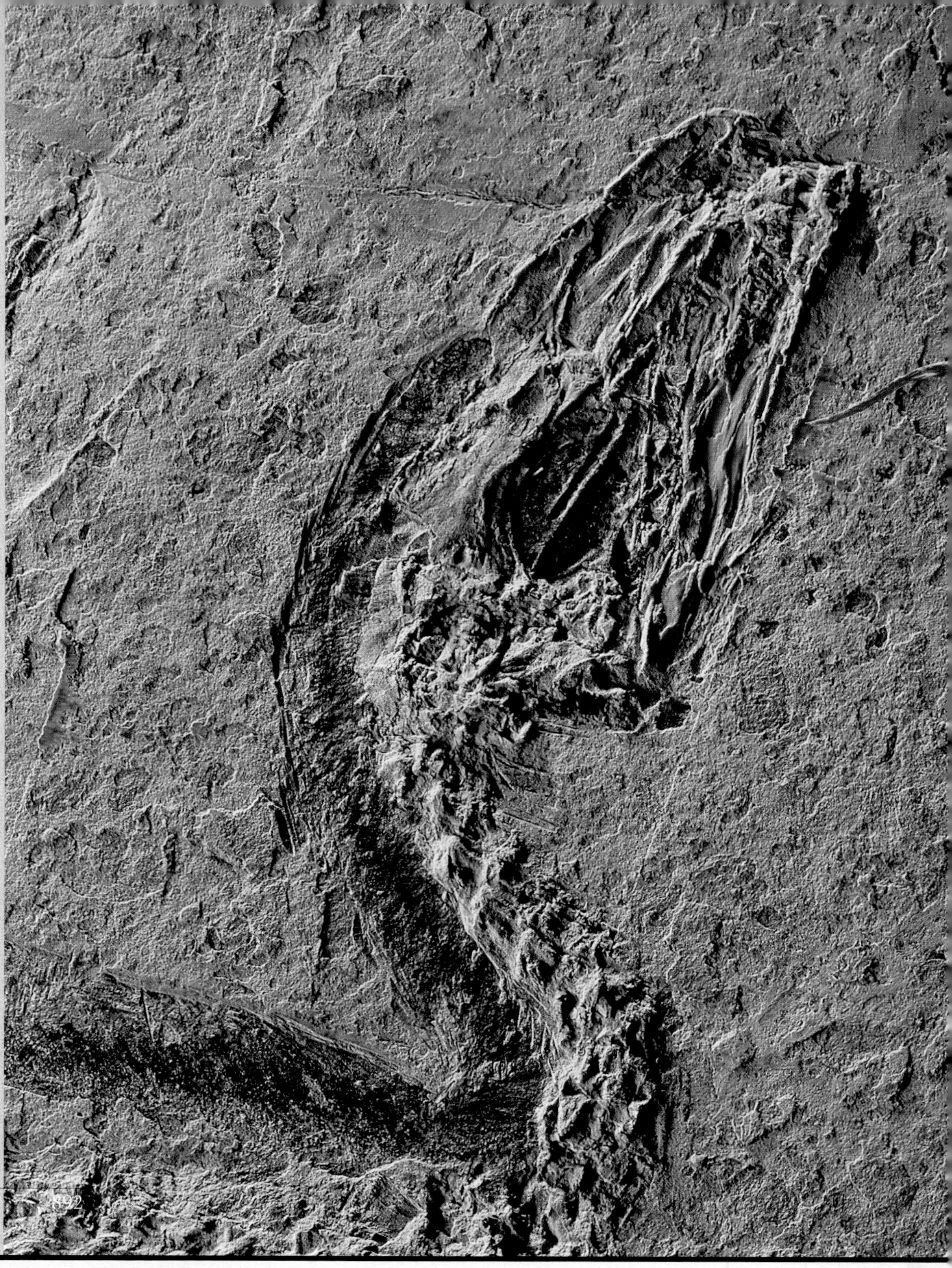

Portfolio

Dinosaur–Bird Characteristics

What makes a bird a bird and a dinosaur a dinosaur? Have students research defining characteristics of both modern birds and dinosaurs and draw labeled diagrams of both. Birds are defined as feathered, warm-blooded vertebrates that occupy most natural habitats. Their forelimbs are modified as wings and their hind legs are for walking. Not all birds can fly. Dinosaurs are defined as land-dwelling reptiles with an upright posture that lived from 228 to 66 million years ago. There are two major groups of dinosaurs based on their hipbones, the Ornithischia and the Saurischia. Birds are thought to have descended from saurischian dinosaurs.

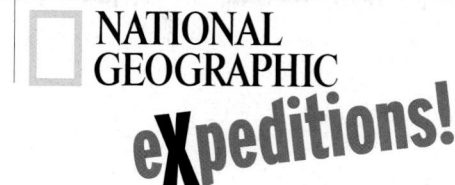
Fossils With Feathers

Dinosaurs Take Wing

Ji Qiang gasped aloud as he opened the green silk box. As director of the National Geological Museum in Beijing, China, Ji was used to seeing fossils. But this one, sent to Ji in 1996 by a dealer in the far northeastern province of Liaoning, was extraordinary.

The more than 120-million-year-old remains belonged to a creature about the size of a chicken (see model at left). The large skull held needle-sharp teeth, and the bony tail was nearly twice as long as the rest of the body. The creature had short, stout forelimbs.

Ji and his fellow scientists named the new creature *Sinosauropteryx prima*, which means "first Chinese dragon feather." They classified it as a theropod, or carnivorous dinosaur. (*Sinosauropteryx*'s gut actually held remains from its last meal, a small mammal.) "The fossil looked a lot like a small meat-eating dinosaur," Ji told National Geographic, "except for one thing."

"ONE THING" THAT STIRRED SCIENTISTS

The "one thing" was a thin, dark ridge along *Sinosauropteryx*'s back. Looking closer, Ji realized the ridge consisted of tiny fibers—thousands of them (see photograph, opposite). They appeared to be the incredibly well-preserved remains of protofeathers, precursors of the feathers that cover modern-day birds. The find reheated a smoldering debate about the relationship between birds and dinosaurs. Most experts today believe that birds evolved from dinosaurs, a view first espoused by naturalist Thomas Henry Huxley in the 1860s. Hux-

● **ABOVE:** A *Sinosauropteryx* model peers down with arms extended, ready to pounce on a lizard or small mammal. If its body covering first evolved to preserve heat rather than for display, it would suggest that *Sinosauropteryx* was warm-blooded. Scientists have long debated the question of dinosaur metabolism.

● **LEFT:** Sealed at death more than 120 million years ago, the eye of a juvenile *Sinosauropteryx* glints with black carbon that crystalized during fossilization. If growths on the head and neck were primitive plumage, they may have served to trap body heat or as courtship display. *Sinosauropteryx* has been classified as a theropod, a meat-eating dinosaur.

893

Interpreting the Photo

The fossilized *Sinosauropteryx*, which means "Chinese dragon wing," was the first feathered dinosaur to be discovered. It had feathers covering its back and sides. There was also a manelike tuft on the back of its head, that was composed of fine filaments that branched from hollow quills. *Sinosauropteryx* had a mouth full of sharp teeth to aid in its meat-eating habits. Unlike modern birds, *Sinosauropteryx* had special ligaments connecting its lower jaw so that the lower jaw could spread apart to eat large prey. One fossilized *Sinosauropteryx* was found with mammal bones in its stomach.

Enrichment

Logical-Mathematical Have interested students research and record the taxonomic classification of one feathered dinosaur and one modern bird. For example, *Sinosauropteryx prima* belongs to Kingdom Animalia, Phylum Chordata, Class Archosauria, Order Saurischia, Family Compsognathidea, Genus Sinosauropteryx and Species prima.

Cultural Diversity

Sankar Chatterjee (1943–) Sankar Chatterjee is the museum science curator of vertebrate paleontology and a professor of geology at Texas Tech University. He earned his Ph.D. at the University of Calcutta in 1970. His research focuses on the link between dinosaurs and birds. Chatterjee has led many expeditions to India, China, the Antarctic, and the American Southwest. On May 21, 1986, he and his graduate students discovered two small, crowlike skeletons, which they named *Protoavis texensis*. These discoveries

are 7.5 million years older than *Archaeopteryx*. There is much controversy among palentologists about whether the discoveries were actually birds. As a result of his research, Chatterjee wrote a book entitled *The Rise of Birds*, which was intended to reach a larger, nonpaleontological audience and convince his contemporaries that *Protoavis* is a bird. In this popular book, Chatterjee put forth the theory that *Protoavis* is a member of a sister group to other early birds that produced modern birds.

Interpreting the Photo

Pigment is rarely preserved in fossils. The tail feathers of *Caudipteryx zoui*, however, exhibit a design of light and dark banded feathers. It is hypothesized that these tail feathers were ornamental in nature. *Caudipteryx zoui* also had downy and quill-like feathers on its arms and body. Their symmetrical shape suggests that they were most likely for warmth only.

Earth Science Online

Be sure to check the Earth Science Web Site for links to chapter material:
earthgeu.com

ley's critics argued, however, that both birds and dinosaurs descended from a common ancestor, and their theory held for decades.

Huxley's hypothesis found a new champion in the 1970s—paleontologist John Ostrom. Ostrom painstakingly compared newly excavated dinosaur fossils to the remains of the earliest known bird, *Archaeopteryx*, and was overwhelmed by the similarities. "Dinosaurs did not become extinct," he proclaimed; they became birds.

But scientists still needed a missing link. *Sinosauropteryx*—a dinosaur that seemed to have feathers—came closer than any other fossil Ji had seen.

MORE FOSSILS, MORE FEATHERS

Soon after *Sinosauropteryx* was discovered, Liaoning Province yielded two more feathered dinosaurs. The region is a paleontologist's dream, thanks to volcanic ash that smothered the landscape more than 120 million years ago. The fallout killed myriad plants and animals, then preserved them beautifully. No place on Earth has provided more information on the origin of birds.

Another Liaoning discovery—*Protarchaeopteryx robusta*—looked like a larger, more primitive version of *Archaeopteryx*, the first known bird. Scientists who have examined *Protarchaeopteryx*'s feathers doubt that the creature could fly. (*Archaeopteryx*, in contrast, was probably able to fly somewhat.)

● Posed in courtship display, a model of *Caudipteryx zoui* depicts a creature nearly a meter (3 feet) long that stunned paleontologists when reconstructed from its fossil—a dinosaur with feathers! It is more than 120 million years old. Months before *Caudipteryx* was found, farmer Li Yin Fang (top, second from right) found the feathered dinosaur *Sinosauropteryx prima* (previous page).

894

Project

Kinesthetic Have students reconstruct the skeleton of a chicken. Have students work in small groups to glue together the pre-boiled and bleached bones of a chicken. Provide a diagram of a chicken skeleton to guide students. Ask students to compare this activity to the work of a vertebrate paleontologist.

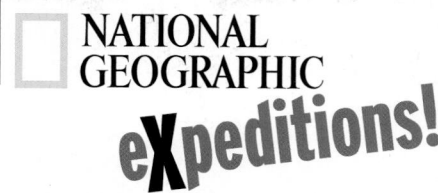
Studying *Protarchaeopteryx* specimens, Ji and Canadian paleontologist Phillip Currie were startled by inconsistencies. "Were we looking at males and females?" Currie wrote. "Was *Protarchaeopteryx* a creature with much variation?" The two scientists watched eagerly as technician Kevin Aulenback used a microscope and dental tools to scrape excess stone from the fossil.

Slowly it became clear that the three men were looking at an entirely new creature. They named it *Caudipteryx zoui* (*Caudipteryx* means "tail feather") for the plumes that the dinosaur probably fanned out when it wooed mates or intimidated enemies (see model at left). A speedy runner, *Caudipteryx* did not fly.

Caudipteryx did, however, share a striking trait with modern birds—a gizzard full of small stones. Such pebbles, called gastroliths, ground food for the dinosaur, which had only a few teeth. Birds today use gastroliths for the same purpose.

"*Caudipteryx* and *Protarchaeopteryx*," wrote Currie, "make the dividing line between dinosaurs and birds even less distinct and strengthen the theory that birds evolved from small, carnivorous, ground-dwelling dinosaurs."

EARLY BIRDS

Hundreds of Liaoning fossils have given scientists an extraordinary look at yet another early bird—*Confuciusornis sanctus* ("sacred Confucius bird"). The species differed from the feathered dinosaurs in a crucial way— it could fly. "*Confuciusornis* is the earliest bird we know of that could fly for any distance," said fossil specialist Hou Lianhai, who named the creature. "It had wings nearly as primitive as those of *Archaeopteryx*, but it had other, more modern features—lighter bones and a shorter tail."

- **ABOVE:** Earliest known bird, 150-million-year-old *Archaeopteryx* was the first fossil evidence linking birds and dinosaurs.

- **LEFT:** The first fossils of the crow-sized *Archaeopteryx* came to light in 1861 in the same Bavarian limestone that yielded this single flight feather.

Interpreting the Photo

In 1861, a well-preserved fossil specimen of *Archaeopteryx lithographica*, which means "ancient wing," was found in the Solnhöfen Limestone of Germany (Upper Jurassic). This animal, the oldest known bird, was about the size of a crow. *Archaeopteryx* had many dinosaur-like characteristics, including teeth, skull shape, lack of a bill, a large tail, and clawed forelimbs. Like a bird, *Archaeopteryx* had feathers, hollow bones, a wishbone, and shortened fingers. A total of seven specimens of *Archaeopteryx lithographica* have been found.

Interpreting the Photo

The feather of the *Archaeopteryx lithographica* is asymmetric in shape, because feathers on either side of the central shaft are different lengths. This asymmetrical shape suggests that the feathers were used for flight.

Going Further

Linguistic Have students research the characteristics of the first known bird, *Archaeopteryx lithographica*, and compare it to both modern birds and dinosaurs.

895

Science Field Book

Earth Science

Journal

Ask students to choose a well-known dinosaur-fossil site to research. Have students each write an essay about their research in their science journals that includes information such as the geographic and stratigraphic location of the site, types of dinosaur fossils found there, the age of the dinosaur fossils, and other fossils found at this site. In addition, ask students to research and write about the environmental conditions that led to the preservation of the fossils.

Display

Have students work in small groups to make posters of either theropod dinosaurs or early birds. Students can obtain pictures by visiting the Earth Science Web Site at **earthgeu.com** and following the appropriate links. Books, magazines, or scientific journals can also be used. Have students present their posters to the class. Follow up with a class discussion about the differences between the two groups of animals.
COOP LEARN

Teaching Strategies

- There are many informative Web sites about dinosaurs on the Internet. Have students visit the Earth Science Web Site at **earthgeu.com** and follow the appropriate links.

- Many scientific terms are new to students and may be difficult to pronounce. Hand out a list of dinosaur names used in the National Geographic *Expeditions!* article, as well as other common dinosaur names. Include the pronunciations of these terms on your list. This will allow students to be more confident about using the correct names in discussions and when asking questions.

Expeditions Activity

One possible answer would be the shape of the beak: sharp for cutting seeds, long for poking into holes, and so on.

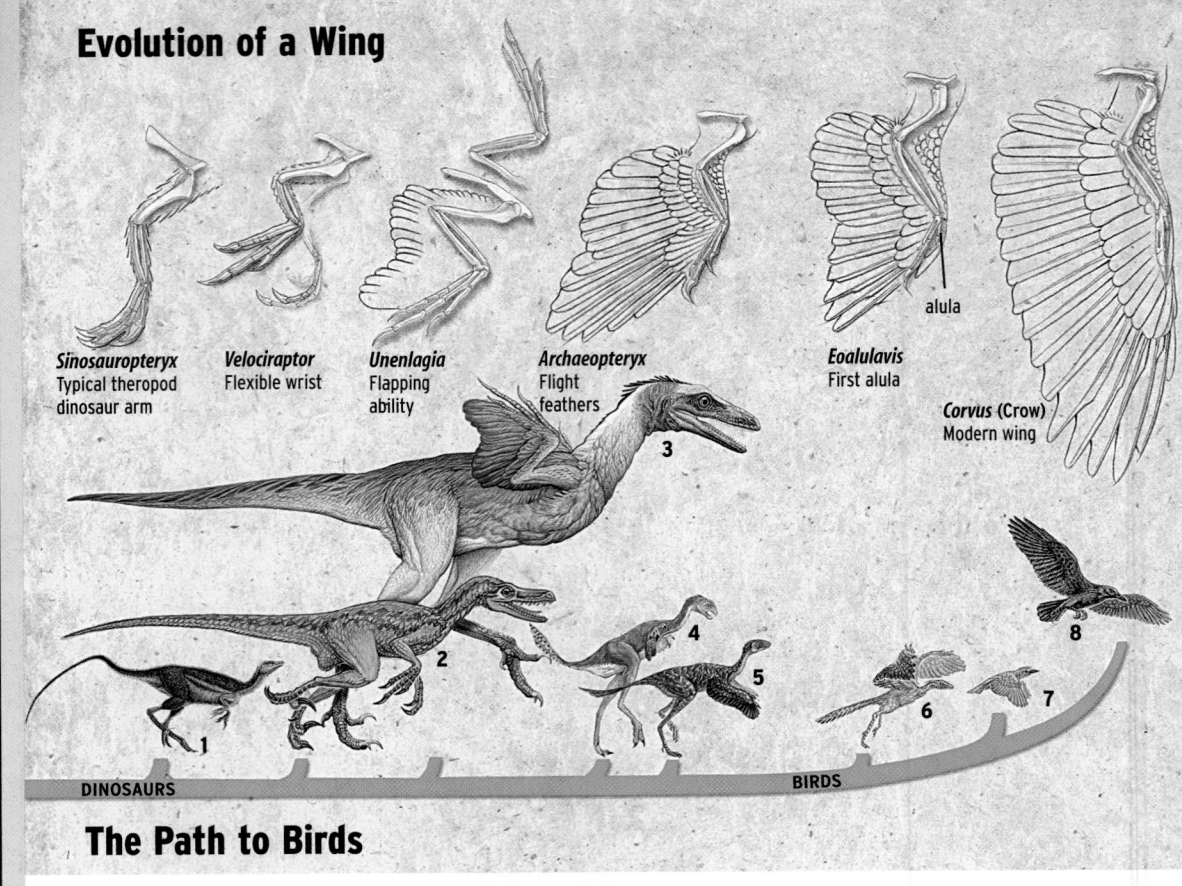

Evolution of a Wing

Sinosauropteryx Typical theropod dinosaur arm

Velociraptor Flexible wrist

Unenlagia Flapping ability

Archaeopteryx Flight feathers

Eoalulavis First alula

alula

Corvus (Crow) Modern wing

DINOSAURS

BIRDS

The Path to Birds

1 Sinosauropteryx
Covered with filaments that may have evolved for insulation or display, *Sinosauropteryx* was a ground-dwelling runner with short arms and three-fingered hands.

2 Velociraptor
This predatory theropod, whose fossils were found in Mongolia, was endowed with a wrist bone that permitted the animal's grasping hands to swivel, helping it capture prey. A flexible wrist is required for powered flight.

3 Unenlagia
Found in Patagonia, this flightless, 2.5-meter-long (8-foot) creature could move its arms up and down much as a person on a surfboard moves the arms for balance. A precursor to flapping, this action is critical to the flight stroke.

4 Caudipteryx
Straddling the realms of dinosaurs and birds, *Caudipteryx* is but one in a series of sensational fossil finds in China. A speedy runner, it was covered with primitive feathers that lacked the aerodynamic quality necessary for flight.

5 Protarchaeopteryx
Another discovery in China, *Protarchaeopteryx* resembles *Archaeopteryx* in many ways but is more primitive. The symmetrical feathers on its arms and tail appear longer than those of *Caudipteryx*, but it probably could not have achieved true powered flight.

6 Archaeopteryx
The feathers of this bird's celebrated fossils are asymmetrical, with the leading edge narrower and more streamlined than the trailing edge. This enabled the wings to slice through the air, permitting at least rudimentary flight.

7 Eoalulavis
Found in Spain, this bird exhibits the earliest known alula, a tuft of feathers attached to the thumb. By altering airflow, the alula permits good maneuverability and control at low flying speeds, crucial for takeoffs and landings.

8 Corvus
At the peak of forelimb evolution, the crow and other modern avian species, with their shortened tailbones and expansive wing surfaces, represent the full flowering of the ability to fly.

896

Earth Science Online

Note Internet addresses that you find useful in the space below for quick reference.

For Internet tips, see Glencoe's **Using the Internet in the Science Classroom.**

Unlike *Archaeopteryx*, which had teeth, *Confuciusornis* had a toothless beak similar to those of modern birds. The discovery indicated that beaks appeared 70 million years earlier than previously believed. Like birds themselves, scientists' knowledge was evolving.

CONSENSUS AND A TOUGH QUESTION

By 2000, science had largely circled back to supporting Thomas Huxley's contention that birds were the descendants of dinosaurs. "The anatomical similarities are overwhelming," said Mark Norell of the American Museum of Natural History, in New York City. Birds and dinosaurs, he pointed out, share more than a hundred features—including wishbones.

Yet critics point out that *Archaeopteryx* is 30 million years older than the feathered dinosaurs from Liaoning. A true missing link, the critics stress, should predate the first bird. Until it appears, they're tracing birds back to a pre-dinosaur reptile.

Even advocates of the dinosaur–bird link concede the need for more, and older, fossils. "We don't have the evidence to support any kind of direct lineal descent," said Ostrom. "We're in the business of connecting dots scattered in time and space."

This text is based on the article "Dinosaurs Take Wing" in the July 1998 NATIONAL GEOGRAPHIC.

● **FAR LEFT:** Just as humans are mammals, birds belong in the clan of dinosaurs in the view of most paleontologists. The idea that the defining traits of birds first arose in dinosaurs dates from the early arguments of evolutionary theory.

This family tree is not a chronological progression, but an illustration of how the traits of the modern wing evolved in different creatures in different places at different times.

Feathers that evolved to keep a ground-dweller warm, for example, might give it the ability to glide and better catch prey, leading to more feather development.

● **LEFT:** Hopes for another big discovery draw scientists to the dig at Sihetun, in China, where layers of rock entomb birds, dinosaurs, plant life, and multitudes of fish. Dating from more than 120 million years ago, the lake bed formation is 31 meters (100 feet) thick and covers 52 square kilometers (20 square miles).

Expeditions Activity

Have you ever stopped to ponder the features that make birds so different from ground-dwelling animals? Think about weight, shape, skeleton structure, and feather design. Now list specific traits, such as webbed feet or bald heads, that various birds have developed that allow them to exercise specific behaviors.

897

Identifying Misconceptions

Most people think of huge animals when they think of dinosaurs. In fact, dinosaurs ranged in size from slightly larger than a chicken to the height of a four-story building. The largest known dinosaur was *Brachiosaurus*. It was 23 m long and 12 m tall. The smallest known dinosaur was *Compsognathus*. It was about 1 m long.

Going Further

Dinosaurs existed through the end of the Cretaceous Period. The Cretaceous-Paleogene boundary is distinguished by a mass extinction event, which occurred 66 million years ago. A mass extinction is classified as an event in which large numbers of unrelated families died out and can no longer be found in the fossil record. For example, 85 percent of all species became extinct at the end of the Cretaceous Period. Most people are not aware of the fact that four other major mass extinction events occurred during the Phanerozoic Eon. These occurred during the Ordovician (438 mybp), the Devonian (360 mybp), at the end of the Permian (the Permo-Triassic Extinction Event) (290 mybp), and during the Triassic (208 mybp). About 90–95 percent of all marine species became extinct as a result of the Permo-Triassic Extinction Event.

898

Purpose

Students will learn about the effects of pollution on rivers and waterways, the steps that need to be taken to clean up such pollution, and the results of one person's campaign to save and restore a seemingly hopelessly polluted river.

Background

For more than 100 years, industries disposed of their wastes in the easiest possible manner. This often included dumping wastes into ravines, rivers, and lakes, with little or no regard for the effects that such dumping might have on the environment. One of the most famous dumping grounds was Love Canal, outside of Niagara Falls, New York. A company named Hooker Chemicals dumped dangerous chemicals into Love Canal for many years with no repercussions. When the company finished with the canal, it was filled in with soil, and the land eventually was sold. Homes and schools were built on top of Love Canal. Over the next few decades, people who lived on Love Canal or went to school there had continual, unexplained health problems. Because Hooker Chemicals was no longer in business, the U.S. government paid for the cleanup of Love Canal. The Love Canal incident served to focus attention on waste-dumping practices across the country, and the name itself became a symbol of technology gone wild—as in the case of the Nashua River— and a rallying point for those who would prevent such pollution and protect the environment.

✓ PORTFOLIO

Sources of Pollution

Pollution that enters our waterways comes in many forms and from several different sources besides industrial waste. Have students list common sources of pollution in waterways. Some nonpoint sources of pollution may be the result of everyday activities, including runoff from excessive use of pesticides and fertilizers, runoff from asphalt highways, discarded motor oil, paints, and the decomposition of other materials. L1 P

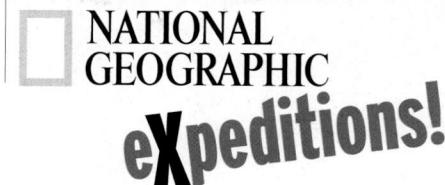

River Restoration

Streams of Hope

● **ABOVE:** Knee-high with muck, a Boys Club member totes trash pulled from a New Hampshire section of the Nashua River.

● **LEFT:** Rank and lifeless by the 1960s (inset), the Nashua River in Massachusetts was a toxic stew of sewage, running red with dye from paper mills. Today it's a haven for anglers and canoeists and a model for communities striving to clean the waters they have fouled.

One day the river ran red. Then green. Then white, or orange, or maybe even blue. Sound like sci-fi or Dr. Seuss? Alas, no. It's an actual part of American environmental history. In the 1960s the Nashua River, which flows quietly for 90 kilometers (56 miles) in Massachusetts and New Hampshire, was one of the most polluted streams in the entire United States.

Mills along the Nashua produced lumber, shoes, paper, and textiles. For more than a century these industries dumped their waste into the water. Dyes in the wastewater turned the river into such a chameleon that locals used to take bets on what color it would be the next day.

People could laugh—darkly—about the changing colors. But there was nothing funny about river fumes that blackened paint on nearby buildings, or about kids being rushed to the doctor for tetanus shots when they got too near the water. It was mortifying that environmental authorities classified the Nashua as unfit for sewage disposal.

Perhaps the river was red because it was dying of embarrassment. It was certainly dying of something.

ONE HERO, MANY HANDS

Marion Stoddart didn't plan on letting the Nashua die quietly. When she explored the watershed in the 1960s, she was appalled. "The highest form of life in the North Nashua was sludge worms," she said. She began a campaign to bring the river back to life.

Stoddart knew that she'd need help—lots of it. She reached out to everyone, including labor leaders and businesspeople. "Marion Stoddart didn't go out there as a lone person in the wilderness," said Geographic reporter Erla Zwingle. "She did it by making key allies."

899

Identifying Misconceptions

Before students study this feature, choose a student at random, and ask him or her to imagine that he or she has just dropped a spoonful of motor oil into a river. Ask the student whether the spoonful of oil will seriously pollute the environment. To demonstrate the concept, collect a liter of drinking water. Ask one student to drop 20 g of salt into the water and stir. Then, have another student taste the water and see whether he or she can taste the salt. Have each student in the class add 20 g of salt to the water, stir, and repeat the tasting. They will most certainly taste the presence of the salt. At the conclusion of the tasting, again ask students whether one spoonful of oil will pollute a river. They should respond that while one spoonful might not be noticeable, one spoonful added repeatedly will pollute the river.

Interpreting the Photo

Tell students that the river is just one type of waterway that can be ravaged by pollution. Streams, lakes, and even oceans can be adversely affected by serious pollution. Have students propose some ways in which pollution might enter large bodies of water. Example: oil spills from ocean-going oil tankers

Earth Science Online

Note Internet addresses that you find useful in the space below for quick reference.

_____

_____

_____

_____

_____

For Internet tips, see Glencoe's **Using the Internet in the Science Classroom.**

Tying to Previous Knowledge

Students have learned how the water cycle moves water through Earth's ecosystems. Point out that the water cycle can move pollutants through ecosystems as well. For example, gases released into the atmosphere by power plants combine with water vapor to form acid precipitation. As this precipitation falls, the chemicals it contains then make their way into surface waters and eventually into the oceans.

Display

 **Visual-Spatial** Have groups of students use photographs from magazines and go to earthgeu.com to find other photographs to make displays of sources of pollution. Groups could focus on sources of water pollution, air pollution, and land pollution. Have students compare their displays and discuss the ways in which the different pollution sources are related. **COOP LEARN** **P**

Earth Science
Science Field Book
Journal

Visual-Spatial Have students assemble a collection of photos depicting pollution. Make sure that students provide captions for each photo describing the location and type of pollution depicted, the dangers that type of pollution might create, and possible sources of the pollution. **L1** **ELL**

"What we were working to do," said Stoddart, "was to get everyone on every level working together." Toward that end, she learned how to present her case in economic as well as environmental terms. Stoddart knew the value of gestures. She presented bottles of polluted river water—emblems of the cost of inaction—to key officials.

"Marion Stoddart qualifies as a hero," said Zwingle, "but the Nashua shows that heroes don't accomplish things on their own. Everything worked because everybody worked."

POSSIBLE DREAM

So what did this hero and her helpers actually do? Stoddart began by setting an "impossible" goal—making the Nashua safe for swimming. When she presented this demand at a water-pollution hearing, almost everyone was flabbergasted. "Come on, be realistic," they responded. But Stoddart stood her ground.

The people who live near and depend on the Nashua then set about doing the impossible. Mill owners began treating their waste, and citizens pitched in to monitor water quality. With help from the

● **ABOVE:** On the leaf-flecked Nashua River, student oarsmen are too young to recall the days when capsized boaters raced to a clinic for tetanus shots because the water was so polluted. Although parts of the Nashua River have been successfully cleaned up, much remains to be done in the watershed to improve water quality.

This text is based on the article "Restoration: New Ideas, New Understanding, New Hope" in NATIONAL GEOGRAPHIC's special issue on water, published in November 1993.

900

Differentiated Instruction

Learning Disabled Make a collection of common food items and food flavorings. Blindfold students and have them try to identify common food items, such as ripe peaches or bananas, by smell. Open bottles of common food flavorings, such as almond or vanilla extracts or peppermint oil, and allow the smell to disperse in a well-ventilated classroom to see whether students can identify the products by smell alone. Use only items that are recognizable. Tell students that their sense of smell helps them taste food as well.

federal government, officials built and upgraded water-treatment plants. There are now eight along the river.

Builders, conservationists, and zoning authorities collaborated on creating a "greenway" along half the Nashua and two of its major tributaries. Development is limited in the greenway, which lessens the amount of pollution entering the river.

Today you can swim in the Nashua River, and you can bet that its water will be clear again tomorrow.

ONE DOWN, THOUSANDS TO GO

Magnificent as the Nashua's rebirth is, it's just one small stream in a nation with two dozen major watersheds. Making all of them healthy requires a daunting, complex interplay of science, economics, and politics. And it can mean serious costs.

Farmers and developers, for instance, may balk at setting fields and houses farther from a stream bank to lessen runoff. Engineers are not often eager to change bridge and highway designs so that a river can meander naturally. Even eco-minded towns gasp at the price tag for separating storm drains from sewer lines. These are but a few examples of the challenges in repairing rivers.

"I'm optimistic about what we can do," said river advocate John Cairns, Jr. "I'm pessimistic about what we will do." Another water expert, pondering the need for cross-border cooperation, asked at a conference, "How do you get people to give up power in order to survive?"

TAKING WATER TO HEART

Perhaps the seed of an answer lies in Marion Stoddart's defiant proposal—a place to swim. When her neighbors looked at the Nashua and imagined themselves immersed in red (or green or white or orange) water, the river suddenly wasn't so distant. They were polluting part of their own lives.

Cleaning up the Nashua didn't magically get cheaper or easier, of course, but a clearer connection to the river may have helped people take hard steps on its behalf. Many river advocates stress the importance of such connections, of seeing streams as more than just water. "Water is a living thing," said Gwichin Indian Chief Clarence Alexander. "We treat it like it's got a soul of its own."

NATIONAL GEOGRAPHIC eXpeditions!

● **ABOVE:** When Marion Stoddard explored the Nashua Basin in the 1960s, almost no form of life survived in the river's polluted waters. Outraged, she has spent 30 years getting industries to treat waste, citizens to monitor water quality, and builders to limit riverbank development. Today the activist canoes the waters she helped revive.

Expeditions Activity

If you had to clean up a river, what measures would you take? What activities would you try to stop in order to reduce pollution? What kinds of plants or animals could you introduce to help clean the river? How would protecting or restoring wetlands affect your project? Investigate these issues and report on the cleanup of a specific river, such as the Cuyahoga, in Ohio.

901

Activity

Naturalist Have students use a map of your area to identify the rivers and streams within a few miles of your location. Then, have students research the various industries in the area and plot their locations on the map. Have students list the waste materials that the industries might produce. Ask students to develop an Endangered Locations list of waterways that might be threatened by industrial pollution. As a follow-up activity, ask students to find out whether these industries have plans in place, or are developing plans, to properly dispose of their wastes and protect the adjacent waterways and communities from possible pollution. **L2**

Enrichment

Some materials may not directly damage the environment, but their presence causes a hazard to living things. One example is the plastic rings used to hold six-packs of soda cans together. Birds and other small animals that get these rings tangled around their necks can be strangled. Have students identify other types of materials that might seem harmless but in reality pose a great danger to wildlife.

Expeditions Activity

Help students to identify what one individual can do to begin the cleanup of a polluted river. Tell students to go to earthgeu.com to investigate polluted rivers that have been cleaned up.

Project

Interpersonal Divide students into several small groups. Have the groups identify different ways in which every person can help to prevent pollution each day. One group can concentrate on activities at school that can help protect the environment, another group can focus on the home, and yet another group can examine ways to work within the community to reduce pollution.

Cultural Diversity

Ruth Patrick (1907–) Ruth Patrick studies microscopic species of algae called diatoms in rivers, focusing on their relationship to water pollution. In 1975, she received the prestigious Tyler Ecology Award and was also an active participant in drafting the Federal Clean Water Act. She has studied rivers in Mexico, Peru, and Brazil. In 1987, she wrote a book about groundwater pollution and policies to manage this problem entitled *Groundwater Contamination in the United States.*

Purpose

Students will learn about the *Hubble Space Telescope*, which has been transmitting images and data back to Earth since its launch in April 1990.

Background

The *Hubble Space Telescope* is named after American astronomer Edwin Powell Hubble, who died in 1953. Following World War I, Hubble did much of his work at the Mount Wilson Observatory in Pasadena, California. He developed the modern classification system for galaxies in which galaxies are grouped by size and shape. He was also instrumental in proving the existence of galaxies beyond the Milky Way. Perhaps Hubble's greatest achievement was his contribution to the Big Bang theory. This theory, which covers the formation of the universe, is based upon Hubble's discovery that the universe is expanding.

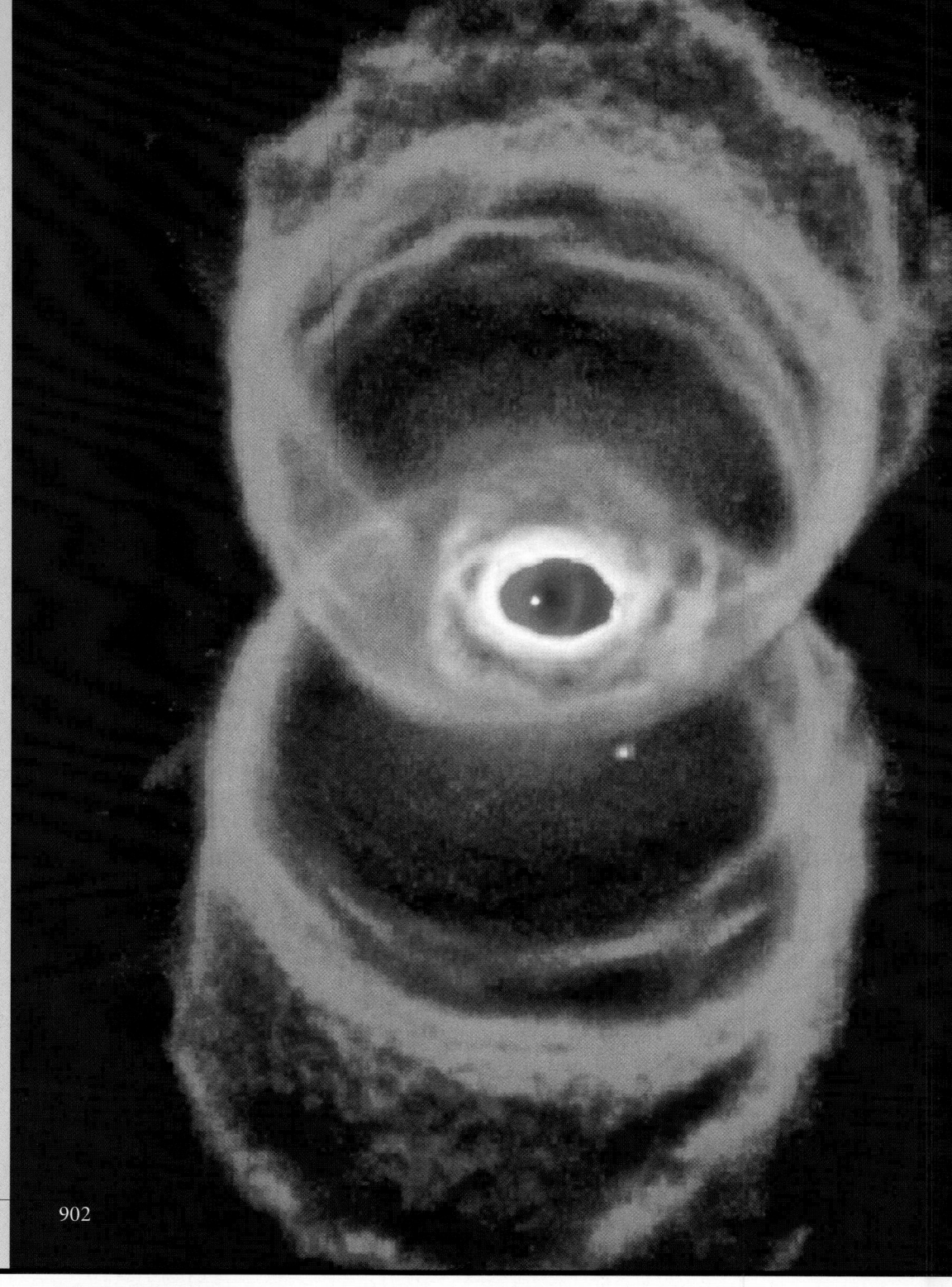

902

✔ PORTFOLIO

Light Pollution

The *Hubble Space Telescope* obtains sharper images than ground-based telescopes because it avoids the blurring effects of Earth's atmosphere as well as the light pollution of Earth. Have students list common sources of light pollution that they've probably taken for granted, such as lights at shopping centers, signs, and streetlights. An example of an attempt to control light pollution is in place in Flagstaff, Arizona, where the streetlights shine down on the ground instead of in all directions. Flagstaff also uses low-pressure sodium lamps, instead of mercury-vapor lamps.

Hubble Space Telescope

NASA's Eye in the Sky

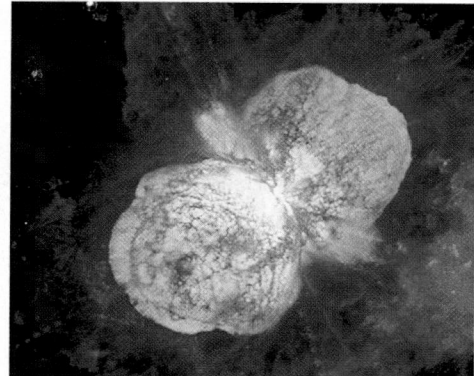

● **ABOVE:** Clouds of gas and dust pour out from the exploding star **Eta Carinae** at 2.4 million kilometers (1.5 million miles) per hour. Still burning five million times brighter than our Sun, Eta Carinae illuminates the clouds from the inside, like frosted Christmas bulbs.

● **LEFT:** The **Etched Hourglass Nebula** is a shell of gas expanding from a dying star.

Hermann Oberth was frustrated.

The German scientist yearned to explore space, but even the best telescopes available to him—to anyone—were hampered by Earth's atmosphere. The gases that make the planet habitable also distort our views of the heavens. Oberth's frustration sparked a bold idea: Why not design a telescope that could orbit the planet? It could offer an unparalleled view of the universe. But would it ever exist?

Oberth conceived his orbiting telescope in 1923. Air travel was still new; space travel was still science fiction. As the saying goes, he was ahead of his time—by decades. NASA launched two small space telescopes in the 1960s and 1970s, but neither came close to being the marvel that Oberth and others yearned for.

ASTRONOMY'S DREAM MACHINE

Five, four, three, two, one—blastoff! In April 1990, four months after Hermann Oberth's death, the shuttle *Discovery* set the *Hubble Space Telescope (HST)* into orbit 595 kilometers (370 miles) above Earth's surface. Named for American astronomer Edwin Hubble, the telescope would finally offer scientists the undistorted images for which they had waited so long. *Hubble* promised to be, as headlines and hype put it, a "window on the universe."

The new telescope could create images that were ten times sharper than anything seen from Earth-based observatories. That's

903

Interpreting the Photo

Tell students that some Earth-based telescopes, such as the twin Keck telescopes in Hawaii, are much larger than the *Hubble Space Telescope*. Yet *HST* is able to achieve better resolution. Ask students to explain why. Being in space, *HST* is able to avoid the distorting effects of Earth's atmosphere.

Tying to Previous Knowledge

Many students have used binoculars to observe distant objects. Tell students that binoculars can be used to view large areas of the night sky. Binoculars are actually two refracting telescopes side by side.

Display

👥 **Interpersonal** Have groups of students use photographs from magazines and images at earthgeu.com to make displays of *Hubble Space Telescope* images. Each group can choose a different year to focus on, or displays can be arranged by topic—that is, one group may focus on *HST* images of planets while another focuses on *HST* images of galaxies. Have students prepare both written and oral presentations to accompany their displays. **L2 ELL COOP LEARN P**

Differentiated Instruction

Learning Disabled Have students observe their reflections in a plane, convex, and concave mirror. **CAUTION:** *Glass mirrors have sharp edges that can cut skin. Handle with care.* Encourage students to describe what they see. A concave mirror enlarges an image. A convex mirror makes an image appear smaller and more distant than it really is. An image in a plane mirror is not distorted. Tell students that different telescopes use different mirrors or lenses to form images. Refracting telescopes use convex lenses; reflecting telescopes use concave mirrors.

Demo

Pass a beam of white light through a prism. Students should note that different colors of light are bent, forming a spectrum. Tell students that telescopes such as *HST* use visible light to obtain images. Ask students to hypothesize how the white light passing through the prism forms a spectrum with violet on one end and red on the other. All colors in the visible spectrum, which have varying wavelengths, are bent at different angles through the prism, and thus they are dispersed. Violet light, which has the shortest wavelength of visible light, is bent the most. Red light, which has the longest wavelength of visible light, is bent the least.

Interpreting the Illustration

Have students research the functioning parts of an Earth-based reflecting telescope. Tell them to sketch cross sections of an Earth-based reflecting telescope and the *Hubble Space Telescope* in their science journals. Have them compare and contrast the two telescopes. Be sure that students label all parts of their diagrams and explain how each contributes to the telescope's function.

comparable to distinguishing the head-lights on a car that is 4800 kilometers (3000 miles) away. *Hubble*'s sharp instruments are sensitive to incredibly faint light; the telescope detects objects that would have to be 50 times brighter before they showed up on a ground-based telescope. Being above the atmosphere, moreover, *Hubble* can observe ultraviolet wavelengths that do not reach the ground.

INFORMATION ODYSSEY

In a day, *Hubble* transmits enough data to fill an encyclopedia. The process begins when instruments aboard the telescope create digital images of what *Hubble* has "seen." *Hubble* transmits the images to the Tracking and Data Relay Satellites that orbit Earth.

The communications satellites route the data stream to NASA's Goddard Space Flight Center in Greenbelt, Maryland. Goddard serves as mission control for *Hubble*. Whenever the telescope is directed to point toward a new target or alter the way it gathers data, the command comes from Greenbelt. Goddard dispatches *Hubble* data, by telephone links, to the Space Telescope Science Institute in Baltimore, Maryland.

"EYE DOCTORS" IN ORBIT

In 1990 *Hubble* was aloft, and the mechanisms for getting data to scientists were in place. But *Hubble* hype turned to horror after the telescope began transmitting images. Where were the crystal-clear shots everyone had expected? Taxpayers roared, and NASA officials cringed. *Hubble*'s blurry pictures looked as if someone had stretched fine gauze over the lens of a camera.

904

Edwin Hubble

● **DIAGRAM (ABOVE):** *Hubble*'s "front door" is the **Aperture (A)**, a long tube that collects light particles called photons. The hinged cover closes when the light is too bright. Once inside, photons bounce from the **Primary Mirror (B)** to the **Secondary Mirror (C)** to a **Spectrograph (D)** and a **Spectrometer (E)** that collect data. The probe's **Solar Panels (F)** collect the minimal energy—only about 150 watts—needed to operate the telescope. The solar panels move constantly to stay aligned with the Sun. *Hubble*'s **Fine Guidance Sensors (G)** aim the satellite with ten times the accuracy of ground-based telescopes.

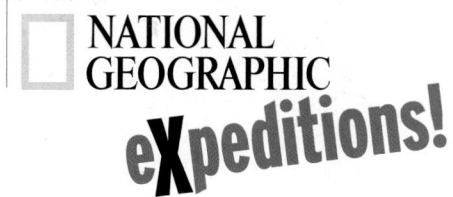

NATIONAL GEOGRAPHIC
eXpeditions!

● **TOP LEFT:** Astronauts from the Space Shuttle *Discovery* make repairs to the *Hubble Space Telescope*. During their week in space in December 1999, the shuttle crew overhauled the telescope for another decade of observation and discovery. Another servicing mission will take place early in the new century.

● **BOTTOM LEFT:** The miracle of star birth unfolds in the **Eagle Nebula.** Deep inside pillars of dense, cool gas and dust—the tallest one here measures three light-years in height—molecular hydrogen and dust condense into lumps that contract and ignite under their own gravity to become stars.

Enrichment

Have interested students find out more about the repairs made to *HST* by the crew of the *Discovery* shuttle in December 1999. The main goal of the mission was to replace the six gyroscopes that provide a reference frame to the rate sensor units, which are part of the telescope's pointing system. In addition, the seven-member crew installed a new advanced computer, changed one of the fine guidance sensors, replaced a tape recorder with a digital data recorder, repaired outside insulation, installed a new radio transmitter, and installed a voltage/temperature improve-ment kit, which will protect the telescope's batteries from over-charging and overheating .

Interpreting the Photo

Tell students that a star begins its life as a nebula, and that the mat-ter in a nebula comes from mat-ter that was once in other stars. Ask students to relate this to the law of conservation of mass. The law of conservation of mass states that matter is neither created nor destroyed. When a star dies, its matter is not destroyed; rather, it is recycled to create new stars.

Note Internet addresses that you find useful in the space below for quick reference.

_____

_____

_____

_____

_____

For Internet tips, see Glencoe's **Using the Internet in the Science Classroom.**

Science Field Book

Earth Science
Journal

Visual-Spatial Have students assemble a collec-tion of images taken by the *HST.* Make sure they provide captions for each photo explaining the sig-nificance of obtaining the image to astronomers.

Going Further

Ask students to research the index of refraction. Have them relate what they learn to the use of lenses in telescope construction. The index of refraction of a substance is equal to the sine of the angle of incidence of light from a vacuum divided by the sine of the angle of refraction. The index of refraction of glass is used when determining how to shape the objective lens of a telescope or the lenses in a pair of glasses.

Interpreting the Photo

Images from *HST* show that Pluto has an extremely varied surface, including 12 distinct areas. A few of these areas are more than 1000 km across. Some are bright; others are dark. In addition, *HST* was on hand to record the collision of comet Shoemaker-Levy 9 with Jupiter. Roughly 21 comet fragments crashed into the gas giant. The largest fragment created an impact the size of Earth on Jupiter.

Teaching Strategies

- NASA has a teacher resource center that will provide free *Hubble Space Telescope* materials.
- Draw a 2.4-m line to show how large the diameter of *HST*'s primary mirror is. A large mirror collects more light than a small mirror, allowing faint, distant objects to be observed.

Mars

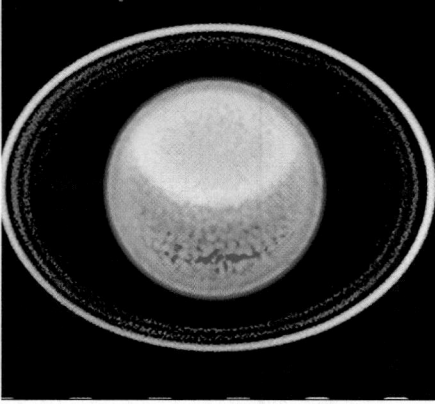

Uranus

Pluto

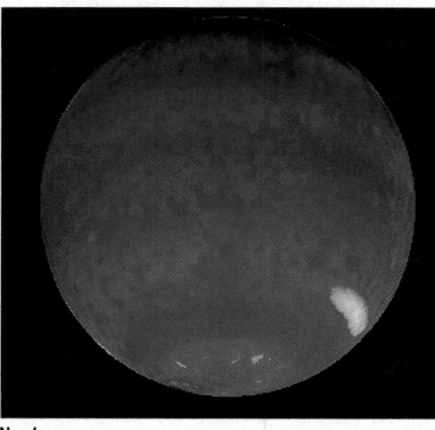

Neptune

NASA quickly diagnosed the problem: The primary mirror was slightly defective. As a result, *Hubble*'s images weren't focused properly. The eye in the sky needed glasses. Responding to a 911 call from space takes time. The shuttle *Endeavour* reached the telescope in December 1993. Replacing the primary mirror was impossible, so the astronauts installed supplementary mirrors that compensated for the flaw. At last the telescope could see clearly.

KEEPING THE TELESCOPE IN SHAPE

Hubble's creators had expected occasional repairs and upgrades, so they made sure astronauts could get to the telescope's key systems. The telescope's parts were made to be removed and replaced easily. Thus, the shuttle crew can repair the *Hubble Space Telescope* in orbit, rather than haul it back to Earth.

● **ABOVE AND RIGHT:** Even the solar system unveiled secrets to *Hubble*'s powerful eye. No one had clearly seen Pluto's face before, and no telescope had captured such a sharp picture of Mars. *Hubble* also provided new looks at clouds on Jupiter and Saturn and at the charcoal black rings of Uranus.

This text is based on "Time Exposures" in the April 1997 issue of NATIONAL GEOGRAPHIC.

906

Cultural Diversity

Kathryn Sullivan (1957–) Among the principle scientists aboard the shuttle *Discovery,* which set the *Hubble Space Telescope* into orbit in 1990, was Dr. Kathryn Sullivan, who was also the first American woman to walk in space. Over the course of her career with NASA, Dr. Sullivan was a crew member for three shuttle missions and spent more than 500 hours in space. She earned her Bachelor of Science degree in Earth Sciences from the University of California in Santa Cruz and her Ph.D. in Geology from Dalhousie University in Nova Scotia. Presently, she is Chief Executive Officer of the Center of Science and Industry in Columbus, Ohio. She devotes much of her time to students and future scientists.

Saturn

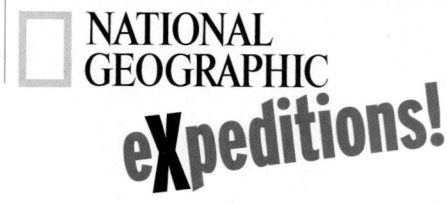

Where *Hubble* Has Looked

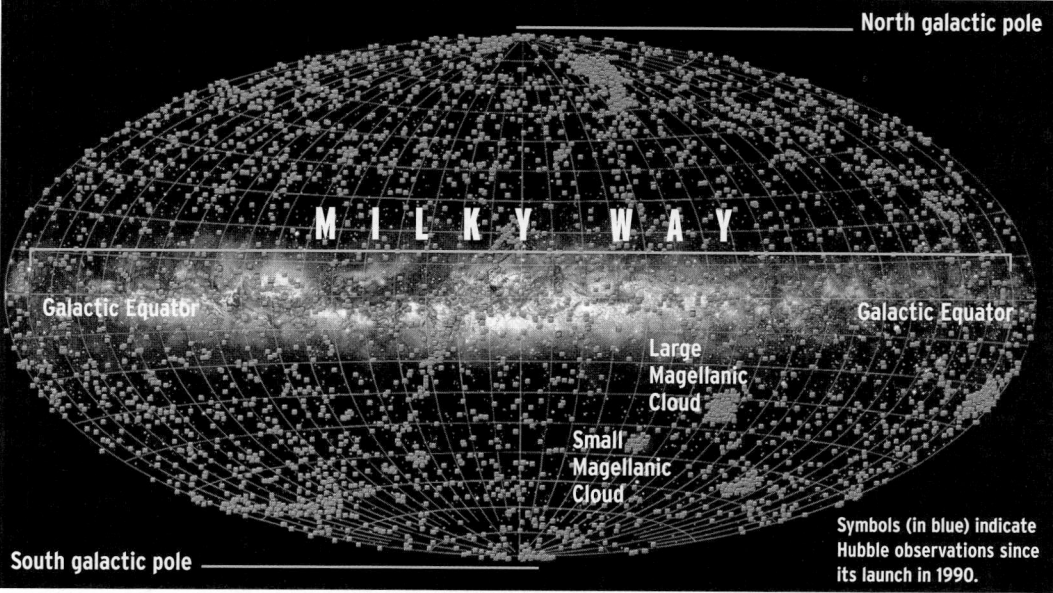

North galactic pole

MILKY WAY

Galactic Equator

Galactic Equator

Large Magellanic Cloud

Small Magellanic Cloud

South galactic pole

Symbols (in blue) indicate Hubble observations since its launch in 1990.

In 1997 the shuttle *Discovery* made the second house call to *Hubble.* In addition to routine maintenance, the astronauts replaced the telescope's scientific instruments with newer, more powerful devices. They also lifted *Hubble* about 15 kilometers (9 miles) higher above the planet's surface.

Discovery visited *Hubble* again in 1999. This third servicing mission replaced the gyroscopes that aim the telescope at targets and installed a new computer that works 20 times faster than its predecessor.

NASA originally planned to retire *Hubble* in 2005, but the telescope's incredible output—120 000 images of 10 000 objects during the first decade of operation—inspired NASA to think again. The agency announced in 1997 that *Hubble* would keep its powerful eyes open until 2010. Despite its problems, the *Hubble Space Telescope* has lived up to—even surpassed—Hermann Oberth's dream.

Space will never look the same again.

Expeditions Activity

Do you want to know more about *Hubble Space Telescope*? Consult the April 1997 NATIONAL GEOGRAPHIC article, "Time Exposures"—or explore science.glencoe.com to compare and contrast photos taken by *Hubble* with earlier images from satellites and space probes.

907

Expeditions Activity

Images from *HST* may or may not be better than images from other sources. *HST* images are better than ground-based telescope images, but many probes provide more detailed images than are possible with *HST*.

Project

Kinesthetic Have students visit the Earth Science Web Site at **earthgeu.com** to find links to the Web site of the Space Telescope Science Institute, the agency charged with interpreting *HST* data. This site has activities and links that students can use to design a model of the Hubble Space Telescope. Have students work in teams to design their models. **L2 COOP LEARN**

Appendix

Contents

Appendix A — International System of Units

The International System of Units (SI) is accepted as the standard for measurement throughout most of the world. Three base units in SI are the meter, the kilogram, and the second. Frequently used SI units are listed below.

Temperature measurements in SI are often made in degrees Celsius. A Celsius degree (°C) is a supplementary unit derived from the base unit Kelvin. The Celsius scale has 100 equal graduations between the freezing temperature (0°C) and the boiling temperature (100°C) of water. The following relationship exists between the Celsius and Kelvin temperature scales:

$$K = {}^\circ C + 273$$

Several other supplementary SI units are listed in Table A-2.

If you want to convert measurements in SI/Metric units to English units, use Table A-3.

Table A-1 Frequently Used SI Units

Length	1 millimeter (mm) = 1000 micrometers (μm)
	1 centimeter (cm) = 10 millimeters (mm)
	1 meter (m) = 100 centimeters (cm)
	1 kilometer (km) = 1000 meters (m)
	1 light-year (ly) = 9 460 000 000 000 kilometers (km)
Area	1 square meter (m²) = 10 000 square centimeters (cm²)
	1 square kilometer (km²) = 1 000 000 square meters (m²)
Volume	1 milliliter (mL) = 1 cubic centimeter (cm³)
	1 liter (L) = 1000 milliliters (mL)
Mass	1 gram (g) = 1000 milligrams (mg)
	1 kilogram (kg) = 1000 grams (g)
	1 metric ton = 1000 kilograms (kg)
Time	1 s = 1 second
	1 h = 1 hour, 60 seconds

Table A-2 Supplementary SI Units

Measurement	Unit	Symbol	Expressed in Base Units
Energy	Joule	J	$kg \cdot m^2/s^2$ or $N \cdot m$
Force	Newton	N	$kg \cdot m/s^2$
Power	Watt	W	$kg \cdot m^2/s^3$ or J/s
Pressure	Pascal	Pa	$kg/(m \cdot s^2)$ or $N \cdot m$

Table A-3 SI/Metric-to-English Conversions

	When You Want to Convert:	Multiply By:	To Find:
Length	Inches	2.54	centimeters
	Centimeters	0.39	inches
	Feet	0.30	meters
	Meters	3.28	feet
	Yards	0.91	meters
	Meters	1.09	yards
	Miles	1.61	kilometers
	Kilometers	0.62	miles
Mass and Weight*	Ounces	28.35	grams
	Grams	0.04	ounces
	Pounds	0.45	kilograms
	Kilograms	2.20	pounds
	Tons	0.91	metric tons
	Metric tons	1.10	tons
	Pounds	4.45	newtons
	Newtons	0.23	pounds
Volume	Cubic inches	16.39	cubic centimeters
	Cubic centimeters	0.06	cubic inches
	Cubic feet	0.03	cubic meters
	Cubic meters	35.31	cubic feet
	Liters	1.06	quarts
	Liters	0.26	gallons
	Gallons	3.78	liters
Area	Square inches	6.45	square centimeters
	Square centimeters	0.16	square inches
	Square feet	0.09	square meters
	Square meters	10.76	square feet
	Square miles	2.59	square kilometers
	Square kilometers	0.39	square miles
	Hectares	2.47	acres
	Acres	0.40	hectares
Temperature	Fahrenheit	5/9 (°F − 32)	Celsius
	Celsius	9/5 °C + 32	Fahrenheit

*Weight as measured in standard Earth gravity

Appendix **B** Safety in the Laboratory

The Earth Science laboratory is a safe place to work if you are aware of important safety rules and if you are careful. You must be responsible for your own safety and for the safety of others. The safety rules given here will protect you and others from harm in the laboratory. While carrying out procedures in any of the activities or *GeoLabs*, take note of the safety symbols and caution statements. The safety symbols are listed and explained in Table B-2.

SAFETY RULES

1. Always obtain your teacher's permission to begin an investigation.

2. Study the procedure outline in the text. If you have questions, ask your teacher. Make sure that you understand all safety symbols shown on the page.

3. Use the safety equipment provided for you. Safety goggles and an apron should be worn during all investigations that involve the use of chemicals.

4. When heating test tubes, always slant them away from yourself and others.

5. Never eat or drink in the lab, and never use lab glassware as food or drink containers. Never inhale chemicals. Do not taste any substances or draw any material into a test tube with your mouth.

6. If you spill any chemical, wash it off immediately with water. Report the spill immediately to your teacher.

7. Know the location and proper use of the fire extinguisher, eye wash, safety shower, fire blanket, first-aid kit, and fire alarm.

8. Keep materials away from flames. Tie back hair and loose clothing when you are working with flames.

9. If a fire should break out in the lab, or if your clothing should catch fire, smother it with the fire blanket or a coat, get under a safety shower, or use the fire department's recommendation for putting out a fire on your clothing: **Stop, Drop, and Roll. NEVER RUN.**

10. Report any accident or injury, no matter how small, to your teacher.

CLEAN-UP PROCEDURES

1. Turn off the water and gas. Disconnect electrical devices.

2. Return all materials to their proper places.

3. Dispose of chemicals and other materials as directed by your teacher. Place broken glass and solid substances in the proper containers. Never discard materials in the sink.

4. Clean your work area.

5. Wash your hands thoroughly after working in the laboratory.

Table B-1 First Aid in the Science Laboratory	
Injury	**Safe Response**
Burns	Apply cold water. Call your teacher immediately.
Cuts and bruises	Stop any bleeding by applying direct pressure. Cover cuts with a clean dressing. Apply cold compresses to bruises. Call your teacher immediately.
Fainting	Leave the person lying down. Loosen any tight clothing and keep crowds away. Call your teacher immediately.
Foreign matter in eye	Flush with plenty of water. Use an eyewash bottle or fountain.
Poisoning	Note the suspected poisoning agent and call your teacher immediately.
Any spills on skin	Flush with large amounts of water or use safety shower. Call your teacher immediately.

Safety symbols in the following table are used in the lab activities to indicate possible hazards. Learn the meaning of each symbol.

We recommend that you wear safety goggles and apron at all times in the lab. This may be required in your school district.

Table B-2 Safety Symbols

SAFETY SYMBOLS	HAZARD	EXAMPLES	PRECAUTION	REMEDY
DISPOSAL	Special disposal procedures need to be followed.	certain chemicals, living organisms	Do not dispose of these materials in the sink or trash can.	Dispose of wastes as directed by your teacher.
BIOLOGICAL	Organisms or other biological materials that might be harmful to humans	bacteria, fungi, blood, unpreserved tissues, plant materials	Avoid skin contact with these materials. Wear mask or gloves.	Notify your teacher if you suspect contact with material. Wash hands thoroughly.
EXTREME TEMPERATURE	Objects that can burn skin by being too cold or too hot	boiling liquids, hot plates, dry ice, liquid nitrogen	Use proper protection when handling.	Go to your teacher for first aid.
SHARP OBJECT	Use of tools or glassware that can easily puncture or slice skin	razor blades, pins, scalpels, pointed tools, dissecting probes, broken glass	Practice commonsense behavior and follow guidelines for use of the tool.	Go to your teacher for first aid.
FUME	Possible danger to respiratory tract from fumes	ammonia, acetone, nail polish remover, heated sulfur, moth balls	Make sure there is good ventilation. Never smell fumes directly. Wear a mask.	Leave foul area and notify your teacher immediately.
ELECTRICAL	Possible danger from electrical shock or burn	improper grounding, liquid spills, short circuits, exposed wires	Double-check setup with teacher. Check condition of wires and apparatus.	Do not attempt to fix electrical problems. Notify your teacher immediately.
IRRITANT	Substances that can irritate the skin or mucous membranes of the respiratory tract	pollen, moth balls, steel wool, fiberglass, potassium permanganate	Wear dust mask and gloves. Practice extra care when handling these materials.	Go to your teacher for first aid.
CHEMICAL	Chemicals can react with and destroy tissue and other materials	bleaches such as hydrogen peroxide; acids such as sulfuric acid, hydrochloric acid; bases such as ammonia, sodium hydroxide	Wear goggles, gloves, and an apron.	Immediately flush the affected area with water and notify your teacher.
TOXIC	Substance may be poisonous if touched, inhaled, or swallowed.	mercury, many metal compounds, iodine, poinsettia plant parts	Follow your teacher's instructions.	Always wash hands thoroughly after use. Go to your teacher for first aid.
FLAMMABLE	Flammable chemicals may be ignited by open flame, spark, or exposed heat.	alcohol, kerosene, potassium permanganate	Avoid open flames and heat when using flammable chemicals.	Notify your teacher immediately. Use fire safety equipment if applicable.
OPEN FLAME	Open flame in use, may cause fire.	hair, clothing, paper, synthetic materials	Tie back hair and loose clothing. Follow teacher's instruction on lighting and extinguishing flames.	Notify your teacher immediately. Use fire safety equipment if applicable.

Eye Safety
Proper eye protection should be worn at all times by anyone performing or observing science activities.

Clothing Protection
This symbol appears when substances could stain or burn clothing.

Animal Safety
This symbol appears when safety of animals and students must be ensured.

Handwashing
After the lab, wash hands with soap and water before removing goggles.

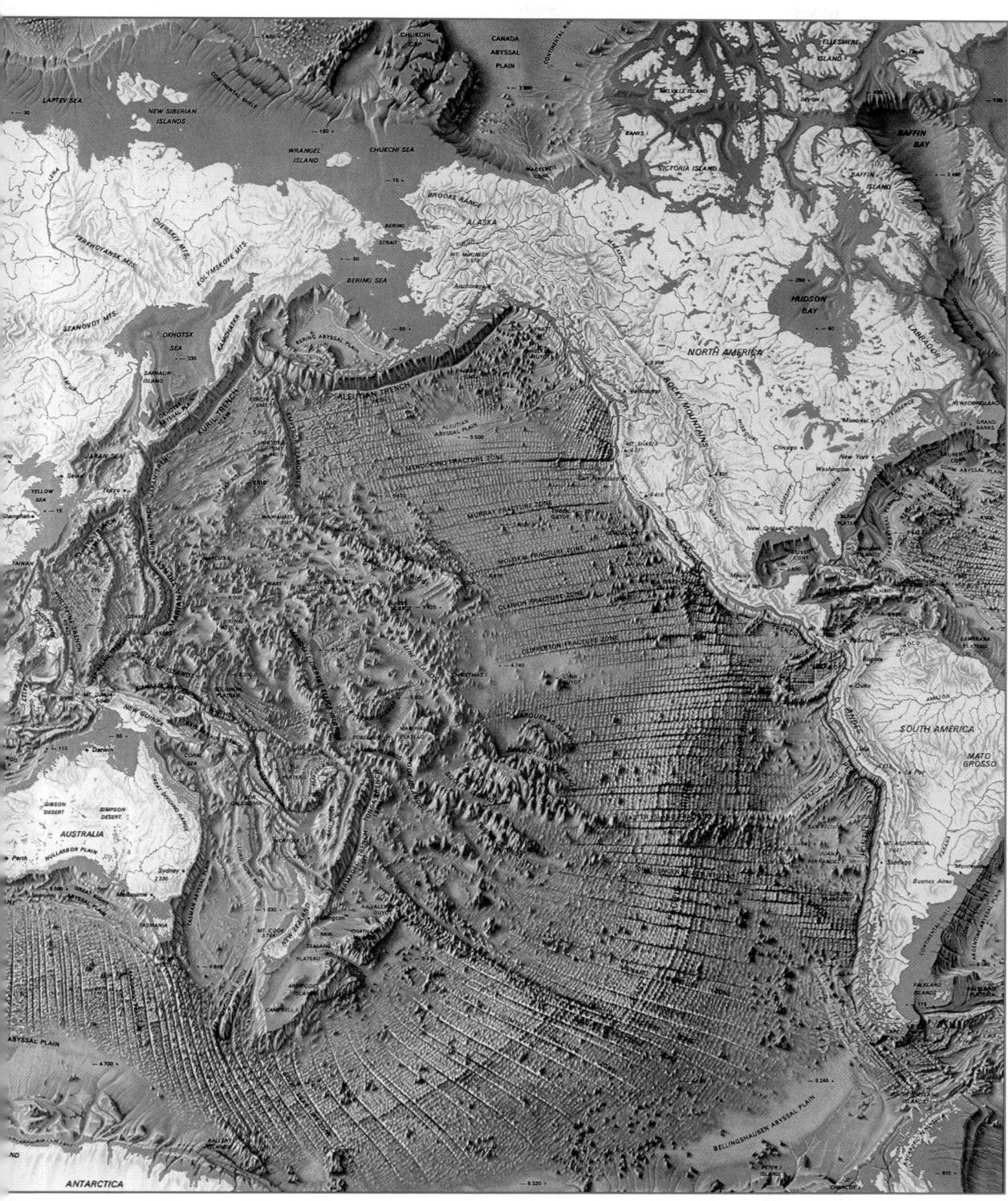

Appendix D Topographic Map Symbols

ROADS AND RAILROADS

Primary highway, hard surface

Secondary highway, hard surface

Light-duty road, hard or improved surface

Unimproved road

Railroad: single track and multiple track

Railroads in juxtaposition

BUILDINGS AND STRUCTURES

Buildings

School, church, and cemetery

Barn and warehouse

Wells, not water (with labels)

o oil   o gas

Tanks: oil, water, etc.

(labeled if water)

water

Open-pit mine, quarry, or prospect

Tunnel

Benchmark

BM Δ 293

Bridge

Campsite

HABITATS

Marsh (swamp)

Wooded marsh

Woods or brushwood

Vineyard

Submerged marsh

Mangrove

Coral reef, rocks

Orchard

Urban area

Perennial streams

Elevated aqueduct

Water well and spring

Small rapids

Large rapids

Intermittent lake

Intermittent stream

Glacier

Large falls

Dry lake bed

SURFACE ELEVATIONS

Spot elevation

x 7369

Water elevation

670

Index contour

100

Intermediate contour

Depression contour

BOUNDARIES

National

State

County, parish, municipal

Civil township, precinct, town, barrio

Incorporated city, village, town, hamlet

Reservation, national or state

Small park, cemetery, airport, etc.

Land grant

Township or range line, United States land survey

Township or range line, approximate location

Appendix E — Weather Map Symbols

Sample Plotted Report at Each Station

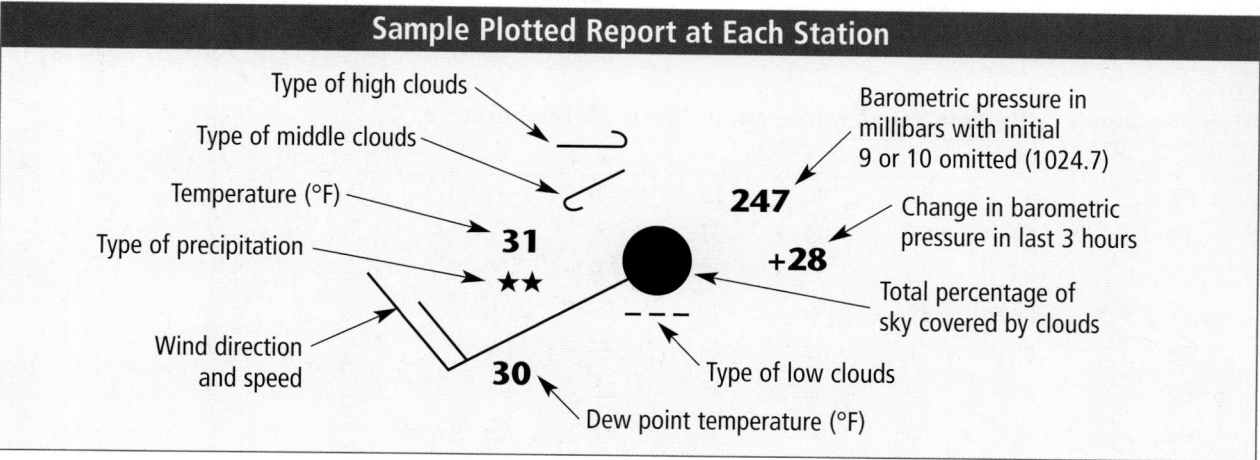

Type of high clouds

Type of middle clouds

Temperature (°F)

Type of precipitation

Wind direction and speed

31

★★

30

Dew point temperature (°F)

Barometric pressure in millibars with initial 9 or 10 omitted (1024.7)

247

+28

Change in barometric pressure in last 3 hours

Total percentage of sky covered by clouds

Type of low clouds

Symbols Used in Plotting Report

Precipitation	Wind Direction and Speed	Sky Coverage	Fronts and Pressure Systems
☰ Fog	◯ 0 calm	◯ No cover	(H) or High — Center of high- or
★ Snow	╱ 1–2 knots	◔ 1/10 or less	(L) or Low — low-pressure system
● Rain	╲ 3–7 knots	◕ 2/10 to 3/10	▲▲▲▲ Cold front
⎁ Thunderstorm	╲ 8–12 knots	◑ 4/10	⌒⌒⌒⌒ Warm front
⦁ Drizzle	╲ 13–17 knots	◐ 1/2	▲⌒▲⌒ Occluded front
▽ Showers	╲ 18–22 knots	◕ 6/10	▲⌒▲⌒ Stationary front
	╲ 23–27 knots	◕ 7/10	
	╲ 48–52 knots	◑ Overcast with openings	
	1 knot = 1.852 km/h	● Completely overcast	

Clouds

Some Types of High Clouds	Some Types of Middle Clouds	Some Types of Low Clouds
⌐⌐ Scattered cirrus	∠ Thin altostratus layer	⌒ Cumulus of fair weather
⌐⌐ Dense cirrus in patches	⫽ Thick altostratus layer	⌣ Stratocumulus
⌐⌐ Veil of cirrus covering entire sky	⌒ Thin altostratus in patches	- - - Fractocumulus of bad weather
⌐⌐ Cirrus not covering entire sky	⌒ Thin altostratus in bands	— Stratus of fair weather

Appendix F — Relative Humidity

Relative Humidity %

Dry-Bulb Temperature	Dry-Bulb Temperature Minus Wet-Bulb Temperature, °C									
	1	2	3	4	5	6	7	8	9	10
0°C	81	64	46	29	13					
1°C	83	66	49	33	18					
2°C	84	68	52	37	22	7				
3°C	84	69	55	40	25	12				
4°C	85	71	57	43	29	16				
5°C	85	72	58	45	32	20				
6°C	86	73	60	48	35	24	11			
7°C	86	74	61	49	38	26	15			
8°C	87	75	63	51	40	29	19	8		
9°C	87	76	65	53	42	32	21	12		
10°C	88	77	66	55	44	34	24	15	6	
11°C	89	78	67	56	46	36	27	18	9	
12°C	89	78	68	58	48	39	29	21	12	
13°C	89	79	69	59	50	41	32	22	15	7
14°C	90	79	70	60	51	42	34	26	18	10
15°C	90	80	71	61	53	44	36	27	20	13
16°C	90	81	71	63	54	46	38	30	23	15
17°C	90	81	72	64	55	47	40	32	25	18
18°C	91	82	73	65	57	49	41	34	27	20
19°C	91	82	74	65	58	50	43	36	29	22
20°C	91	83	74	66	59	51	44	37	31	24
21°C	91	83	75	67	60	53	46	39	32	26
22°C	92	83	76	68	61	54	47	40	34	28
23°C	92	84	76	69	62	55	48	42	36	30
24°C	92	84	77	69	62	56	49	43	37	31
25°C	92	84	77	70	63	57	50	44	39	33
26°C	92	85	78	71	64	58	51	46	40	34
27°C	92	85	78	71	65	58	52	47	41	36
28°C	93	85	78	72	65	59	53	48	42	37
29°C	93	86	79	72	66	60	54	49	43	38
30°C	93	86	79	73	67	61	55	50	44	39
31°C	93	86	80	73	67	62	56	50	45	40
32°C	93	86	80	74	68	62	57	51	46	41

Appendix G — Periodic Table of the Elements

PERIODIC TABLE OF THE ELEMENTS

Key

Element — Hydrogen
Atomic number — 1
Symbol — H
Atomic mass — 1.008
State of matter

State legend:
- Gas
- Liquid
- Solid
- Synthetic elements

Type legend:
- Metal
- Metalloid
- Nonmetal
- Recently discovered

Group 1A / 1

Period	Element
1	Hydrogen 1 H 1.008
2	Lithium 3 Li 6.941
3	Sodium 11 Na 22.990
4	Potassium 19 K 39.098
5	Rubidium 37 Rb 85.468
6	Cesium 55 Cs 132.905
7	Francium 87 Fr 223.020

Group 2A / 2

- Beryllium 4 Be 9.012
- Magnesium 12 Mg 24.305
- Calcium 20 Ca 40.078
- Strontium 38 Sr 87.62
- Barium 56 Ba 137.327
- Radium 88 Ra 226.025

Group 3B / 3

- Scandium 21 Sc 44.956
- Yttrium 39 Y 88.906
- Lanthanum 57 La 138.906
- Actinium 89 Ac 227.028

Group 4B / 4

- Titanium 22 Ti 47.88
- Zirconium 40 Zr 91.224
- Hafnium 72 Hf 178.49
- Rutherfordium 104 Rf (261)

Group 5B / 5

- Vanadium 23 V 50.942
- Niobium 41 Nb 92.906
- Tantalum 73 Ta 180.948
- Dubnium 105 Db (262)

Group 6B / 6

- Chromium 24 Cr 51.996
- Molybdenum 42 Mo 95.94
- Tungsten 74 W 183.84
- Seaborgium 106 Sg (263)

Group 7B / 7

- Manganese 25 Mn 54.938
- Technetium 43 Tc 97.907
- Rhenium 75 Re 186.207
- Bohrium 107 Bh (262)

Group 8B / 8

- Iron 26 Fe 55.847
- Ruthenium 44 Ru 101.07
- Osmium 76 Os 190.2
- Hassium 108 Hs (265)

Group 8B / 9

- Cobalt 27 Co 58.933
- Rhodium 45 Rh 102.906
- Iridium 77 Ir 192.22
- Meitnerium 109 Mt (266)

Group 8B / 10

- Nickel 28 Ni 58.693
- Palladium 46 Pd 106.42
- Platinum 78 Pt 195.08
- Darmstadtium 110 Ds (269)

Group 1B / 11

- Copper 29 Cu 63.546
- Silver 47 Ag 107.868
- Gold 79 Au 196.967
- Unununium ★ 111 Uuu (272)

Group 2B / 12

- Zinc 30 Zn 65.39
- Cadmium 48 Cd 112.411
- Mercury 80 Hg 200.59
- Ununbium ★ 112 Uub (277)

Group 3A / 13

- Boron 5 B 10.811
- Aluminum 13 Al 26.982
- Gallium 31 Ga 69.723
- Indium 49 In 114.82
- Thallium 81 Tl 204.383

Group 4A / 14

- Carbon 6 C 12.011
- Silicon 14 Si 28.086
- Germanium 32 Ge 72.61
- Tin 50 Sn 118.710
- Lead 82 Pb 207.2
- Ununquadium ★ 114 Uuq (285)

Group 5A / 15

- Nitrogen 7 N 14.007
- Phosphorus 15 P 30.974
- Arsenic 33 As 74.922
- Antimony 51 Sb 121.757
- Bismuth 83 Bi 208.980

Group 6A / 16

- Oxygen 8 O 15.999
- Sulfur 16 S 32.066
- Selenium 34 Se 78.96
- Tellurium 52 Te 127.60
- Polonium 84 Po 208.982

Group 7A / 17

- Fluorine 9 F 18.998
- Chlorine 17 Cl 35.453
- Bromine 35 Br 79.904
- Iodine 53 I 126.904
- Astatine 85 At 209.987

Group 8A / 18

- Helium 2 He 4.003
- Neon 10 Ne 20.180
- Argon 18 Ar 39.948
- Krypton 36 Kr 83.80
- Xenon 54 Xe 131.290
- Radon 86 Rn 222.018

The number in parentheses is the mass number of the longest lived isotope for that element.

★ Names not officially assigned. Discovery of element 114 recently reported. Further information not yet available.

Lanthanide series

- Cerium 58 Ce 140.115
- Praseodymium 59 Pr 140.908
- Neodymium 60 Nd 144.24
- Promethium 61 Pm 144.913
- Samarium 62 Sm 150.36
- Europium 63 Eu 151.965
- Gadolinium 64 Gd 157.25
- Terbium 65 Tb 158.925
- Dysprosium 66 Dy 162.50
- Holmium 67 Ho 164.930
- Erbium 68 Er 167.26
- Thulium 69 Tm 168.934
- Ytterbium 70 Yb 173.04
- Lutetium 71 Lu 174.967

Actinide series

- Thorium 90 Th 232.038
- Protactinium 91 Pa 231.036
- Uranium 92 U 238.029
- Neptunium 93 Np 237.048
- Plutonium 94 Pu 244.064
- Americium 95 Am 243.061
- Curium 96 Cm 247.070
- Berkelium 97 Bk 247.070
- Californium 98 Cf 251.080
- Einsteinium 99 Es 252.083
- Fermium 100 Fm 257.095
- Mendelevium 101 Md 258.099
- Nobelium 102 No 259.101
- Lawrencium 103 Lr 260.105

Appendix H — Minerals

Table H-1 Minerals with Metallic Luster

Mineral (Formula)	Color	Streak	Hardness	Specific Gravity	Crystal System	Breakage Pattern	Uses and Other Properties
Bornite (Cu_5FeS_4)	bronze, tarnishes to dark blue purple	gray-black	3	4.9–5.4	tetragonal	uneven fracture	source of copper called "peacock ore" because of the purple shine when it tarnishes
Chalcopyrite ($CuFeS_2$)	brassy to golden yellow	greenish black	3.5–4	4.2	tetragonal	uneven fracture	main ore of copper
Chromite ($FeCr_2O_4$)	black or brown	brown to black	5.5	4.6	cubic	irregular fracture	ore of chromium, stainless steel, metallurgical bricks
Copper (Cu)	copper red	copper red	3	8.5–9	cubic	hackly	coins, pipes, gutters, wire, cooking utensils, jewelry, decorative plaques; malleable and ductile
Galena (PbS)	gray	gray to black	2.5	7.5	cubic	cubic cleavage perfect	source of lead, used in pipes, shields for X rays, fishing equipment sinkers
Gold (Au)	pale to golden yellow	yellow	2.5–3	19.3	cubic	hackly	jewelry, money, gold leaf, fillings for teeth, medicines; does not tarnish
Graphite (C)	black to gray	black to gray	1–2	2.3	hexagonal	basal cleavage (scales)	pencil lead, lubricants for locks, rods to control some small nuclear reactions, battery poles
Hematite (specular) (Fe_2O_3)	black or reddish brown	red or reddish brown	6	5.3	hexagonal	irregular fracture	source of iron; roasted in a blast furnace, converted to "pig" iron, made into steel
Magnetite (Fe_3O_4)	black	black	6	5.2	cubic	conchoidal fracture	source of iron, naturally magnetic, called lodestone
Pyrite (FeS_2)	light, brassy yellow	greenish black	6.5	5.0	cubic	uneven fracture	source of iron, "fool's gold," alters to limonite
Pyrrhotite ($Fe_{1-x}S$)* *contains one less atom of Fe than S	bronze	gray-black	4	4.6	hexagonal	uneven fracture	an ore of iron and sulfur; may be magnetic
Silver (Ag)	silvery white, tarnishes to black	light gray to silver	2.5	10–12	cubic	hackly	coin, fillings for teeth, jewelry, silverplate, wires; malleable and ductile

Table H-2 Minerals with Nonmetallic Luster

Mineral (Formula)	Color	Streak	Hardness	Specific Gravity	Crystal System	Breakage Pattern	Uses and Other Properties
Augite $((Ca, Na)$ (Mg, Fe, Al) $(Al, Si)_2O_6)$	black	colorless	6	3.3	monoclinic	2-directional cleavage	square or 8-sided cross section
Corundum (Al_2O_3)	colorless, blue, brown green, white pink, red	colorless	9	4.0	hexagonal	fracture	gemstones: ruby is red, sapphire is blue; industrial abrasive
Feldspar (orthoclase) $(KAlSi_3O_8)$	colorless white to gray, green, and yellow	colorless	6	2.5	monoclinic	two cleavage planes meet at 90° angle	insoluble in acids; used in the manufacture of porcelain
Feldspar (plagioclase) $(NaAlSi_3O_8)$ $(CaAl_2Si_3O_8)$	gray, green, white	colorless	6	2.5	triclinic	two cleavage planes meet at 86° angle	used in ceramics; striations present on some faces
Fluorite (CaF_2)	colorless, white, blue, green, red, yellow, purple	colorless	4	3–3.2	cubic	cleavage	used in the manufacture of optical equipment; glows under ultraviolet light
Garnet $(Mg, Fe, Ca,$ $Mn)_3, (Al, Fe,$ $Cr)_2, (SiO_4)_3$	deep yellow-red, green, black	colorless	7.5	3.5	cubic	conchoidal fracture	used in jewelry; also used as an abrasive
Hornblende $Ca_2Na(Mg,$ $Fe^2)_4, (Al, Fe^3,$ $Ti)_3, Si_8O_{22}(O,$ $OH)_2$	green to black	gray to white	5–6	3.4	monoclinic	cleavage in two directions	will transmit light on thin edges; 6-sided cross section
Limonite (hydrous iron oxides)	yellow, brown, black	yellow, brown	5.5	2.74–4.3	—	conchoidal fracture	source of iron; weathers easily, coloring matter of soils
Olivine $((Mg, Fe)_2$ $SiO_4)$	olive green	colorless	6.5	3.5	ortho-rhombic	conchoidal fracture	gemstones, refractory sand
Quartz (SiO_2)	colorless, various colors	colorless	7	2.6	hexagonal	conchoidal fracture	used in glass manufacture, electronic equipment, radios, computers, watches, gemstones
Topaz $(Al_2SiO_4$ $(F, OH)_2)$	white, pink, yellow, pale blue, colorless	colorless	8	3.5	ortho-rhombic	basal cleavage	valuable gemstone

Appendix I — Rocks

Rock Types

Rock Type	Rock Name	Characteristics
Igneous (intrusive)	Granite	Large mineral grains of quartz, feldspar, hornblende, and mica. Usually light in color.
	Diorite	Large mineral grains of feldspar, hornblende, and mica. Less quartz than granite. Intermediate in color.
	Gabbro	Large mineral grains of feldspar, hornblende, augite, olivine, and mica. No quartz. Dark in color.
Igneous (extrusive)	Rhyolite	Small or no visible grains of quartz, feldspar, hornblende, and mica. Light in color.
	Andesite	Small or no visible grains of quartz, feldspar, hornblende, and mica. Less quartz than rhyolite. Intermediate in color.
	Basalt	Small or no visible grains of feldspar, hornblende, augite, olivine, and mica. No quartz. Dark in color. Vessicles may be present.
	Obsidian	Glassy texture. No visible grains. Volcanic glass. Fracture is conchoidal. Color is usually black, but may be red-brown or black with white flecks.
	Pumice	Frothy texture. Floats. Usually light in color.
Sedimentary (clastic)	Conglomerate	Coarse-grained. Gravel- or pebble-sized grains.
	Sandstone	Sand-sized grains 1/16 to 2 mm in size. Varies in color.
	Siltstone	Grains are smaller than sand but larger than clay. Varies in color.
	Shale	Smallest grains. Usually dark in color.
Sedimentary (chemical or biochemical)	Limestone	Major mineral is calcite. Usually forms in oceans, lakes, rivers, and caves. Often contains fossils. Effervesces in dilute HCl.
	Coal	Occurs in swampy, low-lying areas. Compacted layers of organic material, mainly plant remains.
Sedimentary (chemical)	Rock salt	Commonly forms by the evaporation of seawater.
Metamorphic	Gneiss	Well-developed banding because of alternating layers of different minerals, usually of different colors. Common parent rock is granite.
	Schist	Well-developed parallel arrangement of flat, sheetlike minerals, mainly micas. Common parent rocks are shale and phyllite.
	Phyllite	Shiny or silky appearance. May look wrinkled. Common parent rocks are shale and slate.
	Slate	Harder, denser, and shinier than shale. Common parent rock is shale.
Metamorphic (nonfoliated)	Marble	Interlocking calcite or dolomite crystals. Common parent rock is limestone.
	Soapstone	Composed mainly of the mineral talc. Soft with a greasy feel.
	Quartzite	Hard and well cemented with interlocking quartz crystals. Common parent rock is sandstone.

The Planets

	Mercury	Venus	Earth	Mars	Jupiter	Saturn	Uranus	Neptune	Pluto
Mass (kg)	3.302×10^{23}	4.8685×10^{24}	5.9736×10^{24}	6.4185×10^{23}	1.8986×10^{27}	5.6846×10^{26}	8.6832×10^{25}	1.0243×10^{26}	1.25×10^{22}
Equatorial radius (km)	2439.7	6051.8	6378.1	3397	71 492	60 268	25 559	24 764	1195
Mean density (kg/m³)	5427	5243	5515	3933	1326	687	1270	1638	1750
Albedo	0.056	0.750	0.306	0.250	0.343	0.342	0.300	0.290	0.145
Semimajor axis (km)	5.791×10^{7}	1.0821×10^{8}	1.4960×10^{8}	2.2792×10^{8}	7.7857×10^{8}	1.43353×10^{9}	2.87246×10^{9}	4.49506×10^{9}	5.86966×10^{9}
Orbital period (Earth days)	87.969	224.701	365.256	686.980	4332.589	10 759.22	30 685.4	60 189	90 465
Orbital inclination (degrees)	7.00	3.39	0.00	1.850	1.304	2.485	0.772	1.769	17.16
Orbital eccentricity	0.2056	0.0067	0.0167	0.0935	0.0489	0.0565	0.0457	0.0113	0.2444
Rotational period (hours)	1407.6	5832.5ᴿ	23.9345	24.6229	9.9250	10.656	17.24ᴿ	16.11	153.2928ᴿ
Axial tilt (degrees)	0.01	177.36	23.45	25.19	3.13	26.73	97.77	28.32	122.53
Average surface temperature (K)	440	737	288	210	129	97	58	58	50
Number of known moons	0	0	1	2	61	31	25*	13	1

*Number as of November 2003.
ᴿ indicates retrograde rotation.

The Moon

Mass (kg)	7.349×10^{22}
Equatorial radius (km)	1737.4
Mean density (kg/m³)	3340
Albedo	0.067
Semimajor axis (km)	3.844×10^{5}
Orbital period (Earth days)	27.3217
Lunar period (Earth days)	29.53
Orbital inclination (degrees)	5.145
Orbital eccentricity	0.0549
Rotational period (hours)	655.728

The Sun

Mass (kg)	1.99×10^{30}
Equatorial radius (km)	6.96×10^{5}
Mean density (kg/m³)	1408
Absolute magnitude	+4.83
Luminosity (W)	384.6
Spectral type	G2
Rotational period (hours)	609.12
Average temperature (K)	5778

Appendix **K** Star Charts

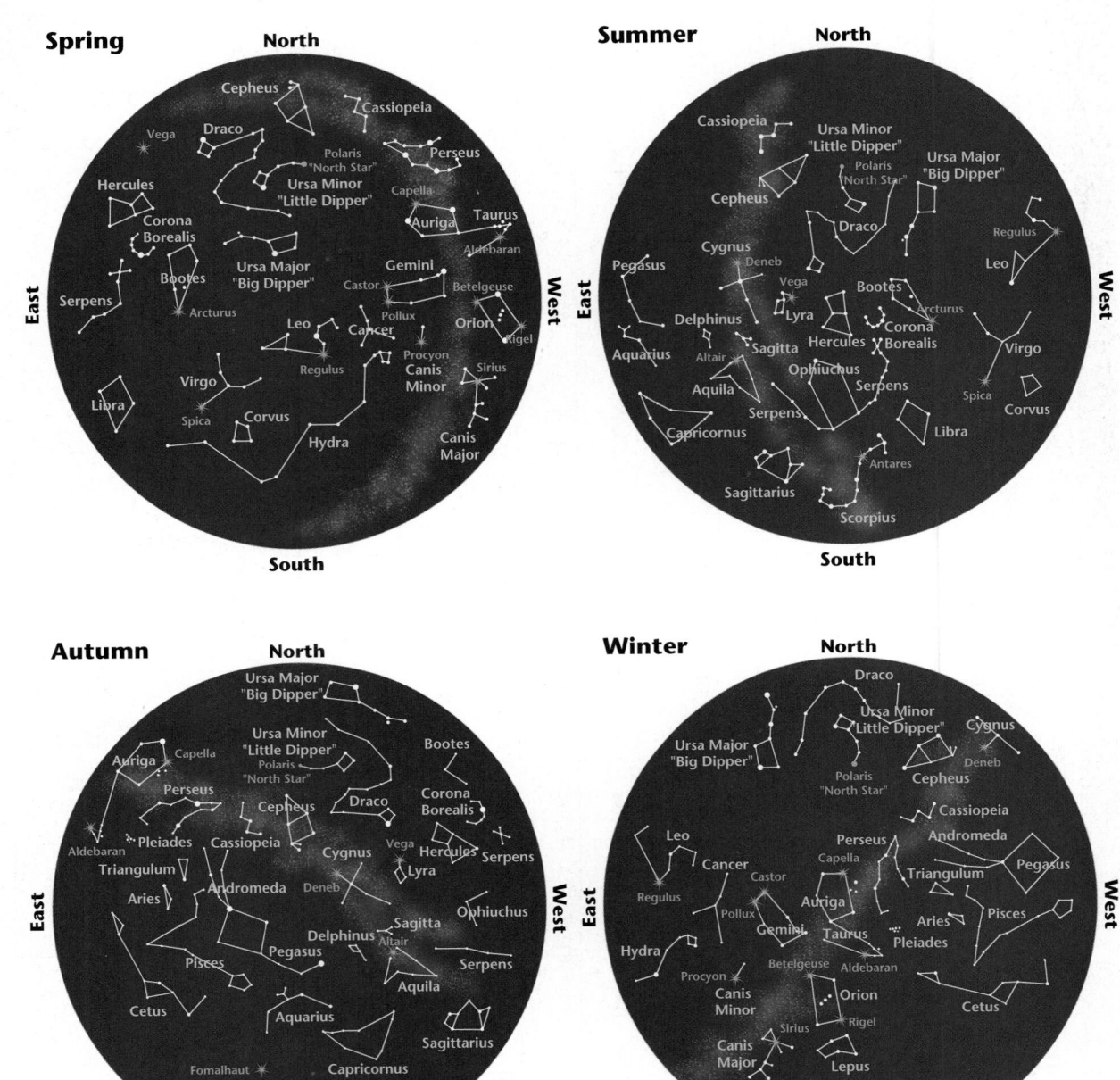

Skill Handbook

Contents

Thinking Critically

OBSERVING AND INFERRING

The process of science often begins with an observation. An observation can be as simple as noticing that the sky is blue, or that seawater is salty. Scientists try to make careful and accurate observations. Some observations describe an event or object using only words. Such observations are called qualitative observations. If you were making qualitative observations of clouds, for example, you might use words such as *puffy, curly, feathery, thin,* or *flat.*

Other observations describe how much of something there is. These are quantitative observations, in which numbers are used as well as words. Quantitative observations of a cloud might include that the cloud's base is at a height of 2000 m and that the cloud extends to a height of 6000 m. When it is possible, scientists use instruments, such as microscopes, thermometers, pan balances, and tape recorders, to make quantitative observations. Measurements provide numerical data, information that can be checked and reproduced. Data collection allows scientists to determine the how and why of their observations.

When you make observations in science, you will find it helpful to first examine an entire object or event. Use your senses of sight, touch, smell, and hearing to examine the object or event in detail. Write down everything that you observe. For example, suppose that you have been given a piece of a quartz crystal. What kinds of observations can you make about that crystal? You might note that it has a specific shape and size. You might also describe how the crystal feels and whether light can pass through it. All of these observations can help you to identify the crystal.

Scientists often use their observations to make inferences. An inference is an attempt to explain, interpret, or determine what caused an observation. For example, if you observed a fist-sized, heavy, round rock called a geode, you might infer that the rock is solid all the way through. However, the rock might be hollow inside, or it might contain beautiful mineral crystals. Or, the rock might be a conglomerate that has a smooth surface. The only way to be sure that your inference is correct is to investigate further. How could you investigate the composition of a rock further?

Before you make an inference, be certain that you have made accurate observations and recorded them carefully. Then, based on everything you know, try to explain or interpret what you have observed. For example, what can you infer from observing the outside of a piece of granite? If possible, investigate further to determine whether your inference is correct.

Thinking Critically

COMPARING AND CONTRASTING

You can analyze and then organize your observations by noting the similarities and differences between two or more objects or events. When you examine objects or events to determine their similarities, you are comparing them. When you examine similar objects or events to determine their differences, you are contrasting them.

Suppose you are asked to compare and contrast the minerals halite and quartz. You could begin by making observations of each type of mineral. Then, you could divide a piece of paper into two columns and list the ways in which the two minerals are similar in one column and the ways in which they are different in the other column. After completing your list, you could organize your findings in a data table or a graph.

Similarities you might point out are that both minerals are solids that occur as crystals, and both are inorganic compounds. Differences might include that halite has a cubic crystal structure, whereas quartz has a hexagonal crystal structure. You could further investigate these two minerals by testing for hardness, luster, color, streak, and cleavage or fracture.

RECOGNIZING CAUSE AND EFFECT

Have you ever seen something happen, and then tried to figure out why or how it happened? If so, you observed an event and inferred a reason for the event. The event or result of an action is an effect, and the reason for the event is the cause.

Suppose that you take a 2-L bottle of soda pop out of the refrigerator and accidentally drop it on the floor. You pick the bottle up, then unscrew the cap and take it off. Immediately, the soda pop fizzes up and spills out of the bottle all over the counter. What was the effect, and what would you infer was the cause? The effect was the soda pop fizzing up and spilling out of the open bottle.

Thinking Critically

You might infer that the cause was your dropping the soda-pop bottle on the floor. In determining the cause and effect, you made a logical inference based on your observations.

Perhaps the soda pop fizzed up and spilled out of the bottle because your little brother or sister shook the bottle before he or she placed it in the refrigerator, or perhaps the soda had been in the refrigerator only for a short time, and it was still warm. When scientists are unsure of the cause of a certain event, they often design controlled experiments to determine what caused the event that they observed. Although you may have made a sound judgment about the cause of the soda pop fizzing and spilling, you would have to perform an experiment to be certain that it was your dropping the bottle on the floor that caused the effect you observed.

INTERPRETING SCIENTIFIC ILLUSTRATIONS

Illustrations are included in your textbook to help you understand, interpret, and remember what you read. Whenever you encounter an illustration, examine it carefully and read the caption. The caption explains or identifies the illustration.

Scientific illustrations often are simplified to enable you to understand a certain portion of a much more complicated object or event. Often, illustrations are simple models of objects or events. Sometimes, scientific illustrations use enhanced or exaggerated figures to help you visualize objects or events.

Some illustrations are designed to show you things that you cannot observe easily on your own. Look at the illustration of a water molecule on the next page. A water molecule, H_2O, is made up of two hydrogen atoms and one oxygen atom. Although you can see water, you cannot see that it is made up of these two types of atoms. A scientific illustration such as the one shown allows you to learn about something that is too small to be seen with the unaided eye. Other illustrations help you to understand something that is too big to be seen easily. A map of the ocean basins, for example, helps you to see the features of the seafloor, something you could not observe yourself.

Some illustrations are designed to show how the internal parts of a structure are arranged. Look at the first illustration of a volcano. The volcano is represented as having been cut lengthwise to show a section that runs along the height of the volcano. An illustration

926 SKILL HANDBOOK

Thinking Critically

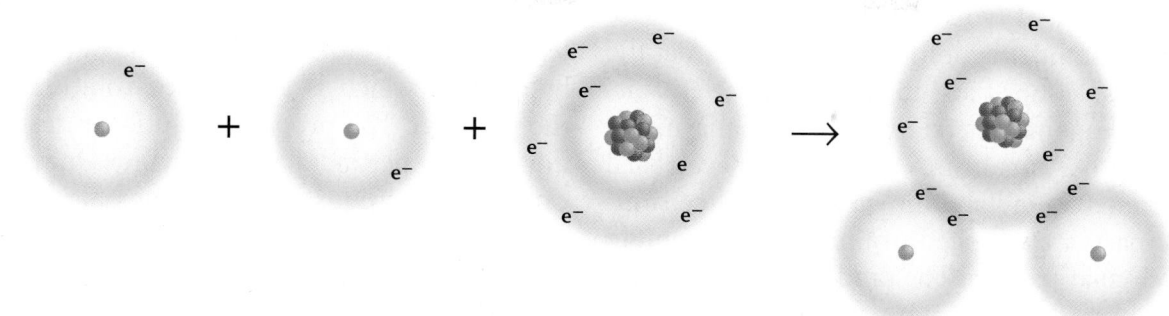

that is represented as having been cut along the length or height of a structure is called a longitudinal section. An illustration that is represented as having been cut crosswise at right angles to the length is a cross section. The second illustration is a cross section of a volcano.

Some scientific illustrations are a series of photographs or diagrams that describe processes. The formation of soil, for example, can best be explained in a series of diagrams that show how rock begins to fracture and break down, then weathers into smaller fragments, then is mixed with organic matter, and finally becomes fertile soil as organic matter decays. Many other processes, such as the

formation of sedimentary rocks, also are best shown in a series of diagrams.

Scientific illustrations also can be used to show events that cannot be observed in a human lifetime. For example, illustrations of tectonic plate movements can show where Earth's landmasses were located millions of years ago. The formation of fossil fuels from organic matter, a process that takes millions of years, can also be described in illustrations.

Symmetry refers to a similarity or likeness of parts. Many organisms and objects have symmetry. When something can be divided into two similar parts lengthwise, it has bilateral symmetry. Look at the photograph of the

Cross section

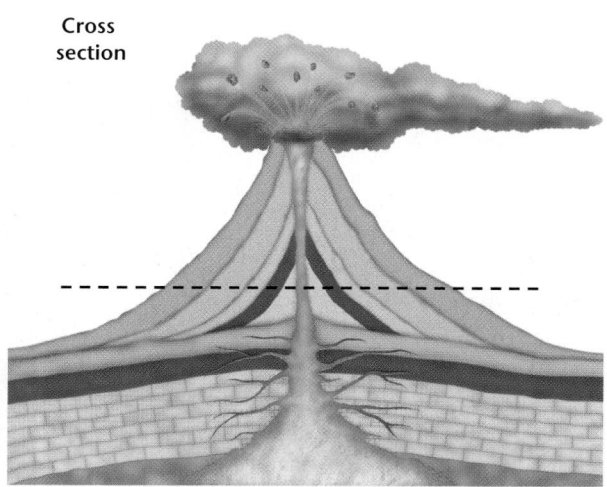

Cross section

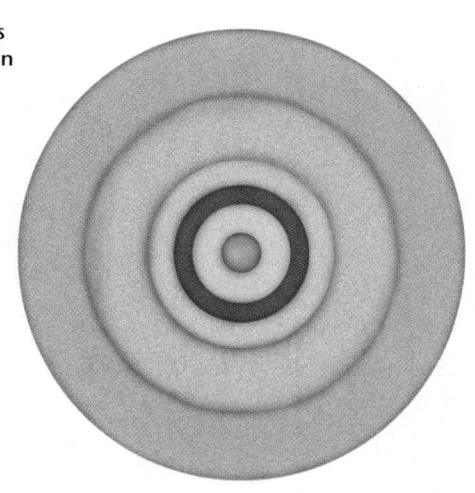

dragonfly. If you drew a line lengthwise through the dragonfly, you would see that the right side looks just the same as the left side. The dragonfly therefore has bilateral symmetry. Other organisms and objects have radial symmetry. Radial symmetry exists when similar parts are arranged around a central point in a circular pattern. The sand dollar in the photograph has radial symmetry because it can be divided anywhere through its center into equal parts. Some organisms and objects cannot be divided into two similar parts. When an organism or an object cannot be divided into two similar parts, it is asymmetrical. Study the amethyst crystal. No matter how you try to divide the crystal, you cannot draw a line that divides it into two equal parts.

Practicing Scientific Methods

The work of a scientist may be described as solving problems. Scientists generally use experiments to solve problems and answer questions. An experiment is a method in which a scientist uses an organized process to attempt to solve a problem or answer a question.

Experimentation involves defining a problem and then formulating and testing a hypothesis, which is a proposed solution to the problem. The proposed solution is tested during an experiment, which includes making careful observations and collecting data. After the collected data have been analyzed, a conclusion is formed and compared to the hypothesis.

FORMING A HYPOTHESIS

Suppose you want to earn a perfect score on an algebra test. You think of several possible ways to accomplish a perfect score. You base these possibilities on your own past experiences and on your observations of your friends' results. All of the following are hypotheses you might consider that could explain how it would be possible to score 100 percent on your test.

If the test is easy, then I will score 100 percent.

If I am intelligent, then I will score 100 percent.

If I study hard, then I will score 100 percent.

Scientists use hypotheses that they can test to explain the observations that they have made. Perhaps a scientist has observed that acid precipitation is damaging the statues in a pioneer cemetery, and also that plants growing nearby are not healthy. The scientist wonders how acid precipitation affects plants. The scientist may form a hypothesis that states: If plants are exposed to increasing levels of acid precipitation, they will become sick and eventually die.

DESIGNING AN EXPERIMENT

Once you have stated a hypothesis, you probably want to find out whether or not it explains an event or an observation. This requires a test. To be valid, a hypothesis must be testable by experimentation. How could you conduct an experiment to test the hypothesis about the effect of acid precipitation on plants?

First, you would obtain identical, young plants in small pots from a garden center. If you were a scientist conducting an experiment, you would use many plants in each experimental group; you would repeat your experiment many times to generate large amounts of data; and you would average your data at the end of all of your experiments. In the science classroom, however, time and resources are more limited, so it is likely that you will only be able to obtain the same number of plants as the number of acidity levels that you want to test, plus one more to serve as the control plant. Perhaps you can obtain six plants for your experiment. Label each plant A, B, C, and so on until each plant has a label. Make a data table that lists each plant by letter, and record the height and width of each plant. In your data table, draw a picture of each plant, noting any areas that are discolored or damaged. Then, collect small spray bottles and label them as well. Pour 200 mL of distilled water (pH 7, neutral) into spray bottle A. This bottle represents your control. In the spray bottle labeled B, pour 200 mL of white vinegar (pH 2, strong acid). This represents the worst case of acid precipitation. In the remaining spray bottles, add vinegar to distilled water to create acid solutions with varying pH values. You can determine the pH values with wide-range indicator paper.

Next, spray each plant, and the soil in each pot, with the corresponding solutions in each

spray bottle once a day for seven days. Each day, record how the plants look. Continue to make daily drawings of each plant and identify any discolored or damaged areas.

From the data you recorded, you will draw a conclusion and make a statement about your results. If your conclusion supports your hypothesis, then you can say that your hypothesis is reliable. If your conclusion does not support your hypothesis, then you will have to make new observations and state a new hypothesis, one that you can also test. Do the data you collected support the hypothesis that acid precipitation causes plants to sicken and die?

SEPARATING AND CONTROLLING VARIABLES

When scientists perform experiments, they must be careful to manipulate or change only one condition and keep all other conditions in the experiment the same. A condition that changes is called a *variable*. A condition that does not change is called a *constant*.

Independent Variable How does a scientist determine if an observation is the result of a certain change in condition? Scientists determine this by setting up an experiment in which only one condition changes, then observing the results. The condition that changes is called the independent variable because it is not influenced by the experimental procedure. The independent variable is the condition that a scientist manipulates in order to observe its effect. In the acid precipitation experiment, the independent variable is the acidity of the solutions sprayed on the plants and the soil.

Constant A constant is a condition that does not change during the course of an experiment. In the acid precipitation experiment, the constants are using plants of the same species, size, and age; using the same amounts of solutions to spray the plants each day; and keeping all the plants in the same conditions of sunlight and temperature at all times during the experiment. For scientists to determine that only the independent variable in an experiment caused any observed changes, they must keep all other factors the same.

Dependent Variable What are these changes observed in an experiment? They are the dependent variables. They are called dependent variables because changes in them depend upon the values of the independent variables. The dependent variables are any changes that result from manipulating the independent variables. In the case of the acid precipitation experiment, the dependent variables are the changes in the health of the plants over seven days as measured by their growth.

Control Scientists also use a control to be certain that the observed changes resulted only from the manipulation of one independent variable. A control is a sample that is treated exactly like each experimental group except that the independent variable is not applied to the control. Controls allow scientists to observe the effect of the independent variable because the assumption is made that whatever changes occur in the control group are not due to the independent variable. The control group provides a means of comparison. The control in the acid precipitation experiment is distilled water, which was sprayed on plant A each day for the same number of times as the other plants in the experiment were sprayed with other solutions. After the experiment, if there has been any change in the dependent variable of the control sample, such as height of the plant, it can be compared to changes in the experimental group. For example, if the control plants had grown several centimeters in seven days, but the other plants had not, you could assume that the lack of growth may be associated with the acidity of the solutions in each spray bottle.

Why is it important to find out what levels of acid precipitation plants can and cannot tolerate? Normal precipitation is slightly acidic, at pH 5.6, and all plants can tolerate normal precipitation. But the use of fossil fuels, such as gasoline in cars and coal in power plants, results in increasing levels of acid precipitation. Knowing how much acidity plants can tolerate can help us determine how much pollution should be allowed.

MEASURING IN SI

The metric system is a uniform system of measurement developed in 1795 by a group of scientists. The development of the metric system helped scientists worldwide avoid problems resulting from the use of different units of measurement by providing an international standard of comparison for measurements. A modern form of the metric system called the International System, or SI, was adopted for worldwide use in 1960. You will find that this text uses metric units, with a few exceptions.

Base Metric Units The metric system is easy to use because it has a systematic method of naming units and a decimal base. For example, the meter is the base unit for measuring length, the gram is the base unit for measuring mass, and the liter is the base unit for measuring volume. Unit sizes vary by multiples of 10. When converting from smaller units to larger ones, you divide by a multiple of 10. When converting from larger units to smaller ones, you multiply by a multiple of 10. Prefixes are used to name larger and smaller units. The following table provides some common metric prefixes and their meanings.

Metric Prefixes		
Prefix	**Symbol**	**Meaning**
kilo-	k	1000 (thousand)
hecto-	h	100 (hundred)
deka-	da	10 (ten)
deci-	d	0.1 (tenth)
centi-	c	0.01 (hundredth)
milli-	m	0.001 (thousandth)

Do you see how the prefix *kilo-* attached to the unit *gram* is *kilogram,* meaning 1000 grams? The prefix *deci-* attached to the unit *meter* is *decimeter,* that is, one-tenth (0.1) of a meter. These prefixes can be attached to any unit of measure in the metric system to form another unit that is a multiple of 10.

Units of Length The meter is the SI unit used to measure length. To visualize the length of a meter, think of a baseball bat, which is about 1 m long. For the measurement of smaller distances, the meter is divided into smaller units called centimeters and millimeters.

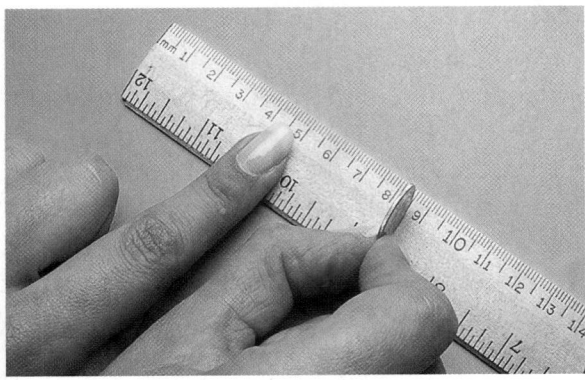

A centimeter is one-hundredth (0.01) of a meter, which is about the width of the fingernail on your index finger. A millimeter is one-thousandth (0.001) of a meter, about the thickness of a dime. The photograph shows this comparison.

Most metric rulers have lines indicating centimeters and millimeters. The centimeter lines are the longer, numbered lines, and the millimeter lines are shorter lines between the centimeter lines. As you might guess, there are 10 millimeters to a centimeter.

Units of length also are used to measure surface area. The standard unit of area is the square meter, m^2, which is a square 1 m long on each side. Similarly, a square centimeter, cm^2, is a square 1 cm long on each side. To find surface area, you multiply the number of units in length times the number of units in width. If you have a surface that is 4 cm long and 5 cm wide, the surface area is 4 cm $\times$ 5 cm = 20 cm^2. Suppose you want to find the surface area of a cubic crystal that is 3 cm long and 3 cm wide. The surface area of a side would be found by multiplying 3 cm $\times$ 3 cm. But because a cube has six sides, you would multiply the surface area of one side by 6 to find the surface area of the cube. The surface area of this cube would be 3 $\times$ 3 $\times$ 6 = 54 cm^2.

Units of Volume The cubic meter (m^3) is the standard SI unit of volume. A cubic meter is a cube 1 m long on each side. You can determine the volume of rectangular solids by multiplying length by width by height.

Liquid volume is measured using a unit called a liter. A liter has a volume of 1000 cubic centimeters. Recall that there are 1000 milliliters in a liter. Thus, a milliliter equals one cubic centimeter. One milliliter of liquid would completely fill a cube measuring 1 cm on each side.

You will measure liquids using beakers and graduated cylinders marked in milliliters. A graduated cylinder is marked with lines from bottom to top. Each graduation represents one milliliter.

Units of Mass You will likely use a beam balance when you want to find the masses of objects. Often, you will measure mass in grams. On one side of the beam balance is a pan, and on the other side is a set of beams. Each beam has an object of a known mass called a rider that slides on the beam.

Before you find the mass of an object, you must set the balance to zero by sliding all the riders back to the zero point. Check the

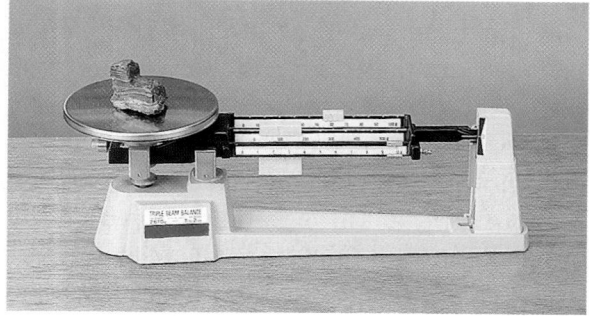

pointer to make sure it swings an equal distance above and below the zero point on the scale. If the swing is unequal, find and turn the adjusting screw until the swing is equal. Then wait until the pointer comes to rest exactly at the zero point.

You can use the balance to find the mass of an object. Place an object on the pan. Slide the rider with the largest mass along the beam until the pointer drops below the zero point. Then move the rider back one notch. Repeat the process for each beam until the pointer comes to a stop on the zero point. Read the masses indicated on the beams. The sum of the masses is the mass of the object.

Never place a hot object or pour chemicals directly on the pan of the balance. Instead, find the mass of a clean container, such as a beaker or glass jar. Place the object or chemical that you want to measure in the container. Next, find the combined mass of the container and the object or chemical. Calculate the mass of the object or chemical by subtracting the mass of the empty container from the combined mass.

Measuring Temperature Most measurements of temperature in SI are made using the Celsius scale. You can easily convert temperatures from the Fahrenheit scale to Celsius using the following formulas.

Conversion of Fahrenheit to Celsius
$$°C = 5/9 \ (°F − 32)$$

Conversion of Celsius to Fahrenheit
$$°F = (9/5 + °C) + 32$$

Organizing Information

CLASSIFYING

Classifying is grouping objects or events based on common features. When you classify, you first make careful observations of the group of items to be classified. Then, you select one feature that is shared by some items in the group but not by others. Place the items that share this feature in a subgroup. Ideally, the items in the second subgroup will have some feature in common with one another. After you decide on the first feature that separates the items into subgroups, examine the items in each subgroup for other features that some items possess but others don't. In this way, form further subgroups until the items no longer can be distinguished enough to identify them as belonging to another distinct subgroup.

How would you classify a collection of minerals? Classify the collection first based on observable features. You might begin classifying minerals by dividing them into two groups: one for minerals with metallic luster, and one for minerals with nonmetallic luster. Within the first group, you could classify minerals by the type of crystal system, by the breakage patterns, and by color. Note that

Organizing Information

Classifying Minerals with Metallic Luster			
Mineral	**Color**	**Crystal System**	**Breakage Pattern**
Copper	copper red	cubic	hackly
Graphite	black to gray	hexagonal	basal cleavage
Hematite	black or reddish brown	hexagonal	irregular fracture
Pyrite	light, brassy yellow	cubic	uneven fracture
Silver	silvery white	cubic	hackly

each mineral can only belong to one group under each type of classification. For example, copper has a cubic crystal system, has a hackly breakage pattern, and is copper red. Continue to select features until all the members of the collection have been classified. The table shows one method of classification.

Remember, when you classify, you are grouping objects or events for a purpose. The purpose could be general, such as how each rock or mineral formed. The classification of your collection might be different, however, if you are interested in the economic value of each specimen or how suitable each would be for use in a piece of jewelry.

SEQUENCING

A sequence is an arrangement of things or events in a particular order. A common sequence with which you may be familiar is the order of steps you must follow to make an omelette. Certain steps of preparation have to be followed for the omelette to be cooked properly.

When you are asked to sequence things or events, you must identify what comes first. You then decide what should come second. Continue to choose things or events until

they are all in order. Then go back over the sequence to make sure that each thing or event logically leads to the next.

Suppose you wanted to watch a movie that just came out on videotape. What sequence of events would you have to follow to watch the movie? You would first turn the television set to the channel that receives images from the videotape player. Then you would turn on the videotape player and insert the videotape. Once the tape began playing, you might adjust the sound and picture. When the movie was over, you would rewind the tape and return it to the video store. What would happen if you did things out of order, such as adjusting the sound before you put in the tape?

CONCEPT MAPPING

If you were taking an automobile trip, you would probably take along a road map. The road map would show your location, your destination, and other places along the way. By examining the map, you would understand where you were in relation to other locations on the map.

A concept map is similar to a road map, except that a concept map shows the relationships among ideas or concepts rather than places. A concept map is a diagram that visually shows how concepts are related. Because a concept map shows the relationships among ideas or concepts, it can clarify their meanings and help you to more clearly understand what you are studying. There is usually not a single correct way to construct a concept map. As you are constructing a concept map, you might discover that an arrangement that is different from the one you began with shows the

Organizing Information

relationships more accurately. There are three common types of concept maps: network trees, events chains, and cycle concept maps.

Network Trees Note that some words in the concept map below are circled. The circled words are science concepts. The lines in the map show related concepts and the words written on the lines describe relationships between the concepts. This map is an example of a network-tree concept map showing the relationships among various types of rocks.

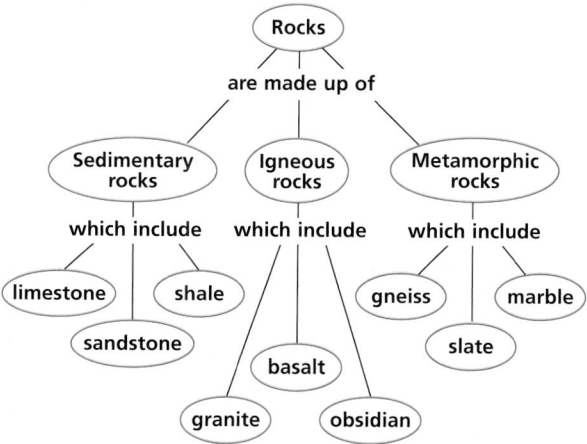

When you begin to construct a network tree, first state the topic and identify the major concepts. Then, identify related concepts and put them in order from most general to most specific. Branch the related concepts from the major concept, and describe each relationship on the lines. Continue in this way with the more specific concepts. Write the relationships between the concepts on the lines until all the concepts are mapped. Examine the concept map for relationships that cross branches, and add them to the concept map as well.

Events Chains An events-chain concept map is used to describe ideas in order. In science, an events-chain concept map can be used to describe a sequence of events, the steps in a procedure, or the stages of a process.

When making an events-chain concept map, you first must identify the one event that starts the chain. This event is called the initiating event. You then identify the next event in the chain, and continue until you reach an outcome. Suppose you wanted to make a concept map of the steps involved in making a fossil. An events-chain map might look like the one shown here. Note that connecting words may not be necessary in this kind of concept map.

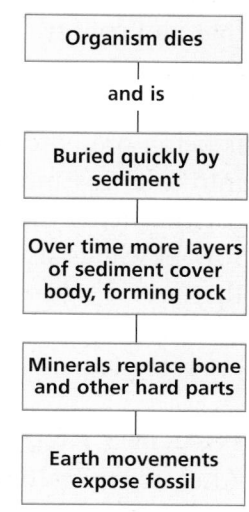

Cycle Concept Maps A cycle concept map is a special type of events-chain map. In a cycle concept map, the series of events does not produce a final outcome. The last event in the chain relates back to the initiating event. Because there is no outcome and the last event relates back to the initiating event, the cycle repeats itself. Follow the stages shown in the concept map of the water cycle.

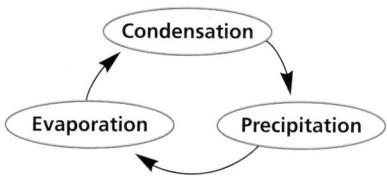

Organizing Information

MAKING AND USING TABLES

Browse through your textbook, and you will notice many data tables both in the text and in the labs. The tables in the text arrange information in such a way that it is easier for you to understand. Also, many labs in your text have tables for you to complete as you do the labs. Lab tables help you organize the data that you collect during a lab so that they can be interpreted more easily.

A data table has a title that describes what is being presented. The table itself is divided into columns and rows. The column headings list the items that are being compared. The row headings list the specific characteristics that are being compared among those items. Within the grid of the table, the collected data are recorded.

MAKING AND USING GRAPHS

After scientists organize data in tables, they often manipulate and then display the data in graphs. A graph is a diagram that shows a comparison between variables. Because graphs show pictures of collected data, they make interpretation and analysis of the data easier. The three basic types of graphs are line graphs, bar graphs, and circle graphs.

Line Graphs A line graph is used to show the relationship between two variables. The variables being compared go on two axes of the graph. The independent variable always goes on the horizontal axis, called the *x*-axis. The independent variable is the one being manipulated. The dependent variable always goes on the vertical axis, the *y*-axis. The dependent variable is any change that results from manipulating the independent variable.

Suppose your class wanted to collect data about humidity. You could make a graph of the amount of water vapor that air can hold at various temperatures. The temperature of the air is the independent variable and therefore should be plotted on the *x*-axis of your graph. The amount of water vapor found per cubic meter of air is the dependent variable and thus it is plotted on the *y*-axis.

You can use unlined paper or graph paper to construct a graph. After drawing your axes, label each axis with a scale. The *x*-axis simply lists the temperatures for which data were collected. To construct the *y*-axis, use the data in the data table below. Because the lowest amount of water vapor in air is 5 g/m^3 of air, you know that you will have to start numbering from at least 5 and continue to number through 80. You might decide to start numbering at 0 and number by 5s spaced at equal distances through 90.

Amount of Water Vapor in Air at Various Temperatures	
Air Temperature (°C)	**grams/cubic meter of air**
0	5
5	8
10	10
15	13
20	18
25	23
30	31
35	39
40	50
45	66
50	80

Organizing Information

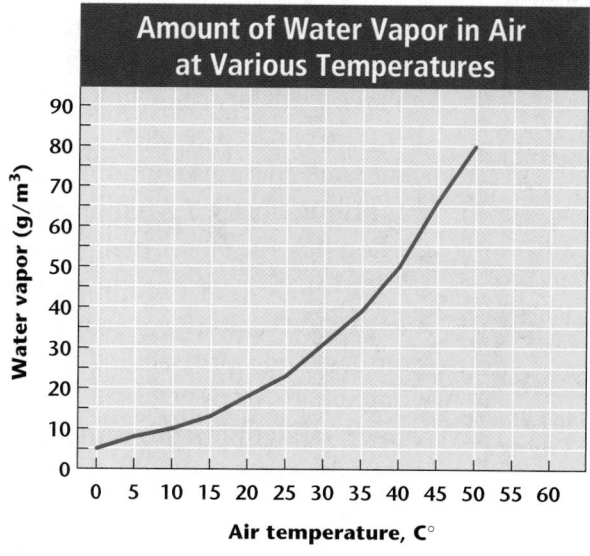

Amount of Water Vapor in Air at Various Temperatures

Y-axis: Water vapor (g/m³), values 0, 10, 20, 30, 40, 50, 60, 70, 80, 90

X-axis: Air temperature, C°, values 0, 5, 10, 15, 20, 25, 30, 35, 40, 45, 50, 55, 60

Next you plot the data points. The first pair of data that you want to plot is the temperature 0°C and the amount 5 g of water vapor in one cubic meter of air. Locate 0°C on the *x*-axis and 5 on the *y*-axis. Where an imaginary vertical line from each axis would meet, place the first data point. Place the other data points in the same way. You can then see if the data have any direction. That is, you can see if water vapor increases or decreases with air temperature. According to the graph, does the amount of water vapor in air increase or decrease with air temperature? Scientists often draw a line that appears to connect the data points on a line graph. Actually, scientists don't draw a line that connects individual data points. Instead, they draw a line that best fits the direction that the data points indicate. Because no one can ever collect enough data to plot every single point on a line graph, lines drawn in a graph come close to clusters of data points and show the general direction of the data points. Although the line graphs used

in this book appear to have straight lines drawn between data points, remember that these are not really continuous lines but rather the best fit for the data points that have been plotted. For the purposes of this book, you may connect the data points plotted on your graph with a smooth line.

What if you wanted to compare the data about humidity collected by your class with similar data collected a year ago by a different class? The data of the other class can be plotted on the same graph to make the comparison. In this case, you would include a key indicating that the two different sets of symbols each indicate a different set of data.

Bar Graphs Bar graphs are similar to line graphs, except that they are used to show comparisons between different sets of data or to display data that are not continuous. In a bar graph, bars rather than data points show the relationships among data.

To make a bar graph, set up the *x*-axis and the *y*-axis as you would for a line graph. The data are plotted by drawing bars from the *x*-axis up to an imaginary point where the *y*-axis would intersect the bar if it were extended.

Look at the bar graph on the next page comparing the net energy efficiency of various ways to heat an enclosed space, such as a house. The independent variable is the way to heat an enclosed space, and the dependent variable is the net energy efficiency of each. The net energy efficiencies of various ways to heat an enclosed space are being compared. Can you see that the heating methods being compared do not have any influence on each

Organizing Information

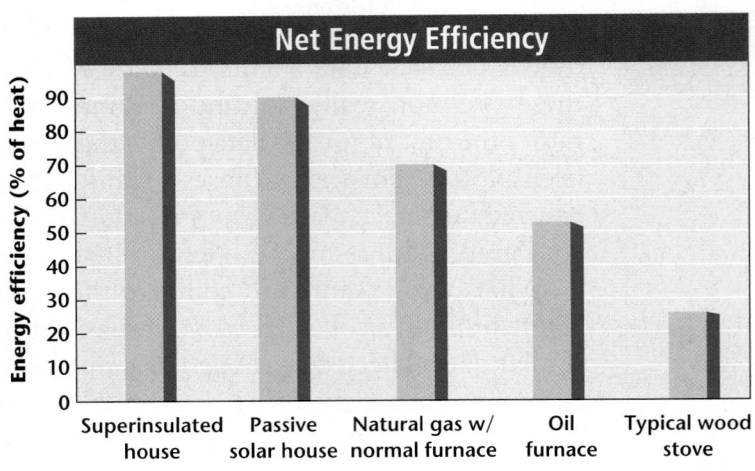

Net Energy Efficiency

(Bar graph: Energy efficiency (% of heat) vs. Heating method)

Heating methods: Superinsulated house, Passive solar house, Natural gas w/ normal furnace, Oil furnace, Typical wood stove

other? That is, the bar graph is illustrating data that are not continuous.

Circle Graphs A circle graph, often called a pie graph, uses a circle divided into sections to display data. Each section represents a part of the whole. When all the sections are added together, they equal 100 percent of the whole.

Suppose you wanted to make a circle graph that shows the percentage of solid waste generated by various industries in the United States each year. The total amount of solid waste generated each year is estimated at 10 billion metric tons. The whole circle graph will therefore represent this amount of solid waste.

Mining and oil and gas production are responsible for approximately 7.5 billion metric tons of solid waste each year. To determine what percentage of the circle graph this represents, divide the amount of solid waste generated by mining and oil and gas production by the total amount of solid waste generated, 10 billion metric tons. To find the number of degrees on a circle this represents, multiply the

answer by 360, the number of degrees in a circle. Round the answer to the nearest whole number. The percentage of solid waste generated by mining and oil and gas production is: 7.5 billion metric tons ÷ 10 billion metric tons × 360° = 270°. To plot these data on the circle graph, you need a compass and a protractor. Use the compass to draw a circle. Then draw a straight line from the center to the edge of the circle. Place your protractor on this line and use it to mark a point on the edge of the circle at 270°. Connect this point with a straight line to the center of the circle. This is the section that represents the percent of solid waste generated by mining and oil and gas production each year. Now, try to perform the same operation for the other data to find the number of degrees of the circle that each represents, and draw them in as well: agriculture, 1.3 billion metric tons; industry, 0.95 billion metric tons; municipal, 0.15 billion metric tons; and sewage sludge, 0.1 billion metric tons. Complete your graph by labeling the sections of the graph and giving the graph a title.

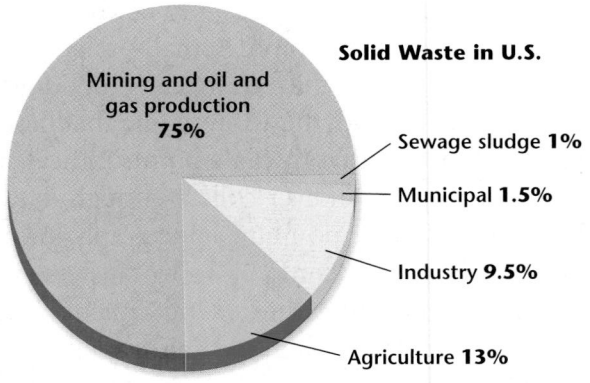

Solid Waste in U.S.

Mining and oil and gas production 75%

Sewage sludge 1%

Municipal 1.5%

Industry 9.5%

Agriculture 13%

English

Español

A

abrasion (p. 193) Process of erosion in which wind-blown or waterborne particles, such as sand, scrape against rock surfaces or other materials and wear them away.

absolute magnitude (p. 816) Brightness an object would have if it were placed at a distance of 10 pc; classification system for stellar brightness that can be calculated only when the actual distance to a star is known.

abyssal plain (p. 426) Smooth, flat part of the seafloor covered with muddy sediments and sedimentary rocks that extends seaward from the continental margin.

Acadian Orogeny (p. 608) Tectonic event in which Avalonia collided with the southeastern margin of Laurasia and added faults, folds, and igneous intrusions to the rocks of the Taconic Orogeny.

acid (p. 65) Solution that contains hydrogen ions (H^+).

acid precipitation (p. 727) Any precipitation with a pH of less than 5.0 that forms when sulfur dioxide and nitrogen oxides combine with moisture in the atmosphere to produce sulfuric acid and nitric acid.

active galactic nucleus (AGN) (p. 844) A galaxy's core in which highly energetic objects or activities are located.

aggregate (p. 660) Naturally accumulating mixture of sand, gravel, and crushed stone found in floodplains, alluvial fans, or glacial deposits.

air mass (p. 301) Large body of air that takes on the characteristics of the area over which it forms; can be described by its stability, temperature, and humidity.

air mass modification (p. 304) Exchange of heat or moisture with the surface over which an air mass moves.

air-mass thunderstorm (p. 331) Type of thunderstorm in which air rises because of unequal heating of Earth's surface within a single air mass and is most common during the afternoon and evening.

abrasion/abrasión (pág. 193) Proceso erosivo en que las partículas arrastradas por el viento o en el agua, como la arena, raspan contra las superficies de piedra las rocas u otros materiales y los desgastan.

absolute magnitude/magnitud absoluta (pág. 816) Brillo que tendría un objeto si estuviera a una distancia de 10 pc; sistema de clasificación para el brillo estelar que puede calcularse sólo cuando se sabe la distancia verdadera hasta una estrella.

abyssal plain/llanura abisal (pág. 426) Parte plana y nivelada del fondo del mar cubierto con sedimentos fangosos y piedras sedimentarias que se extiende desde el margen continental hacia el mar.

Acadian Orogeny/orogenia arcadiana (pág. 608) Acontecimiento tectónico en que Avalonia chocó contra el margen del sudeste de Laurasia y agregó fallas, dobleces e intrusiones ígneas a las rocas de la orogenia Tectónica.

acid/ácido (pág. 65) Solución que contiene iones hidrógeno (H^+).

acid precipitation/precipitación ácida (pág. 727) Cualquier precipitación con un pH de menos de 5.0, que se forma cuando se combinan el dióxido de azufre y óxidos los de nitrógeno con la humedad en la atmósfera para producir ácido sulfúrico y ácido nítrico.

active galactic nucleus (AGN)/núcleo galáctico activo (NGA) (pág. 844) centro de la galaxia en que se localizan cuerpos u ocurren actividades sumamente energéticos.

aggregate/agregado (pág. 660) Mezcla de arena, grava y piedra molida acumulada naturalmente, que se encuentra en llanuras aluviales, abanicos aluviales o depósitos glaciales.

air mass/masa de aire (pág. 301) Cantidad enorme de aire que toma las características del área sobre la cual se forma; puede describirse según su estabilidad, su temperatura y su humedad.

air mass modification/modificación de masa de aire (pág. 304) Intercambio de calor o humedad con la superficie sobre la que se mueve una masa de aire.

air-mass thunderstorm/tormenta eléctrica de masa de aire (pág. 331) Tipo de tormenta en que el aire se eleva debido al calentamiento desigual de la superficie terrestre dentro de una masa de aire y el cual es muy común durante la tarde y el crepúsculo.

air pollution (p. 665) Occurs when air contains harmful levels of pollutants; can be caused by natural phenomena, such as forest fires or volcanic eruptions, or by human activities, such as burning of fossil fuels.

albedo (p. 754) Amount of sunlight that is reflected by the surface of a planet or a satellite, such as the Moon.

Alleghenian Orogeny (p. 615) Mountain-building event that occurred when the part of Gondwana that is now Africa began to collide with Laurasia during the Late Pennsylvanian.

altered hard parts (p. 567) Fossils whose organic material has been removed and whose hard parts have been changed by recrystallization or mineral replacement.

amino acids (p. 590) Building blocks of proteins that were likely abundant on Earth during the Archean.

amniote egg (p. 616) Egg with a shell, providing a complete environment to a developing embryo, that allowed reptiles to colonize land during the Late Mississippian.

analog forecast (p. 320) Weather forecast that compares current weather patterns to patterns that occurred in the past.

Ancestral Rockies (p. 614) Mountain range that formed from the collision between Gondwana and Laurasia during the Late Paleozoic.

anemometer (p. 313) Weather instrument used to measure wind speed.

angiosperms (p. 630) Seed-bearing, flowering plants that evolved during the Cretaceous.

Antler Orogeny (p. 608) Collisional tectonic event that impacted the passive western margin of Laurentia.

aphelion (p. 777) Point in a planet's orbit where it is farthest from the Sun.

apogee (p. 766) Farthest point in the Moon's elliptical orbit to Earth.

apparent magnitude (p. 816) Classification system based on how bright a star appears to be; does not take distance into account so cannot indicate how bright a star actually is.

aquifer (p. 243) Permeable underground layer through which groundwater flows relatively easily.

air pollution/contaminación del aire (pág. 665) Ocurre cuando el aire contiene niveles perjudiciales de contaminantes; puede ser causada por fenómenos naturales, como los incendios forestales o erupciones las volcánicas, o por actividades humanas, como la combustión de combustibles fósiles.

albedo/albedo (pág. 754) Cantidad de luz solar que refleja la superficie de un planeta o un satélite, como por ejemplo, la Luna.

Alleghenian Orogeny/orogenia alegeniana (pág. 615) Acontecimiento formador de montañas que ocurrió cuando la parte de Gondwana que es ahora África empezó a chocar contra Laurasia durante el Pennsylvaniano tardío.

altered hard parts/partes duras alteradas (pág. 567) Fósiles cuya materia orgánica ha desaparecido y cuyas partes duras han sido transformadas por recristalización o por reemplazo mineral.

amino acids/aminoácidos (pág. 590) Componentes de las proteínas que probablemente eran abundantes en la Tierra durante el Arqueano.

amniote egg/huevo amniótico (pág. 616) Huevo con cascarón que provee un ambiente completo para un embrión en desarrollo y el cual permitió que los reptiles colonizaran la tierra firme durante el Mississippiano Tardío.

analog forecast/pronóstico análogo (pág. 320) Pronóstico del tiempo que compara las pautas actuales del clima con pautas que ocurrieron en el pasado.

Ancestral Rockies/Rocosas antiguas (pág. 614) Cordillera de montañas que se formó debido a la colisión entre Gondwana y Laurasia durante el Paleozoico Tardío.

anemometer/anemómetro (pág. 313) Instrumento meteorológico que se utiliza para medir la velocidad de viento.

angiosperms/angiospermas (pág. 630) Plantas con flores, portadoras de semillas que evolucionaron durante el Cretáceo.

Antler Orogeny/orogenia Antler (pág. 608) Evento de colisión tectónica que impactó el margen occidental pasivo de Laurentia.

aphelion/afelio (pág. 777) Punto en la órbita de un planeta cuando se encuentra más alejado del Sol.

apogee/apogeo (pág. 766) Punto de la órbita elíptica de la Luna en que ésta se encuentra más alejada de la Tierra.

apparent magnitude/magnitud aparente (pág. 816) Sistema de clasificación que se basa en el grado de brillo aparente de una estrella; no toma en cuenta la distancia y por lo tanto no puede indicar el brillo real de la estrella.

aquifer/acuífero (pág. 243) Capa subterránea permeable por la cual el agua subterránea fluye de manera relativamente fácil.

artesian well (p. 253) Fountain of water that spurts above the land surface when a well taps a deep, confined aquifer containing water under pressure.

asteroid (p. 578) Metallic or silica-rich object, 1 km to 950 km in diameter, that bombarded early Earth, generating heat energy; (p. 795) rocky remnant of the early solar system found mostly between the orbits of Mars and Jupiter in the asteroid belt.

asthenosphere (p. 8) Partially molten, plasticlike, flowing layer located below the solid part of Earth's mantle.

astronomical unit (AU) (p. 777) A planet's average distance to the Sun; for the Sun and Earth, is 1.496 3 108 km, or 1 AU.

astronomy (p. 6) Study of objects beyond Earth's atmosphere.

atmosphere (p. 9) Blanket of gases surrounding Earth that contains about 78 percent nitrogen, 21 percent oxygen, and 1 percent other gases such as argon, carbon dioxide, and water vapor.

atom (p. 54) Smallest particle of an element, having all the characteristics of that element; the basic building block of matter, consisting of protons, neutrons, and electrons.

atomic mass (p. 58) Average of the mass numbers of the isotopes of an element.

atomic number (p. 54) Number of protons contained in an atom's nucleus.

autumnal equinox (p. 761) Occurs when the Sun is directly overhead at the equator and results in day and night of equal length for both northern and southern hemispheres.

avalanche (p. 187) Landslide that occurs in a mountainous area when snow falls on an icy crust, becomes heavy, slips off, and slides swiftly down a mountainside.

artesian well/pozo artesiano (pág. 253) Fuente de agua que brota hacia la superficie terrestre cuando un pozo conecta con un acuífero profundo y confinado con agua bajo presión.

asteroid/asteroide (pág. 578) Cuerpo metálico o rico en sílice, de 1 a 950 km de diámetro, que bombardeó la Tierra primitiva generando energía térmica; (pág. 795) resto rocoso del sistema solar primitivo que se encuentra principalmente entre las órbitas de Marte y Júpiter en el cinturón de asteroides.

asthenosphere/astenosfera (pág. 8) Capa fluida, parcialmente fundida, tipo plástico, localizada debajo de la parte sólida del manto de la Tierra.

astronomical unit (AU)/unidad astronómica (UA) (pág. 777) La distancia promedio de un planeta al Sol; para el Sol y la Tierra, es de 1.496 3 108 km ó 1 AU.

astronomy/astronomía (pág. 6) Estudio de los cuerpos que se encuentran más allá de la atmósfera de la Tierra.

atmosphere/atmósfera (pág. 9) Manto de gases que rodea la Tierra y que contiene aproximadamente un 78 por ciento de nitrógeno, un 21 por ciento de oxígeno y 1 por ciento de otros gases como el argón, el dióxido de carbono y el vapor del agua.

atom/átomo (pág. 54) La partícula más pequeña de un elemento, la cual posee todas las características de ese elemento; el componente básico de la materia que consiste en protones, neutrones y electrones.

atomic mass/masa atómica (pág. 58) Promedio de los números de masa de los isótopos de un elemento.

atomic number/número atómico (pág. 54) Número de protones que contiene el núcleo de un átomo.

autumnal equinox/equinoccio otoñal (pág. 761) Ocurre cuando el Sol está directamente por encima del ecuador y resulta en que el día y la noche son de igual duración, tanto para el hemisferio norte como para el hemisferio sur.

avalanche/avalancha (pág. 187) Deslizamiento de tierra que ocurre en un área montañosa cuando la nieve cae sobre la corteza helada, se vuelve pesada, se desprende y se resbala rápidamente montaña abajo.

B

banded iron formations (p. 586) Unique, shallow marine deposits made up of alternating bands of chert and iron oxides that formed due to locally high oxygen levels produced by stromatolites.

barometer (p. 312) Weather instrument used to measure air pressure.

banded iron formations/formaciones ferrosas bandeadas (pág. 586) Depósitos marinos, superficiales y poco comunes compuestos de bandas alternadas de óxidos ferrosos y cuarzo criptocristalino que se formaron debido a la cercanía de los altos niveles de oxígeno producidos por estromatolitos.

barometer/barómetro (pág. 312) Instrumento meteorológico que se utiliza para medir la presión atmosférica.

barrier island (p. 418) Long ridge of sand or other sediment deposited or shaped by longshore currents that is separated from the mainland and can be up to tens of kilometers long.

base (p. 66) Solution that contains hydroxide ions (O-).

Basin and Range Province (p. 637) Area in the southwestern United States and North-Central Mexico where extensional tectonism resulted in the formation of mountain ranges separated by long valleys.

batholith (p. 476) Coarse-grained, irregularly shaped, igneous rock mass that covers at least 100 km2, generally forms 10-30 km below Earth's surface, and is common in the interior of major mountain chains.

beach (p. 415) Sloping band of loose sediments, such as sand, pebbles, or mud, deposited along a shoreline.

bedding (p. 126) Horizontal layering in sedimentary rock that can range from a millimeter thick to several meters thick.

bed load (p. 217) Describes sediments that are too heavy or large to be kept in suspension or solution and are pushed or rolled along the bottom of a streambed.

bedrock (p. 660) Unweathered, solid parent rock that may consist of limestone, marble, granite, or other quarried rock.

belt (p. 787) Low, warm, dark-colored cloud that sinks and flows rapidly in the Jovian atmosphere.

Big Bang theory (p. 847) Proposes that the universe began as a single point and has been expanding ever since.

binary star (p. 814) Describes two stars that are bound together by gravity and orbit a common center of mass.

biodiversity (p. 718) Biological diversity of an ecosystem, which is determined by the variety of species of plants and animals.

biogas (p. 696) Biomass fuel that is a mixture of gases, primarily methane, produced when plant and animal wastes are acted on by anaerobic bacteria in a digester.

bioremediation (p. 723) Use of organisms to clean up toxic waste.

biosphere (p. 9) All of Earth's organisms and the environments in which they live.

barrier island/barrera de islas (pág. 418) Grandes ondas de arena u otro sedimento depositado o formado por las corrientes litorales y separadas del continente; pueden medir hasta decenas de kilómetros de largo.

base/base (pág. 66) Solución que contiene iones hidróxido (O⁻).

Basin and Range Province/Provincia Basin and Range (pág. 637) Área en el suroeste de Estados Unidos y el norte y centro de México en donde la tectónica extensional resultó en la formación de cordilleras de montañas separadas por grandes valles.

batholith/batolito (pág. 476) Masa rocosa ígnea de grano grueso irregularmente formada que cubre por lo menos 100 km² y que se forma generalmente de 10 a 30 km bajo de la superficie terrestre y frecuentemente se encuentra en el interior de las principales cadenas montañosas.

beach/playa (pág. 415) Banda inclinada de sedimentos sueltos, como la arena, los guijarros o el barro, depositado a lo largo de una costa.

bedding/estratificación (pág. 126) Capa horizontal de roca sedimentaria que puede medir de un milímetro a varios metros de grueso.

bed load/carga de cauce (pág. 217) Término que describe los sedimentos que son demasiado pesados o grandes para ser mantenidos en suspensión o solución y los cuales son empujados o arrastrados a lo largo del fondo del lecho de una corriente.

bedrock/lecho rocoso (pág. 660) Roca madre sólida no meteorizada que puede consistir en piedra caliza, mármol, granito u otra piedra de cantera.

belt/cinturón (pág. 787) Nube baja, tibia y oscura que desciende y fluye rápidamente en la atmósfera joviana.

Big Bang theory/teoría de la Gran Explosión (pág. 847) Propone que el universo empezó en un solo punto y se ha estado expandiendo desde entonces.

binary star/estrella binaria (pág. 814) Describe dos estrellas unidas por la gravedad, las cuales giran alrededor de un centro común de masa.

biodiversity/biodiversidad (pág. 718) Diversidad biológica de un ecosistema, que está determinada por la variedad de especies de plantas y animales.

biogas/biogas (pág. 696) Combustible de la biomasa que es una mezcla de gases, principalmente metano, que se produce cuando las bacterias anaerobias actúan sobre los desechos de plantas y animales en un aparato digestivo.

bioremediation/biorremediación (pág. 723) Uso de organismos para limpiar desechos tóxicos.

biosphere/biosfera (pág. 9) Todos los organismos de la Tierra y los ambientes en que éstos viven.

black hole (p. 825) Small, extremely dense remnant of a star whose gravity is so immense that not even light can escape its gravity field.

Bowen's reaction series (p. 103) Sequential, predictable, dual-branched pattern in which minerals crystallize from cooling magma.

breaker (p. 400) Collapsing wave that forms when a wave reaches shallow water and is slowed by friction with the ocean bottom.

Burgess Shale (p. 604) Canadian fossil formation that contains Cambrian soft-bodied organisms as well as organisms with hard parts.

black hole/agujero negro (pág. 825) Restos de una estrella, muy densos y pequeños cuya gravedad es tan grande que ni la luz puede escapar de su campo de gravedad.

Bowen's reaction series/serie de reacción de Bowen (pág. 103) Patrón doblemente ramificado, predecible y secuencial en el cual se cristalizan los minerales a partir de magma que se enfría.

breaker/cachón (pág. 400) Ola en estado de colapso que se forma cuando una ola alcanza aguas poco profundas y la cual decelera debido a la fricción contra el fondo del océano.

Burgess Shale/esquisto de Burguess (pág. 604) Formación de fósiles canadiense que contiene tanto organismos Cámbricos de cuerpo blando como organismos con partes duras.

caldera (p. 481) Large crater, up to 50 km in diameter, that can form when the summit or side of a volcano collapses into the magma chamber during or after an eruption.

Caledonian Orogeny (p. 608) Collisional tectonic event that closed the ocean between Laurentia and Baltica, forming the larger continent, Laurasia.

Canadian shield (p. 581) Name given to the Precambrian shield in North America because much of it is exposed in Canada.

carrying capacity (p. 714) Number of organisms that a specific environment can support.

cartography (p. 27) Science of mapmaking.

cast (p. 568) Fossil formed when an earlier fossil of a plant or animal leaves a cavity that becomes filled with minerals or sediment.

cave (p. 245) Underground opening connected to Earth's surface, usually formed when groundwater dissolves limestone.

ceilometer (p. 313) Weather instrument used to measure the height of cloud layers; estimates the amount of sky that is covered by clouds.

cementation (p. 125) Process of sedimentary rock formation that occurs when dissolved minerals precipitate out of groundwater and either a new mineral grows between the sediment grains or the same mineral grows between and over the grains.

Cepheid variable (p. 834) Star with pulsation periods ranging from 1 to 100 days and luminosity that increases with the length of the pulsation period.

caldera/caldera (pág. 481) cráter grande, de hasta 50 km de diámetro, que puede formarse cuando la cumbre o el lado de un volcán se desploman en la cámara de magma, durante o después de una erupción.

Caledonian Orogeny/orogenia Caledoniana (pág. 608) Acontecimiento tectónico de colisión que cerró el océano entre Laurencia y Báltica, formando el continente más grande llamado Laurasia.

Canadian shield/escudo canadiense (pág. 581) Nombre dado al escudo precámbrico en Norteamérica porque la mayor parte está expuesta en Canadá.

carrying capacity/capacidad de carga (pág. 714) Número de organismos que un ambiente específico puede sustentar en un momento dado.

cartography/cartografía (pág. 27) Ciencia de elaboración de mapas.

cast/molde (pág. 568) Fósil que se forma cuando un fósil precedente de una planta o un animal deja una cavidad que se llena con minerales o sedimentos.

cave/cueva (pág. 245) Abertura subterránea conectada a la superficie terrestre, generalmente se forma cuando el agua subterránea disuelve la piedra caliza.

ceilometer/cielómetro (pág. 313) Instrumento meteorológico para medir la altura de las capas de nubes; estima la porción del cielo que está cubierta por nubes.

cementation/cementación (pág. 125) Proceso de formación de roca sedimentaria que ocurre cuando los minerales disueltos se precipitan del agua subterránea y un mineral nuevo crece entre los granos de sedimento o el mismo mineral crece entre los granos y sobre ellos.

Cepheid variable/variable cefeida (pág. 834) Estrella con períodos de pulsación que van desde 1 hasta 100 días y cuya luminosidad aumenta con la longitud del período de la pulsación.

Glossary/Glosario

Glossary

chemical bond (p. 60) Force that holds the atoms of elements together in a compound.

chemical reaction (p. 64) Change of one or more substances into other substances.

chemical weathering (p. 155) Process by which rocks and minerals undergo changes in their composition due to chemical reactions with agents such as acids, water, oxygen, and carbon dioxide.

chromosphere (p. 806) Layer of the Sun's atmosphere above the photosphere and below the corona that is about 2500 km thick and has a temperature around 30 000 K at its top.

cinder-cone volcano (p. 482) Steep-sided, generally small volcano that is built by the accumulation of tephra around the vent.

cirque (p. 201) Deep depression scooped out by a valley glacier.

clastic (p. 122) Describes rock and mineral fragments produced by weathering and erosion and classified according to particle size and shape.

clastic sedimentary rock (p. 128) Most common type of sedimentary rock, such as breccia, sandstone, and shale, formed by lithification of clastic sediments.

cleavage (p. 86) Ability of a mineral to break easily and evenly along one or more flat planes.

climate (p. 300) Average weather of a particular area over a long period of time; (p. 359) includes annual variations in temperature and precipitation, which are influenced by latitude, closeness of lakes and oceans, topography, wind patterns, and air masses.

climatology (p. 359) Study of Earth's climate in order to understand and predict climatic change, based on past and present variations in temperature, precipitation, wind, and other weather variables.

coalescence (p. 289) Process that occurs when cloud droplets collide and form larger droplets, which eventually become too heavy to remain aloft and can fall to Earth as precipitation.

cogeneration (p. 700) Production of two usable forms of energy at the same time from the same process, which can conserve resources and generate income.

cold wave (p. 349) Extended period of lower-than-normal temperatures caused by large, high-pressure systems of continental polar or arctic origin.

chemical bond/enlace químico (pág. 60) Fuerza que mantiene unidos los átomos de los elementos en un compuesto.

chemical reaction/reacción química (pág. 64) Cambio de una o más sustancias en otras sustancias.

chemical weathering/meteorización química (pág. 155) Proceso mediante el cual las rocas y los minerales experimentan cambios en su composición debido a las reacciones químicas con agentes como los ácidos, el agua, el oxígeno y el dióxido de carbono.

chromosphere/cromosfera (pág. 806) Capa de la atmósfera del Sol por encima de la fotosfera y debajo de la corona, la cual mide aproximadamente 2500 km de ancho y tiene una temperatura máxima de alrededor de 30 000 K.

cinder-cone volcano/volcán de cono de carbonilla (pág. 482) Volcán generalmente pequeño de lados empinados que se forma debido a la acumulación de tefrita alrededor de la abertura.

cirque/circo (pág. 201) Depresión profunda formada por un glaciar de valle.

clastic/clástica (pág. 122) Describe los fragmentos de roca y de mineral producidos por la meteorización y la erosión y los cuales se clasifican según su tamaño de partícula y forma.

clastic sedimentary rock/roca sedimentaria clástica (pág. 128) Tipo más común de roca sedimentaria, que incluye rocas como la brecha, la arenisca y el esquisto y la cual se forma por litificación de sedimentos clásticos.

cleavage/crucero (pág. 86) Capacidad de un mineral para romperse fácil y uniformemente a lo largo de uno o más planos lisos.

climate/clima (pág. 300) Tiempo promedio de cierta área a lo largo de un período de tiempo considerable; (pág. 359) incluye las variaciones anuales en temperatura y precipitación y se ve influenciado por la latitud, la cercanía de lagos y océanos, la topografía, los patrones de viento y las masas de aire.

climatology/climatología (pág. 359) Estudio del clima de la Tierra para entender y pronosticar los cambios meteorológicos; se basa en variaciones pasadas y presentes de temperatura, precipitación, viento y otras variables meteorológicas.

coalescence/coalescencia (pág. 289) Proceso que ocurre cuando las gotas de nube chocan y forman gotas más grandes, que a la larga se vuelven demasiado pesadas para permanecer suspendidas y pueden caer a la Tierra como precipitación.

cogeneration/cogeneración (pág. 700) Producción simultánea de dos formas utiles de energía a partir del mismo proceso y la cual puede conservar recursos y ser lucrativa.

cold wave/onda fría (pág. 349) Período extendido de temperaturas más bajas que lo normal causado por grandes sistemas de alta presión de origen polar continental o ártico.

coma (p. 797) Extended volume of glowing gas that forms when a comet's nucleus is heated.

comet (p. 796) Small, eccentrically orbiting body made of rock and ice that consists of a nucleus, a coma, and one or more tails that point away from the Sun.

composite volcano (p. 482) Large, sloping volcano built by violent eruptions of volcanic fragments and lava that accumulate in alternating layers.

compound (p. 60) Substance composed of atoms of two or more different elements that are chemically combined.

condensation (p. 69) Process by which a cooling gas changes into a liquid and releases thermal energy; (p. 279) change of matter from a gas to a liquid.

condensation nuclei (p. 285) Small particles in the atmosphere around which cloud droplets can form.

conduction (p. 276) Energy transfer that occurs when molecules collide; takes place only when substances are in contact with each other.

conic projection (p. 32) Map that is highly accurate for small areas, made by projecting points and lines from a globe onto a cone.

constellation (p. 813) Group of stars that forms a pattern in the sky that resembles an animal, mythological character, or everyday object.

contact metamorphism (p. 135) Local effect that occurs when molten rock meets solid rock.

continental drift (p. 444) Wegener's hypothesis that Earth's continents were joined as a single landmass, called Pangaea, that broke apart about 200 million years ago and slowly moved to their present positions.

continental glacier (p. 200) Glacier that forms over a broad, continent-sized area of land and usually spreads out from its center.

continental margin (p. 422) Submerged part of a continent and shallowest part of the ocean that consists of the continental shelf, the continental slope, and the continental rise.

continental rise (p. 425) Gently sloping accumulation of sediments deposited by a turbidity current at the foot of a continental margin.

coma/cabellera (pág. 797) Volumen extendido de gas resplandeciente que se forma cuando se calienta el núcleo de un cometa.

comet/cometa (pág. 796) Cuerpo pequeño de órbita excéntrica compuesto de roca y hielo y que consta de un núcleo, una cabellera y una o más colas que apuntan hacia el lado contrario del Sol.

composite volcano/volcán compuesto (pág. 482) Volcán grande e inclinado que se forma debido a erupciones violentas de fragmentos y lava volcánicos, los cuales se acumulan en capas alternantes.

compound/compuesto (pág. 60) Sustancia compuesta de átomos de dos o más elementos diferentes que se combinan químicamente.

condensation/condensación (pág. 69) Proceso por el cual un gas enfriador se transforma en un líquido y libera energía térmica; (pág. 279) el cambio de la materia gaseosa a líquida.

condensation nuclei/núcleos de condensación (pág. 285) Partículas pequeñas en la atmósfera alrededor de las cuales se pueden formar las gotas de nubes.

conduction/conducción (pág. 276) Transferencia de energía que ocurre cuando las moléculas chocan; sólo sucede cuando las sustancias están en contacto.

conic projection/proyección cónica (pág. 32) Mapa que es sumamente exacto para áreas pequeñas y el cual se elabora mediante la proyección de puntos y líneas de un globo a un cono.

constellation/constelación (pág. 813) Grupo de estrellas que forman en el firmamento un patrón que parece un animal, un personaje mitológico o un objeto cotidiano.

contact metamorphism/metamorfismo de contacto (pág. 135) Efecto local que ocurre cuando la roca fundida se encuentra con roca sólida.

continental drift/deriva continental (pág. 444) Hipótesis de Wegener que propone que los continentes de la Tierra estaban unidos en una sola masa terrestre, llamada Pangaea, la cual se separó hace aproximadamente 200 millones de años y que los fragmentos se movieron lentamente a sus ubicaciones actuales.

continental glacier/glaciar continental (pág. 200) Glaciar que se forma sobre un área amplia de terreno del tamaño de un continente y que generalmente se extiende a partir de su centro.

continental margin/margen continental (pág. 422) Parte sumergida de un continente y la parte menos profunda del océano formada por la plataforma continental, el talud continental y el declive continental.

continental rise/declive continental (pág. 425) Acumulación de sedimentos levemente inclinados, depositados por una corriente de turbidez al pie de un margen continental.

continental shelf (p. 423) Shallowest part of a continental margin, with an average depth of 130 m and an average width of 60 km, that extends into the ocean from the shore and provides a nutrient-rich home to large numbers of fish.

continental slope (p. 424) Sloping oceanic region found beyond the continental shelf that generally marks the edge of the continental crust and may be cut by submarine canyons.

contour interval (p. 34) Difference in elevation between two side-by-side contour lines on a topographic map.

contour line (p. 33) A line on a topographic map that connects points of equal elevation.

control (p. 12) Standard for comparison in an experiment.

convection (p. 277) Transfer of energy by the flow of a heated substance.

convergent boundary (p. 457) Place where two of Earth's tectonic plates are moving toward each other; is associated with trenches, islands arcs, and folded mountains.

Cordillera (p. 626) Mountain ranges formed in western North America when active subduction along North America's western coast continued through the Middle Triassic.

Coriolis effect (p. 305) Deflects moving particles such as air to the right above the equator and to the left below the equator; caused by Earth's rotation and combines with the heat imbalance found on Earth to create the trade winds, polar easterlies, and prevailing westerlies.

corona (p. 807) Top layer of the Sun's atmosphere that extends from the top of the chromosphere and ranges in temperature from 1 million to 2 million K.

correlation (p. 561) Matching of rock outcrops of one geographic region to another.

cosmic background radiation (p. 848) Weak radiation that is left over from the early, hot stages of the Big Bang expansion of the universe.

cosmology (p. 847) Study of the universe, including its current nature, origin, and evolution, based on observation and the use of theoretical models.

covalent bond (p. 60) Attraction of two atoms for a shared pair of electrons that holds the atoms together.

continental shelf/plataforma continental (pág. 423) Parte más superficial de un margen continental, con una profundidad promedio es de 130 m y un ancho promedio de 60 km que se extiende hacia el océano desde la costa y provee un vivero rico en nutrientes a un gran número de peces.

continental slope/talud continental (pág. 424) Región oceánica inclinada que se encuentra más allá de la plataforma continental, que generalmente marca la orilla de la corteza continental y que puede estar seccionada por cañones submarinos.

contour interval/intervalo entre curvas de nivel (pág. 34) Diferencia en la elevación entre dos curvas de nivel seguidas en un mapa topográfico.

contour line/curva de nivel (pág. 33) Curva en un mapa topográfico que conecta puntos de igual elevación.

control/control (pág. 12) Estándar de comparación en un experimento.

convection/convección (pág. 277) Transferencia de energía debido al flujo de una sustancia calentada.

convergent boundary/límite convergente (pág. 457) Lugar donde dos placas tectónicas terrestres se mueven una hacia la otra. Está asociado con fosas abismales, arcos de islas y montañas plegadas.

Cordillera/cordillera (pág. 626) Conjunto de montañas formado en Norteamérica occidental cuando una subducción activa, a lo largo de la costa occidental de Norteamérica, continuó durante el Triásico Medio.

Coriolis effect/efecto de Coriolis (pág. 305) Desviación de partículas en movimiento, como el aire, hacia la derecha al norte del ecuador y hacia la izquierda al sur del ecuador; lo causa la rotación de la Tierra y se combina con el desequilibrio térmico presente en la Tierra para crear los vientos alisios, los vientos polares del este y los vientos ponientes prevalecientes.

corona/corona (pág. 807) Capa superior de la atmósfera del Sol que se extiende desde la parte superior de la cromosfera y tiene un rango de temperatura de 1 a 2 millones K.

correlation/correlación (pág. 561) Apareamiento de afloramientos rocosos de una región geográfica a otra.

cosmic background radiation/radiación cósmica de fondo (pág. 848) Radiación residual débil de las calientes etapas iniciales de la expansión de la Gran Explosión del universo.

cosmology/cosmología (pág. 847) Estudio del universo que incluye su naturaleza actual, su origen y evolución y el cual se basa en la observación y el uso de modelos teóricos.

covalent bond/enlace covalente (pág. 60) Atracción de dos átomos hacia un par compartido de electrones que mantiene unidos los átomos.

crater (p. 480) Bowl-shaped depression, usually less than 1 km in diameter, that forms around the central vent at the summit of a volcano.

creep (p. 184) Slow, steady downhill movement of loose weathered Earth materials, especially soils, causing objects on a slope to tilt.

crest (p. 399) Highest point of a wave.

cross-bedding (p. 126) Depositional feature of sedimentary rock that forms as inclined layers of sediment are carried forward across a horizontal surface.

cross-cutting relationships (p. 559) Principle stating that a fault or intrusion is younger than the rock it cuts across.

crystal (p. 79) Solid in which atoms are arranged in repeating patterns.

crystalline structure (p. 67) Regular geometric pattern of particles in most solids, giving a solid a definite shape and volume.

cyanobacteria (p. 585) Microscopic, photosynthetic prokaryotes that formed stromatolites and changed early Earth's atmosphere by generating oxygen.

cyclothems (p. 613) Repeating cyclic patterns of stacked sediments that represent cycles of glacial-interglacial periods; from base to top are generally sandstone-shale-coal-shale-limestone-shale.

crater/cráter (pág. 480) Depresión en forma de tazón, generalmente, de menos de 1 km de diámetro que se forma alrededor de la abertura central en la cumbre de un volcán.

creep/corrimiento (pág. 184) Movimiento cuesta abajo constante y lento de materias erosionadas sueltas de la Tierra, especialmente los suelos y la cual hace que se inclinen los objetos en una cuesta.

crest/cresta (pág. 399) Punto más alto de una ola.

cross-bedding/estratificación cruzada (pág. 126) Característica de la depositación de rocas sedimentarias que se forma a medida que las capas inclinadas de sedimento son arrastradas hacia adelante a través de una superficie horizontal.

cross-cutting relationships/relaciones de estratificación cruzada (pág. 559) Principio que establece que una falla o una intrusión es más reciente que la roca que atraviesa.

crystal/cristal (pág. 79) Sólido en el cual los átomos están ordenados en patrones repetitivos.

crystalline structure/estructura cristalina (pág. 67) Patrón geométrico y regular de partículas en la mayoría de los sólidos, la cual le da forma y volumen definidos al sólido.

cyanobacteria/cianobacterias (pág. 585) Organismos procariotas fotosintéticos microscópicos que formaron estromatolitas y cambiaron la atmósfera temprana de la Tierra al producir oxígeno.

cyclothems/ciclotemas (pág. 613) Patrones cíclicos repetitivos de sedimentos amontonados que representan ciclos de períodos glaciales- interglaciales; desde la base hasta la superficie generalmente son: arenisca-esquisto arcilloso–carbón–esquisto arcilloso–piedra caliza-esquisto arcilloso.

D

deep-sea trench (p. 426) Long, relatively narrow depression in the seafloor that can extend for thousands of kilometers, is the deepest part of the ocean basin, and is found primarily in the Pacific Ocean.

deflation (p. 192) Lowering of land surface caused by wind erosion of loose surface particles, often leaving coarse sediments behind.

deforestation (p. 720) Removal of trees from a forested area without adequate replanting, often using clear-cutting, which may result in loss of topsoil and water pollution.

delta (p. 226) Triangular deposit, usually made up of silt and clay particles, that forms where a stream enters a large body of water.

deep-sea trench/fosas abismales submarinas (pág. 426) Depresión larga y relativamente estrecha en el fondo marino que puede extenderse por miles de kilómetros; es la parte más profunda de la cuenca oceánica y se encuentra principalmente en el océano Pacífico.

deflation/deflación (pág. 192) Depresión de la superficie terrestre causada por la erosión eólica de partículas superficiales sueltas, la cual deja a menudo sedimentos gruesos.

deforestation/deforestación (pág. 720) Eliminación de árboles de un área forestal sin replantar adecuadamente, a menudo se utiliza corta a hecho, que puede tener como resultado la pérdida de la capa superficial del suelo y la contaminación del agua.

delta/delta (pág. 226) Depósito triangular, compuesto generalmente de partículas de cieno y arcilla, que se forma en donde una corriente entra a una gran masa de agua.

dendrochronology (p. 564) Science of comparing annual growth rings in trees to date events and environmental changes.

density current (p. 403) Movement of ocean water that occurs in depths too great to be affected by surface winds and is generated by differences in water temperature and salinity.

density-dependent factor (p. 714) Environmental factor, such as disease or lack of food, that increasingly affects a population as the population's size increases.

density-independent factor (p. 714) Environmental factor, such as a storm, flood, or pollution, that limits the growth of all affected populations regardless of size.

dependent variable (p. 12) Factor in an experiment that can change if the independent variable is changed.

deposition (p. 123) Occurs when sediments are laid down on the ground or sink to the bottom of a body of water; (p. 162) final stage of the erosional process in which the movement of transported materials slows and they are dropped in another location.

desalination (p. 674) Process that removes salt from ocean water in order to provide freshwater.

desertification (p. 660) Process by which productive land becomes desert; in arid areas can occur through the loss of topsoil.

dew point (p. 279) Temperature to which air is cooled at a constant pressure to reach saturation, at which point condensation can occur.

differentiation (p. 580) Process in which a planet becomes internally zoned, with the heavy materials sinking toward the center and the lighter materials accumulating near its surface.

digital forecast (p. 319) Weather forecast that uses numerical data to determine how atmospheric variables change over time.

dike (p. 478) Pluton that cuts across preexisting rocks and often forms when magma invades cracks in surrounding rock bodies.

dinosaur (p. 631) Terrestrial reptile that developed an upright posture and dominated the Mesozoic land.

dendrochronology/dendrocronología (pág. 564) Ciencia de la comparación de los anillos de crecimiento anual de los árboles para datar acontecimientos y cambios ambientales.

density current/corriente de densidad (pág. 403) Movimiento de las aguas oceánicas que ocurre a grandes profundidades, no se ve afectado por los vientos superficiales y se genera debido a las diferencias en temperatura y salinidad del agua.

density-dependent factor/factor dependiente de la densidad (pág. 714) Factor ambiental, como las enfermedades o la falta de alimento, que afecta cada vez más una población, a medida que aumenta el tamaño de la población.

density-independent factor/factor independiente de la densidad (pág. 714) Factor ambiental, como las tempestades, las inundaciones o la contaminación, que limita el crecimiento de todas las poblaciones afectadas, sea cual sea el tamaño de la población.

dependent variable/variable dependiente (pág. 12) Factor en un experimento que puede cambiar, si se cambia la variable independiente.

deposition/depositación (pág. 123) Ocurre cuando los sedimentos son depositados en el suelo o se hunden al fondo de una masa de agua; (pág. 162) la etapa final del proceso erosivo en que disminuye el movimiento de materiales transportados y éstos son arrojados en otra ubicación.

desalination/desalinización (pág. 674) Proceso de eliminación de la sal del agua marina para proveer agua dulce.

desertification/desertificación (pág. 660) Proceso mediante el cual la tierra productiva se convierte en desierto; en áreas áridas puede ocurrir debido a la pérdida de la capa superficial del suelo.

dew point/punto de rocío (pág. 279) Temperatura a la cual el aire se enfría a presión constante para alcanzar la saturación y en este punto puede ocurrir la condensación.

differentiation/diferenciación (pág. 580) Proceso en que un planeta se divide internamente en zonas, con el hundimiento de los materiales pesados hacia el centro, mientras que los materiales más ligeros se acumulan cerca de su superficie.

digital forecast/pronóstico digital (pág. 319) Pronóstico del tiempo que utiliza los datos numéricos para determinar cómo cambian las variables atmosféricas con el tiempo.

dike/dique (pág. 478) Plutón que atraviesa las rocas preexistentes y el cual se forma frecuentemente cuando el magma invade las grietas en cuerpos rocosos circundantes.

dinosaur/dinosaurio (pág. 631) Reptil terrestre que desarrolló una postura vertical y dominó la Tierra Mesozoica.

discharge (p. 218) Measure of a volume of stream water that flows over a specific location in a particular amount of time.

divergent boundary (p. 456) Place where two of Earth's tectonic plates are moving apart; is associated with volcanism, earthquakes, and high heat flow, and is found primarily on the seafloor.

divide (p. 215) Elevated land that divides one watershed, or drainage basin, from another.

Doppler effect (p. 315) Change in the wave frequency that occurs in energy when that energy moves toward or away from an observer.

downburst (p. 336) Violent, damaging thunderstorm wind that is concentrated in a local area.

drawdown (p. 252) Difference between the water level in a pumped well and the original water-table level.

drought (p. 347) Extended period of low rainfall, usually caused by shifts in global wind patterns, allowing high-pressure systems to remain for weeks or months over continental areas.

drumlin (p. 202) Elongated landform that results when a glacier moves over an older moraine.

dune (p. 194) Pile of wind-blown sand that develops over time, whose shape depends on sand availability, wind velocity and direction, and amount of vegetation present.

discharge/descarga (pág. 218) Medida de un volumen de agua corriente que fluye sobre una ubicación dada, en cierto lapso de tiempo.

divergent boundary/límite divergente (pág. 456) Lugar donde se alejan dos placas tectónicas terrestres; se asocia con la actividad volcánica, con los terremotos y el flujo de calor alto y se halla principalmente en el fondo marino.

divide/divisoria (pág. 215) Tierra elevada que divide una cuenca hidrográfica de otra.

Doppler effect/efecto Doppler (pág. 315) Cambio en la frecuencia de onda que ocurre en la energía, cuando esa energía se mueve hacia un observador o se aleja de él.

downburst/chaparrón violento (pág. 336) Viento de una tormenta eléctrica violento y dañino, que se concentra en un área local.

drawdown/tasa de agotamiento (pág. 252) Diferencia entre el nivel de agua en un pozo bombeado y el nivel original de la capa freática.

drought/sequía (pág. 347) Período prolongado de poca precipitación, generalmente causado por los cambios en los patrones de vientos globales, que permite que los sistemas de alta presión permanezcan sobre áreas continentales durante semanas o meses.

drumlin/drumlin (pág. 202) Formación alargada de tierra que se forma cuando un glaciar se mueve sobre una morrena más antigua.

dune/duna (pág. 194) Pila de arena arrastrada por el viento, la cual se desarrolla con el tiempo y cuya forma depende de la disponibilidad de la arena, la velocidad y dirección del viento y la cantidad de vegetación presente.

E

eccentricity (p. 777) Ratio of the distance between the foci to the length of the major axis; defines the shape of a planet's elliptical orbit.

ecliptic (p. 759) Plane that contains Earth's orbit around the Sun.

ectotherm (p. 633) Animal whose body temperature is regulated by the temperature of its surroundings.

Ediacaran fauna (p. 592) Fossils of multicellular, varied organisms lacking a mouth, anus, and gut that were widely distributed in the shallow oceans of the late Proterozoic and flourished between 570 and 670 million years ago.

ejecta (p. 754) Material that falls back to the lunar surface after being blasted out by the impact of a space object.

eccentricity/excentricidad (pág. 777) Proporción de la distancia entre los focos a la longitud del eje mayor; define la forma de la órbita elíptica de un planeta.

ecliptic/eclíptica (pág. 759) Plano que contiene la órbita de la Tierra alrededor del Sol.

ectotherm/poiquilotermo (pág. 633) Animal cuya temperatura corporal es regulada por la temperatura de sus alrededores.

Ediacaran fauna/fauna Ediacarana (pág. 592) Fósiles de organismos multicelulares diversos, que carecen de boca, ano, e intestino, los cuales estaban ampliamente distribuidos en los océanos poco profundos del Proterozoico Tardío y que abundaron hace 570 a 670 millones de años.

ejecta/ejecta (pág. 754) Material que regresa a la superficie lunar después de ser expulsado por el impacto de un objeto del espacio.

El Niño (p. 370) Warm ocean current that develops off the western coast of South America and can cause short-term climatic changes felt worldwide.

electromagnetic spectrum (p. 37) Arrangement of electromagnetic radiation, including gamma rays, X rays, and microwaves.

electron (p. 55) Tiny atomic particle with little mass and a negative electrical charge that surrounds the nucleus in energy levels.

element (p. 53) Natural or artificial substance that cannot be broken down into simpler substances by physical or chemical means.

endotherm (p. 633) Animal that maintains a relatively constant body temperature, regardless of its surroundings.

energy efficiency (p. 698) A type of conservation in which energy resources are used in the most productive ways.

energy level (p. 55) Represents the area in an atom where electrons are most likely to occur.

eon (p. 554) Longest time unit in the geological time scale, measured in billions of years.

epicenter (p. 499) Point on Earth's surface directly above the focus of an earthquake.

epoch (p. 556) Time unit in the geological time scale, smaller than a period, measured in millions of years to tens of millions of years.

equator (p. 27) Imaginary line that lies at 0∞ latitude and circles Earth midway between the north and south poles, dividing Earth into the northern hemisphere and the southern hemisphere.

era (p. 554) Second-longest time unit in the geological time scale, measured in hundreds of millions of years, and defined by differences in life-forms that are preserved in rocks.

erosion (p. 153) Movement of weathered materials from one location to another by agents such as water, wind, glaciers, and gravity.

esker (p. 202) Long, winding ridge of layered sediments deposited by streams that flow beneath a melting glacier.

estuary (p. 415) Coastal area of brackish water formed where the lower end of a freshwater river or stream enters the ocean; provides an excellent source of food and shelter to commercially important marine organisms.

eukaryote (p. 591) Organism that is composed of cells that contain nuclei and is generally larger and more complex than a prokaryote.

El Niño/El Niño (pág. 370) Corriente oceánica cálida que se desarrolla lejos de la costa occidental de Sudamérica y que puede causar cambios climáticos a corto plazo y cuyos efectos se sienten por todo el mundo.

electromagnetic spectrum/espectro electromagnético (pág. 37) Arreglo de la radiación electromagnética; incluye los rayos gamma, los rayos X y las microondas.

electron/electrón (pág. 55) Partícula atómica diminuta con masa pequeña y carga eléctrica negativa que rodea el núcleo en los niveles energéticos.

element/elemento (pág. 53) Sustancia natural o artificial que no puede separarse en sustancias más simples por medios físicos o químicos.

endotherm/endotermo (pág. 633) Animal que mantiene una temperatura corporal relativamente constante, sea cual sea la temperatura de sus alrededores.

energy efficiency/eficacia energética (pág. 698) Tipo de conservación en el cual los recursos energéticos se utilizan de maneras más productivas.

energy level/nivel de energía (pág. 55) Representa el área en un átomo donde es más probable que se encuentren los electrones.

eon/eon (pág. 554) Unidad más larga de tiempo en la escala de tiempo geológico; se mide en mil millones de años.

epicenter/epicentro (pág. 499) Lugar en la superficie terrestre directamente encima del foco de un terremoto.

epoch/época (pág. 556) Unidad de tiempo en la escala de tiempo geológico, más pequeña que un período; se mide en millones a decenas de millones de años.

equator/ecuador (pág. 27) Línea imaginaria localizada en la latitud 0° que da vuelta a la Tierra a medio camino entre los polos norte y sur, dividiendo la Tierra en dos hemisferios: el norte y el sur.

era/era (pág. 554) Segunda unidad más larga de tiempo en la escala del tiempo geológico; se mide en centenas de millones de años y se define según las diferencias en las formas de vida preservadas en las rocas.

erosion/erosión (pág. 153) Movimiento de materiales erosionados de un lugar a otro por agentes como el agua, el viento, los glaciares y la gravedad.

esker/ésker (pág. 202) Formación larga y sinuosa de sedimentos en capas, depositados por corrientes que fluyen debajo de un glaciar que se derrite.

estuary/estuario (pág. 415) Área costera de agua salobre que se forma en donde el extremo más bajo de un río o corriente de agua dulce entra al océano; provee una fuente excelente de alimento y refugio para organismos marinos comercialmente importantes.

eukaryote/eucariota (pág. 591) Organismo que está compuesto de células nucleadas; generalmente es más grande y más complejo que un procariota.

eutrophication (p. 230) Process by which lakes become rich in nutrients from the surrounding watershed, resulting in a change in the kinds of organisms in the lake.

evaporation (p. 68) Vaporization—change of state, involving thermal energy; (p. 290) process by which water changes from a liquid to a gas.

evaporite (p. 130) Chemical sedimentary rock that forms mainly in restricted ocean basins in areas with high evaporation rates.

evolution (p. 566) Adaptation of life-forms to changing environmental conditions.

exfoliation (p. 155) Mechanical weathering process in which outer rock layers are stripped away, often resulting in dome-shaped formations.

exosphere (p. 274) Outermost layer of Earth's atmosphere that is located above the thermosphere and contains light gases such as helium and hydrogen.

exponential growth (p. 713) Pattern of growth in which a population of organisms grows faster as it increases in size, resulting in a population explosion.

extrusive (p. 99) Fine-grained igneous rock that is formed when molten rock cools quickly and solidifies on Earth's surface.

eye (p. 344) Calm center of a tropical cyclone that develops when the winds around its center reach at least 120 km/h.

eyewall (p. 344) Band where the strongest winds in a hurricane are usually concentrated, surrounding the eye.

eutrophication/eutroficación (pág. 230) Proceso mediante el cual los lagos se convierten en lugares ricos en alimentos nutritivos provenientes de las cuencas circundantes, lo que resulta en un cambio en los tipos de organismos en el lago.

evaporation/evaporación (pág. 68) Vaporización: cambio de estado que involucra energía térmica; (pág. 290) proceso mediante el cual el agua cambia de un líquido a un gas.

evaporite/evaporita (pág. 130) Roca química sedimentaria que se forma principalmente en cuencas oceánicas restringidas en áreas con tasas de evaporación altas.

evolution/evolución (pág. 566) Adaptación de los seres vivos a las condiciones ambientales cambiantes.

exfoliation/exfoliación (pág. 155) Proceso de meteorización mecánica mediante el cual se eliminan las capas rocosas exteriores, a menudo resultando en formaciones en forma de domo.

exosphere/exosfera (pág. 274) Capa más externa de la atmósfera terrestre localizada por encima de la termosfera y la cual contiene gases livianos como el helio y el hidrógeno.

exponential growth/crecimiento exponencial (pág. 713) Patrón de crecimiento en que una población de organismos crece más rápidamente a medida que aumenta de tamaño, dando como resultado una explosión demográfica.

extrusive/extrusiva (pág. 99) Roca ígnea de grano fino que se forma cuando la roca fundida se enfría rápidamente y se solidifica en la superficie terrestre.

eye/ojo (pág. 344) Centro tranquilo de un ciclón tropical que se desarrolla cuando los vientos alrededor de su centro alcanzan por lo menos 120 km/h.

eyewall/pared del ojo de huracán (pág. 344) Banda que rodea el ojo de un huracán, donde generalmente se concentran los vientos más fuertes.

F

fault (p. 497) Fracture or system of fractures in Earth's crust that occurs when stress is applied too quickly or stress is too great; can form as a result of horizontal compression (reverse fault), horizontal shear (strike-slip fault), or horizontal tension (normal fault).

fault-block mountains (p. 538) Mountains that form when large pieces of crust are tilted, uplifted, or dropped downward between large normal faults.

felsic (p. 107) Light-colored igneous rocks that contain quartz and feldspars and have high silica contents.

fault/falla (pág. 497) Fractura o sistema de fracturas en la corteza terrestre que ocurre cuando se aplica tensión rápidamente o cuando la tensión es demasiado grande; se puede formar como resultado de la compresión horizontal (falla invertida), del cizallamiento horizontal (falla de transformación) o de la tensión horizontal (falla normal).

fault-block mountains/montañas de bloque de falla (pág. 538) Montañas que se forman cuando los trozos grandes de corteza se inclinan, se elevan, o se hunden entre fallas normales grandes.

felsic/félsica (pág. 107) Rocas ígneas de color claro que contienen cuarzo y feldespatos y tienen un contenido alto de sílice.

fission (p. 809) Process in which heavy atomic nuclei split into smaller, lighter nuclei.

flood (p. 219) Potentially devastating natural occurrence in which water spills over the sides of a stream's banks onto adjacent land areas.

floodplain (p. 219) Broad, flat, fertile area extending out from a stream's bank that is covered with water during floods.

focus (p. 499) Point of the initial fault rupture where an earthquake originates that usually lies at least several kilometers beneath Earth's surface.

foliated (p. 136) Metamorphic rock, such as schist or gneiss, whose minerals are squeezed under high pressure and arranged in wavy layers and bands.

fossil (p. 566) Remains or evidence of a once-living plant or animal.

fossil fuel (p. 686) Nonrenewable energy resource formed over geologic time from the compression and partial decomposition of organisms that lived millions of years ago.

fractional crystallization (p. 103) Process in which different minerals crystallize from magma at different temperatures, removing elements from magma.

fracture (p. 87) Ability of a mineral to break into pieces with arclike, rough, or jagged edges.

frequency (p. 38) Number of waves that pass a given point each second.

front (p. 308) Boundary between two air masses of differing densities; can be cold, warm, stationary, or occluded and can stretch over large areas of Earth's surface.

frontal thunderstorm (p. 331) Type of thunderstorm usually produced by an advancing cold front, which can result in a line of thunderstorms hundreds of kilometers long, or, more rarely, an advancing warm front, which can result in a relatively mild thunderstorm.

frost wedging (p. 154) Mechanical weathering process that occurs when water repeatedly freezes and thaws in the cracks of rocks, often resulting in rocks splitting.

fuel (p. 684) Material, such as wood, peat, or coal, burned to provide power or heat.

fission/fisión (pág. 809) Proceso mediante el cual los núcleos atómicos pesados se parten en núcleos más livianos y pequeños.

flood/inundación (pág. 219) Acontecimiento natural potencialmente devastador en que el agua se desborda de las riberas de una corriente y cubre los terrenos adyacentes.

floodplain/llanura aluvial (pág. 219) Área fértil, plana y ancha que se extiende desde las riberas de una corriente, la cual se cubre con agua durante las inundaciones.

focus/foco (pág. 499) Punto de la ruptura de la falla inicial donde se origina un terremoto y el cual generalmente se encuentra por lo menos varios kilómetros debajo de la superficie terrestre.

foliated/foliada (pág. 136) Roca metamórfica, como el esquisto o el gneis, cuyos minerales se comprimen bajo presiones altas y se ordenan en capas y bandas onduladas.

fossil/fósil (pág. 566) Restos o pruebas de una planta o un animal que vivió alguna vez.

fossil fuel/combustible fósil (pág. 686) Recurso energético no renovable que se forma a lo largo del tiempo geológico a partir de la compresión y descomposición parcial de organismos que vivieron hace millones de años.

fractional crystallization/cristalización fraccionaria (pág. 103) Proceso en el cual diferentes minerales se cristalizan a partir del magma a diferentes temperaturas, eliminando elementos del magma.

fracture/fractura (pág. 87) Capacidad de un mineral de romperse en trozos con bordes ásperos, arqueados, o serrados.

frequency/frecuencia (pág. 38) Número de ondas que pasan por un punto dado cada segundo.

front/frente (pág. 308) Frontera entre dos masas de aire con diferentes densidades; puede ser frío, cálido, estacionario u ocluido y puede extenderse sobre grandes áreas de la superficie de la Tierra.

frontal thunderstorm/tormenta eléctrica frontal (pág. 331) Tipo de tormenta que generalmente produce un frente frío en avance y el cual puede resultar en una línea de tormentas de cientos de kilómetros de largo, o con menor frecuencia, en un frente cálido que avanza, el cual puede ocasionar una tormenta relativamente ligera.

frost wedging/grietas causadas por el hielo (pág. 154) Proceso mecánico de meteorización que ocurre cuando el agua se congela y se descongela en repetidas ocasiones en las grietas de rocas, frecuentemente dando como resultado el rompimiento de las rocas.

fuel/combustible (pág. 684) Materiales, incluyendo la leña, la turba o el carbón, que se queman para proporcionar potencia o calor.

Fujita tornado intensity scale (p. 338) Classifies tornados according to their wind speed, duration, and path of destruction on a scale ranging from F0 to F5.

fusion (p. 809) Process in a star's core in which lightweight hydrogen nuclei combine into heavier helium nuclei.

Fujita tornado intensity scale/escala Fujita de intensidad de tornados (pág. 338) Clasifica los tornados según la velocidad de viento, la duración y el daño causado a su paso, en una escala que va de F0 a F5.

fusion/fusión (pág. 809) Proceso en el centro de una estrella en el cual los núcleos livianos de hidrógeno se combinan para formar núcleos más pesados de helio.

G

gangue (p. 663) Material left after ore is extracted that may release harmful chemicals into surface water or groundwater.

gas giant planets (p. 780) Large, gaseous planets that are very cold at their surfaces, have ring systems, many moons, and lack solid surfaces—Jupiter, Saturn, Uranus, and Neptune.

gasohol (p. 696) Biomass fuel that is a mixture of gasoline and ethanol and can be used in conventional gasoline engines.

gem (p. 90) Rare, precious, highly prized mineral that can be cut, polished, and used for jewelry.

geologic time scale (p. 554) Record of Earth's history from its origin to the present used to correlate geologic events, environmental changes, and development of life-forms that are preserved in rocks.

geology (p. 6) Study of materials that make up Earth and the processes that form and change these materials.

geothermal energy (p. 693) Energy produced from Earth's own internal steam and hot water.

geyser (p. 251) Explosive hot spring that erupts regularly.

glacier (p. 198) Large, moving mass of ice that forms near Earth's poles and in mountainous regions at high elevations.

glass (p. 68) Solid that consists of densely packed atoms with a random arrangement and lacks crystals or has crystals that are not visible.

Global Positioning System (GPS) (p. 40) Satellite-based navigation system that permits a user to pinpoint his or her exact location on Earth.

global warming (p. 376) Rise in global temperatures, which may be due to increases in atmospheric CO_2 from deforestation and burning of fossil fuels; (p. 725) a phenomenon related to the greenhouse effect.

gangue/ganga (pág. 663) Material que queda después de que se extrae un mineral y el cual puede liberar sustancias químicas perjudiciales en el agua superficial o subterránea.

gas giant planets/planetas gigantes gaseosos (pág. 780) Planetas grandes y gaseosos con superficies muy frías, sistemas de anillos, muchas lunas y que carecen de superficies sólidas: Júpiter, Saturno, Urano y Neptuno.

gasohol/gasohol (pág. 696) Combustible de biomasa que es una mezcla de gasolina y etanol y que se puede utilizar en motores de gasolina convencionales.

gem/gema (pág. 90) Mineral sumamente valioso, precioso y escaso que se puede cortar, pulir y utilizar en joyería.

geologic time scale/escala del tiempo geológico (pág. 554) Registro de la historia de la Tierra desde su origen hasta el presente; se utiliza para correlacionar los acontecimientos geológicos, los cambios ambientales y el desarrollo de las formas de vida preservadas en las rocas.

geology/geología (pág. 6) Estudio de los materiales que componen la Tierra y de los procesos que forman y cambian estos materiales.

geothermal energy/energía geotérmica (pág. 693) Energía que se produce a partir del vapor interno y del agua caliente que posee la Tierra.

geyser/géiser (pág. 251) Manantial termal explosivo que hace erupción regularmente.

glacier/glaciar (pág. 198) Enorme masa móvil de hielo que se forma cerca de los polos de la Tierra y en regiones montañosas a grandes elevaciones.

glass/vidrio (pág. 68) Sólido que consiste en átomos densamente empacados con un arreglo aleatorio; carece de cristales o tiene cristales que no son visibles.

Global Positioning System (GPS)/Sistema de Posicionamiento Global (GPS) (pág. 40) Sistema de navegación con satélite que le permite a un usuario localizar, con toda precisión, su ubicación exacta sobre la Tierra.

global warming/calentamiento global (pág. 376) Aumento en las temperaturas globales, que puede ser producto de los aumentos en el CO_2 atmosférico debido a la deforestación y la quema de combustibles fósiles; (pág. 725) fenómeno relacionado con el efecto de invernadero.

gnomonic projection (p. 33) Map useful in plotting long-distance trips by boat or plane that is made by projecting points and lines from a globe onto a piece of paper that touches the globe at a single point.

Gondwana (p. 612) Large continent in the southern hemisphere that formed as a result of collisional events during the Late Paleozoic.

graded bedding (p. 126) Depositional feature of sedimentary rock in which particles are progressively heavier and coarser toward the bottom layers of bedding.

greenhouse effect (p. 375) Natural heating of Earth's surface by certain atmospheric gases, which helps keep Earth warm enough to sustain life.

gully erosion (p. 163) Erosion that occurs when a rill channel widens and deepens.

gnomonic projection/proyección gnomónica (pág. 33) Mapa útil en el trazado de viajes de distancias largas por barco o por avión; se elabora proyectando los puntos y las líneas de un globo sobre una hoja de papel que toca el globo en un solo punto.

Gondwana/Gondwana (pág. 612) Inmenso continente en el hemisferio sur que se formó como resultado de las colisiones durante el Paleozoico Tardío.

graded bedding/estratificación graduada (pág. 126) Característica de la depositación de rocas sedimentarias en la cual las partículas son progresivamente más pesadas y toscas hacia las capas inferiores de la estratificación.

greenhouse effect/efecto de invernadero (pág. 375) Calentamiento natural de la superficie terrestre por ciertos gases atmosféricos; ayuda a mantener la Tierra lo suficiente cálida para sustentar vida.

gully erosion/erosión de barrancos (pág. 163) Erosión que ocurre cuando el cauce de un arroyuelo se ensancha y se profundiza.

half-life (p. 563) Period of time it takes for a radioactive isotope, such as carbon-14, to decay to one-half of its original amount.

halo (p. 835) Spherical region that surrounds the Milky Way's nuclear bulge and disk.

hardness (p. 86) Measure of how easily a mineral can be scratched, which is determined by the arrangement of a mineral's atoms.

heat (p. 278) Energy transfer that occurs because of a difference in temperature between substances and flows from an object of higher temperature to an object of lower temperature.

heat island (p. 368) Urban area where climate is warmer than in the surrounding countryside due to factors such as numerous concrete buildings and large expanses of asphalt.

heat wave (p. 348) Extended period of higher-than-normal temperatures caused by large, high-pressure systems that warm by compression and block cooler air masses.

Hertzsprung-Russell diagram (H-R diagram) (p. 819) Graph that relates stellar characteristics—class, mass, temperature, magnitude, diameter, and luminosity.

highlands (p. 754) Light-colored, mountainous, heavily cratered areas of the Moon, composed mostly of lunar breccias.

half-life/media vida (pág. 563) Período de tiempo que demora un isótopo radiactivo, como el carbono 14, en desintegrarse a la mitad de su cantidad radiactiva original.

halo/halo (pág. 835) Región esférica que rodea la protuberancia y el disco nucleares de la Vía Láctea.

hardness/dureza (pág. 86) Medida de la facilidad de un mineral para rayarse, lo cual se determina por el arreglo de los átomos del mineral.

heat/calor (pág. 278) Transferencia de energía que ocurre debido a una diferencia de temperatura entre las sustancias y que fluye de un objeto de temperatura más alta a un objeto de temperatura más baja.

heat island/isla de calor (pág. 368) Área urbana donde el clima es más caliente que en el área rural circundante debido a factores como los numerosos edificios de concreto y las grandes extensiones de asfalto.

heat wave/ola de calor (pág. 348) Período extenso con temperaturas más altas de lo normal; lo causan los grandes sistemas de alta presión que se calientan por compresión y bloquean las masas de aire más frescas.

Hertzsprung-Russell diagram/diagrama de Hertzsprung-Russell (diagrama H-R) (pág. 819) Gráfica que relaciona las características estelares, incluyendo la clase, la masa, la temperatura, la magnitud, el diámetro y la luminosidad.

highlands/tierras altas (pág. 754) Áreas en la Luna de color claro, con muchos cráteres y montañosas, compuestas en su mayor parte de brechas lunares.

hominids (p. 640) Group of upright, bipedal primates, including Homo sapiens.

hominoids (p. 640) Group of primates, including hominids and the great apes.

Homo sapiens (p. 641) Species to which humans belong.

hot spot (p. 486) Unusually hot area in Earth's mantle that is stationary for long periods of time, where high-temperature plumes of mantle material rise toward the surface.

hot spring (p. 251) Thermal spring with temperatures higher than that of the human body.

Hubble constant (p. 843) Value (H) used to calculate the rate that the universe is expanding; measured in kilometers per second per megaparsec.

humidity (p. 283) Amount of water vapor in the air.

hydrolysis (p. 156) Chemical reaction of water with other substances.

hydrosphere (p. 8) All the water in Earth's oceans, lakes, seas, rivers, and glaciers plus all the water in the atmosphere.

hydrothermal metamorphism (p. 135) Occurs when very hot water reacts with rock, altering its mineralogy and chemistry.

hydrothermal vent (p. 591) Hot-water, deep-sea vent that has the energy and nutrients needed for the beginnings of life.

hygrometer (p. 313) Weather instrument used to measure relative humidity.

hypothesis (p. 11) A suggested explanation for an observation often stated in the form of a question that can be answered by the results of an experiment.

hominids/homínidos (pág. 640) Grupo de primates erguidos y bípedos que incluye *Homo sapiens*.

hominoids/hominoideos (pág. 640) Grupo de primates que incluye los homínidos y los grandes simios.

Homo sapiens/Homo sapiens (pág. 641) Especie a la cual pertenecen los seres humanos.

hot spot/foco caliente (pág. 486) Área muy caliente del manto de la Tierra, estacionaria durante largos períodos de tiempo, en donde las plumas de alta temperatura de material del manto suben hacia la superficie.

hot spring/fuente termal (pág. 251) Manantial termal con temperaturas más altas que las del cuerpo humano.

Hubble constant/constante de Hubble (pág. 843) Valor (*H*) utilizado para calcular la velocidad a la que se expande el universo; se mide en kilómetros por segundo por megaparsec.

humidity/humedad (pág. 283) Cantidad de vapor de agua en el aire.

hydrolysis/hidrólisis (pág. 156) Reacción química del agua con otras sustancias.

hydrosphere/hidrosfera (pág. 8) Toda el agua en los océanos, los lagos, los mares, los ríos y los glaciares de la Tierra, además de toda el agua en la atmósfera.

hydrothermal metamorphism/metamorfismo hidrotérmico (pág. 135) Ocurre cuando agua muy caliente reacciona con la roca, alterando su mineralogía y su química.

hydrothermal vent/chimenea hidrotérmica (pág. 591) abertura de agua caliente en las profundidades marinas que contiene la energía y los nutrientes necesarios para el comienzo de la vida.

hygrometer/higrómetro (pág. 313) Instrumento meteorológico que se usa para medir la humedad relativa.

hypothesis/hipótesis (pág. 11) Explicación sugerida para una observación; a menudo se formula en forma de pregunta y puede ser contestada por los resultados de un experimento.

ice age (p. 369) Period of extensive glacial coverage, producing long-term climatic changes.

igneous rock (p. 99) Intrusive or extrusive rock formed from the cooling and crystallization of magma; can be classified as felsic, mafic, intermediate, and ultramafic, according to its mineral composition.

impact crater (p. 754) Moon crater formed when space material impacted on the lunar surface.

ice age/glaciación (pág. 369) Período de amplia cobertura glacial que produce cambios climáticos de largo plazo.

igneous rock/roca ígnea (pág. 99) Roca intrusiva o extrusiva formada por el enfriamiento y cristalización del magma; pueden clasificarse en félsica, máfica, intermedia y ultramáfica, según su composición mineral.

impact crater/cráter de impacto (pág. 754) cráter lunar que se forma cuando el material proveniente del espacio choca contra la superficie lunar.

GLOSSARY/GLOSARIO **955**

independent variable (p. 12) Factor that is manipulated by the experimenter in an experiment.

index fossils (p. 568) Remains of plants or animals that were abundant, widely distributed, and existed briefly that can be used by geologists to correlate or date rock layers.

infiltration (p. 240) Process by which precipitation that has fallen on land surfaces enters the ground and becomes groundwater.

inflationary universe (p. 850) Model predicting that the universe is flat; can explain the walls and voids in the distribution of galaxies.

interferometry (p. 750) Process that links separate telescopes so they act as one telescope, producing more detailed images as the distance between them increases.

International Date Line (p. 31) The 180∞ meridian, which serves as the transition line for calendar days.

intrusive (p. 99) Coarse-grained igneous rock that is formed when molten rock cools slowly and solidifies inside Earth's crust.

ionic bond (p. 63) Attractive force between two ions with opposite charge.

ions (p. 62) Electrically charged atoms or groups of atoms.

iridium (p. 633) Metal that is rare in rocks at Earth's surface but is relatively common in meteorites and asteroids.

isochron (p. 452) Line on a map that connects points of the same age.

isopleth (p. 317) Line drawn on a weather map that connects points of equal or constant values.

isostasy (p. 525) Condition of equilibrium that describes the displacement of Earth's mantle by Earth's continental and oceanic crust.

isostatic rebound (p. 527) Slow process of Earth's crust rising as the result of the removal of mass from the crust.

isotopes (p. 58) Atoms of the same element that have different mass numbers and the same chemical properties.

independent variable/variable independiente (pág. 12) Factor que manipula el investigador en un experimento.

index fossils/fósiles guías (pág. 568) Restos de plantas o animales que fueron abundantes, extensamente distribuidos y de breve existencia, los cuales pueden utilizar los geólogos para correlacionar o para datar las capas rocosas.

infiltration/infiltración (pág. 240) Proceso mediante el cual la precipitación que cae sobre la superficie terrestre entra al suelo y se convierte en agua subterránea.

inflationary universe/universo inflacionario (pág. 850) Modelo que predice que el universo es plano; puede explicar las paredes y los vacíos en la distribución de las galaxias.

interferometry/interferometría (pág. 750) Proceso que une telescopios separados de tal manera que actúan como un solo telescopio, produciendo imágenes más detalladas al aumentar la distancia entre ellos.

International Date Line/Línea Internacional de Cambio de Fecha (pág. 31) El meridiano 180°, que sirve como la línea de transición para los días del calendario.

intrusive/intrusiva (pág. 99) Roca ígnea de grano grueso que se forma cuando roca fundida se enfría lentamente y se solidifica en el interior de la corteza de la Tierra.

ionic bond/enlace iónico (pág. 63) Fuerza atractiva entre dos iones con cargas opuestas.

ions/iones (pág. 62) Átomos o grupos de átomos cargados eléctricamente.

iridium/iridio (pág. 633) Metal escaso en las rocas de la superficie terrestre, pero relativamente común en los meteoritos y los asteroides.

isochron/isocrona (pág. 452) Línea en un mapa que conecta puntos con la misma antigüedad.

isopleth/isopleta (pág. 317) Línea en un mapa meteorológico que conecta los puntos de valores iguales o constantes.

isostasy/isostasia (pág. 525) Condición de equilibrio que describe el desplazamiento del manto terrestre por la corteza continental y la oceánica de la Tierra.

isostatic rebound/rebote isostático (pág. 527) Proceso lento de elevación de la corteza terrestre como resultado de la eliminación de masa de la corteza.

isotopes/isótopos (pág. 58) Átomos del mismo elemento que tienen diferentes números de masa, pero las mismas propiedades químicas.

jet stream (p. 307) High-altitude, narrow, westerly wind band that occurs above large temperature contrasts and can flow as fast as 185 km/h.

jet stream/corriente de chorro (pág. 307) Banda de vientos ponientes, estrecha y de gran altitud situada por encima de los grandes contrastes de temperatura y que puede fluir tan rápido como 185 km/h.

karst topography (p. 246) Irregular topography with sink-holes, sinks, and sinking streams caused by groundwater dissolution of limestone.

key bed (p. 565) Sediment layer that serves as a time marker in the rock record and results from volcanic ash or meteorite-impact debris that spread out and covered large areas of Earth.

kimberlite (p. 113) Rare, ultramafic rock that can contain diamonds and other minerals formed only under very high pressures.

Köeppen classification system (p. 364) Divides climates into five basic types, based on the mean monthly values of temperature and precipitation and types of vegetation.

karst topography/topografía cárstica (pág. 246) Topografía irregular con sumideros, hundimientos y corrientes en declive causados por la disolución de la piedra caliza por el agua subterránea.

key bed/capa clave (pág. 565) Capa de sedimento que sirve como un marcador de tiempo en el registro de las rocas; se origina de las cenizas volcánicas o de los escombros de los impactos de meteoritos que se esparcen y cubren grandes áreas de la Tierra.

kimberlite/kimberlita (pág. 113) Roca ultramáfica escasa que puede contener diamantes y otros minerales; sólo se forma bajo presiones muy altas.

Köeppen classification system/sistema de clasificación de Köeppen (pág. 364) Divide los climas en cinco tipos básicos, basándose en los valores mensuales promedio de temperatura y precipitación y en los tipos de vegetación.

laccolith (p. 477) Relatively small, mushroom-shaped pluton that forms when magma intrudes into parallel rock layers close to Earth's surface.

lake (p. 228) Natural or human-made body of water that can form when a depression on land fills with water.

Landsat satellite (p. 38) Information-gathering satellite that uses visible light and infrared radiation to map Earth's surface.

landslide (p. 186) Rapid downslope movement of a mass of loose soil, rock, or debris that has separated from the bedrock; can be triggered by an earthquake.

latent heat (p. 286) Stored energy in water vapor that is not released to warm the atmosphere until condensation takes place.

latitude (p. 27) Distance in degrees north and south of the equator.

Laurentia (p. 583) Ancient continent formed during the Proterozoic that is the core of modern-day North America.

lava (p. 99) Magma that flows out onto Earth's surface.

law (p. 19) Basic fact that describes the behavior of a natural phenomenon.

laccolith/lacolito (pág. 477) Plutón relativamente pequeño con forma de champiñón que se forma cuando se introduce el magma en las capas rocosas paralelas cerca de la superficie terrestre.

lake/lago (pág. 228) Masa de agua natural o hecha por el hombre que se forma cuando una depresión de la tierra se llena de agua.

Landsat satellite/satélite Landsat (pág. 38) Satélite que recoge información y que utiliza la luz visible y la radiación infrarroja para trazar la superficie terrestre.

landslide/deslizamiento (pág. 186) Rápido desplazamiento cuesta abajo de una masa de tierra, rocas o escombros sueltos que se ha separado de del lecho rocoso; puede ser causado por un terremoto.

latent heat/calor latente (pág. 286) Energía almacenada en el vapor del agua que se libera para calentar la atmósfera hasta que ocurre la condensación.

latitude/latitud (pág. 27) Distancia en grados al norte y al sur del ecuador.

Laurentia/Laurencia (pág. 583) Antiguo continente que se formó durante el Proterozoico y que en la actualidad corresponde al corazón de Norteamérica.

lava/lava (pág. 99) Magma que fluye por la superficie terrestre.

law/ley (pág. 19) Acontecimiento básico que describe el comportamiento de un fenómeno natural.

Glossary

Glossary/Glosario

Le Système International D'Unités (SI) (p. 14) Modern version of the metric system based on a decimal system using the number 10 as the base unit; includes the meter (m), liter (L), second (s), and kilogram (kg).

lifted condensation level (LCL) (p. 279) Height at which condensation occurs, which often corresponds with the base of clouds.

liquid metallic hydrogen (p. 787) Form of hydrogen with both liquid and metallic properties that exists as a layer in the Jovian atmosphere.

lithification (p. 124) Transformation of sediments into rock through compaction and cementation.

lithosphere (p. 8) Earth's rigid outer shell, including the crust and the solid, uppermost part of the mantle.

loess (p. 197) Thick, wind-blown, fertile deposit of silt that contains high levels of nutrients and minerals.

longitude (p. 29) Distance in degrees east and west of the prime meridian.

longshore bar (p. 416) Submerged sandbar located in the surf zone of most beaches.

longshore current (p. 416) Current that flows parallel to the shore, moves large amounts of sediments, and is formed when incoming breakers spill over a long-shore bar.

luminosity (p. 817) Energy output from the surface of a star per second; measured in watts.

lunar eclipse (p. 767) Occurs only during a full moon, when Earth passes between the Sun and the Moon, and Earth's shadow falls on the Moon.

luster (p. 84) Describes the metallic or nonmetallic way that a mineral reflects light from its surface.

Le Système International D'Unités/Sistema Internacional de Unidades (SI) (pág. 14) Versión moderna del sistema métrico basado en un sistema decimal que utiliza el número 10 como unidad base; incluye el metro (m), el litro (L), el segundo (s) y el kilogramo (kg).

lifted condensation level (LCL)/nivel de condensación por ascenso (NCA) (pág. 279) Altura a la cual ocurre la condensación, que a menudo corresponde con la base de nubes.

liquid metallic hydrogen/hidrógeno metálico líquido (pág. 787) Forma del hidrógeno con propiedades tanto líquidas como metálicas que existe en forma de capa en la atmósfera joviana.

lithification/litificación (pág. 124) Transformación de los sedimentos en roca debido a la compactación y la cementación.

lithosphere/litosfera (pág. 8) Parte exterior rígida de la Tierra, que incluye la corteza y la parte sólida más externa del manto.

loess/loes (pág. 197) grueso depósito fértil de cieno, soplado por el viento y el cual contiene niveles altos de nutrientes y minerales.

longitude/longitud (pág. 29) Distancia en grados al este y oeste del primer meridiano.

longshore bar/barra costera (pág. 416) Barra de arena sumergida, localizada en la zona del oleaje de la mayoría de las playas.

longshore current/corriente costera (pág. 416) Corriente que fluye paralela a la costa, transporta grandes cantidades de sedimentos y se forma cuando entran las olas rompientes y se desbordan sobre una barra costera.

luminosity/luminosidad (pág. 817) Energía que irradia la superficie de una estrella por segundo; se mide en vatios.

lunar eclipse/eclipse lunar (pág. 767) Ocurre sólo durante la luna llena, cuando la Tierra pasa entre el Sol y la Luna y la sombra de la Tierra cae sobre la Luna.

luster/lustre (pág. 84) Describe la manera en que un mineral refleja la luz de su superficie; puede ser metálico o no metálico.

mafic (p. 107) Dark-colored igneous rocks that are rich in iron and magnesium.

magma (p. 80) Molten material found beneath Earth's crust that forms minerals with large crystals when it cools slowly and forms minerals with small crystals when it cools rapidly.

mafic/máfica (pág. 107) Rocas ígneas oscuras, ricas en hierro y magnesio.

magma/magma (pág. 80) Material fundido que se encuentra bajo la corteza terrestre; forma minerales con cristales grandes cuando se enfría lentamente y forma minerales con cristales pequeños cuando se enfría rápidamente.

magnetic reversals (p. 451) Changes in Earth's magnetic field over geologic time, recorded in ocean-floor rocks and continental basalt flows.

magnetometer (p. 448) Device used to map the ocean floor that detects small changes in magnetic fields.

magnitude (p. 505) Measure of the energy released during an earthquake, which can be described using the Richter scale.

main sequence (p. 819) In an H-R diagram, the broad, diagonal band that includes about 90 percent of all stars and runs from hot, luminous stars in the upper-left corner to cool, dim stars in the lower-right corner.

map legend (p. 35) Key that explains what the symbols on a map represent.

map scale (p. 35) Ratio between the distances shown on a map and the actual distances on Earth's surface.

mare (p. 754) Dark-colored, basaltic, smooth plain on the Moon, between 3.1 and 3.8 billion years old, that formed from lava welling up and filling in large impact basins.

mass extinction (p. 611) Occurs when an unusually large number of organisms become extinct over a relatively short period of geologic time.

mass movement (p. 181) Downslope movement of Earth materials, due to gravity, that can occur suddenly or very slowly, depending on the weight of the material, its resistance to sliding, and whether a trigger, such as an earthquake, is involved.

mass number (p. 54) Combined number of protons and neutrons in the nucleus of an atom.

Maunder minimum (p. 372) Period of very low sunspot activity that occurred between 1645 and 1716 and closely corresponded with a cold climatic episode known as the "Little Ice Age."

meander (p. 224) Curve or bend in a stream formed when a stream's slope decreases, water builds up in the stream channel, and moving water erodes away the sides of the streambed.

mechanical weathering (p. 154) Process that breaks down rocks and minerals into smaller pieces but does not involve any change in their composition.

magnetic reversals/inversiones magnéticas (pág. 451) Cambios en el campo magnético de la Tierra a lo largo del tiempo geológico, registrado en las rocas del fondo del océano y en los flujos de basalto continentales.

magnetometer/magnetómetro (pág. 448) Dispositivo que se utiliza para hacer mapas del fondo oceánico, el cual detecta los cambios pequeños en los campos magnéticos.

magnitude/magnitud (pág. 505) Medida de la energía que se libera durante un terremoto; se puede describir utilizando la escala de Richter.

main sequence/secuencia principal (pág. 819) En un diagrama H-R, es la banda diagonal ancha que incluye cerca del 90 por ciento de todas las estrellas y que va desde las estrellas calientes y luminosas, en la esquina superior izquierda, hasta las estrellas frías de brillo débil, en la esquina inferior derecha.

map legend/leyenda del mapa (pág. 35) Clave que explica los símbolos en un mapa.

map scale/escala del mapa (pág. 35) Proporción entre las distancias que se muestran en un mapa y las distancias reales en la superficie terrestre.

mare/mar (pág. 754) Planicie lunar lisa, basáltica, de color oscuro, que data entre 3.1 y 3.8 billones de años de antigüedad, que se formó cuando brotó la lava y llenó las grandes cuencas de impacto.

mass extinction/extinción en masa (pág. 611) Ocurre cuando se extingue un número inusualmente grande de organismos, durante un período relativamente corto de tiempo geológico.

mass movement/movimiento de masa (pág. 181) Movimiento cuesta abajo de materiales terrestres debido a la gravedad; puede ocurrir repentina o muy lentamente, dependiendo del peso del material, su resistencia a deslizarse y si está implicado un acontecimiento iniciador, como un terremoto.

mass number/número de masa (pág. 54) Número combinado de protones y neutrones en el núcleo de un átomo.

Maunder minimum/mínimo de Maunder (pág. 372) Período de muy baja actividad de manchas solares que ocurrió entre 1645 y 1716 y correspondió aproximadamente con un episodio climático frío conocido como la "Pequeña Glaciación."

meander/meandro (pág. 224) Curva o recoveco en una corriente que se forma cuando disminuye la inclinación de la corriente, el agua se acumula en el canal y su movimiento erosiona los costados del lecho de la corriente.

mechanical weathering/meteorización mecánica (pág. 154) Proceso que rompe las rocas y los minerales en trozos más pequeños, pero que no implica ningún cambio en la composición del material.

Mercator projection (p. 32) Map with parallel lines of latitude and longitude that shows true direction and the correct shapes of landmasses but distorts areas near the poles.

mesosphere (p. 274) Layer of Earth's atmosphere above the stratopause.

meteor (p. 796) Streak of light produced when a meteoroid falls toward Earth and burns up in Earth's atmosphere.

meteorite (p. 579) Small asteroid or asteroid fragment that fell on early Earth, generating heat; (p. 796) meteoroid that does not completely burn up in Earth's atmosphere and strikes Earth's surface, sometimes causing an impact crater.

meteoroid (p. 796) Piece of interplanetary material that falls toward Earth and enters its atmosphere.

meteorology (p. 6) Branch of Earth science that studies the air that surrounds our planet; (p. 299) study of atmospheric phenomena such as fog, clouds, snow, rain, and lightning.

meteor shower (p. 797) Occurs when Earth intersects a cometary orbit and comet particles burn up as they enter Earth's upper atmosphere.

microclimate (p. 367) Localized climate that differs from the surrounding regional climate.

microcontinents (p. 582) Small pieces of continental crust that collided with one another throughout the Proterozoic, forming the cores of the continents.

mid-ocean ridges (p. 426) Chains of underwater mountains that run throughout the ocean basins, have a total length over 65 000 km, and contain countless active and extinct volcanoes.

mineral (p. 77) Naturally occurring, inorganic solid with a specific chemical composition and a definite crystalline structure that forms from magma or from supersaturated solution.

modern fauna (p. 628) New marine organisms that evolved during the Mesozoic, including crabs, shrimps, sponges, sea urchins, modern corals, snails, and clams, plus major vertebrate groups such as bony fishes, aquatic reptiles, sharks, and aquatic mammals.

modified Mercalli scale (p. 506) Measures earthquake intensity on a scale from I to XII; the higher the number, the greater the damage the earthquake has caused.

Mercator projection/proyección de Mercator (pág. 32) Mapa con las líneas de latitud y de longitud paralelas que muestra la dirección verdadera y las formas correctas de las masas terrestres, pero el cual distorsiona las áreas cercanas a los polos.

mesosphere/mesosfera (pág. 274) Capa de la atmósfera terrestre por encima de la estratopausa.

meteor/meteoro (pág. 796) Rayo luminoso que se produce cuando un meteorito cae a la Tierra y se quema en su atmósfera.

meteorite/meteorito (pág. 579) Asteroide pequeño o fragmento de asteroide que cayó en la Tierra temprana produciendo calor; (pág. 796) meteoroide que no se quema completamente en la atmósfera terrestre y llega a la superficie terrestre, en ocasiones causando un cráter de impacto.

meteoroid/meteoroide (pág. 796) Trozo de material interplanetario que cae a la Tierra y entra a su atmósfera.

meteorology/meteorología (pág. 6) Rama de las ciencias terrestres que estudia el aire que rodea nuestro planeta; (pág. 299) estudio de los fenómenos atmosféricos, como la niebla, las nubes, la nieve, la lluvia y los relámpagos.

meteor shower/lluvia de meteoros (pág. 797) Ocurre cuando la Tierra interseca la órbita de un cometa y las partículas de éste se queman al entrar a la atmósfera superior de la Tierra.

microclimate/microclima (pág. 367) Clima localizado que difiere del clima regional circundante.

microcontinents/microcontinentes (pág. 582) Trozos pequeños de corteza continental que chocaron unos con otros a lo largo del Proterozoico, formando los núcleos de los continentes.

mid-ocean ridges/dorsales mediooceánicas (pág. 426) Cadenas montañosas submarinas que se extienden a través de las cuencas oceánicas, tienen una longitud total de más de 65 000 km y contienen innumerables volcanes activos y extintos.

mineral/mineral (pág. 77) sólido inorgánico de ocurrencia natural con una composición química específica y una estructura cristalina definida que se forma a partir del magma o de una solución sobresaturada.

modern fauna/fauna moderna (pág. 628) Nuevos organismos marinos que evolucionaron durante el Mesozoico; incluyen los cangrejos, los camarones, las esponjas, los erizos de mar, los corales modernos, los caracoles y las almejas, además de grupos de vertebrados principales como los peces óseos, los reptiles acuáticos, los tiburones y los mamíferos acuáticos.

modified Mercalli scale/escala de Mercalli modificada (pág. 506) Mide la intensidad de un terremoto en una escala de I a XII; mientras más alto sea el número, mayor es el daño causado por el terremoto.

960 GLOSSARY/GLOSARIO

mold (p. 568) Fossil that can form when a shelled organism decays in sedimentary rock and is weathered away, leaving a hollowed-out impression.

molecule (p. 61) Combination of two or more atoms joined by covalent bonds.

moment magnitude scale (p. 506) Scale used to measure earthquake magnitude—taking into account the size of the fault rupture, the rocks' stiffness, and amount of movement along the fault—using values that can be estimated from the size of several types of seismic waves.

monoculture (p. 718) Planting of a single plant species, such as corn or wheat, in a field.

moraine (p. 202) Ridge of mixed debris deposited by a melting glacier.

mudflow (p. 185) Rapidly flowing, often destructive mixture of mud and water that may be triggered by an earthquake, intense rainstorm, or volcanic eruption.

mold/molde (pág. 568) Fósil que se puede formar cuando un organismo con concha se desintegra en roca sedimentaria, se meteoriza y queda una impresión hueca.

molecule/molécula (pág. 61) Combinación de dos o más átomos unidos por un enlace covalente.

moment magnitude scale/escala de magnitud momentánea (pág. 506) Escala que se utiliza para medir la intensidad de terremoto (tomando en cuenta el tamaño de la ruptura de la falla, la rigidez de la roca y la cantidad del movimiento a lo largo de la falla) usando valores que pueden estimarse a partir del tamaño de varios tipos de ondas sísmicas.

monoculture/monocultivo (pág. 718) Sembrado de una sola especie de planta, como el maíz o el trigo, en un campo.

moraine/morrena (pág. 202) Acumulación de escombros mezclados que deposita un glaciar que se está derritiendo.

mudflow/flujo o corriente de lodo (pág. 185) Mezcla de lodo y agua que fluye rápidamente y que a menudo es destructiva; puede ser causada por un terremoto, una lluvia intensa o una erupción volcánica.

natural resources (p. 655) Resources provided by Earth, including air, water, land, all living organisms, nutrients, rocks, and minerals.

nebula (p. 822) Large cloud of interstellar gas and dust that collapses on itself, due to its own gravity, and forms a hot, condensed object that will become a new star.

neutron (p. 54) Tiny atomic particle that is electrically neutral and has about the same mass as a proton.

neutron star (p. 825) Collapsed, dense core of a star that forms quickly while its outer layers are falling inward, has a radius of about 10 km, a mass 1.5 to 3 times that of the Sun, and contains only neutrons.

nonfoliated (p. 136) Metamorphic rock that lacks mineral grains with long axes in one direction.

nonpoint source (p. 730) Water-pollution source that generates pollution from widely spread areas, such as runoff from roads.

nonrenewable resource (p. 657) Resource that exists in Earth's crust in a fixed amount and can be replaced only by geological, physical, or chemical processes that take hundreds of millions of years.

natural resources/recursos naturales (pág. 655) Recursos que provee la Tierra; incluyen el aire, el agua, la tierra, todos los organismos vivos, los nutrientes, las rocas y los minerales.

nebula/nebulosa (pág. 822) Nube extensa de gas y polvo interestelares que se hunde sobre sí misma debido a su propia gravedad; forma un cuerpo condensado caliente, que se convertirá en una estrella nueva.

neutron/neutrón (pág. 54) Partícula atómica diminuta, eléctricamente neutra; posee aproximadamente la misma masa de un protón.

neutron star/estrella de neutrones (pág. 825) Centro denso y colapsado de una estrella que se forma rápidamente, mientras sus capas exteriores caen hacia adentro; tiene un radio de aproximadamente 10 km, una masa de 1.5 a 3 veces la del Sol y contiene sólo neutrones.

nonfoliated/no foliada (pág. 136) Roca metamórfica que carece de granos minerales con ejes largos en una dirección.

nonpoint source/fuente no localizada (pág. 730) Fuente de contaminación del agua que genera contaminación a partir de áreas muy separadas, como la escorrentía de los caminos.

nonrenewable resource/recurso no renovable (pág. 657) Recurso que existe en la corteza terrestre en una cantidad fija y sólo puede ser reemplazado por procesos geológicos, físicos o químicos que demoran centenas de millones de años.

normals (p. 360) Standard values for a location, including rainfall, wind speed, and temperatures, based on meteorological records compiled for at least 30 years.

nucleus (p. 54) Positively charged center of an atom, made up of protons and neutrons and surrounded by electrons in energy levels; (p. 797) small, solid core of a comet.

normals/normales (pág. 360) Valores estándares para una ubicación; incluyen la lluvia, la velocidad del viento y las temperaturas y se basan en los registros meteorológicos recopilados durante por lo menos 30 años.

nucleus/núcleo (pág. 54) Centro atómico positivamente cargado, compuesto de protones y neutrones y rodeado por electrones en niveles de energía; (pág. 797) centro pequeño y sólido de un cometa.

oceanography (p. 6) Study of Earth's oceans including the creatures that inhabit its waters, its physical and chemical properties, and the effects of human activities; (p. 385) discipline usually considered to have begun with the Challenger.

ore (p. 89) Mineral that contains a valuable substance that can be mined at a profit; (p. 661) natural resource that may be associated with igneous rocks or formed by processes at Earth's surface.

original horizontality (p. 558) Principle stating that sedimentary rocks are deposited in horizontal or nearly horizontal layers.

original preservation (p. 566) Describes a fossil with soft and hard parts that have not undergone any change since the organism's death.

Ornithischia (p. 632) "Bird-hipped," herbivorous dinosaurs.

orogeny (p. 528) Cycle of processes that form all mountain ranges, resulting in broad mountain belts, most of which are associated with plate boundaries.

orographic lifting (p. 285) Cloud formation that occurs when warm moist air is forced to rise up the side of a mountain.

Ouachita Orogeny (p. 614) Mountain-building event that occurred during the Late Paleozoic when Gondwana collided with the southeastern margin of Laurasia.

outwash plain (p. 202) Area at the leading edge of a glacier, where outwash is deposited by meltwater streams.

oxidation (p. 156) Chemical reaction of oxygen with other substances.

ozone (O3) (p. 273) A gas, formed by the addition of a third oxygen atom to an oxygen molecule, that exists in a layer in the atmosphere and absorbs ultraviolet radiation from the Sun; (p. 724) the major chemical in smog.

oceanography/oceanografía (pág. 6) Estudio de los océanos de la Tierra, incluyendo los seres que habitan en sus aguas, sus propiedades físicas y químicas y los efectos de las actividades humanas sobre ellos; (pág. 385) disciplina que generalmente se considera haber comenzado con las exploraciones del *Challenger*.

ore/mena (pág. 89) Mineral que contiene una sustancia valiosa que se puede extraer con fines de lucro; (pág. 661) recurso natural que puede estar asociado con las rocas ígneas o que puede haberse formado mediante procesos en la superficie terrestre.

original horizontality/horizontalidad original (pág. 558) Principio que establece que rocas sedimentarias se depositan en capas horizontales o casi horizontales.

original preservation/conservación original (pág. 566) Describe un fósil con partes blandas y duras que no han experimentado ningún cambio desde la muerte del organismo.

Ornithischia/Ornithischia (pág. 632) Dinosaurios herbívoros con "caderas de ave".

orogeny/orogenia (pág. 528) Ciclo de procesos que forman todas las cadenas montañosas, dando como resultado cadenas montañosas anchas, la mayor parte de ellos asociados con los límites de las placas.

orographic lifting/levantamiento orográfico (pág. 285) Formación de nubes que ocurre cuando aire húmedo caliente es forzado a elevarse por el costado de una montaña.

Ouachita Orogeny/orogenia Ouachita (pág. 614) Acontecimiento de formación de montañas que ocurrió durante el Paleozoico Tardío, cuando Gondwana chocó contra el margen sureste de Laurasia.

outwash plain/planicie derrubiada (pág. 202) Área en el borde frontal de un glaciar, donde las corrientes de agua de nieve derretida depositan los derrubios.

oxidation/oxidación (pág. 156) Reacción química del oxígeno con otras sustancias.

ozone/ozono (O$_3$) (pág. 273) Gas que se forma al añadir un tercer átomo de oxígeno a una molécula del oxígeno; existe en una capa atmosférica y absorbe la radiación ultravioleta del Sol; (pág. 724) sustancia química principal en el smog.

Glossary

Glossary/Glosario

paleogeography (p. 601) Ancient geographic setting of an area.

paleomagnetism (p. 451) Study of Earth's magnetic record using data gathered from iron-bearing minerals in rocks that have recorded the orientation of Earth's magnetic field at the time of their formation.

Paleozoic fauna (p. 609) Collective name for the animals that dominated the Middle Paleozoic seas.

Pangaea (p. 444) Ancient landmass made up of all the continents that began to break apart about 200 million years ago.

parallax (p. 815) Apparent positional shift of an object caused by the motion of the observer.

partial melting (p. 102) Process in which different minerals melt into magma at different temperatures, changing its composition.

passive margin (p. 602) Edge of a continent along which there is no tectonic activity.

peat (p. 686) Light, spongy, organic fossil fuel derived from moss and other bog plants.

pegmatites (p. 112) Vein deposits of extremely large-grained minerals that can contain rare ores such as lithium and beryllium.

perigee (p. 766) Closest point in the Moon's elliptical orbit to Earth.

perihelion (p. 777) Point in a planet's orbit where it is closest to the Sun.

period (p. 555) Third-longest time unit in the geological time scale, measured in tens of millions of years to hundreds of millions of years, and defined by life-forms that were abundant or became extinct.

permeability (p. 242) Ability of a material to let water pass through, which is high in material with large, well-connected pores and low in material with few pores or small pores.

permineralization (p. 567) Process in which pore spaces in a fossil are filled in with mineral substances.

photosphere (p. 806) Lowest layer of the Sun's atmosphere that is also its visible surface, has an average temperature of 5800 K, and is about 400 km thick.

paleogeography/paleogeografía (pág. 601) Ubicación geográfica antigua de un área.

paleomagnetism/paleomagnetismo (pág. 451) Estudio del registro magnético de la Tierra; utiliza la información recogida de los minerales ferrosos en las rocas, los cuales registraron la orientación del campo magnético de la Tierra en el momento en que se formaron las rocas.

Paleozoic fauna/fauna del Paleozoico (pág. 609) Nombre colectivo para los animales que dominaron los mares del Paleozoico Medio.

Pangaea/Pangaea (pág. 444) Antigua masa terrestre compuesta de todos los continentes, los cuales empezaron a separarse hace aproximadamente 200 millones de años.

parallax/paralaje (pág. 815) Cambio de la posición aparente de un objeto causado por el movimiento del observador.

partial melting/fundición parcial (pág. 102) Proceso en el cual los diferentes minerales se funden en el magma a diferentes temperaturas, cambiando su composición.

passive margin/margen pasivo (pág. 602) Periferia de un continente a lo largo de la cual no ocurre actividad tectónica.

peat/turba (pág. 686) Combustible fósil liviano, esponjoso y orgánico derivado del musgo y otras plantas de ciénaga.

pegmatites/pegmatitas (pág. 112) Vetas de minerales de grano extremadamente grueso que pueden contener minerales raros, como el litio y el berilio.

perigee/perigeo (pág. 766) Punto más cercano a la Tierra en la órbita elíptica de la Luna.

perihelion/perihelio (pág. 777) Punto en la órbita de un planeta cuando está más cercano al Sol.

period/período (pág. 555) Tercera unidad de tiempo más grande en la escala del tiempo geológico; se mide en decenas de millones a centenares de millones de años y se define según las formas de vida que abundaron o que se extinguieron.

permeability/permeabilidad (pág. 242) Capacidad de un material de permitir que el agua lo atraviece, la cual es grande en materiales con poros grandes y bien conectados y baja en materiales con pocos poros o poros pequeños.

permineralization/permineralización (pág. 567) Proceso en que los espacios porosos en un fósil se llenan con minerales.

photosphere/fotosfera (pág. 806) Capa más baja de la atmósfera solar, la cual es su superficie visible. Tiene una temperatura promedio de 5800 K y mide aproximadamente 400 km de ancho.

photovoltaic cells (p. 691) Thin, transparent wafers that convert sunlight into electrical energy and are made up of layers of boron- and phosphorus-enriched silicon.

pillow basalt (p. 536) Igneous rock formed when magma pushes through dikes and erupts onto the seafloor.

planetesimal (p. 794) Space object built of solid particles that can form planets through collisions and mergers.

plasma (p. 69) Hot, highly ionized, electrically conducting gas.

plutons (p. 476) Intrusive igneous rock bodies, including batholiths, stocks, sills, and dikes, formed through mountain-building processes and oceanic-oceanic collisions; can be exposed at Earth's surface due to uplift and erosion.

point source (p. 730) Water-pollution source that generates pollution from a single point of origin, such as an industrial site.

polar easterlies (p. 307) Global wind system that lies between 60∞ latitude and the poles and is characterized by cold air.

polar zones (p. 362) Areas of Earth where solar radiation strikes at a low angle, resulting in temperatures that are nearly always cold; extend from 66.5∞ north and south of the equator to the poles.

pollutant (p. 665) Substance that disrupts Earth's geochemical cycles and can harm the health of living things or adversely affect their activities.

porosity (p. 129) Percentage of open spaces between grains in a rock; (p. 241) is highest in well-sorted sediments.

porphyritic (p. 110) Rock texture characterized by large, well-formed crystals surrounded by finer-grained crystals of the same mineral.

porphyroblasts (p. 136) Large crystals that form in solid rock by the reorganization of atoms during metamorphism.

Precambrian shield (p. 581) Continental core of Archean and Proterozoic rock that may be exposed at the surface or buried by sedimentary rocks.

precession (p. 783) Wobble in Earth's rotational axis.

photovoltaic cells/celdas fotovoltaicas (pág. 691) Láminas delgadas y transparentes que convierten la luz solar en energía eléctrica y que están compuestas de capas de silicio enriquecido con boro y fósforo.

pillow basalt/almohada de basalto (pág. 536) Roca ígnea que se forma cuando el magma atraviesa diques y hace erupción en el fondo del mar.

planetesimal/planetesimal (pág. 794) Cuerpo espacial formado por partículas sólidas y los cuales pueden formar planetas mediante choques y fusiones.

plasma/plasma (pág. 69) Gas caliente, altamente ionizado y conductor de electricidad.

plutons/plutones (pág. 476) Cuerpos rocosos ígneos intrusivos, que incluyen los batolitos, los troncos, las intrusiones y los diques, que se formaron mediante los procesos de creación de montañas y las colisiones oceánicas-oceánicas; pueden estar expuestos a la superficie terrestre debido al levantamiento y la erosión.

point source/fuente localizada (pág. 730) Fuente de contaminación de agua que genera contaminación a partir de un solo punto de origen, como por ejemplo, una ubicación industrial.

polar easterlies/vientos polares del este (pág. 307) Sistema de vientos globales que se encuentra entre los 60° de latitud y los polos y lo caracteriza el aire frío.

polar zones/zonas polares (pág. 362) Áreas de la Tierra donde la radiación solar llega a un ángulo bajo, dando como resultado temperaturas que son casi siempre frías; se extienden desde los 66.5° al norte y al sur del ecuador hasta los polos.

pollutant/contaminante (pág. 665) Sustancia que perturba los ciclos geoquímicos de la Tierra y puede causar daños de salud a los seres vivos o afectar adversamente sus actividades.

porosity/porosidad (pág. 129) Porcentaje de espacios abiertos entre los granos de una roca; (pág. 241) es más alta en sedimentos bien clasificados.

porphyritic/porfirítica (pág. 110) Textura rocosa caracterizada por grandes cristales bien formados y rodeados por cristales del mismo mineral de grano más fino.

porphyroblasts/porfiroblastos (pág. 136) Cristales grandes que se forman en la roca sólida por la reorganización de átomos durante el metamorfismo.

Precambrian shield/escudo precámbrico (pág. 581) Núcleo continental de rocas Arqueanas y Proterozoicas que puede estar expuesto en la superficie o sepultado por rocas sedimentarias.

precession/precesión (pág. 783) Temblor en el eje rotacional de la Tierra.

precipitation (p. 289) All solid and liquid forms of water—including rain, snow, sleet, and hail—that fall from clouds.

prevailing westerlies (p. 306) Global wind system that lies between 30∞ and 60∞ north and south latitude, where surface air moves toward the poles in an easterly direction.

primary wave (p. 498) Seismic wave that squeezes and pulls rocks in the same direction that the wave travels, causing rock particles to move back and forth.

primate (p. 640) Mammal that developed specialized traits, such as opposable thumbs and two eyes directed forward, primarily because of arboreal ancestry.

prime meridian (p. 29) Imaginary line representing 0∞ longitude, running from the north pole, through Greenwich, England, to the south pole.

prokaryote (p. 591) Single-celled organism that lacks a nucleus, is generally small, belongs to the Kingdom Monera, and existed before the Proterozoic.

prominence (p. 809) Arc of gas ejected from the chromosphere, or gas that condenses in the Sun's inner corona and rains back to the surface, that can reach temperatures over 50 000 K and is associated with sunspots.

proton (p. 54) Tiny atomic particle that has mass and a positive electrical charge.

protostar (p. 822) Hot, condensed object at the center of a nebula that will become a new star when nuclear fusion reactions begin.

pyroclastic flow (p. 484) Swift-moving, potentially deadly clouds of gas, ash, and other volcanic material produced by a violent eruption.

precipitation/precipitación (pág. 289) Todas las formas líquidas y sólidas de agua (lluvia, nieve, aguanieve y granizo) que cae de las nubes.

prevailing westerlies/vientos ponientes prevalecientes (pág. 306) Sistema de vientos globales que se localiza entre los 30° y 60° de latitud norte y sur, en donde el aire superficial se mueve hacia los polos en dirección este.

primary wave/onda primaria (pág. 498) Onda sísmica que comprime y hala las rocas en la misma dirección en que se mueve la onda, haciendo que las partículas de la roca se muevan de adelante hacia atrás.

primate/primate (pág. 640) Mamífero que desarrolló rasgos especializados, como los pulgares oponibles y dos ojos dirigidos hacia el frente, principalmente a causa de su ascendencia arbórea.

prime meridian/primer meridiano (pág. 29) Línea imaginaria que representa la longitud 0 y la cual va desde el polo norte, pasa por Greenwich, Inglaterra, hasta el polo sur.

prokaryote/procariota (pág. 591) Organismo unicelular que carece de núcleo, es generalmente pequeño, pertenece al Reino Monera y existió desde antes del Proterozoico.

prominence/prominencia (pág. 809) Arco de gas expulsado de la cromosfera, o gas que se condensa en la corona interna del Sol y que se precipita de nuevo sobre su superficie; puede alcanzar temperaturas mayores a los 50 000 K y se asocia con las manchas solares.

proton/protón (pág. 54) Partícula atómica diminuta que tiene masa y una carga eléctrica positiva.

protostar/protoestrella (pág. 822) Cuerpo condensado caliente en el centro de una nebulosa que se convertirá en una estrella nueva cuando empiecen las reacciones de fusión nuclear.

pyroclastic flow/flujo piroclástico (pág. 484) Nubes de gas, cenizas y otros materiales volcánicos, muy rápidas y potencialmente mortales, producidas por una erupción violenta.

Q

quasars (p. 845) Starlike, very bright, extremely distant objects with emission lines in their spectra.

quasars/cuásares (pág. 845) Cuerpos semejantes a estrellas, muy brillantes y extremadamente lejanos con líneas de emisión en sus espectros.

R

radiation (p. 275) Energy transfer through space by visible light, ultraviolet radiation, and other forms of electromagnetic waves.

radiation/radiación (pág. 275) Transferencia de energía por el espacio a través de luz visible, radiación ultravioleta y otras formas de ondas electromagnéticas.

radioactive decay (p. 562) Emission of atomic particles at a constant rate from a radioactive substance and its resulting change into other elements over time.

radioactivity (p. 58) Spontaneous process of decay, or breaking apart, through which unstable nuclei emit radiation.

radio galaxy (p. 844) Very bright, often giant, elliptical galaxy that emits as much or more energy in the form of radio wavelengths as it does wavelengths of visible light.

radiometric dating (p. 562) Process used to determine the absolute age of a rock or fossil by determining the ratio of parent nuclei to daughter nuclei within a given sample.

radiosonde (p. 314) Balloon-borne weather instrument whose sensors measure air pressure, humidity, temperature, wind speed, and wind direction.

ray (p. 754) Long trail of ejecta that radiates outward from a Moon crater.

recharge (p. 252) Process by which water from precipitation and runoff is added to the zone of saturation.

reclamation (p. 717) Process in which a mining company restores land used during mining operations to its original contours and replants vegetation.

red beds (p. 587) Sedimentary rock deposits that contain oxidized iron, providing evidence that free oxygen existed in the atmosphere during the Proterozoic.

reflecting telescope (p. 749) A type of telescope that uses mirrors to focus visible light.

refracting telescope (p. 749) A type of telescope that uses lenses to focus visible light.

regional metamorphism (p. 134) Process that affects large areas of Earth's crust, producing belts classified as low, medium, or high grade, depending on pressure on the rocks, temperature, and depth below the surface.

regoligh (p. 755) Layer of loose, ground-up rock on the lunar surface.

regression (p. 604) Occurs when sea level falls, causing the shoreline to move seaward, and results in shallower-water deposits overlying deeper-water deposits, with adjacent sediment types overlying each other in vertical succession.

radiactive decay/desintegración radiactiva (pág. 562) Emisión de partículas atómicas de una sustancia radiactiva, a una tasa constante; con el tiempo la sustancia se convierte en otros elementos.

radiactivity/radiactividad (pág. 58) Proceso de desintegración o ruptura espontánea mediante el cual emiten radiación los núcleos inestables.

radio galaxy/radiogalaxia (pág. 844) Galaxia elíptica muy brillante, a menudo gigantesca, que emite tanta o más energía en forma de longitudes de ondas radiales, como lo hace en longitudes de ondas de luz visible.

radiometric dating/datación radiométrica (pág. 562) Proceso que se utiliza para establecer la edad absoluta de una roca o fósil determinando la proporción de núcleos originales a núcleos derivados dentro de una muestra dada.

radiosonde/radiosonda (pág. 314) Instrumento meteorológico que se monta en un globo y cuyos sensores miden la presión atmosférica, la humedad, la temperatura, la velocidad y dirección del viento.

ray/rayo (pág. 754) Largo rastro de ejecta que irradia hacia afuera de un cráter lunar.

recharge/recarga (pág. 252) Proceso mediante el cual el agua de la precipitación y de la escorrentía se añade a la zona de saturación.

reclamation/reclamación (pág. 717) Proceso en que una compañía minera restablece la tierra utilizada durante las operaciones de minería y planta nueva vegetación.

red beds/lechos rojos (pág. 587) Depósitos de roca sedimentaria que contienen hierro oxidado, lo cual proporciona pruebas de que existió oxígeno libre en la atmósfera durante el Proterozoico.

reflecting telescope/telescopio reflector (pág. 749) Tipo de telescopio que utiliza espejos para enfocar la luz visible.

refracting telescope/telescopio refractor (pág. 749) Tipo de telescopio que utiliza lentes para enfocar la luz visible.

regional metamorphism/metamorfismo regional (pág. 134) Proceso que afecta grandes áreas de la corteza terrestre; produce cinturones de bajo, de medio o de alto grado, dependiendo de la presión sobre las rocas, la temperatura y la profundidad debajo de la superficie.

regoligh/regolito (pág. 755) Capa de roca molida suelta en la superficie lunar.

regression/regresión (pág. 604) Ocurre cuando baja el nivel del mar, haciendo que la costa se mueva hacia el mar y resulta en que los depósitos de agua más superficiales cubren los depósitos de aguas profundas con tipos de sedimentos adyacentes que se acumulan uno encima del otro en sucesión vertical.

rejuvenation (p. 227) Process during which a stream resumes downcutting toward its base level, increasing its rate of flow.

relative humidity (p. 283) Ratio of water vapor contained in a specific volume of air compared with how much water vapor that amount of air actually can hold.

remote sensing (p. 37) Process of gathering data about Earth from far above the planet's surface.

renewable resource (p. 656) Natural resource, such as fresh air and most groundwater, than can be used indefinitely without causing a reduction in the available supply.

residual soil (p. 168) Soil located above its parent bedrock.

retrograde motion (p. 776) A planet's backward motion in the sky.

Richter scale (p. 505) Numerical scale used to measure the magnitude of an earthquake, using values based on the size of the earthquake's largest seismic waves.

ridge push (p. 461) Tectonic process associated with convection currents in Earth's mantle that occurs when the weight of an elevated ridge pushes an oceanic plate toward a subduction zone.

rift valley (p. 456) Long, narrow depression that forms when continental crust begins to separate at a divergent boundary.

rill erosion (p. 163) Erosion in which water running down the side of a slope carves a small stream channel.

rille (p. 754) Valleylike structure that meanders across some regions of the Moon's maria.

rock cycle (p. 138) Continuous, dynamic set of processes by which rocks are changed into other types of rock.

RR Lyrae variable (p. 834) Stars with pulsation periods ranging from 1.5 hours to 1 day, generally having the same luminosity, regardless of pulsation period length.

runoff (p. 212) Water that flows downslope on Earth's surface and may enter a stream, river, or lake; its rate is influenced by the angle of the slope, vegetation, rate of precipitation, and soil composition.

rejuvenation/rejuvenecimiento (pág. 227) Proceso en que una corriente reanuda la erosión hacia su nivel base y aumenta su velocidad de flujo.

relative humidity/humedad relativa (pág. 283) Proporción del vapor de agua que contiene un volumen específico de aire comparado con la cantidad de vapor de agua que en realidad puede contener esa cantidad de aire.

remote sensing/percepción remota (pág. 37) Proceso para reunir datos acerca de la Tierra desde muy por encima de la superficie del planeta.

renewable resource/recurso renovable (pág. 656) Recurso natural, como el aire fresco y la mayoría de las aguas subterráneas, que se puede utilizar indefinidamente sin causar una reducción en el suministro disponible.

residual soil/suelo residual (pág. 168) Tierra localizada encima de su lecho rocoso madre.

retrograde motion/movimiento retrógrado (pág. 776) Movimiento hacia atrás de un planeta en el firmamento.

Richter scale/escala de Richter (pág. 505) Escala numérica que se usa para medir la intensidad de un terremoto; emplea valores basados en el tamaño de las ondas sísmicas más grandes del terremoto.

ridge push/empuje de las cordilleras (pág. 461) Proceso tectónico asociado con las corrientes de convección en el manto de la Tierra que ocurre cuando el peso de una cordillera elevada empuja una placa oceánica hacia una zona de subducción.

rift valley/valle de fosas tectónicas (pág. 456) Depresión larga y estrecha que se forma cuando la corteza continental se empieza a separar en un límite divergente.

rill erosion/erosión por surcos (pág. 163) Erosión en la cual el agua que corre cuesta abajo forma un canal pequeño.

rille/surco (pág. 754) Estructura tipo valle que serpentea a través de algunas regiones de los mares lunares.

rock cycle/ciclo de las rocas (pág. 138) Conjunto de procesos continuos y dinámicos a través de los cuales las rocas se transforman en otros tipos de roca.

RR Lyrae variable/variable tipo RR Lyrae (pág. 834) Estrellas con períodos de pulsación que van de 1.5 horas a 1 día; en general tienen la misma luminosidad, a pesar de la longitud del período de la pulsación.

runoff/escorrentía (pág. 212) Agua que fluye cuesta abajo sobre la superficie terrestre y que puede incorporarse a una corriente, río o lago; su velocidad está influenciada por el ángulo de la pendiente, la vegetación, la tasa de precipitación y la composición del suelo.

Saffir-Simpson hurricane scale (p. 344) Classifies hurricanes according to air pressure in the center, wind speed, and property damage potential on a scale ranging from Category 1 to Category 5.

salinity (p. 392) Measure of the amount of salts dissolved in seawater, which is 35 ppt, on average.

Saurischia (p. 632) "Lizard-hipped" dinosaurs—quadrupedal, herbivorous sauropods and bipedal, carnivorous theropods.

scientific notation (p. 16) A type of shorthand used by scientists in which a number is expressed as a multiplier and a power of 10.

sea-breeze thunderstorm (p. 331) Local air-mass thunderstorm that commonly occurs along a coastal area during the summer.

seafloor spreading (p. 453) Hess's theory that new ocean crust is formed at mid-ocean ridges and destroyed at deep-sea trenches; occurs in a continuous cycle of magma intrusion and spreading.

sea level (p. 388) Level of the oceans' surfaces, which is presently rising 1 to 2 mm per year due to melting glaciers

seamount (p. 428) Basaltic, submerged volcano on the seafloor that is more than 1 km high.

season (p. 370) Short-term period of climatic change caused by regular variations in temperature, hours of daylight, and weather patterns that are due to the tilt of Earth's axis as it revolves around the Sun, causing different areas of Earth to receive different amounts of solar radiation.

secondary wave (p. 498) Seismic wave that causes rock particles to move at right angles to the direction of the wave.

sediments (p. 121) Solid particles deposited on Earth's surface that can form sedimentary rocks by processes such as weathering, erosion, deposition, and lithification.

seismic gap (p. 515) Place along an active fault that has not experienced an earthquake for a long time.

seismogram (p. 500) Record produced by a seismometer that can provide individual tracking of each type of seismic wave.

Saffir-Simpson hurricane scale/escala de huracanes de Saffir-Simpson (pág. 344) Clasifica los huracanes según la presión del aire en el centro, la velocidad del viento y el potencial de daño a la propiedad en una escala que va desde la Categoría 1 hasta la Categoría 5.

salinity/salinidad (pág. 392) Medida de la cantidad de sales disueltas en el agua de mar, que en promedio es de 35 ppt.

Saurischia/Saurischia (pág. 632) dinosaurios de "cadera de lagarto"; cuadrúpedos, saurópodos herbívoros y terópodos carnívoros bípedos.

scientific notation/notación científica (pág. 16) Tipo de escritura simplificada que usan los científicos en que un número se expresa como un multiplicador y una potencia de 10.

sea-breeze thunderstorm/tormenta eléctrica de brisa marina (pág. 331) Tormenta de masa de aire local que ocurre comúnmente a lo largo de un área costera durante el verano.

seafloor spreading/expansión del suelo marino (pág. 453) Teoría de Hess que dice que la nueva corteza oceánica se forma en las dorsales mediooceánicas y es destruida en las fosas submarinas profundas; ocurre en un ciclo continuo de intrusión y esparcimiento de magma.

sea level/nivel del mar (pág. 388) Nivel de las superficies de los océanos que actualmente sube de 1 a 2 mm por año, debido al deshielo de los glaciares

seamount/montaña submarina (pág. 428) Volcán basáltico sumergido en el fondo marino y el cual es de más de 1 km de alto.

season/temporada (pág. 370) Período de cambio climático de corto plazo debido a las variaciones regulares en temperatura, horas de luz solar y patrones meteorológicos debido a la inclinación del eje de la Tierra cuando gira alrededor del Sol, lo cual hace que las diferentes áreas de la Tierra reciban diferentes cantidades de radiación solar.

secondary wave/onda secundaria (pág. 498) Onda sísmica que hace que las partículas de las rocas se muevan formando ángulos rectos a la dirección de la onda.

sediments/sedimentos (pág. 121) Partículas sólidas depositadas en la superficie terrestre que puede formar rocas sedimentarias mediante procesos como la metorización, la erosión, la deposición y la litificación.

seismic gap/brecha sísmica (pág. 515) Lugar a lo largo de una falla activa que no ha sufrido un terremoto durante mucho tiempo.

seismogram/sismograma (pág. 500) Registro que produce un sismógrafo y el cual puede proporcionar un registro individual de cada tipo de onda sísmica.

seismometer (p. 500) Instrument used to measure horizontal or vertical motion during an earthquake.

shield volcano (p. 481) Broad volcano with gently sloping sides built by nonexplosive eruptions of basaltic lava that accumulates in layers.

side-scan sonar (p. 386) Technique that directs sound waves at an angle to the seafloor or deep-lake floor, allowing underwater topographic features to be mapped.

silicate (p. 81) Mineral that contains silicon (Si) and oxygen (O) and usually one or more other elements.

sill (p. 477) Pluton that forms when magma intrudes parallel rock layers.

sinkhole (p. 246) Depression in Earth's surface formed when a cave collapses or bedrock is dissolved by acidic rain or moist soil.

slab pull (p. 462) Tectonic process associated with convection currents in Earth's mantle that occurs as the weight of the subducting plate pulls the trailing lithosphere into a subduction zone.

slump (p. 187) Mass movement that occurs when Earth materials in a landslide rotate and slide along a curved surface, leaving a crescent-shaped scar on a slope.

smog (p. 724) Yellow-brown, photochemical haze that occurs when solar radiation acts on air polluted with hydrocarbons and nitrogen oxides from automobile exhausts.

soil (p. 167) Loose covering of weathered rock and decayed organic matter overlying Earth's bedrock that is characterized by texture, fertility, and color and whose composition is determined by its parent rock and environmental conditions.

soil horizon (p. 169) A distinct layer within a soil profile.

soil profile (p. 168) Vertical sequence of soil layers, containing horizon A (topsoil), horizon B (subsoil), and horizon C (weathered parent material).

solar eclipse (p. 765) Occurs when the Moon passes between Earth and the Sun and the Moon casts a shadow on Earth, blocking Earth's view of the Sun; can be partial or total.

solar flare (p. 809) Violent eruption of radiation and particles from the Sun's surface that is associated with sunspots.

solar wind (p. 807) Wind of charged particles that flows throughout the solar system and begins as gas flowing outward from the Sun's corona at high speeds.

seismometer/sismógrafo (pág. 500) Instrumento que se usa para medir los movimientos horizontales o verticales durante un terremoto.

shield volcano/volcán de escudo (pág. 481) Volcán ancho con laderas levemente inclinadas formado por las erupciones no explosivas de lava basáltica que se acumula en capas.

side-scan sonar/sonar de escaneo lateral (pág. 386) Técnica que dirige las ondas sonoras a un ángulo hacia el fondo marino o de un lago profundo, lo que permite trazar el relieve topográfico submarino.

silicate/silicato (pág. 81) Mineral que contiene silicio (Si) y oxígeno (O) y uno o más de otros elementos, generalmente.

sill/intrusión (pág. 477) Plutón que se forma cuando el magma penetra las capas paralelas de roca.

sinkhole/sumidero (pág. 246) Depresión en la superficie terrestre que se forma cuando una caverna se desploma o la lluvia ácida o la tierra húmeda disuelven el lecho rocoso.

slab pull/tracción de placa (pág. 462) Proceso tectónico asociado con las corrientes de convección del manto de la Tierra que ocurre cuando el peso de la placa subductora hala la litosfera hacia una zona de subducción.

slump/desprendimiento (pág. 187) Movimiento de masa que ocurre cuando los materiales terrestres de un deslizamiento giran y se deslizan por una superficie curva y dejan una cicatriz con forma de medialuna en una pendiente.

smog/smog (pág. 724) Neblina fotoquímica ocre que se presenta cuando la radiación solar actúa sobre el aire contaminado con óxidos de nitrógeno e hidrocarburos provenientes de los escapes de automóviles.

soil/suelo (pág. 167) Cubierta suelta de roca erosionada y materia orgánica degradada que cubre el lecho rocoso terrestre; se caracteriza por su textura, fertilidad y color; la roca original y las condiciones ambientales determinan su composición.

soil horizon/horizonte del suelo (pág. 169) Capa distintiva dentro de un perfil del suelo.

soil profile/perfil del suelo (pág. 168) Sucesión vertical de capas de tierra que comprende los horizontes A (capa superficial del suelo), B (subsuelo) y C (material original erosionado).

solar eclipse/eclipse solar (pág. 765) Ocurre cuando la Luna pasa entre la Tierra y el Sol y la Luna proyecta su sombra sobre la Tierra y bloquea el Sol; puede ser parcial o total.

solar flare/erupción solar (pág. 809) Violenta erupción de radiación y partículas desde la superficie del Sol que se asocia con manchas solares.

solar wind/viento solar (pág. 807) Viento de partículas cargadas que fluye a través del sistema solar y comienza como un gas que fluye de la corona del Sol hacia el exterior a altas velocidades.

GLOSSARY/GLOSARIO **969**

solution (p. 65) Homogeneous mixture whose components cannot be distinguished and can be classified as liquid, gaseous, solid, or a combination; (p. 215) in a stream, is created when materials, such as silica ($SiO2$), calcium (Ca), and sodium (Na), dissolve in the stream's water.

sonar (p. 40) Use of sound waves to detect and measure objects underwater.

specific gravity (p. 87) Ratio of the weight of a substance to the weight of an equal volume of $H2O$ at 4∞C.

spectrum (p. 811) Arrangement of visible light ordered according to wavelength.

spinoff (p. 752) NASA technology that has been passed to commercial industries for common use.

spiral density wave (p. 838) Type of wave that creates spiral arms in a galaxy and is composed of alternating regions with variable density that rotate in a fixed pattern.

spring (p. 249) Natural discharge of groundwater at Earth's surface where an aquifer and an aquiclude come in contact.

stability (p. 286) Ability of an air mass to resist rising.

stalactite (p. 248) Cone-shaped or cylindrical dripstone deposit of calcium carbonate that hangs like an icicle from a cave's ceiling.

stalagmite (p. 248) Mound-shaped dripstone deposit of calcium carbonate that forms on a cave's floor beneath a stalactite.

station model (p. 317) Record of weather data for a specific place at a specific time, using meteorological symbols.

steady-state theory (p. 847) Proposes that the universe is the same as it has always been.

stock (p. 477) Irregularly shaped pluton that is similar to a batholith but smaller, generally forms 10-30 km beneath Earth's surface, and cuts across older rocks.

storm surge (p. 345) Occurs when powerful, hurricane-force winds drive a mound of ocean water toward shore, where it washes over the land, often causing enormous damage.

strain (p. 496) Deformation of materials in response to stress.

stratosphere (p. 274) Layer of Earth's atmosphere that is located above the tropopause and is made up primarily of concentrated ozone.

solution/solución (pág. 65) Mezcla homogénea cuyos componentes no se pueden distinguir; puede clasificarse como líquida, gaseosa, sólida o una combinación de éstas; (pág. 215) en una corriente de agua, se crea cuando materiales como el sílice (SiO_2), el calcio (Ca) y el sodio (Na) se disuelven en la corriente de agua.

sonar/sonar (pág. 40) Uso de las ondas sonoras para detectar y medir objetos submarinos.

specific gravity/gravedad específica (pág. 87) Proporción del peso de una sustancia al peso de un volumen igual de H_2O a 4°C.

spectrum/espectro (pág. 811) Arreglo de la luz visible ordenada según su longitud de onda.

spinoff/tecnología derivada (pág. 752) Tecnología de la NASA que se les ha pasado a las industrias comerciales para el uso común.

spiral density wave/onda de densidad espiral (pág. 838) Tipo de onda que crea brazos en espiral en una galaxia y la cual se compone de regiones alternadas con densidad variable que giran en un patrón fijo.

spring/manantial (pág. 249) Descarga natural de agua subterránea en la superficie terrestre donde un acuífero y un acuicludo entran el contacto.

stability/estabilidad (pág. 286) Capacidad de una masa de aire para resistirse a ascender.

stalactite/estalactita (pág. 248) Depósito rocoso de carbonato de calcio, de forma cónica o cilíndrica, que se forma por goteo y que cuelga como un carámbano del techo de una caverna.

stalagmite/estalagmita (pág. 248) Depósito de carbonato de calcio, con forma de montículo, que se forma por goteo en el piso de una caverna, debajo de una estalactita.

station model/código meteorológico (pág. 317) Registro de los datos del tiempo para un lugar específico en un tiempo dado, el cual utiliza símbolos meteorológicos.

steady-state theory/teoría del estado estacionario (pág. 847) Propone que el universo es igual a lo que siempre ha sido.

stock/tronco (pág. 477) Plutón de forma irregular que parece un batolito pero más pequeño, generalmente se forma de 10 a 30 km bajo la superficie terrestre y atraviesa rocas más antiguas.

storm surge/oleaje de tempestad (pág. 345) Ocurre cuando los vientos poderosos con fuerza huracanada arrojan una gran cantidad de agua del océano hacia la costa y la lanzan sobre la tierra, causando a menudo un daño enorme.

strain/tensión (pág. 496) Deformación de materiales en respuesta a un estrés.

stratosphere/estratosfera (pág. 274) Capa de la atmósfera terrestre ubicada por encima de la tropopausa y la cual está compuesta principalmente de ozono concentrado.

streak (p. 85) Color a mineral leaves when it is rubbed across an unglazed porcelain plate or when it is broken up and powdered.

stream bank (p. 222) Ground bordering each side of a stream that keeps the moving water confined.

stream channel (p. 222) Narrow pathway carved into sediment or rock by the movement of surface water.

stress (p. 495) Forces per unit area that act on a material—compression, tension, and shear.

stromatolites (p. 585) Large mats and mounds composed of billions of photosynthesizing cyanobacteria that dominated the Proterozoic's shallow oceans.

subduction (p. 457) Process by which one tectonic plate slips beneath another tectonic plate.

sublimation (p. 68) Process by which a solid slowly changes to a gas without first entering a liquid state.

summer solstice (p. 760) Occurs when the Sun is directly overhead at 23.5∞ north latitude, around June 21, and results in the maximum number of daylight hours for the northern hemisphere and the minimum number for the southern hemisphere.

sunspot (p. 808) Dark spot on the surface of the photosphere that typically lasts two months, occurs in pairs, and has a penumbra and an umbra.

supercell (p. 334) Extremely powerful, self-sustaining thunderstorm characterized by intense, rotating updrafts.

supercluster (p. 842) Gigantic threadlike or sheetlike cluster of galaxies that is hundreds of millions of light-years in size.

supernova (p. 825) Massive explosion that occurs when the outer layers of a star are blown off.

superposition (p. 558) Principle stating that in an undisturbed rock sequence, the oldest rock layers are at the bottom and each successive layer is younger than the layer beneath.

surface current (p. 403) Wind-driven movement of ocean water that primarily affects the upper few hundred meters of the ocean.

surface wave (p. 498) Seismic wave that moves in two directions as it passes through rocks, causing the ground to move both up and down and from side to side.

streak/veta (pág. 85) Color que deja un mineral cuando se frota contra un plato de porcelana sin barnizar o cuando se rompe y se pulveriza.

stream bank/cauce de corriente de agua (pág. 222) Suelo limítrofe a cada lado de una corriente que mantiene restringida el agua en movimiento.

stream channel/canal de corriente de agua (pág. 222) Sendero estrecho labrado en el sedimento o en la roca por el movimiento del agua superficial.

stress/estrés (pág. 495) Fuerzas por unidad de área que actúan sobre un material; compresión, tensión y cizallamiento.

stromatolites/estromatolitos (pág. 585) Montículos grandes compuestos de miles de millones de cianobacterias fotosintéticas que dominaron los océanos superficiales del Proterozoico.

subduction/subducción (pág. 457) Proceso en que una placa tectónica se desliza por debajo de otra.

sublimation/sublimación (pág. 68) Proceso en que un sólido cambia lentamente a un gas, sin pasar primero por el estado líquido.

summer solstice/solsticio de verano (pág. 760) Ocurre cuando el Sol está directamente sobre los 23.5° de latitud norte, alrededor del 21 de junio y tiene como resultado el número máximo de horas de luz de día, para el hemisferio norte y el número mínimo, para el hemisferio sur.

sunspot/mancha solar (pág. 808) Sitio oscuro en la superficie de la fotosfera que dura típicamente dos meses, ocurre en pares y tiene una penumbra y una umbra.

supercell/supercelda (pág. 334) Tormenta autosostenible extremadamente poderosa, caracterizada por intensas corrientes ascendentes giratorias.

supercluster/supercúmulo (pág. 842) Cúmulo gigantesco de galaxias con forma de filamento o lámina que mide centenares de millones de años luz.

supernova/supernova (pág. 825) Enorme explosión que ocurre cuando estallan las capas exteriores de una estrella.

superposition/superposición (pág. 558) Principio que dice que en una sucesión rocosa no alterada, las capas de roca más antiguas están en el fondo y cada capa sucesiva es más reciente que la capa debajo.

surface current/corriente superficial (pág. 403) Movimiento de las aguas del océano producido por el viento y el cual afecta principalmente los primeros cientos de metros superiores del océano.

surface wave/onda superficial (pág. 498) Onda sísmica que se mueve en dos direcciones al pasar a través de las rocas; hace que el suelo se mueva de arriba para abajo y de lado a lado.

suspension (p. 216) State in which small particles, such as silt or sand, are held up and carried along by the turbulence of a stream's moving water.

sustainable energy (p. 703) Involves global management of Earth's natural resources to ensure that current and future energy needs will be met without harming the environment.

sustainable yield (p. 657) Replacement of renewable resources at the same rate at which they are consumed.

synchronous rotation (p. 764) Describes the state at which the Moon's orbital and rotational periods are equal.

suspension/suspensión (pág. 216) Estado en el cual las partículas pequeñas, como el cieno o la arena, no se precipitan y son arrastradas por la turbulencia de una corriente de agua en movimiento.

sustainable energy/energía sostenible (pág. 703) Involucra la administración global de los recursos naturales de la Tierra para asegurar que se satisfagan las necesidades energéticas actuales y futuras sin causar daños al ambiente.

sustainable yield/rendimiento sostenible (pág. 657) Reemplazo de recursos renovables a la misma tasa en que se consumen.

synchronous rotation/rotación sincronizada (pág. 764) Describe el estado en que los períodos de la órbita y de la rotación de la Luna son iguales.

Taconic Orogeny (p. 607) Mountain-building event that occurred during the Middle Ordovician.

temperate zones (p. 362) Areas of Earth that extend between 23.5∞ and 66.5∞ north and south of the equator and have moderate temperatures.

temperature (p. 278) Measurement of how quickly or how slowly molecules move around, which can be measured in degrees Fahrenheit (∞F), degrees Celsius (∞C), or kelvins (K).

temperature inversion (p. 281) Increase in temperature with height in an atmospheric level, which inverts the temperature-altitude relationship and can worsen air-pollution problems.

temperature profile (p. 396) Plots changing ocean water temperatures with depth, which varies, depending on location and season.

tephra (p. 483) Rock fragments, classified by size, that are thrown into the air during a volcanic eruption and fall to the ground.

terrestrial planets (p. 780) Rocky-surfaced, relatively small, dense inner planets closest to the Sun—Mercury, Venus, Earth, and Mars.

Tethys Sea (p. 638) Narrow sea with a strong westward current that moved organisms great distances and, following the breakup of Pangaea, separated Africa and Eurasia before they collided.

Taconic Orogeny/orogenia Tacónica (pág. 607) Acontecimiento de formación de montañas que ocurrió durante el Ordoviciense Medio.

temperate zones/zonas templadas (pág. 362) Áreas de la Tierra que se extienden entre los 23.5° al norte y los 66.5° al sur del ecuador y las cuales experimentan temperaturas moderadas.

temperature/temperatura (pág. 278) Medida de la rapidez con que se mueven las moléculas; puede medirse en grados Fahrenheit (°F), grados centígrados (°C) o Kelvin (K).

temperature inversion/inversión de la temperatura (pág. 281) Aumento de temperatura con la altura en un nivel atmosférico, el cual invierte la relación de la altitud con la temperatura y puede empeorar los problemas de contaminación del aire.

temperature profile/perfil de temperatura (pág. 396) Diagramas que analizan cómo cambia la temperatura del agua oceánica con la profundidad, la cual varía según la ubicación y la temporada.

tephra/tefrita (pág. 483) Fragmentos rocosos que se clasifican por tamaño, son lanzados por el aire durante una erupción volcánica y luego caen al suelo.

terrestrial planets/planetas terrestres (pág. 780) Planetas internos densos, relativamente pequeños con superficie rocosa y cercanos al Sol: Mercurio, Venus, la Tierra y Marte.

Tethys Sea/mar de Tetis (pág. 638) Mar estrecho con una fuerte corriente hacia el oeste que movió los organismos por grandes distancias y, después del rompimiento de Pangaea, separó África y Eurasia antes de que chocaran estos continentes.

972 GLOSSARY/GLOSARIO

theory (p. 19) An explanation based on many observations during repeated experiments that is valid only if it is consistent with observations, makes predictions that can be tested, and is the simplest explanation of observations.

theory of plate tectonics (p. 455) States that Earth's crust and upper mantle are broken into plates, which are huge rock slabs that move in different directions and at different rates over Earth's surface.

thermocline (p. 396) Transitional ocean layer that lies between the relatively warm, sunlit surface layer and the colder, dark, dense bottom layer and is characterized by temperatures that decrease rapidly with depth.

thermometer (p. 312) Weather instrument used to measure temperature that contains a column of mercury or alcohol that expands and rises when heated and contracts and falls when cooled.

thermosphere (p. 274) Layer of Earth's atmosphere that is located above the mesopause and contains only a minute portion of the atmosphere's mass.

tide (p. 400) Periodic rise and fall of sea level caused by the gravitational attraction among Earth, the Moon, and the Sun.

Topex/Poseidon satellite (p. 39) Data-gathering satellite that uses radar to map features on the ocean floor.

topographic map (p. 33) Map that uses contour lines, symbols, and color to show changes in the elevation of Earth's surface and features such as mountains, bridges, and rivers.

tornado (p. 338) Violent, whirling column of air in contact with the ground that forms when wind direction and speed suddenly change with height, is often associated with a supercell, and can be extremely damaging.

trade winds (p. 305) Global wind system that flows at 30∞ north and south latitude, where air sinks, warms, and returns to the equator in a westerly direction.

Transcontinental Arch (p. 601) Series of islands dividing southern Laurentia from north to south during the Cambrian Period, when Laurentia was mostly covered by a shallow, tropical sea.

transform boundary (p. 459) Place where two tectonic plates slide horizontally past each another that is characterized by long faults and shallow earthquakes.

theory/teoría (pág. 19) Una explicación basada en muchas observaciones hechas durante experimentos repetidos que es válida sólo si es consistente con las observaciones, hace predicciones que pueden probarse y es la explicación más sencilla de las observaciones.

theory of plate tectonics/teoría de las placas tectónicas (pág. 455) Establece que la corteza terrestre y su manto superior están separados en placas, que son trozos inmensos de roca que se mueven en diferentes direcciones y a distintas velocidades sobre la superficie terrestre.

thermocline/termoclina (pág. 396) Capa de transición del océano que se encuentra entre la capa superficial iluminada por el Sol y relativamente tibia y la capa inferior, densa, oscura y más fría; se caracteriza por la disminución rápida de las temperaturas con la profundidad.

thermometer/termómetro (pág. 312) Instrumento meteorológico que se utiliza para medir la temperatura que contiene una columna de mercurio o de alcohol, la cual se expande y se eleva cuando se calienta y se contrae y desciende cuando se enfría.

thermosphere/termosfera (pág. 274) Capa de la atmósfera terrestre ubicada por encima de la mesopausa y la cual representa sólo una porción diminuta de la masa de la atmósfera.

tide/marea (pág. 400) Ascenso y descenso periódicos del nivel del mar causados por la atracción gravitatoria entre la Tierra, la Luna y el Sol.

Topex/Poseidon satellite/satélite Topex/Poseidon (pág. 39) Satélite de recolección de datos que usa un radar para trazar el relieve del fondo del océano.

topographic map/mapa topográfico (pág. 33) Mapa que usa curvas de nivel, símbolos y colores para mostrar los cambios en la elevación de la superficie terrestre y rasgos como las montañas, los puentes y los ríos.

tornado/tornado (pág. 338) Violenta columna giratoria de aire en contacto con el suelo, la cual se forma cuando la dirección y la velocidad del viento cambian repentinamente con la altura; se le asocia a menudo con una supercelda y puede ser extremadamente dañino.

trade winds/vientos alisios (pág. 305) Sistema de vientos globales que fluye a 30° de latitud norte y sur, en donde el aire se hunde, se calienta y regresa al ecuador con dirección oeste.

Transcontinental Arch/arco trascontinental (pág. 601) Serie de islas que dividieron el sur de Laurencia de norte a sur durante el Período Cámbrico, cuando Laurencia estaba cubierta, en su mayor parte, por un mar tropical poco profundo.

transform boundary/límite transformante (pág. 459) Lugar donde dos placas tectónicas se deslizan horizontalmente una sobre otra; se caracteriza por fallas grandes y terremotos superficiales.

transgression (p. 603) Occurs when sea level rises and causes the shoreline to move inland, resulting in deeper-water deposits overlying shallower-water deposits with adjacent depositional facies overlying each other in vertical succession.

transported soil (p. 168) Soil that has been moved away from its parent material by water, wind, or a glacier.

travertine (p. 248) A type of limestone found in dripstone formations.

tropical cyclone (p. 341) Large, low-pressure, rotating storm that gets its energy from the evaporation of warm ocean water and the release of heat.

tropics (p. 362) Area of Earth that receives the most solar radiation, is generally warm year-round, and extends between 23.5∞ south and 23.5∞ north of the equator.

troposphere (p. 274) Layer of the atmosphere closest to Earth's surface, where most of the mass of the atmosphere is found and in which most weather takes place and air pollution collects.

trough (p. 399) Lowest point of a wave.

tsunami (p. 513) Large, powerful, ocean wave generated by the vertical motions of the seafloor during an earthquake; in shallow water, can form huge, fast-moving breakers exceeding 30 m in height that can damage coastal areas.

turbidity current (p. 424) Rapidly flowing ocean current that can cut deep-sea canyons in continental slopes and deposit the sediments in the form of a continental rise.

transgression/transgresión (pág. 603) Ocurre cuando el nivel del mar se eleva y hace que la costa se mueva hacia el interior, resultando en depósitos de agua más profunda que cubren los depósitos de agua menos profunda con biofacies depositados adyacentemente unos sobre otros, en sucesión vertical.

transported soil/suelo transportado (pág. 168) Tierra que ha sido retirada de su material de origen por el agua, el viento o un glaciar.

travertine/travertina (pág. 248) Tipo de piedra caliza que se encuentra en en las formaciones rocosas por goteo.

tropical cyclone/ciclón tropical (pág. 341) Tormenta giratoria grande de baja presión, la cual obtiene su energía de la evaporación del agua oceánica tibia y la liberación de calor.

tropics/trópicos (pág. 362) Área de la Tierra que recibe la mayor cantidad de radiación solar, generalmente es caliente todo el año y se extiende entre 23.5° sur y 23.5° norte del ecuador.

troposphere/troposfera (pág. 274) Capa de la atmósfera más cercana a la superficie terrestre donde se encuentra gran parte de la masa atmosférica y en la cual ocurre la mayor parte del tiempo y se acumula la contaminación del aire.

trough/seno (pág. 399) Punto más bajo de una ola.

tsunami/tsunami (pág. 513) Enorme y poderosa ola marina generada por los movimientos verticales del fondo del mar durante un terremoto; en aguas superficiales, puede formar inmensas olas rompientes muy rápidas que exceden 30 m de altura y pueden causar daños a las áreas costeras.

turbidity current/corriente de turbidez (pág. 424) Corriente oceánica de rápido flujo que puede cortar cañones en los taludes continentales y depositar los sedimentos en forma de una elevación continental.

ultramafic (p. 108) Igneous rocks with low silica content and very high levels of magnesium and iron.

unconformity (p. 560) Gap in the rock record caused by erosion or weathering.

Uniformitarianism (p. 557) States that processes such as mountain building, erosion, and sea-level changes that are occurring today have been occurring since Earth formed.

uplifted mountains (p. 537) Mountains that form when large regions of Earth are forced slowly upward without much deformation.

ultramafic/ultramáfica (pág. 108) Rocas ígneas con bajo contenido de sílice y niveles muy altos de magnesio y hierro.

unconformity/disconformidad (pág. 560) Brecha en el registro rocoso causado por la erosión o la meteorización.

uniformitarianism/uniformitarianismo (pág. 557) Establece que los procesos como la formación de montañas, la erosión y los cambios del nivel del mar que ocurren en nuestros días han estado ocurriendo desde que se formó la Tierra.

uplifted mountains/montañas levantadas (pág. 537) Montañas que se forman cuando grandes regiones de la Tierra son forzadas a moverse lentamente hacia arriba sin mucha deformación.

upwelling (p. 405) Upward movement of ocean water that occurs when winds push surface water aside and it is replaced with cold, deep water that originates on the ocean bottom.

upwelling/corriente resurgente (pág. 405) Movimiento ascendente de las aguas del océano que ocurre cuando los vientos empujan hacia un lado el agua superficial y ésta es reemplazada con agua fría profunda que se origina en el fondo de océano.

valence electron (p. 57) Electron in an atom's outermost energy level.

valley glacier (p. 199) Glacier that forms in a valley in a mountainous area and widens V-shaped stream valleys into U-shaped glacial valleys as it moves downslope.

Varangian Glaciation (p. 592) Widespread glaciation event in which ice reached nearly to the equator between 700 and 800 million years ago.

variable star (p. 834) Star in the giant branch of the Hertzsprung-Russell diagram that pulsates in brightness due to its outer layers expanding and contracting.

varves (p. 565) Alternating light-colored and dark-colored sedimentary layers of sand, clay, and silt deposited in a lake that can be used to date cyclic events and changes in the environment.

vascular plants (p. 609) Land plants with the ability to move water through their stems and stalks and which, during the Early Silurian, were small and leafless and grew along the ground.

vent (p. 480) Opening in Earth's crust through which lava erupts and flows out onto the surface.

ventifact (p. 193) Rock shaped by wind-blown sediments.

vernal equinox (p. 761) Occurs when the Sun is directly overhead at the equator and results in day and night of equal length for both northern and southern hemispheres.

viscosity (p. 474) A substance's internal resistance to flow.

valence electron/electrón de valencia (pág. 57) Electrón en el nivel más externo de energía de un átomo.

valley glacier/glaciar de valle (pág. 199) Glaciar que se forma en un valle de un área montañosa; ensancha los valles de corrientes con forma en V generando valles glaciales con forma de U, al moverse cuesta abajo.

Varangian Glaciation/glaciación Varangiana (pág. 592) Amplio acontecimiento glacial en que el hielo casi alcanzó a llegar al ecuador, hace 700 a 800 millones de años.

variable star/estrella variable (pág. 834) Estrella en la rama gigantesca del diagrama de Hertzsprung-Russell cuya luminosidad tiene lugar a impulsos debido a la expansión y contracción de sus capas exteriores.

varves/varves (pág. 565) Capas sedimentarias de colores claros y oscuros alternados, compuestas de arena, arcilla y limo depositados en un lago, las cuales pueden utilizarse para datar acontecimientos cíclicos y cambios en el ambiente.

vascular plants/plantas vasculares (pág. 609) Plantas de tierra con la capacidad de mover agua por sus pedúnculos y tallos y las cuales eran pequeñas y sin hojas y crecían a lo largo del suelo durante el Siluriano Temprano.

vent/chimenea (pág. 480) Abertura en la corteza terrestre por la cual sale lava que fluye hacia la superficie.

ventifact/ventifacto (pág. 193) Roca moldeada por sedimentos arrastrados por el viento.

vernal equinox/equinoccio de invierno (pág. 761) Ocurre cuando el Sol está directamente arriba del ecuador y resulta en que el día y la noche son de igual longitud para los hemisferios norte y sur.

viscosity/viscosidad (pág. 474) Resistencia interna a fluir de una sustancia.

water cycle (p. 290) Continual movement of water between Earth's surface and the atmosphere through evaporation, condensation, and precipitation.

watershed (p. 215) Land area drained by a stream system.

water table (p. 241) Upper boundary of the zone of saturation that rises during wet seasons and drops during dry periods.

water cycle/ciclo del agua (pág. 290) Movimiento continuo del agua entre la superficie terrestre y la atmósfera a través de la evaporación, la condensación y la precipitación.

watershed/cuenca (pág. 215) Área de terreno drenada por un sistema de corrientes de agua.

water table/nivel freático (pág. 241) Límite superior de la zona de saturación que sube durante la temporada de lluvias y disminuye durante los períodos de sequía.

GLOSSARY/GLOSARIO **975**

Glossary

Glossary/Glosario

wave (p. 399) Rhythmic movement that carries energy through matter or space and, in oceans, is generated mainly by wind moving over the surface of the water.

wave refraction (p. 414) Process in which waves advancing toward shore slow when they encounter shallower water, causing the initially straight wave crests to bend toward the headlands.

weather (p. 300) Current state of the atmosphere, including short-term variations such as temperature and precipitation.

weathering (p. 153) Chemical or mechanical process that breaks down and changes rocks on or near Earth's surface and whose rate is influenced by factors such as precipitation and temperature.

well (p. 252) Deep hole drilled or dug into the ground to reach a reservoir of groundwater.

wetland (p. 230) Low-lying land area, such as a bog or marsh, that is covered in water a large part of the year and supports specific plant species.

wind-chill factor (p. 350) Phenomenon measured by the wind-chill index, which estimates the heat loss from human skin caused by a combination of wind and cold air.

winter solstice (p. 761) Occurs when the Sun is directly overhead at 23.5∞ south latitude, around December 21, and results in the minimum number of daylight hours for the northern hemisphere and the maximum number for the southern hemisphere.

wave/onda u ola (pág. 399) Movimiento rítmico que conduce energía a través de la materia o el espacio y, en los océanos, se genera principalmente por el movimiento del viento sobre la superficie del agua.

wave refraction/refracción de onda (pág. 414) Proceso en que las olas avanzan hacia la costa y deceleran cuando encuentran agua menos profunda, lo que hace que sus crestas, inicialmente rectas, se doblen hacia los cabos.

weather/tiempo (pág. 300) Estado actual de la atmósfera que incluye las variaciones a corto plazo, como la temperatura y la precipitación.

weathering/meteorización (pág. 153) Proceso químico o mecánico que rompe y cambia las rocas sobre o cercanas de la superficie terrestre y cuya velocidad se ve influenciada por factores como la precipitación y la temperatura.

well/pozo (pág. 252) Hoyo profundo taladrado o excavado en el suelo para alcanzar un depósito de agua subterránea.

wetland/humedal (pág. 230) Área de tierra baja, como una ciénaga o un pantano, que se encuentra cubierta de agua gran parte del año y la cual alberga especies específicas de plantas.

wind-chill factor/sensación térmica (pág. 350) Fenómeno que mide el índice de sensación térmica y el cual estima la pérdida de calor de la piel humana, causada por una combinación del viento y del aire frío.

winter solstice/solsticio de invierno (pág. 761) Ocurre cuando el Sol está directamente arriba de los 23.5° de latitud sur, alrededor del 21 de diciembre; resulta en el número mínimo de horas de luz solar para el hemisferio norte y el número máximo para el hemisferio sur.

Z

zircon (p. 578) Very stable mineral commonly found in granite that can provide evidence of Earth's crust being at least 4.1 to 4.2 billion years old through radiometric dating.

zone (p. 787) High, cool, light-colored cloud that rises and flows rapidly in the Jovian atmosphere.

zone of saturation (p. 241) Depth below Earth's surface where all the pores of a material are completely filled with groundwater.

zircon/circón (pág. 578) Mineral sumamente estable que se encuentra comúnmente en el granito y que puede proporcionar prueba de que edad de la corteza terrestre es por lo menos de 4.1 a 4.2 mil millones de años por datación radiométrica.

zone/zona (pág. 787) Nube alta, fresca y levemente colorida que se eleva y fluye rápidamente en la atmósfera joviana.

zone of saturation/zona de saturación (pág. 241) Profundidad debajo de la superficie terrestre en donde todos los poros de un material están completamente llenos de agua subterránea.

Page number in boldface indicates the page where the entry is defined.

Evaporites, **130**–131, 148, 613–614, 649
Events, 451 *illus.*
Everest, Sir George, 542
Evolution, **566**. *See also* Life, origins of
Exfoliation, **155**
Exosphere, 273 *illus.*, **274**
Expansion constant. *See* Hubble constant
Experimentation, 12, 929–930. *See also* Discovery Labs; GeoLabs; MiniLabs; Problem-Solving Labs
Exponential growth, **713**, 742
Extinctions. *See* Mass extinctions
Extrasolar planets, 800
Extrusive igneous rocks, **99**, 108 *lab*, 147
Eye, hurricane, **344**
Eyewall, **344**

Fahrenheit scale, 278, 933
Falls, 182
Far Ultraviolet Spectroscopic Explorer, 751
Fault-block mountains, **538**, 548
Faults, **497**, 546, 547; modeling of earthquakes on, 495 *lab*; movement at, 443 *lab*; normal, 497; relative-age dating and, 559; reverse, 497; strike-slip, 497
Fault scarps, 512–513, 548
Fecal materials, energy from, 685, 696
Feedback processes, 584
Feldspars, 919; Bowen's reaction series and, 103–104; crystal structure of, 78 *table*; hardness of, 85 *table*; melting of and magma formation, 102; reaction with carbonic acid, 157
Felsic igneous rocks, **107**, 107 *table*, 147, 180 *lab*
Ferns, 609, 610, 615–616, 650
Fertility, soil, 172–173
Fertilizers, 173, 230, 665, 720
Fetch, 400
Field crops, energy from, 685, 696
Field guide to minerals, 92–93 *lab*
Fine-grained clastics, 128 *table*, 129
Firewood, 685
First aid, 910
First law of thermodynamics, 69
First quarter, 763
Fishes, 432, 609 *illus.*, 615
Fission, 695, **809**
Fissures, 548
Fjords, 420
Flint, 87
Flood basalts, 486 *lab*, 487
Flood monitoring systems, 221
Floodplains, **219**–220
Floods, **219**–221, 265, 347; hurricanes

and, 345; from mild rains, 348 *lab*; from thunderstorms, 337–338, 437
Flood stage, 220
Flowering plants, evolution of, 555
Flows, 182, 185, 265
Flow velocity of groundwater, 242–243
Fluorine, 54 *table*
Fluorite, 85, 85 *table*, 919
Flying reptiles, 631
Focus (earthquake), **499**, 507–508
Focus (orbital), 777, 777 *lab*
Focus on Careers, cosmologists, 860; landscaper, 266; mariculturist, 438; paleoecologists, 650; science teacher, 48; sculptor, 148; urban planners, 742; volcanologist, 548
Foliated metamorphic rocks, 136, 148
Food chains, 683–684
Food, need for by organisms, 711
Fool's gold. *See* Pyrite
Forecasts, weather, 318–321; accuracy of, 320 *illus.*, 321, 436; analog, 320, 437; digital, 319, 437; long-term, 320–321
Forest fires, 335–336
Forestry, 720. *See also* Deforestation
Formaldehyde, 590, 667 *illus.*, 668
Fortified cereals, 53 *lab*
Fossil fuels, 665, 666, **686**–689, 741; formation of, 132, 555; global warming from burning of, 377, 380, 437, 664, 725; locating beds of, 446, 569; as nonrenewable resources, 657, 686
Fossil hunt, 553 *lab*
Fossils, 148, **566**–569, 648; altered hard parts, 567; brachiopod vs. bivalve, 618–619 *lab*; casts, 568; correlating layers of, 561; Ediacaran fauna, 591–592, 648; as evidence of continental drift, 445; as evidence of oxygen in early Earth's atmosphere, 585–586; fossil hunt activity, 553 *lab*; geologic time scale and, 554–556; human origins and, 640–641; index, 568; molds, 568; original preservation, 566; possible evidence of in meteorites, 596; radiometric dating of, 562–563; in sedimentary rocks, 126 *lab*, 127, 131 *illus.*, 132, 148; shape of and buoyancy, 625 *lab*; trace, 568
Foucault pendulum, 758
Fountain Formation, 614 *illus.*
Fractional crystallization, **103**, 147
Fracture, mineral, **87**, 147
Fractures, crust, 495 *lab*, 495–496
Franklin, Benjamin, 354
Freezing, 146
Frequency, wave, **38**, 748

Freshwater. *See also* Freshwater resources; density of, 395; from desalinated seawater, 674–675
Freshwater lakes, 158
Freshwater marshes, 231
Freshwater resources, 8. *See also* Freshwater; conservation of, 732–733; distribution of, 8, 239–240, 240 *table*, 670–671; importance of, 669–670; managing use of, 672–675; pollution of, 255–256, 257 *table*, 730–732; reducing use of, 675; transporting, 673; use of, 254 *illus.*, 671–672, 730
Freshwater wetlands, 230–231, 266
Frontal thunderstorms, **331**
Fronts, **308**–310, 436; cold, 308 *illus.*, 309; occluded, 309 *illus.*, 310; stationary, 309, 309 *illus.*; warm, 308 *illus.*, 309
Frost wedging, **154**, 155 *illus.*
Frozen mammoth carcass, 566, 572
Fuels, **684**, 697. *See also* Alternative energy sources; biomass fuels, 684–686, 696–697; changes in use of, 699 *lab*; earliest uses of, 684; fossil. *See* Fossil fuels; methane hydrates, 736
Fujita, Theodore, 339
Fujita tornado intensity scale, **338**–339, 339 *table*, 437
Full moon, 763
Fungicides, 719
Funnel clouds, 338. *See also* Tornadoes
Fusion, **809**, 810, 821, 822, 859

Gabbro, 107 *table*, 108, 109 *illus.*, 477
Gagarin, Yuri A., 753
Galactic black holes, 836
Galactic center (nucleus), 834, 835
Galactic disk, 834, 835
Galaxies, 839–846, 860; active galactic nuclei (AGNs) and, 844, 846; Andromeda, 839, 841, 842, 846; classification of, 839–840, 852–853 *lab*, 860; distances to, 842–843, 843 *lab*, 845 *lab*; elliptical, 840, 860; groups and clusters of, 841–842; irregular, 840, 860; masses of, 841; Milky Way. *See* Milky Way; movement due to uniform expansion, 842–843, 843 *lab*; quasars in, 845–846; radio, 844; spiral, 839–840, 860; superclusters, 842, 860
Galena, 84, 85 *illus.*, 918
Galilei, Galileo, 778, 858
Galileo, 786
Gamma rays, 38, 747, 748 *illus.*

Gangue, **663**

Ganymede, 787

Garnet, 919

Gas giant planets, **780**, 786–792, 812, 859. *See also Specific planets*

Gasahol, **696**–697, 741

Gaseous solutions, 65, 146

Gases, 68, 146; atmospheric, 272–273; change of state of, 69; pressure-temperature-density relationships, 280–281, 292–293 *lab*

Gasoline, 666

Gastroliths, 568

Gauss normal epoch, 451 *illus.*, 452 *illus.*

Gems, **90**–91, 147

Geocentric model of solar system, 775–776

Geochemical cycles, 664–665, 740

Geochemistry, 7 *table*

GeoDigests, Unit 1 (Earth Science), 48–49; Unit 2 (Composition of Earth), 146–147; Unit 3 (Surface Processes on Earth), 264–266; Unit 4 (The Atmosphere and the Oceans), 436–439; Unit 5 (The Dynamic Earth), 546–549; Unit 6 (Geologic Time), 648–651; Unit 7 (Resources and the Environment), 740–742; Unit 8 (Beyond Earth), 858–861

GeoLabs. *See also* Design Your Own GeoLabs; Discovery Labs; Internet GeoLabs; Mapping GeoLabs; MiniLabs; Problem-Solving Labs; brachiopod vs. bivalve fossils, 618–619 *lab*; crystals, modeling formation of, 114–115 *lab*; epicenters, locating, 516–517 *lab*; precipitation of salt in solution, 70–71 *lab*; pressure-temperature relationships in air, 292–293 *lab*; sedimentary vs. metamorphic rocks, 140–141 *lab*; SI units, measuring with, 20–21 *lab*; stellar spectral lines, 826–827 *lab*; stream velocity and slope, 232–233 *lab*; water masses, modeling, 406–407 *lab*; weathering of halite chips, 174–175 *lab*

Geologic time scale, 554–556, 648. *See also specific eras and periods*; eons, 554; epochs, 554, 556; eras, 554; eras of plant and animal evolution, 555; history-shaping events in, 570–571 *lab*; periods of, 555–556

Geology, **6**, 48

Geomagnetic time scale, 451

Geothermal energy, **693**–694, 741

Geothermal gradient, 101

Geysers, **251**, 693

Gibbs Fracture Zone, 458 *lab*

Gilbert reversal epoch, 451 *illus.*, 452 *illus.*

Ginkgoes, 630

Glacial caves, 875–879

Glacial lakes, 203, 228, 265, 564–565

Glacial till, 202

Glaciation, continental drift and, 446, 447 *illus.*; events of, 198, 570–571 *lab*; Pleistocene, 635; Varangian, 592

Glaciers, **198**–203, 265, 875–879; continental, 200–201; dating of from ice cores, 200 *lab*; deposition by, 168, 202–203, 265, 636 *lab*; distribution of, 198; erosion by, 123, 165, 201–202, 264; evidence of continental drift and, 446; rate of movement of, 206; as source of freshwater, 8 *illus.*, 240 *table*; valley, 199–200

Glasses, **68**

Glass factory, 678

Glassmaking, 678

Glen Canyon Dam, 871, 872–873

Global cooling, 611

Global Positioning Systems (GPS), **40**, 49, 466

Global warming, **376**, 380, 437, **725**–726; combating, 377; deforestation and, 664, 665 *lab*; sea level changes and, 420

Globular star clusters, 834

Glossopteris, 445

Gneiss, 136, 137

Gnomonic projections, 33, 49

Gold, 53, 54, 54 *table*, 84, 85, 662, 716, 918

Gondwana, 444, 612, 613, 614

GPS. *See* Global Positioning Systems (GPS)

Graded bedding, **126**

Gradient, 35; calculating from topographic map, 35 *lab*

Grain size, igneous rock, 108–109

Grand Tetons (Wyoming), 538, 540–541 *lab*

Granite, 68 *illus.*; chemical weathering of, 122 *illus.*; in continental crust, 8; igneous rock classification and, 107 *table*; melting temperature, 102 *illus.*; minerals in, 99 *lab*, 99–100; size of crystals in, 110 *illus.*; uses of, 111

Graphite, 918

Graphs, 17–18, 18 *lab*, 48, 936–938; bar, 937–938; circle, 938; interpreting, 283 *lab*, 423 *lab*, 610 *lab*, 665 *lab*; line, 17–18, 936–937; making and using, 200 *lab*, 217 *lab*

Graptolites, 609 *illus.*

Grasslands, 171, 650

Gravitational contraction, 579, 648

Gravitational water, 242

Gravity, erosion by, 123, 162, 264; mass movements and, 182, 183, 264; Newton's law of universal gravitation, 778–779, 858; planetary orbits and, 778–779

Great Dark Spot, Neptune, 790

Great Lakes, 606, 607 *illus.*

Great Permian Reef Complex, 613–614

Great Red Spot, Jupiter's, 787

Great Rift Valley, 463

Great Salt Lake, 130 *illus.*

Greeks, classification of stars by, 816

Green River Formation, 636

Greenhouse effect, **375**–376, 376 *lab*, 725, 783

Greenwich, England, 29

Grenville Orogeny, 583

Groins, 419

Grooves, 201

Ground subsidence, 255

Groundwater, 8, 239–257, 266, 673–674; cave formation by, 244, 245, 246; dissolution by, 244; karst topography and, 246–247; mineral deposits from, 247–248, 674, 674 *lab*; movement of, 242–243; overuse of, 255, 260, 671–672, 674; pollution of, 255–256, 257 *table*, 258–259 *lab*, 266, 731; protecting, 257; recharge of, 252, 671; stalactite and stalagmite formation, 247–248; storage of, 239 *lab*, 240–241; water *table* and, 241, 242; zone of saturation and, 241–242

Groundwater systems, 249–254, 266. *See also Specific systems*

Growth lines, 609

Gulf of Mexico, 391

Gully erosion, **163**

Guyots, 428

Gypsum, 78 *table*, 80 *illus.*, 85, 85 *table*, 131, 662

Gypsum dunes, 194

Gyres, 404

 H-R diagrams. *See* Hertzsprung-Russell diagram (H-R diagram)

Hachures, 34

Hadley cell, 306

Hadley, George, 306

Hail, 273, 289, 290, 337, 437

Hale-Bopp comet, 796

Half-life, **563**, 563 *table*, 648, 649

Halides, 82 *table*, 83

Halite, 60 *illus.*, 82 *table*, 83; cleavage of, 86–87; from evaporation, 131; pre-

Lightning, 335–336, 437; lightning-protection systems, 354; origins of life and, 590; safety and, 336 *table*; thunder and, 329 *lab*, 335–336

Lightning-protection systems, 354

Light-year (ly), 815

Lignite coal, 687

Limestone, 83; biologic origin of, 131, 148; cave formation and, 65, 157, 244, 245; deposition during Paleozoic, 602, 603 *illus.*, 605, 612; dissolution of, 156 *illus.*, 157, 229, 244, 266; Karst topography and, 246–247; metamorphosis of, 138 *lab*; uses of, 132, 173

Limiting factors, 713–714

Limonite, 661, 919

Line graphs, 17–18, 18 *lab*, 936–937, 938

Lines of longitude, 29

Liquid ethanol, 696, 696–697

Liquid metallic hydrogen, **787**

Liquid methanol, 696

Liquid solutions, 65, 146

Liquids, 68, 69, 146

Liquid volumes, 15

Liter, 15, 48

Lithification, **124**–125, 148

Lithium, 54 *table*, 112

Lithometeors, 299

Lithosphere, 7, **8**, 48; formation of continental, 582–583; information on from seismic waves, 503–504

Lobe-finned fishes, 615

Local Group cluster, 841

Lodestone, 88

Loess, 196–**197**, 265

Logging, 720. *See also* Deforestation

Longitude, **29**, 29 *lab*, 49

Longitudinal dunes, 195, 195 *table*, 265

Longshore bars, **416**, 417 *illus.*

Longshore currents, **416**, 417 *illus.*, 418, 438

Longshore troughs, 416

Low clouds, 287, 287 *table*, 288

Low-grade metamorphism, 137

Low-pressure systems, 310 *illus.*, 311, 436

Luminosity, **817**, 834

Lunar eclipses, **767**, 858

Lunar highlands, **754**, 755

Lunar month, 764, 858

Lunar phases, 762–763, 858

Lunar Prospector, 753

Lunar tides, 402–403

Lung cancer, radon-222 and, 668

Lungfishes, 615

Luster, **84**–85, 147

Lycopods, 609–610, 615–616

 M13, 814

M32, 840 *illus.*

Macrobursts, 336–337

Mafic igneous rocks, **107**, 107 *table*, 108 *lab*, 147

Magellan missions, 781

Magma, 65, **80**, 100–102, 147, 471–475, 546–547. *See also* Volcanoes; andesitic, 473, 474 *table*, 474; basaltic, 473, 474 *table*, 474; Bowen's reaction series and, 103–106; composition of, 100, 474, 474 *table*; crystallization of minerals from, 80, 108–109, 114–115 *lab*; density of, 471 *lab*, 476; formation of, 101–102, 471–473; mountain building and, 478–479; movement of, 471 *lab*; plutons formation, 476–479, 547; rhyolitic, 473, 474 *table*, 475; seafloor spreading and, 453, 454 *illus.*; types of, 100, 101 *table*, 473–475, 546; viscosity of, 474, 474 *lab*, 474 *table*, 475

Magnesium, atomic structure, 55 *table*; chemical symbol, 54 *table*; crystalline structure, 67; ions of, 62; in magma, 100; reaction with oxygen, 63; source of in seawater, 393

Magnesium chloride, 393, 394 *lab*

Magnetic fields, Earth's, 448, 451–452, 464–465 *lab*; Sun's, 808

Magnetic reversals, **451**–452

Magnetism, mineral identification by, 88, 147

Magnetite, 83, 88, 156, 918

Magnetometer, **448**

Magnitude, absolute, 816; apparent, 816; earthquake, 505–506, 547

Main sequence stars, **819**–820, 820 *table*

Major axis, 777

Malachite, 83

Mallory, George, 542

Mammals, 555, 630, 639, 650

Mammoth carcass, frozen, 566, 572

Mammoth Cave, 245, 247

Manganese, 662

Manganese nodules, 429

Mantle, 8, 504, **787**; displacement of, 525–527, 526 *lab*; formation of, 577 *lab*

Mantle convection, plate tectonics and, 460–462

Map legends, **35**, 36 *illus.*, 49

Map profiles, 540–541 *lab*

Mapping GeoLabs. *See also* Discovery Labs; GeoLabs; MiniLabs; Problem-Solving Labs; coastal landforms, 430–431 *lab*; continental growth during Precambrian, 594–595 *lab*;

landslide locations, 204–205 *lab*; map profile of Grand Tetons, 540–541 *lab*; paleomagnetic maps, 464–465 *lab*; pollution plumes, tracking, 258–259 *lab*; relative ages of lunar features, 768–769 *lab*; topographic maps, 42–43 *lab*; weather maps, 322–323 *lab*

Maps, 27–36, 49. *See* Topographic maps; conic projections, 32; equator on, 28; gnomonic projections, 33; hurricane-tracking, 346, 352–353 *lab*; International Date Line on, 31; isochron. *See* Isochron maps; legends on, 35; lines of latitude on, 27–28; lines of longitude on, 29; making and using, 27 *lab*; Mercator projections, 32; physiographic of Earth, 912–913; prime meridian on, 28 *illus.*, 29; scale on, 35–36; time zones on, 30, 31 *illus.*; weather. *see* Weather maps

Map scales, 35 *lab*, **35**–36, 49

Marble, 83

Margins, plate, 601–602. *See also* Plate boundaries

Maria, lunar, **754**, 755, 768–769 *lab*

Marianas Trench, 422, 449, 458

Mariculturist, 438

Marine organisms, anglerfish, 432; Mesozoic, 628–629; Paleozoic, 604, 615; reef formation by, 605–606; sediments from shells of, 429

Mariner 10, 780

Mariner 4, 784

Mariner 9, 784

Marine regression, 617

Marine sediments, 413 *lab*, 428 *lab*, 428–429, 531

Marine terraces, 421

Marine west coast climates, 366

Maritime polar (mP) air masses, 302, 303 *illus.*, 304 *table*

Maritime tropical (mT) air masses, 302, 303 *illus.*, 304 *table*

Mars, 577, 784–785, 859, 921

Mars Global Surveyor, 784

Mars Pathfinder, 784

Marshes, 231, 266

Mass, of galaxies, 836, 841, 842; measurement of, 14–15, 933; units of, 909 *table*

Mass extinctions, 570–571 *lab*, 610–**611**; Mesozoic era, 555, 620, 633–634; Paleozoic era, 555, 611, 617, 620, 649, 650; Permian, 616–617, 620; Proterozoic eon, 592

Massive stars, life cycle of, 824–825

Index

Index

464–465 *lab*
Paleomagnetism, **451**–452
Paleontology, 7 *table*, 22
Paleozoic Era, 554, 601–617, 649–650;
continental setting during, 601–602;
day length, 609, 610 *lab*; life during,
555, 604, 609–611, 615–616, 649,
650; mass extinctions during,
610–611, 616–617, 649; periods of,
602 *table*; reef formation during,
605–606, 613–614; sea level changes,
603–604, 605–606, 612–613, 649,
650; tectonic activity in, 606–608,
614–615
Paleozoic fauna, **609**
Palisades Sill, 477
Pancaking, 511
Pangaea, **444**, 605 *illus.*, 612, 625–626,
635, 649, 650
Papua New Guinea, rain forests of, 706
Parabolas, 777
Parabolic dunes, 195, 195 *table*, 265
Para-dichlorobenzene, 667 *illus.*
Parallax, **815**, 817 *lab*, 859
Parallax shifts, 812, 817 *lab*
Parent elements, 562
Parsec (pc), 815
Partial melting, **102**–103, 147
Partial solar eclipse, 765
Particle accelerators, 854
Particulate matter, 724, 728 *lab*
Pascal (Pa), 909 *table*
Passive margins, **602**
Passive solar heating, 690, 741
Pathfinder, 751
Pearls, 618–619 *lab*
Peat, **686**, 741
Pegmatites, 107 *table*, **112**
Pennsylvanian Period, 554 *illus.*, 555,
612–613, 616
Penumbra, 765, 767, 808 *illus.*
Percussion flaking, 116
Peridotite, 8, 107 *table*, 108, 504
Perigee, **766**
Perihelion, **777**
Periodic comets, 797
Periods, **555**–556, 648
Periodic *Table* of Elements, 55, 58 *illus.*,
917
Permafrost, 171, 566, 572
Permeability, **242**
Permiam Kaibab Formation, 561
Permian mass extinction, 616–617, 620
Permian Period, 554 *illus.*; mass extinc-
tion during, 616–617, 620; orogenic
activity during, 614–615; reef forma-
tion during, 613–614
Permineralization, **567**

Permo-Triassic Extinction Event,
616–617, 620
Pesticides, 719
Petrified wood, 567
Petroleum, 686, 688–689, 741; changes
in use of, 699 *lab*; distribution of,
657–658; drilling for in rain forests,
706; formation of, 688–689; locating
deposits of, 569, 689; migration of,
688 *lab*, 689; storage of in rocks, 132,
601 *lab*, 614; use per day, 658 *illus.*
pH scale, 66, 157–158, 727
Phanerozoic Eon, 554, 583
Phases, moon, 762–763
Phobos, 784
Phosphate, 132
Phosphorus, 54 *table*
Phosphorus fertilizers, 173
Photochemical changes, 667, 724
Photochemical smog, 667
Photos, interpreting, 139
Photosphere, **806**, 859
Photosynthesis, atmospheric oxygen
from, 584, 585–586, 587, 649, 664;
capture of light energy by, 683–684;
eutrophication and, 229–230; global
warming and, 377, 380
Photovoltaic cells, **691**–692
Physical weathering. *See* Mechanical
weathering
Physiographic map of Earth, 912–913
Phytoplankton, 625 *lab*, 628
Pillow basalts, **536**
Pilocene Epoch, 554 *illus.*
Pioneer 10, 786, 788
Pioneer 11, 786, 788
Placer deposits, 662
Plagioclase, 107
Planetary nebula, 823
Planetesimals, **794**–795
Planets, 780–792, 859, 920. *See also*
Specific planets; detecting new, 800;
extrasolar, 800; formation of,
794–795, 859; Kepler's second law
and, 778; Kepler's third law and, 791
lab; missions to, 775 *lab*; orbits of,
776–779, 777 *lab*; relationship
between elliptical orbit and orbital
period, 778, 791 *lab*; retrograde
motion of, 776; scale model of,
798–799 *lab*
Plants, angiosperms (flowering), 630;
appearance of in geologic time scale,
554 *illus.*, 555; capture of light energy by, 683–684; coal from, 555,
612–613; erosion by, 166; fossils of,
566–570; global warming and, 377,
380; as renewable resources,

656–657; seed, 610, 650; terrestrial,
555, 609–610, 649; vascular, 609–610
Plasmas, **69**, 146
Plate boundaries, 455–459, 458 *lab*, 546;
convergent, 455 *illus.*, 457–459;
divergent, 455 *illus.*, 456; earthquakes
and, 509–510; mantle convection
and, 461; transform, 455 *illus.*, 459;
volcanoes on, 484–486
Plates, 546
Plate tectonics, 7 *table*, **455**–459, 546;
absence of on moon, 756; causes of
plate movement, 460–463, 546; continent formation and, 582–583; early
observations of, 443–444; interaction
of plates at boundaries, 443 *lab*,
455–459, 456 *lab*, 458 *lab*; mountain
building and. *See* Orogeny; movement at faults, 443 *lab*; ocean basin
formation, 456, 456 *lab*; seafloor
spreading and, 453–454; unanswered
questions about, 462–463; Wegener's
hypothesis of continental drift,
444–447
Platinum, 106, 661
Pleiades, 814
Pleistocene Epoch, 554 *illus.*, 566, 635,
650
Pleistocene glaciation, 635
Plesiosaurs, 629
Pliocene Epoch, 635, 635 *illus.*
Plucking, 201
Pluto, 791–792, 859, 921
Plutons, **476**–479, 547, 791–792
Point sources, **730**, 731, 734–735 *lab*
Polar bears, range of, 44
Polar climates, 366, 367 *illus.*, 437
Polar easterlies, 305 *illus.*, **307**
Polarity of Earth's magnetic field,
451–452
Polar jet stream, 307
Polar molecules, **61**–62
Polar soils, 170 *illus.*, 171, 264
Polar zones, 44, **362**
Pollutants, **665**, 740; changes in emis-
sions of, 728 *lab*
Pollution, 740, 742; acid precipitation.
See Acid precipitation; from agricul-
ture, 719, 720; air. *See* Air pollution;
climatic change and, 377; groundwa-
ter, 255–256, 257 *table*, 258–259 *lab*,
266, 731; industrial, 234, 255,
721–722; from landfills, 721, 722;
from mining, 663, 716–717; ozone
depletion and, 294, 726; pinpointing
sources of, 734–735 *lab*; from urban
development, 721–723; water. *See*
Water pollution

313, 916
Relative humidity chart, 313
Remote sensing, **37**–41, 49
Renewable resources, **656**–657, 711 *lab*, 740
Reptiles, 616, 629, 631, 633
Reservoirs, 672–673, 741
Residual soil, **168**, 264
Resources, 740–741. *See also* Energy resources; natural resources; everyday use of, 711 *lab*; origins of common, 655 *lab*
Results, communicating, 17–18
Retrograde motion, **776**
Retrograde rotation, 781
Reverse faults, 497, 547
Reversed polarity, 451
Rhyolitic magma, 100, 101 *table*, 473, 474 *table*, 475, 546
Ribonucleic acid (RNA), 590–591
Ribozymes, 590–591
Richter, Charles, 505
Richter scale, **505**, 547
Ridge push, **461**
Rift valleys, **456**, 485
Rift zones, 485–486
Rill erosion, **163**
Rilles, **754**, 755, 768–769 *lab*
Rings, planetary, 787, 788, 789, 790, 859
Rip currents, 417
Ripple marks, 148
Rivers, 214, 266. *See also* Streams
River systems, 214
RNA (ribonucleic acid), 590–591
"RNA world" hypothesis, 590–591
Rock cycle, **138**–139, 140–141 *lab*, 148
Rock falls, 182 *illus.*, 188, 264
Rock gypsum, 128 *table*
Rocks, absolute-age dating of, 562–563, 648; aggregates, 660–661, 740; bedrock, 169, 264, 740; erosion of. *See* Erosion; evidence of atmospheric oxygen from, 585–586; evidence of continental drift from, 444; fossils in. *See* Fossils; igneous. *See* Igneous rocks; magnetism of, 451; matching layers of, 561; melting of, 101–103; metamorphic. *See* Metamorphic rocks; on ocean floor, 450; oldest, 578; permeability of, 242, 601 *lab*; relative-age dating of, 557–561; the rock cycle and, 138–139; sedimentary. *See* Sedimentary rocks; types of, 920; weathering of. *See* Weathering
Rock salt, 128 *table*
Rock slides, 186, 264
Rocky headlands, 413, 414–415
Rocky Mountains, 636

Rodinia, 582–583, 601, 602 *illus.*
Roman aquiducts, 673
Round elliptical galaxies, 840
RR Lyrae variables, 834
Rubidium-87, 563 *table*
Rubies, 90, 91
Rudists, 628
Runoff, 212–214
Rust, 64
Rutile, 89 *illus.*

S S-waves (Secondary waves), 498, 547; information on Earth's interior from, 502–504; locating epicenters by, 501, 508–509, 516–517 *lab*; travel-time curves of, 501, 502 *lab*, 508–509, 516–517 *lab*
Safe Drinking Water Act (1974), 732
Safety, hurricanes and, 346 *table*; laboratory, 12–13, 13 *table*, 910–911; lightning and thunderstorms and, 336 *table*; tornadoes and, 339–340, 340 *table*
Saffir-Simpson hurricane scale, **344**, 344 *table*, 437
Sagittarius A*, 836
Salinity, **392**–393, 395, 406–407 *lab*
Saltation, 191
Salton Sea, 214 *illus.*
Salts. *See also* Seawater; atmospheric, 272, 285; deposits of in Great Lakes region, 606, 607 *illus.*; from desalinated seawater, 676–677 *lab*; groundwater pollution and, 256; mining of, 662; precipitation of from solution, 70–71 *lab*
Salt water. *See* Seawater
Saltwater incursion, 256 *illus.*
San Andreas Fault, 443 *lab*, 459, 497, 515, 636
Sand, 172, 172 *lab*, 172 *table*, 241, 242, 264
Sand dunes. *See* Dunes
Sandbars, 164
Sand-slope activity, modeling, 181 *lab*
Sandstone, 128 *table*, 129, 602, 603 *illus.*
Sandstone-shale-limestone sequence, deposition of, 602, 603 *illus.*
Sap, fossil insects in, 566
Sapphires, 91
Satellites. *See also specific satellites*; GPS, 40, 466; planets and moons, 775; remote sensing with, 38–41; space-based observatories, 751; weather, 315–316, 436
Saturated solutions, 70–71 *lab*, 80
Saturn, 788–789, 859, 921
Saurischian dinosaurs, **632**

Sauropods, 632
Savannas, 365
Scale, map. *See* Map scale
Scale models, dinosaur weight from, 644; solar system, 798–799 *lab*
Scanning electron microscopes (SEM), 72
Scarps, 780–781
Schist, 136
Science & Math, carbon dioxide increases and global warming, 380; diamonds, price of, 94; Earth's circumference, determining, 770; glacial movement, rate of, 206; Mount Everest, measuring height of, 542; polar bears, range of, 44
Science & Technology, atmospheric change, tracking, 324; CT scanning of fossil remains, 22; electron microscopes, 72; global positioning systems (GPS), 466; lightning-protection systems, 354; obsidian scalpels, 116; particle accelerators and study of universe, 854; weight of a dinosaur, 644
Science & the Environment, climate change from Tambora eruption, 490; deep-sea fishes, 432; erosion on barrier islands, 176; High Plains (Ogallala) Aquifer, 260; mass extinctions, 620; methane hydrates, 736; pollution of Lake Baikal, 234
Science in the News, crayons, safety of, 142; discovery of extrasolar planets, 800; the *Endurance* (Antarctic exploration), 408; frozen mammoth carcass, 572; Izmet, Turkey, earthquake (1999), 518; ozone depletion, 294; so-called fossils in meteorites, 596; Wistar's glass factory, 678
Science teacher, 48
Scientific diagrams, interpreting, 510
Scientific illustrations, interpreting, 36, 63 *lab*, 110 *lab*, 138 *lab*, 311, 926–928
Scientific law, **19**, 48
Scientific method, 11–13, 48, 928–931; analysis and conclusions, 13; experimentation, 12, 929–930; hypotheses, 11, 928–929
Scientific notation, **16**, 48
Scientific theory, **19**, 48
Sculptors, 148
Sea Beam technology, 40–41
Sea-breeze thunderstorms, **331**
Sea caves, 414–415
Seafloor. *See* Ocean floor
Seafloor spreading, **453**–454, 546; at divergent boundaries, 456, 456 *lab*;

Index

Index

Index

Index

formation and, 413–415, 438; height of, 400; landforms formed by, 417–419; refraction of, 414; sediment transport by, 415, 416

Waves, seismic. *See* Seismic waves

Waxing, 762

Waxing crescent, 762

Waxing gibbous, 762–763

Weather, **300**–321, 436–437. *See also Specific events*; air masses and, 299 *lab*, 301–304; analysis of, 317–318, 318 *lab*, 436–437; angle of Sun's rays and, 300–301, 302 *lab*, 436; climate vs., 300, 436; forecasting, 318–321, 436; mapping of, 317–318, 318 *lab*, 322–323 *lab*; measurement tools for, 312–316; systems of. *See* Weather systems

Weather forecasts, 318–321, 324, 436

Weathering, 121–122, 148, **153**–161, 264; chemical, 155–159, 264; concentration of ores by, 662; mechanical, 154–155, 159–160, 163 *lab*, 174–175 *lab*, 264; rate of, 158–161, 174–175 *lab*; soil formation and, 167, 168; surface area and, 153 *lab*, 161

Weather instruments, 312–315, 436; anemometers, 313; barometers, 312–313; ceilometers, 313; hydrometers, 313; radiosonde, 314, 436; rain gauges, 313; thermometers, 312; weather radar, 314–315, 436; weather satellites, 315–316, 436

Weather maps, 317, 317–318, 436; create and analyze, 318 *lab*; interpreting, 322–323 *lab*; symbols on, 317 *table*, 436, 915

Weather radar, 314–315, 436

Weather satellites, 315–316, 436

Weather systems, 305–311; Coriolis effect and, 305; fronts, 308–310; jet streams, 307–308; pressure systems, 310–311; wind systems, 305–307

Wegener, Alfred, 444–447, 532, 546

Weight, of a dinosaur, 644; measurement of, 14

Wells, **252**–253, 253 *lab*, 254 *lab*, 266

Wetlands, freshwater, **230**–231, 266

Wet scrubbers, 729

White dwarfs, 820, 823, 824, 859

White smokers, 427

Wildlife refuges, 659

Willo (*Thescelosaurus* fossil), 22

Wind, 282, 436; deposition by, 194–197, 265; energy from, 694–695; erosion by, 123, 165–166, 191–193, 194 *lab*, 264, 265; measurement of, 313; thunderstorms and, 336–337, 437

Wind barriers, 166, 264

Wind-chill factor, **350**

Wind-chill index, **350**–351

Wind farms, 694

Windmills, 694

Windows, energy efficient, 703

Wind speed, 400, 436

Wind systems, 305–307, 436; polar easterlies, 307; prevailing westerlies, 306–307; trade winds, 305–306

Wind transport, 191–193

Wind turbines, 694

Winter solstice, **762**

Wistar, Caspar, 678

Wobble, Earth's axis, 373, 437, 783

Wood, energy from, 685, 696

Worm trails, 568, 569 *illus.*

Wulfenite, 78 *table*

 X rays, 747, 748

X–ray telescopes, 828

Xenon, 272 *illus.*

Xeriscaping, 733 *illus.*

Year, determining length of during periods, 609

Yucatan Peninsula, 565, 633 *illus.*, 634

Zenith of the observer, 759 *illus.*

Zircon, 88, **578**

Zone of saturation, **241**–242, 266

Zones, Jupiter's, **787**

Credits

ART CREDITS

Morgan-Cain and Associates: xvii, 11, 18, 25, 30(b), 31, 34, 35(t), 38-39, 41, 45(c), 47(l), 78, 81(t), 59, 66, 100-104, 106-107, 110, 122, 125, 130, 133, 134(b), 135-136, 139, 145, 157-158, 160-161, 173, 179, 200, 209, 212-214, 217, 219-220, 223, 225, 233, 236, 241-243, 246, 250, 252, 254-256, 261, 263, 272, 274-275, 278-279, 283, 296-297, 301, 305-311, 317, 320, 326, 331, 332-335, 338, 343, 345, 356, 361-364, 367, 369-370, 372-373, 375, 383, 388-389, 395-403, 405-406, 411, 414, 416-417, 422-423, 435, 448, 450-452, 454, 456-457, 459, 461, 465-466, 468-469, 472, 476, 493, 496-504, 509, 519-520, 525-526, 529-531, 533, 535-538, 541(b), 544-545, 554, 558-562, 567-569, 575, 578, 580-581, 595, 597, 599, 602(t), 603, 606, 610, 613, 622, 623, 626, 630(b), 631, 632(t), 635, 646, 658, 665, 667, 672, 681, 689, 698, 705, 708-709, 714-715, 721-722, 725, 727, 730, 738-739, 748-749, 756-757, 759-767, 770, 772-773, 776-780, 782-784, 787-791, 795, 797, 801-803, 811-813, 815-816, 818-819, 821-824, 827, 835-838, 840-841, 847, 849, 851, 855-857, 914-915, 922, 927(b), 937-938

Barbara Hoopes Ambler: 604, 609, 615, 629, 630(t), 632(b), 640-641

Michael Woods: 167, 169, 592

Glencoe: 56-58, 61-63, 67, 73-74, 81(b), 82, 726, 917

Precision Graphics: 28, 30(t), 32-33, 35(b), 45(t), 47(r), 126, 134(t), 159, 170, 182-184, 186-187, 191-193,195-198, 201, 205, 215, 251, 273, 276, 285-288, 291, 303, 315, 319, 323, 330, 342, 353, 390, 393, 404, 415, 434, 443-445, 455, 473, 477, 481-483, 485, 487, 508, 510, 514, 517, 524, 528, 582-583, 602(b), 605, 607-608, 612, 633, 637-638, 671, 735, 908, 927(t)

PHOTO CREDITS

Cover Galen Rowell/Mountain Light Photography; **vii** EIT/SOHO/NASA; **ix** (t)Geoff Tompkinson/Science Photo Library/Photo Researchers, (b)Poulet/Liaison; **x** (t)M.I. Walker/Photo Researchers, (b)Galen Rowell/CORBIS; **xi** Joe Sohm/The Stock Market; **xii** Jack Dykinga, **xiii** NASA; **xiv** Matt Meadows; **xv** James L. Amos/Photo Researchers; **xvi** Warren Faidley/Weatherstock; **xviii** Wolfgang Kaehler/Science Photo Library; **xx** AP/Wide World Photos; **xxi** CXC/SAO/NASA; **xxii** Ed Viesturs; **xxiii** John Noel Photographic Collection; **2-3** Jack Dykinga; **4** Larry Ulrich; **5** Matt Meadows; **6** (t)Roger Ressmeyer/CORBIS, (b)Simon Fraser/Science Photo Library/Photo Researchers; **7** (tl)Everett Johnson/Stone, (tr)Jeremy Woodhouse/DRK Photo, (cl)Paul A. Souders/CORBIS, (cr)Chip Clark, (bl)Laurence Parent, (br)Herb Lingl/Black Star; **8** Flip Nicklin/Minden Pictures; **9** Jeremy Woodhouse/DRK Photo; **10** Larry Lefever/Grant Heilman Photography; **12** Matt Meadows; **14** NASA; **15** (t)Matt Meadows, (b)Runk/Schoenberger/Grant Heilman Photography; **16** David Malin/Anglo-Australian Observatory; **17** Matt Meadows; **19** (l)Victoria & Albert Museum, London/Art Resource, NY, (r)Bettmann/CORBIS; **20** Matt Meadows; **22** Ira Block/National Geographic Image Collection; **23** (t)Jeremy Woodhouse/DRK Photo, (c,b)Matt Meadows; **26** CORBIS; **27** Aaron Haupt; **35** USGS; **36** National Geographic Maps; **37** Boeing; **38** NASA/AP/Wide World Photos; **40** Doug Martin; **43** USGS; **44** Geostock/PhotoDisc; **45** Boeing; **48** Wayne Newton/PhotoEdit; **49** USGS/NASA; **50-51** Roger Du Buisson/The Stock Market; **52** James L. Stanfield/National Geographic Image Collection; **53** Doug Martin; **54** (l)Richard Megna/Fundamental Photographs, (c)L.S. Stepanowicz/Visuals Unlimited, (r)Kaj R. Svenson/Science Photo Library/Photo Researchers; **55** Matt Meadows; **60** Richard Megna/Fundamental Photographs; **64** (t)Bruce Iverson, (b)PhotoDisc; **65** (t)Matt Meadows, (b)John Evans; **66** (l to r) StudiOhio, Mark Burnett, StudiOhio, Matt Meadows, Amanita Pictures, StudiOhio, Aaron Haupt; **67** (l)Andrew Syred/Science Photo Library/Photo Researchers, (r)Chip Clark; **68** (t)Aaron Haupt, (c)John Evans, (b)Tony Freeman/PhotoEdit; **69** EIT/SOHO/NASA; **70 71** Matt Meadows; **72** (l)Andrew Syred/Science Photo Library/Photo Researchers, (c)Dr. Jeremy Burgess/Science Photo Library/Photo Researchers, (r)SCIMAT/Photo Researchers; **73** (t)Bruce Iverson, (b)Tony Freeman/PhotoEdit; **76** Chip Clark;

77 Matt Meadows; **78** (t)M. Claye Jacana/Photo Researchers, (b, l to r)Charles D. Winters/Photo Researchers, Mark A. Schneider/Visuals Unlimited, Mark A. Schneider/Visuals Unlimited, Biophoto Associates/Photo Researchers, Runk/Schoenberger/Grant Heilman Photography, Doug Martin; **79** (l)Robert De Gugliemo/Science Library/Photo Researchers, (r)Barry L. Runk/Grant Heilman Photography; **80** Martin Miller/Visuals Unlimited; **83** Chip Clark; **84** (l)Mark A. Schneider/Visuals Unlimited, (c)Charles D. Winters/Photo Researchers, (r)Runk/Schoenberger/Grant Heilman Photography; **85** (tl)Mark A. Schneider/Visuals Unlimited, (tr)Runk/Schoenberger/Grant Heilman Photography, (b)Fundamental Photographs; **87** (l)Tom Ives/The Stock Market, (c)Runk/Schoenberger/Grant Heilman Photography, (r)Doug Martin; **88** Paul Silverman/Fundamental Photographs; **89** (t,br)Paul Silverman/Fundamental Photographs, (bl)AP/Wide World Photos; **90** AFP/CORBIS; **91** (l)Biophoto Associates/Photo Researchers, (r)Chip Clark; **92** Matt Meadows; **94** Rick Gayle/The Stock Market; **95** (t)Biophoto Associates/Photo Researchers, (b)Tom Ives/The Stock Market;
97 Photo Researchers; **98** Alfred Pasieka/Science Photo Library/Photo Researchers; **99** Matt Meadows; **100** (l)Runk/Schoenberger/Grant Heilman Photography, (r)Phillip Hayson/Photo Researchers; **101** Robert Garvey/CORBIS; **104** A.J. Copley/Visuals Unlimited; **105** Craig A. Cox; **108** (l)Paul Silverman/Fundamental Photographs, (r)Christena M. Cox; **109** (tl)Andrew J. Martinez/Photo Researchers, (tr)Doug Martin, (b)Andrew J. Copley/Visuals Unlimited; **110** (l)Barry L. Runk/Grant Heilman Photography, (r)Doug Martin; **111** (t)Aaron Haupt, (bl)Jeremy Woodhouse/DRK Photo, (br)AFP/CORBIS; **112** (t)Tom McHugh/Photo Researchers, (bl)Doug Martin, (br)University of Houston; **113** (l)Chip Clark, (r)Jeremy Woodhouse/DRK Photo; **115 116** Matt Meadows; **117** (t)A.J. Copley/Visuals Unlimited, (b)Jeremy Woodhouse/DRK Photo; **120** Tim Fitzharris/Minden Pictures; **121** Matt Meadows; **122** William E. Ferguson; **123** (tl)T.A. Wiewandt/DRK Photo, (tr)Kim Heacox Photography/DRK Photo, (bl)William E. Ferguson, (br)Grant Heilman/Grant Heilman Photography; **124** (l)Kazuyoshi Nomachi/Photo Researchers, (r)Anthony Bannister/Photo Researchers; **125** Christena M. Cox; **126** (t)John Cancalosi/Peter Arnold, Inc.; (b)Jim Steinberg/Photo Researchers; **127** (t)Marc Epstein/Visuals Unlimited, (b)Adrienne T. Gibson/Earth Scenes; **129** (t,c)Doug Martin, (b)John Sohlden/Visuals Unlimited; **130** Scott T. Smith/CORBIS; **131** (l)Mark Burnett/Photo Researchers, (r)M.I. Walker/Photo Researchers; **135** Farley Lewis/Photo Researchers; **136** (t)Alfred Pasieka/Science Photo Library/Photo Researchers, (bl,bcl) William E. Ferguson, (bcr)Doug Martin, (br)Andrew J. Martinez/Photo Researchers; **137** (tl)A.J. Copley/Visuals Unlimited, (tr)Doug Martin, (b)Breck P. Kent/Earth Scenes; **140** Matt Meadows; **142** Dr. Jeremy Burgess/Science Photo Library/Photo Researchers; **143** (t)Marc Epstein/Visuals Unlimited, (c)Scott T. Smith/CORBIS, (b)Breck P. Kent/Earth Scenes; **146** Yoav Levy/Phototake; **147** Mark A. Schneider/Photo Researchers; **148** Craig Blacklock/Larry Ulrich Stock; **150-151** Jack Dykinga/Stone; **152** Jack Dykinga; **153** Matt Meadows; **154** (t)Catherine Ursillo/Photo Researchers, (b)William E. Ferguson; **155** (tl)Susan Rayfield/Photo Researchers, (tc)Cliff Leight, (tr)Bud Lehnhausen/Photo Researchers, (b)J. Serrao/Photo Researchers; **156** (t)Scott T. Smith/CORBIS, (b)Wilbur E. Garrett/National Geographic Image Collection; **160** Jack Dykinga; **162** Gary Braasch; **163** (l)Jack Dykinga, (r)William E. Ferguson; **164** (t)NASA, (c)Arthur Morris/Visuals Unlimited, (b)John Shelton; **165** (t)Cliff Leight, (b)Jeff Foott/DRK Photo; **166** Vince Streano/CORBIS; **168** Kevin Fleming/CORBIS; **169** Doug Martin; **171** Fletcher & Baylis/Photo Researchers; **174** Matt Meadows; **176** Bob Jordan/AP/Wide World Photos; **177** (t)Susan Rayfield/Photo Researchers, (c)William E. Ferguson, (b)Kevin Fleming/CORBIS; **180** Andres Leighton/AP/Wide World Photos; **182** Daniel D. Lamoreux/Visuals Unlimited; **185** (l)Gary Braasch, (r)Giuseppe Mastullo/Grazia Neri/Sygma; **186** Michael Gallacher/Missoulian/Liaison Agency; **187** Chuck Place/Stock Boston; **188** (t)Gilbert Vogt/Liaison Agency, (bl)Don & Pat Valenti/DRK Photo, (br)Stouffer Productions/Earth Scenes; **189** Ricardo Mazalan/AP/Wide World Photos; **190** (l)Michael Habicht/Earth Scenes, (r)Jim Steinberg/Photo Researchers; **191** Tony Freeman/PhotoEdit; **192** David Muench/Corbis; **193** (t)Jeff Foott/DRK Photo, (b)Galen Rowell/CORBIS; **194** Tony Wilson-Bligh/CORBIS; **196** Scott W. Smith/Earth Scenes; **199** (t)Kim Heacox Photography/DRK Photos, (b)John Gerlach/Earth Scenes; **201** Tom Bean/DRK Photo; **202** Ken M. Johns/Photo Researchers; **203** (l)Tom Bean/DRK Photo, (r)Cliff Leight; **206** Johnny Johnson/Stone; **207** (t)Michael Gallacher/Missoulian/Liaison Agency, (c)Tony Wilson-Bligh/CORBIS, (b)Kim Heacox Photography/DRK Photo; **210** Tom Bean/Stone; **211** Matt Meadows; **214** John Shelton; **217** Jack Dykinga; **218**

Tom Bean/DRK Photo; **219** Geoff Tompkinson/Science Photo Library/Photo Researchers; **220** John Eastcott & Yva Momatiuk/Photo Researchers; **221** Cliff Leight; **222** Jack Dykinga; **223** Norbert Rosing/Earth Scenes; **224** (t)Bob Krist/CORBIS, (b)Brian Milne/Earth Scenes; **225** Jeff Lapore/Photo Researchers; **226** (t)Michael Collier/DRK Photo, (b)NASA/TSADO/Tom Stack & Associates; **227** Jack Dykinga; **228** Scott T. Smith/CORBIS; **229** Cliff Leight; **230** (t)W. Banaszewski/Visuals Unlimited, (b)Farrell Grehan/Photo Researchers; **231** Gordon & Cathy Illg/Animals Animals; **232** Matt Meadows; **234** Konrad Wothe/Minden Pictures; **235** (t)Jack Dykinga, (c)Jeff Lapore/Photo Researchers, (b)Gordon & Cathy Illg/Animals Animals; **238** Peter & Ann Bosted/Tom Stack & Associates; **239** Doug Martin; **244** Keren Su/CORBIS; **245** John W. Bova/Photo Researchers; **246** John Shelton; **247** Sheila Terry/Science Photo Library/Photo Researchers; **248** Richard Thom/Visuals Unlimited; **249** A.J. Copley/Visuals Unlimited; **251** Jeff Foott/Tom Stack & Associates; **259** USGS; **260** T.A. Wiewandt/DRK Photo; **261** (t)Richard Thom/Visuals Unlimited, (b)A.J. Copley/Visuals Unlimited; **264** Cliff Leight; **265** (l)Larry Ulrich, (r)Theo Allofs/Stone; **267** Oldrich Karasek/Stone; **268-269** Laurence Parent; **270** Art Wolfe; **271** Matt Meadows; **277** (l)Chuck Savage/The Stock Market, (r)Chris Bartlett/FPG; **281** Tom Prettyman/PhotoEdit; **282** Bernhard Edmaier/Science Photo Library/Photo Researchers; **284** CORBIS; **284** (t)Chris Bartlett/FPG, (c)Bernhard Edmaier/Science Photo Library/Photo Researchers, (b)Michael Collier/DRK Photo; **289** Michael Collier/DRK Photo; **290** NCAR/Tom Stack & Associates; **292** Matt Meadows; **294** TOMS/NASA; **298** Larry Ulrich; **299** Matt Meadows; **300** (l)Nuridsany Et Perennou/Science Source/Photo Researchers, (c)Warren Faidley/Weatherstock, (r)Adam Jones/Photo Researchers; **307** NASA; **312** (tl)Greg Vaughn/Tom Stack & Associates, (tr,br)Doug Martin, (bl)Leonard Lessin, FBPA/Photo Researchers; **313** Randy Trine; **314** United Nations; **316** TSADO/NCDC/NOAA/Tom Stack & Associates; **319** Bob Daemmrich/Stock Boston; **321** Science Visualization Studio/The SeaWiFs Project/Goddard Space Flight Center/NASA; **324** William L. Wantland/Tom Stack & Associates; **325** (t to b)Adam Jones/Photo Researchers, NASA, Randy Trine, Bob Daemmrich/Stock Boston; **327** United Nations; **328** Warren Faidley/Weatherstock; **329** Matt Meadows; **333** CORBIS; **334** Warren Faidley/Weatherstock; **337** (tl)CORBIS, (tr)Gene Moore/Phototake/PictureQuest, (b)Warren Faidley/Weatherstock; **339** (t)H. Baker/Weatherstock, (c)Keith Brewster/Weatherstock, (b)W. Balzer/Weatherstock; **341** NASA/TSADO/Tom Stack & Associates; **343** NASA; **345** Mark Allen Stack/Tom Stack & Associates; **347** CORBIS; **351** (l)Dick Blume, Syracuse Newspapers/AP/Wide World Photos, (r)Gary Walts, Syracuse Newspapers/AP/Wide World Photos; **354** CORBIS; **355** (t to b)CORBIS, W. Balzer/Weatherstock, NASA/TSADO/Tom Stack & Associates, Gary Walts Syracuse Newspapers /AP/Wide World Photos; **358** David Barnes/Stone; **363** Francois Gohier/Photo Researchers; **365** Frans Lanting/Minden Pictures; **366** Baron Wolman/Stone; **367** (l)Tui De Roy/Minden Pictures, (r)Peter B. Kaplan/Photo Researchers; **368** SVS/Goddard Space Flight Center/NASA; **371** (l)Mitch Reardon/Photo Researchers, (r)Doug Sokell/Tom Stack & Associates; **374** NASA/Roger Ressmeyer/CORBIS; **377** (t)Howard Buffett/Grant Heilman Photography, (b)Bill Bachman/PhotoEdit; **378** Tom Stack; **380** Jacques Jangoux/Stone; **381** (t to b)Francois Gohier/Photo Researchers, Frans Lanting/Minden Pictures, Doug Sokell/Tom Stack & Associates, Howard Buffett/Grant Heilman Photography; **384** Kim Heacox/Stone; **385** Matt Meadows; **386** (l)AP/Wide World Photos, (r)USGS/AP/Wide World Photos; **387** (t)NASA/Science Photo Library/Photo Researchers, (b)S. Nielsen/DRK Photo; **389** Los Almos National Laboratory/Science Photo Library/Photo Researchers; **390** Perry Conway/Tom Stack & Associates; **391** TSADO/NASA/Tom Stack & Associates; **392** Jose Manuel Sanchis Calvete/CORBIS; **393** CORBIS; **394** Randy Morse/Tom Stack & Associates; **396** Peter David/Photo Researchers; **400** Paul Berger/Stone; **408** Underwood & Underwood/CORBIS; **409** (t)NASA/Science Photo Library/Photo Researchers, (c)Randy Morse/Tom Stack & Associates, (b)Paul Berger/Stone; **412** Jack Dykinga; **413** Geoff Butler; **415** Wolfgang Kaehler/CORBIS; **418** (l)Melvin B. Zucker/Visuals Unlimited, (r)Philip Gould/CORBIS; **419** Tom Bean/DRK Photo; **420** Tom Stack/Tom Stack & Associates; **421** John Shelton; **424** Official U.S. Navy Photo by R.F. Diel; **425 426** Marie Tharp; **427** Dr. Ken MacDonald/Science Photo Library/Photo Researchers; **428** Doug Martin; **429** Science VU/Visuals Unlimted; **431** USGS; **432** Peter David/Photo Researchers; **433** (t)Wolfgang Kaehler/CORBIS, (b)Science VU/Visuals Unlimited; **436** William L. Wantland/Tom Stack & Associates; **437** StockTrek/The Stock Market; **438** Larry Ulrich; **439** (t)Jeff Foott/DRK Photo, (b)Andrew Syred/Science Photo Library/Photo Researchers; **440-441** David Ball/Stone; **442** Emory Kristoff/National Geographic Society Image Collection; **446** Betty

Crowell/Faraway Places; **449** Dr. Ken MacDonald/Science Photo Library/Photo Researchers; **453** NOAA/NGDC; **458** (t)Harold E. Wilson/Earth Scenes, (b)Marie Tharp; **460** Richard Megna/Fundamental Photographs; **462** Stephen P. Grand/Rob D. van der Hilst/Sri Widiyantoro/*GSA Today* 4/97; **463** NASA/Tom Stack & Associates; **467** (t to b)Betty Crowell/Faraway Places, NOAA/NGDC, Harold E. Wilson/Earth Scenes, NASA/Tom Stack & Associates; **470** Richard A. Cooke III/Stone; **471** Aaron Haupt; **474** G. Brad Lewis/Stone; **475** J.D. Griggs/CORBIS; **478** (l)Art Attack/Photo Researchers, (r)Tom Bean/DRK Photo; **479** Larry Ulrich; **480** Michael Collier/DRK Photo; **481** C.C. Lockwood/DRK Photo; **482** David Muench Photography; **483** (l)C. Sharp/Earth Scenes, (r)Pat & Tom Leeson/Photo Researchers; **484** Morris J. Elsing/National Geographic Image Collection; **486** Yann Arthus-Bertrand/CORBIS; **488** PhotoDisc; **490** NASA; **491** (t)G. Brad Lewis/Stone, (c)Larry Ulrich, (b)Pat & Tom Leeson/Photo Researchers; **494** Wally Santana/AP/Wide World Photos; **495** Bob Daemmrich; **497** John Shelton; **505** Winfield Parks/National Geographic Image Collection; **506** Barry Sweet/AP/Wide World; **511** Nik Wheeler/CORBIS; **512** William H. Mullins/Photo Researchers; **513** James Mori/Institute of Geophysics, National Central University, Taiwan, and Kyoto University, Japan; **515** David Parker/Science Photo Library/Photo Researchers; **518** (l)Earl & Nazima Kowall/CORBIS, (r)Shahpari Sohaie/CORBIS; **519** (t)John Shelton, (c)Winfield Parks/National Geographic Image Collection, (b)David Parker/Science Photo Library/Photo Researchers; **522** Barbara Rowell/Mountain Light Photography; **523** Doug Martin; **527** Warren Morgan/CORBIS; **529** Roger Ressmeyer/CORBIS; **530** Betty Crowell/Faraway Places; **531** Galen Rowell/CORBIS; **532** William Felger/Grant Heilman Photography; **534** Kenneth Murray/Photo Researchers; **536** B. Murton/Southampton Oceanography Centre/Science Photo Library/Photo Researchers; **537** Lynn Gerig Photography/Tom Stack & Associates; **538** A.J. Copley/Visuals Unlimited; **539** Richard A. Cooke/CORBIS; **541** USGS; **542** AP/Wide World Photos; **543** (t)Warren Morgan/CORBIS, (c)Roger Ressmeyer/CORBIS, (b)A.J. Copley/Visuals Unlimited; **546** Yann Arthus-Bertrand/CORBIS; **547** Sharna Balfour/Gallo Images/CORBIS; **548** Wilbur Garrett/National Geographic Image Collection; **549** Cliff Leight; **550-551** John M. Roberts/ The Stock Market; **552** Larry Ulrich; **553** Matt Meadows; **555** Tom Bean/DRK Photo; **556** Laynne Kennedy/CORBIS; **557** Tom Bean/DRK Photo; **559** William E. Ferguson; **561** Christena M. Cox; **564** Tom Till/DRK Photo; **565** Charlie Ott/Photo Researchers; **566** C. Munoz-Yague/Phototake; **567** (tl)Dr. Dennis Kunkel/Phototake, (tr)Tom Bean/DRK Photo, (b)James L. Amos/CORBIS; **568** (t)Mark A. Schneider/Photo Researchers, (b)Tom Bean/DRK Photo; **569** (tl)Fred Bruemmer/Peter Arnold, Inc., (tr)Ray Nelson/Phototake, (b)Matt Meadows; **572** Francis Latreille; **573** (t to b)Tom Bean/DRK Photo, William E. Ferguson, Charlie Ott/Photo Researchers, Tom Bean/DRK Photo; **576** Chip Clark; **577** Matt Meadows; **579** Keith Bedford/AP/Wide World Photos; **584** Erwin and Peggy Bauer/Tom Stack & Associates; **585** (tl)Sinclair Stammers/Science Photo Library/ Photo Researchers, (tr)M. Abbey/Photo Researchers, (bl)Roland Seitre/Peter Arnold, Inc., (br)Sinclair Stammers/Science Photo Library/Photo Researchers; **586** (l)John Cancalosi/Peter Arnold, Inc., (r)Jim Wark/Peter Arnold, Inc.; **587** Jack Dykinga; **589** Jim Sugar Photography/CORBIS; **590** (l)Prof. Oscar L. Miller/Science Photo Library/Photo Researchers, (r)Science Source/Photo Researchers; **591** Fred McConnaughey/Photo Researchers; **596** NASA/Science Photo Library/Photo Researchers; **597** (t)Keith Bedford/AP/Wide World Photos, (c)John Cancalosi/Peter Arnold, Inc., (b)Fred McConnaughey/Photo Researchers; **600** Adam Jones/Photo Researchers; **601** Doug Martin; **603** Tom Bean/DRK Photo; **604** Chip Clark; **606** David Cavagnaro/DRK Photo; **607** Michael P. Gadomski/Photo Researchers; **608** Don Duckson/Visuals Unlimited; **609** (tl)William E. Ferguson, (tr)Doug Martin, (b)Dick Keen/Visuals Unlimited; **610** (l)Gregory K. Scott/Photo Researchers, (c)John Cancalosi/DRK Photo, (r)John Cancaloci/DRK Photo; **614** (t)Laurence Parent, (b)ProFiles West/Index Stock Photography; **615** (l)Kaj R. Svensson/Science Photo Library/Photo Researchers, (r)Fred McConnaughey/Photo Researchers; **618** Doug Martin; **620** Sinclair Stammers/Science Photo Library/Photo Researchers; **621** (t)Tom Bean/DRK Photo, (c)Doug Martin, (b)Kaj R. Svensson/Science Photo Library/Photo Researchers; **624** Francois Gohier/Photo Researchers; **625** (t)Dee Breger/Photo Researchers, (b)Juergen Berger/Max-Planck Institute/Science Photo Library/Photo Researchers; **626** Christena M. Cox; **627** Jack Dykinga; **628** M.I. Walker/Photo Researchers; **629** Sinclair Stammers/Science Photo Library/Photo Researchers; **631** Ken Lucas/Visuals Unlimited; **636** Dominique Braud/Tom Stack & Associates; **639** John Shaw/Tom Stack & Associates; **642** Ken Lucas Photo/Visuals Unlimited; **643** Stephen J. Krasemann/DRK Photo; **644** Mark Burnett; **645** (t to b)Dee Breger/Photo Researchers, Sinclair Stammers/Science

Geologic Time Scale

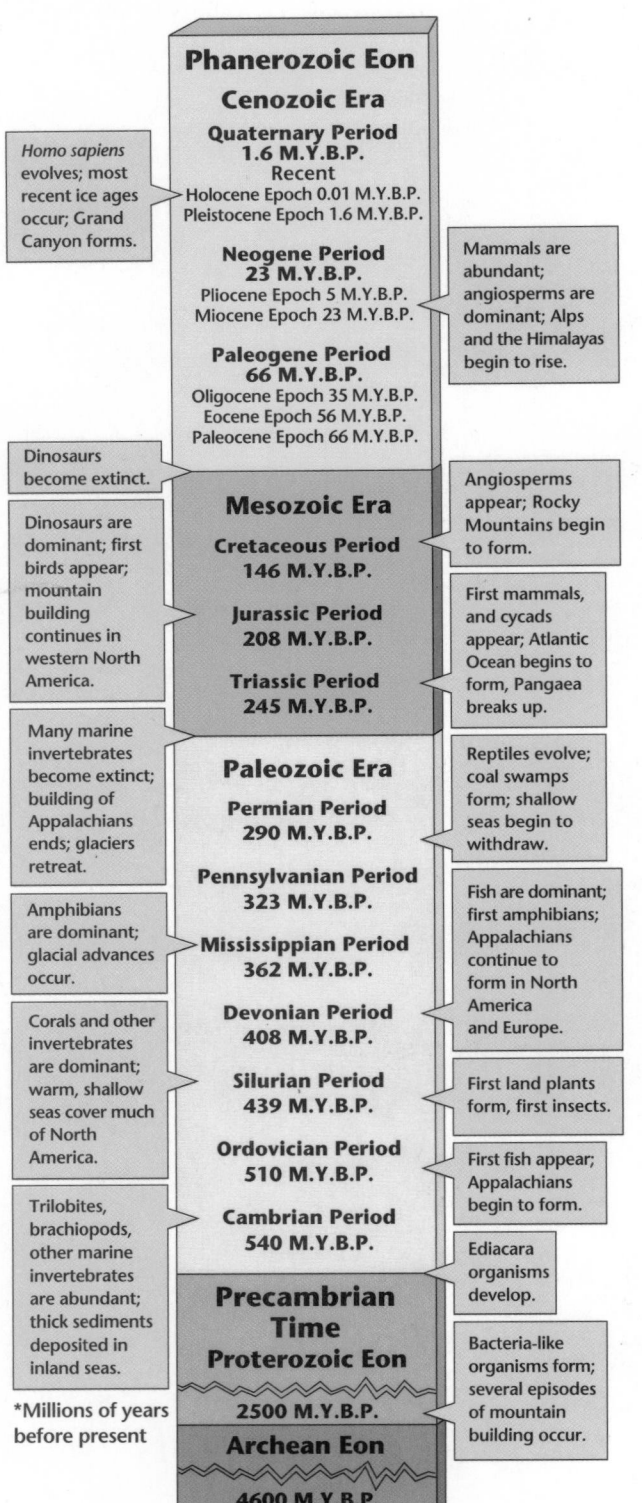

Homo sapiens evolves; most recent ice ages occur; Grand Canyon forms.

Phanerozoic Eon

Cenozoic Era

Quaternary Period
1.6 M.Y.B.P.
Recent
Holocene Epoch 0.01 M.Y.B.P.
Pleistocene Epoch 1.6 M.Y.B.P.

Neogene Period
23 M.Y.B.P.
Pliocene Epoch 5 M.Y.B.P.
Miocene Epoch 23 M.Y.B.P.

Paleogene Period
66 M.Y.B.P.
Oligocene Epoch 35 M.Y.B.P.
Eocene Epoch 56 M.Y.B.P.
Paleocene Epoch 66 M.Y.B.P.

Mammals are abundant; angiosperms are dominant; Alps and the Himalayas begin to rise.

Dinosaurs become extinct.

Angiosperms appear; Rocky Mountains begin to form.

Mesozoic Era

Cretaceous Period
146 M.Y.B.P.

Jurassic Period
208 M.Y.B.P.

Triassic Period
245 M.Y.B.P.

Dinosaurs are dominant; first birds appear; mountain building continues in western North America.

First mammals, and cycads appear; Atlantic Ocean begins to form, Pangaea breaks up.

Many marine invertebrates become extinct; building of Appalachians ends; glaciers retreat.

Reptiles evolve; coal swamps form; shallow seas begin to withdraw.

Paleozoic Era

Permian Period
290 M.Y.B.P.

Pennsylvanian Period
323 M.Y.B.P.

Mississippian Period
362 M.Y.B.P.

Devonian Period
408 M.Y.B.P.

Silurian Period
439 M.Y.B.P.

Ordovician Period
510 M.Y.B.P.

Cambrian Period
540 M.Y.B.P.

Amphibians are dominant; glacial advances occur.

Corals and other invertebrates are dominant; warm, shallow seas cover much of North America.

Trilobites, brachiopods, other marine invertebrates are abundant; thick sediments deposited in inland seas.

Fish are dominant; first amphibians; Appalachians continue to form in North America and Europe.

First land plants form, first insects.

First fish appear; Appalachians begin to form.

Ediacara organisms develop.

Precambrian Time

Proterozoic Eon

2500 M.Y.B.P.

Bacteria-like organisms form; several episodes of mountain building occur.

*Millions of years before present

Archean Eon

4600 M.Y.B.P.

Properties of Earth's Interior

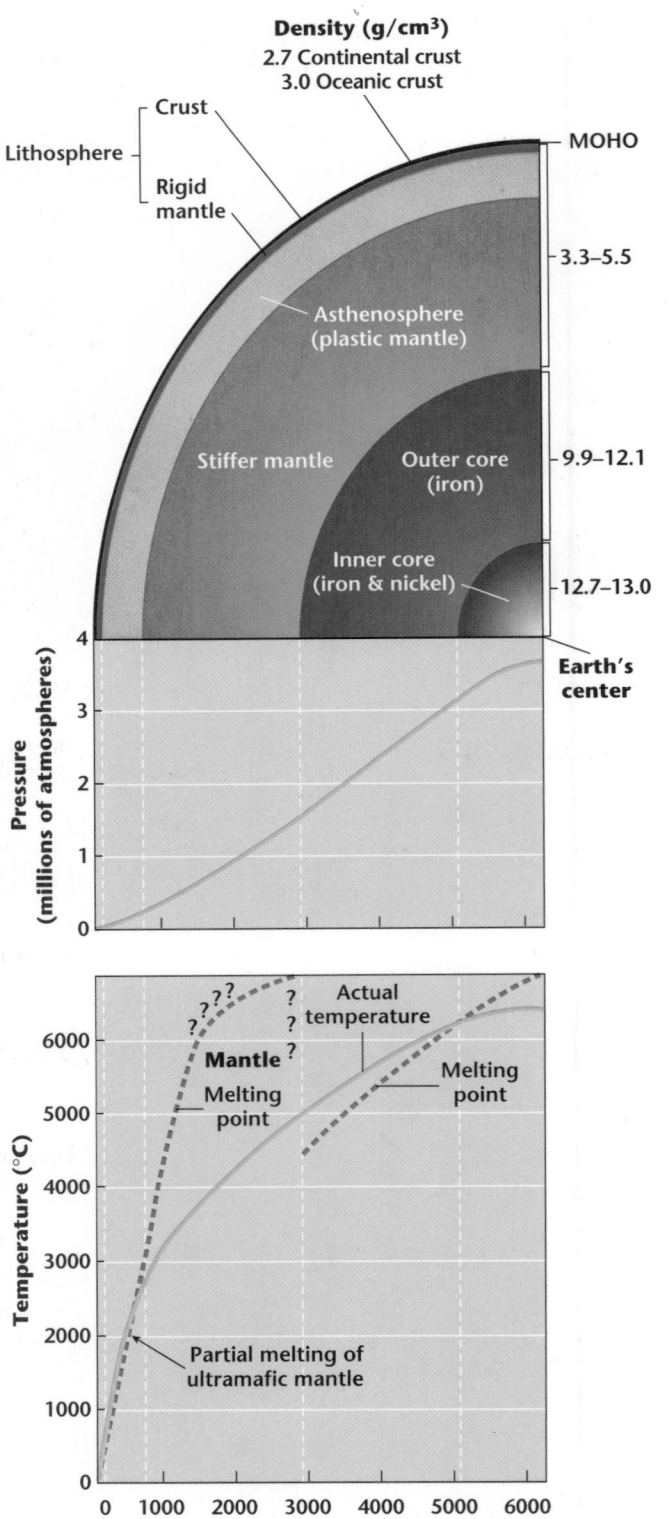

Density (g/cm³)
2.7 Continental crust
3.0 Oceanic crust

Lithosphere

Crust

Rigid mantle

MOHO

3.3–5.5

Asthenosphere (plastic mantle)

Stiffer mantle

Outer core (iron)

9.9–12.1

Inner core (iron & nickel)

12.7–13.0

Earth's center

Pressure (millions of atmospheres)

Temperature (°C)

Actual temperature

Mantle

Melting point

Melting point

Partial melting of ultramafic mantle

Depth (km)